$156.95 per copy (in United States)
Price is subject to change without prior notice.

0044

The 2014 *Commercial Rennovation Cost Data*, 35th annual edition, and all of the RSMeans annual cost data books for 2014, are dedicated to the memory of our respected colleague and friend, Paula Reale-Camelio.

RSMeans Commercial Renovation Cost Data

35TH ANNUAL EDITION

2014

RSMeans
A division of Reed Construction Data, LLC
Construction Publishers & Consultants
700 Longwater Drive
Norwell, MA 02061
USA
1-800-334-3509
www.rsmeans.com

Copyright 2013 by RSMeans
A division of Reed Construction Data, LLC
All rights reserved.

Printed in the United States of America
ISSN 2161-4628
ISBN 978-1-940238-02-9

Senior Editor

Bob Mewis, CCC *(4, 6, 7, 14, 41, 44)**

Contributing Editors

Christopher Babbitt
Adrian C. Charest, PE *(26, 27, 28, 48)*
Gary W. Christensen
David G. Drain, PE *(33)*
Cheryl Elsmore
David Fiske
Robert Fortier, PE *(2, 31, 32, 34, 35, 46)*
Robert J. Kuchta *(8)*
Thomas Lane
Robert C. McNichols
Genevieve Medeiros
Melville J. Mossman, PE *(21, 22, 23)**
Jeannene D. Murphy
Marilyn Phelan, AIA *(9, 10, 11, 12)*
Stephen C. Plotner *(3, 5)*
Siobhan Soucie
Phillip R. Waier, PE *(1, 13)*

Cover Design

Wendy McBay
Paul Robertson
Wayne Engebretson

Chief Operating Officer

Richard Remington

Vice President, Business Development

Steven Ritchie

Vice President, Finance & Operations

Renée Pinczes

Senior Director, Inside Sales

Derek F. Dean

Sales Manager

Reid Clanton

Director, Engineering

Bob Mewis, CCC

Senior Director, Product Management

Jennifer Johnson

Senior Product Marketing Manager

Andrea Sillah

Senior Director, Operations

Rodney L. Sharples

Production Manager

Michael Kokernak

Production

Jill Goodman
Jonathan Forgit
Debbie Panarelli
Sara Rutan
Mary Lou Geary

Technical Support

Christopher Anderson
Gary L. Hoitt
Kathryn S. Rodriguez

* Numbers in italics are the divisional responsibilities for each editor. Please contact the designated editor directly with any questions.

This book is printed on 90% recycled paper using soy-based ink and is entirely recyclable.

Related RSMeans Products and Services

This book is aimed primarily at commercial renovation projects. The information contained within has provisions for estimating small jobs with small quantities of work and large jobs that encompass major renovations. As with all RSMeans cost data, with reasonable exercise of judgment, this book can be used for estimating jobs with a wide range of costs.

The engineers at RSMeans suggest the following products and services as companion information resources to *RSMeans Commercial Renovation Cost Data*:

Construction Cost Data Books

Facilities Construction Cost Data 2014
Facilities Construction & Maintenance Cost Data 2014

Reference Books

Estimating Building Costs
RSMeans Estimating Handbook
Green Building: Project Planning & Estimating
How to Estimate with RSMeans Data
Plan Reading & Material Takeoff
Project Scheduling & Management for Construction
Universal Design for Style, Comfort & Safety

Seminars and In-House Training

Facilities Construction Estimating
RSMeans Online® Training
RSMeans Data for Job Order Contracting (JOC)
Practical Project Management for Construction Professionals
Scheduling with MSProject for Construction Professionals
Mechanical & Electrical Estimating

RSMeans Online Bookstore

Visit RSMeans at **www.rsmeans.com** for a one-stop portal for the most reliable and current resources available on the market. Here you can learn about our more than 20 annual cost data books, also available on CD and online versions, as well as our libary of reference books and RSMeans seminars.

RSMeans Electronic Data

Get the information found in RSMeans cost books electronically at **RSMeansOnline.com**.

RSMeans Business Solutions

Cost engineers and analysts conduct facility life cycle and benchmark research studies and predictive cost modeling, as well as offer consultation services for conceptual estimating, real property management, and job order contracting. Research studies are designed with the application of proprietary cost and project data from Reed Construction Data and RSMeans' extensive North American databases. Analysts offer building product manufacturers qualitative and quantitative market research, as well as time/motion studies for new products, and Web-based dashboards for market opportunity analysis. Clients are from both the public and private sectors, including federal, state, and municipal agencies; corporations; institutions; construction management firms; hospitals; and associations.

RSMeans for Job Order Contracting (JOC)

Best practice job order contracting (JOC) services support the owner in the development of their program. RSMeans develops all required contracting documents, works with stakeholders, and develops qualified and experienced contractor lists. RSMeans JOCWorks® software is the best of class in the functional tools that meet JOC specific requirements. RSMeans data is organized to meet JOC cost estimating requirements.

Construction Costs for Software Applications

More than 25 unit price and assemblies cost databases are available through a number of leading estimating and facilities management software providers (listed below). For more information see the "Other RSMeans Products" pages at the back of this publication.

RSMeansData™ is also available to federal, state, and local government agencies as multi-year, multi-seat licenses.

- 4Clicks-Solutions, LLC
- Assetworks
- Beck Technology
- BSD – Building Systems Design, Inc.
- CMS – Construction Management Software
- Corecon Technologies, Inc.
- CorVet Systems
- Hard Dollar Corporation
- Maxwell Systems
- MC^2
- MOCA Systems
- Parsons Corporation
- ProEst
- Refined Data
- Sage Timberline Office
- UDA Technologies, Inc.
- US Cost, Inc.
- VFA – Vanderweil Facility Advisers
- WinEstimator, Inc.
- R & K Solutions
- Tririga

Table of Contents

Foreword

Our Mission

Since 1942, RSMeans has been actively engaged in construction cost publishing and consulting throughout North America.

Today, more than 70 years after RSMeans began, our primary objective remains the same: to provide you, the construction and facilities professional, with the most current and comprehensive construction cost data possible.

Whether you are a contractor, owner, architect, engineer, facilities manager, or anyone else who needs a reliable construction cost estimate, you'll find this publication to be a highly useful and necessary tool.

With the constant flow of new construction methods and materials today, it's difficult to find the time to look at and evaluate all the different construction cost possibilities. In addition, because labor and material costs keep changing, last year's cost information is not a reliable basis for today's estimate or budget.

That's why so many construction professionals turn to RSMeans. We keep track of the costs for you, along with a wide range of other key information, from city cost indexes . . . to productivity rates . . . to crew composition . . . to contractor's overhead and profit rates.

RSMeans performs these functions by collecting data from all facets of the industry and organizing it in a format that is instantly accessible to you. From the preliminary budget to the detailed unit price estimate, you'll find the data in this book useful for all phases of construction cost determination.

The Staff, the Organization, and Our Services

When you purchase one of RSMeans' publications, you are, in effect, hiring the services of a full-time staff of construction and engineering professionals.

Our thoroughly experienced and highly qualified staff works daily at collecting, analyzing, and disseminating comprehensive cost information for your needs. These staff members have years of practical construction experience and engineering training prior to joining the firm. As a result, you can count on them not only for accurate cost figures, but also for additional background reference information that will help you create a realistic estimate.

The RSMeans organization is always prepared to help you solve construction problems through its variety of data solutions, including online, CD, and print book formats, as well as cost estimating expertise available via our business solutions, training, and seminars.

Besides a full array of construction cost estimating books, RSMeans also publishes a number of other reference works for the construction industry. Subjects include construction estimating and project and business management, special topics such as green building and job order contracting, and a library of facility management references.

In addition, you can access all of our construction cost data electronically in convenient CD format or on the web. Visit **RSMeansonline.com** for more information on our 24/7 online cost data.

What's more, you can increase your knowledge and improve your construction estimating and management performance with an RSMeans construction seminar or in-house training program. These two-day seminar programs offer unparalleled opportunities for everyone in your organization to become updated on a wide variety of construction-related issues.

RSMeans is also a worldwide provider of construction cost management and analysis services for commercial and government owners.

In short, RSMeans can provide you with the tools and expertise for constructing accurate and dependable construction estimates and budgets in a variety of ways.

Robert Snow Means Established a Tradition of Quality That Continues Today

Robert Snow Means spent years building RSMeans, making certain he always delivered a quality product.

Today, at RSMeans, we do more than talk about the quality of our data and the usefulness of our books. We stand behind all of our data, from historical cost indexes to construction materials and techniques to current costs.

If you have any questions about our products or services, please call us toll-free at 1-800-334-3509. Our customer service representatives will be happy to assist you. You can also visit our website at **www.rsmeans.com**

How the Book is Built: an Overview

The Construction Specifications Institute (CSI) and Construction Specifications Canada (CSC) have produced the 2012 edition of MasterFormat®, a system of titles and numbers used extensively to organize construction information.

All unit price data in the RSMeans cost data books is now arranged in the 50-division MasterFormat® 2012 system.

A Powerful Construction Tool

You have in your hands one of the most powerful construction tools available today. A successful project is built on the foundation of an accurate and dependable estimate. This book will enable you to construct just such an estimate.

For the casual user the book is designed to be:

- quickly and easily understood so you can get right to your estimate.
- filled with valuable information so you can understand the necessary factors that go into the cost estimate.

For the regular user, the book is designed to be:

- a handy desk reference that can be quickly referred to for key costs.
- a comprehensive, fully reliable source of current construction costs and productivityrates so you'll be prepared to estimate any project.
- a source book for preliminary project cost, product selections, and alternate materials and methods.

To meet all of these requirements, we have organized the book into the following clearly defined sections.

Quick Start

See our "Quick Start" instructions on the following page to get started right away.

Estimating with RSMeans Unit Price Cost Data

Please refer to these steps for guidance on completing an estimate using RSMeans unit price cost data.

How to Use the Book: The Details

This section contains an in-depth explanation of how the book is arranged . . . and how you can use it to determine a reliable construction cost estimate. It includes information about how we develop our cost figures and how to completely prepare your estimate.

Unit Price Section

All cost data has been divided into the 50 divisions according to the MasterFormat system of classification and numbering. For a listing of these divisions and an outline of their subdivisions, see the Unit Price Section Table of Contents.

Estimating tips are included at the beginning of each division.

Assemblies Section

The cost data in this section has been organized in an "Assemblies" format. These assemblies are the functional elements of a building and are arranged according to the 7 elements of the UNIFORMAT II classification system. For a complete explanation of a typical "Assemblies" page, see "How RSMeans Assemblies Data Works."

Reference Section

This section includes information on Equipment Rental Costs, Crew Listings, Historical Cost Indexes, City Cost Indexes, Location Factors, Reference Tables, Change Orders, Square Foot Costs, and a listing of Abbreviations.

Equipment Rental Costs: This section contains the average costs to rent and operate hundreds of pieces of construction equipment.

Crew Listings: This section lists all of the crews referenced in the book. For the purposes of this book, a crew is composed of more than one trade classification and/or the addition of power equipment to any trade classification. Power equipment is included in the cost of the crew. Costs are shown both with bare labor rates and with the installing contractor's overhead and profit added. For each, the total crew cost per eight-hour day and the composite cost per labor-hour are listed.

Historical Cost Indexes: These indexes provide you with data to adjust construction costs over time.

City Cost Indexes: All costs in this book are U.S. national averages. Costs vary because of the regional economy. You can adjust costs by CSI Division to over 700 locations throughout the U.S. and Canada by using the data in this section.

Location Factors: You can adjust total project costs to over 900 locations throughout the U.S. and Canada by using the data in this section.

Reference Tables: At the beginning of selected major classifications in the Unit Price section are reference numbers shown in a shaded box. These numbers refer you to related information in the Reference Section. In this section, you'll find reference tables, explanations, estimating information that support how we develop the unit price data, technical data, and estimating procedures.

Change Orders: This section includes information on the factors that influence the pricing of change orders.

Square Foot Costs: This section contains costs for 59 different building types that allow you to make a rough estimate for the overall cost of a project or its major components.

Abbreviations: A listing of abbreviations used throughout this book, along with the terms they represent, is included in this section.

Index

A comprehensive listing of all terms and subjects in this book will help you quickly find what you need when you are not sure where it occurs in MasterFormat.

The Scope of This Book

This book is designed to be as comprehensive and as easy to use as possible. To that end we have made certain assumptions and limited its scope in two key ways:

1. We have established material prices based on a national average.
2. We have computed labor costs based on a 30-city national average of union wage rates.

For a more detailed explanation of how the cost data is developed, see "How To Use the Book: The Details."

Project Size/Type

The material prices in RSMeans cost data books are "contractor's prices." They are the prices that contractors can expect to pay at the lumberyards, suppliers/distributers warehouses, etc. Small orders of speciality items would be higher than the costs shown, while very large orders, such as truckload lots, would be less. The variation would depend on the size, timing, and negotiating power of the contractor. The labor costs are primarily for new construction or major renovation rather than repairs or minor alterations.

With reasonable exercise of judgment, the figures can be used for any building work.

Absolute Essentials for a Quick Start

If you feel you are ready to use this book and don't think you will need the detailed instructions that begin on the following page, this Absolute Essentials for a Quick Start page is for you. These steps will allow you to get started estimating in a matter of minutes.

1 Scope

Think through the project that you will be estimating, and identify the many individual work tasks that will need to be covered in your estimate.

2 Quantify

Determine the number of units that will be required for each work task that you identified.

3 Pricing

Locate individual Unit Price line items that match the work tasks you identified. The Unit Price Section Table of Contents that begins on page 1 and the Index in the back of the book will help you find these line items.

4 Multiply

Multiply the Total Incl O&P cost for a Unit Price line item in the book by your quantity for that item. The price you calculate will be an estimate for a completed item of work performed by a subcontractor. Keep adding line items in this manner to build your estimate.

5 Project Overhead

Include project overhead items in your estimate. These items are needed to make the job run and are typically, but not always, provided by the General Contractor. They can be found in Division 1. An alternate method of estimating project overhead costs is to apply a percentage of the total project cost.

Include rented tools not included in crews, waste, rubbish handling, and cleanup.

6 Estimate Summary

Include General Contractor's markup on subcontractors, General Contractor's office overhead and profit, and sales tax on materials and equipment.

Adjust your estimate to the project's location by using the City Cost Indexes or Location Factors found in the Reference Section.

Editors' Note: We urge you to spend time reading and understanding the supporting material in the front of this book. An accurate estimate requires experience, knowledge, and careful calculation. The more you know about how we at RSMeans developed the data, the more accurate your estimate will be. In addition, it is important to take into consideration the reference material in the back of the book such as Equipment Listings, Crew Listings, City Cost Indexes, Location Factors, and Reference Tables.

Estimating with RSMeans Unit Price Cost Data

Following these steps will allow you to complete an accurate estimate using RSMeans Unit Price cost data.

1 Scope Out the Project

- Identify the individual work tasks that will need to be covered in your estimate.
- The Unit Price data in this book has been divided into 50 Divisions according to the CSI MasterFormat 2012—their titles are listed on the back cover of your book.
- Think through the project and identify those CSI Divisions needed in your estimate.
- The Unit Price Section Table of Contents on page 1 may also be helpful when scoping out your project.
- Experienced estimators find it helpful to begin with Division 2 and continue through completion. Division 1 can be estimated after the full project scope is known.

2 Quantify

- Determine the number of units required for each work task that you identified.
- Experienced estimators include an allowance for waste in their quantities. (Waste is not included in RSMeans Unit Price line items unless so stated.)

3 Price the Quantities

- Use the Unit Price Table of Contents, and the Index, to locate individual Unit Price line items for your estimate.
- Reference Numbers indicated within a Unit Price section refer to additional information that you may find useful.
- The crew indicates who is performing the work for that task. Crew codes are expanded in the Crew Listings in the Reference Section to include all trades and equipment that comprise the crew.

- The Daily Output is the amount of work the crew is expected to do in one day.
- The Labor-Hours value is the amount of time it will take for the crew to install one unit of work.
- The abbreviated Unit designation indicates the unit of measure upon which the crew, productivity, and prices are based.
- Bare Costs are shown for materials, labor, and equipment needed to complete the Unit Price line item. Bare costs do not include waste, project overhead, payroll insurance, payroll taxes, main office overhead, or profit.
- The Total Incl O&P cost is the billing rate or invoice amount of the installing contractor or subcontractor who performs the work for the Unit Price line item.

4 Multiply

- Multiply the total number of units needed for your project by the Total Incl O&P cost for each Unit Price line item.
- Be careful that your take off unit of measure matches the unit of measure in the Unit column.
- The price you calculate is an estimate for a completed item of work.
- Keep scoping individual tasks, determining the number of units required for those tasks, matching each task with individual Unit Price line items in the book, and multiply quantities by Total Incl O&P costs.
- An estimate completed in this manner is priced as if a subcontractor, or set of subcontractors, is performing the work. The estimate does not yet include Project Overhead or Estimate Summary components such as General Contractor markups on subcontracted work, General Contractor office overhead and profit, contingency, and location factor.

5 Project Overhead

- Include project overhead items from Division 1 – General Requirements.
- These items are needed to make the job run. They are typically, but not always, provided by the General Contractor. Items include, but are not limited to, field personnel, insurance, performance bond, permits, testing, temporary utilities, field office and storage facilities, temporary scaffolding and platforms, equipment mobilization and demobilization, temporary roads and sidewalks, winter protection, temporary barricades and fencing, temporary security, temporary signs, field engineering and layout, final cleaning and commissioning.
- Each item should be quantified, and matched to individual Unit Price line items in Division 1, and then priced and added to your estimate.
- An alternate method of estimating project overhead costs is to apply a percentage of the total project cost, usually 5% to 15% with an average of 10% (see General Conditions, page ix).
- Include other project related expenses in your estimate such as:
  - Rented equipment not itemized in the Crew Listings
  - Rubbish handling throughout the project (see 02 41 19.19)

6 Estimate Summary

- Include sales tax as required by laws of your state or county.
- Include the General Contractor's markup on self-performed work, usually 5% to 15% with an average of 10%.
- Include the General Contractor's markup on subcontracted work, usually 5% to 15% with an average of 10%.
- Include General Contractor's main office overhead and profit:
  - RSMeans gives general guidelines on the General Contractor's main office overhead (see section 01 31 13.50 and Reference Number R013113-50).
  - RSMeans gives no guidance on the General Contractor's profit.
  - Markups will depend on the size of the General Contractor's operations, his projected annual revenue, the level of risk he is taking on, and on the level of competition in the local area and for this project in particular.
- Include a contingency, usually 3% to 5%, if appropriate.
- Adjust your estimate to the project's location by using the City Cost Indexes or the Location Factors in the Reference Section:
  - Look at the rules on the pages for How to Use the City Cost Indexes to see how to apply the Indexes for your location.
  - When the proper Index or Factor has been identified for the project's location, convert it to a multiplier by dividing it by 100, and then multiply that multiplier by your estimated total cost. The original estimated total cost will now be adjusted up or down from the national average to a total that is appropriate for your location.

Editors' Notes:

1) *We urge you to spend time reading and understanding the supporting material in the front of this book. An accurate estimate requires experience, knowledge, and careful calculation. The more you know about how we at RSMeans developed the data, the more accurate your estimate will be. In addition, it is important to take into consideration the reference material in the back of the book such as Equipment Listings, Crew Listings, City Cost Indexes, Location Factors, and Reference Tables.*

2) *Contractors who are bidding or are involved in JOC, DOC, SABER, or IDIQ type contracts are cautioned that workers' compensation insurance, federal and state payroll taxes, waste, project supervision, project overhead, main office overhead, and profit are not included in bare costs. The coefficient or multiplier must cover these costs.*

How to Use the Book: The Details

What's Behind the Numbers? The Development of Cost Data

The staff at RSMeans continually monitors developments in the construction industry in order to ensure reliable, thorough, and up-to-date cost information. While overall construction costs may vary relative to general economic conditions, price fluctuations within the industry are dependent upon many factors. Individual price variations may, in fact, be opposite to overall economic trends. Therefore, costs are constantly tracked and complete updates are published yearly. Also, new items are frequently added in response to changes in materials and methods.

Costs—$ (U.S.)

All costs represent U.S. national averages and are given in U.S. dollars. The RSMeans City Cost Indexes can be used to adjust costs to a particular location. The City Cost Indexes for Canada can be used to adjust U.S. national averages to local costs in Canadian dollars. No exchange rate conversion is necessary.

G The processes or products identified by the green symbol in our publications have been determined to be environmentally responsible and/or resource-efficient solely by the RSMeans engineering staff. The inclusion of the green symbol does not represent compliance with any specific industry association or standard.

Material Costs

The RSMeans staff contacts manufacturers, dealers, distributors, and contractors all across the U.S. and Canada to determine national average material costs. If you have access to current material costs for your specific location, you may wish to make adjustments to reflect differences from the national average. Included within material costs are fasteners for a normal installation. RSMeans engineers use manufacturers' recommendations, written specifications, and/or standard construction practice for size and spacing of fasteners. Adjustments to material costs may be required for your specific application or location. The manufacturer's warranty is assumed. Extended warranties are not included in the material costs. Material costs do not include sales tax.

Labor Costs

Labor costs are based on the average of wage rates from 30 major U.S. cities. Rates are determined from labor union agreements or prevailing wages for construction trades for the current year. Rates, along with overhead and profit markups, are listed on the inside back cover of this book.

- If wage rates in your area vary from those used in this book, or if rate increases are expected within a given year, labor costs should be adjusted accordingly.

Labor costs reflect productivity based on actual working conditions. In addition to actual installation, these figures include time spent during a normal weekday on tasks such as, material receiving and handling, mobilization at site, site movement, breaks, and cleanup. Productivity data is developed over an extended period so as not to be influenced by abnormal variations and reflects a typical average.

Equipment Costs

Equipment costs include not only rental, but also operating costs for equipment under normal use. The operating costs include parts and labor for routine servicing such as repair and replacement of pumps, filters, and worn lines. Normal operating expendables, such as fuel, lubricants, tires, and electricity (where applicable), are also included. Extraordinary operating expendables with highly variable wear patterns, such as diamond bits and blades, are excluded. These costs are included under materials. Equipment rental rates are obtained from industry sources throughout North America—contractors, suppliers, dealers, manufacturers, and distributors.

Rental rates can also be treated as reimbursement costs for contractor-owned equipment. Owned equipment costs include depreciation, loan payments, interest, taxes, insurance, storage and major repairs.

Equipment costs do not include operators' wages; nor do they include the cost to move equipment to a job site (mobilization) or from a job site (demobilization).

Equipment Cost/Day——The cost of power equipment required for each crew is included in the Crew Listings in the Reference Section (small tools that are considered as essential everyday tools are not listed out separately). The Crew Listings itemize specialized tools and heavy equipment along with labor trades. The daily cost of itemized equipment included in a crew is based on dividing the weekly bare rental rate by 5 (number of working days per week) and then adding the hourly operating cost times 8 (the number of hours per day). This Equipment Cost/Day is shown in the last column of the Equipment Rental Cost pages in the Reference Section.

Mobilization/Demobilization——The cost to move construction equipment from an equipment yard or rental company to the job site and back again is not included in equipment costs. Mobilization (to the site) and demobilization (from the site) costs can be found in the Unit Price Section. If a piece of equipment is already at the job site, it is not appropriate to utilize mob./demob. costs again in an estimate.

Overhead and Profit

Total Cost including O&P for the *Installing Contractor* is shown in the last column on the Unit Price and/or the Assemblies pages of this book. This figure is the sum of the bare material cost plus 10% for profit, the bare labor cost plus total overhead and profit, and the bare equipment cost plus 10% for profit. Details for the calculation of Overhead and Profit on labor are shown on the inside back cover and in the Reference Section of this book. (See "How RSMeans Data Works" for an example of this calculation.)

General Conditions

Cost data in this book is presented in two ways: Bare Costs and Total Cost including O&P (Overhead and Profit). General Conditions, or General Requirements, of the contract, should also be added to the Total Cost including O&P when applicable. Costs for General Conditions are listed in Division 1 of the Unit Price Section and the Reference Section of this book. General Conditions for the *Installing Contractor* may range from 0%

to 10% of the Total Cost including O&P. For the *General* or *Prime Contractor*, costs for General Conditions may range from 5% to 15% of the Total Cost including O&P, with a figure of 10% as the most typical allowance.

Factors Affecting Costs

Costs can vary depending upon a number of variables. Here's how we have handled the main factors affecting costs.

Quality——The prices for materials and the workmanship upon which productivity is based represent sound construction work. They are also in line with U.S. government specifications.

Overtime——We have made no allowance for overtime. If you anticipate premium time or work beyond normal working hours, be sure to make an appropriate adjustment to your labor costs.

Productivity——The productivity, daily output, and labor-hour figures for each line item are based on working an eight-hour day in daylight hours in moderate temperatures. For work that extends beyond normal work hours or is performed under adverse conditions, productivity may decrease. (See "How RSMeans Data Works" for more on productivity.)

Size of Project——The size, scope of work, and type of construction project will have a significant impact on cost. Economies of scale can reduce costs for large projects. Unit costs can often run higher for small projects.

Location——Material prices in this book are for metropolitan areas. However, in dense urban areas, traffic and site storage limitations may increase costs. Beyond a 20-mile radius

of large cities, extra trucking or transportation charges may also increase the material costs slightly. On the other hand, lower wage rates may be in effect. Be sure to consider both of these factors when preparing an estimate, particularly if the job site is located in a central city or remote rural location.

In addition, highly specialized subcontract items may require travel and per-diem expenses for mechanics.

Other Factors——

• season of year
• contractor management
• weather conditions
• local union restrictions
• building code requirements
• availability of:
    • adequate energy
    • skilled labor
    • building materials
• owner's special requirements/restrictions
• safety requirements
• environmental considerations

Unpredictable Factors——General business conditions influence "in-place" costs of all items. Substitute materials and construction methods may have to be employed. These may affect the installed cost and/or life cycle costs. Such factors may be difficult to evaluate and cannot necessarily be predicted on the basis of the job's location in a particular section of the country. Thus, where these factors apply, you may find significant but unavoidable cost variations for which you will have to apply a measure of judgment to your estimate.

Rounding of Costs

In general, all unit prices in excess of $5.00 have been rounded to make them easier to use and still maintain adequate precision of the results. The rounding rules we have chosen are in the following table.

Prices from . . .	Rounded to the nearest . . .
$.01 to $5.00	$.01
$5.01 to $20.00	$.05
$20.01 to $100.00	$.50
$100.01 to $300.00	$1.00
$300.01 to $1,000.00	$5.00
$1,000.01 to $10,000.00	$25.00
$10,000.01 to $50,000.00	$100.00
$50,000.01 and above	$500.00

How Subcontracted Items Affect Costs

A considerable portion of all large construction jobs is usually subcontracted. In fact, the percentage done by subcontractors is constantly increasing and may run over 90%. Since the workers employed by these companies do nothing else but install their particular product, they soon become expert in that line. The result is, installation by these firms is accomplished so efficiently that the total in-place cost, even adding the general contractor's overhead and profit, is no more, and often less, than if the principal contractor had handled the installation himself/herself. Companies that deal with construction specialties are anxious to have their product perform well and, consequently, the installation will be the best possible.

Contingencies

The allowance for contingencies generally provides for unforeseen construction difficulties. On alterations or repair jobs, 20% is not too much. If drawings are final and only field contingencies are being considered, 2% or 3% is probably sufficient, and often nothing need be added. Contractually, changes in plans will be covered by extras. The contractor should consider inflationary price trends and possible material shortages during the course of the job. These escalation factors are dependent upon both economic conditions and the anticipated time between the estimate and actual construction. If drawings are not complete or approved, or a budget cost is wanted, it is wise to add 5% to 10%. Contingencies, then, are a matter of judgment. Additional allowances for contingencies are shown in Division 1.

Important Estimating Considerations

The "productivity," or daily output, of each craftsman includes mobilization and cleanup time, break time and plan layout time, as well as an allowance to carry stock from the storage trailer or location on the job site up to 200' into the building and to the first or second floor. If material has to be transported over greater distances or to higher floors, an additional allowance should be considered by the estimator. An allowance has also been included in the piping and fittings installation time for leak checking and minor tightening. Equipment installation time includes the following applicable items: positioning, leveling and securing the unit in place, connecting all associated piping, ducts, vents, etc., which shall have been estimated separately, connecting to an adjacent power source, filling/bleeding, startup, adjusting the controls up and down to ensure proper response, setting the integral controls/valves/regulators/thermostats for proper operation (does not include external building type control systems, DDC systems, etc.), explaining/training owner's operator, and warranty. A reasonable breakdown of the labor costs is as follows:

1. Movement into building, installation/setting of equipment — 35%
2. Connection to piping/duct/power, etc. — 25%
3. Filling/flushing/cleaning/touchup, etc. — 15%
4. Startup/running adjustments — 5%
5. Training owner's representative — 5%
6. Warranty/call back/service — 15%

Note that cranes or other lifting equipment are not included on any lines in the Mechanical divisions. For example, if a crane is required to lift a heavy piece of pipe into place high above a gym floor, or to put a rooftop unit on the roof of a four-story building, etc., it must be added. Due to the potential for extreme variation—from nothing additional required to a major crane or helicopter—we feel that including a nominal amount for "lifting contingency" would be useless and detract from the accuracy of the estimate. When using equipment rental from RSMeans, remember to include the cost of the operator(s).

Estimating Labor-Hours

The labor-hours expressed in this publication are based on Average Installation time, using an efficiency level of approximately 60%–65% (see item 7), which has been found reasonable and acceptable by many contractors. The book uses this national efficiency average to establish a consistent benchmark. For bid situations, adjustments to this efficiency level should be the responsibility of the contractor bidding the project. The unit labor-hour is divided in the following manner. A typical day for a journeyman might be:

1.	Study Plans	3%	14.4 min.
2.	Material Procurement	3%	14.4 min.
3.	Receiving and Storing	3%	14.4 min.
4.	Mobilization	5%	24.0 min.
5.	Site Movement	5%	24.0 min.
6.	Layout and Marking	8%	38.4 min.
7.	Actual Installation	64%	307.2 min.
8.	Cleanup	3%	14.4 min.
9.	Breaks, Nonproductive	6%	28.8 min.
		100%	480.0 min.

If any of the percentages expressed in this breakdown do not apply to the particular work or project situation, then that percentage or a portion of it may be deducted from or added to labor-hours.

Final Checklist

Estimating can be a straightforward process provided you remember the basics. Here's a checklist of some of the steps you should remember to complete before finalizing your estimate.

Did you remember to . . .

- factor in the City Cost Index for your locale?
- take into consideration which items have been marked up and by how much?
- mark up the entire estimate sufficiently for your purposes?
- read the background information on techniques and technical matters that could impact your project time span and cost?
- include all components of your project in the final estimate?
- make use of Minimum Labor/Equipment Charges for Small Quantities (see the following page for more details)?
- double check your figures for accuracy?
- call RSMeans if you have any questions about your estimate or the data you've found in our publications?

Remember, RSMeans stands behind its publications. If you have any questions about your estimate . . . about the costs you've used from our books . . . or even about the technical aspects of the job that may affect your estimate, feel free to call the RSMeans editors at 1-800-334-3509.

Free Quarterly Updates

Stay up-to-date throughout 2014 with RSMeans' free cost data updates four times a year. Sign up online to make sure you have access to the newest data. Every quarter we provide the city cost adjustment factors for hundreds of cities and key materials. Register at: **www.rsmeans2014updates.com**

Using Minimum Labor/Equipment Charges for Small Quantities

Estimating small construction or repair tasks often creates situations in which the quantity of work to be performed is very small. When this occurs, the labor and/or equipment costs to perform the work may be too low to allow for the crew to get to the job, receive instructions, find materials, get set up, perform the work, clean up, and get to the next job. In these situations, the estimator should compare the developed labor and/or equipment costs for performing the work (e.g., quantity × labor and/or equipment costs) with the "*minimum labor/equipment charge*" within that Unit Price section of the book.(These minimum labor/equipment charge line items appear only in *Facilities Construction Cost Data* and *Commercial Renovation Cost Data*.)

If the labor and/or equipment costs developed by the estimator are LOWER THAN the "*minimum labor/equipment charge*" listed at the bottom of specific sections of Unit Price costs, the estimator should adjust the developed costs upward to the "*minimum labor/equipment charge*." The proper use of a "minimum labor/equipment charge" results in having enough money in the estimate to cover the contractor's higher cost of performing a very small amount of work during a partial workday.

A "*minimum labor/equipment charge*" should be used only when the task being estimated is the only task the crew will perform at the job site that day. If, however, the crew will be able to perform other tasks at the job site that day, the use of a "*minimum labor/equipment charge*" is not appropriate.

08 52 Wood Windows

08 52 10 – Plain Wood Windows

08 52 10.40 Casement Window		Crew	Daily Output	Labor-Hours	Unit	Material	2014 Bare Costs Labor	Equipment	Total	Total Incl O&P
0010	**CASEMENT WINDOW**, including frame, screen and grilles									
0100	2'-0" x 3'-0" H, dbl. insulated glass [G]	1 Carp	10	.800	Ea.	268	36.50		304.50	355
0150	Low E glass [G]		10	.800		259	36.50		295.50	345
0200	2'-0" x 4'-6" high, double insulated glass [G]		9	.889		360	41		401	460
0250	Low E glass [G]		9	.889		370	41		411	470
9000	Minimum labor/equipment charge	1 Carp	3	2.667	Job		122		122	201

Example:

Establish the bid price to install two casement windows. Assume installation of 2'×4'-6" metal clad windows with insulating glass [Unit Price line number 08 52 10.40 0250], and that this is the only task this crew will perform at the job site that day.

Solution:

Step One — Develop the Bare Labor Cost for this task:
Bare Labor Cost = 2 windows @ $41.00/each = $82.00

Step Two — Evaluate the "*minimum labor/equipment charge*" for this Unit Price section against the developed Bare Labor Cost for this task:

"*Minimum labor/equipment charge*" = $122.00 (compare with $82.00)

Step Three — Choose to adjust the developed labor cost upward to the "*minimum labor/equipment charge*."

Step Four — Develop the bid price for this task (including O&P):

Add together the marked-up Bare Material Cost for this task and the marked-up "*minimum labor/equipment charge*" for this Unit Price section.

$$2 \times (\$370.00 + 10\%) + (\$122.00 + 64.3\%)$$
$$= 2 \times (\$370.00 + \$37.00) + (\$122.00 + \$78.45)$$
$$= 2 \times (\$407.00) + \$200.45$$
$$= \$814.00 + \$200.45$$
$$= \$1014.45$$

ANSWER: $1014.45 is the correct bid price to use. This sum takes into consideration the Material Cost (with 10% for profit) for these two windows, plus the "*minimum labor/equipment charge*" (with O&P included) for this section of the Unit Price.

Unit Price Section

Table of Contents

1

Table of Contents (cont.)

Table of Contents (cont.)

How RSMeans Unit Price Works

All RSMeans unit price data is organized in the same way.

It is important to understand the structure, so that you can find information easily and use it correctly.

RSMeans **Line Numbers** consist of 12 characters, which identify a unique location in the database for each task. The first 6 or 8 digits conform to the Construction Specifications Institute MasterFormat® 2012. The remainder of the digits are a further breakdown by RSMeans in order to arrange items in understandable groups of similar tasks. Line numbers are consistent across all RSMeans publications, so a line number in any RSMeans product will always refer to the same unit of work.

RSMeans engineers have created **reference** information to assist you in your estimate. If there is information that applies to a section, it will be indicated at the start of the section. In this case, R033105-10 provides information on the proportionate quantities of formwork, reinforcing, and concrete used in cast-in-place concrete items such as footings, slabs, beams, and columns. The Reference Section is located in the back of the book on the pages with a gray edge.

RSMeans **Descriptions** are shown in a hierarchical structure to make them readable. In order to read a complete description, read up through the indents to the top of the section. Include everything that is above and to the left that is not contradicted by information below. For instance, the complete description for line 03 30 53.40 3550 is "Concrete in place, including forms (4 uses), Grade 60 rebar, concrete (Portland cement Type 1), placement and finishing unless otherwise indicated; Equipment pad (3000 psi), 4' x 4' x 6" thick."

When using **RSMeans data**, it is important to read through an entire section to ensure that you use the data that most closely matches your work. Note that sometimes there is additional information shown in the section that may improve your price. There are frequently lines that further describe, add to, or adjust data for specific situations.

03 30 Cast-In-Place Concrete

03 30 53 – Miscellaneous Cast-In-Place Concrete

03 30 53.40 Concrete In Place

0010	**CONCRETE IN PLACE**	R033105-10
0020	Including forms (4 uses), Grade 60 rebar, concrete (Portland cement	R033105-20
0050	Type I), placement and finishing unless otherwise indicated	R033105-70
0300	Beams (3500 psi), 5 kip per L.F., 10' span	R033105-85
0350	25' span	
0500	Chimney foundations (5000 psi), over 5 C.Y.	
0510	(3500 psi), under 5 C.Y.	
0700	Columns, square (4000 psi), 12" x 12", less than 2% reinforcing	
3450	Over 10,000 S.F.	
3500	Add per floor for 3 to 6 stories high	
3520	For 7 to 20 stories high	
3540	Equipment pad (3000 psi), 3' x 3' x 6" thick	
3550	4' x 4' x 6" thick	
3560	5' x 5' x 8" thick	
3570	6' x 6' x 8" thick	

The data published in RSMeans print books represents a "national average" cost. This data should be modified to the project location using the **City Cost Indexes** or **Location Factors** tables found in the reference section (see pages 748–796). Use the location factors to adjust estimate totals if the project covers multiple trades. Use the city cost indexes (CCI) for single trade projects or projects where a more detailed analysis is required. All figures in the two tables are derived from the same research. The last row of data in the CCI, the weighted average, is the same as the numbers reported for each location in the location factor table.

Crews include labor or labor and equipment necessary to accomplish each task. In this case, Crew C-14H is used. RSMeans selects a crew to represent the workers and equipment that are typically used for that task. In this case, Crew C-14H consists of one carpenter foreman (outside), two carpenters, one rodman, one laborer, one cement finisher, and one gas engine vibrator. Details of all crews can be found in the reference section.

Crews

Crew No.	Bare Costs		Incl. Subs O&P		Cost Per Labor-Hour	
1 Carpenter Foreman (outside)	$47.85	$382.80	$78.60	$628.80	$45.15	$73.68
2 Carpenters	45.85	733.60	75.35	1205.60		
1 Rodman (reinf.)	50.65	405.20	83.10	664.80		
1 Laborer	36.65	293.20	60.20	481.60		
1 Cement Finisher	44.05	352.40	69.50	556.00		
1 Gas Engine Vibrator		33.00		36.30	.69	.76
48 L.H., Daily Totals		$2200.20		$3573.10	$45.84	$74.44

The **Daily Output** is the amount of work that the crew can do in a normal 8-hour workday, including mobilization, layout, movement of materials, and cleanup. In this case, crew C-14H can install thirty .4' x 4' x 6" thick concrete pads in a day. Daily output is variable, based on many factors, including the size of the job, location, and environmental conditions. RSMeans data represents work done in daylight (or adequate lighting) and temperate conditions.

Bare Costs are the costs of materials, labor, and equipment that the installing contractor pays. They represent the cost, in U.S. dollars, for one unit of work. They do not include any markups for profit or labor burden.

Crew	Daily Output	Labor-Hours	Unit	Material	2014 Bare Costs			Total	Total Incl O&P
					Labor	Equipment		Total	
C-14A	15.62	12.804	C.Y.	315	590	47.50		952.50	1,375
"	18.55	10.782		335	495	40		870	1,225
C-14C	32.22	3.476		147	153	1.01		301.01	415
"	23.71	4.724		173	207	1.37		381.37	535
C-14A	11.96	16.722		355	770	62		1,187	1,725
	2200	.025		.80	1.04	.32		2.16	2.92
	31800	.002		.07	.07	.02		.09	.14
	21200	.003		.11	.11	.03		.14	.21
C-14H	45	1.067	Ea.	44.50	48	.74		93.24	128
	30	1.600		66.50	72	1.10		139.60	192
	18	2.667		119	120	1.84		240.84	330
	14	3.429		160	155	2.37		317.37	430

The **Total Incl O&P column** is the total cost, including overhead and profit, that the installing contractor will charge the customer. This represents the cost of materials plus 10% profit, the cost of labor plus labor burden and 10% profit, and the cost of equipment plus 10% profit. It does not include the general contractor's overhead and profit. Note: See the inside back cover for details of how RSMeans calculates labor burden.

The **Total column** represents the total bare cost for the installing contractor, in U.S. dollars. In this case, the sum of $66.50 for material + $72.00 for labor + $1.10 for equipment is $139.60.

The figure in the **Labor Hours** column is the amount of labor required to perform one unit of work—in this case the amount of labor required to construct one 4' x 4' equipment pad. This figure is calculated by dividing the number of hours of labor in the crew by the daily output (48 labor hours divided by 30 pads = 1.6 hours of labor per pad). Multiply 1.600 times 60 to see the value in minutes: 60 x 1.6 = 96 minutes. Note: the labor hour figure is not dependent on the crew size. A change in crew size will result in a corresponding change in daily output, but the labor hours per unit of work will not change.

All RSMeans unit cost data includes the typical **Unit of Measure** used for estimating that item. For concrete-in-place the typical unit is cubic yards (C.Y.) or each (Ea.). For installing broadloom carpet it is square yard, and for gypsum board it is square foot. The estimator needs to take special care that the unit in the data matches the unit in the take-off. Unit conversions may be found in the Reference Section.

Sample Estimate

This sample demonstrates the elements of an estimate, including a tally of the RSMeans data lines, and a summary of the markups on a contractor's work to arrive at a total cost to the owner. The RSMeans Location Factor is added at the bottom of the estimate to adjust the cost of the work to a specific location.

Work Performed: The body of the estimate shows the RSMeans data selected, including line number, a brief description of each item, its take-off unit and quantity, and the bare costs of materials, labor, and equipment. This estimate also includes a column titled "SubContract." This data is taken from the RSMeans column "Total Incl O&P," and represents the total that a subcontractor would charge a general contractor for the work, including the sub's markup for overhead and profit.

Division 1, General Requirements: This is the first division numerically, but the last division estimated. Division 1 includes project-wide needs provided by the general contractor. These requirements vary by project, but may include temporary facilities and utilities, security, testing, project cleanup, etc. For small projects a percentage can be used, typically between 5% and 15% of project cost. For large projects the costs may be itemized and priced individually.

Bonds: Bond costs should be added to the estimate. The figures here represent a typical performance bond, ensuring the owner that if the general contractor does not complete the obligations in the construction contract the bonding company will pay the cost for completion of the work.

Location Adjustment: RSMeans published data is based on national average costs. If necessary, adjust the total cost of the project using a location factor from the "Location Factor" table or the "City Cost Index" table. Use location factors if the work is general, covering multiple trades. If the work is by a single trade (e.g., masonry) use the more specific data found in the "City Cost Indexes."

This estimate is based on an interactive spreadsheet. A copy of this spreadsheet is located on the RSMeans website at **http://www.reedconstructiondata.com/rsmeans/extras/546011**. You are free to download it and adjust it to your methodology.

Project Name: Pre-Engineered Steel Building				Architect: As Shown	
Location:	**Anywhere, USA**				
Line Number	**Description**	**Qty**	**Unit**		**Material**
03 30 53.40 3940	Strip footing, 12" x 24", reinforced	34	C.Y.		$4,624.00
03 30 53.40 3950	Strip footing, 12" x 36", reinforced	15	C.Y.		$1,950.00
03 11 13.65 3000	Concrete slab edge forms	500	L.F.		$155.00
03 22 11.10 0200	Welded wire fabric reinforcing	150	C.S.F.		$2,580.00
03 31 13.35 0300	Ready mix concrete, 4000 psi for slab on grade	278	C.Y.		$28,912.00
03 31 13.70 4300	Place, strike off & consolidate concrete slab	278	C.Y.		$0.00
03 35 13.30 0250	Machine float & trowel concrete slab	15,000	S.F.		$0.00
03 15 16.20 0140	Cut control joints in concrete slab	950	L.F.		$57.00
03 39 23.13 0300	Sprayed concrete curing membrane	150	C.S.F.		$1,642.50
Division 03	**Subtotal**				**$39,920.50**
08 36 13.10 2650	Manual 10' x 10' steel sectional overhead door	8	Ea.		$8,800.00
08 36 13.10 2860	Insulation and steel back panel for OH door	800	S.F.		$3,760.00
Division 08	**Subtotal**				**$12,560.00**
13 34 19.50 1100	Pre-Engineered Steel Building, 100' x 150' x 24'	15,000	SF Flr.		$0.00
13 34 19.50 6050	Framing for PESB door opening, 3' x 7'	4	Opng.		$0.00
13 34 19.50 6100	Framing for PESB door opening, 10' x 10'	8	Opng.		$0.00
13 34 19.50 6200	Framing for PESB window opening, 4' x 3'	6	Opng.		$0.00
13 34 19.50 5750	PESB door, 3' x 7', single leaf	4	Opng.		$2,340.00
13 34 19.50 7750	PESB sliding window, 4' x 3' with screen	6	Opng.		$2,250.00
13 34 19.50 6550	PESB gutter, eave type, 26 ga., painted	300	L.F.		$2,010.00
13 34 19.50 8650	PESB roof vent, 12" wide x 10' long	15	Ea.		$540.00
13 34 19.50 6900	PESB insulation, vinyl faced, 4" thick	27,400	S.F.		$10,960.00
Division 13	**Subtotal**				**$18,100.00**
				Subtotal	$70,580.50
Division 01	**General Requirements @ 7%**				**4,940.64**
				Estimate Subtotal	$75,521.14
				Sales Tax @ 5%	3,776.06
				Subtotal A	79,297.19
				GC O & P	7,929.72
				Subtotal B	87,226.91
				Contingency @ 5%	
				Subtotal C	
				Bond @ $12/1000 +10% O&P	
				Subtotal D	
				Location Adjustment Factor	
				Grand Total	

This example shows the cost to construct a pre-engineered steel building. The foundation, doors, windows, and insulation will be installed by the general contractor. A subcontractor will install the structural steel, roofing, and siding.

Labor	Equipment	SubContract	Estimate Total	R+R
		01/01/14		
$3,468.00	$23.12	$0.00		
$1,230.00	$8.10	$0.00		
$1,160.00	$0.00	$0.00		
$3,900.00	$0.00	$0.00		
$0.00	$0.00	$0.00		
$4,642.60	$166.80	$0.00		
$8,700.00	$450.00	$0.00		
$370.50	$95.00	$0.00		
$922.50	$0.00	$0.00		
24,393.60	$743.02	$0.00	$65,057.12	Division 03
$3,280.00	$0.00	$0.00		
$0.00	$0.00	$0.00		
$3,280.00	$0.00	$0.00	$15,840.00	Division 08
$0.00	$0.00	$352,500.00		
$0.00	$0.00	$2,320.00		
$0.00	$0.00	$9,400.00		
$0.00	$0.00	$3,390.00		
$656.00	$0.00	$0.00		
$558.00	$65.70	$0.00		
$768.00	$0.00	$0.00		
$3,060.00	$0.00	$0.00		
$8,768.00	$0.00	$0.00		
13,810.00	$65.70	$367,610.00	$399,585.70	Division 13
$41,483.60	$808.72	$367,610.00	$480,482.82	Subtotal
2,903.85	56.61	25,732.70		Gen. Requirements
$44,387.45	$865.33	$393,342.70	$480,482.82	Estimate Subtotal
	43.27	9,833.57		Sales tax
44,387.45	908.60	403,176.27		Subtotal
27,919.71	90.86	40,317.63		GC O & P
72,307.16	999.46	443,493.89	$604,027.42	Subtotal
			30,201.37	Contingency
			$634,228.79	Subtotal
			8,371.82	Bond
			$642,600.61	Subtotal
102.30			14,779.81	Location Adjustment
			$657,380.43	Grand Total

Sales Tax: If the work is subject to state or local sales taxes, the amount must be added to the estimate. Sales tax may be added to material costs, equipment costs, and subcontracted work. In this case, sales tax was added in all three categories. It was assumed that approximately half the subcontracted work would be material cost, so the tax was applied to 50% of the subcontract total.

GC O&P: This entry represents the general contractor's markup on material, labor, equipment, and subcontractor costs. RSMeans' standard markup on materials, equipment, and subcontracted work is 10%. In this estimate, the markup on the labor performed by the GC's workers uses "Skilled Workers Average" shown in Column F on the table "Installing Contractor's Overhead & Profit," which can be found on the inside-back cover of the book.

Contingency: A factor for contingency may be added to any estimate to represent the cost of unknowns that may occur between the time that the estimate is performed and the time the project is constructed. The amount of the allowance will depend on the stage of design at which the estimate is done, and the contractor's assessment of the risk involved. Refer to section 01 21 16.50 for contigency allowances.

Estimating Tips

01 20 00 Price and Payment Procedures

- Allowances that should be added to estimates to cover contingencies and job conditions that are not included in the national average material and labor costs are shown in section 01 21.
- When estimating historic preservation projects (depending on the condition of the existing structure and the owner's requirements), a 15%–20% contingency or allowance is recommended, regardless of the stage of the drawings.

01 30 00 Administrative Requirements

- Before determining a final cost estimate, it is a good practice to review all the items listed in Subdivisions 01 31 and 01 32 to make final adjustments for items that may need customizing to specific job conditions.
- Requirements for initial and periodic submittals can represent a significant cost to the General Requirements of a job. Thoroughly check the submittal specifications when estimating a project to determine any costs that should be included.

01 40 00 Quality Requirements

- All projects will require some degree of Quality Control. This cost is not included in the unit cost of construction listed in each division. Depending upon the terms of the contract, the various costs of inspection and testing can be the responsibility of either the owner or the contractor. Be sure to include the required costs in your estimate.

01 50 00 Temporary Facilities and Controls

- Barricades, access roads, safety nets, scaffolding, security, and many more requirements for the execution of a safe project are elements of direct cost. These costs can easily be overlooked when preparing an estimate. When looking through the major classifications of this subdivision, determine which items apply to each division in your estimate.
- Construction Equipment Rental Costs can be found in the Reference Section in section 01 54 33. Operators' wages are not included in equipment rental costs.
- Equipment mobilization and demobilization costs are not included in equipment rental costs and must be considered separately in section 01 54 36.50.
- The cost of small tools provided by the installing contractor for his workers is covered in the "Overhead" column on the "Installing Contractor's Overhead and Profit" table that lists labor trades, base rates and markups and, therefore, is included in the "Total Incl. O&P" cost of any Unit Price line item. For those users who are constrained by contract terms to use only bare costs, there are two line items in section 01 54 39.70 for small tools as a percentage of bare labor cost. If some of those users are further constrained by contract terms to refrain from using line items from Division 1, you are advised to cover the cost of small tools within your coefficient or multiplier.

01 70 00 Execution and Closeout Requirements

- When preparing an estimate, thoroughly read the specifications to determine the requirements for Contract Closeout. Final cleaning, record documentation, operation and maintenance data, warranties and bonds, and spare parts and maintenance materials can all be elements of cost for the completion of a contract. Do not overlook these in your estimate.

Reference Numbers

Reference numbers are shown in shaded boxes at the beginning of some major classifications. These numbers refer to related items in the Reference Section. The reference information may be an estimating procedure, an alternate pricing method, or technical information.

Note: Not all subdivisions listed here necessarily appear in this publication.

01 11 Summary of Work

01 11 31 – Professional Consultants

01 11 31.10 Architectural Fees	Crew	Daily Output	Labor-Hours	Unit	Material	2014 Bare Costs Labor	Equipment	Total	Total Incl O&P
0010 **ARCHITECTURAL FEES** R011110-10									
0020 For new construction									
0060 Minimum				Project				4.90%	4.90%
0090 Maximum								16%	16%
0100 For alteration work, to $500,000, add to new construction fee								50%	50%
0150 Over $500,000, add to new construction fee								25%	25%

01 11 31.20 Construction Management Fees									
0010 **CONSTRUCTION MANAGEMENT FEES**									
0060 For work to $100,000				Project				10%	10%
0070 To $250,000								9%	9%
0090 To $1,000,000								6%	6%
0100 To $5,000,000								5%	5%
0110 To $10,000,000								4%	4%

01 11 31.30 Engineering Fees									
0010 **ENGINEERING FEES** R011110-30									
0020 Educational planning consultant, minimum				Project				.50%	.50%
0100 Maximum				"				2.50%	2.50%
0400 Elevator & conveying systems, minimum				Contrct				2.50%	2.50%
0500 Maximum								5%	5%
1000 Mechanical (plumbing & HVAC), minimum								4.10%	4.10%
1100 Maximum								10.10%	10.10%
1200 Structural, minimum				Project				1%	1%
1300 Maximum				"				2.50%	2.50%

01 11 31.75 Renderings									
0010 **RENDERINGS** Color, matted, 20" x 30", eye level,									
0020 1 building, minimum				Ea.	2,050			2,050	2,275
0050 Average					2,875			2,875	3,175
0100 Maximum					4,625			4,625	5,100
1000 5 buildings, minimum					4,125			4,125	4,525
1100 Maximum					8,250			8,250	9,075

01 21 Allowances

01 21 16 – Contingency Allowances

01 21 16.50 Contingencies

	Crew	Daily Output	Labor-Hours	Unit	Material	2014 Bare Costs Labor	Equipment	Total	Total Incl O&P
0010 **CONTINGENCIES**, Add to estimate									
0020 Conceptual stage				Project				20%	20%
0050 Schematic stage								15%	15%
0100 Preliminary working drawing stage (Design Dev.)								10%	10%
0150 Final working drawing stage								3%	3%

01 21 53 – Factors Allowance

01 21 53.50 Factors

	Crew	Daily Output	Labor-Hours	Unit	Material	2014 Bare Costs Labor	Equipment	Total	Total Incl O&P
0010 **FACTORS** Cost adjustments R012153-10									
0100 Add to construction costs for particular job requirements									
0500 Cut & patch to match existing construction, add, minimum				Costs	2%	3%			
0550 Maximum					5%	9%			
0800 Dust protection, add, minimum					1%	2%			
0850 Maximum					4%	11%			
1100 Equipment usage curtailment, add, minimum					1%	1%			
1150 Maximum					3%	10%			
1400 Material handling & storage limitation, add, minimum					1%	1%			

01 21 Allowances

01 21 53 – Factors Allowance

01 21 53.50 Factors

		Crew	Daily Output	Labor-Hours	Unit	Material	2014 Bare Costs Labor	Equipment	Total	Total Incl O&P
1450	Maximum				Costs	6%	7%			
1700	Protection of existing work, add, minimum					2%	2%			
1750	Maximum					5%	7%			
2000	Shift work requirements, add, minimum						5%			
2050	Maximum						30%			
2300	Temporary shoring and bracing, add, minimum					2%	5%			
2350	Maximum					5%	12%			
2400	Work inside prisons and high security areas, add, minimum						30%			
2450	Maximum						50%			

01 21 55 – Job Conditions Allowance

01 21 55.50 Job Conditions

		Crew	Daily Output	Labor-Hours	Unit	Material	2014 Bare Costs Labor	Equipment	Total	Total Incl O&P
0010	**JOB CONDITIONS** Modifications to applicable									
0020	cost summaries									
0100	Economic conditions, favorable, deduct				Project				2%	2%
0200	Unfavorable, add								5%	5%
0300	Hoisting conditions, favorable, deduct								2%	2%
0400	Unfavorable, add								5%	5%
0500	General Contractor management, experienced, deduct								2%	2%
0600	Inexperienced, add								10%	10%
0700	Labor availability, surplus, deduct								1%	1%
0800	Shortage, add								10%	10%
0900	Material storage area, available, deduct								1%	1%
1000	Not available, add								2%	2%
1100	Subcontractor availability, surplus, deduct								5%	5%
1200	Shortage, add								12%	12%
1300	Work space, available, deduct								2%	2%
1400	Not available, add								5%	5%

01 21 63 – Taxes

01 21 63.10 Taxes

		Crew	Daily Output	Labor-Hours	Unit	Material	2014 Bare Costs Labor	Equipment	Total	Total Incl O&P
0010	**TAXES**	R012909-80								
0020	Sales tax, State, average				%	5.06%				
0050	Maximum	R012909-85				7.25%				
0200	Social Security, on first $115,800 of wages						7.65%			
0300	Unemployment, combined Federal and State, minimum						.60%			
0350	Average						7.80%			
0400	Maximum						13.50%			

01 31 Project Management and Coordination

01 31 13 – Project Coordination

01 31 13.20 Field Personnel

		Crew	Daily Output	Labor-Hours	Unit	Material	2014 Bare Costs Labor	Equipment	Total	Total Incl O&P
0010	**FIELD PERSONNEL**									
0020	Clerk, average				Week		435		435	710
0180	Project manager, minimum						1,925		1,925	3,150
0200	Average						2,225		2,225	3,600
0220	Maximum						2,525		2,525	4,125
0240	Superintendent, minimum						1,875		1,875	3,050
0260	Average						2,050		2,050	3,350
0280	Maximum						2,350		2,350	3,825

01 31 Project Management and Coordination

01 31 13 – Project Coordination

01 31 13.30 Insurance		Crew	Daily Output	Labor-Hours	Unit	Material	2014 Bare Costs Labor	Equipment	Total	Total Incl O&P
0010	**INSURANCE** R013113-40									
0020	Builders risk, standard, minimum				Job				.24%	.24%
0050	Maximum R013113-60								.64%	.64%
0200	All-risk type, minimum								.25%	.25%
0250	Maximum								.62%	.62%
0400	Contractor's equipment floater, minimum				Value				.50%	.50%
0450	Maximum				"				1.50%	1.50%
0600	Public liability, average				Job				2.02%	2.02%
0810	Workers' compensation & employer's liability									
2000	Range of 35 trades in 50 states, excl. wrecking, min.				Payroll		2.48%			
2100	Average						14%			
2200	Maximum						150%			

01 31 13.40 Main Office Expense

0010	**MAIN OFFICE EXPENSE** Average for General Contractors									
0020	As a percentage of their annual volume									
0030	Annual volume to $300,000, minimum				% Vol.				20%	
0040	Maximum								30%	
0060	To $500,000, minimum								17%	
0070	Maximum								22%	
0080	To $1,000,000, minimum								16%	
0090	Maximum								19%	
0110	To $3,000,000, minimum								14%	
0120	Maximum								16%	
0130	To $5,000,000, minimum								8%	
0140	Maximum								10%	

01 31 13.50 General Contractor's Mark-Up

0010	**GENERAL CONTRACTOR'S MARK-UP** on Change Orders									
0200	Extra work, by subcontractors, add				%				10%	10%
0250	By General Contractor, add								15%	15%
0400	Omitted work, by subcontractors, deduct all but								5%	5%
0450	By General Contractor, deduct all but								7.50%	7.50%
0600	Overtime work, by subcontractors, add								15%	15%
0650	By General Contractor, add								10%	10%

01 31 13.60 Installing Contractor's Main Office Overhead

0010	**INSTALLING CONTRACTOR'S MAIN OFFICE OVERHEAD** R013113-50									
0020	As percent of direct costs, minimum				%				5%	
0050	Average								13%	
0100	Maximum								30%	

01 31 13.80 Overhead and Profit

0010	**OVERHEAD & PROFIT** Allowance to add to items in this R013113-50									
0020	book that do not include Subs O&P, average				%				25%	
0100	Allowance to add to items in this book that									
0110	do include Subs O&P, minimum				%				5%	5%
0150	Average								10%	10%
0200	Maximum								15%	15%
0290	Typical, by size of project, under $50,000								40%	
0310	$50,000 to $100,000								35%	
0320	$100,000 to $500,000								25%	
0330	$500,000 to $1,000,000								20%	

01 31 Project Management and Coordination

01 31 13 – Project Coordination

01 31 13.90 Performance Bond	Crew	Daily Output	Labor-Hours	Unit	Material	2014 Bare Costs Labor	Equipment	Total	Total Incl O&P
0010 **PERFORMANCE BOND**									
0020 For buildings, minimum				Job				.60%	.60%
0100 Maximum				"				2.50%	2.50%

01 41 Regulatory Requirements

01 41 26 – Permit Requirements

01 41 26.50 Permits

	Crew	Daily Output	Labor-Hours	Unit	Material	Labor	Equipment	Total	Total Incl O&P
0010 **PERMITS**									
0020 Rule of thumb, most cities, minimum				Job				.50%	.50%
0100 Maximum				"				2%	2%

01 45 Quality Control

01 45 23 – Testing and Inspecting Services

01 45 23.50 Testing

	Crew	Daily Output	Labor-Hours	Unit	Material	Labor	Equipment	Total	Total Incl O&P
0010 **TESTING** and Inspecting Services									
1800 Compressive test, cylinder, delivered to lab, ASTM C 39				Ea.				12	13
1900 Picked up by lab, minimum								14	15
1950 Average								18	20
2000 Maximum								27	30
2200 Compressive strength, cores (not incl. drilling), ASTM C 42								36	40
2300 Patching core holes								22	24
4730 Soil testing									
4735 Soil density, nuclear method, ASTM D2922				Ea.				35	38.50
4740 Sand cone method ASTM D1556								27	30
4750 Moisture content, ASTM D 2216								9	10
4780 Permeability test, double ring infiltrometer								500	550
4800 Permeability, var. or constant head, undist., ASTM D 2434								227	250
4850 Recompacted								250	275
4900 Proctor compaction, 4" standard mold, ASTM D 698								123	135
4950 6" modified mold								68	75
5100 Shear tests, triaxial, minimum								410	450
5150 Maximum								545	600
5550 Technician for inspection, per day, earthwork								320	350
5650 Bolting								400	440
5750 Roofing								480	530
5790 Welding								480	530
5820 Non-destructive metal testing, dye penetrant				Day				310	340
5840 Magnetic particle								310	340
5860 Radiography								450	495
5880 Ultrasonic								310	340
6000 Welding certification, minimum				Ea.				91	100
6100 Maximum				"				250	275
7000 Underground storage tank									
7500 Volumetric tightness test ,<=12,000 gal.				Ea.				435	480
7510 <=30,000 gal.				"				615	675
7600 Vadose zone (soil gas) sampling, 10-40 samples, min.				Day				1,375	1,500
7610 Maximum				"				2,275	2,500
7700 Ground water monitoring incl. drilling 3 wells, min.				Total				4,550	5,000
7710 Maximum				"				6,375	7,000

01 45 Quality Control

01 45 23 - Testing and Inspecting Services

01 45 23.50 Testing	Crew	Daily Output	Labor-Hours	Unit	Material	2014 Bare Costs Labor	Equipment	Total	Total Incl O&P
8000	X-ray concrete slabs				Ea.				182	200

01 51 Temporary Utilities

01 51 13 - Temporary Electricity

01 51 13.80 Temporary Utilities

		Crew	Daily Output	Labor-Hours	Unit	Material	2014 Bare Costs Labor	Equipment	Total	Total Incl O&P
0010	**TEMPORARY UTILITIES**									
0100	Heat, incl. fuel and operation, per week, 12 hrs. per day	1 Skwk	100	.080	CSF Flr	28	3.78		31.78	36.50
0200	24 hrs. per day	"	60	.133		53.50	6.30		59.80	69
0350	Lighting, incl. service lamps, wiring & outlets, minimum	1 Elec	34	.235		2.80	12.55		15.35	22.50
0360	Maximum	"	17	.471		5.85	25		30.85	45.50
0400	Power for temp lighting only, 6.6 KWH, per month								.92	1.01
0430	11.8 KWH, per month								1.65	1.82
0450	23.6 KWH, per month								3.30	3.63
0600	Power for job duration incl. elevator, etc., minimum								47	51.50
0650	Maximum								110	121

01 52 Construction Facilities

01 52 13 - Field Offices and Sheds

01 52 13.20 Office and Storage Space

		Crew	Daily Output	Labor-Hours	Unit	Material	2014 Bare Costs Labor	Equipment	Total	Total Incl O&P
0010	**OFFICE AND STORAGE SPACE**									
0020	Office trailer, furnished, no hookups, 20' x 8', buy	2 Skwk	1	16	Ea.	9,150	755		9,905	11,300
0250	Rent per month					169			169	185
0300	32' x 8', buy	2 Skwk	.70	22.857		14,000	1,075		15,075	17,200
0350	Rent per month					203			203	223
0400	50' x 10', buy	2 Skwk	.60	26.667		22,400	1,250		23,650	26,700
0450	Rent per month					305			305	335
0500	50' x 12', buy	2 Skwk	.50	32		27,000	1,525		28,525	32,200
0550	Rent per month					350			350	385
0700	For air conditioning, rent per month, add					48.50			48.50	53.50
0800	For delivery, add per mile				Mile	11			11	12.10
0890	Delivery each way				Ea.	200			200	220
1200	Storage boxes, 20' x 8', buy	2 Skwk	1.80	8.889		2,775	420		3,195	3,725
1250	Rent per month					78.50			78.50	86
1300	40' x 8', buy	2 Skwk	1.40	11.429		3,700	540		4,240	4,950
1350	Rent per month					99			99	109

01 54 Construction Aids

01 54 16 - Temporary Hoists

01 54 16.50 Weekly Forklift Crew

		Crew	Daily Output	Labor-Hours	Unit	Material	2014 Bare Costs Labor	Equipment	Total	Total Incl O&P
0010	**WEEKLY FORKLIFT CREW**									
0100	All-terrain forklift, 45' lift, 35' reach, 9000 lb. capacity	A-3P	.20	40	Week		1,875	2,650	4,525	5,900

01 54 19 - Temporary Cranes

01 54 19.50 Daily Crane Crews

		Crew	Daily Output	Labor-Hours	Unit	Material	2014 Bare Costs Labor	Equipment	Total	Total Incl O&P
0010	**DAILY CRANE CREWS** for small jobs, portal to portal									
0100	12-ton truck-mounted hydraulic crane	A-3H	1	8	Day		400	875	1,275	1,600
0200	25-ton	A-3I	1	8			400	1,000	1,400	1,750
0300	40-ton	A-3J	1	8			400	1,250	1,650	2,025

01 54 Construction Aids

01 54 19 – Temporary Cranes

01 54 19.50 Daily Crane Crews

		Crew	Daily Output	Labor-Hours	Unit	Material	2014 Bare Costs Labor	Equipment	Total	Total Incl O&P
0400	55-ton	A-3K	1	16	Day		750	1,650	2,400	3,025
0500	80-ton	A-3L	1	16			750	2,400	3,150	3,825
0600	100-ton	A-3M	1	16	↓		750	2,375	3,125	3,825
0900	If crane is needed on a Saturday, Sunday or Holiday									
0910	At time-and-a-half, add				Day		50%			
0920	At double time, add				"		100%			

01 54 19.60 Monthly Tower Crane Crew

		Crew	Daily Output	Labor-Hours	Unit	Material	Labor	Equipment	Total	Total Incl O&P
0010	**MONTHLY TOWER CRANE CREW**, excludes concrete footing									
0100	Static tower crane, 130' high, 106' jib, 6200 lb. capacity	A-3N	.05	176	Month		8,850	24,200	33,050	40,600

01 54 23 – Temporary Scaffolding and Platforms

01 54 23.60 Pump Staging

			Crew	Daily Output	Labor-Hours	Unit	Material	Labor	Equipment	Total	Total Incl O&P
0010	**PUMP STAGING**, Aluminum	R015423-20									
0200	24' long pole section, buy					Ea.	355			355	390
0300	18' long pole section, buy						275			275	300
0400	12' long pole section, buy						185			185	204
0500	6' long pole section, buy						103			103	113
0600	6' long splice joint section, buy						72.50			72.50	80
0700	Pump jack, buy						148			148	163
0900	Foldable brace, buy						58			58	64
1000	Workbench/back safety rail support, buy						78			78	85.50
1100	Scaffolding planks/workbench, 14" wide x 24' long, buy						715			715	785
1200	Plank end safety rail, buy						291			291	320
1250	Safety net, 22' long, buy						355			355	390
1300	System in place, 50' working height, per use based on 50 uses		2 Carp	84.80	.189	C.S.F.	6.10	8.65		14.75	21
1400	100 uses			84.80	.189		3.06	8.65		11.71	17.55
1500	150 uses		↓	84.80	.189	↓	2.05	8.65		10.70	16.45

01 54 23.70 Scaffolding

			Crew	Daily Output	Labor-Hours	Unit	Material	Labor	Equipment	Total	Total Incl O&P
0010	**SCAFFOLDING**	R015423-10									
0015	Steel tube, regular, no plank, labor only to erect & dismantle										
0090	Building exterior, wall face, 1 to 5 stories, 6'-4" x 5' frames		3 Carp	8	3	C.S.F.		138		138	226
0200	6 to 12 stories		4 Carp	8	4			183		183	300
0301	13 to 20 stories		5 Clab	8	5			183		183	300
0460	Building interior, wall face area, up to 16' high		3 Carp	12	2			91.50		91.50	151
0560	16' to 40' high			10	2.400	↓		110		110	181
0800	Building interior floor area, up to 30' high		↓	150	.160	C.C.F.		7.35		7.35	12.05
0900	Over 30' high		4 Carp	160	.200	"		9.15		9.15	15.05
0906	Complete system for face of walls, no plank, material only rent/mo					C.S.F.	35			35	38.50
0908	Interior spaces, no plank, material only rent/mo					C.C.F.	3.35			3.35	3.68
0910	Steel tubular, heavy duty shoring, buy										
0920	Frames 5' high 2' wide					Ea.	81.50			81.50	90
0925	5' high 4' wide						93			93	102
0930	6' high 2' wide						93.50			93.50	103
0935	6' high 4' wide					↓	109			109	120
0940	Accessories										
0945	Cross braces					Ea.	15.50			15.50	17.05
0950	U-head, 8" x 8"						19.10			19.10	21
0955	J-head, 4" x 8"						13.90			13.90	15.30
0960	Base plate, 8" x 8"						15.50			15.50	17.05
0965	Leveling jack					↓	33.50			33.50	36.50
1000	Steel tubular, regular, buy										
1100	Frames 3' high 5' wide					Ea.	72.50			72.50	80
1150	5' high 5' wide						86.50			86.50	95

01 54 Construction Aids

01 54 23 – Temporary Scaffolding and Platforms

01 54 23.70 Scaffolding	Crew	Daily Output	Labor-Hours	Unit	Material	2014 Bare Costs Labor	Equipment	Total	Total Incl O&P
1200 6'-4" high 5' wide				Ea.	118			118	129
1350 7'-6" high 6' wide					158			158	173
1500 Accessories cross braces					15.50			15.50	17.05
1550 Guardrail post					16.40			16.40	18.05
1600 Guardrail 7' section					6.30			6.30	6.95
1650 Screw jacks & plates					21.50			21.50	24
1700 Sidearm brackets					25.50			25.50	28.50
1750 8" casters					31			31	34
1800 Plank 2" x 10" x 16'-0"					52			52	57.50
1900 Stairway section					276			276	305
1910 Stairway starter bar					32			32	35
1920 Stairway inside handrail					53			53	58
1930 Stairway outside handrail					81.50			81.50	90
1940 Walk-thru frame guardrail					41.50			41.50	46
2000 Steel tubular, regular, rent/mo.									
2100 Frames 3' high 5' wide				Ea.	5			5	5.50
2150 5' high 5' wide					5			5	5.50
2200 6'-4" high 5' wide					5.15			5.15	5.65
2250 7'-6" high 6' wide					7			7	7.70
2500 Accessories, cross braces					1			1	1.10
2550 Guardrail post					1			1	1.10
2600 Guardrail 7' section					1			1	1.10
2650 Screw jacks & plates					2			2	2.20
2700 Sidearm brackets					2			2	2.20
2750 8" casters					8			8	8.80
2800 Outrigger for rolling tower					3			3	3.30
2850 Plank 2" x 10" x 16'-0"					6			6	6.60
2900 Stairway section					35.50			35.50	39
2940 Walk-thru frame guardrail					2.50			2.50	2.75
3000 Steel tubular, heavy duty shoring, rent/mo.									
3250 5' high 2' & 4' wide				Ea.	5			5	5.50
3300 6' high 2' & 4' wide					5			5	5.50
3500 Accessories, cross braces					1			1	1.10
3600 U - head, 8" x 8"					1			1	1.10
3650 J - head, 4" x 8"					1			1	1.10
3700 Base plate, 8" x 8"					1			1	1.10
3750 Leveling jack					2			2	2.20
5700 Planks, 2" x 10" x 16'-0", labor only to erect & remove to 50' H	3 Carp	72	.333			15.30		15.30	25
5800 Over 50' high	4 Carp	80	.400			18.35		18.35	30

01 54 23.75 Scaffolding Specialties

	Crew	Daily Output	Labor-Hours	Unit	Material	Labor	Equipment	Total	Total Incl O&P
0010 **SCAFFOLDING SPECIALTIES**									
1200 Sidewalk bridge, heavy duty steel posts & beams, including									
1210 parapet protection & waterproofing (material cost is rent/month)									
1220 8' to 10' wide, 2 posts	3 Carp	15	1.600	L.F.	37	73.50		110.50	162
1230 3 posts	"	10	2.400	"	56.50	110		166.50	243
1500 Sidewalk bridge using tubular steel scaffold frames including									
1510 planking (material cost is rent/month)	3 Carp	45	.533	L.F.	5.60	24.50		30.10	46
1600 For 2 uses per month, deduct from all above					50%				
1700 For 1 use every 2 months, add to all above					100%				
1900 Catwalks, 20" wide, no guardrails, 7' span, buy				Ea.	133			133	146
2000 10' span, buy					186			186	205
3720 Putlog, standard, 8' span, with hangers, buy					66.50			66.50	73

01 54 23 – Temporary Scaffolding and Platforms

01 54 23.75 Scaffolding Specialties

		Crew	Daily Output	Labor-Hours	Unit	Material	2014 Bare Costs Labor	2014 Bare Costs Equipment	Total	Total Incl O&P
3730	Rent per month				Ea.	10			10	11
3750	12' span, buy					99			99	109
3755	Rent per month					15			15	16.50
3760	Trussed type, 16' span, buy					229			229	252
3770	Rent per month					20			20	22
3790	22' span, buy					274			274	300
3795	Rent per month					30			30	33
4000	7 step					760			760	835
4100	Rolling towers, buy, 5' wide, 7' long, 10' high					1,150			1,150	1,275
4200	For 5' high added sections, to buy, add					204			204	224
4300	Complete incl. wheels, railings, outriggers,									
4350	21' high, to buy				Ea.	1,975			1,975	2,175
4400	Rent/month = 5% of purchase cost				"	170			170	187
5000	Motorized work platform, mast climber									
5050	Base unit, 50' W, less than 100' tall, rent/mo				Ea.	3,100			3,100	3,400
5100	Less than 200' tall, rent/mo					3,900			3,900	4,300
5150	Less than 300' tall, rent/mo					4,575			4,575	5,050
5200	Less than 400' tall, rent/mo					5,200			5,200	5,700
5250	Set up and demob, per unit, less than 100' tall	B-68F	16.60	1.446	C.S.F.		69.50	19.55	89.05	135
5300	Less than 200' tall		25	.960			46	13	59	89.50
5350	Less than 300' tall		30	.800			38.50	10.80	49.30	74.50
5400	Less than 400' tall		33	.727			35	9.85	44.85	68
5500	Mobilization (price includes freight in and out) per unit				Ea.				1,100	1,225

01 54 23.80 Staging Aids

		Crew	Daily Output	Labor-Hours	Unit	Material	2014 Bare Costs Labor	2014 Bare Costs Equipment	Total	Total Incl O&P
0010	**STAGING AIDS** and fall protection equipment									
0100	Sidewall staging bracket, tubular, buy				Ea.	51			51	56
0110	Cost each per day, based on 250 days use				Day	.20			.20	.22
0200	Guard post, buy				Ea.	48			48	53
0210	Cost each per day, based on 250 days use				Day	.19			.19	.21
0300	End guard chains, buy per pair				Pair	36			36	39.50
0310	Cost per set per day, based on 250 days use				Day	.20			.20	.22
1010	Cost each per day, based on 250 days use				"	.04			.04	.04
1100	Wood bracket, buy				Ea.	16.80			16.80	18.50
1110	Cost each per day, based on 250 days use				Day	.07			.07	.07
2010	Cost per pair per day, based on 250 days use				"	.47			.47	.52
2100	Steel siderail jack, buy per pair				Pair	97.50			97.50	107
2110	Cost per pair per day, based on 250 days use				Day	.39			.39	.43
3010	Cost each per day, based on 250 days use				"	.21			.21	.23
3100	Aluminum scaffolding plank, 20" wide x 24' long, buy				Ea.	820			820	900
3110	Cost each per day, based on 250 days use				Day	3.28			3.28	3.60
4000	Nylon full body harness, lanyard and rope grab				Ea.	176			176	193
4010	Cost each per day, based on 250 days use				Day	.70			.70	.77
4100	Rope for safety line, 5/8" x 100' nylon, buy				Ea.	56			56	61.50
4110	Cost each per day, based on 250 days use				Day	.22			.22	.25
4200	Permanent U-Bolt roof anchor, buy				Ea.	30			30	33
4300	Temporary (one use) roof ridge anchor, buy				"	32			32	35.50
5000	Installation (setup and removal) of staging aids									
5010	Sidewall staging bracket	2 Carp	64	.250	Ea.		11.45		11.45	18.85
5020	Guard post with 2 wood rails	"	64	.250			11.45		11.45	18.85
5030	End guard chains, set	1 Carp	64	.125			5.75		5.75	9.40
5100	Roof shingling bracket		96	.083			3.82		3.82	6.30
5200	Ladder jack		64	.125			5.75		5.75	9.40

01 54 23 – Temporary Scaffolding and Platforms

01 54 23.80 Staging Aids	Crew	Daily Output	Labor-Hours	Unit	Material	2014 Bare Costs Labor	Equipment	Total	Total Incl O&P
5300 Wood plank, 2" x 10" x 16'	2 Carp	80	.200	Ea.		9.15		9.15	15.05
5310 Aluminum scaffold plank, 20" x 24'	"	40	.400			18.35		18.35	30
5410 Safety rope	1 Carp	40	.200			9.15		9.15	15.05
5420 Permanent U-Bolt roof anchor (install only)	2 Carp	40	.400			18.35		18.35	30
5430 Temporary roof ridge anchor (install only)	1 Carp	64	.125	↓		5.75		5.75	9.40

01 54 26 – Temporary Swing Staging

01 54 26.50 Swing Staging

	Crew	Daily Output	Labor-Hours	Unit	Material	2014 Bare Costs Labor	Equipment	Total	Total Incl O&P
0010 **SWING STAGING**, 500 lb. cap., 2' wide to 24' long, hand operated									
0020 steel cable type, with 60' cables, buy				Ea.	4,900			4,900	5,375
0030 Rent per month				"	490			490	540
0600 Lightweight (not for masons) 24' long for 150' height,									
0610 manual type, buy				Ea.	10,200			10,200	11,200
0620 Rent per month					1,025			1,025	1,125
0700 Powered, electric or air, to 150' high, buy					25,600			25,600	28,200
0710 Rent per month					1,800			1,800	1,975
0780 To 300' high, buy					26,000			26,000	28,600
0800 Rent per month					1,825			1,825	2,000
1000 Bosun's chair or work basket 3' x 3.5', to 300' high, electric, buy					10,400			10,400	11,400
1010 Rent per month				↓	730			730	800
2200 Move swing staging (setup and remove)	E-4	2	16	Move		825	71	896	1,600

01 54 36 – Equipment Mobilization

01 54 36.50 Mobilization

	Crew	Daily Output	Labor-Hours	Unit	Material	2014 Bare Costs Labor	Equipment	Total	Total Incl O&P
0010 **MOBILIZATION** (Use line item again for demobilization) R015433-10									
0015 Up to 25 mi. haul dist. (50 mi. RT for mob/demob crew)									
0020 Dozer, loader, backhoe, excav., grader, paver, roller, 70 to 150 H.P.	B-34N	4	2	Ea.		75	142	217	279
0100 Above 150 HP	B-34K	3	2.667			100	320	420	520
0300 Scraper, towed type (incl. tractor), 6 C.Y. capacity		3	2.667			100	320	420	520
0400 10 C.Y.		2.50	3.200			120	385	505	620
0600 Self-propelled scraper, 15 C.Y.		2.50	3.200			120	385	505	620
0700 24 C.Y.		2	4			150	480	630	775
0900 Shovel or dragline, 3/4 C.Y.		3.60	2.222			83.50	267	350.50	430
1000 1-1/2 C.Y.		3	2.667			100	320	420	520
1100 Small equipment, placed in rear of, or towed by pickup truck	A-3A	8	1			36.50	21	57.50	82.50
1150 Equip up to 70 HP, on flatbed trailer behind pickup truck	A-3D	4	2			73	70.50	143.50	197
2000 Crane, truck-mounted, up to 75 ton, (driver only, one-way)	1 Eqhv	7.20	1.111			56		56	88.50
2100 Crane, truck-mounted, over 75 ton	A-3E	2.50	6.400			281	67.50	348.50	525
2200 Crawler-mounted, up to 75 ton	A-3F	2	8			350	500	850	1,125
2300 Over 75 ton	A-3G	1.50	10.667	↓		470	755	1,225	1,575
2500 For each additional 5 miles haul distance, add						10%	10%		
3000 For large pieces of equipment, allow for assembly/knockdown									
3100 For mob/demob of micro-tunneling equip, see Section 33 05 23.19									
3200 For mob/demob of pile driving equip, see Section 31 62 19.10									

01 54 39 – Construction Equipment

01 54 39.70 Small Tools

	Crew	Daily Output	Labor-Hours	Unit	Material	2014 Bare Costs Labor	Equipment	Total	Total Incl O&P
0010 **SMALL TOOLS** R013113-50									
0020 As % of contractor's bare labor cost for project, minimum				Total		.50%			
0100 Maximum				"		2%			

01 55 Vehicular Access and Parking

01 55 23 – Temporary Roads

01 55 23.50 Roads and Sidewalks	Crew	Daily Output	Labor-Hours	Unit	Material	2014 Bare Costs Labor	Equipment	Total	Total Incl O&P
0010 **ROADS AND SIDEWALKS** Temporary									
0050 Roads, gravel fill, no surfacing, 4" gravel depth	B-14	715	.067	S.Y.	3.98	2.60	.51	7.09	9.20
0100 8" gravel depth	"	615	.078	"	7.95	3.02	.59	11.56	14.35

01 56 Temporary Barriers and Enclosures

01 56 13 – Temporary Air Barriers

01 56 13.60 Tarpaulins

01 56 13.60 Tarpaulins	Crew	Daily Output	Labor-Hours	Unit	Material	2014 Bare Costs Labor	Equipment	Total	Total Incl O&P
0010 **TARPAULINS**									
0020 Cotton duck, 10 oz. to 13.13 oz. per S.Y., 6'x8'				S.F.	.75			.75	.83
0050 30'x30'					.43			.43	.47
0100 Polyvinyl coated nylon, 14 oz. to 18 oz., minimum					1.30			1.30	1.43
0150 Maximum					1.19			1.19	1.31
0200 Reinforced polyethylene 3 mils thick, white					.03			.03	.03
0300 4 mils thick, white, clear or black					.09			.09	.10
0400 5.5 mils thick, clear					.17			.17	.19
0500 White, fire retardant					.41			.41	.45
0600 12 mils, oil resistant, fire retardant					.27			.27	.30
0700 8.5 mils, black					.57			.57	.63
0720 Steel reinforced polyethylene, 20 mils thick					.46			.46	.51
0730 Polyester reinforced w/integral fastening system 11 mils thick					.24			.24	.26
0740 Mylar polyester, non-reinforced, 7 mils thick					1.17			1.17	1.29

01 56 13.90 Winter Protection

01 56 13.90 Winter Protection	Crew	Daily Output	Labor-Hours	Unit	Material	2014 Bare Costs Labor	Equipment	Total	Total Incl O&P
0010 **WINTER PROTECTION**									
0100 Framing to close openings	2 Clab	500	.032	S.F.	.41	1.17		1.58	2.38
0200 Tarpaulins hung over scaffolding, 8 uses, not incl. scaffolding		1500	.011		.25	.39		.64	.92
0250 Tarpaulin polyester reinf. w/integral fastening system 11 mils thick		1600	.010		.24	.37		.61	.86
0300 Prefab fiberglass panels, steel frame, 8 uses		1200	.013		2.20	.49		2.69	3.22

01 56 16 – Temporary Dust Barriers

01 56 16.10 Dust Barriers, Temporary

01 56 16.10 Dust Barriers, Temporary	Crew	Daily Output	Labor-Hours	Unit	Material	2014 Bare Costs Labor	Equipment	Total	Total Incl O&P
0010 **DUST BARRIERS, TEMPORARY**									
0020 Spring loaded telescoping pole & head, to 12', erect and dismantle	1 Clab	240	.033	Ea.		1.22		1.22	2.01
0025 Cost per day (based upon 250 days)				Day	.24			.24	.26
0030 To 21', erect and dismantle	1 Clab	240	.033	Ea.		1.22		1.22	2.01
0035 Cost per day (based upon 250 days)				Day	.38			.38	.42
0040 Accessories, caution tape reel, erect and dismantle	1 Clab	480	.017	Ea.		.61		.61	1
0045 Cost per day (based upon 250 days)				Day	.36			.36	.40
0060 Foam rail and connector, erect and dismantle	1 Clab	240	.033	Ea.		1.22		1.22	2.01
0065 Cost per day (based upon 250 days)				Day	.10			.10	.11
0070 Caution tape	1 Clab	384	.021	C.L.F.	2.70	.76		3.46	4.22
0080 Zipper, standard duty		60	.133	Ea.	15.95	4.89		20.84	25.50
0090 Heavy duty		48	.167	"	18.90	6.10		25	31
0100 Polyethylene sheet, 4 mil		37	.216	Sq.	2.91	7.90		10.81	16.20
0110 6 mil		37	.216	"	3.98	7.90		11.88	17.40
1000 Dust partition, 6 mil polyethylene, 1" x 3" frame	2 Carp	2000	.008	S.F.	.29	.37		.66	.92
1080 2" x 4" frame	"	2000	.008	"	.32	.37		.69	.95

19

01 56 Temporary Barriers and Enclosures

01 56 23 – Temporary Barricades

01 56 23.10 Barricades	Crew	Daily Output	Labor-Hours	Unit	Material	2014 Bare Costs Labor	Equipment	Total	Total Incl O&P
0010 **BARRICADES**									
0020 5' high, 3 rail @ 2" x 8", fixed	2 Carp	20	.800	L.F.	5.75	36.50		42.25	67
0150 Movable	"	30	.533	"	4.77	24.50		29.27	45.50
0300 Stock units, 6' high, 8' wide, plain, buy				Ea.	390			390	430
0350 With reflective tape, buy				"	405			405	445
0400 Break-a-way 3" PVC pipe barricade									
0410 with 3 ea. 1' x 4' reflectorized panels, buy				Ea.	128			128	141
0500 Plywood with steel legs, 24" wide					59			59	65
0600 Warning signal flag tree, 11' high, 2 flags, buy					238			238	262
0800 Traffic cones, PVC, 18" high					11			11	12.10
0850 28" high					18.60			18.60	20.50
0900 Barrels, 55 gal., with flasher	1 Clab	96	.083		91	3.05		94.05	105
1000 Guardrail, wooden, 3' high, 1" x 6", on 2" x 4" posts	2 Carp	200	.080	L.F.	1.29	3.67		4.96	7.45
1100 2" x 6", on 4" x 4" posts	"	165	.097		2.35	4.45		6.80	9.90
1200 Portable metal with base pads, buy					15.55			15.55	17.10
1250 Typical installation, assume 10 reuses	2 Carp	600	.027		2.55	1.22		3.77	4.82
1300 Barricade tape, polyethylene, 7 mil, 3" wide x 500' long roll				Ea.	25			25	27.50
3000 Detour signs, set up and remove									
3010 Reflective aluminum, MUTCD, 24" x 24", post mounted	1 Clab	20	.400	Ea.	2.35	14.65		17	26.50

01 56 26 – Temporary Fencing

01 56 26.50 Temporary Fencing	Crew	Daily Output	Labor-Hours	Unit	Material	2014 Bare Costs Labor	Equipment	Total	Total Incl O&P
0010 **TEMPORARY FENCING**									
0020 Chain link, 11 ga., 4' high	2 Clab	400	.040	L.F.	2.95	1.47		4.42	5.65
0100 6' high		300	.053		2.95	1.95		4.90	6.45
0200 Rented chain link, 6' high, to 1000' (up to 12 mo.)		400	.040		4.39	1.47		5.86	7.25
0250 Over 1000' (up to 12 mo.)		300	.053		4.29	1.95		6.24	7.95
0350 Plywood, painted, 2" x 4" frame, 4' high	A-4	135	.178		6.25	7.80		14.05	19.55
0400 4" x 4" frame, 8' high	"	110	.218		11.45	9.55		21	28
0500 Wire mesh on 4" x 4" posts, 4' high	2 Carp	100	.160		9.75	7.35		17.10	23
0550 8' high	"	80	.200		14.70	9.15		23.85	31

01 56 29 – Temporary Protective Walkways

01 56 29.50 Protection	Crew	Daily Output	Labor-Hours	Unit	Material	2014 Bare Costs Labor	Equipment	Total	Total Incl O&P
0010 **PROTECTION**									
0020 Stair tread, 2" x 12" planks, 1 use	1 Carp	75	.107	Tread	4.57	4.89		9.46	13.10
0100 Exterior plywood, 1/2" thick, 1 use		65	.123		1.79	5.65		7.44	11.20
0200 3/4" thick, 1 use		60	.133		2.64	6.10		8.74	12.95
2200 Sidewalks, 2" x 12" planks, 2 uses		350	.023	S.F.	.76	1.05		1.81	2.56
2300 Exterior plywood, 2 uses, 1/2" thick		750	.011		.30	.49		.79	1.13
2400 5/8" thick		650	.012		.37	.56		.93	1.34
2500 3/4" thick		600	.013		.44	.61		1.05	1.48

01 56 32 – Temporary Security

01 56 32.50 Watchman	Crew	Daily Output	Labor-Hours	Unit	Material	2014 Bare Costs Labor	Equipment	Total	Total Incl O&P
0010 **WATCHMAN**									
0020 Service, monthly basis, uniformed person, minimum				Hr.				25	27.50
0100 Maximum								45.50	50
0200 Person and command dog, minimum								31	34
0300 Maximum								54.50	60
0500 Sentry dog, leased, with job patrol (yard dog), 1 dog				Week				290	320
0600 2 dogs				"				390	430
0800 Purchase, trained sentry dog, minimum				Ea.				1,375	1,500

01 56 Temporary Barriers and Enclosures

01 56 32 – Temporary Security

01 56 32.50 Watchman	Crew	Daily Output	Labor-Hours	Unit	Material	2014 Bare Costs Labor	Equipment	Total	Total Incl O&P
0900 Maximum				Ea.				2,725	3,000

01 58 Project Identification

01 58 13 – Temporary Project Signage

01 58 13.50 Signs

	Crew	Daily Output	Labor-Hours	Unit	Material	2014 Bare Costs Labor	Equipment	Total	Total Incl O&P
0010 **SIGNS**									
0020 High intensity reflectorized, no posts, buy				S.F.	31.50			31.50	34.50

01 71 Examination and Preparation

01 71 23 – Field Engineering

01 71 23.13 Construction Layout

	Crew	Daily Output	Labor-Hours	Unit	Material	2014 Bare Costs Labor	Equipment	Total	Total Incl O&P
0010 **CONSTRUCTION LAYOUT**									
1100 Crew for layout of building, trenching or pipe laying, 2 person crew	A-6	1	16	Day		730	71.50	801.50	1,275
1200 3 person crew	A-7	1	24	↓		1,200	71.50	1,271.50	2,025
1400 Crew for roadway layout, 4 person crew	A-8	1	32	↓		1,575	71.50	1,646.50	2,600

01 74 Cleaning and Waste Management

01 74 13 – Progress Cleaning

01 74 13.20 Cleaning Up

	Crew	Daily Output	Labor-Hours	Unit	Material	2014 Bare Costs Labor	Equipment	Total	Total Incl O&P
0010 **CLEANING UP**									
0020 After job completion, allow, minimum				Job				.30%	.30%
0040 Maximum				"				1%	1%
0052 Cleanup of floor area, continuous, per day, during const.	A-5	16	1.125	M.S.F.	.81	41	4.22	46.03	73
0100 Final by GC at end of job	"	11.50	1.565	"	.86	57.50	5.85	64.21	101

01 76 Protecting Installed Construction

01 76 13 – Temporary Protection of Installed Construction

01 76 13.20 Temporary Protection

	Crew	Daily Output	Labor-Hours	Unit	Material	2014 Bare Costs Labor	Equipment	Total	Total Incl O&P
0010 **TEMPORARY PROTECTION**									
0020 Flooring, 1/8" tempered hardboard, taped seams	2 Carp	1500	.011	S.F.	.39	.49		.88	1.23
0030 Peel away carpet protection	1 Clab	3200	.003	"	.11	.09		.20	.27

01 91 Commissioning

01 91 13 – General Commissioning Requirements

01 91 13.50 Building Commissioning

	Crew	Daily Output	Labor-Hours	Unit	Material	2014 Bare Costs Labor	Equipment	Total	Total Incl O&P
0010 **BUILDING COMMISSIONING**									
0100 Basic building commissioning, minimum				%				.25%	.25%
0150 Maximum								.50%	.50%
0200 Enhanced building commissioning, minimum								.50%	.50%
0250 Maximum				↓				1%	1%

01 93 09 – Facility Equipment

01 93 09.50 Moving Equipment	Crew	Daily Output	Labor-Hours	Unit	Material	2014 Bare Costs Labor	Equipment	Total	Total Incl O&P
0010 **MOVING EQUIPMENT**, Remove and reset, 100' distance,									
0020 No obstructions, no assembly or leveling unless noted									
0100 Annealing furnace, 24' overall	B-67	4	4	Ea.		190	78.50	268.50	385
0200 Annealing oven, small		14	1.143			54.50	22.50	77	111
0240 Very large		1	16			760	315	1,075	1,550
0400 Band saw, small		12	1.333			63.50	26	89.50	129
0440 Large		8	2			95	39.50	134.50	193
0500 Blue print copy machine		7	2.286			109	45	154	222
0600 Bonding mill, 6"		7	2.286			109	45	154	222
0620 12"		6	2.667			127	52.50	179.50	258
0640 18"		4	4			190	78.50	268.50	385
0660 24"		2	8			380	157	537	775
0700 Boring machine (jig)	B-68	7	3.429			164	45	209	310
0800 Bridgeport mill, standard	B-67	14	1.143			54.50	22.50	77	111
1000 Calibrator, 6 unit	"	14	1.143			54.50	22.50	77	111
1100 Comparitor, bench top	2 Clab	14	1.143			42		42	69
1140 Floor mounted	B-67	7	2.286			109	45	154	222
1200 Computer, desk top	2 Clab	25	.640			23.50		23.50	38.50
1300 Copy machine	"	25	.640			23.50		23.50	38.50
1500 Deflasher	B-67	14	1.143			54.50	22.50	77	111
1600 Degreaser, small		14	1.143			54.50	22.50	77	111
1640 Large 24' overall		1	16			760	315	1,075	1,550
1700 Desk with chair	2 Clab	25	.640			23.50		23.50	38.50
1800 Dial press	B-67	7	2.286			109	45	154	222
1900 Drafting table	2 Clab	14	1.143			42		42	69
2000 Drill press, bench top	"	14	1.143			42		42	69
2040 Floor mounted	B-67	14	1.143			54.50	22.50	77	111
2080 Industrial radial	"	7	2.286			109	45	154	222
2100 Dust collector, portable	2 Clab	25	.640			23.50		23.50	38.50
2140 Stationary, small	B-67	7	2.286			109	45	154	222
2180 Stationary, large	"	2	8			380	157	537	775
2300 Electric discharge machine	B-68	7	3.429			164	45	209	310
2400 Environmental chamber walls, including assembly	4 Clab	18	1.778	L.F.		65		65	107
2600 File cabinet	2 Clab	25	.640	Ea.		23.50		23.50	38.50
2800 Grinder/sander, pedestal mount	B-67	14	1.143			54.50	22.50	77	111
3000 Hack saw, power	2 Clab	24	.667			24.50		24.50	40
3100 Hydraulic press	B-67	14	1.143			54.50	22.50	77	111
3500 Laminar flow tables	"	14	1.143			54.50	22.50	77	111
3600 Lathe, bench	2 Clab	14	1.143			42		42	69
3640 6"	B-67	14	1.143			54.50	22.50	77	111
3680 10"		13	1.231			58.50	24	82.50	119
3720 12"		12	1.333			63.50	26	89.50	129
4000 Milling machine		8	2			95	39.50	134.50	193
4100 Molding press, 25 ton		5	3.200			152	63	215	310
4140 60 ton		4	4			190	78.50	268.50	385
4180 100 ton		2	8			380	157	537	775
4220 150 ton		1.50	10.667			510	209	719	1,025
4260 200 ton		1	16			760	315	1,075	1,550
4300 300 ton		.75	21.333			1,025	420	1,445	2,050
4700 Oil pot stand		14	1.143			54.50	22.50	77	111
5000 Press, 10 ton		14	1.143			54.50	22.50	77	111
5040 15 ton		12	1.333			63.50	26	89.50	129
5080 20 ton		10	1.600			76	31.50	107.50	155

01 93 09 – Facility Equipment

01 93 09.50 Moving Equipment	Crew	Daily Output	Labor-Hours	Unit	Material	2014 Bare Costs Labor	2014 Bare Costs Equipment	Total	Total Incl O&P
5120	30 ton	B-67	8	2	Ea.		95	39.50	134.50	193
5160	45 ton		6	2.667			127	52.50	179.50	258
5200	60 ton		4	4			190	78.50	268.50	385
5240	75 ton		2.50	6.400			305	126	431	620
5280	100 ton		2	8			380	157	537	775
5500	Raised floor, including assembly	2 Carp	250	.064	S.F.		2.93		2.93	4.82
5600	Rolling mill, 6"	B-67	7	2.286	Ea.		109	45	154	222
5640	9"		6	2.667			127	52.50	179.50	258
5680	12"		4	4			190	78.50	268.50	385
5720	13"		3.50	4.571			218	90	308	445
5760	18"		2	8			380	157	537	775
5800	25"		1	16			760	315	1,075	1,550
6000	Sander, floor stand		14	1.143			54.50	22.50	77	111
6100	Screw machine		7	2.286			109	45	154	222
6200	Shaper, 16"		14	1.143			54.50	22.50	77	111
6300	Shear, power assist		4	4			190	78.50	268.50	385
6400	Slitter, 6"		14	1.143			54.50	22.50	77	111
6440	8"		13	1.231			58.50	24	82.50	119
6480	10"		12	1.333			63.50	26	89.50	129
6520	12"		11	1.455			69	28.50	97.50	141
6560	16"		10	1.600			76	31.50	107.50	155
6600	20"		8	2			95	39.50	134.50	193
6640	24"		6	2.667			127	52.50	179.50	258
6800	Snag and tap machine		7	2.286			109	45	154	222
6900	Solder machine (auto)		7	2.286			109	45	154	222
7000	Storage cabinet metal, small	2 Clab	36	.444			16.30		16.30	27
7040	Large		25	.640			23.50		23.50	38.50
7100	Storage rack open, small		14	1.143			42		42	69
7140	Large		7	2.286			84		84	138
7200	Surface bench, small	B-67	14	1.143			54.50	22.50	77	111
7240	Large	"	5	3.200			152	63	215	310
7300	Surface grinder, large wet	B-68	5	4.800			229	63	292	430
7500	Time check machine	2 Clab	14	1.143			42		42	69
8000	Welder, 30 kVA (bench)		14	1.143			42		42	69
8100	Work bench with chair		25	.640			23.50		23.50	38.50
8110	For haul up to 200 feet, add				%		25%			

Division Notes

	CREW	DAILY OUTPUT	LABOR-HOURS	UNIT	BARE COSTS				TOTAL INCL O&P
					MAT.	LABOR	EQUIP.	TOTAL	

Estimating Tips

02 30 00 Subsurface Investigation

In preparing estimates on structures involving earthwork or foundations, all information concerning soil characteristics should be obtained. Look particularly for hazardous waste, evidence of prior dumping of debris, and previous stream beds.

02 40 00 Demolition and Structure Moving

The costs shown for selective demolition do not include rubbish handling or disposal. These items should be estimated separately using RSMeans data or other sources.

- Historic preservation often requires that the contractor remove materials from the existing structure, rehab them, and replace them. The estimator must be aware of any related measures and precautions that must be taken when doing selective demolition and cutting and patching. Requirements may include special handling and storage, as well as security.

- In addition to Subdivision 02 41 00, you can find selective demolition items in each division. Example: Roofing demolition is in Division 7.

02 40 00 Building Deconstruction

This section provides costs for the careful dismantling and recycling of most of low-rise building materials.

02 50 00 Containment of Hazardous Waste

This section addresses on-site hazardous waste disposal costs.

02 80 00 Hazardous Material Disposal/ Remediation

This subdivision includes information on hazardous waste handling, asbestos remediation, lead remediation, and mold remediation. See reference R028213-20 and R028319-60 for further guidance in using these unit price lines.

02 90 00 Monitoring Chemical Sampling, Testing Analysis

This section provides costs for on-site sampling and testing hazardous waste.

Reference Numbers

Reference numbers are shown in shaded boxes at the beginning of some major classifications. These numbers refer to related items in the Reference Section. The reference information may be an estimating procedure, an alternate pricing method, or technical information.

Note: Not all subdivisions listed here necessarily appear in this publication.

Division 2 - Existing Conditions

02 21 Surveys

02 21 13 – Site Surveys

02 21 13.09 Topographical Surveys	Crew	Daily Output	Labor-Hours	Unit	Material	2014 Bare Costs Labor	2014 Bare Costs Equipment	Total	Total Incl O&P
0010 **TOPOGRAPHICAL SURVEYS**									
0020 Topographical surveying, conventional, minimum	A-7	3.30	7.273	Acre	19.20	365	21.50	405.70	635
0100 Maximum	A-8	.60	53.333	"	58.50	2,600	119	2,777.50	4,400

02 21 13.13 Boundary and Survey Markers

	Crew	Daily Output	Labor-Hours	Unit	Material	Labor	Equipment	Total	Total Incl O&P
0010 **BOUNDARY AND SURVEY MARKERS**									
0300 Lot location and lines, large quantities, minimum	A-7	2	12	Acre	34	605	35.50	674.50	1,050
0320 Average	"	1.25	19.200		54	970	57	1,081	1,675
0400 Small quantities, maximum	A-8	1	32		71.50	1,575	71.50	1,718	2,675

02 32 Geotechnical Investigations

02 32 13 – Subsurface Drilling and Sampling

02 32 13.10 Boring and Exploratory Drilling

	Crew	Daily Output	Labor-Hours	Unit	Material	Labor	Equipment	Total	Total Incl O&P
0010 **BORING AND EXPLORATORY DRILLING**									
0020 Borings, initial field stake out & determination of elevations	A-6	1	16	Day		730	71.50	801.50	1,275
0100 Drawings showing boring details				Total		335		335	425
0200 Report and recommendations from P.E.						775		775	970
0300 Mobilization and demobilization	B-55	4	6			220	280	500	670
0350 For over 100 miles, per added mile		450	.053	Mile		1.95	2.49	4.44	5.95
0600 Auger holes in earth, no samples, 2-1/2" diameter		78.60	.305	L.F.		11.20	14.25	25.45	34
0650 4" diameter		67.50	.356			13	16.60	29.60	40
0800 Cased borings in earth, with samples, 2-1/2" diameter		55.50	.432		22	15.85	20	57.85	72
0850 4" diameter		32.60	.736		33.50	27	34.50	95	119
1000 Drilling in rock, "BX" core, no sampling	B-56	34.90	.458			19.20	46	65.20	81.50
1050 With casing & sampling		31.70	.505		22	21	50.50	93.50	114
1200 "NX" core, no sampling		25.92	.617			26	62	88	110
1250 With casing and sampling		25	.640		26	27	64.50	117.50	143
1400 Borings, earth, drill rig and crew with truck mounted auger	B-55	1	24	Day		880	1,125	2,005	2,675
1450 Rock using crawler type drill	B-56	1	16	"		670	1,600	2,270	2,850
1500 For inner city borings add, minimum								10%	10%
1510 Maximum								20%	20%

02 41 Demolition

02 41 13 – Selective Site Demolition

02 41 13.15 Hydrodemolition

	Crew	Daily Output	Labor-Hours	Unit	Material	Labor	Equipment	Total	Total Incl O&P
0010 **HYDRODEMOLITION**									
0015 Hydrodemolition, concrete pavement, 4000 PSI, 2" depth	B-5	500	.112	S.F.		4.53	2.85	7.38	10.50
0120 4" depth		450	.124			5.05	3.17	8.22	11.65
0130 6" depth		400	.140			5.65	3.56	9.21	13.10
0410 6000 PSI, 2" depth		410	.137			5.50	3.47	8.97	12.75
0420 4" depth		350	.160			6.45	4.07	10.52	15
0430 6" depth		300	.187			7.55	4.75	12.30	17.45
0510 8000 PSI, 2" depth		330	.170			6.85	4.32	11.17	15.90
0520 4" depth		280	.200			8.10	5.10	13.20	18.75
0530 6" depth		240	.233			9.45	5.95	15.40	22

02 41 13.17 Demolish, Remove Pavement and Curb

	Crew	Daily Output	Labor-Hours	Unit	Material	Labor	Equipment	Total	Total Incl O&P
0010 **DEMOLISH, REMOVE PAVEMENT AND CURB** R024119-10									
5010 Pavement removal, bituminous roads, up to 3" thick	B-38	690	.058	S.Y.		2.41	1.86	4.27	5.95
5050 4" to 6" thick		420	.095			3.96	3.05	7.01	9.75
5100 Bituminous driveways		640	.063			2.60	2	4.60	6.40

02 41 Demolition

02 41 13 – Selective Site Demolition

02 41 13.17 Demolish, Remove Pavement and Curb

		Crew	Daily Output	Labor-Hours	Unit	Material	2014 Bare Costs Labor	2014 Bare Costs Equipment	Total	Total Incl O&P
5200	Concrete to 6" thick, hydraulic hammer, mesh reinforced	B-38	255	.157	S.Y.		6.50	5	11.50	16.05
5300	Rod reinforced		200	.200	↓		8.30	6.40	14.70	20.50
5400	Concrete, 7" to 24" thick, plain		33	1.212	C.Y.		50.50	39	89.50	124
5500	Reinforced		24	1.667	"		69.50	53.50	123	171
5590	Minimum labor/equipment charge	↓	6	6.667	Job		277	213	490	685
5600	With hand held air equipment, bituminous, to 6" thick	B-39	1900	.025	S.F.		.98	.12	1.10	1.74
5700	Concrete to 6" thick, no reinforcing		1600	.030			1.16	.15	1.31	2.05
5800	Mesh reinforced		1400	.034			1.33	.17	1.50	2.35
5900	Rod reinforced	↓	765	.063	↓		2.43	.31	2.74	4.30
5990	Minimum labor/equipment charge	B-38	6	6.667	Job		277	213	490	685
6000	Curbs, concrete, plain	B-6	360	.067	L.F.		2.67	1.01	3.68	5.45
6100	Reinforced		275	.087			3.50	1.33	4.83	7.10
6200	Granite		360	.067			2.67	1.01	3.68	5.45
6300	Bituminous		528	.045	↓		1.82	.69	2.51	3.71
6390	Minimum labor/equipment charge	↓	6	4	Job		160	61	221	325

02 41 13.33 Minor Site Demolition

		Crew	Daily Output	Labor-Hours	Unit	Material	2014 Bare Costs Labor	2014 Bare Costs Equipment	Total	Total Incl O&P
0010	**MINOR SITE DEMOLITION** R024119-10									
0015	No hauling, abandon catch basin or manhole	B-6	7	3.429	Ea.		138	52	190	281
0020	Remove existing catch basin or manhole, masonry		4	6			241	91.50	332.50	490
0030	Catch basin or manhole frames and covers, stored		13	1.846			74	28	102	151
0040	Remove and reset	↓	7	3.429			138	52	190	281
0100	Roadside delineators, remove only	B-80	175	.183			7.25	4.33	11.58	16.55
0110	Remove and reset	"	100	.320	↓		12.70	7.60	20.30	29
0400	Minimum labor/equipment charge	B-6	4	6	Job		241	91.50	332.50	490
0800	Guiderail, corrugated steel, remove only	B-80A	100	.240	L.F.		8.80	3.33	12.13	18.10
0850	Remove and reset	"	40	.600	"		22	8.35	30.35	45
0860	Guide posts, remove only	B-80B	120	.267	Ea.		10.45	2.07	12.52	19.30
0870	Remove and reset	B-55	50	.480	"		17.55	22.50	40.05	53.50
0890	Minimum labor/equipment charge	2 Clab	4	4	Job		147		147	241
0900	Hydrants, fire, remove only	B-21A	5	8	Ea.		365	96	461	690
0950	Remove and reset	"	2	20	"		915	241	1,156	1,725
0990	Minimum labor/equipment charge	2 Plum	2	8	Job		460		460	720
1000	Masonry walls, block, solid	B-5	1800	.031	C.F.		1.26	.79	2.05	2.91
1200	Brick, solid		900	.062			2.52	1.58	4.10	5.80
1400	Stone, with mortar		900	.062			2.52	1.58	4.10	5.80
1500	Dry set	↓	1500	.037	↓		1.51	.95	2.46	3.49
1600	Median barrier, precast concrete, remove and store	B-3	430	.112	L.F.		4.39	6	10.39	13.75
1610	Remove and reset	"	390	.123	"		4.84	6.60	11.44	15.10
1650	Minimum labor/equipment charge	A-1	4	2	Job		73.50	21	94.50	143
2900	Pipe removal, sewer/water, no excavation, 12" diameter	B-6	175	.137	L.F.		5.50	2.09	7.59	11.20
2930	15"-18" diameter	B-12Z	150	.160			6.60	10.90	17.50	22.50
2960	21"-24" diameter		120	.200			8.25	13.65	21.90	28.50
3000	27"-36" diameter	↓	90	.267			11	18.20	29.20	38
3200	Steel, welded connections, 4" diameter	B-6	160	.150			6	2.28	8.28	12.25
3300	10" diameter		80	.300	↓		12.05	4.57	16.62	24.50
3390	Minimum labor/equipment charge	↓	3	8	Job		320	122	442	655
3500	Railroad track removal, ties and track	B-13	330	.170	L.F.		6.75	2.26	9.01	13.50
3600	Ballast	B-14	500	.096	C.Y.		3.72	.73	4.45	6.85
3700	Remove and re-install, ties & track using new bolts & spikes		50	.960	L.F.		37	7.30	44.30	68.50
3800	Turnouts using new bolts and spikes		1	48	Ea.		1,850	365	2,215	3,425
3890	Minimum labor/equipment charge	↓	5	9.600	Job		370	73	443	685
4000	Sidewalk removal, bituminous, 2" thick	B-6	350	.069	S.Y.		2.75	1.04	3.79	5.60

27

02 41 Demolition

02 41 13 – Selective Site Demolition

02 41 13.33 Minor Site Demolition

		Crew	Daily Output	Labor-Hours	Unit	Material	2014 Bare Costs Labor	2014 Bare Costs Equipment	Total	Total Incl O&P
4010	2-1/2" thick	B-6	325	.074	S.Y.		2.96	1.12	4.08	6.05
4050	Brick, set in mortar		185	.130			5.20	1.97	7.17	10.60
4100	Concrete, plain, 4"		160	.150			6	2.28	8.28	12.25
4110	Plain, 5"		140	.171			6.90	2.61	9.51	14
4120	Plain, 6"		120	.200			8	3.04	11.04	16.35
4200	Mesh reinforced, concrete, 4 "		150	.160			6.40	2.44	8.84	13.10
4210	5 " thick		131	.183			7.35	2.79	10.14	14.95
4220	6 " thick		112	.214			8.60	3.26	11.86	17.55
4290	Minimum labor/equipment charge	B-39	12	4	Job		155	19.50	174.50	275

02 41 13.60 Selective Demolition Fencing

		Crew	Daily Output	Labor-Hours	Unit	Material	2014 Bare Costs Labor	2014 Bare Costs Equipment	Total	Total Incl O&P
0010	**SELECTIVE DEMOLITION FENCING** R024119-10									
1600	Fencing, barbed wire, 3 strand	2 Clab	430	.037	L.F.		1.36		1.36	2.24
1650	5 strand	"	280	.057			2.09		2.09	3.44
1700	Chain link, posts & fabric, 8' to 10' high, remove only	B-6	445	.054			2.16	.82	2.98	4.41
1750	Remove and reset	"	70	.343			13.75	5.20	18.95	28.50

02 41 16 – Structure Demolition

02 41 16.13 Building Demolition

		Crew	Daily Output	Labor-Hours	Unit	Material	2014 Bare Costs Labor	2014 Bare Costs Equipment	Total	Total Incl O&P
0010	**BUILDING DEMOLITION** Large urban projects, incl. 20 mi. haul R024119-10									
0011	No foundation or dump fees, C.F. is vol. of building standing									
0020	Steel	B-8	21500	.003	C.F.		.12	.15	.27	.37
0050	Concrete		15300	.004			.17	.22	.39	.52
0080	Masonry		20100	.003			.13	.17	.30	.39
0100	Mixture of types		20100	.003			.13	.17	.30	.39
0500	Small bldgs, or single bldgs, no salvage included, steel	B-3	14800	.003			.13	.17	.30	.40
0600	Concrete		11300	.004			.17	.23	.40	.52
0650	Masonry		14800	.003			.13	.17	.30	.40
0700	Wood		14800	.003			.13	.17	.30	.40
0750	For buildings with no interior walls, deduct								50%	50%
1000	Demoliton single family house, one story, wood 1600 S.F.	B-3	1	48	Ea.		1,900	2,575	4,475	5,900
1020	3200 S.F.		.50	96			3,775	5,150	8,925	11,800
1200	Demoliton two family house, two story, wood 2400 S.F.		.67	71.964			2,825	3,850	6,675	8,850
1220	4200 S.F.		.38	128			5,025	6,875	11,900	15,700
1300	Demoliton three family house, three story, wood 3200 S.F.		.50	96			3,775	5,150	8,925	11,800
1320	5400 S.F.		.30	160			6,300	8,575	14,875	19,700
5000	For buildings with no interior walls, deduct								50%	50%

02 41 16.17 Building Demolition Footings and Foundations

		Crew	Daily Output	Labor-Hours	Unit	Material	2014 Bare Costs Labor	2014 Bare Costs Equipment	Total	Total Incl O&P
0010	**BUILDING DEMOLITION FOOTINGS AND FOUNDATIONS** R024119-10									
0200	Floors, concrete slab on grade,									
0240	4" thick, plain concrete	B-9	500	.080	S.F.		2.96	.47	3.43	5.40
0280	Reinforced, wire mesh		470	.085			3.15	.50	3.65	5.75
0300	Rods		400	.100			3.71	.58	4.29	6.75
0400	6" thick, plain concrete		375	.107			3.95	.62	4.57	7.20
0420	Reinforced, wire mesh		340	.118			4.36	.69	5.05	7.90
0440	Rods		300	.133			4.94	.78	5.72	8.95
1000	Footings, concrete, 1' thick, 2' wide	B-5	300	.187	L.F.		7.55	4.75	12.30	17.45
1080	1'-6" thick, 2' wide		250	.224			9.05	5.70	14.75	21
1120	3' wide		200	.280			11.30	7.10	18.40	26.50
1140	2' thick, 3' wide		175	.320			12.95	8.15	21.10	30
1200	Average reinforcing, add								10%	10%
1220	Heavy reinforcing, add								20%	20%
2000	Walls, block, 4" thick	1 Clab	180	.044	S.F.		1.63		1.63	2.68
2040	6" thick		170	.047			1.72		1.72	2.83

02 41 Demolition

02 41 16 – Structure Demolition

02 41 16.17 Building Demolition Footings and Foundations

		Crew	Daily Output	Labor-Hours	Unit	Material	2014 Bare Costs Labor	2014 Bare Costs Equipment	Total	Total Incl O&P
2080	8" thick	1 Clab	150	.053	S.F.		1.95		1.95	3.21
2100	12" thick	↓	150	.053			1.95		1.95	3.21
2200	For horizontal reinforcing, add								10%	10%
2220	For vertical reinforcing, add								20%	20%
2400	Concrete, plain concrete, 6" thick	B-9	160	.250			9.25	1.46	10.71	16.80
2420	8" thick		140	.286			10.60	1.67	12.27	19.25
2440	10" thick		120	.333			12.35	1.95	14.30	22.50
2500	12" thick	↓	100	.400			14.80	2.34	17.14	27
2600	For average reinforcing, add								10%	10%
2620	For heavy reinforcing, add				↓				20%	20%
9000	Minimum labor/equipment charge	A-1	2	4	Job		147	42	189	287

02 41 16.19 Minor Building Deconstruction

			Crew	Daily Output	Labor-Hours	Unit	Material	2014 Bare Costs Labor	2014 Bare Costs Equipment	Total	Total Incl O&P
0010	**MINOR BUILDING DECONSTRUCTION**		R024119-10								
0011	For salvage, avg house										
0225	2 story, pre 1970 house, 1400 S.F., labor for all salv mat, min	G	6 Clab	25	1.920	SF Flr.		70.50		70.50	116
0230	Maximum	G	"	15	3.200	"		117		117	193
0235	Salvage of carpet, tackless	G	2 Clab	2400	.007	S.F.		.24		.24	.40
0240	Wood floors, incl denailing and packaging	G	3 Clab	270	.089	"		3.26		3.26	5.35
0260	Wood doors and trim, standard	G	1 Clab	16	.500	Ea.		18.35		18.35	30
0280	Base or cove mouldings, incl denailing and packaging	G		500	.016	L.F.		.59		.59	.96
0320	Closet shelving and trim, incl denailing and packaging	G	↓	18	.444	Set		16.30		16.30	27
0340	Kitchen cabinets, uppers and lowers, prefab type	G	2 Clab	24	.667	L.F.		24.50		24.50	40
0360	Kitchen cabinets, uppers and lowers, built-in	G		12	1.333	"		49		49	80.50
0370	Bath fixt, incl toilet, tub, vanity, and med cabinet	G	↓	3	5.333	Set		195		195	320

02 41 19 – Selective Demolition

02 41 19.13 Selective Building Demolition

		Crew	Daily Output	Labor-Hours	Unit	Material	2014 Bare Costs Labor	2014 Bare Costs Equipment	Total	Total Incl O&P
0010	**SELECTIVE BUILDING DEMOLITION**									
0020	Costs related to selective demolition of specific building components									
0025	are included under Common Work Results (XX 05)									
0030	in the component's appropriate division.									

02 41 19.16 Selective Demolition, Cutout

			Crew	Daily Output	Labor-Hours	Unit	Material	2014 Bare Costs Labor	2014 Bare Costs Equipment	Total	Total Incl O&P
0010	**SELECTIVE DEMOLITION, CUTOUT**		R024119-10								
0020	Concrete, elev. slab, light reinforcement, under 6 C.F.		B-9	65	.615	C.F.		23	3.59	26.59	41.50
0050	Light reinforcing, over 6 C.F.			75	.533	"		19.75	3.11	22.86	36
0200	Slab on grade to 6" thick, not reinforced, under 8 S.F.			85	.471	S.F.		17.45	2.75	20.20	31.50
0250	8 – 16 S.F.		↓	175	.229	"		8.45	1.33	9.78	15.35
0255	For over 16 S.F. see Line 02 41 16.17 0400										
0600	Walls, not reinforced, under 6 C.F.		B-9	60	.667	C.F.		24.50	3.89	28.39	45
0650	6 – 12 C.F.		"	80	.500	"		18.55	2.92	21.47	33.50
0655	For over 12 C.F. see Line 02 41 16.17 2500										
1000	Concrete, elevated slab, bar reinforced, under 6 C.F.		B-9	45	.889	C.F.		33	5.20	38.20	59.50
1050	Bar reinforced, over 6 C.F.			50	.800	"		29.50	4.67	34.17	53.50
1200	Slab on grade to 6" thick, bar reinforced, under 8 S.F.			75	.533	S.F.		19.75	3.11	22.86	36
1250	8 – 16 S.F.		↓	150	.267	"		9.90	1.56	11.46	17.95
1255	For over 16 S.F. see Line 02 41 16.17 0440										
1400	Walls, bar reinforced, under 6 C.F.		B-9	50	.800	C.F.		29.50	4.67	34.17	53.50
1450	6 – 12 C.F.		"	70	.571	"		21	3.34	24.34	38.50
1455	For over 12 C.F. see Lines 02 41 16.17 2500 and 2600										
2000	Brick, to 4 S.F. opening, not including toothing										
2040	4" thick		B-9	30	1.333	Ea.		49.50	7.80	57.30	89.50
2060	8" thick			18	2.222			82.50	13	95.50	149
2080	12" thick		↓	10	4	↓		148	23.50	171.50	269

02 41 Demolition

02 41 19 – Selective Demolition

02 41 19.16 Selective Demolition, Cutout	Crew	Daily Output	Labor-Hours	Unit	Material	2014 Bare Costs Labor	Equipment	Total	Total Incl O&P
2400 Concrete block, to 4 S.F. opening, 2" thick	B-9	35	1.143	Ea.		42.50	6.65	49.15	77
2420 4" thick		30	1.333			49.50	7.80	57.30	89.50
2440 8" thick		27	1.481			55	8.65	63.65	99.50
2460 12" thick		24	1.667			62	9.75	71.75	112
2600 Gypsum block, to 4 S.F. opening, 2" thick		80	.500			18.55	2.92	21.47	33.50
2620 4" thick		70	.571			21	3.34	24.34	38.50
2640 8" thick		55	.727			27	4.25	31.25	49
2800 Terra cotta, to 4 S.F. opening, 4" thick		70	.571			21	3.34	24.34	38.50
2840 8" thick		65	.615			23	3.59	26.59	41.50
2880 12" thick		50	.800			29.50	4.67	34.17	53.50
4000 For toothing masonry, see Section 04 01 20.50									
6000 Walls, interior, not including re-framing,									
6010 openings to 5 S.F.									
6100 Drywall to 5/8" thick	1 Clab	24	.333	Ea.		12.20		12.20	20
6200 Paneling to 3/4" thick		20	.400			14.65		14.65	24
6300 Plaster, on gypsum lath		20	.400			14.65		14.65	24
6340 On wire lath		14	.571			21		21	34.50
7000 Wood frame, not including re-framing, openings to 5 S.F.									
7200 Floors, sheathing and flooring to 2" thick	1 Clab	5	1.600	Ea.		58.50		58.50	96.50
7310 Roofs, sheathing to 1" thick, not including roofing		6	1.333			49		49	80.50
7410 Walls, sheathing to 1" thick, not including siding		7	1.143			42		42	69
8500 Minimum labor/equipment charge		4	2	Job		73.50		73.50	120

02 41 19.18 Selective Demolition, Disposal Only	Crew	Daily Output	Labor-Hours	Unit	Material	2014 Bare Costs Labor	Equipment	Total	Total Incl O&P
0010 **SELECTIVE DEMOLITION, DISPOSAL ONLY** R024119-10									
0015 Urban bldg w/salvage value allowed									
0020 Including loading and 5 mile haul to dump									
0200 Steel frame	B-3	430	.112	C.Y.		4.39	6	10.39	13.75
0300 Concrete frame		365	.132			5.15	7.05	12.20	16.15
0400 Masonry construction		445	.108			4.24	5.80	10.04	13.25
0500 Wood frame		247	.194			7.65	10.45	18.10	24

02 41 19.19 Selective Facility Services Demolition	Crew	Daily Output	Labor-Hours	Unit	Material	2014 Bare Costs Labor	Equipment	Total	Total Incl O&P
0010 **SELECTIVE FACILITY SERVICES DEMOLITION**, Rubbish Handling R024119-10									
0020 The following are to be added to the demolition prices									
0050 The following are components for a complete chute system									
0100 Top chute circular steel, 4' long, 18" diameter	B-1C	15	1.600	Ea.	256	59.50	30.50	346	415
0102 23" diameter		15	1.600		277	59.50	30.50	367	435
0104 27" diameter		15	1.600		299	59.50	30.50	389	460
0106 30" diameter		15	1.600		320	59.50	30.50	410	480
0108 33" diameter		15	1.600		340	59.50	30.50	430	505
0110 36" diameter		15	1.600		365	59.50	30.50	455	530
0112 Regular chute, 18" diameter		15	1.600		192	59.50	30.50	282	345
0114 23" diameter		15	1.600		213	59.50	30.50	303	365
0116 27" diameter		15	1.600		234	59.50	30.50	324	390
0118 30" diameter		15	1.600		256	59.50	30.50	346	415
0120 33" diameter		15	1.600		277	59.50	30.50	367	435
0122 36" diameter		15	1.600		299	59.50	30.50	389	460
0124 Control door chute, 18" diameter		15	1.600		365	59.50	30.50	455	530
0126 23" diameter		15	1.600		385	59.50	30.50	475	550
0128 27" diameter		15	1.600		405	59.50	30.50	495	575
0130 30" diameter		15	1.600		425	59.50	30.50	515	600
0132 33" diameter		15	1.600		445	59.50	30.50	535	620
0134 36" diameter		15	1.600		470	59.50	30.50	560	645

02 41 Demolition

02 41 19 - Selective Demolition

02 41 19.19 Selective Facility Services Demolition	Crew	Daily Output	Labor-Hours	Unit	Material	2014 Bare Costs Labor	Equipment	Total	Total Incl O&P
0136	Chute liners, 14 ga., 18-30" diameter	B-1C	15	1.600	Ea.	215	59.50	30.50	305	370
0138	33-36" diameter		15	1.600		269	59.50	30.50	359	430
0140	17% thinner chute, 30" diameter		15	1.600		213	59.50	30.50	303	365
0142	33% thinner chute, 30" diameter		15	1.600		160	59.50	30.50	250	310
0144	Top chute cover	1 Clab	24	.333		147	12.20		159.20	182
0146	Door chute cover	"	24	.333		147	12.20		159.20	182
0148	Top chute trough	2 Clab	12	1.333		490	49		539	620
0150	Bolt down frame & counter weights, 250 lb.	B-1	4	6		4,075	224		4,299	4,850
0152	500 lb.		4	6		5,950	224		6,174	6,925
0154	750 lb.		4	6		8,750	224		8,974	10,000
0156	1000 lb.		2.67	8.989		9,775	335		10,110	11,400
0158	1500 lb.		2.67	8.989		12,500	335		12,835	14,400
0160	Chute warning light system, 5 stories	B-1C	4	6		8,625	224	114	8,963	9,975
0162	10 stories	"	2	12		13,700	450	228	14,378	16,100
0164	Dust control device for dumpsters	1 Clab	8	1		98	36.50		134.50	168
0166	Install or replace breakaway cord		8	1		26	36.50		62.50	88.50
0168	Install or replace warning sign		16	.500		11	18.35		29.35	42
0600	Dumpster, weekly rental, 1 dump/week, 6 C.Y. capacity (2 Tons)				Week	415			415	455
0700	10 C.Y. capacity (3 Tons)					480			480	530
0725	20 C.Y. capacity (5 Tons)	R024119-20				565			565	625
0800	30 C.Y. capacity (7 Tons)					730			730	800
0840	40 C.Y. capacity (10 Tons)					775			775	850
0900	Alternate pricing for dumpsters									
0910	Delivery, average for all sizes				Ea.	75			75	82.50
0920	Haul, average for all sizes					235			235	259
0930	Rent per day, average for all sizes					20			20	22
0940	Rent per month, average for all sizes					80			80	88
0950	Disposal fee per ton, average for all sizes				Ton	88			88	97
2000	Load, haul, dump and return, 50' haul, hand carried	2 Clab	24	.667	C.Y.		24.50		24.50	40
2005	Wheeled		37	.432			15.85		15.85	26
2040	51' to 100' haul, hand carried		16.50	.970			35.50		35.50	58.50
2045	Wheeled		25	.640			23.50		23.50	38.50
2080	Over 100' haul, add per 100 L.F., hand carried		35.50	.451			16.50		16.50	27
2085	Wheeled		54	.296			10.85		10.85	17.85
2120	In elevators, per 10 floors, add		140	.114			4.19		4.19	6.90
2130	Load, haul, dump and return, up to 50' haul, incl. up to 5 rsr stair, hand		23	.696			25.50		25.50	42
2135	Wheeled		35	.457			16.75		16.75	27.50
2140	6 – 10 riser stairs, hand carried		22	.727			26.50		26.50	44
2145	Wheeled		34	.471			17.25		17.25	28.50
2150	11 – 20 riser stairs, hand carried		20	.800			29.50		29.50	48
2155	Wheeled		31	.516			18.90		18.90	31
2160	21 – 40 riser stairs, hand carried		16	1			36.50		36.50	60
2165	Wheeled		24	.667			24.50		24.50	40
2170	100' haul, incl. 5 riser stair, hand carried		15	1.067			39		39	64
2175	Wheeled		23	.696			25.50		25.50	42
2180	6 – 10 riser stair, hand carried		14	1.143			42		42	69
2185	Wheeled		21	.762			28		28	46
2190	11 – 20 riser stair, hand carried		12	1.333			49		49	80.50
2195	Wheeled		18	.889			32.50		32.50	53.50
2200	21 – 40 riser stair, hand carried		8	2			73.50		73.50	120
2205	Wheeled		12	1.333			49		49	80.50
2210	Over 100' haul, add per 100 L.F., hand carried		35.50	.451			16.50		16.50	27
2215	Wheeled		54	.296			10.85		10.85	17.85

02 41 19.19 Selective Facility Services Demolition

		Crew	Daily Output	Labor-Hours	Unit	Material	2014 Bare Costs Labor	Equipment	Total	Total Incl O&P
2220	For each additional flight of stairs, up to 5 risers, add	2 Clab	550	.029	Flight		1.07		1.07	1.75
2225	6 – 10 risers, add		275	.058			2.13		2.13	3.50
2230	11 – 20 risers, add		138	.116			4.25		4.25	7
2235	21 – 40 risers, add		69	.232			8.50		8.50	13.95
3000	Loading & trucking, including 2 mile haul, chute loaded	B-16	45	.711	C.Y.		26.50	15.40	41.90	60.50
3040	Hand loading truck, 50' haul	"	48	.667			25	14.40	39.40	57
3080	Machine loading truck	B-17	120	.267			10.55	6.50	17.05	24
3120	Wheeled 50' and ramp dump loaded	2 Clab	24	.667			24.50		24.50	40
5000	Haul, per mile, up to 8 C.Y. truck	B-34B	1165	.007			.26	.59	.85	1.07
5100	Over 8 C.Y. truck	"	1550	.005			.19	.45	.64	.81

02 41 19.20 Selective Demolition, Dump Charges

		Crew	Daily Output	Labor-Hours	Unit	Material	2014 Bare Costs Labor	Equipment	Total	Total Incl O&P
0010	**SELECTIVE DEMOLITION, DUMP CHARGES** R024119-10									
0020	Dump charges, typical urban city, tipping fees only									
0100	Building construction materials				Ton	74			74	81
0200	Trees, brush, lumber					63			63	69.50
0300	Rubbish only					63			63	69.50
0500	Reclamation station, usual charge					74			74	81

02 41 19.21 Selective Demolition, Gutting

		Crew	Daily Output	Labor-Hours	Unit	Material	2014 Bare Costs Labor	Equipment	Total	Total Incl O&P
0010	**SELECTIVE DEMOLITION, GUTTING** R024119-10									
0020	Building interior, including disposal, dumpster fees not included									
0500	Residential building									
0560	Minimum	B-16	400	.080	SF Flr.		2.99	1.73	4.72	6.80
0580	Maximum	"	360	.089	"		3.32	1.92	5.24	7.55
0900	Commercial building									
1000	Minimum	B-16	350	.091	SF Flr.		3.42	1.98	5.40	7.80
1020	Maximum	"	250	.128	"		4.78	2.77	7.55	10.90
3000	Minimum labor/equipment charge		4	8	Job		299	173	472	680

02 41 19.25 Selective Demolition, Saw Cutting

		Crew	Daily Output	Labor-Hours	Unit	Material	2014 Bare Costs Labor	Equipment	Total	Total Incl O&P
0010	**SELECTIVE DEMOLITION, SAW CUTTING** R024119-10									
0015	Asphalt, up to 3" deep	B-89	1050	.015	L.F.	.14	.64	.50	1.28	1.72
0020	Each additional inch of depth	"	1800	.009		.05	.37	.29	.71	.97
1200	Masonry walls, hydraulic saw, brick, per inch of depth	B-89B	300	.053		.05	2.23	3.03	5.31	6.95
1220	Block walls, solid, per inch of depth	"	250	.064		.05	2.67	3.64	6.36	8.35
2000	Brick or masonry w/hand held saw, per inch of depth	A-1	125	.064		.06	2.35	.67	3.08	4.66
5000	Wood sheathing to 1" thick, on walls	1 Carp	200	.040			1.83		1.83	3.01
5020	On roof	"	250	.032			1.47		1.47	2.41
9000	Minimum labor/equipment charge	A-1	2	4	Job		147	42	189	287

02 41 19.27 Selective Demolition, Torch Cutting

		Crew	Daily Output	Labor-Hours	Unit	Material	2014 Bare Costs Labor	Equipment	Total	Total Incl O&P
0010	**SELECTIVE DEMOLITION, TORCH CUTTING** R024119-10									
0020	Steel, 1" thick plate	E-25	333	.024	L.F.	.76	1.28	.03	2.07	3.21
0040	1" diameter bar	"	600	.013	Ea.	.13	.71	.02	.86	1.46
1000	Oxygen lance cutting, reinforced concrete walls									
1040	12" to 16" thick walls	1 Clab	10	.800	L.F.		29.50		29.50	48
1080	24" thick walls	"	6	1.333	"		49		49	80.50
1090	Minimum labor/equipment charge	E-25	2	4	Job		212	5.70	217.70	395
1100	See Section 05 05 21.10									

02 42 10 – Building Deconstruction

02 42 10.10 Estimated Salvage Value or Savings		Crew	Daily Output	Labor-Hours	Unit	Material	2014 Bare Costs Labor	Equipment	Total	Total Incl O&P
0010	**ESTIMATED SALVAGE VALUE OR SAVINGS**									
0015	Excludes material handling, packaging, container costs and									
0020	transportation for salvage or disposal									
0050	All Items in Section 02 42 10.10 are credit deducts and not costs									
0100	Copper Wire Salvage Value	G				Lb.			1.60	1.60
0110	Disposal Savings	G							.04	.04
0200	Copper Pipe Salvage Value	G							2.50	2.50
0210	Disposal Savings	G							.05	.05
0300	Steel Pipe Salvage Value	G							.06	.06
0310	Disposal Savings	G							.03	.03
0400	Cast Iron Pipe Salvage Value	G							.03	.03
0410	Disposal Savings	G							.01	.01
0500	Steel Doors or Windows Salvage Value	G							.06	.06
0510	Aluminum	G							.55	.55
0520	Disposal Savings	G							.03	.03
0600	Aluminum Siding Salvage Value	G							.49	.49
0630	Disposal Savings	G				▼			.03	.03
0640	Wood Siding (no lead or asbestos)	G				C.Y.			12	12
0800	Clean Concrete Disposal Savings	G				Ton			62	62
0850	Asphalt Shingles Disposal Savings	G				"			60	60
1000	Wood wall framing clean salvage value	G				M.B.F.			55	55
1010	Painted	G							44	44
1020	Floor framing	G							55	55
1030	Painted	G							44	44
1050	Roof framing	G							55	55
1060	Painted	G							44	44
1100	Wood beams salvage value	G				▼			55	55
1200	Wood framing and beams disposal savings	G				Ton			66	66
1220	Wood sheating and sub-base flooring	G							72.50	72.50
1230	Wood wall paneling (1/4 inch thick)	G				▼			66	66
1300	Wood panel 3/4-1 inch thick low salvage value	G				S.F.			.55	.55
1350	high salvage value	G				"			2.20	2.20
1400	Disposal savings	G				Ton			66	66
1500	Flooring tongue and groove 25/32 inch thick low salvage value	G				S.F.			.55	.55
1530	High salvage value	G				"			1.10	1.10
1560	Disposal savings	G				Ton			66	66
1600	Drywall or sheet rock salvage value	G							22	22
1650	Disposal savings	G				▼			66	66

02 42 10.20 Deconstruction of Building Components

02 42 10.20 Deconstruction of Building Components		Crew	Daily Output	Labor-Hours	Unit	Material	2014 Bare Costs Labor	Equipment	Total	Total Incl O&P
0010	**DECONSTRUCTION OF BUILDING COMPONENTS**									
0012	Buildings one or two stories only									
0015	Excludes material handling, packaging, container costs and									
0020	transportation for salvage or disposal									
0050	Deconstruction of Plumbing Fixtures									
0100	Wall hung or countertop lavatory	G	2 Clab	16	1	Ea.		36.50	36.50	60
0110	Single or double compartment kitchen sink	G		14	1.143			42	42	69
0120	Wall hung urinal	G		14	1.143			42	42	69
0130	Floor mounted	G		8	2			73.50	73.50	120
0140	Floor mounted water closet	G		16	1			36.50	36.50	60
0150	Wall hung	G		14	1.143			42	42	69
0160	Water fountain, free standing	G		16	1			36.50	36.50	60
0170	Wall hung or deck mounted	G	▼	12	1.333	▼		49	49	80.50

02 42 10.20 Deconstruction of Building Components		Crew	Daily Output	Labor-Hours	Unit	Material	2014 Bare Costs Labor	Equipment	Total	Total Incl O&P
0180	Bathtub, steel or fiberglass	G	2 Clab	10	1.600	Ea.		58.50		58.50	96.50
0190	Cast iron	G		8	2			73.50		73.50	120
0200	Shower, single	G		6	2.667			97.50		97.50	161
0210	Group	G		7	2.286			84		84	138
0300	Deconstruction of Electrical Fixtures										
0310	Surface mount incandescent fixtures	G	2 Clab	48	.333	Ea.		12.20		12.20	20
0320	Fluorescent, 2 lamp	G		32	.500			18.35		18.35	30
0330	4 lamp	G		24	.667			24.50		24.50	40
0340	Strip Fluorescent, 1 lamp	G		40	.400			14.65		14.65	24
0350	2 lamp	G		32	.500			18.35		18.35	30
0400	Recessed drop-in fluorescent fixture, 2 lamp	G		27	.593			21.50		21.50	35.50
0410	4 lamp	G		18	.889			32.50		32.50	53.50
0500	Deconstruction of appliances										
0510	Cooking stoves	G	2 Clab	26	.615	Ea.		22.50		22.50	37
0520	Dishwashers	G	"	26	.615	"		22.50		22.50	37
0600	Deconstruction of millwork and trim										
0610	Cabinets, wood	G	2 Carp	40	.400	L.F.		18.35		18.35	30
0620	Countertops	G		100	.160	"		7.35		7.35	12.05
0630	Wall paneling, 1 inch thick	G		500	.032	S.F.		1.47		1.47	2.41
0640	Ceiling trim	G		500	.032	L.F.		1.47		1.47	2.41
0650	Wainscoting	G		500	.032	S.F.		1.47		1.47	2.41
0660	Base, 3/4" to 1" thick	G		600	.027	L.F.		1.22		1.22	2.01
0700	Deconstruction of doors and windows										
0710	Doors, wrap, interior, wood, single, no closers	G	2 Carp	21	.762	Ea.	4.25	35		39.25	62
0720	Double	G		13	1.231		8.50	56.50		65	102
0730	Solid core, single, exterior or interior	G		10	1.600		4.25	73.50		77.75	126
0740	Double	G		8	2		8.50	91.50		100	160
0810	Windows, wrap, wood, single										
0812	with no casement or cladding	G	2 Carp	21	.762	Ea.	4.25	35		39.25	62
0820	with casement and/or cladding	G	"	18	.889	"	4.25	41		45.25	71.50
0900	Deconstruction of interior finishes										
0910	Drywall for recycling	G	2 Clab	1775	.009	S.F.		.33		.33	.54
0920	Plaster wall, first floor	G		1775	.009			.33		.33	.54
0930	Second floor	G		1330	.012			.44		.44	.72
1000	Deconstruction of roofing and accessories										
1010	Built-up roofs	G	2 Clab	570	.028	S.F.		1.03		1.03	1.69
1020	Gutters, facia and rakes	G	"	1140	.014	L.F.		.51		.51	.85
2000	Deconstruction of wood components										
2010	Roof sheeting	G	2 Clab	570	.028	S.F.		1.03		1.03	1.69
2020	Main roof framing	G		760	.021	L.F.		.77		.77	1.27
2030	Porch roof framing	G		445	.036			1.32		1.32	2.16
2040	Beams 4" x 8"	G	B-1	375	.064			2.39		2.39	3.92
2050	4" x 10"	G		300	.080			2.99		2.99	4.90
2055	4" x 12"	G		250	.096			3.58		3.58	5.90
2060	6" x 8"	G		250	.096			3.58		3.58	5.90
2065	6" x 10"	G		200	.120			4.48		4.48	7.35
2070	6" x 12"	G		170	.141			5.25		5.25	8.65
2075	8" x 12"	G		126	.190			7.10		7.10	11.70
2080	10" x 12"	G		100	.240			8.95		8.95	14.70
2100	Ceiling joists	G	2 Clab	800	.020			.73		.73	1.20
2150	Wall framing, interior	G		1230	.013			.48		.48	.78
2160	Sub-floor	G		2000	.008	S.F.		.29		.29	.48
2170	Floor joists	G		2000	.008	L.F.		.29		.29	.48

02 42 Removal and Salvage of Construction Materials

02 42 10 – Building Deconstruction

02 42 10.20 Deconstruction of Building Components

			Crew	Daily Output	Labor-Hours	Unit	Material	2014 Bare Costs Labor	Equipment	Total	Total Incl O&P
2200	Wood siding (no lead or asbestos)	G	2 Clab	1300	.012	S.F.		.45		.45	.74
2300	Wall framing, exterior	G		1600	.010	L.F.		.37		.37	.60
2400	Stair risers	G		53	.302	Ea.		11.05		11.05	18.15
2500	Posts	G		800	.020	L.F.		.73		.73	1.20
3000	Deconstruction of exterior brick walls										
3010	Exterior brick walls, first floor	G	2 Clab	200	.080	S.F.		2.93		2.93	4.82
3020	Second floor	G		64	.250	"		9.15		9.15	15.05
3030	Brick chimney	G		100	.160	C.F.		5.85		5.85	9.65
4000	Deconstruction of concrete										
4010	Slab on grade, 4" thick, plain concrete	G	B-9	500	.080	S.F.		2.96	.47	3.43	5.40
4020	Wire mesh reinforced	G		470	.085			3.15	.50	3.65	5.75
4030	Rod reinforced	G		400	.100			3.71	.58	4.29	6.75
4110	Foundation wall, 6" thick, plain concrete	G		160	.250			9.25	1.46	10.71	16.80
4120	8" thick	G		140	.286			10.60	1.67	12.27	19.25
4130	10" thick	G		120	.333			12.35	1.95	14.30	22.50
9000	Deconstruction process, support equipment as needed										
9010	Daily use, portal to portal, 12-ton truck-mounted hydraulic crane crew	G	A-3H	1	8	Day		400	875	1,275	1,600
9020	Daily use, skid steer and operator	G	A-3C	1	8			375	310	685	935
9030	Daily use, backhoe 48 H.P., operator and labor	G	"	1	8			375	310	685	935

02 42 10.30 Deconstruction Material Handling

			Crew	Daily Output	Labor-Hours	Unit	Material	2014 Bare Costs Labor	Equipment	Total	Total Incl O&P
0010	**DECONSTRUCTION MATERIAL HANDLING**										
0012	Buildings one or two stories only										
0100	Clean and stack brick on pallet	G	2 Clab	1200	.013	Ea.		.49		.49	.80
0200	Haul 50' and load rough lumber up to 2" x 8" size	G		2000	.008	"		.29		.29	.48
0210	Lumber larger than 2" x 8"	G		3200	.005	B.F.		.18		.18	.30
0300	Finish wood for recycling stack and wrap per pallet	G		8	2	Ea.	34	73.50		107.50	158
0350	Light fixtures			6	2.667		61	97.50		158.50	229
0375	Windows			6	2.667		58	97.50		155.50	225
0400	Miscellaneous materials			8	2		17	73.50		90.50	139
1000	See Section 02 41 19.19 for bulk material handling										

02 43 Structure Moving

02 43 13 – Structure Relocation

02 43 13.13 Building Relocation

			Crew	Daily Output	Labor-Hours	Unit	Material	2014 Bare Costs Labor	Equipment	Total	Total Incl O&P
0010	**BUILDING RELOCATION**										
0011	One day move, up to 24' wide										
0020	Reset on new foundation, patch & hook-up, average move					Total					11,500
0040	Wood or steel frame bldg., based on ground floor area	G	B-4	185	.259	S.F.		9.65	2.80	12.45	18.90
0060	Masonry bldg., based on ground floor area	G	"	137	.350			13	3.78	16.78	25.50
0200	For 24' to 42' wide, add									15%	15%
0220	For each additional day on road, add	G	B-4	1	48	Day		1,775	520	2,295	3,500
0240	Construct new basement, move building, 1 day										
0300	move, patch & hook-up, based on ground floor area	G	B-3	155	.310	S.F.	10.25	12.20	16.60	39.05	49.50

02 58 Snow Control

02 58 13 – Snow Fencing

02 58 13.10 Snow Fencing System	Crew	Daily Output	Labor-Hours	Unit	Material	2014 Bare Costs Labor	Equipment	Total	Total Incl O&P
0010 **SNOW FENCING SYSTEM**									
7001 Snow fence on steel posts 10' O.C., 4' high	B-1	500	.048	L.F.	.96	1.79		2.75	4

02 65 Underground Storage Tank Removal

02 65 10 – Underground Tank and Contaminated Soil Removal

02 65 10.30 Removal of Underground Storage Tanks

		Crew	Daily Output	Labor-Hours	Unit	Material	2014 Bare Costs Labor	Equipment	Total	Total Incl O&P
0010	**REMOVAL OF UNDERGROUND STORAGE TANKS** R026510-20									
0011	Petroleum storage tanks, non-leaking									
0100	Excavate & load onto trailer									
0110	3000 gal. to 5000 gal. tank [G]	B-14	4	12	Ea.		465	91.50	556.50	860
0120	6000 gal. to 8000 gal. tank [G]	B-3A	3	13.333			520	345	865	1,225
0130	9000 gal. to 12000 gal. tank [G]	"	2	20	↓		780	515	1,295	1,850
0190	Known leaking tank, add				%				100%	100%
0200	Remove sludge, water and remaining product from tank bottom									
0201	of tank with vacuum truck									
0300	3000 gal. to 5000 gal. tank [G]	A-13	5	1.600	Ea.		75.50	154	229.50	289
0310	6000 gal. to 8000 gal. tank [G]		4	2			94	193	287	360
0320	9000 gal. to 12000 gal. tank [G]	↓	3	2.667	↓		125	257	382	480
0390	Dispose of sludge off-site, average				Gal.				6.25	6.80
0400	Insert inert solid CO_2 "dry ice" into tank									
0401	For cleaning/transporting tanks (1.5 lb./100 gal. cap) [G]	1 Clab	500	.016	Lb.	1.08	.59		1.67	2.15
0403	Insert solid carbon dioxide, 1.5 lb./100 gal. [G]	"	400	.020	"	1.08	.73		1.81	2.39
0503	Disconnect and remove piping [G]	1 Plum	160	.050	L.F.		2.88		2.88	4.49
0603	Transfer liquids, 10% of volume [G]	"	1600	.005	Gal.		.29		.29	.45
0703	Cut accessway into underground storage tank [G]	1 Clab	5.33	1.501	Ea.		55		55	90.50
0813	Remove sludge, wash and wipe tank, 500 gal. [G]	1 Plum	8	1			57.50		57.50	90
0823	3,000 gal. [G]		6.67	1.199			69		69	108
0833	5,000 gal. [G]		6.15	1.301			75		75	117
0843	8,000 gal. [G]		5.33	1.501			86.50		86.50	135
0853	10,000 gal. [G]		4.57	1.751			101		101	157
0863	12,000 gal. [G]	↓	4.21	1.900	↓		109		109	171
1020	Haul tank to certified salvage dump, 100 miles round trip									
1023	3000 gal. to 5000 gal. tank				Ea.				760	830
1026	6000 gal. to 8000 gal. tank								880	960
1029	9,000 gal. to 12,000 gal. tank				↓				1,050	1,150
1100	Disposal of contaminated soil to landfill									
1110	Minimum				C.Y.				145	160
1111	Maximum				"				400	440
1120	Disposal of contaminated soil to									
1121	bituminous concrete batch plant									
1130	Minimum				C.Y.				80	88
1131	Maximum				"				115	125
1203	Excavate, pull, & load tank, backfill hole, 8,000 gal. + [G]	B-12C	.50	32	Ea.		1,400	2,350	3,750	4,825
1213	Haul tank to certified dump, 100 miles rt, 8,000 gal. + [G]	B-34K	1	8			300	960	1,260	1,550
1223	Excavate, pull, & load tank, backfill hole, 500 gal. [G]	B-11C	1	16			685	365	1,050	1,500
1233	Excavate, pull, & load tank, backfill hole, 3,000 – 5,000 gal. [G]	B-11M	.50	32			1,375	795	2,170	3,075
1243	Haul tank to certified dump, 100 miles rt, 500 gal. [G]	B-34L	1	8			375	270	645	890
1253	Haul tank to certified dump, 100 miles rt, 3,000 – 5,000 gal. [G]	B-34M	1	8	↓		375	335	710	960
2010	Decontamination of soil on site incl poly tarp on top/bottom									
2011	Soil containment berm, and chemical treatment									
2020	Minimum [G]	B-11C	100	.160	C.Y.	7.80	6.85	3.65	18.30	23.50

02 65 Underground Storage Tank Removal

02 65 10 - Underground Tank and Contaminated Soil Removal

02 65 10.30 Removal of Underground Storage Tanks		Crew	Daily Output	Labor-Hours	Unit	Material	2014 Bare Costs Labor	Equipment	Total	Total Incl O&P
2021	Maximum	G B-11C	100	.160	C.Y.	10.10	6.85	3.65	20.60	26
2050	Disposal of decontaminated soil, minimum								135	150
2055	Maximum								400	440

02 81 Transportation and Disposal of Hazardous Materials

02 81 20 - Hazardous Waste Handling

02 81 20.10 Hazardous Waste Cleanup/Pickup/Disposal

		Crew	Daily Output	Labor-Hours	Unit	Material	2014 Bare Costs Labor	Equipment	Total	Total Incl O&P
0010	**HAZARDOUS WASTE CLEANUP/PICKUP/DISPOSAL**									
0100	For contractor rental equipment, i.e., Dozer,									
0110	Front end loader, Dump truck, etc., see 01 54 33 Reference Section									
1000	Solid pickup									
1100	55 gal. drums				Ea.				240	265
1120	Bulk material, minimum				Ton				190	210
1130	Maximum				"				595	655
1200	Transportation to disposal site									
1220	Truckload = 80 drums or 25 C.Y. or 18 tons									
1260	Minimum				Mile				3.95	4.45
1270	Maximum				"				7.25	7.35
3000	Liquid pickup, vacuum truck, stainless steel tank									
3100	Minimum charge, 4 hours									
3110	1 compartment, 2200 gallon				Hr.				140	155
3120	2 compartment, 5000 gallon				"				200	225
3400	Transportation in 6900 gallon bulk truck				Mile				7.95	8.75
3410	In teflon lined truck				"				10.20	11.25
5000	Heavy sludge or dry vacuumable material				Hr.				140	160
6000	Dumpsite disposal charge, minimum				Ton				140	155
6020	Maximum				"				415	455

02 82 Asbestos Remediation

02 82 13 - Asbestos Abatement

02 82 13.39 Asbestos Remediation Plans and Methods

		Crew	Daily Output	Labor-Hours	Unit	Material	2014 Bare Costs Labor	Equipment	Total	Total Incl O&P
0010	**ASBESTOS REMEDIATION PLANS AND METHODS**									
0100	Building Survey-Commercial Building				Ea.				2,200	2,400
0200	Asbestos Abatement Remediation Plan				"				1,350	1,475

02 82 13.41 Asbestos Abatement Equipment

		Crew	Daily Output	Labor-Hours	Unit	Material	2014 Bare Costs Labor	Equipment	Total	Total Incl O&P
0010	**ASBESTOS ABATEMENT EQUIPMENT** R028213-20									
0011	Equipment and supplies, buy									
0200	Air filtration device, 2000 CFM				Ea.	940			940	1,025
0250	Large volume air sampling pump, minimum					340			340	375
0260	Maximum					330			330	360
0300	Airless sprayer unit, 2 gun					4,425			4,425	4,850
0350	Light stand, 500 watt					48			48	53
0400	Personal respirators									
0410	Negative pressure, 1/2 face, dual operation, min.				Ea.	26			26	28.50
0420	Maximum					29			29	31.50
0450	P.A.P.R., full face, minimum					122			122	134
0460	Maximum					162			162	178
0470	Supplied air, full face, incl. air line, minimum					165			165	182
0480	Maximum					395			395	435

02 82 13 – Asbestos Abatement

02 82 13.41 Asbestos Abatement Equipment

		Crew	Daily Output	Labor-Hours	Unit	Material	2014 Bare Costs Labor	2014 Bare Costs Equipment	Total	Total Incl O&P
0500	Personnel sampling pump				Ea.	222			222	244
1500	Power panel, 20 unit, incl. GFI					590			590	650
1600	Shower unit, including pump and filters					1,250			1,250	1,375
1700	Supplied air system (type C)					3,350			3,350	3,675
1750	Vacuum cleaner, HEPA, 16 gal., stainless steel, wet/dry					1,175			1,175	1,300
1760	55 gallon					1,225			1,225	1,350
1800	Vacuum loader, 9 – 18 ton/hr.					92,500			92,500	102,000
1900	Water atomizer unit, including 55 gal. drum					275			275	305
2000	Worker protection, whole body, foot, head cover & gloves, plastic					14.50			14.50	15.95
2500	Respirator, single use					24.50			24.50	27
2550	Cartridge for respirator					7.15			7.15	7.85
2570	Glove bag, 7 mil, 50" x 64"					16.25			16.25	17.90
2580	10 mil, 44" x 60"					5.65			5.65	6.20
3000	HEPA vacuum for work area, minimum					1,400			1,400	1,550
3050	Maximum					1,450			1,450	1,600
6000	Disposable polyethylene bags, 6 mil, 3 C.F.					1.65			1.65	1.82
6300	Disposable fiber drums, 3 C.F.					17.85			17.85	19.65
6400	Pressure sensitive caution labels, 3" x 5"					3.40			3.40	3.74
6450	11" x 17"					7.20			7.20	7.90
6500	Negative air machine, 1800 CFM					830			830	915

02 82 13.42 Preparation of Asbestos Containment Area

		Crew	Daily Output	Labor-Hours	Unit	Material	2014 Bare Costs Labor	2014 Bare Costs Equipment	Total	Total Incl O&P
0010	**PREPARATION OF ASBESTOS CONTAINMENT AREA**									
0100	Pre-cleaning, HEPA vacuum and wet wipe, flat surfaces	A-9	12000	.005	S.F.	.02	.27		.29	.47
0200	Protect carpeted area, 2 layers 6 mil poly on 3/4" plywood	"	1000	.064		2	3.28		5.28	7.45
0300	Separation barrier, 2" x 4" @ 16", 1/2" plywood ea. side, 8' high	2 Carp	400	.040		3.25	1.83		5.08	6.60
0310	12' high		320	.050		3.25	2.29		5.54	7.35
0320	16' high		200	.080		2.25	3.67		5.92	8.55
0400	Personnel decontam. chamber, 2" x 4" @ 16", 3/4" ply ea. side		280	.057		4.25	2.62		6.87	9
0450	Waste decontam. chamber, 2" x 4" studs @ 16", 3/4" ply ea. side		360	.044		4.25	2.04		6.29	8.05
0500	Cover surfaces with polyethylene sheeting									
0501	Including glue and tape									
0550	Floors, each layer, 6 mil	A-9	8000	.008	S.F.	.04	.41		.45	.71
0551	4 mil		9000	.007		.03	.36		.39	.61
0560	Walls, each layer, 6 mil		6000	.011		.04	.55		.59	.93
0561	4 mil		7000	.009		.03	.47		.50	.78
0570	For heights above 12', add						20%			
0575	For heights above 20', add						30%			
0580	For fire retardant poly, add					100%				
0590	For large open areas, deduct					10%	20%			
0600	Seal floor penetrations with foam firestop to 36 sq. in.	2 Carp	200	.080	Ea.	9.25	3.67		12.92	16.25
0610	36 sq. in. to 72 sq. in.		125	.128		18.50	5.85		24.35	30
0615	72 sq. in. to 144 sq. in.		80	.200		37	9.15		46.15	56
0620	Wall penetrations, to 36 square inches		180	.089		9.25	4.08		13.33	16.90
0630	36 sq. in. to 72 sq. in.		100	.160		18.50	7.35		25.85	32.50
0640	72 sq. in. to 144 sq. in.		60	.267		37	12.25		49.25	61
0800	Caulk seams with latex	1 Carp	230	.035	L.F.	.17	1.59		1.76	2.81
0900	Set up neg. air machine, 1-2k CFM/25 M.C.F. volume	1 Asbe	4.30	1.860	Ea.		95		95	153
0950	Set up and remove portable shower unit	2 Asbe	4	4	"		205		205	330

02 82 13 – Asbestos Abatement

02 82 13.43 Bulk Asbestos Removal		Crew	Daily Output	Labor-Hours	Unit	Material	2014 Bare Costs Labor	Equipment	Total	Total Incl O&P
0010	**BULK ASBESTOS REMOVAL**									
0020	Includes disposable tools and 2 suits and 1 respirator filter/day/worker									
0100	Beams, W 10 x 19	A-9	235	.272	L.F.	1.23	13.95		15.18	24
0110	W 12 x 22		210	.305		1.38	15.60		16.98	26.50
0120	W 14 x 26		180	.356		1.61	18.20		19.81	31
0130	W 16 x 31		160	.400		1.81	20.50		22.31	35
0140	W 18 x 40		140	.457		2.06	23.50		25.56	40
0150	W 24 x 55		110	.582		2.63	30		32.63	51
0160	W 30 x 108		85	.753		3.40	38.50		41.90	65.50
0170	W 36 x 150		72	.889		4.01	45.50		49.51	77.50
0200	Boiler insulation		480	.133	S.F.	.67	6.85		7.52	11.70
0210	With metal lath, add				%				50%	50%
0300	Boiler breeching or flue insulation	A-9	520	.123	S.F.	.56	6.30		6.86	10.70
0310	For active boiler, add				%				100%	100%
0400	Duct or AHU insulation	A-10B	440	.073	S.F.	.33	3.73		4.06	6.35
0500	Duct vibration isolation joints, up to 24 sq. in. duct	A-9	56	1.143	Ea.	5.15	58.50		63.65	99.50
0520	25 sq. in. to 48 sq. in. duct		48	1.333		6	68.50		74.50	117
0530	49 sq. in. to 76 sq. in. duct		40	1.600		7.25	82		89.25	140
0600	Pipe insulation, air cell type, up to 4" diameter pipe		900	.071	L.F.	.32	3.64		3.96	6.20
0610	4" to 8" diameter pipe		800	.080		.36	4.10		4.46	7
0620	10" to 12" diameter pipe		700	.091		.41	4.68		5.09	7.95
0630	14" to 16" diameter pipe		550	.116		.53	5.95		6.48	10.15
0650	Over 16" diameter pipe		650	.098	S.F.	.44	5.05		5.49	8.60
0700	With glove bag up to 3" diameter pipe		200	.320	L.F.	8.95	16.40		25.35	36.50
1000	Pipe fitting insulation up to 4" diameter pipe		320	.200	Ea.	.90	10.25		11.15	17.45
1100	6" to 8" diameter pipe		304	.211		.95	10.80		11.75	18.35
1110	10" to 12" diameter pipe		192	.333		1.51	17.05		18.56	29
1120	14" to 16" diameter pipe		128	.500		2.26	25.50		27.76	43.50
1130	Over 16" diameter pipe		176	.364	S.F.	1.64	18.60		20.24	32
1200	With glove bag, up to 8" diameter pipe		75	.853	L.F.	6.15	43.50		49.65	77
2000	Scrape foam fireproofing from flat surface		2400	.027	S.F.	.12	1.37		1.49	2.32
2100	Irregular surfaces		1200	.053		.24	2.73		2.97	4.65
3000	Remove cementitious material from flat surface		1800	.036		.16	1.82		1.98	3.10
3100	Irregular surface		1000	.064		.21	3.28		3.49	5.50
4000	Scrape acoustical coating/fireproofing, from ceiling		3200	.020		.09	1.02		1.11	1.75
5000	Remove VAT and mastic from floor by hand		2400	.027		.12	1.37		1.49	2.32
5100	By machine	A-11	4800	.013		.06	.68	.01	.75	1.18
5150	For 2 layers, add				%				50%	50%
6000	Remove contaminated soil from crawl space by hand	A-9	400	.160	C.F.	.72	8.20		8.92	13.95
6100	With large production vacuum loader	A-12	700	.091	"	.41	4.68	1.10	6.19	9.15
7000	Radiator backing, not including radiator removal	A-9	1200	.053	S.F.	.24	2.73		2.97	4.65
8000	Cement-asbestos transite board and cement wall board	2 Asbe	1000	.016		.17	.82		.99	1.50
8100	Transite shingle siding	A-10B	750	.043		.28	2.19		2.47	3.82
8200	Shingle roofing	"	2000	.016		.08	.82		.90	1.41
8250	Built-up, no gravel, non-friable	B-2	1400	.029		.08	1.06		1.14	1.83
8260	Bituminous flashing	1 Rofc	300	.027		.08	1.04		1.12	1.97
8300	Asbestos millboard, flat board and VAT contaminated plywood	2 Asbe	1000	.016		.08	.82		.90	1.40
9000	For type B (supplied air) respirator equipment, add				%				10%	10%

02 82 Asbestos Remediation

02 82 13 – Asbestos Abatement

02 82 13.44 Demolition In Asbestos Contaminated Area

		Crew	Daily Output	Labor-Hours	Unit	Material	2014 Bare Costs Labor	Equipment	Total	Total Incl O&P
0010	**DEMOLITION IN ASBESTOS CONTAMINATED AREA**									
0200	Ceiling, including suspension system, plaster and lath	A-9	2100	.030	S.F.	.14	1.56		1.70	2.66
0210	Finished plaster, leaving wire lath		585	.109		.49	5.60		6.09	9.55
0220	Suspended acoustical tile		3500	.018		.08	.94		1.02	1.59
0230	Concealed tile grid system		3000	.021		.10	1.09		1.19	1.86
0240	Metal pan grid system		1500	.043		.19	2.19		2.38	3.72
0250	Gypsum board		2500	.026		.12	1.31		1.43	2.24
0260	Lighting fixtures up to 2' x 4'	↓	72	.889	Ea.	4.01	45.50		49.51	77.50
0400	Partitions, non load bearing									
0410	Plaster, lath, and studs	A-9	690	.093	S.F.	1.02	4.75		5.77	8.75
0450	Gypsum board and studs	"	1390	.046	"	.21	2.36		2.57	4.02
9000	For type B (supplied air) respirator equipment, add				%				10%	10%

02 82 13.45 OSHA Testing

		Crew	Daily Output	Labor-Hours	Unit	Material	2014 Bare Costs Labor	Equipment	Total	Total Incl O&P
0010	**OSHA TESTING**									
0100	Certified technician, minimum				Day				200	220
0110	Maximum								300	330
0120	Industrial hygienist, minimum								250	250
0130	Maximum				↓				400	440
0200	Asbestos sampling and PCM analysis, NIOSH 7400, minimum	1 Asbe	8	1	Ea.	2.90	51		53.90	85
0210	Maximum		4	2		3.20	102		105.20	168
1000	Cleaned area samples		8	1		2.75	51		53.75	85
1100	PCM air sample analysis, NIOSH 7400, minimum		8	1		31	51		82	116
1110	Maximum	↓	4	2		3.35	102		105.35	168
1200	TEM air sample analysis, NIOSH 7402, minimum								80	106
1210	Maximum				↓				360	450

02 82 13.46 Decontamination of Asbestos Containment Area

		Crew	Daily Output	Labor-Hours	Unit	Material	2014 Bare Costs Labor	Equipment	Total	Total Incl O&P
0010	**DECONTAMINATION OF ASBESTOS CONTAINMENT AREA**									
0100	Spray exposed substrate with surfactant (bridging)									
0200	Flat surfaces	A-9	6000	.011	S.F.	.35	.55		.90	1.27
0250	Irregular surfaces		4000	.016	"	.30	.82		1.12	1.65
0300	Pipes, beams, and columns		2000	.032	L.F.	.55	1.64		2.19	3.24
1000	Spray encapsulate polyethylene sheeting		8000	.008	S.F.	.33	.41		.74	1.02
1100	Roll down polyethylene sheeting		8000	.008	"		.41		.41	.66
1500	Bag polyethylene sheeting		400	.160	Ea.	.79	8.20		8.99	14
2000	Fine clean exposed substrate, with nylon brush		2400	.027	S.F.		1.37		1.37	2.19
2500	Wet wipe substrate		4800	.013			.68		.68	1.10
2600	Vacuum surfaces, fine brush	↓	6400	.010	↓		.51		.51	.82
3000	Structural demolition									
3100	Wood stud walls	A-9	2800	.023	S.F.		1.17		1.17	1.88
3500	Window manifolds, not incl. window replacement		4200	.015			.78		.78	1.25
3600	Plywood carpet protection	↓	2000	.032	↓		1.64		1.64	2.63
4000	Remove custom decontamination facility	A-10A	8	3	Ea.	15.10	154		169.10	264
4100	Remove portable decontamination facility	3 Asbe	12	2	"	12.80	102		114.80	178
5000	HEPA vacuum, shampoo carpeting	A-9	4800	.013	S.F.	.07	.68		.75	1.18
9000	Final cleaning of protected surfaces	A-10A	8000	.003	"		.15		.15	.25

02 82 13.47 Asbestos Waste Pkg., Handling, and Disp.

		Crew	Daily Output	Labor-Hours	Unit	Material	2014 Bare Costs Labor	Equipment	Total	Total Incl O&P
0010	**ASBESTOS WASTE PACKAGING, HANDLING, AND DISPOSAL**									
0100	Collect and bag bulk material, 3 C.F. bags, by hand	A-9	400	.160	Ea.	1.65	8.20		9.85	14.95
0200	Large production vacuum loader	A-12	880	.073		.84	3.72	.88	5.44	7.90
1000	Double bag and decontaminate	A-9	960	.067		1.65	3.41		5.06	7.30
2000	Containerize bagged material in drums, per 3 C.F. drum	"	800	.080	↓	17.85	4.10		21.95	26.50

02 82 Asbestos Remediation

02 82 13 – Asbestos Abatement

02 82 13.47 Asbestos Waste Pkg., Handling, and Disp.

		Crew	Daily Output	Labor-Hours	Unit	Material	2014 Bare Costs Labor	Equipment	Total	Total Incl O&P
3000	Cart bags 50' to dumpster	2 Asbe	400	.040	Ea.		2.05		2.05	3.29
5000	Disposal charges, not including haul, minimum				C.Y.				61	67
5020	Maximum				"				355	395
9000	For type B (supplied air) respirator equipment, add				%				10%	10%

02 82 13.48 Asbestos Encapsulation With Sealants

		Crew	Daily Output	Labor-Hours	Unit	Material	2014 Bare Costs Labor	Equipment	Total	Total Incl O&P
0010	**ASBESTOS ENCAPSULATION WITH SEALANTS**									
0100	Ceilings and walls, minimum	A-9	21000	.003	S.F.	.30	.16		.46	.58
0110	Maximum		10600	.006		.44	.31		.75	.98
0200	Columns and beams, minimum		13300	.005		.30	.25		.55	.73
0210	Maximum		5325	.012		.50	.62		1.12	1.54
0300	Pipes to 12" diameter including minor repairs, minimum		800	.080	L.F.	.42	4.10		4.52	7.05
0310	Maximum		400	.160	"	1.10	8.20		9.30	14.35

02 83 Lead Remediation

02 83 19 – Lead-Based Paint Remediation

02 83 19.21 Lead Paint Remediation Plans and Methods

		Crew	Daily Output	Labor-Hours	Unit	Material	2014 Bare Costs Labor	Equipment	Total	Total Incl O&P
0010	**LEAD PAINT REMEDIATION PLANS AND METHODS**									
0100	Building Survey-Commercial Building				Ea.				2,050	2,250
0200	Lead Abatement Remediation Plan								1,225	1,350
0300	Lead Paint Testing, AAS Analysis								51	56
0400	Lead Paint Testing, X-Ray Fluorescence								51	56

02 83 19.22 Preparation of Lead Containment Area

		Crew	Daily Output	Labor-Hours	Unit	Material	2014 Bare Costs Labor	Equipment	Total	Total Incl O&P
0010	**PREPARATION OF LEAD CONTAINMENT AREA**									
0020	Lead abatement work area, test kit, per swab	1 Skwk	16	.500	Ea.	4.13	23.50		27.63	43
0025	For dust barriers see Section 01 56 16.10									
0050	Caution sign	1 Skwk	48	.167	Ea.	10.45	7.90		18.35	24.50
0100	Pre-cleaning, HEPA vacuum and wet wipe, floor and wall surfaces	3 Skwk	5000	.005	S.F.	.02	.23		.25	.39
0105	Ceiling, 6' - 11' high		4100	.006		.09	.28		.37	.55
0108	12' - 15' high		3550	.007		.08	.32		.40	.60
0115	Over 15' high		3000	.008		.11	.38		.49	.74
0500	Cover surfaces with polyethylene sheeting									
0550	Floors, each layer, 6 mil	3 Skwk	8000	.003	S.F.	.04	.14		.18	.28
0560	Walls, each layer, 6 mil	"	6000	.004	"	.04	.19		.23	.36
0570	For heights above 12', add						20%			
2400	Post abatement cleaning of protective sheeting, HEPA vacuum & wet wipe	3 Skwk	5000	.005	S.F.	.02	.23		.25	.39
2450	Doff, bag and seal protective sheeting		12000	.002		.01	.09		.10	.16
2500	Post abatement cleaning, HEPA vacuum & wet wipe		5000	.005		.02	.23		.25	.39

02 83 19.23 Encapsulation of Lead-Based Paint

		Crew	Daily Output	Labor-Hours	Unit	Material	2014 Bare Costs Labor	Equipment	Total	Total Incl O&P
0010	**ENCAPSULATION OF LEAD-BASED PAINT**									
0020	Interior, brushwork, trim, under 6"	1 Pord	240	.033	L.F.	2.25	1.32		3.57	4.59
0030	6" to 12" wide		180	.044		3	1.76		4.76	6.10
0040	Balustrades		300	.027		1.80	1.05		2.85	3.67
0050	Pipe to 4" diameter		500	.016		1.10	.63		1.73	2.23
0060	To 8" diameter		375	.021		1.45	.84		2.29	2.95
0070	To 12" diameter		250	.032		2.15	1.27		3.42	4.40
0080	To 16" diameter		170	.047		3.20	1.86		5.06	6.50
0090	Cabinets, ornate design		200	.040	S.F.	2.75	1.58		4.33	5.55
0100	Simple design		250	.032	"	2.20	1.27		3.47	4.45
0110	Doors, 3' x 7', both sides, incl. frame & trim									
0120	Flush	1 Pord	6	1.333	Ea.	27.50	52.50		80	115

02 83 Lead Remediation

02 83 19 – Lead-Based Paint Remediation

02 83 19.23 Encapsulation of Lead-Based Paint

		Crew	Daily Output	Labor-Hours	Unit	Material	2014 Bare Costs Labor	Equipment	Total	Total Incl O&P
0130	French, 10 – 15 lite	1 Pord	3	2.667	Ea.	5.55	105		110.55	175
0140	Panel		4	2		33.50	79		112.50	164
0150	Louvered		2.75	2.909		30.50	115		145.50	219
0160	Windows, per interior side, per 15 S.F.									
0170	1 to 6 lite	1 Pord	14	.571	Ea.	19	22.50		41.50	57.50
0180	7 to 10 lite		7.50	1.067		21	42		63	91
0190	12 lite		5.75	1.391		28.50	55		83.50	120
0200	Radiators		8	1		67.50	39.50		107	138
0210	Grilles, vents		275	.029	S.F.	2	1.15		3.15	4.05
0220	Walls, roller, drywall or plaster		1000	.008		.55	.32		.87	1.12
0230	With spunbonded reinforcing fabric		720	.011		.62	.44		1.06	1.38
0240	Wood		800	.010		.68	.40		1.08	1.38
0250	Ceilings, roller, drywall or plaster		900	.009		.62	.35		.97	1.24
0260	Wood		700	.011		.76	.45		1.21	1.57
0270	Exterior, brushwork, gutters and downspouts		300	.027	L.F.	1.80	1.05		2.85	3.67
0280	Columns		400	.020	S.F.	1.35	.79		2.14	2.76
0290	Spray, siding		600	.013	"	.91	.53		1.44	1.85
0300	Miscellaneous									
0310	Electrical conduit, brushwork, to 2" diameter	1 Pord	500	.016	L.F.	1.10	.63		1.73	2.23
0320	Brick, block or concrete, spray		500	.016	S.F.	1.10	.63		1.73	2.23
0330	Steel, flat surfaces and tanks to 12"		500	.016		1.10	.63		1.73	2.23
0340	Beams, brushwork		400	.020		1.35	.79		2.14	2.76
0350	Trusses		400	.020		1.35	.79		2.14	2.76

02 83 19.26 Removal of Lead-Based Paint

		Crew	Daily Output	Labor-Hours	Unit	Material	2014 Bare Costs Labor	Equipment	Total	Total Incl O&P
0010	**REMOVAL OF LEAD-BASED PAINT** R028319-60									
0011	By chemicals, per application									
0050	Baseboard, to 6" wide	1 Pord	64	.125	L.F.	.71	4.94		5.65	8.75
0070	To 12" wide		32	.250	"	1.37	9.90		11.27	17.35
0200	Balustrades, one side		28	.286	S.F.	1.42	11.30		12.72	19.70
1400	Cabinets, simple design		32	.250		1.28	9.90		11.18	17.25
1420	Ornate design		25	.320		1.55	12.65		14.20	22
1600	Cornice, simple design		60	.133		1.47	5.25		6.72	10.05
1620	Ornate design		20	.400		5.25	15.80		21.05	31.50
2800	Doors, one side, flush		84	.095		1.84	3.77		5.61	8.05
2820	Two panel		80	.100		1.28	3.96		5.24	7.75
2840	Four panel		45	.178		1.37	7.05		8.42	12.80
2880	For trim, one side, add		64	.125	L.F.	.70	4.94		5.64	8.70
3000	Fence, picket, one side		30	.267	S.F.	1.28	10.55		11.83	18.30
3200	Grilles, one side, simple design		30	.267		1.30	10.55		11.85	18.35
3220	Ornate design		25	.320		1.40	12.65		14.05	22
3240	Handrails		90	.089	L.F.	1.30	3.52		4.82	7.10
4400	Pipes, to 4" diameter		90	.089		1.84	3.52		5.36	7.65
4420	To 8" diameter		50	.160		3.68	6.35		10.03	14.20
4440	To 12" diameter		36	.222		5.50	8.80		14.30	20
4460	To 16" diameter		20	.400		7.35	15.80		23.15	33.50
4500	For hangers, add		40	.200	Ea.	2.44	7.90		10.34	15.40
4800	Siding		90	.089	S.F.	1.22	3.52		4.74	7
5000	Trusses, open		55	.145	SF Face	1.92	5.75		7.67	11.35
6200	Windows, one side only, double hung, 1/1 light, 24" x 48" high		4	2	Ea.	23	79		102	152
6220	30" x 60" high		3	2.667		30.50	105		135.50	203
6240	36" x 72" high		2.50	3.200		36.50	127		163.50	243
6280	40" x 80" high		2	4		45.50	158		203.50	305

42

02 83 Lead Remediation

02 83 19 – Lead-Based Paint Remediation

02 83 19.26 Removal of Lead-Based Paint		Crew	Daily Output	Labor-Hours	Unit	Material	2014 Bare Costs Labor	2014 Bare Costs Equipment	Total	Total Incl O&P
6400	Colonial window, 6/6 light, 24" x 48" high	1 Pord	2	4	Ea.	45.50	158		203.50	305
6420	30" x 60" high		1.50	5.333		61	211		272	405
6440	36" x 72" high		1	8		91	315		406	610
6480	40" x 80" high		1	8		91	315		406	610
6600	8/8 light, 24" x 48" high		2	4		45.50	158		203.50	305
6620	40" x 80" high		1	8		91	315		406	610
6800	12/12 light, 24" x 48" high		1	8		91	315		406	610
6820	40" x 80" high		.75	10.667		122	420		542	810
6840	Window frame & trim items, included in pricing above									
7000	Hand scraping and HEPA vacuum, less than 4 S.F.	1 Pord	8	1	Ea.	1.65	39.50		41.15	65.50
8000	Collect and bag bulk material, 3 C.F. bags, by hand		30	.267	"	1.65	10.55		12.20	18.70
9000	Minimum labor/equipment charge		3	2.667	Job		105		105	169

02 85 Mold Remediation

02 85 16 – Mold Remediation Preparation and Containment

02 85 16.40 Mold Remediation Plans and Methods

		Crew	Daily Output	Labor-Hours	Unit	Material	2014 Bare Costs Labor	2014 Bare Costs Equipment	Total	Total Incl O&P
0010	**MOLD REMEDIATION PLANS AND METHODS**									
0020	Initial inspection, areas to 2500 S.F.				Total				268	295
0030	Areas to 5000 S.F.								440	485
0032	Areas to 10000 S.F.								440	485
0040	Testing, air sample each								126	139
0050	Swab sample								115	127
0060	Tape sample								125	140
0070	Post remediation air test								126	139
0080	Mold abatement plan, area to 2500 S.F.								1,225	1,325
0090	Areas to 5000 S.F.								1,625	1,775
0095	Areas to 10000 S.F.								2,550	2,800
0100	Packup & removal of contents, average 3 bedroom home, excl storage								8,150	8,975
0110	Average 5 bedroom home, excl storage								15,300	16,800
0600	For demolition in mold contaminated areas, see Section 02 85 33.50									
0610	For personal protection equipment, see Section 02 82 13.41									

02 85 16.50 Preparation of Mold Containment Area

		Crew	Daily Output	Labor-Hours	Unit	Material	2014 Bare Costs Labor	2014 Bare Costs Equipment	Total	Total Incl O&P
0010	**PREPARATION OF MOLD CONTAINMENT AREA**									
0100	Pre-cleaning, HEPA vacuum and wet wipe, flat surfaces	A-9	12000	.005	S.F.	.02	.27		.29	.47
0300	Separation barrier, 2" x 4" @ 16", 1/2" plywood ea. side, 8' high	2 Carp	400	.040		3.25	1.83		5.08	6.60
0310	12' high		320	.050		3.25	2.29		5.54	7.35
0320	16' high		200	.080		2.25	3.67		5.92	8.55
0400	Personnel decontam. chamber, 2" x 4" @ 16", 3/4" ply ea. side		280	.057		4.25	2.62		6.87	9
0450	Waste decontam. chamber, 2" x 4" studs @ 16", 3/4" ply each side		360	.044		4.25	2.04		6.29	8.05
0500	Cover surfaces with polyethylene sheeting									
0501	Including glue and tape									
0550	Floors, each layer, 6 mil	A-9	8000	.008	S.F.	.04	.41		.45	.71
0551	4 mil		9000	.007		.03	.36		.39	.61
0560	Walls, each layer, 6 mil		6000	.011		.04	.55		.59	.93
0561	4 mil		7000	.009		.03	.47		.50	.78
0570	For heights above 12', add						20%			
0575	For heights above 20', add						30%			
0580	For fire retardant poly, add					100%				
0590	For large open areas, deduct					10%	20%			
0600	Seal floor penetrations with foam firestop to 36 sq. in.	2 Carp	200	.080	Ea.	9.25	3.67		12.92	16.25
0610	36 sq. in. to 72 sq. in.		125	.128		18.50	5.85		24.35	30

43

02 85 Mold Remediation

02 85 16 – Mold Remediation Preparation and Containment

02 85 16.50 Preparation of Mold Containment Area	Crew	Daily Output	Labor-Hours	Unit	Material	2014 Bare Costs Labor	Equipment	Total	Total Incl O&P
0615 72 sq. in. to 144 sq. in.	2 Carp	80	.200	Ea.	37	9.15		46.15	56
0620 Wall penetrations, to 36 square inches		180	.089		9.25	4.08		13.33	16.90
0630 36 sq. in. to 72 sq. in.		100	.160		18.50	7.35		25.85	32.50
0640 72 sq. in. to 144 sq. in.		60	.267		37	12.25		49.25	61
0800 Caulk seams with latex caulk	1 Carp	230	.035	L.F.	.17	1.59		1.76	2.81
0900 Set up neg. air machine, 1-2k CFM/25 M.C.F. volume	1 Asbe	4.30	1.860	Ea.		95		95	153

02 85 33 – Removal and Disposal of Materials with Mold

02 85 33.50 Demolition in Mold Contaminated Area	Crew	Daily Output	Labor-Hours	Unit	Material	2014 Bare Costs Labor	Equipment	Total	Total Incl O&P
0010 **DEMOLITION IN MOLD CONTAMINATED AREA**									
0200 Ceiling, including suspension system, plaster and lath	A-9	2100	.030	S.F.	.14	1.56		1.70	2.66
0210 Finished plaster, leaving wire lath		585	.109		.49	5.60		6.09	9.55
0220 Suspended acoustical tile		3500	.018		.08	.94		1.02	1.59
0230 Concealed tile grid system		3000	.021		.10	1.09		1.19	1.86
0240 Metal pan grid system		1500	.043		.19	2.19		2.38	3.72
0250 Gypsum board		2500	.026		.12	1.31		1.43	2.24
0255 Plywood		2500	.026		.12	1.31		1.43	2.24
0260 Lighting fixtures up to 2' x 4'		72	.889	Ea.	4.01	45.50		49.51	77.50
0400 Partitions, non load bearing									
0410 Plaster, lath, and studs	A-9	690	.093	S.F.	1.02	4.75		5.77	8.75
0450 Gypsum board and studs		1390	.046		.21	2.36		2.57	4.02
0465 Carpet & pad		1390	.046		.21	2.36		2.57	4.02
0600 Pipe insulation, air cell type, up to 4" diameter pipe		900	.071	L.F.	.32	3.64		3.96	6.20
0610 4" to 8" diameter pipe		800	.080		.36	4.10		4.46	7
0620 10" to 12" diameter pipe		700	.091		.41	4.68		5.09	7.95
0630 14" to 16" diameter pipe		550	.116		.53	5.95		6.48	10.15
0650 Over 16" diameter pipe		650	.098	S.F.	.44	5.05		5.49	8.60
9000 For type B (supplied air) respirator equipment, add				%				10%	10%

Estimating Tips

General

- Carefully check all the plans and specifications. Concrete often appears on drawings other than structural drawings, including mechanical and electrical drawings for equipment pads. The cost of cutting and patching is often difficult to estimate. See Subdivision 03 81 for Concrete Cutting, Subdivision 02 41 19.16 for Cutout Demolition, Subdivision 03 05 05.10 for Concrete Demolition, and Subdivision 02 41 19.19 for Rubbish Handling (handling, loading and hauling of debris).
- Always obtain concrete prices from suppliers near the job site. A volume discount can often be negotiated, depending upon competition in the area. Remember to add for waste, particularly for slabs and footings on grade.

03 10 00 Concrete Forming and Accessories

- A primary cost for concrete construction is forming. Most jobs today are constructed with prefabricated forms. The selection of the forms best suited for the job and the total square feet of forms required for efficient concrete forming and placing are key elements in estimating concrete construction. Enough forms must be available for erection to make efficient use of the concrete placing equipment and crew.
- Concrete accessories for forming and placing depend upon the systems used. Study the plans and specifications to ensure that all special accessory requirements have been included in the cost estimate, such as anchor bolts, inserts, and hangers.
- Included within costs for forms-in-place are all necessary bracing and shoring.

03 20 00 Concrete Reinforcing

- Ascertain that the reinforcing steel supplier has included all accessories, cutting, bending, and an allowance for lapping, splicing, and waste. A good rule of thumb is 10% for lapping, splicing, and waste. Also, 10% waste should be allowed for welded wire fabric.
- The unit price items in the subdivisions for Reinforcing In Place, Glass Fiber Reinforcing, and Welded Wire Fabric include the labor to install accessories such as beam and slab bolsters, high chairs, and bar ties and tie wire. The material cost for these accessories is not included; they may be obtained from the Accessories Division.

03 30 00 Cast-In-Place Concrete

- When estimating structural concrete, pay particular attention to requirements for concrete additives, curing methods, and surface treatments. Special consideration for climate, hot or cold, must be included in your estimate. Be sure to include requirements for concrete placing equipment, and concrete finishing.
- For accurate concrete estimating, the estimator must consider each of the following major components individually: forms, reinforcing steel, ready-mix concrete, placement of the concrete, and finishing of the top surface. For faster estimating, Subdivision 03 30 53.40 for Concrete-In-Place can be used; here, various items of concrete work are presented that include the costs of all five major components (unless specifically stated otherwise).

03 40 00 Precast Concrete
03 50 00 Cast Decks and Underlayment

- The cost of hauling precast concrete structural members is often an important factor. For this reason, it is important to get a quote from the nearest supplier. It may become economically feasible to set up precasting beds on the site if the hauling costs are prohibitive.

Reference Numbers

Reference numbers are shown in shaded boxes at the beginning of some major classifications. These numbers refer to related items in the Reference Section. The reference information may be an estimating procedure, an alternate pricing method, or technical information.

Note: Not all subdivisions listed here necessarily appear in this publication.

03 01 30 – Maintenance of Cast-In-Place Concrete

03 01 30.62 Concrete Patching	Crew	Daily Output	Labor-Hours	Unit	Material	2014 Bare Costs Labor	Equipment	Total	Total Incl O&P
0010 **CONCRETE PATCHING**									
0100 Floors, 1/4" thick, small areas, regular grout	1 Cefi	170	.047	S.F.	1.42	2.07		3.49	4.83
0150 Epoxy grout	"	100	.080	"	7.80	3.52		11.32	14.10
2000 Walls, including chipping, cleaning and epoxy grout									
2100 1/4" deep	1 Cefi	65	.123	S.F.	7.20	5.40		12.60	16.45
2150 1/2" deep		50	.160		14.40	7.05		21.45	27
2200 3/4" deep		40	.200		21.50	8.80		30.30	38
9000 Minimum labor/equipment charge		4.50	1.778	Job		78.50		78.50	124

03 01 30.71 Concrete Crack Repair

	Crew	Daily Output	Labor-Hours	Unit	Material	2014 Bare Costs Labor	Equipment	Total	Total Incl O&P
0010 **CONCRETE CRACK REPAIR**									
1000 Structural repair of concrete cracks by epoxy injection (ACI RAP-1)									
1001 suitable for horizontal, vertical and overhead repairs									
1010 Clean/grind concrete surface(s) free of contaminants	1 Cefi	400	.020	L.F.		.88		.88	1.39
1015 Rout crack with v-notch crack chaser, if needed	C-32	600	.027		.04	1.08	.15	1.27	1.94
1020 Blow out crack with oil-free dry compressed air (1 pass)	C-28	3000	.003			.12	.01	.13	.20
1030 Install surface-mounted entry ports (spacing = concrete depth)	1 Cefi	400	.020	Ea.	1.34	.88		2.22	2.86
1040 Cap crack at surface with epoxy gel (per side/face)		400	.020	L.F.	.33	.88		1.21	1.75
1050 Snap off ports, grind off epoxy cap residue after injection		200	.040	"		1.76		1.76	2.78
1100 Manual injection with 2-part epoxy cartridge, excludes prep									
1110 Up to 1/32" (0.03125") wide x 4" deep	1 Cefi	160	.050	L.F.	.17	2.20		2.37	3.66
1120 6" deep		120	.067		.25	2.94		3.19	4.90
1130 8" deep		107	.075		.33	3.29		3.62	5.55
1140 10" deep		100	.080		.41	3.52		3.93	6
1150 12" deep		96	.083		.50	3.67		4.17	6.35
1210 Up to 1/16" (0.0625") wide x 4" deep		160	.050		.33	2.20		2.53	3.84
1220 6" deep		120	.067		.50	2.94		3.44	5.20
1230 8" deep		107	.075		.66	3.29		3.95	5.95
1240 10" deep		100	.080		.83	3.52		4.35	6.45
1250 12" deep		96	.083		.99	3.67		4.66	6.90
1310 Up to 3/32" (0.09375") wide x 4" deep		160	.050		.50	2.20		2.70	4.03
1320 6" deep		120	.067		.74	2.94		3.68	5.45
1330 8" deep		107	.075		.99	3.29		4.28	6.30
1340 10" deep		100	.080		1.24	3.52		4.76	6.90
1350 12" deep		96	.083		1.49	3.67		5.16	7.45
1410 Up to 1/8" (0.125") wide x 4" deep		160	.050		.66	2.20		2.86	4.21
1420 6" deep		120	.067		.99	2.94		3.93	5.70
1430 8" deep		107	.075		1.32	3.29		4.61	6.65
1440 10" deep		100	.080		1.65	3.52		5.17	7.35
1450 12" deep		96	.083		1.98	3.67		5.65	8
1500 Pneumatic injection with 2-part bulk epoxy, excludes prep									
1510 Up to 5/32" (0.15625") wide x 4" deep	C-31	240	.033	L.F.	.23	1.47	1.54	3.24	4.28
1520 6" deep		180	.044		.35	1.96	2.06	4.37	5.75
1530 8" deep		160	.050		.47	2.20	2.32	4.99	6.55
1540 10" deep		150	.053		.58	2.35	2.47	5.40	7.05
1550 12" deep		144	.056		.70	2.45	2.57	5.72	7.45
1610 Up to 3/16" (0.1875") wide x 4" deep		240	.033		.28	1.47	1.54	3.29	4.33
1620 6" deep		180	.044		.42	1.96	2.06	4.44	5.80
1630 8" deep		160	.050		.56	2.20	2.32	5.08	6.65
1640 10" deep		150	.053		.70	2.35	2.47	5.52	7.20
1650 12" deep		144	.056		.84	2.45	2.57	5.86	7.60
1710 Up to 1/4" (0.1875") wide x 4" deep		240	.033		.37	1.47	1.54	3.38	4.43
1720 6" deep		180	.044		.56	1.96	2.06	4.58	5.95

03 01 Maintenance of Concrete

03 01 30 – Maintenance of Cast-In-Place Concrete

03 01 30.71 Concrete Crack Repair

		Crew	Daily Output	Labor-Hours	Unit	Material	2014 Bare Costs Labor	2014 Bare Costs Equipment	Total	Total Incl O&P
1730	8" deep	C-31	160	.050	L.F.	.75	2.20	2.32	5.27	6.85
1740	10" deep		150	.053		.94	2.35	2.47	5.76	7.45
1750	12" deep	↓	144	.056	↓	1.12	2.45	2.57	6.14	7.90
2000	Non-structural filling of concrete cracks by gravity-fed resin (ACI RAP-2)									
2001	suitable for individual cracks in stable horizontal surfaces only									
2010	Clean/grind concrete surface(s) free of contaminants	1 Cefi	400	.020	L.F.		.88		.88	1.39
2020	Rout crack with v-notch crack chaser, if needed	C-32	600	.027		.04	1.08	.15	1.27	1.94
2030	Blow out crack with oil-free dry compressed air (1 pass)	C-28	3000	.003			.12	.01	.13	.20
2040	Cap crack with epoxy gel at underside of elevated slabs, if needed	1 Cefi	400	.020		.33	.88		1.21	1.75
2050	Insert backer rod into crack, if needed		400	.020		.02	.88		.90	1.42
2060	Partially fill crack with fine dry sand, if needed		800	.010		.02	.44		.46	.72
2070	Apply two beads of sealant alongside crack to form reservoir, if needed	↓	400	.020	↓	.25	.88		1.13	1.67
2100	Manual filling with squeeze bottle of 2-part epoxy resin									
2110	Full depth crack up to 1/16" (0.0625") wide x 4" deep	1 Cefi	300	.027	L.F.	.09	1.17		1.26	1.95
2120	6" deep		240	.033		.14	1.47		1.61	2.47
2130	8" deep		200	.040		.18	1.76		1.94	2.98
2140	10" deep		185	.043		.23	1.90		2.13	3.26
2150	12" deep		175	.046		.27	2.01		2.28	3.48
2210	Full depth crack up to 1/8" (0.125") wide x 4" deep		270	.030		.18	1.31		1.49	2.26
2220	6" deep		215	.037		.27	1.64		1.91	2.89
2230	8" deep		180	.044		.36	1.96		2.32	3.49
2240	10" deep		165	.048		.46	2.14		2.60	3.87
2250	12" deep		155	.052		.55	2.27		2.82	4.19
2310	Partial depth crack up to 3/16" (0.1875") wide x 1" deep		300	.027		.07	1.17		1.24	1.93
2410	Up to 1/4" (0.250") wide x 1" deep		270	.030		.09	1.31		1.40	2.16
2510	Up to 5/16" (0.3125") wide x 1" deep		250	.032		.11	1.41		1.52	2.35
2610	Up to 3/8" (0.375") wide x 1" deep	↓	240	.033	↓	.14	1.47		1.61	2.47

03 01 30.72 Concrete Surface Repairs

		Crew	Daily Output	Labor-Hours	Unit	Material	2014 Bare Costs Labor	2014 Bare Costs Equipment	Total	Total Incl O&P
0010	**CONCRETE SURFACE REPAIRS**									
9000	Surface repair by Methacrylate flood coat (ACI RAP-13)									
9010	Suitable for healing and sealing horizontal surfaces only									
9020	Large cracks must previously have been repaired or filled									
9100	Shotblast entire surface to remove contaminants	A-1A	4000	.002	S.F.		.09	.05	.14	.21
9200	Blow off dust and debris with oil-free dry compressed air	C-28	16000	.001			.02		.02	.03
9300	Flood coat surface w/Methacrylate, distribute w/broom/squeegee, no prep.	3 Cefi	8000	.003		.96	.13		1.09	1.27
9400	Lightly broadcast even coat of dry silica sand while sealer coat is tacky	1 Cefi	8000	.001	↓	.01	.04		.05	.08

03 05 Common Work Results for Concrete

03 05 05 – Selective Concrete Demolition

03 05 05.10 Selective Demolition, Concrete

		Crew	Daily Output	Labor-Hours	Unit	Material	2014 Bare Costs Labor	2014 Bare Costs Equipment	Total	Total Incl O&P
0010	**SELECTIVE DEMOLITION, CONCRETE** R024119-10									
0012	Excludes saw cutting, torch cutting, loading or hauling									
0050	Break into small pieces, reinf. less than 1% of cross-sectional area	B-9	24	1.667	C.Y.		62	9.75	71.75	112
0060	Reinforcing 1% to 2% of cross-sectional area		16	2.500			92.50	14.60	107.10	168
0070	Reinforcing more than 2% of cross-sectional area	↓	8	5	↓		185	29	214	335
0150	Remove whole pieces, up to 2 tons per piece	E-18	36	1.111	Ea.		56.50	26.50	83	131
0160	2 – 5 tons per piece		30	1.333			68	32	100	157
0170	5 – 10 tons per piece		24	1.667			85	40	125	196
0180	10 – 15 tons per piece		18	2.222			113	53.50	166.50	262
0250	Precast unit embedded in masonry, up to 1 C.F.	D-1	16	1			41.50		41.50	67
0260	1 – 2 C.F.	↓	12	1.333			55		55	89.50

03 05 Common Work Results for Concrete

03 05 05 – Selective Concrete Demolition

03 05 05.10 Selective Demolition, Concrete	Crew	Daily Output	Labor-Hours	Unit	Material	2014 Bare Costs Labor	Equipment	Total	Total Incl O&P
0270	2 – 5 C.F.	D-1	10	1.600	Ea.		66		66	107
0280	5 – 10 C.F.	↓	8	2	↓		82.50		82.50	134
0990	For hydrodemolition see Section 02 41 13.15									
1910	Minimum labor/equipment charge	B-9	2	20	Job		740	117	857	1,350

03 05 13 – Basic Concrete Materials

03 05 13.20 Concrete Admixtures and Surface Treatments

		Crew	Daily Output	Labor-Hours	Unit	Material	2014 Bare Costs Labor	Equipment	Total	Total Incl O&P
0010	**CONCRETE ADMIXTURES AND SURFACE TREATMENTS**									
0040	Abrasives, aluminum oxide, over 20 tons				Lb.	1.82			1.82	2
0050	1 to 20 tons					1.95			1.95	2.14
0070	Under 1 ton					2.03			2.03	2.23
0100	Silicon carbide, black, over 20 tons					2.78			2.78	3.06
0110	1 to 20 tons					2.96			2.96	3.25
0120	Under 1 ton				↓	3.08			3.08	3.39
0200	Air entraining agent, .7 to 1.5 oz. per bag, 55 gallon drum				Gal.	13.35			13.35	14.65
0220	5 gallon pail					18.35			18.35	20
0300	Bonding agent, acrylic latex, 250 S.F. per gallon, 5 gallon pail					22			22	24.50
0320	Epoxy resin, 80 S.F. per gallon, 4 gallon case				↓	61.50			61.50	67.50
0400	Calcium chloride, 50 lb. bags, TL lots				Ton	770			770	845
0420	Less than truckload lots				Bag	23.50			23.50	25.50
0500	Carbon black, liquid, 2 to 8 lb. per bag of cement				Lb.	8.65			8.65	9.55
0600	Colored pigments, integral, 2 to 10 lb. per bag of cement, subtle colors					2.40			2.40	2.64
0610	Standard colors					3.25			3.25	3.58
0620	Premium colors				↓	5.40			5.40	5.95
0920	Dustproofing compound, 250 S.F./gal., 5 gallon pail				Gal.	6.20			6.20	6.80
1010	Epoxy based, 125 S.F./gal., 5 gallon pail				"	53			53	58
1100	Hardeners, metallic, 55 lb. bags, natural (grey)				Lb.	.66			.66	.73
1200	Colors					2.17			2.17	2.38
1300	Non-metallic, 55 lb. bags, natural grey					.41			.41	.45
1320	Colors				↓	.90			.90	.99
1550	Release agent, for tilt slabs, 5 gallon pail				Gal.	16.20			16.20	17.80
1570	For forms, 5 gallon pail					13.35			13.35	14.70
1590	Concrete release agent for forms, 100% biodegradeable, zero VOC, 5 gal pail G					19.20			19.20	21
1595	55 gallon drum G					15.75			15.75	17.35
1600	Sealer, hardener and dustproofer, epoxy-based, 125 S.F./gal., 5 gallon unit					53			53	58
1620	3 gallon unit					58			58	64
1630	Sealer, solvent-based, 250 S.F./gal., 55 gallon drum					23.50			23.50	25.50
1640	5 gallon pail					29.50			29.50	32.50
1650	Sealer, water based, 350 S.F., 55 gallon drum					22			22	24.50
1660	5 gallon pail					25			25	27.50
1900	Set retarder, 100 S.F./gal., 1 gallon pail				↓	22			22	24
2000	Waterproofing, integral 1 lb. per bag of cement				Lb.	2.02			2.02	2.22
2100	Powdered metallic, 40 lb. per 100 S.F., standard colors					2.40			2.40	2.64
2120	Premium colors				↓	3.36			3.36	3.70
3000	For integral colored pigments, 2500 psi (5 bag mix)									
3100	Standard colors, 1.8 lb. per bag, add				C.Y.	21.50			21.50	24
3200	9.4 lb. per bag, add					113			113	124
3400	Premium colors, 1.8 lb. per bag, add					29.50			29.50	32
3500	7.5 lb. per bag, add					122			122	134
3700	Ultra premium colors, 1.8 lb. per bag, add					48.50			48.50	53.50
3800	7.5 lb. per bag, add				↓	203			203	223

03 05 Common Work Results for Concrete

03 05 13 – Basic Concrete Materials

03 05 13.85 Winter Protection	Crew	Daily Output	Labor-Hours	Unit	Material	2014 Bare Costs Labor	Equipment	Total	Total Incl O&P
0010 **WINTER PROTECTION**									
0012 For heated ready mix, add				C.Y.	4.50			4.50	4.95
0100 Temporary heat to protect concrete, 24 hours	2 Clab	50	.320	M.S.F.	535	11.75		546.75	605
0200 Temporary shelter for slab on grade, wood frame/polyethylene sheeting									
0201 Build or remove, light framing for short spans	2 Carp	10	1.600	M.S.F.	284	73.50		357.50	430
0210 Large framing for long spans	"	3	5.333	"	380	245		625	820
0710 Electrically, heated pads, 15 watts/S.F., 20 uses				S.F.	.52			.52	.57

03 11 Concrete Forming

03 11 13 – Structural Cast-In-Place Concrete Forming

03 11 13.20 Forms In Place, Beams and Girders

03 11 13.20 Forms In Place, Beams and Girders		Crew	Daily Output	Labor-Hours	Unit	Material	2014 Bare Costs Labor	Equipment	Total	Total Incl O&P
0010 **FORMS IN PLACE, BEAMS AND GIRDERS**	R031113-40									
0500 Exterior spandrel, job-built plywood, 12" wide, 1 use	R031113-60	C-2	225	.213	SFCA	2.98	9.55		12.53	18.95
0650 4 use			310	.155		.97	6.90		7.87	12.40
1000 18" wide, 1 use			250	.192		2.69	8.55		11.24	17.05
1150 4 use			315	.152		.88	6.80		7.68	12.15
1500 24" wide, 1 use			265	.181		2.47	8.10		10.57	16
1650 4 use			325	.148		.80	6.60		7.40	11.75
2000 Interior beam, job-built plywood, 12" wide, 1 use			300	.160		3.54	7.15		10.69	15.65
2150 4 use			377	.127		1.15	5.70		6.85	10.60
2500 24" wide, 1 use			320	.150		2.52	6.70		9.22	13.75
2650 4 use			395	.122		.81	5.45		6.26	9.80
3000 Encasing steel beam, hung, job-built plywood, 1 use			325	.148		3.09	6.60		9.69	14.25
3150 4 use			430	.112		1	4.98		5.98	9.30
9000 Minimum labor/equipment charge		2 Carp	2	8	Job		365		365	605

03 11 13.25 Forms In Place, Columns

03 11 13.25 Forms In Place, Columns		Crew	Daily Output	Labor-Hours	Unit	Material	2014 Bare Costs Labor	Equipment	Total	Total Incl O&P
0010 **FORMS IN PLACE, COLUMNS**	R031113-40									
0500 Round fiberglass, 4 use per mo., rent, 12" diameter		C-1	160	.200	L.F.	8.15	8.70		16.85	23.50
0550 16" diameter	R031113-60		150	.213		9.70	9.30		19	26
0600 18" diameter			140	.229		10.85	9.95		20.80	28.50
0650 24" diameter			135	.237		13.50	10.30		23.80	32
0700 28" diameter			130	.246		15.10	10.70		25.80	34
0800 30" diameter			125	.256		15.75	11.15		26.90	35.50
0850 36" diameter			120	.267		21	11.60		32.60	42
1500 Round fiber tube, recycled paper, 1 use, 8" diameter	G		155	.206		1.66	9		10.66	16.60
1550 10" diameter	G		155	.206		2.24	9		11.24	17.20
1600 12" diameter	G		150	.213		2.60	9.30		11.90	18.10
1650 14" diameter	G		145	.221		3.77	9.60		13.37	19.95
1700 16" diameter	G		140	.229		4.52	9.95		14.47	21.50
1720 18" diameter	G		140	.229		5.30	9.95		15.25	22
1750 20" diameter	G		135	.237		7.30	10.30		17.60	25
1800 24" diameter	G		130	.246		9.30	10.70		20	28
1850 30" diameter	G		125	.256		13.60	11.15		24.75	33.50
1900 36" diameter	G		115	.278		17.05	12.10		29.15	38.50
1950 42" diameter	G		100	.320		42	13.95		55.95	69.50
2000 48" diameter	G		85	.376		48.50	16.40		64.90	80.50
2200 For seamless type, add						15%				
3000 Round, steel, 4 use per mo., rent, regular duty, 14" diameter	G	C-1	145	.221	L.F.	17.55	9.60		27.15	35
3050 16" diameter	G		125	.256		17.90	11.15		29.05	38
3100 Heavy duty, 20" diameter	G		105	.305		19.75	13.25		33	43.50

03 11 13 – Structural Cast-In-Place Concrete Forming

03 11 13.25 Forms In Place, Columns

		Crew	Daily Output	Labor-Hours	Unit	Material	2014 Bare Costs Labor	Equipment	Total	Total Incl O&P
3150	24" diameter [G]	C-1	85	.376	L.F.	21.50	16.40		37.90	50.50
3200	30" diameter [G]		70	.457		25	19.90		44.90	59.50
3250	36" diameter [G]		60	.533		26.50	23		49.50	67
3300	48" diameter [G]		50	.640		39.50	28		67.50	89.50
3350	60" diameter [G]		45	.711		48.50	31		79.50	105
4500	For second and succeeding months, deduct					50%				
5000	Job-built plywood, 8" x 8" columns, 1 use	C-1	165	.194	SFCA	2.67	8.45		11.12	16.85
5050	2 use		195	.164		1.53	7.15		8.68	13.45
5100	3 use		210	.152		1.07	6.65		7.72	12.10
5150	4 use		215	.149		.88	6.50		7.38	11.60
5500	12" x 12" columns, 1 use		180	.178		2.56	7.75		10.31	15.50
5550	2 use		210	.152		1.41	6.65		8.06	12.45
5600	3 use		220	.145		1.02	6.35		7.37	11.55
5650	4 use		225	.142		.83	6.20		7.03	11.10
6000	16" x 16" columns, 1 use		185	.173		2.55	7.55		10.10	15.20
6050	2 use		215	.149		1.36	6.50		7.86	12.15
6100	3 use		230	.139		1.02	6.05		7.07	11.10
6150	4 use		235	.136		.83	5.95		6.78	10.65
6500	24" x 24" columns, 1 use		190	.168		2.87	7.35		10.22	15.20
6550	2 use		216	.148		1.58	6.45		8.03	12.35
6600	3 use		230	.139		1.15	6.05		7.20	11.20
6650	4 use		238	.134		.93	5.85		6.78	10.65
7000	36" x 36" columns, 1 use		200	.160		2.30	6.95		9.25	14
7050	2 use		230	.139		1.30	6.05		7.35	11.40
7100	3 use		245	.131		.92	5.70		6.62	10.35
7150	4 use		250	.128		.75	5.55		6.30	9.95
7400	Steel framed plywood, based on 50 uses of purchased									
7420	forms, and 4 uses of bracing lumber									
7500	8" x 8" column	C-1	340	.094	SFCA	2.11	4.10		6.21	9.05
7550	10" x 10"		350	.091		1.84	3.98		5.82	8.55
7600	12" x 12"		370	.086		1.56	3.77		5.33	7.90
7650	16" x 16"		400	.080		1.22	3.48		4.70	7.05
7700	20" x 20"		420	.076		1.08	3.32		4.40	6.65
7750	24" x 24"		440	.073		.78	3.17		3.95	6.05
7755	30" x 30"		440	.073		.99	3.17		4.16	6.30
7760	36" x 36"		460	.070		.87	3.03		3.90	5.95
9000	Minimum labor/equipment charge	2 Carp	2	8	Job		365		365	605

03 11 13.35 Forms In Place, Elevated Slabs

		Crew	Daily Output	Labor-Hours	Unit	Material	2014 Bare Costs Labor	Equipment	Total	Total Incl O&P
0010	**FORMS IN PLACE, ELEVATED SLABS** R031113-40									
1000	Flat plate, job-built plywood, to 15' high, 1 use	C-2	470	.102	S.F.	3.64	4.56		8.20	11.50
1150	4 use R031113-60		560	.086		1.18	3.83		5.01	7.60
1500	15' to 20' high ceilings, 4 use		495	.097		1.25	4.33		5.58	8.45
2000	Flat slab, drop panels, job-built plywood, to 15' high, 1 use		449	.107		4.20	4.77		8.97	12.45
2150	4 use		544	.088		1.37	3.94		5.31	7.95
2250	15' to 20' high ceilings, 4 use		480	.100		2.43	4.47		6.90	10
3500	Floor slab, with 1-way joist pans, 1 use		415	.116		5.95	5.15		11.10	15.05
3650	4 use		500	.096		3.12	4.29		7.41	10.50
4500	With 2-way waffle domes, 1 use		405	.119		6.10	5.30		11.40	15.40
4550	4 use		470	.102		3.25	4.56		7.81	11.10
5000	Box out for slab openings, over 16" deep, 1 use		190	.253	SFCA	4.14	11.30		15.44	23
5050	2 use		240	.200	"	2.28	8.95		11.23	17.15
5500	Shallow slab box outs, to 10 S.F.		42	1.143	Ea.	10.50	51		61.50	95.50

03 11 Concrete Forming

03 11 13 – Structural Cast-In-Place Concrete Forming

03 11 13.35 Forms In Place, Elevated Slabs

		Crew	Daily Output	Labor-Hours	Unit	Material	2014 Bare Costs Labor	Equipment	Total	Total Incl O&P
5550	Over 10 S.F. (use perimeter)	C-2	600	.080	L.F.	1.41	3.57		4.98	7.40
6000	Bulkhead forms for slab, with keyway, 1 use, 2 piece		500	.096		1.95	4.29		6.24	9.20
6100	3 piece (see also edge forms)	↓	460	.104		2.14	4.66		6.80	10
6200	Slab bulkhead form, 4-1/2" high, exp metal, w/keyway & stakes [G]	C-1	1200	.027		.88	1.16		2.04	2.88
6210	5-1/2" high [G]		1100	.029		1.01	1.27		2.28	3.19
6215	7-1/2" high [G]		960	.033		1.25	1.45		2.70	3.77
6220	9-1/2" high [G]		840	.038	↓	1.36	1.66		3.02	4.23
6500	Curb forms, wood, 6" to 12" high, on elevated slabs, 1 use		180	.178	SFCA	1.51	7.75		9.26	14.35
6550	2 use		205	.156		.83	6.80		7.63	12.05
6600	3 use		220	.145		.60	6.35		6.95	11.05
6650	4 use		225	.142	↓	.49	6.20		6.69	10.75
7000	Edge forms to 6" high, on elevated slab, 4 use		500	.064	L.F.	.18	2.79		2.97	4.78
7070	7" to 12" high, 1 use		162	.198	SFCA	1.14	8.60		9.74	15.40
7080	2 use		198	.162		.62	7.05		7.67	12.25
7090	3 use		222	.144		.45	6.30		6.75	10.80
7101	4 use		350	.091	↓	.18	3.98		4.16	6.75
7500	Depressed area forms to 12" high, 4 use		300	.107	L.F.	.92	4.65		5.57	8.65
7550	12" to 24" high, 4 use		175	.183		1.26	7.95		9.21	14.50
8000	Perimeter deck and rail for elevated slabs, straight		90	.356		12	15.50		27.50	38.50
8050	Curved		65	.492	↓	16.45	21.50		37.95	53
8500	Void forms, round plastic, 8" high x 3" diameter [G]		450	.071	Ea.	2.08	3.10		5.18	7.40
8550	4" diameter [G]		425	.075		3.23	3.28		6.51	8.95
8600	6" diameter [G]		400	.080		5.05	3.48		8.53	11.25
8650	8" diameter [G]	↓	375	.085	↓	8.80	3.72		12.52	15.75
9000	Minimum labor/equipment charge	2 Carp	2	8	Job		365		365	605

03 11 13.40 Forms In Place, Equipment Foundations

		Crew	Daily Output	Labor-Hours	Unit	Material	2014 Bare Costs Labor	Equipment	Total	Total Incl O&P
0010	**FORMS IN PLACE, EQUIPMENT FOUNDATIONS** R031113-40									
0020	1 use	C-2	160	.300	SFCA	3.09	13.40		16.49	25.50
0050	2 use R031113-60		190	.253		1.70	11.30		13	20.50
0100	3 use		200	.240		1.24	10.70		11.94	18.95
0150	4 use	↓	205	.234	↓	1.01	10.45		11.46	18.30
9000	Minimum labor/equipment charge	1 Carp	3	2.667	Job		122		122	201

03 11 13.45 Forms In Place, Footings

		Crew	Daily Output	Labor-Hours	Unit	Material	2014 Bare Costs Labor	Equipment	Total	Total Incl O&P
0010	**FORMS IN PLACE, FOOTINGS** R031113-40									
0020	Continuous wall, plywood, 1 use	C-1	375	.085	SFCA	6.25	3.72		9.97	12.95
0150	4 use R031113-60	"	485	.066	"	2.03	2.87		4.90	6.95
1500	Keyway, 4 use, tapered wood, 2" x 4"	1 Carp	530	.015	L.F.	.20	.69		.89	1.36
1550	2" x 6"	"	500	.016	"	.28	.73		1.01	1.52
3000	Pile cap, square or rectangular, job-built plywood, 1 use	C-1	290	.110	SFCA	2.79	4.81		7.60	10.95
3150	4 use		383	.084		.91	3.64		4.55	7
5000	Spread footings, job-built lumber, 1 use		305	.105		2	4.57		6.57	9.70
5150	4 use	↓	414	.077	↓	.65	3.37		4.02	6.25
9000	Minimum labor/equipment charge	1 Carp	3	2.667	Job		122		122	201

03 11 13.47 Forms In Place, Gas Station Forms

		Crew	Daily Output	Labor-Hours	Unit	Material	2014 Bare Costs Labor	Equipment	Total	Total Incl O&P
0010	**FORMS IN PLACE, GAS STATION FORMS**									
0050	Curb fascia, with template, 12 ga. steel, left in place, 9" high [G]	1 Carp	50	.160	L.F.	13.90	7.35		21.25	27.50
1000	Sign or light bases, 18" diameter, 9" high [G]		9	.889	Ea.	87.50	41		128.50	163
1050	30" diameter, 13" high [G]		8	1	"	139	46		185	229
1990	Minimum labor/equipment charge	↓	2	4	Job		183		183	300
2000	Island forms, 10' long, 9" high, 3'- 6" wide [G]	C-1	10	3.200	Ea.	390	139		529	655
2050	4' wide [G]		9	3.556		400	155		555	695
2500	20' long, 9" high, 4' wide [G]	↓	6	5.333	↓	645	232		877	1,100

51

03 11 Concrete Forming

03 11 13 – Structural Cast-In-Place Concrete Forming

03 11 13.47 Forms In Place, Gas Station Forms		Crew	Daily Output	Labor-Hours	Unit	Material	2014 Bare Costs Labor	2014 Bare Costs Equipment	Total	Total Incl O&P
2550	5' wide	[G] C-1	5	6.400	Ea.	670	279		949	1,200
9000	Minimum labor/equipment charge	1 Carp	3	2.667	Job		122		122	201

03 11 13.50 Forms In Place, Grade Beam

		Crew	Daily Output	Labor-Hours	Unit	Material	Labor	Equipment	Total	Total Incl O&P
0010	**FORMS IN PLACE, GRADE BEAM** R031113-40									
0020	Job-built plywood, 1 use	C-2	530	.091	SFCA	2.82	4.04		6.86	9.75
0150	4 use R031113-60	"	605	.079	"	.92	3.54		4.46	6.80
9000	Minimum labor/equipment charge	2 Carp	2	8	Job		365		365	605

03 11 13.65 Forms In Place, Slab On Grade

		Crew	Daily Output	Labor-Hours	Unit	Material	Labor	Equipment	Total	Total Incl O&P
0010	**FORMS IN PLACE, SLAB ON GRADE** R031113-40									
1000	Bulkhead forms w/keyway, wood, 6" high, 1 use R031113-60	C-1	510	.063	L.F.	.93	2.73		3.66	5.50
1400	Bulkhead form for slab, 4-1/2" high, exp metal, incl keyway & stakes [G]		1200	.027		.88	1.16		2.04	2.88
1410	5-1/2" high [G]		1100	.029		1.01	1.27		2.28	3.19
1420	7-1/2" high [G]		960	.033		1.25	1.45		2.70	3.77
1430	9-1/2" high [G]		840	.038		1.36	1.66		3.02	4.23
2000	Curb forms, wood, 6" to 12" high, on grade, 1 use		215	.149	SFCA	2.43	6.50		8.93	13.30
2150	4 use		275	.116	"	.79	5.05		5.84	9.20
3000	Edge forms, wood, 4 use, on grade, to 6" high		600	.053	L.F.	.31	2.32		2.63	4.16
3050	7" to 12" high		435	.074	SFCA	.77	3.20		3.97	6.10
3060	Over 12"		350	.091	"	.82	3.98		4.80	7.45
3500	For depressed slabs, 4 use, to 12" high		300	.107	L.F.	.67	4.65		5.32	8.40
3550	To 24" high		175	.183		.88	7.95		8.83	14.05
4000	For slab blockouts, to 12" high, 1 use		200	.160		.71	6.95		7.66	12.25
4050	To 24" high, 1 use		120	.267		.90	11.60		12.50	20
4100	Plastic (extruded), to 6" high, multiple use, on grade		800	.040		8.20	1.74		9.94	11.85
5000	Screed, 24 ga. metal key joint, see Section 03 15 16.30									
5020	Wood, incl. wood stakes, 1" x 3"	C-1	900	.036	L.F.	.77	1.55		2.32	3.38
5050	2" x 4"		900	.036	"	.76	1.55		2.31	3.37
6000	Trench forms in floor, wood, 1 use		160	.200	SFCA	1.68	8.70		10.38	16.15
6150	4 use		185	.173	"	.55	7.55		8.10	13
8760	Void form, corrugated fiberboard, 4" x 12", 4' long [G]		3000	.011	S.F.	3.01	.46		3.47	4.07
8770	6" x 12", 4' long		3000	.011		3.59	.46		4.05	4.71
8780	1/4" thick hardboard protective cover for void form	2 Carp	1500	.011		.57	.49		1.06	1.43
9000	Minimum labor/equipment charge	1 Carp	2	4	Job		183		183	300

03 11 13.85 Forms In Place, Walls

		Crew	Daily Output	Labor-Hours	Unit	Material	Labor	Equipment	Total	Total Incl O&P
0010	**FORMS IN PLACE, WALLS** R031113-10									
0100	Box out for wall openings, to 16" thick, to 10 S.F.	C-2	24	2	Ea.	25	89.50		114.50	175
0150	Over 10 S.F. (use perimeter) R031113-40	"	280	.171	L.F.	2.13	7.65		9.78	14.95
0250	Brick shelf, 4" w, add to wall forms, use wall area above shelf									
0260	1 use R031113-60	C-2	240	.200	SFCA	2.28	8.95		11.23	17.15
0350	4 use		300	.160	"	.91	7.15		8.06	12.75
0500	Bulkhead, wood with keyway, 1 use, 2 piece		265	.181	L.F.	1.90	8.10		10	15.40
0600	Bulkhead forms with keyway, 1 piece expanded metal, 8" wall [G]	C-1	1000	.032		1.25	1.39		2.64	3.67
0610	10" wall [G]		800	.040		1.36	1.74		3.10	4.36
0620	12" wall [G]		525	.061		1.63	2.65		4.28	6.15
0700	Buttress, to 8' high, 1 use	C-2	350	.137	SFCA	4.19	6.10		10.29	14.65
0850	4 use		480	.100	"	1.38	4.47		5.85	8.85
1000	Corbel or haunch, to 12" wide, add to wall forms, 1 use		150	.320	L.F.	2.28	14.30		16.58	26
1150	4 use		180	.267	"	.74	11.90		12.64	20.50
2000	Wall, job-built plywood, to 8' high, 1 use		370	.130	SFCA	2.64	5.80		8.44	12.40
2050	2 use		435	.110		1.67	4.93		6.60	9.95
2100	3 use		495	.097		1.21	4.33		5.54	8.45
2150	4 use		505	.095		.99	4.24		5.23	8.05

03 11 Concrete Forming

03 11 13 – Structural Cast-In-Place Concrete Forming

03 11 13.85 Forms In Place, Walls

		Crew	Daily Output	Labor-Hours	Unit	Material	2014 Bare Costs Labor	Equipment	Total	Total Incl O&P
2400	8' to 16' high, 1 use	C-2	280	.171	SFCA	2.91	7.65		10.56	15.80
2450	2 use		345	.139		1.24	6.20		7.44	11.55
2500	3 use		375	.128		.89	5.70		6.59	10.35
2550	4 use		395	.122		.73	5.45		6.18	9.70
2700	Over 16' high, 1 use		235	.204		2.51	9.10		11.61	17.75
2750	2 use		290	.166		1.38	7.40		8.78	13.65
2800	3 use		315	.152		1	6.80		7.80	12.30
2850	4 use		330	.145		.82	6.50		7.32	11.55
4000	Radial, smooth curved, job-built plywood, 1 use		245	.196		2.41	8.75		11.16	17
4150	4 use		335	.143		.78	6.40		7.18	11.35
4200	Below grade, job-built plywood, 1 use		225	.213		2.48	9.55		12.03	18.35
4210	2 use		225	.213		1.36	9.55		10.91	17.15
4220	3 use		225	.213		1.13	9.55		10.68	16.90
4230	4 use		225	.213		.81	9.55		10.36	16.55
4600	Retaining wall, battered, job-built plyw'd, to 8' high, 1 use		300	.160		1.89	7.15		9.04	13.85
4750	4 use		390	.123		.61	5.50		6.11	9.75
4900	Over 8' to 16' high, 1 use		240	.200		2.06	8.95		11.01	16.90
5050	4 use		320	.150		.67	6.70		7.37	11.75
7500	Lintel or sill forms, 1 use	1 Carp	30	.267		3.06	12.25		15.31	23.50
7560	4 use	"	37	.216		1	9.90		10.90	17.40
7800	Modular prefabricated plywood, based on 20 uses of purchased									
7820	forms, and 4 uses of bracing lumber									
7860	To 8' high	C-2	800	.060	SFCA	.85	2.68		3.53	5.35
8060	Over 8' to 16' high		600	.080		.90	3.57		4.47	6.85
8600	Pilasters, 1 use		270	.178		3.05	7.95		11	16.40
8660	4 use		385	.125		.99	5.55		6.54	10.25
9010	Steel framed plywood, based on 50 uses of purchased									
9020	forms, and 4 uses of bracing lumber									
9060	To 8' high	C-2	600	.080	SFCA	.68	3.57		4.25	6.60
9260	Over 8' to 16' high		450	.107		.68	4.76		5.44	8.60
9460	Over 16' to 20' high		400	.120		.68	5.35		6.03	9.55
9475	For elevated walls, add						10%			
9480	For battered walls, 1 side battered, add					10%	10%			
9485	For battered walls, 2 sides battered, add					15%	15%			
9900	Minimum labor/equipment charge	2 Carp	2	8	Job		365		365	605

03 11 16 – Architectural Cast-in Place Concrete Forming

03 11 16.13 Concrete Form Liners

		Crew	Daily Output	Labor-Hours	Unit	Material	2014 Bare Costs Labor	Equipment	Total	Total Incl O&P
0010	**CONCRETE FORM LINERS**									
5750	Liners for forms (add to wall forms), ABS plastic									
5800	Aged wood, 4" wide, 1 use	1 Carp	256	.031	SFCA	3.30	1.43		4.73	6
5820	2 use		256	.031		1.82	1.43		3.25	4.35
5830	3 use		256	.031		1.32	1.43		2.75	3.80
5840	4 use		256	.031		1.07	1.43		2.50	3.53
5900	Fractured rope rib, 1 use		192	.042		4.79	1.91		6.70	8.40
5925	2 use		192	.042		2.63	1.91		4.54	6.05
5950	3 use		192	.042		1.92	1.91		3.83	5.25
6000	4 use		192	.042		1.56	1.91		3.47	4.85
6100	Ribbed, 3/4" deep x 1-1/2" O.C., 1 use		224	.036		4.79	1.64		6.43	7.95
6125	2 use		224	.036		2.63	1.64		4.27	5.60
6150	3 use		224	.036		1.92	1.64		3.56	4.80
6200	4 use		224	.036		1.56	1.64		3.20	4.40
6300	Rustic brick pattern, 1 use		224	.036		3.30	1.64		4.94	6.30

53

03 11 16 – Architectural Cast-in Place Concrete Forming

03 11 16.13 Concrete Form Liners		Crew	Daily Output	Labor-Hours	Unit	Material	2014 Bare Costs Labor	Equipment	Total	Total Incl O&P
6325	2 use	1 Carp	224	.036	SFCA	1.82	1.64		3.46	4.69
6350	3 use		224	.036		1.32	1.64		2.96	4.14
6400	4 use		224	.036		1.07	1.64		2.71	3.87
6500	3/8" striated, random, 1 use		224	.036		3.30	1.64		4.94	6.30
6525	2 use		224	.036		1.82	1.64		3.46	4.69
6550	3 use		224	.036		1.32	1.64		2.96	4.14
6600	4 use		224	.036		1.07	1.64		2.71	3.87

03 15 Concrete Accessories

03 15 05 – Concrete Forming Accessories

03 15 05.70 Shores

			Crew	Daily Output	Labor-Hours	Unit	Material	Labor	Equipment	Total	Total Incl O&P
0010	**SHORES**										
0020	Erect and strip, by hand, horizontal members										
0500	Aluminum joists and stringers	G	2 Carp	60	.267	Ea.		12.25		12.25	20
0600	Steel, adjustable beams	G		45	.356			16.30		16.30	27
0700	Wood joists			50	.320			14.65		14.65	24
0800	Wood stringers			30	.533			24.50		24.50	40
1000	Vertical members to 10' high	G		55	.291			13.35		13.35	22
1050	To 13' high	G		50	.320			14.65		14.65	24
1100	To 16' high	G		45	.356			16.30		16.30	27
1500	Reshoring	G		1400	.011	S.F.	.58	.52		1.10	1.50
1600	Flying truss system	G	C-17D	9600	.009	SFCA		.42	.09	.51	.77
1760	Horizontal, aluminum joists, 6-1/4" high x 5' to 21' span, buy	G				L.F.	15.45			15.45	17
1770	Beams, 7-1/4" high x 4' to 30' span	G				"	18.10			18.10	19.90
1810	Horizontal, steel beam, W8x10, 7' span, buy	G				Ea.	54.50			54.50	60
1830	10' span	G					64.50			64.50	71
1920	15' span	G					111			111	122
1940	20' span	G					156			156	172
1970	Steel stringer, W8x10, 4' to 16' span, buy	G				L.F.	6.45			6.45	7.10
3000	Rent for job duration, aluminum joist @ 2' O.C., per mo.	G				SF Flr.	.39			.39	.43
3050	Steel W8x10	G					.16			.16	.18
3060	Steel adjustable	G					.16			.16	.18
3500	#1 post shore, steel, 5'-7" to 9'-6" high, 10000# cap., buy	G				Ea.	148			148	163
3550	#2 post shore, 7'-3" to 12'-10" high, 7800# capacity	G					171			171	188
3600	#3 post shore, 8'-10" to 16'-1" high, 3800# capacity	G					187			187	206
5010	Frame shoring systems, steel, 12000#/leg, buy										
5040	Frame, 2' wide x 6' high	G				Ea.	93.50			93.50	103
5250	X-brace	G					15.50			15.50	17.05
5550	Base plate	G					15.50			15.50	17.05
5600	Screw jack	G					33.50			33.50	36.50
5650	U-head, 8" x 8"	G					19.10			19.10	21

03 15 05.85 Stair Tread Inserts

		Crew	Daily Output	Labor-Hours	Unit	Material	Labor	Equipment	Total	Total Incl O&P
0010	**STAIR TREAD INSERTS**									
0105	Cast nosing insert, abrasive surface, pre-drilled, includes screws									
0110	Aluminum, 3" wide x 3' long	1 Cefi	32	.250	Ea.	52.50	11		63.50	75
0120	4' long		31	.258		67	11.35		78.35	91.50
0130	5' long		30	.267		82.50	11.75		94.25	110
0135	Extruded nosing insert, black abrasive strips, continuous anchor									
0140	Aluminum, 3" wide x 3' long	1 Cefi	64	.125	Ea.	34	5.50		39.50	46
0150	4' long		60	.133		34	5.85		39.85	47
0160	5' long		56	.143		52.50	6.30		58.80	67.50

03 15 Concrete Accessories

03 15 05 – Concrete Forming Accessories

03 15 05.85 Stair Tread Inserts		Crew	Daily Output	Labor-Hours	Unit	Material	2014 Bare Costs Labor	Equipment	Total	Total Incl O&P
0165	Extruded nosing insert, black abrasive strips, pre-drilled, incl. screws									
0170	Aluminum, 3" wide x 3' long	1 Cefi	32	.250	Ea.	46.50	11		57.50	68.50
0180	4' long		31	.258		60.50	11.35		71.85	84.50
0190	5' long	↓	30	.267	↓	71	11.75		82.75	96.50
9000	Minimum labor/equipment charge	1 Carp	4	2	Job		91.50		91.50	151

03 15 13 – Waterstops

03 15 13.50 Waterstops

		Crew	Daily Output	Labor-Hours	Unit	Material	Labor	Equipment	Total	Total Incl O&P
0010	**WATERSTOPS**, PVC and Rubber									
0020	PVC, ribbed 3/16" thick, 4" wide	1 Carp	155	.052	L.F.	1.22	2.37		3.59	5.25
0050	6" wide		145	.055		2.16	2.53		4.69	6.55
0500	With center bulb, 6" wide, 3/16" thick		135	.059		1.88	2.72		4.60	6.55
0550	3/8" thick		130	.062		3.35	2.82		6.17	8.35
0600	9" wide x 3/8" thick	↓	125	.064	↓	5.45	2.93		8.38	10.80

03 15 16 – Concrete Construction Joints

03 15 16.20 Control Joints, Saw Cut

		Crew	Daily Output	Labor-Hours	Unit	Material	Labor	Equipment	Total	Total Incl O&P
0010	**CONTROL JOINTS, SAW CUT**									
0100	Sawcut control joints in green concrete									
0120	1" depth	C-27	2000	.008	L.F.	.04	.35	.09	.48	.70
0140	1-1/2" depth		1800	.009		.06	.39	.10	.55	.79
0160	2" depth	↓	1600	.010	↓	.07	.44	.11	.62	.90
0180	Sawcut joint reservoir in cured concrete									
0182	3/8" wide x 3/4" deep, with single saw blade	C-27	1000	.016	L.F.	.06	.70	.18	.94	1.36
0184	1/2" wide x 1" deep, with double saw blades		900	.018		.11	.78	.19	1.08	1.57
0186	3/4" wide x 1-1/2" deep, with double saw blades	↓	800	.020		.22	.88	.22	1.32	1.88
0190	Water blast joint to wash away laitance, 2 passes	C-29	2500	.003			.12	.03	.15	.22
0200	Air blast joint to blow out debris and air dry, 2 passes	C-28	2000	.004	↓		.18	.01	.19	.29
0300	For backer rod, see Section 07 91 23.10									
0340	For joint sealant, see Sections 03 15 16.30 or 07 92 13.20									
0900	For replacement of joint sealant, see Section 07 01 90.81									

03 15 16.30 Expansion Joints

			Crew	Daily Output	Labor-Hours	Unit	Material	Labor	Equipment	Total	Total Incl O&P
0010	**EXPANSION JOINTS**										
0020	Keyed, cold, 24 ga., incl. stakes, 3-1/2" high	G	1 Carp	200	.040	L.F.	.77	1.83		2.60	3.86
0050	4-1/2" high	G		200	.040		.88	1.83		2.71	3.98
0100	5-1/2" high	G		195	.041		1.01	1.88		2.89	4.20
0150	7-1/2" high	G		190	.042		1.25	1.93		3.18	4.55
0160	9-1/2" high	G	↓	185	.043		1.36	1.98		3.34	4.76
0300	Poured asphalt, plain, 1/2" x 1"		1 Clab	450	.018		.76	.65		1.41	1.91
0350	1" x 2"			400	.020		3.02	.73		3.75	4.52
0500	Neoprene, liquid, cold applied, 1/2" x 1"			450	.018		2.88	.65		3.53	4.24
0550	1" x 2"			400	.020		11.50	.73		12.23	13.85
0700	Polyurethane, poured, 2 part, 1/2" x 1"			400	.020		1.33	.73		2.06	2.66
0750	1" x 2"			350	.023		5.30	.84		6.14	7.25
0900	Rubberized asphalt, hot or cold applied, 1/2" x 1"			450	.018		.40	.65		1.05	1.51
0950	1" x 2"			400	.020		1.60	.73		2.33	2.96
1100	Hot applied, fuel resistant, 1/2" x 1"			450	.018		.60	.65		1.25	1.73
1150	1" x 2"		↓	400	.020		2.40	.73		3.13	3.84
2000	Premolded, bituminous fiber, 1/2" x 6"		1 Carp	375	.021		.43	.98		1.41	2.08
2050	1" x 12"			300	.027		1.95	1.22		3.17	4.16
2140	Concrete expansion joint, recycled paper and fiber, 1/2" x 6"	G		390	.021		.42	.94		1.36	2.01
2150	1/2" x 12"	G		360	.022		.83	1.02		1.85	2.59
2250	Cork with resin binder, 1/2" x 6"		↓	375	.021	↓	.96	.98		1.94	2.67

03 15 Concrete Accessories

03 15 16 – Concrete Construction Joints

03 15 16.30 Expansion Joints

	Crew	Daily Output	Labor-Hours	Unit	Material	2014 Bare Costs Labor	Equipment	Total	Total Incl O&P
2300 1" x 12"	1 Carp	300	.027	L.F.	2.70	1.22		3.92	4.98
2500 Neoprene sponge, closed cell, 1/2" x 6"		375	.021		2.37	.98		3.35	4.22
2550 1" x 12"		300	.027		8.25	1.22		9.47	11.10
2750 Polyethylene foam, 1/2" x 6"		375	.021		.68	.98		1.66	2.36
2800 1" x 12"		300	.027		2.19	1.22		3.41	4.42
3000 Polyethylene backer rod, 3/8" diameter		460	.017		.03	.80		.83	1.34
3050 3/4" diameter		460	.017		.06	.80		.86	1.37
3100 1" diameter		460	.017		.09	.80		.89	1.41
3500 Polyurethane foam, with polybutylene, 1/2" x 1/2"		475	.017		1.14	.77		1.91	2.52
3550 1" x 1"		450	.018		2.88	.82		3.70	4.51
3750 Polyurethane foam, regular, closed cell, 1/2" x 6"		375	.021		.84	.98		1.82	2.53
3800 1" x 12"		300	.027		3	1.22		4.22	5.30
4000 Polyvinyl chloride foam, closed cell, 1/2" x 6"		375	.021		2.28	.98		3.26	4.12
4050 1" x 12"		300	.027		7.85	1.22		9.07	10.65
4250 Rubber, gray sponge, 1/2" x 6"		375	.021		1.92	.98		2.90	3.72
4300 1" x 12"		300	.027		6.90	1.22		8.12	9.60
4400 Redwood heartwood, 1" x 4"		400	.020		1.16	.92		2.08	2.79
4450 1" x 6"		375	.021		1.75	.98		2.73	3.54
5000 For installation in walls, add						75%			
5250 For installation in boxouts, add						25%			

03 15 19 – Cast-In Concrete Anchors

03 15 19.05 Anchor Bolt Accessories

	Crew	Daily Output	Labor-Hours	Unit	Material	2014 Bare Costs Labor	Equipment	Total	Total Incl O&P
0010 **ANCHOR BOLT ACCESSORIES**									
0015 For anchor bolts set in fresh concrete, see Section 03 15 19.10									
8150 Anchor bolt sleeve, plastic, 1" diam. bolts	1 Carp	60	.133	Ea.	8.10	6.10		14.20	18.95
8500 1-1/2" diameter		28	.286		14.35	13.10		27.45	37.50
8600 2" diameter		24	.333		18.10	15.30		33.40	45
8650 3" diameter		20	.400		33	18.35		51.35	66.50

03 15 19.10 Anchor Bolts

		Crew	Daily Output	Labor-Hours	Unit	Material	2014 Bare Costs Labor	Equipment	Total	Total Incl O&P
0010 **ANCHOR BOLTS**										
0015 Made from recycled materials										
0025 Single bolts installed in fresh concrete, no templates										
0030 Hooked w/nut and washer, 1/2" diameter, 8" long	G	1 Carp	132	.061	Ea.	1.49	2.78		4.27	6.20
0040 12" long	G		131	.061		1.66	2.80		4.46	6.45
0050 5/8" diameter, 8" long	G		129	.062		3.25	2.84		6.09	8.25
0060 12" long	G		127	.063		4	2.89		6.89	9.15
0070 3/4" diameter, 8" long	G		127	.063		4	2.89		6.89	9.15
0080 12" long	G		125	.064		5	2.93		7.93	10.30
0090 2-bolt pattern, including job-built 2-hole template, per set										
0100 J-type, incl. hex nut & washer, 1/2" diameter x 6" long	G	1 Carp	21	.381	Set	5.60	17.45		23.05	34.50
0110 12" long	G		21	.381		6.30	17.45		23.75	35.50
0120 18" long	G		21	.381		7.30	17.45		24.75	36.50
0130 3/4" diameter x 8" long	G		20	.400		10.95	18.35		29.30	42
0140 12" long	G		20	.400		12.95	18.35		31.30	44.50
0150 18" long	G		20	.400		15.95	18.35		34.30	47.50
0160 1" diameter x 12" long	G		19	.421		22	19.30		41.30	56
0170 18" long	G		19	.421		26	19.30		45.30	60
0180 24" long	G		19	.421		31	19.30		50.30	65.50
0190 36" long	G		18	.444		41.50	20.50		62	79
0200 1-1/2" diameter x 18" long	G		17	.471		65.50	21.50		87	108
0210 24" long	G		16	.500		77.50	23		100.50	123
0300 L-type, incl. hex nut & washer, 3/4" diameter x 12" long	G		20	.400		12.20	18.35		30.55	43.50

03 15 19 – Cast-In Concrete Anchors

03 15 19.10 Anchor Bolts		Crew	Daily Output	Labor-Hours	Unit	Material	2014 Bare Costs Labor	Equipment	Total	Total Incl O&P
0310	18" long	G 1 Carp	20	.400	Set	14.80	18.35		33.15	46.50
0320	24" long	G	20	.400		17.40	18.35		35.75	49
0330	30" long	G	20	.400		21.50	18.35		39.85	53.50
0340	36" long	G	20	.400		24	18.35		42.35	56.50
0350	1" diameter x 12" long	G	19	.421		18.90	19.30		38.20	52.50
0360	18" long	G	19	.421		23	19.30		42.30	56.50
0370	24" long	G	19	.421		27.50	19.30		46.80	61.50
0380	30" long	G	19	.421		32	19.30		51.30	66.50
0390	36" long	G	18	.444		36	20.50		56.50	73
0400	42" long	G	18	.444		43	20.50		63.50	81
0410	48" long	G	18	.444		48	20.50		68.50	86.50
0420	1-1/4" diameter x 18" long	G	18	.444		33	20.50		53.50	70
0430	24" long	G	18	.444		39	20.50		59.50	76
0440	30" long	G	17	.471		44.50	21.50		66	84.50
0450	36" long	G	17	.471		50	21.50		71.50	90.50
1000	4-bolt pattern, including job-built 4-hole template, per set									
1100	J-type, incl. hex nut & washer, 1/2" diameter x 6" long	G 1 Carp	19	.421	Set	8.25	19.30		27.55	40.50
1110	12" long	G	19	.421		9.60	19.30		28.90	42
1120	18" long	G	18	.444		11.60	20.50		32.10	46.50
1130	3/4" diameter x 8" long	G	17	.471		18.95	21.50		40.45	56.50
1140	12" long	G	17	.471		23	21.50		44.50	61
1150	18" long	G	17	.471		29	21.50		50.50	67.50
1160	1" diameter x 12" long	G	16	.500		41	23		64	82.50
1170	18" long	G	15	.533		49	24.50		73.50	94
1180	24" long	G	15	.533		59	24.50		83.50	105
1190	36" long	G	15	.533		80	24.50		104.50	128
1200	1-1/2" diameter x 18" long	G	13	.615		128	28		156	188
1210	24" long	G	12	.667		152	30.50		182.50	218
1300	L-type, incl. hex nut & washer, 3/4" diameter x 12" long	G	17	.471		21.50	21.50		43	59
1310	18" long	G	17	.471		26.50	21.50		48	65
1320	24" long	G	17	.471		32	21.50		53.50	70.50
1330	30" long	G	16	.500		39.50	23		62.50	81
1340	36" long	G	16	.500		45	23		68	87
1350	1" diameter x 12" long	G	16	.500		35	23		58	76
1360	18" long	G	15	.533		42.50	24.50		67	87
1370	24" long	G	15	.533		52	24.50		76.50	97
1380	30" long	G	15	.533		61	24.50		85.50	107
1390	36" long	G	15	.533		69	24.50		93.50	116
1400	42" long	G	14	.571		83.50	26		109.50	135
1410	48" long	G	14	.571		93	26		119	145
1420	1-1/4" diameter x 18" long	G	14	.571		63.50	26		89.50	113
1430	24" long	G	14	.571		74.50	26		100.50	125
1440	30" long	G	13	.615		86	28		114	141
1450	36" long	G	13	.615		97.50	28		125.50	154

03 15 19.45 Machinery Anchors

		Crew	Daily Output	Labor-Hours	Unit	Material	2014 Bare Costs Labor	Equipment	Total	Total Incl O&P
0010	**MACHINERY ANCHORS**, heavy duty, incl. sleeve, floating base nut,									
0020	lower stud & coupling nut, fiber plug, connecting stud, washer & nut.									
0030	For flush mounted embedment in poured concrete heavy equip. pads.									
0200	Stud & bolt, 1/2" diameter	G E-16	40	.400	Ea.	72.50	21	3.55	97.05	122
0300	5/8" diameter	G	35	.457		80.50	24	4.06	108.56	136
0500	3/4" diameter	G	30	.533		93	28	4.74	125.74	158
0600	7/8" diameter	G	25	.640		101	33.50	5.70	140.20	178

03 15 Concrete Accessories

03 15 19 – Cast-In Concrete Anchors

03 15 19.45 Machinery Anchors		Crew	Daily Output	Labor-Hours	Unit	Material	2014 Bare Costs Labor	Equipment	Total	Total Incl O&P
0800	1" diameter	G E-16	20	.800	Ea.	117	41.50	7.10	165.60	213
0900	1-1/4" diameter	G	15	1.067		141	55.50	9.45	205.95	267

03 21 Reinforcement Bars

03 21 11 – Plain Steel Reinforcement Bars

03 21 11.60 Reinforcing In Place

		Crew	Daily Output	Labor-Hours	Unit	Material	2014 Bare Costs Labor	Equipment	Total	Total Incl O&P
0010	**REINFORCING IN PLACE**, 50-60 ton lots, A615 Grade 60 R032110-10									
0020	Includes labor, but not material cost, to install accessories									
0030	Made from recycled materials									
0102	Beams & Girders, #3 to #7	G 4 Rodm	3200	.010	Lb.	.50	.51		1.01	1.38
0152	#8 to #18	G	5400	.006		.50	.30		.80	1.04
0202	Columns, #3 to #7	G	3000	.011		.50	.54		1.04	1.44
0252	#8 to #18	G	4600	.007		.50	.35		.85	1.13
0402	Elevated slabs, #4 to #7	G	5800	.006		.50	.28		.78	1.01
0502	Footings, #4 to #7	G	4200	.008		.50	.39		.89	1.18
0552	#8 to #18	G	7200	.004		.50	.22		.72	.92
0602	Slab on grade, #3 to #7	G	4200	.008		.50	.39		.89	1.18
0702	Walls, #3 to #7	G	6000	.005		.50	.27		.77	.99
0752	#8 to #18	G	8000	.004		.50	.20		.70	.88
0900	For other than 50 – 60 ton lots									
1000	Under 10 ton job, #3 to #7, add					25%	10%			
1010	#8 to #18, add					20%	10%			
1050	10 – 50 ton job, #3 to #7, add					10%				
1060	#8 to #18, add					5%				
1100	60 – 100 ton job, #3 to #7, deduct					5%				
1110	#8 to #18, deduct					10%				
1150	Over 100 ton job, #3 to #7, deduct					10%				
1160	#8 to #18, deduct					15%				
2000	Unloading & sorting, add to above	C-5	100	.560	Ton		28	7.45	35.45	53.50
2200	Crane cost for handling, 90 picks/day, up to 1.5 Tons/bundle, add to above		135	.415			20.50	5.55	26.05	39.50
2210	1.0 Ton/bundle		92	.609			30.50	8.10	38.60	58.50
2220	0.5 Ton/bundle		35	1.600			80	21.50	101.50	154
2400	Dowels, 2 feet long, deformed, #3	G 2 Rodm	520	.031	Ea.	.41	1.56		1.97	3.01
2410	#4	G	480	.033		.73	1.69		2.42	3.58
2420	#5	G	435	.037		1.15	1.86		3.01	4.32
2430	#6	G	360	.044		1.65	2.25		3.90	5.50
2450	Longer and heavier dowels, add	G	725	.022	Lb.	.55	1.12		1.67	2.44
2500	Smooth dowels, 12" long, 1/4" or 3/8" diameter	G	140	.114	Ea.	.72	5.80		6.52	10.30
2520	5/8" diameter	G	125	.128		1.26	6.50		7.76	12.05
2530	3/4" diameter	G	110	.145		1.57	7.35		8.92	13.80
2600	Dowel sleeves for CIP concrete, 2-part system									
2610	Sleeve base, plastic, for 5/8" smooth dowel sleeve, fasten to edge form	1 Rodm	200	.040	Ea.	.52	2.03		2.55	3.89
2615	Sleeve, plastic, 12" long, for 5/8" smooth dowel, snap onto base		400	.020		1.16	1.01		2.17	2.94
2620	Sleeve base, for 3/4" smooth dowel sleeve		175	.046		.52	2.32		2.84	4.37
2625	Sleeve, 12" long, for 3/4" smooth dowel		350	.023		1.30	1.16		2.46	3.33
2630	Sleeve base, for 1" smooth dowel sleeve		150	.053		.66	2.70		3.36	5.15
2635	Sleeve, 12" long, for 1" smooth dowel		300	.027		1.37	1.35		2.72	3.73
2700	Dowel caps, visual warning only, plastic, #3 to #8	2 Rodm	800	.020		.27	1.01		1.28	1.96
2720	#8 to #18		750	.021		.68	1.08		1.76	2.52
2750	Impalement protective, plastic, #4 to #9		800	.020		1.50	1.01		2.51	3.31
9000	Minimum labor/equipment charge	1 Rodm	4	2	Job		101		101	166

03 21 Reinforcement Bars

03 21 21 – Composite Reinforcement Bars

03 21 21.11 Glass Fiber-Reinforced Polymer Reinf. Bars

03 21 21.11 Glass Fiber-Reinforced Polymer Reinf. Bars	Crew	Daily Output	Labor-Hours	Unit	Material	2014 Bare Costs Labor	Equipment	Total	Total Incl O&P
0010 **GLASS FIBER-REINFORCED POLYMER REINFORCEMENT BARS**									
0020 Includes labor, but not material cost, to install accessories									
0050 #2 bar, .043 lb./L.F.	4 Rodm	9500	.003	L.F.	.36	.17		.53	.68
0100 #3 bar, .092 lb./L.F.		9300	.003		.49	.17		.66	.83
0150 #4 bar, .160 lb./L.F.		9100	.004		.71	.18		.89	1.07
0200 #5 bar, .258 lb./L.F.		8700	.004		1.09	.19		1.28	1.51
0250 #6 bar, .372 lb./L.F.		8300	.004		1.41	.20		1.61	1.87
0300 #7 bar, .497 lb./L.F.		7900	.004		1.84	.21		2.05	2.36
0350 #8 bar, .620 lb./L.F.		7400	.004		2.50	.22		2.72	3.11
0400 #9 bar, .800 lb./L.F.		6800	.005		3.16	.24		3.40	3.87
0450 #10 bar, 1.08 lb./L.F.	↓	5800	.006	↓	3.93	.28		4.21	4.78
0500 For Bends, add per bend				Ea.	1.48			1.48	1.63

03 22 Fabric and Grid Reinforcing

03 22 11 – Plain Welded Wire Fabric Reinforcing

03 22 11.10 Plain Welded Wire Fabric

03 22 11.10 Plain Welded Wire Fabric		Crew	Daily Output	Labor-Hours	Unit	Material	2014 Bare Costs Labor	Equipment	Total	Total Incl O&P
0010 **PLAIN WELDED WIRE FABRIC** ASTM A185	R032205-30									
0020 Includes labor, but not material cost, to install accessories										
0030 Made from recycled materials										
0050 Sheets										
0100 6 x 6 - W1.4 x W1.4 (10 x 10) 21 lb. per C.S.F.	G	2 Rodm	35	.457	C.S.F.	14.50	23		37.50	54
0200 6 x 6 - W2.1 x W2.1 (8 x 8) 30 lb. per C.S.F.	G		31	.516		17.20	26		43.20	62
0300 6 x 6 - W2.9 x W2.9 (6 x 6) 42 lb. per C.S.F.	G		29	.552		22.50	28		50.50	70.50
0400 6 x 6 - W4 x W4 (4 x 4) 58 lb. per C.S.F.	G		27	.593		31.50	30		61.50	83.50
0500 4 x 4 - W1.4 x W1.4 (10 x 10) 31 lb. per C.S.F.	G		31	.516		20	26		46	65
0600 4 x 4 - W2.1 x W2.1 (8 x 8) 44 lb. per C.S.F.	G		29	.552		25	28		53	73.50
0650 4 x 4 - W2.9 x W2.9 (6 x 6) 61 lb. per C.S.F.	G		27	.593		40.50	30		70.50	93.50
0700 4 x 4 - W4 x W4 (4 x 4) 85 lb. per C.S.F.	G	↓	25	.640	↓	50.50	32.50		83	109
0750 Rolls										
0800 2 x 2 - #14 galv., 21 lb./C.S.F., beam & column wrap	G	2 Rodm	6.50	2.462	C.S.F.	41.50	125		166.50	251
0900 2 x 2 - #12 galv. for gunite reinforcing	G	"	6.50	2.462	"	62.50	125		187.50	274
9000 Minimum labor/equipment charge		1 Rodm	4	2	Job		101		101	166

03 22 13 – Galvanized Welded Wire Fabric Reinforcing

03 22 13.10 Galvanized Welded Wire Fabric

03 22 13.10 Galvanized Welded Wire Fabric	Crew	Daily Output	Labor-Hours	Unit	Material	2014 Bare Costs Labor	Equipment	Total	Total Incl O&P
0010 **GALVANIZED WELDED WIRE FABRIC**									
0100 Add to plain welded wire pricing for galvanized welded wire				Lb.	.23			.23	.25

03 22 16 – Epoxy-Coated Welded Wire Fabric Reinforcing

03 22 16.10 Epoxy-Coated Welded Wire Fabric

03 22 16.10 Epoxy-Coated Welded Wire Fabric	Crew	Daily Output	Labor-Hours	Unit	Material	2014 Bare Costs Labor	Equipment	Total	Total Incl O&P
0010 **EPOXY-COATED WELDED WIRE FABRIC**									
0100 Add to plain welded wire pricing for epoxy-coated welded wire				Lb.	.21			.21	.23

03 24 Fibrous Reinforcing

03 24 05 – Reinforcing Fibers

03 24 05.30 Synthetic Fibers		Crew	Daily Output	Labor-Hours	Unit	Material	2014 Bare Costs Labor	Equipment	Total	Total Incl O&P
0010	**SYNTHETIC FIBERS**									
0100	Synthetic fibers, add to concrete				Lb.	4.80			4.80	5.30
0110	1-1/2 lb. per C.Y.				C.Y.	7.40			7.40	8.15

03 24 05.70 Steel Fibers

0010	**STEEL FIBERS**									
0140	ASTM A850, Type V, continuously deformed, 1-1/2" long x 0.045" diam.									
0150	Add to price of ready mix concrete	G			Lb.	1.25			1.25	1.38
0205	Alternate pricing, dosing at 5 lb. per C.Y., add to price of RMC	G			C.Y.	6.25			6.25	6.90
0210	10 lb. per C.Y.	G				12.50			12.50	13.75
0215	15 lb. per C.Y.	G				18.75			18.75	20.50
0220	20 lb. per C.Y.	G				25			25	27.50
0225	25 lb. per C.Y.	G				31.50			31.50	34.50
0230	30 lb. per C.Y.	G				37.50			37.50	41.50
0235	35 lb. per C.Y.	G				44			44	48
0240	40 lb. per C.Y.	G				50			50	55
0250	50 lb. per C.Y.	G				62.50			62.50	69
0275	75 lb. per C.Y.	G				94			94	103
0300	100 lb. per C.Y.	G				125			125	138

03 30 Cast-In-Place Concrete

03 30 53 – Miscellaneous Cast-In-Place Concrete

03 30 53.40 Concrete In Place		Crew	Daily Output	Labor-Hours	Unit	Material	2014 Bare Costs Labor	Equipment	Total	Total Incl O&P
0010	**CONCRETE IN PLACE**	R033105-10								
0020	Including forms (4 uses), Grade 60 rebar, concrete (Portland cement	R033105-20								
0050	Type I), placement and finishing unless otherwise indicated	R033105-70								
0300	Beams (3500 psi), 5 kip per L.F., 10' span	R033105-85 C-14A	15.62	12.804	C.Y.	315	590	47.50	952.50	1,375
0350	25' span	"	18.55	10.782		335	495	40	870	1,225
0500	Chimney foundations (5000 psi), over 5 C.Y.	C-14C	32.22	3.476		147	153	1.01	301.01	415
0510	(3500 psi), under 5 C.Y.	"	23.71	4.724		173	207	1.37	381.37	535
0700	Columns, square (4000 psi), 12" x 12", less than 2% reinforcing	C-14A	11.96	16.722		355	770	62	1,187	1,725
0720	2% to 3% reinforcing reinforcing		10.13	19.743		565	910	73.50	1,548.50	2,200
0740	Over 3% reinforcing		9.03	22.148		850	1,025	82.50	1,957.50	2,700
0800	16" x 16", less than 2% reinforcing		16.22	12.330		282	565	46	893	1,300
0820	2% to 3% reinforcing reinforcing		12.57	15.911		480	730	59	1,269	1,800
0840	Over 3% reinforcing		10.25	19.512		745	900	72.50	1,717.50	2,375
0900	24" x 24", less than 2% reinforcing		23.66	8.453		238	390	31.50	659.50	930
0920	2% to 3% reinforcing reinforcing		17.71	11.293		425	520	42	987	1,375
0940	Over 3% reinforcing		14.15	14.134		680	650	52.50	1,382.50	1,875
1000	36" x 36", less than 2% reinforcing		33.69	5.936		210	273	22	505	700
1020	2% to 3% reinforcing reinforcing		23.32	8.576		375	395	32	802	1,100
1040	Over 3% reinforcing		17.82	11.223		635	515	42	1,192	1,600
1100	Columns, round (4000 psi), tied, 12" diameter, less than 2% reinforcing		20.97	9.537		305	440	35.50	780.50	1,100
1120	2% to 3% reinforcing reinforcing		15.27	13.098		515	605	48.50	1,168.50	1,600
1140	Over 3% reinforcing		12.11	16.515		785	760	61.50	1,606.50	2,175
1200	16" diameter, less than 2% reinforcing		31.49	6.351		280	292	23.50	595.50	815
1220	2% to 3% reinforcing reinforcing		19.12	10.460		490	480	39	1,009	1,375
1240	Over 3% reinforcing		13.77	14.524		740	670	54	1,464	1,975
1300	20" diameter, less than 2% reinforcing		41.04	4.873		283	224	18.15	525.15	695
1320	2% to 3% reinforcing reinforcing		24.05	8.316		475	385	31	891	1,175
1340	Over 3% reinforcing		17.01	11.758		740	540	43.50	1,323.50	1,750
1400	24" diameter, less than 2% reinforcing		51.85	3.857		264	177	14.35	455.35	600

03 30 53 – Miscellaneous Cast-In-Place Concrete

03 30 53.40 Concrete In Place	Crew	Daily Output	Labor-Hours	Unit	Material	2014 Bare Costs Labor	Equipment	Total	Total Incl O&P
1420	2% to 3% reinforcing reinforcing	C-14A	27.06	7.391	C.Y.	475	340	27.50	842.50	1,100
1440	Over 3% reinforcing		18.29	10.935		725	505	40.50	1,270.50	1,675
1500	36" diameter, less than 2% reinforcing		75.04	2.665		265	123	9.90	397.90	505
1520	2% to 3% reinforcing reinforcing		37.49	5.335		450	245	19.85	714.85	915
1540	Over 3% reinforcing		22.84	8.757		705	405	32.50	1,142.50	1,475
1900	Elevated slab (4000 psi), flat slab with drops, 125 psf Sup. Load, 20' span	C-14B	38.45	5.410		256	249	19.30	524.30	710
1950	30' span		50.99	4.079		273	187	14.55	474.55	620
2100	Flat plate, 125 psf Sup. Load, 15' span		30.24	6.878		234	315	24.50	573.50	800
2150	25' span		49.60	4.194		245	193	14.95	452.95	600
2300	Waffle const., 30" domes, 125 psf Sup. Load, 20' span		37.07	5.611		254	258	20	532	720
2350	30' span		44.07	4.720		237	217	16.85	470.85	635
2500	One way joists, 30" pans, 125 psf Sup. Load, 15' span		27.38	7.597		299	350	27	676	930
2550	25' span		31.15	6.677		283	305	24	612	835
2700	One way beam & slab, 125 psf Sup. Load, 15' span		20.59	10.102		253	465	36	754	1,075
2750	25' span		28.36	7.334		241	335	26	602	845
2900	Two way beam & slab, 125 psf Sup. Load, 15' span		24.04	8.652		245	395	31	671	955
2950	25' span		35.87	5.799		212	266	20.50	498.50	690
3100	Elevated slabs, flat plate, including finish, not									
3110	including forms or reinforcing									
3150	Regular concrete (4000 psi), 4" slab	C-8	2613	.021	S.F.	1.39	.87	.27	2.53	3.24
3200	6" slab		2585	.022		2.03	.88	.27	3.18	3.96
3250	2-1/2" thick floor fill		2685	.021		.91	.85	.26	2.02	2.66
3300	Lightweight, 110# per C.F., 2-1/2" thick floor fill		2585	.022		1.24	.88	.27	2.39	3.09
3400	Cellular concrete, 1-5/8" fill, under 5000 S.F.		2000	.028		.84	1.14	.36	2.34	3.16
3450	Over 10,000 S.F.		2200	.025		.80	1.04	.32	2.16	2.92
3500	Add per floor for 3 to 6 stories high		31800	.002			.07	.02	.09	.14
3520	For 7 to 20 stories high		21200	.003			.11	.03	.14	.21
3540	Equipment pad (3000 psi), 3' x 3' x 6" thick	C-14H	45	1.067	Ea.	44.50	48	.74	93.24	128
3550	4' x 4' x 6" thick		30	1.600		66.50	72	1.10	139.60	192
3560	5' x 5' x 8" thick		18	2.667		119	120	1.84	240.84	330
3570	6' x 6' x 8" thick		14	3.429		160	155	2.37	317.37	430
3580	8' x 8' x 10" thick		8	6		335	271	4.14	610.14	815
3590	10' x 10' x 12" thick		5	9.600		575	435	6.60	1,016.60	1,350
3800	Footings (3000 psi), spread under 1 C.Y.	C-14C	28	4	C.Y.	164	176	1.16	341.16	470
3825	1 C.Y. to 5 C.Y.		43	2.605		198	114	.76	312.76	405
3850	Over 5 C.Y.		75	1.493		180	65.50	.43	245.93	305
3900	Footings, strip (3000 psi), 18" x 9", unreinforced	C-14L	40	2.400		120	103	.82	223.82	300
3920	18" x 9", reinforced	C-14C	35	3.200		144	141	.93	285.93	390
3925	20" x 10", unreinforced	C-14L	45	2.133		117	91.50	.73	209.23	279
3930	20" x 10", reinforced	C-14C	40	2.800		136	123	.81	259.81	350
3935	24" x 12", unreinforced	C-14L	55	1.745		116	74.50	.59	191.09	250
3940	24" x 12", reinforced	C-14C	48	2.333		136	102	.68	238.68	320
3945	36" x 12", unreinforced	C-14L	70	1.371		112	58.50	.47	170.97	220
3950	36" x 12", reinforced	C-14C	60	1.867		130	82	.54	212.54	278
4000	Foundation mat (3000 psi), under 10 C.Y.		38.67	2.896		204	127	.84	331.84	435
4050	Over 20 C.Y.		56.40	1.986		178	87	.58	265.58	340
4200	Wall, free-standing (3000 psi), 8" thick, 8' high	C-14D	45.83	4.364		152	199	16.25	367.25	510
4250	14' high		27.26	7.337		188	335	27.50	550.50	785
4260	12" thick, 8' high		64.32	3.109		142	142	11.55	295.55	400
4270	14' high		40.01	4.999		152	228	18.60	398.60	565
4300	15" thick, 8' high		80.02	2.499		137	114	9.30	260.30	350
4350	12' high		51.26	3.902		137	178	14.50	329.50	460
4500	18' high		48.85	4.094		155	187	15.25	357.25	490

03 30 53.40 Concrete In Place	Crew	Daily Output	Labor-Hours	Unit	Material	2014 Bare Costs Labor	Equipment	Total	Total Incl O&P
4520 Handicap access ramp (4000 psi), railing both sides, 3' wide	C-14H	14.58	3.292	L.F.	315	149	2.27	466.27	595
4525 5' wide		12.22	3.928		330	177	2.71	509.71	650
4530 With 6" curb and rails both sides, 3' wide		8.55	5.614		325	253	3.87	581.87	780
4535 5' wide		7.31	6.566		330	296	4.53	630.53	855
4650 Slab on grade (3500 psi), not including finish, 4" thick	C-14E	60.75	1.449	C.Y.	120	65.50	.55	186.05	240
4700 6" thick	"	92	.957	"	115	43	.36	158.36	198
4701 Thickened slab edge (3500 psi), for slab on grade poured									
4702 monolithically with slab; depth is in addition to slab thickness;									
4703 formed vertical outside edge, earthen bottom and inside slope									
4705 8" deep x 8" wide bottom, unreinforced	C-14L	2190	.044	L.F.	3.33	1.88	.01	5.22	6.75
4710 8" x 8", reinforced	C-14C	1670	.067		5.70	2.95	.02	8.67	11.10
4715 12" deep x 12" wide bottom, unreinforced	C-14L	1800	.053		6.75	2.28	.02	9.05	11.20
4720 12" x 12", reinforced	C-14C	1310	.086		11.05	3.76	.02	14.83	18.35
4725 16" deep x 16" wide bottom, unreinforced	C-14L	1440	.067		11.40	2.85	.02	14.27	17.25
4730 16" x 16", reinforced	C-14C	1120	.100		16.50	4.39	.03	20.92	25.50
4735 20" deep x 20" wide bottom, unreinforced	C-14L	1150	.083		17.25	3.57	.03	20.85	25
4740 20" x 20", reinforced	C-14C	920	.122		24	5.35	.04	29.39	35
4745 24" deep x 24" wide bottom, unreinforced	C-14L	930	.103		24.50	4.42	.04	28.96	34.50
4750 24" x 24", reinforced	C-14C	740	.151		33	6.65	.04	39.69	47
4751 Slab on grade (3500 psi), incl. troweled finish, not incl. forms									
4760 or reinforcing, over 10,000 S.F., 4" thick	C-14F	3425	.021	S.F.	1.31	.88	.01	2.20	2.85
4820 6" thick		3350	.021		1.91	.90	.01	2.82	3.54
4840 8" thick		3184	.023		2.62	.95	.01	3.58	4.40
4900 12" thick		2734	.026		3.92	1.10	.01	5.03	6.10
4950 15" thick		2505	.029		4.93	1.20	.01	6.14	7.35
5000 Slab on grade (3000 psi), incl. broom finish, not incl. forms									
5001 or reinforcing, 4" thick	C-14G	2873	.019	S.F.	1.29	.80	.01	2.10	2.71
5010 6" thick		2590	.022		2.01	.89	.01	2.91	3.65
5020 8" thick		2320	.024		2.62	.99	.01	3.62	4.50
5200 Lift slab in place above the foundation, incl. forms, reinforcing,									
5210 concrete (4000 psi) and columns, over 20,000 S.F. per floor	C-14B	2113	.098	S.F.	6.80	4.52	.35	11.67	15.30
5250 10,000 S.F. to 20,000 S.F. per floor		1650	.126		7.45	5.80	.45	13.70	18.15
5300 Under 10,000 S.F. per floor		1500	.139		8.10	6.35	.50	14.95	19.90
5500 Lightweight, ready mix, including screed finish only,									
5510 not including forms or reinforcing									
5550 1:4 (2500 psi) for structural roof decks	C-14B	260	.800	C.Y.	138	37	2.86	177.86	215
5600 1:6 (3000 psi) for ground slab with radiant heat	C-14F	92	.783		140	32.50	.36	172.86	207
5650 1:3:2 (2000 psi) with sand aggregate, roof deck	C-14B	260	.800		135	37	2.86	174.86	212
5700 Ground slab (2000 psi)	C-14F	107	.673		135	28	.31	163.31	194
5900 Pile caps (3000 psi), incl. forms and reinf., sq. or rect., under 10 C.Y.	C-14C	54.14	2.069		165	91	.60	256.60	330
5950 Over 10 C.Y.		75	1.493		155	65.50	.43	220.93	277
6000 Triangular or hexagonal, under 10 C.Y.		53	2.113		121	93	.61	214.61	286
6050 Over 10 C.Y.		85	1.318		137	58	.38	195.38	245
6200 Retaining walls (3000 psi), gravity, 4' high see Section 32 32	C-14D	66.20	3.021		137	138	11.25	286.25	390
6250 10' high		125	1.600		131	73	5.95	209.95	271
6300 Cantilever, level backfill loading, 8' high		70	2.857		147	130	10.65	287.65	385
6350 16' high		91	2.198		142	100	8.20	250.20	330
6800 Stairs (3500 psi), not including safety treads, free standing, 3'-6" wide	C-14H	83	.578	LF Nose	5.40	26	.40	31.80	49
6850 Cast on ground		125	.384	"	4.49	17.35	.27	22.11	33.50
7000 Stair landings, free standing		200	.240	S.F.	4.39	10.85	.17	15.41	22.50
7050 Cast on ground		475	.101	"	3.45	4.56	.07	8.08	11.30
9000 Minimum labor/equipment charge	2 Carp	1	16	Job		735		735	1,200

03 31 Structural Concrete

03 31 13 – Heavyweight Structural Concrete

03 31 13.25 Concrete, Hand Mix		Crew	Daily Output	Labor-Hours	Unit	Material	2014 Bare Costs Labor	Equipment	Total	Total Incl O&P
0010	**CONCRETE, HAND MIX** for small quantities or remote areas									
0050	Includes bulk local aggregate, bulk sand, bagged Portland									
0060	cement (Type I) and water, using gas powered cement mixer									
0125	2500 psi	C-30	135	.059	C.F.	3.14	2.17	1.31	6.62	8.45
0130	3000 psi		135	.059		3.37	2.17	1.31	6.85	8.70
0135	3500 psi		135	.059		3.50	2.17	1.31	6.98	8.85
0140	4000 psi		135	.059		3.66	2.17	1.31	7.14	9.05
0145	4500 psi		135	.059		3.83	2.17	1.31	7.31	9.20
0150	5000 psi		135	.059		4.09	2.17	1.31	7.57	9.50
0300	Using pre-bagged dry mix and wheelbarrow (80-lb. bag = 0.6 C.F.)									
0340	4000 psi	1 Clab	48	.167	C.F.	6.25	6.10		12.35	16.95

03 31 13.30 Concrete, Volumetric Site-Mixed

		Crew	Daily Output	Labor-Hours	Unit	Material	2014 Bare Costs Labor	Equipment	Total	Total Incl O&P
0010	**CONCRETE, VOLUMETRIC SITE-MIXED**									
0015	Mixed on-site in volumetric truck									
0020	Includes local aggregate, sand, Portland cement (Type I) and water									
0025	Excludes all additives and treatments									
0100	3000 psi, 1 C.Y. mixed and discharged				C.Y.	159			159	175
0110	2 C.Y.					136			136	150
0120	3 C.Y.					122			122	134
0130	4 C.Y.					114			114	125
0140	5 C.Y.					106			106	116
0200	For truck holding/waiting time past first 2 on-site hours, add				Hr.	72			72	79
0210	For trip charge beyond first 20 miles, each way, add				Mile	2.25			2.25	2.48
0220	For each additional increase of 500 psi, add				Ea.	4.17			4.17	4.59

03 31 13.35 Heavyweight Concrete, Ready Mix

		Crew	Daily Output	Labor-Hours	Unit	Material	2014 Bare Costs Labor	Equipment	Total	Total Incl O&P
0010	**HEAVYWEIGHT CONCRETE, READY MIX,** delivered									
0012	Includes local aggregate, sand, Portland cement (Type I) and water									
0015	Excludes all additives and treatments R033105-20									
0020	2000 psi				C.Y.	93			93	102
0100	2500 psi					95.50			95.50	105
0150	3000 psi					99			99	109
0200	3500 psi					101			101	111
0300	4000 psi					104			104	114
0350	4500 psi					107			107	117
0400	5000 psi					110			110	121
0411	6000 psi					113			113	124
0412	8000 psi					119			119	130
0413	10,000 psi					125			125	137
0414	12,000 psi					131			131	144
1000	For high early strength (Portland cement Type III), add					10%				
1300	For winter concrete (hot water), add					4.50			4.50	4.95
1400	For hot weather concrete (ice), add					7.65			7.65	8.40
1410	For mid-range water reducer, add					3.69			3.69	4.06
1420	For high-range water reducer/superplasticizer, add					5.70			5.70	6.30
1430	For retarder, add					3.06			3.06	3.37
1440	For non-Chloride accelerator, add					5.65			5.65	6.20
1450	For Chloride accelerator, per 1%, add					3.32			3.32	3.65
1460	For fiber reinforcing, synthetic (1 lb./C.Y.), add					6.95			6.95	7.60
1500	For Saturday delivery, add					4.93			4.93	5.40
1510	For truck holding/waiting time past 1st hour per load, add				Hr.	97			97	107
1520	For short load (less than 4 C.Y.), add per load				Ea.	77.50			77.50	85
2000	For all lightweight aggregate, add				C.Y.	45%				

03 31 13 – Heavyweight Structural Concrete

03 31 13.70 Placing Concrete	Crew	Daily Output	Labor-Hours	Unit	Material	2014 Bare Costs Labor	Equipment	Total	Total Incl O&P
0010 **PLACING CONCRETE** R033105-70									
0020 Includes labor and equipment to place, level (strike off) and consolidate									
0050 Beams, elevated, small beams, pumped	C-20	60	1.067	C.Y.		42	12.95	54.95	82.50
0100 With crane and bucket	C-7	45	1.600			63.50	27.50	91	133
0200 Large beams, pumped	C-20	90	.711			28	8.65	36.65	55
0250 With crane and bucket	C-7	65	1.108			44	18.85	62.85	92.50
0400 Columns, square or round, 12" thick, pumped	C-20	60	1.067			42	12.95	54.95	82.50
0450 With crane and bucket	C-7	40	1.800			71.50	30.50	102	150
0600 18" thick, pumped	C-20	90	.711			28	8.65	36.65	55
0650 With crane and bucket	C-7	55	1.309			52	22.50	74.50	109
0800 24" thick, pumped	C-20	92	.696			27.50	8.45	35.95	54
0850 With crane and bucket	C-7	70	1.029			41	17.50	58.50	86
1000 36" thick, pumped	C-20	140	.457			18	5.55	23.55	35
1050 With crane and bucket	C-7	100	.720			28.50	12.25	40.75	60
1400 Elevated slabs, less than 6" thick, pumped	C-20	140	.457			18	5.55	23.55	35
1450 With crane and bucket	C-7	95	.758			30	12.90	42.90	63
1500 6" to 10" thick, pumped	C-20	160	.400			15.75	4.85	20.60	31
1550 With crane and bucket	C-7	110	.655			26	11.15	37.15	54.50
1600 Slabs over 10" thick, pumped	C-20	180	.356			14	4.31	18.31	27
1650 With crane and bucket	C-7	130	.554			22	9.45	31.45	46
1900 Footings, continuous, shallow, direct chute	C-6	120	.400			15.30	.55	15.85	25.50
1950 Pumped	C-20	150	.427			16.80	5.20	22	33
2000 With crane and bucket	C-7	90	.800			32	13.60	45.60	66.50
2100 Footings, continuous, deep, direct chute	C-6	140	.343			13.10	.47	13.57	22
2150 Pumped	C-20	160	.400			15.75	4.85	20.60	31
2200 With crane and bucket	C-7	110	.655			26	11.15	37.15	54.50
2400 Footings, spread, under 1 C.Y., direct chute	C-6	55	.873			33.50	1.20	34.70	56
2450 Pumped	C-20	65	.985			39	11.95	50.95	76
2500 With crane and bucket	C-7	45	1.600			63.50	27.50	91	133
2600 Over 5 C.Y., direct chute	C-6	120	.400			15.30	.55	15.85	25.50
2650 Pumped	C-20	150	.427			16.80	5.20	22	33
2700 With crane and bucket	C-7	100	.720			28.50	12.25	40.75	60
2900 Foundation mats, over 20 C.Y., direct chute	C-6	350	.137			5.25	.19	5.44	8.75
2950 Pumped	C-20	400	.160			6.30	1.94	8.24	12.40
3000 With crane and bucket	C-7	300	.240			9.55	4.09	13.64	20
3200 Grade beams, direct chute	C-6	150	.320			12.25	.44	12.69	20.50
3250 Pumped	C-20	180	.356			14	4.31	18.31	27
3300 With crane and bucket	C-7	120	.600			24	10.20	34.20	50
3500 High rise, for more than 5 stories, pumped, add per story	C-20	2100	.030			1.20	.37	1.57	2.36
3510 With crane and bucket, add per story	C-7	2100	.034			1.37	.58	1.95	2.85
3700 Pile caps, under 5 C.Y., direct chute	C-6	90	.533			20.50	.74	21.24	34
3750 Pumped	C-20	110	.582			23	7.05	30.05	45
3800 With crane and bucket	C-7	80	.900			36	15.35	51.35	75
3850 Pile cap, 5 C.Y. to 10 C.Y., direct chute	C-6	175	.274			10.50	.38	10.88	17.50
3900 Pumped	C-20	200	.320			12.60	3.88	16.48	25
3950 With crane and bucket	C-7	150	.480			19.10	8.15	27.25	40
4000 Over 10 C.Y., direct chute	C-6	215	.223			8.55	.31	8.86	14.25
4050 Pumped	C-20	240	.267			10.50	3.23	13.73	20.50
4100 With crane and bucket	C-7	185	.389			15.50	6.65	22.15	32.50
4300 Slab on grade, up to 6" thick, direct chute	C-6	110	.436			16.70	.60	17.30	27.50
4350 Pumped	C-20	130	.492			19.40	5.95	25.35	38
4400 With crane and bucket	C-7	110	.655			26	11.15	37.15	54.50

03 31 Structural Concrete

03 31 13 – Heavyweight Structural Concrete

03 31 13.70 Placing Concrete	Crew	Daily Output	Labor-Hours	Unit	Material	2014 Bare Costs Labor	Equipment	Total	Total Incl O&P
4600	Over 6" thick, direct chute	C-6	165	.291	C.Y.		11.10	.40	11.50	18.55
4650	Pumped	C-20	185	.346			13.60	4.20	17.80	26.50
4700	With crane and bucket	C-7	145	.497			19.75	8.45	28.20	41.50
4900	Walls, 8" thick, direct chute	C-6	90	.533			20.50	.74	21.24	34
4950	Pumped	C-20	100	.640			25	7.75	32.75	49.50
5000	With crane and bucket	C-7	80	.900			36	15.35	51.35	75
5050	12" thick, direct chute	C-6	100	.480			18.35	.66	19.01	30.50
5100	Pumped	C-20	110	.582			23	7.05	30.05	45
5200	With crane and bucket	C-7	90	.800			32	13.60	45.60	66.50
5300	15" thick, direct chute	C-6	105	.457			17.45	.63	18.08	29
5350	Pumped	C-20	120	.533			21	6.45	27.45	41
5400	With crane and bucket	C-7	95	.758			30	12.90	42.90	63
5600	Wheeled concrete dumping, add to placing costs above									
5610	Walking cart, 50' haul, add	C-18	32	.281	C.Y.		10.35	1.88	12.23	19.10
5620	150' haul, add		24	.375			13.85	2.51	16.36	25.50
5700	250' haul, add		18	.500			18.45	3.35	21.80	34
5800	Riding cart, 50' haul, add	C-19	80	.113			4.15	1.26	5.41	8.20
5810	150' haul, add		60	.150			5.55	1.69	7.24	10.95
5900	250' haul, add		45	.200			7.35	2.25	9.60	14.55
6000	Concrete in-fill for pan-type metal stairs and landings. Manual placement									
6010	includes up to 50' horizontal haul from point of concrete discharge.									
6100	Stair pan treads, 2" deep									
6110	Flights in 1st floor level up/down from discharge point	C-8A	3200	.015	S.F.		.59		.59	.96
6120	2nd floor level		2500	.019			.76		.76	1.23
6130	3rd floor level		2000	.024			.95		.95	1.53
6140	4th floor level		1800	.027			1.05		1.05	1.70
6200	Intermediate stair landings, pan-type 4" deep									
6210	Flights in 1st floor level up/down from discharge point	C-8A	2000	.024	S.F.		.95		.95	1.53
6220	2nd floor level		1500	.032			1.26		1.26	2.04
6230	3rd floor level		1200	.040			1.58		1.58	2.55
6240	4th floor level		1000	.048			1.89		1.89	3.06
9000	Minimum labor/equipment charge	C-6	2	24	Job		915	33	948	1,525

03 35 Concrete Finishing

03 35 13 – High-Tolerance Concrete Floor Finishing

03 35 13.30 Finishing Floors, High Tolerance	Crew	Daily Output	Labor-Hours	Unit	Material	2014 Bare Costs Labor	Equipment	Total	Total Incl O&P
0010	**FINISHING FLOORS, HIGH TOLERANCE**									
0012	Finishing requires that concrete first be placed, struck off & consolidated									
0015	Basic finishing for various unspecified flatwork									
0100	Bull float only	C-10	4000	.006	S.F.		.25		.25	.40
0125	Bull float & manual float		2000	.012			.50		.50	.80
0150	Bull float, manual float, & broom finish, w/edging & joints		1850	.013			.54		.54	.86
0200	Bull float, manual float & manual steel trowel		1265	.019			.79		.79	1.26
0210	For specified Random Access Floors in ACI Classes 1, 2, 3 and 4 to achieve									
0215	Composite Overall Floor Flatness and Levelness values up to FF35/FL25									
0250	Bull float, machine float & machine trowel (walk-behind)	C-10C	1715	.014	S.F.		.58	.03	.61	.96
0300	Power screed, bull float, machine float & trowel (walk-behind)	C-10D	2400	.010			.42	.05	.47	.71
0350	Power screed, bull float, machine float & trowel (ride-on)	C-10E	4000	.006			.25	.07	.32	.47
0352	For specified Random Access Floors in ACI Classes 5, 6, 7 and 8 to achieve									
0354	Composite Overall Floor Flatness and Levelness values up to FF50/FL50									
0356	Add for two-dimensional restraightening after power float	C-10	6000	.004	S.F.		.17		.17	.27

03 35 Concrete Finishing

03 35 13 – High-Tolerance Concrete Floor Finishing

03 35 13.30 Finishing Floors, High Tolerance	Crew	Daily Output	Labor-Hours	Unit	Material	2014 Bare Costs Labor	Equipment	Total	Total Incl O&P
0358	For specified Random or Defined Access Floors in ACI Class 9 to achieve									
0360	Composite Overall Floor Flatness and Levelness values up to FF100/FL100									
0362	Add for two-dimensional restraightening after bull float & power float	C-10	3000	.008	S.F.		.33		.33	.53
0364	For specified Superflat Defined Access Floors in ACI Class 9 to achieve									
0366	Minimum Floor Flatness and Levelness values of FF100/FL100									
0368	Add for 2-dim'l restraightening after bull float, power float, power trowel	C-10	2000	.012	S.F.		.50		.50	.80
9100	Minimum labor/equipment charge	"	2	12	Job		500		500	795

03 35 29 – Tooled Concrete Finishing

03 35 29.60 Finishing Walls

		Crew	Daily Output	Labor-Hours	Unit	Material	2014 Bare Costs Labor	Equipment	Total	Total Incl O&P
0010	**FINISHING WALLS**									
0020	Break ties and patch voids	1 Cefi	540	.015	S.F.	.04	.65		.69	1.07
0050	Burlap rub with grout	"	450	.018		.04	.78		.82	1.28
0300	Bush hammer, green concrete	B-39	1000	.048			1.86	.23	2.09	3.29
0350	Cured concrete	"	650	.074			2.86	.36	3.22	5.05
0500	Acid etch	1 Cefi	575	.014		.14	.61		.75	1.12
0700	Sandblast, light penetration	E-11	1100	.029		.50	1.20	.22	1.92	2.89
0750	Heavy penetration	"	375	.085		1	3.51	.63	5.14	7.95
0850	Grind form fins flush	1 Clab	700	.011	L.F.		.42		.42	.69
9000	Minimum labor/equipment charge	C-10	2	12	Job		500		500	795

03 35 33 – Stamped Concrete Finishing

03 35 33.50 Slab Texture Stamping

		Crew	Daily Output	Labor-Hours	Unit	Material	2014 Bare Costs Labor	Equipment	Total	Total Incl O&P
0010	**SLAB TEXTURE STAMPING**									
0050	Stamping requires that concrete first be placed, struck off, consolidated,									
0060	bull floated and free of bleed water. Decorative stamping tasks include:									
0100	Step 1 - first application of dry shake colored hardener	1 Cefi	6400	.001	S.F.	.43	.06		.49	.56
0110	Step 2 - bull float		6400	.001			.06		.06	.09
0130	Step 3 - second application of dry shake colored hardener		6400	.001		.21	.06		.27	.32
0140	Step 4 - bull float, manual float & steel trowel	3 Cefi	1280	.019			.83		.83	1.30
0150	Step 5 - application of dry shake colored release agent	1 Cefi	6400	.001		.10	.06		.16	.20
0160	Step 6 - place, tamp & remove mats	3 Cefi	2400	.010		1.43	.44		1.87	2.28
0170	Step 7 - touch up edges, mat joints & simulated grout lines	1 Cefi	1280	.006			.28		.28	.43
0300	Alternate stamping estimating method includes all tasks above	4 Cefi	800	.040		2.17	1.76		3.93	5.15
0400	Step 8 - pressure wash @ 3000 psi after 24 hours	1 Cefi	1600	.005			.22		.22	.35
0500	Step 9 - roll 2 coats cure/seal compound when dry	"	800	.010		.59	.44		1.03	1.35

03 35 43 – Polished Concrete Finishing

03 35 43.10 Polished Concrete Floors

		Crew	Daily Output	Labor-Hours	Unit	Material	2014 Bare Costs Labor	Equipment	Total	Total Incl O&P
0010	**POLISHED CONCRETE FLOORS**									
0015	Processing of cured concrete to include grinding, honing,									
0020	and polishing of interior floors with 22" segmented diamond									
0025	planetary floor grinder (2 passes in different directions per grit)									
0100	Removal of pre-existing coatings, dry, with carbide discs using									
0105	dry vacuum pick-up system, final hand sweeping									
0110	Glue, adhesive or tar	J-4	1.60	15	M.S.F.	24	625	124	773	1,150
0120	Paint, epoxy, 1 coat		3.60	6.667		24	277	55	356	530
0130	2 coats		1.80	13.333		24	555	110	689	1,025
0200	Grinding and edging, wet, including wet vac pick-up and auto									
0205	scrubbing between grit changes									
0210	40-grit diamond/metal matrix	J-4A	1.60	20	M.S.F.	31.50	805	256	1,092.50	1,625
0220	80-grit diamond/metal matrix		2	16		31.50	645	205	881.50	1,300
0230	120-grit diamond/metal matrix		2.40	13.333		31.50	540	171	742.50	1,100
0240	200-grit diamond/metal matrix		2.80	11.429		31.50	460	146	637.50	935

03 35 Concrete Finishing

03 35 43 – Polished Concrete Finishing

03 35 43.10 Polished Concrete Floors	Crew	Daily Output	Labor-Hours	Unit	Material	2014 Bare Costs Labor	Equipment	Total	Total Incl O&P
0300	Spray on dye or stain (1 coat)	1 Cefi	16	.500	M.S.F.	212	22		234	268
0400	Spray on densifier/hardener (2 coats)	"	8	1		340	44		384	445
0410	Auto scrubbing after 2nd coat, when dry	J-4B	16	.500	↓		18.35	13.25	31.60	44.50
0500	Honing and edging, wet, including wet vac pick-up and auto									
0505	scrubbing between grit changes									
0510	100-grit diamond/resin matrix	J-4A	2.80	11.429	M.S.F.	31.50	460	146	637.50	935
0520	200-grit diamond/resin matrix	"	2.80	11.429	"	31.50	460	146	637.50	935
0530	Dry, including dry vacuum pick-up system, final hand sweeping									
0540	400-grit diamond/resin matrix	J-4A	2.80	11.429	M.S.F.	31.50	460	146	637.50	935
0600	Polishing and edging, dry, including dry vac pick-up and hand									
0605	sweeping between grit changes									
0610	800-grit diamond/resin matrix	J-4A	2.80	11.429	M.S.F.	31.50	460	146	637.50	935
0620	1500-grit diamond/resin matrix		2.80	11.429		31.50	460	146	637.50	935
0630	3000-grit diamond/resin matrix	↓	2.80	11.429	↓	31.50	460	146	637.50	935
0700	Auto scrubbing after final polishing step	J-4B	16	.500	↓		18.35	13.25	31.60	44.50

03 37 Specialty Placed Concrete

03 37 13 – Shotcrete

03 37 13.30 Gunite (Dry-Mix)

		Crew	Daily Output	Labor-Hours	Unit	Material	Labor	Equipment	Total	Total Incl O&P
0010	**GUNITE (DRY-MIX)**									
0020	Typical in place, 1" layers, no mesh included	C-16	2000	.028	S.F.	.32	1.14	.20	1.66	2.41
0300	Typical in place, including mesh, 2" thick, flat surfaces		1000	.056		1.26	2.28	.39	3.93	5.50
0350	Curved surfaces		500	.112		1.26	4.57	.79	6.62	9.60
0500	4" thick, flat surfaces		750	.075		1.90	3.05	.52	5.47	7.60
0550	Curved surfaces	↓	350	.160		1.90	6.55	1.12	9.57	13.85
0900	Prepare old walls, no scaffolding, good condition	C-10	1000	.024			1		1	1.59
0950	Poor condition	"	275	.087	↓		3.63		3.63	5.80
1100	For high finish requirement or close tolerance, add						50%			
1150	Very high				↓		110%			
9000	Minimum labor/equipment charge	C-10	1	24	Job		1,000		1,000	1,600

03 37 13.60 Shotcrete (Wet-Mix)

		Crew	Daily Output	Labor-Hours	Unit	Material	Labor	Equipment	Total	Total Incl O&P
0010	**SHOTCRETE (WET-MIX)**									
0020	Wet mix, placed @ up to 12 C.Y. per hour, 3000 psi	C-8C	80	.600	C.Y.	103	24	5.70	132.70	158
0100	Up to 35 C.Y. per hour	C-8E	240	.200	"	92.50	8	2.23	102.73	117
1010	Fiber reinforced, 1" thick	C-8C	1740	.028	S.F.	.76	1.11	.26	2.13	2.93
1020	2" thick		900	.053		1.53	2.15	.51	4.19	5.70
1030	3" thick		825	.058		2.29	2.34	.55	5.18	6.90
1040	4" thick	↓	750	.064	↓	3.06	2.58	.61	6.25	8.20

03 39 Concrete Curing

03 39 13 – Water Concrete Curing

03 39 13.50 Water Curing		Crew	Daily Output	Labor-Hours	Unit	Material	2014 Bare Costs Labor	Equipment	Total	Total Incl O&P
0010	**WATER CURING**									
0015	With burlap, 4 uses assumed, 7.5 oz.	2 Clab	55	.291	C.S.F.	14.70	10.65		25.35	33.50
0100	10 oz.	"	55	.291	"	26.50	10.65		37.15	46.50
0400	Curing blankets, 1" to 2" thick, buy				S.F.	.19			.19	.21
9000	Minimum labor/equipment charge	1 Clab	5	1.600	Job		58.50		58.50	96.50

03 39 23 – Membrane Concrete Curing

03 39 23.13 Chemical Compound Membrane Concrete Curing

		Crew	Daily Output	Labor-Hours	Unit	Material	2014 Bare Costs Labor	Equipment	Total	Total Incl O&P
0010	**CHEMICAL COMPOUND MEMBRANE CONCRETE CURING**									
0300	Sprayed membrane curing compound	2 Clab	95	.168	C.S.F.	10.95	6.15		17.10	22
0700	Curing compound, solvent based, 400 S.F./gal., 55 gallon lots				Gal.	23.50			23.50	25.50
0720	5 gallon lots					29.50			29.50	32.50
0800	Curing compound, water based, 250 S.F./gal., 55 gallon lots					22			22	24.50
0820	5 gallon lots					25			25	27.50

03 39 23.23 Sheet Membrane Concrete Curing

		Crew	Daily Output	Labor-Hours	Unit	Material	2014 Bare Costs Labor	Equipment	Total	Total Incl O&P
0010	**SHEET MEMBRANE CONCRETE CURING**									
0200	Curing blanket, burlap/poly, 2-ply	2 Clab	70	.229	C.S.F.	19.05	8.40		27.45	35

03 41 Precast Structural Concrete

03 41 13 – Precast Concrete Hollow Core Planks

03 41 13.50 Precast Slab Planks

			Crew	Daily Output	Labor-Hours	Unit	Material	2014 Bare Costs Labor	Equipment	Total	Total Incl O&P
0010	**PRECAST SLAB PLANKS**	R034105-30									
0020	Prestressed roof/floor members, grouted, solid, 4" thick		C-11	2400	.030	S.F.	5.85	1.51	.77	8.13	10
0050	6" thick			2800	.026		6.30	1.30	.66	8.26	9.95
0100	Hollow, 8" thick			3200	.023		7.10	1.13	.57	8.80	10.45
0150	10" thick			3600	.020		7.30	1.01	.51	8.82	10.35
0200	12" thick			4000	.018		7.90	.91	.46	9.27	10.80

03 41 23 – Precast Concrete Stairs

03 41 23.50 Precast Stairs

		Crew	Daily Output	Labor-Hours	Unit	Material	2014 Bare Costs Labor	Equipment	Total	Total Incl O&P
0010	**PRECAST STAIRS**									
0020	Precast concrete treads on steel stringers, 3' wide	C-12	75	.640	Riser	134	29	8.85	171.85	204
0300	Front entrance, 5' wide with 48" platform, 2 risers		16	3	Flight	485	136	41.50	662.50	800
0350	5 risers		12	4		765	182	55	1,002	1,200
0500	6' wide, 2 risers		15	3.200		535	145	44	724	875
0550	5 risers		11	4.364		845	198	60.50	1,103.50	1,325
1200	Basement entrance stairwell, 6 steps, incl. steel bulkhead door	B-51	22	2.182		1,450	80.50	12.30	1,542.80	1,725
1250	14 steps	"	11	4.364		2,400	161	24.50	2,585.50	2,925

03 41 33 – Precast Structural Pretensioned Concrete

03 41 33.10 Precast Beams

			Crew	Daily Output	Labor-Hours	Unit	Material	2014 Bare Costs Labor	Equipment	Total	Total Incl O&P
0010	**PRECAST BEAMS**	R034105-30									
0011	L-shaped, 20' span, 12" x 20"		C-11	32	2.250	Ea.	2,900	113	57.50	3,070.50	3,475
0060	18" x 36"			24	3		3,975	151	76.50	4,202.50	4,725
0100	24" x 44"			22	3.273		4,775	165	83.50	5,023.50	5,625
0150	30' span, 12" x 36"			24	3		5,375	151	76.50	5,602.50	6,275
0200	18" x 44"			20	3.600		6,550	181	92	6,823	7,625
0250	24" x 52"			16	4.500		7,850	227	115	8,192	9,175
0400	40' span, 12" x 52"			20	3.600		8,350	181	92	8,623	9,600
0450	18" x 52"			16	4.500		9,325	227	115	9,667	10,800
0500	24" x 52"			12	6		10,500	300	153	10,953	12,200
1200	Rectangular, 20' span, 12" x 20"			32	2.250		2,825	113	57.50	2,995.50	3,375

03 41 Precast Structural Concrete

03 41 33 – Precast Structural Pretensioned Concrete

03 41 33.10 Precast Beams		Crew	Daily Output	Labor-Hours	Unit	Material	2014 Bare Costs		Total	Total Incl O&P
							Labor	Equipment		
1250	18" x 36"	C-11	24	3	Ea.	3,500	151	76.50	3,727.50	4,200
1300	24" x 44"		22	3.273		4,175	165	83.50	4,423.50	4,975
1400	30' span, 12" x 36"		24	3		4,700	151	76.50	4,927.50	5,525
1450	18" x 44"		20	3.600		5,675	181	92	5,948	6,650
1500	24" x 52"		16	4.500		6,850	227	115	7,192	8,050
1600	40' span, 12" x 52"		20	3.600		6,975	181	92	7,248	8,100
1650	18" x 52"		16	4.500		7,950	227	115	8,292	9,275
1700	24" x 52"		12	6		9,125	300	153	9,578	10,700
2000	"T" shaped, 20' span, 12" x 20"		32	2.250		3,325	113	57.50	3,495.50	3,925
2050	18" x 36"		24	3		4,450	151	76.50	4,677.50	5,250
2100	24" x 44"		22	3.273		5,350	165	83.50	5,598.50	6,250
2200	30' span, 12" x 36"		24	3		6,125	151	76.50	6,352.50	7,075
2250	18" x 44"		20	3.600		7,425	181	92	7,698	8,575
2300	24" x 52"		16	4.500		8,875	227	115	9,217	10,300
2500	40' span, 12" x 52"		20	3.600		10,100	181	92	10,373	11,500
2550	18" x 52"		16	4.500		10,700	227	115	11,042	12,300
2600	24" x 52"		12	6		11,800	300	153	12,253	13,700

03 41 33.15 Precast Columns

		Crew	Daily Output	Labor-Hours	Unit	Material	Labor	Equipment	Total	Total Incl O&P
0010	**PRECAST COLUMNS** R034105-30									
0020	Rectangular to 12' high, 16" x 16"	C-11	120	.600	L.F.	166	30	15.30	211.30	254
0050	24" x 24"	"	96	.750	"	228	38	19.15	285.15	340

03 45 Precast Architectural Concrete

03 45 13 – Faced Architectural Precast Concrete

03 45 13.50 Precast Wall Panels

		Crew	Daily Output	Labor-Hours	Unit	Material	Labor	Equipment	Total	Total Incl O&P
0010	**PRECAST WALL PANELS**									
2200	Fiberglass reinforced cement with urethane core									
2210	R20, 8' x 8', 5" plain finish	E-2	750	.075	S.F.	21	3.75	2.04	26.79	32.50
2220	Exposed aggregate or brick finish	"	600	.093	"	32	4.68	2.55	39.23	46

03 48 Precast Concrete Specialties

03 48 43 – Precast Concrete Trim

03 48 43.40 Precast Lintels

		Crew	Daily Output	Labor-Hours	Unit	Material	Labor	Equipment	Total	Total Incl O&P
0010	**PRECAST LINTELS**, smooth gray, prestressed, stock units only									
0800	4" wide, 8" high, x 4' long	D-10	28	1.143	Ea.	23.50	51.50	17.20	92.20	128
0850	8' long		24	1.333		57	60	20	137	182
1000	6" wide, 8" high, x 4' long		26	1.231		33.50	55.50	18.50	107.50	147
1050	10' long		22	1.455		86	65.50	22	173.50	225
1200	8" wide, 8" high, x 4' long		24	1.333		42.50	60	20	122.50	166
1250	12' long		20	1.600		138	72	24	234	295
1275	For custom sizes, types, colors, or finishes of precast lintels, add					150%				

03 48 43.90 Precast Window Sills

		Crew	Daily Output	Labor-Hours	Unit	Material	Labor	Equipment	Total	Total Incl O&P
0010	**PRECAST WINDOW SILLS**									
0600	Precast concrete, 4" tapers to 3", 9" wide	D-1	70	.229	L.F.	11.90	9.45		21.35	28.50
0650	11" wide		60	.267		15.55	11		26.55	35
0700	13" wide, 3 1/2" tapers to 2 1/2", 12" wall		50	.320		15.50	13.20		28.70	38.50

03 51 Cast Roof Decks

03 51 13 – Cementitious Wood Fiber Decks

03 51 13.50 Cementitious/Wood Fiber Planks		Crew	Daily Output	Labor-Hours	Unit	Material	2014 Bare Costs Labor	Equipment	Total	Total Incl O&P
0010	CEMENTITIOUS/WOOD FIBER PLANKS									
0050	Plank, beveled edge, 1" thick	2 Carp	1000	.016	S.F.	2.20	.73		2.93	3.63
0100	1-1/2" thick		975	.016		2.90	.75		3.65	4.43
0150	T & G, 2" thick		950	.017		2.40	.77		3.17	3.91
0200	2-1/2" thick	↓	925	.017		2.70	.79		3.49	4.27
1000	Bulb tee, sub-purlin and grout, 6' span, add	E-1	5000	.005		2.14	.24	.03	2.41	2.81
1100	8' span	"	4200	.006	↓	2.14	.29	.03	2.46	2.90

03 52 Lightweight Concrete Roof Insulation

03 52 16 – Lightweight Insulating Concrete

03 52 16.13 Lightweight Cellular Insulating Concrete

			Crew	Daily Output	Labor-Hours	Unit	Material	Labor	Equipment	Total	Total Incl O&P
0010	LIGHTWEIGHT CELLULAR INSULATING CONCRETE	R035216-10									
0020	Portland cement and foaming agent	G	C-8	50	1.120	C.Y.	115	45.50	14.20	174.70	215

03 52 16.16 Lightweight Aggregate Insulating Concrete

			Crew	Daily Output	Labor-Hours	Unit	Material	Labor	Equipment	Total	Total Incl O&P
0010	LIGHTWEIGHT AGGREGATE INSULATING CONCRETE	R035216-10									
0100	Poured vermiculite or perlite, field mix,										
0110	1:6 field mix	G	C-8	50	1.120	C.Y.	251	45.50	14.20	310.70	365
0200	Ready mix, 1:6 mix, roof fill, 2" thick	G		10000	.006	S.F.	1.39	.23	.07	1.69	1.98
0250	3" thick	G	↓	7700	.007	"	2.09	.30	.09	2.48	2.88

03 53 Concrete Topping

03 53 16 – Iron-Aggregate Concrete Topping

03 53 16.50 Floor Topping

		Crew	Daily Output	Labor-Hours	Unit	Material	Labor	Equipment	Total	Total Incl O&P
0010	FLOOR TOPPING									
0400	Integral topping and finish, using 1:1:2 mix, 3/16" thick	C-10B	1000	.040	S.F.	.10	1.58	.28	1.96	2.98
0450	1/2" thick		950	.042		.26	1.67	.30	2.23	3.31
0500	3/4" thick		850	.047		.39	1.86	.33	2.58	3.81
0600	1" thick		750	.053		.52	2.11	.38	3.01	4.41
0800	Granolithic topping, laid after, 1:1:1-1/2 mix, 1/2" thick		590	.068		.29	2.69	.48	3.46	5.20
0820	3/4" thick		580	.069		.43	2.73	.49	3.65	5.45
0850	1" thick		575	.070		.58	2.76	.49	3.83	5.65
0950	2" thick	↓	500	.080	↓	1.16	3.17	.57	4.90	7

03 54 Cast Underlayment

03 54 13 – Gypsum Cement Underlayment

03 54 13.50 Poured Gypsum Underlayment

		Crew	Daily Output	Labor-Hours	Unit	Material	Labor	Equipment	Total	Total Incl O&P
0010	POURED GYPSUM UNDERLAYMENT									
0400	Underlayment, gypsum based, self-leveling 2500 psi, pumped, 1/2" thick	C-8	24000	.002	S.F.	.33	.10	.03	.46	.55
0500	3/4" thick		20000	.003		.50	.11	.04	.65	.77
0600	1" thick	↓	16000	.004		.67	.14	.04	.85	1.02
1400	Hand placed, 1/2" thick	C-18	450	.020		.33	.74	.13	1.20	1.73
1500	3/4" thick	"	300	.030	↓	.50	1.11	.20	1.81	2.59

03 54 16 – Hydraulic Cement Underlayment

03 54 16.50 Cement Underlayment

		Crew	Daily Output	Labor-Hours	Unit	Material	Labor	Equipment	Total	Total Incl O&P
0010	CEMENT UNDERLAYMENT									
2510	Underlayment, P.C based, self-leveling, 4100 psi, pumped, 1/4" thick	C-8	20000	.003	S.F.	1.49	.11	.04	1.64	1.86
2520	1/2" thick	↓	19000	.003	↓	2.99	.12	.04	3.15	3.52

03 54 Cast Underlayment

03 54 16 – Hydraulic Cement Underlayment

03 54 16.50 Cement Underlayment	Crew	Daily Output	Labor-Hours	Unit	Material	2014 Bare Costs Labor	Equipment	Total	Total Incl O&P
2530	3/4" thick	C-8	18000	.003	S.F.	4.48	.13	.04	4.65	5.15
2540	1" thick		17000	.003		6	.13	.04	6.17	6.85
2550	1-1/2" thick	↓	15000	.004		8.95	.15	.05	9.15	10.15
2560	Hand placed, 1/2" thick	C-18	450	.020		2.99	.74	.13	3.86	4.65
2610	Topping, P.C based, self-leveling, 6100 psi, pumped, 1/4" thick	C-8	20000	.003		2.18	.11	.04	2.33	2.62
2620	1/2" thick		19000	.003		4.37	.12	.04	4.53	5.05
2630	3/4" thick		18000	.003		6.55	.13	.04	6.72	7.45
2660	1" thick		17000	.003		8.75	.13	.04	8.92	9.85
2670	1-1/2" thick	↓	15000	.004		13.10	.15	.05	13.30	14.70
2680	Hand placed, 1/2" thick	C-18	450	.020	↓	4.37	.74	.13	5.24	6.15

03 63 Epoxy Grouting

03 63 05 – Grouting of Dowels and Fasteners

03 63 05.10 Epoxy Only

		Crew	Daily Output	Labor-Hours	Unit	Material	2014 Bare Costs Labor	Equipment	Total	Total Incl O&P
0010	**EPOXY ONLY**									
1500	Chemical anchoring, epoxy cartridge, excludes layout, drilling, fastener									
1530	For fastener 3/4" diam. x 6" embedment	2 Skwk	72	.222	Ea.	5.55	10.50		16.05	23
1535	1" diam. x 8" embedment		66	.242		8.30	11.45		19.75	28
1540	1-1/4" diam. x 10" embedment		60	.267		16.60	12.60		29.20	39
1545	1-3/4" diam. x 12" embedment		54	.296		27.50	14		41.50	53.50
1550	14" embedment		48	.333		33	15.75		48.75	62
1555	2" diam. x 12" embedment		42	.381		44.50	18		62.50	78
1560	18" embedment	↓	32	.500	↓	55.50	23.50		79	99.50

03 81 Concrete Cutting

03 81 13 – Flat Concrete Sawing

03 81 13.50 Concrete Floor/Slab Cutting

		Crew	Daily Output	Labor-Hours	Unit	Material	2014 Bare Costs Labor	Equipment	Total	Total Incl O&P
0010	**CONCRETE FLOOR/SLAB CUTTING**									
0050	Includes blade cost, layout and set-up time									
0300	Saw cut concrete slabs, plain, up to 3" deep	B-89	1060	.015	L.F.	.13	.63	.50	1.26	1.71
0320	Each additional inch of depth		3180	.005		.04	.21	.17	.42	.57
0400	Mesh reinforced, up to 3" deep		980	.016		.15	.68	.54	1.37	1.84
0420	Each additional inch of depth		2940	.005		.05	.23	.18	.46	.61
0500	Rod reinforced, up to 3" deep		800	.020		.19	.84	.66	1.69	2.26
0520	Each additional inch of depth		2400	.007	↓	.06	.28	.22	.56	.76
0590	Minimum labor/equipment charge	↓	2	8	Job		335	263	598	825

03 81 13.75 Concrete Saw Blades

		Crew	Daily Output	Labor-Hours	Unit	Material	2014 Bare Costs Labor	Equipment	Total	Total Incl O&P
0010	**CONCRETE SAW BLADES**									
3000	Blades for saw cutting, included in cutting line items									
3020	Diamond, 12" diameter				Ea.	244			244	269
3040	18" diameter					445			445	490
3080	24" diameter					755			755	830
3120	30" diameter					1,100			1,100	1,200
3160	36" diameter					1,425			1,425	1,575
3200	42" diameter				↓	2,700			2,700	2,975

03 81 Concrete Cutting

03 81 16 – Track Mounted Concrete Wall Sawing

03 81 16.50 Concrete Wall Cutting	Crew	Daily Output	Labor-Hours	Unit	Material	2014 Bare Costs Labor	Equipment	Total	Total Incl O&P
0010 **CONCRETE WALL CUTTING**									
0750 Includes blade cost, layout and set-up time									
0800 Concrete walls, hydraulic saw, plain, per inch of depth	B-89B	250	.064	L.F.	.04	2.67	3.64	6.35	8.35
0820 Rod reinforcing, per inch of depth		150	.107	"	.06	4.46	6.05	10.57	13.85
0890 Minimum labor/equipment charge	↓	2	8	Job		335	455	790	1,025

03 82 Concrete Boring

03 82 13 – Concrete Core Drilling

03 82 13.10 Core Drilling	Crew	Daily Output	Labor-Hours	Unit	Material	2014 Bare Costs Labor	Equipment	Total	Total Incl O&P
0010 **CORE DRILLING**									
0015 Includes bit cost, layout and set-up time									
0020 Reinforced concrete slab, up to 6" thick									
0100 1" diameter core	B-89A	17	.941	Ea.	.18	39.50	6.85	46.53	72
0150 For each additional inch of slab thickness in same hole, add		1440	.011		.03	.47	.08	.58	.88
0200 2" diameter core		16.50	.970		.29	40.50	7.05	47.84	74.50
0250 For each additional inch of slab thickness in same hole, add		1080	.015		.05	.62	.11	.78	1.19
0300 3" diameter core		16	1		.39	42	7.25	49.64	77
0350 For each additional inch of slab thickness in same hole, add		720	.022		.07	.93	.16	1.16	1.78
0500 4" diameter core		15	1.067		.50	45	7.75	53.25	82
0550 For each additional inch of slab thickness in same hole, add		480	.033		.08	1.40	.24	1.72	2.65
0700 6" diameter core		14	1.143		.78	48	8.30	57.08	88.50
0750 For each additional inch of slab thickness in same hole, add		360	.044		.13	1.87	.32	2.32	3.55
0900 8" diameter core		13	1.231		1.08	51.50	8.95	61.53	95.50
0950 For each additional inch of slab thickness in same hole, add		288	.056		.18	2.33	.40	2.91	4.45
1100 10" diameter core		12	1.333		1.51	56	9.70	67.21	104
1150 For each additional inch of slab thickness in same hole, add		240	.067		.25	2.80	.48	3.53	5.40
1300 12" diameter core		11	1.455		1.79	61	10.55	73.34	114
1350 For each additional inch of slab thickness in same hole, add		206	.078		.30	3.26	.56	4.12	6.30
1500 14" diameter core		10	1.600		2.11	67	11.60	80.71	125
1550 For each additional inch of slab thickness in same hole, add		180	.089		.35	3.73	.65	4.73	7.20
1700 18" diameter core		9	1.778		2.84	74.50	12.90	90.24	139
1750 For each additional inch of slab thickness in same hole, add		144	.111		.47	4.66	.81	5.94	9.05
1754 24" diameter core		8	2		3.99	84	14.50	102.49	157
1756 For each additional inch of slab thickness in same hole, add	↓	120	.133		.67	5.60	.97	7.24	10.95
1760 For horizontal holes, add to above				↓		20%	20%		
1770 Prestressed hollow core plank, 8" thick									
1780 1" diameter core	B-89A	17.50	.914	Ea.	.24	38.50	6.65	45.39	70.50
1790 For each additional inch of plank thickness in same hole, add		3840	.004		.03	.18	.03	.24	.35
1794 2" diameter core		17.25	.928		.38	39	6.75	46.13	71.50
1796 For each additional inch of plank thickness in same hole, add		2880	.006		.05	.23	.04	.32	.47
1800 3" diameter core		17	.941		.52	39.50	6.85	46.87	72.50
1810 For each additional inch of plank thickness in same hole, add		1920	.008		.07	.35	.06	.48	.71
1820 4" diameter core		16.50	.970		.66	40.50	7.05	48.21	75
1830 For each additional inch of plank thickness in same hole, add		1280	.013		.08	.52	.09	.69	1.05
1840 6" diameter core		15.50	1.032		1.04	43.50	7.50	52.04	80.50
1850 For each additional inch of plank thickness in same hole, add		960	.017		.13	.70	.12	.95	1.41
1860 8" diameter core		15	1.067		1.44	45	7.75	54.19	83
1870 For each additional inch of plank thickness in same hole, add		768	.021		.18	.87	.15	1.20	1.80
1880 10" diameter core		14	1.143		2.01	48	8.30	58.31	90
1890 For each additional inch of plank thickness in same hole, add	↓	640	.025		.25	1.05	.18	1.48	2.20

03 82 Concrete Boring

03 82 13 – Concrete Core Drilling

03 82 13.10 Core Drilling		Crew	Daily Output	Labor-Hours	Unit	Material	2014 Bare Costs Labor	Equipment	Total	Total Incl O&P
1900	12" diameter core	B-89A	13.50	1.185	Ea.	2.39	50	8.60	60.99	93.50
1910	For each additional inch of plank thickness in same hole, add		548	.029		.30	1.23	.21	1.74	2.56
1999	Drilling, core, minimum labor/equipment charge		2	8	Job		335	58	393	615
3000	Bits for core drilling, included in drilling line items									
3010	Diamond, premium, 1" diameter				Ea.	72			72	79.50
3020	2" diameter					115			115	127
3030	3" diameter					157			157	173
3040	4" diameter					199			199	219
3060	6" diameter					315			315	345
3080	8" diameter					435			435	475
3110	10" diameter					605			605	665
3120	12" diameter					715			715	790
3140	14" diameter					845			845	930
3180	18" diameter					1,125			1,125	1,250
3240	24" diameter					1,600			1,600	1,750

03 82 16 – Concrete Drilling

03 82 16.10 Concrete Impact Drilling		Crew	Daily Output	Labor-Hours	Unit	Material	2014 Bare Costs Labor	Equipment	Total	Total Incl O&P
0010	**CONCRETE IMPACT DRILLING**									
0020	Includes bit cost, layout and set-up time, no anchors									
0050	Up to 4" deep in concrete/brick floors/walls									
0100	Holes, 1/4" diameter	1 Carp	75	.107	Ea.	.06	4.89		4.95	8.10
0150	For each additional inch of depth in same hole, add		430	.019		.02	.85		.87	1.42
0200	3/8" diameter		63	.127		.05	5.80		5.85	9.60
0250	For each additional inch of depth in same hole, add		340	.024		.01	1.08		1.09	1.78
0300	1/2" diameter		50	.160		.05	7.35		7.40	12.10
0350	For each additional inch of depth in same hole, add		250	.032		.01	1.47		1.48	2.42
0400	5/8" diameter		48	.167		.08	7.65		7.73	12.65
0450	For each additional inch of depth in same hole, add		240	.033		.02	1.53		1.55	2.53
0500	3/4" diameter		45	.178		.11	8.15		8.26	13.50
0550	For each additional inch of depth in same hole, add		220	.036		.03	1.67		1.70	2.77
0600	7/8" diameter		43	.186		.15	8.55		8.70	14.15
0650	For each additional inch of depth in same hole, add		210	.038		.04	1.75		1.79	2.91
0700	1" diameter		40	.200		.16	9.15		9.31	15.25
0750	For each additional inch of depth in same hole, add		190	.042		.04	1.93		1.97	3.21
0800	1-1/4" diameter		38	.211		.23	9.65		9.88	16.10
0850	For each additional inch of depth in same hole, add		180	.044		.06	2.04		2.10	3.41
0900	1-1/2" diameter		35	.229		.32	10.50		10.82	17.55
0950	For each additional inch of depth in same hole, add		165	.048		.08	2.22		2.30	3.74
1000	For ceiling installations, add						40%			

Division Notes

	CREW	DAILY OUTPUT	LABOR-HOURS	UNIT	BARE COSTS				TOTAL INCL O&P
					MAT.	LABOR	EQUIP.	TOTAL	

Estimating Tips

04 05 00 Common Work Results for Masonry

- The terms *mortar* and *grout* are often used interchangeably, and incorrectly. Mortar is used to bed masonry units, seal the entry of air and moisture, provide architectural appearance, and allow for size variations in the units. Grout is used primarily in reinforced masonry construction and is used to bond the masonry to the reinforcing steel. Common mortar types are M(2500 psi), S(1800 psi), N(750 psi), and O(350 psi), and conform to ASTM C270. Grout is either fine or coarse and conforms to ASTM C476, and in-place strengths generally exceed 2500 psi. Mortar and grout are different components of masonry construction and are placed by entirely different methods. An estimator should be aware of their unique uses and costs.

- Mortar is included in all assembled masonry line items. The mortar cost, part of the assembled masonry material cost, includes all ingredients, all labor, and all equipment required. Please see reference number R040513-10.

- Waste, specifically the loss/ droppings of mortar and the breakage of brick and block, is included in all masonry assemblies in this division. A factor of 25% is added for mortar and 3% for brick and concrete masonry units.

- Scaffolding or staging is not included in any of the Division 4 costs. Refer to Subdivision 01 54 23 for scaffolding and staging costs.

04 20 00 Unit Masonry

- The most common types of unit masonry are brick and concrete masonry. The major classifications of brick are building brick (ASTM C62), facing brick (ASTM C216), glazed brick, fire brick, and pavers. Many varieties of texture and appearance can exist within these classifications, and the estimator would be wise to check local custom and availability within the project area. For repair and remodeling jobs, matching the existing brick may be the most important criteria.

- Brick and concrete block are priced by the piece and then converted into a price per square foot of wall. Openings less than two square feet are generally ignored by the estimator because any savings in units used is offset by the cutting and trimming required.

- It is often difficult and expensive to find and purchase small lots of historic brick. Costs can vary widely. Many design issues affect costs, selection of mortar mix, and repairs or replacement of masonry materials. Cleaning techniques must be reflected in the estimate.

- All masonry walls, whether interior or exterior, require bracing. The cost of bracing walls during construction should be included by the estimator, and this bracing must remain in place until permanent bracing is complete. Permanent bracing of masonry walls is accomplished by masonry itself, in the form of pilasters or abutting wall corners, or by anchoring the walls to the structural frame. Accessories in the form of anchors, anchor slots, and ties are used, but their supply and installation can be by different trades. For instance, anchor slots on spandrel beams and columns are supplied and welded in place by the steel fabricator, but the ties from the slots into the masonry are installed by the bricklayer. Regardless of the installation method, the estimator must be certain that these accessories are accounted for in pricing.

Reference Numbers

Reference numbers are shown in shaded boxes at the beginning of some major classifications. These numbers refer to related items in the Reference Section. The reference information may be an estimating procedure, an alternate pricing method, or technical information.

Note: Not all subdivisions listed here necessarily appear in this publication.

04 01 20 – Maintenance of Unit Masonry

04 01 20.20 Pointing Masonry

		Crew	Daily Output	Labor-Hours	Unit	Material	2014 Bare Costs Labor	Equipment	Total	Total Incl O&P
0010	**POINTING MASONRY**									
0300	Cut and repoint brick, hard mortar, running bond	1 Bric	80	.100	S.F.	.51	4.56		5.07	7.95
0320	Common bond		77	.104		.51	4.74		5.25	8.25
0360	Flemish bond		70	.114		.54	5.20		5.74	9.05
0400	English bond		65	.123		.54	5.60		6.14	9.70
0600	Soft old mortar, running bond		100	.080		.51	3.65		4.16	6.45
0620	Common bond		96	.083		.51	3.80		4.31	6.70
0640	Flemish bond		90	.089		.54	4.05		4.59	7.20
0680	English bond		82	.098	↓	.54	4.45		4.99	7.80
0700	Stonework, hard mortar		140	.057	L.F.	.68	2.61		3.29	4.98
0720	Soft old mortar		160	.050	"	.68	2.28		2.96	4.45
1000	Repoint, mask and grout method, running bond		95	.084	S.F.	.68	3.84		4.52	7
1020	Common bond		90	.089		.68	4.05		4.73	7.35
1040	Flemish bond		86	.093		.72	4.24		4.96	7.70
1060	English bond		77	.104		.72	4.74		5.46	8.50
2000	Scrub coat, sand grout on walls, thin mix, brushed		120	.067		2.72	3.04		5.76	7.95
2020	Troweled		98	.082	↓	3.79	3.72		7.51	10.20
9000	Minimum labor/equipment charge	↓	3	2.667	Job		122		122	197

04 01 20.30 Pointing CMU

		Crew	Daily Output	Labor-Hours	Unit	Material	2014 Bare Costs Labor	Equipment	Total	Total Incl O&P
0010	**POINTING CMU**									
0300	Cut and repoint block, hard mortar, running bond	1 Bric	190	.042	S.F.	.21	1.92		2.13	3.35
0310	Stacked bond		200	.040		.21	1.82		2.03	3.19
0600	Soft old mortar, running bond		230	.035		.21	1.59		1.80	2.81
0610	Stacked bond	↓	245	.033	↓	.21	1.49		1.70	2.65

04 01 20.41 Unit Masonry Stabilization

		Crew	Daily Output	Labor-Hours	Unit	Material	2014 Bare Costs Labor	Equipment	Total	Total Incl O&P
0010	**UNIT MASONRY STABILIZATION**									
0100	Structural repointing method									
0110	Cut / grind mortar joint	1 Bric	240	.033	L.F.		1.52		1.52	2.47
0120	Clean and mask joint		2500	.003		.13	.15		.28	.38
0130	Epoxy paste and 1/4" FRP rod		240	.033		1.07	1.52		2.59	3.65
0132	3/8" FRP rod		160	.050		1.63	2.28		3.91	5.50
0134	1/4" CFRP rod		240	.033		13.90	1.52		15.42	17.70
0136	3/8" CFRP rod		160	.050		17.50	2.28		19.78	23
0140	Remove masking	↓	14400	.001	↓		.03		.03	.04
0300	Structural fabric method									
0310	Primer	1 Bric	600	.013	S.F.	.46	.61		1.07	1.49
0320	Apply filling/leveling paste		720	.011		.43	.51		.94	1.29
0330	Epoxy, glass fiber fabric		720	.011		5.65	.51		6.16	7
0340	Carbon fiber fabric	↓	720	.011	↓	15.45	.51		15.96	17.80

04 01 20.50 Toothing Masonry

		Crew	Daily Output	Labor-Hours	Unit	Material	2014 Bare Costs Labor	Equipment	Total	Total Incl O&P
0010	**TOOTHING MASONRY**									
0500	Brickwork, soft old mortar	1 Clab	40	.200	V.L.F.		7.35		7.35	12.05
0520	Hard mortar		30	.267			9.75		9.75	16.05
0700	Blockwork, soft old mortar		70	.114			4.19		4.19	6.90
0720	Hard mortar	↓	50	.160	↓		5.85		5.85	9.65
9000	Minimum labor/equipment charge	↓	4	2	Job		73.50		73.50	120

04 01 30 – Unit Masonry Cleaning

04 01 30.20 Cleaning Masonry

		Crew	Daily Output	Labor-Hours	Unit	Material	2014 Bare Costs Labor	Equipment	Total	Total Incl O&P
0010	**CLEANING MASONRY**									
0200	By chemical, brush and rinse, new work, light construction dust	D-1	1000	.016	S.F.	.06	.66		.72	1.13
0220	Medium construction dust	↓	800	.020	↓	.08	.83		.91	1.43

04 01 Maintenance of Masonry

04 01 30 – Unit Masonry Cleaning

04 01 30.20 Cleaning Masonry

		Crew	Daily Output	Labor-Hours	Unit	Material	2014 Bare Costs Labor	Equipment	Total	Total Incl O&P
0240	Heavy construction dust, drips or stains	D-1	600	.027	S.F.	.11	1.10		1.21	1.91
0260	Low pressure wash and rinse, light restoration, light soil		800	.020		.12	.83		.95	1.48
0270	Average soil, biological staining		400	.040		.18	1.65		1.83	2.88
0280	Heavy soil, biological and mineral staining, paint		330	.048		.25	2		2.25	3.52
0300	High pressure wash and rinse, heavy restoration, light soil		600	.027		.11	1.10		1.21	1.91
0310	Average soil, biological staining		400	.040		.16	1.65		1.81	2.86
0320	Heavy soil, biological and mineral staining, paint		250	.064		.22	2.64		2.86	4.53
0400	High pressure wash, water only, light soil	C-29	500	.016			.59	.14	.73	1.11
0420	Average soil, biological staining		375	.021			.78	.19	.97	1.48
0440	Heavy soil, biological and mineral staining, paint		250	.032			1.17	.28	1.45	2.24
0800	High pressure water and chemical, light soil		450	.018		.15	.65	.15	.95	1.40
0820	Average soil, biological staining		300	.027		.22	.98	.23	1.43	2.10
0840	Heavy soil, biological and mineral staining, paint		200	.040		.30	1.47	.35	2.12	3.12
1200	Sandblast, wet system, light soil	J-6	1750	.018		.33	.74	.14	1.21	1.72
1220	Average soil, biological staining		1100	.029		.50	1.18	.22	1.90	2.69
1240	Heavy soil, biological and mineral staining, paint		700	.046		.67	1.86	.34	2.87	4.10
1400	Dry system, light soil		2500	.013		.33	.52	.09	.94	1.31
1420	Average soil, biological staining		1750	.018		.50	.74	.14	1.38	1.90
1440	Heavy soil, biological and mineral staining, paint		1000	.032		.67	1.30	.24	2.21	3.09
1800	For walnut shells, add					.82			.82	.90
1820	For corn chips, add					.82			.82	.90
2000	Steam cleaning, light soil	A-1H	750	.011			.39	.10	.49	.75
2020	Average soil, biological staining		625	.013			.47	.12	.59	.90
2040	Heavy soil, biological and mineral staining		375	.021			.78	.20	.98	1.50
4000	Add for masking doors and windows	1 Clab	800	.010		.04	.37		.41	.64
4200	Add for pedestrian protection				Job				10%	10%
9000	Minimum labor/equipment charge	D-4	2	16	"		665	67.50	732.50	1,150

04 01 30.60 Brick Washing

		Crew	Daily Output	Labor-Hours	Unit	Material	2014 Bare Costs Labor	Equipment	Total	Total Incl O&P
0010	**BRICK WASHING**									
0012	Acid cleanser, smooth brick surface	1 Bric	560	.014	S.F.	.06	.65		.71	1.13
0050	Rough brick		400	.020		.09	.91		1	1.58
0060	Stone, acid wash		600	.013		.10	.61		.71	1.10
1000	Muriatic acid, price per gallon in 5 gallon lots				Gal.	13			13	14.30

04 05 Common Work Results for Masonry

04 05 05 – Selective Masonry Demolition

04 05 05.10 Selective Demolition

		Crew	Daily Output	Labor-Hours	Unit	Material	2014 Bare Costs Labor	Equipment	Total	Total Incl O&P
0010	**SELECTIVE DEMOLITION** R024119-10									
0200	Bond beams, 8" block with #4 bar	2 Clab	32	.500	L.F.		18.35		18.35	30
0300	Concrete block walls, unreinforced, 2" thick		1200	.013	S.F.		.49		.49	.80
0310	4" thick		1150	.014			.51		.51	.84
0320	6" thick		1100	.015			.53		.53	.88
0330	8" thick		1050	.015			.56		.56	.92
0340	10" thick		1000	.016			.59		.59	.96
0360	12" thick		950	.017			.62		.62	1.01
0380	Reinforced alternate courses, 2" thick		1130	.014			.52		.52	.85
0390	4" thick		1080	.015			.54		.54	.89
0400	6" thick		1035	.015			.57		.57	.93
0410	8" thick		990	.016			.59		.59	.97
0420	10" thick		940	.017			.62		.62	1.02
0430	12" thick		890	.018			.66		.66	1.08

04 05 Common Work Results for Masonry

04 05 05 – Selective Masonry Demolition

04 05 05.10 Selective Demolition	Crew	Daily Output	Labor-Hours	Unit	Material	2014 Bare Costs Labor	Equipment	Total	Total Incl O&P
0440 Reinforced alternate courses & vertically 48" OC, 4" thick	2 Clab	900	.018	S.F.		.65		.65	1.07
0450 6" thick		850	.019			.69		.69	1.13
0460 8" thick		800	.020			.73		.73	1.20
0480 10" thick		750	.021			.78		.78	1.28
0490 12" thick		700	.023			.84		.84	1.38
1000 Chimney, 16" x 16", soft old mortar	1 Clab	55	.145	C.F.		5.35		5.35	8.75
1020 Hard mortar		40	.200			7.35		7.35	12.05
1030 16" x 20", soft old mortar		55	.145			5.35		5.35	8.75
1040 Hard mortar		40	.200			7.35		7.35	12.05
1050 16" x 24", soft old mortar		55	.145			5.35		5.35	8.75
1060 Hard mortar		40	.200			7.35		7.35	12.05
1080 20" x 20", soft old mortar		55	.145			5.35		5.35	8.75
1100 Hard mortar		40	.200			7.35		7.35	12.05
1110 20" x 24", soft old mortar		55	.145			5.35		5.35	8.75
1120 Hard mortar		40	.200			7.35		7.35	12.05
1140 20" x 32", soft old mortar		55	.145			5.35		5.35	8.75
1160 Hard mortar		40	.200			7.35		7.35	12.05
1200 48" x 48", soft old mortar		55	.145			5.35		5.35	8.75
1220 Hard mortar		40	.200			7.35		7.35	12.05
1250 Metal, high temp steel jacket, 24" diameter	E-2	130	.431	V.L.F.		21.50	11.75	33.25	51
1260 60" diameter	"	60	.933			47	25.50	72.50	111
1280 Flue lining, up to 12" x 12"	1 Clab	200	.040			1.47		1.47	2.41
1282 Up to 24" x 24"		150	.053			1.95		1.95	3.21
2000 Columns, 8" x 8", soft old mortar		48	.167			6.10		6.10	10.05
2020 Hard mortar		40	.200			7.35		7.35	12.05
2060 16" x 16", soft old mortar		16	.500			18.35		18.35	30
2100 Hard mortar		14	.571			21		21	34.50
2140 24" x 24", soft old mortar		8	1			36.50		36.50	60
2160 Hard mortar		6	1.333			49		49	80.50
2200 36" x 36", soft old mortar		4	2			73.50		73.50	120
2220 Hard mortar		3	2.667			97.50		97.50	161
2230 Alternate pricing method, soft old mortar		30	.267	C.F.		9.75		9.75	16.05
2240 Hard mortar		23	.348	"		12.75		12.75	21
3000 Copings, precast or masonry, to 8" wide									
3020 Soft old mortar	1 Clab	180	.044	L.F.		1.63		1.63	2.68
3040 Hard mortar	"	160	.050	"		1.83		1.83	3.01
3100 To 12" wide									
3120 Soft old mortar	1 Clab	160	.050	L.F.		1.83		1.83	3.01
3140 Hard mortar	"	140	.057	"		2.09		2.09	3.44
4000 Fireplace, brick, 30" x 24" opening									
4020 Soft old mortar	1 Clab	2	4	Ea.		147		147	241
4040 Hard mortar		1.25	6.400			235		235	385
4100 Stone, soft old mortar		1.50	5.333			195		195	320
4120 Hard mortar		1	8			293		293	480
5000 Veneers, brick, soft old mortar		140	.057	S.F.		2.09		2.09	3.44
5020 Hard mortar		125	.064			2.35		2.35	3.85
5050 Glass block, up to 4" thick		500	.016			.59		.59	.96
5100 Granite and marble, 2" thick		180	.044			1.63		1.63	2.68
5120 4" thick		170	.047			1.72		1.72	2.83
5140 Stone, 4" thick		180	.044			1.63		1.63	2.68
5160 8" thick		175	.046			1.68		1.68	2.75
5400 Alternate pricing method, stone, 4" thick		60	.133	C.F.		4.89		4.89	8.05
5420 8" thick		85	.094	"		3.45		3.45	5.65

04 05 05 – Selective Masonry Demolition

04 05 05.10 Selective Demolition	Crew	Daily Output	Labor-Hours	Unit	Material	2014 Bare Costs Labor	Equipment	Total	Total Incl O&P
9000 Minimum labor/equipment charge	1 Clab	2	4	Job		147		147	241

04 05 13 – Masonry Mortaring

04 05 13.10 Cement

	Crew	Daily Output	Labor-Hours	Unit	Material	2014 Bare Costs Labor	Equipment	Total	Total Incl O&P
0010 **CEMENT**									
0100 Masonry, 70 lb. bag, T.L. lots				Bag	11.05			11.05	12.15
0150 L.T.L. lots					11.70			11.70	12.90
0200 White, 70 lb. bag, T.L. lots					15.65			15.65	17.25
0250 L.T.L. lots					18.30			18.30	20

04 05 13.20 Lime

	Crew	Daily Output	Labor-Hours	Unit	Material	2014 Bare Costs Labor	Equipment	Total	Total Incl O&P
0010 **LIME**									
0020 Masons, hydrated, 50 lb. bag, T.L. lots				Bag	10.10			10.10	11.10
0050 L.T.L. lots					11.10			11.10	12.20
0200 Finish, double hydrated, 50 lb. bag, T.L. lots					8.65			8.65	9.55
0250 L.T.L. lots					9.55			9.55	10.50

04 05 13.23 Surface Bonding Masonry Mortaring

	Crew	Daily Output	Labor-Hours	Unit	Material	2014 Bare Costs Labor	Equipment	Total	Total Incl O&P
0010 **SURFACE BONDING MASONRY MORTARING**									
0020 Gray or white colors, not incl. block work	1 Bric	540	.015	S.F.	.13	.68		.81	1.25

04 05 13.30 Mortar

	Crew	Daily Output	Labor-Hours	Unit	Material	2014 Bare Costs Labor	Equipment	Total	Total Incl O&P
0010 **MORTAR**									
0020 With masonry cement									
0100 Type M, 1:1:6 mix	1 Brhe	143	.056	C.F.	4.91	2.07		6.98	8.75
0200 Type N, 1:3 mix		143	.056		4.94	2.07		7.01	8.80
0300 Type O, 1:3 mix		143	.056		4.78	2.07		6.85	8.60
0400 Type PM, 1:1:6 mix, 2500 psi		143	.056		3.99	2.07		6.06	7.75
0500 Type S, 1/2:1:4 mix		143	.056		5.35	2.07		7.42	9.25
2000 With portland cement and lime									
2100 Type M, 1:1/4:3 mix	1 Brhe	143	.056	C.F.	8.45	2.07		10.52	12.65
2200 Type N, 1:1:6 mix, 750 psi		143	.056		6.60	2.07		8.67	10.60
2300 Type O, 1:2:9 mix (Pointing Mortar)		143	.056		7	2.07		9.07	11.05
2400 Type PL, 1:1/2:4 mix, 2500 psi		143	.056		3.99	2.07		6.06	7.75
2600 Type S, 1:1/2:4 mix, 1800 psi		143	.056		7.75	2.07		9.82	11.85
2650 Pre-mixed, type S or N					5.05			5.05	5.55
2700 Mortar for glass block	1 Brhe	143	.056		10.40	2.07		12.47	14.75
2900 Mortar for fire brick, dry mix, 10 lb. pail				Ea.	26			26	28.50

04 05 13.91 Masonry Restoration Mortaring

	Crew	Daily Output	Labor-Hours	Unit	Material	2014 Bare Costs Labor	Equipment	Total	Total Incl O&P
0010 **MASONRY RESTORATION MORTARING**									
0020 Masonry restoration mix				Lb.	.23			.23	.25
0050 White				"	.23			.23	.25

04 05 13.93 Mortar Pigments

	Crew	Daily Output	Labor-Hours	Unit	Material	2014 Bare Costs Labor	Equipment	Total	Total Incl O&P
0010 **MORTAR PIGMENTS**, 50 lb. bags (2 bags per M bricks)									
0020 Color admixture, range 2 to 10 lb. per bag of cement, light colors				Lb.	4.25			4.25	4.68
0050 Medium colors					6.20			6.20	6.80
0100 Dark colors					12.90			12.90	14.20

04 05 13.95 Sand

	Crew	Daily Output	Labor-Hours	Unit	Material	2014 Bare Costs Labor	Equipment	Total	Total Incl O&P
0010 **SAND**, screened and washed at pit									
0020 For mortar, per ton				Ton	17.40			17.40	19.15
0050 With 10 mile haul					32			32	35
0100 With 30 mile haul					52			52	57
0200 Screened and washed, at the pit				C.Y.	24			24	26.50
0250 With 10 mile haul					44			44	48.50

04 05 13 – Masonry Mortaring

04 05 13.95 Sand	Crew	Daily Output	Labor-Hours	Unit	Material	2014 Bare Costs Labor	Equipment	Total	Total Incl O&P
0300　　With 30 mile haul				C.Y.	72			72	79.50

04 05 13.98 Mortar Admixtures	Crew	Daily Output	Labor-Hours	Unit	Material	Labor	Equipment	Total	Total Incl O&P
0010　**MORTAR ADMIXTURES**									
0020　　Waterproofing admixture, per quart (1 qt. to 2 bags of masonry cement)				Qt.	3.50			3.50	3.85

04 05 16 – Masonry Grouting

04 05 16.30 Grouting	Crew	Daily Output	Labor-Hours	Unit	Material	Labor	Equipment	Total	Total Incl O&P
0010　**GROUTING**									
0011　　Bond beams & lintels, 8" deep, 6" thick, 0.15 C.F. per L.F.	D-4	1480	.022	L.F.	.66	.90	.09	1.65	2.27
0020　　　8" thick, 0.2 C.F. per L.F.		1400	.023		1.04	.95	.10	2.09	2.79
0050　　　10" thick, 0.25 C.F. per L.F.		1200	.027		1.09	1.11	.11	2.31	3.11
0060　　　12" thick, 0.3 C.F. per L.F.		1040	.031		1.31	1.28	.13	2.72	3.65
0200　　Concrete block cores, solid, 4" thk., by hand, 0.067 C.F./S.F. of wall	D-8	1100	.036	S.F.	.29	1.53		1.82	2.81
0210　　　6" thick, pumped, 0.175 C.F. per S.F.	D-4	720	.044		.76	1.85	.19	2.80	4.04
0250　　　8" thick, pumped, 0.258 C.F. per S.F.		680	.047		1.13	1.96	.20	3.29	4.62
0300　　　10" thick, pumped, 0.340 C.F. per S.F.		660	.048		1.49	2.02	.20	3.71	5.10
0350　　　12" thick, pumped, 0.422 C.F. per S.F.		640	.050		1.84	2.08	.21	4.13	5.60
0500　　Cavity walls, 2" space, pumped, 0.167 C.F./S.F. of wall		1700	.019		.73	.78	.08	1.59	2.15
0550　　　3" space, 0.250 C.F./S.F.		1200	.027		1.09	1.11	.11	2.31	3.11
0600　　　4" space, 0.333 C.F. per S.F.		1150	.028		1.46	1.16	.12	2.74	3.60
0700　　　6" space, 0.500 C.F. per S.F.		800	.040		2.19	1.67	.17	4.03	5.30
0800　　Door frames, 3' x 7' opening, 2.5 C.F. per opening		60	.533	Opng.	10.95	22	2.25	35.20	50.50
0850　　　6' x 7' opening, 3.5 C.F. per opening		45	.711	"	15.30	29.50	2.99	47.79	68
2000　　Grout, C476, for bond beams, lintels and CMU cores		350	.091	C.F.	4.37	3.81	.38	8.56	11.40
9000　　Minimum labor/equipment charge	1 Bric	2	4	Job		182		182	296

04 05 19 – Masonry Anchorage and Reinforcing

04 05 19.05 Anchor Bolts	Crew	Daily Output	Labor-Hours	Unit	Material	Labor	Equipment	Total	Total Incl O&P
0010　**ANCHOR BOLTS**									
0015　　Installed in fresh grout in CMU bond beams or filled cores, no templates									
0020　　　Hooked, with nut and washer, 1/2" diam., 8" long	1 Bric	132	.061	Ea.	1.49	2.76		4.25	6.15
0030　　　　12" long		131	.061		1.66	2.78		4.44	6.35
0040　　　5/8" diameter, 8" long		129	.062		3.25	2.83		6.08	8.15
0050　　　　12" long		127	.063		4	2.87		6.87	9.05
0060　　　3/4" diameter, 8" long		127	.063		4	2.87		6.87	9.05
0070　　　　12" long		125	.064		5	2.92		7.92	10.25

04 05 19.16 Masonry Anchors	Crew	Daily Output	Labor-Hours	Unit	Material	Labor	Equipment	Total	Total Incl O&P
0010　**MASONRY ANCHORS**									
0020　　For brick veneer, galv., corrugated, 7/8" x 7", 22 Ga.	1 Bric	10.50	.762	C	13.45	34.50		47.95	71.50
0100　　　24 Ga.		10.50	.762		9.50	34.50		44	67
0150　　　16 Ga.		10.50	.762		26.50	34.50		61	85.50
0200　　Buck anchors, galv., corrugated, 16 ga., 2" bend, 8" x 2"		10.50	.762		49	34.50		83.50	111
0250　　　8" x 3"		10.50	.762		51	34.50		85.50	113
0300　　Adjustable, rectangular, 4-1/8" wide									
0350　　　Anchor and tie, 3/16" wire, mill galv.									
0400　　　2-3/4" eye, 3-1/4" tie	1 Bric	1.05	7.619	M	430	345		775	1,050
0500　　　　4-3/4" tie		1.05	7.619		465	345		810	1,075
0520　　　　5-1/2" tie		1.05	7.619		505	345		850	1,125
0550　　　4-3/4" eye, 3-1/4" tie		1.05	7.619		475	345		820	1,100
0570　　　　4-3/4" tie		1.05	7.619		515	345		860	1,125
0580　　　　5-1/2" tie		1.05	7.619		560	345		905	1,175
0660　　Cavity wall, Z-type, galvanized, 6" long, 1/8" diam.		10.50	.762	C	23.50	34.50		58	82.50
0670　　　3/16" diameter		10.50	.762		27	34.50		61.50	86

04 05 19 - Masonry Anchorage and Reinforcing

04 05 19.16 Masonry Anchors		Crew	Daily Output	Labor-Hours	Unit	Material	2014 Bare Costs Labor	Equipment	Total	Total Incl O&P
0680	1/4" diameter	1 Bric	10.50	.762	C	40.50	34.50		75	101
0850	8" long, 3/16" diameter		10.50	.762		25	34.50		59.50	84
0855	1/4" diameter		10.50	.762		48.50	34.50		83	110
1000	Rectangular type, galvanized, 1/4" diameter, 2" x 6"		10.50	.762		70	34.50		104.50	134
1050	4" x 6"		10.50	.762		85	34.50		119.50	150
1100	3/16" diameter, 2" x 6"		10.50	.762		42	34.50		76.50	103
1150	4" x 6"	↓	10.50	.762	↓	48.50	34.50		83	110
1200	Mesh wall tie, 1/2" mesh, hot dip galvanized									
1400	16 ga., 12" long, 3" wide	1 Bric	9	.889	C	84.50	40.50		125	159
1420	6" wide		9	.889		122	40.50		162.50	201
1440	12" wide		8.50	.941		198	43		241	287
1500	Rigid partition anchors, plain, 8" long, 1" x 1/8"		10.50	.762		235	34.50		269.50	315
1550	1" x 1/4"		10.50	.762		277	34.50		311.50	360
1580	1-1/2" x 1/8"		10.50	.762		259	34.50		293.50	340
1600	1-1/2" x 1/4"		10.50	.762		325	34.50		359.50	410
1650	2" x 1/8"		10.50	.762		305	34.50		339.50	390
1700	2" x 1/4"	↓	10.50	.762	↓	405	34.50		439.50	500
2000	Column flange ties, wire, galvanized									
2300	3/16" diameter, up to 3" wide	1 Bric	10.50	.762	C	87	34.50		121.50	153
2350	To 5" wide		10.50	.762		94.50	34.50		129	161
2400	To 7" wide		10.50	.762		102	34.50		136.50	169
2600	To 9" wide		10.50	.762		109	34.50		143.50	176
2650	1/4" diameter, up to 3" wide		10.50	.762		110	34.50		144.50	178
2700	To 5" wide		10.50	.762		118	34.50		152.50	187
2800	To 7" wide		10.50	.762		133	34.50		167.50	203
2850	To 9" wide	↓	10.50	.762		143	34.50		177.50	214
2900	For hot dip galvanized, add				↓	35%				
4000	Channel slots, 1-3/8" x 1/2" x 8"									
4100	12 ga., plain	1 Bric	10.50	.762	C	212	34.50		246.50	290
4150	16 ga., galvanized	"	10.50	.762	"	145	34.50		179.50	216
4200	Channel slot anchors									
4300	16 ga., galvanized, 1-1/4" x 3-1/2"				C	56.50			56.50	62
4350	1-1/4" x 5-1/2"					66			66	72.50
4400	1-1/4" x 7-1/2"					74.50			74.50	82
4500	1/8" plain, 1-1/4" x 3-1/2"					143			143	157
4550	1-1/4" x 5-1/2"					152			152	167
4600	1-1/4" x 7-1/2"					166			166	183
4700	For corrugation, add					76.50			76.50	84.50
4750	For hot dip galvanized, add				↓	35%				
5000	Dowels									
5100	Plain, 1/4" diameter, 3" long				C	55.50			55.50	61
5150	4" long					61.50			61.50	67.50
5200	6" long					75			75	82.50
5300	3/8" diameter, 3" long					73			73	80.50
5350	4" long					91			91	100
5400	6" long					105			105	115
5500	1/2" diameter, 3" long					107			107	117
5550	4" long					127			127	139
5600	6" long					164			164	180
5700	5/8" diameter, 3" long					146			146	161
5750	4" long					180			180	198
5800	6" long					247			247	272
6000	3/4" diameter, 3" long				↓	182			182	200

04 05 Common Work Results for Masonry

04 05 19 – Masonry Anchorage and Reinforcing

04 05 19.16 Masonry Anchors	Crew	Daily Output	Labor-Hours	Unit	Material	2014 Bare Costs Labor	Equipment	Total	Total Incl O&P
6100 4" long				C	231			231	254
6150 6" long					330			330	365
6300 For hot dip galvanized, add					35%				

04 05 19.26 Masonry Reinforcing Bars

	Crew	Daily Output	Labor-Hours	Unit	Material	Labor	Equipment	Total	Total Incl O&P
0010 **MASONRY REINFORCING BARS**									
0015 Steel bars A615, placed horiz., #3 & #4 bars	1 Bric	450	.018	Lb.	.50	.81		1.31	1.87
0020 #5 & #6 bars		800	.010		.50	.46		.96	1.29
0050 Placed vertical, #3 & #4 bars		350	.023		.50	1.04		1.54	2.24
0060 #5 & #6 bars		650	.012		.50	.56		1.06	1.46
0200 Joint reinforcing, regular truss, to 6" wide, mill std galvanized		30	.267	C.L.F.	21	12.15		33.15	43
0250 12" wide		20	.400		24.50	18.25		42.75	56.50
0400 Cavity truss with drip section, to 6" wide		30	.267		22.50	12.15		34.65	44.50
0450 12" wide		20	.400		26	18.25		44.25	58
0500 Joint reinforcing, ladder type, mill std galvanized									
0600 9 ga. sides, 9 ga. ties, 4" wall	1 Bric	30	.267	C.L.F.	15.30	12.15		27.45	36.50
0650 6" wall		30	.267		17.70	12.15		29.85	39
0700 8" wall		25	.320		18.95	14.60		33.55	44.50
0750 10" wall		20	.400		16.25	18.25		34.50	47.50
0800 12" wall		20	.400		16.45	18.25		34.70	47.50
1000 Truss type									
1100 9 ga. sides, 9 ga. ties, 4" wall	1 Bric	30	.267	C.L.F.	20.50	12.15		32.65	42.50
1150 6" wall		30	.267		21	12.15		33.15	43
1200 8" wall		25	.320		22	14.60		36.60	47.50
1250 10" wall		20	.400		20.50	18.25		38.75	52
1300 12" wall		20	.400		21	18.25		39.25	53
1500 3/16" sides, 9 ga. ties, 4" wall		30	.267		23.50	12.15		35.65	46
1550 6" wall		30	.267		29.50	12.15		41.65	52.50
1600 8" wall		25	.320		30.50	14.60		45.10	57.50
1650 10" wall		20	.400		31.50	18.25		49.75	64
1700 12" wall		20	.400		32	18.25		50.25	65
2000 3/16" sides, 3/16" ties, 4" wall		30	.267		33	12.15		45.15	56.50
2050 6" wall		30	.267		34	12.15		46.15	57.50
2100 8" wall		25	.320		35	14.60		49.60	62
2150 10" wall		20	.400		37	18.25		55.25	70
2200 12" wall		20	.400		39	18.25		57.25	72.50
2500 Cavity truss type, galvanized									
2600 9 ga. sides, 9 ga. ties, 4" wall	1 Bric	25	.320	C.L.F.	35.50	14.60		50.10	62.50
2650 6" wall		25	.320		31	14.60		45.60	58
2700 8" wall		20	.400		37.50	18.25		55.75	70.50
2750 10" wall		15	.533		39.50	24.50		64	82.50
2800 12" wall		15	.533		36	24.50		60.50	79
3000 3/16" sides, 9 ga. ties, 4" wall		25	.320		33.50	14.60		48.10	60
3050 6" wall		25	.320		30.50	14.60		45.10	57
3100 8" wall		20	.400		44.50	18.25		62.75	78.50
3150 10" wall		15	.533		29.50	24.50		54	71.50
3200 12" wall		15	.533		35	24.50		59.50	78
3500 For hot dip galvanizing, add				Ton	460			460	505

04 05 23 – Masonry Accessories

04 05 23.13 Masonry Control and Expansion Joints

	Crew	Daily Output	Labor-Hours	Unit	Material	Labor	Equipment	Total	Total Incl O&P
0010 **MASONRY CONTROL AND EXPANSION JOINTS**									
0020 Rubber, for double wythe 8" minimum wall (Brick/CMU)	1 Bric	400	.020	L.F.	1.77	.91		2.68	3.43
0025 "T" shaped		320	.025		1.16	1.14		2.30	3.13

04 05 Common Work Results for Masonry

04 05 23 – Masonry Accessories

04 05 23.13 Masonry Control and Expansion Joints

	Crew	Daily Output	Labor-Hours	Unit	Material	2014 Bare Costs Labor	2014 Bare Costs Equipment	Total	Total Incl O&P
0030 Cross-shaped for CMU units	1 Bric	280	.029	L.F.	1.42	1.30		2.72	3.68
0050 PVC, for double wythe 8" minimum wall (Brick/CMU)		400	.020		1.27	.91		2.18	2.88
0120 "T" shaped		320	.025		.73	1.14		1.87	2.65
0160 Cross-shaped for CMU units	↓	280	.029	↓	.92	1.30		2.22	3.13

04 05 23.19 Masonry Cavity Drainage, Weepholes, and Vents

	Crew	Daily Output	Labor-Hours	Unit	Material	2014 Bare Costs Labor	2014 Bare Costs Equipment	Total	Total Incl O&P
0010 **MASONRY CAVITY DRAINAGE, WEEPHOLES, AND VENTS**									
0020 Extruded aluminum, 4" deep, 2-3/8" x 8-1/8"	1 Bric	30	.267	Ea.	31.50	12.15		43.65	54.50
0050 5" x 8-1/8"		25	.320		41	14.60		55.60	69
0100 2-1/4" x 25"		25	.320		71.50	14.60		86.10	103
0150 5" x 16-1/2"		22	.364		62.50	16.60		79.10	95.50
0175 5" x 24"		22	.364		77.50	16.60		94.10	112
0200 6" x 16-1/2"		22	.364		83.50	16.60		100.10	119
0250 7-3/4" x 16-1/2"	↓	20	.400		71	18.25		89.25	108
0400 For baked enamel finish, add					35%				
0500 For cast aluminum, painted, add					60%				
1000 Stainless steel ventilators, 6" x 6"	1 Bric	25	.320		188	14.60		202.60	230
1050 8" x 8"		24	.333		208	15.20		223.20	253
1100 12" x 12"		23	.348		228	15.85		243.85	276
1150 12" x 6"		24	.333		228	15.20		243.20	275
1200 Foundation block vent, galv., 1-1/4" thk, 8" high, 16" long, no damper	↓	30	.267		16.20	12.15		28.35	37.50
1250 For damper, add				↓	3.11			3.11	3.42

04 05 23.95 Wall Plugs

	Crew	Daily Output	Labor-Hours	Unit	Material	2014 Bare Costs Labor	2014 Bare Costs Equipment	Total	Total Incl O&P
0010 **WALL PLUGS** (for nailing to brickwork)									
0020 25 ga., galvanized, plain	1 Bric	10.50	.762	C	26.50	34.50		61	85.50
0050 Wood filled	"	10.50	.762	"	63.50	34.50		98	127

04 21 Clay Unit Masonry

04 21 13 – Brick Masonry

04 21 13.13 Brick Veneer Masonry

		Crew	Daily Output	Labor-Hours	Unit	Material	2014 Bare Costs Labor	2014 Bare Costs Equipment	Total	Total Incl O&P
0010 **BRICK VENEER MASONRY**, T.L. lots, excl. scaff., grout & reinforcing	R042110-20									
0015 Material costs incl. 3% brick and 25% mortar waste										
2000 Standard, sel. common, 4" x 2-2/3" x 8", (6.75/S.F.)	R042110-50	D-8	230	.174	S.F.	4.43	7.35		11.78	16.80
2020 Red, 4" x 2-2/3" x 8", running bond			220	.182		4	7.65		11.65	16.85
2050 Full header every 6th course (7.88/S.F.)			185	.216		4.66	9.10		13.76	19.90
2100 English, full header every 2nd course (10.13/S.F.)			140	.286		5.95	12.05		18	26
2150 Flemish, alternate header every course (9.00/S.F.)			150	.267		5.30	11.25		16.55	24
2200 Flemish, alt. header every 6th course (7.13/S.F.)			205	.195		4.22	8.25		12.47	18
2250 Full headers throughout (13.50/S.F.)			105	.381		7.95	16.05		24	35
2300 Rowlock course (13.50/S.F.)			100	.400		7.95	16.85		24.80	36.50
2350 Rowlock stretcher (4.50/S.F.)			310	.129		2.69	5.45		8.14	11.80
2400 Soldier course (6.75/S.F.)			200	.200		4	8.45		12.45	18.10
2450 Sailor course (4.50/S.F.)			290	.138		2.69	5.80		8.49	12.40
2600 Buff or gray face, running bond, (6.75/S.F.)			220	.182		4.23	7.65		11.88	17.10
2700 Glazed face brick, running bond			210	.190		11.40	8.05		19.45	25.50
2750 Full header every 6th course (7.88/S.F.)			170	.235		13.30	9.90		23.20	31
3000 Jumbo, 6" x 4" x 12" running bond (3.00/S.F.)			435	.092		4.51	3.88		8.39	11.25
3050 Norman, 4" x 2-2/3" x 12" running bond, (4.5/S.F.)			320	.125		5.80	5.25		11.05	14.95
3100 Norwegian, 4" x 3-1/5" x 12" (3.75/S.F.)			375	.107		4.66	4.50		9.16	12.40
3150 Economy, 4" x 4" x 8" (4.50/S.F.)			310	.129		3.95	5.45		9.40	13.20
3200 Engineer, 4" x 3-1/5" x 8" (5.63/S.F.)		↓	260	.154		3.48	6.50		9.98	14.40

04 21 Clay Unit Masonry

04 21 13 – Brick Masonry

04 21 13.13 Brick Veneer Masonry

		Crew	Daily Output	Labor-Hours	Unit	Material	2014 Bare Costs Labor	2014 Bare Costs Equipment	Total	Total Incl O&P
3250	Roman, 4" x 2" x 12" (6.00/S.F.)	D-8	250	.160	S.F.	7.70	6.75		14.45	19.45
3300	SCR, 6" x 2-2/3" x 12" (4.50/S.F.)		310	.129		6.55	5.45		12	16.05
3350	Utility, 4" x 4" x 12" (3.00/S.F.)	↓	360	.111	↓	4.56	4.68		9.24	12.60
3360	For less than truck load lots, add				M	15%				
3400	For cavity wall construction, add						15%			
3450	For stacked bond, add						10%			
3500	For interior veneer construction, add						15%			
3550	For curved walls, add						30%			
9000	Minimum labor/equipment charge	D-1	2	8	Job		330		330	535

04 21 13.14 Thin Brick Veneer

		Crew	Daily Output	Labor-Hours	Unit	Material	2014 Bare Costs Labor	2014 Bare Costs Equipment	Total	Total Incl O&P
0010	**THIN BRICK VENEER**									
0015	Material costs incl. 3% brick and 25% mortar waste									
0020	On & incl. metal panel support sys, modular, 2-2/3" x 5/8" x 8", red	D-7	92	.174	S.F.	8.75	6.55		15.30	19.95
0100	Closure, 4" x 5/8" x 8"		110	.145		8.75	5.45		14.20	18.25
0110	Norman, 2-2/3" x 5/8" x 12"		110	.145		8.95	5.45		14.40	18.45
0120	Utility, 4" x 5/8" x 12"		125	.128		8.95	4.81		13.76	17.45
0130	Emperor, 4" x 3/4" x 16"		175	.091		10.15	3.44		13.59	16.60
0140	Super emperor, 8" x 3/4" x 16"	↓	195	.082	↓	10.15	3.09		13.24	16.05
0150	For L shaped corners with 4" return, add				L.F.	9.25			9.25	10.20
0200	On masonry/plaster back-up, modular, 2-2/3" x 5/8" x 8", red	D-7	137	.117	S.F.	3.95	4.39		8.34	11.25
0210	Closure, 4" x 5/8" x 8"		165	.097		3.95	3.65		7.60	10.10
0220	Norman, 2-2/3" x 5/8" x 12"		165	.097		4.15	3.65		7.80	10.30
0230	Utility, 4" x 5/8" x 12"		185	.086		4.15	3.25		7.40	9.65
0240	Emperor, 4" x 3/4" x 16"		260	.062		5.35	2.31		7.66	9.55
0250	Super emperor, 8" x 3/4" x 16"	↓	285	.056	↓	5.35	2.11		7.46	9.20
0260	For L shaped corners with 4" return, add				L.F.	9.25			9.25	10.20
0270	For embedment into pre-cast concrete panels, add				S.F.	14.40			14.40	15.85

04 21 13.15 Chimney

		Crew	Daily Output	Labor-Hours	Unit	Material	2014 Bare Costs Labor	2014 Bare Costs Equipment	Total	Total Incl O&P
0010	**CHIMNEY**, excludes foundation, scaffolding, grout and reinforcing									
0100	Brick, 16" x 16", 8" flue	D-1	18.20	.879	V.L.F.	25	36.50		61.50	86.50
0150	16" x 20" with one 8" x 12" flue		16	1		38.50	41.50		80	110
0200	16" x 24" with two 8" x 8" flues		14	1.143		55.50	47		102.50	138
0250	20" x 20" with one 12" x 12" flue		13.70	1.168		50	48		98	133
0300	20" x 24" with two 8" x 12" flues		12	1.333		63	55		118	159
0350	20" x 32" with two 12" x 12" flues	↓	10	1.600	↓	87.50	66		153.50	204

04 21 13.18 Columns

		Crew	Daily Output	Labor-Hours	Unit	Material	2014 Bare Costs Labor	2014 Bare Costs Equipment	Total	Total Incl O&P
0010	**COLUMNS**, solid, excludes scaffolding, grout and reinforcing									
0050	Brick, 8" x 8", 9 brick per V.L.F.	D-1	56	.286	V.L.F.	5.20	11.80		17	25
0100	12" x 8", 13.5 brick per V.L.F.		37	.432		7.80	17.85		25.65	37.50
0200	12" x 12", 20 brick per V.L.F.		25	.640		11.55	26.50		38.05	55.50
0300	16" x 12", 27 brick per V.L.F.		19	.842		15.60	35		50.60	73.50
0400	16" x 16", 36 brick per V.L.F.		14	1.143		21	47		68	99.50
0500	20" x 16", 45 brick per V.L.F.		11	1.455		26	60		86	126
0600	20" x 20", 56 brick per V.L.F.		9	1.778		32.50	73.50		106	155
0700	24" x 20", 68 brick per V.L.F.		7	2.286		39	94.50		133.50	196
0800	24" x 24", 81 brick per V.L.F.		6	2.667		46.50	110		156.50	231
1000	36" x 36", 182 brick per V.L.F.		3	5.333	↓	105	220		325	475
9000	Minimum labor/equipment charge	↓	2	8	Job		330		330	535

04 21 13.30 Oversized Brick

		Crew	Daily Output	Labor-Hours	Unit	Material	2014 Bare Costs Labor	2014 Bare Costs Equipment	Total	Total Incl O&P
0010	**OVERSIZED BRICK**, excludes scaffolding, grout and reinforcing									
0100	Veneer, 4" x 2.25" x 16"	D-8	387	.103	S.F.	5.05	4.36		9.41	12.65
0105	4" x 2.75" x 16"	↓	412	.097	↓	5.25	4.09		9.34	12.45

04 21 13.30 Oversized Brick	Crew	Daily Output	Labor-Hours	Unit	Material	2014 Bare Costs Labor	2014 Bare Costs Equipment	Total	Total Incl O&P
0110 4" x 4" x 16"	D-8	460	.087	S.F.	5.90	3.67		9.57	12.45
0120 4" x 8" x 16"		533	.075		6	3.16		9.16	11.75
0125 Loadbearing, 6" x 4" x 16", grouted and reinforced		387	.103		14.10	4.36		18.46	22.50
0130 8" x 4" x 16", grouted and reinforced		327	.122		14.95	5.15		20.10	25
0135 6" x 8" x 16", grouted and reinforced		440	.091		13.40	3.83		17.23	21
0140 8" x 8" x 16", grouted and reinforced		400	.100		14.65	4.22		18.87	23
0145 Curtainwall/reinforced veneer, 6" x 4" x 16"		387	.103		18.35	4.36		22.71	27
0150 8" x 4" x 16"		327	.122		21.50	5.15		26.65	32
0155 6" x 8" x 16"		440	.091		18.15	3.83		21.98	26
0160 8" x 8" x 16"	↓	400	.100		26	4.22		30.22	35.50
0200 For 1 to 3 slots in face, add					15%				
0210 For 4 to 7 slots in face, add					25%				
0220 For bond beams, add					20%				
0230 For bullnose shapes, add					20%				
0240 For open end knockout, add					10%				
0250 For white or gray color group, add					10%				
0260 For 135 degree corner, add					250%				

04 21 13.35 Common Building Brick									
0010 **COMMON BUILDING BRICK**, C62, TL lots, material only R042110-20									
0020 Standard				M	490			490	540
0050 Select				"	550			550	605

04 21 13.40 Structural Brick									
0010 **STRUCTURAL BRICK** C652, Grade SW, incl. mortar, scaffolding not incl.									
0100 Standard unit, 4-5/8" x 2-3/4" x 9-5/8"	D-8	245	.163	S.F.	4.51	6.90		11.41	16.15
0120 Bond beam		225	.178		7	7.50		14.50	19.85
0140 V cut bond beam		225	.178		7.60	7.50		15.10	20.50
0160 Stretcher quoin, 5-5/8" x 2-3/4" x 9-5/8"		245	.163		7.40	6.90		14.30	19.35
0180 Corner quoin		245	.163		8.20	6.90		15.10	20.50
0200 Corner, 45 deg, 4-5/8" x 2-3/4" x 10-7/16"	↓	235	.170	↓	8.45	7.20		15.65	21

04 21 13.45 Face Brick									
0010 **FACE BRICK** Material Only, C216, TL lots R042110-20									
0300 Standard modular, 4" x 2-2/3" x 8", minimum				M	490			490	540
0350 Maximum R042110-50					695			695	760
0450 Economy, 4" x 4" x 8", minimum					765			765	840
0500 Maximum					990			990	1,100
0510 Economy, 4" x 4" x 12", minimum					1,200			1,200	1,325
0520 Maximum					1,575			1,575	1,725
0550 Jumbo, 6" x 4" x 12", minimum					1,375			1,375	1,500
0600 Maximum					1,825			1,825	2,000
0610 Jumbo, 8" x 4" x 12", minimum					1,375			1,375	1,500
0620 Maximum					1,825			1,825	2,000
0650 Norwegian, 4" x 3-1/5" x 12", minimum					1,125			1,125	1,225
0700 Maximum					1,450			1,450	1,600
0710 Norwegian, 6" x 3-1/5" x 12", minimum					1,475			1,475	1,600
0720 Maximum					1,900			1,900	2,100
0850 Standard glazed, plain colors, 4" x 2-2/3" x 8", minimum					1,550			1,550	1,725
0900 Maximum					2,025			2,025	2,225
1000 Deep trim shades, 4" x 2-2/3" x 8", minimum					1,975			1,975	2,150
1050 Maximum					2,200			2,200	2,425
1080 Jumbo utility, 4" x 4" x 12"					1,375			1,375	1,525
1120 4" x 8" x 8"					1,725			1,725	1,875
1140 4" x 8" x 16"				↓	5,050			5,050	5,550

04 21 Clay Unit Masonry

04 21 13 – Brick Masonry

04 21 13.45 Face Brick

		Crew	Daily Output	Labor-Hours	Unit	Material	2014 Bare Costs Labor	Equipment	Total	Total Incl O&P
1260	Engineer, 4" x 3-1/5" x 8", minimum				M	515			515	565
1270	Maximum					715			715	785
1350	King, 4" x 2-3/4" x 10", minimum					465			465	515
1360	Maximum					575			575	630
1770	Standard modular, double glazed, 4" x 2-2/3" x 8"					2,325			2,325	2,550
1850	Jumbo, colored glazed ceramic, 6" x 4" x 12"					2,450			2,450	2,700
2050	Jumbo utility, glazed, 4" x 4" x 12"					4,600			4,600	5,050
2100	4" x 8" x 8"					5,400			5,400	5,950
2150	4" x 16" x 8"					6,325			6,325	6,950
2170	For less than truck load lots, add					15			15	16.50
2180	For buff or gray brick, add					16			16	17.60
3050	Used brick, minimum					405			405	445
3150	Add for brick to match existing work, minimum					5%				
3200	Maximum					50%				

04 21 26 – Glazed Structural Clay Tile Masonry

04 21 26.10 Structural Facing Tile

		Crew	Daily Output	Labor-Hours	Unit	Material	2014 Bare Costs Labor	Equipment	Total	Total Incl O&P
0010	**STRUCTURAL FACING TILE**, std. colors, excl. scaffolding, grout, reinforcing									
0020	6T series, 5-1/3" x 12", 2.3 pieces per S.F., glazed 1 side, 2" thick	D-8	225	.178	S.F.	8.80	7.50		16.30	22
0100	4" thick		220	.182		11.95	7.65		19.60	25.50
0150	Glazed 2 sides		195	.205		15.75	8.65		24.40	31.50
0250	6" thick		210	.190		17.85	8.05		25.90	32.50
0300	Glazed 2 sides		185	.216		21	9.10		30.10	38.50
0400	8" thick		180	.222		23.50	9.35		32.85	41
0500	Special shapes, group 1		400	.100	Ea.	7.55	4.22		11.77	15.15
0550	Group 2		375	.107		12.25	4.50		16.75	21
0600	Group 3		350	.114		15.75	4.82		20.57	25
0650	Group 4		325	.123		32.50	5.20		37.70	44.50
0700	Group 5		300	.133		39	5.60		44.60	52
0750	Group 6		275	.145		53	6.15		59.15	68
1000	Fire rated, 4" thick, 1 hr. rating		210	.190	S.F.	17.05	8.05		25.10	32
1050	2 hr. rating		170	.235		26.50	9.90		36.40	45
1300	Acoustic, 4" thick		210	.190		34	8.05		42.05	50.50
1310	6" thick		170	.235		35	9.90		44.90	54.50
1320	8" thick		145	.276		37	11.65		48.65	60
1350	8T acoustic, 4" thick		265	.151		18.25	6.35		24.60	30.50
1360	6" thick		256	.156		25	6.60		31.60	38
1370	8" thick		208	.192		26.50	8.10		34.60	42.50
2000	8W series, 8" x 16", 1.125 pieces per S.F.									
2050	2" thick, glazed 1 side	D-8	360	.111	S.F.	10.25	4.68		14.93	18.85
2100	4" thick, glazed 1 side		345	.116		14.10	4.89		18.99	23.50
2150	Glazed 2 sides		325	.123		16.95	5.20		22.15	27
2200	6" thick, glazed 1 side		330	.121		24	5.10		29.10	35
2210	Glazed 2 sides		250	.160		29	6.75		35.75	43
2250	8" thick, glazed 1 side		310	.129		24	5.45		29.45	35.50
2260	Glazed 2 sides		220	.182		19.75	7.65		27.40	34
2500	Special shapes, group 1		300	.133	Ea.	14.60	5.60		20.20	25
2550	Group 2		280	.143		19.50	6		25.50	31.50
2600	Group 3		260	.154		20.50	6.50		27	33.50
2650	Group 4		250	.160		43	6.75		49.75	58
2700	Group 5		240	.167		38.50	7.05		45.55	53.50
2750	Group 6		230	.174		83	7.35		90.35	103
2900	Fire rated, 2" thick, glazed 1 side		360	.111	S.F.	14.05	4.68		18.73	23

04 21 Clay Unit Masonry

04 21 26 – Glazed Structural Clay Tile Masonry

	04 21 26.10 Structural Facing Tile	Crew	Daily Output	Labor-Hours	Unit	Material	2014 Bare Costs Labor	Equipment	Total	Total Incl O&P
3000	4" thick, glazed 1 side	D-8	345	.116	S.F.	13.75	4.89		18.64	23
3020	Gazed 2 sides		345	.116		19.60	4.89		24.49	29.50
3040	6" thick, glazed 1 side		330	.121		20.50	5.10		25.60	31.50
3045	Glazed 2 sides		250	.160		20.50	6.75		27.25	33.50
3047	8" thick, glazed 1 side		310	.129		34	5.45		39.45	46
3048	Glazed 2 sides		220	.182		35.50	7.65		43.15	52
3050	Special shapes, group 1, fire rated		300	.133		17.65	5.60		23.25	28.50
3060	Group 2		280	.143		23.50	6		29.50	36
3070	Group 3		260	.154		25	6.50		31.50	38
3080	Group 4		250	.160		48	6.75		54.75	64
3090	Group 5		240	.167		56	7.05		63.05	73.50
3100	Acoustic, 4" thick	↓	345	.116	↓	18	4.89		22.89	28
3120	4W series, 8" x 8", 2.25 pieces per S.F.									
3125	2" thick, glazed 1 side	D-8	360	.111	S.F.	9.45	4.68		14.13	18
3130	4" thick, glazed 1 side		345	.116		11.15	4.89		16.04	20
3135	Glazed 2 sides		325	.123		15.35	5.20		20.55	25.50
3140	6" thick, glazed 1 side		330	.121		15.85	5.10		20.95	25.50
3145	Glazed 2 sides		250	.160	↓	19.10	6.75		25.85	32
3150	8" thick, glazed 1 side		310	.129		23	5.45		28.45	34.50
3155	Special shapes, group I		300	.133	Ea.	7.40	5.60		13	17.30
3160	Group II	↓	280	.143	"	8.55	6		14.55	19.20
3200	For designer colors, add					25%				
3300	For epoxy mortar joints, add				S.F.	1.69			1.69	1.86
9000	Minimum labor/equipment charge	D-1	2	8	Job		330		330	535

04 21 29 – Terra Cotta Masonry

04 21 29.10 Terra Cotta Masonry Components

		Crew	Daily Output	Labor-Hours	Unit	Material	2014 Bare Costs Labor	Equipment	Total	Total Incl O&P
0010	**TERRA COTTA MASONRY COMPONENTS**									
0020	Coping, split type, not glazed, 9" wide	D-1	90	.178	L.F.	13.15	7.35		20.50	26.50
0100	13" wide		80	.200		18.35	8.25		26.60	33.50
0200	Coping, split type, glazed, 9" wide		90	.178		11.70	7.35		19.05	25
0250	13" wide	↓	80	.200	↓	15.45	8.25		23.70	30.50
0500	Partition or back-up blocks, scored, in C.L. lots									
0700	Non-load bearing 12" x 12", 3" thick, special order	D-8	550	.073	S.F.	16.85	3.07		19.92	23.50
0750	4" thick, standard		500	.080		5.35	3.37		8.72	11.35
0800	6" thick		450	.089		7.20	3.75		10.95	14
0850	8" thick		400	.100		9.05	4.22		13.27	16.80
1000	Load bearing, 12" x 12", 4" thick, in walls		500	.080		5.45	3.37		8.82	11.50
1050	In floors		750	.053		5.45	2.25		7.70	9.65
1200	6" thick, in walls		450	.089		7.35	3.75		11.10	14.20
1250	In floors		675	.059		7.35	2.50		9.85	12.15
1400	8" thick, in walls		400	.100		9.15	4.22		13.37	16.90
1450	In floors		575	.070		9.15	2.93		12.08	14.80
1600	10" thick, in walls, special order		350	.114		23	4.82		27.82	33.50
1650	In floors, special order		500	.080		23	3.37		26.37	31
1800	12" thick, in walls, special order		300	.133		23	5.60		28.60	34.50
1850	In floors, special order	↓	450	.089		23	3.75		26.75	31.50
2000	For reinforcing with steel rods, add to above				↓	15%	5%			
2025	Placed vertical, #3 & #4 bars	1 Bric	350	.023	Lb.	.50	1.04		1.54	2.24
2100	For smooth tile instead of scored, add				S.F.	3.66			3.66	4.03
2200	For L.C.L. quantities, add				"	10%	10%			
9000	Minimum labor/equipment charge	D-1	2	8	Job		330		330	535

04 21 Clay Unit Masonry

04 21 29 – Terra Cotta Masonry

04 21 29.20 Terra Cotta Tile		Crew	Daily Output	Labor-Hours	Unit	Material	2014 Bare Costs Labor	Equipment	Total	Total Incl O&P
0010	**TERRA COTTA TILE**, on walls, dry set, 1/2" thick									
0100	Square, hexagonal or lattice shapes, unglazed	1 Tilf	135	.059	S.F.	4.62	2.49		7.11	9
0300	Glazed, plain colors		130	.062		7.10	2.58		9.68	11.85
0400	Intense colors		125	.064		8.30	2.68		10.98	13.40

04 22 Concrete Unit Masonry

04 22 10 – Concrete Masonry Units

04 22 10.11 Autoclave Aerated Concrete Block

			Crew	Daily Output	Labor-Hours	Unit	Material	2014 Bare Costs Labor	Equipment	Total	Total Incl O&P
0010	**AUTOCLAVE AERATED CONCRETE BLOCK**, excl. scaffolding, grout & reinforcing										
0050	Solid, 4" x 8" x 24", incl. mortar	G	D-8	600	.067	S.F.	1.48	2.81		4.29	6.20
0060	6" x 8" x 24"	G		600	.067		2.23	2.81		5.04	7
0070	8" x 8" x 24"	G		575	.070		2.97	2.93		5.90	8.05
0080	10" x 8" x 24"	G		575	.070		3.63	2.93		6.56	8.75
0090	12" x 8" x 24"	G		550	.073		4.45	3.07		7.52	9.90

04 22 10.14 Concrete Block, Back-Up

		Crew	Daily Output	Labor-Hours	Unit	Material	2014 Bare Costs Labor	Equipment	Total	Total Incl O&P
0010	**CONCRETE BLOCK, BACK-UP**, C90, 2000 psi									
0020	Normal weight, 8" x 16" units, tooled joint 1 side									
0050	Not-reinforced, 2000 psi, 2" thick	D-8	475	.084	S.F.	1.40	3.55		4.95	7.30
0200	4" thick		460	.087		1.66	3.67		5.33	7.80
0300	6" thick		440	.091		2.18	3.83		6.01	8.60
0350	8" thick		400	.100		2.45	4.22		6.67	9.55
0400	10" thick		330	.121		2.95	5.10		8.05	11.55
0450	12" thick	D-9	310	.155		3.76	6.40		10.16	14.55
1000	Reinforced, alternate courses, 4" thick	D-8	450	.089		1.82	3.75		5.57	8.10
1100	6" thick		430	.093		2.34	3.92		6.26	8.90
1150	8" thick		395	.101		2.62	4.27		6.89	9.85
1200	10" thick		320	.125		3.10	5.25		8.35	11.95
1250	12" thick	D-9	300	.160		3.92	6.60		10.52	15.05
9000	Minimum labor/equipment charge	D-1	2	8	Job		330		330	535

04 22 10.16 Concrete Block, Bond Beam

		Crew	Daily Output	Labor-Hours	Unit	Material	2014 Bare Costs Labor	Equipment	Total	Total Incl O&P
0010	**CONCRETE BLOCK, BOND BEAM**, C90, 2000 psi									
0020	Not including grout or reinforcing									
0125	Regular block, 6" thick	D-8	584	.068	L.F.	2.25	2.89		5.14	7.15
0130	8" high, 8" thick	"	565	.071		2.63	2.98		5.61	7.75
0150	12" thick	D-9	510	.094		3.91	3.89		7.80	10.60
0525	Lightweight, 6" thick	D-8	592	.068		2.67	2.85		5.52	7.55
0530	8" high, 8" thick	"	575	.070		3.22	2.93		6.15	8.30
0550	12" thick	D-9	520	.092		4.33	3.81		8.14	10.95
2000	Including grout and 2 #5 bars									
2100	Regular block, 8" high, 8" thick	D-8	300	.133	L.F.	4.72	5.60		10.32	14.35
2150	12" thick	D-9	250	.192		6.55	7.95		14.50	20
2500	Lightweight, 8" high, 8" thick	D-8	305	.131		5.30	5.55		10.85	14.85
2550	12" thick	D-9	255	.188		7	7.75		14.75	20.50
9000	Minimum labor/equipment charge	D-1	2	8	Job		330		330	535

04 22 10.19 Concrete Block, Insulation Inserts

		Crew	Daily Output	Labor-Hours	Unit	Material	2014 Bare Costs Labor	Equipment	Total	Total Incl O&P
0010	**CONCRETE BLOCK, INSULATION INSERTS**									
0100	Styrofoam, plant installed, add to block prices									
0200	8" x 16" units, 6" thick				S.F.	1.20			1.20	1.32
0250	8" thick					1.35			1.35	1.49
0300	10" thick					1.50			1.50	1.65

04 22 Concrete Unit Masonry

04 22 10 – Concrete Masonry Units

04 22 10.19 Concrete Block, Insulation Inserts	Crew	Daily Output	Labor-Hours	Unit	Material	2014 Bare Costs Labor	Equipment	Total	Total Incl O&P
0350	12" thick				S.F.	1.65			1.65	1.82
0500	8" x 8" units, 8" thick					1.20			1.20	1.32
0550	12" thick					1.20			1.20	1.32

04 22 10.23 Concrete Block, Decorative	Crew	Daily Output	Labor-Hours	Unit	Material	2014 Bare Costs Labor	Equipment	Total	Total Incl O&P
0010	**CONCRETE BLOCK, DECORATIVE**, C90, 2000 psi									
0020	Embossed, simulated brick face									
0100	8" x 16" units, 4" thick	D-8	400	.100	S.F.	2.73	4.22		6.95	9.85
0200	8" thick		340	.118		3.92	4.96		8.88	12.35
0250	12" thick		300	.133		4.26	5.60		9.86	13.85
0400	Embossed both sides									
0500	8" thick	D-8	300	.133	S.F.	2.53	5.60		8.13	11.95
0550	12" thick	"	275	.145	"	3.67	6.15		9.82	14
1000	Fluted high strength									
1100	8" x 16" x 4" thick, flutes 1 side,	D-8	345	.116	S.F.	4.17	4.89		9.06	12.55
1150	Flutes 2 sides		335	.119		4.73	5.05		9.78	13.40
1200	8" thick		300	.133		5	5.60		10.60	14.65
1250	For special colors, add					.46			.46	.51
1400	Deep grooved, smooth face									
1450	8" x 16" x 4" thick	D-8	345	.116	S.F.	2.59	4.89		7.48	10.80
1500	8" thick	"	300	.133	"	4.55	5.60		10.15	14.15
2000	Formblock, incl. inserts & reinforcing									
2100	8" x 16" x 8" thick	D-8	345	.116	S.F.	3.38	4.89		8.27	11.65
2150	12" thick	"	310	.129	"	4.42	5.45		9.87	13.70
2500	Ground face									
2600	8" x 16" x 4" thick	D-8	345	.116	S.F.	3.45	4.89		8.34	11.75
2650	6" thick		325	.123		3.86	5.20		9.06	12.70
2700	8" thick		300	.133		4.26	5.60		9.86	13.85
2725	10" thick		280	.143		4.93	6		10.93	15.25
2750	12" thick	D-9	265	.181		5.40	7.50		12.90	18.10
2900	For special colors, add, minimum					15%				
2950	For special colors, add, maximum					45%				
4000	Slump block									
4100	4" face height x 16" x 4" thick	D-1	165	.097	S.F.	3.68	4		7.68	10.55
4150	6" thick		160	.100		5.30	4.13		9.43	12.55
4200	8" thick		155	.103		5.35	4.26		9.61	12.80
4250	10" thick		140	.114		10.50	4.72		15.22	19.20
4300	12" thick		130	.123		11.05	5.10		16.15	20.50
4400	6" face height x 16" x 6" thick		155	.103		5.05	4.26		9.31	12.50
4450	8" thick		150	.107		7.45	4.41		11.86	15.35
4500	10" thick		130	.123		11	5.10		16.10	20.50
4550	12" thick		120	.133		11.25	5.50		16.75	21.50
5000	Split rib profile units, 1" deep ribs, 8 ribs									
5100	8" x 16" x 4" thick	D-8	345	.116	S.F.	3.62	4.89		8.51	11.95
5150	6" thick		325	.123		4.17	5.20		9.37	13.05
5200	8" thick		300	.133		4.83	5.60		10.43	14.45
5225	10" thick		300	.133		5.25	5.60		10.85	14.90
5250	12" thick	D-9	275	.175		5.65	7.20		12.85	17.90
5400	For special deeper colors, 4" thick, add					1.23			1.23	1.35
5450	12" thick, add					1.27			1.27	1.39
5600	For white, 4" thick, add					1.23			1.23	1.35
5650	6" thick, add					1.25			1.25	1.38
5700	8" thick, add					1.28			1.28	1.40

04 22 10.23 Concrete Block, Decorative

		Crew	Daily Output	Labor-Hours	Unit	Material	2014 Bare Costs Labor	Equipment	Total	Total Incl O&P
5750	12" thick, add				S.F.	1.32			1.32	1.45
6000	Split face									
6100	8" x 16" x 4" thick	D-8	350	.114	S.F.	3.27	4.82		8.09	11.45
6150	6" thick		325	.123		3.79	5.20		8.99	12.60
6200	8" thick		300	.133		4.36	5.60		9.96	13.95
6225	10" thick		275	.145		4.88	6.15		11.03	15.30
6250	12" thick	D-9	270	.178		5.25	7.35		12.60	17.70
6300	For scored, add					.37			.37	.41
6400	For special deeper colors, 4" thick, add					.59			.59	.65
6450	6" thick, add					.70			.70	.77
6500	8" thick, add					.72			.72	.80
6550	12" thick, add					.75			.75	.82
6650	For white, 4" thick, add					1.22			1.22	1.34
6700	6" thick, add					1.23			1.23	1.35
6750	8" thick, add					1.24			1.24	1.37
6800	12" thick, add					1.27			1.27	1.39
7000	Scored ground face, 2 to 5 scores									
7100	8" x 16" x 4" thick	D-8	340	.118	S.F.	6.55	4.96		11.51	15.30
7150	6" thick		310	.129		7.30	5.45		12.75	16.90
7200	8" thick		290	.138		8.30	5.80		14.10	18.55
7250	12" thick	D-9	265	.181		12.55	7.50		20.05	26
8000	Hexagonal face profile units, 8" x 16" units									
8100	4" thick, hollow	D-8	340	.118	S.F.	3.45	4.96		8.41	11.85
8200	Solid		340	.118		4.42	4.96		9.38	12.90
8300	6" thick, hollow		310	.129		3.72	5.45		9.17	12.95
8350	8" thick, hollow		290	.138		4.12	5.80		9.92	14
8500	For stacked bond, add						26%			
8550	For high rise construction, add per story	D-8	67.80	.590	M.S.F.		25		25	40.50
8600	For scored block, add					10%				
8650	For honed or ground face, per face, add				Ea.	.98			.98	1.08
8700	For honed or ground end, per end, add				"	.98			.98	1.08
8750	For bullnose block, add					10%				
8800	For special color, add					13%				
9000	Minimum labor/equipment charge	D-1	2	8	Job		330		330	535

04 22 10.24 Concrete Block, Exterior

		Crew	Daily Output	Labor-Hours	Unit	Material	2014 Bare Costs Labor	Equipment	Total	Total Incl O&P
0010	**CONCRETE BLOCK, EXTERIOR**, C90, 2000 psi									
0020	Reinforced alt courses, tooled joints 2 sides									
0100	Normal weight, 8" x 16" x 6" thick	D-8	395	.101	S.F.	2.27	4.27		6.54	9.45
0200	8" thick		360	.111		3.92	4.68		8.60	11.90
0250	10" thick		290	.138		4.08	5.80		9.88	13.95
0300	12" thick	D-9	250	.192		4.68	7.95		12.63	18.05
9000	Minimum labor/equipment charge	D-1	2	8	Job		330		330	535

04 22 10.26 Concrete Block Foundation Wall

		Crew	Daily Output	Labor-Hours	Unit	Material	2014 Bare Costs Labor	Equipment	Total	Total Incl O&P
0010	**CONCRETE BLOCK FOUNDATION WALL**, C90/C145									
0050	Normal-weight, cut joints, horiz joint reinf, no vert reinf.									
0200	Hollow, 8" x 16" x 6" thick	D-8	455	.088	S.F.	2.64	3.71		6.35	8.90
0250	8" thick		425	.094		2.93	3.97		6.90	9.70
0300	10" thick		350	.114		3.43	4.82		8.25	11.60
0350	12" thick	D-9	300	.160		4.25	6.60		10.85	15.45
0500	Solid, 8" x 16" block, 6" thick	D-8	440	.091		2.81	3.83		6.64	9.30
0550	8" thick	"	415	.096		4.12	4.06		8.18	11.15
0600	12" thick	D-9	350	.137		5.95	5.65		11.60	15.75

04 22 10 – Concrete Masonry Units

04 22 10.26 Concrete Block Foundation Wall

		Crew	Daily Output	Labor-Hours	Unit	Material	2014 Bare Costs Labor	Equipment	Total	Total Incl O&P
1000	Reinforced, #4 vert @ 48"									
1100	Hollow, 8" x 16" block, 4" thick	D-8	455	.088	S.F.	2.66	3.71		6.37	8.90
1125	6" thick		445	.090		3.51	3.79		7.30	10
1150	8" thick		415	.096		4.16	4.06		8.22	11.20
1200	10" thick		340	.118		5	4.96		9.96	13.55
1250	12" thick	D-9	290	.166		6.20	6.85		13.05	17.90
1500	Solid, 8" x 16" block, 6" thick	D-8	430	.093		2.82	3.92		6.74	9.45
1600	8" thick	"	405	.099		4.12	4.16		8.28	11.30
1650	12" thick	D-9	340	.141		5.95	5.85		11.80	16
9000	Minimum labor/equipment charge	D-1	2	8	Job		330		330	535

04 22 10.30 Concrete Block, Interlocking

		Crew	Daily Output	Labor-Hours	Unit	Material	2014 Bare Costs Labor	Equipment	Total	Total Incl O&P
0010	**CONCRETE BLOCK, INTERLOCKING**									
0100	Not including grout or reinforcing									
0200	8" x 16" units, 2,000 psi, 8" thick	D-1	245	.065	S.F.	2.83	2.70		5.53	7.50
0300	12" thick	"	220	.073		4.20	3		7.20	9.50
0400	Including grout & reinforcing, 8" thick	D-4	245	.131		7.60	5.45	.55	13.60	17.80
0450	12" thick		220	.145		9.20	6.05	.61	15.86	20.50
0500	16" thick		185	.173		11.50	7.20	.73	19.43	25
9000	Minimum labor/equipment charge	D-1	2	8	Job		330		330	535

04 22 10.32 Concrete Block, Lintels

		Crew	Daily Output	Labor-Hours	Unit	Material	2014 Bare Costs Labor	Equipment	Total	Total Incl O&P
0010	**CONCRETE BLOCK, LINTELS**, C90, normal weight									
0100	Including grout and horizontal reinforcing									
0200	8" x 8" x 8", 1 #4 bar	D-4	300	.107	L.F.	5.20	4.44	.45	10.09	13.40
0250	2 #4 bars		295	.108		5.45	4.52	.46	10.43	13.80
0400	8" x 16" x 8", 1 #4 bar		275	.116		3.65	4.85	.49	8.99	12.35
0450	2 #4 bars		270	.119		3.87	4.94	.50	9.31	12.75
1000	12" x 8" x 8", 1 #4 bar		275	.116		6.80	4.85	.49	12.14	15.85
1100	2 #4 bars		270	.119		7.05	4.94	.50	12.49	16.25
1150	2 #5 bars		270	.119		7.30	4.94	.50	12.74	16.50
1200	2 #6 bars		265	.121		7.60	5.05	.51	13.16	17
1500	12" x 16" x 8", 1 #4 bar		250	.128		7.40	5.35	.54	13.29	17.35
1600	2 #3 bars		245	.131		7.40	5.45	.55	13.40	17.55
1650	2 #4 bars		245	.131		7.60	5.45	.55	13.60	17.80
1700	2 #5 bars		240	.133		7.85	5.55	.56	13.96	18.20
9000	Minimum labor/equipment charge	D-1	2	8	Job		330		330	535

04 22 10.33 Lintel Block

		Crew	Daily Output	Labor-Hours	Unit	Material	2014 Bare Costs Labor	Equipment	Total	Total Incl O&P
0010	**LINTEL BLOCK**									
3481	Lintel block 6" x 8" x 8"	D-1	300	.053	Ea.	1.29	2.20		3.49	5
3501	6" x 16" x 8"		275	.058		2	2.40		4.40	6.10
3521	8" x 8" x 8"		275	.058		1.06	2.40		3.46	5.05
3561	8" x 16" x 8"		250	.064		1.84	2.64		4.48	6.30

04 22 10.34 Concrete Block, Partitions

		Crew	Daily Output	Labor-Hours	Unit	Material	2014 Bare Costs Labor	Equipment	Total	Total Incl O&P
0010	**CONCRETE BLOCK, PARTITIONS**, excludes scaffolding									
1000	Lightweight block, tooled joints, 2 sides, hollow									
1100	Not reinforced, 8" x 16" x 4" thick	D-8	440	.091	S.F.	1.72	3.83		5.55	8.10
1150	6" thick		410	.098		2.45	4.11		6.56	9.40
1200	8" thick		385	.104		2.98	4.38		7.36	10.40
1250	10" thick		370	.108		3.61	4.56		8.17	11.35
1300	12" thick	D-9	350	.137		3.81	5.65		9.46	13.40
1500	Reinforced alternate courses, 4" thick	D-8	435	.092		1.83	3.88		5.71	8.30
1600	6" thick		405	.099		2.58	4.16		6.74	9.60
1650	8" thick		380	.105		3.12	4.44		7.56	10.65

04 22 10 – Concrete Masonry Units

04 22 10.34 Concrete Block, Partitions

		Crew	Daily Output	Labor-Hours	Unit	Material	2014 Bare Costs Labor	2014 Bare Costs Equipment	Total	Total Incl O&P
1700	10" thick	D-8	365	.110	S.F.	3.73	4.62		8.35	11.60
1750	12" thick	D-9	345	.139	↓	3.93	5.75		9.68	13.65
4000	Regular block, tooled joints, 2 sides, hollow									
4100	Not reinforced, 8" x 16" x 4" thick	D-8	430	.093	S.F.	1.58	3.92		5.50	8.10
4150	6" thick		400	.100		2.10	4.22		6.32	9.15
4200	8" thick		375	.107		2.37	4.50		6.87	9.90
4250	10" thick	↓	360	.111		2.86	4.68		7.54	10.75
4300	12" thick	D-9	340	.141		3.67	5.85		9.52	13.50
4500	Reinforced alternate courses, 8" x 16" x 4" thick	D-8	425	.094		1.73	3.97		5.70	8.35
4550	6" thick		395	.101		2.25	4.27		6.52	9.45
4600	8" thick		370	.108		2.53	4.56		7.09	10.20
4650	10" thick	↓	355	.113		3.70	4.75		8.45	11.75
4700	12" thick	D-9	335	.143	↓	3.83	5.90		9.73	13.80
9000	Minimum labor/equipment charge	D-1	2	8	Job		330		330	535

04 22 10.38 Concrete Brick

		Crew	Daily Output	Labor-Hours	Unit	Material	2014 Bare Costs Labor	2014 Bare Costs Equipment	Total	Total Incl O&P
0010	**CONCRETE BRICK**, C55, grade N, type 1									
0100	Regular, 4 x 2-1/4 x 8	D-8	660	.061	Ea.	.52	2.56		3.08	4.72
0125	Rusticated, 4 x 2-1/4 x 8		660	.061		.58	2.56		3.14	4.79
0150	Frog, 4 x 2-1/4 x 8		660	.061		.56	2.56		3.12	4.77
0200	Double, 4 x 4-7/8 x 8	↓	535	.075	↓	.91	3.15		4.06	6.10

04 22 10.44 Glazed Concrete Block

		Crew	Daily Output	Labor-Hours	Unit	Material	2014 Bare Costs Labor	2014 Bare Costs Equipment	Total	Total Incl O&P
0010	**GLAZED CONCRETE BLOCK** C744									
0100	Single face, 8" x 16" units, 2" thick	D-8	360	.111	S.F.	9.55	4.68		14.23	18.10
0200	4" thick		345	.116		9.80	4.89		14.69	18.75
0250	6" thick		330	.121		10.60	5.10		15.70	19.95
0300	8" thick		310	.129		11.30	5.45		16.75	21.50
0350	10" thick	↓	295	.136		12.95	5.70		18.65	23.50
0400	12" thick	D-9	280	.171		13.80	7.10		20.90	26.50
0700	Double face, 8" x 16" units, 4" thick	D-8	340	.118		13.85	4.96		18.81	23.50
0750	6" thick		320	.125		16.85	5.25		22.10	27
0800	8" thick		300	.133	↓	17.65	5.60		23.25	28.50
1000	Jambs, bullnose or square, single face, 8" x 16", 2" thick		315	.127	Ea.	18.25	5.35		23.60	28.50
1050	4" thick		285	.140	"	21.50	5.90		27.40	33
1200	Caps, bullnose or square, 8" x 16", 2" thick		420	.095	L.F.	16.95	4.02		20.97	25
1250	4" thick		380	.105	"	18.45	4.44		22.89	27.50
1256	Corner, bullnose or square, 2" thick		280	.143	Ea.	19.80	6		25.80	32
1258	4" thick		270	.148		21.50	6.25		27.75	33.50
1260	6" thick		260	.154		26.50	6.50		33	40
1270	8" thick		250	.160		32.50	6.75		39.25	47
1280	10" thick		240	.167		33	7.05		40.05	48
1290	12" thick		230	.174	↓	34.50	7.35		41.85	50
1500	Cove base, 8" x 16", 2" thick		315	.127	L.F.	8.55	5.35		13.90	18.10
1550	4" thick		285	.140		8.65	5.90		14.55	19.10
1600	6" thick		265	.151		9.25	6.35		15.60	20.50
1650	8" thick	↓	245	.163	↓	9.70	6.90		16.60	22
9000	Minimum labor/equipment charge	D-1	2	8	Job		330		330	535

04 23 Glass Unit Masonry

04 23 13 – Vertical Glass Unit Masonry

04 23 13.10 Glass Block		Crew	Daily Output	Labor-Hours	Unit	Material	2014 Bare Costs Labor	Equipment	Total	Total Incl O&P
0010	**GLASS BLOCK**									
0100	Plain, 4" thick, under 1,000 S.F., 6" x 6"	D-8	115	.348	S.F.	29	14.65		43.65	56
0150	8" x 8"		160	.250		16.65	10.55		27.20	35.50
0160	end block		160	.250		59	10.55		69.55	82
0170	90 deg corner		160	.250		53.50	10.55		64.05	76
0180	45 deg corner		160	.250		44	10.55		54.55	65.50
0200	12" x 12"		175	.229		23.50	9.65		33.15	41.50
0210	4" x 8"		160	.250		32	10.55		42.55	52
0220	6" x 8"		160	.250		22.50	10.55		33.05	42
0300	1,000 to 5,000 S.F., 6" x 6"		135	.296		28.50	12.50		41	52
0350	8" x 8"		190	.211		16.30	8.90		25.20	32.50
0400	12" x 12"		215	.186		23	7.85		30.85	38.50
0410	4" x 8"		215	.186		31	7.85		38.85	47.50
0420	6" x 8"		215	.186		22	7.85		29.85	37.50
0500	Over 5,000 S.F., 6" x 6"		145	.276		27.50	11.65		39.15	49.50
0700	For solar reflective blocks, add					100%				
1000	Thinline, plain, 3-1/8" thick, under 1,000 S.F., 6" x 6"	D-8	115	.348	S.F.	21	14.65		35.65	47
1050	8" x 8"		160	.250		11.85	10.55		22.40	30
1250	8" x 8"		215	.186		11.30	7.85		19.15	25
1400	For cleaning block after installation (both sides), add		1000	.040		.16	1.69		1.85	2.92
9000	Minimum labor/equipment charge	D-1	2	8	Job		330		330	535

04 27 Multiple-Wythe Unit Masonry

04 27 10 – Multiple-Wythe Masonry

04 27 10.10 Cornices

		Crew	Daily Output	Labor-Hours	Unit	Material	2014 Bare Costs Labor	Equipment	Total	Total Incl O&P
0010	**CORNICES**									
0110	Face bricks, 12 brick/S.F.	D-1	30	.533	SF Face	5.45	22		27.45	42
0150	15 brick/S.F.		23	.696	"	6.55	28.50		35.05	53.50
9000	Minimum labor/equipment charge		1.50	10.667	Job		440		440	715

04 27 10.30 Brick Walls

		Crew	Daily Output	Labor-Hours	Unit	Material	2014 Bare Costs Labor	Equipment	Total	Total Incl O&P
0010	**BRICK WALLS**, including mortar, excludes scaffolding									
0020	Estimating by number of brick									
0140	Face brick, 4" thick wall, 6.75 brick/S.F.	D-8	1.45	27.586	M	585	1,175		1,760	2,550
0150	Common brick, 4" thick wall, 6.75 brick/S.F.		1.60	25		585	1,050		1,635	2,350
0204	8" thick, 13.50 bricks per S.F.		1.80	22.222		600	935		1,535	2,175
0250	12" thick, 20.25 bricks per S.F.		1.90	21.053		605	890		1,495	2,125
0304	16" thick, 27.00 bricks per S.F.		2	20		610	845		1,455	2,050
0500	Reinforced, face brick, 4" thick wall, 6.75 brick/S.F.		1.40	28.571		610	1,200		1,810	2,625
0520	Common brick, 4" thick wall, 6.75 brick/S.F.		1.55	25.806		610	1,100		1,710	2,450
0550	8" thick, 13.50 bricks per S.F.		1.75	22.857		625	965		1,590	2,275
0600	12" thick, 20.25 bricks per S.F.		1.85	21.622		630	910		1,540	2,175
0650	16" thick, 27.00 bricks per S.F.		1.95	20.513		635	865		1,500	2,100
0790	Alternate method of figuring by square foot									
0800	Face brick, 4" thick wall, 6.75 brick/S.F.	D-8	215	.186	S.F.	3.93	7.85		11.78	17.10
0850	Common brick, 4" thick wall, 6.75 brick/S.F.	R042110-50	240	.167		3.94	7.05		10.99	15.75
0900	8" thick, 13.50 bricks per S.F.		135	.296		8.10	12.50		20.60	29.50
1000	12" thick, 20.25 bricks per S.F.		95	.421		12.20	17.75		29.95	42.50
1050	16" thick, 27.00 bricks per S.F.		75	.533		16.50	22.50		39	54.50
1200	Reinforced, face brick, 4" thick wall, 6.75 brick/S.F.		210	.190		4.10	8.05		12.15	17.55
1220	Common brick, 4" thick wall, 6.75 brick/S.F.		235	.170		4.11	7.20		11.31	16.15
1250	8" thick, 13.50 bricks per S.F.		130	.308		8.45	12.95		21.40	30.50

04 27 Multiple-Wythe Unit Masonry

04 27 10 – Multiple-Wythe Masonry

04 27 10.30 Brick Walls		Crew	Daily Output	Labor-Hours	Unit	Material	2014 Bare Costs Labor	Equipment	Total	Total Incl O&P
1300	12" thick, 20.25 bricks per S.F.	D-8	90	.444	S.F.	12.75	18.75		31.50	44.50
1350	16" thick, 27.00 bricks per S.F.	↓	70	.571	↓	17.20	24		41.20	58
9000	Minimum labor/equipment charge	D-1	2	8	Job		330		330	535

04 27 10.40 Steps

		Crew	Daily Output	Labor-Hours	Unit	Material	Labor	Equipment	Total	Total Incl O&P
0010	**STEPS**									
0012	Entry steps, select common brick	D-1	.30	53.333	M	550	2,200		2,750	4,175

04 41 Dry-Placed Stone

04 41 10 – Dry Placed Stone

04 41 10.10 Rough Stone Wall

			Crew	Daily Output	Labor-Hours	Unit	Material	Labor	Equipment	Total	Total Incl O&P
0011	**ROUGH STONE WALL**, Dry										
0012	Dry laid (no mortar), under 18" thick	G	D-1	60	.267	C.F.	12.40	11		23.40	31.50
0100	Random fieldstone, under 18" thick	G	D-12	60	.533		12.40	22.50		34.90	49.50
0150	Over 18" thick	G	"	63	.508	↓	14.85	21		35.85	51
0500	Field stone veneer	G	D-8	120	.333	S.F.	11.45	14.05		25.50	35.50
0510	Valley stone veneer	G	↓	120	.333	↓	11.45	14.05		25.50	35.50
0520	River stone veneer	G	↓	120	.333	↓	11.45	14.05		25.50	35.50
0600	Rubble stone walls, in mortar bed, up to 18" thick	G	D-11	75	.320	C.F.	14.95	13.90		28.85	39
9000	Minimum labor/equipment charge		D-1	2	8	Job		330		330	535

04 43 Stone Masonry

04 43 10 – Masonry with Natural and Processed Stone

04 43 10.05 Ashlar Veneer

		Crew	Daily Output	Labor-Hours	Unit	Material	Labor	Equipment	Total	Total Incl O&P
0011	**ASHLAR VENEER** 4" + or - thk, random or random rectangular									
0150	Sawn face, split joints, low priced stone	D-8	140	.286	S.F.	11.55	12.05		23.60	32.50
0200	Medium priced stone		130	.308		13.30	12.95		26.25	35.50
0300	High priced stone		120	.333		17.85	14.05		31.90	42.50
0600	Seam face, split joints, medium price stone		125	.320		20	13.50		33.50	44
0700	High price stone		120	.333		20.50	14.05		34.55	45.50
1000	Split or rock face, split joints, medium price stone		125	.320		14.70	13.50		28.20	38
1100	High price stone	↓	120	.333	↓	19.05	14.05		33.10	44

04 43 10.10 Bluestone

		Crew	Daily Output	Labor-Hours	Unit	Material	Labor	Equipment	Total	Total Incl O&P
0010	**BLUESTONE**, cut to size									
0500	Sills, natural cleft, 10" wide to 6' long, 1-1/2" thick	D-11	70	.343	L.F.	13.35	14.90		28.25	38.50
0550	2" thick		63	.381		14.60	16.55		31.15	43
0600	Smooth finish, 1-1/2" thick		70	.343		12	14.90		26.90	37
0650	2" thick		63	.381		13	16.55		29.55	41.50
0800	Thermal finish, 1-1/2" thick		70	.343		12	14.90		26.90	37
0850	2" thick	↓	63	.381		13	16.55		29.55	41.50
1000	Stair treads, natural cleft, 12" wide, 6' long, 1-1/2" thick	D-10	115	.278		12	12.55	4.19	28.74	38.50
1050	2" thick		105	.305		13	13.75	4.58	31.33	41.50
1100	Smooth finish, 1-1/2" thick		115	.278		12	12.55	4.19	28.74	38.50
1150	2" thick		105	.305		13	13.75	4.58	31.33	41.50
1300	Thermal finish, 1-1/2" thick		115	.278		12	12.55	4.19	28.74	38.50
1350	2" thick	↓	105	.305	↓	13	13.75	4.58	31.33	41.50
9000	Minimum labor/equipment charge	D-1	2.50	6.400	Job		264		264	430

04 43 Stone Masonry

04 43 10 – Masonry with Natural and Processed Stone

04 43 10.45 Granite		Crew	Daily Output	Labor-Hours	Unit	Material	2014 Bare Costs Labor	2014 Bare Costs Equipment	Total	Total Incl O&P
0010	**GRANITE**, cut to size									
0050	Veneer, polished face, 3/4" to 1-1/2" thick									
0150	Low price, gray, light gray, etc.	D-10	130	.246	S.F.	26.50	11.10	3.70	41.30	51.50
0180	Medium price, pink, brown, etc.		130	.246		29.50	11.10	3.70	44.30	54.50
0220	High price, red, black, etc.	↓	130	.246	↓	42	11.10	3.70	56.80	68.50
0300	1-1/2" to 2-1/2" thick, veneer									
0350	Low price, gray, light gray, etc.	D-10	130	.246	S.F.	28.50	11.10	3.70	43.30	53.50
0500	Medium price, pink, brown, etc.	"	130	.246	"	33.50	11.10	3.70	48.30	59
2500	Steps, copings, etc., finished on more than one surface									
2550	Minimum	D-10	50	.640	C.F.	91	29	9.65	129.65	157
2600	Maximum	"	50	.640	"	146	29	9.65	184.65	217
9000	Minimum labor/equipment charge	D-1	2	8	Job		330		330	535

04 43 10.55 Limestone

04 43 10.55 Limestone		Crew	Daily Output	Labor-Hours	Unit	Material	2014 Bare Costs Labor	2014 Bare Costs Equipment	Total	Total Incl O&P
0010	**LIMESTONE**, cut to size									
0020	Veneer facing panels									
0500	Texture finish, light stick, 4-1/2" thick, 5' x 12'	D-4	300	.107	S.F.	47.50	4.44	.45	52.39	60
0750	5" thick, 5' x 14' panels	D-10	275	.116		51.50	5.25	1.75	58.50	67.50
1000	Sugarcube finish, 2" Thick, 3' x 5' panels		275	.116		35	5.25	1.75	42	49
1050	3" Thick, 4' x 9' panels		275	.116		38	5.25	1.75	45	52
1200	4" Thick, 5' x 11' panels		275	.116		40.50	5.25	1.75	47.50	55.50
1400	Sugarcube, textured finish, 4-1/2" thick, 5' x 12'		275	.116		44.50	5.25	1.75	51.50	59.50
1450	5" thick, 5' x 14' panels		275	.116	↓	53	5.25	1.75	60	68.50
2000	Coping, sugarcube finish, top & 2 sides		30	1.067	C.F.	67.50	48	16.05	131.55	169
2100	Sills, lintels, jambs, trim, stops, sugarcube finish, average		20	1.600		67.50	72	24	163.50	217
2150	Detailed		20	1.600	↓	67.50	72	24	163.50	217
2300	Steps, extra hard, 14" wide, 6" rise	↓	50	.640	L.F.	25	29	9.65	63.65	84.50
3000	Quoins, plain finish, 6" x 12" x 12"	D-12	25	1.280	Ea.	37.50	53.50		91	129
3050	6" x 16" x 24"	"	25	1.280	"	50	53.50		103.50	142
9000	Minimum labor/equipment charge	D-1	2	8	Job		330		330	535

04 43 10.60 Marble

04 43 10.60 Marble		Crew	Daily Output	Labor-Hours	Unit	Material	2014 Bare Costs Labor	2014 Bare Costs Equipment	Total	Total Incl O&P
0011	**MARBLE**, ashlar, split face, 4" + or - thick, random									
0040	Lengths 1' to 4' & heights 2" to 7-1/2", average	D-8	175	.229	S.F.	14.25	9.65		23.90	31.50
0100	Base, polished, 3/4" or 7/8" thick, polished, 6" high	D-10	65	.492	L.F.	10.55	22	7.40	39.95	56
0300	Carvings or bas relief, from templates, average		80	.400	S.F.	144	18.05	6	168.05	194
0350	Maximum	↓	80	.400	"	335	18.05	6	359.05	405
1000	Facing, polished finish, cut to size, 3/4" to 7/8" thick									
1050	Average	D-10	130	.246	S.F.	23.50	11.10	3.70	38.30	47.50
1100	Maximum		130	.246		33.50	11.10	3.70	48.30	59
1300	1-1/4" thick, average		125	.256		17.75	11.55	3.85	33.15	42.50
1350	Maximum		125	.256		40	11.55	3.85	55.40	67
1500	2" thick, average		120	.267	↓	40	12.05	4.01	56.06	68
1550	Maximum	↓	120	.267	↓	62	12.05	4.01	78.06	92
1700	Rubbed finish, cut to size, 4" thick									
1740	Average	D-10	100	.320	S.F.	40	14.45	4.81	59.26	73
1780	Maximum	"	100	.320	"	69	14.45	4.81	88.26	105
2200	Window sills, 6" x 3/4" thick	D-1	85	.188	L.F.	10.45	7.75		18.20	24
2500	Flooring, polished tiles, 12" x 12" x 3/8" thick									
2510	Thin set, average	D-11	90	.267	S.F.	8.45	11.55		20	28
2600	Maximum		90	.267		86	11.55		97.55	113
2700	Mortar bed, average		65	.369		8.45	16		24.45	35.50
2740	Maximum	↓	65	.369		90.50	16		106.50	126
2780	Travertine, 3/8" thick, average	D-10	130	.246	↓	9.25	11.10	3.70	24.05	32

04 43 Stone Masonry

04 43 10 – Masonry with Natural and Processed Stone

04 43 10.60 Marble

		Crew	Daily Output	Labor-Hours	Unit	Material	2014 Bare Costs Labor	Equipment	Total	Total Incl O&P
2790	Maximum	D-10	130	.246	S.F.	25.50	11.10	3.70	40.30	50
2800	Patio tile, non-slip, 1/2" thick, flame finish	D-11	75	.320	↓	11	13.90		24.90	34.50
2900	Shower or toilet partitions, 7/8" thick partitions									
3050	3/4" or 1-1/4" thick stiles, polished 2 sides, average	D-11	75	.320	S.F.	45.50	13.90		59.40	72.50
3201	Soffits, add to above prices				"	20%	100%			
3210	Stairs, risers, 7/8" thick x 6" high	D-10	115	.278	L.F.	15.25	12.55	4.19	31.99	42
3360	Treads, 12" wide x 1-1/4" thick	"	115	.278	"	42.50	12.55	4.19	59.24	71.50
3500	Thresholds, 3' long, 7/8" thick, 4" to 5" wide, plain	D-12	24	1.333	Ea.	31.50	55.50		87	125
3550	Beveled		24	1.333	"	67.50	55.50		123	165
3700	Window stools, polished, 7/8" thick, 5" wide	↓	85	.376	L.F.	20.50	15.75		36.25	48
9000	Minimum labor/equipment charge	D-1	2	8	Job		330		330	535

04 43 10.75 Sandstone or Brownstone

		Crew	Daily Output	Labor-Hours	Unit	Material	2014 Bare Costs Labor	Equipment	Total	Total Incl O&P
0011	**SANDSTONE OR BROWNSTONE**									
0100	Sawed face veneer, 2-1/2" thick, to 2' x 4' panels	D-10	130	.246	S.F.	19	11.10	3.70	33.80	43
0150	4" thick, to 3'-6" x 8' panels		100	.320		19	14.45	4.81	38.26	50
0300	Split face, random sizes	↓	100	.320	↓	13.65	14.45	4.81	32.91	44
9000	Minimum labor/equipment charge	D-1	2.50	6.400	Job		264		264	430

04 43 10.80 Slate

		Crew	Daily Output	Labor-Hours	Unit	Material	2014 Bare Costs Labor	Equipment	Total	Total Incl O&P
0010	**SLATE**									
0040	Pennsylvania - blue gray to black									
0050	Vermont - unfading green, mottled green & purple, gray & purple									
0100	Virginia - blue black									
3100	Stair landings, 1" thick, black, clear	D-1	65	.246	S.F.	20	10.15		30.15	38.50
3200	Ribbon	"	65	.246	"	22	10.15		32.15	40.50
3500	Stair treads, sand finish, 1" thick x 12" wide									
3550	Under 3 L.F.	D-10	85	.376	L.F.	22	17	5.65	44.65	58
3600	3 L.F. to 6 L.F.	"	120	.267	"	24	12.05	4.01	40.06	50
3700	Ribbon, sand finish, 1" thick x 12" wide									
3750	To 6 L.F.	D-10	120	.267	L.F.	20	12.05	4.01	36.06	46
4000	Stools or sills, sand finish, 1" thick, 6" wide	D-12	160	.200		11.50	8.35		19.85	26.50
4100	Honed finish		160	.200		11	8.35		19.35	25.50
4200	10" wide		90	.356		17.75	14.85		32.60	43.50
4250	Honed finish		90	.356		16.50	14.85		31.35	42
4400	2" thick, 6" wide		140	.229		18.50	9.55		28.05	36
4450	Honed finish		140	.229		17.60	9.55		27.15	35
4600	10" wide		90	.356		29	14.85		43.85	56
4650	Honed finish	↓	90	.356		27.50	14.85		42.35	54.50
4800	For lengths over 3', add				↓	25%				
9000	Minimum labor/equipment charge	D-1	2.50	6.400	Job		264		264	430

04 43 10.85 Window Sill

		Crew	Daily Output	Labor-Hours	Unit	Material	2014 Bare Costs Labor	Equipment	Total	Total Incl O&P
0010	**WINDOW SILL**									
0020	Bluestone, thermal top, 10" wide, 1-1/2" thick	D-1	85	.188	S.F.	9.25	7.75		17	23
0050	2" thick		75	.213	"	8.85	8.80		17.65	24
0100	Cut stone, 5" x 8" plain		48	.333	L.F.	11.90	13.75		25.65	35.50
0200	Face brick on edge, brick, 8" wide		80	.200		5.30	8.25		13.55	19.20
0400	Marble, 9" wide, 1" thick		85	.188		8.50	7.75		16.25	22
0900	Slate, colored, unfading, honed, 12" wide, 1" thick		85	.188		8.50	7.75		16.25	22
0950	2" thick	↓	70	.229	↓	8.50	9.45		17.95	24.50
9000	Minimum labor/equipment charge	1 Bric	2	4	Job		182		182	296

04 54 Refractory Brick Masonry

04 54 10 – Refractory Brick Work

04 54 10.10 Fire Brick	Crew	Daily Output	Labor-Hours	Unit	Material	2014 Bare Costs Labor	Equipment	Total	Total Incl O&P
0010 **FIRE BRICK**									
0012 Low duty, 2000°F, 9" x 2-1/2" x 4-1/2"	D-1	.60	26.667	M	1,375	1,100		2,475	3,325
0050 High duty, 3000°F	"	.60	26.667	"	1,800	1,100		2,900	3,775

04 54 10.20 Fire Clay

	Crew	Daily Output	Labor-Hours	Unit	Material	Labor	Equipment	Total	Total Incl O&P
0010 **FIRE CLAY**									
0020 Gray, high duty, 100 lb. bag				Bag	30			30	33
0050 100 lb. drum, premixed (400 brick per drum)				Drum	41			41	45

04 57 Masonry Fireplaces

04 57 10 – Brick or Stone Fireplaces

04 57 10.10 Fireplace

	Crew	Daily Output	Labor-Hours	Unit	Material	Labor	Equipment	Total	Total Incl O&P
0010 **FIREPLACE**									
0100 Brick fireplace, not incl. foundations or chimneys									
0110 30" x 29" opening, incl. chamber, plain brickwork	D-1	.40	40	Ea.	550	1,650		2,200	3,275
0200 Fireplace box only (110 brick)	"	2	8	"	157	330		487	705
0300 For elaborate brickwork and details, add					35%	35%			
0400 For hearth, brick & stone, add	D-1	2	8	Ea.	205	330		535	760
0410 For steel, damper, cleanouts, add		4	4		19.40	165		184.40	290
0600 Plain brickwork, incl. metal circulator		.50	32		985	1,325		2,310	3,225
0800 Face brick only, standard size, 8" x 2-2/3" x 4"		.30	53.333	M	550	2,200		2,750	4,175
0900 Stone fireplace, fieldstone, add				SF Face	8.50			8.50	9.35
1000 Cut stone, add				"	6.25			6.25	6.90
9000 Minimum labor/equipment charge	D-1	2	8	Job		330		330	535

04 71 Manufactured Brick Masonry

04 71 10 – Simulated or Manufactured Brick

04 71 10.10 Simulated Brick

	Crew	Daily Output	Labor-Hours	Unit	Material	Labor	Equipment	Total	Total Incl O&P
0010 **SIMULATED BRICK**									
0020 Aluminum, baked on colors	1 Carp	200	.040	S.F.	3.92	1.83		5.75	7.30
0050 Fiberglass panels		200	.040		8.05	1.83		9.88	11.85
0100 Urethane pieces cemented in mastic		150	.053		8.25	2.45		10.70	13.05
0150 Vinyl siding panels		200	.040		9.70	1.83		11.53	13.70

04 72 Cast Stone Masonry

04 72 10 – Cast Stone Masonry Features

04 72 10.10 Coping

	Crew	Daily Output	Labor-Hours	Unit	Material	Labor	Equipment	Total	Total Incl O&P
0010 **COPING**, stock units									
0050 Precast concrete, 10" wide, 4" tapers to 3-1/2", 8" wall	D-1	75	.213	L.F.	17.10	8.80		25.90	33
0100 12" wide, 3-1/2" tapers to 3", 10" wall		70	.229		18.45	9.45		27.90	36
0110 14" wide, 4" tapers to 3-1/2", 12" wall		65	.246		20.50	10.15		30.65	39
0150 16" wide, 4" tapers to 3-1/2", 14" wall		60	.267		22	11		33	42.50
0300 Limestone for 12" wall, 4" thick		90	.178		14.70	7.35		22.05	28
0350 6" thick		80	.200		22	8.25		30.25	38
0500 Marble, to 4" thick, no wash, 9" wide		90	.178		13.70	7.35		21.05	27
0550 12" wide		80	.200		15.70	8.25		23.95	30.50
0700 Terra cotta, 9" wide		90	.178		6.15	7.35		13.50	18.70
0750 12" wide		80	.200		8.40	8.25		16.65	22.50

04 72 Cast Stone Masonry

04 72 10 – Cast Stone Masonry Features

04 72 10.10 Coping	Crew	Daily Output	Labor-Hours	Unit	Material	2014 Bare Costs Labor	Equipment	Total	Total Incl O&P
0800	Aluminum, for 12" wall	D-1	80	.200	L.F.	8.90	8.25		17.15	23
9000	Minimum labor/equipment charge	↓	2	8	Job		330		330	535

04 72 20 – Cultured Stone Veneer

04 72 20.10 Cultured Stone Veneer Components

		Crew	Daily Output	Labor-Hours	Unit	Material	2014 Bare Costs Labor	Equipment	Total	Total Incl O&P
0010	**CULTURED STONE VENEER COMPONENTS**									
0110	On wood frame and sheathing substrate, random sized cobbles, corner stones	D-8	70	.571	V.L.F.	9.10	24		33.10	49
0120	Field stones		140	.286	S.F.	6.65	12.05		18.70	27
0130	Random sized flats, corner stones		70	.571	V.L.F.	9.35	24		33.35	49.50
0140	Field stones		140	.286	S.F.	7.55	12.05		19.60	28
0150	Horizontal lined ledgestones, corner stones		75	.533	V.L.F.	9.30	22.50		31.80	46.50
0160	Field stones		150	.267	S.F.	6.85	11.25		18.10	26
0170	Random shaped flats, corner stones		65	.615	V.L.F.	9.30	26		35.30	52
0180	Field stones		150	.267	S.F.	6.85	11.25		18.10	26
0190	Random shaped/textured face, corner stones		65	.615	V.L.F.	9.10	26		35.10	52
0200	Field stones		130	.308	S.F.	6.85	12.95		19.80	28.50
0210	Random shaped river rock, corner stones		65	.615	V.L.F.	9.10	26		35.10	52
0220	Field stones		130	.308	S.F.	6.85	12.95		19.80	28.50
0240	On concrete or CMU substrate, random sized cobbles, corner stones		70	.571	V.L.F.	8.45	24		32.45	48.50
0250	Field stones		140	.286	S.F.	6.30	12.05		18.35	26.50
0260	Random sized flats, corner stones		70	.571	V.L.F.	8.70	24		32.70	48.50
0270	Field stones		140	.286	S.F.	7.20	12.05		19.25	27.50
0280	Horizontal lined ledgestones, corner stones		75	.533	V.L.F.	8.60	22.50		31.10	46
0290	Field stones		150	.267	S.F.	6.50	11.25		17.75	25.50
0300	Random shaped flats, corner stones		70	.571	V.L.F.	8.60	24		32.60	48.50
0310	Field stones		140	.286	S.F.	6.50	12.05		18.55	26.50
0320	Random shaped/textured face, corner stones		65	.615	V.L.F.	8.45	26		34.45	51.50
0330	Field stones		130	.308	S.F.	6.55	12.95		19.50	28
0340	Random shaped river rock, corner stones		65	.615	V.L.F.	8.45	26		34.45	51.50
0350	Field stones	↓	130	.308	S.F.	6.55	12.95		19.50	28
0360	Cultured stone veneer, #15 felt weather resistant barrier	1 Clab	3700	.002	Sq.	5.40	.08		5.48	6.10
0370	Expanded metal lath, diamond, 2.5 lb./S.Y., galvanized	1 Lath	85	.094	S.Y.	3.05	3.82		6.87	9.35
0390	Water table or window sill, 18" long	1 Bric	80	.100	Ea.	9.50	4.56		14.06	17.85

04 73 Manufactured Stone Masonry

04 73 20 – Simulated or Manufactured Stone

04 73 20.10 Simulated Stone

		Crew	Daily Output	Labor-Hours	Unit	Material	2014 Bare Costs Labor	Equipment	Total	Total Incl O&P
0010	**SIMULATED STONE**									
0100	Insulated fiberglass panels, 5/8" ply backer	L-4	200	.120	S.F.	10.55	5.15		15.70	20

Estimating Tips

05 05 00 Common Work Results for Metals

- Nuts, bolts, washers, connection angles, and plates can add a significant amount to both the tonnage of a structural steel job and the estimated cost. As a rule of thumb, add 10% to the total weight to account for these accessories.

- Type 2 steel construction, commonly referred to as "simple construction," consists generally of field-bolted connections with lateral bracing supplied by other elements of the building, such as masonry walls or x-bracing. The estimator should be aware, however, that shop connections may be accomplished by welding or bolting. The method may be particular to the fabrication shop and may have an impact on the estimated cost.

05 10 00 Structural Steel

- Steel items can be obtained from two sources: a fabrication shop or a metals service center. Fabrication shops can fabricate items under more controlled conditions than can crews in the field. They are also more efficient and can produce items more economically. Metal service centers serve as a source of long mill shapes to both fabrication shops and contractors.

- Most line items in this structural steel subdivision, and most items in 05 50 00 Metal Fabrications, are indicated as being shop fabricated. The bare material cost for these shop fabricated items is the "Invoice Cost" from the shop and includes the mill base price of steel plus mill extras, transportation to the shop, shop drawings and detailing where warranted, shop fabrication and handling, sandblasting and a shop coat of primer paint, all necessary structural bolts, and delivery to the job site. The bare labor cost and bare equipment cost for these shop fabricated items is for field installation or erection.

- Line items in Subdivision 05 12 23.40 Lightweight Framing, and other items scattered in Division 5, are indicated as being field fabricated. The bare material cost for these field fabricated items is the "Invoice Cost" from the metals service center and includes the mill base price of steel plus mill extras, transportation to the metals service center, material handling, and delivery of long lengths of mill shapes to the job site. Material costs for structural bolts and welding rods should be added to the estimate. The bare labor cost and bare equipment cost for these items is for both field fabrication and field installation or erection, and include time for cutting, welding and drilling in the fabricated metal items. Drilling into concrete and fasteners to fasten field fabricated items to other work are not included and should be added to the estimate.

05 20 00 Steel Joist Framing

- In any given project the total weight of open web steel joists is determined by the loads to be supported and the design. However, economies can be realized in minimizing the amount of labor used to place the joists. This is done by maximizing the joist spacing, and therefore minimizing the number of joists required to be installed on the job. Certain spacings and locations may be required by the design, but in other cases maximizing the spacing and keeping it as uniform as possible will keep the costs down.

05 30 00 Steel Decking

- The takeoff and estimating of metal deck involves more than simply the area of the floor or roof and the type of deck specified or shown on the drawings. Many different sizes and types of openings may exist. Small openings for individual pipes or conduits may be drilled after the floor/roof is installed, but larger openings may require special deck lengths as well as reinforcing or structural support. The estimator should determine who will be supplying this reinforcing. Additionally, some deck terminations are part of the deck package, such as screed angles and pour stops, and others will be part of the steel contract, such as angles attached to structural members and cast-in-place angles and plates. The estimator must ensure that all pieces are accounted for in the complete estimate.

05 50 00 Metal Fabrications

- The most economical steel stairs are those that use common materials, standard details, and most importantly, a uniform and relatively simple method of field assembly. Commonly available A36 channels and plates are very good choices for the main stringers of the stairs, as are angles and tees for the carrier members. Risers and treads are usually made by specialty shops, and it is most economical to use a typical detail in as many places as possible. The stairs should be pre-assembled and shipped directly to the site. The field connections should be simple and straightforward to be accomplished efficiently, and with minimum equipment and labor.

Reference Numbers

Reference numbers are shown in shaded boxes at the beginning of some major classifications. These numbers refer to related items in the Reference Section. The reference information may be an estimating procedure, an alternate pricing method, or technical information. *Note:* Not all subdivisions listed here necessarily appear in this publication.

05 05 Common Work Results for Metals

05 05 05 – Selective Metals Demolition

05 05 05.10 Selective Demolition, Metals

		Crew	Daily Output	Labor-Hours	Unit	Material	2014 Bare Costs Labor	Equipment	Total	Total Incl O&P
0010	SELECTIVE DEMOLITION, METALS	R024119-10								
0015	Excludes shores, bracing, cutting, loading, hauling, dumping									
0020	Remove nuts only up to 3/4" diameter	1 Sswk	480	.017	Ea.		.85		.85	1.56
0030	7/8" to 1-1/4" diameter		240	.033			1.70		1.70	3.12
0040	1-3/8" to 2" diameter		160	.050			2.56		2.56	4.69
0060	Unbolt and remove structural bolts up to 3/4" diameter		240	.033			1.70		1.70	3.12
0070	7/8" to 2" diameter		160	.050			2.56		2.56	4.69
0140	Light weight framing members, remove whole or cut up, up to 20 lb.		240	.033			1.70		1.70	3.12
0150	21 – 40 lb.	2 Sswk	210	.076			3.89		3.89	7.15
0160	41 – 80 lb.	3 Sswk	180	.133			6.80		6.80	12.50
0170	81 – 120 lb.	4 Sswk	150	.213			10.90		10.90	20
0230	Structural members, remove whole or cut up, up to 500 lb.	E-19	48	.500			25	20	45	66.50
0240	1/4 – 2 tons	E-18	36	1.111			56.50	26.50	83	131
0250	2 – 5 tons	E-24	30	1.067			54	25	79	123
0260	5 – 10 tons	E-20	24	2.667			134	49	183	292
0270	10 – 15 tons	E-2	18	3.111			156	85	241	370
0340	Fabricated item, remove whole or cut up, up to 20 lb.	1 Sswk	96	.083			4.26		4.26	7.80
0350	21 – 40 lb.	2 Sswk	84	.190			9.75		9.75	17.85
0360	41 – 80 lb.	3 Sswk	72	.333			17.05		17.05	31.50
0370	81 – 120 lb.	4 Sswk	60	.533			27.50		27.50	50
0380	121 – 500 lb.	E-19	48	.500			25	20	45	66.50
0390	501 – 1000 lb.	"	36	.667			33.50	26.50	60	88.50
0500	Steel roof decking, uncovered, bare	B-2	5000	.008	S.F.		.30		.30	.49
2950	Minimum labor/equipment charge	E-19	2	12	Job		605	480	1,085	1,600

05 05 19 – Post-Installed Concrete Anchors

05 05 19.10 Chemical Anchors

		Crew	Daily Output	Labor-Hours	Unit	Material	2014 Bare Costs Labor	Equipment	Total	Total Incl O&P
0010	CHEMICAL ANCHORS									
0020	Includes layout & drilling									
1430	Chemical anchor, w/rod & epoxy cartridge, 3/4" diam. x 9-1/2" long	B-89A	27	.593	Ea.	9.75	25	4.30	39.05	56
1435	1" diameter x 11-3/4" long		24	.667		16.70	28	4.84	49.54	69.50
1440	1-1/4" diameter x 14" long		21	.762		36	32	5.55	73.55	98.50
1445	1-3/4" diameter x 15" long		20	.800		64.50	33.50	5.80	103.80	132
1450	18" long		17	.941		77.50	39.50	6.85	123.85	157
1455	2" diameter x 18" long		16	1		102	42	7.25	151.25	189
1460	24" long		15	1.067		132	45	7.75	184.75	228

05 05 19.20 Expansion Anchors

			Crew	Daily Output	Labor-Hours	Unit	Material	2014 Bare Costs Labor	Equipment	Total	Total Incl O&P
0010	EXPANSION ANCHORS										
0100	Anchors for concrete, brick or stone, no layout and drilling										
0200	Expansion shields, zinc, 1/4" diameter, 1-5/16" long, single	G	1 Carp	90	.089	Ea.	.48	4.08		4.56	7.25
0300	1-3/8" long, double	G		85	.094		.59	4.32		4.91	7.75
0400	3/8" diameter, 1-1/2" long, single	G		85	.094		.81	4.32		5.13	8
0500	2" long, double	G		80	.100		1.32	4.59		5.91	9
0600	1/2" diameter, 2-1/16" long, single	G		80	.100		1.62	4.59		6.21	9.35
0700	2-1/2" long, double	G		75	.107		2.10	4.89		6.99	10.35
0800	5/8" diameter, 2-5/8" long, single	G		75	.107		2.85	4.89		7.74	11.20
0900	2-3/4" long, double	G		70	.114		2.99	5.25		8.24	11.90
1000	3/4" diameter, 2-3/4" long, single	G		70	.114		3.25	5.25		8.50	12.20
1100	3-15/16" long, double	G		65	.123		5.80	5.65		11.45	15.65
2100	Hollow wall anchors for gypsum wall board, plaster or tile										
2300	1/8" diameter, short	G	1 Carp	160	.050	Ea.	.23	2.29		2.52	4.02
2400	Long	G		150	.053		.23	2.45		2.68	4.27
2500	3/16" diameter, short	G		150	.053		.40	2.45		2.85	4.46

05 05 19 – Post-Installed Concrete Anchors

05 05 19.20 Expansion Anchors		Crew	Daily Output	Labor-Hours	Unit	Material	2014 Bare Costs Labor	Equipment	Total	Total Incl O&P
2600	Long	G	1 Carp	140	.057	Ea.	.58	2.62		3.20	4.95
2700	1/4" diameter, short	G		140	.057		.62	2.62		3.24	4.99
2800	Long	G		130	.062		.61	2.82		3.43	5.30
3000	Toggle bolts, bright steel, 1/8" diameter, 2" long	G		85	.094		.19	4.32		4.51	7.30
3100	4" long	G		80	.100		.25	4.59		4.84	7.85
3200	3/16" diameter, 3" long	G		80	.100		.26	4.59		4.85	7.85
3300	6" long	G		75	.107		.35	4.89		5.24	8.45
3400	1/4" diameter, 3" long	G		75	.107		.34	4.89		5.23	8.40
3500	6" long	G		70	.114		.50	5.25		5.75	9.15
3600	3/8" diameter, 3" long	G		70	.114		.82	5.25		6.07	9.50
3700	6" long	G		60	.133		1.24	6.10		7.34	11.40
3800	1/2" diameter, 4" long	G		60	.133		1.84	6.10		7.94	12.05
3900	6" long	G	↓	50	.160	↓	2.40	7.35		9.75	14.70
4000	Nailing anchors										
4100	Nylon nailing anchor, 1/4" diameter, 1" long		1 Carp	3.20	2.500	C	16.35	115		131.35	206
4200	1-1/2" long			2.80	2.857		21	131		152	239
4300	2" long			2.40	3.333		25.50	153		178.50	279
4400	Metal nailing anchor, 1/4" diameter, 1" long	G		3.20	2.500		17.60	115		132.60	207
4500	1-1/2" long	G		2.80	2.857		22.50	131		153.50	240
4600	2" long	G	↓	2.40	3.333	↓	28	153		181	282
8000	Wedge anchors, not including layout or drilling										
8050	Carbon steel, 1/4" diameter, 1-3/4" long	G	1 Carp	150	.053	Ea.	.40	2.45		2.85	4.46
8100	3-1/4" long	G		140	.057		.53	2.62		3.15	4.89
8150	3/8" diameter, 2-1/4" long	G		145	.055		.49	2.53		3.02	4.70
8200	5" long	G		140	.057		.86	2.62		3.48	5.25
8250	1/2" diameter, 2-3/4" long	G		140	.057		.97	2.62		3.59	5.40
8300	7" long	G		125	.064		1.66	2.93		4.59	6.65
8350	5/8" diameter, 3-1/2" long	G		130	.062		1.69	2.82		4.51	6.50
8400	8-1/2" long	G		115	.070		3.60	3.19		6.79	9.20
8450	3/4" diameter, 4-1/4" long	G		115	.070		2.81	3.19		6	8.35
8500	10" long	G		95	.084		6.40	3.86		10.26	13.40
8550	1" diameter, 6" long	G		100	.080		9.05	3.67		12.72	16
8575	9" long	G		85	.094		11.75	4.32		16.07	20
8600	12" long	G		75	.107		12.70	4.89		17.59	22
8650	1-1/4" diameter, 9" long	G		70	.114		24	5.25		29.25	34.50
8700	12" long	G		60	.133	↓	30.50	6.10		36.60	43.50
8750	For type 303 stainless steel, add						350%				
8800	For type 316 stainless steel, add						450%				
8950	Self-drilling concrete screw, hex washer head, 3/16" diam. x 1-3/4" long	G	1 Carp	300	.027	Ea.	.20	1.22		1.42	2.23
8960	2-1/4" long	G		250	.032		.23	1.47		1.70	2.66
8970	Phillips flat head, 3/16" diam. x 1-3/4" long	G		300	.027		.20	1.22		1.42	2.23
8980	2-1/4" long	G		250	.032	↓	.23	1.47		1.70	2.66
9000	Minimum labor/equipment charge		↓	4	2	Job		91.50		91.50	151

05 05 21 – Fastening Methods for Metal

05 05 21.10 Cutting Steel

		Crew	Daily Output	Labor-Hours	Unit	Material	2014 Bare Costs Labor	Equipment	Total	Total Incl O&P
0010	**CUTTING STEEL**										
0020	Hand burning, incl. preparation, torch cutting & grinding, no staging										
0050	Steel to 1/4" thick	E-25	400	.020	L.F.	.17	1.06	.03	1.26	2.17
0100	1/2" thick		320	.025		.32	1.33	.04	1.69	2.83
0150	3/4" thick		260	.031		.53	1.63	.04	2.20	3.63
0200	1" thick		200	.040	↓	.76	2.12	.06	2.94	4.79
9000	Minimum labor/equipment charge	↓	2	4	Job		212	5.70	217.70	395

05 05 21 – Fastening Methods for Metal

05 05 21.15 Drilling Steel		Crew	Daily Output	Labor-Hours	Unit	Material	2014 Bare Costs Labor	2014 Bare Costs Equipment	Total	Total Incl O&P
0010	**DRILLING STEEL**									
1910	Drilling & layout for steel, up to 1/4" deep, no anchor									
1920	Holes, 1/4" diameter	1 Sswk	112	.071	Ea.	.08	3.65		3.73	6.80
1925	For each additional 1/4" depth, add		336	.024		.08	1.22		1.30	2.32
1930	3/8" diameter		104	.077		.09	3.93		4.02	7.30
1935	For each additional 1/4" depth, add		312	.026		.09	1.31		1.40	2.50
1940	1/2" diameter		96	.083		.09	4.26		4.35	7.90
1945	For each additional 1/4" depth, add		288	.028		.09	1.42		1.51	2.70
1950	5/8" diameter		88	.091		.13	4.65		4.78	8.65
1955	For each additional 1/4" depth, add		264	.030		.13	1.55		1.68	2.99
1960	3/4" diameter		80	.100		.17	5.10		5.27	9.60
1965	For each additional 1/4" depth, add		240	.033		.17	1.70		1.87	3.30
1970	7/8" diameter		72	.111		.22	5.70		5.92	10.65
1975	For each additional 1/4" depth, add		216	.037		.22	1.89		2.11	3.71
1980	1" diameter		64	.125		.23	6.40		6.63	11.95
1985	For each additional 1/4" depth, add		192	.042		.23	2.13		2.36	4.16
1990	For drilling up, add						40%			
2000	Minimum labor/equipment charge	1 Carp	4	2	Job		91.50		91.50	151

05 05 21.90 Welding Steel

		Crew	Daily Output	Labor-Hours	Unit	Material	2014 Bare Costs Labor	2014 Bare Costs Equipment	Total	Total Incl O&P
0010	**WELDING STEEL**, Structural R050521-20									
0020	Field welding, 1/8" E6011, cost per welder, no operating engineer	E-14	8	1	Hr.	4.33	53	17.75	75.08	122
0200	With 1/2 operating engineer	E-13	8	1.500		4.33	76.50	17.75	98.58	159
0300	With 1 operating engineer	E-12	8	2		4.33	100	17.75	122.08	196
0500	With no operating engineer, 2# weld rod per ton	E-14	8	1	Ton	4.33	53	17.75	75.08	122
0600	8# E6011 per ton	"	2	4		17.30	212	71	300.30	485
0800	With one operating engineer per welder, 2# E6011 per ton	E-12	8	2		4.33	100	17.75	122.08	196
0900	8# E6011 per ton	"	2	8		17.30	400	71	488.30	785
1200	Continuous fillet, down welding									
1300	Single pass, 1/8" thick, 0.1#/L.F.	E-14	150	.053	L.F.	.22	2.83	.95	4	6.50
1400	3/16" thick, 0.2#/L.F.		75	.107		.43	5.65	1.89	7.97	12.95
1500	1/4" thick, 0.3#/L.F.		50	.160		.65	8.50	2.84	11.99	19.45
1610	5/16" thick, 0.4#/L.F.		38	.211		.87	11.20	3.74	15.81	25.50
1800	3 passes, 3/8" thick, 0.5#/L.F.		30	.267		1.08	14.15	4.73	19.96	32.50
2010	4 passes, 1/2" thick, 0.7#/L.F.		22	.364		1.52	19.30	6.45	27.27	44.50
2200	5 to 6 passes, 3/4" thick, 1.3#/L.F.		12	.667		2.81	35.50	11.85	50.16	81
2400	8 to 11 passes, 1" thick, 2.4#/L.F.		6	1.333		5.20	71	23.50	99.70	162
2600	For vertical joint welding, add						20%			
2700	Overhead joint welding, add						300%			
2900	For semi-automatic welding, obstructed joints, deduct						5%			
3000	Exposed joints, deduct						15%			
4000	Cleaning and welding plates, bars, or rods									
4010	to existing beams, columns, or trusses	E-14	12	.667	L.F.	1.08	35.50	11.85	48.43	79
9000	Minimum labor/equipment charge	"	4	2	Job		106	35.50	141.50	234

05 05 23 – Metal Fastenings

05 05 23.30 Lag Screws

			Crew	Daily Output	Labor-Hours	Unit	Material	2014 Bare Costs Labor	2014 Bare Costs Equipment	Total	Total Incl O&P
0010	**LAG SCREWS**										
0020	Steel, 1/4" diameter, 2" long	G	1 Carp	200	.040	Ea.	.09	1.83		1.92	3.11
0200	1/2" diameter, 3" long	G		130	.062		.63	2.82		3.45	5.35
0300	5/8" diameter, 3" long	G		120	.067		1.13	3.06		4.19	6.25

05 05 Common Work Results for Metals

05 05 23 – Metal Fastenings

05 05 23.50 Powder Actuated Tools and Fasteners

05 05 23.50 Powder Actuated Tools and Fasteners		Crew	Daily Output	Labor-Hours	Unit	Material	2014 Bare Costs Labor	Equipment	Total	Total Incl O&P
0010	**POWDER ACTUATED TOOLS & FASTENERS**									
0020	Stud driver, .22 caliber, single shot				Ea.	147			147	161
0100	.27 caliber, semi automatic, strip				"	435			435	475
0300	Powder load, single shot, .22 cal, power level 2, brown				C	5.30			5.30	5.80
0400	Strip, .27 cal, power level 4, red					7.60			7.60	8.35
0600	Drive pin, .300 x 3/4" long	G	1 Carp	4.80	1.667		4.86	76.50		81.36	131
0700	.300 x 3" long with washer	G	"	4	2		12.50	91.50		104	165

05 05 23.70 Structural Blind Bolts

05 05 23.70 Structural Blind Bolts		Crew	Daily Output	Labor-Hours	Unit	Material	Labor	Equipment	Total	Total Incl O&P
0010	**STRUCTURAL BLIND BOLTS**									
0100	1/4" diameter x 1/4" grip	G	1 Sswk	240	.033	Ea.	1.24	1.70		2.94	4.48
0150	1/2" grip	G		216	.037		1.33	1.89		3.22	4.93
0200	3/8" diameter x 1/2" grip	G		232	.034		1.75	1.76		3.51	5.15
0250	3/4" grip	G		208	.038		1.84	1.97		3.81	5.65
0300	1/2" diameter x 1/2" grip	G		224	.036		3.99	1.82		5.81	7.75
0350	3/4" grip	G		200	.040		5.60	2.04		7.64	9.90
0400	5/8" diameter x 3/4" grip	G		216	.037		8.25	1.89		10.14	12.55
0450	1" grip	G		192	.042		9.50	2.13		11.63	14.35

05 05 23.87 Weld Studs

05 05 23.87 Weld Studs		Crew	Daily Output	Labor-Hours	Unit	Material	Labor	Equipment	Total	Total Incl O&P
0010	**WELD STUDS**									
0020	1/4" diameter, 2-11/16" long	G	E-10	1120	.014	Ea.	.35	.74	.42	1.51	2.23
0100	4-1/8" long	G		1080	.015		.33	.77	.44	1.54	2.26
0200	3/8" diameter, 4-1/8" long	G		1080	.015		.38	.77	.44	1.59	2.32
0300	6-1/8" long	G		1040	.015		.49	.80	.46	1.75	2.51
9000	Minimum labor/equipment charge		1 Sswk	2	4	Job		204		204	375

05 12 Structural Steel Framing

05 12 23 – Structural Steel for Buildings

05 12 23.05 Canopy Framing

05 12 23.05 Canopy Framing		Crew	Daily Output	Labor-Hours	Unit	Material	Labor	Equipment	Total	Total Incl O&P
0010	**CANOPY FRAMING**									
0020	6" and 8" members, shop fabricated	G	E-4	3000	.011	Lb.	1.59	.55	.05	2.19	2.81
9000	Minimum labor/equipment charge		1 Sswk	1	8	Job		410		410	750

05 12 23.10 Ceiling Supports

05 12 23.10 Ceiling Supports		Crew	Daily Output	Labor-Hours	Unit	Material	Labor	Equipment	Total	Total Incl O&P
0010	**CEILING SUPPORTS**									
1000	Entrance door/folding partition supports, shop fabricated	G	E-4	60	.533	L.F.	26.50	27.50	2.37	56.37	82
1100	Linear accelerator door supports	G		14	2.286		121	118	10.15	249.15	360
1200	Lintels or shelf angles, hung, exterior hot dipped galv.	G		267	.120		18.10	6.20	.53	24.83	32
1250	Two coats primer paint instead of galv.	G		267	.120		15.65	6.20	.53	22.38	29
1400	Monitor support, ceiling hung, expansion bolted	G		4	8	Ea.	420	415	35.50	870.50	1,250
1450	Hung from pre-set inserts	G		6	5.333		450	275	23.50	748.50	1,025
1600	Motor supports for overhead doors	G		4	8		214	415	35.50	664.50	1,025
1700	Partition support for heavy folding partitions, without pocket	G		24	1.333	L.F.	60.50	69	5.90	135.40	199
1750	Supports at pocket only	G		12	2.667		121	138	11.85	270.85	400
2000	Rolling grilles & fire door supports	G		34	.941		51.50	48.50	4.18	104.18	151
2100	Spider-leg light supports, expansion bolted to ceiling slab	G		8	4	Ea.	172	206	17.75	395.75	590
2150	Hung from pre-set inserts	G		12	2.667	"	186	138	11.85	335.85	470
2400	Toilet partition support	G		36	.889	L.F.	60.50	46	3.95	110.45	155
2500	X-ray travel gantry support	G		12	2.667	"	207	138	11.85	356.85	490

05 12 Structural Steel Framing

05 12 23 – Structural Steel for Buildings

05 12 23.17 Columns, Structural		Crew	Daily Output	Labor-Hours	Unit	Material	2014 Bare Costs Labor	Equipment	Total	Total Incl O&P
0010	**COLUMNS, STRUCTURAL**	R051223-10								
0015	Made from recycled materials									
0020	Shop fab'd for 100-ton, 1-2 story project, bolted connections									
0800	Steel, concrete filled, extra strong pipe, 3-1/2" diameter	E-2	660	.085	L.F.	43.50	4.26	2.32	50.08	58
0830	4" diameter		780	.072		48.50	3.60	1.96	54.06	62
0890	5" diameter		1020	.055		58	2.76	1.50	62.26	70.50
0930	6" diameter		1200	.047		77	2.34	1.27	80.61	90
0940	8" diameter		1100	.051		77	2.56	1.39	80.95	90.50
1500	Steel pipe, extra strong, no concrete, 3" to 5" diameter [G]		16000	.004	Lb.	1.33	.18	.10	1.61	1.88
3300	Structural tubing, square, A500GrB, 4" to 6" square, light section [G]		11270	.005	"	1.33	.25	.14	1.72	2.05
8090	For projects 75 to 99 tons, add				All	10%				
8092	50 to 74 tons, add					20%				
8094	25 to 49 tons, add					30%	10%			
8096	10 to 24 tons, add					50%	25%			
8098	2 to 9 tons, add					75%	50%			
8099	Less than 2 tons, add					100%	100%			
9000	Minimum labor/equipment charge	1 Sswk	1	8	Job		410		410	750

05 12 23.20 Curb Edging		Crew	Daily Output	Labor-Hours	Unit	Material	2014 Bare Costs Labor	Equipment	Total	Total Incl O&P
0010	**CURB EDGING**									
0020	Steel angle w/anchors, shop fabricated, on forms, 1" x 1", 0.8#/L.F. [G]	E-4	350	.091	L.F.	1.67	4.72	.41	6.80	10.95
0300	4" x 4" angles, 8.2#/L.F. [G]		275	.116	"	13.85	6	.52	20.37	27
9000	Minimum labor/equipment charge		4	8	Job		415	35.50	450.50	795

05 12 23.40 Lightweight Framing		Crew	Daily Output	Labor-Hours	Unit	Material	2014 Bare Costs Labor	Equipment	Total	Total Incl O&P
0010	**LIGHTWEIGHT FRAMING**									
0015	Made from recycled materials									
0200	For load-bearing steel studs see Section 05 41 13.30									
0400	Angle framing, field fabricated, 4" and larger [G]	E-3	440	.055	Lb.	.77	2.82	.32	3.91	6.40
0450	Less than 4" angles [G]		265	.091		.80	4.69	.54	6.03	10.05
0600	Channel framing, field fabricated, 8" and larger [G]		500	.048		.80	2.49	.28	3.57	5.75
0650	Less than 8" channels [G]		335	.072		.80	3.71	.42	4.93	8.15
1000	Continuous slotted channel framing system, shop fab, simple framing [G]	2 Sswk	2400	.007		4.11	.34		4.45	5.15
1200	Complex framing [G]	"	1600	.010		4.64	.51		5.15	6.05
1250	Plate & bar stock for reinforcing beams and trusses [G]					1.46			1.46	1.60
1300	Cross bracing, rods, shop fabricated, 3/4" diameter [G]	E-3	700	.034		1.59	1.78	.20	3.57	5.25
1310	7/8" diameter [G]		850	.028		1.59	1.46	.17	3.22	4.61
1320	1" diameter [G]		1000	.024		1.59	1.24	.14	2.97	4.19
1330	Angle, 5" x 5" x 3/8" [G]		2800	.009		1.59	.44	.05	2.08	2.62
1350	Hanging lintels, shop fabricated [G]		850	.028		1.59	1.46	.17	3.22	4.61
1380	Roof frames, shop fabricated, 3'-0" square, 5' span [G]	E-2	4200	.013		1.59	.67	.36	2.62	3.33
1400	Tie rod, not upset, 1-1/2" to 4" diameter, with turnbuckle [G]	2 Sswk	800	.020		1.72	1.02		2.74	3.77
1420	No turnbuckle [G]		700	.023		1.66	1.17		2.83	3.96
1500	Upset, 1-3/4" to 4" diameter, with turnbuckle [G]		800	.020		1.72	1.02		2.74	3.77
1520	No turnbuckle [G]		700	.023		1.66	1.17		2.83	3.96
9000	Minimum labor/equipment charge		2	8	Job		410		410	750

05 12 23.45 Lintels		Crew	Daily Output	Labor-Hours	Unit	Material	2014 Bare Costs Labor	Equipment	Total	Total Incl O&P
0010	**LINTELS**									
0015	Made from recycled materials									
0020	Plain steel angles, shop fabricated, under 500 lb. [G]	1 Bric	550	.015	Lb.	1.02	.66		1.68	2.20
0100	500 to 1000 lb. [G]		640	.013		.99	.57		1.56	2.02
0200	1,000 to 2,000 lb. [G]		640	.013		.97	.57		1.54	1.99
0300	2,000 to 4,000 lb. [G]		640	.013		.94	.57		1.51	1.96

05 12 23 – Structural Steel for Buildings

05 12 23.45 **Lintels**		Crew	Daily Output	Labor-Hours	Unit	Material	2014 Bare Costs Labor	Equipment	Total	Total Incl O&P
0500	For built-up angles and plates, add to above	G			Lb.	.33			.33	.36
0700	For engineering, add to above					.13			.13	.15
0900	For galvanizing, add to above, under 500 lb.					.30			.30	.33
0950	500 to 2,000 lb.					.28			.28	.30
1000	Over 2,000 lb.					.25			.25	.28
2000	Steel angles, 3-1/2" x 3", 1/4" thick, 2'-6" long	G	1 Bric	47	.170	Ea.	14.30	7.75		22.05	28.50
2100	4'-6" long	G		26	.308		26	14.05		40.05	51.50
2500	3-1/2" x 3-1/2" x 5/16", 5'-0" long	G		18	.444		38	20.50		58.50	75
2600	4" x 3-1/2", 1/4" thick, 5'-0" long	G		21	.381		33	17.35		50.35	64
2700	9'-0" long	G		12	.667		59	30.50		89.50	115
2800	4" x 3-1/2" x 5/16", 7'-0" long	G		12	.667		57	30.50		87.50	113
2900	5" x 3-1/2" x 5/16", 10'-0" long	G		8	1		92	45.50		137.50	175
9000	Minimum labor/equipment charge			4	2	Job		91		91	148

05 12 23.60 Pipe Support Framing

		Crew	Daily Output	Labor-Hours	Unit	Material	Labor	Equipment	Total	Total Incl O&P
0010	**PIPE SUPPORT FRAMING**									
0020	Under 10#/L.F., shop fabricated	G	E-4	3900	.008	Lb.	1.78	.42	.04	2.24	2.77
0200	10.1 to 15#/L.F.	G		4300	.007		1.75	.38	.03	2.16	2.66
0400	15.1 to 20#/L.F.	G		4800	.007		1.72	.34	.03	2.09	2.55
0600	Over 20#/L.F.	G		5400	.006		1.70	.31	.03	2.04	2.46

05 12 23.65 Plates

		Crew	Daily Output	Labor-Hours	Unit	Material	Labor	Equipment	Total	Total Incl O&P
0010	**PLATES**									
0015	Made from recycled materials									
0020	For connections & stiffener plates, shop fabricated									
0050	1/8" thick (5.1 lb./S.F.)	G				S.F.	6.75			6.75	7.45
0100	1/4" thick (10.2 lb./S.F.)	G					13.50			13.50	14.85
0300	3/8" thick (15.3 lb./S.F.)	G					20.50			20.50	22.50
0400	1/2" thick (20.4 lb./S.F.)	G					27			27	29.50
0450	3/4" thick (30.6 lb./S.F.)	G					40.50			40.50	44.50
0500	1" thick (40.8 lb./S.F.)	G					54			54	59.50
2000	Steel plate, warehouse prices, no shop fabrication									
2100	1/4" thick (10.2 lb./S.F.)	G				S.F.	8.05			8.05	8.85

05 12 23.75 Structural Steel Members

		Crew	Daily Output	Labor-Hours	Unit	Material	Labor	Equipment	Total	Total Incl O&P
0010	**STRUCTURAL STEEL MEMBERS** R051223-10									
0015	Made from recycled materials									
0020	Shop fab'd for 100-ton, 1-2 story project, bolted connections									
0102	Beam or girder, W 6 x 9 R051223-15	G	E-2	600	.093	L.F.	13.10	4.68	2.55	20.33	25.50
0302	W 8 x 10	G		600	.093		14.60	4.68	2.55	21.83	27
0502	x 31	G		550	.102		45	5.10	2.78	52.88	61.50
0702	W 10 x 22	G		600	.093		32	4.68	2.55	39.23	46.50
0902	x 49	G		550	.102		71.50	5.10	2.78	79.38	90.50
1102	W 12 x 16	G		880	.064		23.50	3.19	1.74	28.43	33
1302	x 22	G		880	.064		32	3.19	1.74	36.93	43
1502	x 26	G		880	.064		38	3.19	1.74	42.93	49
1902	W 14 x 26	G		990	.057		38	2.84	1.54	42.38	48
2102	x 30	G		900	.062		43.50	3.12	1.70	48.32	55.50
2702	W 16 x 26	G		1000	.056		38	2.81	1.53	42.34	48
2902	x 31	G		900	.062		45	3.12	1.70	49.82	57
8490	For projects 75 to 99 tons, add						10%				
8492	50 to 74 tons, add						20%				
8494	25 to 49 tons, add						30%	10%			
8496	10 to 24 tons, add						50%	25%			
8498	2 to 9 tons, add						75%	50%			

05 12 Structural Steel Framing

05 12 23 – Structural Steel for Buildings

05 12 23.75 Structural Steel Members

05 12 23.75 Structural Steel Members		Crew	Daily Output	Labor-Hours	Unit	Material	2014 Bare Costs Labor	Equipment	Total	Total Incl O&P
8499	Less than 2 tons, add				L.F.	100%	100%			
9000	Minimum labor/equipment charge	E-2	2	28	Job		1,400	765	2,165	3,325

05 12 23.77 Structural Steel Projects

05 12 23.77 Structural Steel Projects			Crew	Daily Output	Labor-Hours	Unit	Material	2014 Bare Costs Labor	Equipment	Total	Total Incl O&P
0010	**STRUCTURAL STEEL PROJECTS**										
0015	Made from recycled materials										
0020	Shop fab'd for 100-ton, 1-2 story project, bolted connections										
0700	Offices, hospitals, etc., steel bearing, 1 to 2 stories	R050521-20 G	E-5	10.30	7.767	Ton	2,650	395	162	3,207	3,800
1300	Industrial bldgs., 1 story, beams & girders, steel bearing	G		12.90	6.202		2,650	315	130	3,095	3,625
1400	Masonry bearing	R051223-10 G		10	8		2,650	405	167	3,222	3,825
1600	1 story with roof trusses, steel bearing	G		10.60	7.547		3,125	380	158	3,663	4,300
1700	Masonry bearing	R051223-15 G		8.30	9.639		3,125	490	201	3,816	4,550
5390	For projects 75 to 99 tons, add						10%				
5392	50 to 74 tons, add						20%				
5394	25 to 49 tons, add						30%	10%			
5396	10 to 24 tons, add						50%	25%			
5398	2 to 9 tons, add						75%	50%			
5399	Less than 2 tons, add						100%	100%			

05 12 23.78 Structural Steel Secondary Members

05 12 23.78 Structural Steel Secondary Members		Crew	Daily Output	Labor-Hours	Unit	Material	2014 Bare Costs Labor	Equipment	Total	Total Incl O&P
0010	**STRUCTURAL STEEL SECONDARY MEMBERS**									
0015	Made from recycled materials									
0020	Shop fabricated for 20-ton girt/purlin framing package, materials only									
0100	Girts/purlins, C/Z-shapes, includes clips and bolts									
0110	6" x 2-1/2" x 2-1/2", 16 ga., 3.0 lb./L.F.				L.F.	3.58			3.58	3.94
0115	14 ga., 3.5 lb./L.F.					4.17			4.17	4.59
0120	8" x 2-3/4" x 2-3/4", 16 ga., 3.4 lb./L.F.					4.05			4.05	4.46
0125	14 ga., 4.1 lb./L.F.					4.89			4.89	5.40
0130	12 ga., 5.6 lb./L.F.					6.70			6.70	7.35
0135	10" x 3-1/2" x 3-1/2", 14 ga., 4.7 lb./L.F.					5.60			5.60	6.15
0140	12 ga., 6.7 lb./L.F.					8			8	8.80
0145	12" x 3-1/2" x 3-1/2", 14 ga., 5.3 lb./L.F.					6.30			6.30	6.95
0150	12 ga., 7.4 lb./L.F.					8.80			8.80	9.70
0200	Eave struts, C-shape, includes clips and bolts									
0210	6" x 4" x 3", 16 ga., 3.1 lb./L.F.				L.F.	3.70			3.70	4.07
0215	14 ga., 3.9 lb./L.F.					4.65			4.65	5.10
0220	8" x 4" x 3", 16 ga., 3.5 lb./L.F.					4.17			4.17	4.59
0225	14 ga., 4.4 lb./L.F.					5.25			5.25	5.75
0230	12 ga., 6.2 lb./L.F.					7.40			7.40	8.15
0235	10" x 5" x 3", 14 ga., 5.2 lb./L.F.					6.20			6.20	6.80
0240	12 ga., 7.3 lb./L.F.					8.70			8.70	9.60
0245	12" x 5" x 4", 14 ga., 6.0 lb./L.F.					7.15			7.15	7.85
0250	12 ga., 8.4 lb./L.F.					10			10	11
0300	Rake/base angle, excludes concrete drilling and expansion anchors									
0310	2" x 2", 14 ga., 1.0 lb./L.F.	2 Sswk	640	.025	L.F.	1.19	1.28		2.47	3.65
0315	3" x 2", 14 ga., 1.3 lb./L.F.		535	.030		1.55	1.53		3.08	4.51
0320	3" x 3", 14 ga., 1.6 lb./L.F.		500	.032		1.91	1.64		3.55	5.10
0325	4" x 3", 14 ga., 1.8 lb./L.F.		480	.033		2.15	1.70		3.85	5.50
0600	Installation of secondary members, erection only									
0610	Girts, purlins, eave struts, 16 ga., 6" deep	E-18	100	.400	Ea.		20.50	9.60	30.10	47
0615	8" deep		80	.500			25.50	12	37.50	58.50
0620	14 ga., 6" deep		80	.500			25.50	12	37.50	58.50
0625	8" deep		65	.615			31.50	14.80	46.30	72.50
0630	10" deep		55	.727			37	17.45	54.45	85.50

05 12 Structural Steel Framing

05 12 23 – Structural Steel for Buildings

05 12 23.78 Structural Steel Secondary Members		Crew	Daily Output	Labor-Hours	Unit	Material	2014 Bare Costs Labor	Equipment	Total	Total Incl O&P
0635	12" deep	E-18	50	.800	Ea.		41	19.20	60.20	94
0640	12 ga., 8" deep		50	.800			41	19.20	60.20	94
0645	10" deep		45	.889			45.50	21.50	67	105
0650	12" deep	↓	40	1	↓		51	24	75	118
0900	For less than 20-ton job lots									
0905	For 15 to 19 tons, add					10%				
0910	For 10 to 14 tons, add					25%				
0915	For 5 to 9 tons, add					50%	50%	50%		
0920	For 1 to 4 tons, add					75%	75%	75%		
0925	For less than 1 ton, add					100%	100%	100%		
0990	Minimum labor/equipment charge	E-18	1	40	Job		2,050	960	3,010	4,700

05 15 Wire Rope Assemblies

05 15 16 – Steel Wire Rope Assemblies

05 15 16.70 Temporary Cable Safety Railing

			Crew	Daily Output	Labor-Hours	Unit	Material	Labor	Equipment	Total	Total Incl O&P
0010	**TEMPORARY CABLE SAFETY RAILING**, Each 100' strand incl.										
0020	2 eyebolts, 1 turnbuckle, 100' cable, 2 thimbles, 6 clips										
0025	Made from recycled materials										
0100	One strand using 1/4" cable & accessories	G	2 Sswk	4	4	C.L.F.	205	204		409	600
0200	1/2" cable & accessories	G	"	2	8	"	430	410		840	1,225

05 21 Steel Joist Framing

05 21 13 – Deep Longspan Steel Joist Framing

05 21 13.50 Deep Longspan Joists

			Crew	Daily Output	Labor-Hours	Unit	Material	Labor	Equipment	Total	Total Incl O&P
0010	**DEEP LONGSPAN JOISTS**										
3010	DLH series, 40-ton job lots, bolted cross bridging, shop primer										
3015	Made from recycled materials										
3040	Spans to 144' (shipped in 2 pieces)	G	E-7	13	6.154	Ton	1,925	310	139	2,374	2,850
3500	For less than 40-ton job lots										
3502	For 30 to 39 tons, add						10%				
3504	20 to 29 tons, add						20%				
3506	10 to 19 tons, add						30%				
3507	5 to 9 tons, add						50%	25%			
3508	1 to 4 tons, add						75%	50%			
3509	Less than 1 ton, add						100%	100%			
4010	SLH series, 40-ton job lots, bolted cross bridging, shop primer										
4040	Spans to 200' (shipped in 3 pieces)	G	E-7	13	6.154	Ton	1,975	310	139	2,424	2,900
6100	For less than 40-ton job lots										
6102	For 30 to 39 tons, add						10%				
6104	20 to 29 tons, add						20%				
6106	10 to 19 tons, add						30%				
6107	5 to 9 tons, add						50%	25%			
6108	1 to 4 tons, add						75%	50%			
6109	Less than 1 ton, add						100%	100%			

05 21 Steel Joist Framing

05 21 16 – Longspan Steel Joist Framing

05 21 16.50 Longspan Joists

	05 21 16.50 Longspan Joists		Crew	Daily Output	Labor-Hours	Unit	Material	2014 Bare Costs Labor	Equipment	Total	Total Incl O&P
0010	**LONGSPAN JOISTS**										
2000	LH series, 40-ton job lots, bolted cross bridging, shop primer										
2015	Made from recycled materials										
2040	Longspan joists, LH series, up to 96'	G	E-7	13	6.154	Ton	1,825	310	139	2,274	2,750
2600	For less than 40-ton job lots										
2602	For 30 to 39 tons, add						10%				
2604	20 to 29 tons, add						20%				
2606	10 to 19 tons, add						30%				
2607	5 to 9 tons, add						50%	25%			
2608	1 to 4 tons, add						75%	50%			
2609	Less than 1 ton, add						100%	100%			

05 21 19 – Open Web Steel Joist Framing

05 21 19.10 Open Web Joists

	05 21 19.10 Open Web Joists		Crew	Daily Output	Labor-Hours	Unit	Material	2014 Bare Costs Labor	Equipment	Total	Total Incl O&P
0010	**OPEN WEB JOISTS**										
0015	Made from recycled materials										
0050	K series, 40-ton lots, horiz. bridging, spans to 30', shop primer	G	E-7	12	6.667	Ton	1,650	340	151	2,141	2,600
0440	K series, 30' to 50' spans	G	"	17	4.706	"	1,625	238	107	1,970	2,350
0800	For less than 40-ton job lots										
0802	For 30 to 39 tons, add						10%				
0804	20 to 29 tons, add						20%				
0806	10 to 19 tons, add						30%				
0807	5 to 9 tons, add						50%	25%			
0808	1 to 4 tons, add						75%	50%			
0809	Less than 1 ton, add						100%	100%			
1010	CS series, 40-ton job lots, horizontal bridging, shop primer										
1040	Spans to 30'	G	E-7	12	6.667	Ton	1,700	340	151	2,191	2,650
1500	For less than 40-ton job lots										
1502	For 30 to 39 tons, add						10%				
1504	20 to 29 tons, add						20%				
1506	10 to 19 tons, add						30%				
1507	5 to 9 tons, add						50%	25%			
1508	1 to 4 tons, add						75%	50%			
1509	Less than 1 ton, add						100%	100%			
6400	Individual steel bearing plate, 6" x 6" x 1/4" with J-hook	G	1 Bric	160	.050	Ea.	7.95	2.28		10.23	12.45
9000	Minimum labor and equipment, bar joists		F-6	1	40	Job		1,725	665	2,390	3,525

05 31 Steel Decking

05 31 13 – Steel Floor Decking

05 31 13.50 Floor Decking

	05 31 13.50 Floor Decking		Crew	Daily Output	Labor-Hours	Unit	Material	2014 Bare Costs Labor	Equipment	Total	Total Incl O&P
0010	**FLOOR DECKING** R053100-10										
0015	Made from recycled materials										
5100	Non-cellular composite decking, galvanized, 1-1/2" deep, 16 ga.	G	E-4	3500	.009	S.F.	3.31	.47	.04	3.82	4.55
5120	18 ga.	G		3650	.009		2.68	.45	.04	3.17	3.82
5140	20 ga.	G		3800	.008		2.13	.43	.04	2.60	3.19
5200	2" deep, 22 ga.	G		3860	.008		1.86	.43	.04	2.33	2.87
5300	20 ga.	G		3600	.009		2.05	.46	.04	2.55	3.14
5400	18 ga.	G		3380	.009		2.62	.49	.04	3.15	3.83
5500	16 ga.	G		3200	.010		3.27	.52	.04	3.83	4.60
5700	3" deep, 22 ga.	G		3200	.010		2.03	.52	.04	2.59	3.23
5800	20 ga.	G		3000	.011		2.26	.55	.05	2.86	3.54

05 31 Steel Decking

05 31 13 - Steel Floor Decking

05 31 13.50 Floor Decking

		Crew	Daily Output	Labor-Hours	Unit	Material	2014 Bare Costs Labor	Equipment	Total	Total Incl O&P
5900	18 ga.	G	E-4	2850	.011	S.F.	2.79	.58	.05	3.42	4.18
6000	16 ga.	G	↓	2700	.012	↓	3.72	.61	.05	4.38	5.25
9000	Minimum labor/equipment charge		1 Sswk	1	8	Job		410		410	750

05 31 23 - Steel Roof Decking

05 31 23.50 Roof Decking

		Crew	Daily Output	Labor-Hours	Unit	Material	2014 Bare Costs Labor	Equipment	Total	Total Incl O&P
0010	**ROOF DECKING**										
0015	Made from recycled materials										
2100	Open type, 1-1/2" deep, Type B, wide rib, galv., 22 ga., under 50 sq.	G	E-4	4500	.007	S.F.	1.97	.37	.03	2.37	2.87
2400	Over 500 squares	G	"	5100	.006	"	1.42	.32	.03	1.77	2.18

05 31 33 - Steel Form Decking

05 31 33.50 Form Decking

		Crew	Daily Output	Labor-Hours	Unit	Material	2014 Bare Costs Labor	Equipment	Total	Total Incl O&P
0010	**FORM DECKING**										
0015	Made from recycled materials										
6100	Slab form, steel, 28 ga., 9/16" deep, Type UFS, uncoated	G	E-4	4000	.008	S.F.	1.49	.41	.04	1.94	2.44
6200	Galvanized	G	"	4000	.008	"	1.32	.41	.04	1.77	2.25

05 35 Raceway Decking Assemblies

05 35 13 - Steel Cellular Decking

05 35 13.50 Cellular Decking

		Crew	Daily Output	Labor-Hours	Unit	Material	2014 Bare Costs Labor	Equipment	Total	Total Incl O&P
0010	**CELLULAR DECKING**										
0015	Made from recycled materials										
0200	Cellular units, galv, 1-1/2" deep, Type BC, 20-20 ga., over 15 squares	G	E-4	1460	.022	S.F.	7.75	1.13	.10	8.98	10.75
0400	3" deep, Type NC, galvanized, 20-20 ga.	G	↓	1375	.023	↓	8.55	1.20	.10	9.85	11.70
1000	4-1/2" deep, Type JC, galvanized, 18-20 ga.	G	↓	1100	.029	↓	11.90	1.50	.13	13.53	16
1500	For acoustical deck, add						15%				
1900	For multi-story or congested site, add							50%			

05 41 Structural Metal Stud Framing

05 41 13 - Load-Bearing Metal Stud Framing

05 41 13.05 Bracing

		Crew	Daily Output	Labor-Hours	Unit	Material	2014 Bare Costs Labor	Equipment	Total	Total Incl O&P
0010	**BRACING**, shear wall X-bracing, per 10' x 10' bay, one face										
0015	Made of recycled materials										
0120	Metal strap, 20 ga. x 4" wide	G	2 Carp	18	.889	Ea.	17.55	41		58.55	86.50
0130	6" wide	G		18	.889		29.50	41		70.50	99
0160	18 ga. x 4" wide	G		16	1		30.50	46		76.50	109
0170	6" wide	G	↓	16	1	↓	45	46		91	125
0410	Continuous strap bracing, per horizontal row on both faces										
0420	Metal strap, 20 ga. x 2" wide, studs 12" O.C.	G	1 Carp	7	1.143	C.L.F.	53	52.50		105.50	144
0430	16" O.C.	G		8	1		53	46		99	134
0440	24" O.C.	G		10	.800		53	36.50		89.50	119
0450	18 ga. x 2" wide, studs 12" O.C.	G		6	1.333		75	61		136	183
0460	16" O.C.	G		7	1.143		75	52.50		127.50	169
0470	24" O.C.	G	↓	8	1		75	46		121	158

05 41 13.10 Bridging

		Crew	Daily Output	Labor-Hours	Unit	Material	2014 Bare Costs Labor	Equipment	Total	Total Incl O&P
0010	**BRIDGING**, solid between studs w/1-1/4" leg track, per stud bay										
0015	Made from recycled materials										
0200	Studs 12" O.C., 18 ga. x 2-1/2" wide	G	1 Carp	125	.064	Ea.	.89	2.93		3.82	5.80
0210	3-5/8" wide	G	↓	120	.067	↓	1.07	3.06		4.13	6.20

05 41 Structural Metal Stud Framing

05 41 13 – Load-Bearing Metal Stud Framing

05 41 13.10 Bridging

			Crew	Daily Output	Labor-Hours	Unit	Material	2014 Bare Costs Labor	Equipment	Total	Total Incl O&P
0220	4" wide	G	1 Carp	120	.067	Ea.	1.13	3.06		4.19	6.25
0230	6" wide	G		115	.070		1.48	3.19		4.67	6.90
0240	8" wide	G		110	.073		1.84	3.33		5.17	7.50
0300	16 ga. x 2-1/2" wide	G		115	.070		1.13	3.19		4.32	6.50
0310	3-5/8" wide	G		110	.073		1.38	3.33		4.71	7
0320	4" wide	G		110	.073		1.47	3.33		4.80	7.10
0330	6" wide	G		105	.076		1.87	3.49		5.36	7.80
0340	8" wide	G		100	.080		2.34	3.67		6.01	8.65
1200	Studs 16" O.C., 18 ga. x 2-1/2" wide	G		125	.064		1.14	2.93		4.07	6.05
1210	3-5/8" wide	G		120	.067		1.37	3.06		4.43	6.50
1220	4" wide	G		120	.067		1.45	3.06		4.51	6.60
1230	6" wide	G		115	.070		1.90	3.19		5.09	7.35
1240	8" wide	G		110	.073		2.36	3.33		5.69	8.10
1300	16 ga. x 2-1/2" wide	G		115	.070		1.45	3.19		4.64	6.85
1310	3-5/8" wide	G		110	.073		1.77	3.33		5.10	7.45
1320	4" wide	G		110	.073		1.88	3.33		5.21	7.55
1330	6" wide	G		105	.076		2.39	3.49		5.88	8.40
1340	8" wide	G		100	.080		3	3.67		6.67	9.35
2200	Studs 24" O.C., 18 ga. x 2-1/2" wide	G		125	.064		1.65	2.93		4.58	6.65
2210	3-5/8" wide	G		120	.067		1.98	3.06		5.04	7.20
2220	4" wide	G		120	.067		2.10	3.06		5.16	7.30
2230	6" wide	G		115	.070		2.75	3.19		5.94	8.25
2240	8" wide	G		110	.073		3.41	3.33		6.74	9.25
2300	16 ga. x 2-1/2" wide	G		115	.070		2.10	3.19		5.29	7.55
2310	3-5/8" wide	G		110	.073		2.55	3.33		5.88	8.30
2320	4" wide	G		110	.073		2.72	3.33		6.05	8.50
2330	6" wide	G		105	.076		3.46	3.49		6.95	9.55
2340	8" wide	G		100	.080		4.34	3.67		8.01	10.85
3000	Continuous bridging, per row										
3100	16 ga. x 1-1/2" channel thru studs 12" O.C.	G	1 Carp	6	1.333	C.L.F.	48	61		109	153
3110	16" O.C.	G		7	1.143		48	52.50		100.50	139
3120	24" O.C.	G		8.80	.909		48	41.50		89.50	122
4100	2" x 2" angle x 18 ga., studs 12" O.C.	G		7	1.143		75	52.50		127.50	169
4110	16" O.C.	G		9	.889		75	41		116	150
4120	24" O.C.	G		12	.667		75	30.50		105.50	133
4200	16 ga., studs 12" O.C.	G		5	1.600		94.50	73.50		168	225
4210	16" O.C.	G		7	1.143		94.50	52.50		147	190
4220	24" O.C.	G		10	.800		94.50	36.50		131	165

05 41 13.25 Framing, Boxed Headers/Beams

			Crew	Daily Output	Labor-Hours	Unit	Material	2014 Bare Costs Labor	Equipment	Total	Total Incl O&P
0010	**FRAMING, BOXED HEADERS/BEAMS**										
0015	Made from recycled materials										
0200	Double, 18 ga. x 6" deep	G	2 Carp	220	.073	L.F.	5.10	3.33		8.43	11.10
0210	8" deep	G		210	.076		5.65	3.49		9.14	11.95
0220	10" deep	G		200	.080		6.90	3.67		10.57	13.65
0230	12" deep	G		190	.084		7.55	3.86		11.41	14.65
0300	16 ga. x 8" deep	G		180	.089		6.50	4.08		10.58	13.85
0310	10" deep	G		170	.094		7.90	4.32		12.22	15.75
0320	12" deep	G		160	.100		8.60	4.59		13.19	17
0400	14 ga. x 10" deep	G		140	.114		9.10	5.25		14.35	18.60
0410	12" deep	G		130	.123		10	5.65		15.65	20
1210	Triple, 18 ga. x 8" deep	G		170	.094		8.20	4.32		12.52	16.10
1220	10" deep	G		165	.097		9.85	4.45		14.30	18.15

05 41 Structural Metal Stud Framing

05 41 13 – Load-Bearing Metal Stud Framing

05 41 13.25 Framing, Boxed Headers/Beams

			Crew	Daily Output	Labor-Hours	Unit	Material	2014 Bare Costs Labor	Equipment	Total	Total Incl O&P
1230	12" deep	G	2 Carp	160	.100	L.F.	10.85	4.59		15.44	19.45
1300	16 ga. x 8" deep	G		145	.110		9.50	5.05		14.55	18.70
1310	10" deep	G		140	.114		11.35	5.25		16.60	21
1320	12" deep	G		135	.119		12.40	5.45		17.85	22.50
1400	14 ga. x 10" deep	G		115	.139		12.40	6.40		18.80	24
1410	12" deep	G		110	.145		13.70	6.65		20.35	26

05 41 13.30 Framing, Stud Walls

			Crew	Daily Output	Labor-Hours	Unit	Material	2014 Bare Costs Labor	Equipment	Total	Total Incl O&P
0010	**FRAMING, STUD WALLS** w/top & bottom track, no openings,										
0020	Headers, beams, bridging or bracing										
0025	Made from recycled materials										
4100	8' high walls, 18 ga. x 2-1/2" wide, studs 12" O.C.	G	2 Carp	54	.296	L.F.	8.50	13.60		22.10	32
4110	16" O.C.	G		77	.208		6.80	9.55		16.35	23
4120	24" O.C.	G		107	.150		5.10	6.85		11.95	16.85
4130	3-5/8" wide, studs 12" O.C.	G		53	.302		10.05	13.85		23.90	34
4140	16" O.C.	G		76	.211		8.05	9.65		17.70	24.50
4150	24" O.C.	G		105	.152		6.05	7		13.05	18.15
4160	4" wide, studs 12" O.C.	G		52	.308		10.55	14.10		24.65	34.50
4170	16" O.C.	G		74	.216		8.45	9.90		18.35	25.50
4180	24" O.C.	G		103	.155		6.35	7.10		13.45	18.70
4190	6" wide, studs 12" O.C.	G		51	.314		13.40	14.40		27.80	38
4200	16" O.C.	G		73	.219		10.75	10.05		20.80	28.50
4210	24" O.C.	G		101	.158		8.10	7.25		15.35	21
4220	8" wide, studs 12" O.C.	G		50	.320		16.30	14.65		30.95	42
4230	16" O.C.	G		72	.222		13.10	10.20		23.30	31
4240	24" O.C.	G		100	.160		9.90	7.35		17.25	23
4300	16 ga. x 2-1/2" wide, studs 12" O.C.	G		47	.340		10.10	15.60		25.70	36.50
4310	16" O.C.	G		68	.235		8	10.80		18.80	26.50
4320	24" O.C.	G		94	.170		5.90	7.80		13.70	19.35
4330	3-5/8" wide, studs 12" O.C.	G		46	.348		12.05	15.95		28	39.50
4340	16" O.C.	G		66	.242		9.55	11.10		20.65	29
4350	24" O.C.	G		92	.174		7.05	7.95		15	21
4360	4" wide, studs 12" O.C.	G		45	.356		12.65	16.30		28.95	41
4370	16" O.C.	G		65	.246		10	11.30		21.30	29.50
4380	24" O.C.	G		90	.178		7.40	8.15		15.55	21.50
4390	6" wide, studs 12" O.C.	G		44	.364		15.80	16.65		32.45	45
4400	16" O.C.	G		64	.250		12.55	11.45		24	32.50
4410	24" O.C.	G		88	.182		9.30	8.35		17.65	24
4420	8" wide, studs 12" O.C.	G		43	.372		19.50	17.05		36.55	49.50
4430	16" O.C.	G		63	.254		15.50	11.65		27.15	36
4440	24" O.C.	G		86	.186		11.50	8.55		20.05	26.50
5100	10' high walls, 18 ga. x 2-1/2" wide, studs 12" O.C.	G		54	.296		10.20	13.60		23.80	33.50
5110	16" O.C.	G		77	.208		8.05	9.55		17.60	24.50
5120	24" O.C.	G		107	.150		5.95	6.85		12.80	17.80
5130	3-5/8" wide, studs 12" O.C.	G		53	.302		12.05	13.85		25.90	36.50
5140	16" O.C.	G		76	.211		9.55	9.65		19.20	26.50
5150	24" O.C.	G		105	.152		7.05	7		14.05	19.25
5160	4" wide, studs 12" O.C.	G		52	.308		12.65	14.10		26.75	37
5170	16" O.C.	G		74	.216		10.05	9.90		19.95	27.50
5180	24" O.C.	G		103	.155		7.40	7.10		14.50	19.85
5190	6" wide, studs 12" O.C.	G		51	.314		16	14.40		30.40	41
5200	16" O.C.	G		73	.219		12.70	10.05		22.75	30.50
5210	24" O.C.	G		101	.158		9.40	7.25		16.65	22.50

05 41 Structural Metal Stud Framing

05 41 13 – Load-Bearing Metal Stud Framing

05 41 13.30 Framing, Stud Walls		Crew	Daily Output	Labor-Hours	Unit	Material	2014 Bare Costs Labor	Equipment	Total	Total Incl O&P
5220	8" wide, studs 12" O.C.	G	2 Carp	50	.320	L.F.	19.50	14.65		34.15	45.50
5230	16" O.C.	G		72	.222		15.50	10.20		25.70	34
5240	24" O.C.	G		100	.160		11.50	7.35		18.85	24.50
5300	16 ga. x 2-1/2" wide, studs 12" O.C.	G		47	.340		12.20	15.60		27.80	39
5310	16" O.C.	G		68	.235		9.55	10.80		20.35	28.50
5320	24" O.C.	G		94	.170		6.95	7.80		14.75	20.50
5330	3-5/8" wide, studs 12" O.C.	G		46	.348		14.55	15.95		30.50	42
5340	16" O.C.	G		66	.242		11.40	11.10		22.50	31
5350	24" O.C.	G		92	.174		8.30	7.95		16.25	22
5360	4" wide, studs 12" O.C.	G		45	.356		15.25	16.30		31.55	44
5370	16" O.C.	G		65	.246		12	11.30		23.30	32
5380	24" O.C.	G		90	.178		8.70	8.15		16.85	23
5390	6" wide, studs 12" O.C.	G		44	.364		19	16.65		35.65	48.50
5400	16" O.C.	G		64	.250		14.95	11.45		26.40	35.50
5410	24" O.C.	G		88	.182		10.90	8.35		19.25	25.50
5420	8" wide, studs 12" O.C.	G		43	.372		23.50	17.05		40.55	54
5430	16" O.C.	G		63	.254		18.50	11.65		30.15	39.50
5440	24" O.C.	G		86	.186		13.50	8.55		22.05	29
6190	12' high walls, 18 ga. x 6" wide, studs 12" O.C.	G		41	.390		18.65	17.90		36.55	50
6200	16" O.C.	G		58	.276		14.70	12.65		27.35	37
6210	24" O.C.	G		81	.198		10.75	9.05		19.80	26.50
6220	8" wide, studs 12" O.C.	G		40	.400		22.50	18.35		40.85	55
6230	16" O.C.	G		57	.281		17.90	12.85		30.75	40.50
6240	24" O.C.	G		80	.200		13.10	9.15		22.25	29.50
6390	16 ga. x 6" wide, studs 12" O.C.	G		35	.457		22.50	21		43.50	59
6400	16" O.C.	G		51	.314		17.40	14.40		31.80	42.50
6410	24" O.C.	G		70	.229		12.55	10.50		23.05	31
6420	8" wide, studs 12" O.C.	G		34	.471		27.50	21.50		49	66
6430	16" O.C.	G		50	.320		21.50	14.65		36.15	47.50
6440	24" O.C.	G		69	.232		15.50	10.65		26.15	34.50
6530	14 ga. x 3-5/8" wide, studs 12" O.C.	G		34	.471		21	21.50		42.50	59
6540	16" O.C.	G		48	.333		16.55	15.30		31.85	43.50
6550	24" O.C.	G		65	.246		11.90	11.30		23.20	31.50
6560	4" wide, studs 12" O.C.	G		33	.485		22.50	22		44.50	61
6570	16" O.C.	G		47	.340		17.55	15.60		33.15	45
6580	24" O.C.	G		64	.250		12.65	11.45		24.10	33
6730	12 ga. x 3-5/8" wide, studs 12" O.C.	G		31	.516		29.50	23.50		53	71.50
6740	16" O.C.	G		43	.372		23	17.05		40.05	53
6750	24" O.C.	G		59	.271		16.05	12.45		28.50	38
6760	4" wide, studs 12" O.C.	G		30	.533		31.50	24.50		56	74.50
6770	16" O.C.	G		42	.381		24.50	17.45		41.95	55
6780	24" O.C.	G		58	.276		17.15	12.65		29.80	40
7390	16' high walls, 16 ga. x 6" wide, studs 12" O.C.	G		33	.485		28.50	22		50.50	68
7400	16" O.C.	G		48	.333		22.50	15.30		37.80	49.50
7410	24" O.C.	G		67	.239		15.80	10.95		26.75	35.50
7420	8" wide, studs 12" O.C.	G		32	.500		35.50	23		58.50	76.50
7430	16" O.C.	G		47	.340		27.50	15.60		43.10	56
7440	24" O.C.	G		66	.242		19.50	11.10		30.60	40
7560	14 ga. x 4" wide, studs 12" O.C.	G		31	.516		29	23.50		52.50	71
7570	16" O.C.	G		45	.356		22.50	16.30		38.80	51.50
7580	24" O.C.	G		61	.262		15.90	12.05		27.95	37.50
7590	6" wide, studs 12" O.C.	G		30	.533		36.50	24.50		61	80
7600	16" O.C.	G		44	.364		28.50	16.65		45.15	58.50

05 41 Structural Metal Stud Framing

05 41 13 – Load-Bearing Metal Stud Framing

05 41 13.30 Framing, Stud Walls

		Crew	Daily Output	Labor-Hours	Unit	Material	2014 Bare Costs Labor	Equipment	Total	Total Incl O&P
7610	24" O.C.	G 2 Carp	60	.267	L.F.	20	12.25		32.25	42
7760	12 ga. x 4" wide, studs 12" O.C.	G	29	.552		41	25.50		66.50	86.50
7770	16" O.C.	G	40	.400		31.50	18.35		49.85	64.50
7780	24" O.C.	G	55	.291		22	13.35		35.35	46
7790	6" wide, studs 12" O.C.	G	28	.571		51.50	26		77.50	100
7800	16" O.C.	G	39	.410		39.50	18.80		58.30	74.50
7810	24" O.C.	G	54	.296		27.50	13.60		41.10	53
8590	20' high walls, 14 ga. x 6" wide, studs 12" O.C.	G	29	.552		45	25.50		70.50	90.50
8600	16" O.C.	G	42	.381		34.50	17.45		51.95	66.50
8610	24" O.C.	G	57	.281		24	12.85		36.85	47.50
8620	8" wide, studs 12" O.C.	G	28	.571		48.50	26		74.50	96.50
8630	16" O.C.	G	41	.390		37.50	17.90		55.40	70.50
8640	24" O.C.	G	56	.286		26.50	13.10		39.60	50.50
8790	12 ga. x 6" wide, studs 12" O.C.	G	27	.593		64	27		91	115
8800	16" O.C.	G	37	.432		48.50	19.85		68.35	86
8810	24" O.C.	G	51	.314		33.50	14.40		47.90	60.50
8820	8" wide, studs 12" O.C.	G	26	.615		77.50	28		105.50	132
8830	16" O.C.	G	36	.444		59	20.50		79.50	98.50
8840	24" O.C.	G	50	.320		41	14.65		55.65	69
9000	Minimum labor/equipment charge		4	4	Job		183		183	300

05 42 Cold-Formed Metal Joist Framing

05 42 13 – Cold-Formed Metal Floor Joist Framing

05 42 13.05 Bracing

		Crew	Daily Output	Labor-Hours	Unit	Material	2014 Bare Costs Labor	Equipment	Total	Total Incl O&P
0010	**BRACING**, continuous, per row, top & bottom									
0015	Made from recycled materials									
0120	Flat strap, 20 ga. x 2" wide, joists at 12" O.C.	G 1 Carp	4.67	1.713	C.L.F.	55	78.50		133.50	190
0130	16" O.C.	G	5.33	1.501		53.50	69		122.50	172
0140	24" O.C.	G	6.66	1.201		51.50	55		106.50	147
0150	18 ga. x 2" wide, joists at 12" O.C.	G	4	2		74	91.50		165.50	233
0160	16" O.C.	G	4.67	1.713		73	78.50		151.50	209
0170	24" O.C.	G	5.33	1.501		71.50	69		140.50	192

05 42 13.10 Bridging

		Crew	Daily Output	Labor-Hours	Unit	Material	2014 Bare Costs Labor	Equipment	Total	Total Incl O&P
0010	**BRIDGING**, solid between joists w/1-1/4" leg track, per joist bay									
0015	Made from recycled materials									
0230	Joists 12" O.C., 18 ga. track x 6" wide	G 1 Carp	80	.100	Ea.	1.48	4.59		6.07	9.20
0240	8" wide	G	75	.107		1.84	4.89		6.73	10.05
0250	10" wide	G	70	.114		2.29	5.25		7.54	11.10
0260	12" wide	G	65	.123		2.60	5.65		8.25	12.10
0330	16 ga. track x 6" wide	G	70	.114		1.87	5.25		7.12	10.65
0340	8" wide	G	65	.123		2.34	5.65		7.99	11.85
0350	10" wide	G	60	.133		2.91	6.10		9.01	13.25
0360	12" wide	G	55	.145		3.35	6.65		10	14.65
0440	14 ga. track x 8" wide	G	60	.133		2.93	6.10		9.03	13.30
0450	10" wide	G	55	.145		3.64	6.65		10.29	14.95
0460	12" wide	G	50	.160		4.20	7.35		11.55	16.65
0550	12 ga. track x 10" wide	G	45	.178		5.35	8.15		13.50	19.25
0560	12" wide	G	40	.200		5.45	9.15		14.60	21
1230	16" O.C., 18 ga. track x 6" wide	G	80	.100		1.90	4.59		6.49	9.65
1240	8" wide	G	75	.107		2.36	4.89		7.25	10.65
1250	10" wide	G	70	.114		2.94	5.25		8.19	11.85

05 42 13 – Cold-Formed Metal Floor Joist Framing

05 42 13.10 Bridging

			Crew	Daily Output	Labor-Hours	Unit	Material	2014 Bare Costs Labor	Equipment	Total	Total Incl O&P
1260	12" wide	G	1 Carp	65	.123	Ea.	3.33	5.65		8.98	12.90
1330	16 ga. track x 6" wide	G		70	.114		2.39	5.25		7.64	11.25
1340	8" wide	G		65	.123		3	5.65		8.65	12.55
1350	10" wide	G		60	.133		3.73	6.10		9.83	14.15
1360	12" wide	G		55	.145		4.29	6.65		10.94	15.65
1440	14 ga. track x 8" wide	G		60	.133		3.76	6.10		9.86	14.20
1450	10" wide	G		55	.145		4.67	6.65		11.32	16.10
1460	12" wide	G		50	.160		5.40	7.35		12.75	17.95
1550	12 ga. track x 10" wide	G		45	.178		6.85	8.15		15	21
1560	12" wide	G		40	.200		7	9.15		16.15	23
2230	24" O.C., 18 ga. track x 6" wide	G		80	.100		2.75	4.59		7.34	10.55
2240	8" wide	G		75	.107		3.41	4.89		8.30	11.80
2250	10" wide	G		70	.114		4.25	5.25		9.50	13.25
2260	12" wide	G		65	.123		4.82	5.65		10.47	14.55
2330	16 ga. track x 6" wide	G		70	.114		3.46	5.25		8.71	12.40
2340	8" wide	G		65	.123		4.34	5.65		9.99	14.05
2350	10" wide	G		60	.133		5.40	6.10		11.50	16
2360	12" wide	G		55	.145		6.20	6.65		12.85	17.80
2440	14 ga. track x 8" wide	G		60	.133		5.45	6.10		11.55	16.05
2450	10" wide	G		55	.145		6.75	6.65		13.40	18.40
2460	12" wide	G		50	.160		7.80	7.35		15.15	20.50
2550	12 ga. track x 10" wide	G		45	.178		9.90	8.15		18.05	24.50
2560	12" wide	G		40	.200		10.10	9.15		19.25	26

05 42 13.25 Framing, Band Joist

			Crew	Daily Output	Labor-Hours	Unit	Material	2014 Bare Costs Labor	Equipment	Total	Total Incl O&P
0010	**FRAMING, BAND JOIST** (track) fastened to bearing wall										
0015	Made from recycled materials										
0220	18 ga. track x 6" deep	G	2 Carp	1000	.016	L.F.	1.21	.73		1.94	2.54
0230	8" deep	G		920	.017		1.50	.80		2.30	2.96
0240	10" deep	G		860	.019		1.87	.85		2.72	3.46
0320	16 ga. track x 6" deep	G		900	.018		1.52	.82		2.34	3.01
0330	8" deep	G		840	.019		1.91	.87		2.78	3.54
0340	10" deep	G		780	.021		2.37	.94		3.31	4.16
0350	12" deep	G		740	.022		2.73	.99		3.72	4.63
0430	14 ga. track x 8" deep	G		750	.021		2.39	.98		3.37	4.24
0440	10" deep	G		720	.022		2.97	1.02		3.99	4.94
0450	12" deep	G		700	.023		3.42	1.05		4.47	5.50
0540	12 ga. track x 10" deep	G		670	.024		4.35	1.09		5.44	6.60
0550	12" deep	G		650	.025		4.45	1.13		5.58	6.75

05 42 13.30 Framing, Boxed Headers/Beams

			Crew	Daily Output	Labor-Hours	Unit	Material	2014 Bare Costs Labor	Equipment	Total	Total Incl O&P
0010	**FRAMING, BOXED HEADERS/BEAMS**										
0015	Made from recycled materials										
0200	Double, 18 ga. x 6" deep	G	2 Carp	220	.073	L.F.	5.10	3.33		8.43	11.10
0210	8" deep	G		210	.076		5.65	3.49		9.14	11.95
0220	10" deep	G		200	.080		6.90	3.67		10.57	13.65
0230	12" deep	G		190	.084		7.55	3.86		11.41	14.65
0300	16 ga. x 8" deep	G		180	.089		6.50	4.08		10.58	13.85
0310	10" deep	G		170	.094		7.90	4.32		12.22	15.75
0320	12" deep	G		160	.100		8.60	4.59		13.19	17
0400	14 ga. x 10" deep	G		140	.114		9.10	5.25		14.35	18.60
0410	12" deep	G		130	.123		10	5.65		15.65	20
0500	12 ga. x 10" deep	G		110	.145		12	6.65		18.65	24
0510	12" deep	G		100	.160		13.25	7.35		20.60	26.50

05 42 Cold-Formed Metal Joist Framing

05 42 13 – Cold-Formed Metal Floor Joist Framing

05 42 13.30 Framing, Boxed Headers/Beams

			Crew	Daily Output	Labor-Hours	Unit	Material	2014 Bare Costs Labor	Equipment	Total	Total Incl O&P
1210	Triple, 18 ga. x 8" deep	G	2 Carp	170	.094	L.F.	8.20	4.32		12.52	16.10
1220	10" deep	G		165	.097		9.85	4.45		14.30	18.15
1230	12" deep	G		160	.100		10.85	4.59		15.44	19.45
1300	16 ga. x 8" deep	G		145	.110		9.50	5.05		14.55	18.70
1310	10" deep	G		140	.114		11.35	5.25		16.60	21
1320	12" deep	G		135	.119		12.40	5.45		17.85	22.50
1400	14 ga. x 10" deep	G		115	.139		13.15	6.40		19.55	25
1410	12" deep	G		110	.145		14.50	6.65		21.15	27
1500	12 ga. x 10" deep	G		90	.178		17.50	8.15		25.65	32.50
1510	12" deep	G		85	.188		19.40	8.65		28.05	35.50

05 42 13.40 Framing, Joists

			Crew	Daily Output	Labor-Hours	Unit	Material	2014 Bare Costs Labor	Equipment	Total	Total Incl O&P
0010	**FRAMING, JOISTS**, no band joists (track), web stiffeners, headers,										
0020	Beams, bridging or bracing										
0025	Made from recycled materials										
0030	Joists (2" flange) and fasteners, materials only										
0220	18 ga. x 6" deep	G				L.F.	1.58			1.58	1.73
0230	8" deep	G					1.86			1.86	2.04
0240	10" deep	G					2.18			2.18	2.40
0320	16 ga. x 6" deep	G					1.93			1.93	2.13
0330	8" deep	G					2.31			2.31	2.54
0340	10" deep	G					2.70			2.70	2.97
0350	12" deep	G					3.07			3.07	3.37
0430	14 ga. x 8" deep	G					2.90			2.90	3.19
0440	10" deep	G					3.34			3.34	3.67
0450	12" deep	G					3.80			3.80	4.18
0540	12 ga. x 10" deep	G					4.86			4.86	5.35
0550	12" deep	G					5.50			5.50	6.10
1010	Installation of joists to band joists, beams & headers, labor only										
1220	18 ga. x 6" deep		2 Carp	110	.145	Ea.		6.65		6.65	10.95
1230	8" deep			90	.178			8.15		8.15	13.40
1240	10" deep			80	.200			9.15		9.15	15.05
1320	16 ga. x 6" deep			95	.168			7.70		7.70	12.70
1330	8" deep			70	.229			10.50		10.50	17.20
1340	10" deep			60	.267			12.25		12.25	20
1350	12" deep			55	.291			13.35		13.35	22
1430	14 ga. x 8" deep			65	.246			11.30		11.30	18.55
1440	10" deep			45	.356			16.30		16.30	27
1450	12" deep			35	.457			21		21	34.50
1540	12 ga. x 10" deep			40	.400			18.35		18.35	30
1550	12" deep			30	.533			24.50		24.50	40
9000	Minimum labor/equipment charge			4	4	Job		183		183	300

05 42 13.45 Framing, Web Stiffeners

			Crew	Daily Output	Labor-Hours	Unit	Material	2014 Bare Costs Labor	Equipment	Total	Total Incl O&P
0010	**FRAMING, WEB STIFFENERS** at joist bearing, fabricated from										
0020	Stud piece (1-5/8" flange) to stiffen joist (2" flange)										
0025	Made from recycled materials										
2120	For 6" deep joist, with 18 ga. x 2-1/2" stud	G	1 Carp	120	.067	Ea.	.85	3.06		3.91	5.95
2130	3-5/8" stud	G		110	.073		1	3.33		4.33	6.60
2140	4" stud	G		105	.076		1.05	3.49		4.54	6.90
2150	6" stud	G		100	.080		1.32	3.67		4.99	7.50
2160	8" stud	G		95	.084		1.60	3.86		5.46	8.10
2220	8" deep joist, with 2-1/2" stud	G		120	.067		1.14	3.06		4.20	6.25
2230	3-5/8" stud	G		110	.073		1.34	3.33		4.67	6.95

115

05 42 13 – Cold-Formed Metal Floor Joist Framing

05 42 13.45 Framing, Web Stiffeners		Crew	Daily Output	Labor-Hours	Unit	Material	2014 Bare Costs Labor	Equipment	Total	Total Incl O&P
2240	4" stud	G	1 Carp	105	.076	Ea.	1.41	3.49		4.90	7.30
2250	6" stud	G		100	.080		1.77	3.67		5.44	8
2260	8" stud	G		95	.084		2.14	3.86		6	8.70
2320	10" deep joist, with 2-1/2" stud	G		110	.073		1.41	3.33		4.74	7.05
2330	3-5/8" stud	G		100	.080		1.66	3.67		5.33	7.90
2340	4" stud	G		95	.084		1.74	3.86		5.60	8.25
2350	6" stud	G		90	.089		2.19	4.08		6.27	9.10
2360	8" stud	G		85	.094		2.66	4.32		6.98	10
2420	12" deep joist, with 2-1/2" stud	G		110	.073		1.70	3.33		5.03	7.35
2430	3-5/8" stud	G		100	.080		2	3.67		5.67	8.25
2440	4" stud	G		95	.084		2.10	3.86		5.96	8.65
2450	6" stud	G		90	.089		2.64	4.08		6.72	9.60
2460	8" stud	G		85	.094		3.20	4.32		7.52	10.60
3130	For 6" deep joist, with 16 ga. x 3-5/8" stud	G		100	.080		1.25	3.67		4.92	7.45
3140	4" stud	G		95	.084		1.31	3.86		5.17	7.80
3150	6" stud	G		90	.089		1.62	4.08		5.70	8.50
3160	8" stud	G		85	.094		2	4.32		6.32	9.30
3230	8" deep joist, with 3-5/8" stud	G		100	.080		1.68	3.67		5.35	7.90
3240	4" stud	G		95	.084		1.76	3.86		5.62	8.30
3250	6" stud	G		90	.089		2.17	4.08		6.25	9.10
3260	8" stud	G		85	.094		2.68	4.32		7	10.05
3330	10" deep joist, with 3-5/8" stud	G		85	.094		2.08	4.32		6.40	9.40
3340	4" stud	G		80	.100		2.17	4.59		6.76	9.95
3350	6" stud	G		75	.107		2.69	4.89		7.58	11
3360	8" stud	G		70	.114		3.32	5.25		8.57	12.25
3430	12" deep joist, with 3-5/8" stud	G		85	.094		2.50	4.32		6.82	9.85
3440	4" stud	G		80	.100		2.62	4.59		7.21	10.45
3450	6" stud	G		75	.107		3.24	4.89		8.13	11.60
3460	8" stud	G		70	.114		4	5.25		9.25	13
4230	For 8" deep joist, with 14 ga. x 3-5/8" stud	G		90	.089		2.08	4.08		6.16	9
4240	4" stud	G		85	.094		2.20	4.32		6.52	9.50
4250	6" stud	G		80	.100		2.76	4.59		7.35	10.60
4260	8" stud	G		75	.107		2.95	4.89		7.84	11.30
4330	10" deep joist, with 3-5/8" stud	G		75	.107		2.57	4.89		7.46	10.90
4340	4" stud	G		70	.114		2.72	5.25		7.97	11.60
4350	6" stud	G		65	.123		3.42	5.65		9.07	13
4360	8" stud	G		60	.133		3.65	6.10		9.75	14.05
4430	12" deep joist, with 3-5/8" stud	G		75	.107		3.10	4.89		7.99	11.45
4440	4" stud	G		70	.114		3.28	5.25		8.53	12.20
4450	6" stud	G		65	.123		4.12	5.65		9.77	13.80
4460	8" stud	G		60	.133		4.40	6.10		10.50	14.90
5330	For 10" deep joist, with 12 ga. x 3-5/8" stud	G		65	.123		3.72	5.65		9.37	13.35
5340	4" stud	G		60	.133		3.97	6.10		10.07	14.40
5350	6" stud	G		55	.145		5	6.65		11.65	16.45
5360	8" stud	G		50	.160		6.05	7.35		13.40	18.70
5430	12" deep joist, with 3-5/8" stud	G		65	.123		4.48	5.65		10.13	14.20
5440	4" stud	G		60	.133		4.78	6.10		10.88	15.30
5450	6" stud	G		55	.145		6	6.65		12.65	17.55
5460	8" stud	G		50	.160		7.30	7.35		14.65	20

05 42 23 – Cold-Formed Metal Roof Joist Framing

05 42 23.05 Framing, Bracing

0010	FRAMING, BRACING										

05 42 Cold-Formed Metal Joist Framing

05 42 23 – Cold-Formed Metal Roof Joist Framing

05 42 23.05 Framing, Bracing

		Crew	Daily Output	Labor-Hours	Unit	Material	2014 Bare Costs Labor	Equipment	Total	Total Incl O&P
0015	Made from recycled materials									
0020	Continuous bracing, per row									
0100	16 ga. x 1-1/2" channel thru rafters/trusses @ 16" O.C.	G 1 Carp	4.50	1.778	C.L.F.	48	81.50		129.50	187
0120	24" O.C.	G	6	1.333		48	61		109	153
0300	2" x 2" angle x 18 ga., rafters/trusses @ 16" O.C.	G	6	1.333		75	61		136	183
0320	24" O.C.	G	8	1		75	46		121	158
0400	16 ga., rafters/trusses @ 16" O.C.	G	4.50	1.778		94.50	81.50		176	238
0420	24" O.C.	G	6.50	1.231		94.50	56.50		151	197

05 42 23.10 Framing, Bridging

		Crew	Daily Output	Labor-Hours	Unit	Material	2014 Bare Costs Labor	Equipment	Total	Total Incl O&P
0010	**FRAMING, BRIDGING**									
0015	Made from recycled materials									
0020	Solid, between rafters w/1-1/4" leg track, per rafter bay									
1200	Rafters 16" O.C., 18 ga. x 4" deep	G 1 Carp	60	.133	Ea.	1.45	6.10		7.55	11.65
1210	6" deep	G	57	.140		1.90	6.45		8.35	12.70
1220	8" deep	G	55	.145		2.36	6.65		9.01	13.55
1230	10" deep	G	52	.154		2.94	7.05		9.99	14.85
1240	12" deep	G	50	.160		3.33	7.35		10.68	15.70
2200	24" O.C., 18 ga. x 4" deep	G	60	.133		2.10	6.10		8.20	12.35
2210	6" deep	G	57	.140		2.75	6.45		9.20	13.60
2220	8" deep	G	55	.145		3.41	6.65		10.06	14.70
2230	10" deep	G	52	.154		4.25	7.05		11.30	16.25
2240	12" deep	G	50	.160		4.82	7.35		12.17	17.35

05 42 23.50 Framing, Parapets

		Crew	Daily Output	Labor-Hours	Unit	Material	2014 Bare Costs Labor	Equipment	Total	Total Incl O&P
0010	**FRAMING, PARAPETS**									
0015	Made from recycled materials									
0100	3' high installed on 1st story, 18 ga. x 4" wide studs, 12" O.C.	G 2 Carp	100	.160	L.F.	5.30	7.35		12.65	17.90
0110	16" O.C.	G	150	.107		4.52	4.89		9.41	13
0120	24" O.C.	G	200	.080		3.73	3.67		7.40	10.15
0200	6" wide studs, 12" O.C.	G	100	.160		6.80	7.35		14.15	19.50
0210	16" O.C.	G	150	.107		5.80	4.89		10.69	14.40
0220	24" O.C.	G	200	.080		4.80	3.67		8.47	11.35
1100	Installed on 2nd story, 18 ga. x 4" wide studs, 12" O.C.	G	95	.168		5.30	7.70		13	18.55
1110	16" O.C.	G	145	.110		4.52	5.05		9.57	13.25
1120	24" O.C.	G	190	.084		3.73	3.86		7.59	10.45
1200	6" wide studs, 12" O.C.	G	95	.168		6.80	7.70		14.50	20
1210	16" O.C.	G	145	.110		5.80	5.05		10.85	14.65
1220	24" O.C.	G	190	.084		4.80	3.86		8.66	11.65
2100	Installed on gable, 18 ga. x 4" wide studs, 12" O.C.	G	85	.188		5.30	8.65		13.95	20
2110	16" O.C.	G	130	.123		4.52	5.65		10.17	14.20
2120	24" O.C.	G	170	.094		3.73	4.32		8.05	11.20
2200	6" wide studs, 12" O.C.	G	85	.188		6.80	8.65		15.45	21.50
2210	16" O.C.	G	130	.123		5.80	5.65		11.45	15.60
2220	24" O.C.	G	170	.094		4.80	4.32		9.12	12.40

05 42 23.60 Framing, Roof Rafters

		Crew	Daily Output	Labor-Hours	Unit	Material	2014 Bare Costs Labor	Equipment	Total	Total Incl O&P
0010	**FRAMING, ROOF RAFTERS**									
0015	Made from recycled materials									
0100	Boxed ridge beam, double, 18 ga. x 6" deep	G 2 Carp	160	.100	L.F.	5.10	4.59		9.69	13.15
0110	8" deep	G	150	.107		5.65	4.89		10.54	14.25
0120	10" deep	G	140	.114		6.90	5.25		12.15	16.20
0130	12" deep	G	130	.123		7.55	5.65		13.20	17.55
0200	16 ga. x 6" deep	G	150	.107		5.80	4.89		10.69	14.40
0210	8" deep	G	140	.114		6.50	5.25		11.75	15.75

05 42 Cold-Formed Metal Joist Framing

05 42 23 – Cold-Formed Metal Roof Joist Framing

05 42 23.60 Framing, Roof Rafters

		Crew	Daily Output	Labor-Hours	Unit	Material	2014 Bare Costs Labor	Equipment	Total	Total Incl O&P
0220	10" deep	G 2 Carp	130	.123	L.F.	7.90	5.65		13.55	17.90
0230	12" deep	G	120	.133		8.60	6.10		14.70	19.50
1100	Rafters, 2" flange, material only, 18 ga. x 6" deep	G				1.58			1.58	1.73
1110	8" deep	G				1.86			1.86	2.04
1120	10" deep	G				2.18			2.18	2.40
1130	12" deep	G				2.52			2.52	2.77
1200	16 ga. x 6" deep	G				1.93			1.93	2.13
1210	8" deep	G				2.31			2.31	2.54
1220	10" deep	G				2.70			2.70	2.97
1230	12" deep	G				3.07			3.07	3.37
2100	Installation only, ordinary rafter to 4:12 pitch, 18 ga. x 6" deep	2 Carp	35	.457	Ea.		21		21	34.50
2110	8" deep		30	.533			24.50		24.50	40
2120	10" deep		25	.640			29.50		29.50	48
2130	12" deep		20	.800			36.50		36.50	60.50
2200	16 ga. x 6" deep		30	.533			24.50		24.50	40
2210	8" deep		25	.640			29.50		29.50	48
2220	10" deep		20	.800			36.50		36.50	60.50
2230	12" deep		15	1.067			49		49	80.50
8100	Add to labor, ordinary rafters on steep roofs						25%			
8110	Dormers & complex roofs						50%			
8200	Hip & valley rafters to 4:12 pitch						25%			
8210	Steep roofs						50%			
8220	Dormers & complex roofs						75%			
8300	Hip & valley jack rafters to 4:12 pitch						50%			
8310	Steep roofs						75%			
8320	Dormers & complex roofs						100%			
9000	Minimum labor/equipment charge	2 Carp	4	4	Job		183		183	300

05 42 23.70 Framing, Soffits and Canopies

		Crew	Daily Output	Labor-Hours	Unit	Material	2014 Bare Costs Labor	Equipment	Total	Total Incl O&P
0010	**FRAMING, SOFFITS & CANOPIES**									
0015	Made from recycled materials									
0130	Continuous ledger track @ wall, studs @ 16" O.C., 18 ga. x 4" wide	G 2 Carp	535	.030	L.F.	.97	1.37		2.34	3.31
0140	6" wide	G	500	.032		1.27	1.47		2.74	3.80
0150	8" wide	G	465	.034		1.57	1.58		3.15	4.32
0160	10" wide	G	430	.037		1.96	1.71		3.67	4.95
0230	Studs @ 24" O.C., 18 ga. x 4" wide	G	800	.020		.92	.92		1.84	2.53
0240	6" wide	G	750	.021		1.21	.98		2.19	2.94
0250	8" wide	G	700	.023		1.50	1.05		2.55	3.37
0260	10" wide	G	650	.025		1.87	1.13		3	3.92
1000	Horizontal soffit and canopy members, material only									
1030	1-5/8" flange studs, 18 ga. x 4" deep	G			L.F.	1.26			1.26	1.39
1040	6" deep	G				1.58			1.58	1.74
1050	8" deep	G				1.92			1.92	2.11
1140	2" flange joists, 18 ga. x 6" deep	G				1.80			1.80	1.98
1150	8" deep	G				2.12			2.12	2.34
1160	10" deep	G				2.50			2.50	2.75
4030	Installation only, 18 ga., 1-5/8" flange x 4" deep	2 Carp	130	.123	Ea.		5.65		5.65	9.25
4040	6" deep		110	.145			6.65		6.65	10.95
4050	8" deep		90	.178			8.15		8.15	13.40
4140	2" flange, 18 ga. x 6" deep		110	.145			6.65		6.65	10.95
4150	8" deep		90	.178			8.15		8.15	13.40
4160	10" deep		80	.200			9.15		9.15	15.05
6010	Clips to attach facia to rafter tails, 2" x 2" x 18 ga. angle	G 1 Carp	120	.067		.88	3.06		3.94	5.95

118

05 42 Cold-Formed Metal Joist Framing

05 42 23 – Cold-Formed Metal Roof Joist Framing

05 42 23.70 Framing, Soffits and Canopies		Crew	Daily Output	Labor-Hours	Unit	Material	2014 Bare Costs Labor	2014 Bare Costs Equipment	Total	Total Incl O&P
6020	16 ga. angle	G 1 Carp	100	.080	Ea.	1.12	3.67		4.79	7.30
9000	Minimum labor/equipment charge	2 Carp	4	4	Job		183		183	300

05 44 Cold-Formed Metal Trusses

05 44 13 – Cold-Formed Metal Roof Trusses

05 44 13.60 Framing, Roof Trusses

		Crew	Daily Output	Labor-Hours	Unit	Material	2014 Bare Costs Labor	2014 Bare Costs Equipment	Total	Total Incl O&P
0010	**FRAMING, ROOF TRUSSES**									
0015	Made from recycled materials									
0020	Fabrication of trusses on ground, Fink (W) or King Post, to 4:12 pitch									
0120	18 ga. x 4" chords, 16' span	G 2 Carp	12	1.333	Ea.	59	61		120	165
0130	20' span	G	11	1.455		73.50	66.50		140	191
0140	24' span	G	11	1.455		88	66.50		154.50	207
0150	28' span	G	10	1.600		103	73.50		176.50	234
0160	32' span	G	10	1.600		118	73.50		191.50	250
0250	6" chords, 28' span	G	9	1.778		129	81.50		210.50	276
0260	32' span	G	9	1.778		148	81.50		229.50	297
0270	36' span	G	8	2		166	91.50		257.50	335
0280	40' span	G	8	2		185	91.50		276.50	355
1120	5:12 to 8:12 pitch, 18 ga. x 4" chords, 16' span	G	10	1.600		67	73.50		140.50	195
1130	20' span	G	9	1.778		84	81.50		165.50	227
1140	24' span	G	9	1.778		101	81.50		182.50	245
1150	28' span	G	8	2		118	91.50		209.50	280
1160	32' span	G	8	2		134	91.50		225.50	299
1250	6" chords, 28' span	G	7	2.286		148	105		253	335
1260	32' span	G	7	2.286		169	105		274	360
1270	36' span	G	6	2.667		190	122		312	410
1280	40' span	G	6	2.667		211	122		333	435
2120	9:12 to 12:12 pitch, 18 ga. x 4" chords, 16' span	G	8	2		84	91.50		175.50	244
2130	20' span	G	7	2.286		105	105		210	288
2140	24' span	G	7	2.286		126	105		231	310
2150	28' span	G	6	2.667		147	122		269	365
2160	32' span	G	6	2.667		168	122		290	385
2250	6" chords, 28' span	G	5	3.200		185	147		332	445
2260	32' span	G	5	3.200		211	147		358	475
2270	36' span	G	4	4		238	183		421	560
2280	40' span	G	4	4		264	183		447	590
4900	Minimum labor/equipment charge		4	4	Job		183		183	300
5120	Erection only of roof trusses, to 4:12 pitch, 16' span	F-6	48	.833	Ea.		36	13.80	49.80	73.50
5130	20' span		46	.870			37.50	14.40	51.90	77
5140	24' span		44	.909			39	15.05	54.05	80.50
5150	28' span		42	.952			41	15.80	56.80	84.50
5160	32' span		40	1			43	16.60	59.60	88.50
5170	36' span		38	1.053			45.50	17.45	62.95	93
5180	40' span		36	1.111			48	18.40	66.40	98.50
5220	5:12 to 8:12 pitch, 16' span		42	.952			41	15.80	56.80	84.50
5230	20' span		40	1			43	16.60	59.60	88.50
5240	24' span		38	1.053			45.50	17.45	62.95	93
5250	28' span		36	1.111			48	18.40	66.40	98.50
5260	32' span		34	1.176			50.50	19.50	70	104
5270	36' span		32	1.250			54	20.50	74.50	111
5280	40' span		30	1.333			57.50	22	79.50	118

119

05 44 Cold-Formed Metal Trusses

05 44 13 – Cold-Formed Metal Roof Trusses

05 44 13.60 Framing, Roof Trusses		Crew	Daily Output	Labor-Hours	Unit	Material	2014 Bare Costs		Total	Total Incl O&P
							Labor	Equipment		
5320	9:12 to 12:12 pitch, 16' span	F-6	36	1.111	Ea.		48	18.40	66.40	98.50
5330	20' span		34	1.176			50.50	19.50	70	104
5340	24' span		32	1.250			54	20.50	74.50	111
5350	28' span		30	1.333			57.50	22	79.50	118
5360	32' span		28	1.429			61.50	23.50	85	126
5370	36' span		26	1.538			66	25.50	91.50	136
5380	40' span		24	1.667			72	27.50	99.50	148
9000	Minimum labor/equipment charge		2	20	Job		860	330	1,190	1,775

05 51 Metal Stairs

05 51 13 – Metal Pan Stairs

05 51 13.50 Pan Stairs

			Crew	Daily Output	Labor-Hours	Unit	Material	Labor	Equipment	Total	Total Incl O&P
0010	**PAN STAIRS**, shop fabricated, steel stringers										
0015	Made from recycled materials										
0200	Cement fill metal pan, picket rail, 3'-6" wide	G	E-4	35	.914	Riser	500	47	4.06	551.06	640
0300	4'-0" wide	G		30	1.067		560	55	4.74	619.74	720
0350	Wall rail, both sides, 3'-6" wide	G		53	.604		380	31	2.68	413.68	480
1500	Landing, steel pan, conventional	G		160	.200	S.F.	66	10.30	.89	77.19	93

05 51 16 – Metal Floor Plate Stairs

05 51 16.50 Floor Plate Stairs

			Crew	Daily Output	Labor-Hours	Unit	Material	Labor	Equipment	Total	Total Incl O&P
0010	**FLOOR PLATE STAIRS**, shop fabricated, steel stringers										
0015	Made from recycled materials										
0400	Cast iron tread and pipe rail, 3'-6" wide	G	E-4	35	.914	Riser	535	47	4.06	586.06	675
0450	4'-0" wide	G		30	1.067		560	55	4.74	619.74	720
0475	5'-0" wide	G		28	1.143		615	59	5.05	679.05	795
0500	Checkered plate tread, industrial, 3'-6" wide	G		28	1.143		330	59	5.05	394.05	475
0550	Circular, for tanks, 3'-0" wide	G		33	.970		370	50	4.31	424.31	500
0600	For isolated stairs, add							100%			
0800	Custom steel stairs, 3'-6" wide, economy	G	E-4	35	.914		500	47	4.06	551.06	640
0810	Medium priced	G		30	1.067		660	55	4.74	719.74	835
0900	Deluxe	G		20	1.600		825	82.50	7.10	914.60	1,075
1100	For 4' wide stairs, add							5%	5%		
1300	For 5' wide stairs, add							10%	10%		

05 51 19 – Metal Grating Stairs

05 51 19.50 Grating Stairs

			Crew	Daily Output	Labor-Hours	Unit	Material	Labor	Equipment	Total	Total Incl O&P
0010	**GRATING STAIRS**, shop fabricated, steel stringers, safety nosing on treads										
0015	Made from recycled materials										
0020	Grating tread and pipe railing, 3'-6" wide	G	E-4	35	.914	Riser	330	47	4.06	381.06	450
0100	4'-0" wide	G		30	1.067	"	430	55	4.74	489.74	580
9000	Minimum labor/equipment charge			2	16	Job		825	71	896	1,600

05 51 23 – Metal Fire Escapes

05 51 23.25 Fire Escapes

			Crew	Daily Output	Labor-Hours	Unit	Material	Labor	Equipment	Total	Total Incl O&P
0010	**FIRE ESCAPES**, shop fabricated										
0200	2' wide balcony, 1" x 1/4" bars 1-1/2" O.C., with railing	G	2 Sswk	10	1.600	L.F.	58.50	82		140.50	215
0400	1st story cantilevered stair, standard, with railing	G		.50	32	Ea.	2,425	1,625		4,050	5,675
0500	Cable counterweighted, with railing	G		.40	40	"	2,250	2,050		4,300	6,225
0700	36" x 40" platform & fixed stair, with railing	G		.40	40	Flight	1,075	2,050		3,125	4,925
0900	For 3'-6" wide escapes, add to above							100%	150%		

05 51 Metal Stairs

05 51 23 – Metal Fire Escapes

05 51 23.50 Fire Escape Stairs		Crew	Daily Output	Labor-Hours	Unit	Material	2014 Bare Costs Labor	Equipment	Total	Total Incl O&P
0010	**FIRE ESCAPE STAIRS**, portable									
0100	Portable ladder				Ea.	128			128	141

05 51 33 – Metal Ladders

05 51 33.13 Vertical Metal Ladders

			Crew	Daily Output	Labor-Hours	Unit	Material	Labor	Equipment	Total	Total Incl O&P
0010	**VERTICAL METAL LADDERS**, shop fabricated										
0015	Made from recycled materials										
0020	Steel, 20" wide, bolted to concrete, with cage	G	E-4	50	.640	V.L.F.	64	33	2.84	99.84	134
0100	Without cage	G		85	.376		37	19.45	1.67	58.12	78
0300	Aluminum, bolted to concrete, with cage	G		50	.640		115	33	2.84	150.84	190
0400	Without cage	G		85	.376		49.50	19.45	1.67	70.62	92
9000	Minimum labor/equipment charge			2	16	Job		825	71	896	1,600

05 51 33.16 Inclined Metal Ladders

			Crew	Daily Output	Labor-Hours	Unit	Material	Labor	Equipment	Total	Total Incl O&P
0010	**INCLINED METAL LADDERS**, shop fabricated										
0015	Made from recycled materials										
3900	Industrial ships ladder, steel, 24" W, grating treads, 2 line pipe rail	G	E-4	30	1.067	Riser	193	55	4.74	252.74	320
4000	Aluminum	G	"	30	1.067	"	270	55	4.74	329.74	405

05 51 33.23 Alternating Tread Ladders

			Crew	Daily Output	Labor-Hours	Unit	Material	Labor	Equipment	Total	Total Incl O&P
0010	**ALTERNATING TREAD LADDERS**, shop fabricated										
0015	Made from recycled materials										
1350	Alternating tread stair, 56/68°, steel, standard paint color	G	2 Sswk	50	.320	V.L.F.	266	16.35		282.35	320
1360	Non-standard paint color	G		50	.320		300	16.35		316.35	360
1370	Galvanized steel	G		50	.320		310	16.35		326.35	370
1380	Stainless steel	G		50	.320		445	16.35		461.35	520
1390	68°, aluminum	G		50	.320		325	16.35		341.35	390

05 52 Metal Railings

05 52 13 – Pipe and Tube Railings

05 52 13.50 Railings, Pipe

			Crew	Daily Output	Labor-Hours	Unit	Material	Labor	Equipment	Total	Total Incl O&P
0010	**RAILINGS, PIPE**, shop fab'd, 3'-6" high, posts @ 5' O.C.										
0015	Made from recycled materials										
0020	Aluminum, 2 rail, satin finish, 1-1/4" diameter	G	E-4	160	.200	L.F.	36	10.30	.89	47.19	59.50
0030	Clear anodized	G		160	.200		44	10.30	.89	55.19	68.50
0040	Dark anodized	G		160	.200		49	10.30	.89	60.19	74
0080	1-1/2" diameter, satin finish	G		160	.200		42.50	10.30	.89	53.69	66.50
0090	Clear anodized	G		160	.200		47.50	10.30	.89	58.69	72
0100	Dark anodized	G		160	.200		52.50	10.30	.89	63.69	77.50
0140	Aluminum, 3 rail, 1-1/4" diam., satin finish	G		137	.234		54.50	12.05	1.04	67.59	82.50
0150	Clear anodized	G		137	.234		67.50	12.05	1.04	80.59	97.50
0160	Dark anodized	G		137	.234		75	12.05	1.04	88.09	106
0200	1-1/2" diameter, satin finish	G		137	.234		64.50	12.05	1.04	77.59	94
0210	Clear anodized	G		137	.234		74	12.05	1.04	87.09	104
0220	Dark anodized	G		137	.234		80.50	12.05	1.04	93.59	112
0500	Steel, 2 rail, on stairs, primed, 1-1/4" diameter	G		160	.200		25	10.30	.89	36.19	47.50
0520	1-1/2" diameter	G		160	.200		27	10.30	.89	38.19	50
0540	Galvanized, 1-1/4" diameter	G		160	.200		34	10.30	.89	45.19	57.50
0560	1-1/2" diameter	G		160	.200		38.50	10.30	.89	49.69	62
0580	Steel, 3 rail, primed, 1-1/4" diameter	G		137	.234		37.50	12.05	1.04	50.59	64
0600	1-1/2" diameter	G		137	.234		39	12.05	1.04	52.09	66
0620	Galvanized, 1-1/4" diameter	G		137	.234		52.50	12.05	1.04	65.59	80.50

05 52 Metal Railings

05 52 13 – Pipe and Tube Railings

05 52 13.50 Railings, Pipe		Crew	Daily Output	Labor-Hours	Unit	Material	2014 Bare Costs Labor	Equipment	Total	Total Incl O&P
0640	1-1/2" diameter	G	E-4	137	.234	L.F.	60.50	12.05	1.04	73.59	89.50
0700	Stainless steel, 2 rail, 1-1/4" diam. #4 finish	G		137	.234		110	12.05	1.04	123.09	144
0720	High polish	G		137	.234		178	12.05	1.04	191.09	219
0740	Mirror polish	G		137	.234		223	12.05	1.04	236.09	268
0760	Stainless steel, 3 rail, 1-1/2" diam., #4 finish	G		120	.267		166	13.75	1.18	180.93	210
0770	High polish	G		120	.267		275	13.75	1.18	289.93	330
0780	Mirror finish	G		120	.267		335	13.75	1.18	349.93	395
0900	Wall rail, alum. pipe, 1-1/4" diam., satin finish	G		213	.150		20	7.75	.67	28.42	37
0905	Clear anodized	G		213	.150		25	7.75	.67	33.42	42.50
0910	Dark anodized	G		213	.150		29.50	7.75	.67	37.92	47.50
0915	1-1/2" diameter, satin finish	G		213	.150		22.50	7.75	.67	30.92	40
0920	Clear anodized	G		213	.150		28	7.75	.67	36.42	46
0925	Dark anodized	G		213	.150		35	7.75	.67	43.42	53.50
0930	Steel pipe, 1-1/4" diameter, primed	G		213	.150		15	7.75	.67	23.42	31.50
0935	Galvanized	G		213	.150		22	7.75	.67	30.42	39
0940	1-1/2" diameter	G		176	.182		15.50	9.40	.81	25.71	35
0945	Galvanized	G		213	.150		22	7.75	.67	30.42	39
0955	Stainless steel pipe, 1-1/2" diam., #4 finish	G		107	.299		88	15.45	1.33	104.78	127
0960	High polish	G		107	.299		179	15.45	1.33	195.78	227
0965	Mirror polish	G		107	.299		212	15.45	1.33	228.78	263
2000	2-line pipe rail (1-1/2" T&B) with 1/2" pickets @ 4-1/2" O.C.,										
2005	attached handrail on brackets										
2010	42" high aluminum, satin finish, straight & level	G	E-4	120	.267	L.F.	198	13.75	1.18	212.93	245
2050	42" high steel, primed, straight & level	G	"	120	.267		127	13.75	1.18	141.93	167
4000	For curved and level rails, add						10%	10%			
4100	For sloped rails for stairs, add						30%	30%			
9000	Minimum labor/equipment charge		1 Sswk	2	4	Job		204		204	375

05 52 16 – Industrial Railings

05 52 16.50 Railings, Industrial		Crew	Daily Output	Labor-Hours	Unit	Material	2014 Bare Costs Labor	Equipment	Total	Total Incl O&P
0010	**RAILINGS, INDUSTRIAL**, shop fab'd, 3'-6" high, posts @ 5' O.C.										
0020	2 rail, 3'-6" high, 1-1/2" pipe	G	E-4	255	.125	L.F.	27	6.50	.56	34.06	42.50
0200	For 4" high kick plate, 10 ga., add	G					5.65			5.65	6.20
0500	For curved level rails, add						10%	10%			
0550	For sloped rails for stairs, add						30%	30%			
9000	Minimum labor/equipment charge		1 Sswk	2	4	Job		204		204	375

05 55 Metal Stair Treads and Nosings

05 55 13 – Metal Stair Treads

05 55 13.50 Stair Treads		Crew	Daily Output	Labor-Hours	Unit	Material	2014 Bare Costs Labor	Equipment	Total	Total Incl O&P
0010	**STAIR TREADS**, stringers and bolts not included										
3000	Diamond plate treads, steel, 1/8" thick										
3005	Open riser, black enamel										
3010	9" deep x 36" long	G	2 Sswk	48	.333	Ea.	91.50	17.05		108.55	132
3020	42" long	G		48	.333		96.50	17.05		113.55	138
3030	48" long	G		48	.333		101	17.05		118.05	143
3040	11" deep x 36" long	G		44	.364		96.50	18.60		115.10	140
3050	42" long	G		44	.364		102	18.60		120.60	146
3060	48" long	G		44	.364		108	18.60		126.60	153
3110	Galvanized, 9" deep x 36" long	G		48	.333		144	17.05		161.05	191
3120	42" long	G		48	.333		154	17.05		171.05	201

05 55 Metal Stair Treads and Nosings

05 55 13 – Metal Stair Treads

05 55 13.50 Stair Treads	Crew	Daily Output	Labor-Hours	Unit	Material	2014 Bare Costs Labor	Equipment	Total	Total Incl O&P
3130	48" long	G	2 Sswk	48	.333	Ea.	163	17.05		180.05	211
3140	11" deep x 36" long	G		44	.364		149	18.60		167.60	198
3150	42" long	G		44	.364		163	18.60		181.60	213
3160	48" long	G		44	.364		169	18.60		187.60	220
3200	Closed riser, black enamel										
3210	12" deep x 36" long	G	2 Sswk	40	.400	Ea.	110	20.50		130.50	159
3220	42" long	G		40	.400		119	20.50		139.50	169
3230	48" long	G		40	.400		126	20.50		146.50	176
3240	Galvanized, 12" deep x 36" long	G		40	.400		173	20.50		193.50	229
3250	42" long	G		40	.400		189	20.50		209.50	246
3260	48" long	G		40	.400		198	20.50		218.50	256
4000	Bar grating treads										
4005	Steel, 1-1/4" x 3/16" bars, anti-skid nosing, black enamel										
4010	8-5/8" deep x 30" long	G	2 Sswk	48	.333	Ea.	54	17.05		71.05	91
4020	36" long	G		48	.333		63.50	17.05		80.55	101
4030	48" long	G		48	.333		97.50	17.05		114.55	139
4040	10-15/16" deep x 36" long	G		44	.364		70	18.60		88.60	111
4050	48" long	G		44	.364		100	18.60		118.60	144
4060	Galvanized, 8-5/8" deep x 30" long	G		48	.333		62	17.05		79.05	100
4070	36" long	G		48	.333		73.50	17.05		90.55	113
4080	48" long	G		48	.333		108	17.05		125.05	151
4090	10-15/16" deep x 36" long	G		44	.364		86.50	18.60		105.10	129
4100	48" long	G		44	.364		112	18.60		130.60	157
4200	Aluminum, 1-1/4" x 3/16" bars, serrated, with nosing										
4210	7-5/8" deep x 18" long	G	2 Sswk	52	.308	Ea.	50	15.70		65.70	84
4220	24" long	G		52	.308		59	15.70		74.70	94
4230	30" long	G		52	.308		68.50	15.70		84.20	104
4240	36" long	G		52	.308		177	15.70		192.70	224
4250	8-13/16" deep x 18" long	G		48	.333		67	17.05		84.05	106
4260	24" long	G		48	.333		99.50	17.05		116.55	141
4270	30" long	G		48	.333		115	17.05		132.05	158
4280	36" long	G		48	.333		194	17.05		211.05	246
4290	10" deep x 18" long	G		44	.364		130	18.60		148.60	177
4300	30" long	G		44	.364		173	18.60		191.60	224
4310	36" long	G		44	.364		210	18.60		228.60	265
5000	Channel grating treads										
5005	Steel, 14 ga., 2-12" thick, galvanized										
5010	9" deep x 36" long	G	2 Sswk	48	.333	Ea.	103	17.05		120.05	145
5020	48" long	G		48	.333	"	139	17.05		156.05	184
9000	Minimum labor/equipment charge			4	4	Job		204		204	375

05 55 19 – Metal Stair Tread Covers

05 55 19.50 Stair Tread Covers for Renovation

		Crew	Daily Output	Labor-Hours	Unit	Material	Labor	Equipment	Total	Total Incl O&P
0010	**STAIR TREAD COVERS FOR RENOVATION**									
0205	Extruded tread cover with nosing, pre-drilled, includes screws									
0210	Aluminum with black abrasive strips, 9" wide x 3' long	1 Carp	24	.333	Ea.	106	15.30		121.30	141
0220	4' long		22	.364		140	16.65		156.65	181
0230	5' long		20	.400		174	18.35		192.35	221
0240	11" wide x 3' long		24	.333		136	15.30		151.30	175
0250	4' long		22	.364		175	16.65		191.65	221
0260	5' long		20	.400		225	18.35		243.35	278
0305	Black abrasive strips with yellow front strips									
0310	Aluminum, 9" wide x 3' long	1 Carp	24	.333	Ea.	114	15.30		129.30	150

05 55 19.50 Stair Tread Covers for Renovation		Crew	Daily Output	Labor-Hours	Unit	Material	2014 Bare Costs Labor	Equipment	Total	Total Incl O&P
0320	4' long	1 Carp	22	.364	Ea.	152	16.65		168.65	195
0330	5' long		20	.400		193	18.35		211.35	242
0340	11" wide x 3' long		24	.333		146	15.30		161.30	185
0350	4' long		22	.364		188	16.65		204.65	235
0360	5' long		20	.400		242	18.35		260.35	297
0405	Black abrasive strips with photoluminescent front strips									
0410	Aluminum, 9" wide x 3' long	1 Carp	24	.333	Ea.	151	15.30		166.30	191
0420	4' long		22	.364		172	16.65		188.65	217
0430	5' long		20	.400		215	18.35		233.35	266
0440	11" wide x 3' long		24	.333		153	15.30		168.30	193
0450	4' long		22	.364		204	16.65		220.65	252
0460	5' long		20	.400		255	18.35		273.35	310
9000	Minimum labor/equipment charge		4	2	Job		91.50		91.50	151

05 56 13.50 Construction Castings			Crew	Daily Output	Labor-Hours	Unit	Material	2014 Bare Costs Labor	Equipment	Total	Total Incl O&P
0010	**CONSTRUCTION CASTINGS**										
0020	Manhole covers and frames, see Section 33 44 13.13										
0100	Column bases, cast iron, 16" x 16", approx. 65 lb.	G	E-4	46	.696	Ea.	153	36	3.09	192.09	237
0200	32" x 32", approx. 256 lb.	G		23	1.391	"	570	72	6.20	648.20	770
0600	Miscellaneous C.I. castings, light sections, less than 150 lb.	G		3200	.010	Lb.	2.38	.52	.04	2.94	3.62
1300	Special low volume items	G		3200	.010	"	4.13	.52	.04	4.69	5.55

05 58 13.05 Column Covers			Crew	Daily Output	Labor-Hours	Unit	Material	2014 Bare Costs Labor	Equipment	Total	Total Incl O&P
0010	**COLUMN COVERS**										
0015	Made from recycled materials										
0020	Excludes structural steel, light ga. metal framing, misc. metals, sealants										
0100	Round covers, 2 halves with 2 vertical joints for backer rod and sealant										
0110	Up to 12' high, no horizontal joints										
0120	12" diameter, 0.125" aluminum, anodized/painted finish	G	2 Sswk	32	.500	V.L.F.	31.50	25.50		57	81.50
0130	Type 304 stainless steel, 16 gauge, #4 brushed finish	G		32	.500		47	25.50		72.50	98.50
0140	Type 316 stainless steel, 16 gauge, #4 brushed finish	G		32	.500		54	25.50		79.50	107
0150	18" diameter, aluminum	G		32	.500		47	25.50		72.50	98.50
0160	Type 304 stainless steel	G		32	.500		70.50	25.50		96	125
0170	Type 316 stainless steel	G		32	.500		81.50	25.50		107	137
0180	24" diameter, aluminum	G		32	.500		62.50	25.50		88	116
0190	Type 304 stainless steel	G		32	.500		94	25.50		119.50	150
0200	Type 316 stainless steel	G		32	.500		108	25.50		133.50	166
0210	30" diameter, aluminum	G		30	.533		78.50	27.50		106	136
0220	Type 304 stainless steel	G		30	.533		117	27.50		144.50	179
0230	Type 316 stainless steel	G		30	.533		135	27.50		162.50	199
0240	36" diameter, aluminum	G		30	.533		94	27.50		121.50	153
0250	Type 304 stainless steel	G		30	.533		141	27.50		168.50	205
0260	Type 316 stainless steel	G		30	.533		163	27.50		190.50	229
0400	Up to 24' high, 2 stacked sections with 1 horizontal joint										
0410	18" diameter, aluminum	G	2 Sswk	28	.571	V.L.F.	49.50	29		78.50	108

05 58 Formed Metal Fabrications

05 58 13 – Column Covers

05 58 13.05 Column Covers		Crew	Daily Output	Labor-Hours	Unit	Material	2014 Bare Costs Labor	Equipment	Total	Total Incl O&P
0450	Type 304 stainless steel	G	2 Sswk	28	.571	V.L.F.	74	29		103	135
0460	Type 316 stainless steel	G		28	.571		85.50	29		114.50	148
0470	24" diameter, aluminum	G		28	.571		66	29		95	126
0480	Type 304 stainless steel	G		28	.571		98.50	29		127.50	162
0490	Type 316 stainless steel	G		28	.571		114	29		143	179
0500	30" diameter, aluminum	G		24	.667		82	34		116	153
0510	Type 304 stainless steel	G		24	.667		123	34		157	198
0520	Type 316 stainless steel	G		24	.667		142	34		176	219
0530	36" diameter, aluminum	G		24	.667		98.50	34		132.50	172
0540	Type 304 stainless steel	G		24	.667		148	34		182	226
0550	Type 316 stainless steel	G		24	.667		171	34		205	251

05 58 23 – Formed Metal Guards

05 58 23.90 Window Guards

		Crew	Daily Output	Labor-Hours	Unit	Material	2014 Bare Costs Labor	Equipment	Total	Total Incl O&P
0010	**WINDOW GUARDS**, shop fabricated										
0015	Expanded metal, steel angle frame, permanent	G	E-4	350	.091	S.F.	23	4.72	.41	28.13	34
0025	Steel bars, 1/2" x 1/2", spaced 5" O.C.	G	"	290	.110	"	15.90	5.70	.49	22.09	28.50
0030	Hinge mounted, add	G				Opng.	46			46	50.50
0040	Removable type, add	G				"	29			29	32
0050	For galvanized guards, add					S.F.	35%				
0070	For pivoted or projected type, add						105%	40%			
0100	Mild steel, stock units, economy	G	E-4	405	.079		6.25	4.08	.35	10.68	14.80
0200	Deluxe	G		405	.079		12.70	4.08	.35	17.13	22
0400	Woven wire, stock units, 3/8" channel frame, 3' x 5' opening	G		40	.800	Opng.	169	41.50	3.55	214.05	265
0500	4' x 6' opening	G		38	.842		270	43.50	3.74	317.24	380
0800	Basket guards for above, add	G					233			233	256
1000	Swinging guards for above, add	G					79.50			79.50	87.50
9000	Minimum labor/equipment charge		1 Sswk	2	4	Job		204		204	375

05 58 25 – Formed Lamp Posts

05 58 25.40 Lamp Posts

		Crew	Daily Output	Labor-Hours	Unit	Material	2014 Bare Costs Labor	Equipment	Total	Total Incl O&P
0010	**LAMP POSTS**										
0020	Aluminum, 7' high, stock units, post only	G	1 Carp	16	.500	Ea.	82	23		105	128
0100	Mild steel, plain	G		16	.500	"	71	23		94	116
9000	Minimum labor/equipment charge			4	2	Job		91.50		91.50	151

05 71 Decorative Metal Stairs

05 71 13 – Fabricated Metal Spiral Stairs

05 71 13.50 Spiral Stairs

		Crew	Daily Output	Labor-Hours	Unit	Material	2014 Bare Costs Labor	Equipment	Total	Total Incl O&P
0010	**SPIRAL STAIRS**										
1805	Shop fabricated, custom ordered										
1810	Aluminum, 5'-0" diameter, plain units	G	E-4	45	.711	Riser	575	36.50	3.16	614.66	705
1820	Fancy units	G		45	.711		1,100	36.50	3.16	1,139.66	1,275
1900	Cast iron, 4'-0" diameter, plain units	G		45	.711		540	36.50	3.16	579.66	665
1920	Fancy Units	G		25	1.280		735	66	5.70	806.70	935
2000	Steel, industrial checkered plate, 4' diameter	G		45	.711		540	36.50	3.16	579.66	665
2200	6' diameter	G		40	.800		650	41.50	3.55	695.05	795
3100	Spiral stair kits, 12 stacking risers to fit exact floor height										
3110	Steel, flat metal treads, primed, 3'-6" diameter	G	2 Carp	1.60	10	Flight	1,275	460		1,735	2,150
3120	4'-0" diameter	G		1.45	11.034		1,450	505		1,955	2,425
3130	4'-6" diameter	G		1.35	11.852		1,600	545		2,145	2,675
3140	5'-0" diameter	G		1.25	12.800		1,750	585		2,335	2,900

05 71 Decorative Metal Stairs

05 71 13 – Fabricated Metal Spiral Stairs

05 71 13.50 Spiral Stairs			Crew	Daily Output	Labor-Hours	Unit	Material	2014 Bare Costs Labor	Equipment	Total	Total Incl O&P
3210	Galvanized, 3'-6" diameter	G	2 Carp	1.60	10	Flight	1,525	460		1,985	2,425
3220	4'-0" diameter	G		1.45	11.034		1,750	505		2,255	2,750
3230	4'-6" diameter	G		1.35	11.852		1,925	545		2,470	3,025
3240	5'-0" diameter	G		1.25	12.800		2,100	585		2,685	3,275
3310	Checkered plate tread, primed, 3'-6" diameter	G		1.45	11.034		1,500	505		2,005	2,475
3320	4'-0" diameter	G		1.35	11.852		1,700	545		2,245	2,775
3330	4'-6" diameter	G		1.25	12.800		1,850	585		2,435	3,025
3340	5'-0" diameter	G		1.15	13.913		2,025	640		2,665	3,275
3410	Galvanized, 3'-6" diameter	G		1.45	11.034		1,800	505		2,305	2,825
3420	4'-0" diameter	G		1.35	11.852		2,050	545		2,595	3,150
3430	4'-6" diameter	G		1.25	12.800		2,225	585		2,810	3,425
3440	5'-0" diameter	G		1.15	13.913		2,425	640		3,065	3,725
3510	Red oak covers on flat metal treads, 3'-6" diameter			1.35	11.852		2,600	545		3,145	3,775
3520	4'-0" diameter			1.25	12.800		2,875	585		3,460	4,150
3530	4'-6" diameter			1.15	13.913		3,100	640		3,740	4,450
3540	5'-0" diameter			1.05	15.238		3,375	700		4,075	4,875

05 73 Decorative Metal Railings

05 73 16 – Wire Rope Decorative Metal Railings

05 73 16.10 Cable Railings

			Crew	Daily Output	Labor-Hours	Unit	Material	2014 Bare Costs Labor	Equipment	Total	Total Incl O&P
0010	**CABLE RAILINGS**, with 316 stainless steel 1 x 19 cable, 3/16" diameter										
0015	Made from recycled materials										
0100	1-3/4" diameter stainless steel posts x 42" high, cables 4" OC	G	2 Sswk	25	.640	L.F.	34	32.50		66.50	97.50

05 73 23 – Ornamental Railings

05 73 23.50 Railings, Ornamental

			Crew	Daily Output	Labor-Hours	Unit	Material	2014 Bare Costs Labor	Equipment	Total	Total Incl O&P
0010	**RAILINGS, ORNAMENTAL**, 3'-6" high, posts @ 6' O.C.										
0020	Bronze or stainless, hand forged, plain	G	2 Sswk	24	.667	L.F.	118	34		152	193
0100	Fancy	G		18	.889		195	45.50		240.50	299
0200	Aluminum, panelized, plain	G		24	.667		12.65	34		46.65	76.50
0300	Fancy	G		18	.889		28.50	45.50		74	115
0400	Wrought iron, hand forged, plain	G		24	.667		79	34		113	150
0500	Fancy	G		18	.889		139	45.50		184.50	237
0550	Steel, panelized, plain	G		24	.667		19.75	34		53.75	84
0560	Fancy	G		18	.889		28	45.50		73.50	114
0600	Composite metal/wood/glass, plain			18	.889		119	45.50		164.50	215
0700	Fancy			12	1.333		238	68		306	385
9000	Minimum labor/equipment charge		1 Sswk	2	4	Job		204		204	375

05 75 Decorative Formed Metal

05 75 13 – Columns

05 75 13.10 Aluminum Columns

			Crew	Daily Output	Labor-Hours	Unit	Material	2014 Bare Costs Labor	Equipment	Total	Total Incl O&P
0010	**ALUMINUM COLUMNS**										
0015	Made from recycled materials										
0020	Aluminum, extruded, stock units, no cap or base, 6" diameter	G	E-4	240	.133	L.F.	10.85	6.90	.59	18.34	25
0100	8" diameter	G	"	170	.188	"	14.25	9.70	.84	24.79	34.50
0460	Caps, ornamental, plain	G				Set	340			340	370
0470	Fancy	G				"	1,675			1,675	1,850
0500	For square columns, add to column prices above					L.F.	50%				

Estimating Tips

06 05 00 Common Work Results for Wood, Plastics, and Composites

- Common to any wood-framed structure are the accessory connector items such as screws, nails, adhesives, hangers, connector plates, straps, angles, and hold-downs. For typical wood-framed buildings, such as residential projects, the aggregate total for these items can be significant, especially in areas where seismic loading is a concern. For floor and wall framing, the material cost is based on 10 to 25 lbs. per MBF. Hold-downs, hangers, and other connectors should be taken off by the piece.

  Included with material costs are fasteners for a normal installation. RSMeans engineers use manufacturer's recommendations, written specifications, and/or standard construction practice for size and spacing of fasteners. Prices for various fasteners are shown for informational purposes only. Adjustments should be made if unusual fastening conditions exist.

06 10 00 Carpentry

- Lumber is a traded commodity and therefore sensitive to supply and demand in the marketplace. Even in "budgetary" estimating of wood-framed projects, it is advisable to call local suppliers for the latest market pricing.

- Common quantity units for wood-framed projects are "thousand board feet" (MBF). A board foot is a volume of wood, 1" x 1' x 1', or 144 cubic inches. Board-foot quantities are generally calculated using nominal material dimensions—dressed sizes are ignored. Board foot per lineal foot of any stick of lumber can be calculated by dividing the nominal cross-sectional area by 12. As an example, 2,000 lineal feet of 2 x 12 equates to 4 MBF by dividing the nominal area, 2 x 12, by 12, which equals 2, and multiplying by 2,000 to give 4,000 board feet. This simple rule applies to all nominal dimensioned lumber.

- Waste is an issue of concern at the quantity takeoff for any area of construction. Framing lumber is sold in even foot lengths, i.e., 10', 12', 14', 16', and depending on spans, wall heights, and the grade of lumber, waste is inevitable. A rule of thumb for lumber waste is 5%–10% depending on material quality and the complexity of the framing.

- Wood in various forms and shapes is used in many projects, even where the main structural framing is steel, concrete, or masonry. Plywood as a back-up partition material and 2x boards used as blocking and cant strips around roof edges are two common examples. The estimator should ensure that the costs of all wood materials are included in the final estimate.

06 20 00 Finish Carpentry

- It is necessary to consider the grade of workmanship when estimating labor costs for erecting millwork and interior finish. In practice, there are three grades: premium, custom, and economy. The RSMeans daily output for base and case moldings is in the range of 200 to 250 L.F. per carpenter per day. This is appropriate for most average custom-grade projects. For premium projects, an adjustment to productivity of 25%–50% should be made, depending on the complexity of the job.

Reference Numbers

Reference numbers are shown in shaded boxes at the beginning of some major classifications. These numbers refer to related items in the Reference Section. The reference information may be an estimating procedure, an alternate pricing method, or technical information.

Note: Not all subdivisions listed here necessarily appear in this publication.

06 05 05.10 Selective Demolition Wood Framing		Crew	Daily Output	Labor-Hours	Unit	Material	2014 Bare Costs Labor	Equipment	Total	Total Incl O&P
0010	**SELECTIVE DEMOLITION WOOD FRAMING**	R024119-10								
0100	Timber connector, nailed, small	1 Clab	96	.083	Ea.		3.05		3.05	5
0110	Medium		60	.133			4.89		4.89	8.05
0120	Large		48	.167			6.10		6.10	10.05
0130	Bolted, small		48	.167			6.10		6.10	10.05
0140	Medium		32	.250			9.15		9.15	15.05
0150	Large		24	.333			12.20		12.20	20
2958	Beams, 2" x 6"	2 Clab	1100	.015	L.F.		.53		.53	.88
2960	2" x 8"		825	.019			.71		.71	1.17
2965	2" x 10"		665	.024			.88		.88	1.45
2970	2" x 12"		550	.029			1.07		1.07	1.75
2972	2" x 14"		470	.034			1.25		1.25	2.05
2975	4" x 8"	B-1	413	.058			2.17		2.17	3.56
2980	4" x 10"		330	.073			2.71		2.71	4.46
2985	4" x 12"		275	.087			3.26		3.26	5.35
3000	6" x 8"		275	.087			3.26		3.26	5.35
3040	6" x 10"		220	.109			4.07		4.07	6.70
3080	6" x 12"		185	.130			4.84		4.84	7.95
3120	8" x 12"		140	.171			6.40		6.40	10.50
3160	10" x 12"		110	.218			8.15		8.15	13.35
3162	Alternate pricing method		1.10	21.818	M.B.F.		815		815	1,325
3170	Blocking, in 16" OC wall framing, 2" x 4"	1 Clab	600	.013	L.F.		.49		.49	.80
3172	2" x 6"		400	.020			.73		.73	1.20
3174	In 24" OC wall framing, 2" x 4"		600	.013			.49		.49	.80
3176	2" x 6"		400	.020			.73		.73	1.20
3178	Alt method, wood blocking removal from wood framing		.40	20	M.B.F.		735		735	1,200
3179	Wood blocking removal from steel framing		.36	22.222	"		815		815	1,350
3180	Bracing, let in, 1" x 3", studs 16" OC		1050	.008	L.F.		.28		.28	.46
3181	Studs 24" OC		1080	.007			.27		.27	.45
3182	1" x 4", studs 16" OC		1050	.008			.28		.28	.46
3183	Studs 24" OC		1080	.007			.27		.27	.45
3184	1" x 6", studs 16" OC		1050	.008			.28		.28	.46
3185	Studs 24" OC		1080	.007			.27		.27	.45
3186	2" x 3", studs 16" OC		800	.010			.37		.37	.60
3187	Studs 24" OC		830	.010			.35		.35	.58
3188	2" x 4", studs 16" OC		800	.010			.37		.37	.60
3189	Studs 24" OC		830	.010			.35		.35	.58
3190	2" x 6", studs 16" OC		800	.010			.37		.37	.60
3191	Studs 24" OC		830	.010			.35		.35	.58
3192	2" x 8", studs 16" OC		800	.010			.37		.37	.60
3193	Studs 24" OC		830	.010			.35		.35	.58
3194	"T" shaped metal bracing, studs at 16" OC		1060	.008			.28		.28	.45
3195	Studs at 24" OC		1200	.007			.24		.24	.40
3196	Metal straps, studs at 16" OC		1200	.007			.24		.24	.40
3197	Studs at 24" OC		1240	.006			.24		.24	.39
3200	Columns, round, 8' to 14' tall		40	.200	Ea.		7.35		7.35	12.05
3202	Dimensional lumber sizes	2 Clab	1.10	14.545	M.B.F.		535		535	875
3250	Blocking, between joists	1 Clab	320	.025	Ea.		.92		.92	1.51
3252	Bridging, metal strap, between joists		320	.025	Pr.		.92		.92	1.51
3254	Wood, between joists		320	.025	"		.92		.92	1.51
3260	Door buck, studs, header & access., 8' high 2" x 4" wall, 3' wide		32	.250	Ea.		9.15		9.15	15.05
3261	4' wide		32	.250			9.15		9.15	15.05
3262	5' wide		32	.250			9.15		9.15	15.05

06 05 Common Work Results for Wood, Plastics, and Composites

06 05 05 – Selective Wood and Plastics Demolition

06 05 05.10 Selective Demolition Wood Framing		Crew	Daily Output	Labor-Hours	Unit	Material	2014 Bare Costs Labor	Equipment	Total	Total Incl O&P
3263	6' wide	1 Clab	32	.250	Ea.		9.15		9.15	15.05
3264	8' wide		30	.267			9.75		9.75	16.05
3265	10' wide		30	.267			9.75		9.75	16.05
3266	12' wide		30	.267			9.75		9.75	16.05
3267	2" x 6" wall, 3' wide		32	.250			9.15		9.15	15.05
3268	4' wide		32	.250			9.15		9.15	15.05
3269	5' wide		32	.250			9.15		9.15	15.05
3270	6' wide		32	.250			9.15		9.15	15.05
3271	8' wide		30	.267			9.75		9.75	16.05
3272	10' wide		30	.267			9.75		9.75	16.05
3273	12' wide		30	.267			9.75		9.75	16.05
3274	Window buck, studs, header & access, 8' high 2" x 4" wall, 2' wide		24	.333			12.20		12.20	20
3275	3' wide		24	.333			12.20		12.20	20
3276	4' wide		24	.333			12.20		12.20	20
3277	5' wide		24	.333			12.20		12.20	20
3278	6' wide		24	.333			12.20		12.20	20
3279	7' wide		24	.333			12.20		12.20	20
3280	8' wide		22	.364			13.35		13.35	22
3281	10' wide		22	.364			13.35		13.35	22
3282	12' wide		22	.364			13.35		13.35	22
3283	2" x 6" wall, 2' wide		24	.333			12.20		12.20	20
3284	3' wide		24	.333			12.20		12.20	20
3285	4' wide		24	.333			12.20		12.20	20
3286	5' wide		24	.333			12.20		12.20	20
3287	6' wide		24	.333			12.20		12.20	20
3288	7' wide		24	.333			12.20		12.20	20
3289	8' wide		22	.364			13.35		13.35	22
3290	10' wide		22	.364			13.35		13.35	22
3291	12' wide		22	.364	▼		13.35		13.35	22
3360	Deck or porch decking		825	.010	L.F.		.36		.36	.58
3400	Fascia boards, 1" x 6"		500	.016			.59		.59	.96
3440	1" x 8"		450	.018			.65		.65	1.07
3480	1" x 10"		400	.020			.73		.73	1.20
3490	2" x 6"		450	.018			.65		.65	1.07
3500	2" x 8"		400	.020			.73		.73	1.20
3510	2" x 10"		350	.023	▼		.84		.84	1.38
3610	Furring, on wood walls or ceiling		4000	.002	S.F.		.07		.07	.12
3620	On masonry or concrete walls or ceiling		1200	.007	"		.24		.24	.40
3800	Headers over openings, 2 @ 2" x 6"		110	.073	L.F.		2.67		2.67	4.38
3840	2 @ 2" x 8"		100	.080			2.93		2.93	4.82
3880	2 @ 2" x 10"		90	.089	▼		3.26		3.26	5.35
3885	Alternate pricing method		.26	30.651	M.B.F.		1,125		1,125	1,850
3920	Joists, 1" x 4"		1250	.006	L.F.		.23		.23	.39
3930	1" x 6"		1135	.007			.26		.26	.42
3940	1" x 8"		1000	.008			.29		.29	.48
3950	1" x 10"		895	.009			.33		.33	.54
3960	1" x 12"	▼	765	.010			.38		.38	.63
4200	2" x 4"	2 Clab	1000	.016			.59		.59	.96
4230	2" x 6"		970	.016			.60		.60	.99
4240	2" x 8"		940	.017			.62		.62	1.02
4250	2" x 10"		910	.018			.64		.64	1.06
4280	2" x 12"		880	.018			.67		.67	1.09
4281	2" x 14"	▼	850	.019	▼		.69		.69	1.13

129

06 05 05 – Selective Wood and Plastics Demolition

06 05 05.10 Selective Demolition Wood Framing	Crew	Daily Output	Labor-Hours	Unit	Material	2014 Bare Costs Labor	Equipment	Total	Total Incl O&P
4282 Composite joists, 9-1/2"	2 Clab	960	.017	L.F.		.61		.61	1
4283 11-7/8"		930	.017			.63		.63	1.04
4284 14"		897	.018			.65		.65	1.07
4285 16"		865	.019			.68		.68	1.11
4290 Wood joists, alternate pricing method		1.50	10.667	M.B.F.		390		390	640
4500 Open web joist, 12" deep		500	.032	L.F.		1.17		1.17	1.93
4505 14" deep		475	.034			1.23		1.23	2.03
4510 16" deep		450	.036			1.30		1.30	2.14
4520 18" deep		425	.038			1.38		1.38	2.27
4530 24" deep		400	.040			1.47		1.47	2.41
4550 Ledger strips, 1" x 2"	1 Clab	1200	.007			.24		.24	.40
4560 1" x 3"		1200	.007			.24		.24	.40
4570 1" x 4"		1200	.007			.24		.24	.40
4580 2" x 2"		1100	.007			.27		.27	.44
4590 2" x 4"		1000	.008			.29		.29	.48
4600 2" x 6"		1000	.008			.29		.29	.48
4601 2" x 8" or 2" x 10"		800	.010			.37		.37	.60
4602 4" x 6"		600	.013			.49		.49	.80
4604 4" x 8"		450	.018			.65		.65	1.07
5400 Posts, 4" x 4"	2 Clab	800	.020			.73		.73	1.20
5405 4" x 6"		550	.029			1.07		1.07	1.75
5410 4" x 8"		440	.036			1.33		1.33	2.19
5425 4" x 10"		390	.041			1.50		1.50	2.47
5430 4" x 12"		350	.046			1.68		1.68	2.75
5440 6" x 6"		400	.040			1.47		1.47	2.41
5445 6" x 8"		350	.046			1.68		1.68	2.75
5450 6" x 10"		320	.050			1.83		1.83	3.01
5455 6" x 12"		290	.055			2.02		2.02	3.32
5480 8" x 8"		300	.053			1.95		1.95	3.21
5500 10" x 10"		240	.067			2.44		2.44	4.01
5660 Tongue and groove floor planks		2	8	M.B.F.		293		293	480
5682 Rafters, ordinary, 16" OC, 2" x 4"		880	.018	S.F.		.67		.67	1.09
5683 2" x 6"		840	.019			.70		.70	1.15
5684 2" x 8"		820	.020			.72		.72	1.17
5685 2" x 10"		820	.020			.72		.72	1.17
5686 2" x 12"		810	.020			.72		.72	1.19
5687 24" OC, 2" x 4"		1170	.014			.50		.50	.82
5688 2" x 6"		1117	.014			.52		.52	.86
5689 2" x 8"		1091	.015			.54		.54	.88
5690 2" x 10"		1091	.015			.54		.54	.88
5691 2" x 12"		1077	.015			.54		.54	.89
5795 Rafters, ordinary, 2" x 4" (alternate method)		862	.019	L.F.		.68		.68	1.12
5800 2" x 6" (alternate method)		850	.019			.69		.69	1.13
5840 2" x 8" (alternate method)		837	.019			.70		.70	1.15
5855 2" x 10" (alternate method)		825	.019			.71		.71	1.17
5865 2" x 12" (alternate method)		812	.020			.72		.72	1.19
5870 Sill plate, 2" x 4"	1 Clab	1170	.007			.25		.25	.41
5871 2" x 6"		780	.010			.38		.38	.62
5872 2" x 8"		586	.014			.50		.50	.82
5873 Alternate pricing method		.78	10.256	M.B.F.		375		375	615
5885 Ridge board, 1" x 4"	2 Clab	900	.018	L.F.		.65		.65	1.07
5886 1" x 6"		875	.018			.67		.67	1.10
5887 1" x 8"		850	.019			.69		.69	1.13

06 05 Common Work Results for Wood, Plastics, and Composites

06 05 05 – Selective Wood and Plastics Demolition

06 05 05.10 Selective Demolition Wood Framing		Crew	Daily Output	Labor-Hours	Unit	Material	2014 Bare Costs Labor	Equipment	Total	Total Incl O&P
5888	1" x 10"	2 Clab	825	.019	L.F.		.71		.71	1.17
5889	1" x 12"		800	.020			.73		.73	1.20
5890	2" x 4"		900	.018			.65		.65	1.07
5892	2" x 6"		875	.018			.67		.67	1.10
5894	2" x 8"		850	.019			.69		.69	1.13
5896	2" x 10"		825	.019			.71		.71	1.17
5898	2" x 12"		800	.020			.73		.73	1.20
5900	Hip & valley rafters, 2" x 6"		500	.032			1.17		1.17	1.93
5940	2" x 8"		420	.038			1.40		1.40	2.29
6050	Rafter tie, 1" x 4"		1250	.013			.47		.47	.77
6052	1" x 6"		1135	.014			.52		.52	.85
6054	2" x 4"		1000	.016			.59		.59	.96
6056	2" x 6"		970	.016			.60		.60	.99
6070	Sleepers, on concrete, 1" x 2"	1 Clab	4700	.002			.06		.06	.10
6075	1" x 3"		4000	.002			.07		.07	.12
6080	2" x 4"		3000	.003			.10		.10	.16
6085	2" x 6"		2600	.003			.11		.11	.19
6086	Sheathing from roof, 5/16"	2 Clab	1600	.010	S.F.		.37		.37	.60
6088	3/8"		1525	.010			.38		.38	.63
6090	1/2"		1400	.011			.42		.42	.69
6092	5/8"		1300	.012			.45		.45	.74
6094	3/4"		1200	.013			.49		.49	.80
6096	Board sheathing from roof		1400	.011			.42		.42	.69
6100	Sheathing, from walls, 1/4"		1200	.013			.49		.49	.80
6110	5/16"		1175	.014			.50		.50	.82
6120	3/8"		1150	.014			.51		.51	.84
6130	1/2"		1125	.014			.52		.52	.86
6140	5/8"		1100	.015			.53		.53	.88
6150	3/4"		1075	.015			.55		.55	.90
6152	Board sheathing from walls		1500	.011			.39		.39	.64
6158	Subfloor, with boards		1050	.015			.56		.56	.92
6160	Plywood, 1/2" thick		768	.021			.76		.76	1.25
6162	5/8" thick		760	.021			.77		.77	1.27
6164	3/4" thick		750	.021			.78		.78	1.28
6165	1-1/8" thick		720	.022			.81		.81	1.34
6166	Underlayment, particle board, 3/8" thick	1 Clab	780	.010			.38		.38	.62
6168	1/2" thick		768	.010			.38		.38	.63
6170	5/8" thick		760	.011			.39		.39	.63
6172	3/4" thick		750	.011			.39		.39	.64
6200	Stairs and stringers, minimum	2 Clab	40	.400	Riser		14.65		14.65	24
6240	Maximum	"	26	.615	"		22.50		22.50	37
6300	Components, tread	1 Clab	110	.073	Ea.		2.67		2.67	4.38
6320	Riser		80	.100	"		3.67		3.67	6
6390	Stringer, 2" x 10"		260	.031	L.F.		1.13		1.13	1.85
6400	2" x 12"		260	.031			1.13		1.13	1.85
6410	3" x 10"		250	.032			1.17		1.17	1.93
6420	3" x 12"		250	.032			1.17		1.17	1.93
6590	Wood studs, 2" x 3"	2 Clab	3076	.005			.19		.19	.31
6600	2" x 4"		2000	.008			.29		.29	.48
6640	2" x 6"		1600	.010			.37		.37	.60
6720	Wall framing, including studs, plates and blocking, 2" x 4"	1 Clab	600	.013	S.F.		.49		.49	.80
6740	2" x 6"		480	.017	"		.61		.61	1
6750	Headers, 2" x 4"		1125	.007	L.F.		.26		.26	.43

131

06 05 05.10 Selective Demolition Wood Framing

		Crew	Daily Output	Labor-Hours	Unit	Material	2014 Bare Costs Labor	Equipment	Total	Total Incl O&P
6755	2" x 6"	1 Clab	1125	.007	L.F.		.26		.26	.43
6760	2" x 8"		1050	.008			.28		.28	.46
6765	2" x 10"		1050	.008			.28		.28	.46
6770	2" x 12"		1000	.008			.29		.29	.48
6780	4" x 10"		525	.015			.56		.56	.92
6785	4" x 12"		500	.016			.59		.59	.96
6790	6" x 8"		560	.014			.52		.52	.86
6795	6" x 10"		525	.015			.56		.56	.92
6797	6" x 12"		500	.016			.59		.59	.96
7000	Trusses									
7050	12' span	2 Clab	74	.216	Ea.		7.90		7.90	13
7150	24' span	F-3	66	.606			28.50	10.05	38.55	57
7200	26' span		64	.625			29	10.35	39.35	59
7250	28' span		62	.645			30	10.70	40.70	61
7300	30' span		58	.690			32	11.45	43.45	65
7350	32' span		56	.714			33.50	11.85	45.35	67.50
7400	34' span		54	.741			34.50	12.30	46.80	70
7450	36' span		52	.769			36	12.75	48.75	72.50
8000	Soffit, T & G wood	1 Clab	520	.015	S.F.		.56		.56	.93
8010	Hardboard, vinyl or aluminum	"	640	.013			.46		.46	.75
8030	Plywood	2 Carp	315	.051			2.33		2.33	3.83
9000	Minimum labor/equipment charge	1 Clab	4	2	Job		73.50		73.50	120
9500	See Section 02 41 19.19 for rubbish handling									

06 05 05.20 Selective Demolition Millwork and Trim

		Crew	Daily Output	Labor-Hours	Unit	Material	2014 Bare Costs Labor	Equipment	Total	Total Incl O&P
0010	SELECTIVE DEMOLITION MILLWORK AND TRIM R024119-10									
1000	Cabinets, wood, base cabinets, per L.F.	2 Clab	80	.200	L.F.		7.35		7.35	12.05
1020	Wall cabinets, per L.F.	"	80	.200	"		7.35		7.35	12.05
1060	Remove and reset, base cabinets	2 Carp	18	.889	Ea.		41		41	67
1070	Wall cabinets	"	20	.800	"		36.50		36.50	60.50
1100	Steel, painted, base cabinets	2 Clab	60	.267	L.F.		9.75		9.75	16.05
1120	Wall cabinets		60	.267	"		9.75		9.75	16.05
1200	Casework, large area		320	.050	S.F.		1.83		1.83	3.01
1220	Selective		200	.080	"		2.93		2.93	4.82
1500	Counter top, minimum		200	.080	L.F.		2.93		2.93	4.82
1510	Maximum		120	.133			4.89		4.89	8.05
1550	Remove and reset, minimum	2 Carp	50	.320			14.65		14.65	24
1560	Maximum	"	40	.400			18.35		18.35	30
2000	Paneling, 4' x 8' sheets	2 Clab	2000	.008	S.F.		.29		.29	.48
2100	Boards, 1" x 4"		700	.023			.84		.84	1.38
2120	1" x 6"		750	.021			.78		.78	1.28
2140	1" x 8"		800	.020			.73		.73	1.20
3000	Trim, baseboard, to 6" wide		1200	.013	L.F.		.49		.49	.80
3040	Greater than 6" and up to 12" wide		1000	.016			.59		.59	.96
3080	Remove and reset, minimum	2 Carp	400	.040			1.83		1.83	3.01
3090	Maximum	"	300	.053			2.45		2.45	4.02
3100	Ceiling trim	2 Clab	1000	.016			.59		.59	.96
3120	Chair rail		1200	.013			.49		.49	.80
3140	Railings with balusters		240	.067			2.44		2.44	4.01
3160	Wainscoting		700	.023	S.F.		.84		.84	1.38
9000	Minimum labor/equipment charge	1 Clab	4	2	Job		73.50		73.50	120

06 05 23 – Wood, Plastic, and Composite Fastenings

06 05 23.10 Nails

		Crew	Daily Output	Labor-Hours	Unit	Material	2014 Bare Costs Labor	Equipment	Total	Total Incl O&P
0010	**NAILS**, material only, based upon 50# box purchase									
0020	Copper nails, plain				Lb.	9.65			9.65	10.60
0400	Stainless steel, plain					9.25			9.25	10.15
0500	Box, 3d to 20d, bright					1.28			1.28	1.41
0520	Galvanized					1.76			1.76	1.94
0600	Common, 3d to 60d, plain					1.10			1.10	1.21
0700	Galvanized					1.97			1.97	2.17
0800	Aluminum					5.85			5.85	6.45
1000	Annular or spiral thread, 4d to 60d, plain					2.56			2.56	2.82
1200	Galvanized					3.03			3.03	3.33
1400	Drywall nails, plain					1.37			1.37	1.51
1600	Galvanized					2			2	2.20
1800	Finish nails, 4d to 10d, plain					1.25			1.25	1.38
2000	Galvanized					1.86			1.86	2.05
2100	Aluminum					5.85			5.85	6.45
2300	Flooring nails, hardened steel, 2d to 10d, plain					2.63			2.63	2.89
2400	Galvanized					4.04			4.04	4.44
2500	Gypsum lath nails, 1-1/8", 13 ga. flathead, blued					2			2	2.20
2600	Masonry nails, hardened steel, 3/4" to 3" long, plain					1.71			1.71	1.88
2700	Galvanized					3.79			3.79	4.17
2900	Roofing nails, threaded, galvanized					1.76			1.76	1.94
3100	Aluminum					4.85			4.85	5.35
3300	Compressed lead head, threaded, galvanized					2.49			2.49	2.74
3600	Siding nails, plain shank, galvanized					2.02			2.02	2.22
3800	Aluminum					5.85			5.85	6.45
5000	Add to prices above for cement coating					.11			.11	.12
5200	Zinc or tin plating					.14			.14	.15
5500	Vinyl coated sinkers, 8d to 16d					2.50			2.50	2.75

06 05 23.50 Wood Screws

		Crew	Daily Output	Labor-Hours	Unit	Material	2014 Bare Costs Labor	Equipment	Total	Total Incl O&P
0010	**WOOD SCREWS**									
0020	#8 x 1" long, steel				C	2.70			2.70	2.97
0100	Brass					12.20			12.20	13.40
0200	#8, 2" long, steel					4.16			4.16	4.58
0300	Brass					22			22	24
0400	#10, 1" long, steel					3.30			3.30	3.63
0500	Brass					15.60			15.60	17.15
0600	#10, 2" long, steel					5.30			5.30	5.85
0700	Brass					27			27	29.50
0800	#10, 3" long, steel					8.85			8.85	9.75
1000	#12, 2" long, steel					7.30			7.30	8.05
1100	Brass					34.50			34.50	38
1500	#12, 3" long, steel					11.15			11.15	12.30
2000	#12, 4" long, steel					18.75			18.75	20.50

06 05 23.60 Timber Connectors

		Crew	Daily Output	Labor-Hours	Unit	Material	2014 Bare Costs Labor	Equipment	Total	Total Incl O&P
0010	**TIMBER CONNECTORS**									
0020	Add up cost of each part for total cost of connection									
0100	Connector plates, steel, with bolts, straight	2 Carp	75	.213	Ea.	30.50	9.80		40.30	49.50
0110	Tee, 7 ga.		50	.320		35	14.65		49.65	62.50
0120	T- Strap, 14 ga., 12" x 8" x 2"		50	.320		35	14.65		49.65	62.50
0150	Anchor plates, 7 ga., 9" x 7"		75	.213		30.50	9.80		40.30	49.50
0200	Bolts, machine, sq. hd. with nut & washer, 1/2" diameter, 4" long	1 Carp	140	.057		.75	2.62		3.37	5.15
0300	7-1/2" long		130	.062		1.37	2.82		4.19	6.15

06 05 23 – Wood, Plastic, and Composite Fastenings

06 05 23.60 Timber Connectors		Crew	Daily Output	Labor-Hours	Unit	Material	2014 Bare Costs Labor	Equipment	Total	Total Incl O&P
0500	3/4" diameter, 7-1/2" long	1 Carp	130	.062	Ea.	3.20	2.82		6.02	8.15
0610	Machine bolts, w/nut, washer, 3/4" diam., 15" L, HD's & beam hangers		95	.084	↓	5.95	3.86		9.81	12.90
0800	Drilling bolt holes in timber, 1/2" diameter		450	.018	Inch		.82		.82	1.34
0900	1" diameter		350	.023	"		1.05		1.05	1.72
1100	Framing anchor, angle, 3" x 3" x 1-1/2", 12 ga		175	.046	Ea.	2.61	2.10		4.71	6.30
1150	Framing anchors, 18 ga., 4-1/2" x 2-3/4"		175	.046		2.61	2.10		4.71	6.30
1160	Framing anchors, 18 ga., 4-1/2" x 3"		175	.046		2.61	2.10		4.71	6.30
1170	Clip anchors plates, 18 ga., 12" x 1-1/8"		175	.046		2.61	2.10		4.71	6.30
1250	Holdowns, 3 ga. base, 10 ga. body		8	1		25	46		71	103
1260	Holdowns, 7 ga. 11-1/16" x 3-1/4"		8	1		25	46		71	103
1270	Holdowns, 7 ga. 14-3/8" x 3-1/8"		8	1		25	46		71	103
1275	Holdowns, 12 ga. 8" x 2-1/2"		8	1		25	46		71	103
1300	Joist and beam hangers, 18 ga. galv., for 2" x 4" joist		175	.046		.73	2.10		2.83	4.24
1400	2" x 6" to 2" x 10" joist		165	.048		1.39	2.22		3.61	5.20
1600	16 ga. galv., 3" x 6" to 3" x 10" joist		160	.050		2.96	2.29		5.25	7.05
1700	3" x 10" to 3" x 14" joist		160	.050		4.92	2.29		7.21	9.15
1800	4" x 6" to 4" x 10" joist		155	.052		3.07	2.37		5.44	7.25
1900	4" x 10" to 4" x 14" joist		155	.052		5	2.37		7.37	9.40
2000	Two-2" x 6" to two-2" x 10" joists		150	.053		4.19	2.45		6.64	8.65
2100	Two-2" x 10" to two-2" x 14" joists		150	.053		4.68	2.45		7.13	9.15
2300	3/16" thick, 6" x 8" joist		145	.055		65	2.53		67.53	75.50
2400	6" x 10" joist		140	.057		67.50	2.62		70.12	79
2500	6" x 12" joist		135	.059		70.50	2.72		73.22	82
2700	1/4" thick, 6" x 14" joist		130	.062		73	2.82		75.82	85
2900	Plywood clips, extruded aluminum H clip, for 3/4" panels					.24			.24	.26
3000	Galvanized 18 ga. back-up clip					.18			.18	.20
3200	Post framing, 16 ga. galv. for 4" x 4" base, 2 piece	1 Carp	130	.062		16.40	2.82		19.22	22.50
3300	Cap		130	.062		23	2.82		25.82	29.50
3500	Rafter anchors, 18 ga. galv., 1-1/2" wide, 5-1/4" long		145	.055		.49	2.53		3.02	4.70
3600	10-3/4" long		145	.055		1.46	2.53		3.99	5.75
3800	Shear plates, 2-5/8" diameter		120	.067		2.38	3.06		5.44	7.60
3900	4" diameter		115	.070		5.65	3.19		8.84	11.45
4000	Sill anchors, embedded in concrete or block, 25-1/2" long		115	.070		12.70	3.19		15.89	19.20
4100	Spike grids, 3" x 6"		120	.067		.96	3.06		4.02	6.05
4400	Split rings, 2-1/2" diameter		120	.067		1.96	3.06		5.02	7.15
4500	4" diameter		110	.073		2.97	3.33		6.30	8.75
4550	Tie plate, 20 ga., 7" x 3 1/8"		110	.073		2.97	3.33		6.30	8.75
4560	Tie plate, 20 ga., 5" x 4 1/8"		110	.073		2.97	3.33		6.30	8.75
4575	Twist straps, 18 ga., 12" x 1 1/4"		110	.073		2.97	3.33		6.30	8.75
4580	Twist straps, 18 ga., 16" x 1 1/4"		110	.073		2.97	3.33		6.30	8.75
4600	Strap ties, 20 ga., 2-1/16" wide, 12 13/16" long		180	.044		.94	2.04		2.98	4.38
4700	Strap ties, 16 ga., 1-3/8" wide, 12" long		180	.044		.94	2.04		2.98	4.38
4800	21-5/8" x 1-1/4"		160	.050		2.96	2.29		5.25	7.05
5000	Toothed rings, 2-5/8" or 4" diameter		90	.089	↓	1.78	4.08		5.86	8.65
5200	Truss plates, nailed, 20 ga., up to 32' span	▽	17	.471	Truss	12.90	21.50		34.40	49.50
5400	Washers, 2" x 2" x 1/8"				Ea.	.40			.40	.44
5500	3" x 3" x 3/16"				"	1.06			1.06	1.17
9000	Minimum labor/equipment charge	1 Carp	4	2	Job		91.50		91.50	151

06 05 23.70 Rough Hardware

					Unit	Material				
0010	**ROUGH HARDWARE**, average percent of carpentry material									
0020	Minimum				Job	.50%				
0200	Maximum				↓	1.50%				

06 05 Common Work Results for Wood, Plastics, and Composites

06 05 23 – Wood, Plastic, and Composite Fastenings

06 05 23.70 Rough Hardware

	Crew	Daily Output	Labor-Hours	Unit	Material	2014 Bare Costs Labor	Equipment	Total	Total Incl O&P
0210 In seismic or hurricane areas, up to				Job	10%				

06 05 23.80 Metal Bracing

	Crew	Daily Output	Labor-Hours	Unit	Material	2014 Bare Costs Labor	Equipment	Total	Total Incl O&P
0010 **METAL BRACING**									
0302 Let-in, "T" shaped, 22 ga. galv. steel, studs at 16" O.C.	1 Carp	580	.014	L.F.	.81	.63		1.44	1.93
0402 Studs at 24" O.C.		600	.013		.81	.61		1.42	1.89
0502 16 ga. galv. steel straps, studs at 16" O.C.		600	.013		1.05	.61		1.66	2.16
0602 Studs at 24" O.C.	↓	620	.013	↓	1.05	.59		1.64	2.13

06 11 Wood Framing

06 11 10 – Framing with Dimensional, Engineered or Composite Lumber

06 11 10.01 Forest Stewardship Council Certification

	Crew	Daily Output	Labor-Hours	Unit	Material	2014 Bare Costs Labor	Equipment	Total	Total Incl O&P
0010 **FOREST STEWARDSHIP COUNCIL CERTIFICATION**									
0020 For Forest Stewardship Council (FSC) cert dimension lumber, add [G]					65%				

06 11 10.02 Blocking

	Crew	Daily Output	Labor-Hours	Unit	Material	2014 Bare Costs Labor	Equipment	Total	Total Incl O&P
0010 **BLOCKING**									
2600 Miscellaneous, to wood construction									
2620 2" x 4"	1 Carp	.17	47.059	M.B.F.	570	2,150		2,720	4,175
2625 Pneumatic nailed		.21	38.095		575	1,750		2,325	3,500
2660 2" x 8"		.27	29.630		645	1,350		1,995	2,925
2665 Pneumatic nailed	↓	.33	24.242	↓	650	1,100		1,750	2,550
2720 To steel construction									
2740 2" x 4"	1 Carp	.14	57.143	M.B.F.	570	2,625		3,195	4,925
2780 2" x 8"		.21	38.095	"	645	1,750		2,395	3,575
9000 Minimum labor/equipment charge	↓	4	2	Job		91.50		91.50	151

06 11 10.04 Wood Bracing

	Crew	Daily Output	Labor-Hours	Unit	Material	2014 Bare Costs Labor	Equipment	Total	Total Incl O&P
0010 **WOOD BRACING**									
0012 Let-in, with 1" x 6" boards, studs @ 16" O.C.	1 Carp	150	.053	L.F.	.80	2.45		3.25	4.90
0202 Studs @ 24" O.C.	"	230	.035	"	.80	1.59		2.39	3.50

06 11 10.06 Bridging

	Crew	Daily Output	Labor-Hours	Unit	Material	2014 Bare Costs Labor	Equipment	Total	Total Incl O&P
0010 **BRIDGING**									
0012 Wood, for joists 16" O.C., 1" x 3"	1 Carp	130	.062	Pr.	.62	2.82		3.44	5.30
0017 Pneumatic nailed		170	.047		.68	2.16		2.84	4.30
0102 2" x 3" bridging		130	.062		.64	2.82		3.46	5.35
0107 Pneumatic nailed		170	.047		.66	2.16		2.82	4.28
0302 Steel, galvanized, 18 ga., for 2" x 10" joists at 12" O.C.		130	.062		.90	2.82		3.72	5.65
0352 16" O.C.		135	.059		.93	2.72		3.65	5.50
0402 24" O.C.		140	.057		1.90	2.62		4.52	6.40
0602 For 2" x 14" joists at 16" O.C.		130	.062		1.40	2.82		4.22	6.20
0902 Compression type, 16" O.C., 2" x 8" joists		200	.040		.93	1.83		2.76	4.03
1002 2" x 12" joists	↓	200	.040	↓	.93	1.83		2.76	4.03

06 11 10.10 Beam and Girder Framing

	Crew	Daily Output	Labor-Hours	Unit	Material	2014 Bare Costs Labor	Equipment	Total	Total Incl O&P
0010 **BEAM AND GIRDER FRAMING** R061110-30									
1000 Single, 2" x 6"	2 Carp	700	.023	L.F.	.57	1.05		1.62	2.35
1005 Pneumatic nailed		812	.020		.58	.90		1.48	2.11
1020 2" x 8"		650	.025		.86	1.13		1.99	2.80
1025 Pneumatic nailed		754	.021		.87	.97		1.84	2.55
1040 2" x 10"		600	.027		1.14	1.22		2.36	3.26
1045 Pneumatic nailed		696	.023		1.15	1.05		2.20	2.99
1060 2" x 12"		550	.029		1.54	1.33		2.87	3.89
1065 Pneumatic nailed	↓	638	.025		1.55	1.15		2.70	3.60

06 11 Wood Framing

06 11 10 – Framing with Dimensional, Engineered or Composite Lumber

06 11 10.10 Beam and Girder Framing

		Crew	Daily Output	Labor-Hours	Unit	Material	2014 Bare Costs Labor	Equipment	Total	Total Incl O&P
1080	2" x 14"	2 Carp	500	.032	L.F.	1.80	1.47		3.27	4.39
1085	Pneumatic nailed		580	.028		1.81	1.27		3.08	4.07
1100	3" x 8"		550	.029		2.55	1.33		3.88	4.99
1120	3" x 10"		500	.032		3.21	1.47		4.68	5.95
1140	3" x 12"		450	.036		3.86	1.63		5.49	6.90
1160	3" x 14"		400	.040		4.50	1.83		6.33	7.95
1170	4" x 6"	F-3	1100	.036		2.59	1.70	.60	4.89	6.30
1180	4" x 8"		1000	.040		3.49	1.87	.66	6.02	7.60
1200	4" x 10"		950	.042		4.28	1.97	.70	6.95	8.70
1220	4" x 12"		900	.044		5.15	2.08	.74	7.97	9.85
1240	4" x 14"		850	.047		6.75	2.20	.78	9.73	11.85
1250	6" x 8"		525	.076		6.35	3.56	1.26	11.17	14.20
1260	6" x 10"		500	.080		7.95	3.74	1.33	13.02	16.30
1290	8" x 12"		300	.133		14.10	6.25	2.21	22.56	28
2000	Double, 2" x 6"	2 Carp	625	.026		1.14	1.17		2.31	3.18
2005	Pneumatic nailed		725	.022		1.15	1.01		2.16	2.93
2020	2" x 8"		575	.028		1.72	1.28		3	3.99
2025	Pneumatic nailed		667	.024		1.73	1.10		2.83	3.72
2040	2" x 10"		550	.029		2.27	1.33		3.60	4.69
2045	Pneumatic nailed		638	.025		2.30	1.15		3.45	4.42
2060	2" x 12"		525	.030		3.08	1.40		4.48	5.70
2065	Pneumatic nailed		610	.026		3.11	1.20		4.31	5.40
2080	2" x 14"		475	.034		3.60	1.54		5.14	6.50
2085	Pneumatic nailed		551	.029		3.63	1.33		4.96	6.20
3000	Triple, 2" x 6"		550	.029		1.71	1.33		3.04	4.07
3005	Pneumatic nailed		638	.025		1.73	1.15		2.88	3.79
3020	2" x 8"		525	.030		2.58	1.40		3.98	5.15
3025	Pneumatic nailed		609	.026		2.60	1.20		3.80	4.84
3040	2" x 10"		500	.032		3.41	1.47		4.88	6.15
3045	Pneumatic nailed		580	.028		3.44	1.27		4.71	5.85
3060	2" x 12"		475	.034		4.62	1.54		6.16	7.65
3065	Pneumatic nailed		551	.029		4.66	1.33		5.99	7.35
3080	2" x 14"		450	.036		5.95	1.63		7.58	9.25
3085	Pneumatic nailed		522	.031		5.45	1.41		6.86	8.30
9000	Minimum labor/equipment charge	1 Carp	2	4	Job		183		183	300

06 11 10.12 Ceiling Framing

		Crew	Daily Output	Labor-Hours	Unit	Material	2014 Bare Costs Labor	Equipment	Total	Total Incl O&P
0010	**CEILING FRAMING**									
6000	Suspended, 2" x 3"	2 Carp	1000	.016	L.F.	.37	.73		1.10	1.62
6050	2" x 4"		900	.018		.38	.82		1.20	1.76
6100	2" x 6"		800	.020		.57	.92		1.49	2.14
6150	2" x 8"		650	.025		.86	1.13		1.99	2.80
9000	Minimum labor/equipment charge	1 Carp	4	2	Job		91.50		91.50	151

06 11 10.14 Posts and Columns

		Crew	Daily Output	Labor-Hours	Unit	Material	2014 Bare Costs Labor	Equipment	Total	Total Incl O&P
0010	**POSTS AND COLUMNS**									
0100	4" x 4"	2 Carp	390	.041	L.F.	1.71	1.88		3.59	4.97
0150	4" x 6"		275	.058		2.59	2.67		5.26	7.25
0200	4" x 8"		220	.073		3.49	3.33		6.82	9.35
0250	6" x 6"		215	.074		4.76	3.41		8.17	10.85
0300	6" x 8"		175	.091		6.35	4.19		10.54	13.90
0350	6" x 10"		150	.107		7.95	4.89		12.84	16.80
9000	Minimum labor/equipment charge	1 Carp	2	4	Job		183		183	300

06 11 10 – Framing with Dimensional, Engineered or Composite Lumber

06 11 10.18 Joist Framing		Crew	Daily Output	Labor-Hours	Unit	Material	2014 Bare Costs Labor	Equipment	Total	Total Incl O&P
0010	**JOIST FRAMING** R061110-30									
2000	Joists, 2" x 4"	2 Carp	1250	.013	L.F.	.38	.59		.97	1.38
2005	Pneumatic nailed		1438	.011		.38	.51		.89	1.26
2100	2" x 6"		1250	.013		.57	.59		1.16	1.59
2105	Pneumatic nailed		1438	.011		.58	.51		1.09	1.47
2150	2" x 8"		1100	.015		.86	.67		1.53	2.04
2155	Pneumatic nailed		1265	.013		.87	.58		1.45	1.90
2200	2" x 10"		900	.018		1.14	.82		1.96	2.59
2205	Pneumatic nailed		1035	.015		1.15	.71		1.86	2.42
2250	2" x 12"		875	.018		1.54	.84		2.38	3.08
2255	Pneumatic nailed		1006	.016		1.55	.73		2.28	2.91
2300	2" x 14"		770	.021		1.80	.95		2.75	3.55
2305	Pneumatic nailed		886	.018		1.81	.83		2.64	3.35
2350	3" x 6"		925	.017		1.41	.79		2.20	2.85
2400	3" x 10"		780	.021		3.21	.94		4.15	5.10
2450	3" x 12"		600	.027		3.86	1.22		5.08	6.25
2500	4" x 6"		800	.020		2.59	.92		3.51	4.36
2550	4" x 10"		600	.027		4.28	1.22		5.50	6.70
2600	4" x 12"		450	.036		5.15	1.63		6.78	8.35
2605	Sister joist, 2" x 6"		800	.020		.57	.92		1.49	2.14
2606	Pneumatic nailed		960	.017		.58	.76		1.34	1.89
2610	2" x 8"		640	.025		.86	1.15		2.01	2.82
2611	Pneumatic nailed		768	.021		.87	.96		1.83	2.52
2615	2" x 10"		535	.030		1.14	1.37		2.51	3.50
2616	Pneumatic nailed		642	.025		1.15	1.14		2.29	3.14
2620	2" x 12"		455	.035		1.54	1.61		3.15	4.35
2625	Pneumatic nailed		546	.029		1.55	1.34		2.89	3.92
3000	Composite wood joist 9-1/2" deep		.90	17.778	M.L.F.	1,725	815		2,540	3,250
3010	11-1/2" deep		.88	18.182		1,950	835		2,785	3,525
3020	14" deep		.82	19.512		2,325	895		3,220	4,025
3030	16" deep		.78	20.513		3,425	940		4,365	5,325
4000	Open web joist 12" deep		.88	18.182		3,100	835		3,935	4,775
4002	Per linear foot		880	.018	L.F.	3.10	.83		3.93	4.78
4004	Treated, per linear foot		880	.018	"	3.97	.83		4.80	5.75
4010	14" deep		.82	19.512	M.L.F.	3,275	895		4,170	5,075
4012	Per linear foot		820	.020	L.F.	3.27	.89		4.16	5.05
4014	Treated, per linear foot		820	.020	"	4.28	.89		5.17	6.20
4020	16" deep		.78	20.513	M.L.F.	3,650	940		4,590	5,575
4022	Per linear foot		780	.021	L.F.	3.66	.94		4.60	5.55
4024	Treated, per linear foot		780	.021	"	4.81	.94		5.75	6.85
4030	18" deep		.74	21.622	M.L.F.	4,000	990		4,990	6,025
4032	Per linear foot		740	.022	L.F.	3.99	.99		4.98	6
4034	Treated, per linear foot		740	.022	"	5.30	.99		6.29	7.45
6000	Composite rim joist, 1-1/4" x 9-1/2"		.90	17.778	M.L.F.	1,875	815		2,690	3,400
6010	1-1/4" x 11-1/2"		.88	18.182		2,300	835		3,135	3,900
6020	1-1/4" x 14-1/2"		.82	19.512		2,775	895		3,670	4,525
6030	1-1/4" x 16-1/2"		.78	20.513		3,300	940		4,240	5,175
9000	Minimum labor/equipment charge	1 Carp	4	2	Job		91.50		91.50	151

06 11 10.24 Miscellaneous Framing

		Crew	Daily Output	Labor-Hours	Unit	Material	2014 Bare Costs Labor	Equipment	Total	Total Incl O&P
0010	**MISCELLANEOUS FRAMING**									
2000	Firestops, 2" x 4"	2 Carp	780	.021	L.F.	.38	.94		1.32	1.97
2005	Pneumatic nailed		952	.017		.38	.77		1.15	1.69

06 11 10 – Framing with Dimensional, Engineered or Composite Lumber

06 11 10.24 Miscellaneous Framing

		Crew	Daily Output	Labor-Hours	Unit	Material	2014 Bare Costs Labor	Equipment	Total	Total Incl O&P
2100	2" x 6"	2 Carp	600	.027	L.F.	.57	1.22		1.79	2.64
2105	Pneumatic nailed		732	.022		.58	1		1.58	2.28
5000	Nailers, treated, wood construction, 2" x 4"		800	.020		.49	.92		1.41	2.05
5005	Pneumatic nailed		960	.017		.50	.76		1.26	1.80
5100	2" x 6"		750	.021		.76	.98		1.74	2.44
5105	Pneumatic nailed		900	.018		.77	.82		1.59	2.18
5120	2" x 8"		700	.023		1.01	1.05		2.06	2.83
5125	Pneumatic nailed		840	.019		1.02	.87		1.89	2.56
5200	Steel construction, 2" x 4"		750	.021		.49	.98		1.47	2.15
5220	2" x 6"		700	.023		.76	1.05		1.81	2.56
5240	2" x 8"		650	.025		1.01	1.13		2.14	2.98
7000	Rough bucks, treated, for doors or windows, 2" x 6"		400	.040		.76	1.83		2.59	3.84
7005	Pneumatic nailed		480	.033		.77	1.53		2.30	3.35
7100	2" x 8"		380	.042		1.01	1.93		2.94	4.28
7105	Pneumatic nailed		456	.035		1.02	1.61		2.63	3.76
8000	Stair stringers, 2" x 10"		130	.123		1.14	5.65		6.79	10.50
8100	2" x 12"		130	.123		1.54	5.65		7.19	10.95
8150	3" x 10"		125	.128		3.21	5.85		9.06	13.20
8200	3" x 12"		125	.128		3.86	5.85		9.71	13.90
8870	Laminated structural lumber, 1-1/4" x 11-1/2"		130	.123		2.30	5.65		7.95	11.80
8880	1-1/4" x 14-1/2"		130	.123		2.76	5.65		8.41	12.30
9000	Minimum labor/equipment charge	1 Carp	4	2	Job		91.50		91.50	151

06 11 10.26 Partitions

		Crew	Daily Output	Labor-Hours	Unit	Material	2014 Bare Costs Labor	Equipment	Total	Total Incl O&P
0010	**PARTITIONS**									
0020	Single bottom and double top plate, no waste, std. & better lumber									
0180	2" x 4" studs, 8' high, studs 12" O.C.	2 Carp	80	.200	L.F.	4.17	9.15		13.32	19.65
0185	12" O.C., pneumatic nailed		96	.167		4.22	7.65		11.87	17.20
0200	16" O.C.		100	.160		3.41	7.35		10.76	15.80
0205	16" O.C., pneumatic nailed		120	.133		3.45	6.10		9.55	13.85
0300	24" O.C.		125	.128		2.65	5.85		8.50	12.55
0305	24" O.C., pneumatic nailed		150	.107		2.68	4.89		7.57	11
0380	10' high, studs 12" O.C.		80	.200		4.93	9.15		14.08	20.50
0385	12" O.C., pneumatic nailed		96	.167		4.98	7.65		12.63	18.05
0400	16" O.C.		100	.160		3.98	7.35		11.33	16.45
0405	16" O.C., pneumatic nailed		120	.133		4.03	6.10		10.13	14.50
0500	24" O.C.		125	.128		3.03	5.85		8.88	13
0505	24" O.C., pneumatic nailed		150	.107		3.07	4.89		7.96	11.40
0580	12' high, studs 12" O.C.		65	.246		5.70	11.30		17	25
0585	12" O.C., pneumatic nailed		78	.205		5.75	9.40		15.15	22
0600	16" O.C.		80	.200		4.55	9.15		13.70	20
0605	16" O.C., pneumatic nailed		96	.167		4.60	7.65		12.25	17.60
0700	24" O.C.		100	.160		3.41	7.35		10.76	15.80
0705	24" O.C., pneumatic nailed		120	.133		3.45	6.10		9.55	13.85
0780	2" x 6" studs, 8' high, studs 12" O.C.		70	.229		6.25	10.50		16.75	24
0785	12" O.C., pneumatic nailed		84	.190		6.35	8.75		15.10	21.50
0800	16" O.C.		90	.178		5.10	8.15		13.25	19.05
0805	16" O.C., pneumatic nailed		108	.148		5.20	6.80		12	16.85
0900	24" O.C.		115	.139		3.98	6.40		10.38	14.90
0905	24" O.C., pneumatic nailed		138	.116		4.03	5.30		9.33	13.20
0980	10' high, studs 12" O.C.		70	.229		7.40	10.50		17.90	25.50
0985	12" O.C., pneumatic nailed		84	.190		7.50	8.75		16.25	22.50
1000	16" O.C.		90	.178		5.95	8.15		14.10	19.95

06 11 Wood Framing

06 11 10 – Framing with Dimensional, Engineered or Composite Lumber

06 11 10.26 Partitions

		Crew	Daily Output	Labor-Hours	Unit	Material	2014 Bare Costs Labor	Equipment	Total	Total Incl O&P
1005	16" O.C., pneumatic nailed	2 Carp	108	.148	L.F.	6.05	6.80		12.85	17.80
1100	24" O.C.		115	.139		4.55	6.40		10.95	15.50
1105	24" O.C., pneumatic nailed		138	.116		4.60	5.30		9.90	13.80
1180	12' high, studs 12" O.C.		55	.291		8.55	13.35		21.90	31.50
1185	12" O.C., pneumatic nailed		66	.242		8.65	11.10		19.75	28
1200	16" O.C.		70	.229		6.85	10.50		17.35	24.50
1205	16" O.C., pneumatic nailed		84	.190		6.90	8.75		15.65	22
1300	24" O.C.		90	.178		5.10	8.15		13.25	19.05
1305	24" O.C., pneumatic nailed		108	.148		5.20	6.80		12	16.85
1400	For horizontal blocking, 2" x 4", add		600	.027		.38	1.22		1.60	2.43
1500	2" x 6", add		600	.027		.57	1.22		1.79	2.64
1600	For openings, add	▼	250	.064	▼		2.93		2.93	4.82
1702	Headers for above openings, material only, add				B.F.	.71			.71	.78
9000	Minimum labor/equipment charge	1 Carp	4	2	Job		91.50		91.50	151

06 11 10.28 Porch or Deck Framing

		Crew	Daily Output	Labor-Hours	Unit	Material	2014 Bare Costs Labor	Equipment	Total	Total Incl O&P
0010	**PORCH OR DECK FRAMING**									
0100	Treated lumber, posts or columns, 4" x 4"	2 Carp	390	.041	L.F.	1.22	1.88		3.10	4.43
0110	4" x 6"		275	.058		1.77	2.67		4.44	6.30
0120	4" x 8"		220	.073		3.07	3.33		6.40	8.90
0130	Girder, single, 4" x 4"		675	.024		1.22	1.09		2.31	3.13
0140	4" x 6"		600	.027		1.77	1.22		2.99	3.95
0150	4" x 8"		525	.030		3.07	1.40		4.47	5.70
0160	Double, 2" x 4"		625	.026		1.01	1.17		2.18	3.04
0170	2" x 6"		600	.027		1.56	1.22		2.78	3.73
0180	2" x 8"		575	.028		2.08	1.28		3.36	4.39
0190	2" x 10"		550	.029		2.72	1.33		4.05	5.20
0200	2" x 12"		525	.030		4.07	1.40		5.47	6.80
0210	Triple, 2" x 4"		575	.028		1.51	1.28		2.79	3.76
0220	2" x 6"		550	.029		2.34	1.33		3.67	4.76
0230	2" x 8"		525	.030		3.12	1.40		4.52	5.75
0240	2" x 10"		500	.032		4.08	1.47		5.55	6.90
0250	2" x 12"		475	.034		6.10	1.54		7.64	9.25
0260	Ledger, bolted 4' O.C., 2" x 4"		400	.040		.64	1.83		2.47	3.72
0270	2" x 6"		395	.041		.91	1.86		2.77	4.05
0280	2" x 8"		390	.041		1.16	1.88		3.04	4.36
0290	2" x 10"		385	.042		1.47	1.91		3.38	4.75
0300	2" x 12"		380	.042		2.13	1.93		4.06	5.50
0310	Joists, 2" x 4"		1250	.013		.50	.59		1.09	1.51
0320	2" x 6"		1250	.013		.78	.59		1.37	1.81
0330	2" x 8"		1100	.015		1.04	.67		1.71	2.24
0340	2" x 10"		900	.018		1.36	.82		2.18	2.83
0350	2" x 12"	▼	875	.018		1.63	.84		2.47	3.17
0360	Railings and trim , 1" x 4"	1 Carp	300	.027		.47	1.22		1.69	2.53
0370	2" x 2"		300	.027		.33	1.22		1.55	2.38
0380	2" x 4"		300	.027		.50	1.22		1.72	2.56
0390	2" x 6"		300	.027	▼	.77	1.22		1.99	2.85
0400	Decking, 1" x 4"		275	.029	S.F.	1.95	1.33		3.28	4.34
0410	2" x 4"		300	.027		1.67	1.22		2.89	3.85
0420	2" x 6"		320	.025		1.65	1.15		2.80	3.70
0430	5/4" x 6"	▼	320	.025	▼	2.04	1.15		3.19	4.12
0440	Balusters, square, 2" x 2"	2 Carp	660	.024	L.F.	.34	1.11		1.45	2.20
0450	Turned, 2" x 2"	▼	420	.038		.45	1.75		2.20	3.36

06 11 10 – Framing with Dimensional, Engineered or Composite Lumber

06 11 10.28 Porch or Deck Framing

		Crew	Daily Output	Labor-Hours	Unit	Material	2014 Bare Costs Labor	Equipment	Total	Total Incl O&P
0460	Stair stringer, 2" x 10"	2 Carp	130	.123	L.F.	1.36	5.65		7.01	10.75
0470	2" x 12"		130	.123		1.63	5.65		7.28	11.05
0480	Stair treads, 1" x 4"		140	.114		1.96	5.25		7.21	10.75
0490	2" x 4"		140	.114		.50	5.25		5.75	9.15
0500	2" x 6"		160	.100		.75	4.59		5.34	8.40
0510	5/4" x 6"		160	.100	↓	.95	4.59		5.54	8.60
0520	Turned handrail post, 4" x 4"		64	.250	Ea.	31	11.45		42.45	53
0530	Lattice panel, 4' x 8', 1/2"		1600	.010	S.F.	.80	.46		1.26	1.63
0535	3/4"		1600	.010	"	1.20	.46		1.66	2.07
0540	Cedar, posts or columns, 4" x 4"		390	.041	L.F.	3.80	1.88		5.68	7.25
0550	4" x 6"		275	.058		5.90	2.67		8.57	10.85
0560	4" x 8"		220	.073		10	3.33		13.33	16.50
0800	Decking, 1" x 4"		550	.029		1.81	1.33		3.14	4.18
0810	2" x 4"		600	.027		3.63	1.22		4.85	6
0820	2" x 6"		640	.025		6.60	1.15		7.75	9.15
0830	5/4" x 6"		640	.025		4.45	1.15		5.60	6.75
0840	Railings and trim, 1" x 4"		600	.027		1.81	1.22		3.03	4
0860	2" x 4"		600	.027		3.63	1.22		4.85	6
0870	2" x 6"		600	.027		6.60	1.22		7.82	9.25
0920	Stair treads, 1" x 4"		140	.114		1.81	5.25		7.06	10.60
0930	2" x 4"		140	.114		3.63	5.25		8.88	12.60
0940	2" x 6"		160	.100		6.60	4.59		11.19	14.80
0950	5/4" x 6"		160	.100		4.45	4.59		9.04	12.45
0980	Redwood, posts or columns, 4" x 4"		390	.041		6.45	1.88		8.33	10.15
0990	4" x 6"		275	.058		11.20	2.67		13.87	16.70
1000	4" x 8"	↓	220	.073	↓	20.50	3.33		23.83	28
1240	Redwood decking, 1" x 4"	1 Carp	275	.029	S.F.	3.97	1.33		5.30	6.55
1260	2" x 6"		340	.024		7.50	1.08		8.58	10
1270	5/4" x 6"	↓	320	.025	↓	4.77	1.15		5.92	7.15
1280	Railings and trim, 1" x 4"	2 Carp	600	.027	L.F.	1.17	1.22		2.39	3.30
1310	2" x 6"		600	.027		7.50	1.22		8.72	10.25
1420	Alternative decking, wood/plastic composite, 5/4" x 6" G		640	.025		3.04	1.15		4.19	5.20
1440	1" x 4" square edge fir		550	.029		1.97	1.33		3.30	4.36
1450	1" x 4" tongue and groove fir		450	.036		1.31	1.63		2.94	4.12
1460	1" x 4" mahogany		550	.029		1.81	1.33		3.14	4.18
1462	5/4" x 6" PVC	↓	550	.029	↓	3.62	1.33		4.95	6.15
1465	Framing, porch or deck, alt deck fastening, screws, add	1 Carp	240	.033	S.F.		1.53		1.53	2.51
1470	Accessories, joist hangers, 2" x 4"		160	.050	Ea.	.73	2.29		3.02	4.57
1480	2" x 6" through 2" x 12"	↓	150	.053	↓	1.39	2.45		3.84	5.55
1530	Post footing, incl excav, backfill, tube form & concrete, 4' deep, 8" dia	F-7	12	2.667		11.60	110		121.60	194
1540	10" diameter		11	2.909		16.90	120		136.90	216
1550	12" diameter	↓	10	3.200	↓	22.50	132		154.50	242

06 11 10.30 Roof Framing

		Crew	Daily Output	Labor-Hours	Unit	Material	2014 Bare Costs Labor	Equipment	Total	Total Incl O&P
0010	**ROOF FRAMING** R061110-30									
1900	Rough fascia, 2" x 6"	2 Carp	250	.064	L.F.	.57	2.93		3.50	5.45
2000	2" x 8"		225	.071		.86	3.26		4.12	6.30
2100	2" x 10"		180	.089		1.14	4.08		5.22	7.95
5000	Rafters, to 4 in 12 pitch, 2" x 6", ordinary		1000	.016		.57	.73		1.30	1.84
5060	2" x 8", ordinary		950	.017		.86	.77		1.63	2.21
5120	2" x 10", ordinary		630	.025		1.14	1.16		2.30	3.16
5180	2" x 12", ordinary		575	.028		1.54	1.28		2.82	3.80
5250	Composite rafter, 9-1/2" deep	↓	575	.028	↓	1.72	1.28		3	4

06 11 Wood Framing

06 11 10 – Framing with Dimensional, Engineered or Composite Lumber

06 11 10.30 Roof Framing

	Crew	Daily Output	Labor-Hours	Unit	Material	Labor	Equipment	Total	Total Incl O&P
5260	11-1/2" deep	2 Carp	575	.028	L.F.	1.95	1.28		3.23	4.25
5300	Hip and valley rafters, 2" x 6", ordinary		760	.021		.57	.97		1.54	2.22
5360	2" x 8", ordinary		720	.022		.86	1.02		1.88	2.61
5420	2" x 10", ordinary		570	.028		1.14	1.29		2.43	3.37
5480	2" x 12", ordinary		525	.030		1.54	1.40		2.94	4
5540	Hip and valley jacks, 2" x 6", ordinary		600	.027		.57	1.22		1.79	2.64
5600	2" x 8", ordinary		490	.033		.86	1.50		2.36	3.40
5660	2" x 10", ordinary		450	.036		1.14	1.63		2.77	3.93
5720	2" x 12", ordinary		375	.043		1.54	1.96		3.50	4.92
5761	For slopes steeper than 4 in 12, add						30%			
5780	Rafter tie, 1" x 4", #3	2 Carp	800	.020	L.F.	.47	.92		1.39	2.02
5790	2" x 4", #3		800	.020		.38	.92		1.30	1.93
5800	Ridge board, #2 or better, 1" x 6"		600	.027		.80	1.22		2.02	2.89
5820	1" x 8"		550	.029		1.20	1.33		2.53	3.51
5840	1" x 10"		500	.032		1.55	1.47		3.02	4.12
5860	2" x 6"		500	.032		.57	1.47		2.04	3.04
5880	2" x 8"		450	.036		.86	1.63		2.49	3.62
5900	2" x 10"		400	.040		1.14	1.83		2.97	4.26
5920	Roof cants, split, 4" x 4"		650	.025		1.71	1.13		2.84	3.74
5940	6" x 6"		600	.027		4.76	1.22		5.98	7.25
5960	Roof curbs, untreated, 2" x 6"		520	.031		.57	1.41		1.98	2.95
5980	2" x 12"		400	.040		1.54	1.83		3.37	4.71
6000	Sister rafters, 2" x 6"		800	.020		.57	.92		1.49	2.14
6020	2" x 8"		640	.025		.86	1.15		2.01	2.82
6040	2" x 10"		535	.030		1.14	1.37		2.51	3.50
6060	2" x 12"		455	.035		1.54	1.61		3.15	4.35
9000	Minimum labor/equipment charge	1 Carp	4	2	Job		91.50		91.50	151

06 11 10.32 Sill and Ledger Framing

	Crew	Daily Output	Labor-Hours	Unit	Material	Labor	Equipment	Total	Total Incl O&P
0010	**SILL AND LEDGER FRAMING**									
2002	Ledgers, nailed, 2" x 4"	2 Carp	755	.021	L.F.	.38	.97		1.35	2.02
2052	2" x 6"		600	.027		.57	1.22		1.79	2.64
2102	Bolted, not including bolts, 3" x 6"		325	.049		1.39	2.26		3.65	5.25
2152	3" x 12"		233	.069		3.83	3.15		6.98	9.35
2602	Mud sills, redwood, construction grade, 2" x 4"		895	.018		2.26	.82		3.08	3.84
2622	2" x 6"		780	.021		3.40	.94		4.34	5.30
4002	Sills, 2" x 4"		600	.027		.37	1.22		1.59	2.42
4052	2" x 6"		550	.029		.56	1.33		1.89	2.81
4082	2" x 8"		500	.032		.85	1.47		2.32	3.34
4101	2" x 10"		450	.036		1.12	1.63		2.75	3.91
4121	2" x 12"		400	.040		1.52	1.83		3.35	4.69
4202	Treated, 2" x 4"		550	.029		.48	1.33		1.81	2.72
4222	2" x 6"		500	.032		.75	1.47		2.22	3.24
4242	2" x 8"		450	.036		1	1.63		2.63	3.78
4261	2" x 10"		400	.040		1.31	1.83		3.14	4.45
4281	2" x 12"		350	.046		1.98	2.10		4.08	5.60
4402	4" x 4"		450	.036		1.18	1.63		2.81	3.98
4422	4" x 6"		350	.046		1.71	2.10		3.81	5.30
4462	4" x 8"		300	.053		2.99	2.45		5.44	7.30
4481	4" x 10"		260	.062		4.64	2.82		7.46	9.75
9000	Minimum labor/equipment charge	1 Carp	4	2	Job		91.50		91.50	151

06 11 Wood Framing

06 11 10 – Framing with Dimensional, Engineered or Composite Lumber

06 11 10.34 Sleepers		Crew	Daily Output	Labor-Hours	Unit	Material	2014 Bare Costs Labor	2014 Bare Costs Equipment	Total	Total Incl O&P
0010	**SLEEPERS**									
0100	On concrete, treated, 1" x 2"	2 Carp	2350	.007	L.F.	.27	.31		.58	.81
0150	1" x 3"		2000	.008		.45	.37		.82	1.10
0200	2" x 4"		1500	.011		.53	.49		1.02	1.38
0250	2" x 6"		1300	.012		.84	.56		1.40	1.85
9000	Minimum labor/equipment charge	1 Carp	4	2	Job		91.50		91.50	151

06 11 10.36 Soffit and Canopy Framing		Crew	Daily Output	Labor-Hours	Unit	Material	2014 Bare Costs Labor	2014 Bare Costs Equipment	Total	Total Incl O&P
0010	**SOFFIT AND CANOPY FRAMING**									
1002	Canopy or soffit framing , 1" x 4"	2 Carp	900	.018	L.F.	.47	.82		1.29	1.85
1021	1" x 6"		850	.019		.80	.86		1.66	2.30
1042	1" x 8"		750	.021		1.20	.98		2.18	2.93
1102	2" x 4"		620	.026		.38	1.18		1.56	2.36
1121	2" x 6"		560	.029		.57	1.31		1.88	2.78
1142	2" x 8"		500	.032		.86	1.47		2.33	3.35
1202	3" x 4"		500	.032		1.07	1.47		2.54	3.59
1221	3" x 6"		400	.040		1.41	1.83		3.24	4.56
1242	3" x 10"		300	.053		3.21	2.45		5.66	7.55
9000	Minimum labor/equipment charge	1 Carp	4	2	Job		91.50		91.50	151

06 11 10.38 Treated Lumber Framing Material		Crew	Daily Output	Labor-Hours	Unit	Material	2014 Bare Costs Labor	2014 Bare Costs Equipment	Total	Total Incl O&P
0010	**TREATED LUMBER FRAMING MATERIAL**									
0100	2" x 4"				M.B.F.	725			725	800
0110	2" x 6"					750			750	825
0120	2" x 8"					750			750	825
0130	2" x 10"					785			785	865
0140	2" x 12"					990			990	1,075
0200	4" x 4"					885			885	975
0210	4" x 6"					855			855	940
0220	4" x 8"					1,125			1,125	1,225

06 11 10.40 Wall Framing		Crew	Daily Output	Labor-Hours	Unit	Material	2014 Bare Costs Labor	2014 Bare Costs Equipment	Total	Total Incl O&P
0010	**WALL FRAMING** R061110-30									
0100	Door buck, studs, header, access, 8' H, 2" x 4" wall, 3' W	1 Carp	32	.250	Ea.	15.80	11.45		27.25	36.50
0110	4' wide		32	.250		16.95	11.45		28.40	37.50
0120	5' wide		32	.250		21	11.45		32.45	42
0130	6' wide		32	.250		23	11.45		34.45	44
0140	8' wide		30	.267		30.50	12.25		42.75	54
0150	10' wide		30	.267		43.50	12.25		55.75	68
0160	12' wide		30	.267		56	12.25		68.25	81.50
0170	2" x 6" wall, 3' wide		32	.250		22	11.45		33.45	43
0180	4' wide		32	.250		23	11.45		34.45	44.50
0190	5' wide		32	.250		27	11.45		38.45	49
0200	6' wide		32	.250		29	11.45		40.45	51
0210	8' wide		30	.267		37	12.25		49.25	60.50
0220	10' wide		30	.267		49.50	12.25		61.75	74.50
0230	12' wide		30	.267		62	12.25		74.25	88
0240	Window buck, studs, header & access, 8' high 2" x 4" wall, 2' wide		24	.333		16.85	15.30		32.15	43.50
0250	3' wide		24	.333		19.60	15.30		34.90	46.50
0260	4' wide		24	.333		21.50	15.30		36.80	48.50
0270	5' wide		24	.333		25.50	15.30		40.80	53
0280	6' wide		24	.333		28.50	15.30		43.80	56.50
0290	7' wide		24	.333		35	15.30		50.30	63.50
0300	8' wide		22	.364		38.50	16.65		55.15	70

06 11 Wood Framing

06 11 10 – Framing with Dimensional, Engineered or Composite Lumber

06 11 10.40 Wall Framing	Crew	Daily Output	Labor-Hours	Unit	Material	2014 Bare Costs Labor	Equipment	Total	Total Incl O&P
0310	10' wide	1 Carp	22	.364	Ea.	52.50	16.65		69.15	85.50
0320	12' wide		22	.364		67	16.65		83.65	102
0330	2" x 6" wall, 2' wide		24	.333		24.50	15.30		39.80	52
0340	3' wide		24	.333		27	15.30		42.30	55
0350	4' wide		24	.333		29.50	15.30		44.80	57.50
0360	5' wide		24	.333		34	15.30		49.30	62.50
0370	6' wide		24	.333		37.50	15.30		52.80	66
0380	7' wide		24	.333		45	15.30		60.30	74.50
0390	8' wide		22	.364		49	16.65		65.65	81
0400	10' wide		22	.364		63.50	16.65		80.15	97
0410	12' wide		22	.364		79	16.65		95.65	115
2002	Headers over openings, 2" x 6"	2 Carp	360	.044	L.F.	.57	2.04		2.61	3.98
2007	2" x 6", pneumatic nailed		432	.037		.58	1.70		2.28	3.42
2052	2" x 8"		340	.047		.86	2.16		3.02	4.49
2057	2" x 8", pneumatic nailed		408	.039		.87	1.80		2.67	3.91
2101	2" x 10"		320	.050		1.14	2.29		3.43	5
2106	2" x 10", pneumatic nailed		384	.042		1.15	1.91		3.06	4.40
2152	2" x 12"		300	.053		1.54	2.45		3.99	5.70
2157	2" x 12", pneumatic nailed		360	.044		1.55	2.04		3.59	5.05
2180	4" x 8"		260	.062		3.49	2.82		6.31	8.50
2185	4" x 8", pneumatic nailed		312	.051		3.51	2.35		5.86	7.70
2191	4" x 10"		240	.067		4.28	3.06		7.34	9.70
2196	4" x 10", pneumatic nailed		288	.056		4.30	2.55		6.85	8.90
2202	4" x 12"		190	.084		5.15	3.86		9.01	12
2207	4" x 12", pneumatic nailed		228	.070		5.15	3.22		8.37	11
2241	6" x 10"		165	.097		7.95	4.45		12.40	16.05
2246	6" x 10", pneumatic nailed		198	.081		8	3.71		11.71	14.85
2251	6" x 12"		140	.114		9.55	5.25		14.80	19.10
2256	6" x 12", pneumatic nailed		168	.095		9.55	4.37		13.92	17.75
5002	Plates, untreated, 2" x 3"		850	.019		.37	.86		1.23	1.83
5007	2" x 3", pneumatic nailed		1020	.016		.38	.72		1.10	1.59
5022	2" x 4"		800	.020		.38	.92		1.30	1.93
5027	2" x 4", pneumatic nailed		960	.017		.38	.76		1.14	1.68
5041	2" x 6"		750	.021		.57	.98		1.55	2.24
5046	2" x 6", pneumatic nailed		900	.018		.58	.82		1.40	1.97
5122	Studs, 8' high wall, 2" x 3"		1200	.013		.37	.61		.98	1.41
5127	2" x 3", pneumatic nailed		1440	.011		.38	.51		.89	1.25
5142	2" x 4"		1100	.015		.37	.67		1.04	1.51
5147	2" x 4", pneumatic nailed		1320	.012		.38	.56		.94	1.33
5162	2" x 6"		1000	.016		.57	.73		1.30	1.84
5167	2" x 6", pneumatic nailed		1200	.013		.58	.61		1.19	1.63
5182	3" x 4"		800	.020		1.07	.92		1.99	2.69
5187	3" x 4", pneumatic nailed		960	.017		1.08	.76		1.84	2.44
8200	For 12' high walls, deduct						5%			
8220	For stub wall, 6' high, add						20%			
8240	3' high, add						40%			
8250	For second story & above, add						5%			
8300	For dormer & gable, add						15%			
9000	Minimum labor/equipment charge	1 Carp	4	2	Job		91.50		91.50	151

06 11 Wood Framing

06 11 10 – Framing with Dimensional, Engineered or Composite Lumber

06 11 10.42 Furring

		Crew	Daily Output	Labor-Hours	Unit	Material	2014 Bare Costs Labor	Equipment	Total	Total Incl O&P
0010	**FURRING**									
0012	Wood strips, 1" x 2", on walls, on wood	1 Carp	550	.015	L.F.	.24	.67		.91	1.36
0015	On wood, pneumatic nailed		710	.011		.24	.52		.76	1.11
0300	On masonry		495	.016		.26	.74		1	1.51
0400	On concrete		260	.031		.26	1.41		1.67	2.61
0600	1" x 3", on walls, on wood		550	.015		.38	.67		1.05	1.52
0605	On wood, pneumatic nailed		710	.011		.39	.52		.91	1.27
0700	On masonry		495	.016		.42	.74		1.16	1.68
0800	On concrete		260	.031		.42	1.41		1.83	2.78
0850	On ceilings, on wood		350	.023		.38	1.05		1.43	2.14
0855	On wood, pneumatic nailed		450	.018		.39	.82		1.21	1.76
0900	On masonry		320	.025		.42	1.15		1.57	2.34
0950	On concrete		210	.038		.42	1.75		2.17	3.33
9000	Minimum labor/equipment charge		4	2	Job		91.50		91.50	151

06 11 10.44 Grounds

		Crew	Daily Output	Labor-Hours	Unit	Material	2014 Bare Costs Labor	Equipment	Total	Total Incl O&P
0010	**GROUNDS**									
0020	For casework, 1" x 2" wood strips, on wood	1 Carp	330	.024	L.F.	.24	1.11		1.35	2.09
0100	On masonry		285	.028		.26	1.29		1.55	2.41
0200	On concrete		250	.032		.26	1.47		1.73	2.70
0400	For plaster, 3/4" deep, on wood		450	.018		.24	.82		1.06	1.60
0500	On masonry		225	.036		.26	1.63		1.89	2.97
0600	On concrete		175	.046		.26	2.10		2.36	3.73
0700	On metal lath		200	.040		.26	1.83		2.09	3.30
9000	Minimum labor/equipment charge		4	2	Job		91.50		91.50	151

06 12 Structural Panels

06 12 10 – Structural Insulated Panels

06 12 10.10 OSB Faced Panels

			Crew	Daily Output	Labor-Hours	Unit	Material	2014 Bare Costs Labor	Equipment	Total	Total Incl O&P
0010	**OSB FACED PANELS**										
0100	Structural insul. panels, 7/16" OSB both faces, EPS insul, 3-5/8" T	G	F-3	2075	.019	S.F.	3.06	.90	.32	4.28	5.20
0110	5-5/8" thick	G		1725	.023		3.43	1.08	.38	4.89	5.95
0120	7-3/8" thick	G		1425	.028		3.73	1.31	.47	5.51	6.75
0130	9-3/8" thick	G		1125	.036		4.08	1.66	.59	6.33	7.85
0140	7/16" OSB one face, EPS insul, 3-5/8" thick	G		2175	.018		3.25	.86	.30	4.41	5.30
0150	5-5/8" thick	G		1825	.022		3.72	1.02	.36	5.10	6.15
0160	7-3/8" thick	G		1525	.026		4.15	1.23	.43	5.81	7.05
0170	9-3/8" thick	G		1225	.033		4.62	1.53	.54	6.69	8.20
0190	7/16" OSB - 1/2" GWB faces, EPS insul, 3-5/8" T	G		2075	.019		3.22	.90	.32	4.44	5.35
0200	5-5/8" thick	G		1725	.023		3.69	1.08	.38	5.15	6.25
0210	7-3/8" thick	G		1425	.028		4.11	1.31	.47	5.89	7.15
0220	9-3/8" thick	G		1125	.036		4.82	1.66	.59	7.07	8.65
0240	7/16" OSB - 1/2" MRGWB faces, EPS insul, 3-5/8" T	G		2075	.019		3.22	.90	.32	4.44	5.35
0250	5-5/8" thick	G		1725	.023		3.69	1.08	.38	5.15	6.25
0260	7-3/8" thick	G		1425	.028		4.11	1.31	.47	5.89	7.15
0270	9-3/8" thick	G		1125	.036		4.82	1.66	.59	7.07	8.65
0300	For 1/2" GWB added to OSB skin, add	G					.68			.68	.75
0310	For 1/2" MRGWB added to OSB skin, add	G					.68			.68	.75
0320	For one T1-11 skin, add to OSB-OSB	G					1.55			1.55	1.71
0330	For one 19/32" CDX skin, add to OSB-OSB	G					.79			.79	.87
0500	Structural insulated panel, 7/16" OSB both sides, straw core										

06 12 Structural Panels

06 12 10 – Structural Insulated Panels

06 12 10.10 OSB Faced Panels

		Crew	Daily Output	Labor-Hours	Unit	Material	2014 Bare Costs Labor	Equipment	Total	Total Incl O&P
0510	4-3/8" T, walls (w/sill, splines, plates)	G F-6	2400	.017	S.F.	7.40	.72	.28	8.40	9.55
0520	Floors (w/splines)	G	2400	.017		7.40	.72	.28	8.40	9.55
0530	Roof (w/splines)	G	2400	.017		7.40	.72	.28	8.40	9.55
0550	7-7/8" T, walls (w/sill, splines, plates)	G	2400	.017		11.20	.72	.28	12.20	13.75
0560	Floors (w/splines)	G	2400	.017		11.20	.72	.28	12.20	13.75
0570	Roof (w/splines)	G	2400	.017		11.20	.72	.28	12.20	13.75

06 12 19 – Composite Shearwall Panels

06 12 19.10 Steel and Wood Composite Shearwall Panels

		Crew	Daily Output	Labor-Hours	Unit	Material	Labor	Equipment	Total	Total Incl O&P
0010	**STEEL & WOOD COMPOSITE SHEARWALL PANELS**									
0020	Anchor bolts, 36" long (must be placed in wet concrete)	1 Carp	150	.053	Ea.	35	2.45		37.45	42.50
0030	On concrete, 2 x 4 & 2 x 6 walls, 7' - 10' high, 360 lb. shear, 12" wide	2 Carp	8	2		465	91.50		556.50	660
0040	715 lb. shear, 15" wide		8	2		560	91.50		651.50	765
0050	1860 lb. shear, 18" wide		8	2		580	91.50		671.50	785
0060	2780 lb. shear, 21" wide		8	2		685	91.50		776.50	905
0070	3790 lb. shear, 24" wide		8	2		790	91.50		881.50	1,025
0080	2 x 6 walls, 11' to 13' high, 1180 lb. shear, 18" wide		6	2.667		705	122		827	975
0090	1555 lb. shear, 21" wide		6	2.667		890	122		1,012	1,175
0100	2280 lb. shear, 24" wide		6	2.667		995	122		1,117	1,300
0110	For installing above on wood floor frame, add									
0120	Coupler nuts, threaded rods, bolts, shear transfer plate kit	1 Carp	16	.500	Ea.	70	23		93	115
0130	Framing anchors, angle (2 required)	"	96	.083	"	2.61	3.82		6.43	9.15
0140	For blocking see Section 06 11 10.02									
0150	For installing above, first floor to second floor, wood floor frame, add									
0160	Add stack option to first floor wall panel				Ea.	77			77	84.50
0170	Threaded rods, bolts, shear transfer plate kit	1 Carp	16	.500		84	23		107	130
0180	Framing anchors, angle (2 required)	"	96	.083		2.61	3.82		6.43	9.15
0190	For blocking see 06 11 10.02									
0200	For installing stacked panels, balloon framing									
0210	Add stack option to first floor wall panel				Ea.	77			77	84.50
0220	Threaded rods, bolts kit	1 Carp	16	.500	"	49	23		72	91.50

06 13 Heavy Timber Construction

06 13 23 – Heavy Timber Framing

06 13 23.10 Heavy Framing

		Crew	Daily Output	Labor-Hours	Unit	Material	Labor	Equipment	Total	Total Incl O&P
0010	**HEAVY FRAMING**									
0020	Beams, single 6" x 10"	2 Carp	1.10	14.545	M.B.F.	1,600	665		2,265	2,850
0100	Single 8" x 16"		1.20	13.333	"	2,000	610		2,610	3,200
0202	Built from 2" lumber, multiple 2" x 14"		900	.018	B.F.	.76	.82		1.58	2.18
0212	Built from 3" lumber, multiple 3" x 6"		700	.023		.93	1.05		1.98	2.74
0222	Multiple 3" x 8"		800	.020		1.27	.92		2.19	2.90
0232	Multiple 3" x 10"		900	.018		1.28	.82		2.10	2.74
0242	Multiple 3" x 12"		1000	.016		1.28	.73		2.01	2.61
0252	Built from 4" lumber, multiple 4" x 6"		800	.020		1.29	.92		2.21	2.93
0262	Multiple 4" x 8"		900	.018		1.30	.82		2.12	2.77
0272	Multiple 4" x 10"		1000	.016		1.28	.73		2.01	2.61
0282	Multiple 4" x 12"		1100	.015		1.28	.67		1.95	2.50
0292	Columns, structural grade, 1500f, 4" x 4"		450	.036	L.F.	1.70	1.63		3.33	4.55
0302	6" x 6"		225	.071		4.21	3.26		7.47	10
0402	8" x 8"		240	.067		7.20	3.06		10.26	12.90
0502	10" x 10"		90	.178		12.10	8.15		20.25	26.50

06 13 Heavy Timber Construction

06 13 23 – Heavy Timber Framing

06 13 23.10 Heavy Framing		Crew	Daily Output	Labor-Hours	Unit	Material	2014 Bare Costs Labor	Equipment	Total	Total Incl O&P
0602	12" x 12"	2 Carp	70	.229	L.F.	18.35	10.50		28.85	37
0802	Floor planks, 2" thick, T & G, 2" x 6"		1050	.015	B.F.	1.59	.70		2.29	2.90
0902	2" x 10"		1100	.015		1.59	.67		2.26	2.85
1102	3" thick, 3" x 6"		1050	.015		1.59	.70		2.29	2.90
1202	3" x 10"		1100	.015		1.59	.67		2.26	2.85
1402	Girders, structural grade, 12" x 12"		800	.020		1.53	.92		2.45	3.19
1502	10" x 16"		1000	.016		2.40	.73		3.13	3.85
2302	Roof purlins, 4" thick, structural grade		1050	.015		1.30	.70		2	2.58
9000	Minimum labor/equipment charge	1 Carp	2	4	Job		183		183	300

06 15 Wood Decking

06 15 16 – Wood Roof Decking

06 15 16.10 Solid Wood Roof Decking

		Crew	Daily Output	Labor-Hours	Unit	Material	2014 Bare Costs Labor	Equipment	Total	Total Incl O&P
0010	**SOLID WOOD ROOF DECKING**									
0350	Cedar planks, 2" thick	2 Carp	350	.046	S.F.	5.35	2.10		7.45	9.30
0400	3" thick		320	.050		8	2.29		10.29	12.55
0500	4" thick		250	.064		10.65	2.93		13.58	16.55
0550	6" thick		200	.080		16	3.67		19.67	23.50
0650	Douglas fir, 2" thick		350	.046		2.69	2.10		4.79	6.40
0700	3" thick		320	.050		4.04	2.29		6.33	8.20
0800	4" thick		250	.064		5.40	2.93		8.33	10.70
0850	6" thick		200	.080		8.05	3.67		11.72	14.95
0950	Hemlock, 2" thick		350	.046		2.74	2.10		4.84	6.45
1000	3" thick		320	.050		4.11	2.29		6.40	8.30
1100	4" thick		250	.064		5.50	2.93		8.43	10.80
1150	6" thick		200	.080		8.20	3.67		11.87	15.10
1250	Western white spruce, 2" thick		350	.046		1.75	2.10		3.85	5.35
1300	3" thick		320	.050		2.62	2.29		4.91	6.65
1400	4" thick		250	.064		3.50	2.93		6.43	8.65
1450	6" thick		200	.080		5.25	3.67		8.92	11.80
9000	Minimum labor/equipment charge	1 Carp	2	4	Job		183		183	300

06 15 23 – Laminated Wood Decking

06 15 23.10 Laminated Roof Deck

		Crew	Daily Output	Labor-Hours	Unit	Material	2014 Bare Costs Labor	Equipment	Total	Total Incl O&P
0010	**LAMINATED ROOF DECK**									
0020	Pine or hemlock, 3" thick	2 Carp	425	.038	S.F.	6.30	1.73		8.03	9.80
0100	4" thick		325	.049		8.70	2.26		10.96	13.25
0300	Cedar, 3" thick		425	.038		6.85	1.73		8.58	10.40
0400	4" thick		325	.049		9.15	2.26		11.41	13.80
0600	Fir, 3" thick		425	.038		6.30	1.73		8.03	9.80
0700	4" thick		325	.049		8.70	2.26		10.96	13.25
9000	Minimum labor/equipment charge	1 Carp	3	2.667	Job		122		122	201

06 16 Sheathing

06 16 13 – Insulating Sheathing

06 16 13.10 Insulating Sheathing

		Crew	Daily Output	Labor-Hours	Unit	Material	2014 Bare Costs Labor	Equipment	Total	Total Incl O&P
0010	**INSULATING SHEATHING**									
0020	Expanded polystyrene, 1#/C.F. density, 3/4" thick R2.89 [G]	2 Carp	1400	.011	S.F.	.32	.52		.84	1.22
0030	1" thick R3.85 [G]		1300	.012		.38	.56		.94	1.35
0040	2" thick R7.69 [G]		1200	.013		.62	.61		1.23	1.69
0050	Extruded polystyrene, 15 PSI compressive strength, 1" thick, R5 [G]		1300	.012		.67	.56		1.23	1.67
0060	2" thick, R10 [G]		1200	.013		.83	.61		1.44	1.92
0070	Polyisocyanurate, 2#/C.F. density, 3/4" thick [G]		1400	.011		.58	.52		1.10	1.50
0080	1" thick [G]		1300	.012		.64	.56		1.20	1.64
0090	1-1/2" thick [G]		1250	.013		.77	.59		1.36	1.81
0100	2" thick [G]		1200	.013		.93	.61		1.54	2.03

06 16 23 – Subflooring

06 16 23.10 Subfloor

			Crew	Daily Output	Labor-Hours	Unit	Material	2014 Bare Costs Labor	Equipment	Total	Total Incl O&P
0010	**SUBFLOOR**	R061636-20									
0011	Plywood, CDX, 1/2" thick		2 Carp	1500	.011	SF Flr.	.60	.49		1.09	1.45
0015	Pneumatic nailed			1860	.009		.60	.39		.99	1.30
0102	5/8" thick			1350	.012		.74	.54		1.28	1.71
0107	Pneumatic nailed			1674	.010		.74	.44		1.18	1.54
0202	3/4" thick			1250	.013		.88	.59		1.47	1.93
0207	Pneumatic nailed			1550	.010		.88	.47		1.35	1.75
0302	1-1/8" thick, 2-4-1 including underlayment			1050	.015		2.23	.70		2.93	3.60
0440	With boards, 1" x 6", S4S, laid regular			900	.018		1.74	.82		2.56	3.26
0452	1" x 8", laid regular			1000	.016		1.90	.73		2.63	3.30
0462	Laid diagonal			850	.019		1.90	.86		2.76	3.51
0502	1" x 10", laid regular			1100	.015		1.95	.67		2.62	3.24
0602	Laid diagonal			900	.018		1.95	.82		2.77	3.48
8990	Subfloor adhesive, 3/8" bead		1 Carp	2300	.003	L.F.	.12	.16		.28	.39
9000	Minimum labor/equipment charge		"	4	2	Job		91.50		91.50	151

06 16 26 – Underlayment

06 16 26.10 Wood Product Underlayment

			Crew	Daily Output	Labor-Hours	Unit	Material	2014 Bare Costs Labor	Equipment	Total	Total Incl O&P
0010	**WOOD PRODUCT UNDERLAYMENT**	R061636-20									
0015	Plywood, underlayment grade, 1/4" thick		2 Carp	1500	.011	S.F.	.84	.49		1.33	1.72
0018	Pneumatic nailed			1860	.009		.84	.39		1.23	1.57
0030	3/8" thick			1500	.011		.93	.49		1.42	1.82
0070	Pneumatic nailed			1860	.009		.93	.39		1.32	1.67
0102	1/2" thick			1450	.011		1.06	.51		1.57	2
0107	Pneumatic nailed			1798	.009		1.06	.41		1.47	1.84
0202	5/8" thick			1400	.011		1.18	.52		1.70	2.16
0207	Pneumatic nailed			1736	.009		1.18	.42		1.60	1.99
0302	3/4" thick			1300	.012		1.40	.56		1.96	2.47
0306	Pneumatic nailed			1612	.010		1.40	.46		1.86	2.29
0502	Particle board, 3/8" thick			1500	.011		.40	.49		.89	1.24
0507	Pneumatic nailed			1860	.009		.40	.39		.79	1.09
0602	1/2" thick			1450	.011		.42	.51		.93	1.29
0607	Pneumatic nailed			1798	.009		.42	.41		.83	1.13
0802	5/8" thick			1400	.011		.52	.52		1.04	1.43
0807	Pneumatic nailed			1736	.009		.52	.42		.94	1.26
0902	3/4" thick			1300	.012		.62	.56		1.18	1.61
0907	Pneumatic nailed			1612	.010		.62	.46		1.08	1.43
0955	Particleboard, 100% recycled straw/wheat, 4' x 8' x 1/4" [G]			1450	.011		.29	.51		.80	1.15
0960	4' x 8' x 3/8" [G]			1450	.011		.42	.51		.93	1.29
0965	4' x 8' x 1/2" [G]			1350	.012		.59	.54		1.13	1.54
0970	4' x 8' x 5/8" [G]			1300	.012		.71	.56		1.27	1.71

06 16 26 – Underlayment

06 16 26.10 Wood Product Underlayment		Crew	Daily Output	Labor-Hours	Unit	Material	2014 Bare Costs Labor	Equipment	Total	Total Incl O&P
0975	4' x 8' x 3/4"	G 2 Carp	1250	.013	S.F.	.81	.59		1.40	1.85
0980	4' x 8' x 1"	G	1150	.014		1.08	.64		1.72	2.24
0985	4' x 8' x 1-1/4"	G	1100	.015		1.24	.67		1.91	2.46
1100	Hardboard, underlayment grade, 4' x 4', .215" thick	G	1500	.011		.57	.49		1.06	1.43
9000	Minimum labor/equipment charge	1 Carp	4	2	Job		91.50		91.50	151

06 16 33 – Wood Board Sheathing

06 16 33.10 Board Sheathing

06 16 33.10 Board Sheathing		Crew	Daily Output	Labor-Hours	Unit	Material	Labor	Equipment	Total	Total Incl O&P
0009	**BOARD SHEATHING**									
0010	Roof, 1" x 6" boards, laid horizontal	2 Carp	725	.022	S.F.	1.74	1.01		2.75	3.58
0020	On steep roof		520	.031		1.74	1.41		3.15	4.24
0040	On dormers, hips, & valleys		480	.033		1.74	1.53		3.27	4.43
0050	Laid diagonal		650	.025		1.74	1.13		2.87	3.78
0070	1" x 8" boards, laid horizontal		875	.018		1.90	.84		2.74	3.47
0080	On steep roof		635	.025		1.90	1.16		3.06	3.99
0090	On dormers, hips, & valleys		580	.028		1.95	1.27		3.22	4.22
0100	Laid diagonal		725	.022		1.90	1.01		2.91	3.75
0110	Skip sheathing, 1" x 4", 7" OC	1 Carp	1200	.007		.58	.31		.89	1.14
0120	1" x 6", 9" OC	"	1450	.006		.80	.25		1.05	1.30
0200	Walls, 1" x 6" boards, laid regular	2 Carp	650	.025		1.74	1.13		2.87	3.78
0210	Laid diagonal		585	.027		1.74	1.25		2.99	3.98
0220	1" x 8" boards, laid regular		765	.021		1.90	.96		2.86	3.67
0230	Laid diagonal		650	.025		1.90	1.13		3.03	3.95

06 16 36 – Wood Panel Product Sheathing

06 16 36.10 Sheathing

06 16 36.10 Sheathing			Crew	Daily Output	Labor-Hours	Unit	Material	Labor	Equipment	Total	Total Incl O&P
0010	**SHEATHING**	R061110-30									
0012	Plywood on roofs, CDX										
0032	5/16" thick		2 Carp	1600	.010	S.F.	.55	.46		1.01	1.36
0037	Pneumatic nailed	R061636-20		1952	.008		.55	.38		.93	1.23
0052	3/8" thick			1525	.010		.50	.48		.98	1.34
0057	Pneumatic nailed			1860	.009		.50	.39		.89	1.20
0102	1/2" thick			1400	.011		.60	.52		1.12	1.51
0103	Pneumatic nailed			1708	.009		.60	.43		1.03	1.36
0202	5/8" thick			1300	.012		.74	.56		1.30	1.75
0207	Pneumatic nailed			1586	.010		.74	.46		1.20	1.58
0302	3/4" thick			1200	.013		.88	.61		1.49	1.97
0307	Pneumatic nailed			1464	.011		.88	.50		1.38	1.79
0502	Plywood on walls, with exterior CDX, 3/8" thick			1200	.013		.50	.61		1.11	1.55
0507	Pneumatic nailed			1488	.011		.50	.49		.99	1.36
0602	1/2" thick			1125	.014		.60	.65		1.25	1.72
0607	Pneumatic nailed			1395	.011		.60	.53		1.13	1.51
0702	5/8" thick			1050	.015		.74	.70		1.44	1.97
0707	Pneumatic nailed			1302	.012		.74	.56		1.30	1.75
0802	3/4" thick			975	.016		.88	.75		1.63	2.21
0807	Pneumatic nailed			1209	.013		.88	.61		1.49	1.97
1000	For shear wall construction, add							20%			
1200	For structural 1 exterior plywood, add					S.F.	10%				
3000	Wood fiber, regular, no vapor barrier, 1/2" thick		2 Carp	1200	.013		.60	.61		1.21	1.66
3100	5/8" thick			1200	.013		.76	.61		1.37	1.84
3300	No vapor barrier, in colors, 1/2" thick			1200	.013		.73	.61		1.34	1.80
3400	5/8" thick			1200	.013		.77	.61		1.38	1.85
3600	With vapor barrier one side, white, 1/2" thick			1200	.013		.59	.61		1.20	1.65
3700	Vapor barrier 2 sides, 1/2" thick			1200	.013		.82	.61		1.43	1.90

06 16 Sheathing

06 16 36 – Wood Panel Product Sheathing

06 16 36.10 Sheathing		Crew	Daily Output	Labor-Hours	Unit	Material	2014 Bare Costs Labor	Equipment	Total	Total Incl O&P
3800	Asphalt impregnated, 25/32" thick	2 Carp	1200	.013	S.F.	.32	.61		.93	1.35
3850	Intermediate, 1/2" thick		1200	.013		.24	.61		.85	1.26
4500	Oriented strand board, on roof, 7/16" thick [G]		1460	.011		.50	.50		1	1.38
4505	Pneumatic nailed [G]		1780	.009		.50	.41		.91	1.23
4550	1/2" thick [G]		1400	.011		.50	.52		1.02	1.41
4555	Pneumatic nailed [G]		1736	.009		.50	.42		.92	1.24
4600	5/8" thick [G]		1300	.012		.69	.56		1.25	1.69
4605	Pneumatic nailed [G]		1586	.010		.69	.46		1.15	1.52
4610	On walls, 7/16" thick		1200	.013		.50	.61		1.11	1.55
4615	Pneumatic nailed		1488	.011		.50	.49		.99	1.36
4620	1/2" thick		1195	.013		.50	.61		1.11	1.56
4625	Pneumatic nailed		1325	.012		.50	.55		1.05	1.46
4630	5/8" thick		1050	.015		.69	.70		1.39	1.91
4635	Pneumatic nailed		1302	.012		.69	.56		1.25	1.69
4700	Oriented strand board, factory laminated W.R. barrier, on roof, 1/2" thick [G]		1400	.011		.62	.52		1.14	1.54
4705	Pneumatic nailed [G]		1736	.009		.62	.42		1.04	1.37
4720	5/8" thick [G]		1300	.012		.77	.56		1.33	1.78
4725	Pneumatic nailed [G]		1586	.010		.77	.46		1.23	1.61
4730	5/8" thick, T&G [G]		1150	.014		.78	.64		1.42	1.91
4735	Pneumatic nailed, T&G [G]		1400	.011		.78	.52		1.30	1.72
4740	On walls, 7/16" thick [G]		1200	.013		.56	.61		1.17	1.62
4745	Pneumatic nailed [G]		1488	.011		.56	.49		1.05	1.43
4750	1/2" thick [G]		1195	.013		.62	.61		1.23	1.69
4755	Pneumatic nailed [G]		1325	.012		.62	.55		1.17	1.59
4800	Joint sealant tape, 3-1/2"		7600	.002	L.F.	.28	.10		.38	.47
4810	Joint sealant tape, 6"		7600	.002	"	.44	.10		.54	.64
9000	Minimum labor/equipment charge	1 Carp	2	4	Job		183		183	300

06 16 43 – Gypsum Sheathing

06 16 43.10 Gypsum Sheathing

		Crew	Daily Output	Labor-Hours	Unit	Material	Labor	Equipment	Total	Total Incl O&P
0010	**GYPSUM SHEATHING**									
0020	Gypsum, weatherproof, 1/2" thick	2 Carp	1125	.014	S.F.	.44	.65		1.09	1.55
0040	With embedded glass mats	"	1100	.015	"	.77	.67		1.44	1.95

06 17 Shop-Fabricated Structural Wood

06 17 33 – Wood I-Joists

06 17 33.10 Wood and Composite I-Joists

		Crew	Daily Output	Labor-Hours	Unit	Material	Labor	Equipment	Total	Total Incl O&P
0010	**WOOD AND COMPOSITE I-JOISTS**									
0100	Plywood webs, incl. bridging & blocking, panels 24" O.C.									
1200	15' to 24' span, 50 psf live load	F-5	2400	.013	SF Flr.	1.95	.62		2.57	3.16
1300	55 psf live load		2250	.014		2.21	.66		2.87	3.51
1400	24' to 30' span, 45 psf live load		2600	.012		2.61	.57		3.18	3.82
1500	55 psf live load		2400	.013		3.89	.62		4.51	5.30

06 17 53 – Shop-Fabricated Wood Trusses

06 17 53.10 Roof Trusses

		Crew	Daily Output	Labor-Hours	Unit	Material	Labor	Equipment	Total	Total Incl O&P
0010	**ROOF TRUSSES**									
0100	Fink (W) or King post type, 2'-0" O.C.									
0200	Metal plate connected, 4 in 12 slope									
0210	24' to 29' span	F-3	3000	.013	SF Flr.	1.71	.62	.22	2.55	3.14
0300	30' to 43' span		3000	.013		2.18	.62	.22	3.02	3.66
0400	44' to 60' span		3000	.013		2.36	.62	.22	3.20	3.85

06 17 53 – Shop-Fabricated Wood Trusses

06 17 53.10 Roof Trusses	Crew	Daily Output	Labor-Hours	Unit	Material	2014 Bare Costs Labor	Equipment	Total	Total Incl O&P
0700	Glued and nailed, add				SF Flr.	50%			

06 18 Glued-Laminated Construction

06 18 13 – Glued-Laminated Beams

06 18 13.20 Laminated Framing

		Crew	Daily Output	Labor-Hours	Unit	Material	2014 Bare Costs Labor	Equipment	Total	Total Incl O&P
0010	**LAMINATED FRAMING**									
0020	30 lb., short term live load, 15 lb. dead load									
0200	Straight roof beams, 20' clear span, beams 8' O.C.	F-3	2560	.016	SF Flr.	1.91	.73	.26	2.90	3.57
0300	Beams 16' O.C.		3200	.013		1.38	.58	.21	2.17	2.70
0500	40' clear span, beams 8' O.C.		3200	.013		3.65	.58	.21	4.44	5.20
0600	Beams 16' O.C.		3840	.010		2.99	.49	.17	3.65	4.27
0800	60' clear span, beams 8' O.C.	F-4	2880	.017		6.30	.77	.39	7.46	8.60
0900	Beams 16' O.C.	"	3840	.013		4.68	.58	.30	5.56	6.40
1100	Tudor arches, 30' to 40' clear span, frames 8' O.C.	F-3	1680	.024		8.20	1.11	.39	9.70	11.25
1200	Frames 16' O.C.	"	2240	.018		6.40	.83	.30	7.53	8.75
1400	50' to 60' clear span, frames 8' O.C.	F-4	2200	.022		8.85	1.01	.52	10.38	11.90
1500	Frames 16' O.C.		2640	.018		7.50	.84	.43	8.77	10.10
1700	Radial arches, 60' clear span, frames 8' O.C.		1920	.025		8.25	1.16	.59	10	11.65
1800	Frames 16' O.C.		2880	.017		6.35	.77	.39	7.51	8.70
2000	100' clear span, frames 8' O.C.		1600	.030		8.55	1.39	.71	10.65	12.45
2100	Frames 16' O.C.		2400	.020		7.50	.92	.47	8.89	10.25
2300	120' clear span, frames 8' O.C.		1440	.033		11.35	1.54	.79	13.68	15.85
2400	Frames 16' O.C.		1920	.025		10.35	1.16	.59	12.10	13.95
2600	Bowstring trusses, 20' O.C., 40' clear span	F-3	2400	.017		5.10	.78	.28	6.16	7.20
2700	60' clear span	F-4	3600	.013		4.60	.62	.32	5.54	6.40
2800	100' clear span		4000	.012		6.50	.55	.28	7.33	8.35
2900	120' clear span		3600	.013		7	.62	.32	7.94	9.05
3000	For less than 1000 B.F., add					20%				
3100	For premium appearance, add to S.F. prices					5%				
3300	For industrial type, deduct					15%				
3500	For stain and varnish, add					5%				
3900	For 3/4" laminations, add to straight					25%				
4100	Add to curved					15%				
4300	Alternate pricing method: (use nominal footage of									
4310	components). Straight beams, camber less than 6"	F-3	3.50	11.429	M.B.F.	2,825	535	189	3,549	4,200
4400	Columns, including hardware		2	20		3,050	935	330	4,315	5,250
4600	Curved members, radius over 32'		2.50	16		3,125	750	265	4,140	4,950
4700	Radius 10' to 32'		3	13.333		3,075	625	221	3,921	4,675
4900	For complicated shapes, add maximum					100%				
5100	For pressure treating, add to straight					35%				
5200	Add to curved					45%				
6000	Laminated veneer members, southern pine or western species									
6050	1-3/4" wide x 5-1/2" deep	2 Carp	480	.033	L.F.	2.94	1.53		4.47	5.75
6100	9-1/2" deep		480	.033		4.35	1.53		5.88	7.30
6150	14" deep		450	.036		6.75	1.63		8.38	10.10
6200	18" deep		450	.036		9.50	1.63		11.13	13.15
6300	Parallel strand members, southern pine or western species									
6350	1-3/4" wide x 9-1/4" deep	2 Carp	480	.033	L.F.	4.35	1.53		5.88	7.30
6400	11-1/4" deep		450	.036		4.93	1.63		6.56	8.10
6450	14" deep		400	.040		6.75	1.83		8.58	10.40
6500	3-1/2" wide x 9-1/4" deep		480	.033		15.15	1.53		16.68	19.15

06 18 Glued-Laminated Construction

06 18 13 – Glued-Laminated Beams

06 18 13.20 Laminated Framing		Crew	Daily Output	Labor-Hours	Unit	Material	2014 Bare Costs Labor	Equipment	Total	Total Incl O&P
6550	11-1/4" deep	2 Carp	450	.036	L.F.	18.10	1.63		19.73	22.50
6600	14" deep		400	.040		22.50	1.83		24.33	27.50
6650	7" wide x 9-1/4" deep		450	.036		30.50	1.63		32.13	36
6700	11-1/4" deep		420	.038		38	1.75		39.75	44.50
6750	14" deep		400	.040		44.50	1.83		46.33	52
9000	Minimum labor/equipment charge	F-3	2.50	16	Job		750	265	1,015	1,525

06 22 Millwork

06 22 13 – Standard Pattern Wood Trim

06 22 13.15 Moldings, Base

0010	MOLDINGS, BASE	Crew	Daily Output	Labor-Hours	Unit	Material	2014 Bare Costs Labor	Equipment	Total	Total Incl O&P
5100	Classic profile, 5/8" x 5-1/2", finger jointed and primed	1 Carp	250	.032	L.F.	1.39	1.47		2.86	3.94
5105	Poplar		240	.033		1.47	1.53		3	4.13
5110	Red oak		220	.036		2.15	1.67		3.82	5.10
5115	Maple		220	.036		3.40	1.67		5.07	6.50
5120	Cherry		220	.036		4.04	1.67		5.71	7.20
5125	3/4 x 7-1/2", finger jointed and primed		250	.032		1.76	1.47		3.23	4.34
5130	Poplar		240	.033		2.34	1.53		3.87	5.10
5135	Red oak		220	.036		3.12	1.67		4.79	6.15
5140	Maple		220	.036		4.52	1.67		6.19	7.70
5145	Cherry		220	.036		5.40	1.67		7.07	8.70
5150	Modern profile, 5/8" x 3-1/2", finger jointed and primed		250	.032		.93	1.47		2.40	3.43
5155	Poplar		240	.033		.93	1.53		2.46	3.53
5160	Red oak		220	.036		1.47	1.67		3.14	4.36
5165	Maple		220	.036		2.38	1.67		4.05	5.35
5170	Cherry		220	.036		2.57	1.67		4.24	5.55
5175	Ogee profile, 7/16" x 3", finger jointed and primed		250	.032		.56	1.47		2.03	3.02
5180	Poplar		240	.033		.61	1.53		2.14	3.18
5185	Red oak		220	.036		.82	1.67		2.49	3.64
5200	9/16" x 3-1/2", finger jointed and primed		250	.032		.62	1.47		2.09	3.09
5205	Pine		240	.033		1.44	1.53		2.97	4.09
5210	Red oak		220	.036		2.32	1.67		3.99	5.30
5215	9/16" x 4-1/2", red oak		220	.036		3.47	1.67		5.14	6.55
5220	5/8" x 3-1/2", finger jointed and primed		250	.032		.85	1.47		2.32	3.34
5225	Poplar		240	.033		.93	1.53		2.46	3.53
5230	Red oak		220	.036		1.47	1.67		3.14	4.36
5235	Maple		220	.036		2.38	1.67		4.05	5.35
5240	Cherry		220	.036		2.57	1.67		4.24	5.55
5245	5/8" x 4", finger jointed and primed		250	.032		1.10	1.47		2.57	3.62
5250	Poplar		240	.033		1.20	1.53		2.73	3.83
5255	Red oak		220	.036		1.65	1.67		3.32	4.55
5260	Maple		220	.036		2.66	1.67		4.33	5.65
5265	Cherry		220	.036		2.79	1.67		4.46	5.80
5270	Rectangular profile, oak, 3/8" x 1-1/4"		260	.031		1.25	1.41		2.66	3.70
5275	1/2" x 2-1/2"		255	.031		1.91	1.44		3.35	4.46
5280	1/2" x 3-1/2"		250	.032		2.31	1.47		3.78	4.95
5285	1" x 6"		240	.033		3.64	1.53		5.17	6.50
5290	1" x 8"		240	.033		5.10	1.53		6.63	8.10
5295	Pine, 3/8" x 1-3/4"		260	.031		.62	1.41		2.03	3
5300	7/16" x 2-1/2"		255	.031		.90	1.44		2.34	3.35
5305	1" x 6"		240	.033		.88	1.53		2.41	3.48

06 22 Millwork

06 22 13 – Standard Pattern Wood Trim

06 22 13.15 Moldings, Base

		Crew	Daily Output	Labor-Hours	Unit	Material	2014 Bare Costs Labor	Equipment	Total	Total Incl O&P
5310	1" x 8"	1 Carp	240	.033	L.F.	1.18	1.53		2.71	3.81
5315	Shoe, 1/2" x 3/4", primed		260	.031		.46	1.41		1.87	2.82
5320	Pine		240	.033		.37	1.53		1.90	2.92
5325	Poplar		240	.033		.36	1.53		1.89	2.90
5330	Red oak		220	.036		.47	1.67		2.14	3.26
5335	Maple		220	.036		.66	1.67		2.33	3.46
5340	Cherry		220	.036		.74	1.67		2.41	3.55
5345	11/16" x 1-1/2", pine		240	.033		.80	1.53		2.33	3.39
5350	Caps, 11/16" x 1-3/8", pine		240	.033		.84	1.53		2.37	3.43
5355	3/4" x 1-3/4", finger jointed and primed		260	.031		.67	1.41		2.08	3.06
5360	Poplar		240	.033		.94	1.53		2.47	3.54
5365	Red oak		220	.036		1.08	1.67		2.75	3.93
5370	Maple		220	.036		1.48	1.67		3.15	4.37
5375	Cherry		220	.036		3.12	1.67		4.79	6.15
5380	Combination base & shoe, 9/16" x 3-1/2" & 1/2" x 3/4", pine		125	.064		1.81	2.93		4.74	6.80
5385	Three piece oak, 6" high		80	.100		5.20	4.59		9.79	13.25
5390	Including 3/4" x 1" base shoe		70	.114		5.50	5.25		10.75	14.65
5395	Flooring cant strip, 3/4" x 3/4", pre-finished pine		260	.031		.47	1.41		1.88	2.84
5400	For pre-finished, stain and clear coat, add					.50			.50	.55
5405	Clear coat only, add					.40			.40	.44
9000	Minimum labor/equipment charge	1 Carp	4	2	Job		91.50		91.50	151

06 22 13.30 Moldings, Casings

		Crew	Daily Output	Labor-Hours	Unit	Material	2014 Bare Costs Labor	Equipment	Total	Total Incl O&P
0010	**MOLDINGS, CASINGS**									
0085	Apron, 9/16" x 2-1/2", pine	1 Carp	250	.032	L.F.	1.58	1.47		3.05	4.15
0090	5/8" x 2-1/2", pine		250	.032		1.64	1.47		3.11	4.21
0110	5/8" x 3-1/2", pine		220	.036		2.45	1.67		4.12	5.45
0300	Band, 11/16" x 1-1/8", pine		270	.030		1	1.36		2.36	3.33
0310	11/16" x 1-1/2", finger jointed and primed		270	.030		.67	1.36		2.03	2.97
0320	Pine		270	.030		1.24	1.36		2.60	3.59
0330	11/16" x 1-3/4", finger jointed and primed		270	.030		.75	1.36		2.11	3.05
0350	Pine		270	.030		1.25	1.36		2.61	3.60
0355	Beaded, 3/4" x 3-1/2", finger jointed and primed		220	.036		1.04	1.67		2.71	3.88
0360	Poplar		220	.036		1.04	1.67		2.71	3.88
0365	Red oak		220	.036		1.47	1.67		3.14	4.36
0370	Maple		220	.036		2.38	1.67		4.05	5.35
0375	Cherry		220	.036		2.88	1.67		4.55	5.90
0380	3/4" x 4", finger jointed and primed		220	.036		1.10	1.67		2.77	3.95
0385	Poplar		220	.036		1.34	1.67		3.01	4.21
0390	Red oak		220	.036		1.80	1.67		3.47	4.72
0395	Maple		220	.036		2.48	1.67		4.15	5.45
0400	Cherry		220	.036		3.13	1.67		4.80	6.20
0405	3/4" x 5-1/2", finger jointed and primed		200	.040		1.07	1.83		2.90	4.19
0410	Poplar		200	.040		1.80	1.83		3.63	4.99
0415	Red oak		200	.040		2.53	1.83		4.36	5.80
0420	Maple		200	.040		3.49	1.83		5.32	6.85
0425	Cherry		200	.040		4.02	1.83		5.85	7.45
0430	Classic profile, 3/4" x 2-3/4", finger jointed and primed		250	.032		.73	1.47		2.20	3.21
0435	Poplar		250	.032		.93	1.47		2.40	3.43
0440	Red oak		250	.032		1.30	1.47		2.77	3.84
0445	Maple		250	.032		1.95	1.47		3.42	4.55
0450	Cherry		250	.032		2.21	1.47		3.68	4.84
0455	Fluted, 3/4" x 3-1/2", poplar		220	.036		1.04	1.67		2.71	3.88

06 22 13 – Standard Pattern Wood Trim

06 22 13.30 Moldings, Casings	Crew	Daily Output	Labor-Hours	Unit	Material	2014 Bare Costs Labor	Equipment	Total	Total Incl O&P
0460	Red oak	1 Carp	220	.036	L.F.	1.47	1.67		3.14	4.36
0465	Maple		220	.036		2.38	1.67		4.05	5.35
0470	Cherry		220	.036		2.88	1.67		4.55	5.90
0475	3/4" x 4", poplar		220	.036		1.34	1.67		3.01	4.21
0480	Red oak		220	.036		1.80	1.67		3.47	4.72
0485	Maple		220	.036		2.48	1.67		4.15	5.45
0490	Cherry		220	.036		3.13	1.67		4.80	6.20
0495	3/4" x 5-1/2", poplar		200	.040		1.80	1.83		3.63	4.99
0500	Red oak		200	.040		2.53	1.83		4.36	5.80
0505	Maple		200	.040		3.49	1.83		5.32	6.85
0510	Cherry		200	.040		4.02	1.83		5.85	7.45
0515	3/4" x 7-1/2", poplar		190	.042		1.27	1.93		3.20	4.56
0520	Red oak		190	.042		3.50	1.93		5.43	7
0525	Maple		190	.042		5.30	1.93		7.23	8.95
0530	Cherry		190	.042		6.30	1.93		8.23	10.10
0535	3/4" x 9-1/2", poplar		180	.044		3.85	2.04		5.89	7.60
0540	Red oak		180	.044		5.85	2.04		7.89	9.80
0545	Maple		180	.044		8.40	2.04		10.44	12.60
0550	Cherry		180	.044		9.15	2.04		11.19	13.40
0555	Modern profile, 9/16" x 2-1/4", poplar		250	.032		.53	1.47		2	2.99
0560	Red oak		250	.032		.69	1.47		2.16	3.17
0565	11/16" x 2-1/2", finger jointed & primed		250	.032		.72	1.47		2.19	3.20
0570	Pine		250	.032		1.55	1.47		3.02	4.11
0575	3/4" x 2-1/2", poplar		250	.032		.82	1.47		2.29	3.31
0580	Red oak		250	.032		1.06	1.47		2.53	3.57
0585	Maple		250	.032		1.68	1.47		3.15	4.26
0590	Cherry		250	.032		2.12	1.47		3.59	4.74
0595	Mullion, 5/16" x 2", pine		270	.030		.99	1.36		2.35	3.32
0600	9/16" x 2-1/2", fingerjointed and primed		250	.032		.83	1.47		2.30	3.32
0605	Pine		250	.032		1.64	1.47		3.11	4.21
0610	Red oak		250	.032		2.80	1.47		4.27	5.50
0615	1-1/16" x 3-3/4", red oak		220	.036		6.85	1.67		8.52	10.25
0620	Ogee, 7/16" x 2-1/2", poplar		250	.032		.51	1.47		1.98	2.97
0625	Red oak		250	.032		.67	1.47		2.14	3.15
0630	9/16" x 2-1/4", finger jointed and primed		250	.032		.47	1.47		1.94	2.93
0635	Poplar		250	.032		.53	1.47		2	2.99
0640	Red oak		250	.032		.69	1.47		2.16	3.17
0645	11/16" x 2-1/2", finger jointed and primed		250	.032		.67	1.47		2.14	3.15
0700	Pine		250	.032		1.52	1.47		2.99	4.08
0701	Red oak		250	.032		2.59	1.47		4.06	5.25
0730	11/16" x 3-1/2", finger jointed and primed		220	.036		2.12	1.67		3.79	5.05
0750	Pine		220	.036		2.18	1.67		3.85	5.15
0755	3/4" x 2-1/2", finger jointed and primed		250	.032		.67	1.47		2.14	3.15
0760	Poplar		250	.032		.82	1.47		2.29	3.31
0765	Red oak		250	.032		1.06	1.47		2.53	3.57
0770	Maple		250	.032		1.68	1.47		3.15	4.26
0775	Cherry		250	.032		2.12	1.47		3.59	4.74
0780	3/4" x 3-1/2", finger jointed and primed		220	.036		.85	1.67		2.52	3.67
0785	Poplar		220	.036		1.04	1.67		2.71	3.88
0790	Red oak		220	.036		1.47	1.67		3.14	4.36
0795	Maple		220	.036		2.38	1.67		4.05	5.35
0800	Cherry		220	.036		2.88	1.67		4.55	5.90
4700	Square profile, 1" x 1", teak		215	.037		2.01	1.71		3.72	5

06 22 13 – Standard Pattern Wood Trim

06 22 13.30 Moldings, Casings	Crew	Daily Output	Labor-Hours	Unit	Material	2014 Bare Costs Labor	Equipment	Total	Total Incl O&P
4800	Rectangular profile, 1" x 3", teak	1 Carp	200	.040	L.F.	6	1.83		7.83	9.60
9000	Minimum labor/equipment charge	↓	4	2	Job		91.50		91.50	151

06 22 13.35 Moldings, Ceilings	Crew	Daily Output	Labor-Hours	Unit	Material	Labor	Equipment	Total	Total Incl O&P
0010	**MOLDINGS, CEILINGS**									
0600	Bed, 9/16" x 1-3/4", pine	1 Carp	270	.030	L.F.	1.20	1.36		2.56	3.55
0650	9/16" x 2", pine		270	.030		1.43	1.36		2.79	3.80
0710	9/16" x 1-3/4", oak		270	.030		1.96	1.36		3.32	4.38
1200	Cornice, 9/16" x 1-3/4", pine		270	.030		1.21	1.36		2.57	3.56
1300	9/16" x 2-1/4", pine		265	.030		1.47	1.38		2.85	3.88
1350	Cove, 1/2" x 2-1/4", poplar		265	.030		.92	1.38		2.30	3.28
1360	Red oak		265	.030		1.18	1.38		2.56	3.56
1370	Hard maple		265	.030		1.69	1.38		3.07	4.13
1380	Cherry		265	.030		2.07	1.38		3.45	4.54
2400	9/16" x 1-3/4", pine		270	.030		1.12	1.36		2.48	3.46
2500	11/16" x 2-3/4", pine		265	.030		2.21	1.38		3.59	4.70
2510	Crown, 5/8" x 5/8", poplar		300	.027		.41	1.22		1.63	2.46
2520	Red oak		300	.027		.46	1.22		1.68	2.51
2530	Hard maple		300	.027		.66	1.22		1.88	2.73
2540	Cherry		300	.027		.70	1.22		1.92	2.78
2600	9/16" x 3-5/8", pine		250	.032		2.70	1.47		4.17	5.40
2700	11/16" x 4-1/4", pine		250	.032		4.55	1.47		6.02	7.40
2705	Oak		250	.032		6.30	1.47		7.77	9.35
2710	3/4" x 1-3/4", poplar		270	.030		.65	1.36		2.01	2.94
2720	Red oak		270	.030		.91	1.36		2.27	3.23
2730	Hard maple		270	.030		1.26	1.36		2.62	3.61
2740	Cherry		270	.030		1.55	1.36		2.91	3.93
2750	3/4" x 2", poplar		270	.030		.85	1.36		2.21	3.16
2760	Red oak		270	.030		1.10	1.36		2.46	3.44
2770	Hard maple		270	.030		1.52	1.36		2.88	3.90
2780	Cherry		270	.030		1.70	1.36		3.06	4.10
2790	3/4" x 2-3/4", poplar		265	.030		.92	1.38		2.30	3.28
2800	Red oak		265	.030		1.36	1.38		2.74	3.76
2810	Hard maple		265	.030		1.89	1.38		3.27	4.35
2820	Cherry		265	.030		2.18	1.38		3.56	4.66
2830	3/4" x 3-1/2", poplar		250	.032		1.18	1.47		2.65	3.70
2840	Red oak		250	.032		1.70	1.47		3.17	4.28
2850	Hard maple		250	.032		2.32	1.47		3.79	4.96
2860	Cherry		250	.032		2.72	1.47		4.19	5.40
2870	FJP poplar		250	.032		.84	1.47		2.31	3.33
2880	3/4" x 5", poplar		245	.033		1.75	1.50		3.25	4.38
2890	Red oak		245	.033		2.47	1.50		3.97	5.15
2900	Hard maple		245	.033		3.40	1.50		4.90	6.20
2910	Cherry		245	.033		3.92	1.50		5.42	6.75
2920	FJP poplar		245	.033		1.19	1.50		2.69	3.77
2930	3/4" x 6-1/4", poplar		240	.033		2.09	1.53		3.62	4.80
2940	Red oak		240	.033		3	1.53		4.53	5.80
2950	Hard maple		240	.033		4.11	1.53		5.64	7.05
2960	Cherry		240	.033		4.87	1.53		6.40	7.85
2970	7/8" x 8-3/4", poplar		220	.036		3.24	1.67		4.91	6.30
2980	Red oak		220	.036		4.71	1.67		6.38	7.95
2990	Hard maple		220	.036		6.80	1.67		8.47	10.25
3000	Cherry	↓	220	.036		7.80	1.67		9.47	11.30

06 22 Millwork

06 22 13 – Standard Pattern Wood Trim

06 22 13.35 Moldings, Ceilings

		Crew	Daily Output	Labor-Hours	Unit	Material	2014 Bare Costs Labor	2014 Bare Costs Equipment	Total	Total Incl O&P
3010	1" x 7-1/4", poplar	1 Carp	220	.036	L.F.	3.43	1.67		5.10	6.50
3020	Red oak		220	.036		5.10	1.67		6.77	8.35
3030	Hard maple		220	.036		7.40	1.67		9.07	10.85
3040	Cherry		220	.036		8.60	1.67		10.27	12.25
3050	1-1/16" x 4-1/4", poplar		250	.032		2.08	1.47		3.55	4.69
3060	Red oak		250	.032		2.33	1.47		3.80	4.97
3070	Hard maple		250	.032		3.22	1.47		4.69	5.95
3080	Cherry		250	.032		4.60	1.47		6.07	7.45
3090	Dentil crown, 3/4" x 5", poplar		250	.032		1.75	1.47		3.22	4.33
3100	Red oak		250	.032		2.47	1.47		3.94	5.10
3110	Hard maple		250	.032		3.30	1.47		4.77	6.05
3120	Cherry		250	.032		3.92	1.47		5.39	6.70
3130	Dentil piece for above, 1/2" x 1/2", poplar		300	.027		2.48	1.22		3.70	4.73
3140	Red oak		300	.027		2.72	1.22		3.94	5
3150	Hard maple		300	.027		3.23	1.22		4.45	5.55
3160	Cherry		300	.027		3.52	1.22		4.74	5.90
9000	Minimum labor/equipment charge		4	2	Job		91.50		91.50	151

06 22 13.40 Moldings, Exterior

		Crew	Daily Output	Labor-Hours	Unit	Material	2014 Bare Costs Labor	2014 Bare Costs Equipment	Total	Total Incl O&P
0010	**MOLDINGS, EXTERIOR**									
0100	Band board, cedar, rough sawn, 1" x 2"	1 Carp	300	.027	L.F.	.54	1.22		1.76	2.61
0110	1" x 3"		300	.027		.81	1.22		2.03	2.90
0120	1" x 4"		250	.032		1.07	1.47		2.54	3.59
0130	1" x 6"		250	.032		1.61	1.47		3.08	4.18
0140	1" x 8"		225	.036		2.15	1.63		3.78	5.05
0150	1" x 10"		225	.036		2.67	1.63		4.30	5.60
0160	1" x 12"		200	.040		3.21	1.83		5.04	6.55
0240	STK, 1" x 2"		300	.027		.43	1.22		1.65	2.49
0250	1" x 3"		300	.027		.48	1.22		1.70	2.53
0260	1" x 4"		250	.032		.62	1.47		2.09	3.09
0270	1" x 6"		250	.032		.96	1.47		2.43	3.46
0280	1" x 8"		225	.036		1.41	1.63		3.04	4.23
0290	1" x 10"		225	.036		2.08	1.63		3.71	4.97
0300	1" x 12"		200	.040		3.21	1.83		5.04	6.55
0310	Pine, #2, 1" x 2"		300	.027		.25	1.22		1.47	2.29
0320	1" x 3"		300	.027		.40	1.22		1.62	2.45
0330	1" x 4"		250	.032		.49	1.47		1.96	2.95
0340	1" x 6"		250	.032		.83	1.47		2.30	3.32
0350	1" x 8"		225	.036		1.22	1.63		2.85	4.02
0360	1" x 10"		225	.036		1.59	1.63		3.22	4.43
0370	1" x 12"		200	.040		2.05	1.83		3.88	5.25
0380	D & better, 1" x 2"		300	.027		.41	1.22		1.63	2.47
0390	1" x 3"		300	.027		.61	1.22		1.83	2.69
0400	1" x 4"		250	.032		.82	1.47		2.29	3.31
0410	1" x 6"		250	.032		1.12	1.47		2.59	3.64
0420	1" x 8"		225	.036		1.62	1.63		3.25	4.46
0430	1" x 10"		225	.036		2.03	1.63		3.66	4.92
0440	1" x 12"		200	.040		2.63	1.83		4.46	5.90
0450	Redwood, clear all heart, 1" x 2"		300	.027		.63	1.22		1.85	2.71
0460	1" x 3"		300	.027		.94	1.22		2.16	3.05
0470	1" x 4"		250	.032		1.19	1.47		2.66	3.72
0480	1" x 6"		252	.032		1.78	1.46		3.24	4.35
0490	1" x 8"		225	.036		2.36	1.63		3.99	5.25

06 22 13.40 Moldings, Exterior		Crew	Daily Output	Labor-Hours	Unit	Material	2014 Bare Costs Labor	Equipment	Total	Total Incl O&P
0500	1" x 10"	1 Carp	225	.036	L.F.	3.96	1.63		5.59	7.05
0510	1" x 12"		200	.040		4.75	1.83		6.58	8.25
0530	Corner board, cedar, rough sawn, 1" x 2"		225	.036		.54	1.63		2.17	3.28
0540	1" x 3"		225	.036		.81	1.63		2.44	3.57
0550	1" x 4"		200	.040		1.07	1.83		2.90	4.19
0560	1" x 6"		200	.040		1.61	1.83		3.44	4.78
0570	1" x 8"		200	.040		2.15	1.83		3.98	5.40
0580	1" x 10"		175	.046		2.67	2.10		4.77	6.40
0590	1" x 12"		175	.046		3.21	2.10		5.31	6.95
0670	STK, 1" x 2"		225	.036		.43	1.63		2.06	3.16
0680	1" x 3"		225	.036		.48	1.63		2.11	3.20
0690	1" x 4"		200	.040		.60	1.83		2.43	3.67
0700	1" x 6"		200	.040		.96	1.83		2.79	4.06
0710	1" x 8"		200	.040		1.41	1.83		3.24	4.56
0720	1" x 10"		175	.046		2.08	2.10		4.18	5.75
0730	1" x 12"		175	.046		3.21	2.10		5.31	6.95
0740	Pine, #2, 1" x 2"		225	.036		.25	1.63		1.88	2.96
0750	1" x 3"		225	.036		.40	1.63		2.03	3.12
0760	1" x 4"		200	.040		.49	1.83		2.32	3.55
0770	1" x 6"		200	.040		.83	1.83		2.66	3.92
0780	1" x 8"		200	.040		1.22	1.83		3.05	4.35
0790	1" x 10"		175	.046		1.59	2.10		3.69	5.20
0800	1" x 12"		175	.046		2.05	2.10		4.15	5.70
0810	D & better, 1" x 2"		225	.036		.41	1.63		2.04	3.14
0820	1" x 3"		225	.036		.61	1.63		2.24	3.36
0830	1" x 4"		200	.040		.82	1.83		2.65	3.91
0840	1" x 6"		200	.040		1.12	1.83		2.95	4.24
0850	1" x 8"		200	.040		1.62	1.83		3.45	4.79
0860	1" x 10"		175	.046		2.03	2.10		4.13	5.70
0870	1" x 12"		175	.046		2.63	2.10		4.73	6.35
0880	Redwood, clear all heart, 1" x 2"		225	.036		.63	1.63		2.26	3.38
0890	1" x 3"		225	.036		.94	1.63		2.57	3.72
0900	1" x 4"		200	.040		1.19	1.83		3.02	4.32
0910	1" x 6"		200	.040		1.78	1.83		3.61	4.97
0920	1" x 8"		200	.040		2.36	1.83		4.19	5.60
0930	1" x 10"		175	.046		3.96	2.10		6.06	7.80
0940	1" x 12"		175	.046		4.75	2.10		6.85	8.70
0950	Cornice board, cedar, rough sawn, 1" x 2"		330	.024		.54	1.11		1.65	2.43
0960	1" x 3"		290	.028		.81	1.27		2.08	2.97
0970	1" x 4"		250	.032		1.07	1.47		2.54	3.59
0980	1" x 6"		250	.032		1.61	1.47		3.08	4.18
0990	1" x 8"		200	.040		2.15	1.83		3.98	5.40
1000	1" x 10"		180	.044		2.67	2.04		4.71	6.30
1010	1" x 12"		180	.044		3.21	2.04		5.25	6.90
1020	STK, 1" x 2"		330	.024		.43	1.11		1.54	2.31
1030	1" x 3"		290	.028		.48	1.27		1.75	2.60
1040	1" x 4"		250	.032		.62	1.47		2.09	3.09
1050	1" x 6"		250	.032		.96	1.47		2.43	3.46
1060	1" x 8"		200	.040		1.41	1.83		3.24	4.56
1070	1" x 10"		180	.044		2.08	2.04		4.12	5.65
1080	1" x 12"		180	.044		3.21	2.04		5.25	6.90
1500	Pine, #2, 1" x 2"		330	.024		.25	1.11		1.36	2.11
1510	1" x 3"		290	.028		.27	1.27		1.54	2.38

06 22 13.40 Moldings, Exterior		Crew	Daily Output	Labor-Hours	Unit	Material	2014 Bare Costs Labor	Equipment	Total	Total Incl O&P
1600	1" x 4"	1 Carp	250	.032	L.F.	.49	1.47		1.96	2.95
1700	1" x 6"		250	.032		.83	1.47		2.30	3.32
1800	1" x 8"		200	.040		1.22	1.83		3.05	4.35
1900	1" x 10"		180	.044		1.59	2.04		3.63	5.10
2000	1" x 12"		180	.044		2.05	2.04		4.09	5.60
2020	D & better, 1" x 2"		330	.024		.41	1.11		1.52	2.29
2030	1" x 3"		290	.028		.61	1.27		1.88	2.76
2040	1" x 4"		250	.032		.82	1.47		2.29	3.31
2050	1" x 6"		250	.032		1.12	1.47		2.59	3.64
2060	1" x 8"		200	.040		1.62	1.83		3.45	4.79
2070	1" x 10"		180	.044		2.03	2.04		4.07	5.60
2080	1" x 12"		180	.044		2.63	2.04		4.67	6.25
2090	Redwood, clear all heart, 1" x 2"		330	.024		.63	1.11		1.74	2.53
2100	1" x 3"		290	.028		.94	1.27		2.21	3.12
2110	1" x 4"		250	.032		1.19	1.47		2.66	3.72
2120	1" x 6"		250	.032		1.78	1.47		3.25	4.37
2130	1" x 8"		200	.040		2.36	1.83		4.19	5.60
2140	1" x 10"		180	.044		3.96	2.04		6	7.70
2150	1" x 12"		180	.044		4.75	2.04		6.79	8.60
2160	3 piece, 1" x 2", 1" x 4", 1" x 6", rough sawn cedar		80	.100		3.24	4.59		7.83	11.10
2180	STK cedar		80	.100		2.01	4.59		6.60	9.75
2200	#2 pine		80	.100		1.57	4.59		6.16	9.30
2210	D & better pine		80	.100		2.35	4.59		6.94	10.15
2220	Clear all heart redwood		80	.100		3.60	4.59		8.19	11.50
2230	1" x 8", 1" x 10", 1" x 12", rough sawn cedar		65	.123		8	5.65		13.65	18.05
2240	STK cedar		65	.123		6.65	5.65		12.30	16.60
2300	#2 pine		65	.123		4.83	5.65		10.48	14.55
2320	D & better pine		65	.123		6.25	5.65		11.90	16.15
2330	Clear all heart redwood		65	.123		11.05	5.65		16.70	21.50
2340	Door/window casing, cedar, rough sawn, 1" x 2"		275	.029		.54	1.33		1.87	2.79
2350	1" x 3"		275	.029		.81	1.33		2.14	3.08
2360	1" x 4"		250	.032		1.07	1.47		2.54	3.59
2370	1" x 6"		250	.032		1.61	1.47		3.08	4.18
2380	1" x 8"		230	.035		2.15	1.59		3.74	4.99
2390	1" x 10"		230	.035		2.67	1.59		4.26	5.55
2395	1" x 12"		210	.038		3.21	1.75		4.96	6.40
2410	STK, 1" x 2"		275	.029		.43	1.33		1.76	2.67
2420	1" x 3"		275	.029		.48	1.33		1.81	2.71
2430	1" x 4"		250	.032		.62	1.47		2.09	3.09
2440	1" x 6"		250	.032		.96	1.47		2.43	3.46
2450	1" x 8"		230	.035		1.41	1.59		3	4.17
2460	1" x 10"		230	.035		2.08	1.59		3.67	4.91
2470	1" x 12"		210	.038		3.21	1.75		4.96	6.40
2550	Pine, #2, 1" x 2"		275	.029		.25	1.33		1.58	2.47
2560	1" x 3"		275	.029		.40	1.33		1.73	2.63
2570	1" x 4"		250	.032		.49	1.47		1.96	2.95
2580	1" x 6"		250	.032		.83	1.47		2.30	3.32
2590	1" x 8"		230	.035		1.22	1.59		2.81	3.96
2600	1" x 10"		230	.035		1.59	1.59		3.18	4.37
2610	1" x 12"		210	.038		2.05	1.75		3.80	5.10
2620	Pine, D & better, 1" x 2"		275	.029		.41	1.33		1.74	2.65
2630	1" x 3"		275	.029		.61	1.33		1.94	2.87
2640	1" x 4"		250	.032		.82	1.47		2.29	3.31

06 22 13.40 Moldings, Exterior		Crew	Daily Output	Labor-Hours	Unit	Material	2014 Bare Costs Labor	Equipment	Total	Total Incl O&P
2650	1" x 6"	1 Carp	250	.032	L.F.	1.12	1.47		2.59	3.64
2660	1" x 8"		230	.035		1.62	1.59		3.21	4.40
2670	1" x 10"		230	.035		2.03	1.59		3.62	4.86
2680	1" x 12"		210	.038		2.63	1.75		4.38	5.75
2690	Redwood, clear all heart, 1" x 2"		275	.029		.63	1.33		1.96	2.89
2695	1" x 3"		275	.029		.94	1.33		2.27	3.23
2710	1" x 4"		250	.032		1.19	1.47		2.66	3.72
2715	1" x 6"		250	.032		1.78	1.47		3.25	4.37
2730	1" x 8"		230	.035		2.36	1.59		3.95	5.20
2740	1" x 10"		230	.035		3.96	1.59		5.55	7
2750	1" x 12"		210	.038		4.75	1.75		6.50	8.10
3500	Bellyband, 11/16" x 4-1/4"		250	.032		3.23	1.47		4.70	5.95
3610	Brickmold, pine, 1-1/4" x 2"		200	.040		2.50	1.83		4.33	5.75
3620	FJP, 1-1/4" x 2"		200	.040		1.06	1.83		2.89	4.18
5100	Fascia, cedar, rough sawn, 1" x 2"		275	.029		.54	1.33		1.87	2.79
5110	1" x 3"		275	.029		.81	1.33		2.14	3.08
5120	1" x 4"		250	.032		1.07	1.47		2.54	3.59
5200	1" x 6"		250	.032		1.61	1.47		3.08	4.18
5300	1" x 8"		230	.035		2.15	1.59		3.74	4.99
5310	1" x 10"		230	.035		2.67	1.59		4.26	5.55
5320	1" x 12"		210	.038		3.21	1.75		4.96	6.40
5400	2" x 4"		220	.036		1.05	1.67		2.72	3.90
5500	2" x 6"		220	.036		1.58	1.67		3.25	4.48
5600	2" x 8"		200	.040		2.11	1.83		3.94	5.35
5700	2" x 10"		180	.044		2.62	2.04		4.66	6.25
5800	2" x 12"		170	.047		6.25	2.16		8.41	10.45
6120	STK, 1" x 2"		275	.029		.43	1.33		1.76	2.67
6130	1" x 3"		275	.029		.48	1.33		1.81	2.71
6140	1" x 4"		250	.032		.62	1.47		2.09	3.09
6150	1" x 6"		250	.032		.96	1.47		2.43	3.46
6160	1" x 8"		230	.035		1.41	1.59		3	4.17
6170	1" x 10"		230	.035		2.08	1.59		3.67	4.91
6180	1" x 12"		210	.038		3.21	1.75		4.96	6.40
6185	2" x 2"		260	.031		.56	1.41		1.97	2.94
6190	Pine, #2, 1" x 2"		275	.029		.25	1.33		1.58	2.47
6200	1" x 3"		275	.029		.40	1.33		1.73	2.63
6210	1" x 4"		250	.032		.49	1.47		1.96	2.95
6220	1" x 6"		250	.032		.83	1.47		2.30	3.32
6230	1" x 8"		230	.035		1.22	1.59		2.81	3.96
6240	1" x 10"		230	.035		1.59	1.59		3.18	4.37
6250	1" x 12"		210	.038		2.05	1.75		3.80	5.10
6260	D & better, 1" x 2"		275	.029		.41	1.33		1.74	2.65
6270	1" x 3"		275	.029		.61	1.33		1.94	2.87
6280	1" x 4"		250	.032		.82	1.47		2.29	3.31
6290	1" x 6"		250	.032		1.12	1.47		2.59	3.64
6300	1" x 8"		230	.035		1.62	1.59		3.21	4.40
6310	1" x 10"		230	.035		2.03	1.59		3.62	4.86
6312	1" x 12"		210	.038		2.63	1.75		4.38	5.75
6330	Southern yellow, 1-1/4" x 5"		240	.033		2.27	1.53		3.80	5
6340	1-1/4" x 6"		240	.033		2.52	1.53		4.05	5.30
6350	1-1/4" x 8"		215	.037		3.43	1.71		5.14	6.55
6360	1-1/4" x 12"		190	.042		5.05	1.93		6.98	8.70
6370	Redwood, clear all heart, 1" x 2"		275	.029		.63	1.33		1.96	2.89

06 22 13 – Standard Pattern Wood Trim

06 22 13.40 Moldings, Exterior		Crew	Daily Output	Labor-Hours	Unit	Material	2014 Bare Costs Labor	Equipment	Total	Total Incl O&P
6380	1" x 3"	1 Carp	275	.029	L.F.	1.19	1.33		2.52	3.50
6390	1" x 4"		250	.032		1.19	1.47		2.66	3.72
6400	1" x 6"		250	.032		1.78	1.47		3.25	4.37
6410	1" x 8"		230	.035		2.36	1.59		3.95	5.20
6420	1" x 10"		230	.035		3.96	1.59		5.55	7
6430	1" x 12"		210	.038		4.75	1.75		6.50	8.10
6440	1-1/4" x 5"		240	.033		1.86	1.53		3.39	4.55
6450	1-1/4" x 6"		240	.033		2.22	1.53		3.75	4.95
6460	1-1/4" x 8"		215	.037		3.53	1.71		5.24	6.70
6470	1-1/4" x 12"		190	.042		7.10	1.93		9.03	11
6580	Frieze, cedar, rough sawn, 1" x 2"		275	.029		.54	1.33		1.87	2.79
6590	1" x 3"		275	.029		.81	1.33		2.14	3.08
6600	1" x 4"		250	.032		1.07	1.47		2.54	3.59
6610	1" x 6"		250	.032		1.61	1.47		3.08	4.18
6620	1" x 8"		250	.032		2.15	1.47		3.62	4.78
6630	1" x 10"		225	.036		2.67	1.63		4.30	5.60
6640	1" x 12"		200	.040		3.18	1.83		5.01	6.50
6650	STK, 1" x 2"		275	.029		.43	1.33		1.76	2.67
6660	1" x 3"		275	.029		.48	1.33		1.81	2.71
6670	1" x 4"		250	.032		.62	1.47		2.09	3.09
6680	1" x 6"		250	.032		.96	1.47		2.43	3.46
6690	1" x 8"		250	.032		1.41	1.47		2.88	3.96
6700	1" x 10"		225	.036		2.08	1.63		3.71	4.97
6710	1" x 12"		200	.040		3.21	1.83		5.04	6.55
6790	Pine, #2, 1" x 2"		275	.029		.25	1.33		1.58	2.47
6800	1" x 3"		275	.029		.40	1.33		1.73	2.63
6810	1" x 4"		250	.032		.49	1.47		1.96	2.95
6820	1" x 6"		250	.032		.83	1.47		2.30	3.32
6830	1" x 8"		250	.032		1.22	1.47		2.69	3.75
6840	1" x 10"		225	.036		1.59	1.63		3.22	4.43
6850	1" x 12"		200	.040		2.05	1.83		3.88	5.25
6860	D & better, 1" x 2"		275	.029		.41	1.33		1.74	2.65
6870	1" x 3"		275	.029		.61	1.33		1.94	2.87
6880	1" x 4"		250	.032		.82	1.47		2.29	3.31
6890	1" x 6"		250	.032		1.12	1.47		2.59	3.64
6900	1" x 8"		250	.032		1.62	1.47		3.09	4.19
6910	1" x 10"		225	.036		2.03	1.63		3.66	4.92
6920	1" x 12"		200	.040		2.63	1.83		4.46	5.90
6930	Redwood, clear all heart, 1" x 2"		275	.029		.63	1.33		1.96	2.89
6940	1" x 3"		275	.029		.94	1.33		2.27	3.23
6950	1" x 4"		250	.032		1.19	1.47		2.66	3.72
6960	1" x 6"		250	.032		1.78	1.47		3.25	4.37
6970	1" x 8"		250	.032		2.36	1.47		3.83	5
6980	1" x 10"		225	.036		3.96	1.63		5.59	7.05
6990	1" x 12"		200	.040		4.75	1.83		6.58	8.25
7000	Grounds, 1" x 1", cedar, rough sawn		300	.027		.28	1.22		1.50	2.31
7010	STK		300	.027		.27	1.22		1.49	2.30
7020	Pine, #2		300	.027		.16	1.22		1.38	2.18
7030	D & better		300	.027		.25	1.22		1.47	2.29
7050	Redwood		300	.027		.39	1.22		1.61	2.43
7060	Rake/verge board, cedar, rough sawn, 1" x 2"		225	.036		.54	1.63		2.17	3.28
7070	1" x 3"		225	.036		.81	1.63		2.44	3.57
7080	1" x 4"		200	.040		1.07	1.83		2.90	4.19

06 22 13 – Standard Pattern Wood Trim

06 22 13.40 Moldings, Exterior		Crew	Daily Output	Labor-Hours	Unit	Material	2014 Bare Costs Labor	Equipment	Total	Total Incl O&P
7090	1" x 6"	1 Carp	200	.040	L.F.	1.61	1.83		3.44	4.78
7100	1" x 8"		190	.042		2.15	1.93		4.08	5.55
7110	1" x 10"		190	.042		2.67	1.93		4.60	6.10
7120	1" x 12"		180	.044		3.21	2.04		5.25	6.90
7130	STK, 1" x 2"		225	.036		.43	1.63		2.06	3.16
7140	1" x 3"		225	.036		.48	1.63		2.11	3.20
7150	1" x 4"		200	.040		.62	1.83		2.45	3.69
7160	1" x 6"		200	.040		.96	1.83		2.79	4.06
7170	1" x 8"		190	.042		1.41	1.93		3.34	4.72
7180	1" x 10"		190	.042		2.08	1.93		4.01	5.45
7190	1" x 12"		180	.044		3.21	2.04		5.25	6.90
7200	Pine, #2, 1" x 2"		225	.036		.25	1.63		1.88	2.96
7210	1" x 3"		225	.036		.40	1.63		2.03	3.12
7220	1" x 4"		200	.040		.49	1.83		2.32	3.55
7230	1" x 6"		200	.040		.83	1.83		2.66	3.92
7240	1" x 8"		190	.042		1.22	1.93		3.15	4.51
7250	1" x 10"		190	.042		1.59	1.93		3.52	4.92
7260	1" x 12"		180	.044		2.05	2.04		4.09	5.60
7340	D & better, 1" x 2"		225	.036		.41	1.63		2.04	3.14
7350	1" x 3"		225	.036		.61	1.63		2.24	3.36
7360	1" x 4"		200	.040		.82	1.83		2.65	3.91
7370	1" x 6"		200	.040		1.12	1.83		2.95	4.24
7380	1" x 8"		190	.042		1.62	1.93		3.55	4.95
7390	1" x 10"		190	.042		2.03	1.93		3.96	5.40
7400	1" x 12"		180	.044		2.63	2.04		4.67	6.25
7410	Redwood, clear all heart, 1" x 2"		225	.036		.63	1.63		2.26	3.38
7420	1" x 3"		225	.036		.94	1.63		2.57	3.72
7430	1" x 4"		200	.040		1.19	1.83		3.02	4.32
7440	1" x 6"		200	.040		1.78	1.83		3.61	4.97
7450	1" x 8"		190	.042		2.36	1.93		4.29	5.75
7460	1" x 10"		190	.042		3.96	1.93		5.89	7.55
7470	1" x 12"		180	.044		4.75	2.04		6.79	8.60
7480	2" x 4"		200	.040		2.29	1.83		4.12	5.55
7490	2" x 6"		182	.044		3.43	2.02		5.45	7.10
7500	2" x 8"		165	.048		4.56	2.22		6.78	8.65
7630	Soffit, cedar, rough sawn, 1" x 2"	2 Carp	440	.036		.54	1.67		2.21	3.34
7640	1" x 3"		440	.036		.81	1.67		2.48	3.63
7650	1" x 4"		420	.038		1.07	1.75		2.82	4.05
7660	1" x 6"		420	.038		1.61	1.75		3.36	4.64
7670	1" x 8"		420	.038		2.15	1.75		3.90	5.25
7680	1" x 10"		400	.040		2.67	1.83		4.50	5.95
7690	1" x 12"		400	.040		3.21	1.83		5.04	6.55
7700	STK, 1" x 2"		440	.036		.43	1.67		2.10	3.22
7710	1" x 3"		440	.036		.48	1.67		2.15	3.26
7720	1" x 4"		420	.038		.62	1.75		2.37	3.55
7730	1" x 6"		420	.038		.96	1.75		2.71	3.92
7740	1" x 8"		420	.038		1.41	1.75		3.16	4.42
7750	1" x 10"		400	.040		2.08	1.83		3.91	5.30
7760	1" x 12"		400	.040		3.21	1.83		5.04	6.55
7770	Pine, #2, 1" x 2"		440	.036		.25	1.67		1.92	3.02
7780	1" x 3"		440	.036		.40	1.67		2.07	3.18
7790	1" x 4"		420	.038		.49	1.75		2.24	3.41
7800	1" x 6"		420	.038		.83	1.75		2.58	3.78

06 22 Millwork

06 22 13 – Standard Pattern Wood Trim

06 22 13.40 Moldings, Exterior

		Crew	Daily Output	Labor-Hours	Unit	Material	2014 Bare Costs Labor	Equipment	Total	Total Incl O&P
7810	1" x 8"	2 Carp	420	.038	L.F.	1.22	1.75		2.97	4.21
7820	1" x 10"		400	.040		1.59	1.83		3.42	4.76
7830	1" x 12"		400	.040		2.05	1.83		3.88	5.25
7840	D & better, 1" x 2"		440	.036		.41	1.67		2.08	3.20
7850	1" x 3"		440	.036		.61	1.67		2.28	3.42
7860	1" x 4"		420	.038		.82	1.75		2.57	3.77
7870	1" x 6"		420	.038		1.12	1.75		2.87	4.10
7880	1" x 8"		420	.038		1.62	1.75		3.37	4.65
7890	1" x 10"		400	.040		2.03	1.83		3.86	5.25
7900	1" x 12"		400	.040		2.63	1.83		4.46	5.90
7910	Redwood, clear all heart, 1" x 2"		440	.036		.63	1.67		2.30	3.44
7920	1" x 3"		440	.036		.94	1.67		2.61	3.78
7930	1" x 4"		420	.038		1.19	1.75		2.94	4.18
7940	1" x 6"		420	.038		1.78	1.75		3.53	4.83
7950	1" x 8"		420	.038		2.36	1.75		4.11	5.45
7960	1" x 10"		400	.040		3.96	1.83		5.79	7.35
7970	1" x 12"		400	.040		4.75	1.83		6.58	8.25
8050	Trim, crown molding, pine, 11/16" x 4-1/4"	1 Carp	250	.032		4.54	1.47		6.01	7.40
8060	Back band, 11/16" x 1-1/16"		250	.032		.99	1.47		2.46	3.50
8070	Insect screen frame stock, 1-1/16" x 1-3/4"		395	.020		2.39	.93		3.32	4.16
8080	Dentils, 2-1/2" x 2-1/2" x 4", 6" O.C.		30	.267		1.22	12.25		13.47	21.50
8100	Fluted, 5-1/2"		165	.048		4.52	2.22		6.74	8.60
8110	Stucco bead, 1-3/8" x 1-5/8"		250	.032		2.50	1.47		3.97	5.15
9000	Minimum labor/equipment charge		4	2	Job		91.50		91.50	151

06 22 13.45 Moldings, Trim

		Crew	Daily Output	Labor-Hours	Unit	Material	2014 Bare Costs Labor	Equipment	Total	Total Incl O&P
0010	**MOLDINGS, TRIM**									
0200	Astragal, stock pine, 11/16" x 1-3/4"	1 Carp	255	.031	L.F.	1.42	1.44		2.86	3.92
0250	1-5/16" x 2-3/16"		240	.033		2.10	1.53		3.63	4.82
0800	Chair rail, stock pine, 5/8" x 2-1/2"		270	.030		1.68	1.36		3.04	4.08
0900	5/8" x 3-1/2"		240	.033		2.65	1.53		4.18	5.45
1000	Closet pole, stock pine, 1-1/8" diameter		200	.040		1.22	1.83		3.05	4.35
1100	Fir, 1-5/8" diameter		200	.040		2.36	1.83		4.19	5.60
3300	Half round, stock pine, 1/4" x 1/2"		270	.030		.31	1.36		1.67	2.57
3350	1/2" x 1"		255	.031		.74	1.44		2.18	3.17
3400	Handrail, fir, single piece, stock, hardware not included									
3450	1-1/2" x 1-3/4"	1 Carp	80	.100	L.F.	2.50	4.59		7.09	10.30
3470	Pine, 1-1/2" x 1-3/4"		80	.100		2.38	4.59		6.97	10.15
3500	1-1/2" x 2-1/2"		76	.105		2.67	4.83		7.50	10.90
3600	Lattice, stock pine, 1/4" x 1-1/8"		270	.030		.51	1.36		1.87	2.79
3700	1/4" x 1-3/4"		250	.032		.92	1.47		2.39	3.42
3800	Miscellaneous, custom, pine, 1" x 1"		270	.030		.38	1.36		1.74	2.65
3850	1" x 2"		265	.030		.76	1.38		2.14	3.11
3900	1" x 3"		240	.033		1.14	1.53		2.67	3.76
4100	Birch or oak, nominal 1" x 1"		240	.033		.45	1.53		1.98	3
4200	Nominal 1" x 3"		215	.037		1.34	1.71		3.05	4.27
4400	Walnut, nominal 1" x 1"		215	.037		.54	1.71		2.25	3.40
4500	Nominal 1" x 3"		200	.040		1.63	1.83		3.46	4.80
4700	Teak, nominal 1" x 1"		215	.037		2.54	1.71		4.25	5.60
4800	Nominal 1" x 3"		200	.040		7.60	1.83		9.43	11.35
4900	Quarter round, stock pine, 1/4" x 1/4"		275	.029		.31	1.33		1.64	2.53
4950	3/4" x 3/4"		255	.031		.71	1.44		2.15	3.14
5600	Wainscot moldings, 1-1/8" x 9/16", 2' high, minimum		76	.105	S.F.	12.35	4.83		17.18	21.50

06 22 13 – Standard Pattern Wood Trim

06 22 13.45 Moldings, Trim		Crew	Daily Output	Labor-Hours	Unit	Material	2014 Bare Costs Labor	2014 Bare Costs Equipment	Total	Total Incl O&P
5700	Maximum	1 Carp	65	.123	S.F.	15.65	5.65		21.30	26.50
9000	Minimum labor/equipment charge	↓	4	2	Job		91.50		91.50	151

06 22 13.50 Moldings, Window and Door

		Crew	Daily Output	Labor-Hours	Unit	Material	Labor	Equipment	Total	Total Incl O&P
0010	**MOLDINGS, WINDOW AND DOOR**									
2800	Door moldings, stock, decorative, 1-1/8" wide, plain	1 Carp	17	.471	Set	51.50	21.50		73	92
2900	Detailed		17	.471	"	87.50	21.50		109	132
2960	Clear pine door jamb, no stops, 11/16" x 4-9/16"		240	.033	L.F.	5.15	1.53		6.68	8.20
3150	Door trim set, 1 head and 2 sides, pine, 2-1/2 wide		12	.667	Opng.	25.50	30.50		56	78
3170	3-1/2" wide		11	.727	"	37	33.50		70.50	95.50
3250	Glass beads, stock pine, 3/8" x 1/2"		275	.029	L.F.	.37	1.33		1.70	2.60
3270	3/8" x 7/8"		270	.030		.50	1.36		1.86	2.78
4850	Parting bead, stock pine, 3/8" x 3/4"		275	.029		.45	1.33		1.78	2.69
4870	1/2" x 3/4"		255	.031		.57	1.44		2.01	2.99
5000	Stool caps, stock pine, 11/16" x 3-1/2"		200	.040		2.65	1.83		4.48	5.95
5100	1-1/16" x 3-1/4"		150	.053	↓	4.15	2.45		6.60	8.60
5300	Threshold, oak, 3' long, inside, 5/8" x 3-5/8"		32	.250	Ea.	6.40	11.45		17.85	26
5400	Outside, 1-1/2" x 7-5/8"	↓	16	.500	"	38	23		61	79.50
5900	Window trim sets, including casings, header, stops,									
5910	stool and apron, 2-1/2" wide, minimum	1 Carp	13	.615	Opng.	37	28		65	87
5950	Average		10	.800		43.50	36.50		80	109
6000	Maximum		6	1.333	↓	62.50	61		123.50	169
9000	Minimum labor/equipment charge	↓	4	2	Job		91.50		91.50	151

06 22 13.60 Moldings, Soffits

		Crew	Daily Output	Labor-Hours	Unit	Material	Labor	Equipment	Total	Total Incl O&P
0010	**MOLDINGS, SOFFITS** R061110-30									
0200	Soffits, pine, 1" x 4"	2 Carp	420	.038	L.F.	.47	1.75		2.22	3.38
0210	1" x 6"		420	.038		.80	1.75		2.55	3.75
0220	1" x 8"		420	.038		1.19	1.75		2.94	4.18
0230	1" x 10"		400	.040		1.55	1.83		3.38	4.71
0240	1" x 12"		400	.040		2.01	1.83		3.84	5.20
0250	STK cedar, 1" x 4"		420	.038		.59	1.75		2.34	3.52
0260	1" x 6"		420	.038		.93	1.75		2.68	3.89
0270	1" x 8"		420	.038		1.38	1.75		3.13	4.39
0280	1" x 10"		400	.040		2.04	1.83		3.87	5.25
0290	1" x 12"		400	.040	↓	3.17	1.83		5	6.50
1000	Exterior AC plywood, 1/4" thick		400	.040	S.F.	.62	1.83		2.45	3.69
1050	3/8" thick		400	.040		.93	1.83		2.76	4.03
1100	1/2" thick	↓	400	.040		1.06	1.83		2.89	4.18
1150	Polyvinyl chloride, white, solid	1 Carp	230	.035		2.04	1.59		3.63	4.86
1160	Perforated	"	230	.035	↓	2.04	1.59		3.63	4.86
1170	Accessories, "J" channel 5/8"	2 Carp	700	.023	L.F.	.43	1.05		1.48	2.19
9000	Minimum labor/equipment charge	"	5	3.200	Job		147		147	241

06 25 Prefinished Paneling

06 25 13 – Prefinished Hardboard Paneling

06 25 13.10 Paneling, Hardboard

		Crew	Daily Output	Labor-Hours	Unit	Material	2014 Bare Costs Labor	Equipment	Total	Total Incl O&P
0010	**PANELING, HARDBOARD**									
0050	Not incl. furring or trim, hardboard, tempered, 1/8" thick ⒢	2 Carp	500	.032	S.F.	.39	1.47		1.86	2.84
0100	1/4" thick ⒢		500	.032		.63	1.47		2.10	3.10
0300	Tempered pegboard, 1/8" thick ⒢		500	.032		.40	1.47		1.87	2.85
0400	1/4" thick ⒢		500	.032		.65	1.47		2.12	3.13
0600	Untempered hardboard, natural finish, 1/8" thick ⒢		500	.032		.41	1.47		1.88	2.86
0700	1/4" thick ⒢		500	.032		.50	1.47		1.97	2.96
0900	Untempered pegboard, 1/8" thick ⒢		500	.032		.42	1.47		1.89	2.87
1000	1/4" thick ⒢		500	.032		.46	1.47		1.93	2.92
1200	Plastic faced hardboard, 1/8" thick ⒢		500	.032		.63	1.47		2.10	3.10
1300	1/4" thick ⒢		500	.032		.86	1.47		2.33	3.36
1500	Plastic faced pegboard, 1/8" thick ⒢		500	.032		.64	1.47		2.11	3.11
1600	1/4" thick ⒢		500	.032		.82	1.47		2.29	3.31
1800	Wood grained, plain or grooved, 1/4" thick, minimum ⒢		500	.032		.66	1.47		2.13	3.14
1900	Maximum ⒢		425	.038	↓	1.35	1.73		3.08	4.33
2100	Moldings for hardboard, wood or aluminum, minimum		500	.032	L.F.	.39	1.47		1.86	2.84
2200	Maximum	↓	425	.038	"	1.29	1.73		3.02	4.26
9000	Minimum labor/equipment charge	1 Carp	2	4	Job		183		183	300

06 25 16 – Prefinished Plywood Paneling

06 25 16.10 Paneling, Plywood

		Crew	Daily Output	Labor-Hours	Unit	Material	2014 Bare Costs Labor	Equipment	Total	Total Incl O&P
0010	**PANELING, PLYWOOD** R061636-20									
2400	Plywood, prefinished, 1/4" thick, 4' x 8' sheets									
2410	with vertical grooves. Birch faced, minimum	2 Carp	500	.032	S.F.	.41	1.47		1.88	2.86
2420	Average		420	.038		.83	1.75		2.58	3.78
2430	Maximum		350	.046		1.25	2.10		3.35	4.82
2600	Mahogany, African		400	.040		2.90	1.83		4.73	6.20
2700	Philippine (Lauan)		500	.032		.60	1.47		2.07	3.07
2900	Oak or Cherry, minimum		500	.032		.34	1.47		1.81	2.78
3000	Maximum		400	.040		2.06	1.83		3.89	5.30
3200	Rosewood		320	.050		2.90	2.29		5.19	6.95
3400	Teak		400	.040		2.90	1.83		4.73	6.20
3600	Chestnut		375	.043		4.87	1.96		6.83	8.55
3800	Pecan		400	.040		2.10	1.83		3.93	5.30
3900	Walnut, minimum		500	.032		2.06	1.47		3.53	4.68
3950	Maximum		400	.040		5.30	1.83		7.13	8.85
4000	Plywood, prefinished, 3/4" thick, stock grades, minimum		320	.050		1.56	2.29		3.85	5.50
4100	Maximum		224	.071		4.68	3.28		7.96	10.55
4300	Architectural grade, minimum		224	.071		4.68	3.28		7.96	10.55
4400	Maximum		160	.100		4.68	4.59		9.27	12.70
4600	Plywood, "A" face, birch, VC, 1/2" thick, natural		450	.036		2.18	1.63		3.81	5.10
4700	Select		450	.036		2.18	1.63		3.81	5.10
4900	Veneer core, 3/4" thick, natural		320	.050		2.03	2.29		4.32	6
5000	Select		320	.050		2.27	2.29		4.56	6.25
5200	Lumber core, 3/4" thick, natural		320	.050		3.05	2.29		5.34	7.15
5500	Plywood, knotty pine, 1/4" thick, A2 grade		450	.036		1.67	1.63		3.30	4.52
5600	A3 grade		450	.036		2.10	1.63		3.73	4.99
5800	3/4" thick, veneer core, A2 grade		320	.050		2.15	2.29		4.44	6.15
5900	A3 grade		320	.050		2.42	2.29		4.71	6.45
6100	Aromatic cedar, 1/4" thick, plywood		400	.040		2.12	1.83		3.95	5.35
6200	1/4" thick, particle board	↓	400	.040	↓	1.03	1.83		2.86	4.14
9000	Minimum labor/equipment charge	1 Carp	2	4	Job		183		183	300

163

06 25 Prefinished Paneling

06 25 26 – Panel System

06 25 26.10 Panel Systems	Crew	Daily Output	Labor-Hours	Unit	Material	2014 Bare Costs Labor	Equipment	Total	Total Incl O&P
0010 **PANEL SYSTEMS**									
0100 Raised panel, eng. wood core w/wood veneer, std., paint grade	2 Carp	300	.053	S.F.	10.35	2.45		12.80	15.40
0110 Oak veneer		300	.053		24	2.45		26.45	30
0120 Maple veneer		300	.053		30	2.45		32.45	37
0130 Cherry veneer		300	.053		34.50	2.45		36.95	41.50
0300 Class I fire rated, paint grade		300	.053		12	2.45		14.45	17.20
0310 Oak veneer		300	.053		28	2.45		30.45	34.50
0320 Maple veneer		300	.053		37.50	2.45		39.95	45
0330 Cherry veneer		300	.053		45	2.45		47.45	53.50
0510 Beadboard, 5/8" MDF, standard, primed		300	.053		7.85	2.45		10.30	12.60
0520 Oak veneer, unfinished		300	.053		12.40	2.45		14.85	17.65
0530 Maple veneer, unfinished		300	.053		13.55	2.45		16	18.90
0610 Rustic paneling, 5/8" MDF, standard, maple veneer, unfinished	▼	300	.053	▼	13.60	2.45		16.05	18.95

06 26 Board Paneling

06 26 13 – Profile Board Paneling

06 26 13.10 Paneling, Boards

	Crew	Daily Output	Labor-Hours	Unit	Material	2014 Bare Costs Labor	Equipment	Total	Total Incl O&P
0010 **PANELING, BOARDS**									
6400 Wood board paneling, 3/4" thick, knotty pine	2 Carp	300	.053	S.F.	1.91	2.45		4.36	6.10
6500 Rough sawn cedar		300	.053		3.09	2.45		5.54	7.40
6700 Redwood, clear, 1" x 4" boards		300	.053		4.96	2.45		7.41	9.45
6900 Aromatic cedar, closet lining, boards	▼	275	.058	▼	2.02	2.67		4.69	6.60
9000 Minimum labor/equipment charge	1 Carp	2	4	Job		183		183	300

06 43 Wood Stairs and Railings

06 43 13 – Wood Stairs

06 43 13.20 Prefabricated Wood Stairs

	Crew	Daily Output	Labor-Hours	Unit	Material	2014 Bare Costs Labor	Equipment	Total	Total Incl O&P
0010 **PREFABRICATED WOOD STAIRS**									
0100 Box stairs, prefabricated, 3'-0" wide									
0110 Oak treads, up to 14 risers	2 Carp	39	.410	Riser	92.50	18.80		111.30	133
0600 With pine treads for carpet, up to 14 risers	"	39	.410	"	59.50	18.80		78.30	96.50
1100 For 4' wide stairs, add				Flight	25%				
1550 Stairs, prefabricated stair handrail with balusters	1 Carp	30	.267	L.F.	74	12.25		86.25	102
1700 Basement stairs, prefabricated, pine treads									
1710 Pine risers, 3' wide, up to 14 risers	2 Carp	52	.308	Riser	59.50	14.10		73.60	88.50
4000 Residential, wood, oak treads, prefabricated		1.50	10.667	Flight	1,200	490		1,690	2,125
4200 Built in place	▼	.44	36.364	"	1,900	1,675		3,575	4,850
4400 Spiral, oak, 4'-6" diameter, unfinished, prefabricated,									
4500 incl. railing, 9' high	2 Carp	1.50	10.667	Flight	3,625	490		4,115	4,775
9000 Minimum labor/equipment charge	"	3	5.333	Job		245		245	400

06 43 13.40 Wood Stair Parts

	Crew	Daily Output	Labor-Hours	Unit	Material	2014 Bare Costs Labor	Equipment	Total	Total Incl O&P
0010 **WOOD STAIR PARTS**									
0020 Pin top balusters, 1-1/4", oak, 34"	1 Carp	96	.083	Ea.	7.80	3.82		11.62	14.90
0030 38"		96	.083		9.85	3.82		13.67	17.15
0040 42"		96	.083		12.10	3.82		15.92	19.60
0050 Poplar, 34"		96	.083		3.05	3.82		6.87	9.65
0060 38"		96	.083		3.88	3.82		7.70	10.55
0070 42"	▼	96	.083		8.85	3.82		12.67	16

06 43 13 – Wood Stairs

06 43 13.40 Wood Stair Parts	Crew	Daily Output	Labor-Hours	Unit	Material	2014 Bare Costs Labor	Equipment	Total	Total Incl O&P
0080	Maple, 34"	1 Carp	96	.083	Ea.	4.90	3.82		8.72	11.70
0090	38"		96	.083		5.60	3.82		9.42	12.50
0100	42"		96	.083		6.50	3.82		10.32	13.45
0130	Primed, 34"		96	.083		3	3.82		6.82	9.60
0140	38"		96	.083		3.62	3.82		7.44	10.30
0150	42"		96	.083		4.42	3.82		8.24	11.15
0180	Box top balusters, 1-1/4", oak, 34"		60	.133		10.85	6.10		16.95	22
0190	38"		60	.133		12.50	6.10		18.60	24
0200	42"		60	.133		12.95	6.10		19.05	24.50
0210	Poplar, 34"		60	.133		8.65	6.10		14.75	19.55
0220	38"		60	.133		9.50	6.10		15.60	20.50
0230	42"		60	.133		10	6.10		16.10	21
0240	Maple, 34"		60	.133		11.90	6.10		18	23
0250	38"		60	.133		13.80	6.10		19.90	25.50
0260	42"		60	.133		14.20	6.10		20.30	25.50
0290	Primed, 34"		60	.133		7	6.10		13.10	17.75
0300	38"		60	.133		8	6.10		14.10	18.85
0310	42"		60	.133	▼	8.35	6.10		14.45	19.25
0340	Square balusters, cut from lineal stock, pine, 1-1/16" x 1-1/16"		180	.044	L.F.	1.49	2.04		3.53	4.99
0350	1-5/16" x 1-5/16"		180	.044		2	2.04		4.04	5.55
0360	1-5/8" x 1-5/8"		180	.044	▼	3.29	2.04		5.33	6.95
0370	Turned newel, oak, 3-1/2" square, 48" high		8	1	Ea.	94.50	46		140.50	180
0380	62" high		8	1		138	46		184	228
0390	Poplar, 3-1/2" square, 48" high		8	1		55	46		101	136
0400	62" high		8	1		75	46		121	158
0410	Maple, 3-1/2" square, 48" high		8	1		66	46		112	148
0420	62" high		8	1		93	46		139	178
0430	Square newel, oak, 3-1/2" square, 48" high		8	1		50	46		96	131
0440	58" high		8	1		70	46		116	153
0450	Poplar, 3-1/2" square, 48" high		8	1		35	46		81	114
0460	58" high		8	1		39	46		85	119
0470	Maple, 3" square, 48" high		8	1		50	46		96	131
0480	58" high		8	1	▼	62	46		108	144
0490	Railings, oak, minimum		96	.083	L.F.	9.50	3.82		13.32	16.75
0500	Average		96	.083		12.90	3.82		16.72	20.50
0510	Maximum		96	.083		13.50	3.82		17.32	21
0520	Maple, minimum		96	.083		15	3.82		18.82	23
0530	Average		96	.083		15.25	3.82		19.07	23
0540	Maximum		96	.083		15.50	3.82		19.32	23.50
0550	Oak, for bending rail, minimum		48	.167		22	7.65		29.65	36.50
0560	Average		48	.167		25	7.65		32.65	40
0570	Maximum		48	.167		28	7.65		35.65	43.50
0580	Maple, for bending rail, minimum		48	.167		25	7.65		32.65	39.50
0590	Average		48	.167		27	7.65		34.65	42.50
0600	Maximum		48	.167	▼	29.50	7.65		37.15	45
0610	Risers, oak, 3/4" x 8", 36" long		80	.100	Ea.	18	4.59		22.59	27.50
0620	42" long		80	.100		21	4.59		25.59	30.50
0630	48" long		80	.100		24	4.59		28.59	34
0640	54" long		80	.100		27	4.59		31.59	37
0650	60" long		80	.100		30	4.59		34.59	40.50
0660	72" long		80	.100		36	4.59		40.59	47
0670	Poplar, 3/4" x 8", 36" long		80	.100		12	4.59		16.59	21
0680	42" long	▼	80	.100	▼	14	4.59		18.59	23

06 43 Wood Stairs and Railings

06 43 13 – Wood Stairs

06 43 13.40 Wood Stair Parts

		Crew	Daily Output	Labor-Hours	Unit	Material	2014 Bare Costs Labor	Equipment	Total	Total Incl O&P
0690	48" long	1 Carp	80	.100	Ea.	16	4.59		20.59	25
0700	54" long		80	.100		18	4.59		22.59	27.50
0710	60" long		80	.100		20	4.59		24.59	29.50
0720	72" long		80	.100		24	4.59		28.59	34
0730	Pine, 1" x 8", 36" long		80	.100		3.57	4.59		8.16	11.50
0740	42" long		80	.100		4.17	4.59		8.76	12.15
0750	48" long		80	.100		4.76	4.59		9.35	12.80
0760	54" long		80	.100		5.35	4.59		9.94	13.45
0770	60" long		80	.100		5.95	4.59		10.54	14.10
0780	72" long		80	.100		7.15	4.59		11.74	15.40
0790	Treads, oak, no returns, 1-1/32" x 11-1/2" x 36" long		32	.250		29	11.45		40.45	51
0800	42" long		32	.250		34	11.45		45.45	56
0810	48" long		32	.250		38.50	11.45		49.95	61.50
0820	54" long		32	.250		43.50	11.45		54.95	67
0830	60" long		32	.250		48.50	11.45		59.95	72
0840	72" long		32	.250		58	11.45		69.45	83
0850	Mitred return one end, 1-1/32" x 11-1/2" x 36" long		24	.333		52	15.30		67.30	82
0860	42" long		24	.333		60.50	15.30		75.80	91.50
0870	48" long		24	.333		69.50	15.30		84.80	102
0880	54" long		24	.333		78	15.30		93.30	111
0890	60" long		24	.333		86.50	15.30		101.80	121
0900	72" long		24	.333		104	15.30		119.30	139
0910	Mitred return two ends, 1-1/32" x 11-1/2" x 36" long		12	.667		53	30.50		83.50	109
0920	42" long		12	.667		62	30.50		92.50	118
0930	48" long		12	.667		70.50	30.50		101	128
0940	54" long		12	.667		79.50	30.50		110	138
0950	60" long		12	.667		88.50	30.50		119	147
0960	72" long		12	.667		106	30.50		136.50	167
0970	Starting step, oak, 48", bullnose		8	1		195	46		241	291
0980	Double end bullnose		8	1		345	46		391	455
1030	Skirt board, pine, 1" x 10"		55	.145	L.F.	1.55	6.65		8.20	12.65
1040	1" x 12"		52	.154	"	2.01	7.05		9.06	13.80
1050	Oak landing tread, 1-1/16" thick		54	.148	S.F.	9	6.80		15.80	21
1060	Oak cove molding		96	.083	L.F.	1.45	3.82		5.27	7.90
1070	Oak stringer molding		96	.083	"	3.25	3.82		7.07	9.90
1090	Rail bolt, 5/16" x 3-1/2"		48	.167	Ea.	2.75	7.65		10.40	15.60
1100	5/16" x 4-1/2"		48	.167		2.75	7.65		10.40	15.60
1120	Newel post anchor		16	.500		9.75	23		32.75	48.50
1130	Tapered plug, 1/2"		240	.033		1	1.53		2.53	3.61
1140	1"		240	.033		.99	1.53		2.52	3.60
9000	Minimum labor/equipment charge		3	2.667	Job		122		122	201

06 43 16 – Wood Railings

06 43 16.10 Wood Handrails and Railings

		Crew	Daily Output	Labor-Hours	Unit	Material	2014 Bare Costs Labor	Equipment	Total	Total Incl O&P
0010	**WOOD HANDRAILS AND RAILINGS**									
0020	Custom design, architectural grade, hardwood, minimum	1 Carp	38	.211	L.F.	10	9.65		19.65	27
0100	Maximum		30	.267		62.50	12.25		74.75	89
0300	Stock interior railing with spindles 4" O.C., 4' long		40	.200		41	9.15		50.15	60
0400	8' long		48	.167		41	7.65		48.65	57.50
9000	Minimum labor/equipment charge		3	2.667	Job		122		122	201

166

06 44 Ornamental Woodwork

06 44 19 – Wood Grilles

06 44 19.10 Grilles

06 44 19.10 Grilles	Crew	Daily Output	Labor-Hours	Unit	Material	2014 Bare Costs Labor	Equipment	Total	Total Incl O&P
0010	**GRILLES** and panels, hardwood, sanded									
0020	2' x 4' to 4' x 8', custom designs, unfinished, minimum	1 Carp	38	.211	S.F.	61	9.65		70.65	83
0050	Average		30	.267		67.50	12.25		79.75	94.50
0100	Maximum		19	.421		70.50	19.30		89.80	109
9000	Minimum labor/equipment charge		2	4	Job		183		183	300

06 44 33 – Wood Mantels

06 44 33.10 Fireplace Mantels

06 44 33.10 Fireplace Mantels	Crew	Daily Output	Labor-Hours	Unit	Material	2014 Bare Costs Labor	Equipment	Total	Total Incl O&P
0010	**FIREPLACE MANTELS**									
0015	6" molding, 6' x 3'-6" opening, minimum	1 Carp	5	1.600	Opng.	248	73.50		321.50	395
0100	Maximum		5	1.600		445	73.50		518.50	610
0300	Prefabricated pine, colonial type, stock, deluxe		2	4		1,500	183		1,683	1,950
0400	Economy		3	2.667		690	122		812	960
9000	Minimum labor/equipment charge		3	2.667	Job		122		122	201

06 44 33.20 Fireplace Mantel Beam

06 44 33.20 Fireplace Mantel Beam	Crew	Daily Output	Labor-Hours	Unit	Material	2014 Bare Costs Labor	Equipment	Total	Total Incl O&P
0010	**FIREPLACE MANTEL BEAM**									
0020	Rough texture wood, 4" x 8"	1 Carp	36	.222	L.F.	8.30	10.20		18.50	26
0100	4" x 10"		35	.229	"	10.90	10.50		21.40	29
0300	Laminated hardwood, 2-1/4" x 10-1/2" wide, 6' long		5	1.600	Ea.	110	73.50		183.50	242
0400	8' long		5	1.600	"	150	73.50		223.50	286
0600	Brackets for above, rough sawn		12	.667	Pr.	10	30.50		40.50	61
0700	Laminated		12	.667	"	15	30.50		45.50	66.50
9000	Minimum labor/equipment charge		4	2	Job		91.50		91.50	151

06 44 39 – Wood Posts and Columns

06 44 39.10 Decorative Beams

06 44 39.10 Decorative Beams	Crew	Daily Output	Labor-Hours	Unit	Material	2014 Bare Costs Labor	Equipment	Total	Total Incl O&P
0010	**DECORATIVE BEAMS**									
0020	Rough sawn cedar, non-load bearing, 4" x 4"	2 Carp	180	.089	L.F.	1.20	4.08		5.28	8
0100	4" x 6"		170	.094		1.79	4.32		6.11	9.05
0200	4" x 8"		160	.100		2.39	4.59		6.98	10.20
0300	4" x 10"		150	.107		3.63	4.89		8.52	12.05
0400	4" x 12"		140	.114		4.61	5.25		9.86	13.65
0500	8" x 8"		130	.123		4.78	5.65		10.43	14.50
9000	Minimum labor/equipment charge	1 Carp	3	2.667	Job		122		122	201

06 44 39.20 Columns

06 44 39.20 Columns	Crew	Daily Output	Labor-Hours	Unit	Material	2014 Bare Costs Labor	Equipment	Total	Total Incl O&P
0010	**COLUMNS**									
0050	Aluminum, round colonial, 6" diameter	2 Carp	80	.200	V.L.F.	18.60	9.15		27.75	35.50
0100	8" diameter		62.25	.257		21.50	11.80		33.30	43
0200	10" diameter		55	.291		25.50	13.35		38.85	50
0250	Fir, stock units, hollow round, 6" diameter		80	.200		20	9.15		29.15	37
0300	8" diameter		80	.200		25	9.15		34.15	42
0350	10" diameter		70	.229		32.50	10.50		43	53
0360	12" diameter		65	.246		38.50	11.30		49.80	60.50
0400	Solid turned, to 8' high, 3-1/2" diameter		80	.200		9.10	9.15		18.25	25
0500	4-1/2" diameter		75	.213		13.60	9.80		23.40	31
0600	5-1/2" diameter		70	.229		17.75	10.50		28.25	37
0800	Square columns, built-up, 5" x 5"		65	.246		15.50	11.30		26.80	35.50
0900	Solid, 3-1/2" x 3-1/2"		130	.123		9.10	5.65		14.75	19.30
1600	Hemlock, tapered, T & G, 12" diam., 10' high		100	.160		36.50	7.35		43.85	52.50
1700	16' high		65	.246		71.50	11.30		82.80	97.50
1900	10' high, 14" diameter		100	.160		112	7.35		119.35	135
2000	18' high		65	.246		91	11.30		102.30	119
2200	18" diameter, 12' high		65	.246		163	11.30		174.30	199

167

06 44 Ornamental Woodwork

06 44 39 – Wood Posts and Columns

06 44 39.20 Columns		Crew	Daily Output	Labor-Hours	Unit	Material	2014 Bare Costs Labor	Equipment	Total	Total Incl O&P
2300	20' high	2 Carp	50	.320	V.L.F.	115	14.65		129.65	150
2500	20" diameter, 14' high		40	.400		184	18.35		202.35	232
2600	20' high	↓	35	.457		172	21		193	224
2800	For flat pilasters, deduct				↓	33%				
3000	For splitting into halves, add				Ea.	105			105	116
4000	Rough sawn cedar posts, 4" x 4"	2 Carp	250	.064	V.L.F.	3.33	2.93		6.26	8.50
4100	4" x 6"		235	.068		7.25	3.12		10.37	13.10
4200	6" x 6"		220	.073		11.70	3.33		15.03	18.35
4300	8" x 8"	↓	200	.080	↓	20.50	3.67		24.17	28.50
9000	Minimum labor/equipment charge	1 Carp	3	2.667	Job		122		122	201

06 48 Wood Frames

06 48 13 – Exterior Wood Door Frames

06 48 13.10 Exterior Wood Door Frames and Accessories

		Crew	Daily Output	Labor-Hours	Unit	Material	2014 Bare Costs Labor	Equipment	Total	Total Incl O&P
0010	**EXTERIOR WOOD DOOR FRAMES AND ACCESSORIES**									
0400	Exterior frame, incl. ext. trim, pine, 5/4 x 4-9/16" deep	2 Carp	375	.043	L.F.	6.60	1.96		8.56	10.50
0420	5-3/16" deep		375	.043		7.80	1.96		9.76	11.80
0440	6-9/16" deep		375	.043		7.90	1.96		9.86	11.90
0600	Oak, 5/4 x 4-9/16" deep		350	.046		16.90	2.10		19	22
0620	5-3/16" deep		350	.046		18.55	2.10		20.65	24
0640	6-9/16" deep		350	.046		20	2.10		22.10	25.50
1000	Sills, 8/4 x 8" deep, oak, no horns		100	.160		6.40	7.35		13.75	19.05
1020	2" horns		100	.160		17.10	7.35		24.45	31
1040	3" horns		100	.160		17.10	7.35		24.45	31
1100	8/4 x 10" deep, oak, no horns		90	.178		6	8.15		14.15	20
1120	2" horns		90	.178		22.50	8.15		30.65	38
1140	3" horns		90	.178	↓	22.50	8.15		30.65	38
2000	Exterior, colonial, frame & trim, 3' opng., in-swing, minimum		22	.727	Ea.	355	33.50		388.50	445
2010	Average		21	.762		580	35		615	695
2020	Maximum		20	.800		1,200	36.50		1,236.50	1,375
2100	5'-4" opening, in-swing, minimum		17	.941		420	43		463	535
2120	Maximum		15	1.067		1,200	49		1,249	1,400
2140	Out-swing, minimum		17	.941		420	43		463	535
2160	Maximum		15	1.067		1,200	49		1,249	1,400
2400	6'-0" opening, in-swing, minimum		16	1		420	46		466	540
2420	Maximum		10	1.600		1,200	73.50		1,273.50	1,450
2460	Out-swing, minimum		16	1		420	46		466	540
2480	Maximum		10	1.600	↓	1,200	73.50		1,273.50	1,450
2600	For two sidelights, add, minimum		30	.533	Opng.	67	24.50		91.50	114
2620	Maximum		20	.800	"	845	36.50		881.50	985
2700	Custom birch frame, 3'-0" opening		16	1	Ea.	230	46		276	330
2750	6'-0" opening		16	1		350	46		396	460
2900	Exterior, modern, plain trim, 3' opng., in-swing, minimum		26	.615		45	28		73	96
2920	Average		24	.667		53.50	30.50		84	109
2940	Maximum	↓	22	.727	↓	61.50	33.50		95	123

06 48 16 – Interior Wood Door Frames

06 48 16.10 Interior Wood Door Jamb and Frames

		Crew	Daily Output	Labor-Hours	Unit	Material	2014 Bare Costs Labor	Equipment	Total	Total Incl O&P
0010	**INTERIOR WOOD DOOR JAMB AND FRAMES**									
3000	Interior frame, pine, 11/16" x 3-5/8" deep	2 Carp	375	.043	L.F.	6.10	1.96		8.06	9.90
3020	4-9/16" deep	↓	375	.043	↓	6.25	1.96		8.21	10.05

06 48 Wood Frames

06 48 16 – Interior Wood Door Frames

06 48 16.10 Interior Wood Door Jamb and Frames	Crew	Daily Output	Labor-Hours	Unit	Material	2014 Bare Costs Labor	Equipment	Total	Total Incl O&P
3200	Oak, 11/16" x 3-5/8" deep	2 Carp	350	.046	L.F.	9	2.10		11.10	13.35
3220	4-9/16" deep		350	.046		9	2.10		11.10	13.35
3240	5-3/16" deep		350	.046		12.75	2.10		14.85	17.50
3400	Walnut, 11/16" x 3-5/8" deep		350	.046		8.25	2.10		10.35	12.55
3420	4-9/16" deep		350	.046		9	2.10		11.10	13.35
3440	5-3/16" deep		350	.046	▼	9	2.10		11.10	13.35
3600	Pocket door frame		16	1	Ea.	82	46		128	166
3800	Threshold, oak, 5/8" x 3-5/8" deep		200	.080	L.F.	3.56	3.67		7.23	9.95
3820	4-5/8" deep		190	.084		4.13	3.86		7.99	10.90
3840	5-5/8" deep	▼	180	.089	▼	6.50	4.08		10.58	13.85
9000	Minimum labor/equipment charge	1 Carp	4	2	Job		91.50		91.50	151

06 49 Wood Screens and Exterior Wood Shutters

06 49 19 – Exterior Wood Shutters

06 49 19.10 Shutters, Exterior	Crew	Daily Output	Labor-Hours	Unit	Material	2014 Bare Costs Labor	Equipment	Total	Total Incl O&P
0010	**SHUTTERS, EXTERIOR**									
0012	Aluminum, louvered, 1'-4" wide, 3'-0" long	1 Carp	10	.800	Pr.	75	36.50		111.50	143
0200	4'-0" long		10	.800		89.50	36.50		126	159
0300	5'-4" long		10	.800		118	36.50		154.50	191
0400	6'-8" long		9	.889		150	41		191	233
1000	Pine, louvered, primed, each 1'-2" wide, 3'-3" long		10	.800		215	36.50		251.50	298
1100	4'-7" long		10	.800		282	36.50		318.50	370
1250	Each 1'-4" wide, 3'-0" long		10	.800		224	36.50		260.50	305
1350	5'-3" long		10	.800		355	36.50		391.50	450
1500	Each 1'-6" wide, 3'-3" long		10	.800		262	36.50		298.50	350
1600	4'-7" long		10	.800		350	36.50		386.50	445
1620	Cedar, louvered, 1'-2" wide, 5'-7" long		10	.800		335	36.50		371.50	425
1630	Each 1'-4" wide, 2'-2" long		10	.800		176	36.50		212.50	255
1640	3'-0" long		10	.800		224	36.50		260.50	305
1650	3'-3" long		10	.800		238	36.50		274.50	325
1660	3'-11" long		10	.800		277	36.50		313.50	365
1670	4'-3" long		10	.800		296	36.50		332.50	385
1680	5'-3" long		10	.800		355	36.50		391.50	450
1690	5'-11" long		10	.800		390	36.50		426.50	490
1700	Door blinds, 6'-9" long, each 1'-3" wide		9	.889		415	41		456	525
1710	1'-6" wide		9	.889		490	41		531	605
1720	Cedar, solid raised panel, each 1'-4" wide, 3'-3" long		10	.800		335	36.50		371.50	425
1730	3'-11" long		10	.800		385	36.50		421.50	485
1740	4'-3" long		10	.800		415	36.50		451.50	515
1750	4'-7" long		10	.800		440	36.50		476.50	545
1760	4'-11" long		10	.800		465	36.50		501.50	575
1770	5'-11" long		10	.800		550	36.50		586.50	665
1800	Door blinds, 6'-9" long, each 1'-3" wide		9	.889		415	41		456	525
1900	1'-6" wide		9	.889		490	41		531	605
2500	Polystyrene, solid raised panel, each 1'-4" wide, 3'-3" long		10	.800		72	36.50		108.50	140
2600	3'-11" long		10	.800		97	36.50		133.50	168
2700	4'-7" long		10	.800		109	36.50		145.50	181
2800	5'-3" long		10	.800		126	36.50		162.50	200
2900	6'-8" long		9	.889		161	41		202	244
4500	Polystyrene, louvered, each 1'-2" wide, 3'-3" long		10	.800		65	36.50		101.50	132
4600	4'-7" long		10	.800		88	36.50		124.50	158

06 49 Wood Screens and Exterior Wood Shutters

06 49 19 – Exterior Wood Shutters

06 49 19.10 Shutters, Exterior		Crew	Daily Output	Labor-Hours	Unit	Material	2014 Bare Costs Labor	2014 Bare Costs Equipment	Total	Total Incl O&P
4750	5'-3" long	1 Carp	10	.800	Pr.	102	36.50		138.50	173
4850	6'-8" long		9	.889		126	41		167	206
6000	Vinyl, louvered, each 1'-2" x 4'-7" long		10	.800		88	36.50		124.50	158
6200	Each 1'-4" x 6'-8" long		9	.889		126	41		167	206
9000	Minimum labor/equipment charge		4	2	Job		91.50		91.50	151

06 51 Structural Plastic Shapes and Plates

06 51 13 – Plastic Lumber

06 51 13.10 Recycled Plastic Lumber

			Crew	Daily Output	Labor-Hours	Unit	Material	2014 Bare Costs Labor	2014 Bare Costs Equipment	Total	Total Incl O&P
0010	**RECYCLED PLASTIC LUMBER**										
4000	Sheeting, recycled plastic, black or white, 4' x 8' x 1/8"	G	2 Carp	1100	.015	S.F.	1.58	.67		2.25	2.84
4010	4' x 8' x 3/16"	G		1100	.015		2.27	.67		2.94	3.60
4020	4' x 8' x 1/4"	G		950	.017		2.36	.77		3.13	3.87
4030	4' x 8' x 3/8"	G		950	.017		3.67	.77		4.44	5.30
4040	4' x 8' x 1/2"	G		900	.018		4.85	.82		5.67	6.70
4050	4' x 8' x 5/8"	G		900	.018		6.55	.82		7.37	8.55
4060	4' x 8' x 3/4"	G		850	.019		8.25	.86		9.11	10.50
4070	Add for colors	G				Ea.	5%				
8500	100% recycled plastic, var colors, NLB, 2" x 2"	G				L.F.	1.76			1.76	1.94
8510	2" x 4"	G					3.67			3.67	4.04
8520	2" x 6"	G					5.75			5.75	6.35
8530	2" x 8"	G					7.90			7.90	8.70
8540	2" x 10"	G					11.50			11.50	12.65
8550	5/4" x 4"	G					4.26			4.26	4.69
8560	5/4" x 6"	G					5.05			5.05	5.55
8570	1" x 6"	G					2.86			2.86	3.15
8580	1/2" x 8"	G					3.41			3.41	3.75
8590	2" x 10" T & G	G					11.50			11.50	12.65
8600	3" x 10" T & G	G					13.65			13.65	15
8610	Add for premium colors	G					20%				

06 52 Plastic Structural Assemblies

06 52 10 – Fiberglass Structural Assemblies

06 52 10.30 Fiberglass Grating

		Crew	Daily Output	Labor-Hours	Unit	Material	2014 Bare Costs Labor	2014 Bare Costs Equipment	Total	Total Incl O&P
0010	**FIBERGLASS GRATING**									
0100	Molded, green (for mod. corrosive environment)									
0140	1" x 4" mesh, 1" thick	2 Sswk	400	.040	S.F.	10.65	2.04		12.69	15.45
0180	1-1/2" square mesh, 1" thick		400	.040		18.65	2.04		20.69	24.50
0220	1-1/4" thick		400	.040		11.90	2.04		13.94	16.85
0260	1-1/2" thick		400	.040		26	2.04		28.04	33
0300	2" square mesh, 2" thick		320	.050		24.50	2.56		27.06	31.50
1000	Orange (for highly corrosive environment)									
1040	1" x 4" mesh, 1" thick	2 Sswk	400	.040	S.F.	14.75	2.04		16.79	19.95
1080	1-1/2" square mesh, 1" thick		400	.040		19.55	2.04		21.59	25.50
1120	1-1/4" thick		400	.040		20.50	2.04		22.54	26.50
1160	1-1/2" thick		400	.040		22	2.04		24.04	28
1200	2" square mesh, 2" thick		320	.050		26	2.56		28.56	33.50
3000	Pultruded, green (for mod. corrosive environment)									
3040	1" O.C. bar spacing, 1" thick	2 Sswk	400	.040	S.F.	17.30	2.04		19.34	23

06 52 Plastic Structural Assemblies

06 52 10 – Fiberglass Structural Assemblies

06 52 10.30 Fiberglass Grating	Crew	Daily Output	Labor-Hours	Unit	Material	2014 Bare Costs Labor	Equipment	Total	Total Incl O&P
3080	1-1/2" thick	2 Sswk	320	.050	S.F.	18.30	2.56		20.86	24.50
3120	1-1/2" O.C. bar spacing, 1" thick		400	.040		14.20	2.04		16.24	19.35
3160	1-1/2" thick	↓	400	.040	↓	16.80	2.04		18.84	22
4000	Grating support legs, fixed height, no base				Ea.	45.50			45.50	50
4040	With base					41			41	45
4080	Adjustable to 60"				↓	62			62	68.50

06 52 10.40 Fiberglass Floor Grating

		Crew	Daily Output	Labor-Hours	Unit	Material	Labor	Equipment	Total	Total Incl O&P
0010	**FIBERGLASS FLOOR GRATING**									
0100	Reinforced polyester, fire retardant, 1" x 4" grid, 1" thick	E-4	510	.063	S.F.	14.95	3.24	.28	18.47	22.50
0200	1-1/2" x 6" mesh, 1-1/2" thick		500	.064		17.50	3.30	.28	21.08	25.50
0300	With grit surface, 1-1/2" x 6" grid, 1-1/2" thick	↓	500	.064	↓	17.85	3.30	.28	21.43	26

06 63 Plastic Railings

06 63 10 – Plastic (PVC) Railings

06 63 10.10 Plastic Railings

		Crew	Daily Output	Labor-Hours	Unit	Material	Labor	Equipment	Total	Total Incl O&P
0010	**PLASTIC RAILINGS**									
0100	Horizontal PVC handrail with balusters, 3-1/2" wide, 36" high	1 Carp	96	.083	L.F.	25	3.82		28.82	34
0150	42" high		96	.083		28	3.82		31.82	37.50
0200	Angled PVC handrail with balusters, 3-1/2" wide, 36" high		72	.111		28.50	5.10		33.60	39.50
0250	42" high		72	.111		31.50	5.10		36.60	43.50
0300	Post sleeve for 4 x 4 post		96	.083	↓	14	3.82		17.82	21.50
0400	Post cap for 4 x 4 post, flat profile		48	.167	Ea.	13.90	7.65		21.55	28
0450	Newel post style profile		48	.167		23.50	7.65		31.15	38.50
0500	Raised corbeled profile		48	.167		28.50	7.65		36.15	43.50
0550	Post base trim for 4 x 4 post	↓	96	.083	↓	18.25	3.82		22.07	26.50

06 65 Plastic Simulated Wood Trim

06 65 10 – PVC Trim

06 65 10.10 PVC Trim, Exterior

		Crew	Daily Output	Labor-Hours	Unit	Material	Labor	Equipment	Total	Total Incl O&P
0010	**PVC TRIM, EXTERIOR**									
0100	Cornerboards, 5/4" x 6" x 6"	1 Carp	240	.033	L.F.	8.90	1.53		10.43	12.30
0110	Door/window casing, 1" x 4"		200	.040		1.35	1.83		3.18	4.50
0120	1" x 6"		200	.040		2.12	1.83		3.95	5.35
0130	1" x 8"		195	.041		2.80	1.88		4.68	6.15
0140	1" x 10"		195	.041		3.55	1.88		5.43	7
0150	1" x 12"		190	.042		4.34	1.93		6.27	7.95
0160	5/4" x 4"		195	.041		1.72	1.88		3.60	4.98
0170	5/4" x 6"		195	.041		2.72	1.88		4.60	6.10
0180	5/4" x 8"		190	.042		3.57	1.93		5.50	7.10
0190	5/4" x 10"		190	.042		4.57	1.93		6.50	8.20
0200	5/4" x 12"		185	.043		5	1.98		6.98	8.75
0210	Fascia, 1" x 4"		250	.032		1.35	1.47		2.82	3.90
0220	1" x 6"		250	.032		2.12	1.47		3.59	4.74
0230	1" x 8"		225	.036		2.80	1.63		4.43	5.75
0240	1" x 10"		225	.036		3.55	1.63		5.18	6.60
0250	1" x 12"		200	.040		4.34	1.83		6.17	7.80
0260	5/4" x 4"		240	.033		1.72	1.53		3.25	4.40
0270	5/4" x 6"		240	.033		2.72	1.53		4.25	5.50
0280	5/4" x 8"	↓	215	.037	↓	3.57	1.71		5.28	6.75

06 65 Plastic Simulated Wood Trim

06 65 10 – PVC Trim

06 65 10.10 PVC Trim, Exterior		Crew	Daily Output	Labor-Hours	Unit	Material	2014 Bare Costs Labor	Equipment	Total	Total Incl O&P
0290	5/4" x 10"	1 Carp	215	.037	L.F.	4.57	1.71		6.28	7.85
0300	5/4" x 12"		190	.042		5	1.93		6.93	8.65
0310	Frieze, 1" x 4"		250	.032		1.35	1.47		2.82	3.90
0320	1" x 6"		250	.032		2.12	1.47		3.59	4.74
0330	1" x 8"		225	.036		2.80	1.63		4.43	5.75
0340	1" x 10"		225	.036		3.55	1.63		5.18	6.60
0350	1" x 12"		200	.040		4.34	1.83		6.17	7.80
0360	5/4" x 4"		240	.033		1.72	1.53		3.25	4.40
0370	5/4" x 6"		240	.033		2.72	1.53		4.25	5.50
0380	5/4" x 8"		215	.037		3.57	1.71		5.28	6.75
0390	5/4" x 10"		215	.037		4.57	1.71		6.28	7.85
0400	5/4" x 12"		190	.042		5	1.93		6.93	8.65
0410	Rake, 1" x 4"		200	.040		1.35	1.83		3.18	4.50
0420	1" x 6"		200	.040		2.12	1.83		3.95	5.35
0430	1" x 8"		190	.042		2.80	1.93		4.73	6.25
0440	1" x 10"		190	.042		3.55	1.93		5.48	7.10
0450	1" x 12"		180	.044		4.34	2.04		6.38	8.10
0460	5/4" x 4"		195	.041		1.72	1.88		3.60	4.98
0470	5/4" x 6"		195	.041		2.72	1.88		4.60	6.10
0480	5/4" x 8"		185	.043		3.57	1.98		5.55	7.20
0490	5/4" x 10"		185	.043		4.57	1.98		6.55	8.30
0500	5/4" x 12"		175	.046		5	2.10		7.10	8.95
0510	Rake trim, 1" x 4"		225	.036		1.35	1.63		2.98	4.17
0520	1" x 6"		225	.036		2.12	1.63		3.75	5
0560	5/4" x 4"		220	.036		1.72	1.67		3.39	4.63
0570	5/4" x 6"		220	.036		2.72	1.67		4.39	5.75
0610	Soffit, 1" x 4"	2 Carp	420	.038		1.35	1.75		3.10	4.36
0620	1" x 6"		420	.038		2.12	1.75		3.87	5.20
0630	1" x 8"		420	.038		2.80	1.75		4.55	5.95
0640	1" x 10"		400	.040		3.55	1.83		5.38	6.90
0650	1" x 12"		400	.040		4.34	1.83		6.17	7.80
0660	5/4" x 4"		410	.039		1.72	1.79		3.51	4.83
0670	5/4" x 6"		410	.039		2.72	1.79		4.51	5.95
0680	5/4" x 8"		410	.039		3.57	1.79		5.36	6.85
0690	5/4" x 10"		390	.041		4.57	1.88		6.45	8.15
0700	5/4" x 12"		390	.041		5	1.88		6.88	8.60

Estimating Tips

07 10 00 Dampproofing and Waterproofing

- Be sure of the job specifications before pricing this subdivision. The difference in cost between waterproofing and dampproofing can be great. Waterproofing will hold back standing water. Dampproofing prevents the transmission of water vapor. Also included in this section are vapor retarding membranes.

07 20 00 Thermal Protection

- Insulation and fireproofing products are measured by area, thickness, volume or R-value. Specifications may give only what the specific R-value should be in a certain situation. The estimator may need to choose the type of insulation to meet that R-value.

07 30 00 Steep Slope Roofing
07 40 00 Roofing and Siding Panels

- Many roofing and siding products are bought and sold by the square. One square is equal to an area that measures 100 square feet.

This simple change in unit of measure could create a large error if the estimator is not observant. Accessories necessary for a complete installation must be figured into any calculations for both material and labor.

07 50 00 Membrane Roofing
07 60 00 Flashing and Sheet Metal
07 70 00 Roofing and Wall Specialties and Accessories

- The items in these subdivisions compose a roofing system. No one component completes the installation, and all must be estimated. Built-up or single-ply membrane roofing systems are made up of many products and installation trades. Wood blocking at roof perimeters or penetrations, parapet coverings, reglets, roof drains, gutters, downspouts, sheet metal flashing, skylights, smoke vents, and roof hatches all need to be considered along with the roofing material. Several different installation trades will need to work together on the roofing system. Inherent difficulties in the scheduling and coordination of various trades must be accounted for when estimating labor costs.

07 90 00 Joint Protection

- To complete the weather-tight shell, the sealants and caulkings must be estimated. Where different materials meet—at expansion joints, at flashing penetrations, and at hundreds of other locations throughout a construction project—they provide another line of defense against water penetration. Often, an entire system is based on the proper location and placement of caulking or sealants. The detailed drawings that are included as part of a set of architectural plans show typical locations for these materials. When caulking or sealants are shown at typical locations, this means the estimator must include them for all the locations where this detail is applicable. Be careful to keep different types of sealants separate, and remember to consider backer rods and primers if necessary.

Reference Numbers

Reference numbers are shown in shaded boxes at the beginning of some major classifications. These numbers refer to related items in the Reference Section. The reference information may be an estimating procedure, an alternate pricing method, or technical information.

Note: Not all subdivisions listed here necessarily appear in this publication.

07 01 Operation and Maint. of Thermal and Moisture Protection

07 01 50 – Maintenance of Membrane Roofing

07 01 50.10 Roof Coatings

	07 01 50.10 Roof Coatings	Crew	Daily Output	Labor-Hours	Unit	Material	2014 Bare Costs Labor	Equipment	Total	Total Incl O&P
0010	**ROOF COATINGS**									
0012	Asphalt, brush grade, material only				Gal.	9.15			9.15	10.10
0200	Asphalt base, fibered aluminum coating G					7.65			7.65	8.40
0300	Asphalt primer, 5 gallon				↓	7.60			7.60	8.35
0600	Coal tar pitch, 200 lb. barrels				Ton	1,525			1,525	1,700
0700	Tar roof cement, 5 gal. lots				Gal.	11.55			11.55	12.70
0800	Glass fibered roof & patching cement, 5 gallon				"	7.65			7.65	8.40
0900	Reinforcing glass membrane, 450 S.F./roll				Ea.	59.50			59.50	65.50
1000	Neoprene roof coating, 5 gal., 2 gal./sq.				Gal.	30.50			30.50	33.50
1100	Roof patch & flashing cement, 5 gallon					8.30			8.30	9.10
1200	Roof resaturant, glass fibered, 3 gal./sq.					8.85			8.85	9.75
1600	Reflective roof coating, white, elastomeric, approx. 50 S.F. per gal. G				↓	17.15			17.15	18.90

07 01 90 – Maintenance of Joint Protection

07 01 90.81 Joint Sealant Replacement

	07 01 90.81 Joint Sealant Replacement	Crew	Daily Output	Labor-Hours	Unit	Material	2014 Bare Costs Labor	Equipment	Total	Total Incl O&P
0010	**JOINT SEALANT REPLACEMENT**									
0050	Control joints in concrete floors/slabs									
0100	Option 1 for joints with hard dry sealant									
0110	Step 1: Sawcut to remove 95% of old sealant									
0112	1/4" wide x 1/2" deep, with single saw blade	C-27	4800	.003	L.F.	.02	.15	.04	.21	.29
0114	3/8" wide x 3/4" deep, with single saw blade		4000	.004		.03	.18	.04	.25	.36
0116	1/2" wide x 1" deep, with double saw blades		3600	.004		.06	.20	.05	.31	.43
0118	3/4" wide x 1-1/2" deep, with double saw blades	↓	3200	.005		.13	.22	.05	.40	.55
0120	Step 2: Water blast joint faces and edges	C-29	2500	.003			.12	.03	.15	.22
0130	Step 3: Air blast joint faces and edges	C-28	2000	.004			.18	.01	.19	.29
0140	Step 4: Sand blast joint faces and edges	E-11	2000	.016			.66	.12	.78	1.29
0150	Step 5: Air blast joint faces and edges	C-28	2000	.004	↓		.18	.01	.19	.29
0200	Option 2 for joints with soft pliable sealant									
0210	Step 1: Plow joint with rectangular blade	B-62	2600	.009	L.F.		.37	.07	.44	.67
0220	Step 2: Sawcut to re-face joint faces									
0222	1/4" wide x 1/2" deep, with single saw blade	C-27	2400	.007	L.F.	.02	.29	.07	.38	.56
0224	3/8" wide x 3/4" deep, with single saw blade		2000	.008		.04	.35	.09	.48	.71
0226	1/2" wide x 1" deep, with double saw blades		1800	.009		.08	.39	.10	.57	.82
0228	3/4" wide x 1-1/2" deep, with double saw blades	↓	1600	.010		.17	.44	.11	.72	1
0230	Step 3: Water blast joint faces and edges	C-29	2500	.003			.12	.03	.15	.22
0240	Step 4: Air blast joint faces and edges	C-28	2000	.004			.18	.01	.19	.29
0250	Step 5: Sand blast joint faces and edges	E-11	2000	.016			.66	.12	.78	1.29
0260	Step 6: Air blast joint faces and edges	C-28	2000	.004	↓		.18	.01	.19	.29
0290	For saw cutting new control joints, see Section 03 15 16.20									
8910	For backer rod, see Section 07 91 23.10									
8920	For joint sealant, see Sections 03 15 16.30 or 07 92 13.20									

07 05 Common Work Results for Thermal and Moisture Protection

07 05 05 – Selective Demolition

07 05 05.10 Selective Demo., Thermal and Moist. Protection	Crew	Daily Output	Labor-Hours	Unit	Material	2014 Bare Costs Labor	Equipment	Total	Total Incl O&P
0010 SELECTIVE DEMO., THERMAL AND MOISTURE PROTECTION									
0020 Caulking/sealant, to 1" x 1" joint R024119-10	1 Clab	600	.013	L.F.		.49		.49	.80
0120 Downspouts, including hangers		350	.023	"		.84		.84	1.38
0220 Flashing, sheet metal		290	.028	S.F.		1.01		1.01	1.66
0420 Gutters, aluminum or wood, edge hung		240	.033	L.F.		1.22		1.22	2.01
0520 Built-in		100	.080	"		2.93		2.93	4.82
0620 Insulation, air/vapor barrier		3500	.002	S.F.		.08		.08	.14
0670 Batts or blankets		1400	.006	C.F.		.21		.21	.34
0720 Foamed or sprayed in place	2 Clab	1000	.016	B.F.		.59		.59	.96
0770 Loose fitting	1 Clab	3000	.003	C.F.		.10		.10	.16
0870 Rigid board		3450	.002	B.F.		.09		.09	.14
1120 Roll roofing, cold adhesive		12	.667	Sq.		24.50		24.50	40
1170 Roof accessories, adjustable metal chimney flashing		9	.889	Ea.		32.50		32.50	53.50
1325 Plumbing vent flashing		32	.250	"		9.15		9.15	15.05
1375 Ridge vent strip, aluminum		310	.026	L.F.		.95		.95	1.55
1620 Skylight to 10 S.F.		8	1	Ea.		36.50		36.50	60
2120 Roof edge, aluminum soffit and fascia		570	.014	L.F.		.51		.51	.85
2170 Concrete coping, up to 12" wide	2 Clab	160	.100			3.67		3.67	6
2220 Drip edge	1 Clab	1000	.008			.29		.29	.48
2270 Gravel stop		950	.008			.31		.31	.51
2370 Sheet metal coping, up to 12" wide		240	.033			1.22		1.22	2.01
2470 Roof insulation board, over 2" thick	B-2	7800	.005	B.F.		.19		.19	.31
2520 Up to 2" thick	"	3900	.010	S.F.		.38		.38	.62
2620 Roof ventilation, louvered gable vent	1 Clab	16	.500	Ea.		18.35		18.35	30
2670 Remove, roof hatch	G-3	15	2.133			97.50		97.50	156
2675 Rafter vents	1 Clab	960	.008			.31		.31	.50
2720 Soffit vent and/or fascia vent		575	.014	L.F.		.51		.51	.84
2775 Soffit vent strip, aluminum, 3" to 4" wide		160	.050			1.83		1.83	3.01
2820 Roofing accessories, shingle moulding, to 1" x 4"		1600	.005			.18		.18	.30
2870 Cant strip	B-2	2000	.020			.74		.74	1.22
2920 Concrete block walkway	1 Clab	230	.035			1.27		1.27	2.09
3070 Roofing, felt paper, 15#		70	.114	Sq.		4.19		4.19	6.90
3125 #30 felt		30	.267	"		9.75		9.75	16.05
3170 Asphalt shingles, 1 layer	B-2	3500	.011	S.F.		.42		.42	.70
3180 2 layers		1750	.023	"		.85		.85	1.39
3370 Modified bitumen		26	1.538	Sq.		57		57	93.50
3420 Built-up, no gravel, 3 ply		25	1.600			59.50		59.50	97.50
3470 4 ply		21	1.905			70.50		70.50	116
3620 5 ply		1600	.025	S.F.		.93		.93	1.52
3720 5 ply, with gravel		890	.045			1.67		1.67	2.74
3725 Gravel removal, minimum		5000	.008			.30		.30	.49
3730 Maximum		2000	.020			.74		.74	1.22
3870 Fiberglass sheet		1200	.033			1.23		1.23	2.03
4120 Slate shingles		1900	.021			.78		.78	1.28
4170 Ridge shingles, clay or slate		2000	.020	L.F.		.74		.74	1.22
4320 Single ply membrane, attached at seams		52	.769	Sq.		28.50		28.50	47
4370 Ballasted		75	.533			19.75		19.75	32.50
4420 Fully adhered		39	1.026			38		38	62.50
4550 Roof hatch, 2'-6" x 3'-0"	1 Clab	10	.800	Ea.		29.50		29.50	48
4670 Wood shingles	B-2	2200	.018	S.F.		.67		.67	1.11
4820 Sheet metal roofing	"	2150	.019			.69		.69	1.13
4970 Siding, horizontal wood clapboards	1 Clab	380	.021			.77		.77	1.27
5025 Exterior insulation finish system	"	120	.067			2.44		2.44	4.01

07 05 Common Work Results for Thermal and Moisture Protection

07 05 05 – Selective Demolition

07 05 05.10 Selective Demo., Thermal and Moist. Protection

07 05 05.10 Selective Demo., Thermal and Moist. Protection	Crew	Daily Output	Labor-Hours	Unit	Material	2014 Bare Costs Labor	Equipment	Total	Total Incl O&P
5070	Tempered hardboard, remove and reset	1 Carp	380	.021	S.F.		.97		.97	1.59
5120	Tempered hardboard sheet siding	"	375	.021	▼		.98		.98	1.61
5170	Metal, corner strips	1 Clab	850	.009	L.F.		.34		.34	.57
5225	Horizontal strips		444	.018	S.F.		.66		.66	1.08
5320	Vertical strips		400	.020			.73		.73	1.20
5520	Wood shingles		350	.023			.84		.84	1.38
5620	Stucco siding		360	.022			.81		.81	1.34
5670	Textured plywood		725	.011			.40		.40	.66
5720	Vinyl siding		510	.016	▼		.58		.58	.94
5770	Corner strips		900	.009	L.F.		.33		.33	.54
5870	Wood, boards, vertical	▼	400	.020	S.F.		.73		.73	1.20
5920	Waterproofing, protection/drain board	2 Clab	3900	.004	B.F.		.15		.15	.25
5970	Over 1/2" thick		1750	.009	S.F.		.34		.34	.55
6020	To 1/2" thick	▼	2000	.008	"		.29		.29	.48
9000	Minimum labor/equipment charge	1 Clab	2	4	Job		147		147	241

07 11 Dampproofing

07 11 13 – Bituminous Dampproofing

07 11 13.10 Bituminous Asphalt Coating

07 11 13.10 Bituminous Asphalt Coating	Crew	Daily Output	Labor-Hours	Unit	Material	Labor	Equipment	Total	Total Incl O&P
0010	**BITUMINOUS ASPHALT COATING**									
0030	Brushed on, below grade, 1 coat	1 Rofc	665	.012	S.F.	.23	.47		.70	1.10
0100	2 coat		500	.016		.46	.63		1.09	1.63
0300	Sprayed on, below grade, 1 coat		830	.010		.23	.38		.61	.93
0400	2 coat	▼	500	.016	▼	.45	.63		1.08	1.62
0500	Asphalt coating, with fibers				Gal.	7.65			7.65	8.40
0600	Troweled on, asphalt with fibers, 1/16" thick	1 Rofc	500	.016	S.F.	.33	.63		.96	1.50
0700	1/8" thick		400	.020		.59	.78		1.37	2.06
1000	1/2" thick		350	.023	▼	1.91	.90		2.81	3.71
9000	Minimum labor/equipment charge		3	2.667	Job		104		104	188

07 11 16 – Cementitious Dampproofing

07 11 16.20 Cementitious Parging

07 11 16.20 Cementitious Parging	Crew	Daily Output	Labor-Hours	Unit	Material	Labor	Equipment	Total	Total Incl O&P
0010	**CEMENTITIOUS PARGING**									
0020	Portland cement, 2 coats, 1/2" thick	D-1	250	.064	S.F.	.30	2.64		2.94	4.62
0100	Waterproofed Portland cement, 1/2" thick, 2 coats	"	250	.064	"	3.73	2.64		6.37	8.40

07 12 Built-up Bituminous Waterproofing

07 12 13 – Built-Up Asphalt Waterproofing

07 12 13.20 Membrane Waterproofing

07 12 13.20 Membrane Waterproofing	Crew	Daily Output	Labor-Hours	Unit	Material	Labor	Equipment	Total	Total Incl O&P
0010	**MEMBRANE WATERPROOFING**									
0012	On slabs, 1 ply, felt, mopped	G-1	3000	.019	S.F.	.41	.68	.18	1.27	1.88
0015	On walls, 1 ply, felt, mopped		3000	.019		.41	.68	.18	1.27	1.88
0100	On slabs, 1 ply, glass fiber fabric, mopped		2100	.027		.46	.98	.26	1.70	2.55
0105	On walls, 1 ply, glass fiber fabric, mopped		2100	.027		.46	.98	.26	1.70	2.55
0300	On slabs, 2 ply, felt, mopped		2500	.022		.83	.82	.22	1.87	2.63
0305	On walls, 2 ply, felt, mopped		2500	.022		.83	.82	.22	1.87	2.63
0400	On slabs, 2 ply, glass fiber fabric, mopped		1650	.034		1.01	1.24	.34	2.59	3.72
0405	On walls, 2 ply, glass fiber fabric, mopped		1650	.034		1.01	1.24	.34	2.59	3.72
0600	On slabs, 3 ply, felt, mopped		2100	.027		1.24	.98	.26	2.48	3.41
0605	On walls, 3 ply, felt, mopped	▼	2100	.027	▼	1.24	.98	.26	2.48	3.41

07 12 Built-up Bituminous Waterproofing

07 12 13 – Built-Up Asphalt Waterproofing

07 12 13.20 Membrane Waterproofing	Crew	Daily Output	Labor-Hours	Unit	Material	2014 Bare Costs Labor	Equipment	Total	Total Incl O&P
0700	On slabs, 3 ply, glass fiber fabric, mopped	G-1	1550	.036	S.F.	1.37	1.32	.36	3.05	4.27
0705	On walls, 3 ply, glass fiber fabric, mopped	↓	1550	.036		1.37	1.32	.36	3.05	4.27
0710	Asphaltic hardboard protection board, 1/8" thick	2 Rofc	500	.032		.62	1.25		1.87	2.94
0715	1/4" thick		450	.036		1.70	1.39		3.09	4.38
1000	1/4" EPS membrane protection board		3500	.005		.33	.18		.51	.68
1050	3/8" thick		3500	.005		.36	.18		.54	.72
1060	1/2" thick		3500	.005	↓	.39	.18		.57	.75
1070	Fiberglass fabric, black, 20/10 mesh		116	.138	Sq.	14.70	5.40		20.10	26
9000	Minimum labor/equipment charge	↓	2	8	Job		315		315	565

07 13 Sheet Waterproofing

07 13 53 – Elastomeric Sheet Waterproofing

07 13 53.10 Elastomeric Sheet Waterproofing and Access.

		Crew	Daily Output	Labor-Hours	Unit	Material	2014 Bare Costs Labor	Equipment	Total	Total Incl O&P
0010	**ELASTOMERIC SHEET WATERPROOFING AND ACCESS.**									
0090	EPDM, plain, 45 mils thick	2 Rofc	580	.028	S.F.	1.40	1.08		2.48	3.49
0100	60 mils thick		570	.028		1.52	1.10		2.62	3.65
0300	Nylon reinforced sheets, 45 mils thick		580	.028		1.58	1.08		2.66	3.69
0400	60 mils thick	↓	570	.028	C.L.F.	1.67	1.10		2.77	3.81
0600	Vulcanizing splicing tape for above, 2" wide				C.L.F.	75			75	82.50
0700	4" wide				"	144			144	158
0900	Adhesive, bonding, 60 S.F. per gal.				Gal.	31.50			31.50	35
1000	Splicing, 75 S.F. per gal.				"	37			37	40.50
1200	Neoprene sheets, plain, 45 mils thick	2 Rofc	580	.028	S.F.	1.76	1.08		2.84	3.89
1300	60 mils thick		570	.028		2.23	1.10		3.33	4.43
1500	Nylon reinforced, 45 mils thick		580	.028		2	1.08		3.08	4.15
1600	60 mils thick		570	.028		3.03	1.10		4.13	5.30
1800	120 mils thick	↓	500	.032	↓	6.05	1.25		7.30	8.90
1900	Adhesive, splicing, 150 S.F. per gal. per coat				Gal.	37			37	40.50
2100	Fiberglass reinforced, fluid applied, 1/8" thick	2 Rofc	500	.032	S.F.	1.63	1.25		2.88	4.05
2200	Polyethylene and rubberized asphalt sheets, 60 mils thick		550	.029		.76	1.14		1.90	2.89
2400	Polyvinyl chloride sheets, plain, 10 mils thick		580	.028		.14	1.08		1.22	2.10
2500	20 mils thick		570	.028		.18	1.10		1.28	2.18
2700	30 mils thick	↓	560	.029	↓	.25	1.12		1.37	2.30
3000	Adhesives, trowel grade, 40-100 S.F. per gal.				Gal.	23			23	25.50
3100	Brush grade, 100-250 S.F. per gal.				"	20.50			20.50	23
3300	Bitumen modified polyurethane, fluid applied, 55 mils thick	2 Rofc	665	.024	S.F.	.89	.94		1.83	2.68
9000	Minimum labor/equipment charge	"	2	8	Job		315		315	565

07 16 Cementitious and Reactive Waterproofing

07 16 16 – Crystalline Waterproofing

07 16 16.20 Cementitious Waterproofing

		Crew	Daily Output	Labor-Hours	Unit	Material	2014 Bare Costs Labor	Equipment	Total	Total Incl O&P
0010	**CEMENTITIOUS WATERPROOFING**									
0020	1/8" application, sprayed on	G-2A	1000	.024	S.F.	.60	.84	.74	2.18	2.95
0050	4 coat cementitious metallic slurry	1 Cefi	1.20	6.667	C.S.F.	30.50	294		324.50	500

177

07 19 Water Repellents

07 19 19 – Silicone Water Repellents

07 19 19.10 Silicone Based Water Repellents		Crew	Daily Output	Labor-Hours	Unit	Material	2014 Bare Costs Labor	Equipment	Total	Total Incl O&P
0010	**SILICONE BASED WATER REPELLENTS**									
0020	Water base liquid, roller applied	2 Rofc	7000	.002	S.F.	.49	.09		.58	.70
0200	Silicone or stearate, sprayed on CMU, 1 coat	1 Rofc	4000	.002		.35	.08		.43	.53
0300	2 coats		3000	.003		.71	.10		.81	.97
9000	Minimum labor/equipment charge		3	2.667	Job		104		104	188

07 21 Thermal Insulation

07 21 13 – Board Insulation

07 21 13.10 Rigid Insulation

07 21 13.10 Rigid Insulation			Crew	Daily Output	Labor-Hours	Unit	Material	2014 Bare Costs Labor	Equipment	Total	Total Incl O&P
0010	**RIGID INSULATION**, for walls										
0040	Fiberglass, 1.5#/C.F., unfaced, 1" thick, R4.1	G	1 Carp	1000	.008	S.F.	.27	.37		.64	.90
0060	1-1/2" thick, R6.2	G		1000	.008		.40	.37		.77	1.04
0080	2" thick, R8.3	G		1000	.008		.45	.37		.82	1.10
0120	3" thick, R12.4	G		800	.010		.56	.46		1.02	1.37
0370	3#/C.F., unfaced, 1" thick, R4.3	G		1000	.008		.52	.37		.89	1.17
0390	1-1/2" thick, R6.5	G		1000	.008		.78	.37		1.15	1.46
0400	2" thick, R8.7	G		890	.009		1.05	.41		1.46	1.84
0420	2-1/2" thick, R10.9	G		800	.010		1.10	.46		1.56	1.96
0440	3" thick, R13	G		800	.010		1.59	.46		2.05	2.50
0520	Foil faced, 1" thick, R4.3	G		1000	.008		.90	.37		1.27	1.59
0540	1-1/2" thick, R6.5	G		1000	.008		1.35	.37		1.72	2.09
0560	2" thick, R8.7	G		890	.009		1.69	.41		2.10	2.54
0580	2-1/2" thick, R10.9	G		800	.010		1.98	.46		2.44	2.93
0600	3" thick, R13	G		800	.010		2.18	.46		2.64	3.15
1600	Isocyanurate, 4' x 8' sheet, foil faced, both sides										
1610	1/2" thick	G	1 Carp	800	.010	S.F.	.29	.46		.75	1.07
1620	5/8" thick	G		800	.010		.32	.46		.78	1.10
1630	3/4" thick	G		800	.010		.33	.46		.79	1.11
1640	1" thick	G		800	.010		.51	.46		.97	1.31
1650	1-1/2" thick	G		730	.011		.63	.50		1.13	1.52
1660	2" thick	G		730	.011		.79	.50		1.29	1.70
1670	3" thick	G		730	.011		1.78	.50		2.28	2.79
1680	4" thick	G		730	.011		2	.50		2.50	3.03
1700	Perlite, 1" thick, R2.77	G		800	.010		.36	.46		.82	1.15
1750	2" thick, R5.55	G		730	.011		.72	.50		1.22	1.62
1900	Extruded polystyrene, 25 PSI compressive strength, 1" thick, R5	G		800	.010		.52	.46		.98	1.32
1940	2" thick R10	G		730	.011		1.05	.50		1.55	1.99
1960	3" thick, R15	G		730	.011		1.49	.50		1.99	2.47
2100	Expanded polystyrene, 1" thick, R3.85	G		800	.010		.24	.46		.70	1.01
2120	2" thick, R7.69	G		730	.011		.48	.50		.98	1.36
2140	3" thick, R11.49	G		730	.011		.72	.50		1.22	1.62
9000	Minimum labor/equipment charge			4	2	Job		91.50		91.50	151

07 21 13.13 Foam Board Insulation

07 21 13.13 Foam Board Insulation			Crew	Daily Output	Labor-Hours	Unit	Material	2014 Bare Costs Labor	Equipment	Total	Total Incl O&P
0010	**FOAM BOARD INSULATION**										
0600	Polystyrene, expanded, 1" thick, R4	G	1 Carp	680	.012	S.F.	.24	.54		.78	1.15
0700	2" thick, R8	G		675	.012	"	.48	.54		1.02	1.42
9000	Minimum labor/equipment charge			4	2	Job		91.50		91.50	151

07 21 Thermal Insulation

07 21 16 – Blanket Insulation

07 21 16.10 Blanket Insulation for Floors/Ceilings

		Crew	Daily Output	Labor-Hours	Unit	Material	2014 Bare Costs Labor	Equipment	Total	Total Incl O&P
0010	**BLANKET INSULATION FOR FLOORS/CEILINGS**									
0020	Including spring type wire fasteners									
2000	Fiberglass, blankets or batts, paper or foil backing									
2100	3-1/2" thick, R13	G	1 Carp	700	.011	S.F.	.37	.52		.89	1.27
2150	6-1/4" thick, R19	G		600	.013		.48	.61		1.09	1.53
2210	9-1/2" thick, R30	G		500	.016		.70	.73		1.43	1.98
2220	12" thick, R38	G		475	.017		.89	.77		1.66	2.25
3000	Unfaced, 3-1/2" thick, R13	G		600	.013		.32	.61		.93	1.35
3010	6-1/4" thick, R19	G		500	.016		.37	.73		1.10	1.62
3020	9-1/2" thick, R30	G		450	.018		.60	.82		1.42	2
3030	12" thick, R38	G		425	.019		.75	.86		1.61	2.25
9000	Minimum labor/equipment charge			4	2	Job		91.50		91.50	151

07 21 16.20 Blanket Insulation for Walls

		Crew	Daily Output	Labor-Hours	Unit	Material	2014 Bare Costs Labor	Equipment	Total	Total Incl O&P
0010	**BLANKET INSULATION FOR WALLS**									
0020	Kraft faced fiberglass, 3-1/2" thick, R11, 15" wide	G	1 Carp	1350	.006	S.F.	.26	.27		.53	.74
0030	23" wide	G		1600	.005		.26	.23		.49	.67
0060	R13, 11" wide	G		1150	.007		.31	.32		.63	.86
0080	15" wide	G		1350	.006		.31	.27		.58	.79
0100	23" wide	G		1600	.005		.31	.23		.54	.72
0110	R15, 11" wide	G		1150	.007		.51	.32		.83	1.08
0120	15" wide	G		1350	.006		.51	.27		.78	1.01
0130	23" wide	G		1600	.005		.51	.23		.74	.94
0140	6" thick, R19, 11" wide	G		1150	.007		.42	.32		.74	.98
0160	15" wide	G		1350	.006		.42	.27		.69	.91
0180	23" wide	G		1600	.005		.42	.23		.65	.84
0182	R21, 11" wide	G		1150	.007		.60	.32		.92	1.18
0184	15" wide	G		1350	.006		.60	.27		.87	1.11
0186	23" wide	G		1600	.005		.60	.23		.83	1.04
0188	9" thick, R30, 11" wide	G		985	.008		.70	.37		1.07	1.38
0200	15" wide	G		1150	.007		.70	.32		1.02	1.29
0220	23" wide	G		1350	.006		.70	.27		.97	1.22
0230	12" thick, R38, 11" wide	G		985	.008		.89	.37		1.26	1.59
0240	15" wide	G		1150	.007		.89	.32		1.21	1.50
0260	23" wide	G		1350	.006		.89	.27		1.16	1.43
0410	Foil faced fiberglass, 3-1/2" thick, R13, 11" wide	G		1150	.007		.44	.32		.76	1
0420	15" wide	G		1350	.006		.44	.27		.71	.93
0440	23" wide	G		1600	.005		.44	.23		.67	.86
0442	R15, 11" wide	G		1150	.007		.48	.32		.80	1.05
0444	15" wide	G		1350	.006		.48	.27		.75	.98
0446	23" wide	G		1600	.005		.48	.23		.71	.91
0448	6" thick, R19, 11" wide	G		1150	.007		.57	.32		.89	1.15
0460	15" wide	G		1350	.006		.57	.27		.84	1.08
0480	23" wide	G		1600	.005		.57	.23		.80	1.01
0482	R21, 11" wide	G		1150	.007		.60	.32		.92	1.18
0484	15" wide	G		1350	.006		.60	.27		.87	1.11
0486	23" wide	G		1600	.005		.60	.23		.83	1.04
0488	9" thick, R30, 11" wide	G		985	.008		.89	.37		1.26	1.59
0500	15" wide	G		1150	.007		.89	.32		1.21	1.50
0550	23" wide	G		1350	.006		.89	.27		1.16	1.43
0560	12" thick, R38, 11" wide	G		985	.008		1.03	.37		1.40	1.74
0570	15" wide	G		1150	.007		1.03	.32		1.35	1.65
0580	23" wide	G		1350	.006		1.03	.27		1.30	1.58

179

07 21 Thermal Insulation

07 21 16 – Blanket Insulation

07 21 16.20 Blanket Insulation for Walls

			Crew	Daily Output	Labor-Hours	Unit	Material	2014 Bare Costs Labor	Equipment	Total	Total Incl O&P
0620	Unfaced fiberglass, 3-1/2" thick, R13, 11" wide	G	1 Carp	1150	.007	S.F.	.32	.32		.64	.87
0820	15" wide	G		1350	.006		.32	.27		.59	.80
0830	23" wide	G		1600	.005		.32	.23		.55	.73
0832	R15, 11" wide	G		1150	.007		.46	.32		.78	1.03
0836	23" wide	G		1600	.005		.46	.23		.69	.89
0838	6" thick, R19, 11" wide	G		1150	.007		.37	.32		.69	.93
0860	15" wide	G		1150	.007		.37	.32		.69	.93
0880	23" wide	G		1350	.006		.37	.27		.64	.86
0882	R21, 11" wide	G		1150	.007		.50	.32		.82	1.07
0886	15" wide	G		1350	.006		.50	.27		.77	1
0888	23" wide	G		1600	.005		.50	.23		.73	.93
0890	9" thick, R30, 11" wide	G		985	.008		.60	.37		.97	1.27
0900	15" wide	G		1150	.007		.60	.32		.92	1.18
0920	23" wide	G		1350	.006		.60	.27		.87	1.11
0930	12" thick, R38, 11" wide	G		985	.008		.75	.37		1.12	1.44
0940	15" wide	G		1000	.008		.75	.37		1.12	1.43
0960	23" wide	G		1150	.007		.75	.32		1.07	1.35
1300	Wall or ceiling insulation, mineral wool batts										
1320	3-1/2" thick, R15	G	1 Carp	1600	.005	S.F.	.60	.23		.83	1.04
1340	5-1/2" thick, R23	G		1600	.005		.94	.23		1.17	1.42
1380	7-1/4" thick, R30	G		1350	.006		1.24	.27		1.51	1.82
1850	Friction fit wire insulation supports, 16" O.C.			960	.008	Ea.	.06	.38		.44	.70
9000	Minimum labor/equipment charge			4	2	Job		91.50		91.50	151

07 21 19 – Foamed In Place Insulation

07 21 19.10 Masonry Foamed In Place Insulation

			Crew	Daily Output	Labor-Hours	Unit	Material	Labor	Equipment	Total	Total Incl O&P
0010	**MASONRY FOAMED IN PLACE INSULATION**										
0100	Amino-plast foam, injected into block core, 6" block	G	G-2A	6000	.004	Ea.	.15	.14	.12	.41	.55
0110	8" block	G		5000	.005		.19	.17	.15	.51	.65
0120	10" block	G		4000	.006		.23	.21	.19	.63	.83
0130	12" block	G		3000	.008		.31	.28	.25	.84	1.10
0140	Injected into cavity wall	G		13000	.002	B.F.	.05	.06	.06	.17	.23
0150	Preparation, drill holes into mortar joint every 4 VLF, 5/8" dia		1 Clab	960	.008	Ea.		.31		.31	.50
0160	7/8" dia			680	.012			.43		.43	.71
0170	Patch drilled holes, 5/8" diameter			1800	.004		.03	.16		.19	.30
0180	7/8" diameter			1200	.007		.04	.24		.28	.45
9000	Minimum labor/equipment charge		G-2A	2	12	Job		420	370	790	1,150
9010	Minimum labor/equipment charge		1 Clab	4	2	"		73.50		73.50	120

07 21 23 – Loose-Fill Insulation

07 21 23.10 Poured Loose-Fill Insulation

			Crew	Daily Output	Labor-Hours	Unit	Material	Labor	Equipment	Total	Total Incl O&P
0010	**POURED LOOSE-FILL INSULATION**										
0020	Cellulose fiber, R3.8 per inch	G	1 Carp	200	.040	C.F.	.69	1.83		2.52	3.77
0021	4" thick	G		1000	.008	S.F.	.17	.37		.54	.78
0022	6" thick	G		800	.010	"	.28	.46		.74	1.06
0080	Fiberglass wool, R4 per inch	G		200	.040	C.F.	.53	1.83		2.36	3.60
0081	4" thick	G		600	.013	S.F.	.18	.61		.79	1.20
0082	6" thick	G		400	.020	"	.26	.92		1.18	1.79
0100	Mineral wool, R3 per inch	G		200	.040	C.F.	.39	1.83		2.22	3.44
0101	4" thick	G		600	.013	S.F.	.13	.61		.74	1.14
0102	6" thick	G		400	.020	"	.20	.92		1.12	1.72
0300	Polystyrene, R4 per inch	G		200	.040	C.F.	2.50	1.83		4.33	5.75
0301	4" thick	G		600	.013	S.F.	.83	.61		1.44	1.91
0302	6" thick	G		400	.020	"	1.25	.92		2.17	2.89

07 21 Thermal Insulation

07 21 23 – Loose-Fill Insulation

07 21 23.10 Poured Loose-Fill Insulation

		Crew	Daily Output	Labor-Hours	Unit	Material	2014 Bare Costs Labor	Equipment	Total	Total Incl O&P
0400	Perlite, R2.78 per inch	G 1 Carp	200	.040	C.F.	5.40	1.83		7.23	8.95
0401	4" thick	G	1000	.008	S.F.	1.80	.37		2.17	2.58
0402	6" thick	G	800	.010	"	2.70	.46		3.16	3.72
9000	Minimum labor/equipment charge		4	2	Job		91.50		91.50	151

07 21 23.20 Masonry Loose-Fill Insulation

		Crew	Daily Output	Labor-Hours	Unit	Material	2014 Bare Costs Labor	Equipment	Total	Total Incl O&P
0010	**MASONRY LOOSE-FILL INSULATION**, vermiculite or perlite									
0100	In cores of concrete block, 4" thick wall, .115 C.F./S.F.	G D-1	4800	.003	S.F.	.62	.14		.76	.90
0200	6" thick wall, .175 C.F./S.F.	G	3000	.005		.95	.22		1.17	1.40
0300	8" thick wall, .258 C.F./S.F.	G	2400	.007		1.39	.28		1.67	1.98
0400	10" thick wall, .340 C.F./S.F.	G	1850	.009		1.84	.36		2.20	2.60
0500	12" thick wall, .422 C.F./S.F.	G	1200	.013		2.28	.55		2.83	3.40
0550	For sand fill, deduct from above	G				70%				
0600	Poured cavity wall, vermiculite or perlite, water repellant	G D-1	250	.064	C.F.	5.40	2.64		8.04	10.25
0700	Foamed in place, urethane in 2-5/8" cavity	G G-2A	1035	.023	S.F.	1.38	.81	.72	2.91	3.73
0800	For each 1" added thickness, add	G "	2372	.010	"	.53	.35	.31	1.19	1.54

07 21 26 – Blown Insulation

07 21 26.10 Blown Insulation

		Crew	Daily Output	Labor-Hours	Unit	Material	2014 Bare Costs Labor	Equipment	Total	Total Incl O&P
0010	**BLOWN INSULATION** Ceilings, with open access									
0020	Cellulose, 3-1/2" thick, R13	G G-4	5000	.005	S.F.	.24	.18	.09	.51	.64
0030	5-3/16" thick, R19	G	3800	.006		.35	.24	.11	.70	.90
0050	6-1/2" thick, R22	G	3000	.008		.45	.30	.14	.89	1.15
0100	8-11/16" thick, R30	G	2600	.009		.61	.34	.16	1.11	1.42
0120	10-7/8" thick, R38	G	1800	.013		.78	.50	.24	1.52	1.93
1000	Fiberglass, 5.5" thick, R11	G	3800	.006		.18	.24	.11	.53	.71
1050	6" thick, R12	G	3000	.008		.26	.30	.14	.70	.93
1100	8.8" thick, R19	G	2200	.011		.32	.41	.19	.92	1.23
1200	10" thick, R22	G	1800	.013		.37	.50	.24	1.11	1.49
1300	11.5" thick, R26	G	1500	.016		.44	.60	.29	1.33	1.78
1350	13" thick, R30	G	1400	.017		.52	.64	.31	1.47	1.96
1450	16" thick, R38	G	1145	.021		.66	.78	.37	1.81	2.42
1500	20" thick, R49	G	920	.026		.87	.97	.46	2.30	3.07
9000	Minimum labor/equipment charge		4	6	Job		224	107	331	490

07 21 27 – Reflective Insulation

07 21 27.10 Reflective Insulation Options

		Crew	Daily Output	Labor-Hours	Unit	Material	2014 Bare Costs Labor	Equipment	Total	Total Incl O&P
0010	**REFLECTIVE INSULATION OPTIONS**									
0020	Aluminum foil on reinforced scrim	G 1 Carp	19	.421	C.S.F.	14.20	19.30		33.50	47
0100	Reinforced with woven polyolefin	G	19	.421		22	19.30		41.30	55.50
0500	With single bubble air space, R8.8	G	15	.533		26	24.50		50.50	68.50
0600	With double bubble air space, R9.8	G	15	.533		29	24.50		53.50	71.50
9000	Minimum labor/equipment charge		4	2	Job		91.50		91.50	151

07 21 29 – Sprayed Insulation

07 21 29.10 Sprayed-On Insulation

		Crew	Daily Output	Labor-Hours	Unit	Material	2014 Bare Costs Labor	Equipment	Total	Total Incl O&P
0010	**SPRAYED-ON INSULATION**									
0020	Fibrous/cementitious, finished wall, 1" thick, R3.7	G G-2	2050	.012	S.F.	.29	.45	.07	.81	1.12
0100	Attic, 5.2" thick, R19	G	1550	.015	"	.51	.60	.09	1.20	1.63
0200	Fiberglass, R4 per inch, vertical	G	1600	.015	B.F.	.18	.58	.08	.84	1.22
0210	Horizontal	G	1200	.020	"	.18	.77	.11	1.06	1.56
0300	Closed cell, spray polyurethane foam, 2 pounds per cubic foot density									
0310	1" thick	G G-2A	6000	.004	S.F.	.53	.14	.12	.79	.96
0320	2" thick	G	3000	.008		1.05	.28	.25	1.58	1.92
0330	3" thick	G	2000	.012		1.58	.42	.37	2.37	2.87

07 21 Thermal Insulation

07 21 29 – Sprayed Insulation

07 21 29.10 Sprayed-On Insulation		Crew	Daily Output	Labor-Hours	Unit	Material	2014 Bare Costs Labor	Equipment	Total	Total Incl O&P
0335	3-1/2" thick	G	G-2A	1715	.014	S.F.	1.84	.49	.43	2.76	3.35
0340	4" thick	G		1500	.016		2.10	.56	.49	3.15	3.83
0350	5" thick	G		1200	.020		2.63	.70	.62	3.95	4.79
0355	5-1/2" thick	G		1090	.022		2.89	.77	.68	4.34	5.30
0360	6" thick	G		1000	.024		3.15	.84	.74	4.73	5.75
9000	Minimum labor/equipment charge		G-2	2	12	Job		465	67.50	532.50	825

07 22 Roof and Deck Insulation

07 22 16 – Roof Board Insulation

07 22 16.10 Roof Deck Insulation

			Crew	Daily Output	Labor-Hours	Unit	Material	2014 Bare Costs Labor	Equipment	Total	Total Incl O&P
0010	**ROOF DECK INSULATION**, fastening excluded										
0020	Fiberboard low density, 1/2" thick R1.39	G	1 Rofc	1300	.006	S.F.	.30	.24		.54	.76
0030	1" thick R2.78	G		1040	.008		.52	.30		.82	1.11
0080	1 1/2" thick R4.17	G		1040	.008		.80	.30		1.10	1.42
0100	2" thick R5.56	G		1040	.008		1.06	.30		1.36	1.71
0110	Fiberboard high density, 1/2" thick R1.3	G		1300	.006		.29	.24		.53	.75
0120	1" thick R2.5	G		1040	.008		.60	.30		.90	1.20
0130	1-1/2" thick R3.8	G		1040	.008		.89	.30		1.19	1.52
0200	Fiberglass, 3/4" thick R2.78	G		1300	.006		.61	.24		.85	1.10
0400	15/16" thick R3.70	G		1300	.006		.81	.24		1.05	1.32
0460	1-1/16" thick R4.17	G		1300	.006		1.01	.24		1.25	1.54
0600	1-5/16" thick R5.26	G		1300	.006		1.37	.24		1.61	1.94
0650	2-1/16" thick R8.33	G		1040	.008		1.45	.30		1.75	2.14
0700	2-7/16" thick R10	G		1040	.008		1.68	.30		1.98	2.39
1650	Perlite, 1/2" thick R1.32	G		1365	.006		.31	.23		.54	.75
1655	3/4" thick R2.08	G		1040	.008		.35	.30		.65	.93
1660	1" thick R2.78	G		1040	.008		.49	.30		.79	1.08
1670	1-1/2" thick R4.17	G		1040	.008		.72	.30		1.02	1.33
1680	2" thick R5.56	G		910	.009		.99	.34		1.33	1.71
1685	2-1/2" thick R6.67	G		910	.009		1.30	.34		1.64	2.05
1690	Tapered for drainage	G		1040	.008	B.F.	1.01	.30		1.31	1.65
1700	Polyisocyanurate, 2#/C.F. density, 3/4" thick	G		1950	.004	S.F.	.44	.16		.60	.77
1705	1" thick	G		1820	.004		.50	.17		.67	.86
1715	1-1/2" thick	G		1625	.005		.63	.19		.82	1.04
1725	2" thick	G		1430	.006		.79	.22		1.01	1.26
1735	2-1/2" thick	G		1365	.006		1.01	.23		1.24	1.52
1745	3" thick	G		1300	.006		1.22	.24		1.46	1.77
1755	3-1/2" thick	G		1300	.006		1.95	.24		2.19	2.58
1765	Tapered for drainage	G		1820	.004	B.F.	.57	.17		.74	.94
1900	Extruded Polystyrene										
1910	15 PSI compressive strength, 1" thick, R5	G	1 Rofc	1950	.004	S.F.	.53	.16		.69	.87
1920	2" thick, R10	G		1625	.005		.69	.19		.88	1.11
1930	3" thick R15	G		1300	.006		1.38	.24		1.62	1.95
1932	4" thick R20	G		1300	.006		1.86	.24		2.10	2.47
1934	Tapered for drainage	G		1950	.004	B.F.	.56	.16		.72	.91
1940	25 PSI compressive strength, 1" thick R5	G		1950	.004	S.F.	.66	.16		.82	1.02
1942	2" thick R10	G		1625	.005		1.25	.19		1.44	1.73
1944	3" thick R15	G		1300	.006		1.91	.24		2.15	2.54
1946	4" thick R20	G		1300	.006		2.64	.24		2.88	3.33
1948	Tapered for drainage	G		1950	.004	B.F.	.58	.16		.74	.93
1950	40 psi compressive strength, 1" thick R5	G		1950	.004	S.F.	.51	.16		.67	.85

07 22 Roof and Deck Insulation

07 22 16 – Roof Board Insulation

07 22 16.10 Roof Deck Insulation		Crew	Daily Output	Labor-Hours	Unit	Material	2014 Bare Costs Labor	Equipment	Total	Total Incl O&P
1952	2" thick R10	G 1 Rofc	1625	.005	S.F.	.97	.19		1.16	1.42
1954	3" thick R15	G	1300	.006		1.40	.24		1.64	1.97
1956	4" thick R20	G	1300	.006		1.84	.24		2.08	2.45
1958	Tapered for drainage	G	1820	.004	B.F.	.73	.17		.90	1.11
1960	60 PSI compressive strength, 1" thick R5	G	1885	.004	S.F.	.71	.17		.88	1.08
1962	2" thick R10	G	1560	.005		1.35	.20		1.55	1.84
1964	3" thick R15	G	1270	.006		2.20	.25		2.45	2.86
1966	4" thick R20	G	1235	.006		2.73	.25		2.98	3.47
1968	Tapered for drainage	G	1820	.004	B.F.	.93	.17		1.10	1.33
2010	Expanded polystyrene, 1#/C.F. density, 3/4" thick R2.89	G	1950	.004	S.F.	.18	.16		.34	.49
2020	1" thick R3.85	G	1950	.004		.24	.16		.40	.55
2100	2" thick R7.69	G	1625	.005		.48	.19		.67	.88
2110	3" thick R11.49	G	1625	.005		.72	.19		.91	1.14
2120	4" thick R15.38	G	1625	.005		.96	.19		1.15	1.41
2130	5" thick R19.23	G	1495	.005		1.20	.21		1.41	1.70
2140	6" thick R23.26	G	1495	.005		1.44	.21		1.65	1.96
2150	Tapered for drainage	G	1950	.004	B.F.	.51	.16		.67	.85
2400	Composites with 2" EPS									
2410	1" fiberboard	G 1 Rofc	1325	.006	S.F.	1.33	.24		1.57	1.89
2420	7/16" oriented strand board	G	1040	.008		1.07	.30		1.37	1.72
2430	1/2" plywood	G	1040	.008		1.32	.30		1.62	1.99
2440	1" perlite	G	1040	.008		1.09	.30		1.39	1.74
2450	Composites with 1-1/2" polyisocyanurate									
2460	1" fiberboard	G 1 Rofc	1040	.008	S.F.	1.13	.30		1.43	1.78
2470	1" perlite	G	1105	.007		1.01	.28		1.29	1.62
2480	7/16" oriented strand board	G	1040	.008		.89	.30		1.19	1.52
3000	Fastening alternatives, coated screws, 2"		3744	.002	Ea.	.05	.08		.13	.21
3010	4"		3120	.003		.10	.10		.20	.29
3020	6"		2675	.003		.17	.12		.29	.40
3030	8"		2340	.003		.25	.13		.38	.52
3040	10"		1872	.004		.43	.17		.60	.77
3050	Pre-drill and drive wedge spike, 2-1/2"		1248	.006		.37	.25		.62	.86
3060	3-1/2"		1101	.007		.48	.28		.76	1.04
3070	4-1/2"		936	.009		.60	.33		.93	1.26
3075	3" galvanized deck plates		7488	.001		.07	.04		.11	.16
3080	Spot mop asphalt	G-1	295	.190	Sq.	5.50	6.95	1.88	14.33	20.50
3090	Full mop asphalt	"	192	.292		11	10.65	2.88	24.53	34.50
3100	Low-rise polyurethane adhesive	G-2A	100	.240		.18	8.40	7.40	15.98	23
9000	Minimum labor/equipment charge	1 Rofc	3.25	2.462	Job		96.50		96.50	174

07 24 Exterior Insulation and Finish Systems

07 24 13 – Polymer-Based Exterior Insulation and Finish System

07 24 13.10 Exterior Insulation and Finish Systems

0010	EXTERIOR INSULATION AND FINISH SYSTEMS		Crew	Daily Output	Labor-Hours	Unit	Material	Labor	Equipment	Total	Total Incl O&P
0095	Field applied, 1" EPS insulation	G	J-1	390	.103	S.F.	1.92	4.11	.37	6.40	9.10
0100	With 1/2" cement board sheathing	G		268	.149		2.65	6	.54	9.19	13.10
0105	2" EPS insulation	G		390	.103		2.16	4.11	.37	6.64	9.40
0110	With 1/2" cement board sheathing	G		268	.149		2.89	6	.54	9.43	13.35
0115	3" EPS insulation	G		390	.103		2.40	4.11	.37	6.88	9.65
0120	With 1/2" cement board sheathing	G		268	.149		3.13	6	.54	9.67	13.65
0125	4" EPS insulation	G		390	.103		2.64	4.11	.37	7.12	9.90

07 24 Exterior Insulation and Finish Systems

07 24 13 – Polymer-Based Exterior Insulation and Finish System

07 24 13.10 Exterior Insulation and Finish Systems		Crew	Daily Output	Labor-Hours	Unit	Material	2014 Bare Costs Labor	Equipment	Total	Total Incl O&P
0130	With 1/2" cement board sheathing	G	J-1	268	.149	S.F.	4.11	6	.54	10.65	14.70
0140	Premium finish add			1265	.032		.31	1.27	.11	1.69	2.49
0150	Heavy duty reinforcement add			914	.044		.81	1.75	.16	2.72	3.87
0160	2.5#/S.Y. metal lath substrate add		1 Lath	75	.107	S.Y.	3.05	4.33		7.38	10.15
0170	3.4#/S.Y. metal lath substrate add		"	75	.107	"	3.80	4.33		8.13	11
0180	Color or texture change,		J-1	1265	.032	S.F.	.75	1.27	.11	2.13	2.98
0190	With substrate leveling base coat		1 Plas	530	.015		.75	.63		1.38	1.85
0210	With substrate sealing base coat		1 Pord	1224	.007		.08	.26		.34	.51
0370	V groove shape in panel face					L.F.	.60			.60	.66
0380	U groove shape in panel face					"	.79			.79	.87
0433	Crack repair, acrylic rubber, fluid applied, 20 mils thick		1 Plas	350	.023	S.F.	1.43	.96		2.39	3.11
0437	50 mils thick, reinforced		"	200	.040	"	2.62	1.68		4.30	5.55
0440	For higher than one story, add							25%			

07 25 Weather Barriers

07 25 10 – Weather Barriers or Wraps

07 25 10.10 Weather Barriers

		Crew	Daily Output	Labor-Hours	Unit	Material	2014 Bare Costs Labor	Equipment	Total	Total Incl O&P
0010	**WEATHER BARRIERS**									
0400	Asphalt felt paper, 15#	1 Carp	37	.216	Sq.	5.40	9.90		15.30	22.50
0401	Per square foot	"	3700	.002	S.F.	.05	.10		.15	.22
0450	Housewrap, exterior, spun bonded polypropylene									
0470	Small roll	1 Carp	3800	.002	S.F.	.14	.10		.24	.32
0480	Large roll	"	4000	.002	"	.14	.09		.23	.30
2100	Asphalt felt roof deck vapor barrier, class 1 metal decks	1 Rofc	37	.216	Sq.	22	8.45		30.45	39.50
2200	For all other decks	"	37	.216		16.40	8.45		24.85	33.50
2800	Asphalt felt, 50% recycled content, 15 lb., 4 sq. per roll	1 Carp	36	.222		5.40	10.20		15.60	22.50
2810	30 lb., 2 sq. per roll	"	36	.222		10.80	10.20		21	28.50
3000	Building wrap, spunbonded polyethylene	2 Carp	8000	.002	S.F.	.14	.09		.23	.30
9960	Minimum labor/equipment charge	1 Carp	2	4	Job		183		183	300

07 26 Vapor Retarders

07 26 10 – Above-Grade Vapor Retarders

07 26 10.10 Vapor Retarders

			Crew	Daily Output	Labor-Hours	Unit	Material	2014 Bare Costs Labor	Equipment	Total	Total Incl O&P
0010	**VAPOR RETARDERS**										
0020	Aluminum and kraft laminated, foil 1 side	G	1 Carp	37	.216	Sq.	11.25	9.90		21.15	28.50
0100	Foil 2 sides	G		37	.216		12.50	9.90		22.40	30
0600	Polyethylene vapor barrier, standard, .002" thick	G		37	.216		1.50	9.90		11.40	17.95
0700	.004" thick	G		37	.216		2.91	9.90		12.81	19.50
0900	.006" thick	G		37	.216		3.98	9.90		13.88	20.50
1200	.010" thick	G		37	.216		8.85	9.90		18.75	26
1300	Clear reinforced, fire retardant, .008" thick	G		37	.216		10.50	9.90		20.40	28
1350	Cross laminated type, .003" thick	G		37	.216		7.45	9.90		17.35	24.50
1400	.004" thick	G		37	.216		7.80	9.90		17.70	25
1800	Reinf. waterproof, .002" polyethylene backing, 1 side			37	.216		5.95	9.90		15.85	23
1900	2 sides			37	.216		7.80	9.90		17.70	25
2400	Waterproofed kraft with sisal or fiberglass fibers, minimum			37	.216		12.50	9.90		22.40	30
2500	Maximum			37	.216		13.50	9.90		23.40	31
9950	Minimum labor/equipment charge			4	2	Job		91.50		91.50	151

07 27 Air Barriers

07 27 26 – Fluid-Applied Membrane Air Barriers

07 27 26.10 Fluid Applied Membrane Air Barrier	Crew	Daily Output	Labor-Hours	Unit	Material	2014 Bare Costs Labor	Equipment	Total	Total Incl O&P
0010 **FLUID APPLIED MEMBRANE AIR BARRIER**									
0100 Spray applied vapor barrier, 25 S.F./gallon	1 Pord	1375	.006	S.F.	.01	.23		.24	.39

07 31 Shingles and Shakes

07 31 13 – Asphalt Shingles

07 31 13.10 Asphalt Roof Shingles

	Crew	Daily Output	Labor-Hours	Unit	Material	Labor	Equipment	Total	Total Incl O&P
0010 **ASPHALT ROOF SHINGLES**									
0100 Standard strip shingles									
0150 Inorganic, class A, 210-235 lb./sq.	1 Rofc	5.50	1.455	Sq.	81	57		138	192
0155 Pneumatic nailed		7	1.143		81	44.50		125.50	170
0200 235-240 lb./sq.		5	1.600		96	62.50		158.50	219
0205 Pneumatic nailed		6.25	1.280		96	50		146	197
0250 Standard, laminated multi-layered shingles									
0300 Class A, 240-260 lb./sq.	1 Rofc	4.50	1.778	Sq.	106	69.50		175.50	241
0305 Pneumatic nailed		5.63	1.422		106	55.50		161.50	216
0350 Class A, 260-300 lb./square, 4 bundles/square		4	2		106	78.50		184.50	257
0355 Pneumatic nailed		5	1.600		106	62.50		168.50	229
0400 Premium, laminated multi-layered shingles									
0450 Class A, 260-300 lb., 4 bundles/sq.	1 Rofc	3.50	2.286	Sq.	165	89.50		254.50	340
0455 Pneumatic nailed		4.37	1.831		165	71.50		236.50	310
0500 Class A, 300-385 lb./square, 5 bundles/square		3	2.667		219	104		323	430
0505 Pneumatic nailed		3.75	2.133		219	83.50		302.50	390
0800 #15 felt underlayment		64	.125		5.40	4.89		10.29	14.75
0825 #30 felt underlayment		58	.138		10.80	5.40		16.20	21.50
0850 Self adhering polyethylene and rubberized asphalt underlayment		22	.364		77	14.25		91.25	111
0900 Ridge shingles		330	.024	L.F.	2	.95		2.95	3.91
0905 Pneumatic nailed		412.50	.019	"	2	.76		2.76	3.57
1000 For steep roofs (7 to 12 pitch or greater), add						50%			
9000 Minimum labor/equipment charge	1 Rofc	3	2.667	Job		104		104	188

07 31 16 – Metal Shingles

07 31 16.10 Aluminum Shingles

	Crew	Daily Output	Labor-Hours	Unit	Material	Labor	Equipment	Total	Total Incl O&P
0010 **ALUMINUM SHINGLES**									
0020 Mill finish, .019 thick	1 Carp	5	1.600	Sq.	221	73.50		294.50	365
0100 .020" thick	"	5	1.600		222	73.50		295.50	365
0300 For colors, add					20			20	22
0600 Ridge cap, .024" thick	1 Carp	170	.047	L.F.	3.60	2.16		5.76	7.50
0700 End wall flashing, .024" thick		170	.047		1.99	2.16		4.15	5.75
0900 Valley section, .024" thick		170	.047		3.43	2.16		5.59	7.30
1000 Starter strip, .024" thick		400	.020		1.58	.92		2.50	3.25
1200 Side wall flashing, .024" thick		170	.047		1.99	2.16		4.15	5.75
1500 Gable flashing, .024" thick		400	.020		1.58	.92		2.50	3.25
9000 Minimum labor/equipment charge		3	2.667	Job		122		122	201

07 31 16.20 Steel Shingles

	Crew	Daily Output	Labor-Hours	Unit	Material	Labor	Equipment	Total	Total Incl O&P
0010 **STEEL SHINGLES**									
0012 Galvanized, 26 ga.	1 Rots	2.20	3.636	Sq.	335	143		478	625
0200 24 ga.	"	2.20	3.636		335	143		478	625
0300 For colored galvanized shingles, add					55			55	60.50
9000 Minimum labor/equipment charge	1 Rots	3	2.667	Job		105		105	189

07 31 Shingles and Shakes

07 31 26 – Slate Shingles

07 31 26.10 Slate Roof Shingles		Crew	Daily Output	Labor-Hours	Unit	Material	2014 Bare Costs Labor	Equipment	Total	Total Incl O&P
0010	**SLATE ROOF SHINGLES**									
0100	Buckingham Virginia black, 3/16" - 1/4" thick	G	1 Rots	1.75	4.571	Sq.	475	180		655	850
0200	1/4" thick	G		1.75	4.571		475	180		655	850
0900	Pennsylvania black, Bangor, #1 clear	G		1.75	4.571		490	180		670	865
1200	Vermont, unfading, green, mottled green	G		1.75	4.571		480	180		660	850
1300	Semi-weathering green & gray	G		1.75	4.571		350	180		530	705
1400	Purple	G		1.75	4.571		425	180		605	790
1500	Black or gray	G		1.75	4.571		460	180		640	830
2500	Slate roof repair, extensive replacement			1	8		590	315		905	1,225
2600	Repair individual pieces, scattered			19	.421	Ea.	5.90	16.55		22.45	36.50
2700	Ridge shingles, slate			200	.040	L.F.	9.30	1.57		10.87	13.05
9000	Minimum labor/equipment charge			3	2.667	Job		105		105	189

07 31 29 – Wood Shingles and Shakes

07 31 29.13 Wood Shingles

		Crew	Daily Output	Labor-Hours	Unit	Material	2014 Bare Costs Labor	Equipment	Total	Total Incl O&P
0010	**WOOD SHINGLES** R061110-30									
0012	16" No. 1 red cedar shingles, 5" exposure, on roof	1 Carp	2.50	3.200	Sq.	264	147		411	530
0015	Pneumatic nailed		3.25	2.462		264	113		377	475
0200	7-1/2" exposure, on walls		2.05	3.902		176	179		355	490
0205	Pneumatic nailed		2.67	2.996		176	137		313	420
0300	18" No. 1 red cedar perfections, 5-1/2" exposure, on roof		2.75	2.909		227	133		360	470
0305	Pneumatic nailed		3.57	2.241		227	103		330	420
0500	7-1/2" exposure, on walls		2.25	3.556		167	163		330	450
0505	Pneumatic nailed		2.92	2.740		167	126		293	390
0600	Resquared, and rebutted, 5-1/2" exposure, on roof		3	2.667		280	122		402	510
0605	Pneumatic nailed		3.90	2.051		280	94		374	465
0900	7-1/2" exposure, on walls		2.45	3.265		206	150		356	475
0905	Pneumatic nailed		3.18	2.516		206	115		321	415
1000	Add to above for fire retardant shingles					55			55	60.50
1060	Preformed ridge shingles	1 Carp	400	.020	L.F.	4.50	.92		5.42	6.45
2000	White cedar shingles, 16" long, extras, 5" exposure, on roof		2.40	3.333	Sq.	173	153		326	440
2005	Pneumatic nailed		3.12	2.564		173	118		291	385
2050	5" exposure on walls		2	4		173	183		356	490
2055	Pneumatic nailed		2.60	3.077		173	141		314	420
2100	7-1/2" exposure, on walls		2	4		123	183		306	435
2105	Pneumatic nailed		2.60	3.077		123	141		264	370
2150	"B" grade, 5" exposure on walls		2	4		150	183		333	465
2155	Pneumatic nailed		2.60	3.077		150	141		291	395
2300	For 15# organic felt underlayment on roof, 1 layer, add		64	.125		5.40	5.75		11.15	15.35
2400	2 layers, add		32	.250		10.80	11.45		22.25	31
2600	For steep roofs (7/12 pitch or greater), add to above						50%			
2700	Panelized systems, No.1 cedar shingles on 5/16" CDX plywood									
2800	On walls, 8' strips, 7" or 14" exposure	2 Carp	700	.023	S.F.	6	1.05		7.05	8.30
3500	On roofs, 8' strips, 7" or 14" exposure	1 Carp	3	2.667	Sq.	600	122		722	860
3505	Pneumatic nailed		4	2	"	600	91.50		691.50	810
9000	Minimum labor/equipment charge		3	2.667	Job		122		122	201

07 31 29.16 Wood Shakes

		Crew	Daily Output	Labor-Hours	Unit	Material	2014 Bare Costs Labor	Equipment	Total	Total Incl O&P
0010	**WOOD SHAKES**									
1100	Hand-split red cedar shakes, 1/2" thick x 24" long, 10" exp. on roof	1 Carp	2.50	3.200	Sq.	253	147		400	520
1105	Pneumatic nailed		3.25	2.462		253	113		366	465
1110	3/4" thick x 24" long, 10" exp. on roof		2.25	3.556		253	163		416	545
1115	Pneumatic nailed		2.92	2.740		253	126		379	485

07 31 Shingles and Shakes

07 31 29 – Wood Shingles and Shakes

07 31 29.16 Wood Shakes

		Crew	Daily Output	Labor-Hours	Unit	Material	2014 Bare Costs Labor	Equipment	Total	Total Incl O&P
1200	1/2" thick, 18" long, 8-1/2" exp. on roof	1 Carp	2	4	Sq.	179	183		362	495
1205	Pneumatic nailed		2.60	3.077		179	141		320	430
1210	3/4" thick x 18" long, 8 1/2" exp. on roof		1.80	4.444		179	204		383	530
1215	Pneumatic nailed		2.34	3.419		179	157		336	455
1255	10" exp. on walls		2	4		173	183		356	490
1260	10" exposure on walls, pneumatic nailed		2.60	3.077		173	141		314	420
1700	Add to above for fire retardant shakes, 24" long					55			55	60.50
1800	18" long					55			55	60.50
1810	Ridge shakes	1 Carp	350	.023	L.F.	4.50	1.05		5.55	6.65

07 32 Roof Tiles

07 32 13 – Clay Roof Tiles

07 32 13.10 Clay Tiles

		Crew	Daily Output	Labor-Hours	Unit	Material	2014 Bare Costs Labor	Equipment	Total	Total Incl O&P
0010	**CLAY TILES**, including accessories									
0300	Flat shingle, interlocking, 15", 166 pcs/sq, fireflashed blend	3 Rots	6	4	Sq.	510	157		667	845
0500	Terra cotta red		6	4		510	157		667	845
0600	Roman pan and top, 18", 102 pcs/sq, fireflashed blend		5.50	4.364		560	172		732	925
0640	Terra cotta red	1 Rots	2.40	3.333		560	131		691	850
1100	Barrel mission tile, 18", 166 pcs/sq, fireflashed blend	3 Rots	5.50	4.364		405	172		577	755
1140	Terra cotta red		5.50	4.364		405	172		577	755
1700	Scalloped edge flat shingle, 14", 145 pcs/sq, fireflashed blend		6	4		1,125	157		1,282	1,525
1800	Terra cotta red		6	4		1,125	157		1,282	1,525
3010	#15 felt underlayment	1 Rofc	64	.125		5.40	4.89		10.29	14.75
3020	#30 felt underlayment		58	.138		10.80	5.40		16.20	21.50
3040	Polyethylene and rubberized asph. underlayment		22	.364		77	14.25		91.25	111
9010	Minimum labor/equipment charge	1 Rots	2	4	Job		157		157	284

07 32 16 – Concrete Roof Tiles

07 32 16.10 Concrete Tiles

		Crew	Daily Output	Labor-Hours	Unit	Material	2014 Bare Costs Labor	Equipment	Total	Total Incl O&P
0010	**CONCRETE TILES**									
0020	Corrugated, 13" x 16-1/2", 90 per sq., 950 lb. per sq.									
0050	Earthtone colors, nailed to wood deck	1 Rots	1.35	5.926	Sq.	104	233		337	535
0150	Blues		1.35	5.926		104	233		337	535
0200	Greens		1.35	5.926		108	233		341	540
0250	Premium colors		1.35	5.926		108	233		341	540
0500	Shakes, 13" x 16-1/2", 90 per sq., 950 lb. per sq.									
0600	All colors, nailed to wood deck	1 Rots	1.50	5.333	Sq.	88.50	210		298.50	475
1500	Accessory pieces, ridge & hip, 10" x 16-1/2", 8 lb. each	"	120	.067	Ea.	3.88	2.62		6.50	9
1700	Rake, 6-1/2" x 16-3/4", 9 lb. each					3.88			3.88	4.27
1800	Mansard hip, 10" x 16-1/2", 9.2 lb. each					3.88			3.88	4.27
1900	Hip starter, 10" x 16-1/2", 10.5 lb. each					12.20			12.20	13.40
2000	3 or 4 way apex, 10" each side, 11.5 lb. each					14.10			14.10	15.50
9000	Minimum labor/equipment charge	1 Rots	3	2.667	Job		105		105	189

07 32 19 – Metal Roof Tiles

07 32 19.10 Metal Roof Tiles

		Crew	Daily Output	Labor-Hours	Unit	Material	2014 Bare Costs Labor	Equipment	Total	Total Incl O&P
0010	**METAL ROOF TILES**									
0020	Accessories included, .032" thick aluminum, mission tile	1 Carp	2.50	3.200	Sq.	815	147		962	1,125
0200	Spanish tiles		3	2.667	"	560	122		682	815
9000	Minimum labor/equipment charge		3	2.667	Job		122		122	201

07 33 Natural Roof Coverings

07 33 63 – Vegetated Roofing

07 33 63.10 Green Roof Systems

07 33 63.10 Green Roof Systems		Crew	Daily Output	Labor-Hours	Unit	Material	2014 Bare Costs Labor	Equipment	Total	Total Incl O&P
0010	**GREEN ROOF SYSTEMS**									
0020	Soil mixture for green roof 30% sand, 55% gravel, 15% soil									
0100	Hoist and spread soil mixture 4 inch depth up to five stories tall roof	G B-13B	4000	.014	S.F.	.25	.56	.28	1.09	1.49
0150	6 inch depth	G	2667	.021		.37	.84	.43	1.64	2.24
0200	8 inch depth	G	2000	.028		.50	1.12	.57	2.19	2.99
0250	10 inch depth	G	1600	.035		.62	1.40	.71	2.73	3.73
0300	12 inch depth	G	1335	.042		.75	1.67	.85	3.27	4.48
0310	Alt. man-made soil mix, hoist & spread, 4" deep up to 5 stories tall roof	G	4000	.014		1.80	.56	.28	2.64	3.20
0350	Mobilization 55 ton crane to site	G 1 Eqhv	3.60	2.222	Ea.		112		112	177
0355	Hoisting cost to five stories per day (Avg. 28 picks per day)	G B-13B	1	56	Day		2,225	1,125	3,350	4,875
0360	Mobilization or demobilization, 100 ton crane to site driver & escort	G A-3E	2.50	6.400	Ea.		281	67.50	348.50	525
0365	Hoisting cost six to ten stories per day (Avg. 21 picks per day)	G B-13C	1	56	Day		2,225	1,700	3,925	5,500
0370	Hoist and spread soil mixture 4 inch depth six to ten stories tall roof	G	4000	.014	S.F.	.25	.56	.43	1.24	1.65
0375	6 inch depth	G	2667	.021		.37	.84	.64	1.85	2.47
0380	8 inch depth	G	2000	.028		.50	1.12	.85	2.47	3.30
0385	10 inch depth	G	1600	.035		.62	1.40	1.06	3.08	4.12
0390	12 inch depth	G	1335	.042		.75	1.67	1.28	3.70	4.94
0400	Green roof edging treated lumber 4" x 4" no hoisting included	G 2 Carp	400	.040	L.F.	1.22	1.83		3.05	4.35
0410	4" x 6"	G	400	.040		1.77	1.83		3.60	4.95
0420	4" x 8"	G	360	.044		3.07	2.04		5.11	6.75
0430	4" x 6" double stacked	G	300	.053		3.53	2.45		5.98	7.90
0500	Green roof edging redwood lumber 4" x 4" no hoisting included	G	400	.040		6.45	1.83		8.28	10.05
0510	4" x 6"	G	400	.040		11.20	1.83		13.03	15.30
0520	4" x 8"	G	360	.044		20.50	2.04		22.54	26
0530	4" x 6" double stacked	G	300	.053		22.50	2.45		24.95	28.50
0550	Components, not including membrane or insulation:									
0560	Fluid applied rubber membrane, reinforced, 215 mil thick	G G-5	350	.114	S.F.	.26	4.06	.57	4.89	8.20
0570	Root barrier	G 2 Rofc	775	.021		.55	.81		1.36	2.07
0580	Moisture retention barrier and reservoir	G "	900	.018		2.20	.70		2.90	3.67
0600	Planting sedum, light soil, potted, 2-1/4" diameter, two per S.F.	G 1 Clab	420	.019		5.20	.70		5.90	6.85
0610	one per S.F.	G "	840	.010		2.60	.35		2.95	3.43
0630	Planting sedum mat per S.F. including shipping (4000 S.F. min)	G 4 Clab	4000	.008		6.25	.29		6.54	7.35
0640	Installation sedum mat system (no soil required) per S.F. (4000 S.F. min)	G "	4000	.008		8.70	.29		8.99	10.05
0645	Note: pricing of sedum mats shipped in full truck loads (4000-5000 S.F.)									

07 41 Roof Panels

07 41 13 – Metal Roof Panels

07 41 13.10 Aluminum Roof Panels

07 41 13.10 Aluminum Roof Panels		Crew	Daily Output	Labor-Hours	Unit	Material	2014 Bare Costs Labor	Equipment	Total	Total Incl O&P
0010	**ALUMINUM ROOF PANELS**									
0020	Corrugated or ribbed, .0155" thick, natural	G-3	1200	.027	S.F.	.99	1.22		2.21	3.04
0300	Painted		1200	.027		1.44	1.22		2.66	3.53
0400	Corrugated, .018" thick, on steel frame, natural finish		1200	.027		1.30	1.22		2.52	3.38
0600	Painted		1200	.027		1.60	1.22		2.82	3.71
0700	Corrugated, on steel frame, natural, .024" thick		1200	.027		1.85	1.22		3.07	3.99
0800	Painted		1200	.027		2.25	1.22		3.47	4.43
0900	.032" thick, natural		1200	.027		2.39	1.22		3.61	4.58
1200	Painted		1200	.027		3.06	1.22		4.28	5.30
9000	Minimum labor/equipment charge	1 Rofc	3	2.667	Job		104		104	188

188

07 41 Roof Panels

07 41 13 – Metal Roof Panels

07 41 13.20 Steel Roofing Panels

		Crew	Daily Output	Labor-Hours	Unit	Material	2014 Bare Costs Labor	Equipment	Total	Total Incl O&P
0010	**STEEL ROOFING PANELS**									
0012	Corrugated or ribbed, on steel framing, 30 ga. galv	G-3	1100	.029	S.F.	1.67	1.33		3	3.97
0100	28 ga.		1050	.030		1.79	1.39		3.18	4.20
0300	26 ga.		1000	.032		1.85	1.46		3.31	4.38
0400	24 ga.		950	.034		2.90	1.54		4.44	5.65
0600	Colored, 28 ga.		1050	.030		1.67	1.39		3.06	4.07
0700	26 ga.		1000	.032		1.98	1.46		3.44	4.52
0710	Flat profile, 1-3/4" standing seams, 10" wide, standard finish, 26 ga.		1000	.032		3.75	1.46		5.21	6.45
0715	24 ga.		950	.034		4.35	1.54		5.89	7.25
0720	22 ga.		900	.036		5.35	1.62		6.97	8.50
0725	Zinc aluminum alloy finish, 26 ga.		1000	.032		2.94	1.46		4.40	5.55
0730	24 ga.		950	.034		3.51	1.54		5.05	6.35
0735	22 ga.		900	.036		4.02	1.62		5.64	7
0740	12" wide, standard finish, 26 ga.		1000	.032		3.74	1.46		5.20	6.45
0745	24 ga.		950	.034		4.91	1.54		6.45	7.85
0750	Zinc aluminum alloy finish, 26 ga.		1000	.032		4.26	1.46		5.72	7.05
0755	24 ga.		950	.034		3.50	1.54		5.04	6.30
0840	Flat profile, 1" x 3/8" batten, 12" wide, standard finish, 26 ga.		1000	.032		3.30	1.46		4.76	5.95
0845	24 ga.		950	.034		3.87	1.54		5.41	6.75
0850	22 ga.		900	.036		4.63	1.62		6.25	7.70
0855	Zinc aluminum alloy finish, 26 ga.		1000	.032		3.16	1.46		4.62	5.80
0860	24 ga.		950	.034		3.53	1.54		5.07	6.35
0865	22 ga.		900	.036		4.08	1.62		5.70	7.10
0870	16-1/2" wide, standard finish, 24 ga.		950	.034		3.81	1.54		5.35	6.65
0875	22 ga.		900	.036		4.27	1.62		5.89	7.30
0880	Zinc aluminum alloy finish, 24 ga.		950	.034		3.33	1.54		4.87	6.15
0885	22 ga.		900	.036		3.71	1.62		5.33	6.70
0890	Flat profile, 2" x 2" batten, 12" wide, standard finish, 26 ga.		1000	.032		3.79	1.46		5.25	6.50
0895	24 ga.		950	.034		4.53	1.54		6.07	7.45
0900	22 ga.		900	.036		5.55	1.62		7.17	8.70
0905	Zinc aluminum alloy finish, 26 ga.		1000	.032		3.53	1.46		4.99	6.20
0910	24 ga.		950	.034		4.03	1.54		5.57	6.90
0915	22 ga.		900	.036		4.69	1.62		6.31	7.75
0920	16-1/2" wide, standard finish, 24 ga.		950	.034		4.16	1.54		5.70	7.05
0925	22 ga.		900	.036		4.87	1.62		6.49	7.95
0930	Zinc aluminum alloy finish, 24 ga.		950	.034		3.77	1.54		5.31	6.60
0935	22 ga.		900	.036		4.29	1.62		5.91	7.30
9000	Minimum labor/equipment charge	1 Rofc	2	4	Job		157		157	282

07 41 33 – Plastic Roof Panels

07 41 33.10 Fiberglass Panels

		Crew	Daily Output	Labor-Hours	Unit	Material	2014 Bare Costs Labor	Equipment	Total	Total Incl O&P
0010	**FIBERGLASS PANELS**									
0012	Corrugated panels, roofing, 8 oz. per S.F.	G-3	1000	.032	S.F.	2.08	1.46		3.54	4.63
0100	12 oz. per S.F.		1000	.032		3.55	1.46		5.01	6.25
0300	Corrugated siding, 6 oz. per S.F.		880	.036		1.75	1.66		3.41	4.59
0400	8 oz. per S.F.		880	.036		2.08	1.66		3.74	4.95
0500	Fire retardant		880	.036		3.51	1.66		5.17	6.50
0600	12 oz. siding, textured		880	.036		3.60	1.66		5.26	6.60
0700	Fire retardant		880	.036		4.20	1.66		5.86	7.30
0900	Flat panels, 6 oz. per S.F., clear or colors		880	.036		2.20	1.66		3.86	5.10
1100	Fire retardant, class A		880	.036		3.30	1.66		4.96	6.30
1300	8 oz. per S.F., clear or colors		880	.036		2.42	1.66		4.08	5.30
9000	Minimum labor/equipment charge	1 Rofc	2	4	Job		157		157	282

07 42 Wall Panels

07 42 13 – Metal Wall Panels

07 42 13.10 Mansard Panels

		Crew	Daily Output	Labor-Hours	Unit	Material	2014 Bare Costs Labor	Equipment	Total	Total Incl O&P
0010	**MANSARD PANELS**									
0600	Aluminum, stock units, straight surfaces	1 Shee	115	.070	S.F.	3.79	3.81		7.60	10.15
0700	Concave or convex surfaces		75	.107	"	2	5.85		7.85	11.40
0800	For framing, to 5' high, add		115	.070	L.F.	3.50	3.81		7.31	9.85
0900	Soffits, to 1' wide		125	.064	S.F.	2.14	3.50		5.64	7.85
9000	Minimum labor/equipment charge		2.50	3.200	Job		175		175	276

07 42 13.20 Aluminum Siding Panels

		Crew	Daily Output	Labor-Hours	Unit	Material	2014 Bare Costs Labor	Equipment	Total	Total Incl O&P
0010	**ALUMINUM SIDING PANELS**									
0012	Corrugated, on steel framing, .019 thick, natural finish	G-3	775	.041	S.F.	1.52	1.89		3.41	4.69
0100	Painted		775	.041		1.63	1.89		3.52	4.81
0400	Farm type, .021" thick on steel frame, natural		775	.041		1.53	1.89		3.42	4.70
0600	Painted		775	.041		1.63	1.89		3.52	4.81
0700	Industrial type, corrugated, on steel, .024" thick, mill		775	.041		2.12	1.89		4.01	5.35
0900	Painted		775	.041		2.28	1.89		4.17	5.55
1000	.032" thick, mill		775	.041		2.44	1.89		4.33	5.70
1200	Painted		775	.041		2.97	1.89		4.86	6.30
1300	V-Beam, on steel frame, .032" thick, mill		775	.041		2.75	1.89		4.64	6.05
1500	Painted		775	.041		3.15	1.89		5.04	6.50
1600	.040" thick, mill		775	.041		3.34	1.89		5.23	6.70
1800	Painted		775	.041		3.91	1.89		5.80	7.30
3800	Horizontal, colored clapboard, 8" wide, plain	2 Carp	515	.031		2.36	1.42		3.78	4.94
3810	Insulated		515	.031		2.57	1.42		3.99	5.15
3830	8" embossed, painted		515	.031		2.55	1.42		3.97	5.15
3840	Insulated		515	.031		2.73	1.42		4.15	5.35
3860	12" painted, smooth		600	.027		2.41	1.22		3.63	4.66
3870	Insulated		600	.027		2.57	1.22		3.79	4.84
3890	12" embossed, painted		600	.027		2.55	1.22		3.77	4.82
3900	Insulated		515	.031		2.44	1.42		3.86	5
4000	Vertical board & batten, colored, non-insulated		515	.031		1.83	1.42		3.25	4.35
4200	For simulated wood design, add					.11			.11	.12
4300	Corners for above, outside	2 Carp	515	.031	V.L.F.	3.23	1.42		4.65	5.90
4500	Inside corners	"	515	.031	"	1.55	1.42		2.97	4.05
9000	Minimum labor/equipment charge	1 Carp	3	2.667	Job		122		122	201

07 42 13.30 Steel Siding

		Crew	Daily Output	Labor-Hours	Unit	Material	2014 Bare Costs Labor	Equipment	Total	Total Incl O&P
0010	**STEEL SIDING**									
0020	Beveled, vinyl coated, 8" wide	1 Carp	265	.030	S.F.	1.91	1.38		3.29	4.37
0050	10" wide	"	275	.029		2.04	1.33		3.37	4.43
0080	Galv, corrugated or ribbed, on steel frame, 30 ga.	G-3	800	.040		1.31	1.83		3.14	4.37
0100	28 ga.		795	.040		1.38	1.84		3.22	4.47
0300	26 ga.		790	.041		1.91	1.85		3.76	5.05
0400	24 ga.		785	.041		1.94	1.86		3.80	5.10
0600	22 ga.		770	.042		2.24	1.90		4.14	5.50
0700	Colored, corrugated/ribbed, on steel frame, 10 yr. finish, 28 ga.		800	.040		2.04	1.83		3.87	5.15
0900	26 ga.		795	.040		2.13	1.84		3.97	5.30
1000	24 ga.		790	.041		2.49	1.85		4.34	5.70
1020	20 ga.		785	.041		3.15	1.86		5.01	6.45
9000	Minimum labor/equipment charge	1 Carp	3	2.667	Job		122		122	201

07 46 Siding

07 46 23 – Wood Siding

07 46 23.10 Wood Board Siding

07 46 23.10 Wood Board Siding	Crew	Daily Output	Labor-Hours	Unit	Material	2014 Bare Costs Labor	Equipment	Total	Total Incl O&P
0010 **WOOD BOARD SIDING**									
3200 Wood, cedar bevel, A grade, 1/2" x 6"	1 Carp	295	.027	S.F.	4.14	1.24		5.38	6.60
3300 1/2" x 8"		330	.024		5.90	1.11		7.01	8.35
3500 3/4" x 10", clear grade		375	.021		6.30	.98		7.28	8.50
3600 "B" grade		375	.021		3.79	.98		4.77	5.80
3800 Cedar, rough sawn, 1" x 4", A grade, natural		220	.036		6.35	1.67		8.02	9.75
3900 Stained		220	.036		6.50	1.67		8.17	9.90
4100 1" x 12", board & batten, #3 & Btr., natural		420	.019		4.35	.87		5.22	6.25
4200 Stained		420	.019		4.67	.87		5.54	6.60
4400 1" x 8" channel siding, #3 & Btr., natural		330	.024		4.43	1.11		5.54	6.70
4500 Stained		330	.024		4.78	1.11		5.89	7.10
4700 Redwood, clear, beveled, vertical grain, 1/2" x 4"		220	.036		4.11	1.67		5.78	7.25
4750 1/2" x 6"		295	.027		4.49	1.24		5.73	7
4800 1/2" x 8"		330	.024		4.89	1.11		6	7.25
5000 3/4" x 10"		375	.021		4.50	.98		5.48	6.55
5200 Channel siding, 1" x 10", B grade		375	.021		4.12	.98		5.10	6.15
5250 Redwood, T&G boards, B grade, 1" x 4"		220	.036		2.54	1.67		4.21	5.55
5270 1" x 8"		330	.024		4.10	1.11		5.21	6.35
5400 White pine, rough sawn, 1" x 8", natural		330	.024		2.19	1.11		3.30	4.24
5500 Stained		330	.024		2.19	1.11		3.30	4.24
9000 Minimum labor/equipment charge		2	4	Job		183		183	300

07 46 29 – Plywood Siding

07 46 29.10 Plywood Siding Options

07 46 29.10 Plywood Siding Options	Crew	Daily Output	Labor-Hours	Unit	Material	2014 Bare Costs Labor	Equipment	Total	Total Incl O&P
0010 **PLYWOOD SIDING OPTIONS**									
0900 Plywood, medium density overlaid, 3/8" thick	2 Carp	750	.021	S.F.	1.15	.98		2.13	2.88
1000 1/2" thick		700	.023		1.36	1.05		2.41	3.22
1100 3/4" thick		650	.025		1.74	1.13		2.87	3.77
1600 Texture 1-11, cedar, 5/8" thick, natural		675	.024		2.43	1.09		3.52	4.46
1700 Factory stained		675	.024		2.69	1.09		3.78	4.75
1900 Texture 1-11, fir, 5/8" thick, natural		675	.024		1.57	1.09		2.66	3.52
2000 Factory stained		675	.024		1.80	1.09		2.89	3.77
2050 Texture 1-11, S.Y.P., 5/8" thick, natural		675	.024		1.19	1.09		2.28	3.10
2100 Factory stained		675	.024		1.24	1.09		2.33	3.15
2200 Rough sawn cedar, 3/8" thick, natural		675	.024		1.20	1.09		2.29	3.11
2300 Factory stained		675	.024		1.46	1.09		2.55	3.40
2500 Rough sawn fir, 3/8" thick, natural		675	.024		.82	1.09		1.91	2.69
2600 Factory stained		675	.024		1.04	1.09		2.13	2.93
2800 Redwood, textured siding, 5/8" thick		675	.024		1.92	1.09		3.01	3.90
3000 Polyvinyl chloride coated, 3/8" thick		750	.021		1.11	.98		2.09	2.83
9000 Minimum labor/equipment charge	1 Carp	2	4	Job		183		183	300

07 46 33 – Plastic Siding

07 46 33.10 Vinyl Siding

07 46 33.10 Vinyl Siding	Crew	Daily Output	Labor-Hours	Unit	Material	2014 Bare Costs Labor	Equipment	Total	Total Incl O&P
0010 **VINYL SIDING**									
3995 Clapboard profile, woodgrain texture, .048 thick, double 4	2 Carp	495	.032	S.F.	.97	1.48		2.45	3.51
4000 Double 5		550	.029		.97	1.33		2.30	3.26
4005 Single 8		495	.032		1.08	1.48		2.56	3.63
4010 Single 10		550	.029		1.30	1.33		2.63	3.62
4015 .044 thick, double 4		495	.032		.95	1.48		2.43	3.49
4020 Double 5		550	.029		.95	1.33		2.28	3.24
4025 .042 thick, double 4		495	.032		.90	1.48		2.38	3.44
4030 Double 5		550	.029		.90	1.33		2.23	3.19
4035 Cross sawn texture, .040 thick, double 4		495	.032		.64	1.48		2.12	3.15

07 46 Siding

07 46 33 – Plastic Siding

07 46 33.10 Vinyl Siding

		Crew	Daily Output	Labor-Hours	Unit	Material	2014 Bare Costs Labor	Equipment	Total	Total Incl O&P
4040	Double 5	2 Carp	550	.029	S.F.	.64	1.33		1.97	2.90
4045	Smooth texture, .042 thick, double 4		495	.032		.72	1.48		2.20	3.24
4050	Double 5		550	.029		.72	1.33		2.05	2.99
4055	Single 8		495	.032		.72	1.48		2.20	3.24
4060	Cedar texture, .044 thick, double 4		495	.032		.95	1.48		2.43	3.49
4065	Double 6		600	.027		.96	1.22		2.18	3.07
4070	Dutch lap profile, woodgrain texture, .048 thick, double 5		550	.029		.97	1.33		2.30	3.26
4075	.044 thick, double 4.5		525	.030		.95	1.40		2.35	3.35
4080	.042 thick, double 4.5		525	.030		.80	1.40		2.20	3.19
4085	.040 thick, double 4.5		525	.030		.64	1.40		2.04	3.01
4100	Shake profile, 10" wide		400	.040		3.26	1.83		5.09	6.60
4105	Vertical pattern, .046 thick, double 5		550	.029		1.29	1.33		2.62	3.61
4110	.044 thick, triple 3		550	.029		1.47	1.33		2.80	3.81
4115	.040 thick, triple 4		550	.029		1.47	1.33		2.80	3.81
4120	.040 thick, triple 2.66		550	.029		1.62	1.33		2.95	3.98
4125	Insulation, fan folded extruded polystyrene, 1/4"		2000	.008		.27	.37		.64	.90
4130	3/8"		2000	.008	↓	.30	.37		.67	.93
4135	Accessories, J channel, 5/8" pocket		700	.023	L.F.	.44	1.05		1.49	2.20
4140	3/4" pocket		695	.023		.46	1.06		1.52	2.23
4145	1-1/4" pocket		680	.024		.70	1.08		1.78	2.54
4150	Flexible, 3/4" pocket		600	.027		2.20	1.22		3.42	4.43
4155	Under sill finish trim		500	.032		.49	1.47		1.96	2.95
4160	Vinyl starter strip		700	.023		.50	1.05		1.55	2.27
4165	Aluminum starter strip		700	.023		.26	1.05		1.31	2
4170	Window casing, 2-1/2" wide, 3/4" pocket		510	.031		1.46	1.44		2.90	3.96
4175	Outside corner, woodgrain finish, 4" face, 3/4" pocket		700	.023		1.82	1.05		2.87	3.73
4180	5/8" pocket		700	.023		1.82	1.05		2.87	3.73
4185	Smooth finish, 4" face, 3/4" pocket		700	.023		1.82	1.05		2.87	3.73
4190	7/8" pocket		690	.023		1.82	1.06		2.88	3.76
4195	1-1/4" pocket		700	.023		1.28	1.05		2.33	3.13
4200	Soffit and fascia, 1' overhang, solid		120	.133		4	6.10		10.10	14.45
4205	Vented		120	.133		4	6.10		10.10	14.45
4207	18" overhang, solid		110	.145		4.65	6.65		11.30	16.05
4208	Vented		110	.145		4.65	6.65		11.30	16.05
4210	2' overhang, solid		100	.160		5.30	7.35		12.65	17.85
4215	Vented		100	.160		5.30	7.35		12.65	17.85
4217	3' overhang, solid		100	.160		6.55	7.35		13.90	19.30
4218	Vented	↓	100	.160	↓	6.55	7.35		13.90	19.30
4220	Colors for siding and soffits, add				S.F.	.14			.14	.15
4225	Colors for accessories and trim, add				L.F.	.29			.29	.32
9000	Minimum labor/equipment charge	1 Carp	3	2.667	Job		122		122	201

07 46 33.20 Polypropylene Siding

		Crew	Daily Output	Labor-Hours	Unit	Material	2014 Bare Costs Labor	Equipment	Total	Total Incl O&P
0010	**POLYPROPYLENE SIDING**									
4090	Shingle profile, random grooves, double 7	2 Carp	400	.040	S.F.	2.87	1.83		4.70	6.15
4092	Cornerpost for above	1 Carp	365	.022	L.F.	11.15	1.01		12.16	13.90
4095	Triple 5	2 Carp	400	.040	S.F.	2.87	1.83		4.70	6.15
4097	Cornerpost for above	1 Carp	365	.022	L.F.	10.50	1.01		11.51	13.15
5000	Staggered butt, double 7"	2 Carp	400	.040	S.F.	3.26	1.83		5.09	6.60
5002	Cornerpost for above	1 Carp	365	.022	L.F.	11.30	1.01		12.31	14.10
5010	Half round, double 6-1/4"	2 Carp	360	.044	S.F.	3.25	2.04		5.29	6.95
5020	Shake profile, staggered butt, double 9"	"	510	.031	"	3.25	1.44		4.69	5.95
5022	Cornerpost for above	1 Carp	365	.022	L.F.	8.35	1.01		9.36	10.80

07 46 Siding

07 46 33 – Plastic Siding

07 46 33.20 Polypropylene Siding

07 46 33.20 Polypropylene Siding	Crew	Daily Output	Labor-Hours	Unit	Material	2014 Bare Costs Labor	Equipment	Total	Total Incl O&P
5030	Straight butt, double 7"	2 Carp	400	.040	S.F.	3.25	1.83		5.08	6.60
5032	Cornerpost for above	1 Carp	365	.022	L.F.	11.20	1.01		12.21	13.95
6000	Accessories, J channel, 5/8" pocket	2 Carp	700	.023		.44	1.05		1.49	2.20
6010	3/4" pocket		695	.023		.46	1.06		1.52	2.23
6020	1-1/4" pocket		680	.024		.70	1.08		1.78	2.54
6030	Aluminum starter strip	↓	700	.023	↓	.26	1.05		1.31	2

07 46 46 – Fiber Cement Siding

07 46 46.10 Fiber Cement Siding

07 46 46.10 Fiber Cement Siding	Crew	Daily Output	Labor-Hours	Unit	Material	2014 Bare Costs Labor	Equipment	Total	Total Incl O&P
0010	**FIBER CEMENT SIDING**									
0020	Lap siding, 5/16" thick, 6" wide, 4-3/4" exposure, smooth texture	2 Carp	415	.039	S.F.	1.21	1.77		2.98	4.23
0025	Woodgrain texture		415	.039		1.21	1.77		2.98	4.23
0030	7-1/2" wide, 6-1/4" exposure, smooth texture		425	.038		1.42	1.73		3.15	4.40
0035	Woodgrain texture		425	.038		1.42	1.73		3.15	4.40
0040	8" wide, 6-3/4" exposure, smooth texture		425	.038		1.55	1.73		3.28	4.54
0045	Roughsawn texture		425	.038		1.55	1.73		3.28	4.54
0050	9-1/2" wide, 8-1/4" exposure, smooth texture		440	.036		1.54	1.67		3.21	4.44
0055	Woodgrain texture		440	.036		1.54	1.67		3.21	4.44
0060	12" wide, 10-3/8" exposure, smooth texture		455	.035		1.34	1.61		2.95	4.12
0065	Woodgrain texture		455	.035		1.34	1.61		2.95	4.12
0070	Panel siding, 5/16" thick, smooth texture		750	.021		1.31	.98		2.29	3.05
0075	Stucco texture		750	.021		1.31	.98		2.29	3.05
0080	Grooved woodgrain texture		750	.021		1.31	.98		2.29	3.05
0085	V - grooved woodgrain texture		750	.021		1.31	.98		2.29	3.05
0088	Shingle siding, 48" x 15-1/4" panels, 7" exposure		700	.023		4	1.05		5.05	6.10
0090	Wood starter strip	↓	400	.040	L.F.	.42	1.83		2.25	3.47

07 46 73 – Soffit

07 46 73.10 Soffit Options

07 46 73.10 Soffit Options	Crew	Daily Output	Labor-Hours	Unit	Material	2014 Bare Costs Labor	Equipment	Total	Total Incl O&P
0010	**SOFFIT OPTIONS**									
0012	Aluminum, residential, .020" thick	1 Carp	210	.038	S.F.	1.87	1.75		3.62	4.93
0100	Baked enamel on steel, 16 or 18 ga.		105	.076		5.80	3.49		9.29	12.15
0300	Polyvinyl chloride, white, solid		230	.035		2.04	1.59		3.63	4.86
0400	Perforated	↓	230	.035		2.04	1.59		3.63	4.86
0500	For colors, add				↓	.12			.12	.13
9000	Minimum labor/equipment charge	1 Carp	3	2.667	Job		122		122	201

07 51 Built-Up Bituminous Roofing

07 51 13 – Built-Up Asphalt Roofing

07 51 13.10 Built-Up Roofing Components

07 51 13.10 Built-Up Roofing Components	Crew	Daily Output	Labor-Hours	Unit	Material	2014 Bare Costs Labor	Equipment	Total	Total Incl O&P
0010	**BUILT-UP ROOFING COMPONENTS**									
0012	Asphalt saturated felt, #30, 2 square per roll	1 Rofc	58	.138	Sq.	10.80	5.40		16.20	21.50
0200	#15, 4 sq. per roll, plain or perforated, not mopped		58	.138		5.40	5.40		10.80	15.70
0300	Roll roofing, smooth, #65		15	.533		9.65	21		30.65	48
0500	#90		12	.667		35	26		61	85.50
0520	Mineralized		12	.667		35	26		61	85.50
0540	D.C. (Double coverage), 19" selvage edge	↓	10	.800	↓	52	31.50		83.50	114
0580	Adhesive (lap cement)				Gal.	8.50			8.50	9.35
0800	Steep, flat or dead level asphalt, 10 ton lots, packaged				Ton	915			915	1,000
9000	Minimum labor/equipment charge	1 Rofc	4	2	Job		78.50		78.50	141

193

07 51 13.13 Cold-Applied Built-Up Asphalt Roofing	Crew	Daily Output	Labor-Hours	Unit	Material	2014 Bare Costs Labor	Equipment	Total	Total Incl O&P
0010 **COLD-APPLIED BUILT-UP ASPHALT ROOFING**									
0020 3 ply system, installation only (components listed below)	G-5	50	.800	Sq.		28.50	3.98	32.48	56
0100 Spunbond poly. fabric, 1.35 oz./S.Y., 36"W, 10.8 sq./roll				Ea.	134			134	147
0500 Base & finish coat, 3 gal./sq., 5 gal./can				Gal.	7.75			7.75	8.50
0600 Coating, ceramic granules, 1/2 sq./bag				Ea.	21.50			21.50	23.50
0700 Aluminum, 2 gal./sq.				Gal.	11.80			11.80	13
0800 Emulsion, fibered or non-fibered, 4 gal./sq.				"	6.35			6.35	6.95

07 51 13.20 Built-Up Roofing Systems

	Crew	Daily Output	Labor-Hours	Unit	Material	2014 Bare Costs Labor	Equipment	Total	Total Incl O&P
0010 **BUILT-UP ROOFING SYSTEMS**									
0120 Asphalt flood coat with gravel/slag surfacing, not including									
0140 Insulation, flashing or wood nailers									
0200 Asphalt base sheet, 3 plies #15 asphalt felt, mopped	G-1	22	2.545	Sq.	98.50	93	25	216.50	305
0350 On nailable decks		21	2.667		101	97.50	26.50	225	315
0500 4 plies #15 asphalt felt, mopped		20	2.800		134	102	27.50	263.50	365
0550 On nailable decks		19	2.947		119	108	29	256	355
0700 Coated glass base sheet, 2 plies glass (type IV), mopped		22	2.545		106	93	25	224	315
0850 3 plies glass, mopped		20	2.800		129	102	27.50	258.50	355
0950 On nailable decks		19	2.947		121	108	29	258	360
1100 4 plies glass fiber felt (type IV), mopped		20	2.800		159	102	27.50	288.50	390
1150 On nailable decks		19	2.947		143	108	29	280	385
1200 Coated & saturated base sheet, 3 plies #15 asph. felt, mopped		20	2.800		111	102	27.50	240.50	340
1250 On nailable decks		19	2.947		103	108	29	240	340
1300 4 plies #15 asphalt felt, mopped		22	2.545		129	93	25	247	340
2000 Asphalt flood coat, smooth surface									
2200 Asphalt base sheet & 3 plies #15 asphalt felt, mopped	G-1	24	2.333	Sq.	104	85.50	23	212.50	294
2400 On nailable decks		23	2.435		96	89	24	209	294
2600 4 plies #15 asphalt felt, mopped		24	2.333		122	85.50	23	230.50	315
2700 On nailable decks		23	2.435		114	89	24	227	315
2900 Coated glass fiber base sheet, mopped, and 2 plies of									
2910 glass fiber felt (type IV)	G-1	25	2.240	Sq.	102	82	22	206	285
3100 On nailable decks		24	2.333		96	85.50	23	204.50	286
3200 3 plies, mopped		23	2.435		124	89	24	237	325
3300 On nailable decks		22	2.545		117	93	25	235	325
3800 4 plies glass fiber felt (type IV), mopped		23	2.435		147	89	24	260	350
3900 On nailable decks		22	2.545		139	93	25	257	350
4000 Coated & saturated base sheet, 3 plies #15 asph. felt, mopped		24	2.333		106	85.50	23	214.50	297
4200 On nailable decks		23	2.435		98.50	89	24	211.50	296
4300 4 plies #15 organic felt, mopped		22	2.545		125	93	25	243	335
4500 Coal tar pitch with gravel/slag surfacing									
4600 4 plies #15 tarred felt, mopped	G-1	21	2.667	Sq.	234	97.50	26.50	358	460
4800 3 plies glass fiber felt (type IV), mopped	"	19	2.947	"	193	108	29	330	440
5000 Coated glass fiber base sheet, and 2 plies of									
5010 glass fiber felt, (type IV), mopped	G-1	19	2.947	Sq.	196	108	29	333	440
5300 On nailable decks		18	3.111		170	114	31	315	425
5600 4 plies glass fiber felt (type IV), mopped		21	2.667		264	97.50	26.50	388	495
5800 On nailable decks		20	2.800		238	102	27.50	367.50	475

07 51 13.30 Cants

	Crew	Daily Output	Labor-Hours	Unit	Material	2014 Bare Costs Labor	Equipment	Total	Total Incl O&P
0010 **CANTS**									
0012 Lumber, treated, 4" x 4" cut diagonally	1 Rofc	325	.025	L.F.	1.75	.96		2.71	3.67
0300 Mineral or fiber, trapezoidal, 1" x 4" x 48"		325	.025		.24	.96		1.20	2
0400 1-1/2" x 5-5/8" x 48"		325	.025		.42	.96		1.38	2.20
9000 Minimum labor/equipment charge		4	2	Job		78.50		78.50	141

07 51 Built-Up Bituminous Roofing

07 51 13 – Built-Up Asphalt Roofing

07 51 13.40 Felts

		Crew	Daily Output	Labor-Hours	Unit	Material	2014 Bare Costs Labor	2014 Bare Costs Equipment	Total	Total Incl O&P
0010	**FELTS**									
0012	Glass fibered roofing felt, #15, not mopped	1 Rofc	58	.138	Sq.	9.65	5.40		15.05	20.50
0300	Base sheet, #80, channel vented		58	.138		42.50	5.40		47.90	57
0400	#70, coated		58	.138		17.20	5.40		22.60	28.50
0500	Cap, #87, mineral surfaced		58	.138		80	5.40		85.40	98
0600	Flashing membrane, #65		16	.500		9.65	19.60		29.25	46
0800	Coal tar fibered, #15, no mopping		58	.138		18.10	5.40		23.50	29.50
0900	Asphalt felt, #15, 4 sq. per roll, no mopping		58	.138		5.40	5.40		10.80	15.70
1100	#30, 2 sq. per roll		58	.138		10.80	5.40		16.20	21.50
1200	Double coated, #33		58	.138		11	5.40		16.40	22
1400	#40, base sheet		58	.138		9.65	5.40		15.05	20.50
1450	Coated and saturated		58	.138		12	5.40		17.40	23
1500	Tarred felt, organic, #15, 4 sq. rolls		58	.138		13.95	5.40		19.35	25
1550	#30, 2 sq. roll		58	.138		28	5.40		33.40	40.50
1700	Add for mopping above felts, per ply, asphalt, 24 lb. per sq.	G-1	192	.292		11	10.65	2.88	24.53	34.50
1800	Coal tar mopping, 30 lb. per sq.		186	.301		23	11	2.98	36.98	48.50
1900	Flood coat, with asphalt, 60 lb. per sq.		60	.933		27.50	34	9.25	70.75	102
2000	With coal tar, 75 lb. per sq.		56	1		57.50	36.50	9.90	103.90	140
9000	Minimum labor/equipment charge	1 Rofc	4	2	Job		78.50		78.50	141

07 51 13.50 Walkways for Built-Up Roofs

		Crew	Daily Output	Labor-Hours	Unit	Material	2014 Bare Costs Labor	2014 Bare Costs Equipment	Total	Total Incl O&P
0010	**WALKWAYS FOR BUILT-UP ROOFS**									
0020	Asphalt impregnated, 3' x 6' x 1/2" thick	1 Rofc	400	.020	S.F.	1.56	.78		2.34	3.12
0100	3' x 3' x 3/4" thick		400	.020	"	4.48	.78		5.26	6.35
0600	100% recycled rubber, 3' x 4' x 3/8" [G]		400	.020	L.F.	6.35	.78		7.13	8.35
0610	3' x 4' x 1/2" [G]		400	.020		6.80	.78		7.58	8.85
0620	3' x 4' x 3/4" [G]		400	.020		8.45	.78		9.23	10.70
9000	Minimum labor/equipment charge		2.75	2.909	Job		114		114	205

07 52 Modified Bituminous Membrane Roofing

07 52 13 – Atactic-Polypropylene-Modified Bituminous Membrane Roofing

07 52 13.10 APP Modified Bituminous Membrane

		Crew	Daily Output	Labor-Hours	Unit	Material	2014 Bare Costs Labor	2014 Bare Costs Equipment	Total	Total Incl O&P
0010	**APP MODIFIED BITUMINOUS MEMBRANE** R075213-30									
0020	Base sheet, #15 glass fiber felt, nailed to deck	1 Rofc	58	.138	Sq.	10.65	5.40		16.05	21.50
0030	Spot mopped to deck	G-1	295	.190		15.15	6.95	1.88	23.98	31
0040	Fully mopped to deck	"	192	.292		20.50	10.65	2.88	34.03	45
0050	#15 organic felt, nailed to deck	1 Rofc	58	.138		6.40	5.40		11.80	16.80
0060	Spot mopped to deck	G-1	295	.190		10.90	6.95	1.88	19.73	26.50
0070	Fully mopped to deck	"	192	.292		16.40	10.65	2.88	29.93	40.50
2100	APP mod., smooth surf. cap sheet, poly. reinf., torched, 160 mils	G-5	2100	.019	S.F.	.68	.68	.09	1.45	2.07
2150	170 mils		2100	.019		.70	.68	.09	1.47	2.09
2200	Granule surface cap sheet, poly. reinf., torched, 180 mils		2000	.020		.89	.71	.10	1.70	2.37
2250	Smooth surface flashing, torched, 160 mils		1260	.032		.68	1.13	.16	1.97	2.95
2300	170 mils		1260	.032		.70	1.13	.16	1.99	2.97
2350	Granule surface flashing, torched, 180 mils		1260	.032		.89	1.13	.16	2.18	3.18
2400	Fibrated aluminum coating	1 Rofc	3800	.002		.08	.08		.16	.23

07 52 Modified Bituminous Membrane Roofing

07 52 16 – Styrene-Butadiene-Styrene Modified Bituminous Membrane Roofing

07 52 16.10 SBS Modified Bituminous Membrane	Crew	Daily Output	Labor-Hours	Unit	Material	2014 Bare Costs Labor	2014 Bare Costs Equipment	Total	Total Incl O&P
0010 **SBS MODIFIED BITUMINOUS MEMBRANE**									
0080 SBS modified, granule surf cap sheet, polyester reinf., mopped									
1500 Glass fiber reinforced, mopped, 160 mils	G-1	2000	.028	S.F.	.71	1.02	.28	2.01	2.93
1600 Smooth surface cap sheet, mopped, 145 mils		2100	.027		.78	.98	.26	2.02	2.91
1700 Smooth surface flashing, 145 mils		1260	.044		.78	1.63	.44	2.85	4.27
1800 150 mils		1260	.044		.49	1.63	.44	2.56	3.95
1900 Granular surface flashing, 150 mils		1260	.044		.65	1.63	.44	2.72	4.13
2000 160 mils		1260	.044		.71	1.63	.44	2.78	4.19

07 53 Elastomeric Membrane Roofing

07 53 16 – Chlorosulfonate-Polyethylene Roofing

07 53 16.10 Chlorosulfonated Polyethylene Roofing

	Crew	Daily Output	Labor-Hours	Unit	Material	Labor	Equipment	Total	Total Incl O&P
0010 **CHLOROSULFONATED POLYETHYLENE ROOFING**									
0800 Chlorosulfonated polyethylene (CSPE)									
0900 45 mils, heat welded seams, plate attachment	G-5	35	1.143	Sq.	310	40.50	5.70	356.20	420
1100 Heat welded seams, plate attachment and ballasted		26	1.538		320	54.50	7.65	382.15	455
1200 60 mils, heat welded seams, plate attachment		35	1.143		410	40.50	5.70	456.20	530
1300 Heat welded seams, plate attachment and ballasted		26	1.538		415	54.50	7.65	477.15	565

07 53 23 – Ethylene-Propylene-Diene-Monomer Roofing

07 53 23.20 Ethylene-Propylene-Diene-Monomer Roofing

	Crew	Daily Output	Labor-Hours	Unit	Material	Labor	Equipment	Total	Total Incl O&P
0010 **ETHYLENE-PROPYLENE-DIENE-MONOMER ROOFING (EPDM)**									
3500 Ethylene-propylene-diene-monomer (EPDM), 45 mils, 0.28 psf									
3600 Loose-laid & ballasted with stone (10 psf)	G-5	51	.784	Sq.	83	28	3.91	114.91	146
3700 Mechanically attached		35	1.143		78.50	40.50	5.70	124.70	165
3800 Fully adhered with adhesive		26	1.538		111	54.50	7.65	173.15	229
4500 60 mils, 0.40 psf									
4600 Loose-laid & ballasted with stone (10 psf)	G-5	51	.784	Sq.	97.50	28	3.91	129.41	163
4700 Mechanically attached		35	1.143		92	40.50	5.70	138.20	180
4800 Fully adhered with adhesive		26	1.538		124	54.50	7.65	186.15	244
4810 45 mil, .28 psf, membrane only					50			50	55
4820 60 mil, .40 psf, membrane only					62.50			62.50	69
4850 Seam tape for membrane, 3" x 100' roll				Ea.	39.50			39.50	43.50
4900 Batten strips, 10' sections					3.43			3.43	3.77
4910 Cover tape for batten strips, 6" x 100' roll					186			186	205
4930 Plate anchors				M	75			75	82.50
4970 Adhesive for fully adhered systems, 60 S.F./gal.				Gal.	19.70			19.70	21.50

07 53 29 – Polyisobutylene Roofing

07 53 29.10 Polyisobutylene Roofing

	Crew	Daily Output	Labor-Hours	Unit	Material	Labor	Equipment	Total	Total Incl O&P
0010 **POLYISOBUTYLENE ROOFING**									
7500 Polyisobutylene (PIB), 100 mils, 0.57 psf									
7600 Loose-laid & ballasted with stone/gravel (10 psf)	G-5	51	.784	Sq.	200	28	3.91	231.91	275
7700 Partially adhered with adhesive		35	1.143		240	40.50	5.70	286.20	345
7800 Hot asphalt attachment		35	1.143		230	40.50	5.70	276.20	330
7900 Fully adhered with contact cement		26	1.538		250	54.50	7.65	312.15	380

07 54 Thermoplastic Membrane Roofing

07 54 19 – Polyvinyl-Chloride Roofing

07 54 19.10 Polyvinyl-Chloride Roofing (PVC)	Crew	Daily Output	Labor-Hours	Unit	Material	2014 Bare Costs Labor	Equipment	Total	Total Incl O&P
0010 **POLYVINYL-CHLORIDE ROOFING (PVC)**									
8200 Heat welded seams									
8700 Reinforced, 48 mils, 0.33 psf									
8750 Loose-laid & ballasted with stone/gravel (12 psf)	G-5	51	.784	Sq.	117	28	3.91	148.91	183
8800 Mechanically attached		35	1.143		111	40.50	5.70	157.20	201
8850 Fully adhered with adhesive		26	1.538		153	54.50	7.65	215.15	275
8860 Reinforced, 60 mils, .40 psf									
8870 Loose-laid & ballasted with stone/gravel (12 psf)	G-5	51	.784	Sq.	118	28	3.91	149.91	185
8880 Mechanically attached		35	1.143		112	40.50	5.70	158.20	203
8890 Fully adhered with adhesive		26	1.538		154	54.50	7.65	216.15	277

07 54 23 – Thermoplastic-Polyolefin Roofing

07 54 23.10 Thermoplastic Polyolefin Roofing (T.P.O)	Crew	Daily Output	Labor-Hours	Unit	Material	2014 Bare Costs Labor	Equipment	Total	Total Incl O&P
0010 **THERMOPLASTIC POLYOLEFIN ROOFING (T.P.O.)**									
0100 45 mils, loose laid & ballasted with stone(1/2 ton/sq.)	G-5	51	.784	Sq.	86	28	3.91	117.91	149
0120 Fully adhered		25	1.600		78	57	7.95	142.95	197
0140 Mechanically attached		34	1.176		77	42	5.85	124.85	167
0160 Self adhered		35	1.143		87	40.50	5.70	133.20	175
0180 60 mil membrane, heat welded seams, ballasted		50	.800		98.50	28.50	3.98	130.98	165
0200 Fully adhered		25	1.600		90	57	7.95	154.95	211
0220 Mechanically attached		34	1.176		93.50	42	5.85	141.35	185
0240 Self adhered		35	1.143		107	40.50	5.70	153.20	197

07 55 Protected Membrane Roofing

07 55 10 – Protected Membrane Roofing Components

07 55 10.10 Protected Membrane Roofing Components	Crew	Daily Output	Labor-Hours	Unit	Material	2014 Bare Costs Labor	Equipment	Total	Total Incl O&P
0010 **PROTECTED MEMBRANE ROOFING COMPONENTS**									
0100 Choose roofing membrane from 07 50									
0120 Then choose roof deck insulation from 07 22									
0130 Filter fabric	2 Rofc	10000	.002	S.F.	.12	.06		.18	.25
0140 Ballast, 3/8" - 1/2" in place	G-1	36	1.556	Ton	17.10	57	15.40	89.50	139
0150 3/4" - 1-1/2" in place	"	36	1.556	"	17.10	57	15.40	89.50	139
0200 2" concrete blocks, natural	1 Clab	115	.070	S.F.	3.37	2.55		5.92	7.90
0210 Colors	"	115	.070	"	3.73	2.55		6.28	8.30

07 56 Fluid-Applied Roofing

07 56 10 – Fluid-Applied Roofing Elastomers

07 56 10.10 Elastomeric Roofing

	Crew	Daily Output	Labor-Hours	Unit	Material	2014 Bare Costs Labor	Equipment	Total	Total Incl O&P
0010 **ELASTOMERIC ROOFING**									
0110 Acrylic rubber, fluid applied, 20 mils thick	G-5	2000	.020	S.F.	1.90	.71	.10	2.71	3.48
0120 50 mils, reinforced		1200	.033		2.90	1.18	.17	4.25	5.50
0130 For walking surface, add		900	.044		.96	1.58	.22	2.76	4.15
0300 Neoprene, fluid applied, 20 mil thick, not-reinforced	G-1	1135	.049		1.30	1.80	.49	3.59	5.20
0600 Non-woven polyester, reinforced		960	.058		1.42	2.13	.58	4.13	6.05
0700 5 coat neoprene deck, 60 mil thick, under 10,000 S.F.		325	.172		4.32	6.30	1.70	12.32	17.95
0900 Over 10,000 S.F.		625	.090		4.32	3.28	.89	8.49	11.60
9000 Minimum labor/equipment charge	1 Rofc	2	4	Job		157		157	282

07 57 Coated Foamed Roofing

07 57 13 – Sprayed Polyurethane Foam Roofing

07 57 13.10 Sprayed Polyurethane Foam Roofing (S.P.F.)	Crew	Daily Output	Labor-Hours	Unit	Material	2014 Bare Costs Labor	Equipment	Total	Total Incl O&P
0010 **SPRAYED POLYURETHANE FOAM ROOFING (S.P.F.)**									
0100 Primer for metal substrate (when required)	G-2A	3000	.008	S.F.	.42	.28	.25	.95	1.22
0200 Primer for non-metal substrate (when required)		3000	.008		.16	.28	.25	.69	.94
0300 Closed cell spray, polyurethane foam, 3 lb. per C.F. density, 1", R6.7		15000	.002		.66	.06	.05	.77	.88
0400 2", R13.4		13125	.002		1.32	.06	.06	1.44	1.62
0500 3", R18.6		11485	.002		1.98	.07	.06	2.11	2.38
0550 4", R24.8		10080	.002		2.64	.08	.07	2.79	3.14
0700 Spray-on silicone coating		2500	.010		.95	.34	.30	1.59	1.96
0800 Warranty 5-20 year manufacturer's									.15
0900 Warranty 20 year, no dollar limit									.20

07 58 Roll Roofing

07 58 10 – Asphalt Roll Roofing

07 58 10.10 Roll Roofing

	Crew	Daily Output	Labor-Hours	Unit	Material	2014 Bare Costs Labor	Equipment	Total	Total Incl O&P
0010 **ROLL ROOFING**									
0100 Asphalt, mineral surface									
0200 1 ply #15 organic felt, 1 ply mineral surfaced									
0300 Selvage roofing, lap 19", nailed & mopped	G-1	27	2.074	Sq.	74	76	20.50	170.50	241
0400 3 plies glass fiber felt (type IV), 1 ply mineral surfaced									
0500 Selvage roofing, lapped 19", mopped	G-1	25	2.240	Sq.	125	82	22	229	310
0600 Coated glass fiber base sheet, 2 plies of glass fiber									
0700 Felt (type IV), 1 ply mineral surfaced selvage									
0800 Roofing, lapped 19", mopped	G-1	25	2.240	Sq.	133	82	22	237	320
0900 On nailable decks	"	24	2.333	"	122	85.50	23	230.50	315
1000 3 plies glass fiber felt (type III), 1 ply mineral surfaced									
1100 Selvage roofing, lapped 19", mopped	G-1	25	2.240	Sq.	125	82	22	229	310

07 61 Sheet Metal Roofing

07 61 13 – Standing Seam Sheet Metal Roofing

07 61 13.10 Standing Seam Sheet Metal Roofing, Field Fab.

	Crew	Daily Output	Labor-Hours	Unit	Material	2014 Bare Costs Labor	Equipment	Total	Total Incl O&P
0010 **STANDING SEAM SHEET METAL ROOFING, FIELD FABRICATED**									
0400 Copper standing seam roofing, over 10 squares, 16 oz., 125 lb. per sq.	1 Shee	1.30	6.154	Sq.	870	335		1,205	1,475
0600 18 oz., 140 lb. per sq.		1.20	6.667		975	365		1,340	1,650
0700 20 oz., 150 lb. per sq.		1.10	7.273		1,225	400		1,625	1,975
1200 For abnormal conditions or small areas, add					25%	100%			
1300 For lead-coated copper, add					25%				
1400 Lead standing seam roofing, 5 lb. per S.F.	1 Shee	1.30	6.154		1,300	335		1,635	1,950
1500 Zinc standing seam roofing, .020" thick		1.20	6.667		1,100	365		1,465	1,800
1510 .027" thick		1.15	6.957		1,400	380		1,780	2,125
1520 .032" thick		1.10	7.273		1,775	400		2,175	2,575
1530 .040" thick		1.05	7.619		2,225	415		2,640	3,100
9000 Minimum labor/equipment charge		2	4	Job		219		219	345

07 61 16 – Batten Seam Sheet Metal Roofing

07 61 16.10 Batten Seam Sheet Metal Roofing, Field Fab.

	Crew	Daily Output	Labor-Hours	Unit	Material	2014 Bare Costs Labor	Equipment	Total	Total Incl O&P
0010 **BATTEN SEAM SHEET METAL ROOFING, FIELD FABRICATED**									
0012 Copper batten seam roofing, over 10 sq., 16 oz., 130 lb. per sq.	1 Shee	1.10	7.273	Sq.	1,100	400		1,500	1,825
0020 Lead batten seam roofing, 5 lb. per S.F.		1.20	6.667		1,350	365		1,715	2,075
0100 Zinc/copper alloy batten seam roofing, .020 thick		1.20	6.667		1,150	365		1,515	1,850
0200 Copper roofing, batten seam, over 10 sq., 18 oz., 145 lb. per sq.		1	8		1,225	440		1,665	2,050

07 61 Sheet Metal Roofing

07 61 16 – Batten Seam Sheet Metal Roofing

07 61 16.10 Batten Seam Sheet Metal Roofing, Field Fab.	Crew	Daily Output	Labor-Hours	Unit	Material	2014 Bare Costs Labor	Equipment	Total	Total Incl O&P
0300	20 oz., 160 lb. per sq.	1 Shee	1	8	Sq.	1,550	440		1,990	2,425
0500	Stainless steel batten seam roofing, type 304, 28 ga.		1.20	6.667		555	365		920	1,175
0600	26 ga.		1.15	6.957		515	380		895	1,175
0800	Zinc, copper alloy roofing, batten seam, .027" thick		1.15	6.957		1,450	380		1,830	2,200
0900	.032" thick		1.10	7.273		1,850	400		2,250	2,675
1000	.040" thick		1.05	7.619		2,325	415		2,740	3,200
9000	Minimum labor/equipment charge		2	4	Job		219		219	345

07 61 19 – Flat Seam Sheet Metal Roofing

07 61 19.10 Flat Seam Sheet Metal Roofing, Field Fabricated

		Crew	Daily Output	Labor-Hours	Unit	Material	2014 Bare Costs Labor	Equipment	Total	Total Incl O&P
0010	**FLAT SEAM SHEET METAL ROOFING, FIELD FABRICATED**									
0900	Copper flat seam roofing, over 10 squares, 16 oz., 115 lb./sq.	1 Shee	1.20	6.667	Sq.	805	365		1,170	1,475
0950	18 oz., 130 lb./sq.		1.15	6.957		905	380		1,285	1,600
1000	20 oz., 145 lb./sq.		1.10	7.273		1,150	400		1,550	1,875
1008	Zinc flat seam roofing, .020" thick		1.20	6.667		990	365		1,355	1,675
1010	.027" thick		1.15	6.957		1,250	380		1,630	1,975
1020	.032" thick		1.12	7.143		1,575	390		1,965	2,375
1030	.040" thick		1.05	7.619		1,975	415		2,390	2,825
1100	Lead flat seam roofing, 5 lb. per S.F.		1.30	6.154		1,150	335		1,485	1,800
9000	Minimum labor/equipment charge		2.75	2.909	Job		159		159	251

07 62 Sheet Metal Flashing and Trim

07 62 10 – Sheet Metal Trim

07 62 10.10 Sheet Metal Cladding

		Crew	Daily Output	Labor-Hours	Unit	Material	2014 Bare Costs Labor	Equipment	Total	Total Incl O&P
0010	**SHEET METAL CLADDING**									
0100	Aluminum, up to 6 bends, .032" thick, window casing	1 Carp	180	.044	S.F.	1.39	2.04		3.43	4.88
0200	Window sill		72	.111	L.F.	1.39	5.10		6.49	9.90
0300	Door casing		180	.044	S.F.	1.39	2.04		3.43	4.88
0400	Fascia		250	.032		1.39	1.47		2.86	3.94
0500	Rake trim		225	.036		1.39	1.63		3.02	4.21
0700	.024" thick, window casing		180	.044		1.52	2.04		3.56	5
0800	Window sill		72	.111	L.F.	1.52	5.10		6.62	10
0900	Door casing		180	.044	S.F.	1.52	2.04		3.56	5
1000	Fascia		250	.032		1.52	1.47		2.99	4.08
1100	Rake trim		225	.036		1.52	1.63		3.15	4.35
1200	Vinyl coated aluminum, up to 6 bends, window casing		180	.044		1.18	2.04		3.22	4.65
1300	Window sill		72	.111	L.F.	1.18	5.10		6.28	9.65
1400	Door casing		180	.044	S.F.	1.18	2.04		3.22	4.65
1500	Fascia		250	.032		1.18	1.47		2.65	3.71
1600	Rake trim		225	.036		1.18	1.63		2.81	3.98

07 65 Flexible Flashing

07 65 10 – Sheet Metal Flashing

07 65 10.10 Sheet Metal Flashing and Counter Flashing	Crew	Daily Output	Labor-Hours	Unit	Material	2014 Bare Costs Labor	Equipment	Total	Total Incl O&P
0010 **SHEET METAL FLASHING AND COUNTER FLASHING**									
0011 Including up to 4 bends									
0020 Aluminum, mill finish, .013" thick	1 Rofc	145	.055	S.F.	.79	2.16		2.95	4.76
0030 .016" thick		145	.055		.91	2.16		3.07	4.89
0060 .019" thick		145	.055		1.15	2.16		3.31	5.15
0100 .032" thick		145	.055		1.35	2.16		3.51	5.40
0200 .040" thick		145	.055		2.31	2.16		4.47	6.45
0300 .050" thick		145	.055		2.43	2.16		4.59	6.55
0325 Mill finish 5" x 7" step flashing, .016" thick		1920	.004	Ea.	.15	.16		.31	.46
0350 Mill finish 12" x 12" step flashing, .016" thick		1600	.005	"	.50	.20		.70	.90
0400 Painted finish, add				S.F.	.29			.29	.32
1000 Mastic-coated 2 sides, .005" thick	1 Rofc	330	.024		1.82	.95		2.77	3.71
1100 .016" thick		330	.024		2.01	.95		2.96	3.92
1600 Copper, 16 oz., sheets, under 1000 lb.		115	.070		6.95	2.72		9.67	12.55
1700 Over 4000 lb.		155	.052		6.95	2.02		8.97	11.30
1900 20 oz. sheets, under 1000 lb.		110	.073		9.85	2.85		12.70	16
2000 Over 4000 lb.		145	.055		9.35	2.16		11.51	14.20
2200 24 oz. sheets, under 1000 lb.		105	.076		12.10	2.98		15.08	18.75
2300 Over 4000 lb.		135	.059		11.50	2.32		13.82	16.85
2500 32 oz. sheets, under 1000 lb.		100	.080		16.15	3.13		19.28	23.50
2600 Over 4000 lb.		130	.062		15.35	2.41		17.76	21
2700 W shape for valleys, 16 oz., 24" wide		100	.080	L.F.	14	3.13		17.13	21
5800 Lead, 2.5 lb. per S.F., up to 12" wide		135	.059	S.F.	4.99	2.32		7.31	9.70
5900 Over 12" wide		135	.059		3.99	2.32		6.31	8.55
8900 Stainless steel sheets, 32 ga., .010" thick		155	.052		3	2.02		5.02	6.95
9000 28 ga., .015" thick		155	.052		3.99	2.02		6.01	8.05
9100 26 ga., .018" thick		155	.052		4.25	2.02		6.27	8.30
9200 24 ga., .025" thick		155	.052		4.75	2.02		6.77	8.90
9290 For mechanically keyed flashing, add					40%				
9320 Steel sheets, galvanized, 20 ga.	1 Rofc	130	.062	S.F.	1.25	2.41		3.66	5.70
9322 22 ga.		135	.059		1.21	2.32		3.53	5.50
9324 24 ga.		140	.057		.92	2.24		3.16	5.05
9326 26 ga.		145	.055		.80	2.16		2.96	4.77
9328 28 ga.		155	.052		.69	2.02		2.71	4.40
9340 30 ga.		160	.050		.58	1.96		2.54	4.17
9400 Terne coated stainless steel, .015" thick, 28 ga		155	.052		7.35	2.02		9.37	11.75
9500 .018" thick, 26 ga		155	.052		8.30	2.02		10.32	12.75
9600 Zinc and copper alloy (brass), .020" thick		155	.052		8.55	2.02		10.57	13.05
9700 .027" thick		155	.052		10.70	2.02		12.72	15.40
9800 .032" thick		155	.052		13.65	2.02		15.67	18.70
9900 .040" thick		155	.052		17.10	2.02		19.12	22.50
9950 Minimum labor/equipment charge		3	2.667	Job		104		104	188

07 65 12 – Fabric and Mastic Flashings

07 65 12.10 Fabric and Mastic Flashing and Counter Flashing	Crew	Daily Output	Labor-Hours	Unit	Material	2014 Bare Costs Labor	Equipment	Total	Total Incl O&P
0010 **FABRIC AND MASTIC FLASHING AND COUNTER FLASHING**									
1300 Asphalt flashing cement, 5 gallon				Gal.	8.45			8.45	9.30
4900 Fabric, asphalt-saturated cotton, specification grade	1 Rofc	35	.229	S.Y.	2.96	8.95		11.91	19.40
5000 Utility grade		35	.229		1.42	8.95		10.37	17.70
5300 Close-mesh fabric, saturated, 17 oz. per S.Y.		35	.229		2.15	8.95		11.10	18.50
5500 Fiberglass, resin-coated		35	.229		.97	8.95		9.92	17.20
8500 Shower pan, bituminous membrane, 7 oz.		155	.052	S.F.	1.62	2.02		3.64	5.40

07 65 Flexible Flashing

07 65 13 – Laminated Sheet Flashing

07 65 13.10 Laminated Sheet Flashing	Crew	Daily Output	Labor-Hours	Unit	Material	2014 Bare Costs Labor	Equipment	Total	Total Incl O&P
0010 **LAMINATED SHEET FLASHING**, Including up to 4 bends									
0500 Aluminum, fabric-backed 2 sides, .004" thick	1 Rofc	330	.024	S.F.	1.54	.95		2.49	3.40
0700 .005" thick		330	.024		1.82	.95		2.77	3.71
0750 Mastic-backed, self adhesive		460	.017		3.51	.68		4.19	5.10
0800 Mastic-coated 2 sides, .004" thick		330	.024		1.54	.95		2.49	3.40
2800 Copper, paperbacked 1 side, 2 oz.		330	.024		1.67	.95		2.62	3.55
2900 3 oz.		330	.024		1.97	.95		2.92	3.88
3100 Paperbacked 2 sides, 2 oz.		330	.024		1.72	.95		2.67	3.60
3150 3 oz.		330	.024		2.07	.95		3.02	3.99
3200 5 oz.		330	.024		2.69	.95		3.64	4.67
3250 7 oz.		330	.024		4.81	.95		5.76	7
3400 Mastic-backed 2 sides, copper, 2 oz.		330	.024		1.65	.95		2.60	3.53
3500 3 oz.		330	.024		2	.95		2.95	3.91
3700 5 oz.		330	.024		3	.95		3.95	5
3800 Fabric-backed 2 sides, copper, 2 oz.		330	.024		1.93	.95		2.88	3.83
4000 3 oz.		330	.024		2.19	.95		3.14	4.12
4100 5 oz.		330	.024		3.13	.95		4.08	5.15
4300 Copper-clad stainless steel, .015" thick, under 500 lb.		115	.070		5.80	2.72		8.52	11.30
4400 Over 2000 lb.		155	.052		5.55	2.02		7.57	9.75
4600 .018" thick, under 500 lb.		100	.080		6.55	3.13		9.68	12.85
4700 Over 2000 lb.		145	.055		6.20	2.16		8.36	10.75
8550 Shower pan, 3 ply copper and fabric, 3 oz.		155	.052		3.13	2.02		5.15	7.10
8600 7 oz.		155	.052		3.99	2.02		6.01	8.05
9300 Stainless steel, paperbacked 2 sides, .005" thick	↓	330	.024	↓	3.62	.95		4.57	5.70

07 65 19 – Plastic Sheet Flashing

07 65 19.10 Plastic Sheet Flashing and Counter Flashing

	Crew	Daily Output	Labor-Hours	Unit	Material	2014 Bare Costs Labor	Equipment	Total	Total Incl O&P
0010 **PLASTIC SHEET FLASHING AND COUNTER FLASHING**									
7300 Polyvinyl chloride, black, .010" thick	1 Rofc	285	.028	S.F.	.21	1.10		1.31	2.21
7400 .020" thick		285	.028		.28	1.10		1.38	2.29
7600 .030" thick		285	.028		.35	1.10		1.45	2.37
7700 .056" thick		285	.028		.85	1.10		1.95	2.92
7900 Black or white for exposed roofs, .060" thick	↓	285	.028	↓	1.80	1.10		2.90	3.96
8060 PVC tape, 5" x 45 mils, for joint covers, 100 L.F./roll				Ea.	170			170	187
8850 Polyvinyl chloride, .030" thick	1 Rofc	160	.050	S.F.	1.30	1.96		3.26	4.96

07 65 23 – Rubber Sheet Flashing

07 65 23.10 Rubber Sheet Flashing and Counterflashing

	Crew	Daily Output	Labor-Hours	Unit	Material	2014 Bare Costs Labor	Equipment	Total	Total Incl O&P
0010 **RUBBER SHEET FLASHING AND COUNTERFLASHING**									
4810 EPDM 90 mils, 1" diameter pipe flashing	1 Rofc	32	.250	Ea.	19.45	9.80		29.25	39
4820 2" diameter		30	.267		19.45	10.45		29.90	40.50
4830 3" diameter		28	.286		21	11.20		32.20	43
4840 4" diameter		24	.333		24	13.05		37.05	50
4850 6" diameter		22	.364	↓	24	14.25		38.25	52
8100 Rubber, butyl, 1/32" thick		285	.028	S.F.	1.92	1.10		3.02	4.09
8200 1/16" thick		285	.028		2.60	1.10		3.70	4.84
8300 Neoprene, cured, 1/16" thick		285	.028		2.23	1.10		3.33	4.43
8400 1/8" thick	↓	285	.028	↓	6.05	1.10		7.15	8.65

07 71 Roof Specialties

07 71 16 – Manufactured Counterflashing Systems

07 71 16.10 Roof Drain Boot		Crew	Daily Output	Labor-Hours	Unit	Material	2014 Bare Costs Labor	Equipment	Total	Total Incl O&P
0010	**ROOF DRAIN BOOT**									
0100	Cast iron, 2" x 3"	1 Shee	125	.064	L.F.	114	3.50		117.50	131
0200	3" x 4"		125	.064		240	3.50		243.50	270
0300	4" x 5"		125	.064		238	3.50		241.50	268
0400	4" x 6"		125	.064		286	3.50		289.50	320

07 71 19 – Manufactured Gravel Stops and Fasciae

07 71 19.10 Gravel Stop

		Crew	Daily Output	Labor-Hours	Unit	Material	Labor	Equipment	Total	Total Incl O&P
0010	**GRAVEL STOP**									
0020	Aluminum, .050" thick, 4" face height, mill finish	1 Shee	145	.055	L.F.	6	3.02		9.02	11.35
0080	Duranodic finish		145	.055		6.50	3.02		9.52	11.90
0100	Painted		145	.055		6.85	3.02		9.87	12.25
0300	6" face height		135	.059		6.45	3.24		9.69	12.20
0350	Duranodic finish		135	.059		6.95	3.24		10.19	12.75
0400	Painted		135	.059		8.10	3.24		11.34	14
0600	8" face height		125	.064		7.30	3.50		10.80	13.50
0650	Duranodic finish		125	.064		8	3.50		11.50	14.30
0700	Painted		125	.064		8.15	3.50		11.65	14.45
0900	12" face height, .080 thick, 2 piece		100	.080		10.15	4.38		14.53	18.10
0950	Duranodic finish		100	.080		10.05	4.38		14.43	17.95
1000	Painted		100	.080		11.90	4.38		16.28	20
1200	Copper, 16 oz., 3" face height		145	.055		39.50	3.02		42.52	48
1300	6" face height		135	.059		39.50	3.24		42.74	48
1350	Galv steel, 24 ga., 4" leg, plain, with continuous cleat, 4" face		145	.055		6	3.02		9.02	11.35
1360	6" face height		145	.055		6	3.02		9.02	11.35
1500	Polyvinyl chloride, 6" face height		135	.059		4.90	3.24		8.14	10.50
1600	9" face height		125	.064		5.80	3.50		9.30	11.85
1800	Stainless steel, 24 ga., 6" face height		135	.059		9.85	3.24		13.09	15.90
1900	12" face height		100	.080		19.70	4.38		24.08	28.50
2100	20 ga., 6" face height		135	.059		11.90	3.24		15.14	18.15
2200	12" face height		100	.080		24	4.38		28.38	33
9000	Minimum labor/equipment charge		3.50	2.286	Job		125		125	197

07 71 19.30 Fascia

		Crew	Daily Output	Labor-Hours	Unit	Material	Labor	Equipment	Total	Total Incl O&P
0010	**FASCIA**									
0100	Aluminum, reverse board and batten, .032" thick, colored, no furring incl	1 Shee	145	.055	S.F.	6.25	3.02		9.27	11.65
0200	Residential type, aluminum	1 Carp	200	.040	L.F.	1.72	1.83		3.55	4.90
0220	Vinyl	"	200	.040	"	1.92	1.83		3.75	5.10
0300	Steel, galv and enameled, stock, no furring, long panels	1 Shee	145	.055	S.F.	3.91	3.02		6.93	9.05
0600	Short panels		115	.070	"	5.30	3.81		9.11	11.85
9000	Minimum labor/equipment charge		4	2	Job		109		109	173

07 71 23 – Manufactured Gutters and Downspouts

07 71 23.10 Downspouts

		Crew	Daily Output	Labor-Hours	Unit	Material	Labor	Equipment	Total	Total Incl O&P
0010	**DOWNSPOUTS**									
0020	Aluminum 2" x 3", .020" thick, embossed	1 Shee	190	.042	L.F.	.97	2.30		3.27	4.70
0100	Enameled		190	.042		1.32	2.30		3.62	5.10
0300	Enameled, .024" thick, 2" x 3"		180	.044		2.05	2.43		4.48	6.10
0400	3" x 4"		140	.057		2.88	3.13		6.01	8.10
0600	Round, corrugated aluminum, 3" diameter, .020" thick		190	.042		1.57	2.30		3.87	5.35
0700	4" diameter, .025" thick		140	.057		2.33	3.13		5.46	7.50
0900	Wire strainer, round, 2" diameter		155	.052	Ea.	3.92	2.82		6.74	8.75
1000	4" diameter		155	.052		7.20	2.82		10.02	12.40
1200	Rectangular, perforated, 2" x 3"		145	.055		2.30	3.02		5.32	7.30

07 71 23.10 Downspouts

		Crew	Daily Output	Labor-Hours	Unit	Material	2014 Bare Costs Labor	Equipment	Total	Total Incl O&P
1300	3" x 4"	1 Shee	145	.055	Ea.	3.32	3.02		6.34	8.40
1500	Copper, round, 16 oz., stock, 2" diameter		190	.042	L.F.	8.55	2.30		10.85	13.05
1600	3" diameter		190	.042		8.45	2.30		10.75	12.90
1800	4" diameter		145	.055		10.55	3.02		13.57	16.35
1900	5" diameter		130	.062		18.20	3.37		21.57	25.50
2100	Rectangular, corrugated copper, stock, 2" x 3"		190	.042		8.80	2.30		11.10	13.30
2200	3" x 4"		145	.055		12.20	3.02		15.22	18.20
2400	Rectangular, plain copper, stock, 2" x 3"		190	.042		13.30	2.30		15.60	18.30
2500	3" x 4"		145	.055		16.90	3.02		19.92	23.50
2700	Wire strainers, rectangular, 2" x 3"		145	.055	Ea.	13.50	3.02		16.52	19.60
2800	3" x 4"		145	.055		14.65	3.02		17.67	21
3000	Round, 2" diameter		145	.055		5.95	3.02		8.97	11.25
3100	3" diameter		145	.055		5.95	3.02		8.97	11.25
3300	4" diameter		145	.055		8	3.02		11.02	13.55
3400	5" diameter		115	.070		19.80	3.81		23.61	28
3600	Lead-coated copper, round, stock, 2" diameter		190	.042	L.F.	25	2.30		27.30	31
3700	3" diameter		190	.042		21.50	2.30		23.80	27
3900	4" diameter		145	.055		22.50	3.02		25.52	29.50
4000	5" diameter, corrugated		130	.062		24	3.37		27.37	32
4200	6" diameter, corrugated		105	.076		30	4.17		34.17	39.50
4300	Rectangular, corrugated, stock, 2" x 3"		190	.042		15	2.30		17.30	20
4500	Plain, stock, 2" x 3"		190	.042		24	2.30		26.30	30
4600	3" x 4"		145	.055		33	3.02		36.02	41.50
4800	Steel, galvanized, round, corrugated, 2" or 3" diameter, 28 ga.		190	.042		2.08	2.30		4.38	5.90
4900	4" diameter, 28 ga.		145	.055		2.61	3.02		5.63	7.65
5100	5" diameter, 26 ga.		130	.062		3.46	3.37		6.83	9.10
5400	6" diameter, 28 ga.		105	.076		4.20	4.17		8.37	11.15
5500	26 ga.		105	.076		5.80	4.17		9.97	12.95
5700	Rectangular, corrugated, 28 ga., 2" x 3"		190	.042		1.94	2.30		4.24	5.75
5800	3" x 4"		145	.055		1.82	3.02		4.84	6.75
6000	Rectangular, plain, 28 ga., galvanized, 2" x 3"		190	.042		3.03	2.30		5.33	6.95
6100	3" x 4"		145	.055		3.06	3.02		6.08	8.15
6300	Epoxy painted, 24 ga., corrugated, 2" x 3"		190	.042		2.20	2.30		4.50	6.05
6400	3" x 4"		145	.055		2.75	3.02		5.77	7.80
6600	Wire strainers, rectangular, 2" x 3"		145	.055	Ea.	15.90	3.02		18.92	22.50
6700	3" x 4"		145	.055		16.60	3.02		19.62	23
6900	Round strainers, 2" or 3" diameter		145	.055		3.86	3.02		6.88	9
7000	4" diameter		145	.055		5.80	3.02		8.82	11.10
9000	Minimum labor/equipment charge		4	2	Job		109		109	173

07 71 23.20 Downspout Elbows

		Crew	Daily Output	Labor-Hours	Unit	Material	2014 Bare Costs Labor	Equipment	Total	Total Incl O&P
0010	**DOWNSPOUT ELBOWS**									
0020	Aluminum, 2" x 3", embossed	1 Shee	100	.080	Ea.	.95	4.38		5.33	7.95
0100	Enameled		100	.080		1.75	4.38		6.13	8.85
0200	3" x 4", .025" thick, embossed		100	.080		3.50	4.38		7.88	10.75
0300	Enameled		100	.080		3.75	4.38		8.13	11.05
0400	Round corrugated, 3", embossed, .020" thick		100	.080		2.74	4.38		7.12	9.90
0500	4", .025" thick		100	.080		5.80	4.38		10.18	13.25
0600	Copper, 16 oz. round, 2" diameter		100	.080		9.45	4.38		13.83	17.30
0700	3" diameter		100	.080		9	4.38		13.38	16.80
0800	4" diameter		100	.080		13.15	4.38		17.53	21.50
1000	2" x 3" corrugated		100	.080		9	4.38		13.38	16.80
1100	3" x 4" corrugated		100	.080		13.65	4.38		18.03	22

07 71 23.20 Downspout Elbows	Crew	Daily Output	Labor-Hours	Unit	Material	2014 Bare Costs Labor	Equipment	Total	Total Incl O&P
1300 Vinyl, 2-1/2" diameter, 45° or 75°	1 Shee	100	.080	Ea.	3.88	4.38		8.26	11.15
1400 Tee Y junction		75	.107	↓	12.90	5.85		18.75	23.50
9000 Minimum labor/equipment charge	↓	4	2	Job		109		109	173

07 71 23.30 Gutters	Crew	Daily Output	Labor-Hours	Unit	Material	2014 Bare Costs Labor	Equipment	Total	Total Incl O&P
0010 **GUTTERS**									
0012 Aluminum, stock units, 5" K type, .027" thick, plain	1 Shee	125	.064	L.F.	2.61	3.50		6.11	8.35
0100 Enameled		125	.064		2.60	3.50		6.10	8.35
0300 5" K type type, .032" thick, plain		125	.064		3.20	3.50		6.70	9
0400 Enameled		125	.064		3	3.50		6.50	8.80
0700 Copper, half round, 16 oz., stock units, 4" wide		125	.064		10.50	3.50		14	17.05
0900 5" wide		125	.064		7.70	3.50		11.20	13.95
1000 6" wide		118	.068		14	3.71		17.71	21.50
1200 K type, 16 oz., stock, 5" wide		125	.064		12.60	3.50		16.10	19.35
1300 6" wide		125	.064		8.80	3.50		12.30	15.20
1500 Lead coated copper, half round, stock, 4" wide		125	.064		13.80	3.50		17.30	20.50
1600 6" wide		118	.068		22	3.71		25.71	30.50
1800 K type, stock, 5" wide		125	.064		18.90	3.50		22.40	26.50
1900 6" wide		125	.064		18.40	3.50		21.90	25.50
2100 Copper clad stainless steel, K type, 5" wide		125	.064		7	3.50		10.50	13.20
2200 6" wide		125	.064		8.90	3.50		12.40	15.30
2400 Steel, galv, half round or box, 28 ga., 5" wide, plain		125	.064		2.18	3.50		5.68	7.90
2500 Enameled		125	.064		2.13	3.50		5.63	7.85
2700 26 ga., stock, 5" wide		125	.064		2.18	3.50		5.68	7.90
2800 6" wide	↓	125	.064		2.67	3.50		6.17	8.45
3000 Vinyl, O.G., 4" wide	1 Carp	115	.070		1.19	3.19		4.38	6.55
3100 5" wide		115	.070		1.55	3.19		4.74	6.95
3200 4" half round, stock units	↓	115	.070	↓	1.28	3.19		4.47	6.65
3250 Joint connectors				Ea.	2.88			2.88	3.17
3300 Wood, clear treated cedar, fir or hemlock, 3" x 4"	1 Carp	100	.080	L.F.	12.40	3.67		16.07	19.70
3400 4" x 5"	"	100	.080	"	19.45	3.67		23.12	27.50
5000 Accessories, end cap, K type, aluminum 5"	1 Shee	625	.013	Ea.	.66	.70		1.36	1.83
5010 6"		625	.013		1.44	.70		2.14	2.68
5020 Copper, 5"		625	.013		3.89	.70		4.59	5.40
5030 6"		625	.013		3.54	.70		4.24	4.99
5040 Lead coated copper, 5"		625	.013		12.50	.70		13.20	14.85
5050 6"		625	.013		13.35	.70		14.05	15.80
5060 Copper clad stainless steel, 5"		625	.013		3	.70		3.70	4.40
5070 6"		625	.013		3.60	.70		4.30	5.05
5080 Galvanized steel, 5"		625	.013		1.28	.70		1.98	2.51
5090 6"		625	.013		2.18	.70		2.88	3.50
5100 Vinyl, 4"	1 Carp	625	.013		5.80	.59		6.39	7.35
5110 5"	"	625	.013		6.10	.59		6.69	7.65
5120 Half round, copper, 4"	1 Shee	625	.013		4.40	.70		5.10	5.95
5130 5"		625	.013		4.72	.70		5.42	6.30
5140 6"		625	.013		5.15	.70		5.85	6.75
5150 Lead coated copper, 5"		625	.013		14.15	.70		14.85	16.65
5160 6"		625	.013		21	.70		21.70	24.50
5170 Copper clad stainless steel, 5"		625	.013		4.50	.70		5.20	6.05
5180 6"		625	.013		4.50	.70		5.20	6.05
5190 Galvanized steel, 5"		625	.013		2.25	.70		2.95	3.58
5200 6"	↓	625	.013		2.80	.70		3.50	4.18
5210 Outlet, aluminum, 2" x 3"		420	.019	↓	.62	1.04		1.66	2.32

07 71 Roof Specialties

07 71 23 – Manufactured Gutters and Downspouts

07 71 23.30 Gutters

		Crew	Daily Output	Labor-Hours	Unit	Material	2014 Bare Costs Labor	Equipment	Total	Total Incl O&P
5220	3" x 4"	1 Shee	420	.019	Ea.	1.05	1.04		2.09	2.80
5230	2-3/8" round		420	.019		.56	1.04		1.60	2.26
5240	Copper, 2" x 3"		420	.019		6.50	1.04		7.54	8.80
5250	3" x 4"		420	.019		7.85	1.04		8.89	10.30
5260	2-3/8" round		420	.019		4.55	1.04		5.59	6.65
5270	Lead coated copper, 2" x 3"		420	.019		25.50	1.04		26.54	29.50
5280	3" x 4"		420	.019		28.50	1.04		29.54	33
5290	2-3/8" round		420	.019		25.50	1.04		26.54	29.50
5300	Copper clad stainless steel, 2" x 3"		420	.019		6.50	1.04		7.54	8.80
5310	3" x 4"		420	.019		7.85	1.04		8.89	10.30
5320	2-3/8" round		420	.019		4.55	1.04		5.59	6.65
5330	Galvanized steel, 2" x 3"		420	.019		3.18	1.04		4.22	5.15
5340	3" x 4"		420	.019		4.90	1.04		5.94	7.05
5350	2-3/8" round		420	.019		3.98	1.04		5.02	6
5360	K type mitres, aluminum		65	.123		3	6.75		9.75	13.90
5370	Copper		65	.123		17.40	6.75		24.15	29.50
5380	Lead coated copper		65	.123		54.50	6.75		61.25	70.50
5390	Copper clad stainless steel		65	.123		27.50	6.75		34.25	41
5400	Galvanized steel		65	.123		22.50	6.75		29.25	35.50
5420	Half round mitres, copper		65	.123		63.50	6.75		70.25	80.50
5430	Lead coated copper		65	.123		89.50	6.75		96.25	109
5440	Copper clad stainless steel		65	.123		56	6.75		62.75	72.50
5450	Galvanized steel		65	.123		25.50	6.75		32.25	38.50
5460	Vinyl mitres and outlets		65	.123		9.75	6.75		16.50	21.50
5470	Sealant		940	.009	L.F.	.01	.47		.48	.74
5480	Soldering		96	.083	"	.20	4.56		4.76	7.40
9000	Minimum labor/equipment charge		3.75	2.133	Job		117		117	184

07 71 23.35 Gutter Guard

		Crew	Daily Output	Labor-Hours	Unit	Material	2014 Bare Costs Labor	Equipment	Total	Total Incl O&P
0010	**GUTTER GUARD**									
0020	6" wide strip, aluminum mesh	1 Carp	500	.016	L.F.	2.17	.73		2.90	3.60
0100	Vinyl mesh		500	.016	"	2.25	.73		2.98	3.69
9000	Minimum labor/equipment charge		4	2	Job		91.50		91.50	151

07 71 26 – Reglets

07 71 26.10 Reglets and Accessories

		Crew	Daily Output	Labor-Hours	Unit	Material	2014 Bare Costs Labor	Equipment	Total	Total Incl O&P
0010	**REGLETS AND ACCESSORIES**									
0020	Aluminum, .025" thick, in concrete parapet	1 Carp	225	.036	L.F.	1.84	1.63		3.47	4.70
0300	16 oz.		225	.036		5.85	1.63		7.48	9.10
0400	Galvanized steel, 24 ga.		225	.036		1.28	1.63		2.91	4.09
0600	Stainless steel, .020" thick		225	.036		3.64	1.63		5.27	6.70
0900	Counter flashing for above, 12" wide, .032" aluminum	1 Shee	150	.053		2.29	2.92		5.21	7.10
1200	16 oz.		150	.053		5.45	2.92		8.37	10.60
1300	Galvanized steel, .020" thick		150	.053		1.29	2.92		4.21	6
1500	Stainless steel, .020" thick		150	.053		5.70	2.92		8.62	10.85
9000	Minimum labor/equipment charge	1 Carp	3	2.667	Job		122		122	201

07 71 29 – Manufactured Roof Expansion Joints

07 71 29.10 Expansion Joints

		Crew	Daily Output	Labor-Hours	Unit	Material	2014 Bare Costs Labor	Equipment	Total	Total Incl O&P
0010	**EXPANSION JOINTS**									
0300	Butyl or neoprene center with foam insulation, metal flanges									
0400	Aluminum, .032" thick for openings to 2-1/2"	1 Rofc	165	.048	L.F.	18.40	1.90		20.30	23.50
0600	For joint openings to 3-1/2"		165	.048		18.40	1.90		20.30	23.50
0610	For joint openings to 5"		165	.048		18.90	1.90		20.80	24.50

205

07 71 Roof Specialties

07 71 29.10 Expansion Joints		Crew	Daily Output	Labor-Hours	Unit	Material	2014 Bare Costs Labor	2014 Bare Costs Equipment	Total	Total Incl O&P
0620	For joint openings to 8"	1 Rofc	165	.048	L.F.	21	1.90		22.90	26.50
0700	Copper, 16 oz. for openings to 2-1/2"		165	.048		28.50	1.90		30.40	34.50
0900	For joint openings to 3-1/2"		165	.048		28.50	1.90		30.40	34.50
0910	For joint openings to 5"		165	.048		29	1.90		30.90	35.50
0920	For joint openings to 8"		165	.048		31	1.90		32.90	37.50
1000	Galvanized steel, 26 ga. for openings to 2-1/2"		165	.048		14.85	1.90		16.75	19.75
1200	For joint openings to 3-1/2"		165	.048		14.85	1.90		16.75	19.75
1210	For joint openings to 5"		165	.048		16	1.90		17.90	21
1220	For joint openings to 8"		165	.048		19.85	1.90		21.75	25.50
1300	Lead-coated copper, 16 oz. for openings to 2-1/2"		165	.048		35	1.90		36.90	42
1500	For joint openings to 3-1/2"		165	.048		40	1.90		41.90	47.50
1600	Stainless steel, .018", for openings to 2-1/2"		165	.048		20	1.90		21.90	25.50
1800	For joint openings to 3-1/2"		165	.048		17.90	1.90		19.80	23
1810	For joint openings to 5"		165	.048		18.60	1.90		20.50	24
1820	For joint openings to 8"		165	.048		22	1.90		23.90	27.50
1900	Neoprene, double-seal type with thick center, 4-1/2" wide		125	.064		15	2.51		17.51	21
1950	Polyethylene bellows, with galv steel flat flanges		100	.080		6	3.13		9.13	12.25
1960	With galvanized angle flanges		100	.080		6.50	3.13		9.63	12.80
2000	Roof joint with extruded aluminum cover, 2"	1 Shee	115	.070		38	3.81		41.81	48
2100	Roof joint, plastic curbs, foam center, standard	1 Rofc	100	.080		15	3.13		18.13	22
2200	Large		100	.080		19	3.13		22.13	26.50
2300	Transitions, regular, minimum		10	.800	Ea.	120	31.50		151.50	189
2350	Maximum		4	2		150	78.50		228.50	305
2400	Large, minimum		9	.889		175	35		210	256
2450	Maximum		3	2.667		185	104		289	390
2500	Roof to wall joint with extruded aluminum cover	1 Shee	115	.070	L.F.	32	3.81		35.81	41
2700	Wall joint, closed cell foam on PVC cover, 9" wide	1 Rofc	125	.064		5	2.51		7.51	10
2800	12" wide	"	115	.070		6	2.72		8.72	11.50
9000	Minimum labor/equipment charge	1 Shee	3	2.667	Job		146		146	230

07 71 43.10 Drip Edge, Rake Edge, Ice Belts

		Crew	Daily Output	Labor-Hours	Unit	Material	2014 Bare Costs Labor	2014 Bare Costs Equipment	Total	Total Incl O&P
0010	**DRIP EDGE, RAKE EDGE, ICE BELTS**									
0020	Aluminum, .016" thick, 5" wide, mill finish	1 Carp	400	.020	L.F.	.40	.92		1.32	1.95
0100	White finish		400	.020		.41	.92		1.33	1.96
0200	8" wide, mill finish		400	.020		.69	.92		1.61	2.27
0300	Ice belt, 28" wide, mill finish		100	.080		3.85	3.67		7.52	10.30
0310	Vented, mill finish		400	.020		2.86	.92		3.78	4.66
0320	Painted finish		400	.020		2.90	.92		3.82	4.70
0400	Galvanized, 5" wide		400	.020		.53	.92		1.45	2.09
0500	8" wide, mill finish		400	.020		.69	.92		1.61	2.27
0510	Rake edge, aluminum, 1-1/2" x 1-1/2"		400	.020		.30	.92		1.22	1.84
0520	3-1/2" x 1-1/2"		400	.020		.41	.92		1.33	1.96
9000	Minimum labor/equipment charge		4	2	Job		91.50		91.50	151

07 72 Roof Accessories

07 72 23 – Relief Vents

07 72 23.10 Roof Vents

07 72 23.10 Roof Vents	Crew	Daily Output	Labor-Hours	Unit	Material	2014 Bare Costs Labor	Equipment	Total	Total Incl O&P
0010 **ROOF VENTS**									
0020 Mushroom shape, for built-up roofs, aluminum	1 Rofc	30	.267	Ea.	108	10.45		118.45	138
0100 PVC, 6" high		30	.267	"	28.50	10.45		38.95	50.50
9000 Minimum labor/equipment charge		2.75	2.909	Job		114		114	205

07 72 23.20 Vents

07 72 23.20 Vents	Crew	Daily Output	Labor-Hours	Unit	Material	2014 Bare Costs Labor	Equipment	Total	Total Incl O&P
0010 **VENTS**									
0100 Soffit or eave, aluminum, mill finish, strips, 2-1/2" wide	1 Carp	200	.040	L.F.	.42	1.83		2.25	3.47
0200 3" wide		200	.040		.39	1.83		2.22	3.44
0300 Enamel finish, 3" wide		200	.040		.50	1.83		2.33	3.56
0400 Mill finish, rectangular, 4" x 16"		72	.111	Ea.	1.45	5.10		6.55	9.95
0500 8" x 16"		72	.111		2.26	5.10		7.36	10.85
2420 Roof ventilator	Q-9	16	1		50.50	49		99.50	133
2500 Vent, roof vent	1 Rofc	24	.333		25.50	13.05		38.55	51.50

07 72 26 – Ridge Vents

07 72 26.10 Ridge Vents and Accessories

07 72 26.10 Ridge Vents and Accessories	Crew	Daily Output	Labor-Hours	Unit	Material	2014 Bare Costs Labor	Equipment	Total	Total Incl O&P
0010 **RIDGE VENTS AND ACCESSORIES**									
0100 Aluminum strips, mill finish	1 Rofc	160	.050	L.F.	2.75	1.96		4.71	6.55
0150 Painted finish		160	.050	"	4.05	1.96		6.01	8
0200 Connectors		48	.167	Ea.	4.65	6.55		11.20	16.85
0300 End caps		48	.167	"	1.98	6.55		8.53	13.95
0400 Galvanized strips		160	.050	L.F.	3.58	1.96		5.54	7.45
0430 Molded polyethylene, shingles not included		160	.050	"	2.74	1.96		4.70	6.55
0440 End plugs		48	.167	Ea.	1.98	6.55		8.53	13.95
0450 Flexible roll, shingles not included		160	.050	L.F.	2.38	1.96		4.34	6.15
2300 Ridge vent strip, mill finish	1 Shee	155	.052	"	2.98	2.82		5.80	7.75

07 72 33 – Roof Hatches

07 72 33.10 Roof Hatch Options

07 72 33.10 Roof Hatch Options	Crew	Daily Output	Labor-Hours	Unit	Material	2014 Bare Costs Labor	Equipment	Total	Total Incl O&P
0010 **ROOF HATCH OPTIONS**									
0500 2'-6" x 3', aluminum curb and cover	G-3	10	3.200	Ea.	1,075	146		1,221	1,400
0520 Galvanized steel curb and aluminum cover		10	3.200		640	146		786	940
0540 Galvanized steel curb and cover		10	3.200		635	146		781	930
0600 2'-6" x 4'-6", aluminum curb and cover		9	3.556		915	162		1,077	1,250
0800 Galvanized steel curb and aluminum cover		9	3.556		885	162		1,047	1,225
0900 Galvanized steel curb and cover		9	3.556		890	162		1,052	1,250
1100 4' x 4' aluminum curb and cover		8	4		1,800	183		1,983	2,275
1120 Galvanized steel curb and aluminum cover		8	4		1,725	183		1,908	2,200
1140 Galvanized steel curb and cover		8	4		1,700	183		1,883	2,175
1200 2'-6" x 8'-0", aluminum curb and cover		6.60	4.848		1,800	221		2,021	2,325
1400 Galvanized steel curb and aluminum cover		6.60	4.848		1,800	221		2,021	2,325
1500 Galvanized steel curb and cover		6.60	4.848		1,425	221		1,646	1,925
1800 For plexiglass panels, 2'-6" x 3'-0", add to above					440			440	485
9000 Minimum labor/equipment charge	2 Carp	2	8	Job		365		365	605

07 72 36 – Smoke Vents

07 72 36.10 Smoke Hatches

07 72 36.10 Smoke Hatches	Crew	Daily Output	Labor-Hours	Unit	Material	2014 Bare Costs Labor	Equipment	Total	Total Incl O&P
0010 **SMOKE HATCHES**									
0200 For 3'-0" long, add to roof hatches from Section 07 72 33.10				Ea.	25%	5%			
0250 For 4'-0" long, add to roof hatches from Section 07 72 33.10					20%	5%			
0300 For 8'-0" long, add to roof hatches from Section 07 72 33.10					10%	5%			

07 72 Roof Accessories

07 72 36 – Smoke Vents

07 72 36.20 Smoke Vent Options		Crew	Daily Output	Labor-Hours	Unit	Material	2014 Bare Costs		Total	Total Incl O&P
							Labor	Equipment		
0010	**SMOKE VENT OPTIONS**									
0100	4' x 4' aluminum cover and frame	G-3	13	2.462	Ea.	2,050	112		2,162	2,425
0200	Galvanized steel cover and frame		13	2.462		1,800	112		1,912	2,150
0300	4' x 8' aluminum cover and frame		8	4		2,800	183		2,983	3,375
0400	Galvanized steel cover and frame		8	4		2,375	183		2,558	2,925
9000	Minimum labor/equipment charge	2 Carp	2	8	Job		365		365	605

07 72 53 – Snow Guards

07 72 53.10 Snow Guard Options

		Crew	Daily Output	Labor-Hours	Unit	Material	Labor	Equipment	Total	Total Incl O&P
0010	**SNOW GUARD OPTIONS**									
0100	Slate & asphalt shingle roofs, fastened with nails	1 Rofc	160	.050	Ea.	12.55	1.96		14.51	17.35
0200	Standing seam metal roofs, fastened with set screws		48	.167		16.95	6.55		23.50	30.50
0300	Surface mount for metal roofs, fastened with solder		48	.167		6.05	6.55		12.60	18.40
0400	Double rail pipe type, including pipe		130	.062	L.F.	32	2.41		34.41	39.50

07 72 73 – Pitch Pockets

07 72 73.10 Pitch Pockets, Variable Sizes

		Crew	Daily Output	Labor-Hours	Unit	Material	Labor	Equipment	Total	Total Incl O&P
0010	**PITCH POCKETS, VARIABLE SIZES**									
0100	Adjustable, 4" to 7", welded corners, 4" deep	1 Rofc	48	.167	Ea.	15.75	6.55		22.30	29
0200	Side extenders, 6"	"	240	.033	"	2.15	1.30		3.45	4.72

07 72 80 – Vents

07 72 80.30 Vent Options

		Crew	Daily Output	Labor-Hours	Unit	Material	Labor	Equipment	Total	Total Incl O&P
0010	**VENT OPTIONS**									
0020	Plastic, for insulated decks, 1 per M.S.F., minimum	1 Rofc	40	.200	Ea.	19.15	7.85		27	35
0100	Maximum		20	.400		36	15.65		51.65	67.50
0300	Aluminum		30	.267		19.50	10.45		29.95	40.50
0800	Polystyrene baffles, 12" wide for 16" O.C. rafter spacing	1 Carp	90	.089		.40	4.08		4.48	7.15
0900	For 24" O.C. rafter spacing		110	.073		.75	3.33		4.08	6.35
9000	Minimum labor/equipment charge		3	2.667	Job		122		122	201

07 76 Roof Pavers

07 76 16 – Roof Decking Pavers

07 76 16.10 Roof Pavers and Supports

		Crew	Daily Output	Labor-Hours	Unit	Material	Labor	Equipment	Total	Total Incl O&P
0010	**ROOF PAVERS AND SUPPORTS**									
1000	Roof decking pavers, concrete blocks, 2" thick, natural	1 Clab	115	.070	S.F.	3.37	2.55		5.92	7.90
1100	Colors		115	.070	"	3.73	2.55		6.28	8.30
1200	Support pedestal, bottom cap		960	.008	Ea.	2.99	.31		3.30	3.79
1300	Top cap		960	.008		4.79	.31		5.10	5.75
1400	Leveling shims, 1/16"		1920	.004		1.19	.15		1.34	1.56
1500	1/8"		1920	.004		1.19	.15		1.34	1.56
1600	Buffer pad		960	.008		2.49	.31		2.80	3.24
1700	PVC legs (4" SDR 35)		2880	.003	Inch	.12	.10		.22	.30
2000	Alternate pricing method, system in place		101	.079	S.F.	7	2.90		9.90	12.45

07 81 Applied Fireproofing

07 81 16 – Cementitious Fireproofing

07 81 16.10 Sprayed Cementitious Fireproofing	Crew	Daily Output	Labor-Hours	Unit	Material	2014 Bare Costs Labor	Equipment	Total	Total Incl O&P
0010 **SPRAYED CEMENTITIOUS FIREPROOFING**									
0050 Not including canvas protection, normal density									
0100 Per 1" thick, on flat plate steel	G-2	3000	.008	S.F.	.53	.31	.05	.89	1.13
0200 Flat decking		2400	.010		.53	.39	.06	.98	1.26
0400 Beams		1500	.016		.53	.62	.09	1.24	1.68
0500 Corrugated or fluted decks		1250	.019		.79	.74	.11	1.64	2.19
0700 Columns, 1-1/8" thick		1100	.022		.59	.84	.12	1.55	2.14
0800 2-3/16" thick		700	.034		1.20	1.32	.19	2.71	3.67
0900 For canvas protection, add		5000	.005		.07	.19	.03	.29	.41
9000 Minimum labor/equipment charge		3	8	Job		310	45	355	550

07 84 Firestopping

07 84 13 – Penetration Firestopping

07 84 13.10 Firestopping

	Crew	Daily Output	Labor-Hours	Unit	Material	2014 Bare Costs Labor	Equipment	Total	Total Incl O&P
0010 **FIRESTOPPING** R078413-30									
0100 Metallic piping, non insulated									
0110 Through walls, 2" diameter	1 Carp	16	.500	Ea.	15.90	23		38.90	55
0120 4" diameter		14	.571		24.50	26		50.50	69.50
0130 6" diameter		12	.667		32.50	30.50		63	86
0140 12" diameter		10	.800		57.50	36.50		94	124
0150 Through floors, 2" diameter		32	.250		9.65	11.45		21.10	29.50
0160 4" diameter		28	.286		13.85	13.10		26.95	37
0170 6" diameter		24	.333		18.20	15.30		33.50	45
0180 12" diameter		20	.400		31	18.35		49.35	64
0190 Metallic piping, insulated									
0200 Through walls, 2" diameter	1 Carp	16	.500	Ea.	22.50	23		45.50	62.50
0210 4" diameter		14	.571		31	26		57	77
0220 6" diameter		12	.667		39	30.50		69.50	93
0230 12" diameter		10	.800		64	36.50		100.50	131
0240 Through floors, 2" diameter		32	.250		16.30	11.45		27.75	37
0250 4" diameter		28	.286		20.50	13.10		33.60	44
0260 6" diameter		24	.333		25	15.30		40.30	52.50
0270 12" diameter		20	.400		31	18.35		49.35	64
0280 Non metallic piping, non insulated									
0290 Through walls, 2" diameter	1 Carp	12	.667	Ea.	65.50	30.50		96	122
0300 4" diameter		10	.800		82	36.50		118.50	151
0310 6" diameter		8	1		114	46		160	202
0330 Through floors, 2" diameter		16	.500		51.50	23		74.50	94
0340 4" diameter		6	1.333		63.50	61		124.50	170
0350 6" diameter		6	1.333		76.50	61		137.50	184
0370 Ductwork, insulated & non insulated, round									
0380 Through walls, 6" diameter	1 Carp	12	.667	Ea.	33.50	30.50		64	86.50
0390 12" diameter		10	.800		66	36.50		102.50	133
0400 18" diameter		8	1		108	46		154	195
0410 Through floors, 6" diameter		16	.500		18.20	23		41.20	57.50
0420 12" diameter		14	.571		33.50	26		59.50	79.50
0430 18" diameter		12	.667		57.50	30.50		88	114
0440 Ductwork, insulated & non insulated, rectangular									
0450 With stiffener/closure angle, through walls, 6" x 12"	1 Carp	8	1	Ea.	27.50	46		73.50	106
0460 12" x 24"		6	1.333		36.50	61		97.50	140
0470 24" x 48"		4	2		105	91.50		196.50	266

07 84 13.10 Firestopping		Crew	Daily Output	Labor-Hours	Unit	Material	2014 Bare Costs Labor	Equipment	Total	Total Incl O&P
0480	With stiffener/closure angle, through floors, 6" x 12"	1 Carp	10	.800	Ea.	14.95	36.50		51.45	77
0490	12" x 24"		8	1		27	46		73	105
0500	24" x 48"		6	1.333		52.50	61		113.50	158
0510	Multi trade openings									
0520	Through walls, 6" x 12"	1 Carp	2	4	Ea.	57.50	183		240.50	365
0530	12" x 24"	"	1	8		234	365		599	860
0540	24" x 48"	2 Carp	1	16		935	735		1,670	2,225
0550	48" x 96"	"	.75	21.333		3,750	980		4,730	5,725
0560	Through floors, 6" x 12"	1 Carp	2	4		57.50	183		240.50	365
0570	12" x 24"	"	1	8		234	365		599	860
0580	24" x 48"	2 Carp	.75	21.333		935	980		1,915	2,625
0590	48" x 96"	"	.50	32		3,750	1,475		5,225	6,525
0600	Structural penetrations, through walls									
0610	Steel beams, W8 x 10	1 Carp	8	1	Ea.	36.50	46		82.50	116
0620	W12 x 14		6	1.333		57.50	61		118.50	164
0630	W21 x 44		5	1.600		116	73.50		189.50	249
0640	W36 x 135		3	2.667		282	122		404	510
0650	Bar joists, 18" deep		6	1.333		53.50	61		114.50	159
0660	24" deep		6	1.333		66	61		127	173
0670	36" deep		5	1.600		99.50	73.50		173	230
0680	48" deep		4	2		116	91.50		207.50	279
0690	Construction joints, floor slab at exterior wall									
0700	Precast, brick, block or drywall exterior									
0710	2" wide joint	1 Carp	125	.064	L.F.	8.30	2.93		11.23	13.90
0720	4" wide joint	"	75	.107	"	16.55	4.89		21.44	26.50
0730	Metal panel, glass or curtain wall exterior									
0740	2" wide joint	1 Carp	40	.200	L.F.	19.60	9.15		28.75	36.50
0750	4" wide joint	"	25	.320	"	27	14.65		41.65	53.50
0760	Floor slab to drywall partition									
0770	Flat joint	1 Carp	100	.080	L.F.	8.15	3.67		11.82	15
0780	Fluted joint		50	.160		16.55	7.35		23.90	30.50
0790	Etched fluted joint		75	.107		10.75	4.89		15.64	19.90
0800	Floor slab to concrete/masonry partition									
0810	Flat joint	1 Carp	75	.107	L.F.	18.20	4.89		23.09	28
0820	Fluted joint	"	50	.160	"	21.50	7.35		28.85	35.50
0830	Concrete/CMU wall joints									
0840	1" wide	1 Carp	100	.080	L.F.	9.95	3.67		13.62	16.95
0850	2" wide		75	.107		18.20	4.89		23.09	28
0860	4" wide		50	.160		34.50	7.35		41.85	50
0870	Concrete/CMU floor joints									
0880	1" wide	1 Carp	200	.040	L.F.	4.99	1.83		6.82	8.50
0890	2" wide		150	.053		9.10	2.45		11.55	14
0900	4" wide		100	.080		17.40	3.67		21.07	25

07 91 Preformed Joint Seals

07 91 13 – Compression Seals

07 91 13.10 Compression Seals

		Crew	Daily Output	Labor-Hours	Unit	Material	2014 Bare Costs Labor	Equipment	Total	Total Incl O&P
0010	**COMPRESSION SEALS**									
4900	O-ring type cord, 1/4"	1 Bric	472	.017	L.F.	.48	.77		1.25	1.79
4910	1/2"		440	.018		1.79	.83		2.62	3.32
4920	3/4"		424	.019		3.62	.86		4.48	5.40
4930	1"		408	.020		6.95	.89		7.84	9.10
4940	1-1/4"		384	.021		13.75	.95		14.70	16.65
4950	1-1/2"		368	.022		17.40	.99		18.39	20.50
4960	1-3/4"		352	.023		36.50	1.04		37.54	41.50
4970	2"		344	.023		64.50	1.06		65.56	72

07 91 16 – Joint Gaskets

07 91 16.10 Joint Gaskets

		Crew	Daily Output	Labor-Hours	Unit	Material	2014 Bare Costs Labor	Equipment	Total	Total Incl O&P
0010	**JOINT GASKETS**									
4400	Joint gaskets, neoprene, closed cell w/adh, 1/8" x 3/8"	1 Bric	240	.033	L.F.	.28	1.52		1.80	2.78
4500	1/4" x 3/4"		215	.037		.59	1.70		2.29	3.41
4700	1/2" x 1"		200	.040		1.30	1.82		3.12	4.39
4800	3/4" x 1-1/2"		165	.048		1.45	2.21		3.66	5.20

07 91 23 – Backer Rods

07 91 23.10 Backer Rods

		Crew	Daily Output	Labor-Hours	Unit	Material	2014 Bare Costs Labor	Equipment	Total	Total Incl O&P
0010	**BACKER RODS**									
0032	Backer rod, polyethylene, 1/4" diameter	1 Bric	460	.017	L.F.	.02	.79		.81	1.32
0052	1/2" diameter		460	.017		.04	.79		.83	1.33
0072	3/4" diameter		460	.017		.06	.79		.85	1.35
0092	1" diameter		460	.017		.09	.79		.88	1.39

07 91 26 – Joint Fillers

07 91 26.10 Joint Fillers

		Crew	Daily Output	Labor-Hours	Unit	Material	2014 Bare Costs Labor	Equipment	Total	Total Incl O&P
0010	**JOINT FILLERS**									
4360	Butyl rubber filler, 1/4" x 1/4"	1 Bric	290	.028	L.F.	.23	1.26		1.49	2.29
4365	1/2" x 1/2"		250	.032		.92	1.46		2.38	3.38
4370	1/2" x 3/4"		210	.038		1.38	1.74		3.12	4.34
4375	3/4" x 3/4"		230	.035		2.08	1.59		3.67	4.86
4380	1" x 1"		180	.044		2.77	2.03		4.80	6.35
4390	For coloring, add					12%				
4980	Polyethylene joint backing, 1/4" x 2"	1 Bric	2.08	3.846	C.L.F.	12	175		187	298
4990	1/4" x 6"		1.28	6.250	"	28	285		313	495
5600	Silicone, room temp vulcanizing foam seal, 1/4" x 1/2"		1312	.006	L.F.	.33	.28		.61	.82
5610	1/2" x 1/2"		656	.012		.67	.56		1.23	1.64
5620	1/2" x 3/4"		442	.018		1	.83		1.83	2.44
5630	3/4" x 3/4"		328	.024		1.50	1.11		2.61	3.46
5640	1/8" x 1"		1312	.006		.33	.28		.61	.82
5650	1/8" x 3"		442	.018		1	.83		1.83	2.44
5670	1/4" x 3"		295	.027		2.01	1.24		3.25	4.22
5680	1/4" x 6"		148	.054		4.01	2.46		6.47	8.40
5690	1/2" x 6"		82	.098		8	4.45		12.45	16
5700	1/2" x 9"		52.50	.152		12.05	6.95		19	24.50
5710	1/2" x 12"		33	.242		16.05	11.05		27.10	35.50

07 92 Joint Sealants

07 92 13 – Elastomeric Joint Sealants

07 92 13.10 Masonry Joint Sealants		Crew	Daily Output	Labor-Hours	Unit	Material	2014 Bare Costs Labor	Equipment	Total	Total Incl O&P
0010	**MASONRY JOINT SEALANTS**, 1/2" x 1/2" joint									
0050	Re-caulk only, oil base	1 Bric	225	.036	L.F.	.54	1.62		2.16	3.22
0100	Acrylic latex		205	.039		.19	1.78		1.97	3.10
0200	Polyurethane		200	.040		4.25	1.82		6.07	7.65
0300	Silicone		195	.041		3.75	1.87		5.62	7.15
1000	Cut out and re-caulk, oil base		145	.055		.54	2.52		3.06	4.68
1050	Acrylic latex		130	.062		.19	2.81		3	4.77
1100	Polyurethane		125	.064		4.25	2.92		7.17	9.40
1150	Silicone		120	.067		3.75	3.04		6.79	9.05
9000	Minimum labor/equipment charge		4	2	Job		91		91	148

07 92 13.20 Caulking and Sealant Options		Crew	Daily Output	Labor-Hours	Unit	Material	2014 Bare Costs Labor	Equipment	Total	Total Incl O&P
0010	**CAULKING AND SEALANT OPTIONS**									
0050	Latex acrylic based, bulk				Gal.	29.50			29.50	32.50
0055	Bulk in place 1/4" x 1/4" bead	1 Bric	300	.027	L.F.	.09	1.22		1.31	2.07
0060	1/4" x 3/8"		294	.027		.16	1.24		1.40	2.18
0065	1/4" x 1/2"		288	.028		.21	1.27		1.48	2.29
0075	3/8" x 3/8"		284	.028		.23	1.28		1.51	2.34
0080	3/8" x 1/2"		280	.029		.31	1.30		1.61	2.46
0085	3/8" x 5/8"		276	.029		.39	1.32		1.71	2.58
0095	3/8" x 3/4"		272	.029		.46	1.34		1.80	2.69
0100	1/2" x 1/2"		275	.029		.41	1.33		1.74	2.61
0105	1/2" x 5/8"		269	.030		.52	1.36		1.88	2.77
0110	1/2" x 3/4"		263	.030		.62	1.39		2.01	2.93
0115	1/2" x 7/8"		256	.031		.72	1.43		2.15	3.11
0120	1/2" x 1"		250	.032		.83	1.46		2.29	3.28
0125	3/4" x 3/4"		244	.033		.93	1.50		2.43	3.46
0130	3/4" x 1"		225	.036		1.24	1.62		2.86	4
0135	1" x 1"		200	.040		1.66	1.82		3.48	4.78
0190	Cartridges				Gal.	26.50			26.50	29
0200	11 fl. oz. cartridge				Ea.	2.28			2.28	2.51
0500	1/4" x 1/2"	1 Bric	288	.028	L.F.	.19	1.27		1.46	2.26
0600	1/2" x 1/2"		275	.029		.37	1.33		1.70	2.56
0800	3/4" x 3/4"		244	.033		.84	1.50		2.34	3.35
0900	3/4" x 1"		225	.036		1.12	1.62		2.74	3.86
1000	1" x 1"		200	.040		1.40	1.82		3.22	4.50
1400	Butyl based, bulk				Gal.	34			34	37.50
1500	Cartridges				"	38.50			38.50	42.50
1700	1/4" x 1/2", 154 L.F./gal.	1 Bric	288	.028	L.F.	.22	1.27		1.49	2.30
1800	1/2" x 1/2", 77 L.F./gal.	"	275	.029	"	.44	1.33		1.77	2.64
2300	Polysulfide compounds, 1 component, bulk				Gal.	61			61	67
2400	Cartridges				"	59			59	65
2600	1 or 2 component, in place, 1/4" x 1/4", 308 L.F./gal.	1 Bric	300	.027	L.F.	.20	1.22		1.42	2.19
2700	1/2" x 1/4", 154 L.F./gal.		288	.028		.40	1.27		1.67	2.50
2900	3/4" x 3/8", 68 L.F./gal.		272	.029		.90	1.34		2.24	3.17
3000	1" x 1/2", 38 L.F./gal.		250	.032		1.61	1.46		3.07	4.14
3200	Polyurethane, 1 or 2 component				Gal.	51			51	56
3300	Cartridges				"	64			64	70.50
3500	Bulk, in place, 1/4" x 1/4"	1 Bric	300	.027	L.F.	.17	1.22		1.39	2.15
3655	1/2" x 1/4"		288	.028		.33	1.27		1.60	2.42
3800	3/4" x 3/8"		272	.029		.75	1.34		2.09	3.01
3900	1" x 1/2"		250	.032		1.33	1.46		2.79	3.83
4100	Silicone rubber, bulk				Gal.	45.50			45.50	50

07 92 Joint Sealants

07 92 13 – Elastomeric Joint Sealants

07 92 13.20 Caulking and Sealant Options	Crew	Daily Output	Labor-Hours	Unit	Material	2014 Bare Costs Labor	Equipment	Total	Total Incl O&P
4200 Cartridges				Gal.	45			45	49.50
4300 Bulk in place, 1/4" x 1/2", 154 L.F./gal.	1 Bric	235	.034	L.F.	.29	1.55		1.84	2.84

07 92 16 – Rigid Joint Sealants

07 92 16.10 Rigid Joint Sealants

	Crew	Daily Output	Labor-Hours	Unit	Material	2014 Bare Costs Labor	Equipment	Total	Total Incl O&P
0010 **RIGID JOINT SEALANTS**									
5802 Tapes, sealant, PVC foam adhesive, 1/16" x 1/4"				L.F.	.06			.06	.07
5902 1/16" x 1/2"					.08			.08	.09
5952 1/16" x 1"					.15			.15	.17
6002 1/8" x 1/2"					.09			.09	.10

07 92 19 – Acoustical Joint Sealants

07 92 19.10 Acoustical Sealant

	Crew	Daily Output	Labor-Hours	Unit	Material	2014 Bare Costs Labor	Equipment	Total	Total Incl O&P
0010 **ACOUSTICAL SEALANT**									
0020 Acoustical sealant, elastomeric, cartridges				Ea.	8.50			8.50	9.35
0025 In place, 1/4" x 1/4"	1 Bric	300	.027	L.F.	.35	1.22		1.57	2.35
0030 1/4" x 1/2"		288	.028		.69	1.27		1.96	2.82
0035 1/2" x 1/2"		275	.029		1.39	1.33		2.72	3.67
0040 1/2" x 3/4"		263	.030		2.08	1.39		3.47	4.54
0045 3/4" x 3/4"		244	.033		3.12	1.50		4.62	5.85
0050 1" x 1"		200	.040		5.55	1.82		7.37	9.05

07 95 Expansion Control

07 95 13 – Expansion Joint Cover Assemblies

07 95 13.50 Expansion Joint Assemblies

	Crew	Daily Output	Labor-Hours	Unit	Material	2014 Bare Costs Labor	Equipment	Total	Total Incl O&P
0010 **EXPANSION JOINT ASSEMBLIES**									
0200 Floor cover assemblies, 1" space, aluminum	1 Sswk	38	.211	L.F.	21.50	10.75		32.25	44
0300 Bronze		38	.211		51	10.75		61.75	76
0500 2" space, aluminum		38	.211		26.50	10.75		37.25	49
0600 Bronze		38	.211		55	10.75		65.75	80.50
0800 Wall and ceiling assemblies, 1" space, aluminum		38	.211		12.90	10.75		23.65	34
0900 Bronze		38	.211		48	10.75		58.75	72.50
1100 2" space, aluminum		38	.211		22	10.75		32.75	44
1200 Bronze		38	.211		59	10.75		69.75	84.50
1400 Floor to wall assemblies, 1" space, aluminum		38	.211		19.70	10.75		30.45	41.50
1500 Bronze or stainless		38	.211		58	10.75		68.75	83.50
1700 Gym floor angle covers, aluminum, 3" x 3" angle		46	.174		17.05	8.90		25.95	35
1800 3" x 4" angle		46	.174		23.50	8.90		32.40	42.50
2000 Roof closures, aluminum, flat roof, low profile, 1" space		57	.140		39.50	7.15		46.65	56.50
2100 High profile		57	.140		56.50	7.15		63.65	75.50
2300 Roof to wall, low profile, 1" space		57	.140		22	7.15		29.15	37
2400 High profile		57	.140		28.50	7.15		35.65	44
9000 Minimum labor/equipment charge		2	4	Job		204		204	375

Division Notes

	CREW	DAILY OUTPUT	LABOR-HOURS	UNIT	BARE COSTS				TOTAL INCL O&P
					MAT.	LABOR	EQUIP.	TOTAL	

Estimating Tips

08 10 00 Doors and Frames

All exterior doors should be addressed for their energy conservation (insulation and seals).

- Most metal doors and frames look alike, but there may be significant differences among them. When estimating these items, be sure to choose the line item that most closely compares to the specification or door schedule requirements regarding:
  - type of metal
  - metal gauge
  - door core material
  - fire rating
  - finish
- Wood and plastic doors vary considerably in price. The primary determinant is the veneer material. Lauan, birch, and oak are the most common veneers. Other variables include the following:
  - hollow or solid core
  - fire rating
  - flush or raised panel
  - finish
- Door pricing includes bore for cylindrical lockset and mortise for hinges.

08 30 00 Specialty Doors and Frames

- There are many varieties of special doors, and they are usually priced per each. Add frames, hardware, or operators required for a complete installation.

08 40 00 Entrances, Storefronts, and Curtain Walls

- Glazed curtain walls consist of the metal tube framing and the glazing material. The cost data in this subdivision is presented for the metal tube framing alone or the composite wall. If your estimate requires a detailed takeoff of the framing, be sure to add the glazing cost.

08 50 00 Windows

- Most metal windows are delivered preglazed. However, some metal windows are priced without glass. Refer to 08 80 00 Glazing for glass pricing. The grade C indicates commercial grade windows, usually ASTM C-35.
- All wood windows and vinyl are priced preglazed. The glazing is insulating glass. Some wood windows may have single pane float glass. Add the cost of screens and grills if required, and not already included.

08 70 00 Hardware

- Hardware costs add considerably to the cost of a door. The most efficient method to determine the hardware requirements for a project is to review the door and hardware schedule together.

- Door hinges are priced by the pair, with most doors requiring 1-1/2 pairs per door. The hinge prices do not include installation labor because it is included in door installation. Hinges are classified according to the frequency of use, base material, and finish.

08 80 00 Glazing

- Different openings require different types of glass. The most common types are:
  - float
  - tempered
  - insulating
  - impact-resistant
  - ballistic-resistant
- Most exterior windows are glazed with insulating glass. Entrance doors and window walls, where the glass is less than 18" from the floor, are generally glazed with tempered glass. Interior windows and some residential windows are glazed with float glass.
- Coastal communities require the use of impact-resistant glass, dependant on wind speed.
- The insulation or 'u' value is a strong consideration, along with solar heat gain, to determine total energy efficiency.

Reference Numbers

Reference numbers are shown in shaded boxes at the beginning of some major classifications. These numbers refer to related items in the Reference Section. The reference information may be an estimating procedure, an alternate pricing method, or technical information.

Note: Not all subdivisions listed here necessarily appear in this publication.

08 01 Operation and Maintenance of Openings

08 01 11 – Operation and Maintenance of Metal Doors and Frames

08 01 11.10 Door and Window Maintenance		Crew	Daily Output	Labor-Hours	Unit	Material	2014 Bare Costs Labor	Equipment	Total	Total Incl O&P
0010	**DOOR & WINDOW MAINTENANCE**									
1130	Install door	2 Carp	13.07	1.224	Ea.		56		56	92
1140	Remove deadbolt	1 Carp	13.85	.578			26.50		26.50	43.50
1420	Remove door, plane to fit, rail, reinstall door	"	9.60	.833			38		38	63

08 01 14 – Operation and Maintenance of Wood Doors

08 01 14.15 Door and Window Maintenance

		Crew	Daily Output	Labor-Hours	Unit	Material	Labor	Equipment	Total	Total Incl O&P
0010	**DOOR & WINDOW MAINTENANCE**									
0050	Rehang single door	1 Carp	32	.250	Ea.		11.45		11.45	18.85
0100	Rehang, double door		16	.500	Pr.		23		23	37.50
0350	Install window sash cord		32	.250	Ea.	3.70	11.45		15.15	23

08 01 53 – Operation and Maintenance of Plastic Windows

08 01 53.81 Solid Vinyl Replacement Windows

			Crew	Daily Output	Labor-Hours	Unit	Material	Labor	Equipment	Total	Total Incl O&P
0010	**SOLID VINYL REPLACEMENT WINDOWS**	R085313-20									
0020	Double hung, insulated glass, up to 83 united inches	G	2 Carp	8	2	Ea.	340	91.50		431.50	525
0040	84 to 93	G		8	2		380	91.50		471.50	565
0060	94 to 101	G		6	2.667		380	122		502	615
0080	102 to 111	G		6	2.667		395	122		517	635
0100	112 to 120	G		6	2.667		430	122		552	675
0120	For each united inch over 120 , add	G		800	.020	Inch	5.50	.92		6.42	7.55
0140	Casement windows, one operating sash , 42 to 60 united inches	G		8	2	Ea.	222	91.50		313.50	395
0160	61 to 70	G		8	2		248	91.50		339.50	425
0180	71 to 80	G		8	2		269	91.50		360.50	445
0200	81 to 96	G		8	2		286	91.50		377.50	465
0220	Two operating sash, 58 to 78 united inches	G		8	2		440	91.50		531.50	635
0240	79 to 88	G		8	2		470	91.50		561.50	670
0260	89 to 98	G		8	2		515	91.50		606.50	715
0280	99 to 108	G		6	2.667		535	122		657	790
0300	109 to 121	G		6	2.667		575	122		697	835
0320	Two operating.one fixed sash, 73 to 108 united inches	G		8	2		700	91.50		791.50	920
0340	109 to 118	G		8	2		735	91.50		826.50	960
0360	119 to 128	G		6	2.667		755	122		877	1,025
0380	129 to 138	G		6	2.667		805	122		927	1,075
0400	139 to 156	G		6	2.667		850	122		972	1,125
0420	Four operating sash, 98 to 118 united inches	G		8	2		1,000	91.50		1,091.50	1,250
0440	119 to 128	G		8	2		1,075	91.50		1,166.50	1,325
0460	129 to 138	G		6	2.667		1,125	122		1,247	1,450
0480	139 to 148	G		6	2.667		1,175	122		1,297	1,500
0500	149 to 168	G		6	2.667		1,250	122		1,372	1,600
0520	169 to 178	G		6	2.667		1,350	122		1,472	1,700
0540	For venting unit to fixed unit, deduct						16			16	17.60
0560	Fixed picture window, up to 63 united inches	G	2 Carp	8	2		180	91.50		271.50	350
0580	64 to 83	G		8	2		206	91.50		297.50	380
0600	84 to 101	G		8	2		257	91.50		348.50	435
0620	For each united inch over 101, add	G		900	.018	Inch	3.10	.82		3.92	4.75
0780	Diamond shape, per full or partial diamond					Ea.	8.10			8.10	8.90
0800	Cellulose fiber insulation, poured into sash balance cavity	G	1 Carp	36	.222	C.F.	.69	10.20		10.89	17.50
0820	Silicone caulking at perimeter	G	"	800	.010	L.F.	.15	.46		.61	.91

08 05 Common Work Results for Openings

08 05 05 – Selective Windows and Doors Demolition

08 05 05.10 Selective Demolition Doors		Crew	Daily Output	Labor-Hours	Unit	Material	2014 Bare Costs Labor	Equipment	Total	Total Incl O&P
0010	**SELECTIVE DEMOLITION DOORS** R024119-10									
0200	Doors, exterior, 1-3/4" thick, single, 3' x 7' high	1 Clab	16	.500	Ea.		18.35		18.35	30
0202	Doors, exterior, 3' - 6' wide x 7' high		12	.667			24.50		24.50	40
0210	3' x 8' high		10	.800			29.50		29.50	48
0215	Double, 3' x 8' high		6	1.333			49		49	80.50
0220	Double, 6' x 7' high		12	.667			24.50		24.50	40
0500	Interior, 1-3/8" thick, single, 3' x 7' high		20	.400			14.65		14.65	24
0520	Double, 6' x 7' high		16	.500			18.35		18.35	30
0625	Remove Curtain Wall	H-1	390	.082	S.F.		3.90		3.90	6.80
0700	Bi-folding, 3' x 6'-8" high	1 Clab	20	.400	Ea.		14.65		14.65	24
0720	6' x 6'-8" high		18	.444			16.30		16.30	27
0900	Bi-passing, 3' x 6'-8" high		16	.500			18.35		18.35	30
0940	6' x 6'-8" high		14	.571			21		21	34.50
1500	Remove and reset, minimum	1 Carp	8	1			46		46	75.50
1520	Maximum		6	1.333			61		61	100
2000	Frames, including trim, metal		8	1			46		46	75.50
2200	Wood	2 Carp	32	.500			23		23	37.50
2201	Alternate pricing method	1 Carp	200	.040	L.F.		1.83		1.83	3.01
2205	Remove door hardware	"	45.70	.175	Ea.		8.05		8.05	13.20
3000	Special doors, counter doors	2 Carp	6	2.667			122		122	201
3100	Double acting		10	1.600			73.50		73.50	121
3200	Floor door (trap type), or access type		8	2			91.50		91.50	151
3300	Glass, sliding, including frames		12	1.333			61		61	100
3400	Overhead, commercial, 12' x 12' high		4	4			183		183	300
3440	up to 20' x 16' high		3	5.333			245		245	400
3445	up to 35' x 30' high		1	16			735		735	1,200
3500	Residential, 9' x 7' high		8	2			91.50		91.50	151
3540	16' x 7' high		7	2.286			105		105	172
3600	Remove and reset, minimum		4	4			183		183	300
3620	Maximum		2.50	6.400			293		293	480
3700	Roll-up grille		5	3.200			147		147	241
3800	Revolving door		2	8			365		365	605
3900	Storefront swing door		3	5.333			245		245	400
3902	Cafe/bar swing door	2 Clab	8	2			73.50		73.50	120
4000	Residential lockset, exterior	1 Carp	28	.286			13.10		13.10	21.50
4224	Pocket door		8	1			46		46	75.50
4300	Remove and reset deadbolt		8	1			46		46	75.50
5585	Remove panic device	1 Clab	10	.800			29.50		29.50	48
5590	Remove mail slot		45	.178			6.50		6.50	10.70
5595	Remove peep hole		45	.178			6.50		6.50	10.70
5604	Remove 9' x 7' garage door	2 Carp	9.50	1.684			77		77	127
5624	16' x 7' garage door		8	2			91.50		91.50	151
5626	9' x 7' swing up garage door		7	2.286			105		105	172
5628	16' x 7' swing up garage door		7	2.286			105		105	172
5630	Garage door demolition, remove garage door track	1 Carp	6	1.333			61		61	100
5644	Remove overhead door opener	1 Clab	5	1.600			58.50		58.50	96.50
5774	Remove heavy gage sectional door, 20 ga., 8' x 8'	2 Carp	7	2.286			105		105	172
5784	10' x 10'		6	2.667			122		122	201
5794	12' x 12'		5	3.200			147		147	241
5805	14' x 14'		4	4			183		183	300
6384	Remove French door unit	1 Clab	8	1			36.50		36.50	60
7100	Remove double swing pneumatic doors, openers and sensors	2 Skwk	.50	32	Opng.		1,525		1,525	2,475
7570	Remove shock absorbing door	2 Sswk	1.90	8.421	"		430		430	790

08 05 Common Work Results for Openings

08 05 05 – Selective Windows and Doors Demolition

08 05 05.10 Selective Demolition Doors

		Crew	Daily Output	Labor-Hours	Unit	Material	2014 Bare Costs Labor	2014 Bare Costs Equipment	Total	Total Incl O&P
9000	Minimum labor/equipment charge	1 Carp	4	2	Job		91.50		91.50	151

08 05 05.20 Selective Demolition of Windows

		Crew	Daily Output	Labor-Hours	Unit	Material	2014 Bare Costs Labor	2014 Bare Costs Equipment	Total	Total Incl O&P
0010	**SELECTIVE DEMOLITION OF WINDOWS** R024119-10									
0200	Aluminum, including trim, to 12 S.F.	1 Clab	16	.500	Ea.		18.35		18.35	30
0240	To 25 S.F.		11	.727			26.50		26.50	44
0280	To 50 S.F.		5	1.600			58.50		58.50	96.50
0320	Storm windows/screens, to 12 S.F.		27	.296			10.85		10.85	17.85
0360	To 25 S.F.		21	.381			13.95		13.95	23
0400	To 50 S.F.		16	.500			18.35		18.35	30
0600	Glass, minimum		200	.040	S.F.		1.47		1.47	2.41
0620	Maximum		150	.053	"		1.95		1.95	3.21
1000	Steel, including trim, to 12 S.F.		13	.615	Ea.		22.50		22.50	37
1020	To 25 S.F.		9	.889			32.50		32.50	53.50
1040	To 50 S.F.		4	2			73.50		73.50	120
2000	Wood, including trim, to 12 S.F.		22	.364			13.35		13.35	22
2020	To 25 S.F.		18	.444			16.30		16.30	27
2060	To 50 S.F.		13	.615			22.50		22.50	37
2065	To 180 S.F.		8	1			36.50		36.50	60
4400	Remove skylight, prefabricated glass block with metal frame	G-3	180	.178	S.F.		8.10		8.10	13
4410	Remove skylight, plstc domes, flush/curb mtd	"	395	.081	"		3.70		3.70	5.95
5020	Remove and reset window, minimum	1 Carp	6	1.333	Ea.		61		61	100
5040	Average		4	2			91.50		91.50	151
5080	Maximum		2	4			183		183	300
6000	Screening only	1 Clab	4000	.002	S.F.		.07		.07	.12
9000	Minimum labor/equipment charge	"	4	2	Job		73.50		73.50	120

08 11 Metal Doors and Frames

08 11 16 – Aluminum Doors and Frames

08 11 16.10 Entrance Doors

		Crew	Daily Output	Labor-Hours	Unit	Material	2014 Bare Costs Labor	2014 Bare Costs Equipment	Total	Total Incl O&P
0010	**ENTRANCE DOORS** and frame, Aluminum, narrow stile									
0011	Including standard hardware, clear finish, no glass									
0012	Top and bottom offset pivots, 1/4" beveled glass stops, threshold									
0013	Dead bolt lock with inside thumb screw, standard push pull									
0020	3'-0" x 7'-0" opening	2 Sswk	2	8	Ea.	885	410		1,295	1,725
0025	Anodizing aluminum entr. door & frame, add					98.50			98.50	109
0030	3'-6" x 7'-0" opening	2 Sswk	2	8		810	410		1,220	1,650
0100	3'-0" x 10'-0" opening, 3' high transom		1.80	8.889		1,275	455		1,730	2,250
0200	3'-6" x 10'-0" opening, 3' high transom		1.80	8.889		1,350	455		1,805	2,300
0280	5'-0" x 7'-0" opening		2	8		1,425	410		1,835	2,325
0300	6'-0" x 7'-0" opening		1.30	12.308		1,200	630		1,830	2,475
0301	6'-0" x 7'-0" opening		1.30	12.308	Pr.	1,200	630		1,830	2,475
0400	6'-0" x 10'-0" opening, 3' high transom		1.10	14.545		1,625	745		2,370	3,150
0420	7'-0" x 7'-0" opening		1	16		1,350	820		2,170	3,000
0520	3'-0" x 7'-0" opening, wide stile		2	8	Ea.	1,000	410		1,410	1,850
0540	3'-6" x 7'-0" opening		2	8		1,200	410		1,610	2,075
0560	5'-0" x 7'-0" opening		2	8		1,525	410		1,935	2,425
0580	6'-0" x 7'-0" opening		1.30	12.308	Pr.	1,575	630		2,205	2,900
0600	7'-0" x 7'-0" opening		1	16	"	1,725	820		2,545	3,375
1200	For non-standard size, add				Leaf	80%				
1250	For installation of non-standard size, add						20%			
1300	Light bronze finish, add				Leaf	36%				

218

08 11 Metal Doors and Frames

08 11 16 – Aluminum Doors and Frames

08 11 16.10 Entrance Doors

		Crew	Daily Output	Labor-Hours	Unit	Material	2014 Bare Costs Labor	2014 Bare Costs Equipment	Total	Total Incl O&P
1400	Dark bronze finish, add				Leaf	25%				
1500	For black finish, add					40%				
1600	Concealed panic device, add				↓	940			940	1,025
1700	Electric striker release, add				Opng.	260			260	286
1800	Floor check, add				Leaf	650			650	710
1900	Concealed closer, add				"	520			520	570
9000	Minimum labor/equipment charge	2 Carp	4	4	Job		183		183	300

08 11 63 – Metal Screen and Storm Doors and Frames

08 11 63.23 Aluminum Screen and Storm Doors and Frames

		Crew	Daily Output	Labor-Hours	Unit	Material	2014 Bare Costs Labor	2014 Bare Costs Equipment	Total	Total Incl O&P
0010	**ALUMINUM SCREEN AND STORM DOORS AND FRAMES**									
0020	Combination storm and screen									
0420	Clear anodic coating, 2'-8" wide	2 Carp	14	1.143	Ea.	165	52.50		217.50	268
0440	3'-0" wide	"	14	1.143	"	163	52.50		215.50	265
0500	For 7' door height, add					8%				
1020	Mill finish, 2'-8" wide	2 Carp	14	1.143	Ea.	235	52.50		287.50	345
1040	3'-0" wide	"	14	1.143	↓	258	52.50		310.50	370
1100	For 7'-0" door, add					8%				
1520	White painted, 2'-8" wide	2 Carp	14	1.143		286	52.50		338.50	400
1540	3'-0" wide	"	14	1.143		305	52.50		357.50	420
1600	For 7'-0" door, add				↓	8%				
2000	Wood door & screen, see Section 08 14 33.20									
9000	Minimum labor/equipment charge	1 Carp	4	2	Job		91.50		91.50	151

08 12 Metal Frames

08 12 13 – Hollow Metal Frames

08 12 13.13 Standard Hollow Metal Frames

			Crew	Daily Output	Labor-Hours	Unit	Material	2014 Bare Costs Labor	2014 Bare Costs Equipment	Total	Total Incl O&P
0010	**STANDARD HOLLOW METAL FRAMES**										
0020	16 ga., up to 5-3/4" jamb depth										
0025	3'-0" x 6'-8" single	G	2 Carp	16	1	Ea.	145	46		191	236
0028	3'-6" wide, single	G		16	1		152	46		198	243
0030	4'-0" wide, single	G		16	1		151	46		197	242
0040	6'-0" wide, double	G		14	1.143		204	52.50		256.50	310
0045	8'-0" wide, double	G		14	1.143		213	52.50		265.50	320
0100	3'-0" x 7'-0" single	G		16	1		150	46		196	241
0110	3'-6" wide, single			16	1		157	46		203	249
0112	4'-0" wide, single			16	1		157	46		203	249
0140	6'-0" wide, double			14	1.143		194	52.50		246.50	300
0145	8'-0" wide, double			14	1.143		229	52.50		281.50	340
1000	16 ga., up to 4-7/8" deep, 3'-0" x 7'-0" single	G		16	1		166	46		212	259
1140	6'-0" wide, double	G		14	1.143		188	52.50		240.50	293
1200	16 ga., 8-3/4" deep, 3'-0" x 7'-0" single	G		16	1		199	46		245	295
1240	6'-0" wide, double	G		14	1.143		234	52.50		286.50	345
2800	14 ga., up to 3-7/8" deep, 3'-0" x 7'-0" single	G		16	1		181	46		227	275
2840	6'-0" wide, double	G		14	1.143		217	52.50		269.50	325
3000	14 ga., up to 5-3/4" deep, 3'-0" x 6'-8" single	G		16	1		155	46		201	247
3002	3'-6" wide, single	G		16	1		196	46		242	291
3005	4'-0" wide, single	G		16	1		196	46		242	291
3600	up to 5-3/4" jamb depth, 4'-0" x 7'-0" single			15	1.067		185	49		234	284
3620	6'-0" wide, double			12	1.333		235	61		296	360
3640	8'-0" wide, double			12	1.333		246	61		307	370

08 12 Metal Frames

08 12 13 – Hollow Metal Frames

08 12 13.13 Standard Hollow Metal Frames

		Crew	Daily Output	Labor-Hours	Unit	Material	2014 Bare Costs Labor	Equipment	Total	Total Incl O&P
3700	8'-0" high, 4'-0" wide, single	2 Carp	15	1.067	Ea.	235	49		284	340
3740	8'-0" wide, double		12	1.333		290	61		351	420
4000	6-3/4" deep, 4'-0" x 7'-0" single G		15	1.067		220	49		269	325
4020	6'-0" wide, double G		12	1.333		275	61		336	400
4040	8'-0", wide double G		12	1.333		282	61		343	410
4100	8'-0" high, 4'-0" wide, single G		15	1.067		276	49		325	385
4140	8'-0" wide, double G		12	1.333		320	61		381	455
4400	8-3/4" deep, 4'-0" x 7'-0" , single		15	1.067		252	49		301	360
4440	8'-0" wide, double		12	1.333		315	61		376	445
4500	4'-0" x 8'-0" , single		15	1.067		283	49		332	390
4540	8'-0" wide, double		12	1.333		350	61		411	485
4900	For welded frames, add					63			63	69.50
5380	Steel frames, KD, 14 ga., "B" label, to 5-3/4" throat, to 3'-0" x 7'-0"	2 Carp	15	1.067		213	49		262	315
5400	14 ga., "B" label, up to 5-3/4" deep, 4'-0" x 7'-0" single G		15	1.067		208	49		257	310
5440	8'-0" wide, double G		12	1.333		271	61		332	400
5800	6-3/4" deep, 7'-0" high, 4'-0" wide, single G		15	1.067		218	49		267	320
5840	8'-0" wide, double G		12	1.333		385	61		446	525
6200	8-3/4" deep, 4'-0" x 7'-0" single G		15	1.067		289	49		338	400
6240	8'-0" wide, double G		12	1.333		365	61		426	500
6300	For "A" label use same price as "B" label									
6400	For baked enamel finish, add					30%	15%			
6500	For galvanizing, add					20%				
6600	For hospital stop, add				Ea.	295			295	325
6620	For hospital stop, stainless steel add				"	380			380	420
7900	Transom lite frames, fixed, add	2 Carp	155	.103	S.F.	54	4.73		58.73	67.50
8000	Movable, add	"	130	.123	"	68	5.65		73.65	84.50
9000	Minimum labor/equipment charge	1 Carp	4	2	Job		91.50		91.50	151

08 12 13.25 Channel Metal Frames

		Crew	Daily Output	Labor-Hours	Unit	Material	2014 Bare Costs Labor	Equipment	Total	Total Incl O&P
0010	**CHANNEL METAL FRAMES**									
0020	Steel channels with anchors and bar stops									
0100	6" channel @ 8.2#/L.F., 3' x 7' door, weighs 150# G	E-4	13	2.462	Ea.	239	127	10.95	376.95	505
0200	8" channel @ 11.5#/L.F., 6' x 8' door, weighs 275# G		9	3.556		435	183	15.80	633.80	830
0300	8' x 12' door, weighs 400# G		6.50	4.923		635	254	22	911	1,200
0400	10" channel @ 15.3#/L.F., 10' x 10' door, weighs 500# G		6	5.333		795	275	23.50	1,093.50	1,400
0500	12' x 12' door, weighs 600# G		5.50	5.818		955	300	26	1,281	1,625
0600	12" channel @ 20.7#/L.F., 12' x 12' door, weighs 825# G		4.50	7.111		1,300	365	31.50	1,696.50	2,150
0700	12' x 16' door, weighs 1000# G		4	8		1,600	415	35.50	2,050.50	2,550
0800	For frames without bar stops, light sections, deduct					15%				
0900	Heavy sections, deduct					10%				
9000	Minimum labor/equipment charge	E-4	4	8	Job		415	35.50	450.50	795

08 13 Metal Doors

08 13 13 – Hollow Metal Doors

08 13 13.13 Standard Hollow Metal Doors		Crew	Daily Output	Labor-Hours	Unit	Material	2014 Bare Costs Labor	Equipment	Total	Total Incl O&P
0010	**STANDARD HOLLOW METAL DOORS** R081313-20									
0015	Flush, full panel, hollow core									
0017	When noted doors are prepared but do not include glass or louvers									
0020	1-3/8" thick, 20 ga., 2'-0" x 6'-8" G	2 Carp	20	.800	Ea.	335	36.50		371.50	430
0040	2'-8" x 6'-8" G		18	.889		350	41		391	450
0060	3'-0" x 6'-8" G		17	.941		350	43		393	455
0100	3'-0" x 7'-0"		17	.941		360	43		403	465
0120	For vision lite, add					94.50			94.50	104
0140	For narrow lite, add					102			102	112
0320	Half glass, 20 ga., 2'-0" x 6'-8" G	2 Carp	20	.800		490	36.50		526.50	600
0340	2'-8" x 6'-8" G		18	.889		515	41		556	630
0360	3'-0" x 6'-8" G		17	.941		510	43		553	630
0400	3'-0" x 7'-0" G		17	.941		625	43		668	755
0410	1-3/8" thick, 18 ga., 2'-0" x 6'-8" G		20	.800		400	36.50		436.50	500
0420	3'-0" x 6'-8" G		17	.941		405	43		448	515
0425	3'-0" x 7'-0" G		17	.941		415	43		458	530
0450	For vision lite, add					94.50			94.50	104
0452	For narrow lite, add					102			102	112
0460	Half glass, 18 ga., 2'-0" x 6'-8" G	2 Carp	20	.800		555	36.50		591.50	675
0465	2'-8" x 6'-8" G		18	.889		575	41		616	700
0470	3'-0" x 6'-8" G		17	.941		565	43		608	690
0475	3'-0" x 7'-0" G		17	.941		565	43		608	695
0500	Hollow core, 1-3/4" thick, full panel, 20 ga., 2'-8" x 6'-8" G		18	.889		420	41		461	525
0520	3'-0" x 6'-8" G		17	.941		420	43		463	530
0640	3'-0" x 7'-0" G		17	.941		435	43		478	550
0680	4'-0" x 7'-0" G		15	1.067		630	49		679	775
0700	4'-0" x 8'-0" G		13	1.231		735	56.50		791.50	905
1000	18 ga., 2'-8" x 6'-8" G		17	.941		490	43		533	610
1020	3'-0" x 6'-8" G		16	1		475	46		521	600
1120	3'-0" x 7'-0" G		17	.941		515	43		558	635
1150	3'-6" x 7'-0" G	1 Carp	14	.571		570	26		596	675
1180	4'-0" x 7'-0" G	2 Carp	14	1.143		630	52.50		682.50	780
1200	4'-0" x 8'-0" G	"	17	.941		735	43		778	880
1212	For vision lite, add					94.50			94.50	104
1214	For narrow lite, add					102			102	112
1230	Half glass, 20 ga., 2'-8" x 6'-8" G	2 Carp	20	.800		575	36.50		611.50	695
1240	3'-0" x 6'-8" G		18	.889		575	41		616	700
1260	3'-0" x 7'-0" G		18	.889		595	41		636	715
1280	Embossed panel, 1-3/4" thick, poly core, 20 ga., 3'-0" x 7'-0" G		18	.889		415	41		456	520
1290	Half glass, 1-3/4" thick, poly core, 20 ga., 3'-0" x 7'-0" G		18	.889		610	41		651	735
1320	18 ga., 2'-8" x 6'-8" G		18	.889		640	41		681	770
1340	3'-0" x 6'-8" G		17	.941		635	43		678	765
1360	3'-0" x 7'-0" G		17	.941		645	43		688	780
1380	4'-0" x 7'-0" G		15	1.067		785	49		834	945
1400	4'-0" x 8'-0" G		14	1.143		890	52.50		942.50	1,075
1500	Flush full panel, 16 ga., steel hollow core									
1520	2'-0" x 6'-8" G	2 Carp	20	.800	Ea.	555	36.50		591.50	670
1530	2'-8" x 6'-8" G		20	.800		555	36.50		591.50	675
1540	3'-0" x 6'-8" G		20	.800		550	36.50		586.50	665
1560	2'-8" x 7'-0" G		18	.889		575	41		616	695
1570	3'-0" x 7'-0" G		18	.889		560	41		601	680
1580	3'-6" x 7'-0" G		18	.889		655	41		696	785
1590	4'-0" x 7'-0" G		18	.889		725	41		766	860

08 13 Metal Doors

08 13 13 – Hollow Metal Doors

08 13 13.13 Standard Hollow Metal Doors

			Crew	Daily Output	Labor-Hours	Unit	Material	2014 Bare Costs Labor	Equipment	Total	Total Incl O&P
1600	2'-8" x 8'-0"	G	2 Carp	18	.889	Ea.	700	41		741	835
1620	3'-0" x 8'-0"	G		18	.889		720	41		761	855
1630	3'-6" x 8'-0"	G		18	.889		800	41		841	945
1640	4'-0" x 8'-0"	G		18	.889		850	41		891	995
1650	1-13/16", 14 Ga., 2'-8" x 7'-0"	G		10	1.600		1,125	73.50		1,198.50	1,375
1670	3'-0" x 7'-0"	G		10	1.600		1,075	73.50		1,148.50	1,325
1690	3'-6" x 7'-0"	G		10	1.600		1,200	73.50		1,273.50	1,425
1700	4'-0" x 7'-0"	G		10	1.600		1,250	73.50		1,323.50	1,500
1720	Insulated, 1-3/4" thick, full panel, 18 ga., 3'-0" x 6'-8"	G		15	1.067		475	49		524	605
1740	2'-8" x 7'-0"	G		16	1		505	46		551	630
1760	3'-0" x 7'-0"	G		15	1.067		490	49		539	620
1800	4'-0" x 8'-0"	G		13	1.231		740	56.50		796.50	905
1820	Half glass, 18 ga., 3'-0" x 6'-8"	G		16	1		635	46		681	770
1840	2'-8" x 7'-0"	G		17	.941		660	43		703	795
1860	3'-0" x 7'-0"	G		16	1		685	46		731	830
1900	4'-0" x 8'-0"	G		14	1.143		670	52.50		722.50	820
2000	For vision lite, add						94.50			94.50	104
2010	For narrow lite, add						102			102	112
8100	For bottom louver, add						281			281	310
8110	For baked enamel finish, add						30%	15%			
8120	For galvanizing, add						20%				
8170	For soundproofing STC 40, add					Ea.	1,725			1,725	1,900
8190	For 3 hour door, add						370			370	405
8270	For dutch door with shelf, add to standard door						300			300	330
9000	Minimum labor/equipment charge		1 Carp	4	2	Job		91.50		91.50	151

08 13 13.15 Metal Fire Doors

			Crew	Daily Output	Labor-Hours	Unit	Material	2014 Bare Costs Labor	Equipment	Total	Total Incl O&P
0010	**METAL FIRE DOORS** R081313-20										
0015	Steel, flush, "B" label, 90 minute										
0020	Full panel, 20 ga., 2'-0" x 6'-8"		2 Carp	20	.800	Ea.	420	36.50		456.50	520
0040	2'-8" x 6'-8"			18	.889		435	41		476	545
0060	3'-0" x 6'-8"			17	.941		435	43		478	550
0080	3'-0" x 7'-0"			17	.941		455	43		498	570
0140	18 ga., 3'-0" x 6'-8"			16	1		495	46		541	620
0160	2'-8" x 7'-0"			17	.941		520	43		563	640
0180	3'-0" x 7'-0"			16	1		505	46		551	630
0200	4'-0" x 7'-0"			15	1.067		650	49		699	795
0220	For "A" label, 3 hour, 18 ga., use same price as "B" label										
0240	For vision lite, add					Ea.	156			156	172
0300	Full panel, 16 ga., 2'-0" x 6'-8"		2 Carp	20	.800		545	36.50		581.50	660
0310	2'-8" x 6'-8"			18	.889		545	41		586	665
0320	3'-0" x 6'-8"			17	.941		540	43		583	665
0350	2'-8" x 7'-0"			17	.941		565	43		608	690
0360	3'-0" x 7'-0"			16	1		545	46		591	675
0370	4'-0" x 7'-0"			15	1.067		705	49		754	860
0520	Flush, "B" label 90 min., egress core, 20 ga., 2'-0" x 6'-8"			18	.889		655	41		696	785
0540	2'-8" x 6'-8"			17	.941		665	43		708	800
0560	3'-0" x 6'-8"			16	1		665	46		711	805
0580	3'-0" x 7'-0"			16	1		685	46		731	825
0640	Flush, "A" label 3 hour, egress core, 18 ga., 3'-0" x 6'-8"			15	1.067		720	49		769	875
0660	2'-8" x 7'-0"			16	1		750	46		796	895
0680	3'-0" x 7'-0"			15	1.067		740	49		789	895
0700	4'-0" x 7'-0"			14	1.143		885	52.50		937.50	1,050

08 13 13 – Hollow Metal Doors

08 13 13.15 Metal Fire Doors		Crew	Daily Output	Labor-Hours	Unit	Material	2014 Bare Costs Labor	Equipment	Total	Total Incl O&P
9000	Minimum labor/equipment charge		1 Carp	4	2	Job		91.50		91.50	151

08 13 13.20 Residential Steel Doors

			Crew	Daily Output	Labor-Hours	Unit	Material	Labor	Equipment	Total	Total Incl O&P
0010	**RESIDENTIAL STEEL DOORS**										
0020	Prehung, insulated, exterior										
0030	Embossed, full panel, 2'-8" x 6'-8"	G	2 Carp	17	.941	Ea.	305	43		348	405
0040	3'-0" x 6'-8"	G		15	1.067		247	49		296	350
0060	3'-0" x 7'-0"	G		15	1.067		330	49		379	445
0070	5'-4" x 6'-8", double	G		8	2		625	91.50		716.50	835
0220	Half glass, 2'-8" x 6'-8"	G		17	.941		320	43		363	420
0240	3'-0" x 6'-8"	G		16	1		320	46		366	425
0260	3'-0" x 7'-0"	G		16	1		370	46		416	480
0270	5'-4" x 6'-8", double	G		8	2		650	91.50		741.50	865
1320	Flush face, full panel, 2'-8" x 6'-8"	G		16	1		264	46		310	365
1340	3'-0" x 6'-8"	G		15	1.067		264	49		313	370
1360	3'-0" x 7'-0"	G		15	1.067		296	49		345	405
1380	5'-4" x 6'-8", double	G		8	2		560	91.50		651.50	765
1420	Half glass, 2'-8" x 6'-8"	G		17	.941		325	43		368	425
1440	3'-0" x 6'-8"	G		16	1		325	46		371	430
1460	3'-0" x 7'-0"	G		16	1		360	46		406	470
1480	5'-4" x 6'-8", double	G		8	2		640	91.50		731.50	855
1500	Sidelight, full lite, 1'-0" x 6'-8" with grille	G					252			252	277
1510	1'-0" x 6'-8", low e	G					268			268	295
1520	1'-0" x 6'-8", half lite	G					280			280	310
1530	1'-0" x 6'-8", half lite, low e	G					284			284	310
2300	Interior, residential, closet, bi-fold, 2'-0" x 6'-8"	G	2 Carp	16	1		161	46		207	253
2330	3'-0" wide	G		16	1		200	46		246	296
2360	4'-0" wide	G		15	1.067		260	49		309	365
2400	5'-0" wide	G		14	1.143		315	52.50		367.50	435
2420	6'-0" wide	G		13	1.231		335	56.50		391.50	465
9000	Minimum labor/equipment charge		1 Carp	4	2	Job		91.50		91.50	151

08 13 13.25 Doors Hollow Metal

			Crew	Daily Output	Labor-Hours	Unit	Material	Labor	Equipment	Total	Total Incl O&P
0010	**DOORS HOLLOW METAL**										
0500	Exterior, commercial, flush, 20 ga., 1-3/4" x 7'-0" x 2'-6" wide	G	2 Carp	15	1.067	Ea.	395	49		444	510
0530	2'-8" wide	G		15	1.067		435	49		484	555
0560	3'-0" wide	G		14	1.143		435	52.50		487.50	560
0590	3'-6" wide	G		14	1.143		440	52.50		492.50	570
1000	18 ga., 1-3/4" x 7'-0" x 2'-6" wide	G		15	1.067		495	49		544	625
1030	2'-8" wide	G		15	1.067		500	49		549	630
1060	3'-0" wide	G		14	1.143		485	52.50		537.50	620
1500	16 ga., 1-3/4 x 7'-0" x 2'-6" wide	G		15	1.067		560	49		609	695
1530	2'-8" wide	G		15	1.067		565	49		614	705
1560	3'-0" wide	G		14	1.143		555	52.50		607.50	695
1590	3'-6" wide	G		14	1.143		645	52.50		697.50	795
2900	Fire door, "A" label, 18 gauge, 1-3/4" x 2'-6" x 7'-0"	G		15	1.067		645	49		694	790
2930	2'-8" wide	G		15	1.067		665	49		714	810
2960	3'-0" wide	G		14	1.143		640	52.50		692.50	790
2990	3'-6" wide	G		14	1.143		735	52.50		787.50	890
3100	"B" label, 2'-6" wide	G		15	1.067		585	49		634	725
3130	2'-8" wide	G		15	1.067		590	49		639	730
3160	3'-0" wide	G		14	1.143		580	52.50		632.50	725

08 13 Metal Doors

08 13 16 – Aluminum Doors

08 13 16.10 Commercial Aluminum Doors	Crew	Daily Output	Labor-Hours	Unit	Material	2014 Bare Costs Labor	Equipment	Total	Total Incl O&P
0010 **COMMERCIAL ALUMINUM DOORS**, flush, no glazing									
5000 Flush panel doors, pair of 2'-6" x 7'-0"	2 Sswk	2	8	Pr.	1,425	410		1,835	2,325
5050 3'-0" x 7'-0", single		2.50	6.400	Ea.	805	325		1,130	1,475
5100 Pair of 3'-0" x 7'-0"		2	8	Pr.	1,525	410		1,935	2,425
5150 3'-6" x 7'-0", single		2.50	6.400	Ea.	965	325		1,290	1,650

08 14 Wood Doors

08 14 13 – Carved Wood Doors

08 14 13.10 Types of Wood Doors, Carved

	Crew	Daily Output	Labor-Hours	Unit	Material	2014 Bare Costs Labor	Equipment	Total	Total Incl O&P
0010 **TYPES OF WOOD DOORS, CARVED**									
3000 Solid wood, 1-3/4" thick stile and rail									
3020 Mahogany, 3'-0" x 7'-0", minimum	2 Carp	14	1.143	Ea.	1,075	52.50		1,127.50	1,250
3030 Maximum		10	1.600		1,800	73.50		1,873.50	2,100
3040 3'-6" x 8'-0", minimum		10	1.600		1,500	73.50		1,573.50	1,775
3050 Maximum		8	2		2,500	91.50		2,591.50	2,900
3100 Pine, 3'-0" x 7'-0", minimum		14	1.143		490	52.50		542.50	620
3110 Maximum		10	1.600		825	73.50		898.50	1,025
3120 3'-6" x 8'-0", minimum		10	1.600		900	73.50		973.50	1,100
3130 Maximum		8	2		1,825	91.50		1,916.50	2,175
3200 Red oak, 3'-0" x 7'-0", minimum		14	1.143		1,725	52.50		1,777.50	1,975
3210 Maximum		10	1.600		2,300	73.50		2,373.50	2,650
3220 3'-6" x 8'-0", minimum		10	1.600		2,600	73.50		2,673.50	2,975
3230 Maximum		8	2		3,300	91.50		3,391.50	3,775
4000 Hand carved door, mahogany									
4020 3'-0" x 7'-0", minimum	2 Carp	14	1.143	Ea.	1,750	52.50		1,802.50	2,000
4030 Maximum		11	1.455		3,700	66.50		3,766.50	4,175
4040 3'-6" x 8'-0", minimum		10	1.600		3,000	73.50		3,073.50	3,425
4050 Maximum		8	2		3,700	91.50		3,791.50	4,225
4200 Rose wood, 3'-0" x 7'-0", minimum		14	1.143		5,200	52.50		5,252.50	5,800
4210 Maximum		11	1.455		13,700	66.50		13,766.50	15,200
4220 3'-6" x 8'-0", minimum		10	1.600		5,900	73.50		5,973.50	6,625
4225 Maximum		10	1.600		8,900	73.50		8,973.50	9,925
4400 For custom finish, add					475			475	525
4600 Side light, mahogany, 7'-0" x 1'-6" wide, minimum	2 Carp	18	.889		1,100	41		1,141	1,275
4610 Maximum		14	1.143		2,625	52.50		2,677.50	2,975
4620 8'-0" x 1'-6" wide, minimum		14	1.143		1,800	52.50		1,852.50	2,050
4630 Maximum		10	1.600		2,100	73.50		2,173.50	2,425
4640 Side light, oak, 7'-0" x 1'-6" wide, minimum		18	.889		1,200	41		1,241	1,400
4650 Maximum		14	1.143		2,100	52.50		2,152.50	2,375
4660 8'-0" x 1'-6" wide, minimum		14	1.143		1,100	52.50		1,152.50	1,275
4670 Maximum		10	1.600		2,100	73.50		2,173.50	2,425

08 14 16 – Flush Wood Doors

08 14 16.09 Smooth Wood Doors

	Crew	Daily Output	Labor-Hours	Unit	Material	2014 Bare Costs Labor	Equipment	Total	Total Incl O&P
0010 **SMOOTH WOOD DOORS**									
0015 Flush, interior, hollow core									
0025 Lauan face, 1-3/8", 3'-0" x 6'-8"	2 Carp	17	.941	Ea.	54.50	43		97.50	131
0030 4'-0" x 6'-8"		16	1		126	46		172	215
0080 1-3/4", 2'-0" x 6'-8"		17	.941		39	43		82	114
0085 3'-0" x 6'-8"	1 Carp	16	.500		54.50	23		77.50	97.50
0108 3'-0" x 7'-0"	2 Carp	16	1		123	46		169	211

08 14 16.09 Smooth Wood Doors	Crew	Daily Output	Labor-Hours	Unit	Material	2014 Bare Costs Labor	Equipment	Total	Total Incl O&P
0112	Pair of 3'-0" x 7'-0"	2 Carp	9	1.778	Pr.	104	81.50		185.50	248
0140	Birch face, 1-3/8", 2'-6" x 6'-8"		17	.941	Ea.	85	43		128	164
0180	3'-0" x 6'-8"		17	.941		95.50	43		138.50	176
0200	4'-0" x 6'-8"		16	1		158	46		204	250
0202	1-3/4", 2'-0" x 6'-8"		17	.941		50.50	43		93.50	127
0204	2'-4" x 7'-0"		16	1		95.50	46		141.50	181
0206	2'-6" x 7'-0"		16	1		99	46		145	185
0210	3'-0" x 7'-0"		16	1		109	46		155	196
0214	Pair of 3'-0" x 7'-0"		9	1.778	Pr.	211	81.50		292.50	365
0220	Oak face, 1-3/8", 2'-0" x 6'-8"		17	.941	Ea.	104	43		147	185
0280	3'-0" x 6'-8"		17	.941		115	43		158	198
0300	4'-0" x 6'-8"		16	1		139	46		185	229
0305	1-3/4", 2'-6" x 6'-8"		17	.941		110	43		153	192
0310	3'-0" x 7'-0"		16	1		211	46		257	310
0320	Walnut face, 1-3/8", 2'-0" x 6'-8"		17	.941		182	43		225	272
0340	2'-6" x 6'-8"		17	.941		189	43		232	279
0380	3'-0" x 6'-8"		17	.941		197	43		240	287
0400	4'-0" x 6'-8"		16	1		216	46		262	315
0430	For 7'-0" high, add					26			26	28.50
0440	For 8'-0" high, add					36			36	39.50
0480	For prefinishing, clear, add					42			42	46
0500	For prefinishing, stain, add					52			52	57
1320	M.D. overlay on hardboard, 1-3/8", 2'-0" x 6'-8"	2 Carp	17	.941		115	43		158	198
1340	2'-6" x 6'-8"		17	.941		115	43		158	198
1380	3'-0" x 6'-8"		17	.941		126	43		169	210
1400	4'-0" x 6'-8"		16	1		178	46		224	272
1420	For 7'-0" high, add					15.75			15.75	17.35
1440	For 8'-0" high, add					31.50			31.50	34.50
1720	H.P. plastic laminate, 1-3/8", 2'-0" x 6'-8"	2 Carp	16	1		260	46		306	360
1740	2'-6" x 6'-8"		16	1		260	46		306	360
1780	3'-0" x 6'-8"		15	1.067		290	49		339	400
1800	4'-0" x 6'-8"		14	1.143		385	52.50		437.50	505
1820	For 7'-0" high, add					15.75			15.75	17.35
1840	For 8'-0" high, add					31.50			31.50	34.50
2020	Particle core, lauan face, 1-3/8", 2'-6" x 6'-8"	2 Carp	15	1.067		92	49		141	182
2040	3'-0" x 6'-8"		14	1.143		94	52.50		146.50	189
2080	3'-0" x 7'-0"		13	1.231		98.50	56.50		155	201
2085	4'-0" x 7'-0"		12	1.333		123	61		184	235
2110	1-3/4", 3'-0" x 7'-0"		13	1.231		123	56.50		179.50	228
2120	Birch face, 1-3/8", 2'-6" x 6'-8"		15	1.067		103	49		152	194
2140	3'-0" x 6'-8"		14	1.143		113	52.50		165.50	210
2180	3'-0" x 7'-0"		13	1.231		123	56.50		179.50	228
2200	4'-0" x 7'-0"		12	1.333		139	61		200	253
2205	1-3/4", 3'-0" x 7'-0"		13	1.231		123	56.50		179.50	228
2220	Oak face, 1-3/8", 2'-6" x 6'-8"		15	1.067		116	49		165	209
2240	3'-0" x 6'-8"		14	1.143		128	52.50		180.50	227
2280	3'-0" x 7'-0"		13	1.231		133	56.50		189.50	239
2300	4'-0" x 7'-0"		12	1.333		156	61		217	272
2305	1-3/4" 3'-0" x 7'-0"		13	1.231		190	56.50		246.50	300
2320	Walnut face, 1-3/8", 2'-0" x 6'-8"		15	1.067		123	49		172	216
2340	2'-6" x 6'-8"		14	1.143		139	52.50		191.50	239
2380	3'-0" x 6'-8"		13	1.231		156	56.50		212.50	265
2400	4'-0" x 6'-8"		12	1.333		206	61		267	325

08 14 Wood Doors

08 14 16 – Flush Wood Doors

08 14 16.09 Smooth Wood Doors

08 14 16.09 Smooth Wood Doors	Crew	Daily Output	Labor-Hours	Unit	Material	2014 Bare Costs Labor	Equipment	Total	Total Incl O&P
2440	For 8'-0" high, add				Ea.	41			41	45
2460	For 8'-0" high walnut, add					36			36	39.50
2480	For solid wood core, add					40			40	44
2720	For prefinishing, clear, add					36			36	39.50
2740	For prefinishing, stain, add					53			53	58.50
3320	M.D. overlay on hardboard, 1-3/8", 2'-6" x 6'-8"	2 Carp	14	1.143		106	52.50		158.50	203
3340	3'-0" x 6'-8"		13	1.231		115	56.50		171.50	220
3380	3'-0" x 7'-0"		12	1.333		117	61		178	229
3400	4'-0" x 7'-0"	↓	10	1.600		155	73.50		228.50	292
3440	For 8'-0" height, add					37			37	40.50
3460	For solid wood core, add					42			42	46
3720	H.P. plastic laminate, 1-3/8", 2'-6" x 6'-8"	2 Carp	13	1.231		160	56.50		216.50	269
3740	3'-0" x 6'-8"		12	1.333		185	61		246	305
3780	3'-0" x 7'-0"		11	1.455		190	66.50		256.50	320
3800	4'-0" x 7'-0"	↓	8	2		225	91.50		316.50	400
3840	For 8'-0" height, add					37			37	40.50
3860	For solid wood core, add					42			42	46
4000	Exterior, flush, solid core, birch, 1-3/4" x 2'-6" x 7'-0"	2 Carp	15	1.067		173	49		222	271
4020	2'-8" wide		15	1.067		159	49		208	256
4040	3'-0" wide	↓	14	1.143		209	52.50		261.50	315
4045	3'-0" x 8'-0"	1 Carp	8	1		430	46		476	550
4100	Oak faced 1-3/4" x 2'-6" x 7'-0"	2 Carp	15	1.067		.215	49		264	320
4120	2'-8" wide		15	1.067		225	49		274	330
4140	3'-0" wide	↓	14	1.143		230	52.50		282.50	340
4160	Walnut faced, 1-3/4" x 3'-0" x 6'-8"	1 Carp	17	.471		295	21.50		316.50	360
4180	3'-6" wide	"	17	.471		365	21.50		386.50	435
4200	Walnut faced, 1-3/4" x 2'-6" x 7'-0"	2 Carp	15	1.067		310	49		359	420
4220	2'-8" wide		15	1.067		315	49		364	425
4240	3'-0" wide	↓	14	1.143		320	52.50		372.50	435
4300	For 6'-8" high door, deduct from 7'-0" door					16.80			16.80	18.50
5000	Wood doors, for vision lite, add					94.50			94.50	104
5010	Wood doors, for narrow lite, add					102			102	112
5015	Wood doors, for bottom (or top) louver, add				↓	281			281	310
9000	Minimum labor/equipment charge	1 Carp	4	2	Job		91.50		91.50	151

08 14 16.10 Wood Doors Decorator

08 14 16.10 Wood Doors Decorator	Crew	Daily Output	Labor-Hours	Unit	Material	2014 Bare Costs Labor	Equipment	Total	Total Incl O&P
0010	**WOOD DOORS DECORATOR**									
1800	Exterior, flush, solid wood core, birch 1-3/4" x 2'-6" x 7'-0"	2 Carp	15	1.067	Ea.	320	49		369	430
1820	2'-8" wide		15	1.067		325	49		374	440
1840	3'-0" wide		14	1.143		335	52.50		387.50	455
1900	Oak faced, 1-3/4" x 2'-6" x 7'-0"		15	1.067		320	49		369	430
1920	2'-8" wide		15	1.067		330	49		379	445
1940	3'-0" wide		14	1.143		340	52.50		392.50	460
2100	Walnut faced, 1-3/4" x 2'-6" x 7'-0"		15	1.067		385	49		434	505
2120	2'-8" wide		15	1.067		400	49		449	520
2140	3'-0" wide	↓	14	1.143	↓	430	52.50		482.50	560

08 14 16.20 Wood Fire Doors

08 14 16.20 Wood Fire Doors	Crew	Daily Output	Labor-Hours	Unit	Material	2014 Bare Costs Labor	Equipment	Total	Total Incl O&P
0010	**WOOD FIRE DOORS**									
0020	Particle core, 7 face plys, "B" label,									
0040	1 hour, birch face, 1-3/4" x 2'-6" x 6'-8"	2 Carp	14	1.143	Ea.	420	52.50		472.50	545
0080	3'-0" x 6'-8"		13	1.231		400	56.50		456.50	535
0090	3'-0" x 7'-0"		12	1.333		435	61		496	580
0100	4'-0" x 7'-0"	↓	12	1.333	↓	540	61		601	695

08 14 Wood Doors

08 14 16 – Flush Wood Doors

08 14 16.20 Wood Fire Doors		Crew	Daily Output	Labor-Hours	Unit	Material	2014 Bare Costs Labor	Equipment	Total	Total Incl O&P
0140	Oak face, 2'-6" x 6'-8"	2 Carp	14	1.143	Ea.	450	52.50		502.50	580
0180	3'-0" x 6'-8"		13	1.231		455	56.50		511.50	595
0190	3'-0" x 7'-0"		12	1.333		460	61		521	605
0200	4'-0" x 7'-0"		12	1.333		590	61		651	750
0240	Walnut face, 2'-6" x 6'-8"		14	1.143		470	52.50		522.50	600
0280	3'-0" x 6'-8"		13	1.231		490	56.50		546.50	635
0290	3'-0" x 7'-0"		12	1.333		510	61		571	660
0300	4'-0" x 7'-0"		12	1.333		630	61		691	795
0440	M.D. overlay on hardboard, 2'-6" x 6'-8"		15	1.067		315	49		364	425
0480	3'-0" x 6'-8"		14	1.143		375	52.50		427.50	500
0490	3'-0" x 7'-0"		13	1.231		395	56.50		451.50	530
0500	4'-0" x 7'-0"		12	1.333		415	61		476	555
0740	90 minutes, birch face, 1-3/4" x 2'-6" x 6'-8"		14	1.143		325	52.50		377.50	440
0780	3'-0" x 6'-8"		13	1.231		320	56.50		376.50	445
0790	3'-0" x 7'-0"		12	1.333		385	61		446	525
0800	4'-0" x 7'-0"		12	1.333		540	61		601	690
0840	Oak face, 2'-6" x 6'-8"		14	1.143		430	52.50		482.50	560
0880	3'-0" x 6'-8"		13	1.231		440	56.50		496.50	580
0890	3'-0" x 7'-0"		12	1.333		455	61		516	600
0900	4'-0" x 7'-0"		12	1.333		590	61		651	750
0940	Walnut face, 2'-6" x 6'-8"		14	1.143		400	52.50		452.50	525
0980	3'-0" x 6'-8"		13	1.231		410	56.50		466.50	545
0990	3'-0" x 7'-0"		12	1.333		470	61		531	615
1000	4'-0" x 7'-0"		12	1.333		620	61		681	780
1140	M.D. overlay on hardboard, 2'-6" x 6'-8"		15	1.067		355	49		404	470
1180	3'-0" x 6'-8"		14	1.143		375	52.50		427.50	500
1190	3'-0" x 7'-0"		13	1.231		405	56.50		461.50	540
1200	4'-0" x 7'-0"	▼	12	1.333		455	61		516	600
1240	For 8'-0" height, add					75			75	82.50
1260	For 8'-0" height walnut, add					90			90	99
2200	Custom architectural "B" label, flush, 1-3/4" thick, birch,									
2210	Solid core									
2220	2'-6" x 7'-0"	2 Carp	15	1.067	Ea.	305	49		354	415
2260	3'-0" x 7'-0"		14	1.143		315	52.50		367.50	430
2300	4'-0" x 7'-0"		13	1.231		400	56.50		456.50	535
2420	4'-0" x 8'-0"	▼	11	1.455		430	66.50		496.50	585
2480	For oak veneer, add					50%				
2500	For walnut veneer, add					75%				
9000	Minimum labor/equipment charge	1 Carp	4	2	Job		91.50		91.50	151

08 14 23 – Clad Wood Doors

08 14 23.13 Metal-Faced Wood Doors

		Crew	Daily Output	Labor-Hours	Unit	Material	Labor	Equipment	Total	Total Incl O&P
0010	**METAL-FACED WOOD DOORS**									
0020	Interior, flush type, 3' x 7'	2 Carp	4.30	3.721	Opng.	390	171		561	710
9000	Minimum labor/equipment charge	1 Carp	2	4	Job		183		183	300

08 14 23.20 Tin Clad Wood Doors

		Crew	Daily Output	Labor-Hours	Unit	Material	Labor	Equipment	Total	Total Incl O&P
0010	**TIN CLAD WOOD DOORS**									
0020	3 ply, 6' x 7', double sliding, doors only	2 Carp	1	16	Opng.	2,000	735		2,735	3,400
1000	For electric operator, add	1 Elec	2	4	"	3,250	213		3,463	3,900
9000	Minimum labor/equipment charge	2 Carp	1	16	Job		735		735	1,200

08 14 Wood Doors

08 14 33 – Stile and Rail Wood Doors

08 14 33.10 Wood Doors Paneled

		Crew	Daily Output	Labor-Hours	Unit	Material	2014 Bare Costs Labor	Equipment	Total	Total Incl O&P
0010	**WOOD DOORS PANELED**									
0020	Interior, six panel, hollow core, 1-3/8" thick									
0040	Molded hardboard, 2'-0" x 6'-8"	2 Carp	17	.941	Ea.	62	43		105	139
0060	2'-6" x 6'-8"		17	.941		64	43		107	142
0070	2'-8" x 6'-8"		17	.941		67	43		110	145
0080	3'-0" x 6'-8"		17	.941		72	43		115	150
0140	Embossed print, molded hardboard, 2'-0" x 6'-8"		17	.941		64	43		107	142
0160	2'-6" x 6'-8"		17	.941		64	43		107	142
0180	3'-0" x 6'-8"		17	.941		72	43		115	150
0540	Six panel, solid, 1-3/8" thick, pine, 2'-0" x 6'-8"		15	1.067		155	49		204	252
0560	2'-6" x 6'-8"		14	1.143		170	52.50		222.50	273
0580	3'-0" x 6'-8"		13	1.231		145	56.50		201.50	253
1020	Two panel, bored rail, solid, 1-3/8" thick, pine, 1'-6" x 6'-8"		16	1		270	46		316	375
1040	2'-0" x 6'-8"		15	1.067		355	49		404	470
1060	2'-6" x 6'-8"		14	1.143		400	52.50		452.50	525
1340	Two panel, solid, 1-3/8" thick, fir, 2'-0" x 6'-8"		15	1.067		160	49		209	257
1360	2'-6" x 6'-8"		14	1.143		210	52.50		262.50	315
1380	3'-0" x 6'-8"		13	1.231		415	56.50		471.50	550
1740	Five panel, solid, 1-3/8" thick, fir, 2'-0" x 6'-8"		15	1.067		280	49		329	390
1760	2'-6" x 6'-8"		14	1.143		420	52.50		472.50	545
1780	3'-0" x 6'-8"		13	1.231		420	56.50		476.50	555
4190	Exterior, Knotty pine, paneled, 1-3/4", 3'-0" x 6'-8"		16	1		775	46		821	930
4195	Double 1-3/4", 3'-0" x 6'-8"		16	1		1,550	46		1,596	1,775
4200	Ash, paneled, 1-3/4", 3'-0" x 6'-8"		16	1		875	46		921	1,050
4205	Double 1-3/4", 3'-0" x 6'-8"		16	1		1,750	46		1,796	2,000
4210	Cherry, paneled, 1-3/4", 3'-0" x 6'-8"		16	1		875	46		921	1,050
4215	Double 1-3/4", 3'-0" x 6'-8"		16	1		1,750	46		1,796	2,000
4230	Ash, paneled, 1-3/4", 3'-0" x 8'-0"		16	1		950	46		996	1,125
4235	Double 1-3/4", 3'-0" x 8'-0"		16	1		1,900	46		1,946	2,175
4240	Hard Maple, paneled, 1-3/4", 3'-0" x 8'-0"		16	1		950	46		996	1,125
4245	Double 1-3/4", 3'-0" x 8'-0"		16	1		1,900	46		1,946	2,175
4250	Cherry, paneled, 1-3/4", 3'-0" x 8'-0"		16	1		950	46		996	1,125
4255	Double 1-3/4", 3'-0" x 8'-0"		16	1		1,900	46		1,946	2,175
9000	Minimum labor/equipment charge	1 Carp	4	2	Job		91.50		91.50	151

08 14 33.20 Wood Doors Residential

		Crew	Daily Output	Labor-Hours	Unit	Material	2014 Bare Costs Labor	Equipment	Total	Total Incl O&P
0010	**WOOD DOORS RESIDENTIAL**									
0200	Exterior, combination storm & screen, pine									
0260	2'-8" wide	2 Carp	10	1.600	Ea.	300	73.50		373.50	450
0280	3'-0" wide		9	1.778		310	81.50		391.50	475
0300	7'-1" x 3'-0" wide		9	1.778		335	81.50		416.50	505
0400	Full lite, 6'-9" x 2'-6" wide		11	1.455		320	66.50		386.50	460
0420	2'-8" wide		10	1.600		320	73.50		393.50	470
0440	3'-0" wide		9	1.778		325	81.50		406.50	490
0500	7'-1" x 3'-0" wide		9	1.778		355	81.50		436.50	525
0700	Dutch door, pine, 1-3/4" x 2'-8" x 6'-8", minimum		12	1.333		790	61		851	965
0720	Maximum		10	1.600		900	73.50		973.50	1,100
0800	3'-0" wide, minimum		12	1.333		790	61		851	965
0820	Maximum		10	1.600		900	73.50		973.50	1,100
1000	Entrance door, colonial, 1-3/4" x 6'-8" x 2'-8" wide		16	1		500	46		546	620
1020	6 panel pine, 3'-0" wide		15	1.067		445	49		494	570
1100	8 panel pine, 2'-8" wide		16	1		575	46		621	710
1120	3'-0" wide		15	1.067		570	49		619	705

08 14 Wood Doors

08 14 33 – Stile and Rail Wood Doors

08 14 33.20 Wood Doors Residential	Crew	Daily Output	Labor-Hours	Unit	Material	2014 Bare Costs Labor	Equipment	Total	Total Incl O&P
1200	For tempered safety glass lites, (min of 2) add				Ea.	76.50			76.50	84.50
1300	Flush, birch, solid core, 1-3/4" x 6'-8" x 2'-8" wide	2 Carp	16	1		113	46		159	201
1320	3'-0" wide		15	1.067		119	49		168	211
1350	7'-0" x 2'-8" wide		16	1		121	46		167	210
1360	3'-0" wide		15	1.067		143	49		192	238
1380	For tempered safety glass lites, add					103			103	113
1420	6'-8" x 3'-0" wide, fir	2 Carp	16	1		470	46		516	590
1720	Carved mahogany 3'-0" x 6'-8"		15	1.067		1,375	49		1,424	1,600
1800	Lauan, solid core, 1-3/4" x 7'-0" x 2'-4" wide		16	1		110	46		156	197
1810	2'-6" wide		15	1.067		113	49		162	205
1820	2'-8" wide		9	1.778		117	81.50		198.50	263
1830	3'-0" wide		16	1		129	46		175	218
1840	3'-4" wide		16	1		203	46		249	300
1850	Pair of 3'-0" wide		15	1.067	Pr.	257	49		306	365
2700	Interior, closet, bi-fold, w/hardware, no frame or trim incl.									
2720	Flush, birch, 6'-6" or 6'-8" x 2'-6" wide	2 Carp	13	1.231	Ea.	67.50	56.50		124	167
2740	3'-0" wide		13	1.231		71.50	56.50		128	171
2760	4'-0" wide		12	1.333		109	61		170	220
2780	5'-0" wide		11	1.455		105	66.50		171.50	226
2800	6'-0" wide		10	1.600		128	73.50		201.50	262
2820	Flush, hardboard, primed, 6'-8" x 2'-6" wide		13	1.231		56.50	56.50		113	155
2840	3'-0" wide		13	1.231		64	56.50		120.50	163
2860	4'-0" wide		12	1.333		94	61		155	203
2880	5'-0" wide		11	1.455		101	66.50		167.50	221
2900	6'-0" wide		10	1.600		139	73.50		212.50	274
3000	Raised panel pine, 6'-6" or 6'-8" x 2'-6" wide		13	1.231		198	56.50		254.50	310
3020	3'-0" wide		13	1.231		278	56.50		334.50	400
3040	4'-0" wide		12	1.333		305	61		366	435
3060	5'-0" wide		11	1.455		365	66.50		431.50	510
3080	6'-0" wide		10	1.600		400	73.50		473.50	560
3200	Louvered, pine 6'-6" or 6'-8" x 2'-6" wide		13	1.231		144	56.50		200.50	251
3220	3'-0" wide		13	1.231		208	56.50		264.50	320
3240	4'-0" wide		12	1.333		235	61		296	360
3260	5'-0" wide		11	1.455		262	66.50		328.50	400
3280	6'-0" wide		10	1.600		289	73.50		362.50	440
4400	Bi-passing closet, incl. hardware and frame, no trim incl.									
4420	Flush, lauan, 6'-8" x 4'-0" wide	2 Carp	12	1.333	Opng.	176	61		237	294
4440	5'-0" wide		11	1.455		187	66.50		253.50	315
4460	6'-0" wide		10	1.600		209	73.50		282.50	350
4600	Flush, birch, 6'-8" x 4'-0" wide		12	1.333		223	61		284	345
4620	5'-0" wide		11	1.455		212	66.50		278.50	345
4640	6'-0" wide		10	1.600		260	73.50		333.50	405
4800	Louvered, pine, 6'-8" x 4'-0" wide		12	1.333		410	61		471	550
4820	5'-0" wide		11	1.455		395	66.50		461.50	545
4840	6'-0" wide		10	1.600		530	73.50		603.50	705
5000	Paneled, pine, 6'-8" x 4'-0" wide		12	1.333		510	61		571	665
5020	5'-0" wide		11	1.455		410	66.50		476.50	560
5040	6'-0" wide		10	1.600		610	73.50		683.50	790
5042	8'-0" wide		12	1.333		1,025	61		1,086	1,225
6100	Folding accordion, closet, including track and frame									
6120	Vinyl, 2 layer, stock	2 Carp	10	1.600	Ea.	66	73.50		139.50	194
6200	Rigid PVC	"	10	1.600	"	55	73.50		128.50	182
7310	Passage doors, flush, no frame included									

08 14 Wood Doors

08 14 33 – Stile and Rail Wood Doors

08 14 33.20 Wood Doors Residential	Crew	Daily Output	Labor-Hours	Unit	Material	2014 Bare Costs Labor	Equipment	Total	Total Incl O&P
7320	Hardboard, hollow core, 1-3/8" x 6'-8" x 1'-6" wide	2 Carp	18	.889	Ea.	40.50	41		81.50	112
7330	2'-0" wide		18	.889		43	41		84	115
7340	2'-6" wide		18	.889		47.50	41		88.50	120
7350	2'-8" wide		18	.889		49	41		90	121
7360	3'-0" wide		17	.941		52	43		95	129
7420	Lauan, hollow core, 1-3/8" x 6'-8" x 1'-6" wide		18	.889		34	41		75	105
7440	2'-0" wide		18	.889		35	41		76	106
7450	2'-4" wide		18	.889		38.50	41		79.50	110
7460	2'-6" wide		18	.889		38.50	41		79.50	110
7480	2'-8" wide		18	.889		40	41		81	111
7500	3'-0" wide		17	.941		42.50	43		85.50	118
7700	Birch, hollow core, 1-3/8" x 6'-8" x 1'-6" wide		18	.889		41	41		82	112
7720	2'-0" wide		18	.889		42.50	41		83.50	114
7740	2'-6" wide		18	.889		50	41		91	122
7760	2'-8" wide		18	.889		50.50	41		91.50	123
7780	3'-0" wide		17	.941		52	43		95	129
8000	Pine louvered, 1-3/8" x 6'-8" x 1'-6" wide		19	.842		120	38.50		158.50	196
8020	2'-0" wide		18	.889		131	41		172	211
8040	2'-6" wide		18	.889		150	41		191	232
8060	2'-8" wide		18	.889		161	41		202	244
8080	3'-0" wide		17	.941		175	43		218	263
8300	Pine paneled, 1-3/8" x 6'-8" x 1'-6" wide		19	.842		128	38.50		166.50	205
8320	2'-0" wide		18	.889		153	41		194	235
8330	2'-4" wide		18	.889		182	41		223	267
8340	2'-6" wide		18	.889		182	41		223	267
8360	2'-8" wide		18	.889		185	41		226	271
8380	3'-0" wide		17	.941		204	43		247	295
8490	3'-0" wide		17	.941		276	43		319	375
8804	Pocket door, 6 panel pine, 2'-6" x 6'-8"		10.50	1.524		355	70		425	505
8814	2'-8" x 6'-8"		10.50	1.524		360	70		430	510
8824	3'-0" x 6'-8"		10.50	1.524		385	70		455	535
9000	Passage doors, flush, no frame, birch, solid core, 1-3/8" x 2'-4" x 7'-0"		16	1		117	46		163	205
9020	2'-8" wide		16	1		124	46		170	213
9040	3'-0" wide		16	1		134	46		180	223
9060	3'-4" wide		15	1.067	▼	155	49		204	252
9080	Pair of 3'-0" wide		9	1.778	Pr.	265	81.50		346.50	425
9100	Lauan, solid core, 1-3/8" x 7'-0" x 2'-4" wide		16	1	Ea.	108	46		154	194
9120	2'-8" wide		16	1		115	46		161	202
9140	3'-0" wide		16	1		122	46		168	210
9160	3'-4" wide		15	1.067	▼	128	49		177	222
9180	Pair of 3'-0" wide		9	1.778	Pr.	221	81.50		302.50	375
9200	Hardboard, solid core, 1-3/8" x 7'-0" x 2'-4" wide		16	1	Ea.	133	46		179	222
9220	2'-8" wide		16	1		138	46		184	228
9240	3'-0" wide		16	1		142	46		188	232
9260	3'-4" wide		15	1.067	▼	157	49		206	253
9900	Minimum labor/equipment charge	1 Carp	4	2	Job		91.50		91.50	151

08 14 40 – Interior Cafe Doors

08 14 40.10 Cafe Style Doors

0010	CAFE STYLE DOORS									
6520	Interior cafe doors, 2'-6" opening, stock, panel pine	2 Carp	16	1	Ea.	218	46		264	315
6540	3'-0" opening	"	16	1	"	240	46		286	340
6550	Louvered pine									

08 14 Wood Doors

08 14 40 – Interior Cafe Doors

08 14 40.10 Cafe Style Doors		Crew	Daily Output	Labor-Hours	Unit	Material	2014 Bare Costs Labor	Equipment	Total	Total Incl O&P
6560	2'-6" opening	2 Carp	16	1	Ea.	180	46		226	274
8000	3'-0" opening		16	1		193	46		239	288
8010	2'-6" opening, hardwood		16	1		264	46		310	365
8020	3'-0" opening		16	1		281	46		327	385
9000	Minimum labor/equipment charge	1 Carp	4	2	Job		91.50		91.50	151

08 16 Composite Doors

08 16 13 – Fiberglass Doors

08 16 13.10 Entrance Doors, Fiberous Glass

0010	ENTRANCE DOORS, FIBEROUS GLASS		Crew	Daily Output	Labor-Hours	Unit	Material	2014 Bare Costs Labor	Equipment	Total	Total Incl O&P
0020	Exterior, fiberglass, door, 2'-8" wide x 6'-8" high	G	2 Carp	15	1.067	Ea.	259	49		308	365
0040	3'-0" wide x 6'-8" high	G		15	1.067		259	49		308	365
0060	3'-0" wide x 7'-0" high	G		15	1.067		460	49		509	585
0080	3'-0" wide x 6'-8" high, with two lites	G		15	1.067		294	49		343	405
0100	3'-0" wide x 8'-0" high, with two lites	G		15	1.067		495	49		544	625
0110	Half glass, 3'-0" wide x 6'-8" high	G		15	1.067		435	49		484	560
0120	3'-0" wide x 6'-8" high, low e	G		15	1.067		465	49		514	590
0130	3'-0" wide x 8'-0" high	G		15	1.067		580	49		629	720
0140	3'-0" wide x 8'-0" high, low e	G		15	1.067		640	49		689	780
0150	Side lights, 1'-0" wide x 6'-8" high	G					251			251	276
0160	1'-0" wide x 6'-8" high, low e	G					256			256	281
0180	1'-0" wide x 6'-8" high, full glass	G					285			285	315
0190	1'-0" wide x 6'-8" high, low e	G					300			300	330

08 16 14 – French Doors

08 16 14.10 Exterior Doors With Glass Lites

0010	EXTERIOR DOORS WITH GLASS LITES	Crew	Daily Output	Labor-Hours	Unit	Material	2014 Bare Costs Labor	Equipment	Total	Total Incl O&P
0020	French, Fir, 1-3/4", 3'-0" wide x 6'-8" high	2 Carp	12	1.333	Ea.	600	61		661	760
0025	Double		12	1.333		1,200	61		1,261	1,425
0030	Maple, 1-3/4", 3'-0" wide x 6'-8" high		12	1.333		675	61		736	845
0035	Double		12	1.333		1,350	61		1,411	1,575
0040	Cherry, 1-3/4", 3'-0" wide x 6'-8" high		12	1.333		790	61		851	965
0045	Double		12	1.333		1,575	61		1,636	1,825
0100	Mahogany, 1-3/4", 3'-0" wide x 8'-0" high		10	1.600		800	73.50		873.50	1,000
0105	Double		10	1.600		1,600	73.50		1,673.50	1,875
0110	Fir, 1-3/4", 3'-0" wide x 8'-0" high		10	1.600		1,200	73.50		1,273.50	1,450
0115	Double		10	1.600		2,400	73.50		2,473.50	2,775
0120	Oak, 1-3/4", 3'-0" wide x 8'-0" high		10	1.600		1,825	73.50		1,898.50	2,125
0125	Double		10	1.600		3,650	73.50		3,723.50	4,125

08 17 Integrated Door Opening Assemblies

08 17 13 – Integrated Metal Door Opening Assemblies

08 17 13.10 Hollow Metal Doors and Frames

		Crew	Daily Output	Labor-Hours	Unit	Material	2014 Bare Costs Labor	Equipment	Total	Total Incl O&P
0010	**HOLLOW METAL DOORS AND FRAMES**									
0100	Prehung, flush, 18 ga., 1-3/4" x 6'-8" x 2'-8" wide	1 Carp	16	.500	Ea.	665	23		688	770
0120	3'-0" wide		15	.533		620	24.50		644.50	725
0130	3'-6" wide		13	.615		710	28		738	825
0140	4'-0" wide		10	.800		770	36.50		806.50	905
0300	Double, 1-3/4" x 3'-0" x 6'-8"		5	1.600		700	73.50		773.50	890
0350	3'-0" x 8'-0"		4	2		1,550	91.50		1,641.50	1,850

08 17 13.20 Stainless Steel Doors and Frames

			Crew	Daily Output	Labor-Hours	Unit	Material	2014 Bare Costs Labor	Equipment	Total	Total Incl O&P
0010	**STAINLESS STEEL DOORS AND FRAMES**										
0020	Stainless Steel(304) prehung 24 g 2'-6" x 6'-8" door w/16 g frame	G	2 Carp	6	2.667	Ea.	1,775	122		1,897	2,150
0025	2'-8" x 6'-8"	G		6	2.667		1,825	122		1,947	2,200
0030	3'-0" x 6'-8"	G		6	2.667		1,825	122		1,947	2,200
0040	3'-0" x 7'-0"	G		6	2.667		1,850	122		1,972	2,225
0050	4'-0" x 7'-0"	G		5	3.200		2,375	147		2,522	2,875
0100	Stainless Steel(316) prehung 24 g 2'-6" x 6'-8" door w/16 g frame	G		6	2.667		2,700	122		2,822	3,175
0110	2'-8" x 6'-8"	G		6	2.667		2,725	122		2,847	3,175
0120	3'-0" x 6'-8"	G		6	2.667		2,500	122		2,622	2,950
0150	3'-0" x 7'-0"	G		6	2.667		2,675	122		2,797	3,150
0160	4'-0" x 7'-0"	G		6	2.667		3,300	122		3,422	3,825
0300	Stainless Steel(304) prehung 18 g 2'-6" x 6'-8" door w/16 g frame	G		6	2.667		3,075	122		3,197	3,575
0310	2'-8" x 6'-8"	G		6	2.667		3,100	122		3,222	3,600
0320	3'-0" x 6'-8"	G		6	2.667		3,150	122		3,272	3,675
0350	3'-0" x 7'-0"	G		6	2.667		3,200	122		3,322	3,725
0360	4'-0" x 7'-0"	G		5	3.200		3,400	147		3,547	3,975
0500	Stainless steel, prehung door, foam core, 14 ga, 3'-0" x 7'-0"	G		5	3.200		3,400	147		3,547	4,000
0600	Stainless steel, prehung double door, foam core, 14 ga, 3'-0" x 7'-0"	G		4	4		6,700	183		6,883	7,675

08 17 23 – Integrated Wood Door Opening Assemblies

08 17 23.10 Pre-Hung Doors

		Crew	Daily Output	Labor-Hours	Unit	Material	2014 Bare Costs Labor	Equipment	Total	Total Incl O&P
0010	**PRE-HUNG DOORS**									
0300	Exterior, wood, comb. storm & screen, 6'-9" x 2'-6" wide	2 Carp	15	1.067	Ea.	296	49		345	405
0320	2'-8" wide		15	1.067		296	49		345	405
0340	3'-0" wide		15	1.067		305	49		354	415
0360	For 7'-0" high door, add					30			30	33
1600	Entrance door, flush, birch, solid core									
1620	4-5/8" solid jamb, 1-3/4" x 6'-8" x 2'-8" wide	2 Carp	16	1	Ea.	289	46		335	395
1640	3'-0" wide		16	1		375	46		421	490
1642	5-5/8" jamb		16	1		325	46		371	435
1680	For 7'-0" high door, add					25			25	27.50
2000	Entrance door, colonial, 6 panel pine									
2020	4-5/8" solid jamb, 1-3/4" x 6'-8" x 2'-8" wide	2 Carp	16	1	Ea.	640	46		686	780
2040	3'-0" wide	"	16	1		675	46		721	815
2060	For 7'-0" high door, add					54			54	59
2200	For 5-5/8" solid jamb, add					41.50			41.50	46
2230	French style, exterior, 1 lite, 1-3/4" x 3'-0" x 6'-8"	1 Carp	14	.571		590	26		616	695
2235	9 lites	"	14	.571		660	26		686	770
2245	15 lites	2 Carp	14	1.143		640	52.50		692.50	790
2250	Double, 15 lites, 2'-0" x 6'-8", 4'-0" opening		7	2.286	Pr.	1,200	105		1,305	1,500
2260	2'-6" x 6'-8", 5'-0" opening		7	2.286		1,325	105		1,430	1,625
2280	3'-0" x 6'-8", 6'-0" opening		7	2.286		1,350	105		1,455	1,650
2430	3'-0" x 7'-0", 15 lites		14	1.143	Ea.	950	52.50		1,002.50	1,125
2432	Two 3'-0" x 7'-0"		7	2.286	Pr.	1,975	105		2,080	2,325
2435	3'-0" x 8'-0"		14	1.143	Ea.	1,000	52.50		1,052.50	1,175

08 17 Integrated Door Opening Assemblies

08 17 23 – Integrated Wood Door Opening Assemblies

08 17 23.10 Pre-Hung Doors

		Crew	Daily Output	Labor-Hours	Unit	Material	2014 Bare Costs Labor	Equipment	Total	Total Incl O&P
2437	Two, 3'-0" x 8'-0"	2 Carp	7	2.286	Pr.	2,075	105		2,180	2,475
4000	Interior, passage door, 4-5/8" solid jamb									
4350	Paneled, primed, hollow core, 2'-8" wide	2 Carp	17	.941	Ea.	116	43		159	199
4360	3'-0" wide		17	.941		180	43		223	269
4400	Lauan, flush, solid core, 1-3/8" x 6'-8" x 2'-6" wide		17	.941		186	43		229	276
4420	2'-8" wide		17	.941		186	43		229	276
4440	3'-0" wide		16	1		201	46		247	297
4600	Hollow core, 1-3/8" x 6'-8" x 2'-6" wide		17	.941		125	43		168	209
4620	2'-8" wide		17	.941		125	43		168	208
4640	3'-0" wide		16	1		140	46		186	230
4700	For 7'-0" high door, add					35.50			35.50	39
5000	Birch, flush, solid core, 1-3/8" x 6'-8" x 2'-6" wide	2 Carp	17	.941		259	43		302	355
5020	2'-8" wide		17	.941		201	43		244	292
5040	3'-0" wide		16	1		288	46		334	390
5200	Hollow core, 1-3/8" x 6'-8" x 2'-6" wide		17	.941		210	43		253	300
5220	2'-8" wide		17	.941		252	43		295	350
5240	3'-0" wide		16	1		216	46		262	315
5280	For 7'-0" high door, add					30.50			30.50	33.50
5500	Hardboard paneled, 1-3/8" x 6'-8" x 2'-6" wide	2 Carp	17	.941		145	43		188	230
5520	2'-8" wide		17	.941		153	43		196	239
5540	3'-0" wide		16	1		150	46		196	241
6000	Pine paneled, 1-3/8" x 6'-8" x 2'-6" wide		17	.941		255	43		298	350
6020	2'-8" wide		17	.941		274	43		317	370
6040	3'-0" wide		16	1		282	46		328	385
6500	For 5-5/8" solid jamb, add					25			25	27.50
6520	For split jamb, deduct					24			24	26.50
8200	Birch, flush, solid core, 1-3/4" x 6'-8" x 2'-4" wide	1 Carp	17	.471		229	21.50		250.50	288
8220	2'-6" wide		17	.471		227	21.50		248.50	286
8240	2'-8" wide		17	.471		221	21.50		242.50	279
8260	3'-0" wide		16	.500		229	23		252	290
8280	3'-6" wide		15	.533		360	24.50		384.50	435
8500	Pocket door frame with lauan, flush, hollow core, 1-3/8" x 3'-0" x 6'-8"		17	.471		224	21.50		245.50	283
9000	Minimum labor/equipment charge		4	2	Job		91.50		91.50	151

08 31 Access Doors and Panels

08 31 13 – Access Doors and Frames

08 31 13.10 Types of Framed Access Doors

		Crew	Daily Output	Labor-Hours	Unit	Material	2014 Bare Costs Labor	Equipment	Total	Total Incl O&P
0010	**TYPES OF FRAMED ACCESS DOORS**									
1000	Fire rated door with lock									
1100	Metal, 12" x 12"	1 Carp	10	.800	Ea.	165	36.50		201.50	243
1150	18" x 18"		9	.889		220	41		261	310
1200	24" x 24"		9	.889		325	41		366	425
1250	24" x 36"		8	1		335	46		381	440
1300	24" x 48"		8	1		430	46		476	550
1350	36" x 36"		7.50	1.067		495	49		544	625
1400	48" x 48"		7.50	1.067		635	49		684	775
1600	Stainless steel, 12" x 12"		10	.800		282	36.50		318.50	370
1650	18" x 18"		9	.889		410	41		451	515
1700	24" x 24"		9	.889		500	41		541	615
1750	24" x 36"		8	1		640	46		686	780
2000	Flush door for finishing									

08 31 13 – Access Doors and Frames

08 31 13.10 Types of Framed Access Doors		Crew	Daily Output	Labor-Hours	Unit	Material	2014 Bare Costs Labor	Equipment	Total	Total Incl O&P
2100	Metal 8" x 8"	1 Carp	10	.800	Ea.	38	36.50		74.50	103
2150	12" x 12"	"	10	.800	"	42	36.50		78.50	107
3000	Recessed door for acoustic tile									
3100	Metal, 12" x 12"	1 Carp	4.50	1.778	Ea.	82	81.50		163.50	224
3150	12" x 24"		4.50	1.778		95	81.50		176.50	239
3200	24" x 24"		4	2		125	91.50		216.50	289
3250	24" x 36"		4	2		175	91.50		266.50	345
4000	Recessed door for drywall									
4100	Metal 12" x 12"	1 Carp	6	1.333	Ea.	80	61		141	188
4150	12" x 24"		5.50	1.455		114	66.50		180.50	235
4200	24" x 36"		5	1.600		182	73.50		255.50	320
6000	Standard door									
6100	Metal, 8" x 8"	1 Carp	10	.800	Ea.	45	36.50		81.50	110
6150	12" x 12"		10	.800		50	36.50		86.50	116
6200	18" x 18"		9	.889		70	41		111	144
6250	24" x 24"		9	.889		85	41		126	161
6300	24" x 36"		8	1		125	46		171	214
6350	36" x 36"		8	1		145	46		191	236
6500	Stainless steel, 8" x 8"		10	.800		85	36.50		121.50	154
6550	12" x 12"		10	.800		110	36.50		146.50	182
6600	18" x 18"		9	.889		205	41		246	293
6650	24" x 24"		9	.889		265	41		306	360
9000	Minimum labor/equipment charge		4	2	Job		91.50		91.50	151

08 31 13.20 Bulkhead/Cellar Doors

		Crew	Daily Output	Labor-Hours	Unit	Material	Labor	Equipment	Total	Total Incl O&P
0010	**BULKHEAD/CELLAR DOORS**									
0020	Steel, not incl. sides, 44" x 62"	1 Carp	5.50	1.455	Ea.	560	66.50		626.50	725
0100	52" x 73"		5.10	1.569		790	72		862	990
0500	With sides and foundation plates, 57" x 45" x 24"		4.70	1.702		810	78		888	1,025
0600	42" x 49" x 51"		4.30	1.860		915	85.50		1,000.50	1,150
9000	Minimum labor/equipment charge		2	4	Job		183		183	300

08 31 13.30 Commercial Floor Doors

		Crew	Daily Output	Labor-Hours	Unit	Material	Labor	Equipment	Total	Total Incl O&P
0010	**COMMERCIAL FLOOR DOORS**									
0020	Aluminum tile, steel frame, one leaf, 2' x 2' opng.	2 Sswk	3.50	4.571	Opng.	800	234		1,034	1,300
0050	3'-6" x 3'-6" opening		3.50	4.571		1,600	234		1,834	2,175
0500	Double leaf, 4' x 4' opening		3	5.333		1,750	273		2,023	2,425
0550	5' x 5' opening		3	5.333		3,100	273		3,373	3,900
9000	Minimum labor/equipment charge		2	8	Job		410		410	750

08 31 13.35 Industrial Floor Doors

		Crew	Daily Output	Labor-Hours	Unit	Material	Labor	Equipment	Total	Total Incl O&P
0010	**INDUSTRIAL FLOOR DOORS**									
0020	Steel 300 psf L.L., single leaf, 2' x 2', 175#	2 Sswk	6	2.667	Opng.	760	136		896	1,075
0050	3' x 3' opening, 300#		5.50	2.909		1,075	149		1,224	1,450
0300	Double leaf, 4' x 4' opening, 455#		5	3.200		1,900	164		2,064	2,400
0350	5' x 5' opening, 645#		4.50	3.556		2,750	182		2,932	3,350
1000	Aluminum, 300 psf L.L., single leaf, 2' x 2', 60#		6	2.667		750	136		886	1,075
1050	3' x 3' opening, 100#		5.50	2.909		1,300	149		1,449	1,700
1500	Double leaf, 4' x 4' opening, 160#		5	3.200		2,100	164		2,264	2,600
1550	5' x 5' opening, 235#		4.50	3.556		2,800	182		2,982	3,400
9000	Minimum labor/equipment charge		2	8	Job		410		410	750

08 32 Sliding Glass Doors

08 32 13 – Sliding Aluminum-Framed Glass Doors

08 32 13.10 Sliding Aluminum Doors

08 32 13.10 Sliding Aluminum Doors	Crew	Daily Output	Labor-Hours	Unit	Material	2014 Bare Costs Labor	Equipment	Total	Total Incl O&P
0010 **SLIDING ALUMINUM DOORS**									
0350 Aluminum, 5/8" tempered insulated glass, 6' wide									
0400 Premium	2 Carp	4	4	Ea.	1,575	183		1,758	2,025
0450 Economy		4	4		905	183		1,088	1,300
0500 8' wide, premium		3	5.333		1,650	245		1,895	2,225
0550 Economy		3	5.333		1,425	245		1,670	1,950
0600 12' wide, premium		2.50	6.400		2,975	293		3,268	3,750
0650 Economy		2.50	6.400		1,525	293		1,818	2,150
4000 Aluminum, baked on enamel, temp glass, 6'-8" x 10'-0" wide		4	4		1,050	183		1,233	1,475
4020 Insulating glass, 6'-8" x 6'-0" wide		4	4		920	183		1,103	1,325
4040 8'-0" wide		3	5.333		1,075	245		1,320	1,575
4060 10'-0" wide		2	8		1,325	365		1,690	2,050
4080 Anodized, temp glass, 6'-8" x 6'-0" wide		4	4		455	183		638	800
4100 8'-0" wide		3	5.333		575	245		820	1,025
4120 10'-0" wide		2	8		645	365		1,010	1,325

08 32 19 – Sliding Wood-Framed Glass Doors

08 32 19.10 Sliding Wood Doors

08 32 19.10 Sliding Wood Doors	Crew	Daily Output	Labor-Hours	Unit	Material	2014 Bare Costs Labor	Equipment	Total	Total Incl O&P
0010 **SLIDING WOOD DOORS**									
0020 Wood, tempered insul. glass, 6' wide, premium	2 Carp	4	4	Ea.	1,425	183		1,608	1,875
0100 Economy		4	4		1,175	183		1,358	1,575
0150 8' wide, wood, premium		3	5.333		1,825	245		2,070	2,400
0200 Economy		3	5.333		1,500	245		1,745	2,050
0235 10' wide, wood, premium		2.50	6.400		2,600	293		2,893	3,325
0240 Economy		2.50	6.400		2,200	293		2,493	2,900
0250 12' wide, wood, premium		2.50	6.400		3,000	293		3,293	3,775
0300 Economy		2.50	6.400		2,450	293		2,743	3,175
9000 Minimum labor/equipment charge	1 Carp	2	4	Job		183		183	300

08 32 19.15 Sliding Glass Vinyl-Clad Wood Doors

08 32 19.15 Sliding Glass Vinyl-Clad Wood Doors		Crew	Daily Output	Labor-Hours	Unit	Material	2014 Bare Costs Labor	Equipment	Total	Total Incl O&P
0010 **SLIDING GLASS VINYL-CLAD WOOD DOORS**										
0020 Glass, sliding vinyl clad, insul. glass, 6'-0" x 6'-8"	G	2 Carp	4	4	Opng.	1,500	183		1,683	1,975
0025 6'-0" x 6'-10" high	G		4	4		1,650	183		1,833	2,125
0030 6'-0" x 8'-0" high	G		4	4		1,975	183		2,158	2,475
0050 5'-0" x 6'-8" high	G		4	4		1,500	183		1,683	1,950
0100 8'-0" x 6'-10" high	G		4	4		2,025	183		2,208	2,525
0150 8'-0" x 8'-0" high	G		4	4		2,225	183		2,408	2,750
0500 4 leaf, 9'-0" x 6'-10" high	G		3	5.333		3,250	245		3,495	3,975
0550 9'-0" x 8'-0" high	G		3	5.333		3,775	245		4,020	4,550
0600 12'-0" x 6'-10" high	G		3	5.333		3,875	245		4,120	4,675
0650 12'-0" x 8'-0" high	G		3	5.333		3,875	245		4,120	4,675
9000 Minimum labor/equipment charge		1 Carp	4	2	Job		91.50		91.50	151

08 33 Coiling Doors and Grilles

08 33 13 – Coiling Counter Doors

08 33 13.10 Counter Doors, Coiling Type	Crew	Daily Output	Labor-Hours	Unit	Material	2014 Bare Costs Labor	Equipment	Total	Total Incl O&P
0010 **COUNTER DOORS, COILING TYPE**									
0020 Manual, incl. frame and hardware, galv. stl., 4' roll-up, 6' long	2 Carp	2	8	Opng.	1,200	365		1,565	1,925
0300 Galvanized steel, UL label		1.80	8.889		1,225	410		1,635	2,025
0600 Stainless steel, 4' high roll-up, 6' long		2	8		2,150	365		2,515	2,950
0700 10' long		1.80	8.889		2,500	410		2,910	3,425
2000 Aluminum, 4' high, 4' long		2.20	7.273		1,475	335		1,810	2,175
2020 6' long		2	8		1,775	365		2,140	2,550
2040 8' long		1.90	8.421		2,000	385		2,385	2,825
2060 10' long		1.80	8.889		2,050	410		2,460	2,925
2080 14' long		1.40	11.429		2,625	525		3,150	3,725
2100 6' high, 4' long		2	8		1,800	365		2,165	2,575
2120 6' long		1.60	10		1,625	460		2,085	2,550
2140 10' long		1.40	11.429		2,150	525		2,675	3,200
9000 Minimum labor/equipment charge	1 Carp	2	4	Job		183		183	300

08 33 16 – Coiling Counter Grilles

08 33 16.10 Coiling Grilles	Crew	Daily Output	Labor-Hours	Unit	Material	2014 Bare Costs Labor	Equipment	Total	Total Incl O&P
0010 **COILING GRILLES**									
2020 Aluminum, manual operated, mill finish	2 Sswk	82	.195	S.F.	28	9.95		37.95	49
2040 Bronze anodized		82	.195	"	44.50	9.95		54.45	67.50
2060 Steel, manual operated, 10' x 10' high		1	16	Opng.	2,500	820		3,320	4,250
2080 15' x 8' high		.80	20	"	2,900	1,025		3,925	5,050
3000 For safety edge bottom bar, electric, add				L.F.	49			49	54
8000 For motor operation, add	2 Sswk	5	3.200	Opng.	1,250	164		1,414	1,675
9000 Minimum labor/equipment charge	"	1	16	Job		820		820	1,500

08 33 23 – Overhead Coiling Doors

08 33 23.10 Coiling Service Doors	Crew	Daily Output	Labor-Hours	Unit	Material	2014 Bare Costs Labor	Equipment	Total	Total Incl O&P
0010 **COILING SERVICE DOORS** Steel, manual, 20 ga., incl. hardware									
0050 8' x 8' high	2 Sswk	1.60	10	Ea.	1,125	510		1,635	2,175
0130 12' x 12' high, standard		1.20	13.333		2,100	680		2,780	3,575
0160 10' x 20' high, standard		.50	32		2,500	1,625		4,125	5,750
2000 Class A fire doors, manual, 20 ga., 8' x 8' high		1.40	11.429		1,525	585		2,110	2,750
2100 10' x 10' high		1.10	14.545		2,075	745		2,820	3,675
2200 20' x 10' high		.80	20		4,250	1,025		5,275	6,550
2300 12' x 12' high		1	16		3,275	820		4,095	5,100
2400 20' x 12' high		.80	20		4,600	1,025		5,625	6,925
2500 14' x 14' high		.60	26.667		3,575	1,375		4,950	6,450
2600 20' x 16' high		.50	32		5,675	1,625		7,300	9,250
2700 10' x 20' high		.40	40		4,450	2,050		6,500	8,650
3000 For 18 ga. doors, add				S.F.	1.55			1.55	1.71
3300 For enamel finish, add				"	1.80			1.80	1.98
3600 For safety edge bottom bar, pneumatic, add				L.F.	21.50			21.50	24
4000 For weatherstripping, extruded rubber, jambs, add					13.70			13.70	15.05
4100 Hood, add					8.45			8.45	9.30
4200 Sill, add					4.86			4.86	5.35
4500 Motor operators, to 14' x 14' opening	2 Sswk	5	3.200	Ea.	1,075	164		1,239	1,500
4700 For fire door, additional fusible link, add				"	27			27	29.50
9000 Minimum labor/equipment charge	2 Sswk	1	16	Job		820		820	1,500

08 34 13 – Cold Storage Doors

08 34 13.10 Doors for Cold Area Storage

08 34 13.10 Doors for Cold Area Storage	Crew	Daily Output	Labor-Hours	Unit	Material	2014 Bare Costs Labor	Equipment	Total	Total Incl O&P
0010 **DOORS FOR COLD AREA STORAGE**									
0020 Single, 20 ga. galvanized steel									
0300 Horizontal sliding, 5' x 7', manual operation, 3.5" thick	2 Carp	2	8	Ea.	3,225	365		3,590	4,150
0400 4" thick		2	8		3,250	365		3,615	4,175
0500 6" thick		2	8		3,425	365		3,790	4,375
0800 5' x 7', power operation, 2" thick		1.90	8.421		5,600	385		5,985	6,775
0900 4" thick		1.90	8.421		5,700	385		6,085	6,900
1000 6" thick		1.90	8.421		6,500	385		6,885	7,775
1300 9' x 10', manual operation, 2" insulation		1.70	9.412		4,550	430		4,980	5,700
1400 4" insulation		1.70	9.412		4,675	430		5,105	5,850
1500 6" insulation		1.70	9.412		5,575	430		6,005	6,850
1800 Power operation, 2" insulation		1.60	10		7,675	460		8,135	9,200
1900 4" insulation		1.60	10		7,900	460		8,360	9,425
2000 6" insulation		1.70	9.412		8,850	430		9,280	10,500
2300 For stainless steel face, add					25%				
3000 Hinged, lightweight, 3' x 7'-0", 2" thick	2 Carp	2	8	Ea.	1,425	365		1,790	2,150
3050 4" thick		1.90	8.421		1,775	385		2,160	2,575
3300 Aluminum doors, 3' x 7'-0", 4" thick		1.90	8.421		1,350	385		1,735	2,100
3350 6" thick		1.40	11.429		2,350	525		2,875	3,425
3600 Stainless steel, 3' x 7'-0", 4" thick		1.90	8.421		1,725	385		2,110	2,525
3650 6" thick		1.40	11.429		2,950	525		3,475	4,075
3900 Painted, 3' x 7'-0", 4" thick		1.90	8.421		1,275	385		1,660	2,025
3950 6" thick		1.40	11.429		2,350	525		2,875	3,425
5000 Bi-parting, electric operated									
5010 6' x 8' opening, galv. faces, 4" thick for cooler	2 Carp	.80	20	Opng.	7,225	915		8,140	9,425
5050 For freezer, 4" thick		.80	20		7,950	915		8,865	10,300
5300 For door buck framing and door protection, add		2.50	6.400		640	293		933	1,175
6000 Galvanized batten door, galvanized hinges, 4' x 7'		2	8		1,825	365		2,190	2,625
6050 6' x 8'		1.80	8.889		2,475	410		2,885	3,400
6500 Fire door, 3 hr., 6' x 8', single slide		.80	20		8,275	915		9,190	10,600
6550 Double, bi-parting		.70	22.857		12,200	1,050		13,250	15,100
9000 Minimum labor/equipment charge	1 Carp	2	4	Job		183		183	300

08 34 36 – Darkroom Doors

08 34 36.10 Various Types of Darkroom Doors

08 34 36.10 Various Types of Darkroom Doors	Crew	Daily Output	Labor-Hours	Unit	Material	2014 Bare Costs Labor	Equipment	Total	Total Incl O&P
0010 **VARIOUS TYPES OF DARKROOM DOORS**									
0015 Revolving, standard, 2 way, 36" diameter	2 Carp	3.10	5.161	Opng.	2,525	237		2,762	3,175
0020 41" diameter		3.10	5.161		2,825	237		3,062	3,525
0050 3 way, 51" diameter		1.40	11.429		3,675	525		4,200	4,900
1000 4 way, 49" diameter		1.40	11.429		3,575	525		4,100	4,800
2000 Hinged safety, 2 way, 41" diameter		2.30	6.957		3,300	320		3,620	4,150
2500 3 way, 51" diameter		1.40	11.429		3,650	525		4,175	4,875
3000 Pop out safety, 2 way, 41" diameter		3.10	5.161		3,925	237		4,162	4,700
4000 3 way, 51" diameter		1.40	11.429		4,775	525		5,300	6,100
5000 Wheelchair-type, pop out, 51" diameter		1.40	11.429		5,675	525		6,200	7,100
5020 72" diameter		.90	17.778		7,800	815		8,615	9,925

08 34 53 – Security Doors and Frames

08 34 53.20 Steel Door

08 34 53.20 Steel Door	Crew	Daily Output	Labor-Hours	Unit	Material	2014 Bare Costs Labor	Equipment	Total	Total Incl O&P
0010 **STEEL DOOR** with ballistic core and welded frame both 14 ga.									
0050 Flush, UL 752 Level 3, 1-3/4", 3'-0" x 6'-8"	2 Carp	1.50	10.667	Opng.	2,300	490		2,790	3,325
0055 1-3/4", 3'-6" x 6'-8"		1.50	10.667		2,400	490		2,890	3,450
0060 1-3/4", 4'-0" x 6'-8"		1.20	13.333		2,625	610		3,235	3,875
0100 UL 752 Level 8, 1-3/4", 3'-0" x 6'-8"		1.50	10.667		10,100	490		10,590	11,900

08 34 Special Function Doors

08 34 53 – Security Doors and Frames

08 34 53.20 Steel Door

		Crew	Daily Output	Labor-Hours	Unit	Material	2014 Bare Costs Labor	Equipment	Total	Total Incl O&P
0105	1-3/4", 3'-6" x 6'-8"	2 Carp	1.50	10.667	Opng.	10,200	490		10,690	12,000
0110	1-3/4", 4'-0" x 6'-8"		1.20	13.333		11,600	610		12,210	13,800
0120	UL 752 Level 3, 1-3/4", 3'-0" x 7'-0"		1.50	10.667		2,325	490		2,815	3,375
0125	1-3/4", 3'-6" x 7'-0"		1.50	10.667		2,450	490		2,940	3,475
0130	1-3/4", 4'-0" x 7'-0"		1.20	13.333		2,650	610		3,260	3,925
0150	UL 752 Level 8, 1-3/4", 3'-0" x 7'-0"		1.50	10.667		10,200	490		10,690	12,000
0155	1-3/4", 3'-6" x 7'-0"		1.50	10.667		10,200	490		10,690	12,000
0160	1-3/4", 4'-0" x 7'-0"		1.20	13.333		11,700	610		12,310	13,900
1000	Safe Room sliding door and hardware, 1-3/4", 3'-0" x 7'-0" UL 752 Level 3		.50	32		23,300	1,475		24,775	28,000
1050	Safe Room swinging door and hardware, 1-3/4", 3'-0" x 7'-0" UL 752 Level 3		.50	32		27,800	1,475		29,275	33,000

08 34 53.30 Wood Ballistic Doors

		Crew	Daily Output	Labor-Hours	Unit	Material	2014 Bare Costs Labor	Equipment	Total	Total Incl O&P
0010	**WOOD BALLISTIC DOORS** with frames and hardware									
0050	Wood, 1-3/4", 3'-0" x 7'-0" UL 752 Level 3	2 Carp	1.50	10.667	Opng.	2,225	490		2,715	3,250

08 34 56 – Security Gates

08 34 56.10 Gates

		Crew	Daily Output	Labor-Hours	Unit	Material	2014 Bare Costs Labor	Equipment	Total	Total Incl O&P
0010	**GATES**									
0015	Driveway Gates include mounting hardware									
0500	Wood, security gate, driveway, dual, 10' wide	H-4	.80	25	Opng.	3,900	1,075		4,975	6,050
0505	12' wide		.80	25		4,300	1,075		5,375	6,475
0510	15' wide		.80	25		5,100	1,075		6,175	7,350
0600	Steel, security gate, driveway, single, 10' wide		.80	25		2,150	1,075		3,225	4,100
0605	12' wide		.80	25		2,225	1,075		3,300	4,175
0620	Steel, security gate, driveway, dual, 12' wide		.80	25		2,050	1,075		3,125	4,025
0625	14' wide		.80	25		2,200	1,075		3,275	4,175
0630	16' wide		.80	25		2,525	1,075		3,600	4,525
0700	Aluminum, security gate, driveway, dual, 10' wide		.80	25		3,000	1,075		4,075	5,050
0705	12' wide		.80	25		3,200	1,075		4,275	5,275
0710	16' wide		.80	25		3,700	1,075		4,775	5,825
1000	Security gate, driveway, opener 12 VDC				Ea.	700			700	770
1010	Wireless					1,700			1,700	1,875
1020	Security gate, driveway, opener 24 VDC					1,100			1,100	1,200
1030	Wireless					1,300			1,300	1,425
1040	Security gate, driveway, opener 12 VDC, solar panel 10 watt	1 Elec	2	4		200	213		413	550
1050	20 watt	"	2	4		320	213		533	680

08 34 73 – Sound Control Door Assemblies

08 34 73.10 Acoustical Doors

		Crew	Daily Output	Labor-Hours	Unit	Material	2014 Bare Costs Labor	Equipment	Total	Total Incl O&P
0010	**ACOUSTICAL DOORS**									
0020	Including framed seals, 3' x 7', wood, 40 STC rating	2 Carp	1.50	10.667	Ea.	1,300	490		1,790	2,225
0100	Steel, 41 STC rating		1.50	10.667		3,200	490		3,690	4,325
0200	45 STC rating		1.50	10.667		3,600	490		4,090	4,750
0300	48 STC rating		1.50	10.667		4,200	490		4,690	5,425
0400	52 STC rating		1.50	10.667		4,800	490		5,290	6,075
9000	Minimum labor/equipment charge	1 Carp	4	2	Job		91.50		91.50	151

08 36 13 – Sectional Doors

08 36 13.10 Overhead Commercial Doors	Crew	Daily Output	Labor-Hours	Unit	Material	2014 Bare Costs Labor	Equipment	Total	Total Incl O&P
0010 **OVERHEAD COMMERCIAL DOORS**									
1000 Stock, sectional, heavy duty, wood, 1-3/4" thick, 8' x 8' high	2 Carp	2	8	Ea.	1,025	365		1,390	1,725
1200 12' x 12' high		1.50	10.667		2,025	490		2,515	3,025
1300 Chain hoist, 14' x 14' high		1.30	12.308		3,250	565		3,815	4,475
1600 20' x 16' high		.65	24.615		5,325	1,125		6,450	7,700
2100 For medium duty custom door, deduct					5%	5%			
2150 For medium duty stock doors, deduct					10%	5%			
2300 Fiberglass and aluminum, heavy duty, sectional, 12' x 12' high	2 Carp	1.50	10.667	Ea.	2,700	490		3,190	3,775
2450 Chain hoist, 20' x 20' high	"	.50	32		6,675	1,475		8,150	9,750
2900 For electric trolley operator, 1/3 H.P., to 12' x 12', add	1 Carp	2	4		935	183		1,118	1,325
2950 Over 12' x 12', 1/2 H.P., add		1	8		1,100	365		1,465	1,825
2980 Overhead, for row of clear lites add		1	8		110	365		475	725
9000 Minimum labor/equipment charge	2 Carp	1.50	10.667	Job		490		490	805

08 36 13.20 Residential Garage Doors

08 36 13.20 Residential Garage Doors	Crew	Daily Output	Labor-Hours	Unit	Material	Labor	Equipment	Total	Total Incl O&P
0010 **RESIDENTIAL GARAGE DOORS**									
0050 Hinged, wood, custom, double door, 9' x 7'	2 Carp	4	4	Ea.	715	183		898	1,100
0070 16' x 7'		3	5.333		1,100	245		1,345	1,600
0200 Overhead, sectional, incl. hardware, fiberglass, 9' x 7', standard		5.28	3.030		930	139		1,069	1,250
0220 Deluxe		5.28	3.030		1,150	139		1,289	1,475
0300 16' x 7', standard		6	2.667		1,575	122		1,697	1,925
0320 Deluxe		6	2.667		2,150	122		2,272	2,550
0500 Hardboard, 9' x 7', standard		8	2		590	91.50		681.50	800
0520 Deluxe		8	2		815	91.50		906.50	1,050
0600 16' x 7', standard		6	2.667		1,225	122		1,347	1,550
0620 Deluxe		6	2.667		1,425	122		1,547	1,775
0700 Metal, 9' x 7', standard		5.28	3.030		685	139		824	985
0720 Deluxe		8	2		910	91.50		1,001.50	1,150
0800 16' x 7', standard		3	5.333		870	245		1,115	1,350
0820 Deluxe		6	2.667		1,400	122		1,522	1,750
0900 Wood, 9' x 7', standard		8	2		920	91.50		1,011.50	1,150
0920 Deluxe		8	2		2,150	91.50		2,241.50	2,500
1000 16' x 7', standard		6	2.667		1,625	122		1,747	2,000
1020 Deluxe		6	2.667		3,025	122		3,147	3,525
1800 Door hardware, sectional	1 Carp	4	2		330	91.50		421.50	515
1810 Door tracks only		4	2		163	91.50		254.50	330
1820 One side only		7	1.143		112	52.50		164.50	209
3000 Swing-up, including hardware, fiberglass, 9' x 7', standard	2 Carp	8	2		1,000	91.50		1,091.50	1,250
3020 Deluxe		8	2		1,100	91.50		1,191.50	1,350
3100 16' x 7', standard		6	2.667		1,250	122		1,372	1,575
3120 Deluxe		6	2.667		1,600	122		1,722	1,950
3200 Hardboard, 9' x 7', standard		8	2		550	91.50		641.50	755
3220 Deluxe		8	2		650	91.50		741.50	865
3300 16' x 7', standard		6	2.667		670	122		792	935
3320 Deluxe		6	2.667		850	122		972	1,125
3400 Metal, 9' x 7', standard		8	2		600	91.50		691.50	810
3420 Deluxe		8	2		965	91.50		1,056.50	1,200
3500 16' x 7', standard		6	2.667		800	122		922	1,075
3520 Deluxe		6	2.667		1,100	122		1,222	1,400
3600 Wood, 9' x 7', standard		8	2		700	91.50		791.50	920
3620 Deluxe		8	2		1,125	91.50		1,216.50	1,375
3700 16' x 7', standard		6	2.667		900	122		1,022	1,200
3720 Deluxe		6	2.667		2,100	122		2,222	2,500

08 36 Panel Doors

08 36 13 – Sectional Doors

08 36 13.20 Residential Garage Doors

		Crew	Daily Output	Labor-Hours	Unit	Material	2014 Bare Costs Labor	2014 Bare Costs Equipment	Total	Total Incl O&P
3900	Door hardware only, swing up	1 Carp	4	2	Ea.	168	91.50		259.50	335
3920	One side only		7	1.143		90	52.50		142.50	185
4000	For electric operator, economy, add		8	1		425	46		471	545
4100	Deluxe, including remote control		8	1		610	46		656	750
4500	For transmitter/receiver control , add to operator				Total	110			110	121
4600	Transmitters, additional				"	60			60	66
6000	Replace section, on sectional door, fiberglass, 9' x 7'	1 Carp	4	2	Ea.	590	91.50		681.50	795
6020	16' x 7'		3.50	2.286		710	105		815	950
6200	Hardboard, 9' x 7'		4	2		115	91.50		206.50	277
6220	16' x 7'		3.50	2.286		218	105		323	410
6300	Metal, 9' x 7'		4	2		184	91.50		275.50	355
6320	16' x 7'		3.50	2.286		300	105		405	500
6500	Wood, 9' x 7'		4	2		116	91.50		207.50	279
6520	16' x 7'		3.50	2.286		225	105		330	420
7010	Garage doors, row of lites					105			105	116
9000	Minimum labor/equipment charge	1 Carp	2.50	3.200	Job		147		147	241

08 36 19 – Multi-Leaf Vertical Lift Doors

08 36 19.10 Sectional Vertical Lift Doors

		Crew	Daily Output	Labor-Hours	Unit	Material	2014 Bare Costs Labor	2014 Bare Costs Equipment	Total	Total Incl O&P
0010	**SECTIONAL VERTICAL LIFT DOORS**									
0020	Motorized, 14 ga. steel, incl. frame and control panel									
0050	16' x 16' high	L-10	.50	48	Ea.	21,500	2,475	1,325	25,300	29,500
0100	10' x 20' high		1.30	18.462		31,900	950	510	33,360	37,300
0120	15' x 20' high		1.30	18.462		39,500	950	510	40,960	45,600
0140	20' x 20' high		1	24		45,900	1,225	665	47,790	53,500
0160	25' x 20' high		1	24		52,500	1,225	665	54,390	61,000
0170	32' x 24' high		.75	32		46,400	1,650	885	48,935	55,000
0180	20' x 25' high		1	24		54,000	1,225	665	55,890	62,500
0200	25' x 25' high		.70	34.286		61,000	1,775	945	63,720	71,000
0220	25' x 30' high		.70	34.286		68,000	1,775	945	70,720	78,500
0240	30' x 30' high		.70	34.286		79,000	1,775	945	81,720	91,000
0260	35' x 30' high		.70	34.286		89,000	1,775	945	91,720	102,000

08 38 Traffic Doors

08 38 19 – Rigid Traffic Doors

08 38 19.20 Double Acting Swing Doors

		Crew	Daily Output	Labor-Hours	Unit	Material	2014 Bare Costs Labor	2014 Bare Costs Equipment	Total	Total Incl O&P
0010	**DOUBLE ACTING SWING DOORS**									
0020	Including frame, closer, hardware and vision panel									
1000	.063" aluminum, 7'-0" high, 4'-0" wide	2 Carp	4.20	3.810	Pr.	2,100	175		2,275	2,575
1025	6'-0" wide		4	4		2,200	183		2,383	2,725
1050	6'-8" wide		4	4		2,400	183		2,583	2,950
2000	Solid core wood, 3/4" thick, metal frame, stainless steel									
2010	base plate, 7' high opening, 4' wide	2 Carp	4	4	Pr.	2,600	183		2,783	3,150
2050	7' wide		3.80	4.211	"	2,800	193		2,993	3,400
9000	Minimum labor/equipment charge		2	8	Job		365		365	605

08 38 19.30 Shock Absorbing Doors

		Crew	Daily Output	Labor-Hours	Unit	Material	2014 Bare Costs Labor	2014 Bare Costs Equipment	Total	Total Incl O&P
0010	**SHOCK ABSORBING DOORS**									
0020	Rigid, no frame, 1-1/2" thick, 5' x 7'	2 Sswk	1.90	8.421	Opng.	1,400	430		1,830	2,350
0100	8' x 8'		1.80	8.889		2,000	455		2,455	3,025
0500	Flexible, no frame, insulated, .16" thick, economy, 5' x 7'		2	8		1,750	410		2,160	2,675
0600	Deluxe		1.90	8.421		2,625	430		3,055	3,675

08 38 Traffic Doors

08 38 19 – Rigid Traffic Doors

08 38 19.30 Shock Absorbing Doors		Crew	Daily Output	Labor-Hours	Unit	Material	2014 Bare Costs Labor	Equipment	Total	Total Incl O&P
1000	8' x 8' opening, economy	2 Sswk	2	8	Opng.	2,750	410		3,160	3,775
1100	Deluxe		1.90	8.421	↓	3,500	430		3,930	4,650
9000	Minimum labor/equipment charge	↓	2	8	Job		410		410	750

08 41 Entrances and Storefronts

08 41 13 – Aluminum-Framed Entrances and Storefronts

08 41 13.20 Tube Framing

08 41 13.20 Tube Framing		Crew	Daily Output	Labor-Hours	Unit	Material	2014 Bare Costs Labor	Equipment	Total	Total Incl O&P
0010	**TUBE FRAMING**, For window walls and store fronts, aluminum stock									
0050	Plain tube frame, mill finish, 1-3/4" x 1-3/4"	2 Glaz	103	.155	L.F.	9.75	6.85		16.60	22
0150	1-3/4" x 4"		98	.163		13.20	7.20		20.40	26
0200	1-3/4" x 4-1/2"		95	.168		14.85	7.40		22.25	28.50
0250	2" x 6"		89	.180		22.50	7.90		30.40	37.50
0350	4" x 4"		87	.184		25.50	8.10		33.60	41
0400	4-1/2" x 4-1/2"		85	.188		28	8.30		36.30	44
0450	Glass bead		240	.067		2.93	2.94		5.87	8
1000	Flush tube frame, mill finish, 1/4" glass, 1-3/4" x 4", open header		80	.200		12.65	8.80		21.45	28
1050	Open sill		82	.195		10.30	8.60		18.90	25.50
1100	Closed back header		83	.193		18.20	8.50		26.70	34
1150	Closed back sill	↓	85	.188	↓	17.35	8.30		25.65	32.50
1160	Tube fmg., spandrel cover both sides, alum 1" wide	1 Sswk	85	.094	S.F.	97	4.81		101.81	116
1170	Tube fmg., spandrel cover both sides, alum 2" wide	"	85	.094	"	37.50	4.81		42.31	50.50
1200	Vertical mullion, one piece	2 Glaz	75	.213	L.F.	19.05	9.40		28.45	36.50
1250	Two piece		73	.219		20	9.65		29.65	37.50
1300	90° or 180° vertical corner post		75	.213		31	9.40		40.40	49.50
1400	1-3/4" x 4-1/2", open header		80	.200		15.40	8.80		24.20	31.50
1450	Open sill		82	.195		12.90	8.60		21.50	28
1500	Closed back header		83	.193		18.35	8.50		26.85	34
1550	Closed back sill		85	.188		18.15	8.30		26.45	33.50
1600	Vertical mullion, one piece		75	.213		20.50	9.40		29.90	38
1650	Two piece		73	.219		21.50	9.65		31.15	39
1700	90° or 180° vertical corner post		75	.213		22	9.40		31.40	39.50
2000	Flush tube frame, mil fin.,ins. glass w/thml brk, 2" x 4-1/2", open header		75	.213		16	9.40		25.40	33
2050	Open sill		77	.208		13.45	9.15		22.60	29.50
2100	Closed back header		78	.205		15	9.05		24.05	31
2150	Closed back sill		80	.200		16.15	8.80		24.95	32
2200	Vertical mullion, one piece		70	.229		16.70	10.05		26.75	34.50
2250	Two piece		68	.235		18	10.35		28.35	36.50
2300	90° or 180° vertical corner post		70	.229		17.20	10.05		27.25	35
5000	Flush tube frame, mill fin., thermal brk., 2-1/4" x 4-1/2", open header		74	.216		16.60	9.50		26.10	33.50
5050	Open sill		75	.213		14.80	9.40		24.20	31.50
5100	Vertical mullion, one piece		69	.232		17.15	10.20		27.35	35.50
5150	Two piece		67	.239		21	10.50		31.50	40
5200	90° or 180° vertical corner post		69	.232		18.50	10.20		28.70	37
5295	Flush tube frame, mill finish, 4-1/2" x 4-1/2"		85	.188		28	8.30		36.30	44
5300	Plain tube frame, mill finish, 2" x 3" jamb		115	.139		10.90	6.15		17.05	22
5310	2" x 4"		115	.139		16.35	6.15		22.50	28
5320	3" x 5-1/2"		107	.150		26.50	6.60		33.10	39.50
5330	Head, 2" x 3"		200	.080		19.65	3.52		23.17	27
5340	Mullion, 2" x 3"		200	.080		20.50	3.52		24.02	28
5350	2" x 4"		115	.139		21.50	6.15		27.65	34
5360	3" x 5-1/2"	↓	107	.150	↓	31	6.60		37.60	45

241

08 41 Entrances and Storefronts

08 41 13 – Aluminum-Framed Entrances and Storefronts

08 41 13.20 Tube Framing		Crew	Daily Output	Labor-Hours	Unit	Material	2014 Bare Costs Labor	Equipment	Total	Total Incl O&P
5370	4" corner mullion	2 Glaz	90	.178	L.F.	29	7.85		36.85	44.50
5380	Horizontal, 2" x 3"		115	.139		23.50	6.15		29.65	35.50
5390	3" x 5-1/2"		107	.150		28.50	6.60		35.10	42
5430	Sill section, 1/8" x 6"		133	.120		35.50	5.30		40.80	47.50
5440	1/8" x 7"		133	.120		42.50	5.30		47.80	55
5450	1/8" x 8-1/2"		133	.120		49.50	5.30		54.80	63
5460	Column covers, aluminum, 1/8" x 26"		57	.281		64	12.35		76.35	90.50
5470	1/8" x 34"		53	.302		82.50	13.30		95.80	113
5480	1/8" x 38"		53	.302		92	13.30		105.30	123
5700	Vertical mullions, clear finish, 1/4" thick glass		528	.030		12.30	1.33		13.63	15.70
5720	3/8" thick		445	.036		12.30	1.58		13.88	16.10
5740	1/2" thick		400	.040		12.75	1.76		14.51	16.90
5760	3/4" thick		344	.047		13.20	2.05		15.25	17.80
5780	1" thick		304	.053		13.35	2.32		15.67	18.45
6980	Door stop (snap in)		380	.042		3.35	1.85		5.20	6.70
7000	For joints, 90°, clip type, add				Ea.	25			25	27.50
7050	Screw spline joint, add					23.50			23.50	26
7100	For joint other than 90°, add					49			49	54
8000	For bronze anodized aluminum, add					15%				
8020	For black finish, add					30%				
8050	For stainless steel materials, add					350%				
8100	For monumental grade, add					53%				
8150	For steel stiffener, add	2 Glaz	200	.080	L.F.	11.25	3.52		14.77	18.10
8200	For 2 to 5 stories, add per story				Story		8%			
9000	Minimum labor/equipment charge	2 Glaz	2	8	Job		350		350	570

08 41 19 – Stainless-Steel-Framed Entrances and Storefronts

08 41 19.10 Stainless-Steel and Glass Entrance Unit

		Crew	Daily Output	Labor-Hours	Unit	Material	2014 Bare Costs Labor	Equipment	Total	Total Incl O&P
0010	**STAINLESS-STEEL AND GLASS ENTRANCE UNIT**, narrow stiles									
0020	3' x 7' opening, including hardware, minimum	2 Sswk	1.60	10	Opng.	6,600	510		7,110	8,200
0050	Average		1.40	11.429		7,050	585		7,635	8,825
0100	Maximum		1.20	13.333		7,600	680		8,280	9,600
1000	For solid bronze entrance units, statuary finish, add					64%				
1100	Without statuary finish, add					45%				
2000	Balanced doors, 3' x 7', economy	2 Sswk	.90	17.778	Ea.	8,950	910		9,860	11,500
2100	Premium		.70	22.857	"	15,300	1,175		16,475	19,000
9000	Minimum labor/equipment charge		2	8	Job		410		410	750

08 41 26 – All-Glass Entrances and Storefronts

08 41 26.10 Window Walls Aluminum, Stock

		Crew	Daily Output	Labor-Hours	Unit	Material	2014 Bare Costs Labor	Equipment	Total	Total Incl O&P
0010	**WINDOW WALLS ALUMINUM, STOCK**, including glazing									
0020	Minimum	H-2	160	.150	S.F.	44.50	6.25		50.75	59
0050	Average		140	.171		61.50	7.15		68.65	79
0100	Maximum		110	.218		168	9.05		177.05	200
0500	For translucent sandwich wall systems, see Section 07 41 33.10									
0850	Cost of the above walls depends on material,									
0860	finish, repetition, and size of units.									
0870	The larger the opening, the lower the S.F. cost									
1200	Double glazed acoustical window wall for airports,									
1220	including 1" thick glass with 2" x 4-1/2" tube frame	H-2	40	.600	S.F.	115	25		140	168

08 42 Entrances

08 42 26 – All-Glass Entrances

08 42 26.10 Swinging Glass Doors	Crew	Daily Output	Labor-Hours	Unit	Material	2014 Bare Costs Labor	Equipment	Total	Total Incl O&P
0010 **SWINGING GLASS DOORS**									
0020 Including hardware, 1/2" thick, tempered, 3' x 7' opening	2 Glaz	2	8	Opng.	2,200	350		2,550	2,975
0100 6' x 7' opening		1.40	11.429	"	4,300	505		4,805	5,550
9000 Minimum labor/equipment charge		2	8	Job		350		350	570

08 42 29 – Automatic Entrances

08 42 29.23 Sliding Automatic Entrances

	Crew	Daily Output	Labor-Hours	Unit	Material	Labor	Equipment	Total	Total Incl O&P
0010 **SLIDING AUTOMATIC ENTRANCES** 12' x 7'-6" opng., 5' x 7' door, 2 way traffic									
0020 Mat or electronic activated, panic pushout, incl. operator & hardware,									
0030 not including glass or glazing	2 Glaz	.70	22.857	Opng.	8,200	1,000		9,200	10,700
9000 Minimum labor/equipment charge	"	.70	22.857	Job		1,000		1,000	1,625

08 42 36 – Balanced Door Entrances

08 42 36.10 Balanced Entrance Doors

	Crew	Daily Output	Labor-Hours	Unit	Material	Labor	Equipment	Total	Total Incl O&P
0010 **BALANCED ENTRANCE DOORS**									
0020 Hardware & frame, alum. & glass, 3' x 7', econ.	2 Sswk	.90	17.778	Ea.	6,600	910		7,510	8,950
0150 Premium		.70	22.857	"	7,925	1,175		9,100	10,900
9000 Minimum labor/equipment charge		1	16	Job		820		820	1,500

08 43 Storefronts

08 43 13 – Aluminum-Framed Storefronts

08 43 13.10 Aluminum-Framed Entrance Doors and Frames

	Crew	Daily Output	Labor-Hours	Unit	Material	Labor	Equipment	Total	Total Incl O&P
0010 **ALUMINUM-FRAMED ENTRANCE DOORS AND FRAMES**									
0015 Standard hardware and glass stops but no glass									
0020 Entrance door, 3' x 7' opening, clear anodized finish	2 Sswk	7	2.286	Opng.	495	117		612	760
0040 Bronze finish		7	2.286		520	117		637	785
0060 Black finish		7	2.286		575	117		692	845
0200 3'-6" x 7'-0", mill finish		7	2.286		615	117		732	890
0220 Bronze finish		7	2.286		625	117		742	905
0240 Black finish		7	2.286		700	117		817	985
0500 6' x 7' opening, clear finish		6	2.667		815	136		951	1,150
0520 Bronze finish		6	2.667		890	136		1,026	1,225
0600 Door Frame for above doors 3'-0" x 7'-0", mill finish		6	2.667		400	136		536	690
0620 Bronze finish		6	2.667		465	136		601	760
0640 Black finish		6	2.667		505	136		641	805
0700 3'-6" x 7'-0", mill finish		6	2.667		330	136		466	615
0720 Bronze finish		6	2.667		330	136		466	615
0740 Black finish		6	2.667		330	136		466	615
0800 6'-0" x 7'-0", mill finish		6	2.667		330	136		466	615
0820 Bronze finish		6	2.667		335	136		471	620
0840 Black finish		6	2.667		360	136		496	645
1000 With 3' high transom above, 3' x 7' opening, clear finish		5.50	2.909		490	149		639	815
1050 Bronze finish		5.50	2.909		510	149		659	835
1100 Black finish		5.50	2.909		535	149		684	860
1300 3'-6" x 7'-0" opening, clear finish		5.50	2.909		340	149		489	650
1320 Bronze finish		5.50	2.909		355	149		504	670
1340 Black finish		5.50	2.909		365	149		514	675
1500 6' x 7' opening, clear finish		5.50	2.909		595	149		744	930
1550 Bronze finish		5.50	2.909		615	149		764	950
1600 Black finish		5.50	2.909		675	149		824	1,025
8000 For 8' high doors add				Ea.	200			200	220
9000 Minimum labor/equipment charge	2 Sswk	4	4	Job		204		204	375

08 43 Storefronts

08 43 13 – Aluminum-Framed Storefronts

08 43 13.20 Storefront Systems	Crew	Daily Output	Labor-Hours	Unit	Material	2014 Bare Costs Labor	Equipment	Total	Total Incl O&P
0010 **STOREFRONT SYSTEMS**, aluminum frame clear 3/8" plate glass									
0020 incl. 3' x 7' door with hardware (400 sq. ft. max. wall)									
0500 Wall height to 12' high, commercial grade	2 Glaz	150	.107	S.F.	21	4.70		25.70	30.50
0600 Institutional grade		130	.123		26	5.40		31.40	37.50
0700 Monumental grade		115	.139		39	6.15		45.15	53
1000 6' x 7' door with hardware, commercial grade		135	.119		21	5.20		26.20	31.50
1100 Institutional grade		115	.139		29	6.15		35.15	42
1200 Monumental grade		100	.160		53	7.05		60.05	70
1500 For bronze anodized finish, add					15%				
1600 For black anodized finish, add					36%				
1700 For stainless steel framing, add to monumental					78%				
9000 Minimum labor/equipment charge	2 Glaz	1	16	Job		705		705	1,150

08 43 29 – Sliding Storefronts

08 43 29.10 Sliding Panels

	Crew	Daily Output	Labor-Hours	Unit	Material	2014 Bare Costs Labor	Equipment	Total	Total Incl O&P
0010 **SLIDING PANELS**									
0020 Mall fronts, aluminum & glass, 15' x 9' high	2 Glaz	1.30	12.308	Opng.	3,375	540		3,915	4,575
0100 24' x 9' high		.70	22.857		4,800	1,000		5,800	6,900
0200 48' x 9' high, with fixed panels		.90	17.778		8,950	785		9,735	11,100
0500 For bronze finish, add					17%				
9000 Minimum labor/equipment charge	2 Glaz	1	16	Job		705		705	1,150

08 45 Translucent Wall and Roof Assemblies

08 45 10 – Translucent Roof Assemblies

08 45 10.10 Skyroofs

	Crew	Daily Output	Labor-Hours	Unit	Material	2014 Bare Costs Labor	Equipment	Total	Total Incl O&P
0010 **SKYROOFS**, Translucent panels, 2-3/4" thick									
0020 Under 5000 S.F.	G-3	395	.081	SF Hor.	35	3.70		38.70	44.50
0100 Over 5000 S.F.		465	.069		32.50	3.14		35.64	41
0300 Continuous vaulted, semi-circular, to 8' wide, double glazed ⬛G		145	.221		54	10.10		64.10	75.50
0400 Single glazed		160	.200		37	9.15		46.15	55
0600 To 20' wide, single glazed		175	.183		48	8.35		56.35	66
0700 Over 20' wide, single glazed		200	.160		47	7.30		54.30	63
0900 Motorized opening type, single glazed, 1/3 opening		145	.221		46.50	10.10		56.60	67.50
1000 Full opening		130	.246		53	11.25		64.25	76.50
1200 Pyramid type units, self-supporting, to 30' clear opening,									
1300 square or circular, single glazed, minimum	G-3	200	.160	SF Hor.	28.50	7.30		35.80	43
1310 Average		165	.194		38.50	8.85		47.35	56.50
1400 Maximum		130	.246		56	11.25		67.25	80
1500 Grid type, 4' to 10' modules, single glass glazed, minimum		200	.160		37.50	7.30		44.80	53
1550 Maximum		128	.250		58	11.40		69.40	82
1600 Preformed acrylic, minimum		300	.107		49.50	4.87		54.37	62
1650 Maximum		175	.183		62	8.35		70.35	82
9000 Minimum labor/equipment charge	2 Carp	8	2	Job		91.50		91.50	151

08 51 Metal Windows

08 51 13 – Aluminum Windows

08 51 13.10 Aluminum Sash

		Crew	Daily Output	Labor-Hours	Unit	Material	2014 Bare Costs Labor	Equipment	Total	Total Incl O&P
0010	**ALUMINUM SASH**									
0020	Stock, grade C, glaze & trim not incl., casement	2 Sswk	200	.080	S.F.	38.50	4.09		42.59	50
0050	Double hung		200	.080		39	4.09		43.09	50.50
0100	Fixed casement		200	.080		17.25	4.09		21.34	26.50
0150	Picture window		200	.080		18.30	4.09		22.39	27.50
0200	Projected window		200	.080		35	4.09		39.09	46
0250	Single hung		200	.080		16.30	4.09		20.39	25.50
0300	Sliding		200	.080		21	4.09		25.09	31
1000	Mullions for above, tubular		240	.067	L.F.	6.10	3.41		9.51	12.95
3100	Triple glazing for above, add	2 Glaz	85	.188	S.F.	15.75	8.30		24.05	31
9000	Minimum labor/equipment charge	1 Sswk	2	4	Job		204		204	375

08 51 13.20 Aluminum Windows

		Crew	Daily Output	Labor-Hours	Unit	Material	2014 Bare Costs Labor	Equipment	Total	Total Incl O&P
0010	**ALUMINUM WINDOWS**, incl. frame and glazing, commercial grade									
1000	Stock units, casement, 3'-1" x 3'-2" opening	2 Sswk	10	1.600	Ea.	370	82		452	555
1050	Add for storms					119			119	131
1600	Projected, with screen, 3'-1" x 3'-2" opening	2 Sswk	10	1.600		350	82		432	535
1700	Add for storms					116			116	128
2000	4'-5" x 5'-3" opening	2 Sswk	8	2		395	102		497	625
2100	Add for storms					124			124	136
2500	Enamel finish windows, 3'-1" x 3'-2"	2 Sswk	10	1.600		355	82		437	540
2600	4'-5" x 5'-3"		8	2		400	102		502	630
3000	Single hung, 2' x 3' opening, enameled, standard glazed		10	1.600		205	82		287	375
3100	Insulating glass		10	1.600		249	82		331	425
3300	2'-8" x 6'-8" opening, standard glazed		8	2		360	102		462	590
3400	Insulating glass		8	2		465	102		567	705
3700	3'-4" x 5'-0" opening, standard glazed		9	1.778		296	91		387	490
3800	Insulating glass		9	1.778		330	91		421	525
4000	Sliding aluminum, 3' x 2' opening, standard glazed		10	1.600		217	82		299	390
4100	Insulating glass		10	1.600		232	82		314	405
4300	5' x 3' opening, standard glazed		9	1.778		330	91		421	530
4400	Insulating glass		9	1.778		385	91		476	590
4600	8' x 4' opening, standard glazed		6	2.667		350	136		486	635
4700	Insulating glass		6	2.667		565	136		701	870
5000	9' x 5' opening, standard glazed		4	4		530	204		734	960
5100	Insulating glass		4	4		850	204		1,054	1,300
5500	Sliding, with thermal barrier and screen, 6' x 4', 2 track		8	2		725	102		827	985
5700	4 track		8	2		910	102		1,012	1,200
6000	For above units with bronze finish, add					15%				
6200	For installation in concrete openings, add					8%				
7000	Double hung, insulating glass, 2'-0" x 2'-0"	2 Sswk	11	1.455		115	74.50		189.50	263
7020	2'-0" x 2'-6"		11	1.455		124	74.50		198.50	272
7040	3'-0" x 1'-6"		10	1.600		270	82		352	445
7060	3'-0" x 2'-0"		10	1.600		315	82		397	495
7080	3'-0" x 2'-6"		10	1.600		380	82		462	570
7100	3'-0" x 3'-0"		10	1.600		425	82		507	615
7120	3'-0" x 3'-6"		10	1.600		445	82		527	640
7140	3'-0" x 4'-0"		10	1.600		480	82		562	680
7160	3'-0" x 5'-0"		10	1.600		530	82		612	730
7180	3'-0" x 6'-0"		9	1.778		560	91		651	780

08 51 Metal Windows

08 51 23 – Steel Windows

08 51 23.10 Steel Sash	Crew	Daily Output	Labor-Hours	Unit	Material	2014 Bare Costs Labor	Equipment	Total	Total Incl O&P
0010 **STEEL SASH** Custom units, glazing and trim not included									
0100 Casement, 100% vented	2 Sswk	200	.080	S.F.	65	4.09		69.09	79
0200 50% vented		200	.080		53.50	4.09		57.59	66
0300 Fixed		200	.080		28.50	4.09		32.59	39
1000 Projected, commercial, 40% vented		200	.080		51	4.09		55.09	63.50
1100 Intermediate, 50% vented		200	.080		58	4.09		62.09	71.50
1500 Industrial, horizontally pivoted		200	.080		53	4.09		57.09	65.50
1600 Fixed		200	.080		31	4.09		35.09	41.50
2000 Industrial security sash, 50% vented		200	.080		57	4.09		61.09	70.50
2100 Fixed		200	.080		46.50	4.09		50.59	59
2500 Picture window		200	.080		30	4.09		34.09	40.50
3000 Double hung		200	.080		58.50	4.09		62.59	71.50
5000 Mullions for above, open interior face		240	.067	L.F.	10.25	3.41		13.66	17.55
5100 With interior cover		240	.067	"	17.05	3.41		20.46	25
5200 Single glazing for above, add	2 Glaz	200	.080	S.F.	6.80	3.52		10.32	13.20
6000 Double glazing for above, add		200	.080		13.05	3.52		16.57	20
6100 Triple glazing for above, add		85	.188		12.30	8.30		20.60	27
9000 Minimum labor/equipment charge	1 Sswk	2	4	Job		204		204	375

08 51 23.20 Steel Windows

	Crew	Daily Output	Labor-Hours	Unit	Material	2014 Bare Costs Labor	Equipment	Total	Total Incl O&P
0010 **STEEL WINDOWS** Stock, including frame, trim and insul. glass R085123-10									
1000 Custom units, double hung, 2'-8" x 4'-6" opening	2 Sswk	12	1.333	Ea.	705	68		773	905
1100 2'-4" x 3'-9" opening		12	1.333		585	68		653	765
1500 Commercial projected, 3'-9" x 5'-5" opening		10	1.600		1,225	82		1,307	1,500
1600 6'-9" x 4'-1" opening		7	2.286		1,625	117		1,742	2,000
2000 Intermediate projected, 2'-9" x 4'-1" opening		12	1.333		685	68		753	880
2100 4'-1" x 5'-5" opening		10	1.600		1,400	82		1,482	1,700
9000 Minimum labor/equipment charge	1 Sswk	3	2.667	Job		136		136	250

08 51 66 – Metal Window Screens

08 51 66.10 Screens

	Crew	Daily Output	Labor-Hours	Unit	Material	2014 Bare Costs Labor	Equipment	Total	Total Incl O&P
0010 **SCREENS**									
0020 For metal sash, aluminum or bronze mesh, flat screen	2 Sswk	1200	.013	S.F.	4.24	.68		4.92	5.90
0500 Wicket screen, inside window		1000	.016		6.55	.82		7.37	8.70
0800 Security screen, aluminum frame with stainless steel cloth		1200	.013		23.50	.68		24.18	27.50
0900 Steel grate, painted, on steel frame		1600	.010		12.90	.51		13.41	15.15
1000 Screens for solar louvers		160	.100		24.50	5.10		29.60	36
4000 See Section 05 58 23.90									

08 52 Wood Windows

08 52 10 – Plain Wood Windows

08 52 10.20 Awning Window

	Crew	Daily Output	Labor-Hours	Unit	Material	2014 Bare Costs Labor	Equipment	Total	Total Incl O&P
0010 **AWNING WINDOW**, Including frame, screens and grilles									
0100 34" x 22", insulated glass	1 Carp	10	.800	Ea.	270	36.50		306.50	360
0200 Low E glass		10	.800		271	36.50		307.50	360
0300 40" x 28", insulated glass		9	.889		315	41		356	410
0400 Low E Glass		9	.889		340	41		381	440
0500 48" x 36", insulated glass		8	1		465	46		511	590
0600 Low E glass		8	1		490	46		536	615
4000 Impact windows, minimum, add					60%				
4010 Impact windows, maximum, add					160%				
9000 Minimum labor/equipment charge	1 Carp	4	2	Job		91.50		91.50	151

08 52 Wood Windows

08 52 10 – Plain Wood Windows

08 52 10.30 Wood Windows

08 52 10.30 Wood Windows		Crew	Daily Output	Labor-Hours	Unit	Material	2014 Bare Costs Labor	Equipment	Total	Total Incl O&P
0010	**WOOD WINDOWS**, double hung									
0020	Including frame, double insulated glass, screens and grilles									
0040	Double hung, 2'-2" x 3'-4" high	2 Carp	15	1.067	Ea.	210	49		259	310
0060	2'-2" x 4'-4"		14	1.143		229	52.50		281.50	340
0080	2'-6" x 3'-4"		13	1.231		219	56.50		275.50	335
0100	2'-6" x 4'-0"		12	1.333		229	61		290	350
0120	2'-6" x 4'-8"		12	1.333		250	61		311	375
0140	2'-10" x 3'-4"		10	1.600		224	73.50		297.50	370
0160	2'-10" x 4'-0"		10	1.600		247	73.50		320.50	395
0180	3'-7" x 3'-4"		9	1.778		254	81.50		335.50	415
0200	3'-7" x 5'-4"		9	1.778		284	81.50		365.50	445
0220	3'-10" x 5'-4"		8	2		510	91.50		601.50	710
3800	Triple glazing for above, add					25%				

08 52 10.40 Casement Window

08 52 10.40 Casement Window			Crew	Daily Output	Labor-Hours	Unit	Material	2014 Bare Costs Labor	Equipment	Total	Total Incl O&P
0010	**CASEMENT WINDOW**, including frame, screen and grilles										
0100	2'-0" x 3'-0" H, dbl. insulated glass	G	1 Carp	10	.800	Ea.	268	36.50		304.50	355
0150	Low E glass	G		10	.800		259	36.50		295.50	345
0200	2'-0" x 4'-6" high, double insulated glass	G		9	.889		360	41		401	460
0250	Low E glass	G		9	.889		370	41		411	470
0260	Casement 4'-2" x 4'-2" double insulated glass	G		11	.727		875	33.50		908.50	1,025
0270	4'-0" x 4'-0" Low E glass	G		11	.727		535	33.50		568.50	645
0290	6'-4" x 5'-7" Low E glass	G		9	.889		1,125	41		1,166	1,300
0300	2'-4" x 6'-0" high, double insulated glass	G		8	1		430	46		476	550
0350	Low E glass	G		8	1		475	46		521	600
0522	Vinyl clad, premium, double insulated glass, 2'-0" x 3'-0"	G		10	.800		271	36.50		307.50	360
0524	2'-0" x 4'-0"	G		9	.889		315	41		356	415
0525	2'-0" x 5'-0"	G		8	1		360	46		406	475
0528	2'-0" x 6'-0"	G		8	1		380	46		426	495
0600	3'-0" x 5'-0"	G		8	1		665	46		711	805
0700	4'-0" x 3'-0"	G		8	1		730	46		776	880
0710	4'-0" x 4'-0"	G		8	1		625	46		671	760
0720	4'-8" x 4'-0"	G		8	1		690	46		736	835
0730	4'-8" x 5'-0"	G		6	1.333		790	61		851	965
0740	4'-8" x 6'-0"	G		6	1.333		880	61		941	1,075
0750	6'-0" x 4'-0"	G		6	1.333		805	61		866	985
0800	6'-0" x 5'-0"	G		6	1.333		895	61		956	1,075
0900	5'-6" x 5'-6"	G	2 Carp	15	1.067		1,425	49		1,474	1,650
8190	For installation, add per leaf							15%			
8200	For multiple leaf units, deduct for stationary sash										
8220	2' high					Ea.	23			23	25.50
8240	4'-6" high						26			26	28.50
8260	6' high						34.50			34.50	38
8300	Impact windows, minimum, add						60%				
8310	Impact windows, maximum, add						160%				
9000	Minimum labor/equipment charge		1 Carp	3	2.667	Job		122		122	201

08 52 10.50 Double Hung

08 52 10.50 Double Hung			Crew	Daily Output	Labor-Hours	Unit	Material	2014 Bare Costs Labor	Equipment	Total	Total Incl O&P
0010	**DOUBLE HUNG**, Including frame, screens and grilles										
0100	2'-0" x 3'-0" high, low E insul. glass	G	1 Carp	10	.800	Ea.	210	36.50		246.50	292
0200	3'-0" x 4'-0" high, double insulated glass	G		9	.889		279	41		320	370
0300	4'-0" x 4'-6" high, low E insulated glass	G		8	1		320	46		366	430
8000	Impact windows, minimum, add						60%				
8010	Impact windows, maximum, add						160%				

08 52 Wood Windows

08 52 10 – Plain Wood Windows

08 52 10.50 Double Hung

08 52 10.50 Double Hung		Crew	Daily Output	Labor-Hours	Unit	Material	2014 Bare Costs Labor	Equipment	Total	Total Incl O&P
9000	Minimum labor/equipment charge	1 Carp	3	2.667	Job		122		122	201

08 52 10.55 Picture Window

		Crew	Daily Output	Labor-Hours	Unit	Material	Labor	Equipment	Total	Total Incl O&P
0010	**PICTURE WINDOW**, Including frame and grilles									
0100	3'-6" x 4'-0" high, dbl. insulated glass	2 Carp	12	1.333	Ea.	420	61		481	565
0150	Low E glass		12	1.333		435	61		496	575
0200	4'-0" x 4'-6" high, double insulated glass		11	1.455		550	66.50		616.50	715
0250	Low E glass		11	1.455		530	66.50		596.50	695
0300	5'-0" x 4'-0" high, double insulated glass		11	1.455		580	66.50		646.50	750
0350	Low E glass		11	1.455		605	66.50		671.50	775
0400	6'-0" x 4'-6" high, double insulated glass		10	1.600		625	73.50		698.50	810
0450	Low E glass		10	1.600		635	73.50		708.50	820

08 52 10.65 Wood Sash

		Crew	Daily Output	Labor-Hours	Unit	Material	Labor	Equipment	Total	Total Incl O&P
0010	**WOOD SASH**, Including glazing but not trim									
0050	Custom, 5'-0" x 4'-0", 1" dbl. glazed, 3/16" thick lites	2 Carp	3.20	5	Ea.	230	229		459	630
0100	1/4" thick lites		5	3.200		245	147		392	510
0200	1" thick, triple glazed		5	3.200		415	147		562	695
0300	7'-0" x 4'-6" high, 1" double glazed, 3/16" thick lites		4.30	3.721		420	171		591	740
0400	1/4" thick lites		4.30	3.721		475	171		646	800
0500	1" thick, triple glazed		4.30	3.721		540	171		711	875
0600	8'-6" x 5'-0" high, 1" double glazed, 3/16" thick lites		3.50	4.571		565	210		775	970
0700	1/4" thick lites		3.50	4.571		620	210		830	1,025
0800	1" thick, triple glazed		3.50	4.571		625	210		835	1,025
0900	Window frames only, based on perimeter length				L.F.	4.02			4.02	4.42
1200	Window sill, stock, per lineal foot					8.50			8.50	9.35
1250	Casing, stock					3.30			3.30	3.63

08 52 10.70 Sliding Windows

			Crew	Daily Output	Labor-Hours	Unit	Material	Labor	Equipment	Total	Total Incl O&P
0010	**SLIDING WINDOWS**										
0100	3'-0" x 3'-0" high, double insulated	G	1 Carp	10	.800	Ea.	284	36.50		320.50	370
0120	Low E glass	G		10	.800		310	36.50		346.50	400
0200	4'-0" x 3'-6" high, double insulated	G		9	.889		355	41		396	455
0220	Low E glass	G		9	.889		360	41		401	465
0300	6'-0" x 5'-0" high, double insulated	G		8	1		490	46		536	610
0320	Low E glass	G		8	1		530	46		576	655
9000	Minimum labor/equipment charge			3	2.667	Job		122		122	201

08 52 13 – Metal-Clad Wood Windows

08 52 13.10 Awning Windows, Metal-Clad

		Crew	Daily Output	Labor-Hours	Unit	Material	Labor	Equipment	Total	Total Incl O&P
0010	**AWNING WINDOWS, METAL-CLAD**									
2000	Metal clad, awning deluxe, double insulated glass, 34" x 22"	1 Carp	9	.889	Ea.	247	41		288	340
2050	36" x 25"		9	.889		272	41		313	365
2100	40" x 22"		9	.889		291	41		332	385
2150	40" x 30"		9	.889		340	41		381	440
2200	48" x 28"		8	1		345	46		391	455
2250	60" x 36"		8	1		370	46		416	485

08 52 13.20 Casement Windows, Metal-Clad

			Crew	Daily Output	Labor-Hours	Unit	Material	Labor	Equipment	Total	Total Incl O&P
0010	**CASEMENT WINDOWS, METAL-CLAD**										
0100	Metal clad, deluxe, dbl. insul. glass, 2'-0" x 3'-0" high	G	1 Carp	10	.800	Ea.	279	36.50		315.50	365
0120	2'-0" x 4'-0" high	G		9	.889		315	41		356	410
0130	2'-0" x 5'-0" high	G		8	1		325	46		371	435
0140	2'-0" x 6'-0" high	G		8	1		365	46		411	475
0300	Metal clad, casement, bldrs mdl, 6'-0" x 4'-0", dbl. insltd gls, 3 panels		2 Carp	10	1.600		1,200	73.50		1,273.50	1,450
0310	9'-0" x 4'-0", 4 panels			8	2		1,550	91.50		1,641.50	1,850

08 52 Wood Windows

08 52 13 – Metal-Clad Wood Windows

08 52 13.20 Casement Windows, Metal-Clad

08 52 13.20 Casement Windows, Metal-Clad		Crew	Daily Output	Labor-Hours	Unit	Material	2014 Bare Costs Labor	Equipment	Total	Total Incl O&P
0320	10'-0" x 5'-0", 5 panels	2 Carp	7	2.286	Ea.	2,100	105		2,205	2,500
0330	12'-0" x 6'-0", 6 panels	↓	6	2.667	↓	2,700	122		2,822	3,150

08 52 13.30 Double-Hung Windows, Metal-clad

08 52 13.30			Crew	Daily Output	Labor-Hours	Unit	Material	Labor	Equipment	Total	Total Incl O&P
0010	**DOUBLE-HUNG WINDOWS, METAL-CLAD**										
0100	Metal clad, deluxe, dbl. insul. glass, 2'-6" x 3'-0" high	G	1 Carp	10	.800	Ea.	272	36.50		308.50	360
0120	3'-0" x 3'-6" high	G		10	.800		315	36.50		351.50	405
0140	3'-0" x 4'-0" high	G		9	.889		325	41		366	425
0160	3'-0" x 4'-6" high	G		9	.889		345	41		386	445
0180	3'-0" x 5'-0" high	G		8	1		370	46		416	485
0200	3'-6" x 6'-0" high	G	↓	8	1	↓	450	46		496	570

08 52 13.35 Picture and Sliding Windows Metal-Clad

08 52 13.35			Crew	Daily Output	Labor-Hours	Unit	Material	Labor	Equipment	Total	Total Incl O&P
0010	**PICTURE AND SLIDING WINDOWS METAL-CLAD**										
2000	Metal clad, dlx picture, dbl. insul. glass, 4'-0" x 4'-0" high		2 Carp	12	1.333	Ea.	375	61		436	510
2100	4'-0" x 6'-0" high			11	1.455		545	66.50		611.50	710
2200	5'-0" x 6'-0" high			10	1.600		610	73.50		683.50	790
2300	6'-0" x 6'-0" high		↓	10	1.600		695	73.50		768.50	885
2400	Metal clad, dlx sliding, double insulated glass, 3'-0" x 3'-0" high	G	1 Carp	10	.800		330	36.50		366.50	420
2420	4'-0" x 3'-6" high	G		9	.889		400	41		441	505
2440	5'-0" x 4'-0" high	G		9	.889		480	41		521	590
2460	6'-0" x 5'-0" high	G	↓	8	1	↓	725	46		771	870
9000	Minimum labor/equipment charge		2 Carp	2.75	5.818	Job		267		267	440

08 52 13.40 Bow and Bay Windows, Metal-Clad

08 52 13.40			Crew	Daily Output	Labor-Hours	Unit	Material	Labor	Equipment	Total	Total Incl O&P
0010	**BOW AND BAY WINDOWS, METAL-CLAD**										
0100	Metal clad, deluxe, dbl. insul. glass, 8'-0" x 5'-0" high, 4 panels		2 Carp	10	1.600	Ea.	1,675	73.50		1,748.50	1,950
0120	10'-0" x 5'-0" high, 5 panels			8	2		1,800	91.50		1,891.50	2,125
0140	10'-0" x 6'-0" high, 5 panels			7	2.286		2,100	105		2,205	2,500
0160	12'-0" x 6'-0" high, 6 panels			6	2.667		2,925	122		3,047	3,425
0400	Double hung, bldrs. model, bay, 8' x 4' high, dbl. insulated glass			10	1.600		1,325	73.50		1,398.50	1,575
0440	Low E glass			10	1.600		1,425	73.50		1,498.50	1,700
0460	9'-0" x 5'-0" high, double insulated glass			6	2.667		1,425	122		1,547	1,775
0480	Low E glass			6	2.667		1,500	122		1,622	1,850
0500	Metal clad, deluxe, dbl. insul. glass, 7'-0" x 4'-0" high			10	1.600		1,275	73.50		1,348.50	1,525
0520	8'-0" x 4'-0" high			8	2		1,300	91.50		1,391.50	1,600
0540	8'-0" x 5'-0" high			7	2.286		1,350	105		1,455	1,675
0560	9'-0" x 5'-0" high		↓	6	2.667	↓	1,450	122		1,572	1,775

08 52 16 – Plastic-Clad Wood Windows

08 52 16.10 Bow Window

08 52 16.10			Crew	Daily Output	Labor-Hours	Unit	Material	Labor	Equipment	Total	Total Incl O&P
0010	**BOW WINDOW** Including frames, screens, and grilles										
0020	End panels operable										
1000	Bow type, casement, wood, bldrs. mdl., 8' x 5' dbl. insltd glass, 4 panel		2 Carp	10	1.600	Ea.	1,500	73.50		1,573.50	1,775
1050	Low E glass			10	1.600		1,325	73.50		1,398.50	1,575
1100	10'-0" x 5'-0", double insulated glass, 6 panels			6	2.667		1,350	122		1,472	1,700
1200	Low E glass, 6 panels			6	2.667		1,450	122		1,572	1,800
1300	Vinyl clad, bldrs. model, double insulated glass, 6'-0" x 4'-0", 3 panel			10	1.600		1,025	73.50		1,098.50	1,250
1340	9'-0" x 4'-0", 4 panel			8	2		1,350	91.50		1,441.50	1,650
1380	10'-0" x 6'-0", 5 panels			7	2.286		2,250	105		2,355	2,650
1420	12'-0" x 6'-0", 6 panels			6	2.667		2,925	122		3,047	3,425
2000	Bay window, 8' x 5', dbl. insul glass			10	1.600		1,875	73.50		1,948.50	2,200
2050	Low E glass			10	1.600		2,275	73.50		2,348.50	2,625
2100	12'-0" x 6'-0", double insulated glass, 6 panels			6	2.667		2,350	122		2,472	2,775
2200	Low E glass		↓	6	2.667	↓	2,375	122		2,497	2,825

08 52 Wood Windows

08 52 16 – Plastic-Clad Wood Windows

08 52 16.10 Bow Window

	08 52 16.10 Bow Window	Crew	Daily Output	Labor-Hours	Unit	Material	2014 Bare Costs Labor	2014 Bare Costs Equipment	Total	Total Incl O&P
2300	Vinyl clad, premium, double insulated glass, 8'-0" x 5'-0"	2 Carp	10	1.600	Ea.	1,750	73.50		1,823.50	2,050
2340	10'-0" x 5'-0"		8	2		2,300	91.50		2,391.50	2,675
2380	10'-0" x 6'-0"		7	2.286		2,625	105		2,730	3,050
2420	12'-0" x 6'-0"		6	2.667		3,200	122		3,322	3,725
3300	Vinyl clad, premium, double insulated glass, 7'-0" x 4'-6"		10	1.600		1,375	73.50		1,448.50	1,625
3340	8'-0" x 4'-6"		8	2		1,400	91.50		1,491.50	1,675
3380	8'-0" x 5'-0"		7	2.286		1,450	105		1,555	1,775
3420	9'-0" x 5'-0"		6	2.667		1,500	122		1,622	1,850
9000	Minimum labor/equipment charge		2.50	6.400	Job		293		293	480

08 52 16.15 Awning Window Vinyl-Clad

	08 52 16.15 Awning Window Vinyl-Clad	Crew	Daily Output	Labor-Hours	Unit	Material	2014 Bare Costs Labor	2014 Bare Costs Equipment	Total	Total Incl O&P
0010	**AWNING WINDOW VINYL-CLAD** Including frames, screens, and grilles									
0240	Vinyl clad, 34" x 22"	1 Carp	10	.800	Ea.	264	36.50		300.50	350
0280	36" x 28"		9	.889		305	41		346	400
0300	36" x 36"		9	.889		340	41		381	440
0340	40" x 22"		10	.800		288	36.50		324.50	375
0360	48" x 28"		8	1		370	46		416	480
0380	60" x 36"		8	1		500	46		546	625

08 52 16.20 Half Round, Vinyl Clad

	08 52 16.20 Half Round, Vinyl Clad	Crew	Daily Output	Labor-Hours	Unit	Material	2014 Bare Costs Labor	2014 Bare Costs Equipment	Total	Total Incl O&P
0010	**HALF ROUND, VINYL CLAD**, double insulated glass, incl. grille									
0800	14" height x 24" base	2 Carp	9	1.778	Ea.	415	81.50		496.50	590
1040	15" height x 25" base		8	2		385	91.50		476.50	570
1060	16" height x 28" base		7	2.286		405	105		510	615
1080	17" height x 29" base		7	2.286		420	105		525	630
2000	19" height x 33" base	1 Carp	6	1.333		465	61		526	610
2100	20" height x 35" base		6	1.333		465	61		526	610
2200	21" height x 37" base		6	1.333		480	61		541	630
2250	23" height x 41" base	2 Carp	6	2.667		520	122		642	770
2300	26" height x 48" base		6	2.667		535	122		657	785
2350	30" height x 56" base		6	2.667		615	122		737	875
3000	36" height x 67" base	1 Carp	4	2		1,050	91.50		1,141.50	1,300
3040	38" height x 71" base	2 Carp	5	3.200		975	147		1,122	1,325
3050	40" height x 75" base	"	5	3.200		1,275	147		1,422	1,650
5000	Elliptical, 71" x 16"	1 Carp	11	.727		975	33.50		1,008.50	1,125
5100	95" x 21"	"	10	.800		1,375	36.50		1,411.50	1,575

08 52 16.35 Double-Hung Window

	08 52 16.35 Double-Hung Window		Crew	Daily Output	Labor-Hours	Unit	Material	2014 Bare Costs Labor	2014 Bare Costs Equipment	Total	Total Incl O&P
0010	**DOUBLE-HUNG WINDOW** Including frames, screens, and grilles										
0300	Vinyl clad, premium, double insulated glass, 2'-6" x 3'-0"	G	1 Carp	10	.800	Ea.	310	36.50		346.50	400
0305	2'-6" x 4'-0"	G		10	.800		360	36.50		396.50	455
0400	3'-0" x 3'-6"	G		10	.800		335	36.50		371.50	430
0500	3'-0" x 4'-0"	G		9	.889		395	41		436	500
0600	3'-0" x 4'-6"	G		9	.889		410	41		451	515
0700	3'-0" x 5'-0"	G		8	1		445	46		491	560
0790	3'-4" x 5'-0"	G		8	1		455	46		501	575
0800	3'-6" x 6'-0"	G		8	1		490	46		536	615
0820	4'-0" x 5'-0"	G		7	1.143		560	52.50		612.50	700
0830	4'-0" x 6'-0"	G		7	1.143		700	52.50		752.50	850

08 52 16.40 Transom Windows

	08 52 16.40 Transom Windows	Crew	Daily Output	Labor-Hours	Unit	Material	2014 Bare Costs Labor	2014 Bare Costs Equipment	Total	Total Incl O&P
0010	**TRANSOM WINDOWS**									
0050	Vinyl clad, premium, double insulated glass, 32" x 8"	1 Carp	16	.500	Ea.	188	23		211	244
0100	36" x 8"		16	.500		199	23		222	257
0110	36" x 12"		16	.500		212	23		235	271
2000	Custom sizes, up to 350 sq. in.		12	.667		256	30.50		286.50	330

08 52 Wood Windows

08 52 16 – Plastic-Clad Wood Windows

08 52 16.40 Transom Windows

		Crew	Daily Output	Labor-Hours	Unit	Material	2014 Bare Costs Labor	Equipment	Total	Total Incl O&P
2100	351 to 750 sq. in.	1 Carp	12	.667	Ea.	325	30.50		355.50	405
2200	751 to 1150 sq. in.		11	.727		400	33.50		433.50	495
2300	1151 to 1450 sq. in.	↓	11	.727		460	33.50		493.50	565
2400	1451 to 1850 sq. in.	2 Carp	12	1.333		530	61		591	685
2500	1851 to 2250 sq. in.		12	1.333		605	61		666	765
2600	2251 to 2650 sq. in.		11	1.455		680	66.50		746.50	860
2700	2651 to 3050 sq. in.		11	1.455		685	66.50		751.50	865
2800	3051 to 3450 sq. in.		11	1.455		755	66.50		821.50	940
2900	3451 to 3850 sq. in.		10	1.600		810	73.50		883.50	1,000
3000	3851 to 4250 sq. in.		10	1.600		870	73.50		943.50	1,075
3100	4251 to 4650 sq. in.		10	1.600		890	73.50		963.50	1,100
3200	4651 to 5050 sq. in.		10	1.600		935	73.50		1,008.50	1,150
3300	5051 to 5450 sq. in.		9	1.778		1,000	81.50		1,081.50	1,225
3400	5451 to 5850 sq. in.		9	1.778		975	81.50		1,056.50	1,200
3600	6251 to 6650 sq. in.		8	2		1,175	91.50		1,266.50	1,425
3700	6651 to 7050 sq. in.	↓	8	2	↓	1,250	91.50		1,341.50	1,525

08 52 16.45 Trapezoid Windows

		Crew	Daily Output	Labor-Hours	Unit	Material	2014 Bare Costs Labor	Equipment	Total	Total Incl O&P
0010	**TRAPEZOID WINDOWS**									
0900	20" base x 44" leg x 53" leg	2 Carp	13	1.231	Ea.	390	56.50		446.50	525
1000	24" base x 90" leg x 102" leg		8	2		670	91.50		761.50	890
3000	36" base x 40" leg x 22" leg		12	1.333		430	61		491	570
3010	36" base x 44" leg x 25" leg		13	1.231		450	56.50		506.50	590
3050	36" base x 26" leg x 48" leg		9	1.778		455	81.50		536.50	635
3100	36" base x 42" legs, 50" peak		9	1.778		545	81.50		626.50	735
3200	36" base x 60" leg x 81" leg		11	1.455		710	66.50		776.50	895
4320	44" base x 23" leg x 56" leg		11	1.455		560	66.50		626.50	730
4350	44" base x 59" leg x 92" leg		10	1.600		840	73.50		913.50	1,050
4500	46" base x 15" leg x 46" leg		8	2		425	91.50		516.50	615
4550	46" base x 16" leg x 48" leg		8	2		450	91.50		541.50	645
4600	46" base x 50" leg x 80" leg		7	2.286		680	105		785	920
6600	66" base x 12" leg x 42" leg		8	2		575	91.50		666.50	785
6650	66" base x 12" legs, 28" peak		9	1.778		455	81.50		536.50	635
6700	68" base x 23" legs, 31" peak	↓	8	2	↓	575	91.50		666.50	785

08 52 16.70 Vinyl Clad, Premium, Dbl. Insulated Glass

			Crew	Daily Output	Labor-Hours	Unit	Material	2014 Bare Costs Labor	Equipment	Total	Total Incl O&P
0010	**VINYL CLAD, PREMIUM, DBL. INSULATED GLASS**										
1000	Sliding, 3'-0" x 3'-0"	G	1 Carp	10	.800	Ea.	605	36.50		641.50	725
1050	4'-0" x 3'-6"	G		9	.889		685	41		726	820
1100	5'-0" x 4'-0"	G		9	.889		900	41		941	1,050
1150	6'-0" x 5'-0"	G	↓	8	1	↓	1,125	46		1,171	1,325

08 52 50 – Window Accessories

08 52 50.10 Window Grille or Muntin

		Crew	Daily Output	Labor-Hours	Unit	Material	2014 Bare Costs Labor	Equipment	Total	Total Incl O&P
0010	**WINDOW GRILLE OR MUNTIN**, snap in type									
0020	Standard pattern interior grilles									
2000	Wood, awning window, glass size 28" x 16" high	1 Carp	30	.267	Ea.	28	12.25		40.25	51
2060	44" x 24" high		32	.250		40	11.45		51.45	63
2100	Casement, glass size, 20" x 36" high		30	.267		32	12.25		44.25	55
2180	20" x 56" high		32	.250	↓	43	11.45		54.45	66.50
2200	Double hung, glass size, 16" x 24" high		24	.333	Set	51	15.30		66.30	81.50
2280	32" x 32" high		34	.235	"	131	10.80		141.80	162
2500	Picture, glass size, 48" x 48" high		30	.267	Ea.	120	12.25		132.25	152
2580	60" x 68" high		28	.286	"	183	13.10		196.10	224
2600	Sliding, glass size, 14" x 36" high	↓	24	.333	Set	35.50	15.30		50.80	64

08 52 Wood Windows

08 52 50 – Window Accessories

08 52 50.10 Window Grille or Muntin		Crew	Daily Output	Labor-Hours	Unit	Material	2014 Bare Costs Labor	Equipment	Total	Total Incl O&P
2680	36" x 36" high	1 Carp	22	.364	Set	43.50	16.65		60.15	75
9000	Minimum labor/equipment charge	↓	5	1.600	Job		73.50		73.50	121

08 52 66 – Wood Window Screens

08 52 66.10 Wood Screens

		Crew	Daily Output	Labor-Hours	Unit	Material	Labor	Equipment	Total	Total Incl O&P
0010	**WOOD SCREENS**									
0020	Over 3 S.F., 3/4" frames	2 Carp	375	.043	S.F.	4.89	1.96		6.85	8.60
0100	1-1/8" frames		375	.043		8.15	1.96		10.11	12.20
0200	Rescreen wood frame	↓	500	.032	↓	1.61	1.47		3.08	4.18
9000	Minimum labor/equipment charge	1 Carp	4	2	Job		91.50		91.50	151

08 52 69 – Wood Storm Windows

08 52 69.10 Storm Windows

			Crew	Daily Output	Labor-Hours	Unit	Material	Labor	Equipment	Total	Total Incl O&P
0010	**STORM WINDOWS**, aluminum residential										
0300	Basement, mill finish, incl. fiberglass screen										
0320	1'-10" x 1'-0" high	G	2 Carp	30	.533	Ea.	35	24.50		59.50	78.50
0340	2'-9" x 1'-6" high	G		30	.533		38	24.50		62.50	82
0360	3'-4" x 2'-0" high	G	↓	30	.533	↓	44	24.50		68.50	88.50
1600	Double-hung, combination, storm & screen										
1700	Custom, clear anodic coating, 2'-0" x 3'-5" high		2 Carp	30	.533	Ea.	90	24.50		114.50	139
1720	2'-6" x 5'-0" high			28	.571		110	26		136	164
1740	4'-0" x 6'-0" high			25	.640		226	29.50		255.50	297
1800	White painted, 2'-0" x 3'-5" high			30	.533		100	24.50		124.50	150
1820	2'-6" x 5'-0" high			28	.571		160	26		186	219
1840	4'-0" x 6'-0" high			25	.640		273	29.50		302.50	350
2000	Clear anodic coating, 2'-0" x 3'-5" high	G		30	.533		86	24.50		110.50	135
2020	2'-6" x 5'-0" high	G		28	.571		114	26		140	168
2040	4'-0" x 6'-0" high	G		25	.640		126	29.50		155.50	187
2400	White painted, 2'-0" x 3'-5" high	G		30	.533		85	24.50		109.50	134
2420	2'-6" x 5'-0" high	G		28	.571		92	26		118	144
2440	4'-0" x 6'-0" high	G		25	.640		100	29.50		129.50	158
2600	Mill finish, 2'-0" x 3'-5" high	G		30	.533		77	24.50		101.50	125
2620	2'-6" x 5'-0" high	G		28	.571		86	26		112	138
2640	4'-0" x 6'-8" high	G	↓	25	.640	↓	100	29.50		129.50	158
4000	Picture window, storm, 1 lite, white or bronze finish										
4020	4'-6" x 4'-6" high		2 Carp	25	.640	Ea.	120	29.50		149.50	180
4040	5'-8" x 4'-6" high			20	.800		144	36.50		180.50	219
4400	Mill finish, 4'-6" x 4'-6" high			25	.640		126	29.50		155.50	187
4420	5'-8" x 4'-6" high		↓	20	.800	↓	144	36.50		180.50	219
4600	3 lite, white or bronze finish										
4620	4'-6" x 4'-6" high		2 Carp	25	.640	Ea.	152	29.50		181.50	215
4640	5'-8" x 4'-6" high			20	.800		166	36.50		202.50	244
4800	Mill finish, 4'-6" x 4'-6" high			25	.640		144	29.50		173.50	206
4820	5'-8" x 4'-6" high		↓	20	.800	↓	152	36.50		188.50	228
6000	Sliding window, storm, 2 lite, white or bronze finish										
6020	3'-4" x 2'-7" high		2 Carp	28	.571	Ea.	130	26		156	186
6040	4'-4" x 3'-3" high			25	.640		150	29.50		179.50	213
6060	5'-4" x 6'-0" high		↓	20	.800	↓	240	36.50		276.50	325
8000	PVC framed										
8100	Double-hung, combination, storm & screen										
8120	2'-6" x 3'-5"		2 Carp	15	1.067	Ea.	135	49		184	230
8140	4' x 6'		"	12.50	1.280	"	162	58.50		220.50	275
8600	Single lite picture storm										
8620	4'-6" x 4'-6"		2 Carp	12.50	1.280	Ea.	159	58.50		217.50	272

08 52 Wood Windows

08 52 69 – Wood Storm Windows

08 52 69.10 Storm Windows		Crew	Daily Output	Labor-Hours	Unit	Material	2014 Bare Costs Labor	Equipment	Total	Total Incl O&P
8640	5'-8" x 4'-6"	2 Carp	10	1.600	Ea.	169	73.50		242.50	305
9000	Magnetic interior storm window									
9100	3/16" plate glass	1 Glaz	107	.075	S.F.	5.55	3.29		8.84	11.45
9410	Minimum labor/equipment charge	1 Carp	4	2	Job		91.50		91.50	151

08 53 Plastic Windows

08 53 13 – Vinyl Windows

08 53 13.20 Vinyl Single Hung Windows

08 53 13.20 Vinyl Single Hung Windows			Crew	Daily Output	Labor-Hours	Unit	Material	2014 Bare Costs Labor	Equipment	Total	Total Incl O&P
0010	**VINYL SINGLE HUNG WINDOWS**, insulated glass										
0100	Grids, low E, J fin, ext. jambs, 21" x 53"	G	2 Carp	18	.889	Ea.	198	41		239	285
0110	21" x 57"	G		17	.941		200	43		243	291
0120	21" x 65"	G		16	1		205	46		251	300
0130	25" x 41"	G		20	.800		190	36.50		226.50	270
0140	25" x 49"	G		18	.889		200	41		241	287
0150	25" x 57"	G		17	.941		205	43		248	297
0160	25" x 65"	G		16	1		240	46		286	340
0170	29" x 41"	G		18	.889		195	41		236	282
0180	29" x 53"	G		18	.889		205	41		246	293
0190	29" x 57"	G		17	.941		210	43		253	300
0200	29" x 65"	G		16	1		215	46		261	315
0210	33" x 41"	G		20	.800		200	36.50		236.50	281
0220	33" x 53"	G		18	.889		215	41		256	305
0230	33" x 57"	G		17	.941		215	43		258	310
0240	33" x 65"	G		16	1		220	46		266	320
0250	37" x 41"	G		20	.800		225	36.50		261.50	310
0260	37" x 53"	G		18	.889		235	41		276	325
0270	37" x 57"	G		17	.941		240	43		283	335
0280	37" x 65"	G		16	1		256	46		302	360

08 53 13.30 Vinyl Double Hung Windows

08 53 13.30 Vinyl Double Hung Windows			Crew	Daily Output	Labor-Hours	Unit	Material	2014 Bare Costs Labor	Equipment	Total	Total Incl O&P
0010	**VINYL DOUBLE HUNG WINDOWS**, insulated glass										
0100	Grids, low E, J fin, ext. jambs, 21" x 53"	G	2 Carp	18	.889	Ea.	215	41		256	305
0102	21" x 37"	G		18	.889		200	41		241	287
0104	21" x 41"	G		18	.889		205	41		246	293
0106	21" x 49"	G		18	.889		221	41		262	310
0110	21" x 57"	G		17	.941		222	43		265	315
0120	21" x 65"	G		16	1		230	46		276	330
0128	25" x 37"	G		20	.800		210	36.50		246.50	292
0130	25" x 41"	G		20	.800		215	36.50		251.50	298
0140	25" x 49"	G		18	.889		220	41		261	310
0145	25" x 53"	G		18	.889		225	41		266	315
0150	25" x 57"	G		17	.941		225	43		268	320
0160	25" x 65"	G		16	1		235	46		281	335
0162	25" x 69"	G		16	1		242	46		288	340
0164	25" x 77"	G		16	1		260	46		306	360
0168	29" x 37"	G		18	.889		215	41		256	305
0170	29" x 41"	G		18	.889		218	41		259	305
0172	29" x 49"	G		18	.889		225	41		266	315
0180	29" x 53"	G		18	.889		230	41		271	320
0190	29" x 57"	G		17	.941		232	43		275	325
0200	29" x 65"	G		16	1		240	46		286	340
0202	29" x 69"	G		16	1		247	46		293	350

08 53 Plastic Windows

08 53 13 – Vinyl Windows

08 53 13.30 Vinyl Double Hung Windows

			Crew	Daily Output	Labor-Hours	Unit	Material	2014 Bare Costs Labor	Equipment	Total	Total Incl O&P
0205	29" x 77"	G	2 Carp	16	1	Ea.	267	46		313	370
0208	33" x 37"	G		20	.800		220	36.50		256.50	305
0210	33" x 41"	G		20	.800		222	36.50		258.50	305
0215	33" x 49"	G		20	.800		230	36.50		266.50	315
0220	33" x 53"	G		18	.889		235	41		276	325
0230	33" x 57"	G		17	.941		238	43		281	335
0240	33" x 65"	G		16	1		242	46		288	340
0242	33" x 69"	G		16	1		257	46		303	360
0246	33" x 77"	G		16	1		263	46		309	365
0250	37" x 41"	G		20	.800		242	36.50		278.50	325
0255	37" x 49"	G		20	.800		250	36.50		286.50	335
0260	37" x 53"	G		18	.889		257	41		298	350
0270	37" x 57"	G		17	.941		262	43		305	360
0280	37" x 65"	G		16	1		280	46		326	385
0282	37" x 69"	G		16	1		287	46		333	390
0286	37" x 77"	G		16	1		295	46		341	400
0300	Solid vinyl, average quality, double insulated glass, 2'-0" x 3'-0"	G	1 Carp	10	.800		291	36.50		327.50	380
0310	3'-0" x 4'-0"	G		9	.889		205	41		246	292
0320	4'-0" x 4'-6"	G		8	1		335	46		381	440
0330	Premium, double insulated glass, 2'-6" x 3'-0"	G		10	.800		260	36.50		296.50	345
0340	3'-0" x 3'-6"	G		9	.889		283	41		324	375
0350	3'-0" x 4'-0"	G		9	.889		310	41		351	405
0360	3'-0" x 4'-6"	G		9	.889		320	41		361	415
0370	3'-0" x 5'-0"	G		8	1		340	46		386	445
0380	3'-6" x 6'-0"	G		8	1		360	46		406	475

08 53 13.40 Vinyl Casement Windows

			Crew	Daily Output	Labor-Hours	Unit	Material	2014 Bare Costs Labor	Equipment	Total	Total Incl O&P
0010	**VINYL CASEMENT WINDOWS**, insulated glass										
0015	Grids, low E, J fin, extension jambs, screens										
0100	One lite, 21" x 41"	G	2 Carp	20	.800	Ea.	271	36.50		307.50	360
0110	21" x 47"	G		20	.800		294	36.50		330.50	385
0120	21" x 53"	G		20	.800		315	36.50		351.50	410
0128	24" x 35"	G		19	.842		263	38.50		301.50	355
0130	24" x 41"	G		19	.842		283	38.50		321.50	375
0140	24" x 47"	G		19	.842		305	38.50		343.50	400
0150	24" x 53"	G		19	.842		325	38.50		363.50	425
0158	28" x 35"	G		19	.842		278	38.50		316.50	370
0160	28" x 41"	G		19	.842		298	38.50		336.50	395
0170	28" x 47"	G		19	.842		320	38.50		358.50	415
0180	28" x 53"	G		19	.842		350	38.50		388.50	450
0184	28" x 59"	G		19	.842		350	38.50		388.50	450
0188	Two lites, 33" x 35"	G		18	.889		435	41		476	545
0190	33" x 41"	G		18	.889		460	41		501	570
0200	33" x 47"	G		18	.889		495	41		536	610
0210	33" x 53"	G		18	.889		525	41		566	645
0212	33" x 59"	G		18	.889		555	41		596	675
0215	33" x 72"	G		18	.889		570	41		611	695
0220	41" x 41"	G		18	.889		455	41		496	565
0230	41" x 47"	G		18	.889		530	41		571	650
0240	41" x 53"	G		17	.941		565	43		608	690
0242	41" x 59"	G		17	.941		590	43		633	720
0246	41" x 72"	G		17	.941		615	43		658	750
0250	47" x 41"	G		17	.941		505	43		548	625

08 53 Plastic Windows

08 53 13 – Vinyl Windows

08 53 13.40 Vinyl Casement Windows

		Crew	Daily Output	Labor-Hours	Unit	Material	2014 Bare Costs Labor	Equipment	Total	Total Incl O&P
0260	47" x 47" G	2 Carp	17	.941	Ea.	535	43		578	660
0270	47" x 53" G		17	.941		565	43		608	690
0272	47" x 59" G		17	.941		615	43		658	750
0280	56" x 41" G		15	1.067		540	49		589	675
0290	56" x 47" G		15	1.067		565	49		614	700
0300	56" x 53" G		15	1.067		615	49		664	755
0302	56" x 59" G		15	1.067		640	49		689	785
0310	56" x 72" G		15	1.067		690	49		739	840
0340	Solid vinyl, premium, double insulated glass, 2'-0" x 3'-0" high G	1 Carp	10	.800		263	36.50		299.50	350
0360	2'-0" x 4'-0" high G		9	.889		293	41		334	385
0380	2'-0" x 5'-0" high G		8	1		325	46		371	430

08 53 13.50 Vinyl Picture Windows

		Crew	Daily Output	Labor-Hours	Unit	Material	2014 Bare Costs Labor	Equipment	Total	Total Incl O&P
0010	**VINYL PICTURE WINDOWS**, insulated glass									
0100	Grids, low E, J fin, ext. jambs, 33" x 47"	2 Carp	12	1.333	Ea.	250	61		311	375
0110	35" x 71"		12	1.333		335	61		396	470
0120	41" x 47"		12	1.333		270	61		331	395
0130	41" x 71"		12	1.333		350	61		411	485
0140	47" x 47"		12	1.333		305	61		366	435
0150	47" x 71"		11	1.455		380	66.50		446.50	530
0160	53" x 47"		11	1.455		330	66.50		396.50	475
0170	53" x 71"		11	1.455		345	66.50		411.50	490
0180	59" x 47"		11	1.455		370	66.50		436.50	515
0190	59" x 71"		11	1.455		380	66.50		446.50	530
0200	71" x 47"		10	1.600		390	73.50		463.50	550
0210	71" x 71"		10	1.600		405	73.50		478.50	565

08 53 13.60 Vinyl Half Round Windows

		Crew	Daily Output	Labor-Hours	Unit	Material	2014 Bare Costs Labor	Equipment	Total	Total Incl O&P
0010	**VINYL HALF ROUND WINDOWS**, Including grille, j fin low E, ext. jambs									
0100	10" height x 20" base	2 Carp	8	2	Ea.	475	91.50		566.50	670
0110	15" height x 30" base		8	2		440	91.50		531.50	635
0120	17" height x 34" base		7	2.286		320	105		425	520
0130	19" height x 38" base		7	2.286		345	105		450	550
0140	19" height x 33" base		7	2.286		555	105		660	785
0150	24" height x 48" base	1 Carp	6	1.333		365	61		426	500
0160	25" height x 50" base	"	6	1.333		755	61		816	930
0170	30" height x 60" base	2 Carp	6	2.667		660	122		782	925

08 54 Composite Windows

08 54 13 – Fiberglass Windows

08 54 13.10 Fiberglass Single Hung Windows

		Crew	Daily Output	Labor-Hours	Unit	Material	2014 Bare Costs Labor	Equipment	Total	Total Incl O&P
0010	**FIBERGLASS SINGLE HUNG WINDOWS**									
0100	Grids, low E, 18" x 24" G	2 Carp	18	.889	Ea.	335	41		376	435
0110	18" x 40" G		17	.941		340	43		383	445
0130	24" x 40" G		20	.800		360	36.50		396.50	455
0230	36" x 36" G		17	.941		370	43		413	475
0250	36" x 48" G		20	.800		405	36.50		441.50	505
0260	36" x 60" G		18	.889		445	41		486	555
0280	36" x 72" G		16	1		470	46		516	590
0290	48" x 40" G		16	1		470	46		516	590

08 54 Composite Windows

08 54 13 – Fiberglass Windows

08 54 13.30 Fiberglass Slider Windows		Crew	Daily Output	Labor-Hours	Unit	Material	2014 Bare Costs Labor	Equipment	Total	Total Incl O&P
0010	**FIBERGLASS SLIDER WINDOWS**									
0100	Grids, low E, 36" x 24"	[G] 2 Carp	20	.800	Ea.	340	36.50		376.50	435
0110	36" x 36"	[G] "	20	.800	"	390	36.50		426.50	490

08 54 13.50 Fiberglass Bay Windows

0010	**FIBERGLASS BAY WINDOWS**									
0150	48" x 36"	[G] 2 Carp	11	1.455	Ea.	1,100	66.50		1,166.50	1,300

08 56 Special Function Windows

08 56 46 – Radio-Frequency-Interference Shielding Windows

08 56 46.10 Radio-Frequency-interference Mesh

		Crew	Daily Output	Labor-Hours	Unit	Material	Labor	Equipment	Total	Total Incl O&P
0010	**RADIO-FREQUENCY-INTERFERENCE MESH**									
0100	16 mesh copper 0.011" wire				S.F.	4.05			4.05	4.46
0150	22 mesh copper 0.015" wire					5.85			5.85	6.45
0200	100 mesh copper 0.022" wire					7.50			7.50	8.25
0250	100 mesh stainless steel 0.0012" wire				↓	13.20			13.20	14.50

08 56 63 – Detention Windows

08 56 63.13 Visitor Cubicle Windows

		Crew	Daily Output	Labor-Hours	Unit	Material	Labor	Equipment	Total	Total Incl O&P
0010	**VISITOR CUBICLE WINDOWS**									
4000	Visitor cubicle, vision panel, no intercom	E-4	2	16	Ea.	3,200	825	71	4,096	5,125

08 61 Roof Windows

08 61 13 – Metal Roof Windows

08 61 13.10 Roof Windows

		Crew	Daily Output	Labor-Hours	Unit	Material	Labor	Equipment	Total	Total Incl O&P
0010	**ROOF WINDOWS**, fixed high perf tmpd glazing, metallic framed									
0020	46" x 21-1/2", Flashed for shingled roof	1 Carp	8	1	Ea.	270	46		316	375
0100	46" x 28"		8	1		300	46		346	405
0125	57" x 44"		6	1.333		370	61		431	505
0130	72" x 28"		7	1.143		370	52.50		422.50	490
0150	Fixed, laminated tempered glazing, 46" x 21-1/2"		8	1		455	46		501	575
0175	46" x 28"		8	1		505	46		551	630
0200	57" x 44"		6	1.333		475	61		536	620
0500	Vented flashing set for shingled roof, 46" x 21-1/2"		7	1.143		455	52.50		507.50	585
0525	46" x 28"		6	1.333		505	61		566	655
0550	57" x 44"		5	1.600		635	73.50		708.50	815
0560	72" x 28"		5	1.600		635	73.50		708.50	815
0575	Flashing set for low pitched roof, 46" x 21-1/2"		7	1.143		525	52.50		577.50	665
0600	46" x 28"		7	1.143		575	52.50		627.50	720
0625	57" x 44"		5	1.600		715	73.50		788.50	905
0650	Flashing set for curb 46" x 21-1/2"		7	1.143		605	52.50		657.50	750
0675	46" x 28"		7	1.143		660	52.50		712.50	810
0700	57" x 44"		5	1.600		810	73.50		883.50	1,000

08 62 Unit Skylights

08 62 13 – Domed Unit Skylights

08 62 13.10 Domed Skylights

		Crew	Daily Output	Labor-Hours	Unit	Material	2014 Bare Costs Labor	2014 Bare Costs Equipment	Total	Total Incl O&P
0010	**DOMED SKYLIGHTS**									
0020	Skylight, fixed dome type, 22" x 22" G	G-3	12	2.667	Ea.	210	122		332	425
0030	22" x 46" G		10	3.200		232	146		378	490
0040	30" x 30" G		12	2.667		235	122		357	455
0050	30" x 46" G		10	3.200		310	146		456	575
0110	Fixed, double glazed, 22" x 27" G		12	2.667		230	122		352	450
0120	22" x 46" G		10	3.200		282	146		428	545
0130	44" x 46" G		10	3.200		430	146		576	710
0210	Operable, double glazed, 22" x 27" G		12	2.667		325	122		447	555
0220	22" x 46" G		10	3.200		390	146		536	665
0230	44" x 46" G		10	3.200		830	146		976	1,150
9000	Minimum labor/equipment charge		2	16	Job		730		730	1,175

08 62 13.20 Skylights

		Crew	Daily Output	Labor-Hours	Unit	Material	2014 Bare Costs Labor	2014 Bare Costs Equipment	Total	Total Incl O&P
0010	**SKYLIGHTS**, flush or curb mounted									
2025	22-1/2" x 46-1/2"	1 Carp	8	1	Ea.	395	46		441	510
2050	46-1/2" x 46-1/2"	"	8	1	"	695	46		741	840
2120	Ventilating insulated plexiglass dome with									
2130	curb mounting, 36" x 36" G	G-3	12	2.667	Ea.	480	122		602	725
2150	52" x 52" G		12	2.667		660	122		782	920
2160	28" x 52" G		10	3.200		485	146		631	770
2170	36" x 52" G		10	3.200		540	146		686	830
2180	For electric opening system, add G					310			310	340
2210	Operating skylight, with thermopane glass, 24" x 48" G	G-3	10	3.200		575	146		721	870
2220	32" x 48" G		9	3.556		600	162		762	920
2300	Insulated safety glass with aluminum frame G		160	.200	S.F.	92	9.15		101.15	116
4000	Skylight, solar tube kit, incl dome, flashing, diffuser, 1 pipe, 10" dia. G	1 Carp	2	4	Ea.	230	183		413	555
4010	14" diam. G		2	4		310	183		493	640
4020	21" diam. G		2	4		410	183		593	750
4030	Accessories for, 1' long x 9" dia pipe G		24	.333		30	15.30		45.30	58
4040	2' long x 9" dia pipe G		24	.333		45	15.30		60.30	74.50
4050	4' long x 9" dia pipe G		20	.400		72	18.35		90.35	109
4060	1' long x 13" dia pipe G		24	.333		45	15.30		60.30	74.50
4070	2' long x 13" dia pipe G		24	.333		60	15.30		75.30	91
4080	4' long x 13" dia pipe G		20	.400		100	18.35		118.35	140
4090	6.5" turret ext for 21" dia pipe G		16	.500		50	23		73	92.50
4100	12' long x 21" dia flexible pipe G		12	.667		90	30.50		120.50	149
4110	45 degree elbow, 10" G		16	.500		50	23		73	92.50
4120	14" G		16	.500		45	23		68	87
4130	Interior decorative ring, 9" G		20	.400		30	18.35		48.35	63
4140	13" G		20	.400		45	18.35		63.35	79.50

08 71 Door Hardware

08 71 13 – Automatic Door Operators

08 71 13.10 Automatic Openers Commercial	Crew	Daily Output	Labor-Hours	Unit	Material	2014 Bare Costs Labor	Equipment	Total	Total Incl O&P
0010 **AUTOMATIC OPENERS COMMERCIAL**									
0020 Pneumatic, incl opener, motion sens, control box, tubing, compressor									
0050 For single swing door, per opening	2 Skwk	.80	20	Ea.	4,550	945		5,495	6,550
0100 Pair, per opening		.50	32	Opng.	7,375	1,525		8,900	10,600
1000 For single sliding door, per opening		.60	26.667		4,975	1,250		6,225	7,525
1300 Bi-parting pair		.50	32		7,475	1,525		9,000	10,700
1420 Electronic door opener incl motion sens, 12 V control box, motor									
1450 For single swing door, per opening	2 Skwk	.80	20	Opng.	3,550	945		4,495	5,475
1500 Pair, per opening		.50	32		6,500	1,525		8,025	9,625
1600 For single sliding door, per opening		.60	26.667		4,300	1,250		5,550	6,775
1700 Bi-parting pair		.50	32		5,250	1,525		6,775	8,250
1750 Handicap actuator buttons, 2, including 12 V DC wiring, add	1 Carp	1.50	5.333	Pr.	470	245		715	915

08 71 20 – Hardware

08 71 20.15 Hardware

	Crew	Daily Output	Labor-Hours	Unit	Material	2014 Bare Costs Labor	Equipment	Total	Total Incl O&P
0010 **HARDWARE**									
0020 Average percentage for hardware, total job cost									
0050 Maximum				Job					5%
0500 Total hardware for building, average distribution				"	85%	15%			
1000 Door hardware, apartment, interior	1 Carp	4	2	Door	450	91.50		541.50	650
1300 Average, door hardware, motel/hotel interior, with access card		4	2		580	91.50		671.50	790
1500 Hospital bedroom, minimum		4	2		620	91.50		711.50	830
2000 Maximum		3	2.667		725	122		847	995
2250 School, single exterior, incl. lever, incl. panic device		3	2.667		1,275	122		1,397	1,600
2500 Single interior, regular use, lever included		3	2.667		615	122		737	880
2600 Average, door hdwe., school, classroom, ANSI F88, incl. lever		3	2.667		905	122		1,027	1,200
2850 Stairway, single interior		3	2.667		540	122		662	795
3100 Double exterior, with panic device		2	4	Pr.	2,375	183		2,558	2,900
6020 Add for fire alarm door holder, electro-magnetic	1 Elec	4	2	Ea.	102	107		209	277

08 71 20.30 Door Closers

	Crew	Daily Output	Labor-Hours	Unit	Material	2014 Bare Costs Labor	Equipment	Total	Total Incl O&P
0010 **DOOR CLOSERS** Adjustable backcheck, multiple mounting									
0015 and rack and pinion									
0020 Standard Regular Arm	1 Carp	6	1.333	Ea.	188	61		249	305
0040 Hold open arm		6	1.333		200	61		261	320
0100 Fusible link		6.50	1.231		162	56.50		218.50	271
1500 Concealed closers, normal use, head, pivot hung, interior		5.50	1.455		325	66.50		391.50	465
1510 Exterior		5.50	1.455		395	66.50		461.50	545
1520 Overhead concealed, all sizes, regular arm		5.50	1.455		200	66.50		266.50	330
1525 Concealed arm		5	1.600		310	73.50		383.50	460
1530 Concealed in door, all sizes, regular arm		5.50	1.455		320	66.50		386.50	460
1535 Concealed arm		5	1.600		253	73.50		326.50	400
1560 Floor concealed, all sizes, single acting		2.20	3.636		500	167		667	825
1565 Double acting		2.20	3.636		410	167		577	725
1570 Interior, floor, offset pivot, single acting		3.50	2.286		760	105		865	1,000
1590 Exterior		3.50	2.286		835	105		940	1,075
1610 Hold open arm		6	1.333		420	61		481	560
1620 Double acting, standard arm		6	1.333		700	61		761	870
1630 Hold open arm		6	1.333		700	61		761	870
1640 Floor, center hung, single acting, bottom arm		6	1.333		410	61		471	550
1650 Double acting		6	1.333		465	61		526	610
1660 Offset hung, single acting, bottom arm		6	1.333		550	61		611	705
2000 Backcheck and adjustable power, hinge face mount									
5000 For cast aluminum cylinder, deduct				Ea.	35			35	38.50

08 71 Door Hardware

08 71 20 – Hardware

08 71 20.30 Door Closers	Crew	Daily Output	Labor-Hours	Unit	Material	2014 Bare Costs Labor	Equipment	Total	Total Incl O&P
5040	For delayed action, add				Ea.	46			46	50.50
5080	For fusible link arm, add					35			35	38.50
5120	For shock absorbing arm, add					50			50	55
5160	For spring power adjustment, add					40			40	44
6000	Closer-holder, hinge face mount, all sizes, exposed arm	1 Carp	6.50	1.231		201	56.50		257.50	315
6500	Electro magnetic closer/holder									
6510	Single point, no detector	1 Carp	4	2	Ea.	470	91.50		561.50	665
6515	Including detector		4	2		665	91.50		756.50	885
6520	Multi-point, no detector		4	2		875	91.50		966.50	1,125
6524	Including detector		4	2		1,275	91.50		1,366.50	1,550
6550	Electric automatic operators									
6555	Operator	1 Carp	4	2	Ea.	1,975	91.50		2,066.50	2,325
6570	Wall plate actuator		4	2		217	91.50		308.50	390
7000	Electronic closer-holder, hinge facemount, concealed arm		5	1.600		420	73.50		493.50	580
7400	With built-in detector		5	1.600		605	73.50		678.50	785
9000	Minimum labor/equipment charge		4	2	Job		91.50		91.50	151

08 71 20.35 Panic Devices

		Crew	Daily Output	Labor-Hours	Unit	Material	Labor	Equipment	Total	Total Incl O&P
0010	**PANIC DEVICES**									
0015	For rim locks, single door exit only	1 Carp	6	1.333	Ea.	460	61		521	605
0020	Outside key and pull		5	1.600		570	73.50		643.50	750
0200	Bar and vertical rod, exit only		5	1.600		865	73.50		938.50	1,075
0210	Outside key and pull		4	2		940	91.50		1,031.50	1,175
0400	Bar and concealed rod		4	2		745	91.50		836.50	970
0600	Touch bar, exit only		6	1.333		555	61		616	710
0610	Outside key and pull		5	1.600		685	73.50		758.50	870
0700	Touch bar and vertical rod, exit only		5	1.600		845	73.50		918.50	1,050
0710	Outside key and pull		4	2		970	91.50		1,061.50	1,225
1000	Mortise, bar, exit only		4	2		690	91.50		781.50	910
1600	Touch bar, exit only		4	2		740	91.50		831.50	965
2000	Narrow stile, rim mounted, bar, exit only		6	1.333		615	61		676	775
2010	Outside key and pull		5	1.600		890	73.50		963.50	1,100
2200	Bar and vertical rod, exit only		5	1.600		920	73.50		993.50	1,125
2210	Outside key and pull		4	2		920	91.50		1,011.50	1,150
2400	Bar and concealed rod, exit only		3	2.667		1,025	122		1,147	1,350
3000	Mortise, bar, exit only		4	2		600	91.50		691.50	810
3600	Touch bar, exit only		4	2		790	91.50		881.50	1,025
4000	Double doors, exit only		2	4	Pr.	1,425	183		1,608	1,850
4500	Exit & entrance		2	4	"	1,975	183		2,158	2,475
9000	Minimum labor/equipment charge		2.50	3.200	Job		147		147	241

08 71 20.40 Lockset

		Crew	Daily Output	Labor-Hours	Unit	Material	Labor	Equipment	Total	Total Incl O&P
0010	**LOCKSET**, Standard duty									
0020	Non-keyed, passage, w/sect.trim	1 Carp	12	.667	Ea.	63.50	30.50		94	120
0100	Privacy		12	.667		75	30.50		105.50	133
0400	Keyed, single cylinder function		10	.800		108	36.50		144.50	179
0420	Hotel (see also Section 08 71 20.15)		8	1		205	46		251	300
0500	Lever handled, keyed, single cylinder function		10	.800		128	36.50		164.50	202
1000	Heavy duty with sectional trim, non-keyed, passages		12	.667		125	30.50		155.50	188
1100	Privacy		12	.667		155	30.50		185.50	221
1400	Keyed, single cylinder function		10	.800		185	36.50		221.50	265
1420	Hotel		8	1		450	46		496	570
1600	Communicating		10	.800		290	36.50		326.50	380
1690	For re-core cylinder, add					50			50	55

08 71 Door Hardware

08 71 20 – Hardware

08 71 20.40 Lockset

		Crew	Daily Output	Labor-Hours	Unit	Material	2014 Bare Costs Labor	Equipment	Total	Total Incl O&P
1700	Residential, interior door, minimum	1 Carp	16	.500	Ea.	30	23		53	70.50
1720	Maximum		8	1		120	46		166	208
1800	Exterior, minimum		14	.571		50	26		76	98
1810	Average		8	1		72.50	46		118.50	156
1820	Maximum		8	1		220	46		266	320
3800	Cipher lockset w/key pad (security item)		13	.615		920	28		948	1,075
3900	Cipher lockset with dial for swinging doors (security item)		13	.615		1,800	28		1,828	2,050
3920	with dial for swinging doors & drill resistant plate (security item)		12	.667		2,200	30.50		2,230.50	2,475
3950	Cipher lockset with dial for safe/vault door (security item)	↓	12	.667	↓	1,500	30.50		1,530.50	1,700
3980	Keyless, pushbutton type									
4000	Residential/light commercial, deadbolt, standard	1 Carp	9	.889	Ea.	140	41		181	221
4010	Heavy duty		9	.889		230	41		271	320
4020	Industrial, heavy duty, with deadbolt		9	.889		355	41		396	455
4030	Key override		9	.889		390	41		431	495
4040	Lever activated handle		9	.889		415	41		456	520
4050	Key override		9	.889		430	41		471	535
4060	Double sided pushbutton type		8	1		755	46		801	905
4070	Key override		8	1	↓	790	46		836	945
9000	Minimum labor/equipment charge	↓	6	1.333	Job		61		61	100

08 71 20.41 Dead Locks

		Crew	Daily Output	Labor-Hours	Unit	Material	2014 Bare Costs Labor	Equipment	Total	Total Incl O&P
0010	**DEAD LOCKS**									
0011	Mortise heavy duty outside key (security item)	1 Carp	9	.889	Ea.	200	41		241	287
0020	Double cylinder		9	.889		200	41		241	287
0100	Medium duty, outside key		10	.800		110	36.50		146.50	182
0110	Double cylinder		10	.800		120	36.50		156.50	193
1000	Tubular, standard duty, outside key		10	.800		45	36.50		81.50	110
1010	Double cylinder		10	.800		60	36.50		96.50	127
1200	Night latch, outside key		10	.800		45	36.50		81.50	110
1203	Deadlock night latch		7.70	1.039		45	47.50		92.50	128
1420	Deadbolt lock, single cylinder		10	.800		48.50	36.50		85	114
1440	Double cylinder	↓	10	.800	↓	63	36.50		99.50	130

08 71 20.42 Mortise Locksets

		Crew	Daily Output	Labor-Hours	Unit	Material	2014 Bare Costs Labor	Equipment	Total	Total Incl O&P
0010	**MORTISE LOCKSETS**, Comm., wrought knobs & full escutcheon trim									
0015	Assumes mortise is cut									
0020	Non-keyed, passage, minimum	1 Carp	9	.889	Ea.	149	41		190	231
0030	Maximum		8	1		405	46		451	520
0040	Privacy, minimum		9	.889		169	41		210	253
0050	Maximum		8	1		455	46		501	575
0100	Keyed, office/entrance/apartment, minimum		8	1		197	46		243	293
0110	Maximum		7	1.143		515	52.50		567.50	655
0120	Single cylinder, typical, minimum		8	1		189	46		235	284
0130	Maximum		7	1.143		495	52.50		547.50	630
0200	Hotel, minimum (see also Section 08 71 20.15)		7	1.143		189	52.50		241.50	294
0210	Maximum (see also Section 08 71 20.15)		6	1.333		505	61		566	660
0300	Communication, double cylinder, minimum		8	1		225	46		271	325
0310	Maximum		7	1.143		515	52.50		567.50	655
1000	Wrought knobs and sectional trim, non-keyed, passage, minimum		10	.800		130	36.50		166.50	204
1010	Maximum		9	.889		405	41		446	510
1040	Privacy, minimum		10	.800		145	36.50		181.50	221
1050	Maximum		9	.889		455	41		496	565
1100	Keyed, entrance, office/apartment, minimum		9	.889		220	41		261	310
1110	Maximum		8	1		515	46		561	645

08 71 Door Hardware

08 71 20 – Hardware

08 71 20.42 Mortise Locksets

		Crew	Daily Output	Labor-Hours	Unit	Material	2014 Bare Costs Labor	2014 Bare Costs Equipment	Total	Total Incl O&P
1120	Single cylinder, typical, minimum	1 Carp	9	.889	Ea.	225	41		266	315
1130	Maximum	↓	8	1	↓	495	46		541	620
2000	Cast knobs and full escutcheon trim									
2010	Non-keyed, passage, minimum	1 Carp	9	.889	Ea.	275	41		316	370
2020	Maximum		8	1		380	46		426	495
2040	Privacy, minimum		9	.889		320	41		361	415
2050	Maximum		8	1		440	46		486	560
2120	Keyed, single cylinder, typical, minimum		8	1		330	46		376	440
2130	Maximum		7	1.143		525	52.50		577.50	665
3000	Cast knob and sectional trim, non-keyed, passage, minimum		10	.800		210	36.50		246.50	292
3010	Maximum		10	.800		380	36.50		416.50	480
3040	Privacy, minimum		10	.800		225	36.50		261.50	310
3050	Maximum		10	.800		440	36.50		476.50	545
3100	Keyed, office/entrance/apartment, minimum		9	.889		255	41		296	350
3110	Maximum		9	.889		580	41		621	700
3120	Single cylinder, typical, minimum		9	.889		260	41		301	355
3130	Maximum	↓	9	.889		525	41		566	645
3190	For re-core cylinder, add				↓	50			50	55

08 71 20.45 Peepholes

		Crew	Daily Output	Labor-Hours	Unit	Material	2014 Bare Costs Labor	2014 Bare Costs Equipment	Total	Total Incl O&P
0010	**PEEPHOLES**									
2010	Peephole	1 Carp	32	.250	Ea.	15.80	11.45		27.25	36.50
2020	Peephole, wide view	"	32	.250	"	16.50	11.45		27.95	37

08 71 20.50 Door Stops

		Crew	Daily Output	Labor-Hours	Unit	Material	2014 Bare Costs Labor	2014 Bare Costs Equipment	Total	Total Incl O&P
0010	**DOOR STOPS**									
0020	Holder & bumper, floor or wall	1 Carp	32	.250	Ea.	34.50	11.45		45.95	56.50
1300	Wall bumper, 4" diameter, with rubber pad, aluminum		32	.250		11.70	11.45		23.15	31.50
1600	Door bumper, floor type, aluminum		32	.250		8.10	11.45		19.55	28
1620	Brass		32	.250		9.65	11.45		21.10	29.50
1630	Bronze		32	.250		18.20	11.45		29.65	39
1900	Plunger type, door mounted		32	.250		28	11.45		39.45	49.50
2500	Holder, floor type, aluminum		32	.250		33.50	11.45		44.95	56
2520	Wall type, aluminum		32	.250		35	11.45		46.45	57.50
2530	Overhead type, bronze		32	.250		101	11.45		112.45	130
2540	Plunger type, aluminum		32	.250		28	11.45		39.45	49.50
2560	Brass		32	.250		43	11.45		54.45	66
3000	Electro-magnetic, wall mounted, US3		3	2.667		258	122		380	485
3020	Floor mounted, US3		3	2.667		315	122		437	550
4000	Doorstop, ceiling mounted		3	2.667		20	122		142	223
4030	Doorstop, header		3	2.667	↓	45	122		167	251
9000	Minimum labor/equipment charge	↓	6	1.333	Job		61		61	100

08 71 20.55 Push-Pull Plates

		Crew	Daily Output	Labor-Hours	Unit	Material	2014 Bare Costs Labor	2014 Bare Costs Equipment	Total	Total Incl O&P
0010	**PUSH-PULL PLATES**									
0090	Push plate, 0.050 thick, 3" x 12", aluminum	1 Carp	12	.667	Ea.	6.25	30.50		36.75	57
0100	4" x 16"		12	.667		11.10	30.50		41.60	62.50
0110	6" x 16"		12	.667		8.50	30.50		39	59.50
0120	8" x 16"		12	.667		9.90	30.50		40.40	61
0200	Push plate, 0.050 thick, 3" x 12", brass		12	.667		14	30.50		44.50	65.50
0210	4" x 16"		12	.667		17.50	30.50		48	69.50
0220	6" x 16"		12	.667		27	30.50		57.50	79.50
0230	8" x 16"		12	.667		35	30.50		65.50	88.50
0250	Push plate, 0.050 thick, 3" x 12", satin brass		12	.667		14.25	30.50		44.75	65.50
0260	4" x 16"	↓	12	.667		17.70	30.50		48.20	69.50

08 71 20.55 Push-Pull Plates

		Crew	Daily Output	Labor-Hours	Unit	Material	2014 Bare Costs Labor	Equipment	Total	Total Incl O&P
0270	6" x 16"	1 Carp	12	.667	Ea.	27	30.50		57.50	79.50
0280	8" x 16"		12	.667		35	30.50		65.50	88.50
0490	Push plate, 0.050 thick, 3" x 12", bronze		12	.667		17	30.50		47.50	68.50
0500	4" x 16"		12	.667		25	30.50		55.50	77.50
0510	6" x 16"		12	.667		32	30.50		62.50	85
0520	8" x 16"		12	.667		38.50	30.50		69	92.50
0740	Push plate, 0.050 thick, 3" x 12", stainless steel		12	.667		12	30.50		42.50	63
0750	4" x 16"		12	.667		27.50	30.50		58	80
0760	6" x 16"		12	.667		18.65	30.50		49.15	70.50
0780	8" x 16"		12	.667		23.50	30.50		54	76
0790	Push plate, 0.050 thick, 3" x 12", satin stainless steel		12	.667		7	30.50		37.50	57.50
0810	4" x 16"		12	.667		8.50	30.50		39	59.50
0820	6" x 16"		12	.667		11.70	30.50		42.20	63
0830	8" x 16"		12	.667		9	30.50		39.50	60
0980	Pull plate, 0.050 thick, 3" x 12", aluminum		12	.667		25.50	30.50		56	78
1000	4" x 16"		12	.667		25.50	30.50		56	78
1050	Pull plate, 0.050 thick, 3" x 12", brass		12	.667		39.50	30.50		70	93.50
1060	4" x 16"		12	.667		34.50	30.50		65	88
1080	Pull plate, 0.050 thick, 3" x 12", bronze		12	.667		50	30.50		80.50	105
1100	4" x 16"		12	.667		56	30.50		86.50	112
1180	Pull plate, 0.050 thick, 3" x 12", stainless steel		12	.667		45.50	30.50		76	100
1200	4" x 16"		12	.667		58.50	30.50		89	115
1250	Pull plate, 0.050 thick, 3" x 12", chrome		12	.667		44.50	30.50		75	99
1270	4" x 16"		12	.667		46.50	30.50		77	101
1500	Pull handle and push bar, aluminum		11	.727		118	33.50		151.50	185
2000	Bronze		10	.800		159	36.50		195.50	236
3000	Push plate both sides, aluminum		14	.571		27	26		53	72.50
3500	Bronze		13	.615		61.50	28		89.50	114
4000	Door pull, designer style, cast aluminum, minimum		12	.667		88.50	30.50		119	148
5000	Maximum		8	1		370	46		416	480
6000	Cast bronze, minimum		12	.667		87	30.50		117.50	146
7000	Maximum		8	1		405	46		451	520
8000	Walnut, minimum		12	.667		70	30.50		100.50	127
9000	Maximum		8	1		380	46		426	495
9800	Minimum labor/equipment charge		5	1.600	Job		73.50		73.50	121

08 71 20.60 Entrance Locks

		Crew	Daily Output	Labor-Hours	Unit	Material	Labor	Equipment	Total	Total Incl O&P
0010	**ENTRANCE LOCKS**									
0015	Cylinder, grip handle deadlocking latch	1 Carp	9	.889	Ea.	175	41		216	260
0020	Deadbolt		8	1		175	46		221	269
0100	Push and pull plate, dead bolt		8	1		225	46		271	325
0900	For handicapped lever, add					150			150	165

08 71 20.65 Thresholds

		Crew	Daily Output	Labor-Hours	Unit	Material	Labor	Equipment	Total	Total Incl O&P
0010	**THRESHOLDS**									
0011	Threshold 3' long saddles aluminum	1 Carp	48	.167	L.F.	8.15	7.65		15.80	21.50
0100	Aluminum, 8" wide, 1/2" thick		12	.667	Ea.	49	30.50		79.50	104
0500	Bronze		60	.133	L.F.	41.50	6.10		47.60	55.50
0600	Bronze, panic threshold, 5" wide, 1/2" thick		12	.667	Ea.	158	30.50		188.50	223
0700	Rubber, 1/2" thick, 5-1/2" wide		20	.400		40	18.35		58.35	74
0800	2-3/4" wide		20	.400		37.50	18.35		55.85	71.50
1950	ADA Compliant Thresholds									
2000	Threshold, wood oak 3-1/2" wide x 24" long	1 Carp	12	.667	Ea.	9	30.50		39.50	60
2010	3-1/2" wide x 36" long		12	.667		13.50	30.50		44	65

08 71 Door Hardware

08 71 20 – Hardware

08 71 20.65 Thresholds

		Crew	Daily Output	Labor-Hours	Unit	Material	2014 Bare Costs Labor	Equipment	Total	Total Incl O&P
2020	3-1/2" wide x 48" long	1 Carp	12	.667	Ea.	18	30.50		48.50	70
2030	4-1/2" wide x 24" long		12	.667		12	30.50		42.50	63
2040	4-1/2" wide x 36" long		12	.667		17	30.50		47.50	68.50
2050	4-1/2" wide x 48" long		12	.667		23	30.50		53.50	75.50
2060	6-1/2" wide x 24" long		12	.667		16.50	30.50		47	68
2070	6-1/2" wide x 36" long		12	.667		25	30.50		55.50	77.50
2080	6-1/2" wide x 48" long		12	.667		33	30.50		63.50	86.50
2090	Threshold, wood cherry 3-1/2" wide x 24" long		12	.667		13.50	30.50		44	65
2100	3-1/2" wide x 36" long		12	.667		21	30.50		51.50	73
2110	3-1/2" wide x 48" long		12	.667		27	30.50		57.50	79.50
2120	4-1/2" wide x 24" long		12	.667		17.50	30.50		48	69.50
2130	4-1/2" wide x 36" long		12	.667		25.50	30.50		56	78
2140	4-1/2" wide x 48" long		12	.667		34	30.50		64.50	87.50
2150	6-1/2" wide x 24" long		12	.667		25.50	30.50		56	78
2160	6-1/2" wide x 36" long		12	.667		36.50	30.50		67	90
2170	6-1/2" wide x 48" long		12	.667		48.50	30.50		79	104
2180	Threshold, wood walnut 3-1/2" wide x 24" long		12	.667		15.50	30.50		46	67
2190	3-1/2" wide x 36" long		12	.667		22	30.50		52.50	74
2200	3-1/2" wide x 48" long		12	.667		30	30.50		60.50	83
2210	4-1/2" wide x 24" long		12	.667		19.50	30.50		50	71.50
2220	4-1/2" wide x 36" long		12	.667		28.50	30.50		59	81.50
2230	4-1/2" wide x 48" long		12	.667		38	30.50		68.50	92
2240	6-1/2" wide x 24" long		12	.667		28	30.50		58.50	81
2250	6-1/2" wide x 36" long		12	.667		41.50	30.50		72	95.50
2260	6-1/2" wide x 48" long		12	.667		55	30.50		85.50	111
2300	Threshold, aluminum 4" wide x 36" long		12	.667		33	30.50		63.50	86.50
2310	4" wide x 48" long		12	.667		41	30.50		71.50	95
2320	4" wide x 72" long		12	.667		66	30.50		96.50	123
2330	5" wide x 36" long		12	.667		45	30.50		75.50	99.50
2340	5" wide x 48" long		12	.667		56	30.50		86.50	112
2350	5" wide x 72" long		12	.667		89	30.50		119.50	148
2360	6" wide x 36" long		12	.667		53	30.50		83.50	109
2370	6" wide x 48" long		12	.667		68	30.50		98.50	125
2380	6" wide x 72" long		12	.667		106	30.50		136.50	167
2390	7" wide x 36" long		12	.667		69	30.50		99.50	126
2400	7" wide x 48" long		12	.667		90	30.50		120.50	149
2410	7" wide x 72" long		12	.667		137	30.50		167.50	201
2500	Threshold, ramp, aluminum or rubber 24" x 24"		12	.667		190	30.50		220.50	259
9000	Minimum labor/equipment charge		4	2	Job		91.50		91.50	151

08 71 20.75 Door Hardware Accessories

		Crew	Daily Output	Labor-Hours	Unit	Material	2014 Bare Costs Labor	Equipment	Total	Total Incl O&P
0010	**DOOR HARDWARE ACCESSORIES**									
0050	Door closing coordinator, 36" (for paired openings up to 56")	1 Carp	8	1	Ea.	98	46		144	184
0060	48" (for paired openings up to 84")		8	1		105	46		151	192
0070	56" (for paired openings up to 96")		8	1		116	46		162	203
1000	Knockers, brass, standard		16	.500		44	23		67	86
1100	Deluxe		10	.800		121	36.50		157.50	194
4500	Rubber door silencers		540	.015		.36	.68		1.04	1.52
9000	Minimum labor/equipment charge		6	1.333	Job		61		61	100

08 71 20.80 Hasps

		Crew	Daily Output	Labor-Hours	Unit	Material	2014 Bare Costs Labor	Equipment	Total	Total Incl O&P
0010	**HASPS**, steel assembly									
0015	3"	1 Carp	26	.308	Ea.	4.90	14.10		19	28.50
0020	4-1/2"		13	.615		6.60	28		34.60	54

263

08 71 Door Hardware

08 71 20 - Hardware

08 71 20.80 Hasps

	08 71 20.80 Hasps	Crew	Daily Output	Labor-Hours	Unit	Material	2014 Bare Costs Labor	Equipment	Total	Total Incl O&P
0040	6"	1 Carp	12.50	.640	Ea.	8.70	29.50		38.20	57.50

08 71 20.90 Hinges

	08 71 20.90 Hinges	Crew	Daily Output	Labor-Hours	Unit	Material	2014 Bare Costs Labor	Equipment	Total	Total Incl O&P
0010	**HINGES** R087120-10									
0012	Full mortise, avg. freq., steel base, USP, 4-1/2" x 4-1/2"				Pr.	36			36	40
0100	5" x 5", USP					57.50			57.50	63
0200	6" x 6", USP					119			119	131
0400	Brass base, 4-1/2" x 4-1/2", US10					58.50			58.50	64.50
0500	5" x 5", US10					86			86	94.50
0600	6" x 6", US10					162			162	178
0800	Stainless steel base, 4-1/2" x 4-1/2", US32					74			74	81.50
0900	For non removable pin, add (security item)				Ea.	4.88			4.88	5.35
0910	For floating pin, driven tips, add					3.30			3.30	3.63
0930	For hospital type tip on pin, add					13.95			13.95	15.35
0940	For steeple type tip on pin, add					18.95			18.95	21
0950	Full mortise, high frequency, steel base, 3-1/2" x 3-1/2", US26D				Pr.	30			30	33
1000	4-1/2" x 4-1/2", USP					63			63	69
1100	5" x 5", USP					50			50	55
1200	6" x 6", USP					134			134	148
1400	Brass base, 3-1/2" x 3-1/2", US4					51			51	56
1430	4-1/2" x 4-1/2", US10					73.50			73.50	81
1500	5" x 5", US10					122			122	134
1600	6" x 6", US10					166			166	183
1800	Stainless steel base, 4-1/2" x 4-1/2", US32					103			103	114
1810	5" x 4-1/2", US32					137			137	151
1930	For hospital type tip on pin, add				Ea.	13.15			13.15	14.45
1950	Full mortise, low frequency, steel base, 3-1/2" x 3-1/2", US26D				Pr.	23			23	25.50
2000	4-1/2" x 4-1/2", USP					22			22	24.50
2100	5" x 5", USP					47.50			47.50	52
2200	6" x 6", USP					89			89	98
2300	4-1/2" x 4-1/2", US3					17.70			17.70	19.45
2310	5" x 5", US3					42.50			42.50	46.50
2400	Brass bass, 4-1/2" x 4-1/2", US10					53			53	58.50
2500	5" x 5", US10					76.50			76.50	84
2800	Stainless steel base, 4-1/2" x 4-1/2", US32					74.50			74.50	82
8000	Install hinge	1 Carp	34	.235			10.80		10.80	17.75

08 71 20.91 Special Hinges

	08 71 20.91 Special Hinges	Crew	Daily Output	Labor-Hours	Unit	Material	2014 Bare Costs Labor	Equipment	Total	Total Incl O&P
0010	**SPECIAL HINGES**									
0015	Paumelle, high frequency									
0020	Steel base, 6" x 4-1/2", US10				Pr.	145			145	160
0100	Brass base, 5" x 4-1/2", US10				Ea.	248			248	273
0200	Paumelle, average frequency, steel base, 4-1/2" x 3-1/2", US10				Pr.	98.50			98.50	108
0400	Olive knuckle, low frequency, brass base, 6" x 4-1/2", US10				Ea.	142			142	156
1000	Electric hinge with concealed conductor, average frequency									
1010	Steel base, 4-1/2" x 4-1/2", US26D				Pr.	310			310	340
1100	Bronze base, 4-1/2" x 4-1/2", US26D				"	320			320	350
1200	Electric hinge with concealed conductor, high frequency									
1210	Steel base, 4-1/2" x 4-1/2", US26D				Pr.	262			262	288
1600	Double weight, 800 lb., steel base, removable pin, 5" x 6", USP					310			310	340
1700	Steel base-welded pin, 5" x 6", USP					166			166	183
1800	Triple weight, 2000 lb., steel base, welded pin, 5" x 6", USP					400			400	440
2000	Pivot reinf., high frequency, steel base, 7-3/4" door plate, USP					149			149	164
2200	Bronze base, 7-3/4" door plate, US10					232			232	255

08 71 Door Hardware

08 71 20 – Hardware

08 71 20.91 Special Hinges

		Crew	Daily Output	Labor-Hours	Unit	Material	2014 Bare Costs Labor	2014 Bare Costs Equipment	Total	Total Incl O&P
3000	Swing clear, full mortise, full or half surface, high frequency,									
3010	Steel base, 5" high, USP				Pr.	143			143	157
3200	Swing clear, full mortise, average frequency									
3210	Steel base, 4-1/2" high, USP				Pr.	128			128	141
4000	Wide throw, average frequency, steel base, 4-1/2" x 6", USP					94.50			94.50	104
4200	High frequency, steel base, 4-1/2" x 6", USP					112			112	124
4440	US26D					89.50			89.50	98
4600	Spring hinge, single acting, 6" flange, steel				Ea.	50			50	55
4700	Brass					94.50			94.50	104
4900	Double acting, 6" flange, steel					80			80	88
4950	Brass					133			133	146
5000	T-strap, galvanized, 4"				Pr.	17.25			17.25	19
5010	6"					29.50			29.50	32.50
5020	8"					52.50			52.50	58
8000	Continuous hinges									
8010	Steel, piano, 2" x 72"	1 Carp	20	.400	Ea.	22	18.35		40.35	54
8020	Brass, piano, 1-1/16" x 30"		30	.267		8	12.25		20.25	29
8030	Acrylic, piano, 1-3/4" x 12"		40	.200		15	9.15		24.15	31.50
8040	Aluminum, door, standard duty, 7'		3	2.667		135	122		257	350
8050	Heavy duty, 7'		3	2.667		142	122		264	355
8060	8'		3	2.667		160	122		282	375
8070	Steel, door, heavy duty, 7'		3	2.667		200	122		322	420
8080	8'		3	2.667		250	122		372	475
8090	Stainless steel, door, heavy duty, 7'		3	2.667		260	122		382	485
8100	8'		3	2.667		280	122		402	510
9000	Continuous hinge, steel, full mortise, heavy duty, 96 inch		2	4		460	183		643	805
9200	Continuous geared hinge, aluminum, full mortise, standard duty, 83 inch		3	2.667		72	122		194	280
9250	Continuous geared hinge, aluminum, full mortise, heavy duty, 83 inch		3	2.667		87	122		209	297

08 71 20.95 Kick Plates

		Crew	Daily Output	Labor-Hours	Unit	Material	2014 Bare Costs Labor	2014 Bare Costs Equipment	Total	Total Incl O&P
0010	**KICK PLATES**									
0020	Stainless steel, .050, 16 ga., 8" x 28", US32	1 Carp	15	.533	Ea.	38	24.50		62.50	82
0030	8" x 30"		15	.533		41	24.50		65.50	85
0040	8" x 34"		15	.533		46	24.50		70.50	90.50
0050	10" x 28"		15	.533		76	24.50		100.50	124
0060	10" x 30"		15	.533		82	24.50		106.50	130
0070	10" x 34"		15	.533		92	24.50		116.50	141
0080	Mop/Kick, 4" x 28"		15	.533		34	24.50		58.50	77.50
0090	4" x 30"		15	.533		36	24.50		60.50	79.50
0100	4" x 34"		15	.533		41	24.50		65.50	85
0110	6" x 28"		15	.533		43	24.50		67.50	87.50
0120	6" x 30"		15	.533		47	24.50		71.50	91.50
0130	6" x 34"		15	.533		53	24.50		77.50	98.50
0500	Bronze, .050", 8" x 28"		15	.533		66.50	24.50		91	114
0510	8" x 30"		15	.533		65	24.50		89.50	112
0520	8" x 34"		15	.533		73	24.50		97.50	121
0530	10" x 28"		15	.533		75	24.50		99.50	123
0540	10" x 30"		15	.533		80	24.50		104.50	128
0550	10" x 34"		15	.533		91	24.50		115.50	140
0560	Mop/Kick, 4" x 28"		15	.533		33	24.50		57.50	76.50
0570	4" x 30"		15	.533		36	24.50		60.50	79.50
0580	4" x 34"		15	.533		37	24.50		61.50	80.50
0590	6" x 28"		15	.533		46	24.50		70.50	90.50

08 71 Door Hardware

08 71 20 – Hardware

08 71 20.95 Kick Plates

		Crew	Daily Output	Labor-Hours	Unit	Material	2014 Bare Costs Labor	Equipment	Total	Total Incl O&P
0600	6" x 30"	1 Carp	15	.533	Ea.	52	24.50		76.50	97
0610	6" x 34"		15	.533		56	24.50		80.50	102
1000	Acrylic, .125", 8" x 26"		15	.533		28	24.50		52.50	71
1010	8" x 36"		15	.533		38	24.50		62.50	82
1020	8" x 42"		15	.533		45	24.50		69.50	89.50
1030	10" x 26"		15	.533		35	24.50		59.50	78.50
1040	10" x 36"		15	.533		48	24.50		72.50	93
1050	10" x 42"		15	.533		68.50	24.50		93	116
1060	Mop/Kick, 4" x 26"		15	.533		17	24.50		41.50	58.50
1070	4" x 36"		15	.533		24	24.50		48.50	66.50
1080	4" x 42"		15	.533		27	24.50		51.50	69.50
1090	6" x 26"		15	.533		23	24.50		47.50	65.50
1100	6" x 36"		15	.533		34	24.50		58.50	77.50
1110	6" x 42"		15	.533		39	24.50		63.50	83
1220	Brass, .050", 8" x 26"		15	.533		56	24.50		80.50	102
1230	8" x 36"		15	.533		75	24.50		99.50	123
1240	8" x 42"		15	.533		86	24.50		110.50	135
1250	10" x 26"		15	.533		71	24.50		95.50	118
1260	10" x 36"		15	.533		91	24.50		115.50	140
1270	10" x 42"		15	.533		105	24.50		129.50	156
1320	Mop/Kick, 4" x 26"		15	.533		28	24.50		52.50	71
1330	4" x 36"		15	.533		39	24.50		63.50	83
1340	4" x 42"		15	.533		44	24.50		68.50	88.50
1350	6" x 26"		15	.533		38	24.50		62.50	82
1360	6" x 36"		15	.533		48	24.50		72.50	93
1370	6" x 42"		15	.533		55	24.50		79.50	101
1800	Aluminum, .050", 8" x 26"		15	.533		29	24.50		53.50	72
1810	8" x 36"		15	.533		40	24.50		64.50	84
1820	8" x 42"		15	.533		47	24.50		71.50	91.50
1830	10" x 26"		15	.533		36	24.50		60.50	79.50
1840	10" x 36"		15	.533		50	24.50		74.50	95
1850	10" x 42"		15	.533		59	24.50		83.50	105
1860	Mop/Kick, 4" x 26"		15	.533		15	24.50		39.50	56.50
1870	4" x 36"		15	.533		20	24.50		44.50	62
1880	4" x 42"		15	.533		24	24.50		48.50	66.50
1890	6" x 26"		15	.533		22	24.50		46.50	64
1900	6" x 36"		15	.533		30	24.50		54.50	73
1910	6" x 42"		15	.533		35	24.50		59.50	78.50
9000	Minimum labor/equipment charge		6	1.333	Job		61		61	100

08 71 21 – Astragals

08 71 21.10 Exterior Mouldings, Astragals

		Crew	Daily Output	Labor-Hours	Unit	Material	2014 Bare Costs Labor	Equipment	Total	Total Incl O&P
0010	**EXTERIOR MOULDINGS, ASTRAGALS**									
0400	One piece, overlapping cadmium plated steel, flat, 3/16" x 2"	1 Carp	90	.089	L.F.	4	4.08		8.08	11.10
0600	Prime coated steel, flat, 1/8" x 3"		90	.089		5.75	4.08		9.83	13.05
0800	Stainless steel, flat, 3/32" x 1-5/8"		90	.089		16	4.08		20.08	24.50
1000	Aluminum, flat, 1/8" x 2"		90	.089		4.10	4.08		8.18	11.20
1200	Nail on, "T" extrusion		120	.067		1.90	3.06		4.96	7.10
1300	Vinyl bulb insert		105	.076		2.50	3.49		5.99	8.50
1600	Screw on, "T" extrusion		90	.089		3.20	4.08		7.28	10.20
1700	Vinyl insert		75	.107		4.50	4.89		9.39	13
2000	"L" extrusion, neoprene bulbs		75	.107		4.10	4.89		8.99	12.55
2100	Neoprene sponge insert		75	.107		6.90	4.89		11.79	15.65

08 71 Door Hardware

08 71 21 – Astragals

08 71 21.10 Exterior Mouldings, Astragals	Crew	Daily Output	Labor-Hours	Unit	Material	2014 Bare Costs Labor	2014 Bare Costs Equipment	Total	Total Incl O&P
2200	Magnetic	1 Carp	75	.107	L.F.	10.60	4.89		15.49	19.70
2400	Spring hinged security seal, with cam		75	.107		6.80	4.89		11.69	15.55
2600	Spring loaded locking bolt, vinyl insert		45	.178		9.20	8.15		17.35	23.50
2800	Neoprene sponge strip, "Z" shaped, aluminum		60	.133		8.25	6.10		14.35	19.15
2900	Solid neoprene strip, nail on aluminum strip		90	.089		4.05	4.08		8.13	11.15
3000	One piece stile protection									
3020	Neoprene fabric loop, nail on aluminum strips	1 Carp	60	.133	L.F.	1.10	6.10		7.20	11.25
3110	Flush mounted aluminum extrusion, 1/2" x 1-1/4"		60	.133		6.90	6.10		13	17.65
3140	3/4" x 1-3/8"		60	.133		4.10	6.10		10.20	14.55
3160	1-1/8" x 1-3/4"		60	.133		4.70	6.10		10.80	15.20
3300	Mortise, 9/16" x 3/4"		60	.133		4.10	6.10		10.20	14.55
3320	13/16" x 1-3/8"		60	.133		4.30	6.10		10.40	14.80
3600	Spring bronze strip, nail on type		105	.076		1.85	3.49		5.34	7.80
3620	Screw on, with retainer		75	.107		2.70	4.89		7.59	11
3800	Flexible stainless steel housing, pile insert, 1/2" door		105	.076		7.25	3.49		10.74	13.75
3820	3/4" door		105	.076		8.10	3.49		11.59	14.65
4000	Extruded aluminum retainer, flush mount, pile insert		105	.076		2.25	3.49		5.74	8.25
4080	Mortise, felt insert		90	.089		4.55	4.08		8.63	11.70
4160	Mortise with spring, pile insert		90	.089		3.40	4.08		7.48	10.45
4400	Rigid vinyl retainer, mortise, pile insert		105	.076		2.70	3.49		6.19	8.70
4600	Wool pile filler strip, aluminum backing		105	.076		2.70	3.49		6.19	8.70
5000	Two piece overlapping astragal, extruded aluminum retainer									
5010	Pile insert	1 Carp	60	.133	L.F.	3.35	6.10		9.45	13.75
5020	Vinyl bulb insert		60	.133		1.85	6.10		7.95	12.10
5040	Vinyl flap insert		60	.133		3.65	6.10		9.75	14.05
5060	Solid neoprene flap insert		60	.133		6.55	6.10		12.65	17.25
5080	Hypalon rubber flap insert		60	.133		6.65	6.10		12.75	17.35
5090	Snap on cover, pile insert		60	.133		9.45	6.10		15.55	20.50
5400	Magnetic aluminum, surface mounted		60	.133		23	6.10		29.10	35
5500	Interlocking aluminum, 5/8" x 1" neoprene bulb insert		45	.178		5.70	8.15		13.85	19.65
5600	Adjustable aluminum, 9/16" x 21/32", pile insert		45	.178		17.55	8.15		25.70	32.50
5790	For vinyl bulb, deduct					.75			.75	.83
5800	Magnetic, adjustable, 9/16" x 21/32"	1 Carp	45	.178		23	8.15		31.15	38.50
6000	Two piece stile protection									
6010	Cloth backed rubber loop, 1" gap, nail on aluminum strips	1 Carp	45	.178	L.F.	4.35	8.15		12.50	18.20
6040	Screw on aluminum strips		45	.178		6.55	8.15		14.70	20.50
6100	1-1/2" gap, screw on aluminum extrusion		45	.178		5.85	8.15		14	19.85
6240	Vinyl fabric loop, slotted aluminum extrusion, 1" gap		45	.178		2.20	8.15		10.35	15.80
6300	1-1/4" gap		45	.178		6.20	8.15		14.35	20

08 71 25 – Weatherstripping

08 71 25.10 Mechanical Seals, Weatherstripping

		Crew	Daily Output	Labor-Hours	Unit	Material	2014 Bare Costs Labor	2014 Bare Costs Equipment	Total	Total Incl O&P
0010	**MECHANICAL SEALS, WEATHERSTRIPPING**									
1000	Doors, wood frame, interlocking, for 3' x 7' door, zinc	1 Carp	3	2.667	Opng.	44	122		166	250
1100	Bronze		3	2.667		56	122		178	263
1300	6' x 7' opening, zinc		2	4		54	183		237	360
1400	Bronze		2	4		65	183		248	370
1700	Wood frame, spring type, bronze									
1800	3' x 7' door	1 Carp	7.60	1.053	Opng.	23	48.50		71.50	105
1900	6' x 7' door	"	7	1.143	"	29.50	52.50		82	119
2200	Metal frame, spring type, bronze									
2300	3' x 7' door	1 Carp	3	2.667	Opng.	46.50	122		168.50	252
2400	6' x 7' door	"	2.50	3.200	"	52	147		199	298

08 71 Door Hardware

08 71 25 - Weatherstripping

08 71 25.10 Mechanical Seals, Weatherstripping

	08 71 25.10 Mechanical Seals, Weatherstripping	Crew	Daily Output	Labor-Hours	Unit	Material	2014 Bare Costs Labor	Equipment	Total	Total Incl O&P
2500	For stainless steel, spring type, add					133%				
2700	Metal frame, extruded sections, 3' x 7' door, aluminum	1 Carp	3	2.667	Opng.	28	122		150	232
2800	Bronze		3	2.667		82	122		204	291
3100	6' x 7' door, aluminum		1.50	5.333		35	245		280	440
3200	Bronze		1.50	5.333		137	245		382	550
3500	Threshold weatherstripping									
3650	Door sweep, flush mounted, aluminum	1 Carp	25	.320	Ea.	19	14.65		33.65	45
3700	Vinyl		25	.320		18	14.65		32.65	44
5000	Garage door bottom weatherstrip, 12' aluminum, clear		14	.571		25	26		51	70.50
5010	Bronze		14	.571		90	26		116	142
5050	Bottom protection, Rubber		14	.571		37	26		63	83.50
5100	Threshold		14	.571		72	26		98	122
9000	Minimum labor/equipment charge		3	2.667	Job		122		122	201

08 74 Access Control Hardware

08 74 13 - Card Key Access Control Hardware

08 74 13.50 Card Key Access

	08 74 13.50 Card Key Access	Crew	Daily Output	Labor-Hours	Unit	Material	2014 Bare Costs Labor	Equipment	Total	Total Incl O&P
0010	**CARD KEY ACCESS**									
0020	Computerized system , processor, proximity reader and cards									
0030	Does not inculde door hardware, lockset or wiring									
0040	Card key system for 1 door				Ea.	1,175			1,175	1,300
0060	Card key system for 2 doors					2,125			2,125	2,350
0080	Card key system for 4 doors					2,650			2,650	2,900
0100	Processor for card key access system					850			850	935
0160	Magnetic lock for electric access, 600 Pound holding force					190			190	209
0170	Magnetic lock for electric access, 1200 Pound holding force					190			190	209
0200	Proximity card reader					125			125	138

08 74 19 - Biometric Identity Access Control Hardware

08 74 19.50 Biometric Identity Access

	08 74 19.50 Biometric Identity Access	Crew	Daily Output	Labor-Hours	Unit	Material	2014 Bare Costs Labor	Equipment	Total	Total Incl O&P
0010	**BIOMETRIC IDENTITY ACCESS**									
0220	Hand geometry scanner, mem of 512 users, excl striker/power	1 Elec	3	2.667	Ea.	2,100	142		2,242	2,525
0230	Memory upgrade for, adds 9,700 user profiles		8	1		300	53.50		353.50	415
0240	Adds 32,500 user profiles		8	1		600	53.50		653.50	745
0250	Prison type, memory of 256 users, excl striker, power		3	2.667		2,600	142		2,742	3,075
0260	Memory upgrade for, adds 3,300 user profiles		8	1		250	53.50		303.50	360
0270	Adds 9,700 user profiles		8	1		460	53.50		513.50	590
0280	Adds 27,900 user profiles		8	1		610	53.50		663.50	755
0290	All weather, mem of 512 users, excl striker/power		3	2.667		3,900	142		4,042	4,525
0300	Facial & fingerprint scanner, combination unit, excl striker/power		3	2.667		4,300	142		4,442	4,950
0310	Access for, for initial setup, excl striker/power		3	2.667		1,100	142		1,242	1,425

08 75 Window Hardware

08 75 10 – Window Handles and Latches

08 75 10.10 Handles and Latches

		Crew	Daily Output	Labor-Hours	Unit	Material	2014 Bare Costs Labor	Equipment	Total	Total Incl O&P
0010	**HANDLES AND LATCHES**									
1000	Handles, surface mounted, aluminum	1 Carp	24	.333	Ea.	4.30	15.30		19.60	29.50
1020	Brass		24	.333		5.55	15.30		20.85	31
1040	Chrome		24	.333		6.90	15.30		22.20	32.50
1500	Recessed, aluminum		12	.667		2.46	30.50		32.96	52.50
1520	Brass		12	.667		3.88	30.50		34.38	54.50
1540	Chrome		12	.667		3.43	30.50		33.93	54
2000	Latches, aluminum		20	.400		3.26	18.35		21.61	33.50
2020	Brass		20	.400		4.18	18.35		22.53	34.50
2040	Chrome		20	.400		3.04	18.35		21.39	33.50
9000	Minimum labor/equipment charge		6	1.333	Job		61		61	100

08 75 30 – Weatherstripping

08 75 30.10 Mechanical Weather Seals

		Crew	Daily Output	Labor-Hours	Unit	Material	2014 Bare Costs Labor	Equipment	Total	Total Incl O&P
0010	**MECHANICAL WEATHER SEALS**, Window, double hung, 3' X 5'									
0020	Zinc	1 Carp	7.20	1.111	Opng.	20	51		71	106
0100	Bronze		7.20	1.111		39	51		90	127
0200	Vinyl V strip		7	1.143		9.25	52.50		61.75	96
0500	As above but heavy duty, zinc		4.60	1.739		20	79.50		99.50	153
0600	Bronze		4.60	1.739		70	79.50		149.50	208
9000	Minimum labor/equipment charge	1 Clab	4.60	1.739	Job		63.50		63.50	105

08 79 Hardware Accessories

08 79 20 – Door Accessories

08 79 20.10 Door Hardware Accessories

		Crew	Daily Output	Labor-Hours	Unit	Material	2014 Bare Costs Labor	Equipment	Total	Total Incl O&P
0010	**DOOR HARDWARE ACCESSORIES**									
0140	Door bolt, surface, 4"	1 Carp	32	.250	Ea.	11.70	11.45		23.15	31.50
0160	Door latch	"	12	.667	"	8.55	30.50		39.05	59.50
0200	Sliding closet door									
0220	Track and hanger, single	1 Carp	10	.800	Ea.	56	36.50		92.50	122
0240	Double		8	1		80	46		126	164
0260	Door guide, single		48	.167		30	7.65		37.65	45.50
0280	Double		48	.167		40	7.65		47.65	56.50
0600	Deadbolt and lock cover plate, brass or stainless steel		30	.267		28	12.25		40.25	51
0620	Hole cover plate, brass or chrome		35	.229		8	10.50		18.50	26
2240	Mortise lockset, passage, lever handle		9	.889		170	41		211	254
4000	Security chain, standard		18	.444		10	20.50		30.50	44.50
4100	Deluxe		18	.444		45	20.50		65.50	83

08 81 Glass Glazing

08 81 10 – Float Glass

08 81 10.10 Various Types and Thickness of Float Glass

		Crew	Daily Output	Labor-Hours	Unit	Material	2014 Bare Costs Labor	Equipment	Total	Total Incl O&P
0010	**VARIOUS TYPES AND THICKNESS OF FLOAT GLASS**									
0020	3/16" Plain	2 Glaz	130	.123	S.F.	4.93	5.40		10.33	14.20
0200	Tempered, clear		130	.123		6.85	5.40		12.25	16.35
0300	Tinted		130	.123		7.80	5.40		13.20	17.40
0600	1/4" thick, clear, plain		120	.133		5.75	5.85		11.60	15.85
0700	Tinted		120	.133		9.10	5.85		14.95	19.50
0800	Tempered, clear		120	.133		8.70	5.85		14.55	19.05
0900	Tinted		120	.133		10.70	5.85		16.55	21.50

08 81 Glass Glazing

08 81 10 – Float Glass

08 81 10.10 Various Types and Thickness of Float Glass

		Crew	Daily Output	Labor-Hours	Unit	Material	2014 Bare Costs Labor	2014 Bare Costs Equipment	Total	Total Incl O&P
1600	3/8" thick, clear, plain	2 Glaz	75	.213	S.F.	10.05	9.40		19.45	26.50
1700	Tinted		75	.213		15.70	9.40		25.10	32.50
1800	Tempered, clear		75	.213		16.40	9.40		25.80	33.50
1900	Tinted		75	.213		18.55	9.40		27.95	36
2200	1/2" thick, clear, plain		55	.291		17	12.80		29.80	39.50
2300	Tinted		55	.291		27.50	12.80		40.30	51
2400	Tempered, clear		55	.291		24.50	12.80		37.30	47.50
2500	Tinted		55	.291		25.50	12.80		38.30	49
2800	5/8" thick, clear, plain		45	.356		27.50	15.65		43.15	55.50
2900	Tempered, clear		45	.356		31.50	15.65		47.15	60
3200	3/4" thick, clear, plain		35	.457		35.50	20		55.50	71.50
3300	Tempered, clear		35	.457		41	20		61	78
3600	1" thick, clear, plain	↓	30	.533		59	23.50		82.50	103
8900	For low emissivity coating for 3/16" & 1/4" only, add to above				↓	18%				
9000	Minimum labor/equipment charge	1 Glaz	2	4	Job		176		176	286

08 81 13 – Decorative Glass Glazing

08 81 13.40 Glass Column Covers

		Crew	Daily Output	Labor-Hours	Unit	Material	2014 Bare Costs Labor	2014 Bare Costs Equipment	Total	Total Incl O&P
0010	**GLASS COLUMN COVERS**									
0020	Tempered glass column cover, 24" dia., up to 12' high	2 Glaz	30	.533	V.L.F.	82	23.50		105.50	128
0040	up to 20' high	"	24	.667	"	120	29.50		149.50	180

08 81 17 – Fire Glass

08 81 17.10 Fire Resistant Glass

		Crew	Daily Output	Labor-Hours	Unit	Material	2014 Bare Costs Labor	2014 Bare Costs Equipment	Total	Total Incl O&P
0010	**FIRE RESISTANT GLASS**									
0020	Fire Glass Minimum	2 Glaz	40	.400	S.F.	30	17.60		47.60	61.50
0030	Mid Range		40	.400		70	17.60		87.60	106
0050	High End	↓	40	.400	↓	310	17.60		327.60	370

08 81 20 – Vision Panels

08 81 20.10 Full Vision

		Crew	Daily Output	Labor-Hours	Unit	Material	2014 Bare Costs Labor	2014 Bare Costs Equipment	Total	Total Incl O&P
0010	**FULL VISION**, window system with 3/4" glass mullions									
0020	Up to 10' high	H-2	130	.185	S.F.	62.50	7.70		70.20	81.50
0100	10' to 20' high, minimum		110	.218		67	9.05		76.05	88.50
0150	Average		100	.240		72	10		82	96
0200	Maximum	↓	80	.300	↓	81	12.45		93.45	110
9000	Minimum labor/equipment charge	1 Glaz	2	4	Job		176		176	286

08 81 25 – Glazing Variables

08 81 25.10 Applications of Glazing

					Unit	Material	2014 Bare Costs Labor	2014 Bare Costs Equipment	Total	Total Incl O&P
0010	**APPLICATIONS OF GLAZING**	R088110-10								
0500	For high rise glazing, exterior, add per S.F. per story				S.F.					.49
0600	For glass replacement, add				"		100%			
0700	For gasket settings, add				L.F.	5.75			5.75	6.35
0900	For sloped glazing, add				S.F.		26%			
2000	Fabrication, polished edges, 1/4" thick				Inch	.55			.55	.61
2100	1/2" thick					1.30			1.30	1.43
2500	Mitered edges, 1/4" thick					1.30			1.30	1.43
2600	1/2" thick				↓	2.15			2.15	2.37

08 81 Glass Glazing

08 81 30 – Insulating Glass

08 81 30.10 Reduce Heat Transfer Glass		Crew	Daily Output	Labor-Hours	Unit	Material	2014 Bare Costs Labor	Equipment	Total	Total Incl O&P
0010	**REDUCE HEAT TRANSFER GLASS**									
0015	2 lites 1/8" float, 1/2" thk under 15 S.F.									
0020	Clear R088110-10	G	2 Glaz	95	.168	S.F.	9.95	7.40		17.35	23
0100	Tinted	G		95	.168		13.80	7.40		21.20	27.50
0200	2 lites 3/16" float, for 5/8" thk unit, 15 to 30 S.F., clear	G		90	.178		13.70	7.85		21.55	28
0400	1" thk, dbl. glazed, 1/4" float, 30-70 S.F., clear	G		75	.213		16.60	9.40		26	33.50
0500	Tinted	G		75	.213		23.50	9.40		32.90	41.50
2000	Both lites, light & heat reflective	G		85	.188		31.50	8.30		39.80	48
2500	Heat reflective, film inside, 1" thick unit, clear	G		85	.188		27.50	8.30		35.80	44
2600	Tinted	G		85	.188		28.50	8.30		36.80	45
3000	Film on weatherside, clear, 1/2" thick unit	G		95	.168		19.60	7.40		27	33.50
3100	5/8" thick unit	G		90	.178		19.90	7.85		27.75	34.50
3200	1" thick unit	G	▼	85	.188		27	8.30		35.30	43.50
3350	Clear heat reflective film on weather side, retrofit minimum	G	1 Glaz	50	.160		12.90	7.05		19.95	25.50
3360	Maximum	G	"	25	.320		13.70	14.10		27.80	38
3370	Reflective or tinted, add	G					4.30			4.30	4.73
5000	Spectrally selective film, on ext, blocks solar gain/allows 70% of light	G	2 Glaz	95	.168	▼	12.50	7.40		19.90	26
9000	Minimum labor/equipment charge		1 Glaz	2	4	Job		176		176	286

08 81 40 – Plate Glass

08 81 40.10 Plate Glass		Crew	Daily Output	Labor-Hours	Unit	Material	2014 Bare Costs Labor	Equipment	Total	Total Incl O&P
0010	**PLATE GLASS** Twin ground, polished,									
0020	3/16" thick		2 Glaz	100	.160	S.F.	5.15	7.05		12.20	17.05
0100	1/4" thick			94	.170		7.05	7.50		14.55	19.95
0200	3/8" thick			60	.267		12.25	11.75		24	32.50
0300	1/2" thick		▼	40	.400	▼	24	17.60		41.60	54.50

08 81 55 – Window Glass

08 81 55.10 Sheet Glass		Crew	Daily Output	Labor-Hours	Unit	Material	2014 Bare Costs Labor	Equipment	Total	Total Incl O&P
0010	**SHEET GLASS** (window), clear float, stops, putty bed									
0015	1/8" thick, clear float		2 Glaz	480	.033	S.F.	3.60	1.47		5.07	6.35
0500	3/16" thick, clear			480	.033		5.80	1.47		7.27	8.80
0600	Tinted			480	.033		7.45	1.47		8.92	10.60
0700	Tempered		▼	480	.033		9.20	1.47		10.67	12.50
2000	Replace broken window lite, 1/8" glass (9 S.F. maximum)		1 Glaz	48	.167		5.15	7.35		12.50	17.55
2100	1/4" plate (16 S.F. maximum)		"	48	.167	▼	6.05	7.35		13.40	18.55
9000	Minimum labor/equipment charge		2 Glaz	5	3.200	Job		141		141	228

08 81 65 – Wire Glass

08 81 65.10 Glass Reinforced With Wire		Crew	Daily Output	Labor-Hours	Unit	Material	2014 Bare Costs Labor	Equipment	Total	Total Incl O&P
0010	**GLASS REINFORCED WITH WIRE**									
0012	1/4" thick rough obscure		2 Glaz	135	.119	S.F.	23.50	5.20		28.70	34
1000	Polished wire, 1/4" thick, diamond, clear			135	.119		27.50	5.20		32.70	38.50
1500	Pinstripe, obscure		▼	135	.119	▼	40.50	5.20		45.70	53

271

08 83 Mirrors

08 83 13 – Mirrored Glass Glazing

08 83 13.10 Mirrors

		Crew	Daily Output	Labor-Hours	Unit	Material	2014 Bare Costs Labor	Equipment	Total	Total Incl O&P
0010	**MIRRORS**, No frames, wall type, 1/4" plate glass, polished edge									
0100	Up to 5 S.F.	2 Glaz	125	.128	S.F.	9.50	5.65		15.15	19.60
0200	Over 5 S.F.		160	.100		9.25	4.41		13.66	17.35
0500	Door type, 1/4" plate glass, up to 12 S.F.		160	.100		8.55	4.41		12.96	16.55
1000	Float glass, up to 10 S.F., 1/8" thick		160	.100		5.65	4.41		10.06	13.35
1100	3/16" thick		150	.107		6.95	4.70		11.65	15.25
1500	12" x 12" wall tiles, square edge, clear		195	.082		2.22	3.61		5.83	8.30
1600	Veined		195	.082		5.80	3.61		9.41	12.25
2000	1/4" thick, stock sizes, one way transparent		125	.128		18.95	5.65		24.60	30
2010	Bathroom, unframed, laminated		160	.100		13.30	4.41		17.71	22
2500	Tempered		160	.100		17.80	4.41		22.21	27

08 83 13.15 Reflective Glass

		Crew	Daily Output	Labor-Hours	Unit	Material	2014 Bare Costs Labor	Equipment	Total	Total Incl O&P
0010	**REFLECTIVE GLASS**									
0100	1/4" float with fused metallic oxide fixed G	2 Glaz	115	.139	S.F.	16.95	6.15		23.10	28.50
0500	1/4" float glass with reflective applied coating G	"	115	.139	"	13.70	6.15		19.85	25

08 84 Plastic Glazing

08 84 10 – Plexiglass Glazing

08 84 10.10 Plexiglass Acrylic

		Crew	Daily Output	Labor-Hours	Unit	Material	2014 Bare Costs Labor	Equipment	Total	Total Incl O&P
0010	**PLEXIGLASS ACRYLIC**, clear, masked,									
0020	1/8" thick, cut sheets	2 Glaz	170	.094	S.F.	12	4.15		16.15	19.90
0200	Full sheets		195	.082		5	3.61		8.61	11.35
0500	1/4" thick, cut sheets		165	.097		14	4.27		18.27	22.50
0600	Full sheets		185	.086		9	3.81		12.81	16.10
0900	3/8" thick, cut sheets		155	.103		20	4.55		24.55	29.50
1000	Full sheets		180	.089		15	3.92		18.92	23
1300	1/2" thick, cut sheets		135	.119		28	5.20		33.20	39.50
1400	Full sheets		150	.107		20	4.70		24.70	29.50
1700	3/4" thick, cut sheets		115	.139		69	6.15		75.15	86
1800	Full sheets		130	.123		40	5.40		45.40	53
2100	1" thick, cut sheets		105	.152		77.50	6.70		84.20	96.50
2200	Full sheets		125	.128		48	5.65		53.65	62
3000	Colored, 1/8" thick, cut sheets		170	.094		18	4.15		22.15	26.50
3200	Full sheets		195	.082		11	3.61		14.61	17.95
3500	1/4" thick, cut sheets		165	.097		20	4.27		24.27	29
3600	Full sheets		185	.086		14	3.81		17.81	21.50
4000	Mirrors, untinted, cut sheets, 1/8" thick		185	.086		12	3.81		15.81	19.40
4200	1/4" thick		180	.089		16	3.92		19.92	24

08 84 20 – Polycarbonate

08 84 20.10 Thermoplastic

		Crew	Daily Output	Labor-Hours	Unit	Material	2014 Bare Costs Labor	Equipment	Total	Total Incl O&P
0010	**THERMOPLASTIC**, clear, masked, cut sheets									
0020	1/8" thick	2 Glaz	170	.094	S.F.	14	4.15		18.15	22
0500	3/16" thick		165	.097		16	4.27		20.27	24.50
1000	1/4" thick		155	.103		17	4.55		21.55	26
1500	3/8" thick		150	.107		26	4.70		30.70	36
9000	Minimum labor/equipment charge	1 Glaz	2	4	Job		176		176	286

08 85 Glazing Accessories

08 85 10 – Miscellaneous Glazing Accessories

08 85 10.10 Glazing Gaskets	Crew	Daily Output	Labor-Hours	Unit	Material	2014 Bare Costs Labor	Equipment	Total	Total Incl O&P
0010 **GLAZING GASKETS**, Neoprene for glass tongued mullion									
0015　　　　1/4" glass	2 Glaz	200	.080	L.F.	.71	3.52		4.23	6.50
0020　　　　3/8"		200	.080		.90	3.52		4.42	6.70
0040　　　　1/2"		200	.080		1.02	3.52		4.54	6.80
0060　　　　3/4"		180	.089		1.49	3.92		5.41	8
0080　　　　1"		180	.089		1.20	3.92		5.12	7.65
1000　　Glazing compound, wood	1 Glaz	58	.138		1.04	6.10		7.14	11
1005　　Glazing compound, per window, up to 30 L.F.					1.04			1.04	1.14
1006　　Glazing compound, per window, up to 30 L.F.				Ea.	31			31	34.50
1020　　Metal	1 Glaz	58	.138	L.F.	1.04	6.10		7.14	11

08 87 Glazing Surface Films

08 87 13 – Solar Control Films

08 87 13.10 Solar Films On Glass

		Crew	Daily Output	Labor-Hours	Unit	Material	2014 Bare Costs Labor	Equipment	Total	Total Incl O&P
0010 **SOLAR FILMS ON GLASS** (glass not included)										
2000　　Minimum	G	2 Glaz	180	.089	S.F.	6.80	3.92		10.72	13.85
2050　　Maximum	G	"	225	.071	"	15.30	3.13		18.43	22

08 87 23 – Safety and Security Films

08 87 23.13 Safety Films

	Crew	Daily Output	Labor-Hours	Unit	Material	2014 Bare Costs Labor	Equipment	Total	Total Incl O&P
0010 **SAFETY FILMS**									
2010　　Window protection film, controls blast damage	2 Glaz	80	.200	S.F.	6.80	8.80		15.60	22

08 87 23.16 Security Films

	Crew	Daily Output	Labor-Hours	Unit	Material	2014 Bare Costs Labor	Equipment	Total	Total Incl O&P
0010 **SECURITY FILMS**, clear, 32000 psi tensile strength, adhered to glass　R088110-10									
0100　　.002" thick, daylight installation	H-2	950	.025	S.F.	2.70	1.05		3.75	4.68
0150　　.004" thick, daylight installation		800	.030		3.35	1.25		4.60	5.70
0200　　.006" thick, daylight installation		700	.034		3.60	1.43		5.03	6.30
0210　　　Install for anchorage		600	.040		4	1.66		5.66	7.10
0400　　.007" thick, daylight installation		600	.040		4.45	1.66		6.11	7.60
0410　　　Install for anchorage		500	.048		4.94	2		6.94	8.70
0500　　.008" thick, daylight installation		500	.048		5	2		7	8.75
0510　　　Install for anchorage		500	.048		5.55	2		7.55	9.35
0600　　.015" thick, daylight installation		400	.060		8.80	2.49		11.29	13.75
0610　　　Install for anchorage		400	.060		5.55	2.49		8.04	10.15
0900　　Security film anchorage, mechanical attachment and cover plate	H-3	370	.043	L.F.	9.75	1.70		11.45	13.50
0950　　Security film anchorage, wet glaze structural caulking	1 Glaz	225	.036	"	.92	1.57		2.49	3.55
1000　　Adhered security film removal	1 Clab	275	.029	S.F.		1.07		1.07	1.75

08 88 Special Function Glazing

08 88 52 – Prefabricated Glass Block Windows

08 88 52.10 Prefabricated Glass Block Windows

	Crew	Daily Output	Labor-Hours	Unit	Material	2014 Bare Costs Labor	Equipment	Total	Total Incl O&P
0010 **PREFABRICATED GLASS BLOCK WINDOWS**									
0015　Includes frame and silicone seal									
0020　　Glass Block Window 16" x 8"	2 Glaz	6	2.667	Ea.	185	117		302	395
0025　　　16" x 16"		6	2.667		223	117		340	435
0030　　　16" x 24"		6	2.667		265	117		382	480
0050　　　16" x 48"		4	4		380	176		556	705
0100　　Glass Block Window 24" x 8"		6	2.667		211	117		328	420
0110　　　24" x 16"		6	2.667		265	117		382	480

08 88 Special Function Glazing

08 88 52 – Prefabricated Glass Block Windows

08 88 52.10 Prefabricated Glass Block Windows

		Crew	Daily Output	Labor-Hours	Unit	Material	2014 Bare Costs Labor	Equipment	Total	Total Incl O&P
0120	24" x 24"	2 Glaz	6	2.667	Ea.	315	117		432	535
0150	24" x 48"		6	2.667		470	117		587	705
0200	Glass Block Window 32" x 8"		6	2.667		211	117		328	420
0210	32" x 16"		6	2.667		300	117		417	520
0220	32" x 24"		4	4		365	176		541	685
0250	32" x 48"		4	4		555	176		731	895
0300	Glass Block Window 40" x 8"		6	2.667		271	117		388	490
0310	40" x 16"		6	2.667		340	117		457	565
0320	40" x 24"		6	2.667		410	117		527	645
0350	40" x 48"		6	2.667		645	117		762	900
0400	Glass Block Window 48" x 8"		6	2.667		299	117		416	520
0410	48" x 16"		6	2.667		380	117		497	605
0420	48" x 24"		6	2.667		470	117		587	705
0450	48" x 48"		6	2.667		730	117		847	995
0500	Glass Block Window 56" x 8"		6	2.667		330	117		447	555
0510	56" x 16"		4	4		415	176		591	745
0520	56" x 24"		4	4		520	176		696	855
0550	56" x 48"		4	4		825	176		1,001	1,200

08 88 52.20 Prefabricated Glass Block Windows Hurricane Resistant

		Crew	Daily Output	Labor-Hours	Unit	Material	2014 Bare Costs Labor	Equipment	Total	Total Incl O&P
0010	**PREFABRICATED GLASS BLOCK WINDOWS HURRICANE RESISTANT**									
0015	Includes frame and silicone seal									
3020	Glass Block Window 16" x 16"	2 Glaz	6	2.667	Ea.	500	117		617	740
3030	16" x 24"		6	2.667		580	117		697	830
3040	16" x 32"		4	4		660	176		836	1,000
3050	16" x 40"		4	4		705	176		881	1,050
3060	16" x 48"		4	4		740	176		916	1,100
3070	16" x 56"		4	4		900	176		1,076	1,275
3080	Glass Block Window 24" x 24"		6	2.667		660	117		777	915
3090	24" x 32"		4	4		740	176		916	1,100
3100	24" x 40"		4	4		900	176		1,076	1,275
3110	24" x 48"		4	4		945	176		1,121	1,325
3120	24" x 56"		4	4		980	176		1,156	1,350
3130	Glass Block Window 32" x 32"		4	4		820	176		996	1,200
3140	32" x 40"		4	4		925	176		1,101	1,300
3150	32" x 48"		4	4		1,050	176		1,226	1,450
3160	32" x 56"		4	4		1,225	176		1,401	1,625
3200	Glass Block Window 40" x 40"		4	4		1,050	176		1,226	1,450
3210	40" x 48"		3	5.333		1,275	235		1,510	1,775
3220	40" x 56"		3	5.333		1,400	235		1,635	1,925
3260	Glass Block Window 48" x 48"		3	5.333		1,450	235		1,685	1,975
3270	48" x 56"		3	5.333		1,625	235		1,860	2,150
3310	Glass Block Window 56" x 56"		3	5.333		1,775	235		2,010	2,325

08 88 56 – Ballistics-Resistant Glazing

08 88 56.10 Laminated Glass

		Crew	Daily Output	Labor-Hours	Unit	Material	2014 Bare Costs Labor	Equipment	Total	Total Incl O&P
0010	**LAMINATED GLASS**									
0020	Clear float .03" vinyl 1/4"	2 Glaz	90	.178	S.F.	12.10	7.85		19.95	26
0100	3/8" thick		78	.205		22.50	9.05		31.55	39
0200	.06" vinyl, 1/2" thick		65	.246		25.50	10.85		36.35	45.50
1000	5/8" thick		90	.178		29.50	7.85		37.35	45
2000	Bullet-resisting, 1-3/16" thick, to 15 S.F.		16	1		93	44		137	174
2100	Over 15 S.F.		16	1		108	44		152	190
2200	2" thick, to 15 S.F.		10	1.600		134	70.50		204.50	261

08 88 Special Function Glazing

08 88 56 – Ballistics-Resistant Glazing

08 88 56.10 Laminated Glass

		Crew	Daily Output	Labor-Hours	Unit	Material	2014 Bare Costs Labor	Equipment	Total	Total Incl O&P
2300	Over 15 S.F.	2 Glaz	10	1.600	S.F.	115	70.50		185.50	241
2500	2-1/4" thick, to 15 S.F.		12	1.333		149	58.50		207.50	259
2600	Over 15 S.F.		12	1.333		140	58.50		198.50	249
2700	Level 2 (.357 magnum), NIJ and UL		12	1.333		76	58.50		134.50	179
2750	Level 3A (.44 magnum) NIJ, UL 3		12	1.333		81	58.50		139.50	184
2800	Level 4 (AK-47) NIJ, UL 7 & 8		12	1.333		112	58.50		170.50	218
2850	Level 5 (M-16) UL		12	1.333		115	58.50		173.50	222
2900	Level 3 (7.62 Armor Piercing) NIJ, UL 4 & 5		12	1.333		136	58.50		194.50	245

08 91 Louvers

08 91 16 – Operable Louvers

08 91 16.10 Movable Blade Louvers

		Crew	Daily Output	Labor-Hours	Unit	Material	2014 Bare Costs Labor	Equipment	Total	Total Incl O&P
0010	**MOVABLE BLADE LOUVERS**									
0100	PVC, commercial grade, 12" x 12"	1 Shee	20	.400	Ea.	82	22		104	125
0110	16" x 16"		14	.571		96	31.50		127.50	156
0120	18" x 18"		14	.571		99	31.50		130.50	159
0130	24" x 24"		14	.571		140	31.50		171.50	204
0140	30" x 30"		12	.667		168	36.50		204.50	243
0150	36" x 36"		12	.667		197	36.50		233.50	275
0300	Stainless steel, commercial grade, 12" x 12"		20	.400		219	22		241	276
0310	16" x 16"		14	.571		265	31.50		296.50	340
0320	18" x 18"		14	.571		282	31.50		313.50	360
0330	20" x 20"		14	.571		325	31.50		356.50	405
0340	24" x 24"		14	.571		385	31.50		416.50	475
0350	30" x 30"		12	.667		430	36.50		466.50	535
0360	36" x 36"		12	.667		520	36.50		556.50	635

08 91 19 – Fixed Louvers

08 91 19.10 Aluminum Louvers

		Crew	Daily Output	Labor-Hours	Unit	Material	2014 Bare Costs Labor	Equipment	Total	Total Incl O&P
0010	**ALUMINUM LOUVERS**									
0020	Aluminum with screen, residential, 8" x 8"	1 Carp	38	.211	Ea.	17.50	9.65		27.15	35
0100	12" x 12"		38	.211		15	9.65		24.65	32.50
0200	12" x 18"		35	.229		19	10.50		29.50	38
0250	14" x 24"		30	.267		26	12.25		38.25	48.50
0300	18" x 24"		27	.296		29	13.60		42.60	54.50
0500	24" x 30"		24	.333		62.50	15.30		77.80	94
0700	Triangle, adjustable, small		20	.400		47.50	18.35		65.85	82.50
0800	Large		15	.533		59	24.50		83.50	105
2100	Midget, aluminum, 3/4" deep, 1" diameter		85	.094		.78	4.32		5.10	7.95
2150	3" diameter		60	.133		2.28	6.10		8.38	12.55
2200	4" diameter		50	.160		3.64	7.35		10.99	16.05
2250	6" diameter		30	.267		4.10	12.25		16.35	24.50
3000	PVC, commercial grade, 12" x 12"	1 Shee	20	.400		97	22		119	142
3010	12" x 18"		20	.400		109	22		131	155
3020	12" x 24"		20	.400		146	22		168	196
3030	14" x 24"		20	.400		152	22		174	202
3100	Aluminum, commercial grade, 12" x 12"		20	.400		171	22		193	223
3110	24" x 24"		16	.500		249	27.50		276.50	315
3120	24" x 36"		16	.500		300	27.50		327.50	375
3130	36" x 24"		16	.500		310	27.50		337.50	385
3140	36" x 36"		14	.571		390	31.50		421.50	480

08 91 Louvers

08 91 19 – Fixed Louvers

08 91 19.10 Aluminum Louvers		Crew	Daily Output	Labor-Hours	Unit	Material	2014 Bare Costs Labor	Equipment	Total	Total Incl O&P
3150	36" x 48"	1 Shee	10	.800	Ea.	400	44		444	510
3160	48" x 36"		10	.800		390	44		434	500
3170	48" x 48"		10	.800		435	44		479	545
3180	60" x 48"		8	1		485	54.50		539.50	620
3190	60" x 60"	↓	8	1	↓	600	54.50		654.50	745

08 91 19.20 Steel Louvers

		Crew	Daily Output	Labor-Hours	Unit	Material	Labor	Equipment	Total	Total Incl O&P
0010	**STEEL LOUVERS**									
3300	Galvanized Steel, fixed blades, commercial grade, 18" x 18"	1 Shee	20	.400	Ea.	197	22		219	252
3310	24" x 24"		20	.400		232	22		254	290
3320	24" x 36"		16	.500		300	27.50		327.50	375
3330	36" x 24"		16	.500		298	27.50		325.50	375
3340	36" x 36"		14	.571		380	31.50		411.50	470
3350	36" x 48"		10	.800		385	44		429	495
3360	48" x 36"		10	.800		385	44		429	495
3370	48" x 48"		10	.800		425	44		469	535
3380	60" x 48"		10	.800		490	44		534	610
3390	60" x 60"	↓	10	.800	↓	590	44		634	715

08 91 26 – Door Louvers

08 91 26.10 Steel Louvers, 18 Gauge, Fixed Blade

		Crew	Daily Output	Labor-Hours	Unit	Material	Labor	Equipment	Total	Total Incl O&P
0010	**STEEL LOUVERS, 18 GAUGE, FIXED BLADE**									
0050	12" x 12", with enamel or powder coat	1 Carp	20	.400	Ea.	82	18.35		100.35	120
0055	18" x 12"		20	.400		94	18.35		112.35	133
0060	18" x 18"		20	.400		87.50	18.35		105.85	127
0065	24" x 12"		20	.400		113	18.35		131.35	154
0070	24" x 18"		20	.400		126	18.35		144.35	169
0075	24" x 24"		20	.400		150	18.35		168.35	195
0100	12" x 12", galvanized		20	.400		65	18.35		83.35	102
0105	18" x 12"		20	.400		76.50	18.35		94.85	114
0115	24" x 12"		20	.400		89.50	18.35		107.85	129
0125	24" x 24"	↓	20	.400	↓	127	18.35		145.35	169

08 95 Vents

08 95 13 – Soffit Vents

08 95 13.10 Wall Louvers

		Crew	Daily Output	Labor-Hours	Unit	Material	Labor	Equipment	Total	Total Incl O&P
0010	**WALL LOUVERS**									
2330	Soffit vent, continuous, 3" wide, aluminum, mill finish	1 Carp	200	.040	L.F.	.62	1.83		2.45	3.69
2340	Baked enamel finish		200	.040	"	.68	1.83		2.51	3.76
2400	Under eaves vent, aluminum, mill finish, 16" x 4"		48	.167	Ea.	1.90	7.65		9.55	14.65
2500	16" x 8"	↓	48	.167	"	2.18	7.65		9.83	14.95

08 95 16 – Wall Vents

08 95 16.10 Louvers

		Crew	Daily Output	Labor-Hours	Unit	Material	Labor	Equipment	Total	Total Incl O&P
0010	**LOUVERS**									
0020	Redwood, 2'-0" diameter, full circle	1 Carp	16	.500	Ea.	190	23		213	247
0100	Half circle		16	.500		190	23		213	247
0200	Octagonal		16	.500		142	23		165	194
0300	Triangular, 5/12 pitch, 5'-0" at base		16	.500		200	23		223	258
1000	Rectangular, 1'-4" x 1'-3"		16	.500		19.50	23		42.50	59
1100	Rectangular, 1'-4" x 1'-8"		16	.500		28	23		51	68.50
1200	1'-4" x 2'-2"		15	.533		31	24.50		55.50	74.50
1300	1'-9" x 2'-2"	↓	15	.533	↓	37.50	24.50		62	81.50

08 95 Vents

08 95 16 – Wall Vents

08 95 16.10 Louvers		Crew	Daily Output	Labor-Hours	Unit	Material	2014 Bare Costs Labor	Equipment	Total	Total Incl O&P
1400	2'-3" x 2'-2"	1 Carp	14	.571	Ea.	49.50	26		75.50	97.50
1700	2'-4" x 2'-11"		13	.615		49.50	28		77.50	101
2000	Aluminum, 12" x 16"		25	.320		20	14.65		34.65	46
2010	16" x 20"		25	.320		27.50	14.65		42.15	54.50
2020	24" x 30"		25	.320		59	14.65		73.65	89
2100	6' triangle		12	.667		168	30.50		198.50	235
3100	Round, 2'-2" diameter		16	.500		124	23		147	174
7000	Vinyl gable vent, 8" x 8"		38	.211		14	9.65		23.65	31.50
7020	12" x 12"		38	.211		27	9.65		36.65	45.50
7080	12" x 18"		35	.229		35	10.50		45.50	55.50
7200	18" x 24"		30	.267		45	12.25		57.25	69.50
9000	Minimum labor/equipment charge		3.50	2.286	Job		105		105	172

Division Notes

		CREW	DAILY OUTPUT	LABOR-HOURS	UNIT	BARE COSTS				TOTAL INCL O&P
						MAT.	LABOR	EQUIP.	TOTAL	

Estimating Tips

General

- Room Finish Schedule: A complete set of plans should contain a room finish schedule. If one is not available, it would be well worth the time and effort to obtain one.

09 20 00 Plaster and Gypsum Board

- Lath is estimated by the square yard plus a 5% allowance for waste. Furring, channels, and accessories are measured by the linear foot. An extra foot should be allowed for each accessory miter or stop.

- Plaster is also estimated by the square yard. Deductions for openings vary by preference, from zero deduction to 50% of all openings over 2 feet in width. The estimator should allow one extra square foot for each linear foot of horizontal interior or exterior angle located below the ceiling level. Also, double the areas of small radius work.

- Drywall accessories, studs, track, and acoustical caulking are all measured by the linear foot. Drywall taping is figured by the square foot. Gypsum wallboard is estimated by the square foot. No material deductions should be made for door or window openings under 32 S.F.

09 60 00 Flooring

- Tile and terrazzo areas are taken off on a square foot basis. Trim and base materials are measured by the linear foot. Accent tiles are listed per each. Two basic methods of installation are used. Mud set is approximately 30% more expensive than thin set. In terrazzo work, be sure to include the linear footage of embedded decorative strips, grounds, machine rubbing, and power cleanup.

- Wood flooring is available in strip, parquet, or block configuration. The latter two types are set in adhesives with quantities estimated by the square foot. The laying pattern will influence labor costs and material waste. In addition to the material and labor for laying wood floors, the estimator must make allowances for sanding and finishing these areas unless the flooring is prefinished.

- Sheet flooring is measured by the square yard. Roll widths vary, so consideration should be given to use the most economical width, as waste must be figured into the total quantity. Consider also the installation methods available, direct glue down or stretched.

09 70 00 Wall Finishes

- Wall coverings are estimated by the square foot. The area to be covered is measured, length by height of wall above baseboards, to calculate the square footage of each wall. This figure is divided by the number of square feet in the single roll which is being used. Deduct, in full, the areas of openings such as doors and windows. Where a pattern match is required allow 25%–30% waste.

09 80 00 Acoustic Treatment

- Acoustical systems fall into several categories. The takeoff of these materials should be by the square foot of area with a 5% allowance for waste. Do not forget about scaffolding, if applicable, when estimating these systems.

09 90 00 Painting and Coating

- A major portion of the work in painting involves surface preparation. Be sure to include cleaning, sanding, filling, and masking costs in the estimate.

- Protection of adjacent surfaces is not included in painting costs. When considering the method of paint application, an important factor is the amount of protection and masking required. These must be estimated separately and may be the determining factor in choosing the method of application.

Reference Numbers

Reference numbers are shown in shaded boxes at the beginning of some major classifications. These numbers refer to related items in the Reference Section. The reference information may be an estimating procedure, an alternate pricing method, or technical information.

Note: Not all subdivisions listed here necessarily appear in this publication.

09 01 Maintenance of Finishes

09 01 70 – Maintenance of Wall Finishes

09 01 70.10 Gypsum Wallboard Repairs

		Crew	Daily Output	Labor-Hours	Unit	Material	2014 Bare Costs Labor	Equipment	Total	Total Incl O&P
0010	**GYPSUM WALLBOARD REPAIRS**									
0100	Fill and sand, pin/nail holes	1 Carp	960	.008	Ea.		.38		.38	.63
0110	Screw head pops		480	.017			.76		.76	1.26
0120	Dents, up to 2" square		48	.167		.01	7.65		7.66	12.55
0130	2" to 4" square		24	.333		.04	15.30		15.34	25
0140	Cut square, patch, sand and finish, holes, up to 2" square		12	.667		.04	30.50		30.54	50
0150	2" to 4" square		11	.727		.09	33.50		33.59	55
0160	4" to 8" square		10	.800		.24	36.50		36.74	61
0170	8" to 12" square		8	1		.47	46		46.47	76
0180	12" to 32" square		6	1.333		1.55	61		62.55	102
0210	16" by 48"		5	1.600		2.61	73.50		76.11	124
0220	32" by 48"		4	2		4.12	91.50		95.62	156
0230	48" square		3.50	2.286		5.80	105		110.80	178
0240	60" square		3.20	2.500		9.35	115		124.35	198
0500	Skim coat surface with joint compound		1600	.005	S.F.	.03	.23		.26	.42
0510	Prepare, retape and refinish joints		60	.133	L.F.	.67	6.10		6.77	10.80
9000	Minimum labor/equipment charge		2	4	Job		183		183	300

09 05 Common Work Results for Finishes

09 05 05 – Selective Finishes Demolition

09 05 05.10 Selective Demolition, Ceilings

		Crew	Daily Output	Labor-Hours	Unit	Material	2014 Bare Costs Labor	Equipment	Total	Total Incl O&P
0010	**SELECTIVE DEMOLITION, CEILINGS**	R024119-10								
0200	Ceiling, drywall, furred and nailed or screwed	2 Clab	800	.020	S.F.		.73		.73	1.20
0220	On metal frame		760	.021			.77		.77	1.27
0240	On suspension system, including system		720	.022			.81		.81	1.34
1000	Plaster, lime and horse hair, on wood lath, incl. lath		700	.023			.84		.84	1.38
1020	On metal lath		570	.028			1.03		1.03	1.69
1100	Gypsum, on gypsum lath		720	.022			.81		.81	1.34
1120	On metal lath		500	.032			1.17		1.17	1.93
1200	Suspended ceiling, mineral fiber, 2' x 2' or 2' x 4'		1500	.011			.39		.39	.64
1250	On suspension system, incl. system		1200	.013			.49		.49	.80
1500	Tile, wood fiber, 12" x 12", glued		900	.018			.65		.65	1.07
1540	Stapled		1500	.011			.39		.39	.64
1580	On suspension system, incl. system		760	.021			.77		.77	1.27
2000	Wood, tongue and groove, 1" x 4"		1000	.016			.59		.59	.96
2040	1" x 8"		1100	.015			.53		.53	.88
2400	Plywood or wood fiberboard, 4' x 8' sheets		1200	.013			.49		.49	.80
9000	Minimum labor/equipment charge	1 Clab	2	4	Job		147		147	241

09 05 05.20 Selective Demolition, Flooring

		Crew	Daily Output	Labor-Hours	Unit	Material	2014 Bare Costs Labor	Equipment	Total	Total Incl O&P
0010	**SELECTIVE DEMOLITION, FLOORING**	R024119-10								
0200	Brick with mortar	2 Clab	475	.034	S.F.		1.23		1.23	2.03
0400	Carpet, bonded, including surface scraping		2000	.008			.29		.29	.48
0480	Tackless		9000	.002			.07		.07	.11
0550	Carpet tile, releasable adhesive		5000	.003			.12		.12	.19
0560	Permanent adhesive		1850	.009			.32		.32	.52
0600	Composition, acrylic or epoxy		400	.040			1.47		1.47	2.41
0700	Concrete, scarify skin	A-1A	225	.036			1.68	.95	2.63	3.79
0800	Resilient, sheet goods	2 Clab	1400	.011			.42		.42	.69
0820	For gym floors	"	900	.018			.65		.65	1.07
0850	Vinyl or rubber cove base	1 Clab	1000	.008	L.F.		.29		.29	.48
0860	Vinyl or rubber cove base, molded corner	"	1000	.008	Ea.		.29		.29	.48

09 05 Common Work Results for Finishes

09 05 05 – Selective Finishes Demolition

09 05 05.20 Selective Demolition, Flooring

		Crew	Daily Output	Labor-Hours	Unit	Material	2014 Bare Costs Labor	Equipment	Total	Total Incl O&P
0870	For glued and caulked installation, add to labor						50%			
0900	Vinyl composition tile, 12" x 12"	2 Clab	1000	.016	S.F.		.59		.59	.96
2000	Tile, ceramic, thin set		675	.024			.87		.87	1.43
2020	Mud set		625	.026			.94		.94	1.54
2200	Marble, slate, thin set		675	.024			.87		.87	1.43
2220	Mud set		625	.026			.94		.94	1.54
2600	Terrazzo, thin set		450	.036			1.30		1.30	2.14
2620	Mud set		425	.038			1.38		1.38	2.27
2640	Terrazzo, cast in place		300	.053			1.95		1.95	3.21
3000	Wood, block, on end	1 Carp	400	.020			.92		.92	1.51
3200	Parquet		450	.018			.82		.82	1.34
3400	Strip flooring, interior, 2-1/4" x 25/32" thick		325	.025			1.13		1.13	1.86
3500	Exterior, porch flooring, 1" x 4"		220	.036			1.67		1.67	2.74
3800	Subfloor, tongue and groove, 1" x 6"		325	.025			1.13		1.13	1.86
3820	1" x 8"		430	.019			.85		.85	1.40
3840	1" x 10"		520	.015			.71		.71	1.16
4000	Plywood, nailed		600	.013			.61		.61	1
4100	Glued and nailed		400	.020			.92		.92	1.51
4200	Hardboard, 1/4" thick		760	.011			.48		.48	.79
8000	Remove flooring, bead blast, minimum	A-1A	1000	.008			.38	.21	.59	.86
8100	Maximum		400	.020			.95	.54	1.49	2.13
8150	Mastic only		1500	.005			.25	.14	.39	.57
9000	Minimum labor/equipment charge	1 Clab	4	2	Job		73.50		73.50	120

09 05 05.30 Selective Demolition, Walls and Partitions

		Crew	Daily Output	Labor-Hours	Unit	Material	2014 Bare Costs Labor	Equipment	Total	Total Incl O&P
0010	**SELECTIVE DEMOLITION, WALLS AND PARTITIONS** R024119-10									
0020	Walls, concrete, reinforced	B-39	120	.400	C.F.		15.50	1.95	17.45	27.50
0025	Plain	"	160	.300			11.60	1.46	13.06	20.50
0100	Brick, 4" to 12" thick	B-9	220	.182			6.75	1.06	7.81	12.20
0200	Concrete block, 4" thick		1150	.035	S.F.		1.29	.20	1.49	2.34
0280	8" thick		1050	.038			1.41	.22	1.63	2.56
0300	Exterior stucco 1" thick over mesh		3200	.013			.46	.07	.53	.84
1000	Drywall, nailed or screwed	1 Clab	1000	.008			.29		.29	.48
1010	2 layers		400	.020			.73		.73	1.20
1020	Glued and nailed		900	.009			.33		.33	.54
1500	Fiberboard, nailed		900	.009			.33		.33	.54
1520	Glued and nailed		800	.010			.37		.37	.60
1568	Plenum barrier, sheet lead		300	.027			.98		.98	1.61
1600	Glass block		65	.123			4.51		4.51	7.40
2000	Movable walls, metal, 5' high		300	.027			.98		.98	1.61
2020	8' high		400	.020			.73		.73	1.20
2200	Metal or wood studs, finish 2 sides, fiberboard	B-1	520	.046			1.72		1.72	2.83
2250	Lath and plaster		260	.092			3.45		3.45	5.65
2300	Plasterboard (drywall)		520	.046			1.72		1.72	2.83
2350	Plywood		450	.053			1.99		1.99	3.27
2800	Paneling, 4' x 8' sheets	1 Clab	475	.017			.62		.62	1.01
3000	Plaster, lime and horsehair, on wood lath		400	.020			.73		.73	1.20
3020	On metal lath		335	.024			.88		.88	1.44
3400	Gypsum or perlite, on gypsum lath		410	.020			.72		.72	1.17
3420	On metal lath		300	.027			.98		.98	1.61
3450	Plaster, interior gypsum, acoustic, or cement		60	.133	S.Y.		4.89		4.89	8.05
3500	Stucco, on masonry		145	.055			2.02		2.02	3.32
3510	Commercial 3-coat		80	.100			3.67		3.67	6

09 05 Common Work Results for Finishes

09 05 05 – Selective Finishes Demolition

09 05 05.30 Selective Demolition, Walls and Partitions

		Crew	Daily Output	Labor-Hours	Unit	Material	2014 Bare Costs Labor	2014 Bare Costs Equipment	Total	Total Incl O&P
3520	Interior stucco	1 Clab	25	.320	S.Y.		11.75		11.75	19.25
3753	Remove damaged glass block	B-1	134.62	.178	S.F.		6.65		6.65	10.95
3760	Tile, ceramic, on walls, thin set	1 Clab	300	.027			.98		.98	1.61
3765	Mud set		250	.032	↓		1.17		1.17	1.93
3800	Toilet partitions, slate or marble		5	1.600	Ea.		58.50		58.50	96.50
3820	Metal or plastic	↓	8	1	"		36.50		36.50	60
5000	Wallcovering, vinyl	1 Pape	700	.011	S.F.		.45		.45	.73
5010	With release agent		1500	.005			.21		.21	.34
5025	Wallpaper, 2 layers or less, by hand		250	.032			1.27		1.27	2.04
5035	3 layers or more		165	.048			1.93		1.93	3.10
5040	Designer	↓	480	.017	↓		.66		.66	1.06
9000	Minimum labor/equipment charge	1 Clab	4	2	Job		73.50		73.50	120

09 21 Plaster and Gypsum Board Assemblies

09 21 16 – Gypsum Board Assemblies

09 21 16.23 Gypsum Board Shaft Wall Assemblies

		Crew	Daily Output	Labor-Hours	Unit	Material	2014 Bare Costs Labor	2014 Bare Costs Equipment	Total	Total Incl O&P
0010	**GYPSUM BOARD SHAFT WALL ASSEMBLIES**									
0020	Cavity type on 25 ga. J-track & C-H studs, 24" O.C.									
0030	1" thick coreboard wall liner on shaft side									
0040	2-hour assembly with double layer									
0060	5/8" fire rated gypsum board on room side	2 Carp	220	.073	S.F.	2.02	3.33		5.35	7.70
0100	3-hour assembly with triple layer									
0300	5/8" fire rated gypsum board on room side	2 Carp	180	.089	S.F.	1.70	4.08		5.78	8.55
0400	4-hour assembly, 1" coreboard, 5/8" fire rated gypsum board									
0600	and 3/4" galv. metal furring channels, 24" O.C., with									
0700	Double layer 5/8" fire rated gypsum board on room side	2 Carp	110	.145	S.F.	1.59	6.65		8.24	12.70
0900	For taping & finishing, add per side	1 Carp	1050	.008	"	.05	.35		.40	.62
1000	For insulation, see Section 07 21									
5200	For work over 8' high, add	2 Carp	3060	.005	S.F.		.24		.24	.39
5300	For distribution cost over 3 stories high, add per story	"	6100	.003	"		.12		.12	.20

09 21 16.33 Partition Wall

		Crew	Daily Output	Labor-Hours	Unit	Material	2014 Bare Costs Labor	2014 Bare Costs Equipment	Total	Total Incl O&P
0010	**PARTITION WALL** Stud wall, 8' to 12' high									
0050	1/2", interior, gypsum board, std, tape & finish 2 sides									
0500	Installed on and incl., 2" x 4" wood studs, 16" O.C.	2 Carp	310	.052	S.F.	1.12	2.37		3.49	5.10
1000	Metal studs, NLB, 25 ga., 16" O.C., 3-5/8" wide		350	.046		1.06	2.10		3.16	4.61
1200	6" wide		330	.048		1.20	2.22		3.42	4.97
1400	Water resistant, on 2" x 4" wood studs, 16" O.C.		310	.052		1.28	2.37		3.65	5.30
1600	Metal studs, NLB, 25 ga., 16" O.C., 3-5/8" wide		350	.046		1.22	2.10		3.32	4.79
1800	6" wide		330	.048		1.36	2.22		3.58	5.15
2000	Fire res., 2 layers, 1-1/2 hr., on 2" x 4" wood studs, 16" O.C.		210	.076		1.80	3.49		5.29	7.75
2200	Metal studs, NLB, 25 ga., 16" O.C., 3-5/8" wide		250	.064		1.74	2.93		4.67	6.75
2400	6" wide		230	.070		1.88	3.19		5.07	7.30
2600	Fire & water res., 2 layers, 1-1/2 hr., 2" x 4" studs, 16" O.C.		210	.076		1.80	3.49		5.29	7.75
2800	Metal studs, NLB, 25 ga., 16" O.C., 3-5/8" wide		250	.064		1.74	2.93		4.67	6.75
3000	6" wide	↓	230	.070	↓	1.88	3.19		5.07	7.30
3200	5/8", interior, gypsum board, standard, tape & finish 2 sides									
3400	Installed on and including 2" x 4" wood studs, 16" O.C.	2 Carp	300	.053	S.F.	1.16	2.45		3.61	5.30
3600	24" O.C.		330	.048		1.07	2.22		3.29	4.82
3800	Metal studs, NLB, 25 ga., 16" O.C., 3-5/8" wide		340	.047		1.10	2.16		3.26	4.76
4000	6" wide		320	.050		1.24	2.29		3.53	5.15
4200	24" O.C., 3-5/8" wide	↓	360	.044	↓	1.01	2.04		3.05	4.46

09 21 Plaster and Gypsum Board Assemblies

09 21 16 – Gypsum Board Assemblies

09 21 16.33 Partition Wall		Crew	Daily Output	Labor-Hours	Unit	Material	2014 Bare Costs Labor	Equipment	Total	Total Incl O&P
4400	6" wide	2 Carp	340	.047	S.F.	1.11	2.16		3.27	4.77
4800	Water resistant, on 2" x 4" wood studs, 16" O.C.		300	.053		1.42	2.45		3.87	5.60
5000	24" O.C.		330	.048		1.33	2.22		3.55	5.10
5200	Metal studs, NLB, 25 ga. 16" O.C., 3-5/8" wide		340	.047		1.36	2.16		3.52	5.05
5400	6" wide		320	.050		1.50	2.29		3.79	5.40
5600	24" O.C., 3-5/8" wide		360	.044		1.27	2.04		3.31	4.74
5800	6" wide		340	.047		1.37	2.16		3.53	5.05
6000	Fire resistant, 2 layers, 2 hr., on 2" x 4" wood studs, 16" O.C.		205	.078		1.79	3.58		5.37	7.85
6200	24" O.C.		235	.068		1.79	3.12		4.91	7.10
6400	Metal studs, NLB, 25 ga., 16" O.C., 3-5/8" wide		245	.065		1.85	2.99		4.84	6.95
6600	6" wide		225	.071		1.96	3.26		5.22	7.50
6800	24" O.C., 3-5/8" wide		265	.060		1.73	2.77		4.50	6.45
7000	6" wide		245	.065		1.83	2.99		4.82	6.95
7200	Fire & water resistant, 2 layers, 2 hr., 2" x 4" studs, 16" O.C.		205	.078		1.88	3.58		5.46	7.95
7400	24" O.C.		235	.068		1.79	3.12		4.91	7.10
7600	Metal studs, NLB, 25 ga., 16" O.C., 3-5/8" wide		245	.065		1.82	2.99		4.81	6.95
7800	6" wide		225	.071		1.96	3.26		5.22	7.50
8000	24" O.C., 3-5/8" wide		265	.060		1.73	2.77		4.50	6.45
8200	6" wide		245	.065		1.83	2.99		4.82	6.95
8600	1/2" blueboard, mesh tape both sides									
8620	Installed on and including 2" x 4" wood studs, 16" O.C.	2 Carp	300	.053	S.F.	1.16	2.45		3.61	5.30
8640	Metal studs, NLB, 25 ga., 16" O.C., 3-5/8" wide		340	.047		1.10	2.16		3.26	4.76
8660	6" wide		320	.050		1.24	2.29		3.53	5.15
9000	Exterior, 1/2" gypsum sheathing, 1/2" gypsum finished, interior,									
9100	including foil faced insulation, metal studs, 20 ga.									
9200	16" O.C., 3-5/8" wide	2 Carp	290	.055	S.F.	1.70	2.53		4.23	6.05
9400	6" wide		270	.059		1.95	2.72		4.67	6.60
9600	Partitions, for work over 8' high, add		1530	.010			.48		.48	.79

09 22 Supports for Plaster and Gypsum Board

09 22 03 – Fastening Methods for Finishes

09 22 03.20 Drilling Plaster/Drywall

		Crew	Daily Output	Labor-Hours	Unit	Material	2014 Bare Costs Labor	Equipment	Total	Total Incl O&P
0010	**DRILLING PLASTER/DRYWALL**									
1100	Drilling & layout for drywall/plaster walls, up to 1" deep, no anchor									
1200	Holes, 1/4" diameter	1 Carp	150	.053	Ea.	.01	2.45		2.46	4.03
1300	3/8" diameter		140	.057		.01	2.62		2.63	4.32
1400	1/2" diameter		130	.062		.01	2.82		2.83	4.65
1500	3/4" diameter		120	.067		.01	3.06		3.07	5
1600	1" diameter		110	.073		.02	3.33		3.35	5.50
1700	1-1/4" diameter		100	.080		.03	3.67		3.70	6.10
1800	1-1/2" diameter		90	.089		.04	4.08		4.12	6.75
1900	For ceiling installations, add						40%			

09 22 13 – Metal Furring

09 22 13.13 Metal Channel Furring

		Crew	Daily Output	Labor-Hours	Unit	Material	2014 Bare Costs Labor	Equipment	Total	Total Incl O&P
0010	**METAL CHANNEL FURRING**									
0030	Beams and columns, 7/8" channels, galvanized, 12" O.C.	1 Lath	155	.052	S.F.	.37	2.10		2.47	3.70
0050	16" O.C.		170	.047		.31	1.91		2.22	3.34
0070	24" O.C.		185	.043		.20	1.76		1.96	2.98
0100	Ceilings, on steel, 7/8" channels, galvanized, 12" O.C.		210	.038		.34	1.55		1.89	2.80
0300	16" O.C.		290	.028		.31	1.12		1.43	2.10

09 22 13 – Metal Furring

09 22 13.13 Metal Channel Furring		Crew	Daily Output	Labor-Hours	Unit	Material	2014 Bare Costs Labor	Equipment	Total	Total Incl O&P
0400	24" O.C.	1 Lath	420	.019	S.F.	.20	.77		.97	1.43
0600	1-5/8" channels, galvanized, 12" O.C.		190	.042		.46	1.71		2.17	3.19
0700	16" O.C.		260	.031		.41	1.25		1.66	2.42
0900	24" O.C.		390	.021		.28	.83		1.11	1.61
0930	7/8" channels with sound isolation clips, 12" O.C.		120	.067		1.72	2.71		4.43	6.15
0940	16" O.C.		100	.080		1.29	3.25		4.54	6.50
0950	24" O.C.		165	.048		.86	1.97		2.83	4.03
0960	1-5/8" channels, galvanized, 12" O.C.		110	.073		1.83	2.95		4.78	6.65
0970	16" O.C.		100	.080		1.38	3.25		4.63	6.60
0980	24" O.C.		155	.052		.92	2.10		3.02	4.30
1000	Walls, 7/8" channels, galvanized, 12" O.C.		235	.034		.34	1.38		1.72	2.54
1200	16" O.C.		265	.030		.31	1.23		1.54	2.26
1300	24" O.C.		350	.023		.20	.93		1.13	1.68
1500	1-5/8" channels, galvanized, 12" O.C.		210	.038		.46	1.55		2.01	2.94
1600	16" O.C.		240	.033		.41	1.35		1.76	2.58
1800	24" O.C.		305	.026		.28	1.06		1.34	1.97
1920	7/8" channels with sound isolation clips, 12" O.C.		125	.064		1.72	2.60		4.32	5.95
1940	16" O.C.		100	.080		1.29	3.25		4.54	6.50
1950	24" O.C.		150	.053		.86	2.17		3.03	4.34
1960	1-5/8" channels, galvanized, 12" O.C.		115	.070		1.83	2.82		4.65	6.45
1970	16" O.C.		95	.084		1.38	3.42		4.80	6.85
1980	24" O.C.		140	.057		.92	2.32		3.24	4.65
9000	Minimum labor/equipment charge		4	2	Job		81		81	128

09 22 16 – Non-Structural Metal Framing

09 22 16.13 Non-Structural Metal Stud Framing

		Crew	Daily Output	Labor-Hours	Unit	Material	2014 Bare Costs Labor	Equipment	Total	Total Incl O&P
0010	**NON-STRUCTURAL METAL STUD FRAMING**									
1600	Non-load bearing, galv., 8' high, 25 ga. 1-5/8" wide, 16" O.C.	1 Carp	619	.013	S.F.	.27	.59		.86	1.27
1610	24" O.C.		950	.008		.20	.39		.59	.86
1620	2-1/2" wide, 16" O.C.		613	.013		.32	.60		.92	1.33
1630	24" O.C.		938	.009		.24	.39		.63	.91
1640	3-5/8" wide, 16" O.C.		600	.013		.39	.61		1	1.42
1650	24" O.C.		925	.009		.29	.40		.69	.97
1660	4" wide, 16" O.C.		594	.013		.42	.62		1.04	1.49
1670	24" O.C.		925	.009		.32	.40		.72	1.11
1680	6" wide, 16" O.C.		588	.014		.53	.62		1.15	1.61
1690	24" O.C.		906	.009		.40	.40		.80	1.11
1700	20 ga. studs, 1-5/8" wide, 16" O.C.		494	.016		.38	.74		1.12	1.63
1710	24" O.C.		763	.010		.28	.48		.76	1.10
1720	2-1/2" wide, 16" O.C.		488	.016		.46	.75		1.21	1.74
1730	24" O.C.		750	.011		.35	.49		.84	1.18
1740	3-5/8" wide, 16" O.C.		481	.017		.50	.76		1.26	1.80
1750	24" O.C.		738	.011		.37	.50		.87	1.23
1760	4" wide, 16" O.C.		475	.017		.60	.77		1.37	1.93
1770	24" O.C.		738	.011		.45	.50		.95	1.32
1780	6" wide, 16" O.C.		469	.017		.76	.78		1.54	2.12
1790	24" O.C.		725	.011		.57	.51		1.08	1.46
2000	Non-load bearing, galv., 10' high, 25 ga. 1-5/8" wide, 16" O.C.		495	.016		.26	.74		1	1.50
2100	24" O.C.		760	.011		.19	.48		.67	1
2200	2-1/2" wide, 16" O.C.		490	.016		.30	.75		1.05	1.56
2250	24" O.C.		750	.011		.22	.49		.71	1.05
2300	3-5/8" wide, 16" O.C.		480	.017		.36	.76		1.12	1.66
2350	24" O.C.		740	.011		.27	.50		.77	1.11

09 22 16 – Non-Structural Metal Framing

09 22 16.13 Non-Structural Metal Stud Framing	Crew	Daily Output	Labor-Hours	Unit	Material	2014 Bare Costs Labor	Equipment	Total	Total Incl O&P
2400 4" wide, 16" O.C.	1 Carp	475	.017	S.F.	.40	.77		1.17	1.71
2450 24" O.C.		740	.011		.30	.50		.80	1.13
2500 6" wide, 16" O.C.		470	.017		.50	.78		1.28	1.83
2550 24" O.C.		725	.011		.37	.51		.88	1.24
2600 20 ga. studs, 1-5/8" wide, 16" O.C.		395	.020		.36	.93		1.29	1.92
2650 24" O.C.		610	.013		.26	.60		.86	1.28
2700 2-1/2" wide, 16" O.C.		390	.021		.43	.94		1.37	2.03
2750 24" O.C.		600	.013		.32	.61		.93	1.35
2800 3-5/8" wide, 16" OC		385	.021		.47	.95		1.42	2.09
2850 24" O.C.		590	.014		.35	.62		.97	1.40
2900 4" wide, 16" O.C.		380	.021		.57	.97		1.54	2.22
2950 24" O.C.		590	.014		.42	.62		1.04	1.48
3000 6" wide, 16" O.C.		375	.021		.72	.98		1.70	2.40
3050 24" O.C.		580	.014		.53	.63		1.16	1.62
3060 Non-load bearing, galv., 12' high, 25 ga. 1-5/8" wide, 16" O.C.		413	.019		.25	.89		1.14	1.73
3070 24" O.C.		633	.013		.18	.58		.76	1.15
3080 2-1/2" wide, 16" O.C.		408	.020		.29	.90		1.19	1.80
3090 24" O.C.		625	.013		.21	.59		.80	1.19
3100 3-5/8" wide, 16" O.C.		400	.020		.35	.92		1.27	1.89
3110 24" O.C.		617	.013		.25	.59		.84	1.26
3120 4" wide, 16" O.C.		396	.020		.38	.93		1.31	1.94
3130 24" O.C.		617	.013		.28	.59		.87	1.29
3140 6" wide, 16" O.C.		392	.020		.48	.94		1.42	2.07
3150 24" O.C.		604	.013		.35	.61		.96	1.38
3160 20 ga. studs, 1-5/8" wide, 16" O.C.		329	.024		.34	1.12		1.46	2.20
3170 24" O.C.		508	.016		.25	.72		.97	1.46
3180 2-1/2" wide, 16" O.C.		325	.025		.41	1.13		1.54	2.31
3190 24" O.C.		500	.016		.30	.73		1.03	1.54
3200 3-5/8" wide, 16" O.C.		321	.025		.45	1.14		1.59	2.38
3210 24" O.C.		492	.016		.33	.75		1.08	1.59
3220 4" wide, 16" O.C.		317	.025		.55	1.16		1.71	2.50
3230 24" O.C.		492	.016		.40	.75		1.15	1.67
3240 6" wide, 16" O.C.		313	.026		.69	1.17		1.86	2.69
3250 24" O.C.	1 Carp	483	.017	S.F.	.50	.76		1.26	1.80
5000 Load bearing studs, see Section 05 41 13.30									
9000 Minimum labor/equipment charge	1 Carp	4	2	Job		91.50		91.50	151

09 22 26 – Suspension Systems

09 22 26.13 Ceiling Suspension Systems

	Crew	Daily Output	Labor-Hours	Unit	Material	Labor	Equipment	Total	Total Incl O&P
0010 **CEILING SUSPENSION SYSTEMS** for gypsum board or plaster									
8000 Suspended ceilings, including carriers									
8200 1-1/2" carriers, 24" O.C. with:									
8300 7/8" channels, 16" O.C.	1 Lath	275	.029	S.F.	.51	1.18		1.69	2.41
8320 24" O.C.		310	.026		.41	1.05		1.46	2.10
8400 1-5/8" channels, 16" O.C.		205	.039		.62	1.58		2.20	3.17
8420 24" O.C.		250	.032		.48	1.30		1.78	2.57
8600 2" carriers, 24" O.C. with:									
8700 7/8" channels, 16" O.C.	1 Lath	250	.032	S.F.	.56	1.30		1.86	2.65
8720 24" O.C.		285	.028		.45	1.14		1.59	2.29
8800 1-5/8" channels, 16" O.C.		190	.042		.66	1.71		2.37	3.41
8820 24" O.C.		225	.036		.53	1.44		1.97	2.85

09 22 36.13 Gypsum Lath

		Crew	Daily Output	Labor-Hours	Unit	Material	2014 Bare Costs Labor	Equipment	Total	Total Incl O&P
0010	**GYPSUM LATH** R092000-50									
0020	Plain or perforated, nailed, 3/8" thick	1 Lath	85	.094	S.Y.	2.70	3.82		6.52	8.95
0100	1/2" thick		80	.100		2.43	4.06		6.49	9.05
0300	Clipped to steel studs, 3/8" thick		75	.107		2.70	4.33		7.03	9.75
0400	1/2" thick		70	.114		2.43	4.64		7.07	9.95
1500	For ceiling installations, add		216	.037			1.50		1.50	2.36
1600	For columns and beams, add		170	.047			1.91		1.91	3
9000	Minimum labor/equipment charge		4.25	1.882	Job		76.50		76.50	120

09 22 36.23 Metal Lath

		Crew	Daily Output	Labor-Hours	Unit	Material	2014 Bare Costs Labor	Equipment	Total	Total Incl O&P
0010	**METAL LATH** R092000-50									
0020	Diamond, expanded, 2.5 lb. per S.Y., painted				S.Y.	4.24			4.24	4.66
0100	Galvanized					3.05			3.05	3.36
0300	3.4 lb. per S.Y., painted					3.47			3.47	3.82
0400	Galvanized					3.80			3.80	4.18
0600	For 15# asphalt sheathing paper, add					.49			.49	.53
0900	Flat rib, 1/8" high, 2.75 lb., painted					3.26			3.26	3.59
1000	Foil backed					3.14			3.14	3.45
1200	3.4 lb. per S.Y., painted					4.28			4.28	4.71
1300	Galvanized					5.85			5.85	6.40
1500	For 15# asphalt sheathing paper, add					.49			.49	.53
1800	High rib, 3/8" high, 3.4 lb. per S.Y., painted					4.39			4.39	4.83
1900	Galvanized					3.71			3.71	4.08
2400	3/4" high, painted, .60 lb. per S.F.				S.F.	.62			.62	.68
2500	.75 lb. per S.F.				"	1.33			1.33	1.46
2800	Stucco mesh, painted, 3.6 lb.				S.Y.	4.03			4.03	4.43
3000	K-lath, perforated, absorbent paper, regular					4.42			4.42	4.86
3100	Heavy duty					5.20			5.20	5.75
3300	Waterproof, heavy duty, grade B backing					5.10			5.10	5.60
3400	Fire resistant backing					5.65			5.65	6.20
3600	2.5 lb. diamond painted, on wood framing, on walls	1 Lath	85	.094		4.24	3.82		8.06	10.65
3700	On ceilings		75	.107		4.24	4.33		8.57	11.45
3900	3.4 lb. diamond painted, on wood framing, on walls		80	.100		4.28	4.06		8.34	11.10
4000	On ceilings		70	.114		4.28	4.64		8.92	12
4200	3.4 lb. diamond painted, wired to steel framing		75	.107		4.28	4.33		8.61	11.50
4300	On ceilings		60	.133		4.28	5.40		9.68	13.20
4600	Cornices, wired to steel		35	.229		4.28	9.30		13.58	19.25
4800	Screwed to steel studs, 2.5 lb.		80	.100		4.24	4.06		8.30	11.05
4900	3.4 lb.		75	.107		3.47	4.33		7.80	10.60
5100	Rib lath, painted, wired to steel, on walls, 2.5 lb.		75	.107		3.26	4.33		7.59	10.40
5200	3.4 lb.		70	.114		4.39	4.64		9.03	12.15
5400	4.0 lb.		65	.123		5.70	5		10.70	14.10
5500	For self-furring lath, add					.11			.11	.12
5700	Suspended ceiling system, incl. 3.4 lb. diamond lath, painted	1 Lath	15	.533		3.58	21.50		25.08	38
5800	Galvanized	"	15	.533		4.53	21.50		26.03	39
6000	Hollow metal stud partitions, 3.4 lb. painted lath both sides									
6010	Non-load bearing, 25 ga., w/rib lath 2-1/2" studs, 12" O.C.	1 Lath	20.30	.394	S.Y.	12.25	16		28.25	38.50
6300	16" O.C.		21.10	.379		11.50	15.40		26.90	36.50
6350	24" O.C.		22.70	.352		10.80	14.30		25.10	34.50
6400	3-5/8" studs, 16" O.C.		19.50	.410		12.05	16.65		28.70	39.50
6600	24" O.C.		20.40	.392		11.20	15.90		27.10	37.50
6700	4" studs, 16" O.C.		20.40	.392		12.40	15.90		28.30	38.50
6900	24" O.C.		21.60	.370		11.45	15.05		26.50	36

09 22 Supports for Plaster and Gypsum Board

09 22 36 – Lath

09 22 36.23 Metal Lath	Crew	Daily Output	Labor-Hours	Unit	Material	2014 Bare Costs Labor	Equipment	Total	Total Incl O&P
7000	6" studs, 16" O.C.	1 Lath	19.50	.410	S.Y.	13.30	16.65		29.95	40.50
7100	24" O.C.		21.10	.379		12.10	15.40		27.50	37.50
7200	L.B. partitions, 16 ga., w/rib lath, 2-1/2" studs, 16" O.C.		20	.400		12.45	16.25		28.70	39
7300	3-5/8" studs, 16 ga.		19.70	.406		14.15	16.50		30.65	41.50
7500	4" studs, 16 ga.		19.50	.410		14.70	16.65		31.35	42
7600	6" studs, 16 ga.		18.70	.428		17.35	17.35		34.70	46.50
9000	Minimum labor/equipment charge		4.25	1.882	Job		76.50		76.50	120

09 23 Gypsum Plastering

09 23 13 – Acoustical Gypsum Plastering

09 23 13.10 Perlite or Vermiculite Plaster

09 23 13.10 Perlite or Vermiculite Plaster		Crew	Daily Output	Labor-Hours	Unit	Material	2014 Bare Costs Labor	Equipment	Total	Total Incl O&P
0010	PERLITE OR VERMICULITE PLASTER	R092000-50								
0020	In 100 lb. bags, under 200 bags				Bag	16.65			16.65	18.30
0300	2 coats, no lath included, on walls	J-1	92	.435	S.Y.	3.78	17.40	1.56	22.74	34
0400	On ceilings		79	.506		3.78	20.50	1.82	26.10	38.50
0900	3 coats, no lath included, on walls		74	.541		6.30	21.50	1.94	29.74	44
1000	On ceilings		63	.635		6.30	25.50	2.28	34.08	50.50
1700	For irregular or curved surfaces, add to above					30%				
1800	For columns and beams, add to above					50%				
1900	For soffits, add to ceiling prices					40%				
9000	Minimum labor/equipment charge	1 Plas	1	8	Job		335		335	540

09 23 20 – Gypsum Plaster

09 23 20.10 Gypsum Plaster On Walls and Ceilings

09 23 20.10 Gypsum Plaster On Walls and Ceilings		Crew	Daily Output	Labor-Hours	Unit	Material	2014 Bare Costs Labor	Equipment	Total	Total Incl O&P
0010	GYPSUM PLASTER ON WALLS AND CEILINGS	R092000-50								
0020	80# bag, less than 1 ton				Bag	14.45			14.45	15.85
0300	2 coats, no lath included, on walls	J-1	105	.381	S.Y.	3.37	15.25	1.37	19.99	29.50
0400	On ceilings		92	.435		3.37	17.40	1.56	22.33	33.50
0900	3 coats, no lath included, on walls		87	.460		4.82	18.40	1.65	24.87	36.50
1000	On ceilings		78	.513		4.82	20.50	1.84	27.16	40.50
1600	For irregular or curved surfaces, add					30%				
1800	For columns & beams, add					50%				
9000	Minimum labor/equipment charge	1 Plas	1	8	Job		335		335	540

09 24 Cement Plastering

09 24 23 – Cement Stucco

09 24 23.40 Stucco

09 24 23.40 Stucco		Crew	Daily Output	Labor-Hours	Unit	Material	2014 Bare Costs Labor	Equipment	Total	Total Incl O&P
0010	STUCCO	R092000-50								
0015	3 coats 1" thick, float finish, with mesh, on wood frame	J-2	63	.762	S.Y.	6.55	30.50	2.28	39.33	58.50
0100	On masonry construction, no mesh incl.	J-1	67	.597		2.50	24	2.14	28.64	43.50
0300	For trowel finish, add	1 Plas	170	.047			1.97		1.97	3.17
0400	For 3/4" thick, on masonry, deduct	J-1	880	.045		.62	1.82	.16	2.60	3.78
0600	For coloring and special finish, add, minimum		685	.058		.39	2.34	.21	2.94	4.41
0700	Maximum		200	.200		1.38	8	.72	10.10	15.15
0900	For soffits, add	J-2	155	.310		2.14	12.45	.93	15.52	23.50
1000	Exterior stucco, with bonding agent, 3 coats, on walls, no mesh incl.	J-1	200	.200		3.58	8	.72	12.30	17.60
1200	Ceilings		180	.222		3.58	8.90	.80	13.28	19.10
1300	Beams		80	.500		3.58	20	1.80	25.38	38
1500	Columns		100	.400		3.58	16	1.44	21.02	31
1550	Minimum labor/equipment charge	1 Plas	1	8	Job		335		335	540

09 24 Cement Plastering

09 24 23 – Cement Stucco

09 24 23.40 Stucco		Crew	Daily Output	Labor-Hours	Unit	Material	2014 Bare Costs Labor	Equipment	Total	Total Incl O&P
1600	Mesh, painted, nailed to wood, 1.8 lb.	1 Lath	60	.133	S.Y.	6.20	5.40		11.60	15.30
1800	3.6 lb.		55	.145		4.03	5.90		9.93	13.70
1900	Wired to steel, painted, 1.8 lb.		53	.151		6.20	6.15		12.35	16.40
2100	3.6 lb.		50	.160		4.03	6.50		10.53	14.65
9000	Minimum labor/equipment charge		4	2	Job		81		81	128

09 25 Other Plastering

09 25 23 – Lime Based Plastering

09 25 23.10 Venetian Plaster

		Crew	Daily Output	Labor-Hours	Unit	Material	2014 Bare Costs Labor	Equipment	Total	Total Incl O&P
0010	**VENETIAN PLASTER**									
0100	Walls, 1 coat primer, roller applied	1 Plas	950	.008	S.F.	.16	.35		.51	.75
0200	Plaster, 3 coats, incl. sanding	2 Plas	700	.023	"	.44	.96		1.40	2.03
0210	For pigment, light colors add per gal. plaster				Gal.	12			12	13.20
0220	For pigment, dark colors add				"	50			50	55
0300	For sealer/wax coat incl. burnishing, add	1 Plas	300	.027	S.F.	.41	1.12		1.53	2.25

09 26 Veneer Plastering

09 26 13 – Gypsum Veneer Plastering

09 26 13.20 Blueboard

		Crew	Daily Output	Labor-Hours	Unit	Material	2014 Bare Costs Labor	Equipment	Total	Total Incl O&P
0010	**BLUEBOARD** For use with thin coat									
0100	plaster application see Section 09 26 13.80									
1000	3/8" thick, on walls or ceilings, standard, no finish included	2 Carp	1900	.008	S.F.	.31	.39		.70	.97
1100	With thin coat plaster finish		875	.018		.41	.84		1.25	1.83
1400	On beams, columns, or soffits, standard, no finish included		675	.024		.36	1.09		1.45	2.18
1450	With thin coat plaster finish		475	.034		.46	1.54		2	3.04
3000	1/2" thick, on walls or ceilings, standard, no finish included		1900	.008		.31	.39		.70	.97
3100	With thin coat plaster finish		875	.018		.41	.84		1.25	1.83
3300	Fire resistant, no finish included		1900	.008		.31	.39		.70	.97
3400	With thin coat plaster finish		875	.018		.41	.84		1.25	1.83
3450	On beams, columns, or soffits, standard, no finish included		675	.024		.36	1.09		1.45	2.18
3500	With thin coat plaster finish		475	.034		.46	1.54		2	3.04
3700	Fire resistant, no finish included		675	.024		.36	1.09		1.45	2.18
3800	With thin coat plaster finish		475	.034		.46	1.54		2	3.04
5000	5/8" thick, on walls or ceilings, fire resistant, no finish included		1900	.008		.33	.39		.72	.99
5100	With thin coat plaster finish		875	.018		.43	.84		1.27	1.85
5500	On beams, columns, or soffits, no finish included		675	.024		.38	1.09		1.47	2.21
5600	With thin coat plaster finish		475	.034		.48	1.54		2.02	3.07
6000	For high ceilings, over 8' high, add		3060	.005			.24		.24	.39
6500	For over 3 stories high, add per story		6100	.003			.12		.12	.20
9000	Minimum labor/equipment charge	1 Carp	2	4	Job		183		183	300

09 26 13.80 Thin Coat Plaster

		Crew	Daily Output	Labor-Hours	Unit	Material	2014 Bare Costs Labor	Equipment	Total	Total Incl O&P
0010	**THIN COAT PLASTER** R092000-50									
0012	1 coat veneer, not incl. lath	J-1	3600	.011	S.F.	.10	.45	.04	.59	.86
1000	In 50 lb. bags				Bag	13.70			13.70	15.10

09 28 Backing Boards and Underlayments

09 28 13 – Cementitious Backing Boards

09 28 13.10 Cementitious Backerboard

		Crew	Daily Output	Labor-Hours	Unit	Material	2014 Bare Costs Labor	Equipment	Total	Total Incl O&P
0010	**CEMENTITIOUS BACKERBOARD**									
0070	Cementitious backerboard, on floor, 3' x 4' x 1/2" sheets	2 Carp	525	.030	S.F.	.80	1.40		2.20	3.18
0080	3' x 5' x 1/2" sheets		525	.030		.74	1.40		2.14	3.12
0090	3' x 6' x 1/2" sheets		525	.030		.74	1.40		2.14	3.11
0100	3' x 4' x 5/8" sheets		525	.030		1.02	1.40		2.42	3.42
0110	3' x 5' x 5/8" sheets		525	.030		.99	1.40		2.39	3.38
0120	3' x 6' x 5/8" sheets		525	.030		.96	1.40		2.36	3.36
0150	On wall, 3' x 4' x 1/2" sheets		350	.046		.80	2.10		2.90	4.32
0160	3' x 5' x 1/2" sheets		350	.046		.74	2.10		2.84	4.26
0170	3' x 6' x 1/2" sheets		350	.046		.74	2.10		2.84	4.25
0180	3' x 4' x 5/8" sheets		350	.046		1.02	2.10		3.12	4.56
0190	3' x 5' x 5/8" sheets		350	.046		.99	2.10		3.09	4.52
0200	3' x 6' x 5/8" sheets		350	.046		.96	2.10		3.06	4.50
0250	On counter, 3' x 4' x 1/2" sheets		180	.089		.80	4.08		4.88	7.60
0260	3' x 5' x 1/2" sheets		180	.089		.74	4.08		4.82	7.50
0270	3' x 6' x 1/2" sheets		180	.089		.74	4.08		4.82	7.50
0300	3' x 4' x 5/8" sheets		180	.089		1.02	4.08		5.10	7.80
0310	3' x 5' x 5/8" sheets		180	.089		.99	4.08		5.07	7.80
0320	3' x 6' x 5/8" sheets		180	.089		.96	4.08		5.04	7.75

09 29 Gypsum Board

09 29 10 – Gypsum Board Panels

09 29 10.30 Gypsum Board

		Crew	Daily Output	Labor-Hours	Unit	Material	2014 Bare Costs Labor	Equipment	Total	Total Incl O&P
0010	**GYPSUM BOARD** on walls & ceilings	R092910-10								
0100	Nailed or screwed to studs unless otherwise noted									
0110	1/4" thick, on walls or ceilings, standard, no finish included	2 Carp	1330	.012	S.F.	.31	.55		.86	1.25
0115	1/4" thick, on walls or ceilings, flexible, no finish included		1050	.015		.47	.70		1.17	1.67
0117	1/4" thick, on columns or soffits, flexible, no finish included		1050	.015		.47	.70		1.17	1.67
0130	1/4" thick, standard, no finish included, less than 800 S.F.		510	.031		.31	1.44		1.75	2.70
0150	3/8" thick, on walls, standard, no finish included		2000	.008		.31	.37		.68	.94
0200	On ceilings, standard, no finish included		1800	.009		.31	.41		.72	1.01
0250	On beams, columns, or soffits, no finish included		675	.024		.31	1.09		1.40	2.13
0300	1/2" thick, on walls, standard, no finish included		2000	.008		.30	.37		.67	.93
0350	Taped and finished (level 4 finish)		965	.017		.35	.76		1.11	1.63
0390	With compound skim coat (level 5 finish)		775	.021		.41	.95		1.36	2.01
0400	Fire resistant, no finish included		2000	.008		.32	.37		.69	.95
0450	Taped and finished (level 4 finish)		965	.017		.37	.76		1.13	1.66
0490	With compound skim coat (level 5 finish)		775	.021		.43	.95		1.38	2.03
0500	Water resistant, no finish included		2000	.008		.38	.37		.75	1.02
0550	Taped and finished (level 4 finish)		965	.017		.43	.76		1.19	1.72
0590	With compound skim coat (level 5 finish)		775	.021		.49	.95		1.44	2.09
0600	Prefinished, vinyl, clipped to studs		900	.018		.48	.82		1.30	1.87
0700	Mold resistant, no finish included		2000	.008		.40	.37		.77	1.04
0710	Taped and finished (level 4 finish)		965	.017		.45	.76		1.21	1.74
0720	With compound skim coat (level 5 finish)		775	.021		.51	.95		1.46	2.12
1000	On ceilings, standard, no finish included		1800	.009		.30	.41		.71	1
1050	Taped and finished (level 4 finish)		765	.021		.35	.96		1.31	1.96
1090	With compound skim coat (level 5 finish)		610	.026		.41	1.20		1.61	2.43
1100	Fire resistant, no finish included		1800	.009		.32	.41		.73	1.02
1150	Taped and finished (level 4 finish)		765	.021		.37	.96		1.33	1.99
1195	With compound skim coat (level 5 finish)		610	.026		.43	1.20		1.63	2.45

09 29 10.30 Gypsum Board		Crew	Daily Output	Labor-Hours	Unit	Material	2014 Bare Costs Labor	Equipment	Total	Total Incl O&P
1200	Water resistant, no finish included	2 Carp	1800	.009	S.F.	.38	.41		.79	1.09
1250	Taped and finished (level 4 finish)		765	.021		.43	.96		1.39	2.05
1290	With compound skim coat (level 5 finish)		610	.026		.49	1.20		1.69	2.51
1310	Mold resistant, no finish included		1800	.009		.40	.41		.81	1.11
1320	Taped and finished (level 4 finish)		765	.021		.45	.96		1.41	2.07
1330	With compound skim coat (level 5 finish)		610	.026		.51	1.20		1.71	2.54
1350	Sag resistant, no finish included		1600	.010		.32	.46		.78	1.10
1360	Taped and finished (level 4 finish)		765	.021		.37	.96		1.33	1.99
1370	With compound skim coat (level 5 finish)		610	.026		.43	1.20		1.63	2.45
1500	On beams, columns, or soffits, standard, no finish included		675	.024		.35	1.09		1.44	2.17
1550	Taped and finished (level 4 finish)		540	.030		.35	1.36		1.71	2.61
1590	With compound skim coat (level 5 finish)		475	.034		.41	1.54		1.95	2.99
1600	Fire resistant, no finish included		675	.024		.32	1.09		1.41	2.14
1650	Taped and finished (level 4 finish)		540	.030		.37	1.36		1.73	2.64
1690	With compound skim coat (level 5 finish)		475	.034		.43	1.54		1.97	3.01
1700	Water resistant, no finish included		675	.024		.44	1.09		1.53	2.27
1750	Taped and finished (level 4 finish)		540	.030		.43	1.36		1.79	2.70
1790	With compound skim coat (level 5 finish)		475	.034		.49	1.54		2.03	3.07
1800	Mold resistant, no finish included		675	.024		.46	1.09		1.55	2.30
1810	Taped and finished (level 4 finish)		540	.030		.45	1.36		1.81	2.72
1820	With compound skim coat (level 5 finish)		475	.034		.51	1.54		2.05	3.10
1850	Sag resistant, no finish included		675	.024		.37	1.09		1.46	2.19
1860	Taped and finished (level 4 finish)		540	.030		.37	1.36		1.73	2.64
1870	With compound skim coat (level 5 finish)		475	.034		.43	1.54		1.97	3.01
2000	5/8" thick, on walls, standard, no finish included		2000	.008		.32	.37		.69	.95
2050	Taped and finished (level 4 finish)		965	.017		.37	.76		1.13	1.66
2090	With compound skim coat (level 5 finish)		775	.021		.43	.95		1.38	2.03
2100	Fire resistant, no finish included		2000	.008		.34	.37		.71	.97
2150	Taped and finished (level 4 finish)		965	.017		.39	.76		1.15	1.68
2195	With compound skim coat (level 5 finish)		775	.021		.45	.95		1.40	2.05
2200	Water resistant, no finish included		2000	.008		.45	.37		.82	1.10
2250	Taped and finished (level 4 finish)		965	.017		.50	.76		1.26	1.80
2290	With compound skim coat (level 5 finish)		775	.021		.56	.95		1.51	2.17
2300	Prefinished, vinyl, clipped to studs		900	.018		.89	.82		1.71	2.32
2510	Mold resistant, no finish included		2000	.008		.45	.37		.82	1.10
2520	Taped and finished (level 4 finish)		965	.017		.50	.76		1.26	1.80
2530	With compound skim coat (level 5 finish)		775	.021		.56	.95		1.51	2.17
3000	On ceilings, standard, no finish included		1800	.009		.32	.41		.73	1.02
3050	Taped and finished (level 4 finish)		765	.021		.37	.96		1.33	1.99
3090	With compound skim coat (level 5 finish)		615	.026		.43	1.19		1.62	2.43
3100	Fire resistant, no finish included		1800	.009		.34	.41		.75	1.04
3150	Taped and finished (level 4 finish)		765	.021		.39	.96		1.35	2.01
3190	With compound skim coat (level 5 finish)		615	.026		.45	1.19		1.64	2.45
3200	Water resistant, no finish included		1800	.009		.45	.41		.86	1.17
3250	Taped and finished (level 4 finish)		765	.021		.50	.96		1.46	2.13
3290	With compound skim coat (level 5 finish)		615	.026		.56	1.19		1.75	2.57
3300	Mold resistant, no finish included		1800	.009		.45	.41		.86	1.17
3310	Taped and finished (level 4 finish)		765	.021		.50	.96		1.46	2.13
3320	With compound skim coat (level 5 finish)		615	.026		.56	1.19		1.75	2.57
3500	On beams, columns, or soffits, no finish included		675	.024		.37	1.09		1.46	2.19
3550	Taped and finished (level 4 finish)		475	.034		.43	1.54		1.97	3.01
3590	With compound skim coat (level 5 finish)		380	.042		.49	1.93		2.42	3.71
3600	Fire resistant, no finish included		675	.024		.39	1.09		1.48	2.22

09 29 10.30 Gypsum Board		Crew	Daily Output	Labor-Hours	Unit	Material	2014 Bare Costs Labor	Equipment	Total	Total Incl O&P
3650	Taped and finished (level 4 finish)	2 Carp	475	.034	S.F.	.45	1.54		1.99	3.03
3690	With compound skim coat (level 5 finish)		380	.042		.45	1.93		2.38	3.66
3700	Water resistant, no finish included		675	.024		.52	1.09		1.61	2.36
3750	Taped and finished (level 4 finish)		475	.034		.56	1.54		2.10	3.15
3790	With compound skim coat (level 5 finish)		380	.042		.57	1.93		2.50	3.80
3800	Mold resistant, no finish included		675	.024		.52	1.09		1.61	2.36
3810	Taped and finished (level 4 finish)		475	.034		.56	1.54		2.10	3.15
3820	With compound skim coat (level 5 finish)		380	.042		.57	1.93		2.50	3.80
4000	Fireproofing, beams or columns, 2 layers, 1/2" thick, incl finish		330	.048		.74	2.22		2.96	4.46
4010	Mold resistant		330	.048		.90	2.22		3.12	4.64
4050	5/8" thick		300	.053		.78	2.45		3.23	4.88
4060	Mold resistant		300	.053		1	2.45		3.45	5.10
4100	3 layers, 1/2" thick		225	.071		1.11	3.26		4.37	6.55
4110	Mold resistant		225	.071		1.35	3.26		4.61	6.85
4150	5/8" thick		210	.076		1.17	3.49		4.66	7.05
4160	Mold resistant		210	.076		1.50	3.49		4.99	7.40
5050	For 1" thick coreboard on columns		480	.033		.74	1.53		2.27	3.32
5100	For foil-backed board, add					.15			.15	.17
5200	For work over 8' high, add	2 Carp	3060	.005			.24		.24	.39
5270	For textured spray, add	2 Lath	1600	.010		.04	.41		.45	.68
5300	For distribution cost over 3 stories high, add per story	2 Carp	6100	.003			.12		.12	.20
5350	For finishing inner corners, add		950	.017	L.F.	.11	.77		.88	1.39
5355	For finishing outer corners, add		1250	.013		.23	.59		.82	1.22
5500	For acoustical sealant, add per bead	1 Carp	500	.016		.04	.73		.77	1.26
5550	Sealant, 1 quart tube				Ea.	7.05			7.05	7.80
6000	Gypsum sound dampening panels									
6010	1/2" thick on walls, multi-layer, light weight, no finish included	2 Carp	1500	.011	S.F.	1.87	.49		2.36	2.86
6015	Taped and finished (level 4 finish)		725	.022		1.92	1.01		2.93	3.77
6020	With compound skim coat (level 5 finish)		580	.028		1.98	1.27		3.25	4.25
6025	5/8" thick on walls, for wood studs, no finish included		1500	.011		2.70	.49		3.19	3.77
6030	Taped and finished (level 4 finish)		725	.022		2.75	1.01		3.76	4.68
6035	With compound skim coat (level 5 finish)		580	.028		2.81	1.27		4.08	5.15
6040	For metal stud, no finish included		1500	.011		2.06	.49		2.55	3.07
6045	Taped and finished (level 4 finish)		725	.022		2.11	1.01		3.12	3.98
6050	With compound skim coat (level 5 finish)		580	.028		2.17	1.27		3.44	4.46
6055	Abuse resist, no finish included		1500	.011		3.75	.49		4.24	4.93
6060	Taped and finished (level 4 finish)		725	.022		3.80	1.01		4.81	5.85
6065	With compound skim coat (level 5 finish)		580	.028		3.86	1.27		5.13	6.30
6070	Shear rated, no finish included		1500	.011		4.30	.49		4.79	5.55
6075	Taped and finished (level 4 finish)		725	.022		4.35	1.01		5.36	6.45
6080	With compound skim coat (level 5 finish)		580	.028		4.41	1.27		5.68	6.95
6085	For SCIF applications, no finish included		1500	.011		4.72	.49		5.21	6
6090	Taped and finished (level 4 finish)		725	.022		4.77	1.01		5.78	6.90
6095	With compound skim coat (level 5 finish)		580	.028		4.83	1.27		6.10	7.40
6100	1-3/8" thick on walls, THX Certified, no finish included		1500	.011		8.40	.49		8.89	10.05
6105	Taped and finished (level 4 finish)		725	.022		8.45	1.01		9.46	10.95
6110	With compound skim coat (level 5 finish)		580	.028		8.50	1.27		9.77	11.45
6115	5/8" thick on walls, score & snap installation, no finish included		2000	.008		1.78	.37		2.15	2.56
6120	Taped and finished (level 4 finish)		965	.017		1.83	.76		2.59	3.26
6125	With compound skim coat (level 5 finish)		775	.021		1.89	.95		2.84	3.63
7020	5/8" thick on ceilings, for wood joists, no finish included		1200	.013		2.70	.61		3.31	3.97
7025	Taped and finished (level 4 finish)		510	.031		2.75	1.44		4.19	5.40
7030	With compound skim coat (level 5 finish)		410	.039		2.81	1.79		4.60	6.05

09 29 Gypsum Board

09 29 10 – Gypsum Board Panels

09 29 10.30 Gypsum Board		Crew	Daily Output	Labor-Hours	Unit	Material	2014 Bare Costs Labor	Equipment	Total	Total Incl O&P
7035	For metal joists, no finish included	2 Carp	1200	.013	S.F.	2.06	.61		2.67	3.27
7040	Taped and finished (level 4 finish)		510	.031		2.11	1.44		3.55	4.68
7045	With compound skim coat (level 5 finish)		410	.039		2.17	1.79		3.96	5.30
7050	Abuse resist, no finish included		1200	.013		3.75	.61		4.36	5.15
7055	Taped and finished (level 4 finish)		510	.031		3.80	1.44		5.24	6.55
7060	With compound skim coat (level 5 finish)		410	.039		3.86	1.79		5.65	7.20
7065	Shear rated, no finish included		1200	.013		4.30	.61		4.91	5.75
7070	Taped and finished (level 4 finish)		510	.031		4.35	1.44		5.79	7.15
7075	With compound skim coat (level 5 finish)		410	.039		4.41	1.79		6.20	7.80
7080	For SCIF applications, no finish included		1200	.013		4.72	.61		5.33	6.20
7085	Taped and finished (level 4 finish)		510	.031		4.77	1.44		6.21	7.60
7090	With compound skim coat (level 5 finish)		410	.039		4.83	1.79		6.62	8.25
8010	5/8" thick on ceilings, score & snap installation, no finish included		1600	.010		1.78	.46		2.24	2.71
8015	Taped and finished (level 4 finish)		680	.024		1.83	1.08		2.91	3.78
8020	With compound skim coat (level 5 finish)		545	.029		1.89	1.35		3.24	4.28
9000	Minimum labor/equipment charge	1 Carp	2	4	Job		183		183	300

09 29 15 – Gypsum Board Accessories

09 29 15.10 Accessories, Gypsum Board

		Crew	Daily Output	Labor-Hours	Unit	Material	2014 Bare Costs Labor	Equipment	Total	Total Incl O&P
0010	**ACCESSORIES, GYPSUM BOARD**									
0020	Casing bead, galvanized steel	1 Carp	2.90	2.759	C.L.F.	24.50	126		150.50	235
0100	Vinyl		3	2.667		22	122		144	225
0300	Corner bead, galvanized steel, 1" x 1"		4	2		15.15	91.50		106.65	168
0400	1-1/4" x 1-1/4"		3.50	2.286		16	105		121	190
0600	Vinyl		4	2		16.25	91.50		107.75	169
0900	Furring channel, galv. steel, 7/8" deep, standard		2.60	3.077		32.50	141		173.50	268
1000	Resilient		2.55	3.137		29	144		173	268
1100	J trim, galvanized steel, 1/2" wide		3	2.667		21.50	122		143.50	225
1120	5/8" wide		2.95	2.712		27.50	124		151.50	234
1500	Z stud, galvanized steel, 1-1/2" wide		2.60	3.077		36	141		177	272
9000	Minimum labor/equipment charge		3	2.667	Job		122		122	201

09 30 Tiling

09 30 13 – Ceramic Tiling

09 30 13.10 Ceramic Tile

		Crew	Daily Output	Labor-Hours	Unit	Material	2014 Bare Costs Labor	Equipment	Total	Total Incl O&P
0010	**CERAMIC TILE**									
0600	Cove base, 4-1/4" x 4-1/4" high, mud set	D-7	91	.176	L.F.	3.88	6.60		10.48	14.65
0700	Thin set		128	.125		3.95	4.70		8.65	11.75
0900	6" x 4-1/4" high, mud set		100	.160		4.05	6		10.05	13.90
1000	Thin set		137	.117		3.93	4.39		8.32	11.20
1200	Sanitary cove base, 6" x 4-1/4" high, mud set		93	.172		4.11	6.45		10.56	14.75
1300	Thin set		124	.129		3.99	4.85		8.84	12.05
1500	6" x 6" high, mud set		84	.190		5.10	7.15		12.25	16.90
1600	Thin set		117	.137		4.96	5.15		10.11	13.55
2400	Bullnose trim, 4-1/4" x 4-1/4", mud set		82	.195		3.81	7.35		11.16	15.75
2500	Thin set		128	.125		3.73	4.70		8.43	11.50
2700	2" x 6" bullnose trim, mud set		84	.190		4.27	7.15		11.42	16
2800	Thin set		124	.129		4.21	4.85		9.06	12.30
3000	Floors, natural clay, random or uniform, thin set, color group 1		183	.087	S.F.	4.15	3.29		7.44	9.75
3100	Color group 2		183	.087		5.85	3.29		9.14	11.65
3300	Porcelain type, 1 color, color group 2, 1" x 1"		183	.087		5.20	3.29		8.49	10.90

09 30 Tiling

09 30 13 – Ceramic Tiling

09 30 13.10 Ceramic Tile

	09 30 13.10 Ceramic Tile	Crew	Daily Output	Labor-Hours	Unit	Material	2014 Bare Costs Labor	Equipment	Total	Total Incl O&P
3310	2" x 2" or 2" x 1", thin set	D-7	190	.084	S.F.	5.95	3.17		9.12	11.55
3350	For random blend, 2 colors, add					1			1	1.10
3360	4 colors, add					1.50			1.50	1.65
4300	Specialty tile, 4-1/4" x 4-1/4" x 1/2", decorator finish	D-7	183	.087		10.40	3.29		13.69	16.65
4500	Add for epoxy grout, 1/16" joint, 1" x 1" tile		800	.020		.66	.75		1.41	1.91
4600	2" x 2" tile		820	.020		.61	.73		1.34	1.83
4800	Pregrouted sheets, walls, 4-1/4" x 4-1/4", 6" x 4-1/4"									
4810	and 8-1/2" x 4-1/4", 4 S.F. sheets, silicone grout	D-7	240	.067	S.F.	5.05	2.51		7.56	9.50
5100	Floors, unglazed, 2 S.F. sheets,									
5110	Urethane adhesive	D-7	180	.089	S.F.	5.05	3.34		8.39	10.80
5400	Walls, interior, thin set, 4-1/4" x 4-1/4" tile		190	.084		2.26	3.17		5.43	7.45
5500	6" x 4-1/4" tile		190	.084		2.92	3.17		6.09	8.20
5700	8-1/2" x 4-1/4" tile		190	.084		4.86	3.17		8.03	10.35
5800	6" x 6" tile		175	.091		3.12	3.44		6.56	8.85
5810	8" x 8" tile		170	.094		4.27	3.54		7.81	10.25
5820	12" x 12" tile		160	.100		4.35	3.76		8.11	10.70
5830	16" x 16" tile		150	.107		4.77	4.01		8.78	11.55
6000	Decorated wall tile, 4-1/4" x 4-1/4", minimum		270	.059		3.18	2.23		5.41	7
6100	Maximum		180	.089		49.50	3.34		52.84	60
6600	Crystalline glazed, 4-1/4" x 4-1/4", mud set, plain		100	.160		4.27	6		10.27	14.15
6700	4-1/4" x 4-1/4", scored tile		100	.160		5.80	6		11.80	15.85
6900	6" x 6" plain		93	.172		6.50	6.45		12.95	17.35
7000	For epoxy grout, 1/16" joints, 4-1/4" tile, add		800	.020		.41	.75		1.16	1.63
7200	For tile set in dry mortar, add		1735	.009			.35		.35	.55
7300	For tile set in Portland cement mortar, add		290	.055		.16	2.07		2.23	3.45
9300	Ceramic tiles, recycled glass, standard colors, 2" x 2" thru 6" x 6" G		190	.084		20	3.17		23.17	27
9310	6" x 6" G		175	.091		20	3.44		23.44	27.50
9320	8" x 8" G		170	.094		22	3.54		25.54	30
9330	12" x 12" G		160	.100		22	3.76		25.76	30.50
9340	Earthtones, 2" x 2" to 4" x 8" G		190	.084		25	3.17		28.17	32.50
9350	6" x 6" G		175	.091		25	3.44		28.44	33
9360	8" x 8" G		170	.094		26	3.54		29.54	34
9370	12" x 12" G		160	.100		26	3.76		29.76	34.50
9380	Deep colors, 2" x 2" to 4" x 8" G		190	.084		29.50	3.17		32.67	37.50
9390	6" x 6" G		175	.091		29.50	3.44		32.94	38
9400	8" x 8" G		170	.094		31	3.54		34.54	39.50
9410	12" x 12" G		160	.100		31	3.76		34.76	40
9500	Minimum labor/equipment charge		3.25	4.923	Job		185		185	291

09 30 13.20 Ceramic Tile Repairs

		Crew	Daily Output	Labor-Hours	Unit	Material	Labor	Equipment	Total	Total Incl O&P
0010	**CERAMIC TILE REPAIRS**									
1000	Grout removal, carbide tipped, rotary grinder	1 Clab	240	.033	L.F.		1.22		1.22	2.01

09 30 13.45 Ceramic Tile Accessories

		Crew	Daily Output	Labor-Hours	Unit	Material	Labor	Equipment	Total	Total Incl O&P
0010	**CERAMIC TILE ACCESSORIES**									
0100	Spacers, 1/8"				C	1.98			1.98	2.18
1310	Sealer for natural stone tile, installed	1 Tilf	650	.012	S.F.	.05	.52		.57	.87

09 30 16 – Quarry Tiling

09 30 16.10 Quarry Tile

		Crew	Daily Output	Labor-Hours	Unit	Material	Labor	Equipment	Total	Total Incl O&P
0010	**QUARRY TILE**									
0100	Base, cove or sanitary, mud set, to 5" high, 1/2" thick	D-7	110	.145	L.F.	5.35	5.45		10.80	14.50
0300	Bullnose trim, red, mud set, 6" x 6" x 1/2" thick		120	.133		4.39	5		9.39	12.75
0400	4" x 4" x 1/2" thick		110	.145		4.50	5.45		9.95	13.55
0600	4" x 8" x 1/2" thick, using 8" as edge		130	.123		4.50	4.63		9.13	12.25

09 30 Tiling

09 30 16 – Quarry Tiling

09 30 16.10 Quarry Tile

		Crew	Daily Output	Labor-Hours	Unit	Material	2014 Bare Costs Labor	Equipment	Total	Total Incl O&P
0700	Floors, mud set, 1,000 S.F. lots, red, 4" x 4" x 1/2" thick	D-7	120	.133	S.F.	7.05	5		12.05	15.65
0900	6" x 6" x 1/2" thick		140	.114		7.30	4.30		11.60	14.80
1000	4" x 8" x 1/2" thick	↓	130	.123		6.05	4.63		10.68	13.95
1300	For waxed coating, add					.74			.74	.81
1500	For non-standard colors, add					.45			.45	.50
1600	For abrasive surface, add					.51			.51	.56
1800	Brown tile, imported, 6" x 6" x 3/4"	D-7	120	.133		7.85	5		12.85	16.50
1900	8" x 8" x 1"		110	.145		8.55	5.45		14	18
2100	For thin set mortar application, deduct		700	.023			.86		.86	1.35
2700	Stair tread, 6" x 6" x 3/4", plain		50	.320		6.95	12.05		19	26.50
2800	Abrasive		47	.340		5.95	12.80		18.75	26.50
3000	Wainscot, 6" x 6" x 1/2", thin set, red		105	.152		4.63	5.75		10.38	14.10
3100	Non-standard colors		105	.152	↓	5.15	5.75		10.90	14.65
3300	Window sill, 6" wide, 3/4" thick		90	.178	L.F.	6.20	6.70		12.90	17.30
3400	Corners		80	.200	Ea.	6.65	7.50		14.15	19.15
9000	Minimum labor/equipment charge	↓	3.25	4.923	Job		185		185	291

09 30 23 – Glass Mosaic Tiling

09 30 23.10 Glass Mosaics

		Crew	Daily Output	Labor-Hours	Unit	Material	2014 Bare Costs Labor	Equipment	Total	Total Incl O&P
0010	**GLASS MOSAICS** 3/4" tile on 12" sheets, standard grout									
1020	1" tile on 12" sheets, opalescent finish	D-7	73	.219	S.F.	17.55	8.25		25.80	32.50
1040	1" x 2" tile on 12" sheet, blend		73	.219		17.30	8.25		25.55	32
1060	2" tile on 12" sheet, blend		73	.219		17.10	8.25		25.35	32
1080	5/8" x random tile, linear, on 12" sheet, blend		73	.219		28	8.25		36.25	44
1600	Dots on 12" sheet		73	.219		28	8.25		36.25	44
1700	For glass mosaic tiles set in dry mortar, add		290	.055		.45	2.07		2.52	3.77
1720	For glass mosaic tile set in Portland cement mortar, add		290	.055	↓	.01	2.07		2.08	3.28
1730	For polyblend sanded tile grout	↓	96.15	.166	Lb.	2.19	6.25		8.44	12.25

09 30 29 – Metal Tiling

09 30 29.10 Metal Tile

		Crew	Daily Output	Labor-Hours	Unit	Material	2014 Bare Costs Labor	Equipment	Total	Total Incl O&P
0010	**METAL TILE** 4' x 4' sheet, 24 ga., tile pattern, nailed									
0200	Stainless steel	2 Carp	512	.031	S.F.	27.50	1.43		28.93	32.50
0400	Aluminized steel	"	512	.031	"	14.80	1.43		16.23	18.60
9000	Minimum labor/equipment charge	1 Carp	4	2	Job		91.50		91.50	151

09 34 Waterproofing-Membrane Tiling

09 34 13 – Waterproofing-Membrane Ceramic Tiling

09 34 13.10 Ceramic Tile Waterproofing Membrane

		Crew	Daily Output	Labor-Hours	Unit	Material	2014 Bare Costs Labor	Equipment	Total	Total Incl O&P
0010	**CERAMIC TILE WATERPROOFING MEMBRANE**									
0020	On floors, including thinset									
0030	Fleece laminated polyethylene grid, 1/8" thick	D-7	250	.064	S.F.	2.23	2.41		4.64	6.25
0040	5/16" thick	"	250	.064	"	2.55	2.41		4.96	6.60
0050	On walls, including thinset									
0060	Fleece laminated polyethylene sheet, 8 mil thick	D-7	480	.033	S.F.	2.23	1.25		3.48	4.42
0070	Accessories, including thinset									
0080	Joint and corner sheet, 4 mils thick, 5" wide	1 Tilf	240	.033	L.F.	1.32	1.40		2.72	3.65
0090	7-1/4" wide		180	.044		1.68	1.86		3.54	4.79
0100	10" wide		120	.067	↓	2.05	2.80		4.85	6.65
0110	Pre-formed corners, inside		32	.250	Ea.	6.20	10.50		16.70	23.50
0120	Outside		32	.250		7.35	10.50		17.85	24.50
0130	2" flanged floor drain with 6" stainless steel grate	↓	16	.500	↓	380	21		401	450

09 34 Waterproofing-Membrane Tiling

09 34 13 – Waterproofing-Membrane Ceramic Tiling

09 34 13.10 Ceramic Tile Waterproofing Membrane	Crew	Daily Output	Labor-Hours	Unit	Material	2014 Bare Costs Labor	Equipment	Total	Total Incl O&P
0140 EPS, sloped shower floor	1 Tilf	480	.017	S.F.	4.77	.70		5.47	6.35
0150 Curb	↓	32	.250	L.F.	13.50	10.50		24	31.50

09 51 Acoustical Ceilings

09 51 23 – Acoustical Tile Ceilings

09 51 23.10 Suspended Acoustic Ceiling Tiles

		Crew	Daily Output	Labor-Hours	Unit	Material	2014 Bare Costs Labor	Equipment	Total	Total Incl O&P
0010	**SUSPENDED ACOUSTIC CEILING TILES**, not including									
0100	suspension system									
0300	Fiberglass boards, film faced, 2' x 2' or 2' x 4', 5/8" thick	1 Carp	625	.013	S.F.	1.02	.59		1.61	2.08
0400	3/4" thick		600	.013		1.67	.61		2.28	2.84
0500	3" thick, thermal, R11		450	.018		1.90	.82		2.72	3.43
0600	Glass cloth faced fiberglass, 3/4" thick		500	.016		2.01	.73		2.74	3.42
0700	1" thick		485	.016		2.74	.76		3.50	4.25
0820	1-1/2" thick, nubby face		475	.017		2.50	.77		3.27	4.02
1110	Mineral fiber tile, lay-in, 2' x 2' or 2' x 4', 5/8" thick, fine texture		625	.013		1.25	.59		1.84	2.34
1115	Rough textured		625	.013		1.21	.59		1.80	2.29
1125	3/4" thick, fine textured		600	.013		1.66	.61		2.27	2.83
1130	Rough textured		600	.013		1.65	.61		2.26	2.82
1135	Fissured		600	.013		2.70	.61		3.31	3.97
1150	Tegular, 5/8" thick, fine textured		470	.017		1.64	.78		2.42	3.08
1155	Rough textured		470	.017		1.18	.78		1.96	2.58
1165	3/4" thick, fine textured		450	.018		2.70	.82		3.52	4.31
1170	Rough textured		450	.018		1.54	.82		2.36	3.03
1175	Fissured		450	.018		2.70	.82		3.52	4.31
1185	For plastic film face, add					.84			.84	.92
1190	For fire rating, add					.45			.45	.50
1300	Mirror tile, acrylic, 2' x 2'	1 Carp	500	.016		10.70	.73		11.43	12.95
1900	Eggcrate, acrylic, 1/2" x 1/2" x 1/2" cubes		500	.016		1.86	.73		2.59	3.26
2100	Polystyrene eggcrate, 3/8" x 3/8" x 1/2" cubes		510	.016		1.56	.72		2.28	2.90
2200	1/2" x 1/2" x 1/2" cubes		500	.016		1.74	.73		2.47	3.12
2400	Luminous panels, prismatic, acrylic		400	.020		2.26	.92		3.18	4
2500	Polystyrene		400	.020		1.16	.92		2.08	2.79
2700	Flat white acrylic		400	.020		3.94	.92		4.86	5.85
2800	Polystyrene		400	.020		2.70	.92		3.62	4.48
3000	Drop pan, white, acrylic		400	.020		5.75	.92		6.67	7.85
3100	Polystyrene		400	.020		4.82	.92		5.74	6.80
3600	Perforated aluminum sheets, .024" thick, corrugated, painted		490	.016		2.34	.75		3.09	3.80
3700	Plain		500	.016		3.92	.73		4.65	5.50
3720	Mineral fiber, 24" x 24" or 48", reveal edge, painted, 5/8" thick		600	.013		1.18	.61		1.79	2.30
3740	3/4" thick		575	.014		1.54	.64		2.18	2.74
5020	66 – 78% recycled content, 3/4" thick [G]		600	.013		1.87	.61		2.48	3.06
5040	Mylar, 42% recycled content, 3/4" thick [G]		600	.013		4.41	.61		5.02	5.85
9000	Minimum labor/equipment charge	↓	4	2	Job		91.50		91.50	151

09 51 23.30 Suspended Ceilings, Complete

		Crew	Daily Output	Labor-Hours	Unit	Material	2014 Bare Costs Labor	Equipment	Total	Total Incl O&P
0010	**SUSPENDED CEILINGS, COMPLETE**, including standard									
0100	suspension system but not incl. 1-1/2" carrier channels									
0600	Fiberglass ceiling board, 2' x 4' x 5/8", plain faced	1 Carp	500	.016	S.F.	1.72	.73		2.45	3.10
0700	Offices, 2' x 4' x 3/4"		380	.021		2.37	.97		3.34	4.20
0800	Mineral fiber, on 15/16" T bar susp. 2' x 2' x 3/4" lay-in board		345	.023		2.57	1.06		3.63	4.57
0810	2' x 4' x 5/8" tile		380	.021		2.65	.97		3.62	4.50
0820	Tegular, 2' x 2' x 5/8" tile on 9/16" grid		250	.032	↓	3.12	1.47		4.59	5.85

09 51 Acoustical Ceilings

09 51 23 – Acoustical Tile Ceilings

09 51 23.30 Suspended Ceilings, Complete	Crew	Daily Output	Labor-Hours	Unit	Material	2014 Bare Costs Labor	Equipment	Total	Total Incl O&P
0830	2' x 4' x 3/4" tile	1 Carp	275	.029	S.F.	3.02	1.33		4.35	5.50
0900	Luminous panels, prismatic, acrylic		255	.031		2.96	1.44		4.40	5.60
1200	Metal pan with acoustic pad, steel		75	.107		4.48	4.89		9.37	13
1300	Painted aluminum		75	.107		3.04	4.89		7.93	11.40
1500	Aluminum, degreased finish		75	.107		5.15	4.89		10.04	13.75
1600	Stainless steel		75	.107		9.70	4.89		14.59	18.70
1800	Tile, Z bar suspension, 5/8" mineral fiber tile		150	.053		2.32	2.45		4.77	6.55
1900	3/4" mineral fiber tile		150	.053		2.48	2.45		4.93	6.75
2402	For strip lighting, see Section 26 51 13.50									
2500	For rooms under 500 S.F., add				S.F.		25%			
9000	Minimum labor/equipment charge	1 Carp	2	4	Job		183		183	300

09 51 53 – Direct-Applied Acoustical Ceilings

09 51 53.10 Ceiling Tile

09 51 53.10 Ceiling Tile	Crew	Daily Output	Labor-Hours	Unit	Material	2014 Bare Costs Labor	Equipment	Total	Total Incl O&P
0010	**CEILING TILE**, stapled or cemented									
0100	12" x 12" or 12" x 24", not including furring									
0600	Mineral fiber, vinyl coated, 5/8" thick	1 Carp	300	.027	S.F.	1.87	1.22		3.09	4.07
0700	3/4" thick		300	.027		1.78	1.22		3	3.97
0900	Fire rated, 3/4" thick, plain faced		300	.027		1.29	1.22		2.51	3.43
1000	Plastic coated face		300	.027		1.29	1.22		2.51	3.43
1200	Aluminum faced, 5/8" thick, plain		300	.027		1.61	1.22		2.83	3.78
3000	Wood fiber tile, 1/2" thick		400	.020		1.09	.92		2.01	2.71
3100	3/4" thick		400	.020		1.19	.92		2.11	2.82
3300	For flameproofing, add					.10			.10	.11
3400	For sculptured 3 dimensional, add					.30			.30	.33
3900	For ceiling primer, add					.13			.13	.14
4000	For ceiling cement, add					.38			.38	.42
9000	Minimum labor/equipment charge	1 Carp	4	2	Job		91.50		91.50	151

09 53 Acoustical Ceiling Suspension Assemblies

09 53 23 – Metal Acoustical Ceiling Suspension Assemblies

09 53 23.30 Ceiling Suspension Systems

09 53 23.30 Ceiling Suspension Systems	Crew	Daily Output	Labor-Hours	Unit	Material	2014 Bare Costs Labor	Equipment	Total	Total Incl O&P
0010	**CEILING SUSPENSION SYSTEMS** for boards and tile									
0050	Class A suspension system, 15/16" T bar, 2' x 4' grid	1 Carp	800	.010	S.F.	.70	.46		1.16	1.52
0300	2' x 2' grid		650	.012		.91	.56		1.47	1.93
0310	25% recycled steel, 2' x 4' grid [G]		800	.010		.76	.46		1.22	1.58
0320	2' x 2' grid [G]		650	.012		.95	.56		1.51	1.97
0350	For 9/16" grid, add					.16			.16	.18
0360	For fire rated grid, add					.09			.09	.10
0370	For colored grid, add					.21			.21	.23
0400	Concealed Z bar suspension system, 12" module	1 Carp	520	.015		.78	.71		1.49	2.02
0600	1-1/2" carrier channels, 4' O.C., add	"	470	.017		.11	.78		.89	1.40
0700	Carrier channels for ceilings with									
0900	recessed lighting fixtures, add	1 Carp	460	.017	S.F.	.20	.80		1	1.53
3000	Seismic ceiling bracing, IBC Site Class D, Occupancy Category II									
3050	For ceilings less than 2500 S.F.									
3060	Seismic clips at attached walls	1 Carp	180	.044	Ea.	1	2.04		3.04	4.45
3100	For ceilings greater than 2500 S.F., add									
3120	Seismic clips, joints at cross tees	1 Carp	120	.067	Ea.	2.90	3.06		5.96	8.20
3140	At cross tees and mains, mains field cut	"	60	.133	"	2.90	6.10		9	13.25
3200	Compression posts, telescopic, attached to structure above									

09 53 Acoustical Ceiling Suspension Assemblies

09 53 23 – Metal Acoustical Ceiling Suspension Assemblies

09 53 23.30 Ceiling Suspension Systems	Crew	Daily Output	Labor-Hours	Unit	Material	2014 Bare Costs Labor	Equipment	Total	Total Incl O&P
3210	To 30" high	1 Carp	26	.308	Ea.	27	14.10		41.10	53
3220	30" to 48" high		25.50	.314		43.50	14.40		57.90	71.50
3230	48" to 84" high		25	.320		52.50	14.65		67.15	81.50
3240	84" to 102" high		24.50	.327		60	14.95		74.95	90.50
3250	102" to 120" high		24	.333		85.50	15.30		100.80	120
3260	120" to 144" high	↓	24	.333	↓	95	15.30		110.30	130
3300	Stabilizer bars									
3310	12" long	1 Carp	240	.033	Ea.	.78	1.53		2.31	3.37
3320	24" long		235	.034		.77	1.56		2.33	3.41
3330	36" long		230	.035		.72	1.59		2.31	3.41
3340	48" long	↓	220	.036	↓	.73	1.67		2.40	3.54
3400	Wire support for light fixtures, per L.F. height to structure above									
3410	Less than 10 lb.	1 Carp	400	.020	L.F.	.28	.92		1.20	1.81
3420	10 lb. to 56 lb.	"	240	.033	"	.55	1.53		2.08	3.12
3500	Retrofit existing suspended ceiling grid to current code									
3510	Less than 2500 S.F. (using clips @ perimeter)	1 Carp	1455	.006	S.F.	.07	.25		.32	.49
3520	Greater than 2500 S.F. (using compression posts and clips)		550	.015		.44	.67		1.11	1.59
4000	Remove and replace ceiling grid, class A, 15/16" T bar, 2' x 2' grid		435	.018		.91	.84		1.75	2.39
4010	2' x 4' grid	↓	535	.015	↓	.70	.69		1.39	1.90

09 54 Specialty Ceilings

09 54 33 – Decorative Panel Ceilings

09 54 33.20 Metal Panel Ceilings

		Crew	Daily Output	Labor-Hours	Unit	Material	2014 Bare Costs Labor	Equipment	Total	Total Incl O&P
0010	**METAL PANEL CEILINGS**									
0020	Lay-in or screwed to furring, not including grid									
0100	Tin ceilings, 2' x 2' or 2' x 4', bare steel finish	2 Carp	300	.053	S.F.	2.46	2.45		4.91	6.70
0120	Painted white finish		300	.053	"	3.67	2.45		6.12	8.05
0140	Copper, chrome or brass finish		300	.053	L.F.	6.45	2.45		8.90	11.10
0200	Cornice molding, 2-1/2" to 3-1/2" wide, 4' long, bare steel finish		200	.080	S.F.	2.21	3.67		5.88	8.50
0220	Painted white finish		200	.080		2.92	3.67		6.59	9.25
0240	Copper, chrome or brass finish		200	.080		3.91	3.67		7.58	10.35
0320	5" to 6-1/2" wide, 4' long, bare steel finish		150	.107		3.19	4.89		8.08	11.55
0340	Painted white finish		150	.107		4.25	4.89		9.14	12.70
0360	Copper, chrome or brass finish		150	.107		6.50	4.89		11.39	15.20
0420	Flat molding, 3-1/2" to 5" wide, 4' long, bare steel finish		250	.064		3.29	2.93		6.22	8.45
0440	Painted white finish		250	.064		3.80	2.93		6.73	9
0460	Copper, chrome or brass finish	↓	250	.064	↓	7.35	2.93		10.28	12.90

09 62 Specialty Flooring

09 62 19 – Laminate Flooring

09 62 19.10 Floating Floor

		Crew	Daily Output	Labor-Hours	Unit	Material	2014 Bare Costs Labor	Equipment	Total	Total Incl O&P
0010	**FLOATING FLOOR**									
8300	Floating floor, laminate, wood pattern strip, complete	1 Clab	133	.060	S.F.	5.05	2.20		7.25	9.15
8310	Components, T & G wood composite strips					4.02			4.02	4.42
8320	Film					.14			.14	.15
8330	Foam					.25			.25	.28
8340	Adhesive					.65			.65	.72
8350	Installation kit				↓	.17			.17	.19
8360	Trim, 2" wide x 3' long				L.F.	3.85			3.85	4.24

09 62 Specialty Flooring

09 62 19 – Laminate Flooring

09 62 19.10 Floating Floor		Crew	Daily Output	Labor-Hours	Unit	Material	2014 Bare Costs Labor	Equipment	Total	Total Incl O&P
8370	Reducer moulding				L.F.	5.20			5.20	5.70

09 62 23 – Bamboo Flooring

09 62 23.10 Flooring, Bamboo

		Crew	Daily Output	Labor-Hours	Unit	Material	Labor	Equipment	Total	Total Incl O&P
0010	**FLOORING, BAMBOO**									
8600	Flooring, wood, bamboo strips, unfinished, 5/8" x 4" x 3'	G 1 Carp	255	.031	S.F.	4.53	1.44		5.97	7.35
8610	5/8" x 4" x 4'	G	275	.029		4.70	1.33		6.03	7.35
8620	5/8" x 4" x 6'	G	295	.027		5.15	1.24		6.39	7.75
8630	Finished, 5/8" x 4" x 3'	G	255	.031		4.99	1.44		6.43	7.85
8640	5/8" x 4" x 4'	G	275	.029		5.20	1.33		6.53	7.95
8650	5/8" x 4" x 6'	G	295	.027		4.54	1.24		5.78	7.05
8660	Stair treads, unfinished, 1-1/16" x 11-1/2" x 4'	G	18	.444	Ea.	43.50	20.50		64	81.50
8670	Finished, 1-1/16" x 11-1/2" x 4'	G	18	.444		77	20.50		97.50	118
8680	Stair risers, unfinished, 5/8" x 7-1/2" x 4'	G	18	.444		16.05	20.50		36.55	51
8690	Finished, 5/8" x 7-1/2" x 4'	G	18	.444		30.50	20.50		51	67
8700	Stair nosing, unfinished, 6' long	G	16	.500		35.50	23		58.50	76.50
8710	Finished, 6' long	G	16	.500		42	23		65	83.50

09 63 Masonry Flooring

09 63 13 – Brick Flooring

09 63 13.10 Miscellaneous Brick Flooring

		Crew	Daily Output	Labor-Hours	Unit	Material	Labor	Equipment	Total	Total Incl O&P
0010	**MISCELLANEOUS BRICK FLOORING**									
0020	Acid-proof shales, red, 8" x 3-3/4" x 1-1/4" thick	D-7	.43	37.209	M	685	1,400		2,085	2,950
0050	2-1/4" thick	D-1	.40	40		950	1,650		2,600	3,725
0200	Acid-proof clay brick, 8" x 3-3/4" x 2-1/4" thick	G	.40	40		930	1,650		2,580	3,700
0250	9" x 4-1/2" x 3"	G	95	.168	S.F.	4.14	6.95		11.09	15.85
0260	Cast ceramic, pressed, 4" x 8" x 1/2", unglazed	D-7	100	.160		6.25	6		12.25	16.35
0270	Glazed		100	.160		8.35	6		14.35	18.60
0280	Hand molded flooring, 4" x 8" x 3/4", unglazed		95	.168		8.25	6.35		14.60	19.05
0290	Glazed		95	.168		10.35	6.35		16.70	21.50
0300	8" hexagonal, 3/4" thick, unglazed		85	.188		9.05	7.10		16.15	21
0310	Glazed		85	.188		16.35	7.10		23.45	29
0400	Heavy duty industrial, cement mortar bed, 2" thick, not incl. brick	D-1	80	.200		.83	8.25		9.08	14.30
0450	Acid-proof joints, 1/4" wide	"	65	.246		1.44	10.15		11.59	18.10
0500	Pavers, 8" x 4", 1" to 1-1/4" thick, red	D-7	95	.168		3.64	6.35		9.99	13.95
0510	Ironspot	"	95	.168		5.15	6.35		11.50	15.60
0540	1-3/8" to 1-3/4" thick, red	D-1	95	.168		3.51	6.95		10.46	15.15
0560	Ironspot		95	.168		5.10	6.95		12.05	16.90
0580	2-1/4" thick, red		90	.178		3.57	7.35		10.92	15.90
0590	Ironspot		90	.178		5.55	7.35		12.90	18.05
0700	Paver, adobe brick, 6" x 12", 1/2" joint	G	42	.381		1.38	15.75		17.13	27
0710	Mexican red, 12" x 12"	G 1 Tilf	48	.167		1.66	7		8.66	12.85
0720	Saltillo, 12" x 12"	G "	48	.167		1.40	7		8.40	12.55
0800	For sidewalks and patios with pavers, see Section 32 14 16.10									
0870	For epoxy joints, add	D-1	600	.027	S.F.	2.77	1.10		3.87	4.84
0880	For Furan underlayment, add	"	600	.027		2.30	1.10		3.40	4.32
0890	For waxed surface, steam cleaned, add	A-1H	1000	.008		.20	.29	.08	.57	.78
9000	Minimum labor/equipment charge	1 Bric	2	4	Job		182		182	296

09 63 Masonry Flooring

09 63 40 – Stone Flooring

09 63 40.10 Marble	Crew	Daily Output	Labor-Hours	Unit	Material	2014 Bare Costs Labor	Equipment	Total	Total Incl O&P
0010 **MARBLE**									
0020 Thin gauge tile, 12" x 6", 3/8", white Carara	D-7	60	.267	S.F.	14.90	10.05		24.95	32
0100 Travertine		60	.267		13.30	10.05		23.35	30.50
0200 12" x 12" x 3/8", thin set, floors		60	.267		9	10.05		19.05	25.50
0300 On walls		52	.308	↓	9.85	11.55		21.40	29
1000 Marble threshold, 4" wide x 36" long x 5/8" thick, white		60	.267	Ea.	9	10.05		19.05	25.50
9000 Minimum labor/equipment charge	↓	3	5.333	Job		201		201	315

09 63 40.20 Slate Tile

	Crew	Daily Output	Labor-Hours	Unit	Material	Labor	Equipment	Total	Total Incl O&P
0010 **SLATE TILE**									
0020 Vermont, 6" x 6" x 1/4" thick, thin set	D-7	180	.089	S.F.	7	3.34		10.34	12.95
9000 Minimum labor/equipment charge	"	3	5.333	Job		201		201	315

09 64 Wood Flooring

09 64 16 – Wood Block Flooring

09 64 16.10 End Grain Block Flooring

	Crew	Daily Output	Labor-Hours	Unit	Material	Labor	Equipment	Total	Total Incl O&P
0010 **END GRAIN BLOCK FLOORING**									
0020 End grain flooring, coated, 2" thick	1 Carp	295	.027	S.F.	3.52	1.24		4.76	5.90
0400 Natural finish, 1" thick, fir		125	.064		3.64	2.93		6.57	8.80
0600 1-1/2" thick, pine		125	.064		3.57	2.93		6.50	8.75
0700 2" thick, pine		125	.064	↓	4.12	2.93		7.05	9.35
9000 Minimum labor/equipment charge	↓	2	4	Job		183		183	300

09 64 23 – Wood Parquet Flooring

09 64 23.10 Wood Parquet

	Crew	Daily Output	Labor-Hours	Unit	Material	Labor	Equipment	Total	Total Incl O&P
0010 **WOOD PARQUET** flooring									
5200 Parquetry, standard, 5/16" thick, not incl. finish, oak, minimum	1 Carp	160	.050	S.F.	4.14	2.29		6.43	8.30
5300 Maximum		100	.080		7	3.67		10.67	13.75
5500 Teak, minimum		160	.050		4.86	2.29		7.15	9.10
5600 Maximum		100	.080		8.50	3.67		12.17	15.40
5650 13/16" thick, select grade oak, minimum		160	.050		9.50	2.29		11.79	14.20
5700 Maximum		100	.080		14.40	3.67		18.07	22
5800 Custom parquetry, including finish, minimum		100	.080		15.65	3.67		19.32	23.50
5900 Maximum		50	.160		21	7.35		28.35	35
6700 Parquetry, prefinished white oak, 5/16" thick, minimum		160	.050		4.27	2.29		6.56	8.45
6800 Maximum		100	.080		4.69	3.67		8.36	11.20
7000 Walnut or teak, parquetry, minimum		160	.050		5.35	2.29		7.64	9.65
7100 Maximum	↓	100	.080	↓	9.35	3.67		13.02	16.35
7200 Acrylic wood parquet blocks, 12" x 12" x 5/16",									
7210 Irradiated, set in epoxy	1 Carp	160	.050	S.F.	7.80	2.29		10.09	12.30

09 64 29 – Wood Strip and Plank Flooring

09 64 29.10 Wood

		Crew	Daily Output	Labor-Hours	Unit	Material	Labor	Equipment	Total	Total Incl O&P
0010 **WOOD**	R061110-30									
0020 Fir, vertical grain, 1" x 4", not incl. finish, grade B & better		1 Carp	255	.031	S.F.	2.74	1.44		4.18	5.35
0100 C grade & better			255	.031		2.58	1.44		4.02	5.20
0300 Flat grain, 1" x 4", not incl. finish, B & better			255	.031		3.13	1.44		4.57	5.80
0400 C & better			255	.031		3.01	1.44		4.45	5.65
4000 Maple, strip, 25/32" x 2-1/4", not incl. finish, select			170	.047		5.75	2.16		7.91	9.90
4100 #2 & better			170	.047		4.29	2.16		6.45	8.25
4300 33/32" x 3-1/4", not incl. finish, #1 grade			170	.047		4.49	2.16		6.65	8.50
4400 #2 & better		↓	170	.047	↓	4	2.16		6.16	7.95

09 64 Wood Flooring

09 64 29 – Wood Strip and Plank Flooring

09 64 29.10 Wood		Crew	Daily Output	Labor-Hours	Unit	Material	2014 Bare Costs Labor	Equipment	Total	Total Incl O&P
4600	Oak, white or red, 25/32" x 2-1/4", not incl. finish									
4700	#1 common	1 Carp	170	.047	S.F.	2.98	2.16		5.14	6.85
4900	Select quartered, 2-1/4" wide		170	.047		4.24	2.16		6.40	8.20
5000	Clear		170	.047		4.12	2.16		6.28	8.10
6100	Prefinished, white oak, prime grade, 2-1/4" wide		170	.047		4.69	2.16		6.85	8.70
6200	3-1/4" wide		185	.043		5.10	1.98		7.08	8.85
6400	Ranch plank		145	.055		7.15	2.53		9.68	12
6500	Hardwood blocks, 9" x 9", 25/32" thick		160	.050		5.90	2.29		8.19	10.25
7400	Yellow pine, 3/4" x 3-1/8", T & G, C & better, not incl. finish		200	.040		1.49	1.83		3.32	4.65
7500	Refinish wood floor, sand, 2 coats poly, wax, soft wood, min.	1 Clab	400	.020		.88	.73		1.61	2.17
7600	Hard wood, max.		130	.062		1.31	2.26		3.57	5.15
7800	Sanding and finishing, 2 coats polyurethane		295	.027		.88	.99		1.87	2.60
7900	Subfloor and underlayment, see Section 06 16									
8015	Transition molding, 2 1/4" wide, 5' long	1 Carp	19.20	.417	Ea.	10.70	19.10		29.80	43.50
9000	Minimum labor/equipment charge	"	2	4	Job		183		183	300

09 65 Resilient Flooring

09 65 10 – Resilient Tile Underlayment

09 65 10.10 Latex Underlayment

09 65 10.10 Latex Underlayment		Crew	Daily Output	Labor-Hours	Unit	Material	Labor	Equipment	Total	Total Incl O&P
0010	**LATEX UNDERLAYMENT**									
3600	Latex underlayment, 1/8" thk., cementitious for resilient flooring	1 Tilf	160	.050	S.F.	1.16	2.10		3.26	4.58
4000	Liquid, fortified				Gal.	34			34	37.50

09 65 13 – Resilient Base and Accessories

09 65 13.13 Resilient Base

09 65 13.13 Resilient Base		Crew	Daily Output	Labor-Hours	Unit	Material	Labor	Equipment	Total	Total Incl O&P
0010	**RESILIENT BASE**									
0690	1/8" vinyl base, 2 1/2" H, straight or cove, standard colors	1 Tilf	315	.025	L.F.	1.34	1.07		2.41	3.15
0700	4" high		315	.025		1.26	1.07		2.33	3.07
0710	6" high		315	.025		1.52	1.07		2.59	3.35
0720	Corners, 2 1/2" high		315	.025	Ea.	2.02	1.07		3.09	3.90
0730	4" high		315	.025		2.56	1.07		3.63	4.50
0740	6" high		315	.025		2.99	1.07		4.06	4.97
0800	1/8" rubber base, 2 1/2" H, straight or cove, standard colors		315	.025	L.F.	1.13	1.07		2.20	2.92
1100	4" high		315	.025		1.26	1.07		2.33	3.07
1110	6" high		315	.025		1.65	1.07		2.72	3.50
1150	Corners, 2 1/2" high		315	.025	Ea.	1.70	1.07		2.77	3.55
1153	4" high		315	.025		2.51	1.07		3.58	4.44
1155	6" high		315	.025		3.15	1.07		4.22	5.15
1450	For premium color/finish add					50%				
1500	Millwork profile	1 Tilf	315	.025	L.F.	5.85	1.07		6.92	8.15

09 65 13.23 Resilient Stair Treads and Risers

09 65 13.23 Resilient Stair Treads and Risers		Crew	Daily Output	Labor-Hours	Unit	Material	Labor	Equipment	Total	Total Incl O&P
0010	**RESILIENT STAIR TREADS AND RISERS**									
0300	Rubber, molded tread, 12" wide, 5/16" thick, black	1 Tilf	115	.070	L.F.	14.10	2.92		17.02	20
0400	Colors		115	.070		14.50	2.92		17.42	20.50
0600	1/4" thick, black		115	.070		13.60	2.92		16.52	19.55
0700	Colors		115	.070		14.10	2.92		17.02	20
0900	Grip strip safety tread, colors, 5/16" thick		115	.070		22	2.92		24.92	29
1000	3/16" thick		120	.067		16.10	2.80		18.90	22
1200	Landings, smooth sheet rubber, 1/8" thick		120	.067	S.F.	6.95	2.80		9.75	12.05
1300	3/16" thick		120	.067	"	8.75	2.80		11.55	14.05
1500	Nosings, 3" wide, 3/16" thick, black		140	.057	L.F.	3.94	2.40		6.34	8.10

09 65 Resilient Flooring

09 65 13 – Resilient Base and Accessories

09 65 13.23 Resilient Stair Treads and Risers		Crew	Daily Output	Labor-Hours	Unit	Material	2014 Bare Costs Labor	2014 Bare Costs Equipment	Total	Total Incl O&P
1600	Colors	1 Tilf	140	.057	L.F.	4.29	2.40		6.69	8.50
1800	Risers, 7" high, 1/8" thick, flat		250	.032		6.65	1.34		7.99	9.45
1900	Coved		250	.032		8.25	1.34		9.59	11.20
2100	Vinyl, molded tread, 12" wide, colors, 1/8" thick		115	.070		6.95	2.92		9.87	12.25
2200	1/4" thick		115	.070		8.75	2.92		11.67	14.25
2300	Landing material, 1/8" thick		200	.040	S.F.	6.95	1.68		8.63	10.30
2400	Riser, 7" high, 1/8" thick, coved		175	.046	L.F.	3.95	1.92		5.87	7.35
2500	Tread and riser combined, 1/8" thick		80	.100	"	10.45	4.20		14.65	18.10
9000	Minimum labor/equipment charge		3	2.667	Job		112		112	176

09 65 16 – Resilient Sheet Flooring

09 65 16.10 Rubber and Vinyl Sheet Flooring

			Crew	Daily Output	Labor-Hours	Unit	Material	Labor	Equipment	Total	Total Incl O&P
0010	**RUBBER AND VINYL SHEET FLOORING**										
5500	Linoleum, sheet goods	G	1 Tilf	360	.022	S.F.	3.59	.93		4.52	5.40
5900	Rubber, sheet goods, 36" wide, 1/8" thick			120	.067		7.65	2.80		10.45	12.80
5950	3/16" thick			100	.080		10.35	3.36		13.71	16.70
6000	1/4" thick			90	.089		12.25	3.73		15.98	19.35
8000	Vinyl sheet goods, backed, .065" thick, minimum			250	.032		4.10	1.34		5.44	6.60
8050	Maximum			200	.040		5	1.68		6.68	8.15
8100	.080" thick, minimum			230	.035		4.10	1.46		5.56	6.80
8150	Maximum			200	.040		5.90	1.68		7.58	9.15
8200	.125" thick, minimum			230	.035		4.25	1.46		5.71	7
8250	Maximum			200	.040		7.50	1.68		9.18	10.90
8400	For welding seams, add			100	.080	L.F.	.20	3.36		3.56	5.50
8700	Adhesive cement, 1 gallon per 200 to 300 S.F.					Gal.	27			27	29.50
8800	Asphalt primer, 1 gallon per 300 S.F.						14			14	15.40
8900	Emulsion, 1 gallon per 140 S.F.						18			18	19.80

09 65 19 – Resilient Tile Flooring

09 65 19.10 Miscellaneous Resilient Tile Flooring

			Crew	Daily Output	Labor-Hours	Unit	Material	Labor	Equipment	Total	Total Incl O&P
0010	**MISCELLANEOUS RESILIENT TILE FLOORING**										
2200	Cork tile, standard finish, 1/8" thick	G	1 Tilf	315	.025	S.F.	7	1.07		8.07	9.40
2250	3/16" thick	G		315	.025		7.75	1.07		8.82	10.25
2300	5/16" thick	G		315	.025		8.45	1.07		9.52	10.95
2350	1/2" thick	G		315	.025		10.70	1.07		11.77	13.45
2500	Urethane finish, 1/8" thick	G		315	.025		9.50	1.07		10.57	12.15
2550	3/16" thick	G		315	.025		10.30	1.07		11.37	13.05
2600	5/16" thick	G		315	.025		11.70	1.07		12.77	14.55
2650	1/2" thick	G		315	.025		15.75	1.07		16.82	19.05
6050	Rubber tile, marbleized colors, 12" x 12", 1/8" thick			400	.020		7.25	.84		8.09	9.25
6100	3/16" thick			400	.020		9.25	.84		10.09	11.50
6300	Special tile, plain colors, 1/8" thick			400	.020		10	.84		10.84	12.30
6350	3/16" thick			400	.020		10.25	.84		11.09	12.60
7000	Vinyl composition tile, 12" x 12", 1/16" thick			500	.016		.86	.67		1.53	2.01
7050	Embossed			500	.016		2.21	.67		2.88	3.49
7100	Marbleized			500	.016		2.21	.67		2.88	3.49
7150	Solid			500	.016		2.85	.67		3.52	4.20
7200	3/32" thick, embossed			500	.016		1.46	.67		2.13	2.67
7250	Marbleized			500	.016		2.54	.67		3.21	3.85
7300	Solid			500	.016		2.36	.67		3.03	3.66
7350	1/8" thick, marbleized			500	.016		2.22	.67		2.89	3.50
7400	Solid			500	.016		2.26	.67		2.93	3.55
7450	Conductive			500	.016		6.70	.67		7.37	8.40
7500	Vinyl tile, 12" x 12", .050" thick, minimum			500	.016		3.42	.67		4.09	4.82

09 65 Resilient Flooring

09 65 19 – Resilient Tile Flooring

09 65 19.10 Miscellaneous Resilient Tile Flooring	Crew	Daily Output	Labor-Hours	Unit	Material	2014 Bare Costs Labor	Equipment	Total	Total Incl O&P
7550	Maximum	1 Tilf	500	.016	S.F.	7	.67		7.67	8.75
7600	1/8" thick, minimum		500	.016		4.99	.67		5.66	6.55
7650	Solid colors		500	.016		3.65	.67		4.32	5.10
7700	Marbleized or Travertine pattern		500	.016		5.90	.67		6.57	7.55
7750	Florentine pattern		500	.016		6.30	.67		6.97	8
7800	Maximum		500	.016	↓	13	.67		13.67	15.35
9500	Minimum labor/equipment charge	↓	4	2	Job		84		84	132

09 65 33 – Conductive Resilient Flooring

09 65 33.10 Conductive Rubber and Vinyl Flooring

0010	CONDUCTIVE RUBBER AND VINYL FLOORING									
1700	Conductive flooring, rubber tile, 1/8" thick	1 Tilf	315	.025	S.F.	6.60	1.07		7.67	8.95
1800	Homogeneous vinyl tile, 1/8" thick	"	315	.025	"	8.75	1.07		9.82	11.35

09 66 Terrazzo Flooring

09 66 13 – Portland Cement Terrazzo Flooring

09 66 13.10 Portland Cement Terrazzo

0010	PORTLAND CEMENT TERRAZZO, cast-in-place									
0020	Cove base, 6" high, 16 ga. zinc	1 Mstz	20	.400	L.F.	3.19	16.65		19.84	29.50
0100	Curb, 6" high and 6" wide		6	1.333		5.60	55.50		61.10	93.50
0300	Divider strip for floors, 14 ga., 1-1/4" deep, zinc		375	.021		1.46	.89		2.35	3.01
0400	Brass		375	.021		2.56	.89		3.45	4.22
0600	Heavy top strip 1/4" thick, 1-1/4" deep, zinc		300	.027		2.08	1.11		3.19	4.04
1200	For thin set floors, 16 ga., 1/2" x 1/2", zinc	↓	350	.023	↓	.98	.95		1.93	2.58
1500	Floor, bonded to concrete, 1-3/4" thick, gray cement	J-3	75	.213	S.F.	3.28	8.15	3.87	15.30	20.50
1600	White cement, mud set		75	.213		3.65	8.15	3.87	15.67	21
1800	Not bonded, 3" total thickness, gray cement		70	.229		4.08	8.75	4.15	16.98	23
1900	White cement, mud set	↓	70	.229	↓	4.76	8.75	4.15	17.66	23.50
9000	Minimum labor/equipment charge	1 Mstz	1	8	Job		335		335	525

09 66 16 – Terrazzo Floor Tile

09 66 16.10 Tile or Terrazzo Base

0010	TILE OR TERRAZZO BASE									
0020	Scratch coat only	1 Mstz	150	.053	S.F.	.43	2.22		2.65	3.97
0500	Scratch and brown coat only		75	.107	"	.82	4.44		5.26	7.90
9000	Minimum labor/equipment charge	↓	1	8	Job		335		335	525

09 66 16.13 Portland Cement Terrazzo Floor Tile

0010	PORTLAND CEMENT TERRAZZO FLOOR TILE									
1200	Floor tiles, non-slip, 1" thick, 12" x 12"	D-1	60	.267	S.F.	19.70	11		30.70	39.50
1300	1-1/4" thick, 12" x 12"		60	.267		20.50	11		31.50	40.50
1500	16" x 16"		50	.320		22	13.20		35.20	46
1600	1-1/2" thick, 16" x 16"	↓	45	.356		20.50	14.70		35.20	46.50
1800	For Venetian terrazzo, add					6.10			6.10	6.70
1900	For white cement, add				↓	.57			.57	.63

09 66 16.16 Plastic Matrix Terrazzo Floor Tile

0010	PLASTIC MATRIX TERRAZZO FLOOR TILE									

09 66 16.30 Terrazzo, Precast

0010	TERRAZZO, PRECAST									
0020	Base, 6" high, straight	1 Mstz	70	.114	L.F.	11.85	4.76		16.61	20.50
0100	Cove		60	.133		12.80	5.55		18.35	23
0300	8" high, straight	↓	60	.133	↓	11.45	5.55		17	21.50

09 66 Terrazzo Flooring

09 66 16 – Terrazzo Floor Tile

09 66 16.30 Terrazzo, Precast

		Crew	Daily Output	Labor-Hours	Unit	Material	2014 Bare Costs Labor	Equipment	Total	Total Incl O&P
0400	Cove	1 Mstz	50	.160	L.F.	16.85	6.65		23.50	29
0600	For white cement, add					.45			.45	.50
0700	For 16 ga. zinc toe strip, add					1.72			1.72	1.89
0900	Curbs, 4" x 4" high	1 Mstz	40	.200		32.50	8.35		40.85	48.50
1000	8" x 8" high	"	30	.267		37.50	11.10		48.60	58.50
2400	Stair treads, 1-1/2" thick, non-slip, three line pattern	2 Mstz	70	.229		41	9.50		50.50	60
2500	Nosing and two lines		70	.229		41	9.50		50.50	60
2700	2" thick treads, straight		60	.267		45.50	11.10		56.60	67.50
2800	Curved		50	.320		59	13.35		72.35	86
3000	Stair risers, 1" thick, to 6" high, straight sections		60	.267		10.30	11.10		21.40	29
3100	Cove		50	.320		15.30	13.35		28.65	38
3300	Curved, 1" thick, to 6" high, vertical		48	.333		21	13.90		34.90	45
3400	Cove		38	.421		42	17.55		59.55	73.50
3600	Stair tread and riser, single piece, straight, minimum		60	.267		52	11.10		63.10	75
3700	Maximum		40	.400		67.50	16.65		84.15	100
3900	Curved tread and riser, minimum		40	.400		73	16.65		89.65	106
4000	Maximum		32	.500		92	21		113	134
4200	Stair stringers, notched, 1" thick		25	.640		30	26.50		56.50	75
4300	2" thick		22	.727		35	30.50		65.50	86
4500	Stair landings, structural, non-slip, 1-1/2" thick		85	.188	S.F.	32.50	7.85		40.35	48
4600	3" thick		75	.213		46	8.90		54.90	64.50
4800	Wainscot, 12" x 12" x 1" tiles	1 Mstz	12	.667		6.85	28		34.85	51
4900	16" x 16" x 1-1/2" tiles	"	8	1		14.25	41.50		55.75	81
9500	Minimum labor/equipment charge	1 Tilf	2	4	Job		168		168	264

09 66 23 – Resinous Matrix Terrazzo Flooring

09 66 23.16 Epoxy-Resin Terrazzo Flooring

		Crew	Daily Output	Labor-Hours	Unit	Material	2014 Bare Costs Labor	Equipment	Total	Total Incl O&P
0010	**EPOXY-RESIN TERRAZZO FLOORING**									
1800	Epoxy terrazzo, 1/4" thick, chemical resistant, minimum	J-3	200	.080	S.F.	5.95	3.06	1.45	10.46	12.90
1900	Maximum	"	150	.107	"	9	4.08	1.94	15.02	18.45

09 67 Fluid-Applied Flooring

09 67 13 – Elastomeric Liquid Flooring

09 67 13.13 Elastomeric Liquid Flooring

		Crew	Daily Output	Labor-Hours	Unit	Material	2014 Bare Costs Labor	Equipment	Total	Total Incl O&P
0010	**ELASTOMERIC LIQUID FLOORING**									
0020	Cementitious acrylic, 1/4" thick	C-6	520	.092	S.F.	1.63	3.53	.13	5.29	7.70
0200	Methyl methachrylate, 1/4" thick	C-8A	3000	.016	"	5.80	.63		6.43	7.35

09 67 26 – Quartz Flooring

09 67 26.26 Quartz Flooring

		Crew	Daily Output	Labor-Hours	Unit	Material	2014 Bare Costs Labor	Equipment	Total	Total Incl O&P
0010	**QUARTZ FLOORING**									
0600	Epoxy, with colored quartz chips, broadcast, minimum	C-6	675	.071	S.F.	2.75	2.72	.10	5.57	7.55
0700	Maximum		490	.098		3.97	3.74	.14	7.85	10.60
0900	Troweled, minimum		560	.086		3.50	3.28	.12	6.90	9.35
1000	Maximum		480	.100		5.25	3.82	.14	9.21	12.20
1200	Heavy duty epoxy topping, 1/4" thick,									
1300	500 to 1,000 S.F.	C-6	420	.114	S.F.	5.55	4.37	.16	10.08	13.35
1500	1,000 to 2,000 S.F.		450	.107		5	4.08	.15	9.23	12.30
1600	Over 10,000 S.F.		480	.100		4.63	3.82	.14	8.59	11.50

09 68 Carpeting

09 68 05 - Carpet Accessories

09 68 05.11 Flooring Transition Strip

		Crew	Daily Output	Labor-Hours	Unit	Material	2014 Bare Costs Labor	2014 Bare Costs Equipment	Total	Total Incl O&P
0010	**FLOORING TRANSITION STRIP**									
0107	Clamp down brass divider, 12' strip, vinyl to carpet	1 Tilf	31.25	.256	Ea.	11.05	10.75		21.80	29
0117	Vinyl to hard surface	"	31.25	.256	"	11.05	10.75		21.80	29

09 68 10 - Carpet Pad

09 68 10.10 Commercial Grade Carpet Pad

		Crew	Daily Output	Labor-Hours	Unit	Material	Labor	Equipment	Total	Total Incl O&P
0010	**COMMERCIAL GRADE CARPET PAD**									
9000	Sponge rubber pad, minimum	1 Tilf	150	.053	S.Y.	4.30	2.24		6.54	8.25
9100	Maximum		150	.053		10.20	2.24		12.44	14.70
9200	Felt pad, minimum		150	.053		5.10	2.24		7.34	9.10
9300	Maximum		150	.053		7.60	2.24		9.84	11.85
9400	Bonded urethane pad, minimum		150	.053		5.05	2.24		7.29	9.05
9500	Maximum		150	.053		9.20	2.24		11.44	13.60
9600	Prime urethane pad, minimum		150	.053		3.21	2.24		5.45	7.05
9700	Maximum		150	.053		5.45	2.24		7.69	9.50

09 68 13 - Tile Carpeting

09 68 13.10 Carpet Tile

		Crew	Daily Output	Labor-Hours	Unit	Material	Labor	Equipment	Total	Total Incl O&P
0010	**CARPET TILE**									
0100	Tufted nylon, 18" x 18", hard back, 20 oz.	1 Tilf	80	.100	S.Y.	22.50	4.20		26.70	31.50
0110	26 oz.		80	.100		38.50	4.20		42.70	49
0200	Cushion back, 20 oz.		80	.100		28.50	4.20		32.70	37.50
0210	26 oz.		80	.100		44.50	4.20		48.70	55.50
1100	Tufted, 24" x 24", hard back, 24 oz. nylon		80	.100		29	4.20		33.20	38.50
1180	35 oz.		80	.100		35.50	4.20		39.70	46
5060	42 oz.		80	.100		46	4.20		50.20	57.50

09 68 16 - Sheet Carpeting

09 68 16.10 Sheet Carpet

		Crew	Daily Output	Labor-Hours	Unit	Material	Labor	Equipment	Total	Total Incl O&P
0010	**SHEET CARPET**									
0700	Nylon, level loop, 26 oz., light to medium traffic	1 Tilf	75	.107	S.Y.	30	4.47		34.47	40
0720	28 oz., light to medium traffic		75	.107		31.50	4.47		35.97	41.50
0900	32 oz., medium traffic		75	.107		38	4.47		42.47	49
1100	40 oz., medium to heavy traffic		75	.107		56	4.47		60.47	68.50
2920	Nylon plush, 30 oz., medium traffic		57	.140		29.50	5.90		35.40	42
3000	36 oz., medium traffic		75	.107		39.50	4.47		43.97	50.50
3100	42 oz., medium to heavy traffic		70	.114		44.50	4.79		49.29	56
3200	46 oz., medium to heavy traffic		70	.114		52	4.79		56.79	64.50
3300	54 oz., heavy traffic		70	.114		56.50	4.79		61.29	69.50
4500	50 oz., medium to heavy traffic		75	.107		132	4.47		136.47	152
4700	Patterned, 32 oz., medium to heavy traffic		70	.114		131	4.79		135.79	152
4900	48 oz., heavy traffic		70	.114		135	4.79		139.79	157
5000	For less than full roll (approx. 1500 S.F.), add					25%				
5100	For small rooms, less than 12' wide, add						25%			
5200	For large open areas (no cuts), deduct						25%			
5600	For bound carpet baseboard, add	1 Tilf	300	.027	L.F.	3	1.12		4.12	5.05
5610	For stairs, not incl. price of carpet, add	"	30	.267	Riser		11.20		11.20	17.60
5620	For borders and patterns, add to labor						18%			
8950	For tackless, stretched installation, add padding from 09 68 10.10 to above									
9850	For brand-named specific fiber, add				S.Y.	25%				
9900	Carpet cleaning machine, rent				Day				38	42
9910	Minimum labor/equipment charge	1 Tilf	3	2.667	Job		112		112	176

09 68 Carpeting

09 68 20 – Athletic Carpet

09 68 20.10 Indoor Athletic Carpet	Crew	Daily Output	Labor-Hours	Unit	Material	2014 Bare Costs Labor	Equipment	Total	Total Incl O&P
0010 **INDOOR ATHLETIC CARPET**									
3700 Polyethylene, in rolls, no base incl., landscape surfaces	1 Tilf	275	.029	S.F.	4.07	1.22		5.29	6.40
3800 Nylon action surface, 1/8" thick		275	.029		3.76	1.22		4.98	6.05
3900 1/4" thick		275	.029		5.45	1.22		6.67	7.85
4000 3/8" thick		275	.029		6.80	1.22		8.02	9.40
5500 Polyvinyl chloride, sheet goods for gyms, 1/4" thick		80	.100		9.60	4.20		13.80	17.15
5600 3/8" thick		60	.133		11	5.60		16.60	21

09 69 Access Flooring

09 69 13 – Rigid-Grid Access Flooring

09 69 13.10 Access Floors

	Crew	Daily Output	Labor-Hours	Unit	Material	2014 Bare Costs Labor	Equipment	Total	Total Incl O&P
0010 **ACCESS FLOORS**									
0015 Access floor package including panel, pedestal, stringers & laminate cover									
0100 Computer room, greater than 6,000 S.F.	4 Carp	750	.043	S.F.	7.50	1.96		9.46	11.45
0110 Less than 6,000 S.F.	2 Carp	375	.043		8.15	1.96		10.11	12.20
0120 Office, greater than 6,000 S.F.	4 Carp	1050	.030		5.35	1.40		6.75	8.20
0250 Panels, particle board or steel, 1250# load, no covering, under 6,000 S.F.	2 Carp	600	.027		3.75	1.22		4.97	6.15
0300 Over 6,000 S.F.		640	.025		3.21	1.15		4.36	5.40
0400 Aluminum, 24" panels		500	.032		32.50	1.47		33.97	38.50
0600 For carpet covering, add					8.75			8.75	9.65
0700 For vinyl floor covering, add					9.05			9.05	9.95
0900 For high pressure laminate covering, add					7.50			7.50	8.25
0910 For snap on stringer system, add	2 Carp	1000	.016		1.56	.73		2.29	2.93
0950 Office applications, steel or concrete panels,									
0960 no covering, over 6,000 S.F.	2 Carp	960	.017	S.F.	10.55	.76		11.31	12.85
1050 Pedestals, 6" to 12"	"	85	.188	Ea.	8.30	8.65		16.95	23.50

09 72 Wall Coverings

09 72 19 – Textile Wall Covering

09 72 19.10 Textile Wall Covering

	Crew	Daily Output	Labor-Hours	Unit	Material	2014 Bare Costs Labor	Equipment	Total	Total Incl O&P
0010 **TEXTILE WALL COVERING**, including sizing; add 10-30% waste @ takeoff									
0020 Silk	1 Pape	640	.013	S.F.	4.09	.50		4.59	5.30
0030 Cotton		640	.013		6.55	.50		7.05	8
0040 Linen		640	.013		1.82	.50		2.32	2.80
0050 Blend		640	.013		2.93	.50		3.43	4.02

09 72 20 – Natural Fiber Wall Covering

09 72 20.10 Natural Fiber Wall Covering

	Crew	Daily Output	Labor-Hours	Unit	Material	2014 Bare Costs Labor	Equipment	Total	Total Incl O&P
0010 **NATURAL FIBER WALL COVERING**, including sizing; add 10-30% waste @ takeoff									
0015 Bamboo	1 Pape	640	.013	S.F.	2.23	.50		2.73	3.25
0030 Burlap		640	.013		2	.50		2.50	3
0045 Jute		640	.013		1.27	.50		1.77	2.20
0060 Sisal		640	.013		1.44	.50		1.94	2.38

09 72 23 – Wallpapering

09 72 23.10 Wallpaper

	Crew	Daily Output	Labor-Hours	Unit	Material	2014 Bare Costs Labor	Equipment	Total	Total Incl O&P
0010 **WALLPAPER** including sizing; add 10-30 percent waste @ takeoff									
0050 Aluminum foil	1 Pape	275	.029	S.F.	1.04	1.16		2.20	3
0100 Copper sheets, .025" thick, vinyl backing		240	.033		5.55	1.33		6.88	8.25
0300 Phenolic backing		240	.033		7.20	1.33		8.53	10.10

09 72 Wall Coverings

09 72 23 – Wallpapering

09 72 23.10 Wallpaper		Crew	Daily Output	Labor-Hours	Unit	Material	2014 Bare Costs Labor	Equipment	Total	Total Incl O&P
0600	Cork tiles, light or dark, 12" x 12" x 3/16"	1 Pape	240	.033	S.F.	5.05	1.33		6.38	7.70
0700	5/16" thick		235	.034		2.95	1.35		4.30	5.40
0900	1/4" basketweave		240	.033		3.50	1.33		4.83	6
1000	1/2" natural, non-directional pattern		240	.033		7.60	1.33		8.93	10.55
1100	3/4" natural, non-directional pattern		240	.033		11.65	1.33		12.98	14.95
1200	Granular surface, 12" x 36", 1/2" thick		385	.021		1.29	.83		2.12	2.75
1300	1" thick		370	.022		1.66	.86		2.52	3.21
1500	Polyurethane coated, 12" x 12" x 3/16" thick		240	.033		4.03	1.33		5.36	6.55
1600	5/16" thick		235	.034		6.30	1.35		7.65	9.05
1800	Cork wallpaper, paperbacked, natural		480	.017		2.04	.66		2.70	3.30
1900	Colors		480	.017		2.84	.66		3.50	4.18
2100	Flexible wood veneer, 1/32" thick, plain woods		100	.080		2.41	3.18		5.59	7.75
2200	Exotic woods		95	.084		3.65	3.35		7	9.40
2400	Gypsum-based, fabric-backed, fire resistant									
2500	for masonry walls, minimum, 21 oz./S.Y.	1 Pape	800	.010	S.F.	.89	.40		1.29	1.62
2600	Average		720	.011		1.25	.44		1.69	2.09
2700	Maximum (small quantities)		640	.013		1.40	.50		1.90	2.34
2750	Acrylic, modified, semi-rigid PVC, .028" thick	2 Carp	330	.048		1.21	2.22		3.43	4.98
2800	.040" thick	"	320	.050		1.78	2.29		4.07	5.75
3000	Vinyl wall covering, fabric-backed, lightweight, type 1 (12-15 oz./S.Y.)	1 Pape	640	.013		.93	.50		1.43	1.82
3300	Medium weight, type 2 (20-24 oz./S.Y.)		480	.017		.90	.66		1.56	2.05
3400	Heavy weight, type 3 (28 oz./S.Y.)		435	.018		1.48	.73		2.21	2.80
3600	Adhesive, 5 gal. lots (18 S.Y./gal.)				Gal.	14.20			14.20	15.60
3700	Wallpaper, average workmanship, solid pattern, low cost paper	1 Pape	640	.013	S.F.	.43	.50		.93	1.27
3900	basic patterns (matching required), avg. cost paper		535	.015		.98	.60		1.58	2.03
4000	Paper at $85 per double roll, quality workmanship		435	.018		1.94	.73		2.67	3.30
4190	Grass cloth, natural fabric [G]		400	.020		1.87	.80		2.67	3.34
4200	Grass cloths with lining paper, minimum [G]		400	.020		.66	.80		1.46	2.01
4300	Maximum [G]		350	.023		2.66	.91		3.57	4.39
5990	Wallpaper removal, 1 layer		800	.010		.02	.40		.42	.66
6000	Wallpaper removal, 3 layer		400	.020		.06	.80		.86	1.35
9000	Minimum labor/equipment charge		2	4	Job		159		159	255

09 77 Special Wall Surfacing

09 77 33 – Fiberglass Reinforced Panels

09 77 33.10 Fiberglass Reinforced Plastic Panels

09 77 33.10		Crew	Daily Output	Labor-Hours	Unit	Material	Labor	Equipment	Total	Total Incl O&P
0010	**FIBERGLASS REINFORCED PLASTIC PANELS**, .090" thick									
0020	On walls, adhesive mounted, embossed surface	2 Carp	640	.025	S.F.	1.11	1.15		2.26	3.10
0030	Smooth surface		640	.025		1.37	1.15		2.52	3.39
0040	Fire rated, embossed surface		640	.025		1.99	1.15		3.14	4.07
0050	Nylon rivet mounted, on drywall, embossed surface		480	.033		1.11	1.53		2.64	3.73
0060	Smooth surface		480	.033		1.37	1.53		2.90	4.02
0070	Fire rated, embossed surface		480	.033		1.99	1.53		3.52	4.70
0080	On masonry, embossed surface		320	.050		1.11	2.29		3.40	4.99
0090	Smooth surface		320	.050		1.37	2.29		3.66	5.30
0100	Fire rated, embossed surface		320	.050		1.99	2.29		4.28	5.95
0110	Nylon rivet and adhesive mounted, on drywall, embossed surface		240	.067		1.26	3.06		4.32	6.40
0120	Smooth surface		240	.067		1.26	3.06		4.32	6.40
0130	Fire rated, embossed surface		240	.067		2.19	3.06		5.25	7.40
0140	On masonry, embossed surface		190	.084		1.26	3.86		5.12	7.75
0150	Smooth surface		190	.084		1.26	3.86		5.12	7.75

09 77 Special Wall Surfacing

09 77 33 – Fiberglass Reinforced Panels

09 77 33.10 Fiberglass Reinforced Plastic Panels	Crew	Daily Output	Labor-Hours	Unit	Material	2014 Bare Costs Labor	Equipment	Total	Total Incl O&P
0160	Fire rated, embossed surface	2 Carp	190	.084	S.F.	2.19	3.86		6.05	8.75
0170	For moldings add	1 Carp	250	.032	L.F.	.26	1.47		1.73	2.70
0180	On ceilings, for lay in grid system, embossed surface		400	.020	S.F.	1.11	.92		2.03	2.73
0190	Smooth surface		400	.020		1.37	.92		2.29	3.02
0200	Fire rated, embossed surface		400	.020		1.99	.92		2.91	3.70

09 77 43 – Panel Systems

09 77 43.20 Slatwall Panels and Accessories

		Crew	Daily Output	Labor-Hours	Unit	Material	2014 Bare Costs Labor	Equipment	Total	Total Incl O&P
0010	**SLATWALL PANELS AND ACCESSORIES**									
0100	Slatwall panel, 4' x 8' x 3/4" T, MDF, paint grade	1 Carp	500	.016	S.F.	1.32	.73		2.05	2.66
0110	Melamine finish		500	.016		1.99	.73		2.72	3.40
0120	High pressure plastic laminate finish		500	.016		3.62	.73		4.35	5.20
0130	Aluminum channel inserts, add					2.29			2.29	2.52
0200	Accessories, corner forms, 8' L				L.F.	5.55			5.55	6.10
0210	T-connector, 8' L					7.50			7.50	8.25
0220	J-mold, 8' L					1.25			1.25	1.38
0230	Edge cap, 8' L					1.09			1.09	1.20
0240	Finish end cap, 8' L					3.37			3.37	3.71
0300	Display hook, metal, 4" L				Ea.	.43			.43	.47
0310	6" L					.47			.47	.52
0320	8" L					.52			.52	.57
0330	10" L					.58			.58	.64
0340	12" L					.64			.64	.70
0350	Acrylic, 4" L					.91			.91	1
0360	6" L					1.05			1.05	1.16
0370	8" L					1.10			1.10	1.21
0380	10" L					1.12			1.12	1.23
0400	Waterfall hanger, metal, 12" - 16"					4			4	4.40
0410	Acrylic					9.85			9.85	10.85
0500	Shelf bracket, metal, 8"					1.92			1.92	2.11
0510	10"					2.16			2.16	2.38
0520	12"					2.36			2.36	2.60
0530	14"					2.60			2.60	2.86
0540	16"					3.04			3.04	3.34
0550	Acrylic, 8"					3.77			3.77	4.15
0560	10"					4.02			4.02	4.42
0570	12"					4.24			4.24	4.66
0580	14"					4.46			4.46	4.91
0600	Shelf, acrylic, 12" x 16" x 1/4"					16.35			16.35	18
0610	12" x 24" x 1/4"					22.50			22.50	25

09 81 Acoustic Insulation

09 81 16 – Acoustic Blanket Insulation

09 81 16.10 Sound Attenuation Blanket

		Crew	Daily Output	Labor-Hours	Unit	Material	2014 Bare Costs Labor	Equipment	Total	Total Incl O&P
0010	**SOUND ATTENUATION BLANKET**									
0020	Blanket, 1" thick	1 Carp	925	.009	S.F.	.26	.40		.66	.94
0500	1-1/2" thick		920	.009		.27	.40		.67	.96
1000	2" thick		915	.009		.36	.40		.76	1.06
1500	3" thick		910	.009		.52	.40		.92	1.23
3400	Urethane plastic foam, open cell, on wall, 2" thick	2 Carp	2050	.008		3.11	.36		3.47	4.01
3500	3" thick		1550	.010		4.13	.47		4.60	5.30

307

09 81 Acoustic Insulation

09 81 16 – Acoustic Blanket Insulation

09 81 16.10 Sound Attenuation Blanket

		Crew	Daily Output	Labor-Hours	Unit	Material	2014 Bare Costs Labor	2014 Bare Costs Equipment	Total	Total Incl O&P
3600	4" thick	2 Carp	1050	.015	S.F.	5.80	.70		6.50	7.50
3700	On ceiling, 2" thick		1700	.009		3.10	.43		3.53	4.12
3800	3" thick		1300	.012		4.13	.56		4.69	5.45
3900	4" thick		900	.018		5.80	.82		6.62	7.70
4000	Nylon matting 0.4" thick, with carbon black spinerette									
4010	plus polyester fabric, on floor	D-7	1600	.010	S.F.	1.36	.38		1.74	2.09
4200	Fiberglass reinf. backer board underlayment, 7/16" thick, on floor	"	1500	.011	"	1.66	.40		2.06	2.46
9000	Minimum labor/equipment charge	1 Carp	5	1.600	Job		73.50		73.50	121

09 84 Acoustic Room Components

09 84 13 – Fixed Sound-Absorptive Panels

09 84 13.10 Fixed Panels

		Crew	Daily Output	Labor-Hours	Unit	Material	2014 Bare Costs Labor	2014 Bare Costs Equipment	Total	Total Incl O&P
0010	**FIXED PANELS** Perforated steel facing, painted with									
0100	Fiberglass or mineral filler, no backs, 2-1/4" thick, modular									
0200	space units, ceiling or wall hung, white or colored	1 Carp	100	.080	S.F.	8.70	3.67		12.37	15.65
0300	Fiberboard sound deadening panels, 1/2" thick	"	600	.013	"	.33	.61		.94	1.36
0500	Fiberglass panels, 4' x 8' x 1" thick, with									
0600	glass cloth face for walls, cemented	1 Carp	155	.052	S.F.	7.60	2.37		9.97	12.25
0700	1-1/2" thick, dacron covered, inner aluminum frame,									
0710	wall mounted	1 Carp	300	.027	S.F.	8.90	1.22		10.12	11.80
0900	Mineral fiberboard panels, fabric covered, 30" x 108",									
1000	3/4" thick, concealed spline, wall mounted	1 Carp	150	.053	S.F.	6.40	2.45		8.85	11.05
9000	Minimum labor/equipment charge	"	4	2	Job		91.50		91.50	151

09 91 Painting

09 91 03 – Paint Restoration

09 91 03.20 Sanding

		Crew	Daily Output	Labor-Hours	Unit	Material	2014 Bare Costs Labor	2014 Bare Costs Equipment	Total	Total Incl O&P
0010	**SANDING** and puttying interior trim, compared to									
0100	Painting 1 coat, on quality work				L.F.		100%			
0300	Medium work						50%			
0400	Industrial grade						25%			
0500	Surface protection, placement and removal									
0510	Basic drop cloths	1 Pord	6400	.001	S.F.		.05		.05	.08
0520	Masking with paper		800	.010		.04	.40		.44	.67
0530	Volume cover up (using plastic sheathing, or building paper)		16000	.001			.02		.02	.03

09 91 03.30 Exterior Surface Preparation

		Crew	Daily Output	Labor-Hours	Unit	Material	2014 Bare Costs Labor	2014 Bare Costs Equipment	Total	Total Incl O&P
0010	**EXTERIOR SURFACE PREPARATION**									
0015	Doors, per side, not incl. frames or trim									
0020	Scrape & sand									
0030	Wood, flush	1 Pord	616	.013	S.F.		.51		.51	.82
0040	Wood, detail		496	.016			.64		.64	1.02
0050	Wood, louvered		280	.029			1.13		1.13	1.81
0060	Wood, overhead		616	.013			.51		.51	.82
0070	Wire brush									
0080	Metal, flush	1 Pord	640	.013	S.F.		.49		.49	.79
0090	Metal, detail		520	.015			.61		.61	.98
0100	Metal, louvered		360	.022			.88		.88	1.41
0110	Metal or fibr., overhead		640	.013			.49		.49	.79
0120	Metal, roll up		560	.014			.57		.57	.91

09 91 Painting

09 91 03 – Paint Restoration

09 91 03.30 Exterior Surface Preparation

	Crew	Daily Output	Labor-Hours	Unit	Material	2014 Bare Costs Labor	2014 Bare Costs Equipment	Total	Total Incl O&P
0130	Metal, bulkhead	1 Pord	640	.013	S.F.		.49		.49	.79
0140	Power wash, based on 2500 lb. operating pressure									
0150	Metal, flush	A-1H	2240	.004	S.F.		.13	.03	.16	.25
0160	Metal, detail		2120	.004			.14	.04	.18	.27
0170	Metal, louvered		2000	.004			.15	.04	.19	.28
0180	Metal or fibr., overhead		2400	.003			.12	.03	.15	.23
0190	Metal, roll up		2400	.003			.12	.03	.15	.23
0200	Metal, bulkhead	▼	2200	.004	▼		.13	.03	.16	.26
0400	Windows, per side, not incl. trim									
0410	Scrape & sand									
0420	Wood, 1-2 lite	1 Pord	320	.025	S.F.		.99		.99	1.59
0430	Wood, 3-6 lite		280	.029			1.13		1.13	1.81
0440	Wood, 7-10 lite		240	.033			1.32		1.32	2.11
0450	Wood, 12 lite		200	.040			1.58		1.58	2.54
0460	Wood, Bay/Bow	▼	320	.025	▼		.99		.99	1.59
0470	Wire brush									
0480	Metal, 1-2 lite	1 Pord	480	.017	S.F.		.66		.66	1.06
0490	Metal, 3-6 lite		400	.020			.79		.79	1.27
0500	Metal, Bay/Bow	▼	480	.017	▼		.66		.66	1.06
0510	Power wash, based on 2500 lb. operating pressure									
0520	1-2 lite	A-1H	4400	.002	S.F.		.07	.02	.09	.13
0530	3-6 lite		4320	.002			.07	.02	.09	.13
0540	7-10 lite		4240	.002			.07	.02	.09	.13
0550	12 lite		4160	.002			.07	.02	.09	.14
0560	Bay/Bow	▼	4400	.002	▼		.07	.02	.09	.13
0600	Siding, scrape and sand, light=10-30%, med.=30-70%									
0610	Heavy=70-100% of surface to sand									
0650	Texture 1-11, light	1 Pord	480	.017	S.F.		.66		.66	1.06
0660	Med.		440	.018			.72		.72	1.15
0670	Heavy		360	.022			.88		.88	1.41
0680	Wood shingles, shakes, light		440	.018			.72		.72	1.15
0690	Med.		360	.022			.88		.88	1.41
0700	Heavy		280	.029			1.13		1.13	1.81
0710	Clapboard, light		520	.015			.61		.61	.98
0720	Med.		480	.017			.66		.66	1.06
0730	Heavy	▼	400	.020	▼		.79		.79	1.27
0740	Wire brush									
0750	Aluminum, light	1 Pord	600	.013	S.F.		.53		.53	.85
0760	Med.		520	.015			.61		.61	.98
0770	Heavy	▼	440	.018	▼		.72		.72	1.15
0780	Pressure wash, based on 2500 lb. operating pressure									
0790	Stucco	A-1H	3080	.003	S.F.		.10	.02	.12	.19
0800	Aluminum or vinyl		3200	.003			.09	.02	.11	.18
0810	Siding, masonry, brick & block	▼	2400	.003	▼		.12	.03	.15	.23
1300	Miscellaneous, wire brush									
1310	Metal, pedestrian gate	1 Pord	100	.080	S.F.		3.16		3.16	5.10
8000	For chemical washing, see Section 04 01 30									
8010	For steam cleaning, see Section 04 01 30.20									

09 91 03.40 Interior Surface Preparation

		Crew	Daily Output	Labor-Hours	Unit	Material	2014 Bare Costs Labor	2014 Bare Costs Equipment	Total	Total Incl O&P
0010	**INTERIOR SURFACE PREPARATION**									
0020	Doors, per side, not incl. frames or trim									
0030	Scrape & sand									
0040	Wood, flush	1 Pord	616	.013	S.F.		.51		.51	.82
0050	Wood, detail		496	.016			.64		.64	1.02
0060	Wood, louvered		280	.029			1.13		1.13	1.81
0070	Wire brush									
0080	Metal, flush	1 Pord	640	.013	S.F.		.49		.49	.79
0090	Metal, detail		520	.015			.61		.61	.98
0100	Metal, louvered		360	.022			.88		.88	1.41
0110	Hand wash									
0120	Wood, flush	1 Pord	2160	.004	S.F.		.15		.15	.23
0130	Wood, detailed		2000	.004			.16		.16	.25
0140	Wood, louvered		1360	.006			.23		.23	.37
0150	Metal, flush		2160	.004			.15		.15	.23
0160	Metal, detail		2000	.004			.16		.16	.25
0170	Metal, louvered		1360	.006			.23		.23	.37
0400	Windows, per side, not incl. trim									
0410	Scrape & sand									
0420	Wood, 1-2 lite	1 Pord	360	.022	S.F.		.88		.88	1.41
0430	Wood, 3-6 lite		320	.025			.99		.99	1.59
0440	Wood, 7-10 lite		280	.029			1.13		1.13	1.81
0450	Wood, 12 lite		240	.033			1.32		1.32	2.11
0460	Wood, Bay/Bow		360	.022			.88		.88	1.41
0470	Wire brush									
0480	Metal, 1-2 lite	1 Pord	520	.015	S.F.		.61		.61	.98
0490	Metal, 3-6 lite		440	.018			.72		.72	1.15
0500	Metal, Bay/Bow		520	.015			.61		.61	.98
0600	Walls, sanding, light=10-30%, medium - 30-70%,									
0610	heavy=70-100% of surface to sand									
0650	Walls, sand									
0660	Gypsum board or plaster, light	1 Pord	3077	.003	S.F.		.10		.10	.17
0670	Gypsum board or plaster, medium		2160	.004			.15		.15	.23
0680	Gypsum board or plaster, heavy		923	.009			.34		.34	.55
0690	Wood, T&G, light		2400	.003			.13		.13	.21
0700	Wood, T&G, med.		1600	.005			.20		.20	.32
0710	Wood, T&G, heavy		800	.010			.40		.40	.63
0720	Walls, wash									
0730	Gypsum board or plaster	1 Pord	3200	.003	S.F.		.10		.10	.16
0740	Wood, T&G		3200	.003			.10		.10	.16
0750	Masonry, brick & block, smooth		2800	.003			.11		.11	.18
0760	Masonry, brick & block, coarse		2000	.004			.16		.16	.25
8000	For chemical washing, see Section 04 01 30									
8010	For steam cleaning, see Section 04 01 30.20									
9010	Minimum labor/equipment charge	1 Pord	3	2.667	Job		105		105	169

09 91 03.41 Scrape After Fire Damage

		Crew	Daily Output	Labor-Hours	Unit	Material	2014 Bare Costs Labor	2014 Bare Costs Equipment	Total	Total Incl O&P
0010	**SCRAPE AFTER FIRE DAMAGE**									
0050	Boards, 1" x 4"	1 Pord	336	.024	L.F.		.94		.94	1.51
0060	1" x 6"		260	.031			1.22		1.22	1.95
0070	1" x 8"		207	.039			1.53		1.53	2.45
0080	1" x 10"		174	.046			1.82		1.82	2.92
0500	Framing, 2" x 4"		265	.030			1.19		1.19	1.92

09 91 Painting

09 91 03 – Paint Restoration

09 91 03.41 Scrape After Fire Damage

		Crew	Daily Output	Labor-Hours	Unit	Material	2014 Bare Costs Labor	Equipment	Total	Total Incl O&P
0510	2" x 6"	1 Pord	221	.036	L.F.		1.43		1.43	2.30
0520	2" x 8"		190	.042			1.67		1.67	2.67
0530	2" x 10"		165	.048			1.92		1.92	3.08
0540	2" x 12"		144	.056			2.20		2.20	3.53
1000	Heavy framing, 3" x 4"		226	.035			1.40		1.40	2.25
1010	4" x 4"		210	.038			1.51		1.51	2.42
1020	4" x 6"		191	.042			1.66		1.66	2.66
1030	4" x 8"		165	.048			1.92		1.92	3.08
1040	4" x 10"		144	.056			2.20		2.20	3.53
1060	4" x 12"		131	.061			2.42		2.42	3.87
2900	For sealing, minimum		825	.010	S.F.	.14	.38		.52	.77
2920	Maximum		460	.017	"	.30	.69		.99	1.43
3000	For sandblasting, see Section 04 01 30.20									
9000	Minimum labor/equipment charge	1 Pord	3	2.667	Job		105		105	169

09 91 13 – Exterior Painting

09 91 13.30 Fences

		Crew	Daily Output	Labor-Hours	Unit	Material	2014 Bare Costs Labor	Equipment	Total	Total Incl O&P
0010	**FENCES**									
0100	Chain link or wire metal, one side, water base									
0110	Roll & brush, first coat	1 Pord	960	.008	S.F.	.08	.33		.41	.61
0120	Second coat		1280	.006		.07	.25		.32	.48
0130	Spray, first coat		2275	.004		.08	.14		.22	.30
0140	Second coat		2600	.003		.08	.12		.20	.28
0150	Picket, water base									
0160	Roll & brush, first coat	1 Pord	865	.009	S.F.	.08	.37		.45	.68
0170	Second coat		1050	.008		.08	.30		.38	.57
0180	Spray, first coat		2275	.004		.08	.14		.22	.31
0190	Second coat		2600	.003		.08	.12		.20	.29
0200	Stockade, water base									
0210	Roll & brush, first coat	1 Pord	1040	.008	S.F.	.08	.30		.38	.58
0220	Second coat		1200	.007		.08	.26		.34	.51
0230	Spray, first coat		2275	.004		.08	.14		.22	.31
0240	Second coat		2600	.003		.08	.12		.20	.29
9000	Minimum labor/equipment charge		2	4	Job		158		158	254

09 91 13.42 Miscellaneous, Exterior

		Crew	Daily Output	Labor-Hours	Unit	Material	2014 Bare Costs Labor	Equipment	Total	Total Incl O&P
0010	**MISCELLANEOUS, EXTERIOR**									
0100	Railing, ext., decorative wood, incl. cap & baluster									
0110	Newels & spindles @ 12" O.C.									
0120	Brushwork, stain, sand, seal & varnish									
0130	First coat	1 Pord	90	.089	L.F.	.75	3.52		4.27	6.45
0140	Second coat	"	120	.067	"	.75	2.64		3.39	5.05
0150	Rough sawn wood, 42" high, 2" x 2" verticals, 6" O.C.									
0160	Brushwork, stain, each coat	1 Pord	90	.089	L.F.	.24	3.52		3.76	5.90
0170	Wrought iron, 1" rail, 1/2" sq. verticals									
0180	Brushwork, zinc chromate, 60" high, bars 6" O.C.									
0190	Primer	1 Pord	130	.062	L.F.	.86	2.43		3.29	4.85
0200	Finish coat		130	.062		1.13	2.43		3.56	5.15
0210	Additional coat		190	.042		1.32	1.67		2.99	4.12
0220	Shutters or blinds, single panel, 2' x 4', paint all sides									
0230	Brushwork, primer	1 Pord	20	.400	Ea.	.69	15.80		16.49	26.50
0240	Finish coat, exterior latex		20	.400		.61	15.80		16.41	26
0250	Primer & 1 coat, exterior latex		13	.615		1.15	24.50		25.65	40.50
0260	Spray, primer		35	.229		1	9.05		10.05	15.60

09 91 13.42 Miscellaneous, Exterior

		Crew	Daily Output	Labor-Hours	Unit	Material	2014 Bare Costs Labor	2014 Bare Costs Equipment	Total	Total Incl O&P
0270	Finish coat, exterior latex	1 Pord	35	.229	Ea.	1.30	9.05		10.35	15.95
0280	Primer & 1 coat, exterior latex	↓	20	.400	↓	1.08	15.80		16.88	26.50
0290	For louvered shutters, add				S.F.	10%				
0300	Stair stringers, exterior, metal									
0310	Roll & brush, zinc chromate, to 14", each coat	1 Pord	320	.025	L.F.	.38	.99		1.37	2
0320	Rough sawn wood, 4" x 12"									
0330	Roll & brush, exterior latex, each coat	1 Pord	215	.037	L.F.	.09	1.47		1.56	2.46
0340	Trellis/lattice, 2" x 2" @ 3" O.C. with 2" x 8" supports									
0350	Spray, latex, per side, each coat	1 Pord	475	.017	S.F.	.09	.67		.76	1.17
0450	Decking, ext., sealer, alkyd, brushwork, sealer coat		1140	.007		.09	.28		.37	.55
0460	1st coat		1140	.007		.09	.28		.37	.55
0470	2nd coat		1300	.006		.07	.24		.31	.47
0500	Paint, alkyd, brushwork, primer coat		1140	.007		.10	.28		.38	.56
0510	1st coat		1140	.007		.16	.28		.44	.62
0520	2nd coat		1300	.006		.12	.24		.36	.52
0600	Sand paint, alkyd, brushwork, 1 coat		150	.053		.13	2.11		2.24	3.52
9000	Minimum labor/equipment charge	↓	2	4	Job		158		158	254

09 91 13.60 Siding Exterior

		Crew	Daily Output	Labor-Hours	Unit	Material	2014 Bare Costs Labor	2014 Bare Costs Equipment	Total	Total Incl O&P
0010	**SIDING EXTERIOR**, Alkyd (oil base)									
0450	Steel siding, oil base, paint 1 coat, brushwork	2 Pord	2015	.008	S.F.	.13	.31		.44	.64
0500	Spray		4550	.004		.19	.14		.33	.43
0800	Paint 2 coats, brushwork		1300	.012		.25	.49		.74	1.06
1000	Spray		2750	.006		.17	.23		.40	.56
1200	Stucco, rough, oil base, paint 2 coats, brushwork		1300	.012		.25	.49		.74	1.06
1400	Roller		1625	.010		.27	.39		.66	.92
1600	Spray		2925	.005		.28	.22		.50	.66
1800	Texture 1-11 or clapboard, oil base, primer coat, brushwork		1300	.012		.13	.49		.62	.93
2000	Spray		4550	.004		.13	.14		.27	.37
2400	Paint 2 coats, brushwork		810	.020		.37	.78		1.15	1.65
2600	Spray		2600	.006		.41	.24		.65	.84
3400	Stain 2 coats, brushwork		950	.017		.16	.67		.83	1.25
4000	Spray		3050	.005		.18	.21		.39	.53
4200	Wood shingles, oil base primer coat, brushwork		1300	.012		.12	.49		.61	.92
4400	Spray		3900	.004		.12	.16		.28	.39
5000	Paint 2 coats, brushwork		810	.020		.31	.78		1.09	1.59
5200	Spray		2275	.007		.29	.28		.57	.77
6500	Stain 2 coats, brushwork		950	.017		.16	.67		.83	1.25
7000	Spray	↓	2660	.006		.22	.24		.46	.63
8000	For latex paint, deduct					10%				
8100	For work over 12' H, from pipe scaffolding, add						15%			
8200	For work over 12' H, from extension ladder, add						25%			
8300	For work over 12' H, from swing staging, add				↓		35%			
9000	Minimum labor/equipment charge	1 Pord	2	4	Job		158		158	254

09 91 13.62 Siding, Misc.

		Crew	Daily Output	Labor-Hours	Unit	Material	2014 Bare Costs Labor	2014 Bare Costs Equipment	Total	Total Incl O&P
0010	**SIDING, MISC.**, latex paint									
0100	Aluminum siding									
0110	Brushwork, primer	2 Pord	2275	.007	S.F.	.06	.28		.34	.52
0120	Finish coat, exterior latex		2275	.007		.05	.28		.33	.51
0130	Primer & 1 coat exterior latex		1300	.012		.13	.49		.62	.92
0140	Primer & 2 coats exterior latex	↓	975	.016	↓	.18	.65		.83	1.24
0150	Mineral fiber shingles									
0160	Brushwork, primer	2 Pord	1495	.011	S.F.	.13	.42		.55	.83

09 91 Painting

09 91 13 – Exterior Painting

09 91 13.62 Siding, Misc.

		Crew	Daily Output	Labor-Hours	Unit	Material	2014 Bare Costs Labor	Equipment	Total	Total Incl O&P
0170	Finish coat, industrial enamel	2 Pord	1495	.011	S.F.	.18	.42		.60	.88
0180	Primer & 1 coat enamel		810	.020		.32	.78		1.10	1.60
0190	Primer & 2 coats enamel		540	.030		.50	1.17		1.67	2.43
0200	Roll, primer		1625	.010		.15	.39		.54	.79
0210	Finish coat, industrial enamel		1625	.010		.20	.39		.59	.85
0220	Primer & 1 coat enamel		975	.016		.35	.65		1	1.42
0230	Primer & 2 coats enamel		650	.025		.54	.97		1.51	2.16
0240	Spray, primer		3900	.004		.12	.16		.28	.39
0250	Finish coat, industrial enamel		3900	.004		.16	.16		.32	.44
0260	Primer & 1 coat enamel		2275	.007		.28	.28		.56	.76
0270	Primer & 2 coats enamel		1625	.010		.44	.39		.83	1.12
0280	Waterproof sealer, first coat		4485	.004		.08	.14		.22	.31
0290	Second coat	▼	5235	.003	▼	.07	.12		.19	.27
0300	Rough wood incl. shingles, shakes or rough sawn siding									
0310	Brushwork, primer	2 Pord	1280	.013	S.F.	.14	.49		.63	.94
0320	Finish coat, exterior latex		1280	.013		.10	.49		.59	.90
0330	Primer & 1 coat exterior latex		960	.017		.23	.66		.89	1.32
0340	Primer & 2 coats exterior latex		700	.023		.33	.90		1.23	1.81
0350	Roll, primer		2925	.005		.18	.22		.40	.55
0360	Finish coat, exterior latex		2925	.005		.12	.22		.34	.48
0370	Primer & 1 coat exterior latex		1790	.009		.30	.35		.65	.90
0380	Primer & 2 coats exterior latex		1300	.012		.42	.49		.91	1.24
0390	Spray, primer		3900	.004		.16	.16		.32	.43
0400	Finish coat, exterior latex		3900	.004		.09	.16		.25	.36
0410	Primer & 1 coat exterior latex		2600	.006		.25	.24		.49	.66
0420	Primer & 2 coats exterior latex		2080	.008		.33	.30		.63	.86
0430	Waterproof sealer, first coat		4485	.004		.14	.14		.28	.38
0440	Second coat	▼	4485	.004	▼	.08	.14		.22	.31
0450	Smooth wood incl. butt, T&G, beveled, drop or B&B siding									
0460	Brushwork, primer	2 Pord	2325	.007	S.F.	.10	.27		.37	.55
0470	Finish coat, exterior latex		1280	.013		.10	.49		.59	.90
0480	Primer & 1 coat exterior latex		800	.020		.20	.79		.99	1.49
0490	Primer & 2 coats exterior latex		630	.025		.29	1		1.29	1.93
0500	Roll, primer		2275	.007		.11	.28		.39	.57
0510	Finish coat, exterior latex		2275	.007		.10	.28		.38	.56
0520	Primer & 1 coat exterior latex		1300	.012		.21	.49		.70	1.02
0530	Primer & 2 coats exterior latex		975	.016		.32	.65		.97	1.39
0540	Spray, primer		4550	.004		.09	.14		.23	.31
0550	Finish coat, exterior latex		4550	.004		.09	.14		.23	.32
0560	Primer & 1 coat exterior latex		2600	.006		.18	.24		.42	.58
0570	Primer & 2 coats exterior latex		1950	.008		.26	.32		.58	.81
0580	Waterproof sealer, first coat		5230	.003		.08	.12		.20	.27
0590	Second coat	▼	5980	.003		.08	.11		.19	.25
0600	For oil base paint, add				▼	10%				
9000	Minimum labor/equipment charge	1 Pord	2	4	Job		158		158	254

09 91 13.70 Doors and Windows, Exterior

		Crew	Daily Output	Labor-Hours	Unit	Material	2014 Bare Costs Labor	Equipment	Total	Total Incl O&P
0010	**DOORS AND WINDOWS, EXTERIOR**									
0100	Door frames & trim, only									
0110	Brushwork, primer	1 Pord	512	.016	L.F.	.06	.62		.68	1.06
0120	Finish coat, exterior latex		512	.016		.08	.62		.70	1.07
0130	Primer & 1 coat, exterior latex		300	.027	▼	.14	1.05		1.19	1.84
0135	2 coats, exterior latex, both sides	▼	15	.533	Ea.	6.85	21		27.85	41.50

09 91 Painting

09 91 13 – Exterior Painting

09 91 13.70 Doors and Windows, Exterior

		Crew	Daily Output	Labor-Hours	Unit	Material	2014 Bare Costs Labor	Equipment	Total	Total Incl O&P
0140	Primer & 2 coats, exterior latex	1 Pord	265	.030	L.F.	.22	1.19		1.41	2.16
0150	Doors, flush, both sides, incl. frame & trim									
0160	Roll & brush, primer	1 Pord	10	.800	Ea.	4.74	31.50		36.24	56
0170	Finish coat, exterior latex		10	.800		5.85	31.50		37.35	57.50
0180	Primer & 1 coat, exterior latex		7	1.143		10.55	45		55.55	84
0190	Primer & 2 coats, exterior latex		5	1.600		16.40	63.50		79.90	120
0200	Brushwork, stain, sealer & 2 coats polyurethane	↓	4	2	↓	26	79		105	156
0210	Doors, French, both sides, 10-15 lite, incl. frame & trim									
0220	Brushwork, primer	1 Pord	6	1.333	Ea.	2.37	52.50		54.87	87
0230	Finish coat, exterior latex		6	1.333		2.92	52.50		55.42	87.50
0240	Primer & 1 coat, exterior latex		3	2.667		5.30	105		110.30	175
0250	Primer & 2 coats, exterior latex		2	4		8.05	158		166.05	263
0260	Brushwork, stain, sealer & 2 coats polyurethane	↓	2.50	3.200	↓	9.45	127		136.45	213
0270	Doors, louvered, both sides, incl. frame & trim									
0280	Brushwork, primer	1 Pord	7	1.143	Ea.	4.74	45		49.74	77.50
0290	Finish coat, exterior latex		7	1.143		5.85	45		50.85	79
0300	Primer & 1 coat, exterior latex		4	2		10.55	79		89.55	139
0310	Primer & 2 coats, exterior latex		3	2.667		16.05	105		121.05	187
0320	Brushwork, stain, sealer & 2 coats polyurethane	↓	4.50	1.778	↓	26	70.50		96.50	142
0330	Doors, panel, both sides, incl. frame & trim									
0340	Roll & brush, primer	1 Pord	6	1.333	Ea.	4.74	52.50		57.24	89.50
0350	Finish coat, exterior latex		6	1.333		5.85	52.50		58.35	91
0360	Primer & 1 coat, exterior latex		3	2.667		10.55	105		115.55	181
0370	Primer & 2 coats, exterior latex		2.50	3.200		16.05	127		143.05	221
0380	Brushwork, stain, sealer & 2 coats polyurethane	↓	3	2.667	↓	26	105		131	198
0400	Windows, per ext. side, based on 15 S.F.									
0410	1 to 6 lite									
0420	Brushwork, primer	1 Pord	13	.615	Ea.	.94	24.50		25.44	40
0430	Finish coat, exterior latex		13	.615		1.15	24.50		25.65	40.50
0440	Primer & 1 coat, exterior latex		8	1		2.09	39.50		41.59	66
0450	Primer & 2 coats, exterior latex		6	1.333		3.17	52.50		55.67	88
0460	Stain, sealer & 1 coat varnish	↓	7	1.143	↓	3.73	45		48.73	76.50
0470	7 to 10 lite									
0480	Brushwork, primer	1 Pord	11	.727	Ea.	.94	29		29.94	47
0490	Finish coat, exterior latex		11	.727		1.15	29		30.15	47.50
0500	Primer & 1 coat, exterior latex		7	1.143		2.09	45		47.09	75
0510	Primer & 2 coats, exterior latex		5	1.600		3.17	63.50		66.67	105
0520	Stain, sealer & 1 coat varnish	↓	6	1.333	↓	3.73	52.50		56.23	88.50
0530	12 lite									
0540	Brushwork, primer	1 Pord	10	.800	Ea.	.94	31.50		32.44	52
0550	Finish coat, exterior latex		10	.800		1.15	31.50		32.65	52.50
0560	Primer & 1 coat, exterior latex		6	1.333		2.09	52.50		54.59	87
0570	Primer & 2 coats, exterior latex		5	1.600		3.17	63.50		66.67	105
0580	Stain, sealer & 1 coat varnish	↓	6	1.333	↓	3.87	52.50		56.37	89
0590	For oil base paint, add				↓	10%				
9000	Minimum labor/equipment charge	1 Pord	2	4	Job		158		158	254

09 91 13.80 Trim, Exterior

		Crew	Daily Output	Labor-Hours	Unit	Material	2014 Bare Costs Labor	Equipment	Total	Total Incl O&P
0010	**TRIM, EXTERIOR**									
0100	Door frames & trim (see Doors, interior or exterior)									
0110	Fascia, latex paint, one coat coverage									
0120	1" x 4", brushwork	1 Pord	640	.013	L.F.	.02	.49		.51	.81
0130	Roll	↓	1280	.006	↓	.03	.25		.28	.43

09 91 Painting

09 91 13 – Exterior Painting

09 91 13.80 Trim, Exterior

		Crew	Daily Output	Labor-Hours	Unit	Material	2014 Bare Costs Labor	Equipment	Total	Total Incl O&P
0140	Spray	1 Pord	2080	.004	L.F.	.02	.15		.17	.26
0150	1" x 6" to 1" x 10", brushwork		640	.013		.08	.49		.57	.88
0160	Roll		1230	.007		.09	.26		.35	.50
0170	Spray		2100	.004		.07	.15		.22	.31
0180	1" x 12", brushwork		640	.013		.08	.49		.57	.88
0190	Roll		1050	.008		.09	.30		.39	.57
0200	Spray		2200	.004		.07	.14		.21	.30
0210	Gutters & downspouts, metal, zinc chromate paint									
0220	Brushwork, gutters, 5", first coat	1 Pord	640	.013	L.F.	.40	.49		.89	1.23
0230	Second coat		960	.008		.38	.33		.71	.94
0240	Third coat		1280	.006		.30	.25		.55	.74
0250	Downspouts, 4", first coat		640	.013		.40	.49		.89	1.23
0260	Second coat		960	.008		.38	.33		.71	.94
0270	Third coat		1280	.006		.30	.25		.55	.74
0280	Gutters & downspouts, wood									
0290	Brushwork, gutters, 5", primer	1 Pord	640	.013	L.F.	.06	.49		.55	.86
0300	Finish coat, exterior latex		640	.013		.07	.49		.56	.87
0310	Primer & 1 coat exterior latex		400	.020		.14	.79		.93	1.42
0320	Primer & 2 coats exterior latex		325	.025		.22	.97		1.19	1.80
0330	Downspouts, 4", primer		640	.013		.06	.49		.55	.86
0340	Finish coat, exterior latex		640	.013		.07	.49		.56	.87
0350	Primer & 1 coat exterior latex		400	.020		.14	.79		.93	1.42
0360	Primer & 2 coats exterior latex		325	.025		.11	.97		1.08	1.68
0370	Molding, exterior, up to 14" wide									
0380	Brushwork, primer	1 Pord	640	.013	L.F.	.07	.49		.56	.87
0390	Finish coat, exterior latex		640	.013		.08	.49		.57	.88
0400	Primer & 1 coat exterior latex		400	.020		.17	.79		.96	1.45
0410	Primer & 2 coats exterior latex		315	.025		.17	1		1.17	1.79
0420	Stain & fill		1050	.008		.10	.30		.40	.59
0430	Shellac		1850	.004		.13	.17		.30	.41
0440	Varnish		1275	.006		.11	.25		.36	.52
9000	Minimum labor/equipment charge		2	4	Job		158		158	254

09 91 13.90 Walls, Masonry (CMU), Exterior

		Crew	Daily Output	Labor-Hours	Unit	Material	2014 Bare Costs Labor	Equipment	Total	Total Incl O&P
0010	**WALLS, MASONRY (CMU), EXTERIOR**									
0360	Concrete masonry units (CMU), smooth surface									
0370	Brushwork, latex, first coat	1 Pord	640	.013	S.F.	.07	.49		.56	.87
0380	Second coat		960	.008		.06	.33		.39	.59
0390	Waterproof sealer, first coat		736	.011		.25	.43		.68	.96
0400	Second coat		1104	.007		.25	.29		.54	.73
0410	Roll, latex, paint, first coat		1465	.005		.09	.22		.31	.44
0420	Second coat		1790	.004		.07	.18		.25	.35
0430	Waterproof sealer, first coat		1680	.005		.25	.19		.44	.57
0440	Second coat		2060	.004		.25	.15		.40	.52
0450	Spray, latex, paint, first coat		1950	.004		.07	.16		.23	.33
0460	Second coat		2600	.003		.05	.12		.17	.26
0470	Waterproof sealer, first coat		2245	.004		.25	.14		.39	.50
0480	Second coat		2990	.003		.25	.11		.36	.44
0490	Concrete masonry unit (CMU), porous									
0500	Brushwork, latex, first coat	1 Pord	640	.013	S.F.	.14	.49		.63	.95
0510	Second coat		960	.008		.07	.33		.40	.61
0520	Waterproof sealer, first coat		736	.011		.25	.43		.68	.96
0530	Second coat		1104	.007		.25	.29		.54	.73

09 91 Painting

09 91 13 – Exterior Painting

09 91 13.90 Walls, Masonry (CMU), Exterior

		Crew	Daily Output	Labor-Hours	Unit	Material	2014 Bare Costs Labor	Equipment	Total	Total Incl O&P
0540	Roll latex, first coat	1 Pord	1465	.005	S.F.	.11	.22		.33	.47
0550	Second coat		1790	.004		.07	.18		.25	.36
0560	Waterproof sealer, first coat		1680	.005		.25	.19		.44	.57
0570	Second coat		2060	.004		.25	.15		.40	.52
0580	Spray latex, first coat		1950	.004		.08	.16		.24	.35
0590	Second coat		2600	.003		.05	.12		.17	.26
0600	Waterproof sealer, first coat		2245	.004		.25	.14		.39	.50
0610	Second coat		2990	.003	▼	.25	.11		.36	.44
9000	Minimum labor/equipment charge	▼	2	4	Job		158		158	254

09 91 23 – Interior Painting

09 91 23.20 Cabinets and Casework

		Crew	Daily Output	Labor-Hours	Unit	Material	2014 Bare Costs Labor	Equipment	Total	Total Incl O&P
0010	**CABINETS AND CASEWORK**									
1000	Primer coat, oil base, brushwork	1 Pord	650	.012	S.F.	.06	.49		.55	.85
2000	Paint, oil base, brushwork, 1 coat		650	.012		.11	.49		.60	.90
3000	Stain, brushwork, wipe off		650	.012		.08	.49		.57	.87
4000	Shellac, 1 coat, brushwork		650	.012		.10	.49		.59	.90
4500	Varnish, 3 coats, brushwork, sand after 1st coat	▼	325	.025		.28	.97		1.25	1.87
5000	For latex paint, deduct				▼	10%				
9010	Minimum labor/equipment charge	1 Pord	2	4	Job		158		158	254

09 91 23.33 Doors and Windows, Interior Alkyd (Oil Base)

		Crew	Daily Output	Labor-Hours	Unit	Material	2014 Bare Costs Labor	Equipment	Total	Total Incl O&P
0010	**DOORS AND WINDOWS, INTERIOR ALKYD (OIL BASE)**									
0500	Flush door & frame, 3' x 7', oil, primer, brushwork	1 Pord	10	.800	Ea.	3.32	31.50		34.82	54.50
1000	Paint, 1 coat		10	.800		4.11	31.50		35.61	55.50
1400	Stain, brushwork, wipe off		18	.444		1.71	17.60		19.31	30
1600	Shellac, 1 coat, brushwork		25	.320		2.20	12.65		14.85	23
1800	Varnish, 3 coats, brushwork, sand after 1st coat		9	.889		5.95	35		40.95	63
2000	Panel door & frame, 3' x 7', oil, primer, brushwork		6	1.333		2.44	52.50		54.94	87
2200	Paint, 1 coat		6	1.333		4.11	52.50		56.61	89
2600	Stain, brushwork, panel door, 3' x 7', not incl. frame		16	.500		1.71	19.80		21.51	33.50
2800	Shellac, 1 coat, brushwork		22	.364		2.20	14.40		16.60	25.50
3000	Varnish, 3 coats, brushwork, sand after 1st coat	▼	7.50	1.067	▼	5.95	42		47.95	74
4400	Windows, including frame and trim, per side									
4600	Colonial type, 6/6 lites, 2' x 3', oil, primer, brushwork	1 Pord	14	.571	Ea.	.38	22.50		22.88	37
5800	Paint, 1 coat		14	.571		.65	22.50		23.15	37
6200	3' x 5' opening, 6/6 lites, primer coat, brushwork		12	.667		.96	26.50		27.46	43.50
6400	Paint, 1 coat		12	.667		1.62	26.50		28.12	44.50
6800	4' x 8' opening, 6/6 lites, primer coat, brushwork		8	1		2.05	39.50		41.55	66
7000	Paint, 1 coat		8	1		3.46	39.50		42.96	67.50
8000	Single lite type, 2' x 3', oil base, primer coat, brushwork		33	.242		.38	9.60		9.98	15.80
8200	Paint, 1 coat		33	.242		.65	9.60		10.25	16.10
8600	3' x 5' opening, primer coat, brushwork		20	.400		.96	15.80		16.76	26.50
8800	Paint, 1 coat		20	.400		1.62	15.80		17.42	27.50
9200	4' x 8' opening, primer coat, brushwork		14	.571		2.05	22.50		24.55	39
9400	Paint, 1 coat		14	.571	▼	3.46	22.50		25.96	40.50
9900	Minimum labor/equipment charge	▼	2	4	Job		158		158	254

09 91 23.35 Doors and Windows, Interior Latex

		Crew	Daily Output	Labor-Hours	Unit	Material	2014 Bare Costs Labor	Equipment	Total	Total Incl O&P
0010	**DOORS & WINDOWS, INTERIOR LATEX**									
0100	Doors, flush, both sides, incl. frame & trim									
0110	Roll & brush, primer	1 Pord	10	.800	Ea.	3.97	31.50		35.47	55.50
0120	Finish coat, latex		10	.800		5.35	31.50		36.85	57
0130	Primer & 1 coat latex		7	1.143		9.35	45		54.35	83
0140	Primer & 2 coats latex	▼	5	1.600	▼	14.40	63.50		77.90	118

09 91 Painting

09 91 23 – Interior Painting

09 91 23.35 Doors and Windows, Interior Latex

		Crew	Daily Output	Labor-Hours	Unit	Material	2014 Bare Costs Labor	2014 Bare Costs Equipment	Total	Total Incl O&P
0160	Spray, both sides, primer	1 Pord	20	.400	Ea.	4.18	15.80		19.98	30
0170	Finish coat, latex		20	.400		5.65	15.80		21.45	31.50
0180	Primer & 1 coat latex		11	.727		9.90	29		38.90	57
0190	Primer & 2 coats latex		8	1		15.25	39.50		54.75	80.50
0200	Doors, French, both sides, 10-15 lite, incl. frame & trim									
0210	Roll & brush, primer	1 Pord	6	1.333	Ea.	1.99	52.50		54.49	86.50
0220	Finish coat, latex		6	1.333		2.68	52.50		55.18	87.50
0230	Primer & 1 coat latex		3	2.667		4.67	105		109.67	174
0240	Primer & 2 coats latex		2	4		7.20	158		165.20	262
0260	Doors, louvered, both sides, incl. frame & trim									
0270	Roll & brush, primer	1 Pord	7	1.143	Ea.	3.97	45		48.97	77
0280	Finish coat, latex		7	1.143		5.35	45		50.35	78.50
0290	Primer & 1 coat, latex		4	2		9.10	79		88.10	137
0300	Primer & 2 coats, latex		3	2.667		14.70	105		119.70	185
0320	Spray, both sides, primer		20	.400		4.18	15.80		19.98	30
0330	Finish coat, latex		20	.400		5.65	15.80		21.45	31.50
0340	Primer & 1 coat, latex		11	.727		9.90	29		38.90	57
0350	Primer & 2 coats, latex		8	1		15.55	39.50		55.05	80.50
0360	Doors, panel, both sides, incl. frame & trim									
0370	Roll & brush, primer	1 Pord	6	1.333	Ea.	4.18	52.50		56.68	89
0380	Finish coat, latex		6	1.333		5.35	52.50		57.85	90.50
0390	Primer & 1 coat, latex		3	2.667		9.35	105		114.35	179
0400	Primer & 2 coats, latex		2.50	3.200		14.70	127		141.70	219
0420	Spray, both sides, primer		10	.800		4.18	31.50		35.68	55.50
0430	Finish coat, latex		10	.800		5.65	31.50		37.15	57
0440	Primer & 1 coat, latex		5	1.600		9.90	63.50		73.40	113
0450	Primer & 2 coats, latex		4	2		15.55	79		94.55	144
0460	Windows, per interior side, based on 15 S.F.									
0470	1 to 6 lite									
0480	Brushwork, primer	1 Pord	13	.615	Ea.	.78	24.50		25.28	40
0490	Finish coat, enamel		13	.615		1.06	24.50		25.56	40
0500	Primer & 1 coat enamel		8	1		1.84	39.50		41.34	65.50
0510	Primer & 2 coats enamel		6	1.333		2.90	52.50		55.40	87.50
0530	7 to 10 lite									
0540	Brushwork, primer	1 Pord	11	.727	Ea.	.78	29		29.78	47
0550	Finish coat, enamel		11	.727		1.06	29		30.06	47
0560	Primer & 1 coat enamel		7	1.143		1.84	45		46.84	74.50
0570	Primer & 2 coats enamel		5	1.600		2.90	63.50		66.40	105
0590	12 lite									
0600	Brushwork, primer	1 Pord	10	.800	Ea.	.78	31.50		32.28	52
0610	Finish coat, enamel		10	.800		1.06	31.50		32.56	52
0620	Primer & 1 coat enamel		6	1.333		1.84	52.50		54.34	86.50
0630	Primer & 2 coats enamel		5	1.600		2.90	63.50		66.40	105
0650	For oil base paint, add					10%				
9000	Minimum labor/equipment charge	1 Pord	2	4	Job		158		158	254

09 91 23.39 Doors and Windows, Interior Latex, Zero VOC

			Crew	Daily Output	Labor-Hours	Unit	Material	2014 Bare Costs Labor	2014 Bare Costs Equipment	Total	Total Incl O&P
0010	**DOORS & WINDOWS, INTERIOR LATEX, ZERO VOC**										
0100	Doors flush, both sides, incl. frame & trim										
0110	Roll & brush, primer	G	1 Pord	10	.800	Ea.	4.84	31.50		36.34	56.50
0120	Finish coat, latex	G		10	.800		5.65	31.50		37.15	57
0130	Primer & 1 coat latex	G		7	1.143		10.45	45		55.45	84
0140	Primer & 2 coats latex	G		5	1.600		15.80	63.50		79.30	119

09 91 Painting

09 91 23 – Interior Painting

09 91 23.39 Doors and Windows, Interior Latex, Zero VOC

			Crew	Daily Output	Labor-Hours	Unit	Material	2014 Bare Costs Labor	Equipment	Total	Total Incl O&P
0160	Spray, both sides, primer	G	1 Pord	20	.400	Ea.	5.10	15.80		20.90	31
0170	Finish coat, latex	G		20	.400		5.90	15.80		21.70	32
0180	Primer & 1 coat latex	G		11	.727		11.10	29		40.10	58
0190	Primer & 2 coats latex	G	↓	8	1	↓	16.70	39.50		56.20	82
0200	Doors, French, both sides, 10-15 lite, incl. frame & trim										
0210	Roll & brush, primer	G	1 Pord	6	1.333	Ea.	2.42	52.50		54.92	87
0220	Finish coat, latex	G		6	1.333		2.81	52.50		55.31	87.50
0230	Primer & 1 coat latex	G		3	2.667		5.25	105		110.25	175
0240	Primer & 2 coats latex	G	↓	2	4	↓	7.90	158		165.90	263
0360	Doors, panel, both sides, incl. frame & trim										
0370	Roll & brush, primer	G	1 Pord	6	1.333	Ea.	5.10	52.50		57.60	90
0380	Finish coat, latex	G		6	1.333		5.65	52.50		58.15	90.50
0390	Primer & 1 coat, latex	G		3	2.667		10.45	105		115.45	181
0400	Primer & 2 coats, latex	G		2.50	3.200		16.10	127		143.10	221
0420	Spray, both sides, primer	G		10	.800		5.10	31.50		36.60	56.50
0430	Finish coat, latex	G		10	.800		5.90	31.50		37.40	57.50
0440	Primer & 1 coat, latex	G		5	1.600		11.10	63.50		74.60	114
0450	Primer & 2 coats, latex	G	↓	4	2	↓	17.05	79		96.05	146
0460	Windows, per interior side, based on 15 S.F.										
0470	1 to 6 lite										
0480	Brushwork, primer	G	1 Pord	13	.615	Ea.	.96	24.50		25.46	40
0490	Finish coat, enamel	G		13	.615		1.11	24.50		25.61	40
0500	Primer & 1 coat enamel	G		8	1		2.07	39.50		41.57	66
0510	Primer & 2 coats enamel	G		6	1.333	↓	3.18	52.50		55.68	88
9000	Minimum labor/equipment charge		↓	2	4	Job		158		158	254

09 91 23.40 Floors, Interior

		Crew	Daily Output	Labor-Hours	Unit	Material	2014 Bare Costs Labor	Equipment	Total	Total Incl O&P
0010	**FLOORS, INTERIOR**									
0100	Concrete paint, latex									
0110	Brushwork									
0120	1st coat	1 Pord	975	.008	S.F.	.15	.32		.47	.69
0130	2nd coat		1150	.007		.10	.28		.38	.55
0140	3rd coat	↓	1300	.006	↓	.08	.24		.32	.48
0150	Roll									
0160	1st coat	1 Pord	2600	.003	S.F.	.20	.12		.32	.42
0170	2nd coat		3250	.002		.12	.10		.22	.29
0180	3rd coat	↓	3900	.002	↓	.09	.08		.17	.23
0190	Spray									
0200	1st coat	1 Pord	2600	.003	S.F.	.18	.12		.30	.39
0210	2nd coat		3250	.002		.10	.10		.20	.27
0220	3rd coat	↓	3900	.002	↓	.08	.08		.16	.21
0300	Acid stain and sealer									
0310	Stain, one coat	1 Pord	650	.012	S.F.	.11	.49		.60	.90
0320	Two coats		570	.014		.22	.56		.78	1.13
0330	Acrylic sealer, one coat		2600	.003		.18	.12		.30	.40
0340	Two coats	↓	1400	.006	↓	.37	.23		.60	.77

09 91 23.52 Miscellaneous, Interior

		Crew	Daily Output	Labor-Hours	Unit	Material	2014 Bare Costs Labor	Equipment	Total	Total Incl O&P
0010	**MISCELLANEOUS, INTERIOR**									
2400	Floors, conc./wood, oil base, primer/sealer coat, brushwork	2 Pord	1950	.008	S.F.	.08	.32		.40	.61
2450	Roller		5200	.003		.09	.12		.21	.30
2600	Spray		6000	.003		.09	.11		.20	.27
2650	Paint 1 coat, brushwork		1950	.008		.08	.32		.40	.61
2800	Roller	↓	5200	.003	↓	.08	.12		.20	.29

09 91 Painting

09 91 23 – Interior Painting

09 91 23.52 Miscellaneous, Interior

		Crew	Daily Output	Labor-Hours	Unit	Material	2014 Bare Costs Labor	Equipment	Total	Total Incl O&P
2850	Spray	2 Pord	6000	.003	S.F.	.09	.11		.20	.27
3000	Stain, wood floor, brushwork, 1 coat		4550	.004		.08	.14		.22	.31
3200	Roller		5200	.003		.09	.12		.21	.29
3250	Spray		6000	.003		.09	.11		.20	.26
3400	Varnish, wood floor, brushwork		4550	.004		.09	.14		.23	.32
3450	Roller		5200	.003		.10	.12		.22	.31
3600	Spray		6000	.003		.11	.11		.22	.29
3800	Grilles, per side, oil base, primer coat, brushwork	1 Pord	520	.015		.13	.61		.74	1.12
3850	Spray		1140	.007		.13	.28		.41	.60
3920	Paint 2 coats, brushwork		325	.025		.42	.97		1.39	2.02
3940	Spray		650	.012		.48	.49		.97	1.31
5000	Pipe, 1" - 4" diameter, primer or sealer coat, oil base, brushwork	2 Pord	1250	.013	L.F.	.09	.51		.60	.91
5100	Spray		2165	.007		.08	.29		.37	.56
5350	Paint 2 coats, brushwork		775	.021		.19	.82		1.01	1.52
5400	Spray		1240	.013		.22	.51		.73	1.06
6300	13" - 16" diameter, primer or sealer coat, brushwork		310	.052		.35	2.04		2.39	3.66
6450	Spray		540	.030		.44	1.17		1.61	2.37
6500	Paint 2 coats, brushwork		195	.082		.78	3.25		4.03	6.05
6550	Spray		310	.052		.86	2.04		2.90	4.22
7000	Trim, wood, incl. puttying, under 6" wide									
7200	Primer coat, oil base, brushwork	1 Pord	650	.012	L.F.	.03	.49		.52	.82
7250	Paint, 1 coat, brushwork		650	.012		.05	.49		.54	.84
7450	3 coats		325	.025		.16	.97		1.13	1.73
7500	Over 6" wide, primer coat, brushwork		650	.012		.06	.49		.55	.85
7550	Paint, 1 coat, brushwork		650	.012		.11	.49		.60	.90
7650	3 coats		325	.025		.31	.97		1.28	1.90
8000	Cornice, simple design, primer coat, oil base, brushwork		650	.012	S.F.	.06	.49		.55	.85
8250	Paint, 1 coat		650	.012		.11	.49		.60	.90
8350	Ornate design, primer coat		350	.023		.06	.90		.96	1.52
8400	Paint, 1 coat		350	.023		.11	.90		1.01	1.57
8600	Balustrades, primer coat, oil base, brushwork		520	.015		.06	.61		.67	1.05
8900	Trusses and wood frames, primer coat, oil base, brushwork		800	.010		.06	.40		.46	.70
8950	Spray		1200	.007		.07	.26		.33	.49
9220	Paint 2 coats, brushwork		500	.016		.21	.63		.84	1.25
9240	Spray		600	.013		.23	.53		.76	1.11
9260	Stain, brushwork, wipe off		600	.013		.08	.53		.61	.94
9280	Varnish, 3 coats, brushwork		275	.029		.28	1.15		1.43	2.16
9350	For latex paint, deduct					10%				
9900	Minimum labor/equipment charge	1 Pord	2	4	Job		158		158	254

09 91 23.62 Electrostatic Painting

		Crew	Daily Output	Labor-Hours	Unit	Material	2014 Bare Costs Labor	Equipment	Total	Total Incl O&P
0010	**ELECTROSTATIC PAINTING**									
0100	In shop									
0200	Flat surfaces (lockers, casework, elevator doors. etc.)									
0300	One coat	1 Pord	200	.040	S.F.	.53	1.58		2.11	3.12
0400	Two coats	"	120	.067	"	.77	2.64		3.41	5.05
0500	Irregular surfaces (furniture, door frames, etc.)									
0600	One coat	1 Pord	150	.053	S.F.	.53	2.11		2.64	3.96
0700	Two coats	"	100	.080	"	.77	3.16		3.93	5.95
0800	On site									
0900	Flat surfaces (lockers, casework, elevator doors, etc.)									
1000	One coat	1 Pord	150	.053	S.F.	.53	2.11		2.64	3.96
1100	Two coats	"	100	.080	"	.77	3.16		3.93	5.95

09 91 Painting

09 91 23 – Interior Painting

09 91 23.62 Electrostatic Painting

		Crew	Daily Output	Labor-Hours	Unit	Material	2014 Bare Costs Labor	2014 Bare Costs Equipment	Total	Total Incl O&P
1200	Irregular surfaces (furniture, door frames, etc)									
1300	One coat	1 Pord	115	.070	S.F.	.53	2.75		3.28	4.99
1400	Two coats	"	70	.114	"	.77	4.52		5.29	8.10

09 91 23.72 Walls and Ceilings, Interior

		Crew	Daily Output	Labor-Hours	Unit	Material	2014 Bare Costs Labor	2014 Bare Costs Equipment	Total	Total Incl O&P
0010	**WALLS AND CEILINGS, INTERIOR**									
0100	Concrete, drywall or plaster, latex , primer or sealer coat									
0200	Smooth finish, brushwork	1 Pord	1150	.007	S.F.	.06	.28		.34	.51
0240	Roller		1350	.006		.06	.23		.29	.45
0280	Spray		2750	.003		.05	.12		.17	.24
0300	Sand finish, brushwork		975	.008		.06	.32		.38	.59
0340	Roller		1150	.007		.06	.28		.34	.51
0380	Spray		2275	.004		.05	.14		.19	.28
0800	Paint 2 coats, smooth finish, brushwork		680	.012		.13	.47		.60	.89
0840	Roller		800	.010		.13	.40		.53	.77
0880	Spray		1625	.005		.12	.19		.31	.44
0900	Sand finish, brushwork		605	.013		.13	.52		.65	.98
0940	Roller		1020	.008		.13	.31		.44	.64
0980	Spray		1700	.005		.12	.19		.31	.43
1600	Glaze coating, 2 coats, spray, clear		1200	.007		.49	.26		.75	.96
1640	Multicolor		1200	.007		.98	.26		1.24	1.50
1660	Painting walls, complete, including surface prep, primer &									
1670	2 coats finish, on drywall or plaster, with roller	1 Pord	325	.025	S.F.	.20	.97		1.17	1.77
1700	For oil base paint, add					10%				
1800	For ceiling installations, add						25%			
2000	Masonry or concrete block, primer/sealer, latex paint									
2100	Primer, smooth finish, brushwork	1 Pord	1000	.008	S.F.	.10	.32		.42	.62
2110	Roller		1150	.007		.10	.28		.38	.55
2180	Spray		2400	.003		.09	.13		.22	.31
2200	Sand finish, brushwork		850	.009		.10	.37		.47	.71
2210	Roller		975	.008		.10	.32		.42	.63
2280	Spray		2050	.004		.09	.15		.24	.35
2800	Primer plus one finish coat, smooth brush		525	.015		.29	.60		.89	1.29
2810	Roller		615	.013		.18	.51		.69	1.03
2880	Spray		1200	.007		.16	.26		.42	.60
2900	Sand finish, brushwork		450	.018		.18	.70		.88	1.33
2910	Roller		515	.016		.18	.61		.79	1.19
2980	Spray		1025	.008		.16	.31		.47	.67
3600	Glaze coating, 3 coats, spray, clear		900	.009		.70	.35		1.05	1.33
3620	Multicolor		900	.009		1.13	.35		1.48	1.81
4000	Block filler, 1 coat, brushwork		425	.019		.12	.74		.86	1.32
4100	Silicone, water repellent, 2 coats, spray		2000	.004		.29	.16		.45	.57
4120	For oil base paint, add					10%				
8200	For work 8' - 15' H, add						10%			
8300	For work over 15' H, add						20%			
8400	For light textured surfaces, add						10%			
8410	Heavy textured, add						25%			
9900	Minimum labor/equipment charge	1 Pord	2	4	Job		158		158	254

09 91 23.74 Walls and Ceilings, Interior, Zero VOC Latex

			Crew	Daily Output	Labor-Hours	Unit	Material	2014 Bare Costs Labor	2014 Bare Costs Equipment	Total	Total Incl O&P
0010	**WALLS AND CEILINGS, INTERIOR, ZERO VOC LATEX**										
0100	Concrete, dry wall or plaster, latex, primer or sealer coat										
0200	Smooth finish, brushwork	G	1 Pord	1150	.007	S.F.	.06	.28		.34	.51
0240	Roller	G		1350	.006		.06	.23		.29	.45

09 91 Painting

09 91 23 – Interior Painting

09 91 23.74 Walls and Ceilings, Interior, Zero VOC Latex

			Crew	Daily Output	Labor-Hours	Unit	Material	2014 Bare Costs Labor	Equipment	Total	Total Incl O&P
0280	Spray	G	1 Pord	2750	.003	S.F.	.05	.12		.17	.23
0300	Sand finish, brushwork	G		975	.008		.06	.32		.38	.59
0340	Roller	G		1150	.007		.07	.28		.35	.51
0380	Spray	G		2275	.004		.05	.14		.19	.28
0800	Paint 2 coats, smooth finish, brushwork	G		680	.012		.14	.47		.61	.91
0840	Roller	G		800	.010		.15	.40		.55	.79
0880	Spray	G		1625	.005		.13	.19		.32	.45
0900	Sand finish, brushwork	G		605	.013		.14	.52		.66	.99
0940	Roller	G		1020	.008		.15	.31		.46	.66
0980	Spray	G		1700	.005		.13	.19		.32	.44
1800	For ceiling installations, add	G						25%			
8200	For work 8' - 15' H, add							10%			
8300	For work over 15' H, add							20%			
9900	Minimum labor/equipment charge		1 Pord	2	4	Job		158		158	254

09 91 23.75 Dry Fall Painting

		Crew	Daily Output	Labor-Hours	Unit	Material	2014 Bare Costs Labor	Equipment	Total	Total Incl O&P
0010	**DRY FALL PAINTING**									
0100	Sprayed on walls, gypsum board or plaster									
0220	One coat	1 Pord	2600	.003	S.F.	.06	.12		.18	.26
0250	Two coats		1560	.005		.11	.20		.31	.45
0280	Concrete or textured plaster, one coat		1560	.005		.06	.20		.26	.39
0310	Two coats		1300	.006		.11	.24		.35	.51
0340	Concrete block, one coat		1560	.005		.06	.20		.26	.39
0370	Two coats		1300	.006		.11	.24		.35	.51
0400	Wood, one coat		877	.009		.06	.36		.42	.64
0430	Two coats		650	.012		.11	.49		.60	.90
0440	On ceilings, gypsum board or plaster									
0470	One coat	1 Pord	1560	.005	S.F.	.06	.20		.26	.39
0500	Two coats		1300	.006		.11	.24		.35	.51
0530	Concrete or textured plaster, one coat		1560	.005		.06	.20		.26	.39
0560	Two coats		1300	.006		.11	.24		.35	.51
0570	Structural steel, bar joists or metal deck, one coat		1560	.005		.06	.20		.26	.39
0580	Two coats		1040	.008		.11	.30		.41	.61
9900	Minimum labor/equipment charge		2	4	Job		158		158	254

09 93 Staining and Transparent Finishing

09 93 23 – Interior Staining and Finishing

09 93 23.10 Varnish

		Crew	Daily Output	Labor-Hours	Unit	Material	2014 Bare Costs Labor	Equipment	Total	Total Incl O&P
0010	**VARNISH**									
0012	1 coat + sealer, on wood trim, brush, no sanding included	1 Pord	400	.020	S.F.	.07	.79		.86	1.35
0020	1 coat + sealer, on wood trim, brush, no sanding included, no VOC		400	.020		.18	.79		.97	1.47
0100	Hardwood floors, 2 coats, no sanding included, roller		1890	.004		.15	.17		.32	.44
9000	Minimum labor/equipment charge		4	2	Job		79		79	127

09 96 23 – Graffiti-Resistant Coatings

09 96 23.10 Graffiti Resistant Treatments

09 96 23.10 Graffiti Resistant Treatments	Crew	Daily Output	Labor-Hours	Unit	Material	2014 Bare Costs Labor	Equipment	Total	Total Incl O&P
0010	**GRAFFITI RESISTANT TREATMENTS**, sprayed on walls									
0100	Non-sacrificial, permanent non-stick coating, clear, on metals	1 Pord	2000	.004	S.F.	2.06	.16		2.22	2.52
0200	Concrete		2000	.004		2.35	.16		2.51	2.83
0300	Concrete block		2000	.004		3.03	.16		3.19	3.59
0400	Brick		2000	.004		3.44	.16		3.60	4.03
0500	Stone		2000	.004		3.44	.16		3.60	4.03
0600	Unpainted wood		2000	.004		3.97	.16		4.13	4.62
2000	Semi-permanent cross linking polymer primer, on metals		2000	.004		.67	.16		.83	.98
2100	Concrete		2000	.004		.80	.16		.96	1.13
2200	Concrete block		2000	.004		1	.16		1.16	1.35
2300	Brick		2000	.004		.80	.16		.96	1.13
2400	Stone		2000	.004		.80	.16		.96	1.13
2500	Unpainted wood		2000	.004		1.11	.16		1.27	1.47
3000	Top coat, on metals		2000	.004		.55	.16		.71	.85
3100	Concrete		2000	.004		.62	.16		.78	.94
3200	Concrete block		2000	.004		.87	.16		1.03	1.21
3300	Brick		2000	.004		.73	.16		.89	1.05
3400	Stone		2000	.004		.73	.16		.89	1.05
3500	Unpainted wood		2000	.004		.87	.16		1.03	1.21
5000	Sacrificial, water based, on metal		2000	.004		.32	.16		.48	.61
5100	Concrete		2000	.004		.32	.16		.48	.61
5200	Concrete block		2000	.004		.32	.16		.48	.61
5300	Brick		2000	.004		.32	.16		.48	.61
5400	Stone		2000	.004		.32	.16		.48	.61
5500	Unpainted wood		2000	.004		.32	.16		.48	.61
8000	Cleaner for use after treatment									
8100	Towels or wipes, per package of 30				Ea.	.63			.63	.70
8200	Aerosol spray, 24 oz. can				"	18			18	19.80

09 96 46 – Intumescent Coatings

09 96 46.10 Coatings, Intumescent

09 96 46.10		Crew	Daily Output	Labor-Hours	Unit	Material	Labor	Equipment	Total	Total Incl O&P
0010	**COATINGS, INTUMESCENT**, spray applied									
0100	On exterior structural steel, 0.25" d.f.t.	1 Pord	475	.017	S.F.	.41	.67		1.08	1.52
0150	0.51" d.f.t.		350	.023		.41	.90		1.31	1.90
0200	0.98" d.f.t.		280	.029		.41	1.13		1.54	2.26
0300	On interior structural steel, 0.108" d.f.t.		300	.027		.41	1.05		1.46	2.14
0350	0.310" d.f.t.		150	.053		.41	2.11		2.52	3.83
0400	0.670" d.f.t.		100	.080		.41	3.16		3.57	5.55

09 96 53 – Elastomeric Coatings

09 96 53.10 Coatings, Elastomeric

09 96 53.10		Crew	Daily Output	Labor-Hours	Unit	Material	Labor	Equipment	Total	Total Incl O&P
0010	**COATINGS, ELASTOMERIC**									
0020	High build, water proof, one coat system									
0100	Concrete, brush	1 Pord	650	.012	S.F.	.31	.49		.80	1.12

09 96 56 – Epoxy Coatings

09 96 56.20 Wall Coatings

09 96 56.20		Crew	Daily Output	Labor-Hours	Unit	Material	Labor	Equipment	Total	Total Incl O&P
0010	**WALL COATINGS**									
0100	Acrylic glazed coatings, minimum	1 Pord	525	.015	S.F.	.31	.60		.91	1.31
0200	Maximum		305	.026		.65	1.04		1.69	2.38
0300	Epoxy coatings, minimum		525	.015		.40	.60		1	1.41
0400	Maximum		170	.047		1.20	1.86		3.06	4.31
2400	Sprayed perlite or vermiculite, 1/16" thick, minimum		2935	.003		.27	.11		.38	.47
2500	Maximum		640	.013		.73	.49		1.22	1.59

09 96 High-Performance Coatings

09 96 56 – Epoxy Coatings

09 96 56.20 Wall Coatings	Crew	Daily Output	Labor-Hours	Unit	Material	2014 Bare Costs Labor	Equipment	Total	Total Incl O&P
2700	Vinyl plastic wall coating, minimum	1 Pord	735	.011	S.F.	.33	.43		.76	1.05
2800	Maximum		240	.033		.81	1.32		2.13	3
3000	Urethane on smooth surface, 2 coats, minimum		1135	.007		.27	.28		.55	.75
3100	Maximum		665	.012		.58	.48		1.06	1.40

323

Division Notes

		CREW	DAILY OUTPUT	LABOR-HOURS	UNIT	BARE COSTS				TOTAL INCL O&P
						MAT.	LABOR	EQUIP.	TOTAL	

Estimating Tips

General

- The items in this division are usually priced per square foot or each.

- Many items in Division 10 require some type of support system or special anchors that are not usually furnished with the item. The required anchors must be added to the estimate in the appropriate division.

- Some items in Division 10, such as lockers, may require assembly before installation. Verify the amount of assembly required. Assembly can often exceed installation time.

10 20 00 Interior Specialties

- Support angles and blocking are not included in the installation of toilet compartments, shower/dressing compartments, or cubicles. Appropriate line items from Divisions 5 or 6 may need to be added to support the installations.

- Toilet partitions are priced by the stall. A stall consists of a side wall, pilaster, and door with hardware. Toilet tissue holders and grab bars are extra.

- The required acoustical rating of a folding partition can have a significant impact on costs. Verify the sound transmission coefficient rating of the panel priced to the specification requirements.

- Grab bar installation does not include supplemental blocking or backing to support the required load. When grab bars are installed at an existing facility, provisions must be made to attach the grab bars to solid structure.

Reference Numbers

Reference numbers are shown in shaded boxes at the beginning of some major classifications. These numbers refer to related items in the Reference Section. The reference information may be an estimating procedure, an alternate pricing method, or technical information.

Note: Not all subdivisions listed here necessarily appear in this publication.

10 11 Visual Display Units

10 11 13 – Chalkboards

10 11 13.13 Fixed Chalkboards

10 11 13.13 Fixed Chalkboards	Crew	Daily Output	Labor-Hours	Unit	Material	2014 Bare Costs Labor	Equipment	Total	Total Incl O&P
0010 **FIXED CHALKBOARDS** Porcelain enamel steel									
3900 Wall hung									
4000 Aluminum frame and chalktrough									
4300 3' x 5'	2 Carp	15	1.067	Ea.	310	49		359	420
4600 4' x 12'	"	13	1.231	"	585	56.50		641.50	740
4700 Wood frame and chalktrough									
4800 3' x 4'	2 Carp	16	1	Ea.	217	46		263	315
5300 4' x 8'	"	13	1.231	"	355	56.50		411.50	485
5400 Liquid chalk, white porcelain enamel, wall hung									
5420 Deluxe units, aluminum trim and chalktrough									
5450 4' x 4'	2 Carp	16	1	Ea.	252	46		298	355
5550 4' x 12'	"	12	1.333	"	535	61		596	690
5700 Wood trim and chalktrough									
5900 4' x 4'	2 Carp	16	1	Ea.	715	46		761	860
6200 4' x 8'		14	1.143	"	970	52.50		1,022.50	1,150
9000 Minimum labor/equipment charge		3	5.333	Job		245		245	400

10 11 13.43 Portable Chalkboards

10 11 13.43 Portable Chalkboards	Crew	Daily Output	Labor-Hours	Unit	Material	2014 Bare Costs Labor	Equipment	Total	Total Incl O&P
0010 **PORTABLE CHALKBOARDS**									
0100 Freestanding, reversible									
0120 Economy, wood frame, 4' x 6'									
0140 Chalkboard both sides				Ea.	615			615	680
0160 Chalkboard one side, cork other side				"	565			565	620
0200 Standard, lightweight satin finished aluminum, 4' x 6'									
0220 Chalkboard both sides				Ea.	675			675	745
0240 Chalkboard one side, cork other side				"	705			705	775
0300 Deluxe, heavy duty extruded aluminum, 4' x 6'									
0320 Chalkboard both sides				Ea.	1,050			1,050	1,150
0340 Chalkboard one side, cork other side				"	1,025			1,025	1,125

10 11 16 – Markerboards

10 11 16.53 Electronic Markerboards

0010 **ELECTRONIC MARKERBOARDS**									

10 11 23 – Tackboards

10 11 23.10 Fixed Tackboards

10 11 23.10 Fixed Tackboards	Crew	Daily Output	Labor-Hours	Unit	Material	2014 Bare Costs Labor	Equipment	Total	Total Incl O&P
0010 **FIXED TACKBOARDS**									
2120 Prefabricated, 1/4" cork, 3' x 5' with aluminum frame	2 Carp	16	1	Ea.	124	46		170	212
2140 Wood frame	"	16	1	"	156	46		202	247
2300 Glass enclosed cabinets, alum., cork panel, hinged doors									
2600 4' x 7', 3 door	2 Carp	10	1.600	Ea.	1,775	73.50		1,848.50	2,075
9000 Minimum labor/equipment charge	"	4	4	Job		183		183	300

10 13 Directories

10 13 10 – Building Directories

10 13 10.10 Directory Boards	Crew	Daily Output	Labor-Hours	Unit	Material	2014 Bare Costs Labor	Equipment	Total	Total Incl O&P
0010 **DIRECTORY BOARDS**									
0050 Plastic, glass covered, 30" x 20"	2 Carp	3	5.333	Ea.	234	245		479	655
0100 36" x 48"		2	8		845	365		1,210	1,525
0900 Outdoor, weatherproof, black plastic, 36" x 24"		2	8		760	365		1,125	1,450
1000 36" x 36"	↓	1.50	10.667	↓	880	490		1,370	1,775
9000 Minimum labor/equipment charge	1 Carp	1	8	Job		365		365	605

10 14 Signage

10 14 19 – Dimensional Letter Signage

10 14 19.10 Exterior Signs

	Crew	Daily Output	Labor-Hours	Unit	Material	2014 Bare Costs Labor	Equipment	Total	Total Incl O&P
0010 **EXTERIOR SIGNS**									
3900 Plaques, custom, 20" x 30", for up to 450 letters, cast aluminum	2 Carp	4	4	Ea.	1,425	183		1,608	1,850
4000 Cast bronze		4	4		1,875	183		2,058	2,350
4200 30" x 36", up to 900 letters cast aluminum		3	5.333		2,350	245		2,595	2,975
4300 Cast bronze	↓	3	5.333		4,225	245		4,470	5,050
5100 Exit signs, 24 ga. alum., 14" x 12" surface mounted	1 Carp	30	.267		47.50	12.25		59.75	72.50
5200 10" x 7"	"	20	.400		25.50	18.35		43.85	58
6400 Replacement sign faces, 6" or 8"	1 Clab	50	.160	↓	62.50	5.85		68.35	78
9000 Minimum labor/equipment charge	1 Carp	4	2	Job		91.50		91.50	151

10 14 23 – Panel Signage

10 14 23.13 Engraved Panel Signage

	Crew	Daily Output	Labor-Hours	Unit	Material	2014 Bare Costs Labor	Equipment	Total	Total Incl O&P
0010 **ENGRAVED PANEL SIGNAGE**, interior									
1010 Flexible door sign, adhesive back, w/Braille, 5/8" letters, 4" x 4"	1 Clab	32	.250	Ea.	30.50	9.15		39.65	48.50
1050 6" x 6"		32	.250		46.50	9.15		55.65	66
1100 8" x 2"		32	.250		30.50	9.15		39.65	48.50
1150 8" x 4"		32	.250		39.50	9.15		48.65	58.50
1200 8" x 8"		32	.250		52.50	9.15		61.65	73
1250 12" x 2"		32	.250		35	9.15		44.15	53.50
1300 12" x 6"		32	.250		50	9.15		59.15	70
1350 12" x 12"		32	.250		105	9.15		114.15	131
1500 Graphic symbols, 2" x 2"		32	.250		12	9.15		21.15	28.50
1550 6" x 6"		32	.250		31	9.15		40.15	49
1600 8" x 8"	↓	32	.250		39	9.15		48.15	57.50
2010 Corridor, stock acrylic, 2-sided, with mounting bracket, 2" x 8"	1 Carp	24	.333		24.50	15.30		39.80	52
2020 2" x 10"		24	.333		33.50	15.30		48.80	62
2050 3" x 8"		24	.333		28.50	15.30		43.80	56.50
2060 3" x 10"		24	.333		42	15.30		57.30	71.50
2070 3" x 12"		24	.333		47	15.30		62.30	76.50
2100 4" x 8"		24	.333		21	15.30		36.30	48
2110 4" x 10"		24	.333		37	15.30		52.30	65.50
2120 4" x 12"	↓	24	.333	↓	50.50	15.30		65.80	80.50

10 14 53 – Traffic Signage

10 14 53.20 Traffic Signs

	Crew	Daily Output	Labor-Hours	Unit	Material	2014 Bare Costs Labor	Equipment	Total	Total Incl O&P
0010 **TRAFFIC SIGNS**									
0012 Stock, 24" x 24", no posts, .080" alum. reflectorized	B-80	70	.457	Ea.	83	18.15	10.85	112	133
0100 High intensity		70	.457		95.50	18.15	10.85	124.50	146
0300 30" x 30", reflectorized		70	.457		121	18.15	10.85	150	174
0400 High intensity		70	.457		133	18.15	10.85	162	187
0600 Guide and directional signs, 12" x 18", reflectorized		70	.457		34.50	18.15	10.85	63.50	79.50
0700 High intensity	↓	70	.457		51	18.15	10.85	80	98

10 14 Signage

10 14 53 – Traffic Signage

10 14 53.20 Traffic Signs		Crew	Daily Output	Labor-Hours	Unit	Material	2014 Bare Costs Labor	2014 Bare Costs Equipment	Total	Total Incl O&P
0900	18" x 24", stock signs, reflectorized	B-80	70	.457	Ea.	46	18.15	10.85	75	92.50
1000	High intensity		70	.457		51	18.15	10.85	80	98
1200	24" x 24", stock signs, reflectorized		70	.457		56	18.15	10.85	85	103
1300	High intensity		70	.457		61	18.15	10.85	90	108
1500	Add to above for steel posts, galvanized, 10'-0" upright, bolted		200	.160		32.50	6.35	3.79	42.64	50.50
1600	12'-0" upright, bolted		140	.229	↓	39	9.10	5.40	53.50	63.50
1800	Highway road signs, aluminum, over 20 S.F., reflectorized		350	.091	S.F.	33.50	3.63	2.17	39.30	45.50
2000	High intensity		350	.091		33.50	3.63	2.17	39.30	45.50
2200	Highway, suspended over road, 80 S.F. min., reflectorized		165	.194		31	7.70	4.59	43.29	51.50
2300	High intensity	↓	165	.194	↓	29.50	7.70	4.59	41.79	50

10 17 Telephone Specialties

10 17 16 – Telephone Enclosures

10 17 16.10 Commercial Telephone Enclosures

		Crew	Daily Output	Labor-Hours	Unit	Material	Labor	Equipment	Total	Total Incl O&P
0010	**COMMERCIAL TELEPHONE ENCLOSURES**									
0300	Shelf type, wall hung, minimum	2 Carp	5	3.200	Ea.	1,025	147		1,172	1,375
0400	Maximum		5	3.200	"	2,850	147		2,997	3,375
9000	Minimum labor/equipment charge	↓	4	4	Job		183		183	300

10 21 Compartments and Cubicles

10 21 13 – Toilet Compartments

10 21 13.13 Metal Toilet Compartments

		Crew	Daily Output	Labor-Hours	Unit	Material	Labor	Equipment	Total	Total Incl O&P
0010	**METAL TOILET COMPARTMENTS**									
0110	Cubicles, ceiling hung									
0200	Powder coated steel	2 Carp	4	4	Ea.	515	183		698	865
0500	Stainless steel	"	4	4		1,075	183		1,258	1,475
0600	For handicap units, incl. 52" grab bars, add				↓	430			430	475
0900	Floor and ceiling anchored									
1000	Powder coated steel	2 Carp	5	3.200	Ea.	590	147		737	885
1300	Stainless steel	"	5	3.200		1,150	147		1,297	1,525
1400	For handicap units, incl. 52" grab bars, add				↓	296			296	325
1610	Floor anchored									
1700	Powder coated steel	2 Carp	7	2.286	Ea.	585	105		690	810
2000	Stainless steel	"	7	2.286		1,400	105		1,505	1,725
2100	For handicap units, incl. 52" grab bars, add					310			310	345
2200	For juvenile units, deduct				↓	41.50			41.50	45.50
2450	Floor anchored, headrail braced									
2500	Powder coated steel	2 Carp	6	2.667	Ea.	380	122		502	615
2804	Stainless steel	"	4.60	3.478		1,050	159		1,209	1,400
2900	For handicap units, incl. 52" grab bars, add					370			370	410
3000	Wall hung partitions, powder coated steel	2 Carp	7	2.286		635	105		740	870
3300	Stainless steel	"	7	2.286		1,650	105		1,755	2,000
3400	For handicap units, incl. 52" grab bars, add				↓	370			370	410
4000	Screens, entrance, floor mounted, 58" high, 48" wide									
4200	Powder coated steel	2 Carp	15	1.067	Ea.	242	49		291	345
4500	Stainless steel	"	15	1.067	"	910	49		959	1,075
4650	Urinal screen, 18" wide									
4704	Powder coated steel	2 Carp	6.15	2.602	Ea.	206	119		325	425
5004	Stainless steel	"	6.15	2.602	"	580	119		699	835

10 21 Compartments and Cubicles

10 21 13 – Toilet Compartments

10 21 13.13 Metal Toilet Compartments

		Crew	Daily Output	Labor-Hours	Unit	Material	2014 Bare Costs Labor	Equipment	Total	Total Incl O&P
5100	Floor mounted, head rail braced									
5300	Powder coated steel	2 Carp	8	2	Ea.	230	91.50		321.50	405
5600	Stainless steel	"	8	2	"	595	91.50		686.50	805
5750	Pilaster, flush									
5800	Powder coated steel	2 Carp	10	1.600	Ea.	278	73.50		351.50	425
6100	Stainless steel		10	1.600		615	73.50		688.50	795
6300	Post braced, powder coated steel		10	1.600		153	73.50		226.50	289
6600	Stainless steel	↓	10	1.600	↓	450	73.50		523.50	615
6700	Wall hung, bracket supported									
6800	Powder coated steel	2 Carp	10	1.600	Ea.	153	73.50		226.50	289
7100	Stainless steel		10	1.600		227	73.50		300.50	370
7400	Flange supported, powder coated steel		10	1.600		106	73.50		179.50	237
7700	Stainless steel		10	1.600		310	73.50		383.50	460
7800	Wedge type, powder coated steel		10	1.600		134	73.50		207.50	269
8100	Stainless steel	↓	10	1.600	↓	575	73.50		648.50	755
9000	Minimum labor/equipment charge	1 Carp	2.50	3.200	Job		147		147	241

10 21 13.14 Metal Toilet Compartment Components

		Crew	Daily Output	Labor-Hours	Unit	Material	2014 Bare Costs Labor	Equipment	Total	Total Incl O&P
0010	**METAL TOILET COMPARTMENT COMPONENTS**									
0100	Pilasters									
0110	Overhead braced, powder coated steel, 7" wide x 82" high	2 Carp	22.20	.721	Ea.	69.50	33		102.50	131
0120	Stainless steel		22.20	.721		124	33		157	192
0130	Floor braced, powder coated steel, 7" wide x 70" high		23.30	.687		123	31.50		154.50	188
0140	Stainless steel		23.30	.687		242	31.50		273.50	320
0150	Ceiling hung, powder coated steel, 7" wide x 83" high		13.30	1.203		131	55		186	235
0160	Stainless steel		13.30	1.203		271	55		326	390
0170	Wall hung, powder coated steel, 3" wide x 58" high		18.90	.847		129	39		168	206
0180	Stainless steel	↓	18.90	.847	↓	191	39		230	274
0200	Panels									
0210	Powder coated steel, 31" wide x 58" high	2 Carp	18.90	.847	Ea.	132	39		171	209
0220	Stainless steel		18.90	.847		360	39		399	465
0230	Powder coated steel, 53" wide x 58" high		18.90	.847		164	39		203	244
0240	Stainless steel		18.90	.847		470	39		509	580
0250	Powder coated steel, 63" wide x 58" high		18.90	.847		200	39		239	284
0260	Stainless steel	↓	18.90	.847	↓	515	39		554	630
0300	Doors									
0310	Powder coated steel, 24" wide x 58" high	2 Carp	14.10	1.135	Ea.	138	52		190	237
0320	Stainless steel		14.10	1.135		287	52		339	400
0330	Powder coated steel, 26" wide x 58" high		14.10	1.135		140	52		192	240
0340	Stainless steel		14.10	1.135		296	52		348	410
0350	Powder coated steel, 28" wide x 58" high		14.10	1.135		160	52		212	262
0360	Stainless steel		14.10	1.135		330	52		382	450
0370	Powder coated steel, 36" wide x 58" high		14.10	1.135		172	52		224	276
0380	Stainless steel	↓	14.10	1.135	↓	370	52		422	495
0400	Headrails									
0410	For powder coated steel, 62" long	2 Carp	65	.246	Ea.	21.50	11.30		32.80	42
0420	Stainless steel		65	.246		22.50	11.30		33.80	43.50
0430	For powder coated steel, 84" long		50	.320		32	14.65		46.65	59.50
0440	Stainless steel		50	.320		34.50	14.65		49.15	62
0450	For powder coated steel, 120" long		30	.533		42.50	24.50		67	87
0460	Stainless steel	↓	30	.533	↓	46.50	24.50		71	91
9000	Minimum labor/equipment charge	1 Carp	4	2	Job		91.50		91.50	151

10 21 13.16 Plastic-Laminate-Clad Toilet Compartments

		Crew	Daily Output	Labor-Hours	Unit	Material	2014 Bare Costs Labor	Equipment	Total	Total Incl O&P
0010	**PLASTIC-LAMINATE-CLAD TOILET COMPARTMENTS**									
0110	Cubicles, ceiling hung									
0300	Plastic laminate on particle board	2 Carp	4	4	Ea.	520	183		703	870
0600	For handicap units, incl. 52" grab bars, add				"	430			430	475
0900	Floor and ceiling anchored									
1100	Plastic laminate on particle board	2 Carp	5	3.200	Ea.	785	147		932	1,100
1400	For handicap units, incl. 52" grab bars, add				"	296			296	325
1610	Floor mounted									
1800	Plastic laminate on particle board	2 Carp	7	2.286	Ea.	490	105		595	710
2450	Floor mounted, headrail braced									
2600	Plastic laminate on particle board	2 Carp	6	2.667	Ea.	750	122		872	1,025
3400	For handicap units, incl. 52" grab bars, add					370			370	410
4300	Entrance screen, floor mtd., plas. lam., 58" high, 48" wide	2 Carp	15	1.067		610	49		659	750
4800	Urinal screen, 18" wide, ceiling braced, plastic laminate		8	2		184	91.50		275.50	355
5400	Floor mounted, headrail braced		8	2		190	91.50		281.50	360
5900	Pilaster, flush, plastic laminate		10	1.600		505	73.50		578.50	680
6400	Post braced, plastic laminate		10	1.600		300	73.50		373.50	450
6700	Wall hung, bracket supported									
6900	Plastic laminate on particle board	2 Carp	10	1.600	Ea.	92.50	73.50		166	223
7450	Flange supported									
7500	Plastic laminate on particle board	2 Carp	10	1.600	Ea.	230	73.50		303.50	375
9000	Minimum labor/equipment charge	1 Carp	2.50	3.200	Job		147		147	241

10 21 13.17 Plastic-Laminate Clad Toilet Compartment Components

		Crew	Daily Output	Labor-Hours	Unit	Material	2014 Bare Costs Labor	Equipment	Total	Total Incl O&P
0010	**PLASTIC-LAMINATE CLAD TOILET COMPARTMENT COMPONENTS**									
0100	Pilasters									
0110	Overhead braced, 7" wide x 82" high	2 Carp	22.20	.721	Ea.	95	33		128	160
0130	Floor anchored, 7" wide x 70" high		23.30	.687		95	31.50		126.50	156
0150	Ceiling hung, 7" wide x 83" high		13.30	1.203		99.50	55		154.50	200
0180	Wall hung, 3" wide x 58" high		18.90	.847		93	39		132	166
0200	Panels									
0210	31" wide x 58" high	2 Carp	18.90	.847	Ea.	143	39		182	221
0230	51" wide x 58" high		18.90	.847		196	39		235	280
0250	63" wide x 58" high		18.90	.847		229	39		268	315
0300	Doors									
0310	24" wide x 58" high	2 Carp	14.10	1.135	Ea.	141	52		193	241
0330	26" wide x 58" high		14.10	1.135		146	52		198	246
0350	28" wide x 58" high		14.10	1.135		150	52		202	251
0370	36" wide x 58" high		14.10	1.135		180	52		232	284
0400	Headrails									
0410	62" long	2 Carp	65	.246	Ea.	22.50	11.30		33.80	43.50
0430	84" long		60	.267		31.50	12.25		43.75	54.50
0450	120" long		30	.533		42	24.50		66.50	86
9000	Minimum labor/equipment charge	1 Carp	4	2	Job		91.50		91.50	151

10 21 13.19 Plastic Toilet Compartments

		Crew	Daily Output	Labor-Hours	Unit	Material	2014 Bare Costs Labor	Equipment	Total	Total Incl O&P
0010	**PLASTIC TOILET COMPARTMENTS**									
0110	Cubicles, ceiling hung									
0250	Phenolic	2 Carp	4	4	Ea.	865	183		1,048	1,250
0600	For handicap units, incl. 52" grab bars, add				"	430			430	475
0900	Floor and ceiling anchored									
1050	Phenolic	2 Carp	5	3.200	Ea.	825	147		972	1,150
1400	For handicap units, incl. 52" grab bars, add				"	296			296	325
1610	Floor mounted									

10 21 Compartments and Cubicles

10 21 13 – Toilet Compartments

10 21 13.19 Plastic Toilet Compartments

		Crew	Daily Output	Labor-Hours	Unit	Material	2014 Bare Costs Labor	Equipment	Total	Total Incl O&P
1750	Phenolic	2 Carp	7	2.286	Ea.	795	105		900	1,050
2100	For handicap units, incl. 52" grab bars, add					310			310	345
2200	For juvenile units, deduct					41.50			41.50	45.50
2450	Floor mounted, headrail braced									
2550	Phenolic	2 Carp	6	2.667	Ea.	795	122		917	1,075
9000	Minimum labor/equipment charge	1 Carp	2.50	3.200	Job		147		147	241

10 21 13.20 Plastic Toilet Compartment Components

		Crew	Daily Output	Labor-Hours	Unit	Material	2014 Bare Costs Labor	Equipment	Total	Total Incl O&P
0010	**PLASTIC TOILET COMPARTMENT COMPONENTS**									
0100	Pilasters									
0110	Overhead braced, polymer plastic, 7" wide x 82" high	2 Carp	22.20	.721	Ea.	121	33		154	188
0120	Phenolic		22.20	.721		148	33		181	218
0130	Floor braced, polymer plastic, 7" wide x 70" high		23.30	.687		169	31.50		200.50	238
0140	Phenolic		23.30	.687		140	31.50		171.50	206
0150	Ceiling hung, polymer plastic, 7" wide x 83" high		13.30	1.203		166	55		221	274
0160	Phenolic		13.30	1.203		158	55		213	265
0180	Wall hung, phenolic, 3" wide x 58" high		18.90	.847		96	39		135	169
0200	Panels									
0203	Polymer plastic, 18" high x 55" high	2 Carp	18.90	.847	Ea.	200	39		239	284
0206	Phenolic, 18" wide x 58" high		18.90	.847		193	39		232	276
0210	Polymer plastic, 31" high x 55" high		18.90	.847		305	39		344	400
0220	Phenolic, 31" wide x 58" high		18.90	.847		260	39		299	350
0223	Polymer plastic, 48" high x 55" high		18.90	.847		470	39		509	580
0226	Phenolic, 48" wide x 58" high		18.90	.847		550	39		589	670
0230	Polymer plastic, 51" wide x 55" high		18.90	.847		405	39		444	510
0240	Phenolic, 51" wide x 58" high		18.90	.847		395	39		434	500
0250	Polymer plastic, 63" wide x 55" high		18.90	.847		555	39		594	675
0260	Phenolic, 63" wide x 58" high		18.90	.847		415	39		454	525
0300	Doors									
0310	Polymer plastic, 24" wide x 55" high	2 Carp	14.10	1.135	Ea.	208	52		260	315
0320	Phenolic, 24" wide x 58" high		14.10	1.135		292	52		344	405
0330	Polymer plastic, 26" high x 55" high		14.10	1.135		222	52		274	330
0340	Phenolic, 26" wide x 58" high		14.10	1.135		310	52		362	425
0350	Polymer plastic, 28" wide x 55" high		14.10	1.135		247	52		299	360
0360	Phenolic, 28" wide x 58" high		14.10	1.135		330	52		382	445
0370	Polymer plastic, 36" wide x 55" high		14.10	1.135		288	52		340	400
0380	Phenolic, 36" wide x 58" high		14.10	1.135		410	52		462	535
0400	Headrails									
0410	For polymer plastic, 62" long	2 Carp	65	.246	Ea.	22.50	11.30		33.80	43.50
0420	Phenolic		65	.246		22.50	11.30		33.80	43.50
0430	For polymer plastic, 84" long		50	.320		33	14.65		47.65	60
0440	Phenolic		50	.320		33	14.65		47.65	60
0450	For polymer plastic, 120" long		30	.533		43	24.50		67.50	87.50
0460	Phenolic		30	.533		43	24.50		67.50	87.50
9000	Minimum labor/equipment charge	1 Carp	4	2	Job		91.50		91.50	151

10 21 13.40 Stone Toilet Compartments

		Crew	Daily Output	Labor-Hours	Unit	Material	2014 Bare Costs Labor	Equipment	Total	Total Incl O&P
0010	**STONE TOILET COMPARTMENTS**									
0100	Cubicles, ceiling hung, marble	2 Marb	2	8	Ea.	1,625	340		1,965	2,325
0600	For handicap units, incl. 52" grab bars, add					430			430	475
0800	Floor & ceiling anchored, marble	2 Marb	2.50	6.400		2,025	270		2,295	2,700
1400	For handicap units, incl. 52" grab bars, add					296			296	325
1600	Floor mounted, marble	2 Marb	3	5.333		1,200	225		1,425	1,700
2400	Floor mounted, headrail braced, marble	"	3	5.333		1,150	225		1,375	1,650

10 21 13 – Toilet Compartments

10 21 13.40 Stone Toilet Compartments		Crew	Daily Output	Labor-Hours	Unit	Material	2014 Bare Costs Labor	Equipment	Total	Total Incl O&P
2900	For handicap units, incl. 52" grab bars, add				Ea.	370			370	410
4100	Entrance screen, floor mounted marble, 58" high, 48" wide	2 Marb	9	1.778		755	75		830	950
4600	Urinal screen, 18" wide, ceiling braced, marble	D-1	6	2.667	↓	755	110		865	1,000
5100	Floor mounted, head rail braced									
5200	Marble	D-1	6	2.667	Ea.	645	110		755	890
5700	Pilaster, flush, marble		9	1.778		840	73.50		913.50	1,050
6200	Post braced, marble	↓	9	1.778	↓	825	73.50		898.50	1,025
9000	Minimum labor/equipment charge	1 Carp	2.50	3.200	Job		147		147	241

10 21 16 – Shower and Dressing Compartments

10 21 16.10 Partitions, Shower

		Crew	Daily Output	Labor-Hours	Unit	Material	2014 Bare Costs Labor	Equipment	Total	Total Incl O&P
0010	**PARTITIONS, SHOWER** floor mounted, no plumbing									
0400	Cabinet, one piece, fiberglass, 32" x 32"	2 Carp	5	3.200	Ea.	510	147		657	800
0420	36" x 36"		5	3.200		610	147		757	910
0440	36" x 48"		5	3.200		1,300	147		1,447	1,675
0460	Acrylic, 32" x 32"		5	3.200		299	147		446	570
0480	36" x 36"		5	3.200		1,000	147		1,147	1,350
0500	36" x 48"	↓	5	3.200		1,500	147		1,647	1,900
0520	Shower door for above, clear plastic, 24" wide	1 Carp	8	1		177	46		223	271
0540	28" wide		8	1		201	46		247	298
0560	Tempered glass, 24" wide		8	1		191	46		237	286
0580	28" wide	↓	8	1		216	46		262	315
4100	Shower doors, economy plastic, 24" wide	1 Shee	9	.889		144	48.50		192.50	235
4200	Tempered glass door, economy		8	1		260	54.50		314.50	375
4700	Deluxe, tempered glass, chrome on brass frame, minimum		8	1		385	54.50		439.50	505
4800	Maximum		1	8	↓	625	440		1,065	1,375
9990	Minimum labor/equipment charge	↓	2.50	3.200	Job		175		175	276

10 22 16 – Folding Gates

10 22 16.10 Security Gates

		Crew	Daily Output	Labor-Hours	Unit	Material	2014 Bare Costs Labor	Equipment	Total	Total Incl O&P
0010	**SECURITY GATES** for roll up type, see Section 08 33 13.10									
0300	Scissors type folding gate, ptd. steel, single, 6-1/2' high, 5-1/2' wide	2 Sswk	4	4	Opng.	223	204		427	620
0350	6-1/2' wide		4	4		243	204		447	640
0400	7-1/2' wide		4	4		253	204		457	655
0600	Double gate, 8' high, 8' wide		2.50	6.400		380	325		705	1,025
0650	10' wide		2.50	6.400		415	325		740	1,050
0700	12' wide		2	8		610	410		1,020	1,425
0750	14' wide		2	8		700	410		1,110	1,525
0900	Door gate, folding steel, 4' wide, 61" high		4	4		138	204		342	525
1000	71" high		4	4		169	204		373	560
1200	81" high		4	4		182	204		386	575
1300	Window gates, 2' to 4' wide, 31" high		4	4		78	204		282	460
1500	55" high		3.75	4.267		122	218		340	535
1600	79" high	↓	3.50	4.571	↓	144	234		378	590

10 22 Partitions

10 22 19 - Demountable Partitions

10 22 19.43 Demountable Composite Partitions	Crew	Daily Output	Labor-Hours	Unit	Material	2014 Bare Costs Labor	Equipment	Total	Total Incl O&P
0010 **DEMOUNTABLE COMPOSITE PARTITIONS**, add for doors									
0100 Do not deduct door openings from total L.F.									
0900 Demountable gypsum system on 2" to 2-1/2"									
1000 steel studs, 9' high, 3" to 3-3/4" thick									
1200 Vinyl clad gypsum	2 Carp	48	.333	L.F.	59	15.30		74.30	90
1300 Fabric clad gypsum		44	.364		147	16.65		163.65	190
1500 Steel clad gypsum		40	.400		164	18.35		182.35	210
1600 1.75 system, aluminum framing, vinyl clad hardboard,									
1800 paper honeycomb core panel, 1-3/4" to 2-1/2" thick									
1900 9' high	2 Carp	48	.333	L.F.	99	15.30		114.30	134
2100 7' high		60	.267		89	12.25		101.25	118
2200 5' high		80	.200		75	9.15		84.15	97.50
2250 Unitized gypsum system									
2300 Unitized panel, 9' high, 2" to 2-1/2" thick									
2350 Vinyl clad gypsum	2 Carp	48	.333	L.F.	127	15.30		142.30	165
2400 Fabric clad gypsum	"	44	.364	"	210	16.65		226.65	259
2500 Unitized mineral fiber system									
2510 Unitized panel, 9' high, 2-1/4" thick, aluminum frame									
2550 Vinyl clad mineral fiber	2 Carp	48	.333	L.F.	127	15.30		142.30	164
2600 Fabric clad mineral fiber	"	44	.364	"	189	16.65		205.65	236
2800 Movable steel walls, modular system									
2900 Unitized panels, 9' high, 48" wide									
3100 Baked enamel, pre-finished	2 Carp	60	.267	L.F.	144	12.25		156.25	178
3200 Fabric clad steel	"	56	.286	"	207	13.10		220.10	250
5500 For acoustical partitions, add, minimum				S.F.	2.31			2.31	2.54
5550 Maximum				"	10.80			10.80	11.85
5700 For doors, see Sections 08 11 & 08 16									
5800 For door hardware, see Section 08 71									
6100 In-plant modular office system, w/prehung hollow core door									
6200 3" thick polystyrene core panels									
6250 12' x 12', 2 wall	2 Clab	3.80	4.211	Ea.	4,125	154		4,279	4,775
6300 4 wall		1.90	8.421		7,300	310		7,610	8,525
6350 16' x 16', 2 wall		3.60	4.444		6,175	163		6,338	7,075
6400 4 wall		1.80	8.889		8,650	325		8,975	10,100
9000 Minimum labor/equipment charge	2 Carp	3	5.333	Job		245		245	400

10 22 23 - Portable Partitions, Screens, and Panels

10 22 23.13 Wall Screens

10 22 23.13 Wall Screens	Crew	Daily Output	Labor-Hours	Unit	Material	2014 Bare Costs Labor	Equipment	Total	Total Incl O&P
0010 **WALL SCREENS**, divider panels, free standing, fiber core									
0020 Fabric face straight									
0100 3'-0" long, 4'-0" high	2 Carp	100	.160	L.F.	149	7.35		156.35	176
0200 5'-0" high		90	.178		105	8.15		113.15	129
0500 6'-0" high		75	.213		122	9.80		131.80	151
0900 5'-0" long, 4'-0" high		175	.091		92	4.19		96.19	108
1000 5'-0" high		150	.107		100	4.89		104.89	118
1500 6'-0" high		125	.128		117	5.85		122.85	138
1600 6'-0" long, 5'-0" high		162	.099		97	4.53		101.53	114
3200 Economical panels, fabric face, 4'-0" long, 5'-0" high		132	.121		49	5.55		54.55	63
3250 6'-0" high		112	.143		53	6.55		59.55	69
3300 5'-0" long, 5'-0" high		150	.107		51.50	4.89		56.39	64.50
3350 6'-0" high		125	.128		43	5.85		48.85	57
3450 Acoustical panels, 60 to 90 NRC, 3'-0" long, 5'-0" high		90	.178		88.50	8.15		96.65	110
3550 6'-0" high		75	.213		98	9.80		107.80	124

10 22 Partitions

10 22 23 – Portable Partitions, Screens, and Panels

10 22 23.13 Wall Screens		Crew	Daily Output	Labor-Hours	Unit	Material	2014 Bare Costs Labor	Equipment	Total	Total Incl O&P
3600	5'-0" long, 5'-0" high	2 Carp	150	.107	L.F.	65	4.89		69.89	79.50
3650	6'-0" high		125	.128		68	5.85		73.85	84.50
3700	6'-0" long, 5'-0" high		162	.099		56	4.53		60.53	69
3750	6'-0" high		138	.116		55	5.30		60.30	69.50
3800	Economy acoustical panels, 40 N.R.C., 4'-0" long, 5'-0" high		132	.121		49	5.55		54.55	63
3850	6'-0" high		112	.143		53	6.55		59.55	69
3900	5'-0" long, 6'-0" high		125	.128		43	5.85		48.85	57
3950	6'-0" long, 5'-0" high		162	.099		43	4.53		47.53	55
9000	Minimum labor/equipment charge		3	5.333	Job		245		245	400

10 22 33 – Accordion Folding Partitions

10 22 33.10 Partitions, Accordion Folding

		Crew	Daily Output	Labor-Hours	Unit	Material	Labor	Equipment	Total	Total Incl O&P
0010	**PARTITIONS, ACCORDION FOLDING**									
0100	Vinyl covered, over 150 S.F., frame not included									
0300	Residential, 1.25 lb. per S.F., 8' maximum height	2 Carp	300	.053	S.F.	23	2.45		25.45	29
0400	Commercial, 1.75 lb. per S.F., 8' maximum height		225	.071		26	3.26		29.26	34
0900	Acoustical, 3 lb. per S.F., 17' maximum height		100	.160		29	7.35		36.35	43.50
1200	5 lb. per S.F., 20' maximum height		95	.168		40	7.70		47.70	56.50
1500	Vinyl clad wood or steel, electric operation, 5.0 psf		160	.100		57	4.59		61.59	70.50
1900	Wood, non-acoustic, birch or mahogany, to 10' high		300	.053		30.50	2.45		32.95	38
9000	Minimum labor/equipment charge		4	4	Job		183		183	300

10 22 39 – Folding Panel Partitions

10 22 39.10 Partitions, Folding Panel

		Crew	Daily Output	Labor-Hours	Unit	Material	Labor	Equipment	Total	Total Incl O&P
0010	**PARTITIONS, FOLDING PANEL**, acoustic, wood									
0100	Vinyl faced, to 18' high, 6 psf, minimum	2 Carp	60	.267	S.F.	57	12.25		69.25	82.50
0150	Average		45	.356		68	16.30		84.30	102
0200	Maximum		30	.533		87.50	24.50		112	137
0400	Plastic laminate or hardwood finish, minimum		60	.267		58.50	12.25		70.75	84.50
0500	Maximum		30	.533		62.50	24.50		87	109
0600	Wood, low acoustical type, 4.5 psf, to 14' high		50	.320		42.50	14.65		57.15	71
9000	Minimum labor/equipment charge		4	4	Job		183		183	300

10 26 Wall and Door Protection

10 26 13 – Corner Guards

10 26 13.10 Metal Corner Guards

		Crew	Daily Output	Labor-Hours	Unit	Material	Labor	Equipment	Total	Total Incl O&P
0010	**METAL CORNER GUARDS**									
0020	Steel angle w/anchors, 1" x 1" x 1/4", 1.5#/L.F.	2 Carp	160	.100	L.F.	6.25	4.59		10.84	14.45
0100	2" x 2" x 1/4" angles, 3.2#/L.F.	"	150	.107	"	10.20	4.89		15.09	19.25
1000	Wall protection, stainless steel, 16 ga, 48" x 36" tall, screwed to studs	2 Skwk	500	.032	S.F.	8.45	1.51		9.96	11.75
1050	Wall end guard, stainless steel, 16 ga, 36" tall, screwed to studs	1 Skwk	30	.267	Ea.	19	12.60		31.60	41.50
9000	Minimum labor/equipment charge	1 Carp	2	4	Job		183		183	300

10 28 Toilet, Bath, and Laundry Accessories

10 28 13 – Toilet Accessories

10 28 13.13 Commercial Toilet Accessories	Crew	Daily Output	Labor-Hours	Unit	Material	2014 Bare Costs Labor	Equipment	Total	Total Incl O&P
0010 **COMMERCIAL TOILET ACCESSORIES**									
0200 Curtain rod, stainless steel, 5' long, 1" diameter	1 Carp	13	.615	Ea.	26.50	28		54.50	75.50
0300 1-1/4" diameter		13	.615		30.50	28		58.50	80
0350 Chrome, 1" diameter		13	.615		32.50	28		60.50	82
0360 For vinyl curtain, add		1950	.004	S.F.	.84	.19		1.03	1.23
0400 Diaper changing station, horizontal, wall mounted, plastic		10	.800	Ea.	223	36.50		259.50	305
0500 Dispenser units, combined soap & towel dispensers,									
0510 mirror and shelf, flush mounted	1 Carp	10	.800	Ea.	310	36.50		346.50	400
0600 Towel dispenser and waste receptacle,									
0610 18 gallon capacity	1 Carp	10	.800	Ea.	286	36.50		322.50	375
0800 Grab bar, straight, 1-1/4" diameter, stainless steel, 18" long		24	.333		29	15.30		44.30	57
0900 24" long		23	.348		29.50	15.95		45.45	58.50
1000 30" long		22	.364		31.50	16.65		48.15	62
1100 36" long		20	.400		38.50	18.35		56.85	72.50
1105 42" long		20	.400		46	18.35		64.35	80.50
1120 Corner, 36" long		20	.400		85.50	18.35		103.85	124
1200 1-1/2" diameter, 24" long		23	.348		31	15.95		46.95	60
1300 36" long		20	.400		33.50	18.35		51.85	67
1310 42" long		18	.444		43	20.50		63.50	81
1500 Tub bar, 1-1/4" diameter, 24" x 36"		14	.571		92.50	26		118.50	145
1600 Plus vertical arm		12	.667		97.50	30.50		128	157
1900 End tub bar, 1" diameter, 90° angle, 16" x 32"		12	.667		109	30.50		139.50	170
2010 Tub/shower/toilet, 2-wall, 36" x 24"		12	.667		83	30.50		113.50	142
2300 Hand dryer, surface mounted, electric, 115 volt, 20 amp		4	2		430	91.50		521.50	625
2400 230 volt, 10 amp		4	2		745	91.50		836.50	970
2450 Hand dryer, touch free, 1400 watt, 81,000 rpm		4	2		1,025	91.50		1,116.50	1,275
2600 Hat and coat strip, stainless steel, 4 hook, 36" long		24	.333		75	15.30		90.30	108
2700 6 hook, 60" long		20	.400		131	18.35		149.35	174
3000 Mirror, with stainless steel 3/4" square frame, 18" x 24"		20	.400		47	18.35		65.35	81.50
3100 36" x 24"		15	.533		103	24.50		127.50	153
3200 48" x 24"		10	.800		139	36.50		175.50	214
3300 72" x 24"		6	1.333		256	61		317	380
3500 With 5" stainless steel shelf, 18" x 24"		20	.400		186	18.35		204.35	235
3600 36" x 24"		15	.533		217	24.50		241.50	279
3700 48" x 24"		10	.800		245	36.50		281.50	330
3800 72" x 24"		6	1.333		300	61		361	430
4100 Mop holder strip, stainless steel, 5 holders, 48" long		20	.400		89	18.35		107.35	128
4200 Napkin/tampon dispenser, recessed		15	.533		525	24.50		549.50	615
4220 Semi-recessed		6.50	1.231		310	56.50		366.50	435
4250 Napkin receptacle, recessed		6.50	1.231		165	56.50		221.50	275
4300 Robe hook, single, regular		36	.222		18.10	10.20		28.30	36.50
4400 Heavy duty, concealed mounting		36	.222		21	10.20		31.20	40
4600 Soap dispenser, chrome, surface mounted, liquid		20	.400		46.50	18.35		64.85	81
4700 Powder		20	.400		55	18.35		73.35	90.50
5000 Recessed stainless steel, liquid		10	.800		137	36.50		173.50	212
5600 Shelf, stainless steel, 5" wide, 18 ga., 24" long		24	.333		68.50	15.30		83.80	101
5700 48" long		16	.500		135	23		158	187
5800 8" wide shelf, 18 ga., 24" long		22	.364		69	16.65		85.65	104
5900 48" long		14	.571		121	26		147	176
6000 Toilet seat cover dispenser, stainless steel, recessed		20	.400		167	18.35		185.35	213
6050 Surface mounted		15	.533		34.50	24.50		59	77.50
6100 Toilet tissue dispenser, surface mounted, SS, single roll		30	.267		17.80	12.25		30.05	39.50
6200 Double roll		24	.333		23.50	15.30		38.80	51

10 28 Toilet, Bath, and Laundry Accessories

10 28 13 – Toilet Accessories

10 28 13.13 Commercial Toilet Accessories	Crew	Daily Output	Labor-Hours	Unit	Material	2014 Bare Costs Labor	Equipment	Total	Total Incl O&P
6240	Plastic, twin/jumbo dbl. roll	1 Carp	24	.333	Ea.	26	15.30		41.30	53.50
6290	Toilet seat	1 Plum	40	.200		30	11.50		41.50	51
6400	Towel bar, stainless steel, 18" long	1 Carp	23	.348		41.50	15.95		57.45	72
6500	30" long		21	.381		111	17.45		128.45	152
6700	Towel dispenser, stainless steel, surface mounted		16	.500		44.50	23		67.50	86.50
6800	Flush mounted, recessed		10	.800		257	36.50		293.50	345
6900	Plastic, touchless, battery operated		16	.500		80.50	23		103.50	126
7000	Towel holder, hotel type, 2 guest size		20	.400		51.50	18.35		69.85	86.50
7200	Towel shelf, stainless steel, 24" long, 8" wide		20	.400		59.50	18.35		77.85	95.50
7400	Tumbler holder, tumbler only		30	.267		15.90	12.25		28.15	37.50
7410	Tumbler holder		20	.400		9.10	18.35		27.45	40
7500	Soap, tumbler & toothbrush		30	.267		19.60	12.25		31.85	41.50
7510	Tumbler & toothbrush holder		20	.400		12.60	18.35		30.95	44
7700	Wall urn ash receiver, surface mount, 11" long		12	.667		95	30.50		125.50	154
8000	Waste receptacles, stainless steel, with top, 13 gallon		10	.800		295	36.50		331.50	385
8100	36 gallon		8	1		395	46		441	510
9000	Minimum labor/equipment charge		5	1.600	Job		73.50		73.50	121

10 28 16 – Bath Accessories

10 28 16.20 Medicine Cabinets

		Crew	Daily Output	Labor-Hours	Unit	Material	2014 Bare Costs Labor	Equipment	Total	Total Incl O&P
0010	**MEDICINE CABINETS**									
0020	With mirror, sst frame, 16" x 22", unlighted	1 Carp	14	.571	Ea.	95	26		121	148
0100	Wood frame		14	.571		136	26		162	193
0300	Sliding mirror doors, 20" x 16" x 4-3/4", unlighted		7	1.143		125	52.50		177.50	223
0400	24" x 19" x 8-1/2", lighted		5	1.600		179	73.50		252.50	320
0600	Triple door, 30" x 32", unlighted, plywood body		7	1.143		320	52.50		372.50	435
0700	Steel body		7	1.143		350	52.50		402.50	470
0900	Oak door, wood body, beveled mirror, single door		7	1.143		195	52.50		247.50	300
1000	Double door		6	1.333		390	61		451	530
1200	Hotel cabinets, stainless, with lower shelf, unlighted		10	.800		200	36.50		236.50	280
1300	Lighted		5	1.600		305	73.50		378.50	455
9000	Minimum labor/equipment charge		4	2	Job		91.50		91.50	151

10 31 Manufactured Fireplaces

10 31 13 – Manufactured Fireplace Chimneys

10 31 13.10 Fireplace Chimneys

		Crew	Daily Output	Labor-Hours	Unit	Material	2014 Bare Costs Labor	Equipment	Total	Total Incl O&P
0010	**FIREPLACE CHIMNEYS**									
0500	Chimney dbl. wall, all stainless, over 8'-6", 7" diam., add to fireplace	1 Carp	33	.242	V.L.F.	83.50	11.10		94.60	110
0600	10" diameter, add to fireplace		32	.250		112	11.45		123.45	143
0700	12" diameter, add to fireplace		31	.258		159	11.85		170.85	194
0800	14" diameter, add to fireplace		30	.267		243	12.25		255.25	287
1000	Simulated brick chimney top, 4' high, 16" x 16"		10	.800	Ea.	425	36.50		461.50	530
1100	24" x 24"		7	1.143	"	540	52.50		592.50	680

10 31 13.20 Chimney Accessories

		Crew	Daily Output	Labor-Hours	Unit	Material	2014 Bare Costs Labor	Equipment	Total	Total Incl O&P
0010	**CHIMNEY ACCESSORIES**									
0020	Chimney screens, galv., 13" x 13" flue	1 Bric	8	1	Ea.	58.50	45.50		104	138
0050	24" x 24" flue		5	1.600		124	73		197	255
0200	Stainless steel, 13" x 13" flue		8	1		97.50	45.50		143	181
0250	20" x 20" flue		5	1.600		152	73		225	285
2400	Squirrel and bird screens, galvanized, 8" x 8" flue		16	.500		53	23		76	95.50
2450	13" x 13" flue		12	.667		55	30.50		85.50	110

10 31 Manufactured Fireplaces

10 31 13 – Manufactured Fireplace Chimneys

10 31 13.20 Chimney Accessories	Crew	Daily Output	Labor-Hours	Unit	Material	2014 Bare Costs Labor	Equipment	Total	Total Incl O&P
9000	Minimum labor/equipment charge	1 Bric	3.50	2.286	Job		104		104	169

10 31 16 – Manufactured Fireplace Forms

10 31 16.10 Fireplace Forms

		Crew	Daily Output	Labor-Hours	Unit	Material	Labor	Equipment	Total	Total Incl O&P
0010	**FIREPLACE FORMS**									
1800	Fireplace forms, no accessories, 32" opening	1 Bric	3	2.667	Ea.	670	122		792	935
1900	36" opening		2.50	3.200		855	146		1,001	1,175
2000	40" opening		2	4		1,125	182		1,307	1,550
2100	78" opening	↓	1.50	5.333	↓	1,650	243		1,893	2,225

10 31 23 – Prefabricated Fireplaces

10 31 23.10 Fireplace, Prefabricated

		Crew	Daily Output	Labor-Hours	Unit	Material	Labor	Equipment	Total	Total Incl O&P
0010	**FIREPLACE, PREFABRICATED**, free standing or wall hung									
0100	With hood & screen, minimum	1 Carp	1.30	6.154	Ea.	1,200	282		1,482	1,800
0150	Average		1	8		1,450	365		1,815	2,200
0200	Maximum		.90	8.889	↓	2,725	410		3,135	3,675
1500	Simulated logs, gas fired, 40,000 BTU, 2' long, minimum		7	1.143	Set	485	52.50		537.50	620
1600	Maximum		6	1.333		1,125	61		1,186	1,350
1700	Electric, 1,500 BTU, 1'-6" long, minimum		7	1.143		200	52.50		252.50	305
1800	11,500 BTU, maximum		6	1.333	↓	300	61		361	435
2000	Fireplace, built-in, 36" hearth, radiant		1.30	6.154	Ea.	660	282		942	1,200
2100	Recirculating, small fan		1	8		945	365		1,310	1,650
2150	Large fan		.90	8.889		1,900	410		2,310	2,775
2200	42" hearth, radiant		1.20	6.667		890	305		1,195	1,475
2300	Recirculating, small fan		.90	8.889		1,175	410		1,585	1,975
2350	Large fan		.80	10		1,300	460		1,760	2,175
2400	48" hearth, radiant		1.10	7.273		2,075	335		2,410	2,825
2500	Recirculating, small fan		.80	10		2,350	460		2,810	3,350
2550	Large fan		.70	11.429		2,375	525		2,900	3,450
3000	See through, including doors		.80	10		2,525	460		2,985	3,550
3200	Corner (2 wall)	↓	1	8	↓	3,250	365		3,615	4,175

10 32 Fireplace Specialties

10 32 13 – Fireplace Dampers

10 32 13.10 Dampers

		Crew	Daily Output	Labor-Hours	Unit	Material	Labor	Equipment	Total	Total Incl O&P
0010	**DAMPERS**									
0800	Damper, rotary control, steel, 30" opening	1 Bric	6	1.333	Ea.	119	61		180	230
0850	Cast iron, 30" opening		6	1.333		125	61		186	236
0880	36" opening		6	1.333		127	61		188	239
0900	48" opening		6	1.333		167	61		228	283
0920	60" opening		6	1.333		355	61		416	490
1000	84" opening, special order		5	1.600		910	73		983	1,125
1050	96" opening, special order		4	2		925	91		1,016	1,175
1200	Steel plate, poker control, 60" opening		8	1		320	45.50		365.50	430
1250	84" opening, special order		5	1.600		585	73		658	765
1400	"Universal" type, chain operated, 32" x 20" opening		8	1		250	45.50		295.50	350
1450	48" x 24" opening	↓	5	1.600	↓	375	73		448	530

10 32 Fireplace Specialties

10 32 23 – Fireplace Doors

10 32 23.10 Doors	Crew	Daily Output	Labor-Hours	Unit	Material	2014 Bare Costs Labor	Equipment	Total	Total Incl O&P
0010 **DOORS**									
0400 Cleanout doors and frames, cast iron, 8" x 8"	1 Bric	12	.667	Ea.	41	30.50		71.50	94.50
0450 12" x 12"		10	.800		108	36.50		144.50	178
0500 18" x 24"		8	1		150	45.50		195.50	239
0550 Cast iron frame, steel door, 24" x 30"		5	1.600		315	73		388	465
1600 Dutch Oven door and frame, cast iron, 12" x 15" opening		13	.615		131	28		159	191
1650 Copper plated, 12" x 15" opening		13	.615		257	28		285	330

10 35 Stoves

10 35 13 – Heating Stoves

10 35 13.10 Woodburning Stoves

	Crew	Daily Output	Labor-Hours	Unit	Material	2014 Bare Costs Labor	Equipment	Total	Total Incl O&P
0010 **WOODBURNING STOVES**									
0015 Cast iron, minimum	2 Carp	1.30	12.308	Ea.	980	565		1,545	2,000
0020 Average		1	16		1,825	735		2,560	3,225
0030 Maximum		.80	20		2,525	915		3,440	4,275
0050 For gas log lighter, add					45			45	49.50

10 43 Emergency Aid Specialties

10 43 13 – Defibrillator Cabinets

10 43 13.05 Defibrillator Cabinets

	Crew	Daily Output	Labor-Hours	Unit	Material	2014 Bare Costs Labor	Equipment	Total	Total Incl O&P
0010 **DEFIBRILLATOR CABINETS**, not equipped, stainless steel									
0050 Defibrillator cabinet, stainless steel with strobe & alarm 12" x 27"	1 Carp	10	.800	Ea.	430	36.50		466.50	530
0100 Automatic External Defibrillator	"	30	.267	"	1,350	12.25		1,362.25	1,500

10 44 Fire Protection Specialties

10 44 13 – Fire Protection Cabinets

10 44 13.53 Fire Equipment Cabinets

	Crew	Daily Output	Labor-Hours	Unit	Material	2014 Bare Costs Labor	Equipment	Total	Total Incl O&P
0010 **FIRE EQUIPMENT CABINETS**, not equipped, 20 ga. steel box									
0040 recessed, D.S. glass in door, box size given									
1000 Portable extinguisher, single, 8" x 12" x 27", alum. door & frame	Q-12	8	2	Ea.	151	99.50		250.50	325
1100 Steel door and frame	"	8	2	"	105	99.50		204.50	271
3000 Hose rack assy., 1-1/2" valve & 100' hose, 24" x 40" x 5-1/2"									
3200 Steel door and frame	Q-12	6	2.667	Ea.	234	133		367	465
4000 Hose rack assy., 2-1/2" x 1-1/2" valve, 100' hose, 24" x 40" x 8"									
4200 Steel door and frame	Q-12	6	2.667	Ea.	241	133		374	475
5000 Hose rack assy., 2-1/2" x 1-1/2" valve, 100' hose									
5010 and extinguisher, 30" x 40" x 8"									
5200 Steel door and frame	Q-12	5	3.200	Ea.	300	160		460	580

10 44 16 – Fire Extinguishers

10 44 16.13 Portable Fire Extinguishers

	Crew	Daily Output	Labor-Hours	Unit	Material	2014 Bare Costs Labor	Equipment	Total	Total Incl O&P
0010 **PORTABLE FIRE EXTINGUISHERS**									
0140 CO_2, with hose and "H" horn, 10 lb.				Ea.	268			268	295
1000 Dry chemical, pressurized									
1040 Standard type, portable, painted, 2-1/2 lb.				Ea.	36.50			36.50	40
1080 10 lb.					79.50			79.50	87.50
1100 20 lb.					134			134	148

10 44 Fire Protection Specialties

10 44 16 – Fire Extinguishers

10 44 16.13 Portable Fire Extinguishers	Crew	Daily Output	Labor-Hours	Unit	Material	2014 Bare Costs Labor	2014 Bare Costs Equipment	Total	Total Incl O&P
1120	30 lb.				Ea.	395			395	435
2000	ABC all purpose type, portable, 2-1/2 lb.					21			21	23.50
2080	9-1/2 lb.					44			44	48
3500	Halotron 1, 2-1/2 lb.					126			126	139
3600	5 lb.					198			198	218
3700	11 lb.					390			390	430

10 51 Lockers

10 51 13 – Metal Lockers

10 51 13.10 Lockers

		Crew	Daily Output	Labor-Hours	Unit	Material	2014 Bare Costs Labor	2014 Bare Costs Equipment	Total	Total Incl O&P
0011	**LOCKERS** steel, baked enamel, pre-assembled									
0110	Single tier box locker, 12" x 15" x 72"	1 Shee	20	.400	Ea.	239	22		261	298
0120	18" x 15" x 72"		20	.400		263	22		285	325
0130	12" x 18" x 72"		20	.400		267	22		289	330
0140	18" x 18" x 72"		20	.400		278	22		300	340
0410	Double tier, 12" x 15" x 36"		30	.267		236	14.60		250.60	283
0420	18" x 15" x 36"		30	.267		235	14.60		249.60	282
0430	12" x 18" x 36"		30	.267		266	14.60		280.60	315
0440	18" x 18" x 36"		30	.267		257	14.60		271.60	305
0500	Two person, 18" x 15" x 72"		20	.400		285	22		307	350
0510	18" x 18" x 72"		20	.400		293	22		315	360
0520	Duplex, 15" x 15" x 72"		20	.400		287	22		309	350
0530	15" x 21" x 72"		20	.400		335	22		357	400
1100	Wire meshed wardrobe, floor. mtd., open front varsity type		7.50	1.067		261	58.50		319.50	380
2400	16-person locker unit with clothing rack									
2500	72 wide x 15" deep x 72" high	1 Shee	15	.533	Ea.	455	29		484	545
2550	18" deep		15	.533	"	625	29		654	735
3250	Rack w/24 wire mesh baskets		1.50	5.333	Set	365	292		657	860
3260	30 baskets		1.25	6.400		360	350		710	945
3270	36 baskets		.95	8.421		475	460		935	1,250
3280	42 baskets		.80	10		540	545		1,085	1,450
3600	For hanger rods, add				Ea.	1.86			1.86	2.05
3650	For number plate kit, 100 plates #1 - #100, add	1 Shee	4	2		70	109		179	250
3700	For locker base, closed front panel		90	.089		7.15	4.86		12.01	15.50
3710	End panel, bolted		36	.222		8.90	12.15		21.05	29
3800	For sloping top, 12" wide		24	.333		30.50	18.25		48.75	63
3810	15" wide		24	.333		33.50	18.25		51.75	66
3820	18" wide		24	.333		35.50	18.25		53.75	68
3850	Sloping top end panel, 12" deep		72	.111		11.10	6.10		17.20	22
3860	15" deep		72	.111		12.90	6.10		19	24
3870	18" deep		72	.111		13.65	6.10		19.75	24.50
3900	For finish end panels, steel, 60" high, 15" deep		12	.667		50	36.50		86.50	113
3910	72" high, 12" deep		12	.667		50	36.50		86.50	113
3920	18" deep		12	.667		56	36.50		92.50	119
5000	For 'ready to assemble' lockers,									
5010	Add to labor						75%			
5020	Deduct from material					20%				
9000	Minimum labor/equipment charge	1 Shee	2.50	3.200	Job		175		175	276

10 55 Postal Specialties

10 55 23 – Mail Boxes

10 55 23.10 Commercial Mail Boxes	Crew	Daily Output	Labor-Hours	Unit	Material	2014 Bare Costs Labor	Equipment	Total	Total Incl O&P
0010 **COMMERCIAL MAIL BOXES**									
0020 Horiz., key lock, 5"H x 6"W x 15"D, alum., rear load	1 Carp	34	.235	Ea.	35	10.80		45.80	56.50
0100 Front loading		34	.235		35	10.80		45.80	56.50
0200 Double, 5"H x 12"W x 15"D, rear loading		26	.308		66.50	14.10		80.60	96.50
0300 Front loading		26	.308		70	14.10		84.10	100
0500 Quadruple, 10"H x 12"W x 15"D, rear loading		20	.400		98.50	18.35		116.85	138
0600 Front loading		20	.400		96.50	18.35		114.85	136
1600 Vault type, horizontal, for apartments, 4" x 5"		34	.235		18.75	10.80		29.55	38.50
1700 Alphabetical directories, 120 names		10	.800		132	36.50		168.50	207
1900 Letter slot, residential		20	.400		80	18.35		98.35	118
2000 Post office type		8	1		105	46		151	192
9000 Minimum labor/equipment charge		5	1.600	Job		73.50		73.50	121

10 56 Storage Assemblies

10 56 13 – Metal Storage Shelving

10 56 13.10 Shelving	Crew	Daily Output	Labor-Hours	Unit	Material	2014 Bare Costs Labor	Equipment	Total	Total Incl O&P
0010 **SHELVING**									
0020 Metal, industrial, cross-braced, 3' wide, 12" deep	1 Sswk	175	.046	SF Shlf	7.45	2.34		9.79	12.50
0100 24" deep		330	.024		4.95	1.24		6.19	7.70
2200 Wide span, 1600 lb. capacity per shelf, 6' wide, 24" deep		380	.021		6.30	1.08		7.38	8.90
2400 36" deep		440	.018		6.75	.93		7.68	9.15
9000 Minimum labor/equipment charge	1 Carp	4	2	Job		91.50		91.50	151

10 57 Wardrobe and Closet Specialties

10 57 23 – Closet and Utility Shelving

10 57 23.19 Wood Closet and Utility Shelving	Crew	Daily Output	Labor-Hours	Unit	Material	2014 Bare Costs Labor	Equipment	Total	Total Incl O&P
0010 **WOOD CLOSET AND UTILITY SHELVING**									
0020 Pine, clear grade, no edge band, 1" x 8"	1 Carp	115	.070	L.F.	3.04	3.19		6.23	8.60
0100 1" x 10"		110	.073		3.78	3.33		7.11	9.65
0200 1" x 12"		105	.076		4.56	3.49		8.05	10.75
0600 Plywood, 3/4" thick with lumber edge, 12" wide		75	.107		1.78	4.89		6.67	10
0700 24" wide		70	.114		3.18	5.25		8.43	12.10
0900 Bookcase, clear grade pine, shelves 12" O.C., 8" deep, per S.F. shelf		70	.114	S.F.	9.90	5.25		15.15	19.45
1000 12" deep shelves		65	.123	"	14.80	5.65		20.45	25.50
1200 Adjustable closet rod and shelf, 12" wide, 3' long		20	.400	Ea.	10.95	18.35		29.30	42
1300 8' long		15	.533	"	20	24.50		44.50	62
1500 Prefinished shelves with supports, stock, 8" wide		75	.107	L.F.	3.38	4.89		8.27	11.75
1600 10" wide		70	.114	"	4.75	5.25		10	13.85
9000 Minimum labor/equipment charge		4	2	Job		91.50		91.50	151

10 73 Protective Covers

10 73 13 – Awnings

10 73 13.10 Awnings, Fabric

	Crew	Daily Output	Labor-Hours	Unit	Material	2014 Bare Costs Labor	Equipment	Total	Total Incl O&P
0010 **AWNINGS, FABRIC**									
0020 Including acrylic canvas and frame, standard design									
0100 Door and window, slope, 3' high, 4' wide	1 Carp	4.50	1.778	Ea.	720	81.50		801.50	925
0110 6' wide		3.50	2.286		925	105		1,030	1,200
0120 8' wide		3	2.667		1,125	122		1,247	1,450
0200 Quarter round convex, 4' wide		3	2.667		1,125	122		1,247	1,425
0210 6' wide		2.25	3.556		1,450	163		1,613	1,875
0220 8' wide		1.80	4.444		1,775	204		1,979	2,275
0300 Dome, 4' wide		7.50	1.067		430	49		479	555
0310 6' wide		3.50	2.286		970	105		1,075	1,250
0320 8' wide		2	4		1,725	183		1,908	2,200
0350 Elongated dome, 4' wide		1.33	6.015		1,625	276		1,901	2,225
0360 6' wide		1.11	7.207		1,925	330		2,255	2,675
0370 8' wide		1	8		2,275	365		2,640	3,100
1000 Entry or walkway, peak, 12' long, 4' wide	2 Carp	.90	17.778		5,125	815		5,940	6,975
1010 6' wide		.60	26.667		7,875	1,225		9,100	10,700
1020 8' wide		.40	40		10,900	1,825		12,725	15,000
1100 Radius with dome end, 4' wide		1.10	14.545		3,875	665		4,540	5,375
1110 6' wide		.70	22.857		6,225	1,050		7,275	8,575
1120 8' wide		.50	32		8,875	1,475		10,350	12,200
2000 Retractable lateral arm awning, manual									
2010 To 12' wide, 8' - 6" projection	2 Carp	1.70	9.412	Ea.	1,150	430		1,580	1,975
2020 To 14' wide, 8' - 6" projection		1.10	14.545		1,350	665		2,015	2,575
2030 To 19' wide, 8' - 6" projection		.85	18.824		1,825	865		2,690	3,450
2040 To 24' wide, 8' - 6" projection		.67	23.881		2,300	1,100		3,400	4,350
2050 Motor for above, add	1 Carp	2.67	3		990	138		1,128	1,325
3000 Patio/deck canopy with frame									
3010 12' wide, 12' projection	2 Carp	2	8	Ea.	1,625	365		1,990	2,400
3020 16' wide, 14' projection	"	1.20	13.333		2,550	610		3,160	3,800
9000 For fire retardant canvas, add					7%				
9010 For lettering or graphics, add					35%				
9020 For painted or coated acrylic canvas, deduct					8%				
9030 For translucent or opaque vinyl canvas, add					10%				
9040 For 6 or more units, deduct					20%	15%			

10 73 16 – Canopies

10 73 16.10 Canopies, Residential

	Crew	Daily Output	Labor-Hours	Unit	Material	2014 Bare Costs Labor	Equipment	Total	Total Incl O&P
0010 **CANOPIES, RESIDENTIAL** Prefabricated									
0500 Carport, free standing, baked enamel, alum., .032", 40 psf									
0520 16' x 8', 4 posts	2 Carp	3	5.333	Ea.	4,475	245		4,720	5,325
0600 20' x 10', 6 posts		2	8		4,600	365		4,965	5,650
0605 30' x 10', 8 posts		2	8		6,900	365		7,265	8,200
1000 Door canopies, extruded alum., .032", 42" projection, 4' wide	1 Carp	8	1		201	46		247	297
1020 6' wide	"	6	1.333		284	61		345	410
1040 8' wide	2 Carp	9	1.778		370	81.50		451.50	545
1060 10' wide		7	2.286		345	105		450	545
1080 12' wide		5	3.200		560	147		707	855
1200 54" projection, 4' wide	1 Carp	8	1		248	46		294	350
1220 6' wide	"	6	1.333		290	61		351	420
1240 8' wide	2 Carp	9	1.778		350	81.50		431.50	520
1260 10' wide		7	2.286		515	105		620	740
1280 12' wide		5	3.200		555	147		702	855
1300 Painted, add					20%				

10 73 Protective Covers

10 73 16 – Canopies

10 73 16.10 Canopies, Residential

		Crew	Daily Output	Labor-Hours	Unit	Material	2014 Bare Costs Labor	2014 Bare Costs Equipment	Total	Total Incl O&P
1310	Bronze anodized, add				Ea.	50%				
3000	Window awnings, aluminum, window 3' high, 4' wide	1 Carp	10	.800		126	36.50		162.50	200
3020	6' wide	"	8	1		180	46		226	274
3040	9' wide	2 Carp	9	1.778		305	81.50		386.50	470
3060	12' wide	"	5	3.200		305	147		452	575
3100	Window, 4' high, 4' wide	1 Carp	10	.800		159	36.50		195.50	236
3120	6' wide	"	8	1		229	46		275	330
3140	9' wide	2 Carp	9	1.778		375	81.50		456.50	545
3160	12' wide	"	5	3.200		375	147		522	650
3200	Window, 6' high, 4' wide	1 Carp	10	.800		295	36.50		331.50	385
3220	6' wide	"	8	1		340	46		386	450
3240	9' wide	2 Carp	9	1.778		900	81.50		981.50	1,125
3260	12' wide	"	5	3.200		1,375	147		1,522	1,775
3400	Roll-up aluminum, 2'-6" wide	1 Carp	14	.571		190	26		216	252
3420	3' wide		12	.667		195	30.50		225.50	264
3440	4' wide		10	.800		244	36.50		280.50	330
3460	6' wide	↓	8	1		290	46		336	395
3480	9' wide	2 Carp	9	1.778		400	81.50		481.50	575
3500	12' wide	"	5	3.200	↓	535	147		682	830
3600	Window awnings, canvas, 24" drop, 3' wide	1 Carp	30	.267	L.F.	50	12.25		62.25	75
3620	4' wide		40	.200		43	9.15		52.15	62.50
3700	30" drop, 3' wide		30	.267		51.50	12.25		63.75	77
3720	4' wide		40	.200		44.50	9.15		53.65	64
3740	5' wide		45	.178		40	8.15		48.15	57.50
3760	6' wide		48	.167		37	7.65		44.65	53
3780	8' wide		48	.167		34.50	7.65		42.15	50.50
3800	10' wide		50	.160	↓	42	7.35		49.35	58
3900	Repair canvas, minimum		8	1	Ea.		46		46	75.50
3920	Maximum		4	2	"		91.50		91.50	151
9000	Minimum labor/equipment charge	↓	3	2.667	Job		122		122	201

10 73 16.20 Metal Canopies

		Crew	Daily Output	Labor-Hours	Unit	Material	2014 Bare Costs Labor	2014 Bare Costs Equipment	Total	Total Incl O&P
0010	**METAL CANOPIES**									
0020	Wall hung, .032", aluminum, prefinished, 8' x 10'	K-2	1.30	18.462	Ea.	1,950	865	256	3,071	3,975
0300	8' x 20'		1.10	21.818		3,425	1,025	305	4,755	5,925
1000	12' x 20'	↓	1	24	↓	5,150	1,125	335	6,610	8,050
2300	Aluminum entrance canopies, flat soffit, .032"									
2500	3'-6" x 4'-0", clear anodized	2 Carp	4	4	Ea.	915	183		1,098	1,300
9000	Minimum labor/equipment charge	"	2	8	Job		365		365	605

10 74 Manufactured Exterior Specialties

10 74 23 – Cupolas

10 74 23.10 Wood Cupolas

		Crew	Daily Output	Labor-Hours	Unit	Material	2014 Bare Costs Labor	2014 Bare Costs Equipment	Total	Total Incl O&P
0010	**WOOD CUPOLAS**									
0020	Stock units, pine, painted, 18" sq., 28" high, alum. roof	1 Carp	4.10	1.951	Ea.	184	89.50		273.50	350
0100	Copper roof		3.80	2.105		255	96.50		351.50	440
0300	23" square, 33" high, aluminum roof		3.70	2.162		360	99		459	560
0400	Copper roof		3.30	2.424		470	111		581	700
0600	30" square, 37" high, aluminum roof		3.70	2.162		560	99		659	780
0700	Copper roof		3.30	2.424		670	111		781	920
0900	Hexagonal, 31" wide, 46" high, copper roof		4	2		860	91.50		951.50	1,100
1000	36" wide, 50" high, copper roof	↓	3.50	2.286	↓	1,400	105		1,505	1,725

10 74 Manufactured Exterior Specialties

10 74 23 – Cupolas

10 74 23.10 Wood Cupolas

	Crew	Daily Output	Labor-Hours	Unit	Material	2014 Bare Costs Labor	Equipment	Total	Total Incl O&P
1200	For deluxe stock units, add to above				Ea.	25%			
1400	For custom built units, add to above				↓	50%	50%		
9000	Minimum labor/equipment charge	1 Carp	2.75	2.909	Job		133		133	219

10 74 29 – Steeples

10 74 29.10 Prefabricated Steeples

		Crew	Daily Output	Labor-Hours	Unit	Material	Labor	Equipment	Total	Total Incl O&P
0010	**PREFABRICATED STEEPLES**									
4000	Steeples, translucent fiberglass, 30" square, 15' high	F-3	2	20	Ea.	8,275	935	330	9,540	11,000
4150	25' high	"	1.80	22.222		9,650	1,050	370	11,070	12,700
4600	Aluminum, baked finish, 16" square, 14' high					5,625			5,625	6,200
4640	35' high, 8' base					36,300			36,300	39,900
4680	152' high, custom				↓	624,500			624,500	687,000

10 74 33 – Weathervanes

10 74 33.10 Residential Weathervanes

		Crew	Daily Output	Labor-Hours	Unit	Material	Labor	Equipment	Total	Total Incl O&P
0010	**RESIDENTIAL WEATHERVANES**									
0020	Residential types, minimum	1 Carp	8	1	Ea.	151	46		197	242
0100	Maximum		2	4	"	1,700	183		1,883	2,175
9000	Minimum labor/equipment charge	↓	4	2	Job		91.50		91.50	151

10 74 46 – Window Wells

10 74 46.10 Area Window Wells

		Crew	Daily Output	Labor-Hours	Unit	Material	Labor	Equipment	Total	Total Incl O&P
0010	**AREA WINDOW WELLS**, Galvanized steel									
0020	20 ga., 3'-2" wide, 1' deep	1 Sswk	29	.276	Ea.	16.95	14.10		31.05	44.50
0100	2' deep		23	.348		27.50	17.75		45.25	62.50
0300	16 ga., 3'-2" wide, 1' deep		29	.276		23	14.10		37.10	51.50
0400	3' deep		23	.348		47	17.75		64.75	84
0600	Welded grating for above, 15 lb., painted		45	.178		87.50	9.10		96.60	113
0700	Galvanized		45	.178		118	9.10		127.10	147
0900	Translucent plastic cap for above	↓	60	.133	↓	17.65	6.80		24.45	32

343

Division Notes

	CREW	DAILY OUTPUT	LABOR-HOURS	UNIT	BARE COSTS				TOTAL INCL O&P
					MAT.	LABOR	EQUIP.	TOTAL	

Estimating Tips

General

- The items in this division are usually priced per square foot or each. Many of these items are purchased by the owner for installation by the contractor. Check the specifications for responsibilities and include time for receiving, storage, installation, and mechanical and electrical hookups in the appropriate divisions.

- Many items in Division 11 require some type of support system that is not usually furnished with the item. Examples of these systems include blocking for the attachment of casework and support angles for ceiling-hung projection screens. The required blocking or supports must be added to the estimate in the appropriate division.

- Some items in Division 11 may require assembly or electrical hookups. Verify the amount of assembly required or the need for a hard electrical connection and add the appropriate costs.

Reference Numbers

Reference numbers are shown in shaded boxes at the beginning of some major classifications. These numbers refer to related items in the Reference Section. The reference information may be an estimating procedure, an alternate pricing method, or technical information.

Note: Not all subdivisions listed here necessarily appear in this publication.

11 11 Vehicle Service Equipment

11 11 13 – Compressed-Air Vehicle Service Equipment

11 11 13.10 Compressed Air Equipment	Crew	Daily Output	Labor-Hours	Unit	Material	2014 Bare Costs Labor	2014 Bare Costs Equipment	Total	Total Incl O&P
0010 **COMPRESSED AIR EQUIPMENT**									
0030 Compressors, electric, 1-1/2 H.P., standard controls	L-4	1.50	16	Ea.	450	690		1,140	1,625
0550 Dual controls		1.50	16		800	690		1,490	2,000
0600 5 H.P., 115/230 volt, standard controls		1	24		2,550	1,025		3,575	4,500
0650 Dual controls		1	24		3,100	1,025		4,125	5,100

11 11 19 – Vehicle Lubrication Equipment

11 11 19.10 Lubrication Equipment

	Crew	Daily Output	Labor-Hours	Unit	Material	Labor	Equipment	Total	Total Incl O&P
0010 **LUBRICATION EQUIPMENT**									
3000 Lube equipment, 3 reel type, with pumps, not including piping	L-4	.50	48	Set	8,700	2,075		10,775	12,900
3100 Hose reel, including hose, oil/lube, 1000 PSI	2 Sswk	2	8	Ea.	730	410		1,140	1,550
3200 Grease, 5000 PSI		2	8		790	410		1,200	1,625
3300 Air, 50 feet, 160 PSI		2	8		865	410		1,275	1,700
3350 25 feet, 160 PSI		2	8		520	410		930	1,325

11 11 33 – Vehicle Spray Painting Equipment

11 11 33.10 Spray Painting Equipment

	Crew	Daily Output	Labor-Hours	Unit	Material	Labor	Equipment	Total	Total Incl O&P
0010 **SPRAY PAINTING EQUIPMENT**									
4000 Spray painting booth, 26' long, complete	L-4	.40	60	Ea.	16,200	2,575		18,775	22,000

11 12 Parking Control Equipment

11 12 13 – Parking Key and Card Control Units

11 12 13.10 Parking Control Units

	Crew	Daily Output	Labor-Hours	Unit	Material	Labor	Equipment	Total	Total Incl O&P
0010 **PARKING CONTROL UNITS**									
5100 Card reader	1 Elec	2	4	Ea.	1,925	213		2,138	2,450
5120 Proximity with customer display	2 Elec	1	16		5,500	855		6,355	7,375
6000 Parking control software, minimum	1 Elec	.50	16		23,600	855		24,455	27,200
6020 Maximum	"	.20	40		103,000	2,125		105,125	117,000

11 12 16 – Parking Ticket Dispensers

11 12 16.10 Ticket Dispensers

	Crew	Daily Output	Labor-Hours	Unit	Material	Labor	Equipment	Total	Total Incl O&P
0010 **TICKET DISPENSERS**									
5900 Ticket spitter with time/date stamp, standard	2 Elec	2	8	Ea.	6,400	425		6,825	7,675
5920 Mag stripe encoding	"	2	8	"	18,600	425		19,025	21,100

11 12 26 – Parking Fee Collection Equipment

11 12 26.13 Parking Fee Coin Collection Equipment

	Crew	Daily Output	Labor-Hours	Unit	Material	Labor	Equipment	Total	Total Incl O&P
0010 **PARKING FEE COIN COLLECTION EQUIPMENT**									
5200 Cashier booth, average	B-22	1	30	Ea.	10,300	1,275	210	11,785	13,600
5300 Collector station, pay on foot	2 Elec	.20	80		109,500	4,275		113,775	127,000
5320 Credit card only	"	.50	32		20,200	1,700		21,900	25,000

11 12 26.23 Fee Equipment

	Crew	Daily Output	Labor-Hours	Unit	Material	Labor	Equipment	Total	Total Incl O&P
0010 **FEE EQUIPMENT**									
5600 Fee computer	1 Elec	1.50	5.333	Ea.	14,000	285		14,285	15,800

11 12 33 – Parking Gates

11 12 33.13 Lift Arm Parking Gates

	Crew	Daily Output	Labor-Hours	Unit	Material	Labor	Equipment	Total	Total Incl O&P
0010 **LIFT ARM PARKING GATES**									
5000 Barrier gate with programmable controller	2 Elec	3	5.333	Ea.	3,350	285		3,635	4,125
5020 Industrial		3	5.333		5,000	285		5,285	5,950
5500 Exit verifier		1	16		17,400	855		18,255	20,500
5700 Full sign, 4" letters	1 Elec	2	4		1,225	213		1,438	1,650
5800 Inductive loop	2 Elec	4	4		169	213		382	515

11 12 Parking Control Equipment

11 12 33 – Parking Gates

11 12 33.13 Lift Arm Parking Gates	Crew	Daily Output	Labor-Hours	Unit	Material	2014 Bare Costs Labor	Equipment	Total	Total Incl O&P
5950 Vehicle detector, microprocessor based	1 Elec	3	2.667	Ea.	420	142		562	685

11 13 Loading Dock Equipment

11 13 13 – Loading Dock Bumpers

11 13 13.10 Dock Bumpers

		Crew	Daily Output	Labor-Hours	Unit	Material	Labor	Equipment	Total	Total Incl O&P
0010	DOCK BUMPERS Bolts not included									
0012	2" x 6" to 4" x 8", average	1 Carp	300	.027	B.F.	.69	1.22		1.91	2.77
0050	Bumpers, rubber blocks 4-1/2" thick, 10" high, 14" long		26	.308	Ea.	63	14.10		77.10	92.50
0200	24" long		22	.364		95	16.65		111.65	132
0300	36" long		17	.471		72.50	21.50		94	115
0500	12" high, 14" long		25	.320		100	14.65		114.65	134

11 13 16 – Loading Dock Seals and Shelters

11 13 16.10 Dock Seals and Shelters

		Crew	Daily Output	Labor-Hours	Unit	Material	Labor	Equipment	Total	Total Incl O&P
0010	DOCK SEALS AND SHELTERS									
6200	Shelters, fabric, for truck or train, scissor arms, minimum	1 Carp	1	8	Ea.	1,750	365		2,115	2,525
6300	Maximum	"	.50	16	"	2,400	735		3,135	3,850

11 13 19 – Stationary Loading Dock Equipment

11 13 19.10 Dock Equipment

		Crew	Daily Output	Labor-Hours	Unit	Material	Labor	Equipment	Total	Total Incl O&P
0010	DOCK EQUIPMENT									
2200	Dock boards, heavy duty, 60" x 60", aluminum, 5,000 lb. capacity				Ea.	1,450			1,450	1,600
4200	Platform lifter, 6' x 6', portable, 3,000 lb. capacity				"	9,150			9,150	10,100

11 16 Vault Equipment

11 16 16 – Safes

11 16 16.10 Commercial Safes

		Crew	Daily Output	Labor-Hours	Unit	Material	Labor	Equipment	Total	Total Incl O&P
0010	COMMERCIAL SAFES									
0800	Money, "B" label, 9" x 14" x 14"				Ea.	540			540	595
0900	Tool resistive, 24" x 24" x 20"					4,125			4,125	4,525
1050	Tool and torch resistive, 24" x 24" x 20"					7,850			7,850	8,625

11 17 Teller and Service Equipment

11 17 13 – Teller Equipment Systems

11 17 13.10 Bank Equipment

		Crew	Daily Output	Labor-Hours	Unit	Material	Labor	Equipment	Total	Total Incl O&P
0010	BANK EQUIPMENT									
0020	Alarm system, police	2 Elec	1.60	10	Ea.	4,900	535		5,435	6,225
0400	Bullet resistant teller window, 44" x 60"	1 Glaz	.60	13.333		3,800	585		4,385	5,150
0500	48" x 60"	"	.60	13.333		5,525	585		6,110	7,025
3000	Counters for banks, frontal only	2 Carp	1	16	Station	1,825	735		2,560	3,225
3100	Complete with steel undercounter		.50	32	"	3,575	1,475		5,050	6,325
5400	Partitions, bullet-resistant, 1-3/16" glass, 8' high		10	1.600	L.F.	198	73.50		271.50	340
5600	Pass thru, bullet-res. window, painted steel, 24" x 36"	2 Sswk	1.60	10	Ea.	2,625	510		3,135	3,850

11 19 Detention Equipment

11 19 30 – Detention Cell Equipment

11 19 30.10 Cell Equipment	Crew	Daily Output	Labor-Hours	Unit	Material	2014 Bare Costs Labor	Equipment	Total	Total Incl O&P
0010 **CELL EQUIPMENT**									
3000 Toilet apparatus including wash basin, average	L-8	1.50	13.333	Ea.	3,350	645		3,995	4,750

11 21 Mercantile and Service Equipment

11 21 13 – Cash Registers and Checking Equipment

11 21 13.10 Checkout Counter

	Crew	Daily Output	Labor-Hours	Unit	Material	2014 Bare Costs Labor	Equipment	Total	Total Incl O&P
0010 **CHECKOUT COUNTER**									
0020 Supermarket conveyor, single belt	2 Clab	10	1.600	Ea.	3,125	58.50		3,183.50	3,550
0100 Double belt, power take-away		9	1.778		4,525	65		4,590	5,075
0400 Double belt, power take-away, incl. side scanning		7	2.286		5,300	84		5,384	5,975
0800 Warehouse or bulk type	↓	6	2.667	↓	6,275	97.50		6,372.50	7,050
1000 Scanning system, 2 lanes, w/registers, scan gun & memory				System	16,400			16,400	18,100
1100 10 lanes, single processor, full scan, with scales				"	156,000			156,000	171,500
2000 Register, restaurant, minimum				Ea.	730			730	805
2100 Maximum					3,075			3,075	3,400
2150 Store, minimum					730			730	805
2200 Maximum				↓	3,075			3,075	3,400

11 21 53 – Barber and Beauty Shop Equipment

11 21 53.10 Barber Equipment

	Crew	Daily Output	Labor-Hours	Unit	Material	2014 Bare Costs Labor	Equipment	Total	Total Incl O&P
0010 **BARBER EQUIPMENT**									
0020 Chair, hydraulic, movable, minimum	1 Carp	24	.333	Ea.	555	15.30		570.30	635
0050 Maximum	"	16	.500		3,425	23		3,448	3,825
0200 Wall hung styling station with mirrors, minimum	L-2	8	2		455	80.50		535.50	635
0300 Maximum	"	4	4		2,300	161		2,461	2,800
0500 Sink, hair washing basin, rough plumbing not incl.	1 Plum	8	1		490	57.50		547.50	630
1000 Sterilizer, liquid solution for tools					159			159	175
1100 Total equipment, rule of thumb, per chair, minimum	L-8	1	20		1,900	965		2,865	3,675
1150 Maximum	"	1	20	↓	5,100	965		6,065	7,175

11 23 Commercial Laundry and Dry Cleaning Equipment

11 23 13 – Dry Cleaning Equipment

11 23 13.13 Dry Cleaners

	Crew	Daily Output	Labor-Hours	Unit	Material	2014 Bare Costs Labor	Equipment	Total	Total Incl O&P
0010 **DRY CLEANERS** Not incl. rough-in									
2000 Dry cleaners, electric, 20 lb. capacity	L-1	.20	80	Ea.	33,300	4,425		37,725	43,500
2050 25 lb. capacity		.17	94.118		48,000	5,225		53,225	61,000
2100 30 lb. capacity		.15	106		50,500	5,925		56,425	64,500
2150 60 lb. capacity	↓	.09	177	↓	78,000	9,850		87,850	101,500

11 23 16 – Drying and Conditioning Equipment

11 23 16.13 Dryers

	Crew	Daily Output	Labor-Hours	Unit	Material	2014 Bare Costs Labor	Equipment	Total	Total Incl O&P
0010 **DRYERS**, Not including rough-in									
1500 Industrial, 30 lb. capacity	1 Plum	2	4	Ea.	3,125	230		3,355	3,800
1600 50 lb. capacity	"	1.70	4.706		3,350	271		3,621	4,125
4700 Lint collector, ductwork not included, 8,000 to 10,000 CFM	Q-10	.30	80		9,100	4,075		13,175	16,500

11 23 19 – Finishing Equipment

11 23 19.13 Folders and Spreaders

	Crew	Daily Output	Labor-Hours	Unit	Material	2014 Bare Costs Labor	Equipment	Total	Total Incl O&P
0010 **FOLDERS AND SPREADERS**									
3500 Folders, blankets & sheets, minimum	1 Elec	.17	47.059	Ea.	32,700	2,500		35,200	39,900
3700 King size with automatic stacker	↓	.10	80	↓	59,000	4,275		63,275	71,500

11 23 Commercial Laundry and Dry Cleaning Equipment

11 23 19 – Finishing Equipment

11 23 19.13 Folders and Spreaders	Crew	Daily Output	Labor-Hours	Unit	Material	2014 Bare Costs Labor	Equipment	Total	Total Incl O&P
3800 For conveyor delivery, add	1 Elec	.45	17.778	Ea.	14,300	950		15,250	17,300

11 23 23 – Commercial Ironing Equipment

11 23 23.13 Irons and Pressers

	Crew	Daily Output	Labor-Hours	Unit	Material	2014 Bare Costs Labor	Equipment	Total	Total Incl O&P
0010 **IRONS AND PRESSERS**									
4500 Ironers, institutional, 110", single roll	1 Elec	.20	40	Ea.	31,700	2,125		33,825	38,200

11 23 26 – Commercial Washers and Extractors

11 23 26.13 Washers and Extractors

	Crew	Daily Output	Labor-Hours	Unit	Material	2014 Bare Costs Labor	Equipment	Total	Total Incl O&P
0010 **WASHERS AND EXTRACTORS**, not including rough-in									
6000 Combination washer/extractor, 20 lb. capacity	L-6	1.50	8	Ea.	5,875	450		6,325	7,150
6100 30 lb. capacity		.80	15		9,150	840		9,990	11,400
6200 50 lb. capacity		.68	17.647		10,700	990		11,690	13,400
6300 75 lb. capacity		.30	40		20,200	2,250		22,450	25,700
6350 125 lb. capacity		.16	75		27,300	4,200		31,500	36,700

11 23 33 – Coin-Operated Laundry Equipment

11 23 33.13 Coin Operated Washers and Dryers

	Crew	Daily Output	Labor-Hours	Unit	Material	2014 Bare Costs Labor	Equipment	Total	Total Incl O&P
0010 **COIN OPERATED WASHERS AND DRYERS**									
0990 Dryer, gas fired									
1000 Commercial, 30 lb. capacity, coin operated, single	1 Plum	3	2.667	Ea.	3,250	153		3,403	3,825
1100 Double stacked	"	2	4	"	7,200	230		7,430	8,275
5290 Clothes washer									
5300 Commercial, coin operated, average	1 Plum	3	2.667	Ea.	1,250	153		1,403	1,625

11 24 Maintenance Equipment

11 24 19 – Vacuum Cleaning Systems

11 24 19.10 Vacuum Cleaning

	Crew	Daily Output	Labor-Hours	Unit	Material	2014 Bare Costs Labor	Equipment	Total	Total Incl O&P
0010 **VACUUM CLEANING**									
0020 Central, 3 inlet, residential	1 Skwk	.90	8.889	Total	1,050	420		1,470	1,850
0200 Commercial		.70	11.429		1,225	540		1,765	2,200
0400 5 inlet system, residential		.50	16		1,475	755		2,230	2,850
0600 7 inlet system, commercial		.40	20		1,675	945		2,620	3,400
4010 Rule of thumb: First 1200 S.F., installed								1,425	1,575
4020 For each additional S.F., add				S.F.					.26

11 26 Unit Kitchens

11 26 13 – Metal Unit Kitchens

11 26 13.10 Commercial Unit Kitchens

	Crew	Daily Output	Labor-Hours	Unit	Material	2014 Bare Costs Labor	Equipment	Total	Total Incl O&P
0010 **COMMERCIAL UNIT KITCHENS**									
1500 Combination range, refrigerator and sink, 30" wide, minimum	L-1	2	8	Ea.	1,100	445		1,545	1,900
1550 Maximum	"	1	16	"	1,450	885		2,335	2,975
1640 Combination range, refrigerator, sink, microwave									
1660 Oven and ice maker	L-1	.80	20	Ea.	4,500	1,100		5,600	6,675

11 27 Photographic Processing Equipment

11 27 13 – Darkroom Processing Equipment

11 27 13.10 Darkroom Equipment	Crew	Daily Output	Labor-Hours	Unit	Material	2014 Bare Costs Labor	2014 Bare Costs Equipment	Total	Total Incl O&P
0010 **DARKROOM EQUIPMENT**									
0020 Developing sink, 5" deep, 24" x 48"	Q-1	2	8	Ea.	4,100	415		4,515	5,175
0050 48" x 52"		1.70	9.412		4,375	490		4,865	5,575
0200 10" deep, 24" x 48"		1.70	9.412		1,525	490		2,015	2,425
0250 24" x 108"		1.50	10.667		3,625	555		4,180	4,825
0500 Dryers, dehumidified filtered air, 36" x 25" x 68" high	L-7	6	4.667		4,250	207		4,457	5,000
0550 48" x 25" x 68" high		5	5.600		10,000	248		10,248	11,400
2000 Processors, automatic, color print, minimum		4	7		15,700	310		16,010	17,800
2050 Maximum		.60	46.667		24,700	2,075		26,775	30,600
2300 Black and white print, minimum		2	14		11,900	620		12,520	14,100
2350 Maximum		.80	35		61,500	1,550		63,050	70,000
2600 Manual processor, 16" x 20" maximum print size		2	14		9,450	620		10,070	11,400
2650 20" x 24" maximum print size		1	28		8,975	1,250		10,225	11,900
3000 Viewing lights, 20" x 24"		6	4.667		285	207		492	650
3100 20" x 24" with color correction		6	4.667		340	207		547	710
3500 Washers, round, minimum sheet 11" x 14"	Q-1	2	8		3,225	415		3,640	4,200
3550 Maximum sheet 20" x 24"		1	16		3,575	830		4,405	5,225
3800 Square, minimum sheet 20" x 24"		1	16		3,125	830		3,955	4,725
3900 Maximum sheet 50" x 56"		.80	20		4,850	1,025		5,875	6,950
4500 Combination tank sink, tray sink, washers, with									
4510 Dry side tables, average	Q-1	.45	35.556	Ea.	10,600	1,850		12,450	14,600

11 31 Residential Appliances

11 31 13 – Residential Kitchen Appliances

11 31 13.13 Cooking Equipment

	Crew	Daily Output	Labor-Hours	Unit	Material	2014 Bare Costs Labor	2014 Bare Costs Equipment	Total	Total Incl O&P
0010 **COOKING EQUIPMENT**									
0020 Cooking range, 30" free standing, 1 oven, minimum	2 Clab	10	1.600	Ea.	435	58.50		493.50	575
0050 Maximum	"	4	4		2,000	147		2,147	2,450
0350 Built-in, 30" wide, 1 oven, minimum	1 Elec	6	1.333		675	71		746	850
0400 Maximum	2 Carp	2	8		1,350	365		1,715	2,075
0900 Countertop cooktops, 4 burner, standard, minimum	1 Elec	6	1.333		293	71		364	430
0950 Maximum		3	2.667		1,300	142		1,442	1,650
1250 Microwave oven, minimum		4	2		119	107		226	296
1300 Maximum		2	4		460	213		673	835
5380 Oven, built in, standard		4	2		625	107		732	855
5390 Deluxe		2	4		2,250	213		2,463	2,775

11 31 13.23 Refrigeration Equipment

	Crew	Daily Output	Labor-Hours	Unit	Material	2014 Bare Costs Labor	2014 Bare Costs Equipment	Total	Total Incl O&P
0010 **REFRIGERATION EQUIPMENT**									
5450 Refrigerator, no frost, 6 C.F.	2 Clab	15	1.067	Ea.	241	39		280	330
5500 Refrigerator, no frost, 10 C.F. to 12 C.F., minimum		10	1.600		420	58.50		478.50	555
5600 Maximum		6	2.667		445	97.50		542.50	645
6790 Energy-star qualified, 18 C.F., minimum [G]	2 Carp	4	4		505	183		688	855
6795 Maximum [G]		2	8		1,150	365		1,515	1,875
6797 21.7 C.F., minimum [G]		4	4		1,025	183		1,208	1,425
6799 Maximum [G]		4	4		2,075	183		2,258	2,600

11 31 13.33 Kitchen Cleaning Equipment

	Crew	Daily Output	Labor-Hours	Unit	Material	2014 Bare Costs Labor	2014 Bare Costs Equipment	Total	Total Incl O&P
0010 **KITCHEN CLEANING EQUIPMENT**									
2750 Dishwasher, built-in, 2 cycles, minimum	L-1	4	4	Ea.	235	222		457	605
2800 Maximum		2	8		430	445		875	1,150
3100 Energy-star qualified, minimum [G]		4	4		365	222		587	745

11 31 Residential Appliances

11 31 13 – Residential Kitchen Appliances

11 31 13.33 Kitchen Cleaning Equipment

		Crew	Daily Output	Labor-Hours	Unit	Material	2014 Bare Costs Labor	Equipment	Total	Total Incl O&P
3110	Maximum	[G] L-1	2	8	Ea.	1,500	445		1,945	2,350

11 31 13.43 Waste Disposal Equipment

		Crew	Daily Output	Labor-Hours	Unit	Material	2014 Bare Costs Labor	Equipment	Total	Total Incl O&P
0010	**WASTE DISPOSAL EQUIPMENT**									
1750	Compactor, residential size, 4 to 1 compaction, minimum	1 Carp	5	1.600	Ea.	640	73.50		713.50	825
1800	Maximum	"	3	2.667		1,000	122		1,122	1,300
3300	Garbage disposal, sink type, minimum	L-1	10	1.600		86.50	88.50		175	233
3350	Maximum	"	10	1.600		217	88.50		305.50	375

11 31 13.53 Kitchen Ventilation Equipment

		Crew	Daily Output	Labor-Hours	Unit	Material	2014 Bare Costs Labor	Equipment	Total	Total Incl O&P
0010	**KITCHEN VENTILATION EQUIPMENT**									
4150	Hood for range, 2 speed, vented, 30" wide, minimum	L-3	5	3.200	Ea.	69.50	160		229.50	335
4200	Maximum		3	5.333		770	266		1,036	1,275
4300	42" wide, minimum		5	3.200		166	160		326	440
4330	Custom		5	3.200		1,650	160		1,810	2,050
4350	Maximum		3	5.333		2,000	266		2,266	2,625
4400	Ventless hood, 2 speed, 30" wide, minimum	1 Elec	8	1		85	53.50		138.50	176
4450	Maximum		7	1.143		585	61		646	740
4510	36" wide, minimum		7	1.143		75	61		136	177
4550	Maximum		6	1.333		565	71		636	730
4580	42" wide, minimum		6	1.333		186	71		257	315
4600	Maximum		5	1.600		680	85.50		765.50	880
4650	For vented 1 speed, deduct from maximum					49.50			49.50	54.50

11 31 23 – Residential Laundry Appliances

11 31 23.13 Washers

		Crew	Daily Output	Labor-Hours	Unit	Material	2014 Bare Costs Labor	Equipment	Total	Total Incl O&P
0010	**WASHERS**									
5000	Residential, 4 cycle, average	1 Plum	3	2.667	Ea.	865	153		1,018	1,200
6750	Energy star qualified, front loading, minimum	[G]	3	2.667		645	153		798	950
6760	Maximum	[G]	1	8		1,575	460		2,035	2,450
6764	Top loading, minimum	[G]	3	2.667		445	153		598	730
6766	Maximum	[G]	3	2.667		1,225	153		1,378	1,600

11 31 23.23 Dryers

		Crew	Daily Output	Labor-Hours	Unit	Material	2014 Bare Costs Labor	Equipment	Total	Total Incl O&P
0010	**DRYERS**									
0500	Gas fired residential, 16 lb. capacity, average	1 Plum	3	2.667	Ea.	665	153		818	975
6770	Electric, front loading, energy-star qualified, minimum	[G] L-2	3	5.333		380	215		595	775
6780	Maximum	[G] "	2	8		1,900	320		2,220	2,600

11 31 33 – Miscellaneous Residential Appliances

11 31 33.13 Sump Pumps

		Crew	Daily Output	Labor-Hours	Unit	Material	2014 Bare Costs Labor	Equipment	Total	Total Incl O&P
0010	**SUMP PUMPS**									
6400	Cellar drainer, pedestal, 1/3 H.P., molded PVC base	1 Plum	3	2.667	Ea.	135	153		288	390
6450	Solid brass	"	2	4	"	289	230		519	680
6460	Sump pump, see also Section 22 14 29.16									

11 33 Retractable Stairs

11 33 10 – Disappearing Stairs

11 33 10.10 Disappearing Stairway	Crew	Daily Output	Labor-Hours	Unit	Material	2014 Bare Costs Labor	Equipment	Total	Total Incl O&P
0010 **DISAPPEARING STAIRWAY** No trim included									
0020 One piece, yellow pine, 8'-0" ceiling	2 Carp	4	4	Ea.	254	183		437	580
0030 9'-0" ceiling		4	4		259	183		442	585
0040 10'-0" ceiling		3	5.333		270	245		515	695
0050 11'-0" ceiling		3	5.333		425	245		670	870
0060 12'-0" ceiling		3	5.333		490	245		735	940
0100 Custom grade, pine, 8'-6" ceiling, minimum	1 Carp	4	2		175	91.50		266.50	345
0150 Average		3.50	2.286		250	105		355	445
0200 Maximum		3	2.667		320	122		442	555
0500 Heavy duty, pivoted, from 7'-7" to 12'-10" floor to floor		3	2.667		735	122		857	1,000
0600 16'-0" ceiling		2	4		1,500	183		1,683	1,950
0800 Economy folding, pine, 8'-6" ceiling		4	2		174	91.50		265.50	340
0900 9'-6" ceiling		4	2		194	91.50		285.50	365
1100 Automatic electric, aluminum, floor to floor height, 8' to 9'	2 Carp	1	16		8,425	735		9,160	10,500
1400 11' to 12'		.90	17.778		8,975	815		9,790	11,200
1700 14' to 15'		.70	22.857		9,675	1,050		10,725	12,300
9000 Minimum labor/equipment charge	1 Carp	2	4	Job		183		183	300

11 41 Foodservice Storage Equipment

11 41 13 – Refrigerated Food Storage Cases

11 41 13.10 Refrigerated Food Cases

	Crew	Daily Output	Labor-Hours	Unit	Material	2014 Bare Costs Labor	Equipment	Total	Total Incl O&P
0010 **REFRIGERATED FOOD CASES**									
0030 Dairy, multi-deck, 12' long	Q-5	3	5.333	Ea.	11,200	281		11,481	12,700
0100 For rear sliding doors, add					1,800			1,800	1,975
0200 Delicatessen case, service deli, 12' long, single deck	Q-5	3.90	4.103		7,650	216		7,866	8,750
0300 Multi-deck, 18 S.F. shelf display		3	5.333		7,075	281		7,356	8,225
0400 Freezer, self-contained, chest-type, 30 C.F.		3.90	4.103		8,425	216		8,641	9,600
0500 Glass door, upright, 78 C.F.		3.30	4.848		10,100	255		10,355	11,500
0600 Frozen food, chest type, 12' long		3.30	4.848		8,125	255		8,380	9,325
0700 Glass door, reach-in, 5 door		3	5.333		13,900	281		14,181	15,700
0800 Island case, 12' long, single deck		3.30	4.848		7,200	255		7,455	8,325
0900 Multi-deck		3	5.333		8,400	281		8,681	9,700
1000 Meat case, 12' long, single deck		3.30	4.848		7,200	255		7,455	8,325
1050 Multi-deck		3.10	5.161		10,300	272		10,572	11,700
1100 Produce, 12' long, single deck		3.30	4.848		6,775	255		7,030	7,850
1200 Multi-deck		3.10	5.161		8,625	272		8,897	9,900

11 41 13.20 Refrigerated Food Storage Equipment

	Crew	Daily Output	Labor-Hours	Unit	Material	2014 Bare Costs Labor	Equipment	Total	Total Incl O&P
0010 **REFRIGERATED FOOD STORAGE EQUIPMENT**									
2350 Cooler, reach-in, beverage, 6' long	Q-1	6	2.667	Ea.	3,550	138		3,688	4,125
4300 Freezers, reach-in, 44 C.F.		4	4		4,350	207		4,557	5,125
4500 68 C.F.		3	5.333		4,775	276		5,051	5,675
4600 Freezer, pre-fab, 8' x 8' w/refrigeration	2 Carp	.45	35.556		10,900	1,625		12,525	14,700
4620 8' x 12'		.35	45.714		11,000	2,100		13,100	15,600
4640 8' x 16'		.25	64		14,900	2,925		17,825	21,200
4660 8' x 20'		.17	94.118		19,200	4,325		23,525	28,200
4680 Reach-in, 1 compartment	Q-1	4	4		2,475	207		2,682	3,050
4685 Energy star rated G	R-18	7.80	3.333		2,550	140		2,690	3,025
4700 2 compartment	Q-1	3	5.333		4,050	276		4,326	4,900
4705 Energy star rated G	R-18	6.20	4.194		3,075	176		3,251	3,650
4710 3 compartment	Q-1	3	5.333		5,225	276		5,501	6,175
4715 Energy star rated G	R-18	5.60	4.643		3,850	194		4,044	4,525

11 41 Foodservice Storage Equipment

11 41 13 – Refrigerated Food Storage Cases

11 41 13.20 Refrigerated Food Storage Equipment

		Crew	Daily Output	Labor-Hours	Unit	Material	2014 Bare Costs Labor	Equipment	Total	Total Incl O&P
8320	Refrigerator, reach-in, 1 compartment	R-18	7.80	3.333	Ea.	2,400	140		2,540	2,850
8325	Energy star rated [G]		7.80	3.333		2,550	140		2,690	3,025
8330	2 compartment		6.20	4.194		3,750	176		3,926	4,400
8335	Energy star rated [G]		6.20	4.194		3,075	176		3,251	3,650
8340	3 compartment		5.60	4.643		4,700	194		4,894	5,475
8345	Energy star rated [G]		5.60	4.643		3,850	194		4,044	4,525
8350	Pre-fab, with refrigeration, 8' x 8'	2 Carp	.45	35.556		6,975	1,625		8,600	10,400
8360	8' x 12'		.35	45.714		7,900	2,100		10,000	12,200
8370	8' x 16'		.25	64		12,200	2,925		15,125	18,200
8380	8' x 20'		.17	94.118		15,500	4,325		19,825	24,100
8390	Pass-thru/roll-in, 1 compartment	R-18	7.80	3.333		4,450	140		4,590	5,125
8400	2 compartment		6.24	4.167		6,250	175		6,425	7,150
8410	3 compartment		5.60	4.643		8,525	194		8,719	9,675
8420	Walk-in, alum, door & floor only, no refrig, 6' x 6' x 7'-6"	2 Carp	1.40	11.429		8,675	525		9,200	10,400
8430	10' x 6' x 7'-6"		.55	29.091		12,500	1,325		13,825	16,000
8440	12' x 14' x 7'-6"		.25	64		17,300	2,925		20,225	23,800
8450	12' x 20' x 7'-6"		.17	94.118		19,100	4,325		23,425	28,100
8460	Refrigerated cabinets, mobile					3,875			3,875	4,275
8470	Refrigerator/freezer, reach-in, 1 compartment	R-18	5.60	4.643		5,725	194		5,919	6,600
8480	2 compartment	"	4.80	5.417		7,475	227		7,702	8,600

11 41 13.30 Wine Cellar

		Crew	Daily Output	Labor-Hours	Unit	Material	2014 Bare Costs Labor	Equipment	Total	Total Incl O&P
0010	**WINE CELLAR**, refrigerated, Redwood interior, carpeted, walk-in type									
0020	6'-8" high, including racks									
0200	80" W x 48" D for 900 bottles	2 Carp	1.50	10.667	Ea.	4,250	490		4,740	5,475
0250	80" W x 72" D for 1300 bottles		1.33	12.030		5,175	550		5,725	6,600
0300	80" W x 94" D for 1900 bottles		1.17	13.675		6,275	625		6,900	7,925
0400	80" W x 124" D for 2500 bottles		1	16		7,375	735		8,110	9,300

11 41 33 – Foodservice Shelving

11 41 33.20 Metal Food Storage Shelving

		Crew	Daily Output	Labor-Hours	Unit	Material	2014 Bare Costs Labor	Equipment	Total	Total Incl O&P
0010	**METAL FOOD STORAGE SHELVING**									
8600	Stainless steel shelving, louvered 4-tier, 20" x 3'	1 Clab	6	1.333	Ea.	1,400	49		1,449	1,600
8605	20" x 4'		6	1.333		1,525	49		1,574	1,750
8610	20" x 6'		6	1.333		2,175	49		2,224	2,475
8615	24" x 3'		6	1.333		1,950	49		1,999	2,225
8620	24" x 4'		6	1.333		2,325	49		2,374	2,650
8625	24" x 6'		6	1.333		3,250	49		3,299	3,625
8630	Flat 4-tier, 20" x 3'		6	1.333		1,150	49		1,199	1,325
8635	20" x 4'		6	1.333		1,400	49		1,449	1,600
8640	20" x 5'		6	1.333		1,600	49		1,649	1,850
8645	24" x 3'		6	1.333		1,250	49		1,299	1,450
8650	24" x 4'		6	1.333		2,200	49		2,249	2,475
8655	24" x 6'		6	1.333		2,650	49		2,699	2,975
8700	Galvanized shelving, louvered 4-tier, 20" x 3'		6	1.333		750	49		799	905
8705	20" x 4'		6	1.333		850	49		899	1,025
8710	20" x 6'		6	1.333		995	49		1,044	1,175
8715	24" x 3'		6	1.333		700	49		749	850
8720	24" x 4'		6	1.333		985	49		1,034	1,150
8725	24" x 6'		6	1.333		1,300	49		1,349	1,525
8730	Flat 4-tier, 20" x 3'		6	1.333		695	49		744	845
8735	20" x 4'		6	1.333		685	49		734	835
8740	20" x 6'		6	1.333		895	49		944	1,075
8745	24" x 3'		6	1.333		660	49		709	810

11 41 Foodservice Storage Equipment

11 41 33 – Foodservice Shelving

11 41 33.20 Metal Food Storage Shelving		Crew	Daily Output	Labor-Hours	Unit	Material	2014 Bare Costs Labor	Equipment	Total	Total Incl O&P
8750	24" x 4'	1 Clab	6	1.333	Ea.	745	49		794	900
8755	24" x 6'		6	1.333		940	49		989	1,100
8760	Stainless steel dunnage rack, 24" x 3'		8	1		325	36.50		361.50	420
8765	24" x 4'		8	1		420	36.50		456.50	520
8770	Galvanized dunnage rack, 24" x 3'		8	1		166	36.50		202.50	243
8775	24" x 4'	▼	8	1	▼	187	36.50		223.50	266

11 42 Food Preparation Equipment

11 42 10 – Commercial Food Preparation Equipment

11 42 10.10 Choppers, Mixers and Misc. Equipment

		Crew	Daily Output	Labor-Hours	Unit	Material	2014 Bare Costs Labor	Equipment	Total	Total Incl O&P
0010	**CHOPPERS, MIXERS AND MISC. EQUIPMENT**									
1700	Choppers, 5 pounds	R-18	7	3.714	Ea.	2,125	156		2,281	2,600
1720	16 pounds		5	5.200		2,175	218		2,393	2,750
1740	35 to 40 pounds		4	6.500		3,500	272		3,772	4,275
1840	Coffee brewer, 5 burners	1 Plum	3	2.667		1,300	153		1,453	1,700
1850	Coffee urn, twin 6 gallon urns		2	4		2,375	230		2,605	2,975
1860	Single, 3 gallon	▼	3	2.667		1,800	153		1,953	2,225
3000	Fast food equipment, total package, minimum	6 Skwk	.08	600		201,000	28,400		229,400	267,500
3100	Maximum	"	.07	685		274,000	32,400		306,400	354,500
3800	Food mixers, bench type, 20 quarts	L-7	7	4		2,925	177		3,102	3,525
3850	40 quarts		5.40	5.185		6,650	230		6,880	7,700
3900	60 quarts		5	5.600		11,200	248		11,448	12,700
4040	80 quarts		3.90	7.179		12,500	320		12,820	14,300
4100	Floor type, 20 quarts		15	1.867		3,200	82.50		3,282.50	3,625
4120	60 quarts		14	2		9,825	88.50		9,913.50	10,900
4140	80 quarts		12	2.333		15,200	103		15,303	17,000
4160	140 quarts	▼	8.60	3.256		25,300	144		25,444	28,000
6700	Peelers, small	R-18	8	3.250		1,875	136		2,011	2,275
6720	Large	"	6	4.333		4,775	181		4,956	5,550
6800	Pulper/extractor, close coupled, 5 HP	1 Plum	1.90	4.211		3,475	242		3,717	4,200
8580	Slicer with table	R-18	9	2.889	▼	4,625	121		4,746	5,275

11 43 Food Delivery Carts and Conveyors

11 43 13 – Food Delivery Carts

11 43 13.10 Mobile Carts, Racks and Trays

		Crew	Daily Output	Labor-Hours	Unit	Material	2014 Bare Costs Labor	Equipment	Total	Total Incl O&P
0010	**MOBILE CARTS, RACKS AND TRAYS**									
1650	Cabinet, heated, 1 compartment, reach-in	R-18	5.60	4.643	Ea.	3,250	194		3,444	3,875
1655	Pass-thru roll-in		5.60	4.643		3,775	194		3,969	4,450
1660	2 compartment, reach-in	▼	4.80	5.417		8,925	227		9,152	10,200
1670	Mobile					3,500			3,500	3,825
6850	Mobile rack w/pan slide					1,375			1,375	1,500
9180	Tray and silver dispenser, mobile	1 Clab	16	.500	▼	905	18.35		923.35	1,025

11 44 Food Cooking Equipment

11 44 13 – Commercial Ranges

11 44 13.10 Cooking Equipment

11 44 13.10 Cooking Equipment	Crew	Daily Output	Labor-Hours	Unit	Material	2014 Bare Costs Labor	Equipment	Total	Total Incl O&P
0010 **COOKING EQUIPMENT**									
0020 Bake oven, gas, one section	Q-1	8	2	Ea.	5,550	104		5,654	6,250
0300 Two sections		7	2.286		8,975	118		9,093	10,100
0600 Three sections		6	2.667		12,400	138		12,538	13,800
0900 Electric convection, single deck	L-7	4	7		6,150	310		6,460	7,250
1300 Broiler, without oven, standard	Q-1	8	2		3,500	104		3,604	4,000
1550 Infrared	L-7	4	7		7,325	310		7,635	8,575
4750 Fryer, with twin baskets, modular model	Q-1	7	2.286		1,250	118		1,368	1,550
5000 Floor model, on 6" legs	"	5	3.200		2,400	166		2,566	2,900
5100 Extra single basket, large					98.50			98.50	108
5170 Energy star rated, 50 lb. capacity [G]	R-18	4	6.500		4,575	272		4,847	5,475
5175 85 lb. capacity [G]	"	4	6.500		8,425	272		8,697	9,700
5300 Griddle, SS, 24" plate, w/4" legs, elec, 208 V, 3 phase, 3' long	Q-1	7	2.286		1,375	118		1,493	1,700
5550 4' long	"	6	2.667		2,225	138		2,363	2,675
6200 Iced tea brewer	1 Plum	3.44	2.326		745	134		879	1,025
6350 Kettle, w/steam jacket, tilting, w/positive lock, SS, 20 gallons	L-7	7	4		8,125	177		8,302	9,250
6600 60 gallons	"	6	4.667		10,800	207		11,007	12,200
6900 Range, restaurant type, 6 burners and 1 standard oven, 36" wide	Q-1	7	2.286		2,575	118		2,693	3,000
6950 Convection		7	2.286		4,400	118		4,518	5,025
7150 2 standard ovens, 24" griddle, 60" wide		6	2.667		4,500	138		4,638	5,200
7200 1 standard, 1 convection oven		6	2.667		9,350	138		9,488	10,500
7450 Heavy duty, single 34" standard oven, open top		5	3.200		4,750	166		4,916	5,475
7500 Convection oven		5	3.200		5,375	166		5,541	6,175
7700 Griddle top		6	2.667		2,825	138		2,963	3,325
7750 Convection oven		6	2.667		7,700	138		7,838	8,675
8850 Steamer, electric 27 KW	L-7	7	4		10,600	177		10,777	12,000
9100 Electric, 10 KW or gas 100,000 BTU	"	5	5.600		6,250	248		6,498	7,275
9150 Toaster, conveyor type, 16-22 slices per minute					1,075			1,075	1,175
9160 Pop-up, 2 slot					610			610	670
9200 For deluxe models of above equipment, add					75%				
9400 Rule of thumb: Equipment cost based									
9410 on kitchen work area									
9420 Office buildings, minimum	L-7	77	.364	S.F.	89.50	16.10		105.60	125
9450 Maximum		58	.483		151	21.50		172.50	201
9550 Public eating facilities, minimum		77	.364		117	16.10		133.10	155
9600 Maximum		46	.609		191	27		218	254
9750 Hospitals, minimum		58	.483		121	21.50		142.50	168
9800 Maximum		39	.718		222	32		254	296

11 46 Food Dispensing Equipment

11 46 16 – Service Line Equipment

11 46 16.10 Commercial Food Dispensing Equipment

	Crew	Daily Output	Labor-Hours	Unit	Material	2014 Bare Costs Labor	Equipment	Total	Total Incl O&P
0010 **COMMERCIAL FOOD DISPENSING EQUIPMENT**									
1050 Butter pat dispenser	1 Clab	13	.615	Ea.	995	22.50		1,017.50	1,125
1100 Bread dispenser, counter top		13	.615		880	22.50		902.50	1,000
1900 Cup and glass dispenser, drop in		4	2		1,075	73.50		1,148.50	1,300
1920 Disposable cup, drop in		16	.500		490	18.35		508.35	570
2650 Dish dispenser, drop in, 12"		11	.727		2,225	26.50		2,251.50	2,500
2660 Mobile		10	.800		2,600	29.50		2,629.50	2,900
3300 Food warmer, counter, 1.2 KW					660			660	725
3550 1.6 KW					2,100			2,100	2,325

11 46 Food Dispensing Equipment

11 46 16 – Service Line Equipment

11 46 16.10 Commercial Food Dispensing Equipment	Crew	Daily Output	Labor-Hours	Unit	Material	2014 Bare Costs Labor	Equipment	Total	Total Incl O&P
3600	Well, hot food, built-in, rectangular, 12" x 20"	R-30	10	2.600	Ea.	805	112		917	1,075
3610	Circular, 7 qt.		10	2.600		415	112		527	635
3620	Refrigerated, 2 compartments		10	2.600		3,025	112		3,137	3,500
3630	3 compartments		9	2.889		3,650	125		3,775	4,225
3640	4 compartments		8	3.250		4,300	141		4,441	4,950
4720	Frost cold plate		9	2.889		18,200	125		18,325	20,200
5700	Hot chocolate dispenser	1 Plum	4	2		1,150	115		1,265	1,450
5750	Ice dispenser 567 pound	Q-1	6	2.667		5,150	138		5,288	5,900
6250	Jet spray dispenser	R-18	4.50	5.778		3,125	242		3,367	3,825
6300	Juice dispenser, concentrate	"	4.50	5.778		1,875	242		2,117	2,425
6690	Milk dispenser, bulk, 2 flavor	R-30	8	3.250		1,825	141		1,966	2,250
6695	3 flavor	"	8	3.250		2,450	141		2,591	2,925
8800	Serving counter, straight	1 Carp	40	.200	L.F.	915	9.15		924.15	1,025
8820	Curved section	"	30	.267	"	1,125	12.25		1,137.25	1,250
8825	Solid surface, see Section 12 36 61.16									
8860	Sneeze guard with lights, 60" L	1 Clab	16	.500	Ea.	390	18.35		408.35	460
9100	Soft serve ice cream machine, medium	R-18	11	2.364		11,900	99		11,999	13,300
9110	Large	"	9	2.889		21,500	121		21,621	23,900

11 47 Ice Machines

11 47 10 – Commercial Ice Machines

11 47 10.10 Commercial Ice Equipment

0010	COMMERCIAL ICE EQUIPMENT									
5800	Ice cube maker, 50 pounds per day	Q-1	6	2.667	Ea.	1,600	138		1,738	1,975
5900	250 pounds per day		1.20	13.333		2,650	690		3,340	4,000
6050	500 pounds per day		4	4		2,750	207		2,957	3,350
6060	With bin		1.20	13.333		3,350	690		4,040	4,775
6090	1000 pounds per day, with bin		1	16		4,875	830		5,705	6,675
6100	Ice flakers, 300 pounds per day		1.60	10		2,750	520		3,270	3,825
6120	600 pounds per day		.95	16.842		3,900	870		4,770	5,625
6130	1000 pounds per day		.75	21.333		4,700	1,100		5,800	6,900
6140	2000 pounds per day		.65	24.615		21,300	1,275		22,575	25,400
6160	Ice storage bin, 500 pound capacity	Q-5	1	16		1,025	840		1,865	2,450
6180	1000 pound	"	.56	28.571		2,500	1,500		4,000	5,100

11 48 Cleaning and Disposal Equipment

11 48 13 – Commercial Dishwashers

11 48 13.10 Dishwashers

0010	DISHWASHERS									
2700	Dishwasher, commercial, rack type									
2720	10 to 12 racks per hour	Q-1	3.20	5	Ea.	3,475	259		3,734	4,225
2730	Energy star rated, 35 to 40 racks/hour [G]		1.30	12.308		4,650	640		5,290	6,100
2740	50 to 60 racks/hour [G]		1.30	12.308		10,100	640		10,740	12,100
2800	Automatic, 190 to 230 racks per hour	L-6	.35	34.286		13,800	1,925		15,725	18,100
2820	235 to 275 racks per hour		.25	48		31,100	2,700		33,800	38,400
2840	8,750 to 12,500 dishes per hour		.10	120		54,500	6,750		61,250	70,500
2950	Dishwasher hood, canopy type	L-3A	10	1.200	L.F.	855	60		915	1,050
2960	Pant leg type	"	2.50	4.800	Ea.	8,600	241		8,841	9,875
5200	Garbage disposal 1.5 HP, 100 GPH	L-1	4.80	3.333		2,150	185		2,335	2,650

11 48 Cleaning and Disposal Equipment

11 48 13 – Commercial Dishwashers

11 48 13.10 Dishwashers

11 48 13.10 Dishwashers		Crew	Daily Output	Labor-Hours	Unit	Material	2014 Bare Costs Labor	Equipment	Total	Total Incl O&P
5210	3 HP, 120 GPH	L-1	4.60	3.478	Ea.	2,600	193		2,793	3,150
5220	5 HP, 250 GPH	↓	4.50	3.556	↓	3,575	197		3,772	4,225
6750	Pot sink, 3 compartment	1 Plum	7.25	1.103	L.F.	970	63.50		1,033.50	1,175
6760	Pot washer, low temp wash/rinse		1.60	5	Ea.	4,000	288		4,288	4,850
6770	High pressure wash, high temperature rinse	↓	1.20	6.667		36,500	385		36,885	40,700
9170	Trash compactor, small, up to 125 lb. compacted weight	L-4	4	6		23,900	258		24,158	26,700
9175	Large, up to 175 lb. compacted weight	"	3	8	↓	29,200	345		29,545	32,700

11 52 Audio-Visual Equipment

11 52 13 – Projection Screens

11 52 13.10 Projection Screens, Wall or Ceiling Hung

11 52 13.10 Projection Screens, Wall or Ceiling Hung		Crew	Daily Output	Labor-Hours	Unit	Material	2014 Bare Costs Labor	Equipment	Total	Total Incl O&P
0010	**PROJECTION SCREENS, WALL OR CEILING HUNG**, matte white									
0100	Manually operated, economy	2 Carp	500	.032	S.F.	5.85	1.47		7.32	8.85
0300	Intermediate		450	.036		6.80	1.63		8.43	10.20
0400	Deluxe		400	.040	↓	9.45	1.83		11.28	13.35
9000	Minimum labor/equipment charge	↓	3	5.333	Job		245		245	400

11 52 16 – Projectors

11 52 16.10 Movie Equipment

11 52 16.10 Movie Equipment		Crew	Daily Output	Labor-Hours	Unit	Material	2014 Bare Costs Labor	Equipment	Total	Total Incl O&P
0011	**MOVIE EQUIPMENT**									
0020	Changeover, minimum				Ea.	465			465	510
3000	Projection screens, rigid, in wall, acrylic, 1/4" thick	2 Glaz	195	.082	S.F.	42	3.61		45.61	52
3100	1/2" thick	"	130	.123	"	48.50	5.40		53.90	62.50
3700	Sound systems, incl. amplifier, mono, minimum	1 Elec	.90	8.889	Ea.	3,300	475		3,775	4,350
3800	Dolby/Super Sound, maximum		.40	20		18,100	1,075		19,175	21,600
4100	Dual system, 2 channel, front surround, minimum		.70	11.429		4,625	610		5,235	6,050
4200	Dolby/Super Sound, 4 channel, maximum	↓	.40	20		16,500	1,075		17,575	19,900
5700	Seating, painted steel, upholstered, minimum	2 Carp	35	.457		132	21		153	180
5800	Maximum	"	28	.571	↓	420	26		446	510

11 53 Laboratory Equipment

11 53 33 – Emergency Safety Appliances

11 53 33.13 Emergency Equipment

11 53 33.13 Emergency Equipment		Crew	Daily Output	Labor-Hours	Unit	Material	2014 Bare Costs Labor	Equipment	Total	Total Incl O&P
0010	**EMERGENCY EQUIPMENT**									
1400	Safety equipment, eye wash, hand held				Ea.	405			405	445
1450	Deluge shower				"	760			760	840

11 53 43 – Service Fittings and Accessories

11 53 43.13 Fittings

11 53 43.13 Fittings		Crew	Daily Output	Labor-Hours	Unit	Material	2014 Bare Costs Labor	Equipment	Total	Total Incl O&P
0010	**FITTINGS**									
1600	Sink, one piece plastic, flask wash, hose, free standing	1 Plum	1.60	5	Ea.	1,925	288		2,213	2,575
1610	Epoxy resin sink, 25" x 16" x 10"	"	2	4	"	218	230		448	600
1630	Steel table, open underneath				L.F.	490			490	540
1640	Doors underneath				"	775			775	850
1900	Utility cabinet, stainless steel				Ea.	925			925	1,025
1950	Utility table, acid resistant top with drawers	2 Carp	30	.533	L.F.	162	24.50		186.50	218
8000	Alternate pricing method: as percent of lab furniture									
8050	Installation, not incl. plumbing & duct work				% Furn.				22%	22%
8100	Plumbing, final connections, simple system								10%	10%
8110	Moderately complex system				↓				15%	15%

357

11 53 Laboratory Equipment

11 53 43 – Service Fittings and Accessories

11 53 43.13 Fittings		Crew	Daily Output	Labor-Hours	Unit	Material	2014 Bare Costs Labor	Equipment	Total	Total Incl O&P
8120	Complex system				% Furn.				20%	20%
8150	Electrical, simple system								10%	10%
8160	Moderately complex system								20%	20%
8170	Complex system				↓				35%	35%

11 57 Vocational Shop Equipment

11 57 10 – Shop Equipment

11 57 10.10 Vocational School Shop Equipment

		Crew	Daily Output	Labor-Hours	Unit	Material	2014 Bare Costs Labor	Equipment	Total	Total Incl O&P
0010	**VOCATIONAL SCHOOL SHOP EQUIPMENT**									
0020	Benches, work, wood, average	2 Carp	5	3.200	Ea.	630	147		777	930
0100	Metal, average		5	3.200		545	147		692	835
0400	Combination belt & disc sander, 6"		4	4		1,650	183		1,833	2,100
0700	Drill press, floor mounted, 12", 1/2 H.P.	↓	4	4		410	183		593	750
0800	Dust collector, not incl. ductwork, 6" diameter	1 Shee	1.10	7.273		4,600	400		5,000	5,700
0810	Dust collector bag, 20" diameter	"	5	1.600		435	87.50		522.50	620
1000	Grinders, double wheel, 1/2 H.P.	2 Carp	5	3.200		215	147		362	475
1300	Jointer, 4", 3/4 H.P.		4	4		1,350	183		1,533	1,800
1600	Kilns, 16 C.F., to 2000°		4	4		1,450	183		1,633	1,900
1900	Lathe, woodworking, 10", 1/2 H.P.		4	4		540	183		723	895
2200	Planer, 13" x 6"		4	4		1,075	183		1,258	1,500
2500	Potter's wheel, motorized		4	4		1,125	183		1,308	1,525
2800	Saws, band, 14", 3/4 H.P.		4	4		920	183		1,103	1,325
3100	Metal cutting band saw, 14"		4	4		2,500	183		2,683	3,050
3400	Radial arm saw, 10", 2 H.P.		4	4		1,350	183		1,533	1,800
3700	Scroll saw, 24"		4	4		580	183		763	940
4000	Table saw, 10", 3 H.P.		4	4		2,675	183		2,858	3,250
4300	Welder AC arc, 30 amp capacity	↓	4	4	↓	3,150	183		3,333	3,750

11 61 Broadcast, Theater, and Stage Equipment

11 61 23 – Folding and Portable Stages

11 61 23.10 Portable Stages

		Crew	Daily Output	Labor-Hours	Unit	Material	2014 Bare Costs Labor	Equipment	Total	Total Incl O&P
0010	**PORTABLE STAGES**									
5000	Stages, portable with steps, folding legs, stock, 8" high				SF Stg.	32			32	35.50
5100	16" high					49			49	54
5200	32" high					53			53	58
5300	40" high				↓	59.50			59.50	65

11 61 33 – Rigging Systems and Controls

11 61 33.10 Controls

		Crew	Daily Output	Labor-Hours	Unit	Material	2014 Bare Costs Labor	Equipment	Total	Total Incl O&P
0010	**CONTROLS**									
0050	Control boards with dimmers and breakers, minimum	1 Elec	1	8	Ea.	12,500	425		12,925	14,400
0150	Maximum	"	.20	40	"	127,500	2,125		129,625	144,000

11 61 43 – Stage Curtains

11 61 43.10 Curtains

		Crew	Daily Output	Labor-Hours	Unit	Material	2014 Bare Costs Labor	Equipment	Total	Total Incl O&P
0010	**CURTAINS**									
0500	Curtain track, straight, light duty	2 Carp	20	.800	L.F.	27.50	36.50		64	90.50
0700	Curved sections		12	1.333	"	175	61		236	293
1000	Curtains, velour, medium weight	↓	600	.027	S.F.	7.90	1.22		9.12	10.70

11 66 Athletic Equipment

11 66 13 - Exercise Equipment

11 66 13.10 Physical Training Equipment

	Crew	Daily Output	Labor-Hours	Unit	Material	2014 Bare Costs Labor	Equipment	Total	Total Incl O&P
0010 **PHYSICAL TRAINING EQUIPMENT**									
0020 Abdominal rack, 2 board capacity				Ea.	480			480	530
0050 Abdominal board, upholstered					655			655	720
0200 Bicycle trainer, minimum					480			480	525
0300 Deluxe, electric					4,300			4,300	4,725
0400 Barbell set, chrome plated steel, 25 lb.					249			249	274
0420 100 lb.					460			460	505
0450 200 lb.					700			700	770
0500 Weight plates, cast iron, per lb.				Lb.	5.20			5.20	5.70
0520 Storage rack, 10 station				Ea.	900			900	990
0600 Circuit training apparatus, 12 machines minimum	2 Clab	1.25	12.800	Set	28,700	470		29,170	32,300
0700 Average		1	16		35,200	585		35,785	39,700
0800 Maximum		.75	21.333		41,700	780		42,480	47,200
0820 Dumbbell set, cast iron, with rack and 5 pair					620			620	680
0900 Squat racks	2 Clab	5	3.200	Ea.	890	117		1,007	1,175
4150 Exercise equipment, bicycle trainer					750			750	825
4180 Chinning bar, adjustable, wall mounted	1 Carp	5	1.600		210	73.50		283.50	350
4200 Exercise ladder, 16' x 1'-7", suspended	L-2	3	5.333		1,350	215		1,565	1,825
4210 High bar, floor plate attached	1 Carp	4	2		2,225	91.50		2,316.50	2,575
4240 Parallel bars, adjustable		4	2		1,750	91.50		1,841.50	2,075
4270 Uneven parallel bars, adjustable		4	2		3,200	91.50		3,291.50	3,650
4280 Wall mounted, adjustable	L-2	1.50	10.667	Set	855	430		1,285	1,650
4300 Rope, ceiling mounted, 18' long	1 Carp	3.66	2.186	Ea.	188	100		288	370
4330 Side horse, vaulting		5	1.600		1,350	73.50		1,423.50	1,600
4360 Treadmill, motorized, deluxe, training type		5	1.600		3,800	73.50		3,873.50	4,300
4390 Weight lifting multi-station, minimum	2 Clab	1	16		330	585		915	1,325

11 66 23 - Gymnasium Equipment

11 66 23.13 Basketball Equipment

	Crew	Daily Output	Labor-Hours	Unit	Material	2014 Bare Costs Labor	Equipment	Total	Total Incl O&P
0010 **BASKETBALL EQUIPMENT**									
1000 Backstops, wall mtd., 6' extended, fixed, minimum	L-2	1	16	Ea.	1,375	645		2,020	2,550
1100 Maximum		1	16		1,875	645		2,520	3,125
1200 Swing up, minimum		1	16		1,425	645		2,070	2,625
1250 Maximum		1	16		2,800	645		3,445	4,150
1300 Portable, manual, heavy duty, spring operated		1.90	8.421		12,600	340		12,940	14,400
1400 Ceiling suspended, stationary, minimum		.78	20.513		4,000	825		4,825	5,750
1450 Fold up, with accessories, maximum		.40	40		6,000	1,600		7,600	9,250
1600 For electrically operated, add	1 Elec	1	8		2,300	425		2,725	3,200
5800 Wall pads, 1-1/2" thick, standard (not fire rated)	2 Carp	640	.025	S.F.	6.20	1.15		7.35	8.70

11 66 23.19 Boxing Ring

	Crew	Daily Output	Labor-Hours	Unit	Material	2014 Bare Costs Labor	Equipment	Total	Total Incl O&P
0010 **BOXING RING**									
4100 Elevated, 22' x 22'	L-4	.10	240	Ea.	7,000	10,300		17,300	24,600
4110 For cellular plastic foam padding, add		.10	240		1,025	10,300		11,325	18,000
4120 Floor level, including posts and ropes only, 20' x 20'		.80	30		4,500	1,300		5,800	7,075
4130 Canvas, 30' x 30'		5	4.800		1,250	207		1,457	1,725

11 66 23.47 Gym Mats

	Crew	Daily Output	Labor-Hours	Unit	Material	2014 Bare Costs Labor	Equipment	Total	Total Incl O&P
0010 **GYM MATS**									
5500 2" thick, naugahyde covered				S.F.	3.67			3.67	4.04
5600 Vinyl/nylon covered					7.95			7.95	8.70
6000 Wrestling mats, 1" thick, heavy duty					5.55			5.55	6.10

11 66 Athletic Equipment

11 66 43 – Interior Scoreboards

11 66 43.10 Scoreboards

		Crew	Daily Output	Labor-Hours	Unit	Material	2014 Bare Costs Labor	Equipment	Total	Total Incl O&P
0010	**SCOREBOARDS**									
7000	Baseball, minimum	R-3	1.30	15.385	Ea.	4,075	815	108	4,998	5,875
7200	Maximum		.05	400		17,900	21,200	2,800	41,900	55,500
7300	Football, minimum		.86	23.256		5,275	1,225	163	6,663	7,900
7400	Maximum		.20	100		15,700	5,300	700	21,700	26,300
7500	Basketball (one side), minimum		2.07	9.662		2,375	510	67.50	2,952.50	3,500
7600	Maximum		.30	66.667		3,475	3,525	465	7,465	9,825
7700	Hockey-basketball (four sides), minimum		.25	80		5,600	4,225	560	10,385	13,400
7800	Maximum		.15	133		5,675	7,050	935	13,660	18,300

11 66 53 – Gymnasium Dividers

11 66 53.10 Divider Curtains

		Crew	Daily Output	Labor-Hours	Unit	Material	2014 Bare Costs Labor	Equipment	Total	Total Incl O&P
0010	**DIVIDER CURTAINS**									
4500	Gym divider curtain, mesh top, vinyl bottom, manual	L-4	500	.048	S.F.	8.90	2.07		10.97	13.20
4700	Electric roll up	L-7	400	.070	"	11.90	3.10		15	18.15

11 82 Solid Waste Handling Equipment

11 82 26 – Facility Waste Compactors

11 82 26.10 Compactors

		Crew	Daily Output	Labor-Hours	Unit	Material	2014 Bare Costs Labor	Equipment	Total	Total Incl O&P
0010	**COMPACTORS**									
0020	Compactors, 115 volt, 250#/hr., chute fed	L-4	1	24	Ea.	11,900	1,025		12,925	14,800
0100	Hand fed		2.40	10		14,900	430		15,330	17,100
1000	Heavy duty industrial compactor, 0.5 C.Y. capacity		1	24		10,000	1,025		11,025	12,700
1050	1.0 C.Y. capacity		1	24		15,000	1,025		16,025	18,200
1400	For handling hazardous waste materials, 55 gallon drum packer, std.					19,500			19,500	21,500
1410	55 gallon drum packer w/HEPA filter					24,300			24,300	26,700
1420	55 gallon drum packer w/charcoal & HEPA filter					32,400			32,400	35,600
1430	All of the above made explosion proof, add					1,425			1,425	1,575

11 91 Religious Equipment

11 91 13 – Baptisteries

11 91 13.10 Baptistry

		Crew	Daily Output	Labor-Hours	Unit	Material	2014 Bare Costs Labor	Equipment	Total	Total Incl O&P
0010	**BAPTISTRY**									
0150	Fiberglass, 3'-6" deep, x 13'-7" long,									
0160	steps at both ends, incl. plumbing, minimum	L-8	1	20	Ea.	5,650	965		6,615	7,800
0200	Maximum	"	.70	28.571		9,225	1,375		10,600	12,300
0250	Add for filter, heater and lights					1,825			1,825	2,025

11 91 23 – Sanctuary Equipment

11 91 23.10 Sanctuary Furnishings

		Crew	Daily Output	Labor-Hours	Unit	Material	2014 Bare Costs Labor	Equipment	Total	Total Incl O&P
0010	**SANCTUARY FURNISHINGS**									
0020	Altar, wood, custom design, plain	1 Carp	1.40	5.714	Ea.	2,525	262		2,787	3,200
0050	Deluxe		.20	40	"	12,200	1,825		14,025	16,400
5000	Wall cross, aluminum, extruded, 2" x 2" section		34	.235	L.F.	215	10.80		225.80	255
5150	4" x 4" section		29	.276		310	12.65		322.65	360
5300	Bronze, extruded, 1" x 2" section		31	.258		425	11.85		436.85	485
5350	2-1/2" x 2-1/2" section		34	.235		640	10.80		650.80	725

Estimating Tips

General

- The items in this division are usually priced per square foot or each. Most of these items are purchased by the owner and installed by the contractor. Do not assume the items in Division 12 will be purchased and installed by the contractor. Check the specifications for responsibilities and include receiving, storage, installation, and mechanical and electrical hookups in the appropriate divisions.

- Some items in this division require some type of support system that is not usually furnished with the item. Examples of these systems include blocking for the attachment of casework and heavy drapery rods. The required blocking must be added to the estimate in the appropriate division.

Reference Numbers

Reference numbers are shown in shaded boxes at the beginning of some major classifications. These numbers refer to related items in the Reference Section. The reference information may be an estimating procedure, an alternate pricing method, or technical information.

Note: Not all subdivisions listed here necessarily appear in this publication.

Division 12 - Furnishings

12 21 Window Blinds

12 21 13 – Horizontal Louver Blinds

12 21 13.13 Metal Horizontal Louver Blinds	Crew	Daily Output	Labor-Hours	Unit	Material	2014 Bare Costs Labor	Equipment	Total	Total Incl O&P
0010 **METAL HORIZONTAL LOUVER BLINDS**									
0020 Horizontal, 1" aluminum slats, solid color, stock	1 Carp	590	.014	S.F.	4.80	.62		5.42	6.30
0070 Horizontal, 1" aluminum slats, custom color	"	590	.014	"	5.30	.62		5.92	6.80

12 21 13.33 Vinyl Horizontal Louver Blinds

	Crew	Daily Output	Labor-Hours	Unit	Material	Labor	Equipment	Total	Total Incl O&P
0010 **VINYL HORIZONTAL LOUVER BLINDS**									
0100 2" composite, 48" wide, 48" high	1 Carp	30	.267	Ea.	90	12.25		102.25	119
0120 72" high		29	.276		129	12.65		141.65	162
0140 96" high		28	.286		177	13.10		190.10	216
0200 60" wide, 60" high		27	.296		97.50	13.60		111.10	130
0220 72" high		25	.320		112	14.65		126.65	147
0240 96" high		24	.333		178	15.30		193.30	221
0300 72" wide, 72" high		25	.320		190	14.65		204.65	234
0320 96" high		23	.348		266	15.95		281.95	320
0400 96" wide, 96" high		20	.400		310	18.35		328.35	370
1000 2" faux wood, 48" wide, 48" high		30	.267		58	12.25		70.25	84
1020 72" high		29	.276		79	12.65		91.65	108
1040 96" high		28	.286		98	13.10		111.10	130
1300 72" wide, 72" high		25	.320		122	14.65		136.65	159
1320 96" high		23	.348		192	15.95		207.95	237
1400 96" wide, 96" high	▼	20	.400	▼	212	18.35		230.35	264

12 23 Interior Shutters

12 23 10 – Wood Interior Shutters

12 23 10.10 Wood Interior Shutters

	Crew	Daily Output	Labor-Hours	Unit	Material	Labor	Equipment	Total	Total Incl O&P
0010 **WOOD INTERIOR SHUTTERS**, louvered									
0200 Two panel, 27" wide, 36" high	1 Carp	5	1.600	Set	147	73.50		220.50	283
0300 33" wide, 36" high		5	1.600		190	73.50		263.50	330
0500 47" wide, 36" high		5	1.600		255	73.50		328.50	400
1000 Four panel, 27" wide, 36" high		5	1.600		216	73.50		289.50	360
1100 33" wide, 36" high		5	1.600		276	73.50		349.50	425
1300 47" wide, 36" high	▼	5	1.600	▼	370	73.50		443.50	525

12 23 10.13 Wood Panels

	Crew	Daily Output	Labor-Hours	Unit	Material	Labor	Equipment	Total	Total Incl O&P
0010 **WOOD PANELS**									
3000 Wood folding panels with movable louvers, 7" x 20" each	1 Carp	17	.471	Pr.	78	21.50		99.50	122
4000 Fixed louver type, stock units, 8" x 20" each		17	.471		92	21.50		113.50	137
4450 18" x 40" each	▼	17	.471	▼	132	21.50		153.50	181

12 24 Window Shades

12 24 13 – Roller Window Shades

12 24 13.10 Shades

	Crew	Daily Output	Labor-Hours	Unit	Material	Labor	Equipment	Total	Total Incl O&P
0010 **SHADES**									
0020 Basswood, roll-up, stain finish, 3/8" slats	1 Carp	300	.027	S.F.	14.65	1.22		15.87	18.10
0030 Double layered, heat reflective		685	.012		9.20	.54		9.74	11
0200 7/8" slats		300	.027		13.85	1.22		15.07	17.20
0900 Mylar, single layer, non-heat reflective		685	.012		4.96	.54		5.50	6.35
0910 Mylar, single layer, heat reflective		685	.012		5.35	.54		5.89	6.80
1000 Double layered, heat reflective		685	.012		5.75	.54		6.29	7.20
1100 Triple layered, heat reflective		685	.012		6.25	.54		6.79	7.80
5000 Thermal, roll up, R4	▼	44	.182	▼	11.80	8.35		20.15	26.50

12 24 Window Shades

12 24 13 – Roller Window Shades

12 24 13.10 Shades		Crew	Daily Output	Labor-Hours	Unit	Material	2014 Bare Costs Labor	Equipment	Total	Total Incl O&P
5030	R10.7	1 Carp	44	.182	S.F.	13.60	8.35		21.95	28.50
5050	Magnetic clips, set of 20				Set	25.50			25.50	28

12 32 Manufactured Wood Casework

12 32 16 – Manufactured Plastic-Laminate-Clad Casework

12 32 16.20 Plastic Laminate Casework Doors

		Crew	Daily Output	Labor-Hours	Unit	Material	Labor	Equipment	Total	Total Incl O&P
0010	**PLASTIC LAMINATE CASEWORK DOORS**									
1000	For casework frames, see Section 12 32 23.15									
1100	For casework hardware, see Section 12 32 23.35									
6000	Plastic laminate on particle board									
6100	12" wide, 18" high	1 Carp	25	.320	Ea.	24	14.65		38.65	50.50
6140	30" high		23	.348		40	15.95		55.95	70
6500	18" wide, 18" high		24	.333		36	15.30		51.30	64.50
6600	30" high		22	.364		60	16.65		76.65	93.50

12 32 16.25 Plastic Laminate Drawer Fronts

		Crew	Daily Output	Labor-Hours	Unit	Material	Labor	Equipment	Total	Total Incl O&P
0010	**PLASTIC LAMINATE DRAWER FRONTS**									
2800	Plastic laminate on particle board front									
3000	4" high, 12" wide	1 Carp	17	.471	Ea.	3.93	21.50		25.43	40
3200	18" wide	"	16	.500	"	5.90	23		28.90	44

12 32 23 – Hardwood Casework

12 32 23.10 Manufactured Wood Casework, Stock Units

		Crew	Daily Output	Labor-Hours	Unit	Material	Labor	Equipment	Total	Total Incl O&P
0010	**MANUFACTURED WOOD CASEWORK, STOCK UNITS**									
0300	Built-in drawer units, pine, 18" deep, 32" high, unfinished									
0400	Minimum	2 Carp	53	.302	L.F.	114	13.85		127.85	148
0500	Maximum	"	40	.400	"	134	18.35		152.35	178
0700	Kitchen base cabinets, hardwood, not incl. counter tops,									
0710	24" deep, 35" high, prefinished									
0800	One top drawer, one door below, 12" wide	2 Carp	24.80	.645	Ea.	254	29.50		283.50	330
0820	15" wide		24	.667		264	30.50		294.50	340
0840	18" wide		23.30	.687		287	31.50		318.50	365
0860	21" wide		22.70	.705		294	32.50		326.50	380
0880	24" wide		22.30	.717		350	33		383	440
1000	Four drawers, 12" wide		24.80	.645		267	29.50		296.50	340
1020	15" wide		24	.667		271	30.50		301.50	350
1040	18" wide		23.30	.687		298	31.50		329.50	380
1060	24" wide		22.30	.717		330	33		363	415
1200	Two top drawers, two doors below, 27" wide		22	.727		375	33.50		408.50	470
1220	30" wide		21.40	.748		405	34.50		439.50	505
1240	33" wide		20.90	.766		420	35		455	525
1260	36" wide		20.30	.788		435	36		471	540
1280	42" wide		19.80	.808		460	37		497	570
1300	48" wide		18.90	.847		495	39		534	610
1500	Range or sink base, two doors below, 30" wide		21.40	.748		335	34.50		369.50	425
1520	33" wide		20.90	.766		360	35		395	460
1540	36" wide		20.30	.788		380	36		416	475
1560	42" wide		19.80	.808		400	37		437	500
1580	48" wide		18.90	.847		415	39		454	525
1800	For sink front units, deduct					154			154	169
2000	Corner base cabinets, 36" wide, standard	2 Carp	18	.889		600	41		641	725
2100	Lazy Susan with revolving door	"	16.50	.970		805	44.50		849.50	960

12 32 Manufactured Wood Casework

12 32 23 – Hardwood Casework

12 32 23.10 Manufactured Wood Casework, Stock Units

		Crew	Daily Output	Labor-Hours	Unit	Material	2014 Bare Costs Labor	Equipment	Total	Total Incl O&P
4000	Kitchen wall cabinets, hardwood, 12" deep with two doors									
4050	12" high, 30" wide	2 Carp	24.80	.645	Ea.	227	29.50		256.50	299
4100	36" wide		24	.667		270	30.50		300.50	345
4400	15" high, 30" wide		24	.667		231	30.50		261.50	305
4420	33" wide		23.30	.687		285	31.50		316.50	365
4440	36" wide		22.70	.705		277	32.50		309.50	360
4450	42" wide		22.70	.705		315	32.50		347.50	400
4700	24" high, 30" wide		23.30	.687		310	31.50		341.50	390
4720	36" wide		22.70	.705		340	32.50		372.50	430
4740	42" wide		22.30	.717		390	33		423	485
5000	30" high, one door, 12" wide		22	.727		207	33.50		240.50	282
5020	15" wide		21.40	.748		231	34.50		265.50	310
5040	18" wide		20.90	.766		254	35		289	335
5060	24" wide		20.30	.788		296	36		332	385
5300	Two doors, 27" wide		19.80	.808		325	37		362	415
5320	30" wide		19.30	.829		345	38		383	445
5340	36" wide		18.80	.851		395	39		434	495
5360	42" wide		18.50	.865		425	39.50		464.50	530
5380	48" wide		18.40	.870		480	40		520	595
6000	Corner wall, 30" high, 24" wide		18	.889		340	41		381	440
6050	30" wide		17.20	.930		360	42.50		402.50	470
6100	36" wide		16.50	.970		410	44.50		454.50	525
6500	Revolving Lazy Susan		15.20	1.053		460	48.50		508.50	585
7000	Broom cabinet, 84" high, 24" deep, 18" wide		10	1.600		625	73.50		698.50	805
7500	Oven cabinets, 84" high, 24" deep, 27" wide		8	2	↓	960	91.50		1,051.50	1,200
7750	Valance board trim	↓	396	.040	L.F.	13	1.85		14.85	17.35
7780	Toe kick trim	1 Carp	256	.031	"	2.79	1.43		4.22	5.40
7790	Base cabinet corner filler		16	.500	Ea.	41.50	23		64.50	83
7800	Cabinet filler, 3" x 24"		20	.400		18.05	18.35		36.40	50
7810	3" x 30"		20	.400		22.50	18.35		40.85	55
7820	3" x 42"		18	.444		31.50	20.50		52	68
7830	3" x 80"		16	.500	↓	60	23		83	104
7850	Cabinet panel	↓	50	.160	S.F.	8.35	7.35		15.70	21
9000	For deluxe models of all cabinets, add					40%				
9500	For custom built in place, add					25%	10%			
9558	Rule of thumb, kitchen cabinets not including									
9560	appliances & counter top, minimum	2 Carp	30	.533	L.F.	168	24.50		192.50	225
9600	Maximum	"	25	.640	"	380	29.50		409.50	465
9700	Minimum labor/equipment charge	1 Carp	3	2.667	Job		122		122	201

12 32 23.15 Manufactured Wood Casework Frames

		Crew	Daily Output	Labor-Hours	Unit	Material	2014 Bare Costs Labor	Equipment	Total	Total Incl O&P
0010	**MANUFACTURED WOOD CASEWORK FRAMES**									
0050	Base cabinets, counter storage, 36" high									
0100	One bay, 18" wide	1 Carp	2.70	2.963	Ea.	164	136		300	405
0400	Two bay, 36" wide		2.20	3.636		250	167		417	550
1100	Three bay, 54" wide		1.50	5.333		298	245		543	725
2800	Bookcases, one bay, 7' high, 18" wide		2.40	3.333		193	153		346	465
3500	Two bay, 36" wide		1.60	5		280	229		509	685
4100	Three bay, 54" wide		1.20	6.667		465	305		770	1,000
5100	Coat racks, one bay, 7' high, 24" wide		4.50	1.778		192	81.50		273.50	345
5300	Two bay, 48" wide		2.75	2.909		268	133		401	515
5800	Three bay, 72" wide		2.10	3.810		395	175		570	720
6100	Wall mounted cabinet, one bay, 24" high, 18" wide	↓	3.60	2.222	↓	106	102		208	283

12 32 Manufactured Wood Casework

12 32 23 – Hardwood Casework

12 32 23.15 Manufactured Wood Casework Frames

		Crew	Daily Output	Labor-Hours	Unit	Material	2014 Bare Costs Labor	Equipment	Total	Total Incl O&P
6800	Two bay, 36" wide	1 Carp	2.20	3.636	Ea.	154	167		321	445
7400	Three bay, 54" wide		1.70	4.706		192	216		408	565
8400	30" high, one bay, 18" wide		3.60	2.222		115	102		217	293
9000	Two bay, 36" wide		2.15	3.721		153	171		324	450
9400	Three bay, 54" wide		1.60	5		191	229		420	585
9800	Wardrobe, 7' high, single, 24" wide		2.70	2.963		212	136		348	455
9880	Partition & adjustable shelves, 48" wide		1.70	4.706		270	216		486	650
9950	Partition, adjustable shelves & drawers, 48" wide		1.40	5.714		405	262		667	875
9970	Minimum labor/equipment charge		4	2	Job		91.50		91.50	151

12 32 23.20 Manufactured Hardwood Casework Doors

		Crew	Daily Output	Labor-Hours	Unit	Material	2014 Bare Costs Labor	Equipment	Total	Total Incl O&P
0010	**MANUFACTURED HARDWOOD CASEWORK DOORS**									
2000	Glass panel, hardwood frame									
2200	12" wide, 18" high	1 Carp	34	.235	Ea.	25.50	10.80		36.30	46
2600	30" high		32	.250		42.50	11.45		53.95	66
4450	18" wide, 18" high		32	.250		38.50	11.45		49.95	61
4550	30" high		29	.276		64	12.65		76.65	91
5000	Hardwood, raised panel									
5100	12" wide, 18" high	1 Carp	16	.500	Ea.	28.50	23		51.50	69
5200	30" high		15	.533		47.50	24.50		72	92.50
5500	18" wide, 18" high		15	.533		43	24.50		67.50	87
5600	30" high		14	.571		71.50	26		97.50	122
9000	Minimum labor/equipment charge		4	2	Job		91.50		91.50	151

12 32 23.25 Manufactured Wood Casework Drawer Fronts

		Crew	Daily Output	Labor-Hours	Unit	Material	2014 Bare Costs Labor	Equipment	Total	Total Incl O&P
0010	**MANUFACTURED WOOD CASEWORK DRAWER FRONTS**									
0100	Solid hardwood front									
1000	4" high, 12" wide	1 Carp	17	.471	Ea.	4.33	21.50		25.83	40.50
1200	18" wide		16	.500	"	6.50	23		29.50	44.50
9000	Minimum labor/equipment charge		4	2	Job		91.50		91.50	151

12 32 23.30 Manufactured Wood Casework Vanities

		Crew	Daily Output	Labor-Hours	Unit	Material	2014 Bare Costs Labor	Equipment	Total	Total Incl O&P
0010	**MANUFACTURED WOOD CASEWORK VANITIES**									
8000	Vanity bases, 2 doors, 30" high, 21" deep, 24" wide	2 Carp	20	.800	Ea.	297	36.50		333.50	385
8050	30" wide		16	1		355	46		401	465
8100	36" wide		13.33	1.200		345	55		400	470
8150	48" wide		11.43	1.400		450	64		514	600
9000	For deluxe models of all vanities, add to above					40%				
9500	For custom built in place, add to above					25%	10%			

12 32 23.35 Manufactured Wood Casework Hardware

		Crew	Daily Output	Labor-Hours	Unit	Material	2014 Bare Costs Labor	Equipment	Total	Total Incl O&P
0010	**MANUFACTURED WOOD CASEWORK HARDWARE**									
1000	Catches, minimum	1 Carp	235	.034	Ea.	1.17	1.56		2.73	3.85
1040	Maximum	"	80	.100	"	7.20	4.59		11.79	15.50
2000	Door/drawer pulls, handles									
2200	Handles and pulls, projecting, metal, minimum	1 Carp	48	.167	Ea.	4.80	7.65		12.45	17.85
2240	Maximum		36	.222		10.15	10.20		20.35	28
2300	Wood, minimum		48	.167		5.05	7.65		12.70	18.10
2340	Maximum		36	.222		9.25	10.20		19.45	27
2600	Flush, metal, minimum		48	.167		5.05	7.65		12.70	18.10
2640	Maximum		36	.222		9.25	10.20		19.45	27
3000	Drawer tracks/glides, minimum		48	.167	Pr.	8.55	7.65		16.20	22
3040	Maximum		24	.333		25	15.30		40.30	52.50
4000	Cabinet hinges, minimum		160	.050		2.90	2.29		5.19	6.95
4040	Maximum		68	.118		11	5.40		16.40	21

12 34 Manufactured Plastic Casework

12 34 16 – Manufactured Solid-Plastic Casework

12 34 16.10 Outdoor Casework		Crew	Daily Output	Labor-Hours	Unit	Material	2014 Bare Costs Labor	Equipment	Total	Total Incl O&P
0010	**OUTDOOR CASEWORK**									
0020	Cabinet, base, sink/range, 36"	2 Carp	20.30	.788	Ea.	1,775	36		1,811	2,025
0100	Base, 36"		20.30	.788		2,000	36		2,036	2,250
0200	Filler strip, 1" x 30"		158	.101		31	4.64		35.64	41.50
0210	Filler strip, 2" x 30"		158	.101		41	4.64		45.64	52.50

12 35 Specialty Casework

12 35 53 – Laboratory Casework

12 35 53.13 Metal Laboratory Casework

		Crew	Daily Output	Labor-Hours	Unit	Material	2014 Bare Costs Labor	Equipment	Total	Total Incl O&P
0010	**METAL LABORATORY CASEWORK**									
0020	Cabinets, base, door units, metal	2 Carp	18	.889	L.F.	228	41		269	320
0300	Drawer units		18	.889		505	41		546	625
0700	Tall storage cabinets, open, 7' high		20	.800		485	36.50		521.50	595
0900	With glazed doors		20	.800		735	36.50		771.50	865
1300	Wall cabinets, metal, 12-1/2" deep, open		20	.800		164	36.50		200.50	242
1500	With doors		20	.800		340	36.50		376.50	435

12 36 Countertops

12 36 16 – Metal Countertops

12 36 16.10 Stainless Steel Countertops

		Crew	Daily Output	Labor-Hours	Unit	Material	2014 Bare Costs Labor	Equipment	Total	Total Incl O&P
0010	**STAINLESS STEEL COUNTERTOPS**									
3200	Stainless steel, custom	1 Carp	24	.333	S.F.	150	15.30		165.30	190

12 36 19 – Wood Countertops

12 36 19.10 Maple Countertops

		Crew	Daily Output	Labor-Hours	Unit	Material	2014 Bare Costs Labor	Equipment	Total	Total Incl O&P
0010	**MAPLE COUNTERTOPS**									
2900	Solid, laminated, 1-1/2" thick, no splash	1 Carp	28	.286	L.F.	74	13.10		87.10	103
3000	With square splash		28	.286	"	88	13.10		101.10	119
3400	Recessed cutting block with trim, 16" x 20" x 1"		8	1	Ea.	90	46		136	175

12 36 23 – Plastic Countertops

12 36 23.13 Plastic-Laminate-Clad Countertops

		Crew	Daily Output	Labor-Hours	Unit	Material	2014 Bare Costs Labor	Equipment	Total	Total Incl O&P
0010	**PLASTIC-LAMINATE-CLAD COUNTERTOPS**									
0020	Stock, 24" wide w/backsplash, minimum	1 Carp	30	.267	L.F.	16.65	12.25		28.90	38.50
0100	Maximum		25	.320		34	14.65		48.65	61
0300	Custom plastic, 7/8" thick, aluminum molding, no splash		30	.267		29.50	12.25		41.75	52.50
0400	Cove splash		30	.267		28.50	12.25		40.75	51.50
0600	1-1/4" thick, no splash		28	.286		34.50	13.10		47.60	59.50
0700	Square splash		28	.286		41.50	13.10		54.60	67
0900	Square edge, plastic face, 7/8" thick, no splash		30	.267		32.50	12.25		44.75	56
1000	With splash		30	.267		38.50	12.25		50.75	62.50
1200	For stainless channel edge, 7/8" thick, add					3.06			3.06	3.37
1300	1-1/4" thick, add					3.65			3.65	4.02
1500	For solid color suede finish, add					4			4	4.40
1700	For end splash, add				Ea.	18			18	19.80
1900	For cut outs, standard, add, minimum	1 Carp	32	.250		12	11.45		23.45	32
2000	Maximum		8	1		6	46		52	82
2100	Postformed, including backsplash and front edge		30	.267	L.F.	10	12.25		22.25	31
2110	Mitred, add		12	.667	Ea.		30.50		30.50	50
2200	Built-in place, 25" wide, plastic laminate		25	.320	L.F.	40.50	14.65		55.15	68.50

12 36 Countertops

12 36 23 – Plastic Countertops

12 36 23.13 Plastic-Laminate-Clad Countertops	Crew	Daily Output	Labor-Hours	Unit	Material	2014 Bare Costs Labor	Equipment	Total	Total Incl O&P
9000 Minimum labor/equipment charge	1 Carp	3.75	2.133	Job		98		98	161

12 36 33 – Tile Countertops

12 36 33.10 Ceramic Tile Countertops

	Crew	Daily Output	Labor-Hours	Unit	Material	2014 Bare Costs Labor	Equipment	Total	Total Incl O&P
0010 **CERAMIC TILE COUNTERTOPS**									
2300 Ceramic tile mosaic	1 Carp	25	.320	L.F.	33	14.65		47.65	60.50

12 36 40 – Stone Countertops

12 36 40.10 Natural Stone Countertops

	Crew	Daily Output	Labor-Hours	Unit	Material	2014 Bare Costs Labor	Equipment	Total	Total Incl O&P
0010 **NATURAL STONE COUNTERTOPS**									
2500 Marble, stock, with splash, 1/2" thick, minimum	1 Bric	17	.471	L.F.	41	21.50		62.50	80
2700 3/4" thick, maximum	"	13	.615	"	103	28		131	159

12 36 53 – Laboratory Countertops

12 36 53.10 Laboratory Countertops and Sinks

	Crew	Daily Output	Labor-Hours	Unit	Material	2014 Bare Costs Labor	Equipment	Total	Total Incl O&P
0010 **LABORATORY COUNTERTOPS AND SINKS**									
0020 Countertops, not incl. base cabinets, acid-proof, minimum	2 Carp	82	.195	S.F.	40	8.95		48.95	58.50
0030 Maximum		70	.229		49.50	10.50		60	71.50
0040 Stainless steel		82	.195		129	8.95		137.95	157

12 36 61 – Simulated Stone Countertops

12 36 61.16 Solid Surface Countertops

	Crew	Daily Output	Labor-Hours	Unit	Material	2014 Bare Costs Labor	Equipment	Total	Total Incl O&P
0010 **SOLID SURFACE COUNTERTOPS**, Acrylic polymer									
0020 Pricing for orders of 100 L.F. or greater									
0100 25" wide, solid colors	2 Carp	28	.571	L.F.	53.50	26		79.50	102
0200 Patterned colors		28	.571		68	26		94	118
0300 Premium patterned colors		28	.571		85	26		111	137
0400 With silicone attached 4" backsplash, solid colors		27	.593		58.50	27		85.50	109
0500 Patterned colors		27	.593		74.50	27		101.50	127
0600 Premium patterned colors		27	.593		92.50	27		119.50	147
0700 With hard seam attached 4" backsplash, solid colors		23	.696		58.50	32		90.50	117
0800 Patterned colors		23	.696		74.50	32		106.50	135
0900 Premium patterned colors		23	.696		92.50	32		124.50	155
1000 Pricing for order of 51 – 99 L.F.									
1100 25" wide, solid colors	2 Carp	24	.667	L.F.	61.50	30.50		92	118
1200 Patterned colors		24	.667		78	30.50		108.50	136
1300 Premium patterned colors		24	.667		97.50	30.50		128	157
1400 With silicone attached 4" backsplash, solid colors		23	.696		67.50	32		99.50	127
1500 Patterned colors		23	.696		85.50	32		117.50	147
1600 Premium patterned colors		23	.696		107	32		139	170
1700 With hard seam attached 4" backsplash, solid colors		20	.800		67.50	36.50		104	135
1800 Patterned colors		20	.800		85.50	36.50		122	155
1900 Premium patterned colors		20	.800		107	36.50		143.50	178
2000 Pricing for order of 1 – 50 L.F.									
2100 25" wide, solid colors	2 Carp	20	.800	L.F.	72.50	36.50		109	140
2200 Patterned colors		20	.800		91.50	36.50		128	162
2300 Premium patterned colors		20	.800		115	36.50		151.50	187
2400 With silicone attached 4" backsplash, solid colors		19	.842		79.50	38.50		118	151
2500 Patterned colors		19	.842		100	38.50		138.50	174
2600 Premium patterned colors		19	.842		125	38.50		163.50	202
2700 With hard seam attached 4" backsplash, solid colors		15	1.067		79.50	49		128.50	168
2800 Patterned colors		15	1.067		100	49		149	191
2900 Premium patterned colors		15	1.067		125	49		174	219
3000 Sinks, pricing for order of 100 or greater units									

12 36 Countertops

12 36 61 – Simulated Stone Countertops

12 36 61.16 Solid Surface Countertops	Crew	Daily Output	Labor-Hours	Unit	Material	2014 Bare Costs Labor	Equipment	Total	Total Incl O&P
3100	Single bowl, hard seamed, solid colors, 13" x 17"	1 Carp	3	2.667	Ea.	360	122		482	600
3200	10" x 15"		7	1.143		167	52.50		219.50	270
3300	Cutouts for sinks		8	1			46		46	75.50
3400	Sinks, pricing for order of 51 – 99 units									
3500	Single bowl, hard seamed, solid colors, 13" x 17"	1 Carp	2.55	3.137	Ea.	415	144		559	690
3600	10" x 15"		6	1.333		192	61		253	310
3700	Cutouts for sinks		7	1.143			52.50		52.50	86
3800	Sinks, pricing for order of 1 – 50 units									
3900	Single bowl, hard seamed, solid colors, 13" x 17"	1 Carp	2	4	Ea.	490	183		673	835
4000	10" x 15"		4.55	1.758		226	80.50		306.50	380
4100	Cutouts for sinks		5.25	1.524			70		70	115
4200	Cooktop cutouts, pricing for 100 or greater units		4	2		26.50	91.50		118	181
4300	51 – 99 units		3.40	2.353		30.50	108		138.50	211
4400	1 – 50 units		3	2.667		36	122		158	241

12 36 61.17 Solid Surface Vanity Tops

0010	SOLID SURFACE VANITY TOPS									
0015	Solid surface, center bowl, 17" x 19"	1 Carp	12	.667	Ea.	186	30.50		216.50	255
0020	19" x 25"		12	.667		190	30.50		220.50	259
0030	19" x 31"		12	.667		223	30.50		253.50	295
0040	19" x 37"		12	.667		259	30.50		289.50	335
0050	22" x 25"		10	.800		340	36.50		376.50	435
0060	22" x 31"		10	.800		395	36.50		431.50	495
0070	22" x 37"		10	.800		460	36.50		496.50	570
0080	22" x 43"		10	.800		525	36.50		561.50	640
0090	22" x 49"		10	.800		585	36.50		621.50	700
0110	22" x 55"		8	1		660	46		706	805
0120	22" x 61"		8	1		755	46		801	905
0220	Double bowl, 22" x 61"		8	1		855	46		901	1,025
0230	Double bowl, 22" x 73"		8	1		930	46		976	1,100
0240	For aggregate colors, add					35%				
0250	For faucets and fittings, see Section 22 41 39.10									

12 36 61.19 Quartz Agglomerate Countertops

0010	QUARTZ AGGLOMERATE COUNTERTOPS									
0100	25" wide, 4" backsplash, color group A, minimum	2 Carp	15	1.067	L.F.	63	49		112	150
0110	Maximum		15	1.067		88.50	49		137.50	178
0120	Color group B, minimum		15	1.067		65.50	49		114.50	153
0130	Maximum		15	1.067		92.50	49		141.50	183
0140	Color group C, minimum		15	1.067		76.50	49		125.50	165
0150	Maximum		15	1.067		105	49		154	196
0160	Color group D, minimum		15	1.067		83	49		132	172
0170	Maximum		15	1.067		112	49		161	205

12 48 Rugs and Mats

12 48 13 – Entrance Floor Mats and Frames

12 48 13.13 Entrance Floor Mats		Crew	Daily Output	Labor-Hours	Unit	Material	2014 Bare Costs Labor	Equipment	Total	Total Incl O&P
0010	**ENTRANCE FLOOR MATS**									
2000	Recycled rubber tire tile, 12" x 12" x 3/8" thick	G	1 Clab	125	.064	S.F.	9.90	2.35		12.25	14.75
2510	Natural cocoa fiber, 1/2" thick	G		125	.064		8.20	2.35		10.55	12.85
2520	3/4" thick	G		125	.064		6.80	2.35		9.15	11.30
2530	1" thick	G		125	.064		9.40	2.35		11.75	14.20

12 51 Office Furniture

12 51 16 – Case Goods

12 51 16.13 Metal Case Goods

		Crew	Daily Output	Labor-Hours	Unit	Material	Labor	Equipment	Total	Total Incl O&P
0010	**METAL CASE GOODS**									
0020	Desks, 29" high, double pedestal, 30" x 60", metal, minimum				Ea.	580			580	635
0030	Maximum				"	1,475			1,475	1,625

12 54 Hospitality Furniture

12 54 13 – Hotel and Motel Furniture

12 54 13.10 Hotel Furniture

		Crew	Daily Output	Labor-Hours	Unit	Material	Labor	Equipment	Total	Total Incl O&P
0010	**HOTEL FURNITURE**									
0020	Standard quality set, minimum				Room	2,375			2,375	2,600
0200	Maximum				"	8,425			8,425	9,275

12 54 16 – Restaurant Furniture

12 54 16.20 Furniture, Restaurant

		Crew	Daily Output	Labor-Hours	Unit	Material	Labor	Equipment	Total	Total Incl O&P
0010	**FURNITURE, RESTAURANT**									
0020	Bars, built-in, front bar	1 Carp	5	1.600	L.F.	274	73.50		347.50	420
0200	Back bar		5	1.600	"	199	73.50		272.50	340
0500	Booth unit, molded plastic, stub wall and 2 seats, minimum		2	4	Set	365	183		548	700
0600	Maximum		1.50	5.333	"	1,400	245		1,645	1,950
0800	Booth seat, upholstered, foursome, single (end) minimum		5	1.600	Ea.	755	73.50		828.50	955
0900	Maximum		4	2		1,025	91.50		1,116.50	1,275
1000	Foursome, double, minimum		4	2		1,250	91.50		1,341.50	1,525
1100	Maximum		3	2.667		1,750	122		1,872	2,125
1300	Circle booth, upholstered, 1/4 circle, minimum		3	2.667		1,375	122		1,497	1,700
1400	Maximum		2	4		1,875	183		2,058	2,375
1500	3/4 circle, minimum		1.50	5.333		5,375	245		5,620	6,300
1600	Maximum		1	8		6,500	365		6,865	7,750

12 55 Detention Furniture

12 55 13 – Detention Bunks

12 55 13.13 Cots

		Crew	Daily Output	Labor-Hours	Unit	Material	Labor	Equipment	Total	Total Incl O&P
0010	**COTS**									
2500	Bolted, single, painted steel	E-4	20	1.600	Ea.	330	82.50	7.10	419.60	525
2700	Stainless steel	"	20	1.600	"	960	82.50	7.10	1,049.60	1,200

12 56 Institutional Furniture

12 56 43 – Dormitory Furniture

12 56 43.10 Dormitory Furnishings

		Crew	Daily Output	Labor-Hours	Unit	Material	2014 Bare Costs Labor	Equipment	Total	Total Incl O&P
0010	**DORMITORY FURNISHINGS**									
0300	Bunkable bed, twin, minimum				Ea.	370			370	405
0320	Maximum				"	540			540	595

12 56 51 – Library Furniture

12 56 51.10 Library Furnishings

		Crew	Daily Output	Labor-Hours	Unit	Material	2014 Bare Costs Labor	Equipment	Total	Total Incl O&P
0010	**LIBRARY FURNISHINGS**									
1710	Carrels, hardwood, 36" x 24", minimum	1 Carp	5	1.600	Ea.	765	73.50		838.50	965
1720	Maximum		4	2		1,950	91.50		2,041.50	2,300
1730	Metal, minimum		5	1.600		255	73.50		328.50	400
1740	Maximum		4	2		440	91.50		531.50	635
6010	Bookshelf, metal, 90" high, 10" shelf, double face		11.50	.696	L.F.	150	32		182	218
6020	Single face		12	.667	"	121	30.50		151.50	183
6050	For 8" shelving, subtract from above					10%				
6070	For 42" high with countertop, subtract from above					20%				

12 56 70 – Healthcare Furniture

12 56 70.10 Furniture, Hospital

		Crew	Daily Output	Labor-Hours	Unit	Material	2014 Bare Costs Labor	Equipment	Total	Total Incl O&P
0010	**FURNITURE, HOSPITAL**									
0020	Beds, manual, minimum				Ea.	785			785	865
0100	Maximum				"	2,500			2,500	2,750
1100	Patient wall systems, not incl. plumbing, minimum				Room	1,400			1,400	1,550
1200	Maximum				"	1,900			1,900	2,100

12 63 Stadium and Arena Seating

12 63 13 – Stadium and Arena Bench Seating

12 63 13.13 Bleachers

		Crew	Daily Output	Labor-Hours	Unit	Material	2014 Bare Costs Labor	Equipment	Total	Total Incl O&P
0010	**BLEACHERS**									
3000	Telescoping, manual to 15 tier, minimum	F-5	65	.492	Seat	90.50	23		113.50	137
3100	Maximum		60	.533		136	24.50		160.50	190
3300	16 to 20 tier, minimum		60	.533		217	24.50		241.50	280
3400	Maximum		55	.582		271	27		298	345
3600	21 to 30 tier, minimum		50	.640		226	29.50		255.50	298
3700	Maximum		40	.800		299	37		336	390
3900	For integral power operation, add, minimum	2 Elec	300	.053		45	2.85		47.85	54.50
4000	Maximum	"	250	.064		72.50	3.41		75.91	85
5000	Benches, folding, in wall, 14' table, 2 benches	L-4	2	12	Set	765	515		1,280	1,675

12 67 Pews and Benches

12 67 13 – Pews

12 67 13.13 Sanctuary Pews

		Crew	Daily Output	Labor-Hours	Unit	Material	2014 Bare Costs Labor	Equipment	Total	Total Incl O&P
0010	**SANCTUARY PEWS**									
1500	Bench type, hardwood, minimum	1 Carp	20	.400	L.F.	93.50	18.35		111.85	133
1550	Maximum	"	15	.533		185	24.50		209.50	244
1570	For kneeler, add					22			22	24.50

12 93 Site Furnishings

12 93 23 – Trash and Litter Receptacles

12 93 23.10 Trash Receptacles

	12 93 23.10 Trash Receptacles		Crew	Daily Output	Labor-Hours	Unit	Material	2014 Bare Costs Labor	Equipment	Total	Total Incl O&P
0010	**TRASH RECEPTACLES**										
0500	Recycled plastic, var colors, round, 32 gal., 28" x 38" H	G	2 Clab	5	3.200	Ea.	500	117		617	745
0510	32 gal., 31" x 32" H	G	"	5	3.200	"	575	117		692	825

12 93 33 – Manufactured Planters

12 93 33.10 Planters

		Crew	Daily Output	Labor-Hours	Unit	Material	Labor	Equipment	Total	Total Incl O&P
0010	**PLANTERS**									
0012	Concrete, sandblasted, precast, 48" diameter, 24" high	2 Clab	15	1.067	Ea.	620	39		659	745
0100	Fluted, precast, 7' diameter, 36" high		10	1.600		1,550	58.50		1,608.50	1,800
0300	Fiberglass, circular, 36" diameter, 24" high		15	1.067		710	39		749	845
0400	60" diameter, 24" high		10	1.600		1,100	58.50		1,158.50	1,300
9000	Minimum labor/equipment charge	1 Clab	2	4	Job		147		147	241

12 93 43 – Site Seating and Tables

12 93 43.13 Site Seating

		Crew	Daily Output	Labor-Hours	Unit	Material	Labor	Equipment	Total	Total Incl O&P
0010	**SITE SEATING**									
0012	Seating, benches, park, precast conc., w/backs, wood rails, 4' long	2 Clab	5	3.200	Ea.	580	117		697	830
0100	8' long		4	4		935	147		1,082	1,275
0300	Fiberglass, without back, one piece, 4' long		10	1.600		605	58.50		663.50	765
0400	8' long		7	2.286		780	84		864	1,000
0500	Steel barstock pedestals w/backs, 2" x 3" wood rails, 4' long		10	1.600		1,100	58.50		1,158.50	1,300
0510	8' long		7	2.286		1,400	84		1,484	1,700
0520	3" x 8" wood plank, 4' long		10	1.600		1,175	58.50		1,233.50	1,400
0530	8' long		7	2.286		1,450	84		1,534	1,750
0540	Backless, 4" x 4" wood plank, 4' square		10	1.600		920	58.50		978.50	1,125
0550	8' long		7	2.286		990	84		1,074	1,250
0600	Aluminum pedestals, with backs, aluminum slats, 8' long		8	2		470	73.50		543.50	635
0610	15' long		5	3.200		955	117		1,072	1,250
0620	Portable, aluminum slats, 8' long		8	2		455	73.50		528.50	620
0630	15' long		5	3.200		550	117		667	800
0800	Cast iron pedestals, back & arms, wood slats, 4' long		8	2		415	73.50		488.50	580
0820	8' long		5	3.200		920	117		1,037	1,225
0840	Backless, wood slats, 4' long		8	2		580	73.50		653.50	760
0860	8' long		5	3.200		1,150	117		1,267	1,450
1700	Steel frame, fir seat, 10' long		10	1.600		345	58.50		403.50	470
9000	Minimum labor/equipment charge		2	8	Job		293		293	480

Division Notes

	CREW	DAILY OUTPUT	LABOR-HOURS	UNIT	BARE COSTS				TOTAL INCL O&P
					MAT.	LABOR	EQUIP.	TOTAL	

Estimating Tips

General

- The items and systems in this division are usually estimated, purchased, supplied, and installed as a unit by one or more subcontractors. The estimator must ensure that all parties are operating from the same set of specifications and assumptions, and that all necessary items are estimated and will be provided. Many times the complex items and systems are covered, but the more common ones, such as excavation or a crane, are overlooked for the very reason that everyone assumes nobody could miss them. The estimator should be the central focus and be able to ensure that all systems are complete.

- Another area where problems can develop in this division is at the interface between systems. The estimator must ensure, for instance, that anchor bolts, nuts, and washers are estimated and included for the air-supported structures and pre-engineered buildings to be bolted to their foundations. Utility supply is a common area where essential items or pieces of equipment can be missed or overlooked due to the fact that each subcontractor may feel it is another's responsibility. The estimator should also be aware of certain items which may be supplied as part of a package but installed by others, and ensure that the installing contractor's estimate includes the cost of installation. Conversely, the estimator must also ensure that items are not costed by two different subcontractors, resulting in an inflated overall estimate.

13 30 00 Special Structures

- The foundations and floor slab, as well as rough mechanical and electrical, should be estimated, as this work is required for the assembly and erection of the structure.

Generally, as noted in the book, the pre-engineered building comes as a shell. Pricing is based on the size and structural design parameters stated in the reference section. Additional features, such as windows and doors with their related structural framing, must also be included by the estimator. Here again, the estimator must have a clear understanding of the scope of each portion of the work and all the necessary interfaces.

Reference Numbers

Reference numbers are shown in shaded boxes at the beginning of some major classifications. These numbers refer to related items in the Reference Section. The reference information may be an estimating procedure, an alternate pricing method, or technical information.

Note: Not all subdivisions listed here necessarily appear in this publication.

13 05 Common Work Results for Special Construction

13 05 05 – Selective Special Construction Demolition

13 05 05.10 Selective Demolition, Air Supported Structures

		Crew	Daily Output	Labor-Hours	Unit	Material	2014 Bare Costs Labor	Equipment	Total	Total Incl O&P
0010	**SELECTIVE DEMOLITION, AIR SUPPORTED STRUCTURES**									
0020	Tank covers, scrim, dbl. layer, vinyl poly w/hdwe., blower & controls									
0050	Round and rectangular R024119-10	B-2	9000	.004	S.F.		.16		.16	.27
0100	Warehouse structures									
0120	Poly/vinyl fabric, 28 oz., incl. tension cables & inflation system	4 Clab	9000	.004	SF Flr.		.13		.13	.21
0150	Reinforced vinyl, 12 oz., 3000 S.F.	"	5000	.006			.23		.23	.39
0200	12,000 to 24,000 S.F.	8 Clab	20000	.003			.12		.12	.19
0250	Tedlar vinyl fabric, 28 oz. w/liner, to 3000 S.F.	4 Clab	5000	.006			.23		.23	.39
0300	12,000 to 24,000 S.F.	8 Clab	20000	.003	↓		.12		.12	.19
0350	Greenhouse/shelter, woven polyethylene with liner									
0400	3000 S.F.	4 Clab	5000	.006	SF Flr.		.23		.23	.39
0450	12,000 to 24,000 S.F.	8 Clab	20000	.003			.12		.12	.19
0500	Tennis/gymnasium, poly/vinyl fabric, 28 oz., incl. thermal liner	4 Clab	9000	.004			.13		.13	.21
0600	Stadium/convention center, teflon coated fiberglass, incl. thermal liner	9 Clab	40000	.002	↓		.07		.07	.11
0700	Doors, air lock, 15' long, 10' x 10'	2 Carp	1.50	10.667	Ea.		490		490	805
0720	15' x 15'		.80	20			915		915	1,500
0750	Revolving personnel door, 6' diam. x 6'-6" high	↓	1.50	10.667	↓		490		490	805

13 05 05.20 Selective Demolition, Garden Houses

		Crew	Daily Output	Labor-Hours	Unit	Material	Labor	Equipment	Total	Total Incl O&P
0010	**SELECTIVE DEMOLITION, GARDEN HOUSES**									
0020	Prefab, wood, excl foundation, average	2 Clab	400	.040	SF Flr.		1.47		1.47	2.41

13 05 05.25 Selective Demolition, Geodesic Domes

		Crew	Daily Output	Labor-Hours	Unit	Material	Labor	Equipment	Total	Total Incl O&P
0010	**SELECTIVE DEMOLITION, GEODESIC DOMES**									
0050	Shell only, interlocking plywood panels, 30' diameter	F-5	3.20	10	Ea.		465		465	760
0060	34' diameter		2.30	13.913			645		645	1,050
0070	39' diameter	↓	2	16			740		740	1,225
0080	45' diameter	F-3	2.20	18.182			850	300	1,150	1,700
0090	55' diameter		2	20			935	330	1,265	1,900
0100	60' diameter		2	20			935	330	1,265	1,900
0110	65' diameter	↓	1.60	25	↓		1,175	415	1,590	2,350

13 05 05.30 Selective Demolition, Greenhouses

		Crew	Daily Output	Labor-Hours	Unit	Material	Labor	Equipment	Total	Total Incl O&P
0010	**SELECTIVE DEMOLITION, GREENHOUSES**									
0020	Resi-type, free standing, excl. foundations, 9' long x 8' wide	2 Clab	160	.100	SF Flr.		3.67		3.67	6
0030	9' long x 11' wide		170	.094			3.45		3.45	5.65
0040	9' long x 14' wide		220	.073			2.67		2.67	4.38
0050	9' long x 17' wide		320	.050			1.83		1.83	3.01
0060	Lean-to type, 4' wide		64	.250			9.15		9.15	15.05
0070	7' wide		120	.133	↓		4.89		4.89	8.05
0080	Geodesic hemisphere, 1/8" plexiglass glazing, 8' diam.		4	4	Ea.		147		147	241
0090	24' diam.		.80	20			735		735	1,200
0100	48' diam.	↓	.40	40	↓		1,475		1,475	2,400

13 05 05.35 Selective Demolition, Hangars

		Crew	Daily Output	Labor-Hours	Unit	Material	Labor	Equipment	Total	Total Incl O&P
0010	**SELECTIVE DEMOLITION, HANGARS**									
0020	T type hangars, prefab, steel , galv roof & walls, incl doors, excl fndtn	E-2	2550	.022	SF Flr.		1.10	.60	1.70	2.61
0030	Circular type, prefab, steel frame, plastic skin, incl foundation, 80' diam	"	.50	112	Total		5,625	3,050	8,675	13,300

13 05 05.45 Selective Demolition, Lightning Protection

		Crew	Daily Output	Labor-Hours	Unit	Material	Labor	Equipment	Total	Total Incl O&P
0010	**SELECTIVE DEMOLITION, LIGHTNING PROTECTION**									
0020	Air terminal & base, copper, 3/8" diam. x 10", to 75' h	1 Clab	16	.500	Ea.		18.35		18.35	30
0030	1/2" diam. x 12", over 75' h		16	.500			18.35		18.35	30
0050	Aluminum, 1/2" diam. x 12", to 75' h		16	.500			18.35		18.35	30
0060	5/8" diam. x 12", over 75' h		16	.500	↓		18.35		18.35	30
0070	Cable, copper, 220 lb. per thousand feet, to 75' high	↓	640	.013	L.F.		.46		.46	.75

13 05 05 – Selective Special Construction Demolition

13 05 05.45 Selective Demolition, Lightning Protection	Crew	Daily Output	Labor-Hours	Unit	Material	2014 Bare Costs		Total	Total Incl O&P
						Labor	Equipment		
0080 375 lb. per thousand feet, over 75' high	1 Clab	460	.017	L.F.		.64		.64	1.05
0090 Aluminum, 101 lb. per thousand feet, to 75' high		560	.014			.52		.52	.86
0100 199 lb. per thousand feet, over 75' high		480	.017	↓		.61		.61	1
0110 Arrester, 175 V AC, to ground		16	.500	Ea.		18.35		18.35	30
0120 650 V AC, to ground	↓	13	.615	"		22.50		22.50	37

13 05 05.50 Selective Demolition, Pre-Engineered Steel Buildings

	Crew	Daily Output	Labor-Hours	Unit	Material	Labor	Equipment	Total	Total Incl O&P
0010 **SELECTIVE DEMOLITION, PRE-ENGINEERED STEEL BUILDINGS**									
0500 Pre-engd. steel bldgs., rigid frame, clear span & multi post, excl. salvage									
0550 3,500 to 7,500 S.F.	L-10	1000	.024	SF Flr.		1.24	.66	1.90	2.90
0600 7,501 to 12,500 S.F.		1500	.016			.82	.44	1.26	1.93
0650 12,500 S.F. or greater	↓	1650	.015	↓		.75	.40	1.15	1.75
0700 Pre-engd. steel building components									
0710 Entrance canopy, including frame 4' x 4'	E-24	8	4	Ea.		202	93	295	465
0720 4' x 8'	"	7	4.571			231	107	338	525
0730 HM doors, self framing, single leaf	2 Skwk	8	2			94.50		94.50	154
0740 Double leaf		5	3.200	↓		151		151	247
0760 Gutter, eave type		600	.027	L.F.		1.26		1.26	2.05
0770 Sash, single slide, double slide or fixed		24	.667	Ea.		31.50		31.50	51.50
0780 Skylight, fiberglass, to 30 S.F.		16	1			47.50		47.50	77
0785 Roof vents, circular, 12" to 24" diameter		12	1.333			63		63	103
0790 Continuous, 10' long	↓	8	2	↓		94.50		94.50	154
0900 Shelters, aluminum frame									
0910 Acrylic glazing, 3' x 9' x 8' high	2 Skwk	2	8	Ea.		380		380	615
0920 9' x 12' x 8' high	"	1.50	10.667	"		505		505	820

13 05 05.60 Selective Demolition, Silos

	Crew	Daily Output	Labor-Hours	Unit	Material	Labor	Equipment	Total	Total Incl O&P
0010 **SELECTIVE DEMOLITION, SILOS**									
0020 Conc stave, indstrl, conical/sloping bott, excl fndtn, 12' diam., 35' h	E-24	.18	177	Ea.		8,975	4,150	13,125	20,500
0030 16' diam., 45' h		.12	266			13,500	6,225	19,725	30,700
0040 25' diam., 75' h	↓	.08	400			20,200	9,325	29,525	46,200
0050 Steel, factory fabricated, 30,000 gal. cap, painted or epoxy lined	L-5	2	28	↓		1,425	375	1,800	2,975

13 05 05.65 Selective Demolition, Sound Control

	Crew	Daily Output	Labor-Hours	Unit	Material	Labor	Equipment	Total	Total Incl O&P
0010 **SELECTIVE DEMOLITION, SOUND CONTROL**									
0120 Acoustical enclosure, 4" thick walls & ceiling panels, 8 lb./S.F.	3 Carp	144	.167	SF Surf		7.65		7.65	12.55
0130 10.5 lb./S.F.		128	.188			8.60		8.60	14.15
0140 Reverb chamber, parallel walls, 4" thick		120	.200			9.15		9.15	15.05
0150 Skewed walls, parallel roof, 4" thick		110	.218			10		10	16.45
0160 Skewed walls/roof, 4" layer/air space		96	.250			11.45		11.45	18.85
0170 Sound-absorbing panels, painted metal, 2'-6" x 8', under 1,000 S.F.		430	.056			2.56		2.56	4.21
0180 Over 1,000 S.F.	↓	480	.050			2.29		2.29	3.77
0190 Flexible transparent curtain, clear	3 Shee	430	.056			3.05		3.05	4.81
0192 50% clear, 50% foam		430	.056			3.05		3.05	4.81
0194 25% clear, 75% foam		430	.056			3.05		3.05	4.81
0196 100% foam	↓	430	.056	↓		3.05		3.05	4.81
0200 Audio-masking sys., incl. speakers, amplfr., signal gnrtr.									
0205 Ceiling mounted, 5,000 S.F.	2 Elec	4800	.003	S.F.		.18		.18	.27
0210 10,000 S.F.		5600	.003			.15		.15	.24
0220 Plenum mounted, 5,000 S.F.		7600	.002			.11		.11	.17
0230 10,000 S.F.	↓	8800	.002	↓		.10		.10	.15

13 05 05.70 Selective Demolition, Special Purpose Rooms

	Crew	Daily Output	Labor-Hours	Unit	Material	Labor	Equipment	Total	Total Incl O&P
0010 **SELECTIVE DEMOLITION, SPECIAL PURPOSE ROOMS**									
0100 Audiometric rooms, under 500 S.F. surface	4 Carp	200	.160	SF Surf		7.35		7.35	12.05
0110 Over 500 S.F. surface	"	240	.133	"		6.10		6.10	10.05

13 05 05.70 Selective Demolition, Special Purpose Rooms

		Crew	Daily Output	Labor-Hours	Unit	Material	2014 Bare Costs Labor	Equipment	Total	Total Incl O&P
0200	Clean rooms, 12' x 12' soft wall, class 100	1 Carp	.30	26.667	Ea.		1,225		1,225	2,000
0210	Class 1000		.30	26.667			1,225		1,225	2,000
0220	Class 10,000		.35	22.857			1,050		1,050	1,725
0230	Class 100,000		.35	22.857			1,050		1,050	1,725
0300	Darkrooms, shell complete, 8' high	2 Carp	220	.073	SF Flr.		3.33		3.33	5.50
0310	12' high		110	.145	"		6.65		6.65	10.95
0350	Darkrooms doors, mini-cylindrical, revolving		4	4	Ea.		183		183	300
0400	Music room, practice modular		140	.114	SF Surf		5.25		5.25	8.60
0500	Refrigeration structures and finishes									
0510	Wall finish, 2 coat portland cement plaster, 1/2" thick	1 Clab	200	.040	S.F.		1.47		1.47	2.41
0520	Fiberglass panels, 1/8" thick		400	.020			.73		.73	1.20
0530	Ceiling finish, polystyrene plastic, 1" to 2" thick		500	.016			.59		.59	.96
0540	4" thick		450	.018			.65		.65	1.07
0550	Refrigerator, prefab aluminum walk-in, 7'-6" high, 6' x 6' OD	2 Carp	100	.160	SF Flr.		7.35		7.35	12.05
0560	10' x 10' OD		160	.100			4.59		4.59	7.55
0570	Over 150 S.F.		200	.080			3.67		3.67	6.05
0600	Sauna, prefabricated, including heater & controls, 7' high, to 30 S.F.		120	.133			6.10		6.10	10.05
0610	To 40 S.F.		140	.114			5.25		5.25	8.60
0620	To 60 S.F.		175	.091			4.19		4.19	6.90
0630	To 100 S.F.		220	.073			3.33		3.33	5.50
0640	To 130 S.F.		250	.064			2.93		2.93	4.82
0650	Steam bath, heater, timer, head, single, to 140 C.F.	1 Plum	2.20	3.636	Ea.		209		209	325
0660	To 300 C.F.		2.20	3.636			209		209	325
0670	Steam bath, comm. size, w/blow-down assembly, to 800 C.F.		1.80	4.444			256		256	400
0680	To 2500 C.F.		1.60	5			288		288	450
0690	Steam bath, comm. size, multiple, for motels, apts, 500 C.F., 2 baths		2	4			230		230	360
0700	1,000 C.F., 4 baths		1.40	5.714			330		330	515

13 05 05.75 Selective Demolition, Storage Tanks

		Crew	Daily Output	Labor-Hours	Unit	Material	2014 Bare Costs Labor	Equipment	Total	Total Incl O&P
0010	**SELECTIVE DEMOLITION, STORAGE TANKS**									
0500	Steel tank, single wall, above ground, not incl. fdn., pumps or piping									
0510	Single wall, 275 gallon	Q-1	3	5.333	Ea.		276		276	430
0520	550 thru 2,000 gallon	B-34P	2	12			575	350	925	1,300
0530	5,000 thru 10,000 gallon	B-34Q	2	12			580	640	1,220	1,625
0540	15,000 thru 30,000 gallon	B-34S	2	16			820	1,800	2,620	3,275
0600	Steel tank, double wall, above ground not incl. fdn., pumps & piping									
0620	500 thru 2,000 gallon	B-34P	2	12	Ea.		575	350	925	1,300

13 05 05.85 Selective Demolition, Swimming Pool Equip

		Crew	Daily Output	Labor-Hours	Unit	Material	2014 Bare Costs Labor	Equipment	Total	Total Incl O&P
0010	**SELECTIVE DEMOLITION, SWIMMING POOL EQUIP**									
0020	Diving stand, stainless steel, 3 meter	2 Clab	3	5.333	Ea.		195		195	320
0030	1 meter		5	3.200			117		117	193
0040	Diving board, 16' long, aluminum		5.40	2.963			109		109	178
0050	Fiberglass		5.40	2.963			109		109	178
0070	Ladders, heavy duty, stainless steel, 2 tread		14	1.143			42		42	69
0080	4 tread		12	1.333			49		49	80.50
0090	Lifeguard chair, stainless steel, fixed		5	3.200			117		117	193
0100	Slide, tubular, fiberglass, aluminum handrails & ladder, 5', straight		4	4			147		147	241
0110	8', curved		6	2.667			97.50		97.50	161
0120	10', curved		3	5.333			195		195	320
0130	12' straight, with platform		2.50	6.400			235		235	385
0140	Removable access ramp, stainless steel		4	4			147		147	241
0150	Removable stairs, stainless steel, collapsible		4	4			147		147	241

13 05 Common Work Results for Special Construction

13 05 05 – Selective Special Construction Demolition

13 05 05.90 Selective Demolition, Tension Structures	Crew	Daily Output	Labor-Hours	Unit	Material	2014 Bare Costs Labor	2014 Bare Costs Equipment	Total	Total Incl O&P
0010 **SELECTIVE DEMOLITION, TENSION STRUCTURES**									
0020 Steel/alum. frame, fabric shell, 60' clear span, 6,000 S.F.	B-41	2000	.022	SF Flr.		.83	.15	.98	1.53
0030 12,000 S.F.		2200	.020			.76	.13	.89	1.39
0040 80' clear span, 20,800 S.F.		2440	.018			.68	.12	.80	1.25
0050 100' clear span, 10,000 S.F.	L-5	4350	.013			.66	.17	.83	1.38
0060 26,000 S.F.		4600	.012			.62	.16	.78	1.30
0070 36,000 S.F.		5000	.011			.57	.15	.72	1.19

13 05 05.95 Selective Demo, X-Ray/Radio Freq Protection	Crew	Daily Output	Labor-Hours	Unit	Material	2014 Bare Costs Labor	2014 Bare Costs Equipment	Total	Total Incl O&P
0010 **SELECTIVE DEMO, X-RAY/RADIO FREQ PROTECTION**									
0020 Shielding lead, lined door frame, excl. hdwe., 1/16" thick	1 Clab	4.80	1.667	Ea.		61		61	100
0030 Lead sheets, 1/16" thick	2 Clab	270	.059	S.F.		2.17		2.17	3.57
0040 1/8" thick		240	.067			2.44		2.44	4.01
0050 Lead shielding, 1/4" thick		270	.059			2.17		2.17	3.57
0060 1/2" thick		240	.067			2.44		2.44	4.01
0070 Lead glass, 1/4" thick, 2.0 mm LE, 12" x 16"	2 Glaz	16	1	Ea.		44		44	71.50
0080 24" x 36"		8	2			88		88	143
0090 36" x 60"		4	4			176		176	286
0100 Lead glass window frame, with 1/16" lead & voice passage, 36" x 60"		4	4			176		176	286
0110 Lead glass window frame, 24" x 36"		8	2			88		88	143
0120 Lead gypsum board, 5/8" thick with 1/16" lead	2 Clab	320	.050	S.F.		1.83		1.83	3.01
0130 1/8" lead		280	.057			2.09		2.09	3.44
0140 1/32" lead		400	.040			1.47		1.47	2.41
0150 Butt joints, 1/8" lead or thicker, 2" x 7' long batten strip		480	.033	Ea.		1.22		1.22	2.01
0160 X-ray protection, average radiography room, up to 300 S.F., 1/16" lead, min		.50	32	Total		1,175		1,175	1,925
0170 Maximum		.30	53.333			1,950		1,950	3,200
0180 Deep therapy X-ray room, 250 kV cap, up to 300 S.F., 1/4" lead, min		.20	80			2,925		2,925	4,825
0190 Maximum		.12	133			4,875		4,875	8,025
0880 Radio frequency shielding, prefab or screen-type copper or steel, minimum		360	.044	SF Surf		1.63		1.63	2.68
0890 Average		310	.052			1.89		1.89	3.11
0895 Maximum		290	.055			2.02		2.02	3.32

13 11 Swimming Pools

13 11 13 – Below-Grade Swimming Pools

13 11 13.50 Swimming Pools	Crew	Daily Output	Labor-Hours	Unit	Material	2014 Bare Costs Labor	2014 Bare Costs Equipment	Total	Total Incl O&P
0011 **SWIMMING POOLS**, Outdoor, incl. equip. & houses, minimum								32.50	36
0300 Maximum								62	68
0400 Residential, incl. equipment, permanent type, minimum								10.90	12
0700 Maximum								22.50	25
0900 Municipal, including equipment only, over 5000 S.F., minimum								22.50	25
1000 Maximum								46.50	51
1300 Motel or apt., incl. equipment only, under 5000 S.F., minimum								20	22
1400 Maximum								31	34

13 12 Fountains

13 12 13 – Exterior Fountains

13 12 13.10 Yard Fountains	Crew	Daily Output	Labor-Hours	Unit	Material	2014 Bare Costs Labor	Equipment	Total	Total Incl O&P
0010 **YARD FOUNTAINS**									
0100 Outdoor fountain, 48" high with bowl and figures	2 Clab	2	8	Ea.	550	293		843	1,075

13 17 Tubs and Pools

13 17 13 – Hot Tubs

13 17 13.10 Redwood Hot Tub System

	Crew	Daily Output	Labor-Hours	Unit	Material	2014 Bare Costs Labor	Equipment	Total	Total Incl O&P
0010 **REDWOOD HOT TUB SYSTEM**									
7050 4' diameter x 4' deep	Q-1	1	16	Ea.	3,225	830		4,055	4,850
7150 6' diameter x 4' deep		.80	20		4,950	1,025		5,975	7,050
7200 8' diameter x 4' deep		.80	20		7,250	1,025		8,275	9,600

13 17 33 – Whirlpool Tubs

13 17 33.10 Whirlpool Bath

	Crew	Daily Output	Labor-Hours	Unit	Material	2014 Bare Costs Labor	Equipment	Total	Total Incl O&P
0010 **WHIRLPOOL BATH**									
6000 Whirlpool, bath with vented overflow, molded fiberglass									
6100 66" x 36" x 24"	Q-1	1	16	Ea.	3,325	830		4,155	4,950
6400 72" x 36" x 21"		1	16		1,800	830		2,630	3,300
6500 60" x 34" x 21"		1	16		1,700	830		2,530	3,175
6600 72" x 42" x 23"		1	16		2,175	830		3,005	3,700
6710 For color add					10%				
6711 For designer colors and trim add					25%				

13 21 Controlled Environment Rooms

13 21 26 – Cold Storage Rooms

13 21 26.50 Refrigeration

	Crew	Daily Output	Labor-Hours	Unit	Material	2014 Bare Costs Labor	Equipment	Total	Total Incl O&P
0010 **REFRIGERATION**									
0020 Curbs, 12" high, 4" thick, concrete	2 Carp	58	.276	L.F.	4.94	12.65		17.59	26.50
6300 Rule of thumb for complete units, w/o doors & refrigeration, cooler		146	.110	SF Flr.	143	5		148	166
6400 Freezer		109.60	.146	"	170	6.70		176.70	197

13 24 Special Activity Rooms

13 24 16 – Saunas

13 24 16.50 Saunas and Heaters

	Crew	Daily Output	Labor-Hours	Unit	Material	2014 Bare Costs Labor	Equipment	Total	Total Incl O&P
0010 **SAUNAS AND HEATERS**									
0020 Prefabricated, incl. heater & controls, 7' high, 6' x 4', C/C	L-7	2.20	12.727	Ea.	5,375	565		5,940	6,850
1700 Door only, cedar, 2'x6', with 1'x4' tempered insulated glass window	2 Carp	3.40	4.706		735	216		951	1,150
1800 Prehung, incl. jambs, pulls & hardware	"	12	1.333		730	61		791	900
2500 Heaters only (incl. above), wall mounted, to 200 C.F.					675			675	745
4480 For additional equipment, see Section 11 66 13.10									

13 24 26 – Steam Baths

13 24 26.50 Steam Baths and Components

	Crew	Daily Output	Labor-Hours	Unit	Material	2014 Bare Costs Labor	Equipment	Total	Total Incl O&P
0010 **STEAM BATHS AND COMPONENTS**									
0020 Heater, timer & head, single, to 140 C.F.	1 Plum	1.20	6.667	Ea.	1,450	385		1,835	2,200
0500 To 300 C.F.	"	1.10	7.273		1,550	420		1,970	2,350
2000 Multiple, motels, apts., 2 baths, w/blow-down assm., 500 C.F.	Q-1	1.30	12.308		7,950	640		8,590	9,750
2500 4 baths	"	.70	22.857		10,700	1,175		11,875	13,700

13 28 Athletic and Recreational Special Construction

13 28 33 – Athletic and Recreational Court Walls

13 28 33.50 Sport Court

13 28 33.50 Sport Court	Crew	Daily Output	Labor-Hours	Unit	Material	2014 Bare Costs Labor	Equipment	Total	Total Incl O&P
0010 **SPORT COURT**									
0020 Floors, No. 2 & better maple, 25/32" thick				SF Flr.				6.05	6.65
0300 Squash, regulation court in existing building, minimum				Court	36,800			36,800	40,400
0400 Maximum				"	41,000			41,000	45,000
0450 Rule of thumb for components:									
0470 Walls	3 Carp	.15	160	Court	11,000	7,325		18,325	24,200
0500 Floor	"	.25	96		8,725	4,400		13,125	16,800
0550 Lighting	2 Elec	.60	26.667	↓	2,100	1,425		3,525	4,500

13 34 Fabricated Engineered Structures

13 34 13 – Glazed Structures

13 34 13.13 Greenhouses

		Crew	Daily Output	Labor-Hours	Unit	Material	2014 Bare Costs Labor	Equipment	Total	Total Incl O&P
0010	**GREENHOUSES**, Shell only, stock units, not incl. 2' stub walls,									
0020	foundation, floors, heat or compartments									
0300	Residential type, free standing, 8'-6" long x 7'-6" wide	2 Carp	59	.271	SF Flr.	31.50	12.45		43.95	55.50
0400	10'-6" wide		85	.188		24	8.65		32.65	40.50
0600	13'-6" wide		108	.148		23.50	6.80		30.30	37
0700	17'-0" wide		160	.100		19.20	4.59		23.79	28.50
0900	Lean-to type, 3'-10" wide		34	.471		36.50	21.50		58	76
1000	6'-10" wide		58	.276		44.50	12.65		57.15	70
1050	8'-0" wide	↓	60	.267	↓	52	12.25		64.25	77
1100	Wall mounted to existing window, 3' x 3'	1 Carp	4	2	Ea.	1,550	91.50		1,641.50	1,850
1120	4' x 5'	"	3	2.667		1,900	122		2,022	2,300
3900	Cooling, 1200 CFM exhaust fan, add					289			289	320
4000	7850 CFM					995			995	1,100
4200	For heaters, 10 MBH, add					209			209	230
4300	60 MBH, add					760			760	835
4500	For benches, 2' x 8', add					157			157	173
4600	4' x 10', add				↓	190			190	209
4800	For controls, add, minimum				Total	240			240	264
4900	Maximum				"	750			750	825
5100	For humidification equipment, add				Ea.	400			400	440
5200	For vinyl shading, add				S.F.	.24			.24	.26

13 34 13.19 Swimming Pool Enclosures

		Crew	Daily Output	Labor-Hours	Unit	Material	2014 Bare Costs Labor	Equipment	Total	Total Incl O&P
0010	**SWIMMING POOL ENCLOSURES** Translucent, free standing									
0020	not including foundations, heat or light									
0200	Economy, minimum	2 Carp	200	.080	SF Hor.	60	3.67		63.67	72
0300	Maximum		100	.160		65	7.35		72.35	83.50
0400	Deluxe, minimum		100	.160		72	7.35		79.35	91
0600	Maximum	↓	70	.229	↓	93	10.50		103.50	119

13 34 23 – Fabricated Structures

13 34 23.16 Fabricated Control Booths

		Crew	Daily Output	Labor-Hours	Unit	Material	2014 Bare Costs Labor	Equipment	Total	Total Incl O&P
0010	**FABRICATED CONTROL BOOTHS**									
0100	Guard House, prefab conc. w/bullet resistant doors & windows, roof & wiring									
0110	8' x 8', Level III	L-10	1	24	Ea.	38,400	1,225	665	40,290	45,200
0120	8' x 8', Level IV	"	1	24	"	43,800	1,225	665	45,690	51,000

13 34 23.45 Kiosks

		Crew	Daily Output	Labor-Hours	Unit	Material	2014 Bare Costs Labor	Equipment	Total	Total Incl O&P
0010	**KIOSKS**									
0020	Round, advertising type, 5' diameter, 7' high, aluminum wall, illuminated				Ea.	23,500			23,500	25,800
0100	Aluminum wall, non-illuminated				↓	22,500			22,500	24,700

13 34 Fabricated Engineered Structures

13 34 23 – Fabricated Structures

13 34 23.45 Kiosks	Crew	Daily Output	Labor-Hours	Unit	Material	2014 Bare Costs Labor	Equipment	Total	Total Incl O&P
0500	Rectangular, 5' x 9', 7'-6" high, aluminum wall, illuminated				Ea.	25,500			25,500	28,000
0600	Aluminum wall, non-illuminated				↓	24,000			24,000	26,400

13 34 63 – Natural Fiber Construction

13 34 63.50 Straw Bale Construction

		Crew	Daily Output	Labor-Hours	Unit	Material	2014 Bare Costs Labor	Equipment	Total	Total Incl O&P
0010	**STRAW BALE CONSTRUCTION**									
2000	Straw bales wall, incl. labor & material complete, minimum	G			SF Flr.					130
2010	Maximum	G			"					160
2020	Straw bales in walls w/modified post and beam frame	G	2 Carp	320	.050	S.F.	6.05	2.29		8.34	10.40

13 42 Building Modules

13 42 63 – Detention Cell Modules

13 42 63.16 Steel Detention Cell Modules

		Crew	Daily Output	Labor-Hours	Unit	Material	2014 Bare Costs Labor	Equipment	Total	Total Incl O&P
0010	**STEEL DETENTION CELL MODULES**									
2000	Cells, prefab., 5' to 6' wide, 7' to 8' high, 7' to 8' deep,									
2010	bar front, cot, not incl. plumbing	E-4	1.50	21.333	Ea.	9,650	1,100	94.50	10,844.50	12,700

13 48 Sound, Vibration, and Seismic Control

13 48 13 – Manufactured Sound and Vibration Control Components

13 48 13.50 Audio Masking

		Crew	Daily Output	Labor-Hours	Unit	Material	2014 Bare Costs Labor	Equipment	Total	Total Incl O&P
0010	**AUDIO MASKING**, acoustical enclosure, 4" thick wall and ceiling									
0020	8# per S.F., up to 12' span	3 Carp	72	.333	SF Surf	33	15.30		48.30	61
0300	Better quality panels, 10.5# per S.F.		64	.375		37	17.20		54.20	69.50
0400	Reverb-chamber, 4" thick, parallel walls	↓	60	.400	↓	46.50	18.35		64.85	81

13 49 Radiation Protection

13 49 13 – Integrated X-Ray Shielding Assemblies

13 49 13.50 Lead Sheets

		Crew	Daily Output	Labor-Hours	Unit	Material	2014 Bare Costs Labor	Equipment	Total	Total Incl O&P
0010	**LEAD SHEETS**									
0300	Lead sheets, 1/16" thick	2 Lath	135	.119	S.F.	10.05	4.81		14.86	18.60
0400	1/8" thick		120	.133		20	5.40		25.40	30.50
0500	Lead shielding, 1/4" thick		135	.119		49	4.81		53.81	61.50
0550	1/2" thick	↓	120	.133	↓	83.50	5.40		88.90	100
1200	X-ray protection, average radiography or fluoroscopy									
1210	room, up to 300 S.F. floor, 1/16" lead, minimum	2 Lath	.25	64	Total	10,100	2,600		12,700	15,200
1500	Maximum, 7'-0" walls	"	.15	106	"	12,200	4,325		16,525	20,200
1600	Deep therapy X-ray room, 250 kV capacity,									
1800	up to 300 S.F. floor, 1/4" lead, minimum	2 Lath	.08	200	Total	28,300	8,125		36,425	43,900
1900	Maximum, 7'-0" walls		.06	266	"	34,900	10,800		45,700	55,500
1999	Minimum labor/equipment charge	↓	4.50	3.556	Job		144		144	227

13 49 21 – Lead Glazing

13 49 21.50 Lead Glazing

		Crew	Daily Output	Labor-Hours	Unit	Material	2014 Bare Costs Labor	Equipment	Total	Total Incl O&P
0010	**LEAD GLAZING**									
0600	Lead glass, 1/4" thick, 2.0 mm LE, 12" x 16"	2 Glaz	13	1.231	Ea.	360	54		414	490
0700	24" x 36"	"	8	2	"	1,275	88		1,363	1,550
2000	X-ray viewing panels, clear lead plastic									
2010	7 mm thick, 0.3 mm LE, 2.3 lb./S.F.	H-3	139	.115	S.F.	234	4.53		238.53	264

13 49 Radiation Protection

13 49 21 – Lead Glazing

	13 49 21.50 Lead Glazing	Crew	Daily Output	Labor-Hours	Unit	Material	2014 Bare Costs Labor	Equipment	Total	Total Incl O&P
2020	12 mm thick, 0.5 mm LE, 3.9 lb./S.F.	H-3	82	.195	S.F.	345	7.70		352.70	395
2030	18 mm thick, 0.8 mm LE, 5.9 lb./S.F.		54	.296		395	11.65		406.65	455
2040	22 mm thick, 1.0 mm LE, 7.2 lb./S.F.		44	.364		515	14.30		529.30	590
2050	35 mm thick, 1.5 mm LE, 11.5 lb./S.F.		28	.571		790	22.50		812.50	905
2060	46 mm thick, 2.0 mm LE, 15.0 lb./S.F.	↓	21	.762	↓	1,025	30		1,055	1,175
2090	For panels 12 S.F. to 48 S.F., add crating charge				Ea.					50

13 49 23 – Integrated RFI/EMI Shielding Assemblies

13 49 23.50 Modular Shielding Partitions

		Crew	Daily Output	Labor-Hours	Unit	Material	2014 Bare Costs Labor	Equipment	Total	Total Incl O&P
0010	**MODULAR SHIELDING PARTITIONS**									
4000	X-ray barriers, modular, panels mounted within framework for									
4002	attaching to floor, wall or ceiling, upper portion is clear lead									
4005	plastic window panels 48"H, lower portion is opaque leaded									
4008	steel panels 36"H, structural supports not incl.									
4010	1-section barrier, 36"W x 84"H overall									
4020	0.5 mm LE panels	H-3	6.40	2.500	Ea.	5,725	98.50		5,823.50	6,450
4030	0.8 mm LE panels		6.40	2.500		6,350	98.50		6,448.50	7,125
4040	1.0 mm LE panels		5.33	3.002		7,775	118		7,893	8,750
4050	1.5 mm LE panels	↓	5.33	3.002	↓	11,100	118		11,218	12,400
4060	2-section barrier, 72"W x 84"H overall									
4070	0.5 mm LE panels	H-3	4	4	Ea.	11,400	157		11,557	12,900
4080	0.8 mm LE panels		4	4		12,700	157		12,857	14,200
4090	1.0 mm LE panels		3.56	4.494		15,600	177		15,777	17,400
5000	1.5 mm LE panels	↓	3.20	5	↓	22,200	197		22,397	24,700
5010	3-section barrier, 108"W x 84"H overall									
5020	0.5 mm LE panels	H-3	3.20	5	Ea.	17,200	197		17,397	19,200
5030	0.8 mm LE panels		3.20	5		19,000	197		19,197	21,200
5040	1.0 mm LE panels		2.67	5.993		23,300	236		23,536	26,100
5050	1.5 mm LE panels	↓	2.46	6.504	↓	33,200	256		33,456	36,900
7000	X-ray barriers, mobile, mounted within framework w/casters on									
7005	bottom, clear lead plastic window panels on upper portion,									
7010	opaque on lower, 30"W x 75"H overall, incl. framework									
7020	24"H upper w/0.5 mm LE, 48"H lower w/0.8 mm LE	1 Carp	16	.500	Ea.	3,700	23		3,723	4,100
7030	48"W x 75"H overall, incl. framework									
7040	36"H upper w/0.5 mm LE, 36"H lower w/0.8 mm LE	1 Carp	16	.500	Ea.	6,000	23		6,023	6,650
7050	36"H upper w/1.0 mm LE, 36"H lower w/1.5 mm LE	"	16	.500	"	7,100	23		7,123	7,850
7060	72"W x 75"H overall, incl. framework									
7070	36"H upper w/0.5 mm LE, 36"H lower w/0.8 mm LE	1 Carp	16	.500	Ea.	7,100	23		7,123	7,850
7080	36"H upper w/1.0 mm LE, 36"H lower w/1.5 mm LE	"	16	.500	"	8,900	23		8,923	9,825

Division Notes

		CREW	DAILY OUTPUT	LABOR-HOURS	UNIT	BARE COSTS				TOTAL INCL O&P
						MAT.	LABOR	EQUIP.	TOTAL	

Estimating Tips

General

- Many products in Division 14 will require some type of support or blocking for installation not included with the item itself. Examples are supports for conveyors or tube systems, attachment points for lifts, and footings for hoists or cranes. Add these supports in the appropriate division.

14 10 00 Dumbwaiters
14 20 00 Elevators

- Dumbwaiters and elevators are estimated and purchased in a method similar to buying a car. The manufacturer has a base unit with standard features. Added to this base unit price will be whatever options the owner or specifications require. Increased load capacity, additional vertical travel, additional stops, higher speed, and cab finish options are items to be considered. When developing an estimate for dumbwaiters and elevators, remember that some items needed by the installers may have to be included as part of the general contract.

Examples are:
— shaftway
— rail support brackets
— machine room
— electrical supply
— sill angles
— electrical connections
— pits
— roof penthouses
— pit ladders

Check the job specifications and drawings before pricing.

- Installation of elevators and handicapped lifts in historic structures can require significant additional costs. The associated structural requirements may involve cutting into and repairing finishes, mouldings, flooring, etc. The estimator must account for these special conditions.

14 30 00 Escalators and Moving Walks

- Escalators and moving walks are specialty items installed by specialty contractors. There are numerous options associated with these items. For specific options, contact a manufacturer or contractor. In a method similar to estimating dumbwaiters and elevators, you should verify the extent of general contract work and add items as necessary.

14 40 00 Lifts
14 90 00 Other Conveying Equipment

- Products such as correspondence lifts, chutes, and pneumatic tube systems, as well as other items specified in this subdivision, may require trained installers. The general contractor might not have any choice as to who will perform the installation or when it will be performed. Long lead times are often required for these products, making early decisions in scheduling necessary.

Reference Numbers

Reference numbers are shown in shaded boxes at the beginning of some major classifications. These numbers refer to related items in the Reference Section. The reference information may be an estimating procedure, an alternate pricing method, or technical information.

Note: Not all subdivisions listed here necessarily appear in this publication.

Division 14 - Conveying Equipment

No part of this publication may be reproduced, stored in a retrieval system, or transmitted in any form or by any means without prior written permission of RSMeans, a division of Reed Construction Data.

14 11 Manual Dumbwaiters

14 11 10 - Hand Operated Dumbwaiters

14 11 10.20 Manual Dumbwaiters		Crew	Daily Output	Labor-Hours	Unit	Material	2014 Bare Costs Labor	Equipment	Total	Total Incl O&P
0010	**MANUAL DUMBWAITERS**									
0020	2 stop, minimum	2 Elev	.75	21.333	Ea.	2,925	1,575		4,500	5,675
0100	Maximum		.50	32	"	6,650	2,375		9,025	11,000
0300	For each additional stop, add	↓	.75	21.333	Stop	1,050	1,575		2,625	3,625

14 12 Electric Dumbwaiters

14 12 10 - Dumbwaiters

14 12 10.10 Electric Dumbwaiters

0010	**ELECTRIC DUMBWAITERS**									
0020	2 stop, minimum	2 Elev	.13	123	Ea.	7,375	9,125		16,500	22,200
0100	Maximum		.11	145	"	22,200	10,800		33,000	41,100
0600	For each additional stop, add	↓	.54	29.630	Stop	3,250	2,200		5,450	6,975
0750	Correspondence lift, 1 floor, 2 stop, 45 lb. capacity	2 Elec	.20	80	Ea.	8,350	4,275		12,625	15,800

14 21 Electric Traction Elevators

14 21 13 - Electric Traction Freight Elevators

14 21 13.10 Electric Traction Freight Elevators and Options

0010	**ELECTRIC TRACTION FREIGHT ELEVATORS AND OPTIONS**	R142000-10								
0425	Electric freight, base unit, 4000 lb., 200 fpm, 4 stop, std. fin.		2 Elev	.05	320	Ea.	106,500	23,700		130,200	154,000
0450	For 5000 lb. capacity, add	R142000-40					5,750			5,750	6,325
0500	For 6000 lb. capacity, add						14,400			14,400	15,800
0525	For 7000 lb. capacity, add						17,900			17,900	19,700
0550	For 8000 lb. capacity, add						35,800			35,800	39,300
0575	For 10000 lb. capacity, add						30,000			30,000	33,000
0600	For 12000 lb. capacity, add						36,400			36,400	40,100
0625	For 16000 lb. capacity, add						44,100			44,100	48,500
0650	For 20000 lb. capacity, add						49,100			49,100	54,000
0675	For increased speed, 250 fpm, add						17,000			17,000	18,700
0700	300 fpm, geared electric, add						21,400			21,400	23,600
0725	350 fpm, geared electric, add						26,100			26,100	28,700
0750	400 fpm, geared electric, add						30,500			30,500	33,600
0775	500 fpm, gearless electric, add						37,600			37,600	41,300
0800	600 fpm, gearless electric, add						45,000			45,000	49,500
0825	700 fpm, gearless electric, add						53,500			53,500	59,000
0850	800 fpm, gearless electric, add						61,500			61,500	68,000
0875	For class "B" loading, add						4,975			4,975	5,475
0900	For class "C-1" loading, add						7,100			7,100	7,825
0925	For class "C-2" loading, add						8,150			8,150	8,975
0950	For class "C-3" loading, add						10,800			10,800	11,900
0975	For travel over 40 V.L.F., add		2 Elev	7.25	2.207	V.L.F.	660	164		824	980
1000	For number of stops over 4, add		"	.27	59.259	Stop	4,075	4,400		8,475	11,300

14 21 23 - Electric Traction Passenger Elevators

14 21 23.10 Electric Traction Passenger Elevators and Options

0010	**ELECTRIC TRACTION PASSENGER ELEVATORS AND OPTIONS**									
1625	Electric pass., base unit, 2000 lb., 200 fpm, 4 stop, std. fin.	2 Elev	.05	320	Ea.	90,000	23,700		113,700	135,500
1650	For 2500 lb. capacity, add					3,675			3,675	4,050
1675	For 3000 lb. capacity, add					4,325			4,325	4,750
1700	For 3500 lb. capacity, add					5,500			5,500	6,050
1725	For 4000 lb. capacity, add	↓				6,700			6,700	7,350

14 21 Electric Traction Elevators

14 21 23 – Electric Traction Passenger Elevators

14 21 23.10 Electric Traction Passenger Elevators and Options	Crew	Daily Output	Labor-Hours	Unit	Material	2014 Bare Costs Labor	Equipment	Total	Total Incl O&P
1750	For 4500 lb. capacity, add				Ea.	8,800			8,800	9,675
1775	For 5000 lb. capacity, add					11,200			11,200	12,300
1800	For increased speed, 250 fpm, geared electric, add					4,975			4,975	5,475
1825	300 fpm, geared electric, add					7,825			7,825	8,600
1850	350 fpm, geared electric, add					9,000			9,000	9,900
1875	400 fpm, geared electric, add					11,800			11,800	12,900
1900	500 fpm, gearless electric, add					27,000			27,000	29,700
1925	600 fpm, gearless electric, add					42,800			42,800	47,100
1950	700 fpm, gearless electric, add					48,300			48,300	53,000
1975	800 fpm, gearless electric, add					53,000			53,000	58,500
2000	For travel over 40 V.L.F., add	2 Elev	7.25	2.207	V.L.F.	805	164		969	1,150
2025	For number of stops over 4, add		.27	59.259	Stop	5,550	4,400		9,950	12,900
2400	Electric hospital, base unit, 4000 lb., 200 fpm, 4 stop, std fin.		.05	320	Ea.	76,000	23,700		99,700	120,000
2425	For 4500 lb. capacity, add					5,225			5,225	5,750
2450	For 5000 lb. capacity, add					6,850			6,850	7,525
2475	For increased speed, 250 fpm, geared electric, add					5,075			5,075	5,575
2500	300 fpm, geared electric, add					7,750			7,750	8,525
2525	350 fpm, geared electric, add					8,950			8,950	9,825
2550	400 fpm, geared electric, add					11,700			11,700	12,800
2575	500 fpm, gearless electric, add					31,100			31,100	34,200
2600	600 fpm, gearless electric, add					45,300			45,300	49,800
2625	700 fpm, gearless electric, add					50,000			50,000	55,000
2650	800 fpm, gearless electric, add					56,000			56,000	61,500
2675	For travel over 40 V.L.F., add	2 Elev	7.25	2.207	V.L.F.	455	164		619	755
2700	For number of stops over 4, add	"	.27	59.259	Stop	4,150	4,400		8,550	11,400

14 21 33 – Electric Traction Residential Elevators

14 21 33.20 Residential Elevators

		Crew	Daily Output	Labor-Hours	Unit	Material	Labor	Equipment	Total	Total Incl O&P
0010	**RESIDENTIAL ELEVATORS**									
7000	Residential, cab type, 1 floor, 2 stop, minimum	2 Elev	.20	80	Ea.	11,200	5,925		17,125	21,600
7100	Maximum		.10	160		19,000	11,900		30,900	39,200
7200	2 floor, 3 stop, minimum		.12	133		16,700	9,875		26,575	33,700
7300	Maximum		.06	266		27,200	19,800		47,000	60,500

14 24 Hydraulic Elevators

14 24 13 – Hydraulic Freight Elevators

14 24 13.10 Hydraulic Freight Elevators and Options

		Crew	Daily Output	Labor-Hours	Unit	Material	Labor	Equipment	Total	Total Incl O&P
0010	**HYDRAULIC FREIGHT ELEVATORS AND OPTIONS**									
1025	Hydraulic freight, base unit, 2000 lb., 50 fpm, 2 stop, std. fin.	2 Elev	.10	160	Ea.	78,500	11,900		90,400	105,000
1050	For 2500 lb. capacity, add					3,775			3,775	4,175
1075	For 3000 lb. capacity, add					6,575			6,575	7,225
1100	For 3500 lb. capacity, add					11,700			11,700	12,800
1125	For 4000 lb. capacity, add					12,600			12,600	13,900
1150	For 4500 lb. capacity, add					14,800			14,800	16,300
1175	For 5000 lb. capacity, add					18,800			18,800	20,700
1200	For 6000 lb. capacity, add					23,000			23,000	25,300
1225	For 7000 lb. capacity, add					28,100			28,100	31,000
1250	For 8000 lb. capacity, add					31,700			31,700	34,900
1275	For 10000 lb. capacity, add					39,100			39,100	43,000
1300	For 12000 lb. capacity, add					50,500			50,500	56,000
1325	For 16000 lb. capacity, add					69,000			69,000	76,000

14 24 Hydraulic Elevators

14 24 13 – Hydraulic Freight Elevators

14 24 13.10 Hydraulic Freight Elevators and Options	Crew	Daily Output	Labor-Hours	Unit	Material	2014 Bare Costs Labor	Equipment	Total	Total Incl O&P
1350	For 20000 lb. capacity, add				Ea.	83,500			83,500	92,000
1375	For increased speed, 100 fpm, add					1,600			1,600	1,775
1400	125 fpm, add					3,525			3,525	3,875
1425	150 fpm, add					4,575			4,575	5,050
1450	175 fpm, add					7,350			7,350	8,075
1475	For class "B" loading, add					4,725			4,725	5,200
1500	For class "C-1" loading, add					7,075			7,075	7,775
1525	For class "C-2" loading, add					8,125			8,125	8,925
1550	For class "C-3" loading, add					10,400			10,400	11,500
1575	For travel over 20 V.L.F., add	2 Elev	7.25	2.207	V.L.F.	1,250	164		1,414	1,625
1600	For number of stops over 2, add	"	.27	59.259	Stop	3,375	4,400		7,775	10,500

14 24 23 – Hydraulic Passenger Elevators

14 24 23.10 Hydraulic Passenger Elevators and Options	Crew	Daily Output	Labor-Hours	Unit	Material	2014 Bare Costs Labor	Equipment	Total	Total Incl O&P
0010	HYDRAULIC PASSENGER ELEVATORS AND OPTIONS									
2050	Hyd. pass., base unit, 1500 lb., 100 fpm, 2 stop, std. fin.	2 Elev	.10	160	Ea.	38,600	11,900		50,500	61,000
2075	For 2000 lb. capacity, add					1,425			1,425	1,575
2100	For 2500 lb. capacity, add					2,750			2,750	3,025
2125	For 3000 lb. capacity, add					3,900			3,900	4,300
2150	For 3500 lb. capacity, add					6,575			6,575	7,250
2175	For 4000 lb. capacity, add					7,875			7,875	8,650
2200	For 4500 lb. capacity, add					10,300			10,300	11,300
2225	For 5000 lb. capacity, add					14,500			14,500	16,000
2250	For increased speed, 125 fpm, add					2,075			2,075	2,275
2275	150 fpm, add					2,800			2,800	3,075
2300	175 fpm, add					4,625			4,625	5,100
2325	200 fpm, add					8,850			8,850	9,725
2350	For travel over 12 V.L.F., add	2 Elev	7.25	2.207	V.L.F.	740	164		904	1,075
2375	For number of stops over 2, add		.27	59.259	Stop	1,800	4,400		6,200	8,800
2725	Hydraulic hospital, base unit, 4000 lb., 100 fpm, 2 stop, std. fin.		.10	160	Ea.	57,000	11,900		68,900	81,500
2775	For 4500 lb. capacity, add					6,400			6,400	7,050
2800	For 5000 lb. capacity, add					9,375			9,375	10,300
2825	For increased speed, 125 fpm, add					2,525			2,525	2,775
2850	150 fpm, add					3,300			3,300	3,625
2875	175 fpm, add					5,500			5,500	6,050
2900	200 fpm, add					8,050			8,050	8,850
2925	For travel over 12 V.L.F., add	2 Elev	7.25	2.207	V.L.F.	545	164		709	855
2950	For number of stops over 2, add	"	.27	59.259	Stop	4,000	4,400		8,400	11,200

14 27 Custom Elevator Cabs and Doors

14 27 13 – Custom Elevator Cab Finishes

14 27 13.10 Cab Finishes	Crew	Daily Output	Labor-Hours	Unit	Material	2014 Bare Costs Labor	Equipment	Total	Total Incl O&P
0010	CAB FINISHES									
3325	Passenger elevator cab finishes (based on 3500 lb. cab size)									
3350	Acrylic panel ceiling				Ea.	730			730	800
3375	Aluminum eggcrate ceiling					890			890	980
3400	Stainless steel doors					3,775			3,775	4,150
3425	Carpet flooring					595			595	655
3450	Epoxy flooring					450			450	495
3475	Quarry tile flooring					850			850	935
3500	Slate flooring					1,525			1,525	1,675

14 27 Custom Elevator Cabs and Doors

14 27 13 - Custom Elevator Cab Finishes

14 27 13.10 Cab Finishes	Crew	Daily Output	Labor-Hours	Unit	Material	2014 Bare Costs Labor	2014 Bare Costs Equipment	Total	Total Incl O&P
3525	Textured rubber flooring				Ea.	635			635	700
3550	Stainless steel walls					4,275			4,275	4,700
3575	Stainless steel returns at door				↓	1,125			1,125	1,225
4450	Hospital elevator cab finishes (based on 3500 lb. cab size)									
4475	Aluminum eggcrate ceiling				Ea.	890			890	980
4500	Stainless steel doors					3,775			3,775	4,150
4525	Epoxy flooring					450			450	495
4550	Quarry tile flooring					850			850	935
4575	Textured rubber flooring					635			635	700
4600	Stainless steel walls					4,375			4,375	4,800
4625	Stainless steel returns at door				↓	940			940	1,025

14 28 Elevator Equipment and Controls

14 28 10 - Elevator Equipment and Control Options

14 28 10.10 Elevator Controls and Doors

	14 28 10.10 Elevator Controls and Doors	Crew	Daily Output	Labor-Hours	Unit	Material	2014 Bare Costs Labor	2014 Bare Costs Equipment	Total	Total Incl O&P
0010	**ELEVATOR CONTROLS AND DOORS**									
2975	Passenger elevator options									
3000	2 car group automatic controls	2 Elev	.66	24.242	Ea.	4,800	1,800		6,600	8,050
3025	3 car group automatic controls		.44	36.364		9,200	2,700		11,900	14,300
3050	4 car group automatic controls		.33	48.485		18,400	3,600		22,000	25,900
3075	5 car group automatic controls		.26	61.538		33,300	4,575		37,875	43,800
3100	6 car group automatic controls		.22	72.727		67,500	5,400		72,900	82,500
3125	Intercom service		3	5.333		995	395		1,390	1,700
3150	Duplex car selective collective		.66	24.242		8,500	1,800		10,300	12,100
3175	Center opening 1 speed doors		2	8		1,900	595		2,495	3,025
3200	Center opening 2 speed doors		2	8		2,650	595		3,245	3,825
3225	Rear opening doors (opposite front)		2	8		4,050	595		4,645	5,400
3250	Side opening 2 speed doors		2	8		4,300	595		4,895	5,650
3275	Automatic emergency power switching		.66	24.242		1,150	1,800		2,950	4,025
3300	Manual emergency power switching	↓	8	2		495	148		643	775
3625	Hall finishes, stainless steel doors					1,625			1,625	1,800
3650	Stainless steel frames					1,400			1,400	1,525
3675	12 month maintenance contract								3,600	3,950
3700	Signal devices, hall lanterns	2 Elev	8	2		505	148		653	785
3725	Position indicators, up to 3		9.40	1.702		470	126		596	710
3750	Position indicators, per each over 3	↓	32	.500		420	37		457	520
3775	High speed heavy duty door opener					3,200			3,200	3,525
3800	Variable voltage, O.H. gearless machine, min.	2 Elev	.16	100		51,500	7,425		58,925	68,000
3815	Maximum		.07	228		80,000	16,900		96,900	114,000
3825	Basement installed geared machine	↓	.33	48.485	↓	49,100	3,600		52,700	59,500
3850	Freight elevator options									
3875	Doors, bi-parting	2 Elev	.66	24.242	Ea.	7,475	1,800		9,275	11,000
3900	Power operated door and gate	"	.66	24.242		23,700	1,800		25,500	28,800
3925	Finishes, steel plate floor					1,800			1,800	1,975
3950	14 ga. 1/4" x 4' steel plate walls					1,950			1,950	2,150
3975	12 month maintenance contract								3,600	3,950
4000	Signal devices, hall lanterns	2 Elev	8	2		495	148		643	775
4025	Position indicators, up to 3		9.40	1.702		485	126		611	725
4050	Position indicators, per each over 3		32	.500		425	37		462	525
4075	Variable voltage basement installed geared machine	↓	.66	24.242	↓	19,500	1,800		21,300	24,200
4100	Hospital elevator options									

387

14 28 Elevator Equipment and Controls

14 28 10 – Elevator Equipment and Control Options

14 28 10.10 Elevator Controls and Doors	Crew	Daily Output	Labor-Hours	Unit	Material	2014 Bare Costs Labor	2014 Bare Costs Equipment	Total	Total Incl O&P
4125	2 car group automatic controls	2 Elev	.66	24.242	Ea.	4,800	1,800		6,600	8,075
4150	3 car group automatic controls		.44	36.364		9,200	2,700		11,900	14,300
4175	4 car group automatic controls		.33	48.485		18,400	3,600		22,000	25,800
4200	5 car group automatic controls		.26	61.538		33,300	4,575		37,875	43,800
4225	6 car group automatic controls		.22	72.727		67,500	5,400		72,900	82,500
4250	Intercom service		3	5.333		990	395		1,385	1,700
4275	Duplex car selective collective		.66	24.242		8,500	1,800		10,300	12,100
4300	Center opening 1 speed doors		2	8		1,900	595		2,495	3,000
4325	Center opening 2 speed doors		2	8		2,475	595		3,070	3,650
4350	Rear opening doors (opposite front)		2	8		4,075	595		4,670	5,400
4375	Side opening 2 speed doors		2	8		6,150	595		6,745	7,700
4400	Automatic emergency power switching		.66	24.242		1,125	1,800		2,925	4,000
4425	Manual emergency power switching	↓	8	2		485	148		633	765
4675	Hall finishes, stainless steel doors					1,575			1,575	1,725
4700	Stainless steel frames					1,400			1,400	1,550
4725	12 month maintenance contract								3,600	3,950
4750	Signal devices, hall lanterns	2 Elev	8	2		475	148		623	755
4775	Position indicators, up to 3		9.40	1.702		470	126		596	710
4800	Position indicators, per each over 3	↓	32	.500		415	37		452	520
4825	High speed heavy duty door opener					3,200			3,200	3,525
4850	Variable voltage, O.H. gearless machine, min.	2 Elev	.16	100		51,000	7,425		58,425	67,500
4865	Maximum		.07	228		78,500	16,900		95,400	112,500
4875	Basement installed geared machine	↓	.33	48.485	↓	20,100	3,600		23,700	27,700
5000	Drilling for piston, casing included, 18" diameter	B-48	80	.700	V.L.F.	53.50	29	36.50	119	146

14 42 Wheelchair Lifts

14 42 13 – Inclined Wheelchair Lifts

14 42 13.10 Inclined Wheelchair Lifts and Stairclimbers

0010	INCLINED WHEELCHAIR LIFTS AND STAIRCLIMBERS									
7700	Stair climber (chair lift), single seat, minimum	2 Elev	1	16	Ea.	5,325	1,175		6,500	7,700
7800	Maximum		.20	80		7,350	5,925		13,275	17,300
8700	Stair lift, minimum		1	16		14,500	1,175		15,675	17,700
8900	Maximum	↓	.20	80	↓	22,900	5,925		28,825	34,400

14 42 16 – Vertical Wheelchair Lifts

14 42 16.10 Wheelchair Lifts

0010	WHEELCHAIR LIFTS									
8000	Wheelchair lift, minimum	2 Elev	1	16	Ea.	7,325	1,175		8,500	9,875
8500	Maximum	"	.50	32	"	17,300	2,375		19,675	22,700

14 45 Vehicle Lifts

14 45 10 – Hydraulic Vehicle Lifts

14 45 10.10 Hydraulic Lifts	Crew	Daily Output	Labor-Hours	Unit	Material	2014 Bare Costs Labor	Equipment	Total	Total Incl O&P
0010 **HYDRAULIC LIFTS**									
2200 Single post, 8000 lb. capacity	L-4	.40	60	Ea.	5,500	2,575		8,075	10,300
2810 Double post, 6000 lb. capacity		2.67	8.989		7,750	385		8,135	9,150
2815 9000 lb. capacity		2.29	10.480		18,400	450		18,850	20,900
2820 15,000 lb. capacity		2	12		20,800	515		21,315	23,600
2822 26,000 lb. capacity		1.80	13.333		13,700	575		14,275	16,000
2825 30,000 lb. capacity		1.60	15		45,900	645		46,545	51,500
2830 Ramp style, 4 post, 25,000 lb. capacity		2	12		18,000	515		18,515	20,600
2835 35,000 lb. capacity		1	24		83,500	1,025		84,525	93,500
2840 50,000 lb. capacity		1	24		93,500	1,025		94,525	104,500
2845 75,000 lb. capacity		1	24		108,500	1,025		109,525	121,000
2850 For drive thru tracks, add, minimum					1,150			1,150	1,275
2855 Maximum					1,975			1,975	2,175
2860 Ramp extensions, 3' (set of 2)					945			945	1,050
2865 Rolling jack platform					3,300			3,300	3,625
2870 Electric/hydraulic jacking beam					8,825			8,825	9,700
2880 Scissor lift, portable, 6000 lb. capacity					8,650			8,650	9,525

14 51 Correspondence and Parcel Lifts

14 51 10 – Electric Correspondence and Parcel Lifts

14 51 10.10 Correspondence Lifts	Crew	Daily Output	Labor-Hours	Unit	Material	2014 Bare Costs Labor	Equipment	Total	Total Incl O&P
0010 **CORRESPONDENCE LIFTS**									
0020 1 floor, 2 stop, 25 lb. capacity, electric	2 Elev	.20	80	Ea.	6,500	5,925		12,425	16,300
0100 Hand, 5 lb. capacity	"	.20	80	"	2,500	5,925		8,425	11,900

14 91 Facility Chutes

14 91 33 – Laundry and Linen Chutes

14 91 33.10 Chutes

	Crew	Daily Output	Labor-Hours	Unit	Material	2014 Bare Costs Labor	Equipment	Total	Total Incl O&P
0011 **CHUTES**, linen, trash or refuse									
0050 Aluminized steel, 16 ga., 18" diameter	2 Shee	3.50	4.571	Floor	1,700	250		1,950	2,275
0100 24" diameter		3.20	5		1,775	274		2,049	2,375
0400 Galvanized steel, 16 ga., 18" diameter		3.50	4.571		1,000	250		1,250	1,500
0500 24" diameter		3.20	5		1,125	274		1,399	1,675
0800 Stainless steel, 18" diameter		3.50	4.571		3,000	250		3,250	3,700
0900 24" diameter		3.20	5		3,150	274		3,424	3,875

14 91 82 – Trash Chutes

14 91 82.10 Trash Chutes and Accessories

	Crew	Daily Output	Labor-Hours	Unit	Material	2014 Bare Costs Labor	Equipment	Total	Total Incl O&P
0010 **TRASH CHUTES AND ACCESSORIES**									
9000 Minimum labor/equipment charge	1 Shee	1	8	Job		440		440	690

14 92 Pneumatic Tube Systems

14 92 10 – Conventional, Automatic and Computer Controlled Pneumatic Tube Systems

14 92 10.10 Pneumatic Tube Systems	Crew	Daily Output	Labor-Hours	Unit	Material	2014 Bare Costs Labor	Equipment	Total	Total Incl O&P
0010 **PNEUMATIC TUBE SYSTEMS**									
0020 100' long, single tube, 2 stations, stock									
0100 3" diameter	2 Stpi	.12	133	Total	6,600	7,800		14,400	19,500
0300 4" diameter	"	.09	177	"	7,450	10,400		17,850	24,400
0400 Twin tube, two stations or more, conventional system									
0700 3" round	2 Stpi	46	.348	L.F.	36	20.50		56.50	71
1050 Add for blower		2	8	System	5,200	470		5,670	6,450
1110 Plus for each round station, add		7.50	2.133	Ea.	1,275	125		1,400	1,600
1200 Alternate pricing method: base cost, minimum		.75	21.333	Total	6,375	1,250		7,625	8,975
1300 Maximum		.25	64	"	12,700	3,750		16,450	19,800
1500 Plus total system length, add, minimum		93.40	.171	L.F.	8.20	10		18.20	24.50
1600 Maximum		37.60	.426	"	24.50	25		49.50	65.50

Estimating Tips

Pipe for fire protection and all uses is located in Subdivisions 21 11 13 and 22 11 13.

The labor adjustment factors listed in Subdivision 22 01 02.20 also apply to Division 21.

Many, but not all, areas in the U.S. require backflow protection in the fire system. It is advisable to check local building codes for specific requirements.

For your reference, the following is a list of the most applicable Fire Codes and Standards which may be purchased from the NFPA, 1 Batterymarch Park, Quincy, MA 02169-7471.

NFPA 1: Uniform Fire Code

NFPA 10: Portable Fire Extinguishers

NFPA 11: Low-, Medium-, and High-Expansion Foam

NFPA 12: Carbon Dioxide Extinguishing Systems (Also companion 12A)

NFPA 13: Installation of Sprinkler Systems (Also companion 13D, 13E, and 13R)

NFPA 14: Installation of Standpipe and Hose Systems

NFPA 15: Water Spray Fixed Systems for Fire Protection

NFPA 16: Installation of Foam-Water Sprinkler and Foam-Water Spray Systems

NFPA 17: Dry Chemical Extinguishing Systems (Also companion 17A)

NFPA 18: Wetting Agents

NFPA 20: Installation of Stationary Pumps for Fire Protection

NFPA 22: Water Tanks for Private Fire Protection

NFPA 24: Installation of Private Fire Service Mains and their Appurtenances

NFPA 25: Inspection, Testing and Maintenance of Water-Based Fire Protection

Reference Numbers

Reference numbers are shown in shaded boxes at the beginning of some major classifications. These numbers refer to related items in the Reference Section. The reference information may be an estimating procedure, an alternate pricing method, or technical information.

Note: Not all subdivisions listed here necessarily appear in this publication.

Note: **Trade Service,** *in part, has been used as a reference source for some of the material prices used in Division 21.*

21 05 Common Work Results for Fire Suppression

21 05 23 – General-Duty Valves for Water-Based Fire-Suppression Piping

21 05 23.50 General-Duty Valves	Crew	Daily Output	Labor-Hours	Unit	Material	2014 Bare Costs Labor	Equipment	Total	Total Incl O&P
0010 **GENERAL-DUTY VALVES**, for water-based fire suppression									
6500 Check, swing, C.I. body, brass fittings, auto. ball drip									
6520 4" size	Q-12	3	5.333	Ea.	335	266		601	780
9990 Minimum labor/equipment charge	1 Spri	3	2.667	Job		148		148	231

21 11 Facility Fire-Suppression Water-Service Piping

21 11 16 – Facility Fire Hydrants

21 11 16.50 Fire Hydrants for Buildings

	Crew	Daily Output	Labor-Hours	Unit	Material	Labor	Equipment	Total	Total Incl O&P
0010 **FIRE HYDRANTS FOR BUILDINGS**									
3750 Hydrants, wall, w/caps, single, flush, polished brass									
3800 2-1/2" x 2-1/2"	Q-12	5	3.200	Ea.	193	160		353	460
4350 Double, projecting, polished brass									
4400 2-1/2" x 2-1/2" x 4"	Q-12	5	3.200	Ea.	242	160		402	515

21 11 19 – Fire-Department Connections

21 11 19.50 Connections for the Fire-Department

	Crew	Daily Output	Labor-Hours	Unit	Material	Labor	Equipment	Total	Total Incl O&P
0010 **CONNECTIONS FOR THE FIRE-DEPARTMENT**									
7140 Standpipe connections, wall, w/plugs & chains									
7280 Double, flush, polished brass									
7300 2-1/2" x 2-1/2" x 4"	Q-12	5	3.200	Ea.	495	160		655	795
9990 Minimum labor/equipment charge	1 Spri	4	2	Job		111		111	173

21 12 Fire-Suppression Standpipes

21 12 13 – Fire-Suppression Hoses and Nozzles

21 12 13.50 Fire Hoses and Nozzles

	Crew	Daily Output	Labor-Hours	Unit	Material	Labor	Equipment	Total	Total Incl O&P
0010 **FIRE HOSES AND NOZZLES**									
0200 Adapters, rough brass, straight hose threads									
0220 One piece, female to male, rocker lugs									
0240 1" x 1"				Ea.	46			46	50.50
0320 2" x 2"					42			42	46
0380 2-1/2" x 2-1/2"					19			19	21
2200 Hose, less couplings									
2260 Synthetic jacket, lined, 300 lb. test, 1-1/2" diameter	Q-12	2600	.006	L.F.	3.09	.31		3.40	3.88
2280 2-1/2" diameter		2200	.007		5.30	.36		5.66	6.40
2360 High strength, 500 lb. test, 1-1/2" diameter		2600	.006		3.18	.31		3.49	3.98
2380 2-1/2" diameter		2200	.007		5.65	.36		6.01	6.75
5600 Nozzles, brass									
5620 Adjustable fog, 3/4" booster line				Ea.	106			106	116
5640 1-1/2" leader line					75.50			75.50	83
5660 2-1/2" direct connection					143			143	158
5680 2-1/2" playpipe nozzle					209			209	230
5780 For chrome plated, add					8%				
9900 Minimum labor/equipment charge	1 Plum	2	4	Job		230		230	360

21 12 19 – Fire-Suppression Hose Racks

21 12 19.50 Fire Hose Racks

	Crew	Daily Output	Labor-Hours	Unit	Material	Labor	Equipment	Total	Total Incl O&P
0010 **FIRE HOSE RACKS**									
2600 Hose rack, swinging, for 1-1/2" diameter hose,									
2620 Enameled steel, 50' & 75' lengths of hose	Q-12	20	.800	Ea.	58	40		98	127

21 12 Fire-Suppression Standpipes

21 12 23 – Fire-Suppression Hose Valves

21 12 23.70 Fire Hose Valves	Crew	Daily Output	Labor-Hours	Unit	Material	2014 Bare Costs Labor	Equipment	Total	Total Incl O&P
0010 **FIRE HOSE VALVES**									
3000 Gate, hose, wheel handle, N.R.S., rough brass, 1-1/2"	1 Spri	12	.667	Ea.	128	37		165	199
3040 2-1/2", 300 lb.	"	7	1.143		180	63.50		243.50	297
3080 For polished brass, add					40%				
3090 For polished chrome, add					50%				

21 13 Fire-Suppression Sprinkler Systems

21 13 13 – Wet-Pipe Sprinkler Systems

21 13 13.50 Wet-Pipe Sprinkler System Components

	Crew	Daily Output	Labor-Hours	Unit	Material	2014 Bare Costs Labor	Equipment	Total	Total Incl O&P
0010 **WET-PIPE SPRINKLER SYSTEM COMPONENTS**									
1220 Water motor, complete with gong	1 Spri	4	2	Ea.	390	111		501	605
1800 Firecycle system, controls, includes panel,									
1820 batteries, solenoid valves and pressure switches	Q-13	1	32	Ea.	19,800	1,700		21,500	24,300
1860 Detector	1 Spri	16	.500	"	680	27.50		707.50	795
1900 Flexible sprinkler head connectors									
1910 Braided stainless steel hose with mounting bracket									
1920 1/2" and 3/4" outlet size									
1940 36" length	1 Spri	30	.267	Ea.	70.50	14.75		85.25	101
1960 60" length	"	22	.364	"	81	20		101	121
1982 May replace hard-pipe armovers									
1984 For wet, pre-action, deluge or dry pipe systems									
2600 Sprinkler heads, not including supply piping									
3700 Standard spray, pendent or upright, brass, 135°F to 286°F									
3740 1/2" NPT, 1/2" orifice	1 Spri	16	.500	Ea.	9.35	27.50		36.85	54
3790 For riser & feeder piping, see Section 22 11 13.00									

21 13 16 – Dry-Pipe Sprinkler Systems

21 13 16.50 Dry-Pipe Sprinkler System Components

	Crew	Daily Output	Labor-Hours	Unit	Material	2014 Bare Costs Labor	Equipment	Total	Total Incl O&P
0010 **DRY-PIPE SPRINKLER SYSTEM COMPONENTS**									
0600 Accelerator	1 Spri	8	1	Ea.	715	55.50		770.50	870
0800 Air compressor for dry pipe system, automatic, complete									
0820 30 gal. system capacity, 3/4 HP	1 Spri	1.30	6.154	Ea.	735	340		1,075	1,350
2600 Sprinkler heads, not including supply piping									
2640 Dry, pendent, 1/2" orifice, 3/4" or 1" NPT									
2660 1/2" to 6" length	1 Spri	14	.571	Ea.	117	31.50		148.50	178
2700 15-1/4" to 18" length	"	14	.571		137	31.50		168.50	201
8200 Dry pipe valve, incl. trim and gauges, 3" size	Q-12	2	8		2,500	400		2,900	3,375
8220 4" size	"	1	16		2,725	800		3,525	4,250

21 13 39 – Foam-Water Systems

21 13 39.50 Foam-Water System Components

	Crew	Daily Output	Labor-Hours	Unit	Material	2014 Bare Costs Labor	Equipment	Total	Total Incl O&P
0010 **FOAM-WATER SYSTEM COMPONENTS**									
2600 Sprinkler heads, not including supply piping									
3600 Foam-water, pendent or upright, 1/2" NPT	1 Spri	12	.667	Ea.	198	37		235	275

Division Notes

		CREW	DAILY OUTPUT	LABOR-HOURS	UNIT	BARE COSTS				TOTAL INCL O&P
						MAT.	LABOR	EQUIP.	TOTAL	

Estimating Tips

22 10 00 Plumbing Piping and Pumps

This subdivision is primarily basic pipe and related materials. The pipe may be used by any of the mechanical disciplines, i.e., plumbing, fire protection, heating, and air conditioning.

Note: CPVC plastic piping approved for fire protection is located in 21 11 13.

- The labor adjustment factors listed in Subdivision 22 01 02.20 apply throughout Divisions 21, 22, and 23. CAUTION: the correct percentage may vary for the same items. For example, the percentage add for the basic pipe installation should be based on the maximum height that the craftsman must install for that particular section. If the pipe is to be located 14' above the floor but it is suspended on threaded rod from beams, the bottom flange of which is 18' high (4' rods), then the height is actually 18' and the add is 20%. The pipe coverer, however, does not have to go above the 14', and so his or her add should be 10%.

- Most pipe is priced first as straight pipe with a joint (coupling, weld, etc.) every 10' and a hanger usually every 10'.

There are exceptions with hanger spacing such as for cast iron pipe (5') and plastic pipe (3 per 10'). Following each type of pipe there are several lines listing sizes and the amount to be subtracted to delete couplings and hangers. This is for pipe that is to be buried or supported together on trapeze hangers. The reason that the couplings are deleted is that these runs are usually long, and frequently longer lengths of pipe are used. By deleting the couplings, the estimator is expected to look up and add back the correct reduced number of couplings.

- When preparing an estimate, it may be necessary to approximate the fittings. Fittings usually run between 25% and 50% of the cost of the pipe. The lower percentage is for simpler runs, and the higher number is for complex areas, such as mechanical rooms.

- For historic restoration projects, the systems must be as invisible as possible, and pathways must be sought for pipes, conduit, and ductwork. While installations in accessible spaces (such as basements and attics) are relatively straightforward to estimate, labor costs may be more difficult to determine when delivery systems must be concealed.

22 40 00 Plumbing Fixtures

- Plumbing fixture costs usually require two lines: the fixture itself and its "rough-in, supply, and waste."

- In the Assemblies Section (Plumbing D2010) for the desired fixture, the System Components Group at the center of the page shows the fixture on the first line. The rest of the list (fittings, pipe, tubing, etc.) will total up to what we refer to in the Unit Price section as "Rough-in, supply, waste, and vent." Note that for most fixtures we allow a nominal 5' of tubing to reach from the fixture to a main or riser.

- Remember that gas- and oil-fired units need venting.

Reference Numbers

Reference numbers are shown in shaded boxes at the beginning of some major classifications. These numbers refer to related items in the Reference Section. The reference information may be an estimating procedure, an alternate pricing method, or technical information.

Note: Not all subdivisions listed here necessarily appear in this publication.

Note: **Trade Service,** *in part, has been used as a reference source for some of the material prices used in Division 22.*

22 01 Operation and Maintenance of Plumbing

22 01 02 – Labor Adjustments

22 01 02.20 Labor Adjustment Factors		Crew	Daily Output	Labor-Hours	Unit	Material	2014 Bare Costs Labor	Equipment	Total	Total Incl O&P
0010	**LABOR ADJUSTMENT FACTORS**, (For Div. 21, 22 and 23) R220102-20									
0100	Labor factors, The below are reasonable suggestions, however									
0110	each project must be evaluated for its own peculiarities, and									
0120	the adjustments be increased or decreased depending on the									
0130	severity of the special conditions.									
1000	Add to labor for elevated installation (Above floor level)									
1080	10' to 14.5' high						10%			
1100	15' to 19.5' high						20%			
1120	20' to 24.5' high						25%			
1140	25' to 29.5' high						35%			
1160	30' to 34.5' high						40%			
1180	35' to 39.5' high						50%			
1200	40' and higher						55%			
2000	Add to labor for crawl space									
2100	3' high						40%			
2140	4' high						30%			
3000	Add to labor for multi-story building									
3100	Add per floor for floors 3 thru 19						2%			
3140	Add per floor for floors 20 and up						4%			
4000	Add to labor for working in existing occupied buildings									
4100	Hospital						35%			
4140	Office building						25%			
4180	School						20%			
4220	Factory or warehouse						15%			
4260	Multi dwelling						15%			
5000	Add to labor, miscellaneous									
5100	Cramped shaft						35%			
5140	Congested area						15%			
5180	Excessive heat or cold						30%			
9000	Labor factors, The above are reasonable suggestions, however									
9010	each project should be evaluated for its own peculiarities.									
9100	Other factors to be considered are:									
9140	Movement of material and equipment through finished areas									
9180	Equipment room									
9220	Attic space									
9260	No service road									
9300	Poor unloading/storage area									
9340	Congested site area/heavy traffic									

22 05 Common Work Results for Plumbing

22 05 05 – Selective Plumbing Demolition

22 05 05.10 Plumbing Demolition

		Crew	Daily Output	Labor-Hours	Unit	Material	Labor	Equipment	Total	Total Incl O&P
0010	**PLUMBING DEMOLITION** R220105-10									
1020	Fixtures, including 10' piping									
1100	Bathtubs, cast iron R024119-10	1 Plum	4	2	Ea.		115		115	180
1120	Fiberglass		6	1.333			76.50		76.50	120
1140	Steel		5	1.600			92		92	144
1200	Lavatory, wall hung		10	.800			46		46	72
1220	Counter top		8	1			57.50		57.50	90
1300	Sink, single compartment		8	1			57.50		57.50	90
1320	Double compartment		7	1.143			66		66	103

22 05 Common Work Results for Plumbing

22 05 05 – Selective Plumbing Demolition

22 05 05.10 Plumbing Demolition

	Crew	Daily Output	Labor-Hours	Unit	Material	2014 Bare Costs Labor	Equipment	Total	Total Incl O&P
1400	Water closet, floor mounted	1 Plum	8	1	Ea.		57.50		57.50	90
1420	Wall mounted		7	1.143			66		66	103
1500	Urinal, floor mounted		4	2			115		115	180
1520	Wall mounted		7	1.143			66		66	103
1600	Water fountains, free standing		8	1			57.50		57.50	90
1620	Wall or deck mounted		6	1.333			76.50		76.50	120
2000	Piping, metal, up thru 1-1/2" diameter		200	.040	L.F.		2.30		2.30	3.59
2050	2" thru 3-1/2" diameter		150	.053			3.07		3.07	4.79
2100	4" thru 6" diameter	2 Plum	100	.160			9.20		9.20	14.35
2150	8" thru 14" diameter	"	60	.267			15.35		15.35	24
2153	16" thru 20" diameter	Q-18	70	.343			18.70	.79	19.49	30
2155	24" thru 26" diameter		55	.436			24	1	25	38
2156	30" thru 36" diameter		40	.600			33	1.38	34.38	52.50
2160	Plastic pipe with fittings, up thru 1-1/2" diameter	1 Plum	250	.032			1.84		1.84	2.87
2162	2" thru 3" diameter	"	200	.040			2.30		2.30	3.59
2164	4" thru 6" diameter	Q-1	200	.080			4.14		4.14	6.45
2166	8" thru 14" diameter		150	.107			5.55		5.55	8.60
2168	16" diameter		100	.160			8.30		8.30	12.95
2250	Water heater, 40 gal.	1 Plum	6	1.333	Ea.		76.50		76.50	120
6000	Remove and reset fixtures, minimum		6	1.333			76.50		76.50	120
6100	Maximum		4	2			115		115	180
9000	Minimum labor/equipment charge		2	4	Job		230		230	360

22 05 23 – General-Duty Valves for Plumbing Piping

22 05 23.20 Valves, Bronze

	Crew	Daily Output	Labor-Hours	Unit	Material	2014 Bare Costs Labor	Equipment	Total	Total Incl O&P
0010	**VALVES, BRONZE**									
1020	Angle, 150 lb., rising stem, threaded									
1070	3/4"	1 Plum	20	.400	Ea.	184	23		207	238
1080	1"		19	.421		265	24		289	330
1100	1-1/2"		13	.615		445	35.50		480.50	545
1110	2"		11	.727		715	42		757	850
1300	Ball									
1398	Threaded, 150 psi									
1460	3/4"	1 Plum	20	.400	Ea.	22.50	23		45.50	60.50
1750	Check, swing, class 150, regrinding disc, threaded									
1850	1/2"	1 Plum	24	.333	Ea.	72	19.20		91.20	109
1860	3/4"		20	.400		95	23		118	140
1870	1"		19	.421		137	24		161	188
1890	1-1/2"		13	.615		230	35.50		265.50	310
1900	2"		11	.727		340	42		382	435
2850	Gate, N.R.S., soldered, 125 psi									
2920	1/2"	1 Plum	24	.333	Ea.	46.50	19.20		65.70	81.50
2940	3/4"		20	.400		53	23		76	94
2950	1"		19	.421		75	24		99	121
2970	1-1/2"		13	.615		129	35.50		164.50	198
2980	2"		11	.727		182	42		224	267
4850	Globe, class 150, rising stem, threaded									
4950	1/2"	1 Plum	24	.333	Ea.	101	19.20		120.20	141
4960	3/4"	"	20	.400	"	135	23		158	184
5600	Relief, pressure & temperature, self-closing, ASME, threaded									
5640	3/4"	1 Plum	28	.286	Ea.	253	16.45		269.45	305
5650	1"		24	.333		405	19.20		424.20	475
5660	1-1/4"		20	.400		895	23		918	1,025

22 05 23 – General-Duty Valves for Plumbing Piping

22 05 23.20 Valves, Bronze

		Crew	Daily Output	Labor-Hours	Unit	Material	2014 Bare Costs Labor	Equipment	Total	Total Incl O&P
5670	1-1/2"	1 Plum	18	.444	Ea.	1,250	25.50		1,275.50	1,425
5680	2"	↓	16	.500	↓	1,350	29		1,379	1,550
6400	Pressure, water, ASME, threaded									
6440	3/4"	1 Plum	28	.286	Ea.	116	16.45		132.45	153
6450	1"		24	.333		260	19.20		279.20	315
6470	1-1/2"	↓	18	.444	↓	570	25.50		595.50	665
6900	Reducing, water pressure									
6920	300 psi to 25-75 psi, threaded or sweat									
6940	1/2"	1 Plum	24	.333	Ea.	395	19.20		414.20	465
6950	3/4"		20	.400		395	23		418	470
6960	1"	↓	19	.421	↓	615	24		639	715
8350	Tempering, water, sweat connections									
8400	1/2"	1 Plum	24	.333	Ea.	109	19.20		128.20	150
8440	3/4"	"	20	.400	"	126	23		149	175
8650	Threaded connections									
8700	1/2"	1 Plum	24	.333	Ea.	126	19.20		145.20	169
8740	3/4"	↓	20	.400	"	770	23		793	880
9000	Minimum labor/equipment charge	↓	4	2	Job		115		115	180

22 05 23.60 Valves, Plastic

		Crew	Daily Output	Labor-Hours	Unit	Material	2014 Bare Costs Labor	Equipment	Total	Total Incl O&P
0010	**VALVES, PLASTIC**									
1150	Ball, PVC, socket or threaded, single union									
1230	1/2"	1 Plum	26	.308	Ea.	28	17.70		45.70	58.50
1240	3/4"		25	.320		32	18.40		50.40	64
1250	1"		23	.348		40	20		60	75.50
1260	1-1/4"		21	.381		54	22		76	93.50
1270	1-1/2"		20	.400		64.50	23		87.50	107
1280	2"	↓	17	.471	↓	93.50	27		120.50	146
1650	CPVC, socket or threaded, single union									
1700	1/2"	1 Plum	26	.308	Ea.	56	17.70		73.70	89
1720	3/4"		25	.320		70	18.40		88.40	106
1730	1"		23	.348		84	20		104	124
1750	1-1/4"		21	.381		134	22		156	182
1760	1-1/2"		20	.400		134	23		157	184
1770	2"	↓	17	.471	↓	185	27		212	246
3150	Ball check, PVC, socket or threaded									
3290	2"	1 Plum	17	.471	Ea.	140	27		167	197
9000	Minimum labor/equipment charge	"	3.50	2.286	Job		132		132	205

22 05 76 – Facility Drainage Piping Cleanouts

22 05 76.10 Cleanouts

		Crew	Daily Output	Labor-Hours	Unit	Material	2014 Bare Costs Labor	Equipment	Total	Total Incl O&P
0010	**CLEANOUTS**									
0060	Floor type									
0080	Round or square, scoriated nickel bronze top									
0100	2" pipe size	1 Plum	10	.800	Ea.	183	46		229	273
0120	3" pipe size		8	1		274	57.50		331.50	390
0140	4" pipe size	↓	6	1.333	↓	274	76.50		350.50	420
0980	Round top, recessed for terrazzo									
1000	2" pipe size	1 Plum	9	.889	Ea.	183	51		234	281
1080	3" pipe size		6	1.333		274	76.50		350.50	420
1100	4" pipe size	↓	4	2		274	115		389	480
1120	5" pipe size	Q-1	6	2.667	↓	345	138		483	595
9000	Minimum labor/equipment charge	1 Plum	3	2.667	Job		153		153	239

22 05 Common Work Results for Plumbing

22 05 76 – Facility Drainage Piping Cleanouts

22 05 76.20 Cleanout Tees		Crew	Daily Output	Labor-Hours	Unit	Material	2014 Bare Costs Labor	Equipment	Total	Total Incl O&P
0010	**CLEANOUT TEES**									
0100	Cast iron, B&S, with countersunk plug									
0220	3" pipe size	1 Plum	3.60	2.222	Ea.	270	128		398	495
0240	4" pipe size	"	3.30	2.424	"	335	140		475	590
0500	For round smooth access cover, same price									
4000	Plastic, tees and adapters. Add plugs									
4010	ABS, DWV									
4020	Cleanout tee, 1-1/2" pipe size	1 Plum	15	.533	Ea.	20	30.50		50.50	70
9000	Minimum labor/equipment charge	"	2.75	2.909	Job		167		167	261

22 07 Plumbing Insulation

22 07 16 – Plumbing Equipment Insulation

22 07 16.10 Insulation for Plumbing Equipment

			Crew	Daily Output	Labor-Hours	Unit	Material	2014 Bare Costs Labor	Equipment	Total	Total Incl O&P
0010	**INSULATION FOR PLUMBING EQUIPMENT**										
2900	Domestic water heater wrap kit										
2920	1-1/2" with vinyl jacket, 20-60 gal.	G	1 Plum	8	1	Ea.	18.60	57.50		76.10	111
2925	50 to 80 gallons	G	"	8	1	"	23.50	57.50		81	116

22 07 19 – Plumbing Piping Insulation

22 07 19.10 Piping Insulation

			Crew	Daily Output	Labor-Hours	Unit	Material	2014 Bare Costs Labor	Equipment	Total	Total Incl O&P
0010	**PIPING INSULATION**										
0100	Rule of thumb, as a percentage of total mechanical costs					Job				10%	10%
0110	Insulation req'd. is based on the surface size/area to be covered										
0230	Insulated protectors, (ADA)										
0235	For exposed piping under sinks or lavatories										
0240	Vinyl coated foam, velcro tabs										
0245	P Trap, 1-1/4" or 1-1/2"		1 Plum	32	.250	Ea.	44.50	14.40		58.90	71.50
0260	Valve and supply cover										
0265	1/2", 3/8", and 7/16" pipe size		1 Plum	32	.250	Ea.	22	14.40		36.40	46.50
0280	Tailpiece offset (wheelchair)										
0285	1-1/4" pipe size		1 Plum	32	.250	Ea.	18.20	14.40		32.60	42.50
0600	Pipe covering (price copper tube one size less than IPS)										
6120	2" wall, 1/2" iron pipe size	G	Q-14	145	.110	L.F.	5	5.10		10.10	13.65
6210	4" iron pipe size	G	"	125	.128	"	9.15	5.90		15.05	19.50
6600	Fiberglass, with all service jacket										
6840	1" wall, 1/2" iron pipe size	G	Q-14	240	.067	L.F.	.89	3.07		3.96	5.90
6860	3/4" iron pipe size	G		230	.070		.97	3.20		4.17	6.20
6870	1" iron pipe size	G		220	.073		1.04	3.35		4.39	6.55
6880	1-1/4" iron pipe size	G		210	.076		1.13	3.51		4.64	6.90
6890	1-1/2" iron pipe size	G		210	.076		1.22	3.51		4.73	7
6900	2" iron pipe size	G		200	.080		1.32	3.68		5	7.35
7080	1-1/2" wall, 1/2" iron pipe size	G		230	.070		1.69	3.20		4.89	7
7140	2" iron pipe size	G		190	.084		2.28	3.88		6.16	8.75
7160	3" iron pipe size	G		170	.094		2.56	4.33		6.89	9.75
7879	Rubber tubing, flexible closed cell foam										
8100	1/2" wall, 1/4" iron pipe size	G	1 Asbe	90	.089	L.F.	.54	4.55		5.09	7.90
8120	3/8" iron pipe size	G		90	.089		.60	4.55		5.15	7.95
8130	1/2" iron pipe size	G		89	.090		.67	4.60		5.27	8.15
8140	3/4" iron pipe size	G		89	.090		.75	4.60		5.35	8.25
8150	1" iron pipe size	G		88	.091		.82	4.65		5.47	8.35
8170	1-1/2" iron pipe size	G		87	.092		1.15	4.70		5.85	8.80

22 07 Plumbing Insulation

22 07 19 – Plumbing Piping Insulation

22 07 19.10 Piping Insulation

		Crew	Daily Output	Labor-Hours	Unit	Material	2014 Bare Costs Labor	Equipment	Total	Total Incl O&P
8180	2" iron pipe size	[G] 1 Asbe	86	.093	L.F.	1.47	4.76		6.23	9.25
8200	3" iron pipe size	[G]	85	.094		2.06	4.81		6.87	10
8220	4" iron pipe size	[G]	80	.100		3.06	5.10		8.16	11.55
8300	3/4" wall, 1/4" iron pipe size	[G]	90	.089		.85	4.55		5.40	8.25
8330	1/2" iron pipe size	[G]	89	.090		1.10	4.60		5.70	8.60
8340	3/4" iron pipe size	[G]	89	.090		1.35	4.60		5.95	8.90
8350	1" iron pipe size	[G]	88	.091		1.54	4.65		6.19	9.15
8360	1-1/4" iron pipe size	[G]	87	.092		2.05	4.70		6.75	9.80
8370	1-1/2" iron pipe size	[G]	87	.092		2.32	4.70		7.02	10.10
8380	2" iron pipe size	[G]	86	.093		2.68	4.76		7.44	10.60
8444	1" wall, 1/2" iron pipe size	[G]	86	.093		2.05	4.76		6.81	9.90
8445	3/4" iron pipe size	[G]	84	.095		2.48	4.87		7.35	10.55
8446	1" iron pipe size	[G]	84	.095		2.89	4.87		7.76	11
8447	1-1/4" iron pipe size	[G]	82	.098		3.23	4.99		8.22	11.55
8448	1-1/2" iron pipe size	[G]	82	.098		3.76	4.99		8.75	12.15
8449	2" iron pipe size	[G]	80	.100		4.95	5.10		10.05	13.65
8450	2-1/2" iron pipe size	[G]	80	.100		6.45	5.10		11.55	15.30
8456	Rubber insulation tape, 1/8" x 2" x 30'	[G]			Ea.	12.05			12.05	13.25
9600	Minimum labor/equipment charge	1 Plum	4	2	Job		115		115	180

22 11 Facility Water Distribution

22 11 13 – Facility Water Distribution Piping

22 11 13.14 Pipe, Brass

		Crew	Daily Output	Labor-Hours	Unit	Material	Labor	Equipment	Total	Total Incl O&P
0010	**PIPE, BRASS**, Plain end									
0900	Field threaded, coupling & clevis hanger assembly 10' O.C.									
0920	Regular weight									
1120	1/2" diameter	1 Plum	48	.167	L.F.	6.40	9.60		16	22
1140	3/4" diameter		46	.174		8.60	10		18.60	25
1160	1" diameter		43	.186		12.50	10.70		23.20	30.50
1180	1-1/4" diameter	Q-1	72	.222		19.10	11.50		30.60	39
1200	1-1/2" diameter		65	.246		23	12.75		35.75	45
1220	2" diameter		53	.302		32	15.65		47.65	60
9000	Minimum labor/equipment charge	1 Plum	4	2	Job		115		115	180

22 11 13.16 Pipe Fittings, Brass

		Crew	Daily Output	Labor-Hours	Unit	Material	Labor	Equipment	Total	Total Incl O&P
0010	**PIPE FITTINGS, BRASS**, Rough bronze, threaded.									
1000	Standard wt., 90° Elbow									
1100	1/2"	1 Plum	12	.667	Ea.	18	38.50		56.50	80
1120	3/4"		11	.727		24	42		66	92
1140	1"		10	.800		39	46		85	115
1160	1-1/4"	Q-1	17	.941		63.50	49		112.50	146
1180	1-1/2"	"	16	1		78.50	52		130.50	167
1500	45° Elbow, 1/8"	1 Plum	13	.615		22	35.50		57.50	80
1580	1/2"		12	.667		22	38.50		60.50	84.50
1600	3/4"		11	.727		31.50	42		73.50	100
1620	1"		10	.800		53.50	46		99.50	131
1640	1-1/4"	Q-1	17	.941		85	49		134	170
1660	1-1/2"	"	16	1		107	52		159	199
2000	Tee, 1/8"	1 Plum	9	.889		21	51		72	104
2080	1/2"		8	1		21	57.50		78.50	114
2100	3/4"		7	1.143		30	66		96	136
2120	1"		6	1.333		54.50	76.50		131	180

22 11 Facility Water Distribution

22 11 13 – Facility Water Distribution Piping

22 11 13.16 Pipe Fittings, Brass

		Crew	Daily Output	Labor-Hours	Unit	Material	2014 Bare Costs Labor	Equipment	Total	Total Incl O&P
2140	1-1/4"	Q-1	10	1.600	Ea.	93.50	83		176.50	232
2160	1-1/2"	"	9	1.778		105	92		197	260
2500	Coupling, 1/8"	1 Plum	26	.308		15.05	17.70		32.75	44
2580	1/2"		15	.533		15.05	30.50		45.55	64.50
2600	3/4"		14	.571		21	33		54	75
2620	1"		13	.615		36	35.50		71.50	95
2640	1-1/4"	Q-1	22	.727		60	37.50		97.50	126
2660	1-1/2"		20	.800		78.50	41.50		120	151
2680	2"		18	.889		130	46		176	214
9000	Minimum labor/equipment charge	1 Plum	4	2	Job		115		115	180

22 11 13.23 Pipe/Tube, Copper

		Crew	Daily Output	Labor-Hours	Unit	Material	2014 Bare Costs Labor	Equipment	Total	Total Incl O&P
0010	**PIPE/TUBE, COPPER**, Solder joints									
1000	Type K tubing, couplings & clevis hanger assemblies 10' O.C.									
1100	1/4" diameter	1 Plum	84	.095	L.F.	4.62	5.50		10.12	13.65
1200	1" diameter		66	.121		10.60	7		17.60	22.50
1260	2" diameter		40	.200		26.50	11.50		38	47
2000	Type L tubing, couplings & clevis hanger assemblies 10' O.C.									
2100	1/4" diameter	1 Plum	88	.091	L.F.	2.30	5.25		7.55	10.70
2120	3/8" diameter		84	.095		3.13	5.50		8.63	12
2140	1/2" diameter		81	.099		3.37	5.70		9.07	12.55
2160	5/8" diameter		79	.101		5.35	5.85		11.20	14.95
2180	3/4" diameter		76	.105		5.15	6.05		11.20	15.10
2200	1" diameter		68	.118		7.85	6.75		14.60	19.20
2220	1-1/4" diameter		58	.138		11.25	7.95		19.20	25
2240	1-1/2" diameter		52	.154		14.35	8.85		23.20	29.50
2260	2" diameter		42	.190		22	10.95		32.95	41
2280	2-1/2" diameter	Q-1	62	.258		35.50	13.35		48.85	60
2300	3" diameter		56	.286		48.50	14.80		63.30	76.50
2320	3-1/2" diameter		43	.372		70.50	19.25		89.75	108
2340	4" diameter		39	.410		85.50	21.50		107	127
2360	5" diameter		34	.471		168	24.50		192.50	223
2380	6" diameter	Q-2	40	.600		244	32		276	320
2410	For other than full hard temper, add					21%				
2590	For silver solder, add						15%			
3000	Type M tubing, couplings & clevis hanger assemblies 10' O.C.									
3140	1/2" diameter	1 Plum	84	.095	L.F.	2.65	5.50		8.15	11.45
3180	3/4" diameter		78	.103		3.99	5.90		9.89	13.60
3200	1" diameter		70	.114		6.50	6.60		13.10	17.40
4000	Type DWV tubing, couplings & clevis hanger assemblies 10' O.C.									
4100	1-1/4" diameter	1 Plum	60	.133	L.F.	9.95	7.65		17.60	23
4120	1-1/2" diameter		54	.148		12.45	8.55		21	27
4140	2" diameter		44	.182		17.05	10.45		27.50	35
4160	3" diameter	Q-1	58	.276		35	14.30		49.30	61
4180	4" diameter		40	.400		62	20.50		82.50	101
4200	5" diameter		36	.444		154	23		177	206
4220	6" diameter	Q-2	42	.571		230	30.50		260.50	300
9000	Minimum labor/equipment charge	1 Plum	4	2	Job		115		115	180

22 11 13.25 Pipe/Tube Fittings, Copper

		Crew	Daily Output	Labor-Hours	Unit	Material	2014 Bare Costs Labor	Equipment	Total	Total Incl O&P
0010	**PIPE/TUBE FITTINGS, COPPER**, Wrought unless otherwise noted									
0040	Solder joints, copper x copper									
0070	90° elbow, 1/4"	1 Plum	22	.364	Ea.	9.70	21		30.70	43
0100	1/2"		20	.400		3.08	23		26.08	39.50

22 11 13 – Facility Water Distribution Piping

22 11 13.25 Pipe/Tube Fittings, Copper		Crew	Daily Output	Labor-Hours	Unit	Material	2014 Bare Costs Labor	Equipment	Total	Total Incl O&P
0120	3/4"	1 Plum	19	.421	Ea.	6.95	24		30.95	45.50
0130	1"		16	.500		17	29		46	63.50
0250	45° elbow, 1/4"		22	.364		17.30	21		38.30	51.50
0270	3/8"		22	.364		14.80	21		35.80	49
0280	1/2"		20	.400		5.65	23		28.65	42.50
0290	5/8"		19	.421		27	24		51	67.50
0300	3/4"		19	.421		9.90	24		33.90	49
0310	1"		16	.500		25	29		54	72.50
0320	1-1/4"		15	.533		33.50	30.50		64	85
0330	1-1/2"		13	.615		40.50	35.50		76	100
0340	2"		11	.727		67.50	42		109.50	140
0350	2-1/2"	Q-1	13	1.231		144	64		208	259
0360	3"		13	1.231		214	64		278	335
0370	3-1/2"		10	1.600		600	83		683	790
0380	4"		9	1.778		455	92		547	645
0390	5"		6	2.667		1,775	138		1,913	2,175
0400	6"	Q-2	9	2.667		2,775	143		2,918	3,300
0450	Tee, 1/4"	1 Plum	14	.571		19.40	33		52.40	73
0470	3/8"		14	.571		15.60	33		48.60	68.50
0480	1/2"		13	.615		5.25	35.50		40.75	61.50
0490	5/8"		12	.667		34	38.50		72.50	97.50
0500	3/4"		12	.667		12.70	38.50		51.20	74
0510	1"		10	.800		39.50	46		85.50	115
0520	1-1/4"		9	.889		53.50	51		104.50	139
0530	1-1/2"		8	1		82.50	57.50		140	181
0540	2"		7	1.143		129	66		195	245
0550	2-1/2"	Q-1	8	2		260	104		364	450
0560	3"		7	2.286		395	118		513	620
0570	3-1/2"		6	2.667		1,150	138		1,288	1,500
0580	4"		5	3.200		960	166		1,126	1,300
0590	5"		4	4		3,150	207		3,357	3,775
0600	6"	Q-2	6	4		4,300	215		4,515	5,050
0612	Tee, reducing on the outlet, 1/4"	1 Plum	15	.533		33	30.50		63.50	84
0613	3/8"		15	.533		31	30.50		61.50	82
0614	1/2"		14	.571		27	33		60	81.50
0615	5/8"		13	.615		54.50	35.50		90	116
0616	3/4"		12	.667		15	38.50		53.50	76.50
0617	1"		11	.727		39.50	42		81.50	109
0618	1-1/4"		10	.800		58	46		104	136
0619	1-1/2"		9	.889		61.50	51		112.50	148
0620	2"		8	1		97.50	57.50		155	197
0621	2-1/2"	Q-1	9	1.778		305	92		397	480
0622	3"		8	2		365	104		469	565
0623	4"		6	2.667		685	138		823	965
0624	5"		5	3.200		3,150	166		3,316	3,700
0625	6"	Q-2	7	3.429		4,075	184		4,259	4,775
0626	8"	"	6	4		16,600	215		16,815	18,500
0630	Tee, reducing on the run, 1/4"	1 Plum	15	.533		41	30.50		71.50	93.50
0631	3/8"		15	.533		47	30.50		77.50	99.50
0632	1/2"		14	.571		37.50	33		70.50	92.50
0633	5/8"		13	.615		55	35.50		90.50	116
0634	3/4"		12	.667		15	38.50		53.50	76.50
0635	1"		11	.727		47	42		89	117

22 11 13.25 Pipe/Tube Fittings, Copper		Crew	Daily Output	Labor-Hours	Unit	Material	2014 Bare Costs Labor	2014 Bare Costs Equipment	Total	Total Incl O&P
0636	1-1/4"	1 Plum	10	.800	Ea.	74.50	46		120.50	154
0637	1-1/2"		9	.889		123	51		174	215
0638	2"		8	1		168	57.50		225.50	274
0639	2-1/2"	Q-1	9	1.778		415	92		507	605
0640	3"		8	2		560	104		664	775
0641	4"		6	2.667		1,275	138		1,413	1,625
0642	5"		5	3.200		2,975	166		3,141	3,525
0643	6"	Q-2	7	3.429		4,550	184		4,734	5,275
0644	8"	"	6	4		16,100	215		16,315	18,000
0650	Coupling, 1/4"	1 Plum	24	.333		2.25	19.20		21.45	32.50
0670	3/8"		24	.333		2.98	19.20		22.18	33.50
0680	1/2"		22	.364		2.34	21		23.34	35
0690	5/8"		21	.381		7.05	22		29.05	42
0700	3/4"		21	.381		4.70	22		26.70	39
0710	1"		18	.444		9.60	25.50		35.10	50.50
0715	1-1/4"		17	.471		16.60	27		43.60	61
0716	1-1/2"		15	.533		22	30.50		52.50	72
0718	2"		13	.615		36.50	35.50		72	96
0721	2-1/2"	Q-1	15	1.067		78	55.50		133.50	172
0722	3"		13	1.231		117	64		181	229
0724	3-1/2"		8	2		224	104		328	410
0726	4"		7	2.286		246	118		364	455
0728	5"		6	2.667		605	138		743	880
0731	6"	Q-2	8	3		1,000	161		1,161	1,350
2000	DWV, solder joints, copper x copper									
2030	90° Elbow, 1-1/4"	1 Plum	13	.615	Ea.	29.50	35.50		65	88
2050	1-1/2"		12	.667		44.50	38.50		83	109
2070	2"		10	.800		58.50	46		104.50	136
2090	3"	Q-1	10	1.600		144	83		227	288
2100	4"	"	9	1.778		1,000	92		1,092	1,250
2250	Tee, Sanitary, 1-1/4"	1 Plum	9	.889		59	51		110	145
2270	1-1/2"		8	1		73.50	57.50		131	171
2290	2"		7	1.143		85.50	66		151.50	197
2310	3"	Q-1	7	2.286		370	118		488	595
2330	4"	"	6	2.667		945	138		1,083	1,275
2400	Coupling, 1-1/4"	1 Plum	14	.571		13.95	33		46.95	67
2420	1-1/2"		13	.615		17.35	35.50		52.85	74.50
2440	2"		11	.727		24	42		66	92
2460	3"	Q-1	11	1.455		49	75.50		124.50	172
2480	4"	"	10	1.600		149	83		232	292
9000	Minimum labor/equipment charge	1 Plum	4	2	Job		115		115	180

22 11 13.44 Pipe, Steel

		Crew	Daily Output	Labor-Hours	Unit	Material	2014 Bare Costs Labor	2014 Bare Costs Equipment	Total	Total Incl O&P
0010	**PIPE, STEEL** R221113-50									
0020	All pipe sizes are to Spec. A-53 unless noted otherwise									
0050	Schedule 40, threaded, with couplings, and clevis hanger									
0060	assemblies sized for covering, 10' O.C.									
0540	Black, 1/4" diameter	1 Plum	66	.121	L.F.	4.51	7		11.51	15.85
0560	1/2" diameter		63	.127		2.73	7.30		10.03	14.40
0570	3/4" diameter		61	.131		3.17	7.55		10.72	15.30
0580	1" diameter		53	.151		4.64	8.70		13.34	18.65
0590	1-1/4" diameter	Q-1	89	.180		5.75	9.30		15.05	21
0600	1-1/2" diameter		80	.200		6.70	10.35		17.05	23.50

22 11 13.44 Pipe, Steel

		Crew	Daily Output	Labor-Hours	Unit	Material	2014 Bare Costs Labor	Equipment	Total	Total Incl O&P
0610	2" diameter	Q-1	64	.250	L.F.	8.95	12.95		21.90	30
0620	2-1/2" diameter		50	.320		14.05	16.60		30.65	41.50
0630	3" diameter		43	.372		18	19.25		37.25	50
0640	3-1/2" diameter		40	.400		24.50	20.50		45	59.50
0650	4" diameter		36	.444		27	23		50	66
1280	All pipe sizes are to Spec. A-53 unless noted otherwise									
1281	Schedule 40, threaded, with couplings and clevis hanger									
1282	assemblies sized for covering, 10' O. C.									
1290	Galvanized, 1/4" diameter	1 Plum	66	.121	L.F.	6.40	7		13.40	17.95
1310	1/2" diameter		63	.127		3.76	7.30		11.06	15.55
1320	3/4" diameter		61	.131		4.45	7.55		12	16.70
1330	1" diameter		53	.151		6.10	8.70		14.80	20.50
1350	1-1/2" diameter	Q-1	80	.200		9.05	10.35		19.40	26
1360	2" diameter		64	.250		12.15	12.95		25.10	33.50
1370	2-1/2" diameter		50	.320		20	16.60		36.60	48
1380	3" diameter		43	.372		25.50	19.25		44.75	58.50
1400	4" diameter		36	.444		38	23		61	77.50
2000	Welded, sch. 40, on yoke & roll hanger assy's, sized for covering, 10' O.C.									
2040	Black, 1" diameter	Q-15	93	.172	L.F.	3.91	8.90	.60	13.41	18.85
2070	2" diameter		61	.262		7.05	13.60	.91	21.56	30
2090	3" diameter		43	.372		15.40	19.25	1.29	35.94	48.50
2110	4" diameter		37	.432		21.50	22.50	1.50	45.50	60
2120	5" diameter		32	.500		34	26	1.73	61.73	80
2130	6" diameter	Q-16	36	.667		42.50	36	1.53	80.03	104
9990	Minimum labor/equipment charge	1 Plum	3	2.667	Job		153		153	239

22 11 13.45 Pipe Fittings, Steel, Threaded

		Crew	Daily Output	Labor-Hours	Unit	Material	2014 Bare Costs Labor	Equipment	Total	Total Incl O&P
0010	**PIPE FITTINGS, STEEL, THREADED** R221113-50									
0020	Cast Iron									
0040	Standard weight, black									
0060	90° Elbow, straight									
0070	1/4"	1 Plum	16	.500	Ea.	9	29		38	55
0080	3/8"		16	.500		13	29		42	59.50
0090	1/2"		15	.533		5.70	30.50		36.20	54.50
0100	3/4"		14	.571		5.95	33		38.95	58
0110	1"		13	.615		7.05	35.50		42.55	63.50
0130	1-1/2"	Q-1	20	.800		13.80	41.50		55.30	79.50
0140	2"		18	.889		21.50	46		67.50	95.50
0150	2-1/2"		14	1.143		51.50	59		110.50	150
0160	3"		10	1.600		84.50	83		167.50	222
0180	4"		6	2.667		157	138		295	390
0500	Tee, straight									
0510	1/4"	1 Plum	10	.800	Ea.	14.05	46		60.05	87.50
0520	3/8"		10	.800		13.65	46		59.65	87
0540	3/4"		9	.889		10.35	51		61.35	91.50
0550	1"		8	1		9.20	57.50		66.70	100
0570	1-1/2"	Q-1	13	1.231		22	64		86	124
0580	2"		11	1.455		30.50	75.50		106	152
0590	2-1/2"		9	1.778		79	92		171	231
0600	3"		6	2.667		121	138		259	350
0620	4"		4	4		245	207		452	595
0700	Standard weight, galvanized cast iron									
0720	90° Elbow, straight									

22 11 13.45 Pipe Fittings, Steel, Threaded		Crew	Daily Output	Labor-Hours	Unit	Material	2014 Bare Costs Labor	Equipment	Total	Total Incl O&P
0730	1/4"	1 Plum	16	.500	Ea.	15.05	29		44.05	61.50
0740	3/8"		16	.500		15.05	29		44.05	61.50
0750	1/2"		15	.533		17.15	30.50		47.65	67
0760	3/4"		14	.571		16.85	33		49.85	70
0770	1"		13	.615		19.50	35.50		55	77
0790	1-1/2"	Q-1	20	.800		41.50	41.50		83	111
0800	2"		18	.889		61.50	46		107.50	140
0810	2-1/2"		14	1.143		126	59		185	232
0820	3"		10	1.600		192	83		275	340
0840	4"		6	2.667		350	138		488	600
1100	Tee, straight									
1110	1/4"	1 Plum	10	.800	Ea.	18.15	46		64.15	92
1120	3/8"		10	.800		18.15	46		64.15	92
1140	3/4"		9	.889		24	51		75	107
1150	1"		8	1		26.50	57.50		84	119
1170	1-1/2"	Q-1	13	1.231		61	64		125	167
1180	2"		11	1.455		76	75.50		151.50	202
1190	2-1/2"		9	1.778		154	92		246	315
1200	3"		6	2.667		345	138		483	595
1220	4"		4	4		485	207		692	860
5000	Malleable iron, 150 lb.									
5020	Black									
5040	90° elbow, straight									
5060	1/4"	1 Plum	16	.500	Ea.	4.42	29		33.42	50
5070	3/8"		16	.500		4.42	29		33.42	50
5090	3/4"		14	.571		3.70	33		36.70	55.50
5100	1"		13	.615		6.40	35.50		41.90	62.50
5120	1-1/2"	Q-1	20	.800		13.95	41.50		55.45	80
5130	2"		18	.889		24	46		70	98.50
5140	2-1/2"		14	1.143		53.50	59		112.50	152
5150	3"		10	1.600		78.50	83		161.50	215
5170	4"		6	2.667		168	138		306	400
5450	Tee, straight									
5470	1/4"	1 Plum	10	.800	Ea.	6.40	46		52.40	79
5480	3/8"		10	.800		6.40	46		52.40	79
5500	3/4"		9	.889		5.85	51		56.85	86.50
5510	1"		8	1		10.05	57.50		67.55	101
5520	1-1/4"	Q-1	14	1.143		16.30	59		75.30	110
5530	1-1/2"		13	1.231		20.50	64		84.50	122
5540	2"		11	1.455		34.50	75.50		110	156
5550	2-1/2"		9	1.778		74.50	92		166.50	226
5560	3"		6	2.667		110	138		248	335
5570	3-1/2"		5	3.200		254	166		420	540
5580	4"		4	4		265	207		472	615
5650	Coupling									
5670	1/4"	1 Plum	19	.421	Ea.	5.50	24		29.50	44
5680	3/8"		19	.421		5.50	24		29.50	44
5690	1/2"		19	.421		4.24	24		28.24	42.50
5700	3/4"		18	.444		4.97	25.50		30.47	45.50
5710	1"		15	.533		7.45	30.50		37.95	56
5720	1-1/4"	Q-1	26	.615		9.65	32		41.65	60
5730	1-1/2"		24	.667		13	34.50		47.50	68.50
5740	2"		21	.762		19.25	39.50		58.75	82.50

22 11 Facility Water Distribution

22 11 13 – Facility Water Distribution Piping

22 11 13.45 Pipe Fittings, Steel, Threaded

		Crew	Daily Output	Labor-Hours	Unit	Material	2014 Bare Costs Labor	Equipment	Total	Total Incl O&P
5750	2-1/2"	Q-1	18	.889	Ea.	53	46		99	131
5760	3"		14	1.143		72	59		131	172
5780	4"	↓	10	1.600		145	83		228	288
6000	For galvanized elbows, tees, and couplings add				↓	20%				
9990	Minimum labor/equipment charge	1 Plum	4	2	Job		115		115	180

22 11 13.47 Pipe Fittings, Steel

		Crew	Daily Output	Labor-Hours	Unit	Material	2014 Bare Costs Labor	Equipment	Total	Total Incl O&P
0010	**PIPE FITTINGS, STEEL**, Flanged, Welded & Special									
3000	Weld joint, butt, carbon steel, standard weight									
3040	90° elbow, long radius									
3050	1/2" pipe size	Q-15	16	1	Ea.	45	52	3.46	100.46	134
3060	3/4" pipe size		16	1		45	52	3.46	100.46	134
3070	1" pipe size		16	1		21	52	3.46	76.46	108
3080	1-1/4" pipe size		14	1.143		21	59	3.95	83.95	120
3090	1-1/2" pipe size		13	1.231		21	64	4.26	89.26	127
3100	2" pipe size		10	1.600		22.50	83	5.55	111.05	160
3110	2-1/2" pipe size		8	2		27.50	104	6.90	138.40	200
3120	3" pipe size		7	2.286		29	118	7.90	154.90	226
3130	4" pipe size		5	3.200		48	166	11.05	225.05	325
3136	5" pipe size	↓	4	4		103	207	13.85	323.85	455
3140	6" pipe size	Q-16	5	4.800	↓	106	258	11.05	375.05	530
3350	Tee, straight									
3360	1/2" pipe size	Q-15	10	1.600	Ea.	110	83	5.55	198.55	256
3370	3/4" pipe size		10	1.600		110	83	5.55	198.55	256
3380	1" pipe size		10	1.600		54.50	83	5.55	143.05	195
3390	1-1/4" pipe size		9	1.778		68.50	92	6.15	166.65	226
3400	1-1/2" pipe size		8	2		68.50	104	6.90	179.40	245
3410	2" pipe size		6	2.667		54.50	138	9.25	201.75	286
3420	2-1/2" pipe size		5	3.200		75.50	166	11.05	252.55	355
3430	3" pipe size		4	4		84	207	13.85	304.85	435
3440	4" pipe size		3	5.333		118	276	18.45	412.45	580
3446	5" pipe size	↓	2.50	6.400		195	330	22	547	755
3450	6" pipe size	Q-16	3	8	↓	203	430	18.40	651.40	915
9990	Minimum labor/equipment charge	Q-15	3	5.333	Job		276	18.45	294.45	450

22 11 13.48 Pipe, Fittings and Valves, Steel, Grooved-Joint

		Crew	Daily Output	Labor-Hours	Unit	Material	2014 Bare Costs Labor	Equipment	Total	Total Incl O&P
0010	**PIPE, FITTINGS AND VALVES, STEEL, GROOVED-JOINT**									
0012	Fittings are ductile iron. Steel fittings noted.									
0020	Pipe includes coupling & clevis type hanger assemblies, 10' O.C.									
1000	Schedule 40, black									
1040	3/4" diameter	1 Plum	71	.113	L.F.	4.62	6.50		11.12	15.20
1050	1" diameter		63	.127		4.41	7.30		11.71	16.25
1060	1-1/4" diameter		58	.138		5.70	7.95		13.65	18.65
1070	1-1/2" diameter		51	.157		6.50	9.05		15.55	21.50
1080	2" diameter	↓	40	.200		7.85	11.50		19.35	26.50
1090	2-1/2" diameter	Q-1	57	.281		13.45	14.55		28	37.50
1100	3" diameter		50	.320		16.55	16.60		33.15	44
1110	4" diameter		45	.356		22.50	18.40		40.90	53.50
1120	5" diameter	↓	37	.432	↓	36.50	22.50		59	75.50
3990	Fittings: coupling material required at joints not incl. in fitting price.									
3994	Add 1 selected coupling, material only, per joint for installed price.									
4000	Elbow, 90° or 45°, painted									
4030	3/4" diameter	1 Plum	50	.160	Ea.	56	9.20		65.20	76.50
4040	1" diameter	↓	50	.160	↓	30	9.20		39.20	47.50

22 11 Facility Water Distribution

22 11 13 – Facility Water Distribution Piping

22 11 13.48 Pipe, Fittings and Valves, Steel, Grooved-Joint

		Crew	Daily Output	Labor-Hours	Unit	Material	2014 Bare Costs Labor	Equipment	Total	Total Incl O&P
4050	1-1/4" diameter	1 Plum	40	.200	Ea.	30	11.50		41.50	51
4060	1-1/2" diameter		33	.242		30	13.95		43.95	55
4070	2" diameter	▼	25	.320		30	18.40		48.40	61.50
4080	2-1/2" diameter	Q-1	40	.400		30	20.50		50.50	65.50
4090	3" diameter		33	.485		53	25		78	97.50
4100	4" diameter		25	.640		57.50	33		90.50	115
4110	5" diameter	▼	20	.800		137	41.50		178.50	216
4250	For galvanized elbows, add				▼	26%				
4690	Tee, painted									
4700	3/4" diameter	1 Plum	38	.211	Ea.	60.50	12.10		72.60	85.50
4740	1" diameter		33	.242		46.50	13.95		60.45	73.50
4750	1-1/4" diameter		27	.296		46.50	17.05		63.55	78
4760	1-1/2" diameter		22	.364		46.50	21		67.50	84
4770	2" diameter	▼	17	.471		46.50	27		73.50	94
4780	2-1/2" diameter	Q-1	27	.593		46.50	30.50		77	99.50
4790	3" diameter		22	.727		64	37.50		101.50	129
4800	4" diameter		17	.941		97	49		146	183
4810	5" diameter	▼	13	1.231		226	64		290	350
4900	For galvanized tees, add					24%				
4933	20" diameter	Q-2	16	1.500	▼	530	80.50		610.50	705
4940	Flexible, standard, painted									
4950	3/4" diameter	1 Plum	100	.080	Ea.	16.60	4.60		21.20	25.50
4960	1" diameter		100	.080		16.60	4.60		21.20	25.50
4970	1-1/4" diameter		80	.100		22	5.75		27.75	33
4980	1-1/2" diameter		67	.119		24	6.85		30.85	36.50
4990	2" diameter	▼	50	.160		25.50	9.20		34.70	42.50
5000	2-1/2" diameter	Q-1	80	.200		29.50	10.35		39.85	48.50
5010	3" diameter		67	.239		33	12.35		45.35	56
5020	3-1/2" diameter		57	.281		47	14.55		61.55	74
5030	4" diameter		50	.320		47.50	16.60		64.10	78
5040	5" diameter	▼	40	.400		72	20.50		92.50	112
5050	6" diameter	Q-2	50	.480		85	26		111	134
5200	For galvanized couplings, add				▼	33%				
9990	Minimum labor/equipment charge	1 Plum	4	2	Job		115		115	180

22 11 13.74 Pipe, Plastic

		Crew	Daily Output	Labor-Hours	Unit	Material	2014 Bare Costs Labor	Equipment	Total	Total Incl O&P
0010	**PIPE, PLASTIC**									
1800	PVC, couplings 10' O.C., clevis hanger assemblies, 3 per 10'									
1820	Schedule 40									
1860	1/2" diameter	1 Plum	54	.148	L.F.	3.02	8.55		11.57	16.65
1870	3/4" diameter		51	.157		3.33	9.05		12.38	17.75
1880	1" diameter		46	.174		3.96	10		13.96	19.95
1890	1-1/4" diameter		42	.190		4.94	10.95		15.89	22.50
1900	1-1/2" diameter	▼	36	.222		4.76	12.80		17.56	25
1910	2" diameter	Q-1	59	.271		5.95	14.05		20	28.50
1920	2-1/2" diameter		56	.286		9.15	14.80		23.95	33
1930	3" diameter		53	.302		11.05	15.65		26.70	36.50
1940	4" diameter		48	.333		14.20	17.25		31.45	42.50
1950	5" diameter		43	.372		28	19.25		47.25	61
1960	6" diameter	▼	39	.410		29.50	21.50		51	65.50
4100	DWV type, schedule 40, couplings 10' O.C., clevis hanger assy's, 3 per 10'									
4210	ABS, schedule 40, foam core type									
4212	Plain end black									

22 11 13 – Facility Water Distribution Piping

22 11 13.74 Pipe, Plastic

		Crew	Daily Output	Labor-Hours	Unit	Material	2014 Bare Costs Labor	Equipment	Total	Total Incl O&P
4214	1-1/2" diameter	1 Plum	39	.205	L.F.	2.96	11.80		14.76	21.50
4216	2" diameter	Q-1	62	.258		3.40	13.35		16.75	24.50
4218	3" diameter		56	.286		6.10	14.80		20.90	29.50
4220	4" diameter		51	.314		8.70	16.25		24.95	35
4222	6" diameter		42	.381		20.50	19.75		40.25	53.50
4240	To delete coupling & hangers, subtract									
4244	1-1/2" diam. to 6" diam.					43%	48%			
4400	PVC									
4410	1-1/4" diameter	1 Plum	42	.190	L.F.	3.41	10.95		14.36	21
4460	2" diameter	Q-1	59	.271		3.39	14.05		17.44	25.50
4470	3" diameter		53	.302		6.05	15.65		21.70	31
4480	4" diameter		48	.333		8.35	17.25		25.60	36
4490	6" diameter		39	.410		17.25	21.50		38.75	52
5300	CPVC, socket joint, couplings 10' O.C., clevis hanger assemblies, 3 per 10'									
5302	Schedule 40									
5304	1/2" diameter	1 Plum	54	.148	L.F.	3.65	8.55		12.20	17.30
5305	3/4" diameter		51	.157		4.30	9.05		13.35	18.85
5306	1" diameter		46	.174		5.50	10		15.50	21.50
5307	1-1/4" diameter		42	.190		6.90	10.95		17.85	24.50
5308	1-1/2" diameter		36	.222		8.05	12.80		20.85	29
5309	2" diameter	Q-1	59	.271		9.90	14.05		23.95	33
5310	2-1/2" diameter		56	.286		16.60	14.80		31.40	41.50
5311	3" diameter		53	.302		20	15.65		35.65	46.50
5360	CPVC, threaded, couplings 10' O.C., clevis hanger assemblies, 3 per 10'									
5380	Schedule 40									
5460	1/2" diameter	1 Plum	54	.148	L.F.	4.45	8.55		13	18.20
5470	3/4" diameter		51	.157		5.70	9.05		14.75	20.50
5480	1" diameter		46	.174		6.95	10		16.95	23
5490	1-1/4" diameter		42	.190		8	10.95		18.95	26
5500	1-1/2" diameter		36	.222		9	12.80		21.80	30
5510	2" diameter	Q-1	59	.271		11.10	14.05		25.15	34
5520	2-1/2" diameter		56	.286		17.85	14.80		32.65	42.50
5530	3" diameter		53	.302		22	15.65		37.65	48.50
9900	Minimum labor/equipment charge	1 Plum	4	2	Job		115		115	180

22 11 13.76 Pipe Fittings, Plastic

		Crew	Daily Output	Labor-Hours	Unit	Material	2014 Bare Costs Labor	Equipment	Total	Total Incl O&P
0010	**PIPE FITTINGS, PLASTIC**									
2700	PVC (white), schedule 40, socket joints									
2760	90° elbow, 1/2"	1 Plum	33.30	.240	Ea.	.48	13.85		14.33	22
2810	2"	Q-1	36.40	.440	"	2.89	23		25.89	38.50
4500	DWV, ABS, non pressure, socket joints									
4540	1/4 Bend, 1-1/4"	1 Plum	20.20	.396	Ea.	6.15	23		29.15	42.50
4560	1-1/2"	"	18.20	.440		4.69	25.50		30.19	44.50
4570	2"	Q-1	33.10	.483		7.45	25		32.45	47
4650	1/8 Bend, same as 1/4 Bend									
4800	Tee, sanitary									
4820	1-1/4"	1 Plum	13.50	.593	Ea.	8.15	34		42.15	62
4830	1-1/2"	"	12.10	.661		7.15	38		45.15	67.50
4840	2"	Q-1	20	.800		11	41.50		52.50	76.50
5000	DWV, PVC, schedule 40, socket joints									
5040	1/4 bend, 1-1/4"	1 Plum	20.20	.396	Ea.	12.55	23		35.55	49.50
5060	1-1/2"	"	18.20	.440		3.45	25.50		28.95	43.50
5070	2"	Q-1	33.10	.483		5.45	25		30.45	45

22 11 Facility Water Distribution

22 11 13 – Facility Water Distribution Piping

22 11 13.76 Pipe Fittings, Plastic		Crew	Daily Output	Labor-Hours	Unit	Material	2014 Bare Costs Labor	Equipment	Total	Total Incl O&P
5080	3"	Q-1	20.80	.769	Ea.	16	40		56	79.50
5090	4"		16.50	.970		31.50	50		81.50	113
5100	6"	↓	10.10	1.584		111	82		193	250
5105	8"	Q-2	9.30	2.581		224	139		363	465
5110	1/4 bend, long sweep, 1-1/2"	1 Plum	18.20	.440		8.30	25.50		33.80	48.50
5112	2"	Q-1	33.10	.483		8.95	25		33.95	49
5114	3"		20.80	.769		21	40		61	85.50
5116	4"	↓	16.50	.970		40	50		90	123
5150	1/8 bend, 1-1/4"	1 Plum	20.20	.396		8.20	23		31.20	44.50
5215	8"	Q-2	9.30	2.581		158	139		297	390
5250	Tee, sanitary 1-1/4"	1 Plum	13.50	.593		12.30	34		46.30	66.50
5254	1-1/2"	"	12.10	.661		6.25	38		44.25	66.50
5255	2"	Q-1	20	.800		9.20	41.50		50.70	74.50
5256	3"		13.90	1.151		23	59.50		82.50	118
5257	4"		11	1.455		43	75.50		118.50	165
5259	6"	↓	6.70	2.388		179	124		303	390
5261	8"	Q-2	6.20	3.871		535	208		743	915
5264	2" x 1-1/2"	Q-1	22	.727		8.10	37.50		45.60	68
5266	3" x 1-1/2"		15.50	1.032		17.05	53.50		70.55	102
5268	4" x 3"		12.10	1.322		52	68.50		120.50	165
5271	6" x 4"	↓	6.90	2.319		173	120		293	375
5314	Combination Y & 1/8 bend, 1-1/2"	1 Plum	12.10	.661		15.10	38		53.10	76
5315	2"	Q-1	20	.800		16.15	41.50		57.65	82.50
5317	3"		13.90	1.151		40	59.50		99.50	137
5318	4"	↓	11	1.455	↓	79.50	75.50		155	206
5324	Combination Y & 1/8 bend, reducing									
5325	2" x 2" x 1-1/2"	Q-1	22	.727	Ea.	21	37.50		58.50	82.50
5327	3" x 3" x 1-1/2"		15.50	1.032		38	53.50		91.50	125
5328	3" x 3" x 2"		15.30	1.046		26.50	54		80.50	114
5329	4" x 4" x 2"	↓	12.20	1.311		43	68		111	154
5331	Wye, 1-1/4"	1 Plum	13.50	.593		16.10	34		50.10	70.50
5332	1-1/2"	"	12.10	.661		11.80	38		49.80	72.50
5333	2"	Q-1	20	.800		11.20	41.50		52.70	77
5334	3"		13.90	1.151		30	59.50		89.50	126
5335	4"		11	1.455		55	75.50		130.50	179
5336	6"	↓	6.70	2.388		165	124		289	375
5337	8"	Q-2	6.20	3.871		385	208		593	750
5341	2" x 1-1/2"	Q-1	22	.727		13.85	37.50		51.35	74.50
5342	3" x 1-1/2"		15.50	1.032		19.85	53.50		73.35	106
5343	4" x 3"		12.10	1.322		44.50	68.50		113	156
5344	6" x 4"	↓	6.90	2.319		122	120		242	320
5345	8" x 6"	Q-2	6.40	3.750		291	201		492	635
5347	Double wye, 1-1/2"	1 Plum	9.10	.879		25.50	50.50		76	107
5348	2"	Q-1	16.60	.964		29.50	50		79.50	111
5349	3"		10.40	1.538		60	79.50		139.50	190
5350	4"	↓	8.25	1.939	↓	122	100		222	291
5353	Double wye, reducing									
5354	2" x 2" x 1-1/2" x 1-1/2"	Q-1	16.80	.952	Ea.	26	49.50		75.50	106
5355	3" x 3" x 2" x 2"		10.60	1.509		44.50	78		122.50	171
5356	4" x 4" x 3" x 3"		8.45	1.893		96.50	98		194.50	259
5357	6" x 6" x 4" x 4"	↓	7.25	2.207		325	114		439	535
5374	Coupling, 1-1/4"	1 Plum	20.20	.396		7.60	23		30.60	44
5376	1-1/2"	"	18.20	.440	↓	1.72	25.50		27.22	41.50

22 11 13 – Facility Water Distribution Piping

22 11 13.76 Pipe Fittings, Plastic		Crew	Daily Output	Labor-Hours	Unit	Material	2014 Bare Costs Labor	Equipment	Total	Total Incl O&P
5378	2"	Q-1	33.10	.483	Ea.	2.24	25		27.24	41.50
5380	3"		20.80	.769		7.70	40		47.70	70.50
5390	4"		16.50	.970		13.65	50		63.65	93.50
5410	Reducer bushing, 2" x 1-1/4"		36.50	.438		7.05	22.50		29.55	43.50
5412	3" x 1-1/2"		27.30	.586		14.15	30.50		44.65	63
5414	4" x 2"		18.20	.879		24.50	45.50		70	98
5416	6" x 4"	↓	11.10	1.441		65.50	74.50		140	189
5418	8" x 6"	Q-2	10.20	2.353	↓	142	126		268	355
5500	CPVC, Schedule 80, threaded joints									
5540	90° Elbow, 1/4"	1 Plum	32	.250	Ea.	12.15	14.40		26.55	36
5560	1/2"		30.30	.264		7.05	15.20		22.25	31.50
5570	3/4"		26	.308		10.55	17.70		28.25	39
5580	1"		22.70	.352		14.80	20.50		35.30	48
5590	1-1/4"		20.20	.396		28.50	23		51.50	67
5600	1-1/2"	↓	18.20	.440		30.50	25.50		56	73.50
5610	2"	Q-1	33.10	.483		41	25		66	84
5620	2-1/2"		24.20	.661		128	34.50		162.50	194
5630	3"	↓	20.80	.769		137	40		177	212
5730	Coupling, 1/4"	1 Plum	32	.250		15.45	14.40		29.85	39.50
5732	1/2"		30.30	.264		12.75	15.20		27.95	37.50
5734	3/4"		26	.308		20.50	17.70		38.20	50
5736	1"		22.70	.352		23.50	20.50		44	57.50
5738	1-1/4"		20.20	.396		25	23		48	62.50
5740	1-1/2"	↓	18.20	.440		26.50	25.50		52	69
5742	2"	Q-1	33.10	.483		31.50	25		56.50	73.50
5744	2-1/2"		24.20	.661		56.50	34.50		91	116
5746	3"	↓	20.80	.769	↓	65.50	40		105.50	134
5900	CPVC, Schedule 80, socket joints									
5904	90° Elbow, 1/4"	1 Plum	32	.250	Ea.	11.55	14.40		25.95	35
5906	1/2"		30.30	.264		4.53	15.20		19.73	28.50
5908	3/4"		26	.308		5.80	17.70		23.50	34
5910	1"		22.70	.352		9.20	20.50		29.70	41.50
5912	1-1/4"		20.20	.396		19.85	23		42.85	57.50
5914	1-1/2"	↓	18.20	.440		22	25.50		47.50	64
5916	2"	Q-1	33.10	.483		26.50	25		51.50	68.50
5918	2-1/2"		24.20	.661		61.50	34.50		96	121
5920	3"	↓	20.80	.769		69.50	40		109.50	139
5930	45° Elbow, 1/4"	1 Plum	32	.250		17.20	14.40		31.60	41.50
5932	1/2"		30.30	.264		5.55	15.20		20.75	29.50
5934	3/4"		26	.308		7.95	17.70		25.65	36.50
5936	1"		22.70	.352		12.75	20.50		33.25	45.50
5938	1-1/4"		20.20	.396		25	23		48	63
5940	1-1/2"	↓	18.20	.440		25.50	25.50		51	67.50
5942	2"	Q-1	33.10	.483		29	25		54	71
5944	2-1/2"		24.20	.661		59	34.50		93.50	118
5946	3"	↓	20.80	.769		75.50	40		115.50	145
5990	Coupling, 1/4"	1 Plum	32	.250		12.30	14.40		26.70	36
5992	1/2"		30.30	.264		4.79	15.20		19.99	29
5994	3/4"		26	.308		6.70	17.70		24.40	35
5996	1"		22.70	.352		9	20.50		29.50	41.50
5998	1-1/4"		20.20	.396		13.50	23		36.50	50.50
6000	1-1/2"	↓	18.20	.440		17	25.50		42.50	58
6002	2"	Q-1	33.10	.483	↓	19.75	25		44.75	60.50

22 11 Facility Water Distribution

22 11 13 – Facility Water Distribution Piping

22 11 13.76 Pipe Fittings, Plastic		Crew	Daily Output	Labor-Hours	Unit	Material	2014 Bare Costs Labor	Equipment	Total	Total Incl O&P
6004	2-1/2"	Q-1	24.20	.661	Ea.	44	34.50		78.50	102
6006	3"	↓	20.80	.769	↓	47.50	40		87.50	115
9990	Minimum labor/equipment charge	1 Plum	4	2	Job		115		115	180

22 11 19 – Domestic Water Piping Specialties

22 11 19.10 Flexible Connectors

		Crew	Daily Output	Labor-Hours	Unit	Material	Labor	Equipment	Total	Total Incl O&P
0010	**FLEXIBLE CONNECTORS**, Corrugated, 7/8" O.D., 1/2" I.D.									
0050	Gas, seamless brass, steel fittings									
0200	12" long	1 Plum	36	.222	Ea.	17.40	12.80		30.20	39
0220	18" long		36	.222		21.50	12.80		34.30	44
0240	24" long		34	.235		25.50	13.55		39.05	49
0260	30" long		34	.235	↓	27.50	13.55		41.05	51.50
9000	Minimum labor/equipment charge	↓	4	2	Job		115		115	180

22 11 19.18 Mixing Valve

		Crew	Daily Output	Labor-Hours	Unit	Material	Labor	Equipment	Total	Total Incl O&P
0010	**MIXING VALVE**, Automatic, water tempering.									
0040	1/2" size	1 Stpi	19	.421	Ea.	555	24.50		579.50	650
0050	3/4" size		18	.444	"	555	26		581	650
9000	Minimum labor/equipment charge	↓	5	1.600	Job		93.50		93.50	146

22 11 19.38 Water Supply Meters

		Crew	Daily Output	Labor-Hours	Unit	Material	Labor	Equipment	Total	Total Incl O&P
0010	**WATER SUPPLY METERS**									
2000	Domestic/commercial, bronze									
2020	Threaded									
2060	5/8" diameter, to 20 GPM	1 Plum	16	.500	Ea.	48.50	29		77.50	98.50
2080	3/4" diameter, to 30 GPM	↓	14	.571		88.50	33		121.50	149
2100	1" diameter, to 50 GPM	↓	12	.667	↓	134	38.50		172.50	208
2300	Threaded/flanged									
2340	1-1/2" diameter, to 100 GPM	1 Plum	8	1	Ea.	330	57.50		387.50	450
9000	Minimum labor/equipment charge	"	3.25	2.462	Job		142		142	221

22 11 19.42 Backflow Preventers

		Crew	Daily Output	Labor-Hours	Unit	Material	Labor	Equipment	Total	Total Incl O&P
0010	**BACKFLOW PREVENTERS**, Includes valves									
0020	and four test cocks, corrosion resistant, automatic operation									
1000	Double check principle									
1010	Threaded, with ball valves									
1020	3/4" pipe size	1 Plum	16	.500	Ea.	231	29		260	299
1030	1" pipe size	↓	14	.571		264	33		297	340
1040	1-1/2" pipe size		10	.800		560	46		606	690
1050	2" pipe size	↓	7	1.143	↓	655	66		721	825
1080	Threaded, with gate valves									
1100	3/4" pipe size	1 Plum	16	.500	Ea.	1,075	29		1,104	1,250
1120	1" pipe size		14	.571		1,100	33		1,133	1,250
1140	1-1/2" pipe size		10	.800		1,400	46		1,446	1,625
1160	2" pipe size	↓	7	1.143	↓	1,725	66		1,791	2,000
4000	Reduced pressure principle									
4100	Threaded, bronze, valves are ball									
4120	3/4" pipe size	1 Plum	16	.500	Ea.	445	29		474	535
4140	1" pipe size		14	.571		480	33		513	575
4150	1-1/4" pipe size		12	.667		845	38.50		883.50	990
4160	1-1/2" pipe size		10	.800		960	46		1,006	1,125
4180	2" pipe size	↓	7	1.143	↓	1,075	66		1,141	1,300
5000	Flanged, bronze, valves are OS&Y									
5060	2-1/2" pipe size	Q-1	5	3.200	Ea.	4,025	166		4,191	4,675
5080	3" pipe size	↓	4.50	3.556	↓	4,650	184		4,834	5,375

411

22 11 Facility Water Distribution

22 11 19 – Domestic Water Piping Specialties

22 11 19.42 Backflow Preventers

		Crew	Daily Output	Labor-Hours	Unit	Material	2014 Bare Costs Labor	2014 Bare Costs Equipment	Total	Total Incl O&P
5100	4" pipe size	Q-1	3	5.333	Ea.	5,500	276		5,776	6,475
5120	6" pipe size	Q-2	3	8	↓	8,750	430		9,180	10,300
5600	Flanged, iron, valves are OS&Y									
5660	2-1/2" pipe size	Q-1	5	3.200	Ea.	3,025	166		3,191	3,575
5680	3" pipe size		4.50	3.556		3,175	184		3,359	3,775
5700	4" pipe size	↓	3	5.333		3,975	276		4,251	4,800
5720	6" pipe size	Q-2	3	8		5,775	430		6,205	7,025
5800	Rebuild 4" diameter reduced pressure	1 Plum	4	2		340	115		455	550
5810	6" diameter		2.66	3.008		355	173		528	665
5820	8" diameter		2	4		440	230		670	845
5830	10" diameter		1.60	5	↓	515	288		803	1,025
9010	Minimum labor/equipment charge	↓	2	4	Job		230		230	360

22 11 19.50 Vacuum Breakers

		Crew	Daily Output	Labor-Hours	Unit	Material	2014 Bare Costs Labor	2014 Bare Costs Equipment	Total	Total Incl O&P
0010	**VACUUM BREAKERS**									
0013	See also backflow preventers Section 22 11 19.42									
1000	Anti-siphon continuous pressure type									
1010	Max. 150 PSI - 210°F									
1020	Bronze body									
1030	1/2" size	1 Stpi	24	.333	Ea.	187	19.50		206.50	237
1040	3/4" size		20	.400		187	23.50		210.50	243
1050	1" size		19	.421		194	24.50		218.50	252
1060	1-1/4" size		15	.533		380	31		411	470
1070	1-1/2" size		13	.615		470	36		506	570
1080	2" size	↓	11	.727	↓	485	42.50		527.50	595
1200	Max. 125 PSI with atmospheric vent									
1210	Brass, in-line construction									
1220	1/4" size	1 Stpi	24	.333	Ea.	117	19.50		136.50	160
1230	3/8" size	"	24	.333	↓	117	19.50		136.50	160
1260	For polished chrome finish, add				↓	13%				
2000	Anti-siphon, non-continuous pressure type									
2010	Hot or cold water 125 PSI - 210°F									
2020	Bronze body									
2030	1/4" size	1 Stpi	24	.333	Ea.	64	19.50		83.50	101
2040	3/8" size		24	.333		64	19.50		83.50	101
2050	1/2" size		24	.333		72.50	19.50		92	111
2060	3/4" size		20	.400		86.50	23.50		110	132
2070	1" size		19	.421		134	24.50		158.50	186
2080	1-1/4" size		15	.533		235	31		266	305
2090	1-1/2" size		13	.615		276	36		312	360
2100	2" size		11	.727		430	42.50		472.50	535
2110	2-1/2" size		8	1		1,225	58.50		1,283.50	1,450
2120	3" size	↓	6	1.333	↓	1,625	78		1,703	1,925
2150	For polished chrome finish, add					50%				

22 11 19.54 Water Hammer Arresters/Shock Absorbers

		Crew	Daily Output	Labor-Hours	Unit	Material	2014 Bare Costs Labor	2014 Bare Costs Equipment	Total	Total Incl O&P
0010	**WATER HAMMER ARRESTERS/SHOCK ABSORBERS**									
0490	Copper									
0500	3/4" male I.P.S. For 1 to 11 fixtures	1 Plum	12	.667	Ea.	28	38.50		66.50	91
0600	1" male I.P.S. For 12 to 32 fixtures		8	1		45.50	57.50		103	140
0700	1-1/4" male I.P.S. For 33 to 60 fixtures		8	1		47	57.50		104.50	142
0800	1-1/2" male I.P.S. For 61 to 113 fixtures		8	1		67.50	57.50		125	164
0900	2" male I.P.S. For 114 to 154 fixtures		8	1		98.50	57.50		156	198
1000	2-1/2" male I.P.S. For 155 to 330 fixtures	↓	4	2	↓	305	115		420	515

22 11 Facility Water Distribution

22 11 19 – Domestic Water Piping Specialties

22 11 19.54 Water Hammer Arresters/Shock Absorbers	Crew	Daily Output	Labor-Hours	Unit	Material	2014 Bare Costs Labor	Equipment	Total	Total Incl O&P
9000	Minimum labor/equipment charge	1 Plum	3.50	2.286	Job		132		132	205

22 11 19.64 Hydrants

		Crew	Daily Output	Labor-Hours	Unit	Material	Labor	Equipment	Total	Total Incl O&P
0010	**HYDRANTS**									
0050	Wall type, moderate climate, bronze, encased									
0200	3/4" IPS connection	1 Plum	16	.500	Ea.	705	29		734	825
1000	Non-freeze, bronze, exposed									
1100	3/4" IPS connection, 4" to 9" thick wall	1 Plum	14	.571	Ea.	480	33		513	575
1120	10" to 14" thick wall	"	12	.667		515	38.50		553.50	630
1280	For anti-siphon type, add					126			126	139
9000	Minimum labor/equipment charge	1 Plum	3	2.667	Job		153		153	239

22 13 Facility Sanitary Sewerage

22 13 16 – Sanitary Waste and Vent Piping

22 13 16.20 Pipe, Cast Iron

		Crew	Daily Output	Labor-Hours	Unit	Material	Labor	Equipment	Total	Total Incl O&P
0010	**PIPE, CAST IRON**, Soil, on clevis hanger assemblies, 5' O.C. R221113-50									
0020	Single hub, service wt., lead & oakum joints 10' O.C.									
2120	2" diameter	Q-1	63	.254	L.F.	9.30	13.15		22.45	31
2140	3" diameter		60	.267		12.95	13.80		26.75	36
2160	4" diameter		55	.291		16.85	15.05		31.90	42
2180	5" diameter	Q-2	76	.316		23	16.95		39.95	52
2200	6" diameter	"	73	.329		29	17.65		46.65	59.50
2220	8" diameter	Q-3	59	.542		44	29.50		73.50	95
4000	No hub, couplings 10' O.C.									
4100	1-1/2" diameter	Q-1	71	.225	L.F.	9.15	11.65		20.80	28.50
4120	2" diameter		67	.239		9.40	12.35		21.75	29.50
4140	3" diameter		64	.250		13.35	12.95		26.30	34.50
4160	4" diameter		58	.276		16.95	14.30		31.25	41
4180	5" diameter	Q-2	83	.289		23	15.55		38.55	49.50
9000	Minimum labor/equipment charge	1 Plum	4	2	Job		115		115	180

22 13 16.30 Pipe Fittings, Cast Iron

		Crew	Daily Output	Labor-Hours	Unit	Material	Labor	Equipment	Total	Total Incl O&P
0010	**PIPE FITTINGS, CAST IRON**, Soil R221113-50									
0040	Hub and spigot, service weight, lead & oakum joints									
0080	1/4 bend, 2"	Q-1	16	1	Ea.	19.25	52		71.25	102
0120	3"		14	1.143		25.50	59		84.50	121
0140	4"		13	1.231		40	64		104	144
0160	5"	Q-2	18	1.333		56	71.50		127.50	174
0180	6"	"	17	1.412		69.50	76		145.50	195
0200	8"	Q-3	11	2.909		208	159		367	480
0340	1/8 bend, 2"	Q-1	16	1		13.65	52		65.65	96
0350	3"		14	1.143		21.50	59		80.50	116
0360	4"		13	1.231		31.50	64		95.50	134
0380	5"	Q-2	18	1.333		43.50	71.50		115	160
0400	6"	"	17	1.412		53	76		129	176
0420	8"	Q-3	11	2.909		158	159		317	425
0500	Sanitary tee, 2"	Q-1	10	1.600		26.50	83		109.50	159
0540	3"		9	1.778		43.50	92		135.50	192
0620	4"		8	2		53	104		157	220
0700	5"	Q-2	12	2		105	107		212	284
0800	6"	"	11	2.182		119	117		236	315
0880	8"	Q-3	7	4.571		315	251		566	740

22 13 16.30 Pipe Fittings, Cast Iron	Crew	Daily Output	Labor-Hours	Unit	Material	2014 Bare Costs Labor	Equipment	Total	Total Incl O&P
5990 No hub									
6000 Cplg. & labor required at joints not incl. in fitting									
6010 price. Add 1 coupling per joint for installed price									
6020 1/4 Bend, 1-1/2"				Ea.	9.85			9.85	10.85
6060 2"					10.70			10.70	11.80
6080 3"					15			15	16.50
6120 4"					22			22	24.50
6184 1/4 Bend, long sweep, 1-1/2"					24.50			24.50	27
6186 2"					23.50			23.50	26
6188 3"					28.50			28.50	31.50
6189 4"					45			45	49.50
6190 5"					87.50			87.50	96.50
6191 6"					99.50			99.50	110
6192 8"					269			269	296
6193 10"					550			550	605
6200 1/8 Bend, 1-1/2"					8.35			8.35	9.15
6210 2"					9.25			9.25	10.15
6212 3"					12.40			12.40	13.65
6214 4"					16.25			16.25	17.85
6380 Sanitary Tee, tapped, 1-1/2"					19.60			19.60	21.50
6382 2" x 1-1/2"					17.35			17.35	19.05
6384 2"					18.55			18.55	20.50
6386 3" x 2"					27.50			27.50	30.50
6388 3"					47.50			47.50	52.50
6390 4" x 1-1/2"					24.50			24.50	27
6392 4" x 2"					28			28	30.50
6393 4"					28			28	30.50
6394 6" x 1-1/2"					64			64	70.50
6396 6" x 2"					65			65	71.50
6459 Sanitary Tee, 1-1/2"					13.85			13.85	15.25
6460 2"					14.75			14.75	16.25
6470 3"					18.25			18.25	20
6472 4"					34.50			34.50	38
8000 Coupling, standard (by CISPI Mfrs.)									
8020 1-1/2"	Q-1	48	.333	Ea.	13.95	17.25		31.20	42.50
8040 2"		44	.364		15.25	18.85		34.10	46.50
8080 3"		38	.421		17.10	22		39.10	53
8120 4"		33	.485		20	25		45	61
8300 Coupling, cast iron clamp & neoprene gasket (by MG)									
8310 1-1/2"	Q-1	48	.333	Ea.	6.40	17.25		23.65	34
8320 2"		44	.364		8.35	18.85		27.20	38.50
8330 3"		38	.421		12.65	22		34.65	48
8340 4"		33	.485		14.60	25		39.60	55
8600 Coupling, Stainless steel, heavy duty									
8620 1-1/2"	Q-1	48	.333	Ea.	9.55	17.25		26.80	37.50
8630 2"		44	.364		9.90	18.85		28.75	40.50
8640 2" x 1-1/2"		44	.364		12.05	18.85		30.90	43
8650 3"		38	.421		10.75	22		32.75	46
8660 4"		33	.485		12.15	25		37.15	52.50
9000 Minimum labor/equipment charge	1 Plum	4	2	Job		115		115	180

22 13 Facility Sanitary Sewerage

22 13 16 – Sanitary Waste and Vent Piping

22 13 16.60 Traps

		Crew	Daily Output	Labor-Hours	Unit	Material	2014 Bare Costs Labor	Equipment	Total	Total Incl O&P
0010	**TRAPS**									
0030	Cast iron, service weight									
0050	Running P trap, without vent									
1100	2"	Q-1	16	1	Ea.	164	52		216	261
1150	4"	"	13	1.231		164	64		228	280
1160	6"	Q-2	17	1.412		605	76		681	785
3000	P trap, B&S, 2" pipe size	Q-1	16	1		32.50	52		84.50	117
3040	3" pipe size	"	14	1.143		49	59		108	146
4700	Copper, drainage, drum trap									
4840	3" x 6" swivel, 1-1/2" pipe size	1 Plum	16	.500	Ea.	455	29		484	545
5100	P trap, standard pattern									
5200	1-1/4" pipe size	1 Plum	18	.444	Ea.	211	25.50		236.50	272
5240	1-1/2" pipe size		17	.471		204	27		231	268
5260	2" pipe size		15	.533		315	30.50		345.50	395
5280	3" pipe size		11	.727		760	42		802	900
9000	Minimum labor/equipment charge		3	2.667	Job		153		153	239

22 13 16.80 Vent Flashing and Caps

		Crew	Daily Output	Labor-Hours	Unit	Material	2014 Bare Costs Labor	Equipment	Total	Total Incl O&P
0010	**VENT FLASHING AND CAPS**									
0120	Vent caps									
0140	Cast iron									
0180	2-1/2" - 3-5/8" pipe	1 Plum	21	.381	Ea.	45	22		67	83.50
0190	4" - 4-1/8" pipe	"	19	.421	"	55	24		79	98.50
0900	Vent flashing									
1000	Aluminum with lead ring									
1050	3" pipe	1 Plum	17	.471	Ea.	14.05	27		41.05	58
1060	4" pipe	"	16	.500	"	16.95	29		45.95	63.50
1350	Copper with neoprene ring									
1440	2" pipe	1 Plum	18	.444	Ea.	21.50	25.50		47	63.50
1450	3" pipe		17	.471		25.50	27		52.50	70.50
1460	4" pipe		16	.500		28	29		57	75.50
9000	Minimum labor/equipment charge		4	2	Job		115		115	180

22 13 19 – Sanitary Waste Piping Specialties

22 13 19.13 Sanitary Drains

		Crew	Daily Output	Labor-Hours	Unit	Material	2014 Bare Costs Labor	Equipment	Total	Total Incl O&P
0010	**SANITARY DRAINS**									
0400	Deck, auto park, C.I., 13" top									
0440	3", 4", 5", and 6" pipe size	Q-1	8	2	Ea.	1,325	104		1,429	1,625
0480	For galvanized body, add				"	720			720	790
2000	Floor, medium duty, C.I., deep flange, 7" diam. top									
2040	2" and 3" pipe size	Q-1	12	1.333	Ea.	186	69		255	315
2080	For galvanized body, add					89.50			89.50	98.50
2120	With polished bronze top					291			291	320
2500	Heavy duty, cleanout & trap w/bucket, C.I., 15" top									
2540	2", 3", and 4" pipe size	Q-1	6	2.667	Ea.	6,075	138		6,213	6,925
2560	For galvanized body, add					1,550			1,550	1,725
2580	With polished bronze top					6,575			6,575	7,250

22 13 19.14 Floor Receptors

		Crew	Daily Output	Labor-Hours	Unit	Material	2014 Bare Costs Labor	Equipment	Total	Total Incl O&P
0010	**FLOOR RECEPTORS**, For connection to 2", 3" & 4" diameter pipe									
0200	12-1/2" square top, 25 sq. in. open area	Q-1	10	1.600	Ea.	900	83		983	1,125
0300	For grate with 4" diam. x 3-3/4" high funnel, add					161			161	177
0400	For grate with 6" diameter x 6" high funnel, add					207			207	227
0700	For acid-resisting bucket, add					253			253	279

22 13 19 – Sanitary Waste Piping Specialties

22 13 19.14 Floor Receptors	Crew	Daily Output	Labor-Hours	Unit	Material	2014 Bare Costs Labor	Equipment	Total	Total Incl O&P
0900	For stainless steel mesh bucket liner, add				Ea.	200			200	220
2000	12-5/8" diameter top, 40 sq. in. open area	Q-1	10	1.600	↓	715	83		798	915
2100	For options, add same prices as square top									
3000	8" x 4" rectangular top, 7.5 sq. in. open area	Q-1	14	1.143	Ea.	690	59		749	855
3100	For trap primer connections, add				"	82			82	90
9000	Minimum labor/equipment charge	Q-1	3	5.333	Job		276		276	430

22 13 19.15 Sink Waste Treatment

0010	SINK WASTE TREATMENT, System for commercial kitchens									
0100	includes clock timer, & fittings									
0200	System less chemical, wall mounted cabinet	1 Plum	16	.500	Ea.	550	29		579	650
2000	Chemical, 1 gallon, add					68.50			68.50	75.50
2100	6 gallons, add					310			310	340
2200	15 gallons, add					840			840	925
2300	30 gallons, add					1,575			1,575	1,725
2400	55 gallons, add				↓	2,675			2,675	2,950

22 13 23 – Sanitary Waste Interceptors

22 13 23.10 Interceptors

0010	INTERCEPTORS									
0150	Grease, fabricated steel, 4 GPM, 8 lb. fat capacity	1 Plum	4	2	Ea.	1,100	115		1,215	1,375
0200	7 GPM, 14 lb. fat capacity		4	2		1,525	115		1,640	1,850
1000	10 GPM, 20 lb. fat capacity	↓	4	2		1,800	115		1,915	2,150
1160	100 GPM, 200 lb. fat capacity	Q-1	2	8		13,600	415		14,015	15,500
1240	300 GPM, 600 lb. fat capacity	"	1	16	↓	30,000	830		30,830	34,300
9000	Minimum labor/equipment charge	1 Plum	3	2.667	Job		153		153	239

22 13 29 – Sanitary Sewerage Pumps

22 13 29.14 Sewage Ejector Pumps

0010	SEWAGE EJECTOR PUMPS, With operating and level controls									
0100	Simplex system incl. tank, cover, pump 15' head									
0500	37 gal. PE tank, 12 GPM, 1/2 HP, 2" discharge	Q-1	3.20	5	Ea.	480	259		739	930
0510	3" discharge		3.10	5.161		520	267		787	985
0530	87 GPM, .7 HP, 2" discharge		3.20	5		735	259		994	1,200
0540	3" discharge		3.10	5.161		795	267		1,062	1,300
0600	45 gal. coated stl. tank, 12 GPM, 1/2 HP, 2" discharge		3	5.333		855	276		1,131	1,375
0610	3" discharge		2.90	5.517		890	286		1,176	1,425
0630	87 GPM, .7 HP, 2" discharge		3	5.333		1,100	276		1,376	1,625
0640	3" discharge		2.90	5.517		1,150	286		1,436	1,725
0660	134 GPM, 1 HP, 2" discharge		2.80	5.714		1,175	296		1,471	1,750
0680	3" discharge		2.70	5.926		1,250	305		1,555	1,850
0700	70 gal. PE tank, 12 GPM, 1/2 HP, 2" discharge		2.60	6.154		920	320		1,240	1,525
0710	3" discharge		2.40	6.667		980	345		1,325	1,625
0730	87 GPM, 0.7 HP, 2" discharge		2.50	6.400		1,200	330		1,530	1,825
0740	3" discharge		2.30	6.957		1,275	360		1,635	1,950
0760	134 GPM, 1 HP, 2" discharge		2.20	7.273	↓	1,300	375		1,675	2,025
0770	3" discharge		2	8		1,375	415		1,790	2,175
9000	Minimum labor/equipment charge	↓	2.50	6.400	Job		330		330	515

22 14 Facility Storm Drainage

22 14 26 – Facility Storm Drains

22 14 26.13 Roof Drains

22 14 26.13 Roof Drains	Crew	Daily Output	Labor-Hours	Unit	Material	2014 Bare Costs Labor	Equipment	Total	Total Incl O&P
0010 **ROOF DRAINS**									
0140 Cornice, C.I., 45° or 90° outlet									
0200 3" and 4" pipe size	Q-1	12	1.333	Ea.	360	69		429	505
0260 For galvanized body, add					70			70	77
0280 For polished bronze dome, add				↓	87.50			87.50	96.50
3860 Roof, flat metal deck, C.I. body, 12" C.I. dome									
3890 3" pipe size	Q-1	14	1.143	Ea.	365	59		424	495
3900 4" pipe size	"	13	1.231	"	365	64		429	500
4620 Main, all aluminum, 12" low profile dome									
4640 2", 3" and 4" pipe size	Q-1	14	1.143	Ea.	405	59		464	540
9000 Minimum labor/equipment charge	1 Plum	4	2	Job		115		115	180

22 14 29 – Sump Pumps

22 14 29.16 Submersible Sump Pumps

22 14 29.16 Submersible Sump Pumps	Crew	Daily Output	Labor-Hours	Unit	Material	2014 Bare Costs Labor	Equipment	Total	Total Incl O&P
0010 **SUBMERSIBLE SUMP PUMPS**									
7000 Sump pump, automatic									
7100 Plastic, 1-1/4" discharge, 1/4 HP	1 Plum	6	1.333	Ea.	134	76.50		210.50	267
7140 1/3 HP		5	1.600		194	92		286	355
7180 1-1/2" discharge, 1/2 HP		4	2		272	115		387	480
7500 Cast iron, 1-1/4" discharge, 1/4 HP		6	1.333		189	76.50		265.50	330
7540 1/3 HP		6	1.333		222	76.50		298.50	365
7560 1/2 HP		5	1.600	↓	269	92		361	440
9000 Minimum labor/equipment charge	↓	4	2	Job		115		115	180

22 15 General Service Compressed-Air Systems

22 15 19 – General Service Packaged Air Compressors and Receivers

22 15 19.10 Air Compressors

22 15 19.10 Air Compressors	Crew	Daily Output	Labor-Hours	Unit	Material	2014 Bare Costs Labor	Equipment	Total	Total Incl O&P
0010 **AIR COMPRESSORS**									
5250 Air, reciprocating air cooled, splash lubricated, tank mounted									
5300 Single stage, 1 phase, 140 psi									
5303 1/2 HP, 30 gal. tank	1 Stpi	3	2.667	Ea.	1,825	156		1,981	2,275
5305 3/4 HP, 30 gal. tank		2.60	3.077		1,875	180		2,055	2,325
5307 1 HP, 30 gal. tank	↓	2.20	3.636	↓	2,300	213		2,513	2,850

22 31 Domestic Water Softeners

22 31 13 – Residential Domestic Water Softeners

22 31 13.10 Residential Water Softeners

22 31 13.10 Residential Water Softeners	Crew	Daily Output	Labor-Hours	Unit	Material	2014 Bare Costs Labor	Equipment	Total	Total Incl O&P
0010 **RESIDENTIAL WATER SOFTENERS**									
7350 Water softener, automatic, to 30 grains per gallon	2 Plum	5	3.200	Ea.	400	184		584	725
7400 To 100 grains per gallon	"	4	4	"	650	230		880	1,075

22 33 Electric Domestic Water Heaters

22 33 13 – Instantaneous Electric Domestic Water Heaters

22 33 13.20 Instantaneous Electric Point-Of-Use Wtr. Htrs.		Crew	Daily Output	Labor-Hours	Unit	Material	2014 Bare Costs Labor	Equipment	Total	Total Incl O&P
0010	**INSTANTANEOUS ELECTRIC POINT-OF-USE WATER HEATERS**									
8965	Point of use, electric, glass lined									
8969	Energy saver									
8970	2.5 gal. single element	G	1 Plum	2.80	2.857	Ea.	245	164		409	525
8971	4 gal. single element	G		2.80	2.857		253	164		417	535
8974	6 gal. single element	G		2.50	3.200		261	184		445	575
8975	10 gal. single element	G		2.50	3.200		330	184		514	645
8976	15 gal. single element	G		2.40	3.333		370	192		562	705
8977	20 gal. single element	G		2.40	3.333		410	192		602	750
8978	30 gal. single element	G		2.30	3.478		480	200		680	840
8979	40 gal. single element	G	▼	2.20	3.636	▼	800	209		1,009	1,200
8988	Commercial (ASHRAE energy std. 90)									
8989	6 gallon	G	1 Plum	2.50	3.200	Ea.	665	184		849	1,025
8990	10 gallon	G		2.50	3.200		710	184		894	1,075
8991	15 gallon	G		2.40	3.333		750	192		942	1,125
8992	20 gallon	G		2.40	3.333		785	192		977	1,175
8993	30 gallon	G	▼	2.30	3.478	▼	1,700	200		1,900	2,175
8995	Under the sink, copper, w/bracket									
8996	2.5 gallon	G	1 Plum	4	2	Ea.	435	115		550	655
9000	Minimum labor/equipment charge		"	1.75	4.571	Job		263		263	410

22 33 30 – Residential, Electric Domestic Water Heaters

22 33 30.13 Residential, Small-Capacity Elec. Water Heaters

		Crew	Daily Output	Labor-Hours	Unit	Material	Labor	Equipment	Total	Total Incl O&P
0010	**RESIDENTIAL, SMALL-CAPACITY ELECTRIC DOMESTIC WATER HEATERS**									
1000	Residential, electric, glass lined tank, 5 yr., 10 gal., single element	1 Plum	2.30	3.478	Ea.	330	200		530	670
1060	30 gallon, double element		2.20	3.636		475	209		684	850
1080	40 gallon, double element		2	4		800	230		1,030	1,250
1100	52 gallon, double element		2	4		895	230		1,125	1,350
1120	66 gallon, double element		1.80	4.444		1,200	256		1,456	1,725
1140	80 gallon, double element	▼	1.60	5	▼	1,350	288		1,638	1,925

22 33 33 – Light-Commercial Electric Domestic Water Heaters

22 33 33.10 Commercial Electric Water Heaters

		Crew	Daily Output	Labor-Hours	Unit	Material	Labor	Equipment	Total	Total Incl O&P
0010	**COMMERCIAL ELECTRIC WATER HEATERS**									
4000	Commercial, 100° rise. NOTE: for each size tank, a range of									
4010	heaters between the ones shown are available									
4020	Electric									
4100	5 gal., 3 kW, 12 GPH, 208 volt	1 Plum	2	4	Ea.	2,750	230		2,980	3,375
4160	50 gal., 36 kW, 148 GPH, 208 volt	"	1.80	4.444		6,400	256		6,656	7,425
4480	400 gal., 210 kW, 860 GPH, 480 volt	Q-1	1	16	▼	38,500	830		39,330	43,600

22 34 Fuel-Fired Domestic Water Heaters

22 34 13 – Instantaneous, Tankless, Gas Domestic Water Heaters

22 34 13.10 Instantaneous, Tankless, Gas Water Heaters

			Crew	Daily Output	Labor-Hours	Unit	Material	Labor	Equipment	Total	Total Incl O&P
0010	**INSTANTANEOUS, TANKLESS, GAS WATER HEATERS**										
9410	Natural gas/propane, 3.2 GPM	G	1 Plum	2	4	Ea.	365	230		595	760
9420	6.4 GPM	G		1.90	4.211		745	242		987	1,200
9430	8.4 GPM	G		1.80	4.444		890	256		1,146	1,375
9440	9.5 GPM	G	▼	1.60	5	▼	1,150	288		1,438	1,700

22 34 Fuel-Fired Domestic Water Heaters

22 34 30 – Residential Gas Domestic Water Heaters

22 34 30.13 Residential, Atmos, Gas Domestic Wtr Heaters

		Crew	Daily Output	Labor-Hours	Unit	Material	2014 Bare Costs Labor	Equipment	Total	Total Incl O&P
0010	**RESIDENTIAL, ATMOSPHERIC, GAS DOMESTIC WATER HEATERS**									
2000	Gas fired, foam lined tank, 10 yr., vent not incl.									
2040	30 gallon	1 Plum	2	4	Ea.	895	230		1,125	1,350
2060	40 gallon		1.90	4.211		895	242		1,137	1,375
2100	75 gallon		1.50	5.333		1,350	305		1,655	1,975

22 34 36 – Commercial Gas Domestic Water Heaters

22 34 36.13 Commercial, Atmos., Gas Domestic Water Htrs.

		Crew	Daily Output	Labor-Hours	Unit	Material	2014 Bare Costs Labor	Equipment	Total	Total Incl O&P
0010	**COMMERCIAL, ATMOSPHERIC, GAS DOMESTIC WATER HEATERS**									
6000	Gas fired, flush jacket, std. controls, vent not incl.									
6040	75 MBH input, 73 GPH	1 Plum	1.40	5.714	Ea.	3,500	330		3,830	4,375
6060	98 MBH input, 95 GPH		1.40	5.714		5,300	330		5,630	6,350
6180	200 MBH input, 192 GPH		.60	13.333		8,925	765		9,690	11,000
6900	For low water cutoff, add		8	1		340	57.50		397.50	460
6960	For bronze body hot water circulator, add		4	2		1,925	115		2,040	2,300

22 34 46 – Oil-Fired Domestic Water Heaters

22 34 46.10 Residential Oil-Fired Water Heaters

		Crew	Daily Output	Labor-Hours	Unit	Material	2014 Bare Costs Labor	Equipment	Total	Total Incl O&P
0010	**RESIDENTIAL OIL-FIRED WATER HEATERS**									
3000	Oil fired, glass lined tank, 5 yr., vent not included, 30 gallon	1 Plum	2	4	Ea.	1,175	230		1,405	1,625
3040	50 gallon	"	1.80	4.444	"	1,375	256		1,631	1,925

22 34 46.20 Commercial Oil-Fired Water Heaters

		Crew	Daily Output	Labor-Hours	Unit	Material	2014 Bare Costs Labor	Equipment	Total	Total Incl O&P
0010	**COMMERCIAL OIL-FIRED WATER HEATERS**									
8000	Oil fired, glass lined, UL listed, std. controls, vent not incl.									
8060	140 gal., 140 MBH input, 134 GPH	Q-1	2.13	7.512	Ea.	19,900	390		20,290	22,500
8080	140 gal., 199 MBH input, 191 GPH		2	8		20,600	415		21,015	23,300
8160	140 gal., 540 MBH input, 519 GPH		.96	16.667		28,100	865		28,965	32,300
8280	201 gal., 1250 MBH input, 1200 GPH	Q-2	1.22	19.672		43,900	1,050		44,950	50,000

22 41 Residential Plumbing Fixtures

22 41 13 – Residential Water Closets, Urinals, and Bidets

22 41 13.40 Water Closets

		Crew	Daily Output	Labor-Hours	Unit	Material	2014 Bare Costs Labor	Equipment	Total	Total Incl O&P
0010	**WATER CLOSETS** R224000-40									
0032	For automatic flush, see Line 22 42 39.10 0972									
0150	Tank type, vitreous china, incl. seat, supply pipe w/stop, 1.6 gpf or noted									
0200	Wall hung									
0400	Two piece, close coupled	Q-1	5.30	3.019	Ea.	630	156		786	935
0960	For rough-in, supply, waste, vent and carrier	"	2.73	5.861	"	810	305		1,115	1,375
0999	Floor mounted									
1100	Two piece, close coupled	Q-1	5.30	3.019	Ea.	233	156		389	500
1102	Economy		5.30	3.019		130	156		286	385
1110	Two piece, close coupled, dual flush		5.30	3.019		299	156		455	575
1140	Two piece, close coupled, 1.28 gpf, ADA ⬚G		5.30	3.019		305	156		461	580
1960	For color, add					30%				
1980	For rough-in, supply, waste and vent	Q-1	3.05	5.246	Ea.	330	272		602	790

22 41 16 – Residential Lavatories and Sinks

22 41 16.10 Lavatories

		Crew	Daily Output	Labor-Hours	Unit	Material	2014 Bare Costs Labor	Equipment	Total	Total Incl O&P
0010	**LAVATORIES**, With trim, white unless noted otherwise R224000-40									
0500	Vanity top, porcelain enamel on cast iron									
0600	20" x 18"	Q-1	6.40	2.500	Ea.	330	130		460	560

22 41 16 – Residential Lavatories and Sinks

22 41 16.10 Lavatories		Crew	Daily Output	Labor-Hours	Unit	Material	2014 Bare Costs Labor	Equipment	Total	Total Incl O&P
0640	33" x 19" oval	Q-1	6.40	2.500	Ea.	690	130		820	960
0860	For color, add					25%				
1000	Cultured marble, 19" x 17", single bowl	Q-1	6.40	2.500	Ea.	175	130		305	395
1120	25" x 22", single bowl	"	6.40	2.500	"	215	130		345	440
1580	For color, same price									
1900	Stainless steel, self-rimming, 25" x 22", single bowl, ledge	Q-1	6.40	2.500	Ea.	365	130		495	605
1960	17" x 22", single bowl		6.40	2.500		355	130		485	590
2600	Steel, enameled, 20" x 17", single bowl		5.80	2.759		197	143		340	440
2900	Vitreous china, 20" x 16", single bowl		5.40	2.963		260	153		413	525
2960	20" x 17", single bowl		5.40	2.963		176	153		329	435
3580	Rough-in, supply, waste and vent for all above lavatories		2.30	6.957		415	360		775	1,025
4000	Wall hung									
4040	Porcelain enamel on cast iron, 16" x 14", single bowl	Q-1	8	2	Ea.	510	104		614	720
4180	20" x 18", single bowl	"	8	2	"	277	104		381	465
4580	For color, add					30%				
6000	Vitreous china, 18" x 15", single bowl with backsplash	Q-1	7	2.286	Ea.	231	118		349	440
6960	Rough-in, supply, waste and vent for above lavatories	"	1.66	9.639	"	470	500		970	1,300
7000	Pedestal type									
7600	Vitreous china, 27" x 21", white	Q-1	6.60	2.424	Ea.	690	126		816	955
7610	27" x 21", colored		6.60	2.424		865	126		991	1,150
7620	27" x 21", premium color		6.60	2.424		970	126		1,096	1,275
7660	26" x 20", white		6.60	2.424		770	126		896	1,050
7670	26" x 20", colored		6.60	2.424		770	126		896	1,050
7680	26" x 20", premium color		6.60	2.424		970	126		1,096	1,275
7700	24" x 20", white		6.60	2.424		395	126		521	630
7710	24" x 20", colored		6.60	2.424		480	126		606	720
7720	24" x 20", premium color		6.60	2.424		535	126		661	785
7760	21" x 18", white		6.60	2.424		284	126		410	510
7770	21" x 18", colored		6.60	2.424		300	126		426	525
7990	Rough-in, supply, waste and vent for pedestal lavatories		1.66	9.639		470	500		970	1,300
9000	Minimum labor/equipment charge	1 Plum	3	2.667	Job		153		153	239

22 41 16.30 Sinks

		Crew	Daily Output	Labor-Hours	Unit	Material	2014 Bare Costs Labor	Equipment	Total	Total Incl O&P
0010	**SINKS**, With faucets and drain									
2000	Kitchen, counter top style, P.E. on C.I., 24" x 21" single bowl	Q-1	5.60	2.857	Ea.	275	148		423	530
2100	31" x 22" single bowl		5.60	2.857		575	148		723	860
2200	32" x 21" double bowl		4.80	3.333		340	173		513	645
3000	Stainless steel, self rimming, 19" x 18" single bowl		5.60	2.857		590	148		738	880
3100	25" x 22" single bowl		5.60	2.857		660	148		808	955
3200	33" x 22" double bowl		4.80	3.333		960	173		1,133	1,325
3300	43" x 22" double bowl		4.80	3.333		1,125	173		1,298	1,500
4000	Steel, enameled, with ledge, 24" x 21" single bowl		5.60	2.857		505	148		653	785
4100	32" x 21" double bowl		4.80	3.333		495	173		668	815
4960	For color sinks except stainless steel, add					10%				
4980	For rough-in, supply, waste and vent, counter top sinks	Q-1	2.14	7.477		460	385		845	1,100
5790	For rough-in, supply, waste & vent, sinks	"	1.85	8.649		460	450		910	1,200

22 41 19 – Residential Bathtubs

22 41 19.10 Baths

		Crew	Daily Output	Labor-Hours	Unit	Material	2014 Bare Costs Labor	Equipment	Total	Total Incl O&P
0010	**BATHS** R224000-40									
0100	Tubs, recessed porcelain enamel on cast iron, with trim									
0180	48" x 42"	Q-1	4	4	Ea.	2,625	207		2,832	3,225
0220	72" x 36"	"	3	5.333	"	2,725	276		3,001	3,425
0300	Mat bottom									

22 41 Residential Plumbing Fixtures

22 41 19 – Residential Bathtubs

22 41 19.10 Baths

		Crew	Daily Output	Labor-Hours	Unit	Material	2014 Bare Costs Labor	2014 Bare Costs Equipment	Total	Total Incl O&P
0380	5' long	Q-1	4.40	3.636	Ea.	1,100	188		1,288	1,525
0560	Corner 48" x 44"		4.40	3.636		2,625	188		2,813	3,200
2000	Enameled formed steel, 4'-6" long		5.80	2.759		495	143		638	770
4600	Module tub & showerwall surround, molded fiberglass									
4610	5' long x 34" wide x 76" high	Q-1	4	4	Ea.	815	207		1,022	1,225
4750	Handicap with 1-1/2" OD grab bar, antiskid bottom									
4760	60" x 32-3/4" x 72" high	Q-1	4	4	Ea.	810	207		1,017	1,225
4770	60" x 30" x 71" high with molded seat		3.50	4.571		795	237		1,032	1,250
9600	Rough-in, supply, waste and vent, for all above tubs, add		2.07	7.729		485	400		885	1,150
9900	Minimum labor/equipment charge		3	5.333	Job		276		276	430

22 41 23 – Residential Showers

22 41 23.20 Showers

		Crew	Daily Output	Labor-Hours	Unit	Material	2014 Bare Costs Labor	2014 Bare Costs Equipment	Total	Total Incl O&P
0011	**SHOWERS**, Stall, with drain only									
1520	32" square	Q-1	5	3.200	Ea.	1,175	166		1,341	1,525
1530	36" square		4.80	3.333		2,925	173		3,098	3,475
1540	Terrazzo receptor, 32" square		5	3.200		1,350	166		1,516	1,725
1580	36" corner angle		4.80	3.333		1,725	173		1,898	2,175
3000	Fiberglass, one piece, with 3 walls, 32" x 32" square		5.50	2.909		490	151		641	775
3100	36" x 36" square		5.50	2.909		505	151		656	790
4200	Rough-in, supply, waste and vent for above showers		2.05	7.805		540	405		945	1,225

22 41 23.40 Shower System Components

		Crew	Daily Output	Labor-Hours	Unit	Material	2014 Bare Costs Labor	2014 Bare Costs Equipment	Total	Total Incl O&P
0010	**SHOWER SYSTEM COMPONENTS**									
5500	Head, water economizer, 1.6 GPM [G]	1 Plum	24	.333	Ea.	43	19.20		62.20	77.50

22 41 36 – Residential Laundry Trays

22 41 36.10 Laundry Sinks

		Crew	Daily Output	Labor-Hours	Unit	Material	2014 Bare Costs Labor	2014 Bare Costs Equipment	Total	Total Incl O&P
0010	**LAUNDRY SINKS**, With trim									
0020	Porcelain enamel on cast iron, black iron frame									
0050	24" x 21", single compartment	Q-1	6	2.667	Ea.	580	138		718	850
0100	26" x 21", single compartment	"	6	2.667	"	610	138		748	885
2000	Molded stone, on wall hanger or legs									
2020	22" x 23", single compartment	Q-1	6	2.667	Ea.	134	138		272	365
2100	45" x 21", double compartment	"	5	3.200	"	330	166		496	625
3000	Plastic, on wall hanger or legs									
3020	18" x 23", single compartment	Q-1	6.50	2.462	Ea.	135	128		263	350
3100	20" x 24", single compartment		6.50	2.462		154	128		282	370
3200	36" x 23", double compartment		5.50	2.909		185	151		336	440
3300	40" x 24", double compartment		5.50	2.909		278	151		429	540
5000	Stainless steel, counter top, 22" x 17" single compartment		6	2.667		64	138		202	287
5200	33" x 22", double compartment		5	3.200		79	166		245	345
9600	Rough-in, supply, waste and vent, for all laundry sinks		2.14	7.477		460	385		845	1,100
9810	Minimum labor/equipment charge	1 Plum	3	2.667	Job		153		153	239

22 41 39 – Residential Faucets, Supplies and Trim

22 41 39.10 Faucets and Fittings

		Crew	Daily Output	Labor-Hours	Unit	Material	2014 Bare Costs Labor	2014 Bare Costs Equipment	Total	Total Incl O&P
0010	**FAUCETS AND FITTINGS**									
0150	Bath, faucets, diverter spout combination, sweat	1 Plum	8	1	Ea.	86.50	57.50		144	185
0200	For integral stops, IPS unions, add					109			109	120
0420	Bath, press-bal mix valve w/diverter, spout, shower head, arm/flange	1 Plum	8	1		168	57.50		225.50	275
0500	Drain, central lift, 1-1/2" IPS male		20	.400		71	23		94	115
0600	Trip lever, 1-1/2" IPS male		20	.400		45	23		68	85.50
0810	Bidet									
0812	Fitting, over the rim, swivel spray/pop-up drain	1 Plum	8	1	Ea.	206	57.50		263.50	315

22 41 Residential Plumbing Fixtures

22 41 39 – Residential Faucets, Supplies and Trim

22 41 39.10 Faucets and Fittings		Crew	Daily Output	Labor-Hours	Unit	Material	2014 Bare Costs Labor	Equipment	Total	Total Incl O&P
1000	Kitchen sink faucets, top mount, cast spout	1 Plum	10	.800	Ea.	61.50	46		107.50	140
1100	For spray, add		24	.333		16.15	19.20		35.35	48
1200	Wall type, swing tube spout		10	.800		74.50	46		120.50	154
1300	Single control lever handle									
1310	With pull out spray									
1320	Polished chrome	1 Plum	10	.800	Ea.	196	46		242	287
2000	Laundry faucets, shelf type, IPS or copper unions		12	.667		49.50	38.50		88	115
2100	Lavatory faucet, centerset, without drain		10	.800		44.50	46		90.50	121
2120	With pop-up drain		6.66	1.201		62.50	69		131.50	177
2210	Porcelain cross handles and pop-up drain									
2220	Polished chrome	1 Plum	6.66	1.201	Ea.	189	69		258	315
2230	Polished brass	"	6.66	1.201	"	284	69		353	420
2260	Single lever handle and pop-up drain									
2280	Satin nickel	1 Plum	6.66	1.201	Ea.	277	69		346	415
2290	Polished chrome		6.66	1.201		198	69		267	325
2800	Self-closing, center set		10	.800		131	46		177	216
2810	Automatic sensor and operator, with faucet head ⑤		6.15	1.301		450	75		525	610
4000	Shower by-pass valve with union		18	.444		68.50	25.50		94	115
4100	Shower arm with flange and head		22	.364		19.25	21		40.25	53.50
4140	Shower, hand held, pin mount, massage action, chrome		22	.364		73	21		94	113
4142	Polished brass		22	.364		136	21		157	183
4144	Shower, hand held, wall mtd, adj. spray, 2 wall mounts, chrome		20	.400		97.50	23		120.50	143
4146	Polished brass		20	.400		185	23		208	240
4148	Shower, hand held head, bar mounted 24", adj. spray, chrome		20	.400		158	23		181	209
4150	Polished brass		20	.400		325	23		348	395
4200	Shower thermostatic mixing valve, concealed, with shower head trim kit		8	1		330	57.50		387.50	450
4220	Shower pressure balancing mixing valve,									
4230	With shower head, arm, flange and diverter tub spout									
4240	Chrome	1 Plum	6.14	1.303	Ea.	350	75		425	500
4250	Satin nickel		6.14	1.303		475	75		550	635
4260	Polished graphite		6.14	1.303		475	75		550	635
5000	Sillcock, compact, brass, IPS or copper to hose		24	.333		9.70	19.20		28.90	40.50
6000	Stop and waste valves, bronze									
6100	Angle, solder end 1/2"	1 Plum	24	.333	Ea.	12.05	19.20		31.25	43.50
6110	3/4"		20	.400		14.15	23		37.15	51.50
6300	Straightway, solder end 3/8"		24	.333		12.35	19.20		31.55	43.50
6310	1/2"		24	.333		12.35	19.20		31.55	43.50
6410	Straightway, threaded 1/2"		24	.333		15.95	19.20		35.15	47.50
6420	3/4"		20	.400		18.30	23		41.30	56
6430	1"		19	.421		13.40	24		37.40	53
7800	Water closet, wax gasket		96	.083		1.38	4.80		6.18	9
7820	Gasket toilet tank to bowl		32	.250		2.38	14.40		16.78	25
7830	Replacement diaphragm washer assy for ballcock valve		12	.667		2.38	38.50		40.88	62.50
7850	Dual flush valve		12	.667		20	38.50		58.50	82
8000	Water supply stops, polished chrome plate									
8200	Angle, 3/8"	1 Plum	24	.333	Ea.	12.90	19.20		32.10	44
8300	1/2"		22	.364		12.90	21		33.90	46.50
8400	Straight, 3/8"		26	.308		13.55	17.70		31.25	42.50
8500	1/2"		24	.333		13.55	19.20		32.75	45
8600	Water closet, angle, w/flex riser, 3/8"		24	.333		44	19.20		63.20	78.50
9000	Minimum labor/equipment charge		4	2	Job		115		115	180

422

22 42 Commercial Plumbing Fixtures

22 42 13 – Commercial Water Closets, Urinals, and Bidets

22 42 13.30 Urinals

		Crew	Daily Output	Labor-Hours	Unit	Material	2014 Bare Costs Labor	Equipment	Total	Total Incl O&P
0010	**URINALS**									
3000	Wall hung, vitreous china, with hanger & self-closing valve									
3100	Siphon jet type	Q-1	3	5.333	Ea.	315	276		591	780
3120	Blowout type		3	5.333		450	276		726	925
3140	Water saving .5 gpf [G]		3	5.333		585	276		861	1,075
3300	Rough-in, supply, waste & vent		2.83	5.654		570	293		863	1,075
5000	Stall type, vitreous china, includes valve		2.50	6.400		715	330		1,045	1,300
6980	Rough-in, supply, waste and vent		1.99	8.040	↓	585	415		1,000	1,300
9000	Minimum labor/equipment charge	↓	4	4	Job		207		207	325

22 42 13.40 Water Closets

		Crew	Daily Output	Labor-Hours	Unit	Material	2014 Bare Costs Labor	Equipment	Total	Total Incl O&P
0010	**WATER CLOSETS**									
3000	Bowl only, with flush valve, seat, 1.6 gpf unless noted									
3100	Wall hung	Q-1	5.80	2.759	Ea.	755	143		898	1,050
3200	For rough-in, supply, waste and vent, single WC		2.56	6.250		890	325		1,215	1,475
3360	With floor outlet, 1.28 gpf [G]		5.80	2.759		585	143		728	870
3362	With floor outlet, 1.28 gpf, ADA [G]	↓	5.80	2.759	↓	620	143		763	910
3390	Floor mounted children's size, 10-3/4" high									
3392	With automatic flush sensor, 1.6 gpf	Q-1	6.20	2.581	Ea.	610	134		744	880
3396	With automatic flush sensor, 1.28 gpf		6.20	2.581	"	610	134		744	880
9000	Minimum labor/equipment charge	↓	4	4	Job		207		207	325

22 42 16 – Commercial Lavatories and Sinks

22 42 16.14 Lavatories

		Crew	Daily Output	Labor-Hours	Unit	Material	2014 Bare Costs Labor	Equipment	Total	Total Incl O&P
0010	**LAVATORIES**, With trim, white unless noted otherwise									
0020	Commercial lavatories same as residential. See Section 22 41 16.10									

22 42 16.40 Service Sinks

		Crew	Daily Output	Labor-Hours	Unit	Material	2014 Bare Costs Labor	Equipment	Total	Total Incl O&P
0010	**SERVICE SINKS**									
6650	Service, floor, corner, P.E. on C.I., 28" x 28"	Q-1	4.40	3.636	Ea.	990	188		1,178	1,400
6790	For rough-in, supply, waste & vent, floor service sinks		1.64	9.756	"	1,475	505		1,980	2,425
9000	Minimum labor/equipment charge	↓	4	4	Job		207		207	325

22 42 23 – Commercial Showers

22 42 23.30 Group Showers

		Crew	Daily Output	Labor-Hours	Unit	Material	2014 Bare Costs Labor	Equipment	Total	Total Incl O&P
0010	**GROUP SHOWERS**									
6000	Group, w/pressure balancing valve, rough-in and rigging not included									
6800	Column, 6 heads, no receptors, less partitions	Q-1	3	5.333	Ea.	3,000	276		3,276	3,725
6900	With stainless steel partitions		1	16		9,250	830		10,080	11,500
7600	5 heads, no receptors, less partitions		3	5.333		2,475	276		2,751	3,150
7620	4 heads (1 handicap) no receptors, less partitions		3	5.333		3,975	276		4,251	4,800
7700	With stainless steel partitions		1	16	↓	7,600	830		8,430	9,650
9000	Minimum labor/equipment charge	↓	4	4	Job		207		207	325

22 42 33 – Wash Fountains

22 42 33.20 Commercial Wash Fountains

		Crew	Daily Output	Labor-Hours	Unit	Material	2014 Bare Costs Labor	Equipment	Total	Total Incl O&P
0010	**COMMERCIAL WASH FOUNTAINS**									
1900	Group, foot control									
2000	Precast terrazzo, circular, 36" diam., 5 or 6 persons	Q-2	3	8	Ea.	5,800	430		6,230	7,050
2100	54" diameter for 8 or 10 persons		2.50	9.600		9,025	515		9,540	10,700
2400	Semi-circular, 36" diam. for 3 persons		3	8		4,775	430		5,205	5,925
2500	54" diam. for 4 or 5 persons	↓	2.50	9.600	↓	6,775	515		7,290	8,250
5610	Group, infrared control, barrier free									
5614	Precast terrazzo									
5620	Semi-circular 36" diam. for 3 persons	Q-2	3	8	Ea.	7,150	430		7,580	8,550

22 42 Commercial Plumbing Fixtures

22 42 33 – Wash Fountains

22 42 33.20 Commercial Wash Fountains

	22 42 33.20 Commercial Wash Fountains	Crew	Daily Output	Labor-Hours	Unit	Material	2014 Bare Costs Labor	Equipment	Total	Total Incl O&P
5630	46" diam. for 4 persons	Q-2	2.80	8.571	Ea.	7,725	460		8,185	9,225
5640	Circular, 54" diam. for 8 persons, button control	↓	2.50	9.600	↓	9,125	515		9,640	10,800
5700	Rough-in, supply, waste and vent for above wash fountains	Q-1	1.82	8.791	↓	660	455		1,115	1,425
9000	Minimum labor/equipment charge	Q-2	3	8	Job		430		430	670

22 42 39 – Commercial Faucets, Supplies, and Trim

22 42 39.10 Faucets and Fittings

	22 42 39.10 Faucets and Fittings	Crew	Daily Output	Labor-Hours	Unit	Material	2014 Bare Costs Labor	Equipment	Total	Total Incl O&P
0010	**FAUCETS AND FITTINGS**									
0840	Flush valves, with vacuum breaker									
0850	Water closet									
0860	Exposed, rear spud	1 Plum	8	1	Ea.	148	57.50		205.50	253
0870	Top spud		8	1		149	57.50		206.50	253
0880	Concealed, rear spud		8	1		197	57.50		254.50	305
0890	Top spud		8	1		159	57.50		216.50	265
0900	Wall hung		8	1		177	57.50		234.50	285
0910	Dual flush flushometer		12	.667		197	38.50		235.50	276
0912	Flushometer retrofit kit	↓	18	.444	↓	16.30	25.50		41.80	58
0920	Urinal									
0930	Exposed, stall	1 Plum	8	1	Ea.	149	57.50		206.50	254
0940	Wall, (washout)		8	1		149	57.50		206.50	253
0950	Pedestal, top spud		8	1		143	57.50		200.50	247
0960	Concealed, stall		8	1		156	57.50		213.50	262
0970	Wall (washout)	↓	8	1	↓	168	57.50		225.50	275
0971	Automatic flush sensor and operator for									
0972	urinals or water closets, standard [G]	1 Plum	8	1	Ea.	450	57.50		507.50	585
0980	High efficiency water saving									
0984	Water closets, 1.28 gpf [G]	1 Plum	8	1	Ea.	415	57.50		472.50	550
0988	Urinals, .5 gpf [G]	"	8	1	"	415	57.50		472.50	550
2790	Faucets for lavatories									
2800	Self-closing, center set	1 Plum	10	.800	Ea.	131	46		177	216
2810	Automatic sensor and operator, with faucet head		6.15	1.301		450	75		525	610
3000	Service sink faucet, cast spout, pail hook, hose end	↓	14	.571	↓	80	33		113	140

22 42 39.30 Carriers and Supports

	22 42 39.30 Carriers and Supports	Crew	Daily Output	Labor-Hours	Unit	Material	2014 Bare Costs Labor	Equipment	Total	Total Incl O&P
0010	**CARRIERS AND SUPPORTS**, For plumbing fixtures									
3000	Lavatory, concealed arm									
3050	Floor mounted, single									
3100	High back fixture	1 Plum	6	1.333	Ea.	465	76.50		541.50	630
3200	Flat slab fixture		6	1.333		400	76.50		476.50	560
3220	Paraplegic	↓	6	1.333	↓	515	76.50		591.50	690
6980	Water closet, siphon jet									
7000	Horizontal, adjustable, caulk									
7040	Single, 4" pipe size	1 Plum	5.33	1.501	Ea.	655	86.50		741.50	855
7060	5" pipe size		5.33	1.501		845	86.50		931.50	1,075
7100	Double, 4" pipe size		5	1.600		1,225	92		1,317	1,500
7120	5" pipe size	↓	5	1.600	↓	1,475	92		1,567	1,775
8200	Water closet, residential									
8220	Vertical centerline, floor mount									
8240	Single, 3" caulk, 2" or 3" vent	1 Plum	6	1.333	Ea.	535	76.50		611.50	705
8260	4" caulk, 2" or 4" vent		6	1.333	"	690	76.50		766.50	875
9990	Minimum labor/equipment charge	↓	3.50	2.286	Job		132		132	205

22 43 Healthcare Plumbing Fixtures

22 43 39 – Healthcare Faucets

22 43 39.10 Faucets and Fittings

22 43 39.10 Faucets and Fittings	Crew	Daily Output	Labor-Hours	Unit	Material	2014 Bare Costs Labor	Equipment	Total	Total Incl O&P
0010 **FAUCETS AND FITTINGS**									
2850 Medical, bedpan cleanser, with pedal valve,	1 Plum	12	.667	Ea.	855	38.50		893.50	1,000
2860 With screwdriver stop valve		12	.667		440	38.50		478.50	545
2870 With self-closing spray valve		12	.667		272	38.50		310.50	360
2900 Faucet, gooseneck spout, wrist handles, grid drain		10	.800		194	46		240	285
2940 Mixing valve, knee action, screwdriver stops	↓	4	2	↓	475	115		590	705

22 45 Emergency Plumbing Fixtures

22 45 13 – Emergency Showers

22 45 13.10 Emergency Showers

22 45 13.10 Emergency Showers	Crew	Daily Output	Labor-Hours	Unit	Material	2014 Bare Costs Labor	Equipment	Total	Total Incl O&P
0010 **EMERGENCY SHOWERS**, Rough-in not included									
5000 Shower, single head, drench, ball valve, pull, freestanding	Q-1	4	4	Ea.	380	207		587	745
5200 Horizontal or vertical supply		4	4		540	207		747	920
6000 Multi-nozzle, eye/face wash combination		4	4		640	207		847	1,025
6400 Multi-nozzle, 12 spray, shower only		4	4		1,950	207		2,157	2,475
6600 For freeze-proof, add		6	2.667	↓	455	138		593	715
9000 Minimum labor/equipment charge	↓	3	5.333	Job		276		276	430

22 45 16 – Eyewash Equipment

22 45 16.10 Eyewash Safety Equipment

22 45 16.10 Eyewash Safety Equipment	Crew	Daily Output	Labor-Hours	Unit	Material	2014 Bare Costs Labor	Equipment	Total	Total Incl O&P
0010 **EYEWASH SAFETY EQUIPMENT**, Rough-in not included									
1000 Eye wash fountain									
1400 Plastic bowl, pedestal mounted	Q-1	4	4	Ea.	269	207		476	620

22 47 Drinking Fountains and Water Coolers

22 47 13 – Drinking Fountains

22 47 13.10 Drinking Water Fountains

22 47 13.10 Drinking Water Fountains	Crew	Daily Output	Labor-Hours	Unit	Material	2014 Bare Costs Labor	Equipment	Total	Total Incl O&P
0010 **DRINKING WATER FOUNTAINS**, For connection to cold water supply									
1000 Wall mounted, non-recessed									
2700 Stainless steel, single bubbler, no back	1 Plum	4	2	Ea.	1,025	115		1,140	1,325
2740 With back		4	2		540	115		655	770
2780 Dual handle & wheelchair projection type		4	2		730	115		845	985
2820 Dual level for handicapped type		3.20	2.500		1,500	144		1,644	1,875
3980 For rough-in, supply and waste, add	↓	2.21	3.620	↓	365	208		573	725
4000 Wall mounted, semi-recessed									
4200 Poly-marble, single bubbler	1 Plum	4	2	Ea.	955	115		1,070	1,225
4600 Stainless steel, satin finish, single bubbler	"	4	2	"	1,125	115		1,240	1,425
6000 Wall mounted, fully recessed									
6400 Poly-marble, single bubbler	1 Plum	4	2	Ea.	1,600	115		1,715	1,925
6800 Stainless steel, single bubbler		4	2		1,525	115		1,640	1,850
7580 For rough-in, supply and waste, add	↓	1.83	4.372	↓	365	252		617	795
7600 Floor mounted, pedestal type									
8600 Enameled iron, heavy duty service, 2 bubblers	1 Plum	2	4	Ea.	2,575	230		2,805	3,200
8880 For freeze-proof valve system, add		2	4		665	230		895	1,100
8900 For rough-in, supply and waste, add		1.83	4.372		365	252		617	795
9000 Minimum labor/equipment charge	↓	2	4	Job		230		230	360

22 47 Drinking Fountains and Water Coolers

22 47 16 – Pressure Water Coolers

22 47 16.10 Electric Water Coolers	Crew	Daily Output	Labor-Hours	Unit	Material	2014 Bare Costs Labor	Equipment	Total	Total Incl O&P
0010 **ELECTRIC WATER COOLERS**									
0100 Wall mounted, non-recessed									
0140 4 GPH	Q-1	4	4	Ea.	680	207		887	1,075
0160 8 GPH, barrier free, sensor operated		4	4		1,025	207		1,232	1,475
1000 Dual height, 8.2 GPH		3.80	4.211		2,025	218		2,243	2,575
1040 14.3 GPH		3.80	4.211		975	218		1,193	1,425
3300 Semi-recessed, 8.1 GPH	↓	4	4	↓	715	207		922	1,100
4600 Floor mounted, flush-to-wall									
4640 4 GPH	1 Plum	3	2.667	Ea.	705	153		858	1,025
4980 For stainless steel cabinet, add					128			128	141
5000 Dual height, 8.2 GPH	1 Plum	2	4	↓	1,100	230		1,330	1,575
9000 Minimum labor/equipment charge	"	2	4	Job		230		230	360

22 66 Chemical-Waste Systems for Lab. and Healthcare Facilities

22 66 53 – Laboratory Chemical-Waste and Vent Piping

22 66 53.30 Glass Pipe

	Crew	Daily Output	Labor-Hours	Unit	Material	2014 Bare Costs Labor	Equipment	Total	Total Incl O&P
0010 **GLASS PIPE**, Borosilicate, couplings & clevis hanger assemblies, 10' O.C.									
0020 Drainage									
1100 1-1/2" diameter	Q-1	52	.308	L.F.	10.60	15.95		26.55	36.50
1120 2" diameter		44	.364		13.85	18.85		32.70	45
1140 3" diameter		39	.410		18.70	21.50		40.20	53.50
1160 4" diameter		30	.533		33.50	27.50		61	79.50
1180 6" diameter	↓	26	.615	↓	58	32		90	114
9000 Minimum labor/equipment charge	1 Plum	4	2	Job		115		115	180

22 66 53.40 Pipe Fittings, Glass

	Crew	Daily Output	Labor-Hours	Unit	Material	2014 Bare Costs Labor	Equipment	Total	Total Incl O&P
0010 **PIPE FITTINGS, GLASS**									
0020 Drainage, beaded ends									
0040 Coupling & labor required at joints not incl. in fitting									
0050 price. Add 1 per joint for installed price									
0070 90° Bend or sweep, 1-1/2"				Ea.	31.50			31.50	35
0090 2"					40			40	44
0100 3"					66			66	72.50
0110 4"					105			105	116
0120 6" (sweep only)					330			330	360
0350 Tee, single sanitary, 1-1/2"					51			51	56.50
0370 2"					51			51	56.50
0380 3"					76.50			76.50	84
0390 4"					137			137	150
0400 6"				↓	365			365	405
0500 Coupling, stainless steel, TFE seal ring									
0520 1-1/2"	Q-1	32	.500	Ea.	23.50	26		49.50	66
0530 2"		30	.533		29.50	27.50		57	75
0540 3"		25	.640		39.50	33		72.50	95
0550 4"		23	.696		67.50	36		103.50	131
0560 6"	↓	20	.800	↓	152	41.50		193.50	232
9000 Minimum labor/equipment charge	1 Plum	4	2	Job		115		115	180

22 66 Chemical-Waste Systems for Lab. and Healthcare Facilities

22 66 53 – Laboratory Chemical-Waste and Vent Piping

22 66 53.60 Corrosion Resistant Pipe

		Crew	Daily Output	Labor-Hours	Unit	Material	2014 Bare Costs Labor	Equipment	Total	Total Incl O&P
0010	**CORROSION RESISTANT PIPE**, No couplings or hangers									
0020	Iron alloy, drain, mechanical joint									
1000	1-1/2" diameter	Q-1	70	.229	L.F.	46	11.85		57.85	69
1100	2" diameter		66	.242		47	12.55		59.55	71
1120	3" diameter		60	.267		60.50	13.80		74.30	88
1140	4" diameter		52	.308		77.50	15.95		93.45	111
2980	Plastic, epoxy, fiberglass filament wound, B&S joint									
3000	2" diameter	Q-1	62	.258	L.F.	12	13.35		25.35	34
3100	3" diameter		51	.314		14	16.25		30.25	41
3120	4" diameter		45	.356		20	18.40		38.40	50.50
3160	8" diameter	Q-2	38	.632		44	34		78	102
3200	12" diameter	"	28	.857		72	46		118	152
9800	Minimum labor/equipment charge	1 Plum	4	2	Job		115		115	180

22 66 53.70 Pipe Fittings, Corrosion Resistant

		Crew	Daily Output	Labor-Hours	Unit	Material	2014 Bare Costs Labor	Equipment	Total	Total Incl O&P
0010	**PIPE FITTINGS, CORROSION RESISTANT**									
0030	Iron alloy									
0050	Mechanical joint									
0060	1/4 Bend, 1-1/2"	Q-1	12	1.333	Ea.	77	69		146	193
0080	2"		10	1.600		126	83		209	268
0090	3"		9	1.778		151	92		243	310
0100	4"		8	2		174	104		278	355
0160	Tee and Y, sanitary, straight									
0170	1-1/2"	Q-1	8	2	Ea.	84	104		188	255
0180	2"		7	2.286		112	118		230	310
0190	3"		6	2.667		174	138		312	405
0200	4"		5	3.200		320	166		486	610
0360	Coupling, 1-1/2"		14	1.143		47.50	59		106.50	145
0380	2"		12	1.333		54	69		123	168
0390	3"		11	1.455		56.50	75.50		132	181
0400	4"		10	1.600		64.50	83		147.50	200
3000	Epoxy, filament wound									
3030	Quick-lock joint									
3040	90° Elbow, 2"	Q-1	28	.571	Ea.	97.50	29.50		127	153
3060	3"		16	1		112	52		164	204
3070	4"		13	1.231		153	64		217	268
3190	Tee, 2"		19	.842		233	43.50		276.50	325
3200	3"		11	1.455		280	75.50		355.50	430
3210	4"		9	1.778		335	92		427	515
9000	Minimum labor/equipment charge	1 Plum	4	2	Job		115		115	180

Division Notes

	CREW	DAILY OUTPUT	LABOR-HOURS	UNIT	BARE COSTS				TOTAL INCL O&P
					MAT.	LABOR	EQUIP.	TOTAL	

Estimating Tips

The labor adjustment factors listed in Subdivision 22 01 02.20 also apply to Division 23.

23 10 00 Facility Fuel Systems

- The prices in this subdivision for above- and below-ground storage tanks do not include foundations or hold-down slabs, unless noted. The estimator should refer to Divisions 3 and 31 for foundation system pricing. In addition to the foundations, required tank accessories, such as tank gauges, leak detection devices, and additional manholes and piping, must be added to the tank prices.

23 50 00 Central Heating Equipment

- When estimating the cost of an HVAC system, check to see who is responsible for providing and installing the temperature control system. It is possible to overlook controls, assuming that they would be included in the electrical estimate.

- When looking up a boiler, be careful on specified capacity. Some manufacturers rate their products on output while others use input.

- Include HVAC insulation for pipe, boiler, and duct (wrap and liner).

- Be careful when looking up mechanical items to get the correct pressure rating and connection type (thread, weld, flange).

23 70 00 Central HVAC Equipment

- Combination heating and cooling units are sized by the air conditioning requirements. (See Reference No. R236000-20 for preliminary sizing guide.)

- A ton of air conditioning is nominally 400 CFM.

- Rectangular duct is taken off by the linear foot for each size, but its cost is usually estimated by the pound. Remember that SMACNA standards now base duct on internal pressure.

- Prefabricated duct is estimated and purchased like pipe: straight sections and fittings.

- Note that cranes or other lifting equipment are not included on any lines in Division 23. For example, if a crane is required to lift a heavy piece of pipe into place high above a gym floor, or to put a rooftop unit on the roof of a four-story building, etc., it must be added. Due to the potential for extreme variation—from nothing additional required to a major crane or helicopter—we feel that including a nominal amount for "lifting contingency" would be useless and detract from the accuracy of the estimate. When using equipment rental cost data from RSMeans, do not forget to include the cost of the operator(s).

Reference Numbers

Reference numbers are shown in shaded boxes at the beginning of some major classifications. These numbers refer to related items in the Reference Section. The reference information may be an estimating procedure, an alternate pricing method, or technical information.

Note: Not all subdivisions listed here necessarily appear in this publication.

Note: **Trade Service,** *in part, has been used as a reference source for some of the material prices used in Division 23.*

23 05 Common Work Results for HVAC

23 05 05 – Selective HVAC Demolition

23 05 05.10 HVAC Demolition

		Crew	Daily Output	Labor-Hours	Unit	Material	2014 Bare Costs Labor	Equipment	Total	Total Incl O&P
0010	**HVAC DEMOLITION** R220105-10									
0100	Air conditioner, split unit, 3 ton	Q-5	2	8	Ea.		420		420	655
0150	Package unit, 3 ton R024119-10	Q-6	3	8	"		435		435	680
0298	Boilers									
0300	Electric, up thru 148 kW	Q-19	2	12	Ea.		635		635	985
0310	150 thru 518 kW	"	1	24			1,275		1,275	1,975
0320	550 thru 2000 kW	Q-21	.40	80			4,350		4,350	6,750
0330	2070 kW and up	"	.30	106			5,800		5,800	9,025
0340	Gas and/or oil, up thru 150 MBH	Q-7	2.20	14.545			810		810	1,275
0350	160 thru 2000 MBH		.80	40			2,225		2,225	3,475
0360	2100 thru 4500 MBH		.50	64			3,575		3,575	5,550
0370	4600 thru 7000 MBH		.30	106			5,950		5,950	9,275
0380	7100 thru 12,000 MBH		.16	200			11,100		11,100	17,400
0390	12,200 thru 25,000 MBH		.12	266			14,900		14,900	23,200
1000	Ductwork, 4" high, 8" wide	1 Clab	200	.040	L.F.		1.47		1.47	2.41
1020	10" wide		190	.042			1.54		1.54	2.54
1040	14" wide		180	.044			1.63		1.63	2.68
1100	6" high, 8" wide		165	.048			1.78		1.78	2.92
1120	12" wide		150	.053			1.95		1.95	3.21
1140	18" wide		135	.059			2.17		2.17	3.57
1200	10" high, 12" wide		125	.064			2.35		2.35	3.85
1220	18" wide		115	.070			2.55		2.55	4.19
1240	24" wide		110	.073			2.67		2.67	4.38
1300	12"-14" high, 16"-18" wide		85	.094			3.45		3.45	5.65
1320	24" wide		75	.107			3.91		3.91	6.40
1340	48" wide		71	.113			4.13		4.13	6.80
1400	18" high, 24" wide		67	.119			4.38		4.38	7.20
1420	36" wide		63	.127			4.65		4.65	7.65
1440	48" wide		59	.136			4.97		4.97	8.15
1500	30" high, 36" wide		56	.143			5.25		5.25	8.60
1520	48" wide		53	.151			5.55		5.55	9.10
1540	72" wide		50	.160			5.85		5.85	9.65
1550	Duct heater, electric strip	1 Elec	8	1	Ea.		53.50		53.50	82.50
1850	Minimum labor/equipment charge	1 Clab	3	2.667	Job		97.50		97.50	161
2200	Furnace, electric	Q-20	2	10	Ea.		500		500	785
2300	Gas or oil, under 120 MBH	Q-9	4	4			197		197	310
2340	Over 120 MBH	"	3	5.333			263		263	415
2800	Heat pump, package unit, 3 ton	Q-5	2.40	6.667			350		350	550
2840	Split unit, 3 ton		2	8			420		420	655
3000	Mechanical equipment, light items. Unit is weight, not cooling.		.90	17.778	Ton		935		935	1,450
3600	Heavy items		1.10	14.545	"		765		765	1,200
5090	Remove refrigerant from system	1 Stpi	40	.200	Lb.		11.70		11.70	18.25
9000	Minimum labor/equipment charge	Q-6	3	8	Job		435		435	680

23 05 23 – General-Duty Valves for HVAC Piping

23 05 23.30 Valves, Iron Body

		Crew	Daily Output	Labor-Hours	Unit	Material	Labor	Equipment	Total	Total Incl O&P
0010	**VALVES, IRON BODY**									
1020	Butterfly, wafer type, gear actuator, 200 lb.									
1030	2"	1 Plum	14	.571	Ea.	96	33		129	157
1060	4"	Q-1	5	3.200	"	113	166		279	385
1650	Gate, 125 lb., N.R.S.									
2150	Flanged									
2240	2-1/2"	Q-1	5	3.200	Ea.	700	166		866	1,025

430

23 05 Common Work Results for HVAC

23 05 23 – General-Duty Valves for HVAC Piping

23 05 23.30 Valves, Iron Body		Crew	Daily Output	Labor-Hours	Unit	Material	2014 Bare Costs Labor	Equipment	Total	Total Incl O&P
2260	3"	Q-1	4.50	3.556	Ea.	780	184		964	1,150
2280	4"	↓	3	5.333	↓	1,125	276		1,401	1,650
3550	OS&Y, 125 lb., flanged									
3680	4"	Q-1	3	5.333	Ea.	730	276		1,006	1,225
3690	5"	Q-2	3.40	7.059		1,175	380		1,555	1,900
3700	6"	"	3	8	↓	1,175	430		1,605	1,975
9000	Minimum labor/equipment charge	1 Plum	3	2.667	Job		153		153	239

23 07 HVAC Insulation

23 07 13 – Duct Insulation

23 07 13.10 Duct Thermal Insulation

			Crew	Daily Output	Labor-Hours	Unit	Material	2014 Bare Costs Labor	Equipment	Total	Total Incl O&P
0010	**DUCT THERMAL INSULATION**										
0100	Rule of thumb, as a percentage of total mechanical costs					Job				10%	10%
0110	Insulation req'd. is based on the surface size/area to be covered										
3000	Ductwork										
3020	Blanket type, fiberglass, flexible										
3140	FSK vapor barrier wrap, .75 lb. density										
3160	1" thick	G	Q-14	350	.046	S.F.	.19	2.10		2.29	3.59
3170	1-1/2" thick	G		320	.050		.23	2.30		2.53	3.95
3180	2" thick	G		300	.053		.27	2.45		2.72	4.24
3190	3" thick	G		260	.062		.38	2.83		3.21	4.97
3200	4" thick	G	↓	242	.066	↓	.64	3.04		3.68	5.60
3210	Vinyl jacket, same as FSK										
9600	Minimum labor/equipment charge		1 Stpi	4	2	Job		117		117	183

23 07 16 – HVAC Equipment Insulation

23 07 16.10 HVAC Equipment Thermal Insulation

		Crew	Daily Output	Labor-Hours	Unit	Material	2014 Bare Costs Labor	Equipment	Total	Total Incl O&P
0010	**HVAC EQUIPMENT THERMAL INSULATION**									
0100	Rule of thumb, as a percentage of total mechanical costs				Job				10%	10%
0110	Insulation req'd. is based on the surface size/area to be covered									
9610	Minimum labor/equipment charge	1 Stpi	4	2	Job		117		117	183

23 09 Instrumentation and Control for HVAC

23 09 53 – Pneumatic and Electric Control System for HVAC

23 09 53.10 Control Components

			Crew	Daily Output	Labor-Hours	Unit	Material	2014 Bare Costs Labor	Equipment	Total	Total Incl O&P
0010	**CONTROL COMPONENTS**										
5000	Thermostats										
5030	Manual		1 Stpi	8	1	Ea.	46.50	58.50		105	143
5040	1 set back, electric, timed	G		8	1		35.50	58.50		94	131
5050	2 set back, electric, timed	G	↓	8	1		179	58.50		237.50	289
5200	24 hour, automatic, clock	G	1 Shee	8	1	↓	158	54.50		212.50	261
6000	Valves, motorized zone										
6100	Sweat connections, 1/2" C x C		1 Stpi	20	.400	Ea.	166	23.50		189.50	219
6110	3/4" C x C		↓	20	.400		166	23.50		189.50	220
6120	1" C x C		↓	19	.421	↓	217	24.50		241.50	277
9000	Minimum labor/equipment charge		1 Plum	4	2	Job		115		115	180

23 21 · Hydronic Piping and Pumps

23 21 20 – Hydronic HVAC Piping Specialties

23 21 20.34 Dielectric Unions

		Crew	Daily Output	Labor-Hours	Unit	Material	2014 Bare Costs Labor	Equipment	Total	Total Incl O&P
0010	**DIELECTRIC UNIONS**, Standard gaskets for water and air									
0020	250 psi maximum pressure									
0280	Female IPT to sweat, straight									
0340	3/4" pipe size	1 Plum	20	.400	Ea.	6.20	23		29.20	43
0780	Female IPT to female IPT, straight									
0800	1/2" pipe size	1 Plum	24	.333	Ea.	13.85	19.20		33.05	45
0840	3/4" pipe size		20	.400	"	15.60	23		38.60	53
9000	Minimum labor/equipment charge		4	2	Job		115		115	180

23 21 20.46 Expansion Tanks

		Crew	Daily Output	Labor-Hours	Unit	Material	2014 Bare Costs Labor	Equipment	Total	Total Incl O&P
0010	**EXPANSION TANKS**									
2000	Steel, liquid expansion, ASME, painted, 15 gallon capacity	Q-5	17	.941	Ea.	640	49.50		689.50	780
2040	30 gallon capacity		12	1.333		715	70		785	895
2080	60 gallon capacity		8	2		1,000	105		1,105	1,275
2120	100 gallon capacity		6	2.667		1,450	140		1,590	1,825
3000	Steel ASME expansion, rubber diaphragm, 19 gal. cap. accept.		12	1.333		2,425	70		2,495	2,775
3020	31 gallon capacity		8	2		2,700	105		2,805	3,150
3040	61 gallon capacity		6	2.667		3,800	140		3,940	4,400
3080	119 gallon capacity		4	4		4,100	211		4,311	4,825
9000	Minimum labor/equipment charge		4	4	Job		211		211	330

23 21 20.70 Steam Traps

		Crew	Daily Output	Labor-Hours	Unit	Material	2014 Bare Costs Labor	Equipment	Total	Total Incl O&P
0010	**STEAM TRAPS**									
0030	Cast iron body, threaded									
0040	Inverted bucket									
0050	1/2" pipe size	1 Stpi	12	.667	Ea.	152	39		191	228
0100	1" pipe size		9	.889		410	52		462	530
0120	1-1/4" pipe size		8	1		615	58.50		673.50	770
1000	Float & thermostatic, 15 psi									
1010	3/4" pipe size	1 Stpi	16	.500	Ea.	124	29.50		153.50	183
1020	1" pipe size		15	.533		150	31		181	213
1040	1-1/2" pipe size		9	.889		263	52		315	370
1060	2" pipe size		6	1.333		485	78		563	650
9000	Minimum labor/equipment charge		4	2	Job		117		117	183

23 21 20.76 Strainers, Y Type, Bronze Body

		Crew	Daily Output	Labor-Hours	Unit	Material	2014 Bare Costs Labor	Equipment	Total	Total Incl O&P
0010	**STRAINERS, Y TYPE, BRONZE BODY**									
0050	Screwed, 125 lb., 1/4" pipe size	1 Stpi	24	.333	Ea.	23	19.50		42.50	56
0100	1/2" pipe size		20	.400		27.50	23.50		51	67
0120	3/4" pipe size		19	.421		34	24.50		58.50	76
0140	1" pipe size		17	.471		40.50	27.50		68	87.50
0160	1-1/2" pipe size		14	.571		87.50	33.50		121	148
0180	2" pipe size		13	.615		116	36		152	184
0182	3" pipe size		12	.667		845	39		884	990
0200	300 lb., 2-1/2" pipe size	Q-5	17	.941		510	49.50		559.50	640
0220	3" pipe size		16	1		1,000	52.50		1,052.50	1,175
0240	4" pipe size		15	1.067		2,300	56		2,356	2,625
1000	Flanged, 150 lb., 1-1/2" pipe size	1 Stpi	11	.727		475	42.50		517.50	585
1020	2" pipe size	"	8	1		640	58.50		698.50	795
1030	2-1/2" pipe size	Q-5	5	3.200		950	168		1,118	1,325
1040	3" pipe size		4.50	3.556		1,175	187		1,362	1,575
1060	4" pipe size		3	5.333		1,775	281		2,056	2,400
1100	6" pipe size	Q-6	3	8		3,400	435		3,835	4,400
1106	8" pipe size	"	2.60	9.231		3,725	505		4,230	4,875
1500	For 300 lb. rating, add					40%				

23 21 Hydronic Piping and Pumps

23 21 20 – Hydronic HVAC Piping Specialties

23 21 20.76 Strainers, Y Type, Bronze Body	Crew	Daily Output	Labor-Hours	Unit	Material	2014 Bare Costs Labor	Equipment	Total	Total Incl O&P
9000	Minimum labor/equipment charge	1 Stpi	3.75	2.133	Job		125		125	195

23 21 23 – Hydronic Pumps

23 21 23.13 In-Line Centrifugal Hydronic Pumps

		Crew	Daily Output	Labor-Hours	Unit	Material	2014 Bare Costs Labor	Equipment	Total	Total Incl O&P
0010	**IN-LINE CENTRIFUGAL HYDRONIC PUMPS**									
0600	Bronze, sweat connections, 1/40 HP, in line									
0640	3/4" size	Q-1	16	1	Ea.	212	52		264	315
1000	Flange connection, 3/4" to 1-1/2" size									
1040	1/12 HP	Q-1	6	2.667	Ea.	545	138		683	815
1060	1/8 HP		6	2.667		940	138		1,078	1,250
1100	1/3 HP		6	2.667		1,050	138		1,188	1,375
1140	2" size, 1/6 HP		5	3.200		1,350	166		1,516	1,725
1180	2-1/2" size, 1/4 HP		5	3.200		1,775	166		1,941	2,200
1220	3" size, 1/4 HP		4	4		1,850	207		2,057	2,375
9000	Minimum labor/equipment charge		3.25	4.923	Job		255		255	400

23 31 HVAC Ducts and Casings

23 31 13 – Metal Ducts

23 31 13.13 Rectangular Metal Ducts

		Crew	Daily Output	Labor-Hours	Unit	Material	2014 Bare Costs Labor	Equipment	Total	Total Incl O&P
0010	**RECTANGULAR METAL DUCTS** R233100-20									
0020	Fabricated rectangular, includes fittings, joints, supports,									
0021	allowance for flexible connections and field sketches.									
0030	Does not include "as-built dwgs." or insulation.									
0031	NOTE: Fabrication and installation are combined									
0040	as LABOR cost. Approx. 25% fittings assumed.									
0042	Fabrication/Inst. is to commercial quality standards									
0043	(SMACNA or equiv.) for structure, sealing, leak testing, etc.									
0100	Aluminum, alloy 3003-H14, under 100 lb.	Q-10	75	.320	Lb.	3.66	16.35		20.01	30
0110	100 to 500 lb.		80	.300		2.38	15.30		17.68	26.50
0120	500 to 1,000 lb.		95	.253		2.25	12.90		15.15	23
0500	Galvanized steel, under 200 lb.		235	.102		.66	5.20		5.86	8.95
0520	200 to 500 lb.		245	.098		.62	5		5.62	8.60
0540	500 to 1,000 lb.		255	.094		.61	4.80	-	5.41	8.25
0560	1,000 to 2,000 lb.		265	.091		.60	4.62		5.22	7.95
0580	Over 5,000 lb.		285	.084		.60	4.30		4.90	7.45
1000	Stainless steel, type 304, under 100 lb.		165	.145		6.35	7.45		13.80	18.65
1020	100 to 500 lb.		175	.137		4.05	7		11.05	15.50
1030	500 to 1,000 lb.		190	.126		2.95	6.45		9.40	13.40

23 31 13.16 Round and Flat-Oval Spiral Ducts

		Crew	Daily Output	Labor-Hours	Unit	Material	2014 Bare Costs Labor	Equipment	Total	Total Incl O&P
0010	**ROUND AND FLAT-OVAL SPIRAL DUCTS**									
5400	Spiral preformed, steel, galv., straight lengths, Max 10" spwg.									
5410	4" diameter, 26 ga.	Q-9	360	.044	L.F.	1.70	2.19		3.89	5.30
5416	5" diameter, 26 ga.		320	.050		1.80	2.46		4.26	5.85
5420	6" diameter, 26 ga.		280	.057		1.90	2.81		4.71	6.55
5425	7" diameter, 26 ga.		240	.067		2.12	3.28		5.40	7.55
5430	8" diameter, 26 ga.		200	.080		2.42	3.94		6.36	8.85
5440	10" diameter, 26 ga.		160	.100		3.02	4.92		7.94	11.05
9990	Minimum labor/equipment charge	1 Shee	3	2.667	Job		146		146	230

23 31 HVAC Ducts and Casings

23 31 16 – Nonmetal Ducts

23 31 16.13 Fibrous-Glass Ducts

	23 31 16.13 Fibrous-Glass Ducts	Crew	Daily Output	Labor-Hours	Unit	Material	2014 Bare Costs Labor	Equipment	Total	Total Incl O&P
0010	**FIBROUS-GLASS DUCTS** R233100-20									
3490	Rigid fiberglass duct board, foil reinf. kraft facing									
3500	Rectangular, 1" thick, alum. faced, (FRK), std. weight	Q-10	350	.069	SF Surf	.77	3.50		4.27	6.35
9990	Minimum labor/equipment charge	1 Shee	3	2.667	Job		146		146	230

23 31 16.19 PVC Ducts

	23 31 16.19 PVC Ducts	Crew	Daily Output	Labor-Hours	Unit	Material	2014 Bare Costs Labor	Equipment	Total	Total Incl O&P
0010	**PVC DUCTS**									
4000	Rigid plastic, corrosive fume resistant PVC									
4020	Straight, 6" diameter	Q-9	220	.073	L.F.	10.05	3.58		13.63	16.70
4040	8" diameter		160	.100		15.35	4.92		20.27	24.50
4060	10" diameter		120	.133		19.40	6.55		25.95	32
4070	12" diameter		100	.160		22.50	7.90		30.40	37.50
4080	14" diameter		70	.229		28	11.25		39.25	49
4090	16" diameter		62	.258		32.50	12.70		45.20	56
4100	18" diameter		58	.276		44.50	13.60		58.10	70.50
4110	20" diameter	Q-10	75	.320		54.50	16.35		70.85	86
4130	24" diameter	"	55	.436		57.50	22.50		80	98
4250	Coupling, 6" diameter	Q-9	88	.182	Ea.	22	8.95		30.95	38
4270	8" diameter		78	.205		28.50	10.10		38.60	47
4290	10" diameter		70	.229		32.50	11.25		43.75	54
4300	12" diameter		55	.291		35.50	14.30		49.80	61.50
4310	14" diameter		44	.364		46	17.90		63.90	78.50
4320	16" diameter		40	.400		48.50	19.70		68.20	84.50
4330	18" diameter		38	.421		63	20.50		83.50	102
4340	20" diameter	Q-10	55	.436		75.50	22.50		98	118
4360	24" diameter	"	45	.533		94.50	27		121.50	147
4470	Elbow, 90°, 6" diameter	Q-9	44	.364		99	17.90		116.90	137
4490	8" diameter		28	.571		111	28		139	168
4510	10" diameter		18	.889		135	44		179	218
4520	12" diameter		15	1.067		154	52.50		206.50	252
4540	16" diameter		10	1.600		231	79		310	380
4550	18" diameter	Q-10	15	1.600		320	81.50		401.50	480
4560	20" diameter		14	1.714		480	87.50		567.50	665
4580	24" diameter		12	2		590	102		692	805
4750	Elbow 45°, use 90° and deduct					25%				
9990	Minimum labor/equipment charge	1 Shee	3	2.667	Job		146		146	230

23 33 Air Duct Accessories

23 33 13 – Dampers

23 33 13.13 Volume-Control Dampers

	23 33 13.13 Volume-Control Dampers	Crew	Daily Output	Labor-Hours	Unit	Material	2014 Bare Costs Labor	Equipment	Total	Total Incl O&P
0010	**VOLUME-CONTROL DAMPERS**									
5990	Multi-blade dampers, opposed blade, 8" x 6"	1 Shee	24	.333	Ea.	21.50	18.25		39.75	53
5994	8" x 8"		22	.364		22.50	19.90		42.40	56
5996	10" x 10"		21	.381		26.50	21		47.50	62.50
6000	12" x 12"		21	.381		29.50	21		50.50	65.50
6020	12" x 18"		18	.444		39.50	24.50		64	82
6030	14" x 10"		20	.400		29	22		51	66
6031	14" x 14"		17	.471		35.50	25.50		61	79.50
6033	16" x 12"		17	.471		35.50	25.50		61	79.50
6035	16" x 16"		16	.500		44	27.50		71.50	91.50
6037	18" x 16"		15	.533		48	29		77	99

23 33 Air Duct Accessories

23 33 13 – Dampers

23 33 13.13 Volume-Control Dampers

		Crew	Daily Output	Labor-Hours	Unit	Material	2014 Bare Costs Labor	2014 Bare Costs Equipment	Total	Total Incl O&P
6038	18" x 18"	1 Shee	15	.533	Ea.	52	29		81	103
6070	20" x 16"		14	.571		52	31.50		83.50	107
6072	20" x 20"		13	.615		62.50	33.50		96	122
6074	22" x 18"		14	.571		62.50	31.50		94	119
6076	24" x 16"		11	.727		61	40		101	130
6078	24" x 20"		8	1		72.50	54.50		127	167
6080	24" x 24"		8	1		85	54.50		139.50	180
6110	26" x 26"		6	1.333		95	73		168	220
6133	30" x 30"	Q-9	6.60	2.424		137	119		256	340
6135	32" x 32"		6.40	2.500		154	123		277	365
6180	48" x 36"		5.60	2.857		253	141		394	500
7500	Variable volume modulating motorized damper, incl. elect. mtr.									
7504	8" x 6"	1 Shee	15	.533	Ea.	118	29		147	176
7506	10" x 6"		14	.571		118	31.50		149.50	180
7510	10" x 10"		13	.615		122	33.50		155.50	187
7520	12" x 12"		12	.667		127	36.50		163.50	197
7522	12" x 16"		11	.727		127	40		167	203
7524	16" x 10"		12	.667		125	36.50		161.50	195
7526	16" x 14"		10	.800		130	44		174	212
7528	16" x 18"		9	.889		135	48.50		183.50	225
7542	18" x 18"		8	1		138	54.50		192.50	238
7544	20" x 14"		8	1		141	54.50		195.50	242
7546	20" x 18"		7	1.143		147	62.50		209.50	261
7560	24" x 12"		8	1		143	54.50		197.50	244
7562	24" x 18"		7	1.143		154	62.50		216.50	268
7564	24" x 24"		6	1.333		160	73		233	291
7568	28" x 10"		7	1.143		143	62.50		205.50	256
7590	30" x 14"		5	1.600		151	87.50		238.50	305
7600	30" x 18"		4	2		198	109		307	390
7610	30" x 24"		3.80	2.105		264	115		379	470
7700	For thermostat, add		8	1		31	54.50		85.50	121
8000	Multi-blade dampers, parallel blade									
8100	8" x 8"	1 Shee	24	.333	Ea.	82	18.25		100.25	119
8140	16" x 10"		20	.400		103	22		125	149
8160	18" x 12"		18	.444		113	24.50		137.50	163
8220	28" x 16"		10	.800		150	44		194	234

23 33 13.16 Fire Dampers

		Crew	Daily Output	Labor-Hours	Unit	Material	2014 Bare Costs Labor	2014 Bare Costs Equipment	Total	Total Incl O&P
0010	**FIRE DAMPERS**									
3000	Fire damper, curtain type, 1-1/2 hr. rated, vertical, 6" x 6"	1 Shee	24	.333	Ea.	24	18.25		42.25	55.50
3020	8" x 6"		22	.364		24	19.90		43.90	58
3240	16" x 14"		18	.444		44	24.50		68.50	87
3400	24" x 20"		8	1		54	54.50		108.50	146

23 33 19 – Duct Silencers

23 33 19.10 Duct Silencers

		Crew	Daily Output	Labor-Hours	Unit	Material	2014 Bare Costs Labor	2014 Bare Costs Equipment	Total	Total Incl O&P
0010	**DUCT SILENCERS**									
9000	Silencers, noise control for air flow, duct				MCFM	57			57	63

23 33 Air Duct Accessories

23 33 23 – Turning Vanes

23 33 23.13 Air Turning Vanes

		Crew	Daily Output	Labor-Hours	Unit	Material	2014 Bare Costs Labor	Equipment	Total	Total Incl O&P
0010	**AIR TURNING VANES**									
9400	Turning vane components									
9410	Turning vane rail	1 Shee	160	.050	L.F.	.75	2.74		3.49	5.15
9420	Double thick, factory fab. vane		300	.027		1.17	1.46		2.63	3.59
9428	12" high set		170	.047		1.68	2.57		4.25	5.90
9432	14" high set		160	.050		1.96	2.74		4.70	6.45
9900	Minimum labor/equipment charge		4	2	Job		109		109	173

23 33 46 – Flexible Ducts

23 33 46.10 Flexible Air Ducts

		Crew	Daily Output	Labor-Hours	Unit	Material	2014 Bare Costs Labor	Equipment	Total	Total Incl O&P
0010	**FLEXIBLE AIR DUCTS** R233100-20									
1280	Add to labor for elevated installation									
1282	of prefabricated (purchased) ductwork									
1283	10' to 15' high						10%			
1284	15' to 20' high						20%			
1285	20' to 25' high						25%			
1286	25' to 30' high						35%			
1287	30' to 35' high						40%			
1288	35' to 40' high						50%			
1289	Over 40' high						55%			
1300	Flexible, coated fiberglass fabric on corr. resist. metal helix									
1400	pressure to 12" (WG) UL-181									
1500	Noninsulated, 3" diameter	Q-9	400	.040	L.F.	1.12	1.97		3.09	4.34
1540	5" diameter		320	.050		1.30	2.46		3.76	5.30
1560	6" diameter		280	.057		1.50	2.81		4.31	6.10
1580	7" diameter		240	.067		1.53	3.28		4.81	6.90
1600	8" diameter		200	.080		1.91	3.94		5.85	8.30
1640	10" diameter		160	.100		2.46	4.92		7.38	10.45
1660	12" diameter		120	.133		2.94	6.55		9.49	13.60
1900	Insulated, 1" thick, PE jacket, 3" diameter G		380	.042		2.60	2.07		4.67	6.15
1910	4" diameter G		340	.047		2.60	2.32		4.92	6.50
1920	5" diameter G		300	.053		2.60	2.63		5.23	7
1940	6" diameter G		260	.062		2.94	3.03		5.97	8
1960	7" diameter G		220	.073		3.20	3.58		6.78	9.15
1980	8" diameter G		180	.089		3.49	4.38		7.87	10.75
2020	10" diameter G		140	.114		4.25	5.65		9.90	13.55
2040	12" diameter G		100	.160		4.90	7.90		12.80	17.80
2060	14" diameter G		80	.200		6.05	9.85		15.90	22.50
9990	Minimum labor/equipment charge	1 Shee	3	2.667	Job		146		146	230

23 33 53 – Duct Liners

23 33 53.10 Duct Liner Board

		Crew	Daily Output	Labor-Hours	Unit	Material	2014 Bare Costs Labor	Equipment	Total	Total Incl O&P
0010	**DUCT LINER BOARD**									
3490	Board type, fiberglass liner, 3 lb. density									
3680	No finish									
3700	1" thick G	Q-14	170	.094	S.F.	.43	4.33		4.76	7.40
3710	1-1/2" thick G		140	.114		.64	5.25		5.89	9.15
3720	2" thick G		130	.123		.86	5.65		6.51	10.05
3940	Board type, non-fibrous foam									
3950	Temperature, bacteria and fungi resistant									
3960	1" thick G	Q-14	150	.107	S.F.	2.38	4.91		7.29	10.50
3970	1-1/2" thick G		130	.123		3.28	5.65		8.93	12.70
3980	2" thick G		120	.133		3.98	6.15		10.13	14.25

23 34 HVAC Fans

23 34 13 – Axial HVAC Fans

23 34 13.10 Axial Flow HVAC Fans

23 34 13.10 Axial Flow HVAC Fans	Crew	Daily Output	Labor-Hours	Unit	Material	2014 Bare Costs Labor	Equipment	Total	Total Incl O&P
0010 **AXIAL FLOW HVAC FANS**									
0020 Air conditioning and process air handling									
0030 Axial flow, compact, low sound, 2.5" S.P.									
0050 3,800 CFM, 5 HP	Q-20	3.40	5.882	Ea.	5,025	294		5,319	6,000
0120 15,600 CFM, 10 HP	"	1.60	12.500	"	8,825	625		9,450	10,700

23 34 14 – Blower HVAC Fans

23 34 14.10 Blower Type HVAC Fans

23 34 14.10 Blower Type HVAC Fans	Crew	Daily Output	Labor-Hours	Unit	Material	2014 Bare Costs Labor	Equipment	Total	Total Incl O&P
0010 **BLOWER TYPE HVAC FANS**									
2500 Ceiling fan, right angle, extra quiet, 0.10" S.P.									
2540 210 CFM	Q-20	19	1.053	Ea.	340	52.50		392.50	460
2580 885 CFM		16	1.250		850	62.50		912.50	1,025
2620 2,960 CFM		11	1.818		1,575	91		1,666	1,875
2640 For wall or roof cap, add	1 Shee	16	.500		287	27.50		314.50	360

23 34 16 – Centrifugal HVAC Fans

23 34 16.10 Centrifugal Type HVAC Fans

23 34 16.10 Centrifugal Type HVAC Fans	Crew	Daily Output	Labor-Hours	Unit	Material	2014 Bare Costs Labor	Equipment	Total	Total Incl O&P
0010 **CENTRIFUGAL TYPE HVAC FANS**									
0200 In-line centrifugal, supply/exhaust booster									
0220 aluminum wheel/hub, disconnect switch, 1/4" S.P.									
0240 500 CFM, 10" diameter connection	Q-20	3	6.667	Ea.	1,250	335		1,585	1,900
0280 1,520 CFM, 16" diameter connection		2	10		1,450	500		1,950	2,375
0320 3,480 CFM, 20" diameter connection		.80	25		1,875	1,250		3,125	4,025
0326 5,080 CFM, 20" diameter connection		.75	26.667		2,025	1,325		3,350	4,325
5000 Utility set, centrifugal, V belt drive, motor									
5020 1/4" S.P., 1200 CFM, 1/4 HP	Q-20	6	3.333	Ea.	1,650	167		1,817	2,075
5040 1520 CFM, 1/3 HP		5	4		2,125	200		2,325	2,675
5060 1850 CFM, 1/2 HP		4	5		2,125	250		2,375	2,725
5080 2180 CFM, 3/4 HP		3	6.667		2,525	335		2,860	3,300
7000 Roof exhauster, centrifugal, aluminum housing, 12" galvanized									
7020 curb, bird screen, back draft damper, 1/4" S.P.									
7100 Direct drive, 320 CFM, 11" sq. damper	Q-20	7	2.857	Ea.	665	143		808	960
7120 600 CFM, 11" sq. damper	"	6	3.333	"	865	167		1,032	1,200
9900 Minimum labor/equipment charge	1 Elec	4	2	Job		107		107	165

23 34 23 – HVAC Power Ventilators

23 34 23.10 HVAC Power Circulators and Ventilators

23 34 23.10 HVAC Power Circulators and Ventilators	Crew	Daily Output	Labor-Hours	Unit	Material	2014 Bare Costs Labor	Equipment	Total	Total Incl O&P
0010 **HVAC POWER CIRCULATORS AND VENTILATORS**									
6650 Residential, bath exhaust, grille, back draft damper									
6660 50 CFM	Q-20	24	.833	Ea.	61	41.50		102.50	133
6670 110 CFM		22	.909		94.50	45.50		140	176
6680 Light combination, squirrel cage, 100 watt, 70 CFM		24	.833		108	41.50		149.50	184
6700 Light/heater combination, ceiling mounted									
6710 70 CFM, 1450 watt	Q-20	24	.833	Ea.	155	41.50		196.50	237
6800 Heater combination, recessed, 70 CFM		24	.833		64.50	41.50		106	137
6820 With 2 infrared bulbs		23	.870		101	43.50		144.50	180
6900 Kitchen exhaust, grille, complete, 160 CFM		22	.909		104	45.50		149.50	186
6910 180 CFM		20	1		87	50		137	174
6920 270 CFM		18	1.111		164	55.50		219.50	269
6940 Residential roof jacks and wall caps									
6944 Wall cap with back draft damper									
6946 3" & 4" diam. round duct	1 Shee	11	.727	Ea.	24.50	40		64.50	89.50
6948 6" diam. round duct	"	11	.727	"	61.50	40		101.50	131
6958 Roof jack with bird screen and back draft damper									

23 34 HVAC Fans

23 34 23 – HVAC Power Ventilators

23 34 23.10 HVAC Power Circulators and Ventilators	Crew	Daily Output	Labor-Hours	Unit	Material	2014 Bare Costs Labor	Equipment	Total	Total Incl O&P
6960	3" & 4" diam. round duct	1 Shee	11	.727	Ea.	25	40		65	90
6962	3-1/4" x 10" rectangular duct	"	10	.800	"	46.50	44		90.50	120
6980	Transition									
6982	3-1/4" x 10" to 6" diam. round	1 Shee	20	.400	Ea.	31	22		53	68.50
8020	Attic, roof type									
8030	Aluminum dome, damper & curb									
8080	12" diameter, 1000 CFM (gravity)	1 Elec	10	.800	Ea.	545	42.50		587.50	665
8090	16" diameter, 1500 CFM (gravity)		9	.889		660	47.50		707.50	800
8100	20" diameter, 2500 CFM (gravity)		8	1		805	53.50		858.50	975
8110	26" diameter, 4000 CFM (gravity)		7	1.143		980	61		1,041	1,175
8120	32" diameter, 6500 CFM (gravity)		6	1.333		1,350	71		1,421	1,575
8130	38" diameter, 8000 CFM (gravity)		5	1.600		2,000	85.50		2,085.50	2,325
8140	50" diameter, 13,000 CFM (gravity)		4	2		2,875	107		2,982	3,350
8160	Plastic, ABS dome									
8180	1050 CFM	1 Elec	14	.571	Ea.	160	30.50		190.50	223
8200	1600 CFM	"	12	.667	"	240	35.50		275.50	320
8240	Attic, wall type, with shutter, one speed									
8250	12" diameter, 1000 CFM	1 Elec	14	.571	Ea.	385	30.50		415.50	470
8260	14" diameter, 1500 CFM		12	.667		420	35.50		455.50	515
8270	16" diameter, 2000 CFM		9	.889		475	47.50		522.50	595
8290	Whole house, wall type, with shutter, one speed									
8300	30" diameter, 4800 CFM	1 Elec	7	1.143	Ea.	1,025	61		1,086	1,225
8310	36" diameter, 7000 CFM		6	1.333		1,100	71		1,171	1,325
8320	42" diameter, 10,000 CFM		5	1.600		1,225	85.50		1,310.50	1,475
8330	48" diameter, 16,000 CFM		4	2		1,525	107		1,632	1,875
8340	For two speed, add					92.50			92.50	102
8350	Whole house, lay-down type, with shutter, one speed									
8360	30" diameter, 4500 CFM	1 Elec	8	1	Ea.	1,075	53.50		1,128.50	1,275
8370	36" diameter, 6500 CFM		7	1.143		1,150	61		1,211	1,375
8380	42" diameter, 9000 CFM		6	1.333		1,275	71		1,346	1,500
8390	48" diameter, 12,000 CFM		5	1.600		1,450	85.50		1,535.50	1,725
8440	For two speed, add					69.50			69.50	76.50
8450	For 12 hour timer switch, add	1 Elec	32	.250		69.50	13.35		82.85	97

23 36 Air Terminal Units

23 36 13 – Constant-Air-Volume Units

23 36 13.10 Constant Volume Mixing Boxes

		Crew	Daily Output	Labor-Hours	Unit	Material	Labor	Equipment	Total	Total Incl O&P
0010	**CONSTANT VOLUME MIXING BOXES**									
5180	Mixing box, includes electric or pneumatic motor									
5200	Constant volume, 150 to 270 CFM	Q-9	12	1.333	Ea.	700	65.50		765.50	875
5210	270 to 600 CFM	"	11	1.455	"	720	71.50		791.50	910

23 36 16 – Variable-Air-Volume Units

23 36 16.10 Variable Volume Mixing Boxes

		Crew	Daily Output	Labor-Hours	Unit	Material	Labor	Equipment	Total	Total Incl O&P
0010	**VARIABLE VOLUME MIXING BOXES**									
5180	Mixing box, includes electric or pneumatic motor									
5500	VAV Cool only, pneumatic, pressure independent 300 to 600 CFM	Q-9	11	1.455	Ea.	730	71.50		801.50	920
5510	500 to 1000 CFM		9	1.778		750	87.50		837.50	965
5520	800 to 1600 CFM		9	1.778		775	87.50		862.50	995
5530	1100 to 2000 CFM		8	2		795	98.50		893.50	1,025
5540	1500 to 3000 CFM		7	2.286		845	113		958	1,100

23 36 Air Terminal Units

23 36 16 – Variable-Air-Volume Units

23 36 16.10 Variable Volume Mixing Boxes	Crew	Daily Output	Labor-Hours	Unit	Material	2014 Bare Costs Labor	Equipment	Total	Total Incl O&P
5550	2000 to 4000 CFM	Q-9	6	2.667	Ea.	855	131		986	1,150
5560	For electric, w/thermostat, pressure dependent, add				▼	23			23	25.50

23 37 Air Outlets and Inlets

23 37 13 – Diffusers, Registers, and Grilles

23 37 13.10 Diffusers

		Crew	Daily Output	Labor-Hours	Unit	Material	2014 Bare Costs Labor	Equipment	Total	Total Incl O&P
0010	**DIFFUSERS**, Aluminum, opposed blade damper unless noted									
0100	Ceiling, linear, also for sidewall									
0120	2" wide	1 Shee	32	.250	L.F.	16.20	13.70		29.90	39.50
0160	4" wide		26	.308		21.50	16.85		38.35	50
0180	6" wide		24	.333		26.50	18.25		44.75	58.50
0200	8" wide		22	.364	▼	31	19.90		50.90	66
0500	Perforated, 24" x 24" lay-in panel size, 6" x 6"		16	.500	Ea.	151	27.50		178.50	209
0520	8" x 8"		15	.533		159	29		188	221
0530	9" x 9"		14	.571		161	31.50		192.50	227
0540	10" x 10"		14	.571		162	31.50		193.50	228
0560	12" x 12"		12	.667		168	36.50		204.50	243
0590	16" x 16"		11	.727		189	40		229	270
0600	18" x 18"		10	.800		202	44		246	291
0610	20" x 20"		10	.800		218	44		262	310
0620	24" x 24"		9	.889		239	48.50		287.50	340
1000	Rectangular, 1 to 4 way blow, 6" x 6"		16	.500		50	27.50		77.50	98
1010	8" x 8"		15	.533		58	29		87	110
1014	9" x 9"		15	.533		66	29		95	119
1016	10" x 10"		15	.533		80	29		109	134
1020	12" x 6"		15	.533		71.50	29		100.50	125
1040	12" x 9"		14	.571		75.50	31.50		107	133
1060	12" x 12"		12	.667		84.50	36.50		121	151
1070	14" x 6"		13	.615		77.50	33.50		111	139
1074	14" x 14"		12	.667		128	36.50		164.50	198
1150	18" x 18"		9	.889		138	48.50		186.50	228
1170	24" x 12"		10	.800		163	44		207	249
2000	T bar mounting, 24" x 24" lay-in frame, 6" x 6"		16	.500		49	27.50		76.50	97
2020	8" x 8"		14	.571		51	31.50		82.50	106
2040	12" x 12"		12	.667		60.50	36.50		97	124
2060	16" x 16"		11	.727		81	40		121	152
2080	18" x 18"	▼	10	.800		90	44		134	168
6000	For steel diffusers instead of aluminum, deduct				▼	10%				
9000	Minimum labor/equipment charge	1 Shee	4	2	Job		109		109	173

23 37 13.30 Grilles

		Crew	Daily Output	Labor-Hours	Unit	Material	2014 Bare Costs Labor	Equipment	Total	Total Incl O&P
0010	**GRILLES**									
0020	Aluminum, unless noted otherwise									
1000	Air return, steel, 6" x 6"	1 Shee	26	.308	Ea.	18.70	16.85		35.55	47
1020	10" x 6"		24	.333		18.70	18.25		36.95	49.50
1080	16" x 8"		22	.364		26.50	19.90		46.40	60.50
1100	12" x 12"		22	.364		26.50	19.90		46.40	60.50
1120	24" x 12"		18	.444		36	24.50		60.50	78
1300	48" x 24"		12	.667	▼	128	36.50		164.50	198
9000	Minimum labor/equipment charge	▼	4	2	Job		109		109	173

23 37 Air Outlets and Inlets

23 37 13 – Diffusers, Registers, and Grilles

23 37 13.60 Registers	Crew	Daily Output	Labor-Hours	Unit	Material	2014 Bare Costs Labor	Equipment	Total	Total Incl O&P
0010 **REGISTERS**									
0980 Air supply									
1000 Ceiling/wall, O.B. damper, anodized aluminum									
1010 One or two way deflection, adj. curved face bars									
1120 12" x 12"	1 Shee	18	.444	Ea.	21	24.50		45.50	62
1140 14" x 8"		17	.471		18.40	25.50		43.90	61
1240 20" x 6"		18	.444		18.90	24.50		43.40	59.50
1340 24" x 8"		13	.615		25.50	33.50		59	81
1350 24" x 18"		12	.667		47.50	36.50		84	110
2700 Above registers in steel instead of aluminum, deduct					10%				
3000 Baseboard, hand adj. damper, enameled steel									
3012 8" x 6"	1 Shee	26	.308	Ea.	4.85	16.85		21.70	32
3020 10" x 6"		24	.333		5.30	18.25		23.55	35
3040 12" x 5"		23	.348		5.60	19.05		24.65	36
3060 12" x 6"		23	.348		5.75	19.05		24.80	36.50
3080 12" x 8"		22	.364		8.30	19.90		28.20	40.50
3100 14" x 6"		20	.400		6.20	22		28.20	41.50
9000 Minimum labor/equipment charge		4	2	Job		109		109	173

23 37 23 – HVAC Gravity Ventilators

23 37 23.10 HVAC Gravity Air Ventilators

	Crew	Daily Output	Labor-Hours	Unit	Material	2014 Bare Costs Labor	Equipment	Total	Total Incl O&P
0010 **HVAC GRAVITY AIR VENTILATORS**, Includes base									
1300 4" neck diameter	Q-9	20	.800	Ea.	64.50	39.50		104	133
1400 12" neck diameter		10	1.600		91	79		170	224
1500 24" neck diameter		8	2		405	98.50		503.50	600
1600 For aluminum, add					300%				
9000 Minimum labor/equipment charge	1 Plum	2	4	Job		230		230	360

23 38 Ventilation Hoods

23 38 13 – Commercial-Kitchen Hoods

23 38 13.10 Hood and Ventilation Equipment

	Crew	Daily Output	Labor-Hours	Unit	Material	2014 Bare Costs Labor	Equipment	Total	Total Incl O&P
0010 **HOOD AND VENTILATION EQUIPMENT**									
2970 Exhaust hood, sst, gutter on all sides, 4' x 4' x 2'	1 Carp	1.80	4.444	Ea.	4,675	204		4,879	5,450
2980 4' x 4' x 7'	"	1.60	5	"	7,425	229		7,654	8,550

23 41 Particulate Air Filtration

23 41 13 – Panel Air Filters

23 41 13.10 Panel Type Air Filters

	Crew	Daily Output	Labor-Hours	Unit	Material	2014 Bare Costs Labor	Equipment	Total	Total Incl O&P
0010 **PANEL TYPE AIR FILTERS**									
2950 Mechanical media filtration units									
3000 High efficiency type, with frame, non-supported G				MCFM	65			65	71.50
3100 Supported type G				"	60			60	66
5500 Throwaway glass or paper media type				Ea.	3.35			3.35	3.69

23 41 16 – Renewable-Media Air Filters

23 41 16.10 Disposable Media Air Filters

	Crew	Daily Output	Labor-Hours	Unit	Material	2014 Bare Costs Labor	Equipment	Total	Total Incl O&P
0010 **DISPOSABLE MEDIA AIR FILTERS**									
5000 Renewable disposable roll				MCFM	19.35			19.35	21.50

23 41 Particulate Air Filtration

23 41 19 – Washable Air Filters

23 41 19.10 Permanent Air Filters		Crew	Daily Output	Labor-Hours	Unit	Material	2014 Bare Costs Labor	Equipment	Total	Total Incl O&P
0010	**PERMANENT AIR FILTERS**									
4500	Permanent washable	G			MCFM	20			20	22

23 41 23 – Extended Surface Filters

23 41 23.10 Expanded Surface Filters

0010	**EXPANDED SURFACE FILTERS**									
4000	Medium efficiency, extended surface	G			MCFM	5.50			5.50	6.05

23 42 Gas-Phase Air Filtration

23 42 13 – Activated-Carbon Air Filtration

23 42 13.10 Charcoal Type Air Filtration

0010	**CHARCOAL TYPE AIR FILTRATION**								
0050	Activated charcoal type, full flow			MCFM	600			600	660
0060	Full flow, impregnated media 12" deep				225			225	248
0070	HEPA filter & frame for field erection				350			350	385
0080	HEPA filter-diffuser, ceiling install.			↓	300			300	330

23 43 Electronic Air Cleaners

23 43 13 – Washable Electronic Air Cleaners

23 43 13.10 Electronic Air Cleaners

0010	**ELECTRONIC AIR CLEANERS**								
2000	Electronic air cleaner, duct mounted								
2150	1000 CFM	1 Shee	4	2	Ea.	420	109		529	640
2200	1200 CFM		3.80	2.105		505	115		620	735
2250	1400 CFM	↓	3.60	2.222	↓	520	122		642	765

23 51 Breechings, Chimneys, and Stacks

23 51 13 – Draft Control Devices

23 51 13.16 Vent Dampers

0010	**VENT DAMPERS**								
5000	Vent damper, bi-metal, gas, 3" diameter	Q-9	24	.667	Ea.	44	33		77	101
5010	4" diameter		24	.667		44	33		77	101
5020	5" diameter		23	.696		44	34.50		78.50	103
5030	6" diameter		22	.727		44	36		80	105
5040	7" diameter		21	.762		45.50	37.50		83	109
5050	8" diameter	↓	20	.800	↓	49	39.50		88.50	116
9000	Minimum labor/equipment charge	1 Shee	4	2	Job		109		109	173

23 51 13.19 Barometric Dampers

0010	**BAROMETRIC DAMPERS**								
1000	Barometric, gas fired system only, 6" size for 5" and 6" pipes	1 Shee	20	.400	Ea.	67	22		89	108
1040	8" size, for 7" and 8" pipes	"	18	.444	"	92.50	24.50		117	141
2000	All fuel, oil, oil/gas, coal								
2020	10" for 9" and 10" pipes	1 Shee	15	.533	Ea.	155	29		184	216
3260	For thermal switch for above, add	"	24	.333	"	64	18.25		82.25	99.50

441

23 51 23 – Gas Vents

23 51 23.10 Gas Chimney Vents	Crew	Daily Output	Labor-Hours	Unit	Material	2014 Bare Costs Labor	Equipment	Total	Total Incl O&P
0010	**GAS CHIMNEY VENTS**, Prefab metal, U.L. listed								
0020	Gas, double wall, galvanized steel								
0080	3" diameter	Q-9	72	.222	V.L.F.	5.55	10.95		16.50	23.50
0100	4" diameter		68	.235		7.20	11.60		18.80	26
0120	5" diameter		64	.250		7.80	12.30		20.10	28
0140	6" diameter		60	.267		9.45	13.15		22.60	31
0160	7" diameter		56	.286		15.10	14.05		29.15	38.50
0180	8" diameter		52	.308		17.40	15.15		32.55	43
0200	10" diameter		48	.333		36	16.40		52.40	66
0220	12" diameter		44	.364		43	17.90		60.90	75.50
0260	16" diameter		40	.400		103	19.70		122.70	145
0300	20" diameter	Q-10	36	.667		150	34		184	219
0340	24" diameter	"	32	.750		236	38.50		274.50	320

23 51 26 – All-Fuel Vent Chimneys

23 51 26.30 All-Fuel Vent Chimneys, Double Wall, St. Stl.

23 51 26.30 All-Fuel Vent Chimneys, Double Wall, St. Stl.	Crew	Daily Output	Labor-Hours	Unit	Material	2014 Bare Costs Labor	Equipment	Total	Total Incl O&P
0010	**ALL-FUEL VENT CHIMNEYS, DOUBLE WALL, STAINLESS STEEL**								
7780	All fuel, pressure tight, double wall, 4" insulation, U.L. listed, 1400°F.								
7790	304 stainless steel liner, aluminized steel outer jacket								
7800	6" diameter	Q-9	60	.267	V.L.F.	62	13.15		75.15	88.50
7804	8" diameter		52	.308		71	15.15		86.15	102
7806	10" diameter		48	.333		79	16.40		95.40	113
7808	12" diameter		44	.364		90.50	17.90		108.40	128
7810	14" diameter		42	.381		102	18.75		120.75	142
7880	For 316 stainless steel liner add				L.F.	30%				
8000	All fuel, double wall, stainless steel fittings								
8010	Roof support 6" diameter	Q-9	30	.533	Ea.	109	26.50		135.50	162
8030	8" diameter		26	.615		127	30.50		157.50	188
8040	10" diameter		24	.667		135	33		168	200
8050	12" diameter		22	.727		143	36		179	214
8060	14" diameter		21	.762		150	37.50		187.50	224
8100	Elbow 45°, 6" diameter		30	.533		233	26.50		259.50	298
8140	8" diameter		26	.615		262	30.50		292.50	335
8160	10" diameter		24	.667		298	33		331	380
8180	12" diameter		22	.727		340	36		376	430
8200	14" diameter		21	.762		380	37.50		417.50	480
8300	Insulated tee, 6" diameter		30	.533		274	26.50		300.50	340
8360	8" diameter		26	.615		300	30.50		330.50	380
8380	10" diameter		24	.667		335	33		368	420
8400	12" diameter		22	.727		380	36		416	475
8420	14" diameter		20	.800		445	39.50		484.50	550
8500	Boot tee, 6" diameter		28	.571		525	28		553	620
8520	8" diameter		24	.667		570	33		603	675
8530	10" diameter		22	.727		665	36		701	785
8540	12" diameter		20	.800		785	39.50		824.50	925
8550	14" diameter		18	.889		895	44		939	1,050
8600	Rain cap with bird screen, 6" diameter		30	.533		280	26.50		306.50	350
8640	8" diameter		26	.615		325	30.50		355.50	405
8660	10" diameter		24	.667		380	33		413	465
8680	12" diameter		22	.727		440	36		476	535
8700	14" diameter		21	.762		495	37.50		532.50	605
8800	Flat roof flashing, 6" diameter		30	.533		103	26.50		129.50	155
8840	8" diameter		26	.615		112	30.50		142.50	171

23 51 Breechings, Chimneys, and Stacks

23 51 26 – All-Fuel Vent Chimneys

23 51 26.30 All-Fuel Vent Chimneys, Double Wall, St. Stl.	Crew	Daily Output	Labor-Hours	Unit	Material	2014 Bare Costs Labor	Equipment	Total	Total Incl O&P
8860	10" diameter	Q-9	24	.667	Ea.	120	33		153	184
8880	12" diameter		22	.727		132	36		168	202
8900	14" diameter		21	.762		135	37.50		172.50	207

23 52 Heating Boilers

23 52 13 – Electric Boilers

23 52 13.10 Electric Boilers, ASME

		Crew	Daily Output	Labor-Hours	Unit	Material	Labor	Equipment	Total	Total Incl O&P
0010	**ELECTRIC BOILERS, ASME**, Standard controls and trim									
1000	Steam, 6 KW, 20.5 MBH	Q-19	1.20	20	Ea.	3,950	1,050		5,000	6,000
1160	60 KW, 205 MBH		1	24		6,650	1,275		7,925	9,300
1300	296 KW, 1010 MBH		.45	53.333		25,000	2,825		27,825	32,000
1400	592 KW, 2020 MBH	Q-21	.34	94.118		35,400	5,100		40,500	46,900
1540	1110 KW, 3788 MBH	"	.19	168		49,600	9,150		58,750	68,500
2000	Hot water, 7.5 KW, 25.6 MBH	Q-19	1.30	18.462		4,975	975		5,950	7,000
2040	30 KW, 102 MBH		1.20	20		5,325	1,050		6,375	7,500
2060	45 KW, 164 MBH		1.20	20		5,425	1,050		6,475	7,600
2070	60 KW, 205 MBH		1.20	20		5,525	1,050		6,575	7,725
2080	75 KW, 256 MBH		1.10	21.818		5,900	1,150		7,050	8,300
2100	90 KW, 307 MBH		1.10	21.818		6,000	1,150		7,150	8,400
9000	Minimum labor/equipment charge	Q-20	1	20	Job		1,000		1,000	1,575

23 52 23 – Cast-Iron Boilers

23 52 23.20 Gas-Fired Boilers

		Crew	Daily Output	Labor-Hours	Unit	Material	Labor	Equipment	Total	Total Incl O&P
0010	**GAS-FIRED BOILERS**, Natural or propane, standard controls, packaged									
1000	Cast iron, with insulated jacket									
2000	Steam, gross output, 81 MBH	Q-7	1.40	22.857	Ea.	2,350	1,275		3,625	4,550
2060	163 MBH		.90	35.556		3,175	1,975		5,150	6,600
2200	440 MBH		.51	62.500		6,000	3,475		9,475	12,000
2320	1,875 MBH		.30	106		22,900	5,950		28,850	34,500
2400	3570 MBH		.18	181		32,600	10,100		42,700	51,500
2540	6,970 MBH		.10	320		110,500	17,800		128,300	149,500
3000	Hot water, gross output, 80 MBH		1.46	21.918		2,150	1,225		3,375	4,275
3020	100 MBH		1.35	23.704		2,300	1,325		3,625	4,575
3040	122 MBH		1.10	29.091		2,625	1,625		4,250	5,400
3060	163 MBH		1	32		3,000	1,775		4,775	6,075
3200	440 MBH		.58	54.983		5,725	3,075		8,800	11,100
3320	2,000 MBH		.26	125		19,600	6,975		26,575	32,500
3540	6,970 MBH		.09	359		110,500	20,000		130,500	152,500
7000	For tankless water heater, add					10%				
7050	For additional zone valves up to 312 MBH add					188			188	207
9900	Minimum labor/equipment charge	Q-6	1	24	Job		1,300		1,300	2,050

23 52 23.30 Gas/Oil Fired Boilers

		Crew	Daily Output	Labor-Hours	Unit	Material	Labor	Equipment	Total	Total Incl O&P
0010	**GAS/OIL FIRED BOILERS**, Combination with burners and controls, packaged									
1000	Cast iron with insulated jacket									
2000	Steam, gross output, 720 MBH	Q-7	.43	74.074	Ea.	14,400	4,125		18,525	22,200
2140	2,700 MBH		.19	165		27,500	9,225		36,725	44,600
2380	6,970 MBH		.09	372		100,500	20,700		121,200	143,000
2900	Hot water, gross output									
2910	200 MBH	Q-6	.62	39.024	Ea.	10,400	2,125		12,525	14,700
2920	300 MBH		.49	49.080		10,400	2,675		13,075	15,600
2930	400 MBH		.41	57.971		12,200	3,175		15,375	18,300

23 52 Heating Boilers

23 52 23 – Cast-Iron Boilers

23 52 23.30 Gas/Oil Fired Boilers

		Crew	Daily Output	Labor-Hours	Unit	Material	2014 Bare Costs Labor	2014 Bare Costs Equipment	Total	Total Incl O&P
2940	500 MBH	Q-6	.36	67.039	Ea.	13,100	3,650		16,750	20,100
3000	584 MBH	Q-7	.44	72.072		14,500	4,025		18,525	22,300
3060	1,460 MBH		.28	113		28,400	6,300		34,700	41,100
3300	13,500 MBH, 403.3 BHP	↓	.04	727	↓	188,500	40,500		229,000	270,000

23 52 23.40 Oil-Fired Boilers

		Crew	Daily Output	Labor-Hours	Unit	Material	2014 Bare Costs Labor	2014 Bare Costs Equipment	Total	Total Incl O&P
0010	**OIL-FIRED BOILERS**, Standard controls, flame retention burner, packaged									
1000	Cast iron, with insulated flush jacket									
2000	Steam, gross output, 109 MBH	Q-7	1.20	26.667	Ea.	2,175	1,475		3,650	4,725
2060	207 MBH		.90	35.556		3,000	1,975		4,975	6,400
2180	1,084 MBH		.38	85.106		10,500	4,750		15,250	19,000
2200	1,360 MBH		.33	98.160		12,100	5,475		17,575	21,800
2240	2,175 MBH		.24	133		17,400	7,450		24,850	30,800
2340	4,360 MBH		.15	214		41,100	12,000		53,100	64,000
2460	6,970 MBH	↓	.09	363	↓	97,500	20,300		117,800	138,500
3000	Hot water, same price as steam									
4000	For tankless coil in smaller sizes, add				Ea.	15%				

23 52 26 – Steel Boilers

23 52 26.40 Oil-Fired Boilers

		Crew	Daily Output	Labor-Hours	Unit	Material	2014 Bare Costs Labor	2014 Bare Costs Equipment	Total	Total Incl O&P
0010	**OIL-FIRED BOILERS**, Standard controls, flame retention burner									
5000	Steel, with insulated flush jacket									
7000	Hot water, gross output, 103 MBH	Q-6	1.60	15	Ea.	1,775	820		2,595	3,225
7020	122 MBH		1.45	16.506		1,875	900		2,775	3,475
7040	137 MBH		1.36	17.595		2,000	960		2,960	3,700
7060	168 MBH		1.30	18.405		2,100	1,000		3,100	3,900
7080	225 MBH		1.22	19.704		2,575	1,075		3,650	4,500
7100	315 MBH		.96	25.105		6,375	1,375		7,750	9,175
7120	420 MBH		.70	34.483	↓	6,700	1,875		8,575	10,300
9000	Minimum labor/equipment charge	↓	1.75	13.714	Job		750		750	1,175

23 52 88 – Burners

23 52 88.10 Replacement Type Burners

		Crew	Daily Output	Labor-Hours	Unit	Material	2014 Bare Costs Labor	2014 Bare Costs Equipment	Total	Total Incl O&P
0010	**REPLACEMENT TYPE BURNERS**									
0990	Residential, conversion, gas fired, LP or natural									
1000	Gun type, atmospheric input 50 to 225 MBH	Q-1	2.50	6.400	Ea.	720	330		1,050	1,300
1020	100 to 400 MBH		2	8		1,200	415		1,615	1,975
1040	300 to 1000 MBH	↓	1.70	9.412	↓	3,625	490		4,115	4,725
3000	Flame retention oil fired assembly, input									
3020	.50 to 2.25 GPH	Q-1	2.40	6.667	Ea.	289	345		634	860
3025	Burner, oil, 0.5 – 2.25 gph [G]					289			289	320
3040	2.0 to 5.0 GPH	Q-1	2	8		345	415		760	1,025
3060	3.0 to 7.0 GPH		1.80	8.889		620	460		1,080	1,400
3080	6.0 to 12.0 GPH	↓	1.60	10	↓	990	520		1,510	1,875

23 54 Furnaces

23 54 13 – Electric-Resistance Furnaces

23 54 13.10 Electric Furnaces

		Crew	Daily Output	Labor-Hours	Unit	Material	2014 Bare Costs Labor	2014 Bare Costs Equipment	Total	Total Incl O&P
0010	**ELECTRIC FURNACES**, Hot air, blowers, std. controls									
0011	not including gas, oil or flue piping									
1000	Electric, UL listed									
1100	34.1 MBH	Q-20	4.40	4.545	Ea.	560	228		788	970

23 54 16 – Fuel-Fired Furnaces

23 54 16.13 Gas-Fired Furnaces

		Crew	Daily Output	Labor-Hours	Unit	Material	Labor	Equipment	Total	Total Incl O&P
0010	**GAS-FIRED FURNACES**									
3000	Gas, AGA certified, upflow, direct drive models									
3020	45 MBH input	Q-9	4	4	Ea.	535	197		732	900
3040	60 MBH input		3.80	4.211		535	207		742	915
3060	75 MBH input		3.60	4.444		575	219		794	980
3100	100 MBH input		3.20	5		625	246		871	1,075
3120	125 MBH input		3	5.333		655	263		918	1,125
3130	150 MBH input		2.80	5.714		670	281		951	1,175
3140	200 MBH input		2.60	6.154		2,800	305		3,105	3,550

23 54 16.16 Oil-Fired Furnaces

		Crew	Daily Output	Labor-Hours	Unit	Material	Labor	Equipment	Total	Total Incl O&P
0010	**OIL-FIRED FURNACES**									
6000	Oil, UL listed, atomizing gun type burner									
6020	56 MBH output	Q-9	3.60	4.444	Ea.	1,550	219		1,769	2,050
6040	95 MBH output		3.40	4.706		1,875	232		2,107	2,450
6060	134 MBH output		3.20	5		2,175	246		2,421	2,800
6080	151 MBH output		3	5.333		2,250	263		2,513	2,900
6100	200 MBH input		2.60	6.154		2,450	305		2,755	3,175
9000	Minimum labor/equipment charge		2.75	5.818	Job		286		286	450

23 54 24 – Furnace Components for Cooling

23 54 24.10 Furnace Components and Combinations

		Crew	Daily Output	Labor-Hours	Unit	Material	Labor	Equipment	Total	Total Incl O&P
0010	**FURNACE COMPONENTS AND COMBINATIONS**									
0080	Coils, A.C. evaporator, for gas or oil furnaces									
0090	Add-on, with holding charge									
0100	Upflow									
0120	1-1/2 ton cooling	Q-5	4	4	Ea.	220	211		431	570
0130	2 ton cooling		3.70	4.324		241	228		469	620
0140	3 ton cooling		3.30	4.848		375	255		630	815
0150	4 ton cooling		3	5.333		465	281		746	955
0160	5 ton cooling		2.70	5.926		505	310		815	1,050
0300	Downflow									
0330	2-1/2 ton cooling	Q-5	3	5.333	Ea.	295	281		576	765
0340	3-1/2 ton cooling		2.60	6.154		435	325		760	980
0350	5 ton cooling		2.20	7.273		505	385		890	1,150
0600	Horizontal									
0630	2 ton cooling	Q-5	3.90	4.103	Ea.	320	216		536	690
0640	3 ton cooling		3.50	4.571		370	241		611	780
0650	4 ton cooling		3.20	5		460	263		723	915
0660	5 ton cooling		2.90	5.517		460	290		750	960
2000	Cased evaporator coils for air handlers									
2100	1-1/2 ton cooling	Q-5	4.40	3.636	Ea.	267	191		458	595
2110	2 ton cooling		4.10	3.902		300	205		505	650
2120	2-1/2 ton cooling		3.90	4.103		320	216		536	685
2130	3 ton cooling		3.70	4.324		360	228		588	750
2140	3-1/2 ton cooling		3.50	4.571		485	241		726	910
2150	4 ton cooling		3.20	5		515	263		778	980

23 54 Furnaces

23 54 24 – Furnace Components for Cooling

23 54 24.10 Furnace Components and Combinations

		Crew	Daily Output	Labor-Hours	Unit	Material	2014 Bare Costs Labor	Equipment	Total	Total Incl O&P
2160	5 ton cooling	Q-5	2.90	5.517	Ea.	525	290		815	1,025
3010	Air handler, modular									
3100	With cased evaporator cooling coil									
3120	1-1/2 ton cooling	Q-5	3.80	4.211	Ea.	1,300	222		1,522	1,775
3130	2 ton cooling		3.50	4.571		1,350	241		1,591	1,850
3140	2-1/2 ton cooling		3.30	4.848		1,450	255		1,705	2,000
3150	3 ton cooling		3.10	5.161		1,550	272		1,822	2,150
3160	3-1/2 ton cooling		2.90	5.517		1,600	290		1,890	2,225
3170	4 ton cooling		2.50	6.400		1,800	335		2,135	2,525
3180	5 ton cooling		2.10	7.619		2,050	400		2,450	2,875
3500	With no cooling coil									
3520	1-1/2 ton coil size	Q-5	12	1.333	Ea.	620	70		690	790
3530	2 ton coil size		10	1.600		620	84		704	815
3540	2-1/2 ton coil size		10	1.600		725	84		809	925
3554	3 ton coil size		9	1.778		825	93.50		918.50	1,050
3560	3-1/2 ton coil size		9	1.778		845	93.50		938.50	1,075
3570	4 ton coil size		8.50	1.882		1,050	99		1,149	1,325
3580	5 ton coil size		8	2		1,075	105		1,180	1,350
4000	With heater									
4120	5 kW, 17.1 MBH	Q-5	16	1	Ea.	670	52.50		722.50	815
4130	7.5 kW, 25.6 MBH		15.60	1.026		680	54		734	830
4140	10 kW, 34.2 MBH		15.20	1.053		845	55.50		900.50	1,025
4150	12.5 KW, 42.7 MBH		14.80	1.081		950	57		1,007	1,150

23 55 Fuel-Fired Heaters

23 55 13 – Fuel-Fired Duct Heaters

23 55 13.16 Gas-Fired Duct Heaters

		Crew	Daily Output	Labor-Hours	Unit	Material	2014 Bare Costs Labor	Equipment	Total	Total Incl O&P
0010	**GAS-FIRED DUCT HEATERS**, Includes burner, controls, stainless steel									
0020	heat exchanger. Gas fired, electric ignition									
1000	Outdoor installation, with power venter									
1120	225 MBH output	Q-5	2.50	6.400	Ea.	4,350	335		4,685	5,325
1160	375 MBH output		1.60	10		7,925	525		8,450	9,525
1180	450 MBH output		1.40	11.429		9,075	600		9,675	10,900

23 55 33 – Fuel-Fired Unit Heaters

23 55 33.16 Gas-Fired Unit Heaters

		Crew	Daily Output	Labor-Hours	Unit	Material	2014 Bare Costs Labor	Equipment	Total	Total Incl O&P
0010	**GAS-FIRED UNIT HEATERS**, Cabinet, grilles, fan, ctrls., burner, no piping									
0022	thermostat, no piping. For flue see Section 23 51 23.10									
1000	Gas fired, floor mounted									
1100	60 MBH output	Q-5	10	1.600	Ea.	870	84		954	1,075
1180	180 MBH output		6	2.667		1,375	140		1,515	1,725
2000	Suspension mounted, propeller fan, 20 MBH output		8.50	1.882		1,025	99		1,124	1,275
2040	60 MBH output		7	2.286		1,225	120		1,345	1,525
2100	130 MBH output		5	3.200		1,725	168		1,893	2,175
2240	320 MBH output		2	8		3,525	420		3,945	4,525
2500	For powered venter and adapter, add					420			420	460
5000	Wall furnace, 17.5 MBH output	Q-5	6	2.667		760	140		900	1,050
5020	24 MBH output		5	3.200		770	168		938	1,100
5040	35 MBH output		4	4		770	211		981	1,175
9000	Minimum labor/equipment charge		3.50	4.571	Job		241		241	375

23 56 Solar Energy Heating Equipment

23 56 16 – Packaged Solar Heating Equipment

23 56 16.40 Solar Heating Systems

		Crew	Daily Output	Labor-Hours	Unit	Material	2014 Bare Costs Labor	2014 Bare Costs Equipment	Total	Total Incl O&P
0010	**SOLAR HEATING SYSTEMS**									
0020	System/Package prices, not including connecting									
0030	pipe, insulation, or special heating/plumbing fixtures									
0500	Hot water, standard package, low temperature									
0580	2 collectors, circulator, fittings, 120 gal. tank	G Q-1	.40	40	Ea.	4,700	2,075		6,775	8,375

23 56 19 – Solar Heating Components

23 56 19.50 Solar Heating Ancillary

		Crew	Daily Output	Labor-Hours	Unit	Material	2014 Bare Costs Labor	2014 Bare Costs Equipment	Total	Total Incl O&P
0010	**SOLAR HEATING ANCILLARY**									
2300	Circulators, air									
2310	Blowers									
2550	Booster fan 6" diameter, 120 CFM	G Q-9	16	1	Ea.	36.50	49		85.50	118
2580	8" diameter, 150 CFM	G	16	1		41	49		90	123
2660	Shutter/damper	G	12	1.333		56	65.50		121.50	166
2670	Shutter motor	G	16	1		139	49		188	231
2800	Circulators, liquid, 1/25 HP, 5.3 GPM	G Q-1	14	1.143		274	59		333	395
2820	1/20 HP, 17 GPM	G "	12	1.333		161	69		230	285
3000	Collector panels, air with aluminum absorber plate									
3010	Wall or roof mount									
3040	Flat black, plastic glazing									
3080	4' x 8'	G Q-9	6	2.667	Ea.	660	131		791	935
3300	Collector panels, liquid with copper absorber plate									
3320	Black chrome, tempered glass glazing									
3330	Alum. frame, 4' x 8', 5/32" single glazing	G Q-1	9.50	1.684	Ea.	995	87		1,082	1,225
3450	Flat black, alum. frame, 3.5' x 7.5'	G	9	1.778		730	92		822	945
3500	4' x 8'	G	5.50	2.909		915	151		1,066	1,225
3600	Liquid, full wetted, plastic, alum. frame, 4' x 10'	G	5	3.200		247	166		413	530
3650	Collector panel mounting, flat roof or ground rack	G	7	2.286		244	118		362	455
3670	Roof clamps	G	70	.229	Set	2.80	11.85		14.65	21.50
3700	Roof strap, teflon	G 1 Plum	205	.039	L.F.	23.50	2.25		25.75	29.50
3900	Differential controller with two sensors									
3930	Thermostat, hard wired	G 1 Plum	8	1	Ea.	101	57.50		158.50	201
4050	Pool valve system	G	2.50	3.200		287	184		471	600
4070	With 12 VAC actuator	G	2	4		300	230		530	690
4150	Sensors									
4220	Freeze prevention	G 1 Plum	32	.250	Ea.	23.50	14.40		37.90	48.50
4300	Heat exchanger									
4315	includes coil, blower, circulator									
4316	and controller for DHW and space hot air									
4330	Fluid to air coil, up flow, 45 MBH	G Q-1	4	4	Ea.	315	207		522	675
4380	70 MBH	G	3.50	4.571		355	237		592	765
4400	80 MBH	G	3	5.333		475	276		751	955
4580	Fluid to fluid package includes two circulating pumps									
4590	expansion tank, check valve, relief valve									
4600	controller, high temperature cutoff and sensors	G Q-1	2.50	6.400	Ea.	770	330		1,100	1,350
4650	Heat transfer fluid									
4700	Propylene glycol, inhibited anti-freeze	G 1 Plum	28	.286	Gal.	15.45	16.45		31.90	42.50
4800	Solar storage tanks, knocked down									
5190	6'-3" high, 7' x 7' = 306 C.F./2000 gallons	G Q-10	1.20	20	Ea.	14,200	1,025		15,225	17,300
5210	7' x 14' = 613 C.F./4000 gallons	G	.60	40		21,400	2,050		23,450	26,700
5230	10'-6" x 14' = 919 C.F./6000 gallons	G	.40	60		24,900	3,075		27,975	32,200
5250	14' x 17'-6" = 1531 C.F./10,000 gallons	G Q-11	.30	106		32,100	5,550		37,650	44,100
7000	Solar control valves and vents									

23 56 Solar Energy Heating Equipment

23 56 19 – Solar Heating Components

23 56 19.50 Solar Heating Ancillary		Crew	Daily Output	Labor-Hours	Unit	Material	2014 Bare Costs Labor	Equipment	Total	Total Incl O&P
7070	Air eliminator, automatic 3/4" size	G	1 Plum	32	.250	Ea.	30	14.40		44.40	55.50
7090	Air vent, automatic, 1/8" fitting	G		32	.250		17.25	14.40		31.65	41.50
7100	Manual, 1/8" NPT	G		32	.250		25.50	14.40		39.90	50.50
7120	Backflow preventer, 1/2" pipe size	G		16	.500		75.50	29		104.50	128
7130	3/4" pipe size	G		16	.500		77	29		106	130
7150	Balancing valve, 3/4" pipe size	G		20	.400		63	23		86	106
7180	Draindown valve, 1/2" copper tube	G		9	.889		212	51		263	315
7200	Flow control valve, 1/2" pipe size	G		22	.364		120	21		141	165
7220	Expansion tank, up to 5 gal.	G		32	.250		68	14.40		82.40	97.50
7400	Pressure gauge, 2" dial	G		32	.250		24	14.40		38.40	49
7450	Relief valve, temp. and pressure 3/4" pipe size	G	↓	30	.267	↓	21	15.35		36.35	47
7500	Solenoid valve, normally closed										
7520	Brass, 3/4" NPT, 24V	G	1 Plum	9	.889	Ea.	119	51		170	210
7530	1" NPT, 24V	G		9	.889		186	51		237	285
7750	Vacuum relief valve, 3/4" pipe size	G	↓	32	.250	↓	29.50	14.40		43.90	55
7800	Thermometers										
7820	Digital temperature monitoring, 4 locations	G	1 Plum	2.50	3.200	Ea.	137	184		321	440
7900	Upright, 1/2" NPT	G	"	8	1	"	28	57.50		85.50	121
8250	Water storage tank with heat exchanger and electric element										
8270	66 gal. with 2" x 2 lb. density insulation	G	1 Plum	1.60	5	Ea.	1,600	288		1,888	2,225
8300	80 gal. with 2" x 2 lb. density insulation	G	"	1.60	5	"	1,600	288		1,888	2,225
8500	Water storage module, plastic										
8600	Tubular, 12" diameter, 4' high	G	1 Carp	48	.167	Ea.	114	7.65		121.65	138
8610	12" diameter, 8' high	G	"	40	.200	↓	175	9.15		184.15	208
8650	Cap, 12" diameter	G				↓	22			22	24
9000	Minimum labor/equipment charge		1 Plum	2	4	Job		230		230	360

23 61 Refrigerant Compressors

23 61 16 – Reciprocating Refrigerant Compressors

23 61 16.10 Reciprocating Compressors

		Crew	Daily Output	Labor-Hours	Unit	Material	2014 Bare Costs Labor	Equipment	Total	Total Incl O&P
0010	**RECIPROCATING COMPRESSORS**										
0990	Refrigeration, recip. hermetic, switches & protective devices										
1000	10 ton	Q-5	1	16	Ea.	12,500	840		13,340	15,000
1100	20 ton	Q-6	.72	33.333		26,600	1,825		28,425	32,100
1400	50 ton	"	.20	120		31,300	6,550		37,850	44,600
1600	130 ton	Q-7	.21	152	↓	39,500	8,500		48,000	56,500

23 62 Packaged Compressor and Condenser Units

23 62 13 – Packaged Air-Cooled Refrigerant Compressor and Condenser Units

23 62 13.10 Packaged Air-Cooled Refrig. Condensing Units

		Crew	Daily Output	Labor-Hours	Unit	Material	2014 Bare Costs Labor	Equipment	Total	Total Incl O&P
0010	**PACKAGED AIR-COOLED REFRIGERANT CONDENSING UNITS**										
0020	Condensing unit										
0030	Air cooled, compressor, standard controls										
0050	1.5 ton	Q-5	2.50	6.400	Ea.	1,300	335		1,635	1,950
0200	2.5 ton	↓	1.70	9.412		1,525	495		2,020	2,450
0300	3 ton		1.30	12.308		1,525	650		2,175	2,675
0400	4 ton		.90	17.778		1,975	935		2,910	3,625
0500	5 ton	↓	.60	26.667	↓	2,475	1,400		3,875	4,900

23 64 Packaged Water Chillers

23 64 19 – Reciprocating Water Chillers

23 64 19.10 Reciprocating Type Water Chillers

23 64 19.10 Reciprocating Type Water Chillers	Crew	Daily Output	Labor-Hours	Unit	Material	2014 Bare Costs Labor	Equipment	Total	Total Incl O&P
0010 **RECIPROCATING TYPE WATER CHILLERS**, With standard controls									
0494 Water chillers, integral air cooled condenser									
0980 Water cooled, multiple compressor, semi-hermetic, tower not incl.									
1090 45 ton cooling	Q-7	.29	111	Ea.	35,100	6,200		41,300	48,300
1100 50 ton cooling		.28	113		36,500	6,350		42,850	50,000
1160 100 ton cooling		.18	179		62,000	10,000		72,000	84,000
1200 145 ton cooling		.16	202		82,000	11,300		93,300	108,000

23 64 23 – Scroll Water Chillers

23 64 23.10 Scroll Water Chillers

	Crew	Daily Output	Labor-Hours	Unit	Material	Labor	Equipment	Total	Total Incl O&P
0010 **SCROLL WATER CHILLERS**, With standard controls									
0480 Packaged w/integral air cooled condenser									
0482 10 ton cooling	Q-7	.34	94.118	Ea.	20,500	5,250		25,750	30,700
0490 15 ton cooling		.37	86.486		22,200	4,825		27,025	31,900
0500 20 ton cooling		.34	94.118		28,200	5,250		33,450	39,200
0520 40 ton cooling		.30	108		36,700	6,025		42,725	49,800
0680 Scroll water cooled, single compressor, hermetic, tower not incl.									
0760 10 ton cooling	Q-6	.36	67.039	Ea.	6,625	3,650		10,275	13,000

23 64 26 – Rotary-Screw Water Chillers

23 64 26.10 Rotary-Screw Type Water Chillers

	Crew	Daily Output	Labor-Hours	Unit	Material	Labor	Equipment	Total	Total Incl O&P
0010 **ROTARY-SCREW TYPE WATER CHILLERS**, With standard controls									
0110 Screw, liquid chiller, air cooled, insulated evaporator									
0120 130 ton	Q-7	.14	228	Ea.	91,500	12,700		104,200	120,500
0124 160 ton	"	.13	246	"	112,500	13,700		126,200	145,000

23 64 33 – Direct Expansion Water Chillers

23 64 33.10 Direct Expansion Type Water Chillers

	Crew	Daily Output	Labor-Hours	Unit	Material	Labor	Equipment	Total	Total Incl O&P
0010 **DIRECT EXPANSION TYPE WATER CHILLERS**, With standard controls									
8000 Direct expansion, shell and tube type, for built up systems									
8020 1 ton	Q-5	2	8	Ea.	7,300	420		7,720	8,675
8030 5 ton		1.90	8.421		12,100	445		12,545	14,000
8040 10 ton		1.70	9.412		15,000	495		15,495	17,300
9000 Minimum labor/equipment charge	Q-6	1	24	Job		1,300		1,300	2,050

23 65 Cooling Towers

23 65 13 – Forced-Draft Cooling Towers

23 65 13.10 Forced-Draft Type Cooling Towers

	Crew	Daily Output	Labor-Hours	Unit	Material	Labor	Equipment	Total	Total Incl O&P
0010 **FORCED-DRAFT TYPE COOLING TOWERS**, Packaged units									
0070 Galvanized steel									
0080 Induced draft, crossflow									
0100 Vertical, belt drive, 61 tons	Q-6	90	.267	TonAC	211	14.55		225.55	255
0150 100 ton		100	.240		203	13.10		216.10	245
0200 115 ton		109	.220		177	12		189	214
0250 131 ton		120	.200		213	10.90		223.90	251
0260 162 ton		132	.182		172	9.95		181.95	205
1000 For higher capacities, use multiples									
1500 Induced air, double flow									
1900 Vertical, gear drive, 167 ton	Q-6	126	.190	TonAC	167	10.40		177.40	199
2000 297 ton		129	.186		103	10.15		113.15	129
2100 582 ton		132	.182		57	9.95		66.95	78.50
2200 1016 ton		150	.160		77.50	8.75		86.25	99

23 65 Cooling Towers

23 65 13 – Forced-Draft Cooling Towers

23 65 13.10 Forced-Draft Type Cooling Towers	Crew	Daily Output	Labor-Hours	Unit	Material	2014 Bare Costs Labor	Equipment	Total	Total Incl O&P
3000	For higher capacities, use multiples								
3500	For pumps and piping, add	Q-6	38	.632	TonAC	105	34.50		139.50	170
4000	For absorption systems, add				"	75%	75%			
4100	Cooling water chemical feeder	Q-5	3	5.333	Ea.	365	281		646	840
5000	Fiberglass tower on galvanized steel support structure									
5010	Draw thru									
5100	100 ton	Q-6	1.40	17.143	Ea.	13,100	935		14,035	15,900
5120	120 ton		1.20	20		15,200	1,100		16,300	18,500
5140	140 ton		1	24		16,500	1,300		17,800	20,200
5160	160 ton		.80	30		18,300	1,650		19,950	22,700
5180	180 ton		.65	36.923		20,800	2,025		22,825	26,100
5200	200 ton		.48	50		23,500	2,725		26,225	30,200
5300	For stainless steel support structure, add					30%				
5360	For higher capacities, use multiples of each size									
6000	Stainless steel									
6010	Induced draft, crossflow, horizontal, belt drive									
6100	57 ton	Q-6	1.50	16	Ea.	26,500	875		27,375	30,600
6120	91 ton		.99	24.242		32,100	1,325		33,425	37,400
6140	111 ton		.43	55.814		40,800	3,050		43,850	49,700
6160	126 ton		.22	109		40,800	5,950		46,750	54,000
6170	Induced draft, crossflow, vertical, gear drive									
6172	167 ton	Q-6	.75	32	Ea.	52,000	1,750		53,750	60,000
6174	297 ton		.43	55.814		58,000	3,050		61,050	68,500
6176	582 ton		.23	104		92,000	5,700		97,700	110,000
6180	1016 ton		.15	160		155,500	8,725		164,225	185,000
9000	Minimum labor/equipment charge		1	24	Job		1,300		1,300	2,050

23 72 Air-to-Air Energy Recovery Equipment

23 72 13 – Heat-Wheel Air-to-Air Energy-Recovery Equipment

23 72 13.10 Heat-Wheel Air-to-Air Energy Recovery Equip.

		Crew	Daily Output	Labor-Hours	Unit	Material	Labor	Equipment	Total	Total Incl O&P
0010	**HEAT-WHEEL AIR-TO-AIR ENERGY RECOVERY EQUIPMENT**									
0100	Air to air									
9000	Minimum labor/equipment charge	1 Shee	4	2	Job		109		109	173

23 73 Indoor Central-Station Air-Handling Units

23 73 39 – Indoor, Direct Gas-Fired Heating and Ventilating Units

23 73 39.10 Make-Up Air Unit

		Crew	Daily Output	Labor-Hours	Unit	Material	Labor	Equipment	Total	Total Incl O&P
0010	**MAKE-UP AIR UNIT**									
0020	Indoor suspension, natural/LP gas, direct fired,									
0032	standard control. For flue see Section 23 51 23.10									
0040	70°F temperature rise, MBH is input									
0100	75 MBH input	Q-6	3.60	6.667	Ea.	4,900	365		5,265	5,975
0220	225 MBH input		2.40	10		6,675	545		7,220	8,200
0300	400 MBH input		1.60	15		16,600	820		17,420	19,500

23 74 Packaged Outdoor HVAC Equipment

23 74 23 – Packaged, Outdoor, Heating-Only Makeup-Air Units

23 74 23.16 Packaged, Ind.-Fired, In/Outdoor	Crew	Daily Output	Labor-Hours	Unit	Material	2014 Bare Costs Labor	Equipment	Total	Total Incl O&P
0010 **PACKAGED, IND.-FIRED, IN/OUTDOOR**, Heat-Only Makeup-Air Units									
1000 Rooftop unit, natural gas, gravity vent, S.S. exchanger									
1010 70°F temperature rise, MBH is input									
1020 250 MBH	Q-6	4	6	Ea.	15,300	330		15,630	17,300
1040 400 MBH		3.60	6.667		15,900	365		16,265	18,100
1060 550 MBH	↓	3.30	7.273	↓	17,700	395		18,095	20,000
1600 For cleanable filters, add					5%				
1700 For electric modulating gas control, add				↓	10%				
9000 Minimum labor/equipment charge	Q-6	2.75	8.727	Job		475		475	745

23 74 33 – Dedicated Outdoor-Air Units

23 74 33.10 Rooftop Air Conditioners

	Crew	Daily Output	Labor-Hours	Unit	Material	2014 Bare Costs Labor	Equipment	Total	Total Incl O&P
0010 **ROOFTOP AIR CONDITIONERS**, Standard controls, curb, economizer									
1000 Single zone, electric cool, gas heat									
1100 3 ton cooling, 60 MBH heating	Q-5	.70	22.857	Ea.	3,850	1,200		5,050	6,100
1120 4 ton cooling, 95 MBH heating		.61	26.403		4,525	1,400		5,925	7,150
1150 7.5 ton cooling, 170 MBH heating		.50	32.258		8,125	1,700		9,825	11,600
1156 8.5 ton cooling, 170 MBH heating	↓	.46	34.783		8,800	1,825		10,625	12,500
1160 10 ton cooling, 200 MBH heating	Q-6	.67	35.982		11,600	1,975		13,575	15,900
1220 30 ton cooling, 540 MBH heating	Q-7	.47	68.376		28,600	3,800		32,400	37,500
1240 40 ton cooling, 675 MBH heating	"	.35	91.168	↓	36,900	5,075		41,975	48,500
2000 Multizone, electric cool, gas heat, economizer									
2120 20 ton cooling, 360 MBH heating	Q-7	.53	60.038	Ea.	70,000	3,350		73,350	82,000
2180 30 ton cooling, 540 MBH heating		.37	85.562		107,000	4,775		111,775	125,000
2210 50 ton cooling, 540 MBH heating		.23	142		152,000	7,925		159,925	180,000
2220 70 ton cooling, 1500 MBH heating		.16	198		164,500	11,100		175,600	198,500
2240 80 ton cooling, 1500 MBH heating		.14	228		188,000	12,700		200,700	227,000
2280 105 ton cooling, 1500 MBH heating	↓	.11	290		217,500	16,200		233,700	264,500
2400 For hot water heat coil, deduct					5%				
2500 For steam heat coil, deduct					2%				
2600 For electric heat, deduct				↓	3%	5%			
9000 Minimum labor/equipment charge	Q-5	1.50	10.667	Job		560		560	875

23 81 Decentralized Unitary HVAC Equipment

23 81 19 – Self-Contained Air-Conditioners

23 81 19.10 Window Unit Air Conditioners

	Crew	Daily Output	Labor-Hours	Unit	Material	2014 Bare Costs Labor	Equipment	Total	Total Incl O&P
0010 **WINDOW UNIT AIR CONDITIONERS**									
4000 Portable/window, 15 amp 125 V grounded receptacle required									
4500 10,000 BTUH	1 Carp	6	1.333	Ea.	570	61		631	725
4520 12,000 BTUH	L-2	8	2	"	695	80.50		775.50	900
9000 Minimum labor/equipment charge	1 Carp	2	4	Job		183		183	300

23 81 19.20 Self-Contained Single Package

	Crew	Daily Output	Labor-Hours	Unit	Material	2014 Bare Costs Labor	Equipment	Total	Total Incl O&P
0010 **SELF-CONTAINED SINGLE PACKAGE**									
0100 Air cooled, for free blow or duct, not incl. remote condenser									
0110 Constant volume									
0200 3 ton cooling	Q-5	1	16	Ea.	3,750	840		4,590	5,425
0210 4 ton cooling	"	.80	20		4,075	1,050		5,125	6,125
0240 10 ton cooling	Q-7	1	32		7,375	1,775		9,150	10,900
0280 30 ton cooling	"	.80	40	↓	25,300	2,225		27,525	31,300
1000 Water cooled for free blow or duct, not including tower									
1010 Constant volume									

23 81 Decentralized Unitary HVAC Equipment

23 81 19 – Self-Contained Air-Conditioners

23 81 19.20 Self-Contained Single Package

		Crew	Daily Output	Labor-Hours	Unit	Material	2014 Bare Costs Labor	Equipment	Total	Total Incl O&P
1100	3 ton cooling	Q-6	1	24	Ea.	3,725	1,300		5,025	6,125
1120	5 ton cooling	"	1	24		4,850	1,300		6,150	7,400
1140	10 ton cooling	Q-7	.90	35.556		9,075	1,975		11,050	13,100
1180	30 ton cooling	"	.70	45.714		37,900	2,550		40,450	45,700
1240	60 ton cooling	Q-8	.30	106		69,500	5,950	185	75,635	86,000
1300	For hot water or steam heat coils, add					12%	10%			
9000	Minimum labor/equipment charge	Q-5	1	16	Job		840		840	1,325

23 81 23 – Computer-Room Air-Conditioners

23 81 23.10 Computer Room Units

		Crew	Daily Output	Labor-Hours	Unit	Material	2014 Bare Costs Labor	Equipment	Total	Total Incl O&P
0010	**COMPUTER ROOM UNITS**									
1000	Air cooled, includes remote condenser but not									
1020	interconnecting tubing or refrigerant									
1160	6 ton	Q-5	.30	53.333	Ea.	35,900	2,800		38,700	43,900
1240	10 ton		.25	64		38,000	3,375		41,375	47,100
1260	12 ton		.24	66.667		39,300	3,500		42,800	48,800
1300	20 ton	Q-6	.26	92.308		50,000	5,050		55,050	63,000
1320	22 ton	"	.24	100		50,500	5,450		55,950	64,000

23 81 26 – Split-System Air-Conditioners

23 81 26.10 Split Ductless Systems

		Crew	Daily Output	Labor-Hours	Unit	Material	2014 Bare Costs Labor	Equipment	Total	Total Incl O&P
0010	**SPLIT DUCTLESS SYSTEMS**									
0100	Cooling only, single zone									
0110	Wall mount									
0120	3/4 ton cooling	Q-5	2	8	Ea.	690	420		1,110	1,425
0130	1 ton cooling		1.80	8.889		765	470		1,235	1,575
0140	1-1/2 ton cooling		1.60	10		1,225	525		1,750	2,175
0150	2 ton cooling		1.40	11.429		1,400	600		2,000	2,500
1000	Ceiling mount									
1020	2 ton cooling	Q-5	1.40	11.429	Ea.	1,250	600		1,850	2,325
1030	3 ton cooling	"	1.20	13.333	"	1,600	700		2,300	2,850
3000	Multizone									
3010	Wall mount									
3020	2 @ 3/4 ton cooling	Q-5	1.80	8.889	Ea.	2,100	470		2,570	3,050
5000	Cooling/Heating									
5010	Wall mount									
5110	1 ton cooling	Q-5	1.70	9.412	Ea.	765	495		1,260	1,625
5120	1-1/2 ton cooling	"	1.50	10.667	"	1,225	560		1,785	2,225
7000	Accessories for all split ductless systems									
7010	Add for ambient frost control	Q-5	8	2	Ea.	79	105		184	251
7020	Add for tube/wiring kit, (Line sets)									
7030	15' kit	Q-5	32	.500	Ea.	103	26.50		129.50	154
7036	25' kit		28	.571		116	30		146	175
7040	35' kit		24	.667		174	35		209	246
7050	50' kit		20	.800		191	42		233	276

23 81 29 – Variable Refrigerant Flow HVAC Systems

23 81 29.10 Heat Pump, Gas Driven

		Crew	Daily Output	Labor-Hours	Unit	Material	2014 Bare Costs Labor	Equipment	Total	Total Incl O&P
0010	**HEAT PUMP, GAS DRIVEN**, Variable refrigerant volume (VRV) type									
0020	Not including interconnecting tubing or multi-zone controls									
1000	For indoor fan VRV type AHU see 23 82 19.40									
1010	Multi-zone split									
1020	Outdoor unit									
1100	8 tons cooling, for up to 17 zones	Q-5	1.30	12.308	Ea.	31,000	650		31,650	35,100

23 81 Decentralized Unitary HVAC Equipment

23 81 29 – Variable Refrigerant Flow HVAC Systems

23 81 29.10 Heat Pump, Gas Driven		Crew	Daily Output	Labor-Hours	Unit	Material	2014 Bare Costs Labor	Equipment	Total	Total Incl O&P
1110	Isolation rails	Q-5	2.60	6.154	Pair	830	325		1,155	1,425
1160	15 tons cooling, for up to 33 zones		1	16	Ea.	42,400	840		43,240	47,900
1170	Isolation rails	↓	2.60	6.154	Pair	830	325		1,155	1,425
2000	Packaged unit									
2020	Outdoor unit									
2200	11 tons cooling	Q-5	1.30	12.308	Ea.	37,200	650		37,850	41,900
2210	Roof curb adapter	"	2.60	6.154		645	325		970	1,225
2220	Thermostat	1 Stpi	1.30	6.154	↓	385	360		745	985

23 81 43 – Air-Source Unitary Heat Pumps

23 81 43.10 Air-Source Heat Pumps

		Crew	Daily Output	Labor-Hours	Unit	Material	2014 Bare Costs Labor	Equipment	Total	Total Incl O&P
0010	**AIR-SOURCE HEAT PUMPS**, Not including interconnecting tubing									
1000	Air to air, split system, not including curbs, pads, fan coil and ductwork									
1012	Outside condensing unit only, for fan coil see Section 23 82 19.10									
1020	2 ton cooling, 8.5 MBH heat @ 0°F	Q-5	2	8	Ea.	2,300	420		2,720	3,200
1040	3 ton cooling, 13 MBH heat @ 0°F		1.20	13.333		2,800	700		3,500	4,175
1080	7.5 ton cooling, 33 MBH heat @ 0°F	↓	.45	35.556		6,325	1,875		8,200	9,900
1120	15 ton cooling, 64 MBH heat @ 0°F	Q-6	.50	48		13,400	2,625		16,025	18,900
1130	20 ton cooling, 85 MBH heat @ 0°F		.35	68.571		17,000	3,750		20,750	24,600
1140	25 ton cooling, 119 MBH heat @ 0°F	↓	.25	96	↓	20,400	5,250		25,650	30,700
1500	Single package, not including curbs, pads, or plenums									
1520	2 ton cooling, 6.5 MBH heat @ 0°F	Q-5	1.50	10.667	Ea.	2,950	560		3,510	4,125
1560	3 ton cooling, 10 MBH heat @ 0°F	"	1.20	13.333	"	3,475	700		4,175	4,925

23 81 46 – Water-Source Unitary Heat Pumps

23 81 46.10 Water Source Heat Pumps

		Crew	Daily Output	Labor-Hours	Unit	Material	2014 Bare Costs Labor	Equipment	Total	Total Incl O&P
0010	**WATER SOURCE HEAT PUMPS**, Not incl. connecting tubing or water source									
2000	Water source to air, single package									
2100	1 ton cooling, 13 MBH heat @ 75°F	Q-5	2	8	Ea.	1,825	420		2,245	2,650
2140	2 ton cooling, 19 MBH heat @ 75°F		1.70	9.412		2,050	495		2,545	3,025
2220	5 ton cooling, 29 MBH heat @ 75°F		.90	17.778	↓	3,025	935		3,960	4,775
9000	Minimum labor/equipment charge	↓	1.75	9.143	Job		480		480	750

23 82 Convection Heating and Cooling Units

23 82 16 – Air Coils

23 82 16.10 Flanged Coils

		Crew	Daily Output	Labor-Hours	Unit	Material	2014 Bare Costs Labor	Equipment	Total	Total Incl O&P
0010	**FLANGED COILS**									
1500	Hot water heating, 1 row, 24" x 48"	Q-5	4	4	Ea.	1,600	211		1,811	2,100
9000	Minimum labor/equipment charge	1 Plum	1	8	Job		460		460	720

23 82 16.20 Duct Heaters

		Crew	Daily Output	Labor-Hours	Unit	Material	2014 Bare Costs Labor	Equipment	Total	Total Incl O&P
0010	**DUCT HEATERS**, Electric, 480 V, 3 Ph.									
0020	Finned tubular insert, 500°F									
0100	8" wide x 6" high, 4.0 kW	Q-20	16	1.250	Ea.	795	62.50		857.50	975
0120	12" high, 8.0 kW		15	1.333		1,325	66.50		1,391.50	1,550
0140	18" high, 12.0 kW		14	1.429		1,850	71.50		1,921.50	2,125
0160	24" high, 16.0 kW		13	1.538		2,375	77		2,452	2,725
0180	30" high, 20.0 kW		12	1.667		2,900	83.50		2,983.50	3,325
0300	12" wide x 6" high, 6.7 kW		15	1.333		845	66.50		911.50	1,025
0320	12" high, 13.3 kW		14	1.429		1,350	71.50		1,421.50	1,600
0340	18" high, 20.0 kW	↓	13	1.538	↓	1,900	77		1,977	2,225
8000	To obtain BTU multiply kW by 3413									
9900	Minimum labor/equipment charge	1 Shee	4	2	Job		109		109	173

23 82 19.10 Fan Coil Air Conditioning

		Crew	Daily Output	Labor-Hours	Unit	Material	2014 Bare Costs Labor	Equipment	Total	Total Incl O&P
0010	**FAN COIL AIR CONDITIONING**									
0030	Fan coil AC, cabinet mounted, filters and controls									
0100	Chilled water, 1/2 ton cooling	Q-5	8	2	Ea.	810	105		915	1,050
0120	1 ton cooling		6	2.667		935	140		1,075	1,250
0160	2.5 ton cooling		5	3.200		1,775	168		1,943	2,225
0180	3 ton cooling	▼	4	4	▼	1,875	211		2,086	2,400
0262	For hot water coil, add					40%	10%			
0940	Direct expansion, for use w/air cooled condensing unit, 1.5 ton cooling	Q-5	5	3.200	Ea.	755	168		923	1,100
1000	5 ton cooling	"	3	5.333		1,450	281		1,731	2,050
1040	10 ton cooling	Q-6	2.60	9.231		3,175	505		3,680	4,275
1060	20 ton cooling	"	.70	34.286		6,250	1,875		8,125	9,800
1500	For hot water coil, add				▼	40%	10%			
1512	For condensing unit add see Section 23 62									
3000	Chilled water, horizontal unit, housing, 2 pipe, fan control, no valves									
3100	1/2 ton cooling	Q-5	8	2	Ea.	1,200	105		1,305	1,500
3110	1 ton cooling		6	2.667		1,450	140		1,590	1,825
3120	1.5 ton cooling		5.50	2.909		1,750	153		1,903	2,175
3130	2 ton cooling		5.25	3.048		2,075	160		2,235	2,550
3140	3 ton cooling		4	4		2,400	211		2,611	2,975
3150	3.5 ton cooling		3.80	4.211		2,650	222		2,872	3,275
3160	4 ton cooling	▼	3.80	4.211	▼	2,650	222		2,872	3,275
4000	With electric heat, 2 pipe									
4100	1/2 ton cooling	Q-5	8	2	Ea.	1,450	105		1,555	1,775
4105	3/4 ton cooling		7	2.286		1,625	120		1,745	1,975
4110	1 ton cooling		6	2.667		1,775	140		1,915	2,175
4120	1.5 ton cooling		5.50	2.909		1,975	153		2,128	2,425
4130	2 ton cooling		5.25	3.048		2,500	160		2,660	3,000
4135	2.5 ton cooling		4.80	3.333		3,450	176		3,626	4,050
4140	3 ton cooling		4	4		4,775	211		4,986	5,575
4150	3.5 ton cooling		3.80	4.211		5,725	222		5,947	6,650
4160	4 ton cooling		3.60	4.444	▼	6,625	234		6,859	7,675
9000	Minimum labor/equipment charge	▼	3.75	4.267	Job		225		225	350

23 82 19.40 Fan Coil Air Conditioning

		Crew	Daily Output	Labor-Hours	Unit	Material	2014 Bare Costs Labor	Equipment	Total	Total Incl O&P
0010	**FAN COIL AIR CONDITIONING**, Variable refrigerant volume (VRV) type									
0020	Not including interconnecting tubing or multi-zone controls									
0030	For VRV condensing unit see section 23 81 29.10									
0050	Indoor type, ducted									
0100	Vertical concealed									
0130	1 ton cooling	G	Q-5	2.97	5.387	Ea.	3,025	284		3,309	3,775
0140	1.5 ton cooling	G		2.77	5.776		3,050	305		3,355	3,825
0150	2 ton cooling	G		2.70	5.926		3,275	310		3,585	4,100
0160	2.5 ton cooling	G		2.60	6.154		3,300	325		3,625	4,125
0170	3 ton cooling	G		2.50	6.400		3,375	335		3,710	4,225
0180	3.5 ton cooling	G		2.30	6.957		3,500	365		3,865	4,425
0190	4 ton cooling	G		2.19	7.306		3,525	385		3,910	4,475
0200	4.5 ton cooling	G	▼	2.08	7.692	▼	3,925	405		4,330	4,925
0230	Outside air connection possible									
1100	Ceiling concealed									
1130	.6 ton cooling	G	Q-5	2.60	6.154	Ea.	1,950	325		2,275	2,625
1140	.75 ton cooling	G		2.60	6.154		2,000	325		2,325	2,700
1150	1 ton cooling	G	▼	2.60	6.154		2,100	325		2,425	2,825
1152	Screening door	G	1 Stpi	5.20	1.538	▼	98	90		188	248

23 82 19 – Fan Coil Units

23 82 19.40 Fan Coil Air Conditioning		Crew	Daily Output	Labor-Hours	Unit	Material	2014 Bare Costs Labor	Equipment	Total	Total Incl O&P
1160	1.5 ton cooling	G	Q-5	2.60	6.154	Ea.	2,200	325		2,525	2,900
1162	Screening door	G	1 Stpi	5.20	1.538		113	90		203	265
1170	2 ton cooling	G	Q-5	2.60	6.154		2,575	325		2,900	3,325
1172	Screening door	G	1 Stpi	5.20	1.538		98	90		188	248
1180	2.5 ton cooling	G	Q-5	2.60	6.154		2,975	325		3,300	3,775
1182	Screening door	G	1 Stpi	5.20	1.538		170	90		260	325
1190	3 ton cooling	G	Q-5	2.60	6.154		3,175	325		3,500	3,975
1192	Screening door	G	1 Stpi	5.20	1.538		170	90		260	325
1200	4 ton cooling	G	Q-5	2.30	6.957		5,250	365		5,615	6,350
1202	Screening door	G	1 Stpi	5.20	1.538		170	90		260	325
1220	6 ton cooling	G	Q-5	2.08	7.692		5,275	405		5,680	6,425
1230	8 ton cooling	G	"	1.89	8.466	↓	5,775	445		6,220	7,050
1260	Outside air connection possible										
4050	Indoor type, duct-free										
4100	Ceiling mounted cassette										
4130	.75 ton cooling	G	Q-5	3.46	4.624	Ea.	2,500	243		2,743	3,125
4140	1 ton cooling	G		2.97	5.387		2,650	284		2,934	3,375
4150	1.5 ton cooling	G		2.77	5.776		2,725	305		3,030	3,475
4160	2 ton cooling	G		2.60	6.154		2,900	325		3,225	3,700
4170	2.5 ton cooling	G		2.50	6.400		2,975	335		3,310	3,800
4180	3 ton cooling	G		2.30	6.957		3,200	365		3,565	4,075
4190	4 ton cooling	G	↓	2.08	7.692		3,600	405		4,005	4,575
4198	For ceiling cassette decoration panel, add	G	1 Stpi	5.20	1.538	↓	294	90		384	465
4230	Outside air connection possible										
4500	Wall mounted										
4530	.6 ton cooling	G	Q-5	5.20	3.077	Ea.	1,050	162		1,212	1,400
4540	.75 ton cooling	G		5.20	3.077		1,100	162		1,262	1,475
4550	1 ton cooling	G		4.16	3.846		1,175	203		1,378	1,625
4560	1.5 ton cooling	G		3.77	4.244		1,400	223		1,623	1,900
4570	2 ton cooling	G	↓	3.46	4.624		1,650	243		1,893	2,175
4590	Condensate pump for the above air handlers	G	1 Stpi	6.46	1.238	↓	211	72.50		283.50	345
4700	Floor standing unit										
4730	1 ton cooling	G	Q-5	2.60	6.154	Ea.	1,700	325		2,025	2,375
4740	1.5 ton cooling	G		2.60	6.154		1,925	325		2,250	2,625
4750	2 ton cooling	G	↓	2.60	6.154	↓	2,050	325		2,375	2,750
4800	Floor standing unit, concealed										
4830	1 ton cooling	G	Q-5	2.60	6.154	Ea.	1,925	325		2,250	2,625
4840	1.5 ton cooling	G		2.60	6.154		2,050	325		2,375	2,775
4850	2 ton cooling	G	↓	2.60	6.154	↓	2,350	325		2,675	3,075
4880	Outside air connection possible										
8000	Accessories										
8100	Branch divergence pipe fitting										
8110	Capacity under 76 MBH		1 Stpi	2.50	3.200	Ea.	149	187		336	455
8120	76 MBH to 112 MBH			2.50	3.200		155	187		342	460
8130	112 MBH to 234 MBH		↓	2.50	3.200	↓	590	187		777	940
8200	Header pipe fitting										
8210	Max 4 branches										
8220	Capacity under 76 MBH		1 Stpi	1.70	4.706	Ea.	325	275		600	785
8260	Max 8 branches										
8270	76 MBH to 112 MBH		1 Stpi	1.70	4.706	Ea.	635	275		910	1,125
8280	112 MBH to 234 MBH		"	1.30	6.154	"	810	360		1,170	1,450

23 82 Convection Heating and Cooling Units

23 82 29 – Radiators

23 82 29.10 Hydronic Heating	Crew	Daily Output	Labor- Hours	Unit	Material	2014 Bare Costs Labor	Equipment	Total	Total Incl O&P
0010 **HYDRONIC HEATING**, Terminal units, not incl. main supply pipe									
1000 Radiation									
1100 Panel, baseboard, C.I., including supports, no covers	Q-5	46	.348	L.F.	36.50	18.30		54.80	68.50
3000 Radiators, cast iron									
3100 Free standing or wall hung, 6 tube, 25" high	Q-5	96	.167	Section	44	8.80		52.80	62
9000 Minimum labor/equipment charge	"	3.20	5	Job		263		263	410

23 82 36 – Finned-Tube Radiation Heaters

23 82 36.10 Finned Tube Radiation

	Crew	Daily Output	Labor- Hours	Unit	Material	2014 Bare Costs Labor	Equipment	Total	Total Incl O&P
0010 **FINNED TUBE RADIATION**, Terminal units, not incl. main supply pipe									
1150 Fin tube, wall hung, 14" slope top cover, with damper									
1200 1-1/4" copper tube, 4-1/4" alum. fin	Q-5	38	.421	L.F.	42	22		64	80.50
1250 1-1/4" steel tube, 4-1/4" steel fin		36	.444		39.50	23.50		63	79.50
1255 2" steel tube, 4-1/4" steel fin		32	.500		43	26.50		69.50	88
1310 Baseboard, pkgd, 1/2" copper tube, alum. fin, 7" high		60	.267		11.20	14.05		25.25	34.50
1320 3/4" copper tube, alum. fin, 7" high		58	.276		7.35	14.50		21.85	30.50
1340 1" copper tube, alum. fin, 8-7/8" high		56	.286		18.85	15.05		33.90	44
1360 1-1/4" copper tube, alum. fin, 8-7/8" high		54	.296		28	15.60		43.60	55
1500 Note: fin tube may also require corners, caps, etc.									

23 82 39 – Unit Heaters

23 82 39.16 Propeller Unit Heaters

	Crew	Daily Output	Labor- Hours	Unit	Material	2014 Bare Costs Labor	Equipment	Total	Total Incl O&P
0010 **PROPELLER UNIT HEATERS**									
3950 Unit heaters, propeller, 115 V 2 psi steam, 60°F entering air									
4000 Horizontal, 12 MBH	Q-5	12	1.333	Ea.	360	70		430	505
4060 43.9 MBH		8	2		545	105		650	765
4240 286.9 MBH		2	8		1,650	420		2,070	2,475
4260 364 MBH		1.80	8.889		2,075	470		2,545	3,000
4270 404 MBH		1.60	10		2,150	525		2,675	3,200
4300 Vertical diffuser same price									
4310 Vertical flow, 40 MBH	Q-5	11	1.455	Ea.	540	76.50		616.50	715
4326 131.0 MBH	"	4	4		845	211		1,056	1,250
4354 420 MBH, (460 V)	Q-6	1.80	13.333		2,150	730		2,880	3,500
4358 500 MBH, (460 V)		1.71	14.035		2,875	765		3,640	4,350
4362 570 MBH, (460 V)		1.40	17.143		3,925	935		4,860	5,775
4366 620 MBH, (460 V)		1.30	18.462		3,925	1,000		4,925	5,900
4370 960 MBH, (460 V)		1.10	21.818		7,450	1,200		8,650	10,100

23 83 Radiant Heating Units

23 83 33 – Electric Radiant Heaters

23 83 33.10 Electric Heating

	Crew	Daily Output	Labor- Hours	Unit	Material	2014 Bare Costs Labor	Equipment	Total	Total Incl O&P
0010 **ELECTRIC HEATING**, not incl. conduit or feed wiring									
1100 Rule of thumb: Baseboard units, including control	1 Elec	4.40	1.818	kW	101	97		198	261
1300 Baseboard heaters, 2' long, 350 watt		8	1	Ea.	30	53.50		83.50	116
1400 3' long, 750 watt		8	1		34.50	53.50		88	121
1600 4' long, 1000 watt		6.70	1.194		41	63.50		104.50	144
1800 5' long, 935 watt		5.70	1.404		51	75		126	172
2000 6' long, 1500 watt		5	1.600		56	85.50		141.50	194
2400 8' long, 2000 watt		4	2		69.50	107		176.50	241
2600 9' long, 1680 watt		3.60	2.222		104	119		223	297
2800 10' long, 1875 watt		3.30	2.424		193	129		322	410

23 83 Radiant Heating Units

23 83 33 – Electric Radiant Heaters

23 83 33.10 Electric Heating

	23 83 33.10 Electric Heating	Crew	Daily Output	Labor-Hours	Unit	Material	2014 Bare Costs Labor	2014 Bare Costs Equipment	Total	Total Incl O&P
2950	Wall heaters with fan, 120 to 277 volt									
3160	Recessed, residential, 750 watt	1 Elec	6	1.333	Ea.	134	71		205	257
3170	1000 watt		6	1.333		134	71		205	257
3180	1250 watt		5	1.600		134	85.50		219.50	279
3190	1500 watt		4	2		134	107		241	310
3230	2500 watt		3.50	2.286		335	122		457	560
3250	4000 watt		2.70	2.963		495	158		653	790
3600	Thermostats, integral		16	.500		30	26.50		56.50	74.50
3800	Line voltage, 1 pole		8	1		20.50	53.50		74	105
3810	2 pole		8	1		29.50	53.50		83	115
9990	Minimum labor/equipment charge		4	2	Job		107		107	165

23 84 Humidity Control Equipment

23 84 13 – Humidifiers

23 84 13.10 Humidifier Units

	23 84 13.10 Humidifier Units	Crew	Daily Output	Labor-Hours	Unit	Material	2014 Bare Costs Labor	2014 Bare Costs Equipment	Total	Total Incl O&P
0010	**HUMIDIFIER UNITS**									
0520	Steam, room or duct, filter, regulators, auto. controls, 220 V									
0560	22 lb. per hour	Q-5	5	3.200	Ea.	2,900	168		3,068	3,450
0580	33 lb. per hour		4	4		2,975	211		3,186	3,600
0620	100 lb. per hour		3	5.333		4,350	281		4,631	5,250
9000	Minimum labor/equipment charge		3.50	4.571	Job		241		241	375

23 91 Prefabricated Equipment Supports

23 91 10 – Prefabricated Curbs, Pads and Stands

23 91 10.10 Prefabricated Pads and Stands

	23 91 10.10 Prefabricated Pads and Stands	Crew	Daily Output	Labor-Hours	Unit	Material	2014 Bare Costs Labor	2014 Bare Costs Equipment	Total	Total Incl O&P
0010	**PREFABRICATED PADS AND STANDS**									
6000	Pad, fiberglass reinforced concrete with polystyrene foam core									
6050	Condenser, 2" thick, 20" x 38"	1 Shee	8	1	Ea.	26.50	54.50		81	116
6090	24" x 36"	"	12	.667		33.50	36.50		70	94.50
6280	36" x 36"	Q-9	8	2		48	98.50		146.50	208
6300	36" x 40"		7	2.286		55	113		168	238
6320	36" x 48"		7	2.286		64	113		177	248

Division Notes

		CREW	DAILY OUTPUT	LABOR-HOURS	UNIT	BARE COSTS				TOTAL INCL O&P
						MAT.	LABOR	EQUIP.	TOTAL	

Estimating Tips

26 05 00 Common Work Results for Electrical

- Conduit should be taken off in three main categories—power distribution, branch power, and branch lighting—so the estimator can concentrate on systems and components, therefore making it easier to ensure all items have been accounted for.

- For cost modifications for elevated conduit installation, add the percentages to labor according to the height of installation, and only to the quantities exceeding the different height levels, not to the total conduit quantities.

- Remember that aluminum wiring of equal ampacity is larger in diameter than copper and may require larger conduit.

- If more than three wires at a time are being pulled, deduct percentages from the labor hours of that grouping of wires.

- When taking off grounding systems, identify separately the type and size of wire, and list each unique type of ground connection.

- The estimator should take the weights of materials into consideration when completing a takeoff. Topics to consider include: How will the materials be supported? What methods of support are available? How high will the support structure have to reach? Will the final support structure be able to withstand the total burden? Is the support material included or separate from the fixture, equipment, and material specified?

- Do not overlook the costs for equipment used in the installation. If scaffolding or highlifts are available in the field, contractors may use them in lieu of the proposed ladders and rolling staging.

26 20 00 Low-Voltage Electrical Transmission

- Supports and concrete pads may be shown on drawings for the larger equipment, or the support system may be only a piece of plywood for the back of a panelboard. In either case, it must be included in the costs.

26 40 00 Electrical and Cathodic Protection

- When taking off cathodic protections systems, identify the type and size of cable, and list each unique type of anode connection.

26 50 00 Lighting

- Fixtures should be taken off room by room, using the fixture schedule, specifications, and the ceiling plan. For large concentrations of lighting fixtures in the same area, deduct the percentages from labor hours.

Reference Numbers

Reference numbers are shown in shaded boxes at the beginning of some major classifications. These numbers refer to related items in the Reference Section. The reference information may be an estimating procedure, an alternate pricing method, or technical information.

Note: Not all subdivisions listed here necessarily appear in this publication.

Note: **Trade Service,** *in part, has been used as a reference source for some of the material prices used in Division 26.*

26 01 Operation and Maintenance of Electrical Systems

26 01 50 – Operation and Maintenance of Lighting

26 01 50.81 Luminaire Replacement	Crew	Daily Output	Labor-Hours	Unit	Material	2014 Bare Costs Labor	Equipment	Total	Total Incl O&P
0010 **LUMINAIRE REPLACEMENT**									
0962 Remove and install new replacement lens, 2' x 2' troffer	1 Elec	16	.500	Ea.	15.75	26.50		42.25	59
0964 2' x 4' troffer		16	.500		14.75	26.50		41.25	57.50
3200 Remove and replace (reinstall), lighting fixture	↓	4	2	↓		107		107	165

26 05 Common Work Results for Electrical

26 05 05 – Selective Electrical Demolition

26 05 05.10 Electrical Demolition

		Crew	Daily Output	Labor-Hours	Unit	Material	2014 Bare Costs Labor	Equipment	Total	Total Incl O&P
0010	**ELECTRICAL DEMOLITION** R260105-30									
0020	Conduit to 15' high, including fittings & hangers									
0100	Rigid galvanized steel, 1/2" to 1" diameter R024119-10	1 Elec	242	.033	L.F.		1.76		1.76	2.73
0120	1-1/4" to 2"	"	200	.040			2.13		2.13	3.30
0140	2-1/2" to 3-1/2"	2 Elec	302	.053			2.83		2.83	4.37
0200	Electric metallic tubing (EMT), 1/2" to 1"	1 Elec	394	.020			1.08		1.08	1.68
0220	1-1/4" to 1-1/2"		326	.025			1.31		1.31	2.03
0240	2" to 3"	↓	236	.034			1.81		1.81	2.80
0400	Wiremold raceway, including fittings & hangers									
0420	No. 3000	1 Elec	250	.032	L.F.		1.71		1.71	2.64
0440	No. 4000	"	217	.037	"		1.97		1.97	3.04
0500	Channels, steel, including fittings & hangers									
0520	3/4" x 1-1/2"	1 Elec	308	.026	L.F.		1.39		1.39	2.14
0540	1-1/2" x 1-1/2"		269	.030			1.59		1.59	2.46
0560	1-1/2" x 1-7/8"	↓	229	.035	↓		1.86		1.86	2.88
0600	Copper bus duct, indoor, 3 phase									
0610	Including hangers & supports									
0620	225 amp	2 Elec	135	.119	L.F.		6.30		6.30	9.80
0640	400 amp		106	.151			8.05		8.05	12.45
0660	600 amp		86	.186			9.95		9.95	15.35
0680	1000 amp		60	.267			14.25		14.25	22
0700	1600 amp		40	.400			21.50		21.50	33
0720	3000 amp	↓	10	1.600	↓		85.50		85.50	132
0800	Plug-in switches, 600V 3 ph., incl. disconnecting									
0820	wire, conduit terminations, 30 amp	1 Elec	15.50	.516	Ea.		27.50		27.50	42.50
0840	60 amp		13.90	.576			30.50		30.50	47.50
0850	100 amp		10.40	.769			41		41	63.50
0860	200 amp	↓	6.20	1.290			69		69	107
0880	400 amp	2 Elec	5.40	2.963			158		158	245
0900	600 amp		3.40	4.706			251		251	390
0920	800 amp		2.60	6.154			330		330	510
0940	1200 amp		2	8			425		425	660
0960	1600 amp	↓	1.70	9.412	↓		500		500	775
1010	Safety switches, 250 or 600V, incl. disconnection									
1050	of wire & conduit terminations									
1100	30 amp	1 Elec	12.30	.650	Ea.		34.50		34.50	53.50
1120	60 amp		8.80	.909			48.50		48.50	75
1140	100 amp		7.30	1.096			58.50		58.50	90.50
1160	200 amp	↓	5	1.600	↓		85.50		85.50	132
1210	Panel boards, incl. removal of all breakers,									
1220	conduit terminations & wire connections									
1230	3 wire, 120/240 V, 100A, to 20 circuits	1 Elec	2.60	3.077	Ea.		164		164	254
1240	200 amps, to 42 circuits	2 Elec	2.60	6.154	↓		330		330	510

26 05 05 – Selective Electrical Demolition

26 05 05.10 Electrical Demolition	Crew	Daily Output	Labor-Hours	Unit	Material	2014 Bare Costs Labor	Equipment	Total	Total Incl O&P
1260	4 wire, 120/208 V, 125A, to 20 circuits	1 Elec	2.40	3.333	Ea.		178		178	275
1270	200 amps, to 42 circuits	2 Elec	2.40	6.667	↓		355		355	550
1300	Transformer, dry type, 1 phase, incl. removal of									
1320	supports, wire & conduit terminations									
1340	1 kVA	1 Elec	7.70	1.039	Ea.		55.50		55.50	86
1360	5 kVA	"	4.70	1.702			91		91	141
1420	75 kVA	2 Elec	2.50	6.400	↓		340		340	530
1440	3 phase to 600V, primary									
1460	3 kVA	1 Elec	3.85	2.078	Ea.		111		111	172
1480	15 kVA	2 Elec	4.20	3.810			203		203	315
1500	30 kVA	"	3.50	4.571			244		244	375
1530	112.5 kVA	R-3	2.90	6.897			365	48.50	413.50	620
1560	500 kVA		1.40	14.286			755	100	855	1,275
1570	750 kVA	↓	1.10	18.182	↓		960	127	1,087	1,650
1600	Pull boxes & cabinets, sheet metal, incl. removal									
1620	of supports and conduit terminations									
1640	6" x 6" x 4"	1 Elec	31.10	.257	Ea.		13.70		13.70	21
1660	12" x 12" x 4"		23.30	.343			18.30		18.30	28.50
1720	Junction boxes, 4" sq. & oct.		80	.100			5.35		5.35	8.25
1740	Handy box		107	.075			3.99		3.99	6.15
1760	Switch box		107	.075			3.99		3.99	6.15
1780	Receptacle & switch plates	↓	257	.031	↓		1.66		1.66	2.57
1800	Wire, THW-THWN-THHN, removed from									
1810	in place conduit, to 15' high									
1830	#14	1 Elec	65	.123	C.L.F.		6.55		6.55	10.15
1840	#12		55	.145			7.75		7.75	12
1850	#10	↓	45.50	.176			9.40		9.40	14.50
1880	#4	2 Elec	53	.302			16.10		16.10	25
1890	#3		50	.320			17.05		17.05	26.50
1910	1/0		33.20	.482			25.50		25.50	40
1920	2/0		29.20	.548			29		29	45
1930	3/0		25	.640			34		34	53
1980	400 kcmil		17	.941			50		50	77.50
1990	500 kcmil	↓	16.20	.988	↓		52.50		52.50	81.50
2000	Interior fluorescent fixtures, incl. supports									
2010	& whips, to 15' high									
2100	Recessed drop-in 2' x 2', 2 lamp	2 Elec	35	.457	Ea.		24.50		24.50	37.50
2120	2' x 4', 2 lamp		33	.485			26		26	40
2140	2' x 4', 4 lamp		30	.533			28.50		28.50	44
2160	4' x 4', 4 lamp	↓	20	.800	↓		42.50		42.50	66
2180	Surface mount, acrylic lens & hinged frame									
2200	1' x 4', 2 lamp	2 Elec	44	.364	Ea.		19.40		19.40	30
2220	2' x 2', 2 lamp		44	.364			19.40		19.40	30
2260	2' x 4', 4 lamp		33	.485			26		26	40
2280	4' x 4', 4 lamp	↓	23	.696	↓		37		37	57.50
2300	Strip fixtures, surface mount									
2320	4' long, 1 lamp	2 Elec	53	.302	Ea.		16.10		16.10	25
2340	4' long, 2 lamp		50	.320			17.05		17.05	26.50
2360	8' long, 1 lamp		42	.381			20.50		20.50	31.50
2380	8' long, 2 lamp	↓	40	.400	↓		21.50		21.50	33
2400	Pendant mount, industrial, incl. removal									
2410	of chain or rod hangers, to 15' high									
2420	4' long, 2 lamp	2 Elec	35	.457	Ea.		24.50		24.50	37.50

26 05 05 – Selective Electrical Demolition

26 05 05.10 Electrical Demolition	Crew	Daily Output	Labor-Hours	Unit	Material	2014 Bare Costs Labor	Equipment	Total	Total Incl O&P
2440	8' long, 2 lamp	2 Elec	27	.593	Ea.		31.50		31.50	49
2460	Interior incandescent, surface, ceiling									
2470	or wall mount, to 12' high									
2480	Metal cylinder type, 75 Watt	2 Elec	62	.258	Ea.		13.75		13.75	21.50
2500	150 Watt	"	62	.258	"		13.75		13.75	21.50
2520	Metal halide, high bay									
2540	400 Watt	2 Elec	15	1.067	Ea.		57		57	88
2560	1000 Watt		12	1.333			71		71	110
2580	150 Watt, low bay	▼	20	.800	▼		42.50		42.50	66
2600	Exterior fixtures, incandescent, wall mount									
2620	100 Watt	2 Elec	50	.320	Ea.		17.05		17.05	26.50
2640	Quartz, 500 Watt		33	.485			26		26	40
2660	1500 Watt	▼	27	.593	▼		31.50		31.50	49
2680	Wall pack, mercury vapor									
2700	175 Watt	2 Elec	25	.640	Ea.		34		34	53
2720	250 Watt	"	25	.640	"		34		34	53
9000	Minimum labor/equipment charge	1 Elec	4	2	Job		107		107	165
9900	Add to labor for higher elevated installation									
9910	15' to 20' high, add						10%			
9920	20' to 25' high, add						20%			
9930	25' to 30' high, add						25%			
9940	30' to 35' high, add						30%			
9950	35' to 40' high, add						35%			
9960	Over 40' high, add						40%			

26 05 19 – Low-Voltage Electrical Power Conductors and Cables

26 05 19.20 Armored Cable

26 05 19.20 Armored Cable	Crew	Daily Output	Labor-Hours	Unit	Material	Labor	Equipment	Total	Total Incl O&P
0010	**ARMORED CABLE**									
0050	600 volt, copper (BX), #14, 2 conductor, solid	1 Elec	2.40	3.333	C.L.F.	54	178		232	335
0100	3 conductor, solid		2.20	3.636		83.50	194		277.50	390
0150	#12, 2 conductor, solid		2.30	3.478		54.50	186		240.50	345
0200	3 conductor, solid		2	4		88.50	213		301.50	430
0250	#10, 2 conductor, solid		2	4		100	213		313	440
0300	3 conductor, solid		1.60	5		139	267		406	570
0340	#8, 2 conductor, stranded		1.50	5.333		262	285		547	730
0350	3 conductor, stranded		1.30	6.154		262	330		592	800
9010	600 volt, copper (MC) steel clad, #14, 2 wire		2.40	3.333		55	178		233	335
9020	3 wire		2.20	3.636		85	194		279	395
9030	4 wire		2	4		118	213		331	460
9040	#12, 2 wire		2.30	3.478		55.50	186		241.50	350
9050	3 wire		2	4		94	213		307	435
9070	#10, 2 wire		2	4		116	213		329	460
9080	3 wire		1.60	5		162	267		429	595
9100	#8, 2 wire, stranded		1.80	4.444		223	237		460	610
9110	3 wire, stranded		1.30	6.154	▼	315	330		645	855
9900	Minimum labor/equipment charge	▼	4	2	Job		107		107	165

26 05 19.50 Mineral Insulated Cable

26 05 19.50 Mineral Insulated Cable	Crew	Daily Output	Labor-Hours	Unit	Material	Labor	Equipment	Total	Total Incl O&P
0010	**MINERAL INSULATED CABLE** 600 volt									
0100	1 conductor, #12	1 Elec	1.60	5	C.L.F.	360	267		627	810
0200	#10		1.60	5		465	267		732	925
0400	#8		1.50	5.333		515	285		800	1,000
0500	#6	▼	1.40	5.714		615	305		920	1,150
0600	#4	2 Elec	2.40	6.667		825	355		1,180	1,450

26 05 19.50 Mineral Insulated Cable		Crew	Daily Output	Labor-Hours	Unit	Material	2014 Bare Costs Labor	Equipment	Total	Total Incl O&P
0800	#2	2 Elec	2.20	7.273	C.L.F.	1,175	390		1,565	1,875
0900	#1		2.10	7.619		1,350	405		1,755	2,100
1000	1/0		2	8		1,575	425		2,000	2,375
1100	2/0		1.90	8.421		1,875	450		2,325	2,775
1200	3/0		1.80	8.889		2,250	475		2,725	3,200
1400	4/0		1.60	10		2,600	535		3,135	3,700
1410	250 kcmil	3 Elec	2.40	10		2,950	535		3,485	4,050
1420	350 kcmil		1.95	12.308		3,350	655		4,005	4,725
1430	500 kcmil		1.95	12.308		4,325	655		4,980	5,775
1500	2 conductor, #12	1 Elec	1.40	5.714		750	305		1,055	1,300
1600	#10		1.20	6.667		925	355		1,280	1,575
1800	#8		1.10	7.273		1,075	390		1,465	1,775
2000	#6		1.05	7.619		1,450	405		1,855	2,225
2100	#4	2 Elec	2	8		1,975	425		2,400	2,825
2200	3 conductor, #12	1 Elec	1.20	6.667		940	355		1,295	1,575
2400	#10		1.10	7.273		1,075	390		1,465	1,775
2600	#8		1.05	7.619		1,325	405		1,730	2,100
2800	#6		1	8		1,750	425		2,175	2,575
3000	#4	2 Elec	1.80	8.889		2,200	475		2,675	3,150
3100	4 conductor, #12	1 Elec	1.20	6.667		990	355		1,345	1,650
3200	#10		1.10	7.273		1,200	390		1,590	1,900
3400	#8		1	8		1,550	425		1,975	2,375
3600	#6		.90	8.889		2,025	475		2,500	2,950
3620	7 conductor, #12		1.10	7.273		1,275	390		1,665	2,000
3640	#10		1	8		1,675	425		2,100	2,475
3800	Terminations, 600 volt, 1 conductor, #12		8	1	Ea.	15.90	53.50		69.40	100
5500	2 conductor, #12		6.70	1.194		15.90	63.50		79.40	116
5600	#10		6.40	1.250		24	66.50		90.50	130
5800	#8		6.20	1.290		24	69		93	134
6000	#6		5.70	1.404		24	75		99	143
6200	#4		5.30	1.509		53	80.50		133.50	184
6400	3 conductor, #12		5.70	1.404		24	75		99	143
6500	#10		5.50	1.455		24	77.50		101.50	147
6600	#8		5.20	1.538		24	82		106	154
6800	#6		4.80	1.667		24	89		113	165
7200	#4		4.60	1.739		53	93		146	203
7400	4 conductor, #12		4.60	1.739		26.50	93		119.50	173
7500	#10		4.40	1.818		26.50	97		123.50	179
7600	#8		4.20	1.905		26.50	102		128.50	186
8400	#6		4	2		56	107		163	227
8500	7 conductor, #12		3.50	2.286		26.50	122		148.50	218
8600	#10		3	2.667		57.50	142		199.50	284
8800	Crimping tool, plier type					59.50			59.50	65.50
9000	Stripping tool					224			224	247
9200	Hand vise					67			67	73.50
9500	Minimum labor/equipment charge	1 Elec	4	2	Job		107		107	165

26 05 19.55 Non-Metallic Sheathed Cable

		Crew	Daily Output	Labor-Hours	Unit	Material	2014 Bare Costs Labor	Equipment	Total	Total Incl O&P
0010	**NON-METALLIC SHEATHED CABLE** 600 volt									
0100	Copper with ground wire, (Romex)									
0150	#14, 2 conductor	1 Elec	2.70	2.963	C.L.F.	25.50	158		183.50	273
0200	3 conductor		2.40	3.333		35.50	178		213.50	315
0220	4 conductor		2.20	3.636		51	194		245	355

26 05 19.55 Non-Metallic Sheathed Cable

		Crew	Daily Output	Labor-Hours	Unit	Material	2014 Bare Costs Labor	Equipment	Total	Total Incl O&P
0250	#12, 2 conductor	1 Elec	2.50	3.200	C.L.F.	38.50	171		209.50	305
0300	3 conductor		2.20	3.636		54	194		248	360
0320	4 conductor		2	4		79.50	213		292.50	420
0350	#10, 2 conductor		2.20	3.636		60	194		254	365
0400	3 conductor		1.80	4.444		85.50	237		322.50	460
0430	#8, 2 conductor		1.60	5		94.50	267		361.50	520
0450	3 conductor		1.50	5.333		138	285		423	590
0500	#6, 3 conductor	▼	1.40	5.714	▼	224	305		529	715
0550	SE type SER aluminum cable, 3 RHW and									
0600	1 bare neutral, 3 #8 & 1 #8	1 Elec	1.60	5	C.L.F.	137	267		404	565
0650	3 #6 & 1 #6	"	1.40	5.714		156	305		461	640
0700	3 #4 & 1 #6	2 Elec	2.40	6.667		144	355		499	710
0750	3 #2 & 1 #4		2.20	7.273		257	390		647	880
0800	3 #1/0 & 1 #2		2	8		390	425		815	1,100
0850	3 #2/0 & 1 #1		1.80	8.889		460	475		935	1,250
0900	3 #4/0 & 1 #2/0	▼	1.60	10	▼	655	535		1,190	1,550
6500	Service entrance cap for copper SEU									
6700	150 amp	1 Elec	10	.800	Ea.	18.90	42.50		61.40	87
6800	200 amp		8	1	"	29	53.50		82.50	114
9000	Minimum labor/equipment charge	▼	4	2	Job		107		107	165

26 05 19.90 Wire

			Crew	Daily Output	Labor-Hours	Unit	Material	2014 Bare Costs Labor	Equipment	Total	Total Incl O&P
0010	**WIRE**	R260533-22									
0020	600 volt, copper type THW, solid, #14		1 Elec	13	.615	C.L.F.	8.30	33		41.30	60
0030	#12			11	.727		12.50	39		51.50	74
0040	#10			10	.800		19.80	42.50		62.30	88
0140	#8			8	1		37.50	53.50		91	124
0160	#6			6.50	1.231		64	65.50		129.50	173
0180	#4		2 Elec	10.60	1.509		101	80.50		181.50	236
0200	#3			10	1.600		126	85.50		211.50	271
0220	#2			9	1.778		160	95		255	325
0240	#1			8	2		202	107		309	385
0260	1/0			6.60	2.424		251	129		380	475
0280	2/0			5.80	2.759		315	147		462	575
0300	3/0			5	3.200		395	171		566	700
0350	4/0			4.40	3.636		505	194		699	855
0400	250 kcmil		3 Elec	6	4		590	213		803	980
0420	300 kcmil			5.70	4.211		705	225		930	1,125
0450	350 kcmil			5.40	4.444		860	237		1,097	1,300
0480	400 kcmil			5.10	4.706		990	251		1,241	1,500
0490	500 kcmil			4.80	5		1,175	267		1,442	1,700
0510	750 kcmil			3.30	7.273		1,975	390		2,365	2,775
0540	600 volt, aluminum type THHN, stranded, #6		1 Elec	8	1		37.50	53.50		91	124
0560	#4		2 Elec	13	1.231		46.50	65.50		112	153
0580	#2			10.60	1.509		63	80.50		143.50	194
0600	#1			9	1.778		92	95		187	248
0620	1/0			8	2		110	107		217	286
0640	2/0			7.20	2.222		130	119		249	325
0680	3/0			6.60	2.424		162	129		291	380
0700	4/0			6.20	2.581		180	138		318	410
0720	250 kcmil		3 Elec	8.70	2.759		219	147		366	470
0740	300 kcmil			8.10	2.963		305	158		463	580
0760	350 kcmil			7.50	3.200		310	171		481	605

26 05 Common Work Results for Electrical

26 05 19 – Low-Voltage Electrical Power Conductors and Cables

26 05 19.90 Wire

	26 05 19.90 Wire	Crew	Daily Output	Labor-Hours	Unit	Material	2014 Bare Costs Labor	Equipment	Total	Total Incl O&P
0780	400 kcmil	3 Elec	6.90	3.478	C.L.F.	360	186		546	680
0800	500 kcmil		6	4		395	213		608	765
0850	600 kcmil		5.70	4.211		505	225		730	905
0880	700 kcmil		5.10	4.706		580	251		831	1,025
9000	Minimum labor/equipment charge	1 Elec	4	2	Job		107		107	165

26 05 26 – Grounding and Bonding for Electrical Systems

26 05 26.80 Grounding

	26 05 26.80 Grounding	Crew	Daily Output	Labor-Hours	Unit	Material	2014 Bare Costs Labor	Equipment	Total	Total Incl O&P
0010	**GROUNDING**									
0030	Rod, copper clad, 8' long, 1/2" diameter	1 Elec	5.50	1.455	Ea.	20.50	77.50		98	143
0040	5/8" diameter		5.50	1.455		19.50	77.50		97	142
0050	3/4" diameter		5.30	1.509		34	80.50		114.50	163
0080	10' long, 1/2" diameter		4.80	1.667		22.50	89		111.50	163
0090	5/8" diameter		4.60	1.739		24.50	93		117.50	171
0100	3/4" diameter		4.40	1.818		39	97		136	193
0130	15' long, 3/4" diameter		4	2		63.50	107		170.50	235
0260	Wire ground bare armored, #8-1 conductor		2	4	C.L.F.	89.50	213		302.50	430
0280	#4-1 conductor		1.60	5		146	267		413	575
0390	Bare copper wire, stranded, #8		11	.727		35	39		74	98.50
0400	#6		10	.800		61	42.50		103.50	133
0600	#2	2 Elec	10	1.600		162	85.50		247.50	310
0800	3/0		6.60	2.424		365	129		494	605
1000	4/0		5.70	2.807		460	150		610	735
1200	250 kcmil	3 Elec	7.20	3.333		545	178		723	875
1800	Water pipe ground clamps, heavy duty									
2000	Bronze, 1/2" to 1" diameter	1 Elec	8	1	Ea.	23.50	53.50		77	108
2100	1-1/4" to 2" diameter		8	1		32.50	53.50		86	119
2200	2-1/2" to 3" diameter		6	1.333		49	71		120	164
2800	Brazed connections, #6 wire		12	.667		16	35.50		51.50	72.50
3000	#2 wire		10	.800		21.50	42.50		64	89.50
3100	3/0 wire		8	1		32	53.50		85.50	118
3200	4/0 wire		7	1.143		37	61		98	135
3400	250 kcmil wire		5	1.600		43	85.50		128.50	179
3600	500 kcmil wire		4	2		53	107		160	223
9000	Minimum labor/equipment charge		4	2	Job		107		107	165

26 05 33 – Raceway and Boxes for Electrical Systems

26 05 33.13 Conduit

	26 05 33.13 Conduit	Crew	Daily Output	Labor-Hours	Unit	Material	2014 Bare Costs Labor	Equipment	Total	Total Incl O&P
0010	**CONDUIT** To 15' high, includes 2 terminations, 2 elbows,	R260533-22								
0020	11 beam clamps, and 11 couplings per 100 L.F.									
1161	Field bends, 45° to 90°, 1/2" diameter	1 Elec	53	.151	Ea.		8.05		8.05	12.45
1162	3/4" diameter		47	.170			9.10		9.10	14.05
1163	1" diameter		44	.182			9.70		9.70	15
1164	1-1/4" diameter		23	.348			18.55		18.55	28.50
1165	1-1/2" diameter		21	.381			20.50		20.50	31.50
1166	2" diameter		16	.500			26.50		26.50	41.50
1991	Field bends, 45° to 90°, 1/2" diameter		44	.182			9.70		9.70	15
1992	3/4" diameter		40	.200			10.65		10.65	16.50
1993	1" diameter		36	.222			11.85		11.85	18.35
1994	1-1/4" diameter		19	.421			22.50		22.50	35
1995	1-1/2" diameter		18	.444			23.50		23.50	36.50
1996	2" diameter		13	.615			33		33	51
2500	Steel, intermediate conduit (IMC), 1/2" diameter		100	.080	L.F.	1.72	4.27		5.99	8.50
2530	3/4" diameter		90	.089		2.06	4.74		6.80	9.60

26 05 33.13 Conduit

		Crew	Daily Output	Labor-Hours	Unit	Material	2014 Bare Costs Labor	Equipment	Total	Total Incl O&P
2550	1" diameter	1 Elec	70	.114	L.F.	3.04	6.10		9.14	12.80
2570	1-1/4" diameter		65	.123		3.73	6.55		10.28	14.25
2600	1-1/2" diameter		60	.133		4.92	7.10		12.02	16.40
2630	2" diameter		50	.160		5.95	8.55		14.50	19.70
2650	2-1/2" diameter		40	.200		10.60	10.65		21.25	28
2670	3" diameter	2 Elec	60	.267		14.50	14.25		28.75	38
2700	3-1/2" diameter		54	.296		19.15	15.80		34.95	45.50
2730	4" diameter		50	.320	Ea.	21	17.05		38.05	49.50
2731	Field bends, 45° to 90°, 1/2" diameter	1 Elec	44	.182	Ea.		9.70		9.70	15
2732	3/4" diameter		40	.200			10.65		10.65	16.50
2733	1" diameter		36	.222			11.85		11.85	18.35
2734	1-1/4" diameter		19	.421			22.50		22.50	35
2735	1-1/2" diameter		18	.444			23.50		23.50	36.50
2736	2" diameter		13	.615			33		33	51
5000	Electric metallic tubing (EMT), 1/2" diameter		170	.047	L.F.	.56	2.51		3.07	4.50
5020	3/4" diameter		130	.062		.86	3.28		4.14	6.05
5040	1" diameter		115	.070		1.48	3.71		5.19	7.40
5060	1-1/4" diameter		100	.080		2.45	4.27		6.72	9.30
5080	1-1/2" diameter		90	.089		3.16	4.74		7.90	10.85
5100	2" diameter		80	.100		4.02	5.35		9.37	12.65
5120	2-1/2" diameter		60	.133		9.55	7.10		16.65	21.50
5140	3" diameter	2 Elec	100	.160		11.05	8.55		19.60	25.50
5160	3-1/2" diameter		90	.178		14	9.50		23.50	30
5180	4" diameter		80	.200		15.35	10.65		26	33.50
5200	Field bends, 45° to 90°, 1/2" diameter	1 Elec	89	.090	Ea.		4.80		4.80	7.40
5220	3/4" diameter		80	.100			5.35		5.35	8.25
5240	1" diameter		73	.110			5.85		5.85	9.05
5260	1-1/4" diameter		38	.211			11.25		11.25	17.40
5280	1-1/2" diameter		36	.222			11.85		11.85	18.35
5300	2" diameter		26	.308			16.40		16.40	25.50
5320	Offsets, 1/2" diameter		65	.123			6.55		6.55	10.15
5340	3/4" diameter		62	.129			6.90		6.90	10.65
5360	1" diameter		53	.151			8.05		8.05	12.45
5380	1-1/4" diameter		30	.267			14.25		14.25	22
5400	1-1/2" diameter		28	.286			15.25		15.25	23.50
7600	EMT, "T" fittings with covers, 1/2" diameter, set screw		16	.500		9.25	26.50		35.75	51.50
9990	Minimum labor/equipment charge		4	2	Job		107		107	165

26 05 33.16 Outlet Boxes

		Crew	Daily Output	Labor-Hours	Unit	Material	2014 Bare Costs Labor	Equipment	Total	Total Incl O&P
0010	**OUTLET BOXES**									
0020	Pressed steel, octagon, 4"	1 Elec	20	.400	Ea.	3.07	21.50		24.57	36.50
0060	Covers, blank		64	.125		1.29	6.65		7.94	11.70
0100	Extension rings		40	.200		5.10	10.65		15.75	22
0150	Square, 4"		20	.400		2.10	21.50		23.60	35.50
0200	Extension rings		40	.200		5.15	10.65		15.80	22
0250	Covers, blank		64	.125		1.39	6.65		8.04	11.85
0300	Plaster rings		64	.125		2.83	6.65		9.48	13.40
0652	Switchbox		24	.333		4.91	17.80		22.71	33
1100	Concrete, floor, 1 gang		5.30	1.509		89	80.50		169.50	223
9000	Minimum labor/equipment charge		4	2	Job		107		107	165

26 05 33.17 Outlet Boxes, Plastic

		Crew	Daily Output	Labor-Hours	Unit	Material	2014 Bare Costs Labor	Equipment	Total	Total Incl O&P
0010	**OUTLET BOXES, PLASTIC**									
0050	4" diameter, round with 2 mounting nails	1 Elec	25	.320	Ea.	2.57	17.05		19.62	29.50

26 05 33 – Raceway and Boxes for Electrical Systems

26 05 33.17 Outlet Boxes, Plastic

		Crew	Daily Output	Labor-Hours	Unit	Material	2014 Bare Costs Labor	Equipment	Total	Total Incl O&P
0100	Bar hanger mounted	1 Elec	25	.320	Ea.	5.30	17.05		22.35	32.50
0200	4", square with 2 mounting nails		25	.320		4.54	17.05		21.59	31.50
0300	Plaster ring		64	.125		2.02	6.65		8.67	12.50
0400	Switch box with 2 mounting nails, 1 gang		30	.267		4.31	14.25		18.56	26.50
0500	2 gang		25	.320		3.68	17.05		20.73	30.50
0600	3 gang		20	.400		5.80	21.50		27.30	39.50
0700	Old work box		30	.267		6.70	14.25		20.95	29.50
9000	Minimum labor/equipment charge		4	2	Job		107		107	165

26 05 33.18 Pull Boxes

		Crew	Daily Output	Labor-Hours	Unit	Material	2014 Bare Costs Labor	Equipment	Total	Total Incl O&P
0010	**PULL BOXES**									
0100	Sheet metal, pull box, NEMA 1, type SC, 6" W x 6" H x 4" D	1 Elec	8	1	Ea.	10.75	53.50		64.25	94.50
0200	8" W x 8" H x 4" D		8	1		15.30	53.50		68.80	99.50
0300	10" W x 12" H x 6" D		5.30	1.509		29	80.50		109.50	157
0400	16" W x 20" H x 8" D		4	2		86	107		193	260
0500	20" W x 24" H x 8" D		3.20	2.500		97.50	133		230.50	315
0600	24" W x 36" H x 8" D		2.70	2.963		140	158		298	400
0650	Pull box, hinged , NEMA 1, 6" W x 6" H x 4" D		8	1		10.90	53.50		64.40	94.50
0800	12" W x 16" H x 6" D		4.70	1.702		43	91		134	189
1000	20" W x 20" H x 6" D		3.60	2.222		74.50	119		193.50	265
1200	20" W x 20" H x 8" D		3.20	2.500		148	133		281	370
1400	24" W x 36" H x 8" D		2.70	2.963		228	158		386	495
1600	24" W x 42" H x 8" D		2	4		345	213		558	710

26 05 33.23 Wireway

		Crew	Daily Output	Labor-Hours	Unit	Material	2014 Bare Costs Labor	Equipment	Total	Total Incl O&P
0010	**WIREWAY** to 15' high									
0100	NEMA 1, Screw cover w/fittings and supports, 2-1/2" x 2-1/2"	1 Elec	45	.178	L.F.	10.35	9.50		19.85	26
0200	4" x 4"	"	40	.200		11.50	10.65		22.15	29
0400	6" x 6"	2 Elec	60	.267		19.50	14.25		33.75	43.50
0600	8" x 8"	"	40	.400		28	21.50		49.50	64
4475	NEMA 3R, Screw cover w/fittings and supports, 4" x 4"	1 Elec	36	.222		19.45	11.85		31.30	40
4480	6" x 6"	2 Elec	55	.291		26	15.50		41.50	52.50
4485	8" x 8"		36	.444		40	23.50		63.50	80.50
4490	12" x 12"		18	.889		64	47.50		111.50	144

26 05 33.95 Cutting and Drilling

		Crew	Daily Output	Labor-Hours	Unit	Material	2014 Bare Costs Labor	Equipment	Total	Total Incl O&P
0010	**CUTTING AND DRILLING**									
0100	Hole drilling to 10' high, concrete wall									
0110	8" thick, 1/2" pipe size	R-31	12	.667	Ea.	.24	35.50	3.85	39.59	59.50
0120	3/4" pipe size		12	.667		.24	35.50	3.85	39.59	59.50
0130	1" pipe size		9.50	.842		.38	45	4.87	50.25	75.50
0140	1-1/4" pipe size		9.50	.842		.38	45	4.87	50.25	75.50
0150	1-1/2" pipe size		9.50	.842		.38	45	4.87	50.25	75.50
0160	2" pipe size		4.40	1.818		.52	97	10.50	108.02	162
0170	2-1/2" pipe size		4.40	1.818		.52	97	10.50	108.02	162
0180	3" pipe size		4.40	1.818		.52	97	10.50	108.02	162
0190	3-1/2" pipe size		3.30	2.424		.66	129	14	143.66	216
0200	4" pipe size		3.30	2.424		.66	129	14	143.66	216
0500	12" thick, 1/2" pipe size		9.40	.851		.36	45.50	4.92	50.78	76.50
0520	3/4" pipe size		9.40	.851		.36	45.50	4.92	50.78	76.50
0540	1" pipe size		7.30	1.096		.58	58.50	6.35	65.43	98
0560	1-1/4" pipe size		7.30	1.096		.58	58.50	6.35	65.43	98
0570	1-1/2" pipe size		7.30	1.096		.58	58.50	6.35	65.43	98
0580	2" pipe size		3.60	2.222		.78	119	12.85	132.63	198
0590	2-1/2" pipe size		3.60	2.222		.78	119	12.85	132.63	198

26 05 Common Work Results for Electrical

26 05 33 – Raceway and Boxes for Electrical Systems

26 05 33.95 Cutting and Drilling	Crew	Daily Output	Labor-Hours	Unit	Material	2014 Bare Costs Labor	Equipment	Total	Total Incl O&P
0600	3" pipe size	R-31	3.60	2.222	Ea.	.78	119	12.85	132.63	198
0610	3-1/2" pipe size		2.80	2.857		.99	152	16.50	169.49	255
0630	4" pipe size		2.50	3.200		.99	171	18.50	190.49	286
0650	16" thick, 1/2" pipe size		7.60	1.053		.48	56	6.10	62.58	94
0670	3/4" pipe size		7	1.143		.48	61	6.60	68.08	102
0690	1" pipe size		6	1.333		.77	71	7.70	79.47	119
0710	1-1/4" pipe size		5.50	1.455		.77	77.50	8.40	86.67	130
0730	1-1/2" pipe size		5.50	1.455		.77	77.50	8.40	86.67	130
0750	2" pipe size		3	2.667		1.05	142	15.40	158.45	238
0770	2-1/2" pipe size		2.70	2.963		1.05	158	17.15	176.20	265
0790	3" pipe size		2.50	3.200		1.05	171	18.50	190.55	286
0810	3-1/2" pipe size		2.30	3.478		1.32	186	20	207.32	310
0830	4" pipe size		2	4		1.32	213	23	237.32	355
0850	20" thick, 1/2" pipe size		6.40	1.250		.60	66.50	7.25	74.35	112
0870	3/4" pipe size		6	1.333		.60	71	7.70	79.30	119
0890	1" pipe size		5	1.600		.96	85.50	9.25	95.71	143
0910	1-1/4" pipe size		4.80	1.667		.96	89	9.65	99.61	150
0930	1-1/2" pipe size		4.60	1.739		.96	93	10.05	104.01	156
0950	2" pipe size		2.70	2.963		1.31	158	17.15	176.46	265
0970	2-1/2" pipe size		2.40	3.333		1.31	178	19.25	198.56	297
0990	3" pipe size		2.20	3.636		1.31	194	21	216.31	325
1010	3-1/2" pipe size		2	4		1.66	213	23	237.66	355
1030	4" pipe size		1.70	4.706		1.66	251	27	279.66	420
1050	24" thick, 1/2" pipe size		5.50	1.455		.72	77.50	8.40	86.62	130
1070	3/4" pipe size		5.10	1.569		.72	83.50	9.05	93.27	140
1090	1" pipe size		4.30	1.860		1.15	99.50	10.75	111.40	167
1110	1-1/4" pipe size		4	2		1.15	107	11.55	119.70	179
1130	1-1/2" pipe size		4	2		1.15	107	11.55	119.70	179
1150	2" pipe size		2.40	3.333		1.57	178	19.25	198.82	298
1170	2-1/2" pipe size		2.20	3.636		1.57	194	21	216.57	325
1190	3" pipe size		2	4		1.57	213	23	237.57	355
1210	3-1/2" pipe size		1.80	4.444		1.99	237	25.50	264.49	395
1230	4" pipe size		1.50	5.333		1.99	285	31	317.99	475
1500	Brick wall, 8" thick, 1/2" pipe size		18	.444		.24	23.50	2.57	26.31	39.50
1520	3/4" pipe size		18	.444		.24	23.50	2.57	26.31	39.50
1540	1" pipe size		13.30	.602		.38	32	3.48	35.86	53.50
1560	1-1/4" pipe size		13.30	.602		.38	32	3.48	35.86	53.50
1580	1-1/2" pipe size		13.30	.602		.38	32	3.48	35.86	53.50
1600	2" pipe size		5.70	1.404		.52	75	8.10	83.62	125
1620	2-1/2" pipe size		5.70	1.404		.52	75	8.10	83.62	125
1640	3" pipe size		5.70	1.404		.52	75	8.10	83.62	125
1660	3-1/2" pipe size		4.40	1.818		.66	97	10.50	108.16	162
1680	4" pipe size		4	2		.66	107	11.55	119.21	178
1700	12" thick, 1/2" pipe size		14.50	.552		.36	29.50	3.19	33.05	49.50
1720	3/4" pipe size		14.50	.552		.36	29.50	3.19	33.05	49.50
1740	1" pipe size		11	.727		.58	39	4.20	43.78	65.50
1760	1-1/4" pipe size		11	.727		.58	39	4.20	43.78	65.50
1780	1-1/2" pipe size		11	.727		.58	39	4.20	43.78	65.50
1800	2" pipe size		5	1.600		.78	85.50	9.25	95.53	143
1820	2-1/2" pipe size		5	1.600		.78	85.50	9.25	95.53	143
1840	3" pipe size		5	1.600		.78	85.50	9.25	95.53	143
1860	3-1/2" pipe size		3.80	2.105		.99	112	12.15	125.14	188
1880	4" pipe size		3.30	2.424		.99	129	14	143.99	216

468

26 05 33 – Raceway and Boxes for Electrical Systems

26 05 33.95 Cutting and Drilling	Crew	Daily Output	Labor-Hours	Unit	Material	2014 Bare Costs Labor	Equipment	Total	Total Incl O&P
1900	16" thick, 1/2" pipe size	R-31	12.30	.650	Ea.	.48	34.50	3.76	38.74	58
1920	3/4" pipe size		12.30	.650		.48	34.50	3.76	38.74	58
1940	1" pipe size		9.30	.860		.77	46	4.97	51.74	77.50
1960	1-1/4" pipe size		9.30	.860		.77	46	4.97	51.74	77.50
1980	1-1/2" pipe size		9.30	.860		.77	46	4.97	51.74	77.50
2000	2" pipe size		4.40	1.818		1.05	97	10.50	108.55	163
2010	2-1/2" pipe size		4.40	1.818		1.05	97	10.50	108.55	163
2030	3" pipe size		4.40	1.818		1.05	97	10.50	108.55	163
2050	3-1/2" pipe size		3.30	2.424		1.32	129	14	144.32	217
2070	4" pipe size		3	2.667		1.32	142	15.40	158.72	238
2090	20" thick, 1/2" pipe size		10.70	.748		.60	40	4.32	44.92	67
2110	3/4" pipe size		10.70	.748		.60	40	4.32	44.92	67
2130	1" pipe size		8	1		.96	53.50	5.80	60.26	90
2150	1-1/4" pipe size		8	1		.96	53.50	5.80	60.26	90
2170	1-1/2" pipe size		8	1		.96	53.50	5.80	60.26	90
2190	2" pipe size		4	2		1.31	107	11.55	119.86	179
2210	2-1/2" pipe size		4	2		1.31	107	11.55	119.86	179
2230	3" pipe size		4	2		1.31	107	11.55	119.86	179
2250	3-1/2" pipe size		3	2.667		1.66	142	15.40	159.06	239
2270	4" pipe size		2.70	2.963		1.66	158	17.15	176.81	266
2290	24" thick, 1/2" pipe size		9.40	.851		.72	45.50	4.92	51.14	76.50
2310	3/4" pipe size		9.40	.851		.72	45.50	4.92	51.14	76.50
2330	1" pipe size		7.10	1.127		1.15	60	6.50	67.65	101
2350	1-1/4" pipe size		7.10	1.127		1.15	60	6.50	67.65	101
2370	1-1/2" pipe size		7.10	1.127		1.15	60	6.50	67.65	101
2390	2" pipe size		3.60	2.222		1.57	119	12.85	133.42	199
2410	2-1/2" pipe size		3.60	2.222		1.57	119	12.85	133.42	199
2430	3" pipe size		3.60	2.222		1.57	119	12.85	133.42	199
2450	3-1/2" pipe size		2.80	2.857		1.99	152	16.50	170.49	256
2470	4" pipe size		2.50	3.200		1.99	171	18.50	191.49	287
3000	Knockouts to 8' high, metal boxes & enclosures									
3020	With hole saw, 1/2" pipe size	1 Elec	53	.151	Ea.		8.05		8.05	12.45
3040	3/4" pipe size		47	.170			9.10		9.10	14.05
3050	1" pipe size		40	.200			10.65		10.65	16.50
3060	1-1/4" pipe size		36	.222			11.85		11.85	18.35
3070	1-1/2" pipe size		32	.250			13.35		13.35	20.50
3080	2" pipe size		27	.296			15.80		15.80	24.50
3090	2-1/2" pipe size		20	.400			21.50		21.50	33
4010	3" pipe size		16	.500			26.50		26.50	41.50
4030	3-1/2" pipe size		13	.615			33		33	51
4050	4" pipe size		11	.727			39		39	60
4070	With hand punch set, 1/2" pipe size		40	.200			10.65		10.65	16.50
4090	3/4" pipe size		32	.250			13.35		13.35	20.50
4110	1" pipe size		30	.267			14.25		14.25	22
4130	1-1/4" pipe size		28	.286			15.25		15.25	23.50
4150	1-1/2" pipe size		26	.308			16.40		16.40	25.50
4170	2" pipe size		20	.400			21.50		21.50	33
4190	2-1/2" pipe size		17	.471			25		25	39
4200	3" pipe size		15	.533			28.50		28.50	44
4220	3-1/2" pipe size		12	.667			35.50		35.50	55
4240	4" pipe size		10	.800			42.50		42.50	66
4260	With hydraulic punch, 1/2" pipe size		44	.182			9.70		9.70	15
4280	3/4" pipe size		38	.211			11.25		11.25	17.40

26 05 Common Work Results for Electrical

26 05 33 – Raceway and Boxes for Electrical Systems

26 05 33.95 Cutting and Drilling		Crew	Daily Output	Labor-Hours	Unit	Material	2014 Bare Costs Labor	Equipment	Total	Total Incl O&P
4300	1" pipe size	1 Elec	38	.211	Ea.		11.25		11.25	17.40
4320	1-1/4" pipe size		38	.211			11.25		11.25	17.40
4340	1-1/2" pipe size		38	.211			11.25		11.25	17.40
4360	2" pipe size		32	.250			13.35		13.35	20.50
4380	2-1/2" pipe size		27	.296			15.80		15.80	24.50
4400	3" pipe size		23	.348			18.55		18.55	28.50
4420	3-1/2" pipe size		20	.400			21.50		21.50	33

26 05 39 – Underfloor Raceways for Electrical Systems

26 05 39.30 Conduit In Concrete Slab

		Crew	Daily Output	Labor-Hours	Unit	Material	Labor	Equipment	Total	Total Incl O&P
0010	**CONDUIT IN CONCRETE SLAB** Including terminations,									
0020	fittings and supports									
3230	PVC, schedule 40, 1/2" diameter	1 Elec	270	.030	L.F.	.64	1.58		2.22	3.15
3250	3/4" diameter		230	.035		.75	1.86		2.61	3.69
3270	1" diameter		200	.040		.94	2.13		3.07	4.34
3300	1-1/4" diameter		170	.047		1.36	2.51		3.87	5.35
3330	1-1/2" diameter		140	.057		1.63	3.05		4.68	6.50
3350	2" diameter		120	.067		2.07	3.56		5.63	7.75
4350	Rigid galvanized steel, 1/2" diameter		200	.040		2.31	2.13		4.44	5.85
4400	3/4" diameter		170	.047		2.44	2.51		4.95	6.55
4450	1" diameter		130	.062		3.36	3.28		6.64	8.80
4500	1-1/4" diameter		110	.073		4.59	3.88		8.47	11.05
4600	1-1/2" diameter		100	.080		5.15	4.27		9.42	12.25
4800	2" diameter		90	.089		6.40	4.74		11.14	14.40
9000	Minimum labor/equipment charge		4	2	Job		107		107	165

26 05 39.40 Conduit In Trench

		Crew	Daily Output	Labor-Hours	Unit	Material	Labor	Equipment	Total	Total Incl O&P
0010	**CONDUIT IN TRENCH** Includes terminations and fittings									
0020	Does not include excavation or backfill, see Section 31 23 16.00									
0200	Rigid galvanized steel, 2" diameter	1 Elec	150	.053	L.F.	6	2.85		8.85	11
0400	2-1/2" diameter	"	100	.080		11.75	4.27		16.02	19.55
0600	3" diameter	2 Elec	160	.100		13.90	5.35		19.25	23.50
0800	3-1/2" diameter		140	.114		18.35	6.10		24.45	29.50
1000	4" diameter		100	.160		20.50	8.55		29.05	35.50
1200	5" diameter		80	.200		42.50	10.65		53.15	63.50
1400	6" diameter		60	.267		62.50	14.25		76.75	91
9000	Minimum labor/equipment charge	1 Elec	4	2	Job		107		107	165

26 05 80 – Wiring Connections

26 05 80.10 Motor Connections

		Crew	Daily Output	Labor-Hours	Unit	Material	Labor	Equipment	Total	Total Incl O&P
0010	**MOTOR CONNECTIONS**									
0020	Flexible conduit and fittings, 115 volt, 1 phase, up to 1 HP motor	1 Elec	8	1	Ea.	7.25	53.50		60.75	90.50
9000	Minimum labor/equipment charge	"	4	2	Job		107		107	165

26 05 90 – Residential Applications

26 05 90.10 Residential Wiring

		Crew	Daily Output	Labor-Hours	Unit	Material	Labor	Equipment	Total	Total Incl O&P
0010	**RESIDENTIAL WIRING**									
0020	20' avg. runs and #14/2 wiring incl. unless otherwise noted									
1000	Service & panel, includes 24' SE-AL cable, service eye, meter,									
1010	Socket, panel board, main bkr., ground rod, 15 or 20 amp									
1020	1-pole circuit breakers, and misc. hardware									
1100	100 amp, with 10 branch breakers	1 Elec	1.19	6.723	Ea.	540	360		900	1,150
1110	With PVC conduit and wire		.92	8.696		595	465		1,060	1,375
1120	With RGS conduit and wire		.73	10.959		740	585		1,325	1,725
1150	150 amp, with 14 branch breakers		1.03	7.767		840	415		1,255	1,575

470

26 05 90 – Residential Applications

26 05 90.10 Residential Wiring		Crew	Daily Output	Labor-Hours	Unit	Material	2014 Bare Costs Labor	Equipment	Total	Total Incl O&P
1170	With PVC conduit and wire	1 Elec	.82	9.756	Ea.	955	520		1,475	1,850
1180	With RGS conduit and wire	↓	.67	11.940		1,225	635		1,860	2,325
1200	200 amp, with 18 branch breakers	2 Elec	1.80	8.889		1,125	475		1,600	1,950
1220	With PVC conduit and wire	↓	1.46	10.959		1,225	585		1,810	2,250
1230	With RGS conduit and wire	↓	1.24	12.903		1,600	690		2,290	2,825
1800	Lightning surge suppressor	1 Elec	32	.250	↓	50.50	13.35		63.85	76.50
2000	Switch devices									
2100	Single pole, 15 amp, Ivory, with a 1-gang box, cover plate,									
2110	Type NM (Romex) cable	1 Elec	17.10	.468	Ea.	12.30	25		37.30	52
2120	Type MC (BX) cable		14.30	.559		23.50	30		53.50	72
2130	EMT & wire		5.71	1.401		29.50	75		104.50	149
2150	3-way, #14/3, type NM cable		14.55	.550		15.60	29.50		45.10	62.50
2170	Type MC cable		12.31	.650		31	34.50		65.50	87.50
2180	EMT & wire		5	1.600		32.50	85.50		118	168
2200	4-way, #14/3, type NM cable		14.55	.550		22.50	29.50		52	70
2220	Type MC cable		12.31	.650		37.50	34.50		72	95
2230	EMT & wire		5	1.600		39.50	85.50		125	176
2250	S.P., 20 amp, #12/2, type NM cable		13.33	.600		21	32		53	73
2270	Type MC cable		11.43	.700		30	37.50		67.50	91
2280	EMT & wire		4.85	1.649		40	88		128	180
2290	S.P. rotary dimmer, 600W, no wiring		17	.471		27	25		52	68.50
2300	S.P. rotary dimmer, 600W, type NM cable		14.55	.550		32	29.50		61.50	80.50
2320	Type MC cable		12.31	.650		43.50	34.50		78	101
2330	EMT & wire		5	1.600		51	85.50		136.50	188
2350	3-way rotary dimmer, type NM cable		13.33	.600		31.50	32		63.50	84
2370	Type MC cable		11.43	.700		42.50	37.50		80	105
2380	EMT & wire	↓	4.85	1.649	↓	50	88		138	191
2400	Interval timer wall switch, 20 amp, 1-30 min., #12/2									
2410	Type NM cable	1 Elec	14.55	.550	Ea.	54	29.50		83.50	105
2420	Type MC cable	↓	12.31	.650		59	34.50		93.50	119
2430	EMT & wire	↓	5	1.600	↓	73	85.50		158.50	213
2500	Decorator style									
2510	S.P., 15 amp, type NM cable	1 Elec	17.10	.468	Ea.	16.15	25		41.15	56.50
2520	Type MC cable		14.30	.559		27.50	30		57.50	76
2530	EMT & wire		5.71	1.401		33.50	75		108.50	153
2550	3-way, #14/3, type NM cable		14.55	.550		19.40	29.50		48.90	67
2570	Type MC cable		12.31	.650		34.50	34.50		69	91.50
2580	EMT & wire		5	1.600		36.50	85.50		122	172
2600	4-way, #14/3, type NM cable		14.55	.550		26.50	29.50		56	74.50
2620	Type MC cable		12.31	.650		41.50	34.50		76	99
2630	EMT & wire		5	1.600		43	85.50		128.50	180
2650	S.P., 20 amp, #12/2, type NM cable		13.33	.600		25	32		57	77
2670	Type MC cable		11.43	.700		34	37.50		71.50	95
2680	EMT & wire		4.85	1.649		44	88		132	184
2700	S.P., slide dimmer, type NM cable		17.10	.468		32	25		57	74
2720	Type MC cable		14.30	.559		43.50	30		73.50	94
2730	EMT & wire		5.71	1.401		51	75		126	172
2750	S.P., touch dimmer, type NM cable		17.10	.468		29.50	25		54.50	70.50
2770	Type MC cable		14.30	.559		40.50	30		70.50	90.50
2780	EMT & wire		5.71	1.401		48	75		123	169
2800	3-way touch dimmer, type NM cable		13.33	.600		51.50	32		83.50	106
2820	Type MC cable		11.43	.700		63	37.50		100.50	127
2830	EMT & wire	↓	4.85	1.649	↓	70.50	88		158.50	214

26 05 90.10 Residential Wiring	Crew	Daily Output	Labor-Hours	Unit	Material	2014 Bare Costs Labor	2014 Bare Costs Equipment	Total	Total Incl O&P
3000	Combination devices								
3100	S.P. switch/15 amp recpt., Ivory, 1-gang box, plate								
3110	Type NM cable	1 Elec	11.43	.700	Ea.	24	37.50		61.50	84.50
3120	Type MC cable		10	.800		35.50	42.50		78	105
3130	EMT & wire		4.40	1.818		43	97		140	197
3150	S.P. switch/pilot light, type NM cable		11.43	.700		24	37.50		61.50	84.50
3170	Type MC cable		10	.800		35.50	42.50		78	105
3180	EMT & wire		4.43	1.806		43	96.50		139.50	197
3190	2-S.P. switches, 2-#14/2, no wiring		14	.571		6.95	30.50		37.45	54.50
3200	2-S.P. switches, 2-#14/2, type NM cables		10	.800		27.50	42.50		70	96.50
3220	Type MC cable		8.89	.900		44.50	48		92.50	124
3230	EMT & wire		4.10	1.951		46.50	104		150.50	212
3250	3-way switch/15 amp recpt., #14/3, type NM cable		10	.800		31.50	42.50		74	101
3270	Type MC cable		8.89	.900		46.50	48		94.50	126
3280	EMT & wire		4.10	1.951		48	104		152	214
3300	2-3 way switches, 2-#14/3, type NM cables		8.89	.900		41	48		89	120
3320	Type MC cable		8	1		66	53.50		119.50	155
3330	EMT & wire		4	2		56	107		163	227
3350	S.P. switch/20 amp recpt., #12/2, type NM cable		10	.800		32	42.50		74.50	102
3370	Type MC cable		8.89	.900		37	48		85	116
3380	EMT & wire		4.10	1.951		51	104		155	217
3400	Decorator style								
3410	S.P. switch/15 amp recpt., type NM cable	1 Elec	11.43	.700	Ea.	28	37.50		65.50	88.50
3420	Type MC cable		10	.800		39	42.50		81.50	109
3430	EMT & wire		4.40	1.818		46.50	97		143.50	202
3450	S.P. switch/pilot light, type NM cable		11.43	.700		28	37.50		65.50	89
3470	Type MC cable		10	.800		39.50	42.50		82	110
3480	EMT & wire		4.40	1.818		47	97		144	202
3500	2-S.P. switches, 2-#14/2, type NM cables		10	.800		31.50	42.50		74	101
3520	Type MC cable		8.89	.900		48.50	48		96.50	128
3530	EMT & wire		4.10	1.951		50	104		154	216
3550	3-way/15 amp recpt., #14/3, type NM cable		10	.800		35	42.50		77.50	105
3570	Type MC cable		8.89	.900		50.50	48		98.50	130
3580	EMT & wire		4.10	1.951		52	104		156	218
3650	2-3 way switches, 2-#14/3, type NM cables		8.89	.900		45	48		93	124
3670	Type MC cable		8	1		69.50	53.50		123	159
3680	EMT & wire		4	2		59.50	107		166.50	231
3700	S.P. switch/20 amp recpt., #12/2, type NM cable		10	.800		36	42.50		78.50	106
3720	Type MC cable		8.89	.900		41	48		89	120
3730	EMT & wire		4.10	1.951		55	104		159	221
4000	Receptacle devices								
4010	Duplex outlet, 15 amp recpt., Ivory, 1-gang box, plate								
4015	Type NM cable	1 Elec	14.55	.550	Ea.	11	29.50		40.50	57.50
4020	Type MC cable		12.31	.650		22.50	34.50		57	78
4030	EMT & wire		5.33	1.501		28	80		108	155
4050	With #12/2, type NM cable		12.31	.650		13.65	34.50		48.15	68.50
4070	Type MC cable		10.67	.750		22.50	40		62.50	86.50
4080	EMT & wire		4.71	1.699		32.50	90.50		123	176
4100	20 amp recpt., #12/2, type NM cable		12.31	.650		21	34.50		55.50	76.50
4120	Type MC cable		10.67	.750		29.50	40		69.50	94.50
4130	EMT & wire		4.71	1.699		39.50	90.50		130	184
4140	For GFI see Section 26 05 90.10 line 4300 below								
4150	Decorator style, 15 amp recpt., type NM cable	1 Elec	14.55	.550	Ea.	14.80	29.50		44.30	62

26 05 90 – Residential Applications

26 05 90.10 Residential Wiring	Crew	Daily Output	Labor-Hours	Unit	Material	2014 Bare Costs Labor	Equipment	Total	Total Incl O&P
4170	Type MC cable	1 Elec	12.31	.650	Ea.	26	34.50		60.50	82
4180	EMT & wire		5.33	1.501		32	80		112	159
4200	With #12/2, type NM cable		12.31	.650		17.45	34.50		51.95	72.50
4220	Type MC cable		10.67	.750		26	40		66	91
4230	EMT & wire		4.71	1.699		36	90.50		126.50	180
4250	20 amp recpt. #12/2, type NM cable		12.31	.650		24.50	34.50		59	80.50
4270	Type MC cable		10.67	.750		33.50	40		73.50	98.50
4280	EMT & wire		4.71	1.699		43.50	90.50		134	188
4300	GFI, 15 amp recpt., type NM cable		12.31	.650		47.50	34.50		82	106
4320	Type MC cable		10.67	.750		58.50	40		98.50	127
4330	EMT & wire		4.71	1.699		64.50	90.50		155	211
4350	GFI with #12/2, type NM cable		10.67	.750		50	40		90	117
4370	Type MC cable		9.20	.870		58.50	46.50		105	137
4380	EMT & wire		4.21	1.900		68.50	101		169.50	233
4400	20 amp recpt., #12/2 type NM cable		10.67	.750		52	40		92	120
4420	Type MC cable		9.20	.870		61	46.50		107.50	139
4430	EMT & wire		4.21	1.900		71	101		172	235
4500	Weather-proof cover for above receptacles, add	↓	32	.250	↓	4.08	13.35		17.43	25
4550	Air conditioner outlet, 20 amp-240 volt recpt.									
4560	30' of #12/2, 2 pole circuit breaker									
4570	Type NM cable	1 Elec	10	.800	Ea.	63	42.50		105.50	135
4580	Type MC cable		9	.889		73	47.50		120.50	154
4590	EMT & wire		4	2		81.50	107		188.50	255
4600	Decorator style, type NM cable		10	.800		67.50	42.50		110	141
4620	Type MC cable		9	.889		78	47.50		125.50	160
4630	EMT & wire	↓	4	2	↓	86.50	107		193.50	260
4650	Dryer outlet, 30 amp-240 volt recpt., 20' of #10/3									
4660	2 pole circuit breaker									
4670	Type NM cable	1 Elec	6.41	1.248	Ea.	64	66.50		130.50	174
4680	Type MC cable	↓	5.71	1.401		69	75		144	192
4690	EMT & wire	↓	3.48	2.299	↓	75.50	123		198.50	273
4700	Range outlet, 50 amp-240 volt recpt., 30' of #8/3									
4710	Type NM cable	1 Elec	4.21	1.900	Ea.	92	101		193	258
4720	Type MC cable		4	2		136	107		243	315
4730	EMT & wire		2.96	2.703		106	144		250	340
4750	Central vacuum outlet, Type NM cable		6.40	1.250		60	66.50		126.50	169
4770	Type MC cable		5.71	1.401		75.50	75		150.50	199
4780	EMT & wire	↓	3.48	2.299	↓	81.50	123		204.50	280
4800	30 amp-110 volt locking recpt., #10/2 circ. bkr.									
4810	Type NM cable	1 Elec	6.20	1.290	Ea.	69	69		138	183
4820	Type MC cable		5.40	1.481		86.50	79		165.50	217
4830	EMT & wire	↓	3.20	2.500	↓	92	133		225	305
4900	Low voltage outlets									
4910	Telephone recpt., 20' of 4/C phone wire	1 Elec	26	.308	Ea.	10.95	16.40		27.35	37.50
4920	TV recpt., 20' of RG59U coax wire, F type connector	"	16	.500	"	19.20	26.50		45.70	62.50
4950	Door bell chime, transformer, 2 buttons, 60' of bellwire									
4970	Economy model	1 Elec	11.50	.696	Ea.	58	37		95	122
4980	Custom model	↓	11.50	.696		123	37		160	193
4990	Luxury model, 3 buttons	↓	9.50	.842	↓	305	45		350	405
6000	Lighting outlets									
6050	Wire only (for fixture), type NM cable	1 Elec	32	.250	Ea.	7.20	13.35		20.55	28.50
6070	Type MC cable		24	.333		13.85	17.80		31.65	42.50
6080	EMT & wire	↓	10	.800	↓	18.65	42.50		61.15	86.50

26 05 90 – Residential Applications

26 05 90.10 Residential Wiring	Crew	Daily Output	Labor-Hours	Unit	Material	2014 Bare Costs Labor	Equipment	Total	Total Incl O&P
6100 Box (4"), and wire (for fixture), type NM cable	1 Elec	25	.320	Ea.	16.10	17.05		33.15	44.50
6120 Type MC cable		20	.400		23	21.50		44.50	58
6130 EMT & wire		11	.727		27.50	39		66.50	90.50
6200 Fixtures (use with lines 6050 or 6100 above)									
6210 Canopy style, economy grade	1 Elec	40	.200	Ea.	37.50	10.65		48.15	57.50
6220 Custom grade		40	.200		57.50	10.65		68.15	79.50
6250 Dining room chandelier, economy grade		19	.421		93.50	22.50		116	138
6270 Luxury grade		15	.533		620	28.50		648.50	725
6310 Kitchen fixture (fluorescent), economy grade		30	.267		69.50	14.25		83.75	98.50
6320 Custom grade		25	.320		190	17.05		207.05	236
6350 Outdoor, wall mounted, economy grade		30	.267		35.50	14.25		49.75	61
6360 Custom grade		30	.267		121	14.25		135.25	156
6370 Luxury grade		25	.320		274	17.05		291.05	325
6410 Outdoor PAR floodlights, 1 lamp, 150 watt		*20	.400		38	21.50		59.50	75
6420 2 lamp, 150 watt each		20	.400		63	21.50		84.50	102
6425 Motion sensing, 2 lamp, 150 watt each		20	.400		76	21.50		97.50	117
6430 For infrared security sensor, add		32	.250		127	13.35		140.35	161
6450 Outdoor, quartz-halogen, 300 watt flood		20	.400		46	21.50		67.50	83.50
6600 Recessed downlight, round, pre-wired, 50 or 75 watt trim		30	.267		47	14.25		61.25	73.50
6610 With shower light trim		30	.267		58	14.25		72.25	86
6620 With wall washer trim		28	.286		70	15.25		85.25	101
6630 With eye-ball trim		28	.286		70	15.25		85.25	101
6640 For direct contact with insulation, add					2.49			2.49	2.74
6700 Porcelain lamp holder	1 Elec	40	.200		3.50	10.65		14.15	20.50
6710 With pull switch		40	.200		5.70	10.65		16.35	23
6750 Fluorescent strip, 1-20 watt tube, wrap around diffuser, 24"		24	.333		58.50	17.80		76.30	92
6760 1-34 watt tube, 48"		24	.333		75.50	17.80		93.30	111
6770 2-34 watt tubes, 48"		20	.400		89.50	21.50		111	132
6780 With residential ballast		20	.400		100	21.50		121.50	143
6800 Bathroom heat lamp, 1-250 watt		28	.286		51.50	15.25		66.75	80
6810 2-250 watt lamps		28	.286		82	15.25		97.25	114
6820 For timer switch, see Section 26 05 90.10 line 2400									
6900 Outdoor post lamp, incl. post, fixture, 35' of #14/2									
6910 Type NMC cable	1 Elec	3.50	2.286	Ea.	226	122		348	435
6920 Photo-eye, add		27	.296		38	15.80		53.80	66.50
6950 Clock dial time switch, 24 hr., w/enclosure, type NM cable		11.43	.700		70.50	37.50		108	136
6970 Type MC cable		11	.727		82	39		121	150
6980 EMT & wire		4.85	1.649		88	88		176	233
7000 Alarm systems									
7050 Smoke detectors, box, #14/3, type NM cable	1 Elec	14.55	.550	Ea.	35	29.50		64.50	84.50
7070 Type MC cable		12.31	.650		46.50	34.50		81	105
7080 EMT & wire		5	1.600		48.50	85.50		134	185
7090 For relay output to security system, add					14.10			14.10	15.55
8000 Residential equipment									
8050 Disposal hook-up, incl. switch, outlet box, 3' of flex									
8060 20 amp-1 pole circ. bkr., and 25' of #12/2									
8070 Type NM cable	1 Elec	10	.800	Ea.	32.50	42.50		75	102
8080 Type MC cable		8	1		42	53.50		95.50	129
8090 EMT & wire		5	1.600		53.50	85.50		139	191
8100 Trash compactor or dishwasher hook-up, incl. outlet box,									
8110 3' of flex, 15 amp-1 pole circ. bkr., and 25' of #14/2									
8120 Type NM cable	1 Elec	10	.800	Ea.	24	42.50		66.50	92.50
8130 Type MC cable		8	1		37	53.50		90.50	123

26 05 90.10 Residential Wiring	Crew	Daily Output	Labor-Hours	Unit	Material	2014 Bare Costs Labor	Equipment	Total	Total Incl O&P
8140 EMT & wire	1 Elec	5	1.600	Ea.	45	85.50		130.50	182
8150 Hot water sink dispensor hook-up, use line 8100									
8200 Vent/exhaust fan hook-up, type NM cable	1 Elec	32	.250	Ea.	7.20	13.35		20.55	28.50
8220 Type MC cable		24	.333		13.85	17.80		31.65	42.50
8230 EMT & wire	↓	10	.800	↓	18.65	42.50		61.15	86.50
8250 Bathroom vent fan, 50 CFM (use with above hook-up)									
8260 Economy model	1 Elec	15	.533	Ea.	27	28.50		55.50	74
8270 Low noise model		15	.533		37	28.50		65.50	84.50
8280 Custom model	↓	12	.667	↓	127	35.50		162.50	195
8300 Bathroom or kitchen vent fan, 110 CFM									
8310 Economy model	1 Elec	15	.533	Ea.	75.50	28.50		104	127
8320 Low noise model	"	15	.533	"	93.50	28.50		122	147
8350 Paddle fan, variable speed (w/o lights)									
8360 Economy model (AC motor)	1 Elec	10	.800	Ea.	125	42.50		167.50	203
8362 With light kit		10	.800		166	42.50		208.50	248
8370 Custom model (AC motor)		10	.800		197	42.50		239.50	283
8372 With light kit		10	.800		238	42.50		280.50	330
8380 Luxury model (DC motor)		8	1		390	53.50		443.50	515
8382 With light kit		8	1		430	53.50		483.50	560
8390 Remote speed switch for above, add	↓	12	.667	↓	32.50	35.50		68	90.50
8500 Whole house exhaust fan, ceiling mount, 36", variable speed									
8510 Remote switch, incl. shutters, 20 amp-1 pole circ. bkr.									
8520 30' of #12/2, type NM cable	1 Elec	4	2	Ea.	1,250	107		1,357	1,550
8530 Type MC cable		3.50	2.286		1,275	122		1,397	1,600
8540 EMT & wire	↓	3	2.667	↓	1,275	142		1,417	1,625
8600 Whirlpool tub hook-up, incl. timer switch, outlet box									
8610 3' of flex, 20 amp-1 pole GFI circ. bkr.									
8620 30' of #12/2, type NM cable	1 Elec	5	1.600	Ea.	127	85.50		212.50	271
8630 Type MC cable		4.20	1.905		131	102		233	300
8640 EMT & wire	↓	3.40	2.353	↓	141	126		267	350
8650 Hot water heater hook-up, incl. 1-2 pole circ. bkr., box;									
8660 3' of flex, 20' of #10/2, type NM cable	1 Elec	5	1.600	Ea.	34	85.50		119.50	169
8670 Type MC cable		4.20	1.905		47.50	102		149.50	209
8680 EMT & wire	↓	3.40	2.353	↓	48.50	126		174.50	247
9000 Heating/air conditioning									
9050 Furnace/boiler hook-up, incl. firestat, local on-off switch									
9060 Emergency switch, and 40' of type NM cable	1 Elec	4	2	Ea.	52.50	107		159.50	223
9070 Type MC cable		3.50	2.286		69.50	122		191.50	266
9080 EMT & wire	↓	1.50	5.333	↓	81	285		366	530
9100 Air conditioner hook-up, incl. local 60 amp disc. switch									
9110 3' sealtite, 40 amp, 2 pole circuit breaker									
9130 40' of #8/2, type NM cable	1 Elec	3.50	2.286	Ea.	182	122		304	390
9140 Type MC cable		3	2.667		249	142		391	495
9150 EMT & wire	↓	1.30	6.154	↓	218	330		548	750
9200 Heat pump hook-up, 1-40 & 1-100 amp 2 pole circ. bkr.									
9210 Local disconnect switch, 3' sealtite									
9220 40' of #8/2 & 30' of #3/2									
9230 Type NM cable	1 Elec	1.30	6.154	Ea.	525	330		855	1,100
9240 Type MC cable		1.08	7.407		600	395		995	1,275
9250 EMT & wire	↓	.94	8.511	↓	590	455		1,045	1,350
9500 Thermostat hook-up, using low voltage wire									
9520 Heating only, 25' of #18-3	1 Elec	24	.333	Ea.	9.60	17.80		27.40	38
9530 Heating/cooling, 25' of #18-4	"	20	.400	"	11.75	21.50		33.25	46

26 22 Low-Voltage Transformers

26 22 13 – Low-Voltage Distribution Transformers

26 22 13.10 Transformer, Dry-Type

		Crew	Daily Output	Labor-Hours	Unit	Material	2014 Bare Costs Labor	Equipment	Total	Total Incl O&P
0010	**TRANSFORMER, DRY-TYPE**									
0050	Single phase, 240/480 volt primary, 120/240 volt secondary									
0100	1 kVA	1 Elec	2	4	Ea.	285	213		498	645
0300	2 kVA		1.60	5		430	267		697	885
0500	3 kVA		1.40	5.714		530	305		835	1,050
0700	5 kVA		1.20	6.667		730	355		1,085	1,350
0900	7.5 kVA	2 Elec	2.20	7.273		1,025	390		1,415	1,725
1100	10 kVA		1.60	10		1,300	535		1,835	2,250
1300	15 kVA		1.20	13.333		1,475	710		2,185	2,725
2300	3 phase, 480 volt primary 120/208 volt secondary									
2310	Ventilated, 3 kVA	1 Elec	1	8	Ea.	785	425		1,210	1,525
2700	6 kVA		.80	10		895	535		1,430	1,800
2900	9 kVA		.70	11.429		1,025	610		1,635	2,100
3100	15 kVA	2 Elec	1.10	14.545		1,075	775		1,850	2,375
3300	30 kVA		.90	17.778		1,175	950		2,125	2,775
3500	45 kVA		.80	20		1,425	1,075		2,500	3,200
9000	Minimum labor/equipment charge	1 Elec	1	8	Job		425		425	660

26 24 Switchboards and Panelboards

26 24 16 – Panelboards

26 24 16.20 Panelboard and Load Center Circuit Breakers

		Crew	Daily Output	Labor-Hours	Unit	Material	2014 Bare Costs Labor	Equipment	Total	Total Incl O&P
0010	**PANELBOARD AND LOAD CENTER CIRCUIT BREAKERS**									
0050	Bolt-on, 10,000 amp I.C., 120 volt, 1 pole									
0100	15 to 50 amp	1 Elec	10	.800	Ea.	14.40	42.50		56.90	82
0200	60 amp		8	1		18.70	53.50		72.20	103
0300	70 amp		8	1		27.50	53.50		81	113
0350	240 volt, 2 pole									
0400	15 to 50 amp	1 Elec	8	1	Ea.	31.50	53.50		85	118
0500	60 amp		7.50	1.067		42.50	57		99.50	135
0600	80 to 100 amp		5	1.600		81.50	85.50		167	222
0700	3 pole, 15 to 60 amp		6.20	1.290		100	69		169	217
0800	70 amp		5	1.600		126	85.50		211.50	271
0900	80 to 100 amp		3.60	2.222		143	119		262	340
1000	22,000 amp I.C., 240 volt, 2 pole, 70 – 225 amp		2.70	2.963		615	158		773	920
1100	3 pole, 70 – 225 amp		2.30	3.478		685	186		871	1,050
1200	14,000 amp I.C., 277 volts, 1 pole, 15 – 30 amp		8	1		38	53.50		91.50	125
1300	22,000 amp I.C., 480 volts, 2 pole, 70 – 225 amp		2.70	2.963		615	158		773	920
1400	3 pole, 70 – 225 amp		2.30	3.478		760	186		946	1,125
2060	Plug-in tandem, 120/240 V, 2-15 A, 1 pole		11	.727		24.50	39		63.50	87
2070	1-15 A & 1-20 A		11	.727		24.50	39		63.50	87
2080	2-20 A		11	.727		24.50	39		63.50	87
2082	Arc fault circuit interrupter, 120/240 V, 1-15 A & 1-20 A, 1 pole		11	.727		76.50	39		115.50	144
9000	Minimum labor/equipment charge		3	2.667	Job		142		142	220

26 24 16.30 Panelboards Commercial Applications

		Crew	Daily Output	Labor-Hours	Unit	Material	2014 Bare Costs Labor	Equipment	Total	Total Incl O&P
0010	**PANELBOARDS COMMERCIAL APPLICATIONS**									
0050	NQOD, w/20 amp 1 pole bolt-on circuit breakers									
0100	3 wire, 120/240 volts, 100 amp main lugs									
0150	10 circuits	1 Elec	1	8	Ea.	535	425		960	1,250
0200	14 circuits		.88	9.091		655	485		1,140	1,475
0250	18 circuits		.75	10.667		710	570		1,280	1,675
0300	20 circuits		.65	12.308		795	655		1,450	1,900

26 24 Switchboards and Panelboards

26 24 16 – Panelboards

26 24 16.30 Panelboards Commercial Applications	Crew	Daily Output	Labor-Hours	Unit	Material	2014 Bare Costs Labor	Equipment	Total	Total Incl O&P
0600 4 wire, 120/208 volts, 100 amp main lugs, 12 circuits	1 Elec	1	8	Ea.	630	425		1,055	1,350
0650 16 circuits		.75	10.667		725	570		1,295	1,675
0700 20 circuits		.65	12.308		835	655		1,490	1,950
0750 24 circuits		.60	13.333		905	710		1,615	2,100
0800 30 circuits		.53	15.094		1,025	805		1,830	2,400
0850 225 amp main lugs, 32 circuits	2 Elec	.90	17.778		1,150	950		2,100	2,750
0900 34 circuits		.84	19.048		1,200	1,025		2,225	2,875
0950 36 circuits		.80	20		1,225	1,075		2,300	3,000
1000 42 circuits		.68	23.529		1,350	1,250		2,600	3,450
1200 NEHB,w/20 amp, 1 pole bolt-on circuit breakers									
1250 4 wire, 277/480 volts, 100 amp main lugs, 12 circuits	1 Elec	.88	9.091	Ea.	1,225	485		1,710	2,075
1300 20 circuits	"	.60	13.333		1,800	710		2,510	3,075
1350 225 amp main lugs, 24 circuits	2 Elec	.90	17.778		2,050	950		3,000	3,725
1400 30 circuits		.80	20		2,450	1,075		3,525	4,350
1450 36 circuits		.72	22.222		2,850	1,175		4,025	4,950
1600 NQOD panel, w/20 amp, 1 pole, circuit breakers									
2000 4 wire, 120/208 volts with main circuit breaker									
2050 100 amp main, 24 circuits	1 Elec	.47	17.021	Ea.	1,175	910		2,085	2,675
2100 30 circuits	"	.40	20		1,325	1,075		2,400	3,100
2200 225 amp main, 32 circuits	2 Elec	.72	22.222		2,200	1,175		3,375	4,225
2250 42 circuits		.56	28.571		2,400	1,525		3,925	4,975
2300 400 amp main, 42 circuits		.48	33.333		3,225	1,775		5,000	6,300
2350 600 amp main, 42 circuits		.40	40		4,775	2,125		6,900	8,550
2400 NEHB, with 20 amp, 1 pole circuit breaker									
2450 4 wire, 277/480 volts with main circuit breaker									
2500 100 amp main, 24 circuits	1 Elec	.42	19.048	Ea.	2,350	1,025		3,375	4,175
2550 30 circuits	"	.38	21.053		2,750	1,125		3,875	4,775
2600 225 amp main, 30 circuits	2 Elec	.72	22.222		3,475	1,175		4,650	5,625
2650 42 circuits	"	.56	28.571		4,275	1,525		5,800	7,050
9000 Minimum labor/equipment charge	1 Elec	1	8	Job		425		425	660

26 27 Low-Voltage Distribution Equipment

26 27 13 – Electricity Metering

26 27 13.10 Meter Centers and Sockets

		Daily Output	Labor-Hours	Unit	Material	2014 Bare Costs Labor	Equipment	Total	Total Incl O&P
0010 **METER CENTERS AND SOCKETS**									
0100 Sockets, single position, 4 terminal, 100 amp	1 Elec	3.20	2.500	Ea.	42	133		175	252
0200 150 amp		2.30	3.478		54.50	186		240.50	345
0300 200 amp		1.90	4.211		89.50	225		314.50	450
0400 Transformer rated, 20 amp		3.20	2.500		147	133		280	370
0500 Double position, 4 terminal, 100 amp		2.80	2.857		198	152		350	455
0600 150 amp		2.10	3.810		233	203		436	570
0700 200 amp		1.70	4.706		440	251		691	870
1100 Meter centers and sockets, three phase, single pos, 7 terminal, 100 amp		2.80	2.857		144	152		296	395
1200 200 amp		2.10	3.810		278	203		481	620
1400 400 amp		1.70	4.706		715	251		966	1,175
9000 Minimum labor/equipment charge		3	2.667	Job		142		142	220

26 27 Low-Voltage Distribution Equipment

26 27 16 – Electrical Cabinets and Enclosures

26 27 16.10 Cabinets	Crew	Daily Output	Labor-Hours	Unit	Material	2014 Bare Costs Labor	Equipment	Total	Total Incl O&P
0010 **CABINETS**									
7000 Cabinets, current transformer									
7050 Single door, 24" H x 24" W x 10" D	1 Elec	1.60	5	Ea.	178	267		445	610
7100 30" H x 24" W x 10" D		1.30	6.154		166	330		496	695
7150 36" H x 24" W x 10" D		1.10	7.273		186	390		576	805
7200 30" H x 30" W x 10" D		1	8		194	425		619	875
7250 36" H x 30" W x 10" D		.90	8.889		227	475		702	985
7300 36" H x 36" W x 10" D		.80	10		235	535		770	1,075
7500 Double door, 48" H x 36" W x 10" D		.60	13.333		555	710		1,265	1,700
7550 24" H x 24" W x 12" D		1	8		165	425		590	840
9990 Minimum labor/equipment charge		2	4	Job		213		213	330

26 27 23 – Indoor Service Poles

26 27 23.40 Surface Raceway

26 27 23.40 Surface Raceway	Crew	Daily Output	Labor-Hours	Unit	Material	2014 Bare Costs Labor	Equipment	Total	Total Incl O&P
0010 **SURFACE RACEWAY**									
0090 Metal, straight section									
0100 No. 500	1 Elec	100	.080	L.F.	1.04	4.27		5.31	7.75
0110 No. 700		100	.080		1.17	4.27		5.44	7.90
0400 No. 1500, small pancake		90	.089		2.15	4.74		6.89	9.70
0600 No. 2000, base & cover, blank		90	.089		2.19	4.74		6.93	9.75
0800 No. 3000, base & cover, blank		75	.107		4.40	5.70		10.10	13.65
1000 No. 4000, base & cover, blank		65	.123		7.30	6.55		13.85	18.20
1200 No. 6000, base & cover, blank		50	.160		11.40	8.55		19.95	25.50
2400 Fittings, elbows, No. 500		40	.200	Ea.	1.90	10.65		12.55	18.60
2800 Elbow cover, No. 2000		40	.200		3.57	10.65		14.22	20.50
2880 Tee, No. 500		42	.190		3.66	10.15		13.81	19.75
2900 No. 2000		27	.296		11.85	15.80		27.65	37.50
3000 Switch box, No. 500		16	.500		11	26.50		37.50	53.50
3400 Telephone outlet, No. 1500		16	.500		14.10	26.50		40.60	57
3600 Junction box, No. 1500		16	.500		9.65	26.50		36.15	52
3800 Plugmold wired sections, No. 2000									
4000 1 circuit, 6 outlets, 3 ft. long	1 Elec	8	1	Ea.	36	53.50		89.50	122
4100 2 circuits, 8 outlets, 6 ft. long	"	5.30	1.509	"	53	80.50		133.50	184
9300 Non-metallic, straight section									
9310 7/16" x 7/8", base & cover, blank	1 Elec	160	.050	L.F.	1.70	2.67		4.37	6
9320 Base & cover w/adhesive		160	.050		1.42	2.67		4.09	5.70
9340 7/16" x 1-5/16", base & cover, blank		145	.055		1.86	2.94		4.80	6.60
9350 Base & cover w/adhesive		145	.055		2.17	2.94		5.11	6.95
9370 11/16" x 2-1/4", base & cover, blank		130	.062		2.63	3.28		5.91	8
9380 Base & cover w/adhesive		130	.062		3.01	3.28		6.29	8.40
9385 1-11/16" x 5-1/4", two compartment base & cover w/screws		80	.100		7.45	5.35		12.80	16.45
9400 Fittings, elbows, 7/16" x 7/8"		50	.160	Ea.	1.88	8.55		10.43	15.25
9410 7/16" x 1-5/16"		45	.178		1.95	9.50		11.45	16.85
9420 11/16" x 2-1/4"		40	.200		2.11	10.65		12.76	18.80
9425 1-11/16" x 5-1/4"		28	.286		11.05	15.25		26.30	35.50
9430 Tees, 7/16" x 7/8"		35	.229		2.42	12.20		14.62	21.50
9440 7/16" x 1-5/16"		32	.250		2.49	13.35		15.84	23
9450 11/16" x 2-1/4"		30	.267		2.56	14.25		16.81	25
9455 1-11/16" x 5-1/4"		24	.333		17.75	17.80		35.55	47
9460 Cover clip, 7/16" x 7/8"		80	.100		.49	5.35		5.84	8.80
9470 7/16" x 1-5/16"		72	.111		.44	5.95		6.39	9.65
9480 11/16" x 2-1/4"		64	.125		.75	6.65		7.40	11.15
9484 1-11/16" x 5-1/4"		42	.190		2.61	10.15		12.76	18.55

26 27 Low-Voltage Distribution Equipment

26 27 23 – Indoor Service Poles

26 27 23.40 Surface Raceway	Crew	Daily Output	Labor-Hours	Unit	Material	2014 Bare Costs Labor	Equipment	Total	Total Incl O&P
9486	Wire clip, 1-11/16" x 5-1/4"	1 Elec	68	.118	Ea.	.45	6.30		6.75	10.20
9490	Blank end, 7/16" x 7/8"		50	.160		.70	8.55		9.25	13.95
9500	7/16" x 1-5/16"		45	.178		.78	9.50		10.28	15.55
9510	11/16" x 2-1/4"		40	.200		1.18	10.65		11.83	17.80
9515	1-11/16" x 5-1/4"		38	.211		5.45	11.25		16.70	23.50
9520	Round fixture box, 5.5" dia x 1"		25	.320		11.10	17.05		28.15	38.50
9530	Device box, 1 gang		30	.267		5	14.25		19.25	27.50
9540	2 gang		25	.320		7.30	17.05		24.35	34.50
9990	Minimum labor/equipment charge		5	1.600	Job		85.50		85.50	132

26 27 26 – Wiring Devices

26 27 26.20 Wiring Devices Elements

		Crew	Daily Output	Labor-Hours	Unit	Material	2014 Bare Costs Labor	Equipment	Total	Total Incl O&P
0010	**WIRING DEVICES ELEMENTS**									
0200	Toggle switch, quiet type, single pole, 15 amp	1 Elec	40	.200	Ea.	5.70	10.65		16.35	23
0500	20 amp		27	.296		8.80	15.80		24.60	34
0550	Rocker, 15 amp		40	.200		4.84	10.65		15.49	22
0560	20 amp		27	.296		11.20	15.80		27	37
0600	3 way, 15 amp		23	.348		5.95	18.55		24.50	35
0850	Rocker, 15 amp		23	.348		6.80	18.55		25.35	36
0860	20 amp		18	.444		16.10	23.50		39.60	54.50
0900	4 way, 15 amp		15	.533		10.75	28.50		39.25	56
1030	Rocker, 15 amp		15	.533		37	28.50		65.50	85
1040	20 amp		11	.727		39.50	39		78.50	104
1650	Dimmer switch, 120 volt, incandescent, 600 watt, 1 pole [G]		16	.500		18.40	26.50		44.90	61.50
2460	Receptacle, duplex, 120 volt, grounded, 15 amp		40	.200		1.22	10.65		11.87	17.85
2470	20 amp		27	.296		8.35	15.80		24.15	33.50
2480	Ground fault interrupting, 15 amp		27	.296		37.50	15.80		53.30	66
2482	20 amp		27	.296		39.50	15.80		55.30	68
2490	Dryer, 30 amp		15	.533		5.20	28.50		33.70	49.50
2500	Range, 50 amp		11	.727		11.85	39		50.85	73
2600	Wall plates, stainless steel, 1 gang		80	.100		2.53	5.35		7.88	11.05
2800	2 gang		53	.151		4.29	8.05		12.34	17.15
3200	Lampholder, keyless		26	.308		11	16.40		27.40	37.50
3400	Pullchain with receptacle		22	.364		20.50	19.40		39.90	52.50
9000	Minimum labor/equipment charge		4	2	Job		107		107	165

26 27 73 – Door Chimes

26 27 73.10 Doorbell System

		Crew	Daily Output	Labor-Hours	Unit	Material	2014 Bare Costs Labor	Equipment	Total	Total Incl O&P
0010	**DOORBELL SYSTEM**, incl. transformer, button & signal									
1000	Door chimes, 2 notes, minimum	1 Elec	16	.500	Ea.	24.50	26.50		51	68.50
1020	Maximum		12	.667		115	35.50		150.50	181
1100	Tube type, 3 tube system		12	.667		187	35.50		222.50	261
1180	4 tube system		10	.800		385	42.50		427.50	490
1900	For transformer & button, minimum add		5	1.600		16.30	85.50		101.80	150
1960	Maximum, add		4.50	1.778		78	95		173	233
3000	For push button only, minimum		24	.333		3.03	17.80		20.83	31
3100	Maximum		20	.400		21.50	21.50		43	56.50
9000	Minimum labor/equipment charge		4	2	Job		107		107	165

26 28 16 – Enclosed Switches and Circuit Breakers

26 28 16.10 Circuit Breakers

		Daily Output	Labor-Hours	Unit	Material	2014 Bare Costs Labor	Equipment	Total	Total Incl O&P
0010	**CIRCUIT BREAKERS** (in enclosure)	Crew							
0100	Enclosed (NEMA 1), 600 volt, 3 pole, 30 amp	1 Elec	3.20	2.500	Ea.	495	133		628	750
0200	60 amp		2.80	2.857		610	152		762	905
0400	100 amp		2.30	3.478		700	186		886	1,050
0500	200 amp		1.50	5.333		1,475	285		1,760	2,075
0600	225 amp		1.50	5.333		1,625	285		1,910	2,225
0700	400 amp	2 Elec	1.60	10		2,750	535		3,285	3,850
9000	Minimum labor/equipment charge	1 Elec	4	2	Job		107		107	165

26 28 16.20 Safety Switches

		Crew	Daily Output	Labor-Hours	Unit	Material	Labor	Equipment	Total	Total Incl O&P
0010	**SAFETY SWITCHES**									
0100	General duty 240 volt, 3 pole NEMA 1, fusible, 30 amp	1 Elec	3.20	2.500	Ea.	86	133		219	300
0200	60 amp		2.30	3.478		146	186		332	450
0300	100 amp		1.90	4.211		250	225		475	625
0400	200 amp		1.30	6.154		535	330		865	1,100
0500	400 amp	2 Elec	1.80	8.889		1,350	475		1,825	2,225
9990	Minimum labor/equipment charge	1 Elec	3	2.667	Job		142		142	220

26 28 16.40 Time Switches

		Crew	Daily Output	Labor-Hours	Unit	Material	Labor	Equipment	Total	Total Incl O&P
0010	**TIME SWITCHES**									
0100	Single pole, single throw, 24 hour dial	1 Elec	4	2	Ea.	138	107		245	315
0200	24 hour dial with reserve power		3.60	2.222		585	119		704	830
0300	Astronomic dial		3.60	2.222		180	119		299	380
0400	Astronomic dial with reserve power		3.30	2.424		665	129		794	930
0500	7 day calendar dial		3.30	2.424		158	129		287	375
0600	7 day calendar dial with reserve power		3.20	2.500		395	133		528	640
0700	Photo cell 2000 watt		8	1		27	53.50		80.50	113
1080	Load management device, 4 loads		2	4		870	213		1,083	1,300
1100	8 loads		1	8		2,200	425		2,625	3,075
9000	Minimum labor/equipment charge		3.50	2.286	Job		122		122	189

26 29 13 – Enclosed Controllers

26 29 13.40 Relays

		Crew	Daily Output	Labor-Hours	Unit	Material	Labor	Equipment	Total	Total Incl O&P
0010	**RELAYS** Enclosed (NEMA 1)									
0050	600 volt AC, 1 pole, 12 amp	1 Elec	5.30	1.509	Ea.	87.50	80.50		168	221
0100	2 pole, 12 amp		5	1.600		87.50	85.50		173	228
0200	4 pole, 10 amp		4.50	1.778		116	95		211	275

26 29 23 – Variable-Frequency Motor Controllers

26 29 23.10 Variable Frequency Drives/Adj. Frequency Drives

			Crew	Daily Output	Labor-Hours	Unit	Material	Labor	Equipment	Total	Total Incl O&P
0010	**VARIABLE FREQUENCY DRIVES/ADJ. FREQUENCY DRIVES**										
0100	Enclosed (NEMA 1), 460 volt, for 3 HP motor size	G	1 Elec	.80	10	Ea.	1,475	535		2,010	2,450
0110	5 HP motor size	G		.80	10		1,675	535		2,210	2,650
0120	7.5 HP motor size	G		.67	11.940		2,000	635		2,635	3,175
0130	10 HP motor size	G		.67	11.940		2,325	635		2,960	3,525
0140	15 HP motor size	G	2 Elec	.89	17.978		2,825	960		3,785	4,575
0150	20 HP motor size	G		.89	17.978		3,325	960		4,285	5,125
0160	25 HP motor size	G		.67	23.881		4,100	1,275		5,375	6,475
0170	30 HP motor size	G		.67	23.881		5,100	1,275		6,375	7,600
0180	40 HP motor size	G		.67	23.881		6,125	1,275		7,400	8,725
0190	50 HP motor size	G		.53	30.189		7,575	1,600		9,175	10,800
0200	60 HP motor size	G	R-3	.56	35.714		9,125	1,900	250	11,275	13,200

26 29 Low-Voltage Controllers

26 29 23 – Variable-Frequency Motor Controllers

26 29 23.10 Variable Frequency Drives/Adj. Frequency Drives		Crew	Daily Output	Labor-Hours	Unit	Material	2014 Bare Costs Labor	Equipment	Total	Total Incl O&P
0210	75 HP motor size [G]	R-3	.56	35.714	Ea.	10,500	1,900	250	12,650	14,800
0220	100 HP motor size [G]		.50	40		12,200	2,125	280	14,605	17,000
0230	125 HP motor size [G]		.50	40		13,600	2,125	280	16,005	18,600
0240	150 HP motor size [G]		.50	40		15,600	2,125	280	18,005	20,800
0250	200 HP motor size [G]		.42	47.619		20,300	2,525	335	23,160	26,600
1100	Custom-engineered, 460 volt, for 3 HP motor size [G]	1 Elec	.56	14.286		2,700	760		3,460	4,150
1110	5 HP motor size [G]		.56	14.286		2,700	760		3,460	4,150
1120	7.5 HP motor size [G]		.47	17.021		2,825	910		3,735	4,525
1130	10 HP motor size [G]		.47	17.021		2,975	910		3,885	4,675
1140	15 HP motor size [G]	2 Elec	.62	25.806		3,725	1,375		5,100	6,200
1150	20 HP motor size [G]		.62	25.806		4,175	1,375		5,550	6,725
1160	25 HP motor size [G]		.47	34.043		4,900	1,825		6,725	8,175
1170	30 HP motor size [G]		.47	34.043		6,100	1,825		7,925	9,525
1180	40 HP motor size [G]		.47	34.043		7,225	1,825		9,050	10,800
1190	50 HP motor size [G]		.37	43.243		8,300	2,300		10,600	12,700
1200	60 HP motor size [G]	R-3	.39	51.282		12,500	2,725	360	15,585	18,400
1210	75 HP motor size [G]		.39	51.282		13,300	2,725	360	16,385	19,200
1220	100 HP motor size [G]		.35	57.143		14,600	3,025	400	18,025	21,100
1230	125 HP motor size [G]		.35	57.143		15,600	3,025	400	19,025	22,200
1240	150 HP motor size [G]		.35	57.143		17,800	3,025	400	21,225	24,700
1250	200 HP motor size [G]		.29	68.966		23,300	3,650	485	27,435	31,800
2000	For complex & special design systems to meet specific									
2010	requirements, obtain quote from vendor.									

26 32 Packaged Generator Assemblies

26 32 13 – Engine Generators

26 32 13.16 Gas-Engine-Driven Generator Sets

		Crew	Daily Output	Labor-Hours	Unit	Material	Labor	Equipment	Total	Total Incl O&P
0010	**GAS-ENGINE-DRIVEN GENERATOR SETS**									
0020	Gas or gasoline operated, includes battery,									
0050	charger, & muffler									
0200	3 phase 4 wire, 277/480 volt, 7.5 kW	R-3	.83	24.096	Ea.	7,275	1,275	169	8,719	10,200
0300	11.5 kW		.71	28.169		10,300	1,500	197	11,997	13,800
0400	20 kW		.63	31.746		12,200	1,675	222	14,097	16,200
0500	35 kW		.55	36.364		14,500	1,925	255	16,680	19,200

26 51 Interior Lighting

26 51 13 – Interior Lighting Fixtures, Lamps, and Ballasts

26 51 13.50 Interior Lighting Fixtures

			Crew	Daily Output	Labor-Hours	Unit	Material	Labor	Equipment	Total	Total Incl O&P
0010	**INTERIOR LIGHTING FIXTURES** Including lamps, mounting										
0030	hardware and connections										
0100	Fluorescent, C.W. lamps, troffer, recess mounted in grid, RS										
0130	Grid ceiling mount										
0200	Acrylic lens, 1'W x 4'L, two 40 watt		1 Elec	5.70	1.404	Ea.	47.50	75		122.50	168
0300	2'W x 2'L, two U40 watt			5.70	1.404		51	75		126	173
0600	2'W x 4'L, four 40 watt			4.70	1.702		57.50	91		148.50	205
0910	Acrylic lens, 1'W x 4'L, two 32 watt T8 [G]			5.70	1.404		52	75		127	173
0930	2'W x 2'L, two U32 watt T8 [G]			5.70	1.404		70.50	75		145.50	194
0940	2'W x 4'L, two 32 watt T8 [G]			5.30	1.509		58	80.50		138.50	189
0950	2'W x 4'L, three 32 watt T8 [G]			5	1.600		59	85.50		144.50	197

26 51 Interior Lighting

26 51 13 – Interior Lighting Fixtures, Lamps, and Ballasts

26 51 13.50 Interior Lighting Fixtures		Crew	Daily Output	Labor-Hours	Unit	Material	2014 Bare Costs Labor	Equipment	Total	Total Incl O&P
0960	2'W x 4'L, four 32 watt T8 **G**	1 Elec	4.70	1.702	Ea.	64.50	91		155.50	212
1000	Surface mounted, RS									
1030	Acrylic lens with hinged & latched door frame									
1100	1'W x 4'L, two 40 watt	1 Elec	7	1.143	Ea.	63.50	61		124.50	165
1200	2'W x 2'L, two U40 watt		7	1.143		68	61		129	170
1500	2'W x 4'L, four 40 watt		5.30	1.509		81	80.50		161.50	214
2100	Strip fixture									
2130	Surface mounted									
2200	4' long, one 40 watt, RS	1 Elec	8.50	.941	Ea.	27.50	50		77.50	108
2300	4' long, two 40 watt, RS	"	8	1		38.50	53.50		92	125
2600	8' long, one 75 watt, SL	2 Elec	13.40	1.194		47.50	63.50		111	151
2700	8' long, two 75 watt, SL	"	12.40	1.290		57.50	69		126.50	170
3000	Strip, pendent mounted, industrial, white porcelain enamel									
3100	4' long, two 40 watt, RS	1 Elec	5.70	1.404	Ea.	52.50	75		127.50	174
3200	4' long, two 60 watt, HO	"	5	1.600		82	85.50		167.50	222
3300	8' long, two 75 watt, SL	2 Elec	8.80	1.818		97	97		194	257
4220	Metal halide, integral ballast, ceiling, recess mounted									
4230	prismatic glass lens, floating door									
4240	2'W x 2'L, 250 watt	1 Elec	3.20	2.500	Ea.	315	133		448	550
4250	2'W x 2'L, 400 watt	2 Elec	5.80	2.759		360	147		507	630
4260	Surface mounted, 2'W x 2'L, 250 watt	1 Elec	2.70	2.963		340	158		498	620
4270	400 watt	2 Elec	4.80	3.333		400	178		578	715
4280	High bay, aluminum reflector,									
4290	Single unit, 400 watt	2 Elec	4.60	3.478	Ea.	405	186		591	735
4300	Single unit, 1000 watt		4	4		585	213		798	975
4310	Twin unit, 400 watt		3.20	5		815	267		1,082	1,300
4320	Low bay, aluminum reflector, 250W DX lamp	1 Elec	3.20	2.500		360	133		493	600
4340	High pressure sodium integral ballast ceiling, recess mounted									
4350	prismatic glass lens, floating door									
4360	2'W x 2'L, 150 watt lamp	1 Elec	3.20	2.500	Ea.	380	133		513	625
4370	2'W x 2'L, 400 watt lamp	2 Elec	5.80	2.759		455	147		602	730
4380	Surface mounted, 2'W x 2'L, 150 watt lamp	1 Elec	2.70	2.963		465	158		623	760
4390	400 watt lamp	2 Elec	4.80	3.333		520	178		698	850
4400	High bay, aluminum reflector,									
4410	Single unit, 400 watt lamp	2 Elec	4.60	3.478	Ea.	375	186		561	700
4430	Single unit, 1000 watt lamp	"	4	4		540	213		753	925
4440	Low bay, aluminum reflector, 150 watt lamp	1 Elec	3.20	2.500		325	133		458	560
4450	Incandescent, high hat can, round alzak reflector, prewired									
4470	100 watt	1 Elec	8	1	Ea.	70.50	53.50		124	161
4480	150 watt		8	1		103	53.50		156.50	196
4500	300 watt		6.70	1.194		238	63.50		301.50	360
4600	Square glass lens with metal trim, prewired									
4630	100 watt	1 Elec	6.70	1.194	Ea.	54.50	63.50		118	159
4700	200 watt		6.70	1.194		96	63.50		159.50	205
6010	Vapor tight, incandescent, ceiling mounted, 200 watt		6.20	1.290		81.50	69		150.50	197
6100	Fluorescent, surface mounted, 2 lamps, 4'L, RS, 40 watt		3.20	2.500		114	133		247	330
6850	Vandalproof, surface mounted, fluorescent, two 32 watt T8 **G**		3.20	2.500		250	133		383	480
6860	Incandescent, one 150 watt		8	1		85	53.50		138.50	176
6900	Mirror light, fluorescent, RS, acrylic enclosure, two 40 watt		8	1		126	53.50		179.50	222
6910	One 40 watt		8	1		105	53.50		158.50	198
6920	One 20 watt		12	.667		81	35.50		116.50	144
7500	Ballast replacement, by weight of ballast, to 15' high									
7520	Indoor fluorescent, less than 2 lb.	1 Elec	10	.800	Ea.	26	42.50		68.50	94.50

26 51 Interior Lighting

26 51 13 – Interior Lighting Fixtures, Lamps, and Ballasts

26 51 13.50 Interior Lighting Fixtures		Crew	Daily Output	Labor-Hours	Unit	Material	2014 Bare Costs Labor	Equipment	Total	Total Incl O&P
7540	Two 40W, watt reducer, 2 to 5 lb.	1 Elec	9.40	.851	Ea.	41	45.50		86.50	116
7560	Two F96 slimline, over 5 lb.		8	1		76	53.50		129.50	166
7580	Vaportite ballast, less than 2 lb.		9.40	.851		26	45.50		71.50	99
7600	2 lb. to 5 lb.		8.90	.899		41	48		89	119
7620	Over 5 lb.		7.60	1.053		76	56		132	171
7630	Electronic ballast for two tubes		8	1		37	53.50		90.50	123
7640	Dimmable ballast one lamp [G]		8	1		105	53.50		158.50	199
7650	Dimmable ballast two-lamp [G]		7.60	1.053		103	56		159	200
9000	Minimum labor/equipment charge		3	2.667	Job		142		142	220

26 51 13.70 Residential Fixtures

26 51 13.70 Residential Fixtures		Crew	Daily Output	Labor-Hours	Unit	Material	2014 Bare Costs Labor	Equipment	Total	Total Incl O&P
0010	**RESIDENTIAL FIXTURES**									
0400	Fluorescent, interior, surface, circline, 32 watt & 40 watt	1 Elec	20	.400	Ea.	118	21.50		139.50	162
0700	Shallow under cabinet, two 20 watt		16	.500		54.50	26.50		81	101
0900	Wall mounted, 4'L, two 32 watt T8, with baffle		10	.800		137	42.50		179.50	217
2000	Incandescent, exterior lantern, wall mounted, 60 watt		16	.500		48	26.50		74.50	94.50
2100	Post light, 150W, with 7' post		4	2		238	107		345	425
2500	Lamp holder, weatherproof with 150W PAR		16	.500		32	26.50		58.50	76.50
2550	With reflector and guard		12	.667		56	35.50		91.50	117
2600	Interior pendent, globe with shade, 150 watt		20	.400		191	21.50		212.50	243
9000	Minimum labor/equipment charge		4	2	Job		107		107	165

26 52 Emergency Lighting

26 52 13 – Emergency Lighting Equipments

26 52 13.10 Emergency Lighting and Battery Units		Crew	Daily Output	Labor-Hours	Unit	Material	2014 Bare Costs Labor	Equipment	Total	Total Incl O&P
0010	**EMERGENCY LIGHTING AND BATTERY UNITS**									
0300	Emergency light units, battery operated									
0350	Twin sealed beam light, 25 watt, 6 volt each									
0500	Lead battery operated	1 Elec	4	2	Ea.	143	107		250	325
0700	Nickel cadmium battery operated		4	2	"	660	107		767	890
9000	Minimum labor/equipment charge		4	2	Job		107		107	165

26 53 Exit Signs

26 53 13 – Exit Lighting

26 53 13.10 Exit Lighting Fixtures		Crew	Daily Output	Labor-Hours	Unit	Material	2014 Bare Costs Labor	Equipment	Total	Total Incl O&P
0010	**EXIT LIGHTING FIXTURES**									
0080	Exit light ceiling or wall mount, incandescent, single face	1 Elec	8	1	Ea.	39	53.50		92.50	125
0100	Double face		6.70	1.194	"	39	63.50		102.50	141
9000	Minimum labor/equipment charge		4	2	Job		107		107	165

26 55 Special Purpose Lighting

26 55 59 – Display Lighting

26 55 59.10 Track Lighting		Crew	Daily Output	Labor-Hours	Unit	Material	2014 Bare Costs Labor	2014 Bare Costs Equipment	Total	Total Incl O&P
0010	**TRACK LIGHTING**									
0080	Track, 1 circuit, 4' section	1 Elec	6.70	1.194	Ea.	48	63.50		111.50	152
0100	8' section	2 Elec	10.60	1.509		74.50	80.50		155	207
0300	3 circuits, 4' section	1 Elec	6.70	1.194		87	63.50		150.50	194
0400	8' section	2 Elec	10.60	1.509	↓	109	80.50		189.50	245
9000	Minimum labor/equipment charge	1 Elec	3	2.667	Job		142		142	220

26 56 Exterior Lighting

26 56 23 – Area Lighting

26 56 23.10 Exterior Fixtures

		Crew	Daily Output	Labor-Hours	Unit	Material	2014 Bare Costs Labor	2014 Bare Costs Equipment	Total	Total Incl O&P
0010	**EXTERIOR FIXTURES** With lamps									
0200	Wall mounted, incandescent, 100 watt	1 Elec	8	1	Ea.	34.50	53.50		88	121
0400	Quartz, 500 watt		5.30	1.509		49.50	80.50		130	180
1100	Wall pack, low pressure sodium, 35 watt		4	2		225	107		332	415
1150	55 watt		4	2		268	107		375	460
1160	High pressure sodium, 70 watt		4	2		221	107		328	410
1170	150 watt		4	2		242	107		349	430
1180	Metal Halide, 175 watt		4	2		245	107		352	435
1190	250 watt		4	2		279	107		386	470
1195	400 watt		4	2		330	107		437	530
1250	Induction lamp, 40 watt		4	2		340	107		447	540
1260	80 watt		4	2		575	107		682	800
1278	LED, poly lens, 26 watt		4	2		325	107		432	525
1280	110 watt		4	2		1,300	107		1,407	1,600
1500	LED, glass lens, 13 watt		4	2		325	107		432	525

26 56 33 – Walkway Lighting

26 56 33.10 Walkway Luminaire

		Crew	Daily Output	Labor-Hours	Unit	Material	2014 Bare Costs Labor	2014 Bare Costs Equipment	Total	Total Incl O&P
0010	**WALKWAY LUMINAIRE**									
9000	Minimum labor/equipment charge	1 Elec	3.75	2.133	Job		114		114	176

26 56 36 – Flood Lighting

26 56 36.20 Floodlights

		Crew	Daily Output	Labor-Hours	Unit	Material	2014 Bare Costs Labor	2014 Bare Costs Equipment	Total	Total Incl O&P
0010	**FLOODLIGHTS** with ballast and lamp,									
1290	floor mtd, mount with swivel bracket									
1400	Pole mounted, pole not included									
2250	Low pressure sodium, 55 watt	1 Elec	2.70	2.963	Ea.	580	158		738	880
2270	90 watt	"	2	4	"	640	213		853	1,025

26 61 Lighting Systems and Accessories

26 61 23 – Lamps Applications

26 61 23.10 Lamps

		Crew	Daily Output	Labor-Hours	Unit	Material	2014 Bare Costs Labor	2014 Bare Costs Equipment	Total	Total Incl O&P
0010	**LAMPS**									
0080	Fluorescent, rapid start, cool white, 2' long, 20 watt	1 Elec	1	8	C	310	425		735	1,000
0100	4' long, 40 watt		.90	8.889		236	475		711	995
0170	4' long, 34 watt energy saver [G]		.90	8.889		425	475		900	1,200
0176	2' long, T8, 17 W energy saver [G]		1	8		390	425		815	1,100
0178	3' long, T8, 25 W energy saver [G]		.90	8.889		415	475		890	1,200
0180	4' long, T8, 32 watt energy saver [G]		.90	8.889		365	475		840	1,125
0560	Twin tube compact lamp [G]		.90	8.889		425	475		900	1,200

26 61 23 – Lamps Applications

26 61 23.10 Lamps		Crew	Daily Output	Labor-Hours	Unit	Material	2014 Bare Costs Labor	2014 Bare Costs Equipment	Total	Total Incl O&P
0570	Double twin tube compact lamp [G]	1 Elec	.80	10	C	945	535		1,480	1,875
0600	Mercury vapor, mogul base, deluxe white, 100 watt		.30	26.667		3,650	1,425		5,075	6,225
0800	400 watt		.30	26.667		5,100	1,425		6,525	7,800
1000	Metal halide, mogul base, 175 watt		.30	26.667		3,000	1,425		4,425	5,500
1100	250 watt		.30	26.667		3,400	1,425		4,825	5,950
1350	High pressure sodium, 70 watt		.30	26.667		3,650	1,425		5,075	6,225
1370	150 watt		.30	26.667		3,925	1,425		5,350	6,525
1500	Low pressure sodium, 35 watt		.30	26.667		12,000	1,425		13,425	15,400
1600	90 watt		.30	26.667		13,300	1,425		14,725	16,800
1800	Incandescent, interior, A21, 100 watt		1.60	5		233	267		500	670
1900	A21, 150 watt		1.60	5		166	267		433	600
2300	R30, 75 watt		1.30	6.154		610	330		940	1,175
2500	Exterior, PAR 38, 75 watt		1.30	6.154		1,850	330		2,180	2,550
2600	PAR 38, 150 watt		1.30	6.154		2,000	330		2,330	2,700
9000	Minimum labor/equipment charge		4	2	Job		107		107	165

Division Notes

	CREW	DAILY OUTPUT	LABOR-HOURS	UNIT	BARE COSTS				TOTAL INCL O&P
					MAT.	LABOR	EQUIP.	TOTAL	

Estimating Tips

27 20 00 Data Communications
27 30 00 Voice Communications
27 40 00 Audio-Video Communications

When estimating material costs for special systems, it is always prudent to obtain manufacturers' quotations for equipment prices and special installation requirements which will affect the total costs.

Reference Numbers

Reference numbers are shown in shaded boxes at the beginning of some major classifications. These numbers refer to related items in the Reference Section. The reference information may be an estimating procedure, an alternate pricing method, or technical information.

Note: Not all subdivisions listed here necessarily appear in this publication.

Note: **Trade Service,** *in part, has been used as a reference source for some of the material prices used in Division 27.*

27 15 Communications Horizontal Cabling

27 15 10 – Special Communications Cabling

27 15 10.23 Sound and Video Cables and Fittings	Crew	Daily Output	Labor-Hours	Unit	Material	2014 Bare Costs Labor	Equipment	Total	Total Incl O&P
0010 **SOUND AND VIDEO CABLES & FITTINGS**									
1250 Nonshielded, #22-2 conductor	1 Elec	10	.800	C.L.F.	14.25	42.50		56.75	81.50

27 15 13 – Communications Copper Horizontal Cabling

27 15 13.13 Communication Cables

	Crew	Daily Output	Labor-Hours	Unit	Material	2014 Bare Costs Labor	Equipment	Total	Total Incl O&P
0010 **COMMUNICATION CABLES**									
5000 High performance unshielded twisted pair (UTP)									
7000 Category 5, #24, 4 pair solid, PVC jacket	1 Elec	7	1.143	C.L.F.	14.80	61		75.80	111
7100 4 pair solid, plenum		7	1.143		45.50	61		106.50	145
7200 4 pair stranded, PVC jacket		7	1.143		22	61		83	119
7210 Category 5e, #24, 4 pair solid, PVC jacket		7	1.143		14.15	61		75.15	110
7212 4 pair solid, plenum		7	1.143		23.50	61		84.50	121
7214 4 pair stranded, PVC jacket		7	1.143		25.50	61		86.50	123
7240 Category 6, #24, 4 pair solid, PVC jacket		7	1.143		20.50	61		81.50	117
7242 4 pair solid, plenum		7	1.143		24.50	61		85.50	122
7244 4 pair stranded, PVC jacket		7	1.143		25.50	61		86.50	123
7300 Connector, RJ-45, category 5		80	.100	Ea.	1.32	5.35		6.67	9.70
7302 Shielded RJ-45, category 5		72	.111		3.36	5.95		9.31	12.85
7310 Jack, UTP RJ-45, category 3		72	.111		2.33	5.95		8.28	11.70
7312 Category 5		65	.123		5	6.55		11.55	15.65
7314 Category 5e		65	.123		3.26	6.55		9.81	13.75
7316 Category 6		65	.123		3.31	6.55		9.86	13.80

27 41 Audio-Video Systems

27 41 33 – Master Antenna Television Systems

27 41 33.10 T.V. Systems

	Crew	Daily Output	Labor-Hours	Unit	Material	2014 Bare Costs Labor	Equipment	Total	Total Incl O&P
0010 **T.V. SYSTEMS**, not including rough-in wires, cables & conduits									
5000 T.V. Antenna, minimum	1 Elec	6	1.333	Ea.	46.50	71		117.50	161
5100 Maximum	"	4	2	"	196	107		303	380

27 51 Distributed Audio-Video Communications Systems

27 51 16 – Public Address and Mass Notification Systems

27 51 16.10 Public Address System

	Crew	Daily Output	Labor-Hours	Unit	Material	2014 Bare Costs Labor	Equipment	Total	Total Incl O&P
0010 **PUBLIC ADDRESS SYSTEM**									
0100 Conventional, office	1 Elec	5.33	1.501	Speaker	134	80		214	271
0200 Industrial		2.70	2.963	"	258	158		416	530
9000 Minimum labor/equipment charge		3.50	2.286	Job		122		122	189

27 51 19 – Sound Masking Systems

27 51 19.10 Sound System

	Crew	Daily Output	Labor-Hours	Unit	Material	2014 Bare Costs Labor	Equipment	Total	Total Incl O&P
0010 **SOUND SYSTEM**, not including rough-in wires, cables & conduits									
2000 Intercom, 30 station capacity, master station	2 Elec	2	8	Ea.	2,300	425		2,725	3,175
2020 10 station capacity	"	4	4		1,275	213		1,488	1,725
3600 House telephone, talking station	1 Elec	1.60	5		460	267		727	925
3800 Press to talk, release to listen	"	5.30	1.509		108	80.50		188.50	243
4000 System-on button					64.50			64.50	71
4200 Door release	1 Elec	4	2		115	107		222	292
4400 Combination speaker and microphone		8	1		196	53.50		249.50	299
4600 Termination box		3.20	2.500		61.50	133		194.50	274
4800 Amplifier or power supply		5.30	1.509		710	80.50		790.50	905

27 51 19 – Sound Masking Systems

27 51 19.10 Sound System		Crew	Daily Output	Labor-Hours	Unit	Material	2014 Bare Costs Labor	Equipment	Total	Total Incl O&P
5000	Vestibule door unit	1 Elec	16	.500	Name	130	26.50		156.50	185
5200	Strip cabinet		27	.296	Ea.	246	15.80		261.80	296
5400	Directory		16	.500	"	116	26.50		142.50	169
9000	Minimum labor/equipment charge	↓	3.50	2.286	Job		122		122	189

Division Notes

	CREW	DAILY OUTPUT	LABOR-HOURS	UNIT	BARE COSTS				TOTAL INCL O&P
					MAT.	LABOR	EQUIP.	TOTAL	

Estimating Tips

- When estimating material costs for electronic safety and security systems, it is always prudent to obtain manufacturers' quotations for equipment prices and special installation requirements that affect the total cost.
- Fire alarm systems consist of control panels, annunciator panels, battery with rack, charger, and fire alarm actuating and indicating devices. Some fire alarm systems include speakers, telephone lines, door closer controls, and other components. Be careful not to overlook the costs related to installation for these items.

Also be aware of costs for integrated automation instrumentation and terminal devices, control equipment, control wiring, and programming.

- Security equipment includes items such as CCTV, access control, and other detection and identification systems to perform alert and alarm functions. Be sure to consider the costs related to installation for this security equipment, such as for integrated automation instrumentation and terminal devices, control equipment, control wiring, and programming.

Reference Numbers

Reference numbers are shown in shaded boxes at the beginning of some major classifications. These numbers refer to related items in the Reference Section. The reference information may be an estimating procedure, an alternate pricing method, or technical information.

Note: Not all subdivisions listed here necessarily appear in this publication.

Division 28 – Electronic Safety and Security

28 13 Access Control

28 13 53 – Security Access Detection

28 13 53.13 Security Access Metal Detectors	Crew	Daily Output	Labor-Hours	Unit	Material	2014 Bare Costs Labor	Equipment	Total	Total Incl O&P
0010 **SECURITY ACCESS METAL DETECTORS**									
0240 Metal detector, hand-held, wand type, unit only				Ea.	89			89	98
0250 Metal detector, walk through portal type, single zone	1 Elec	2	4		3,675	213		3,888	4,350
0260 Multi-zone	"	2	4	↓	4,650	213		4,863	5,450

28 13 53.16 Security Access X-Ray Equipment

	Crew	Daily Output	Labor-Hours	Unit	Material	Labor	Equipment	Total	Total Incl O&P
0010 **SECURITY ACCESS X-RAY EQUIPMENT**									
0290 X-ray machine, desk top, for mail/small packages/letters	1 Elec	4	2	Ea.	3,400	107		3,507	3,900
0300 Conveyor type, incl monitor, minimum	↓	2	4		15,800	213		16,013	17,700
0310 Maximum	↓	2	4		28,300	213		28,513	31,400
0320 X-ray machine, large unit, for airports, incl monitor, min.	2 Elec	1	16		39,600	855		40,455	44,900
0330 Maximum	"	.50	32	↓	68,000	1,700		69,700	77,000

28 13 53.23 Security Access Explosive Detection Equipment

	Crew	Daily Output	Labor-Hours	Unit	Material	Labor	Equipment	Total	Total Incl O&P
0010 **SECURITY ACCESS EXPLOSIVE DETECTION EQUIPMENT**									
0270 Explosives detector, walk through portal type	1 Elec	2	4	Ea.	43,700	213		43,913	48,400
0280 Hand-held, battery operated				"				25,500	28,100

28 16 Intrusion Detection

28 16 16 – Intrusion Detection Systems Infrastructure

28 16 16.50 Intrusion Detection

	Crew	Daily Output	Labor-Hours	Unit	Material	Labor	Equipment	Total	Total Incl O&P
0010 **INTRUSION DETECTION**, not including wires & conduits									
0100 Burglar alarm, battery operated, mechanical trigger	1 Elec	4	2	Ea.	275	107		382	465
0200 Electrical trigger		4	2		330	107		437	525
0400 For outside key control, add		8	1		83	53.50		136.50	174
0600 For remote signaling circuitry, add		8	1		124	53.50		177.50	219
0800 Card reader, flush type, standard		2.70	2.963		920	158		1,078	1,275
1000 Multi-code		2.70	2.963		1,175	158		1,333	1,550
1200 Door switches, hinge switch		5.30	1.509		58	80.50		138.50	189
1400 Magnetic switch		5.30	1.509		68.50	80.50		149	201
1600 Exit control locks, horn alarm		4	2		274	107		381	465
1800 Flashing light alarm		4	2		300	107		407	495
2000 Indicating panels, 1 channel	↓	2.70	2.963		365	158		523	645
2200 10 channel	2 Elec	3.20	5		1,250	267		1,517	1,800
2400 20 channel		2	8		2,425	425		2,850	3,325
2600 40 channel	↓	1.14	14.035		4,425	750		5,175	6,000
2800 Ultrasonic motion detector, 12 volt	1 Elec	2.30	3.478		227	186		413	535
3000 Infrared photoelectric detector		4	2		188	107		295	370
3200 Passive infrared detector		4	2		280	107		387	475
3400 Glass break alarm switch		8	1		92.50	53.50		146	184
3420 Switchmats, 30" x 5'		5.30	1.509		84	80.50		164.50	218
3440 30" x 25'		4	2		201	107		308	385
3460 Police connect panel		4	2		242	107		349	430
3480 Telephone dialer		5.30	1.509		380	80.50		460.50	545
3500 Alarm bell		4	2		103	107		210	279
3520 Siren		4	2		145	107		252	325
3540 Microwave detector, 10' to 200'		2	4		660	213		873	1,050
3560 10' to 350'	↓	2	4	↓	1,925	213		2,138	2,450

28 23 Video Surveillance

28 23 23 – Video Surveillance Systems Infrastructure

28 23 23.50 Video Surveillance Equipments	Crew	Daily Output	Labor-Hours	Unit	Material	2014 Bare Costs Labor	Equipment	Total	Total Incl O&P
0010 **VIDEO SURVEILLANCE EQUIPMENTS**									
0200 Video cameras, wireless, hidden in exit signs, clocks, etc., incl. receiver	1 Elec	3	2.667	Ea.	107	142		249	340
0210 Accessories for video recorder, single camera		3	2.667		181	142		323	420
0220 For multiple cameras		3	2.667		1,750	142		1,892	2,150
0230 Video cameras, wireless, for under vehicle searching, complete	▼	2	4	▼	10,100	213		10,313	11,400

28 31 Fire Detection and Alarm

28 31 23 – Fire Detection and Alarm Annunciation Panels and Fire Stations

28 31 23.50 Alarm Panels and Devices

	Crew	Daily Output	Labor-Hours	Unit	Material	2014 Bare Costs Labor	Equipment	Total	Total Incl O&P
0010 **ALARM PANELS AND DEVICES**, not including wires & conduits									
3594 Fire, alarm control panel									
3600 4 zone	2 Elec	2	8	Ea.	395	425		820	1,100
3800 8 zone		1	16		775	855		1,630	2,175
4000 12 zone	▼	.67	23.988		2,375	1,275		3,650	4,575
4200 Battery and rack	1 Elec	4	2		410	107		517	615
4400 Automatic charger		8	1		580	53.50		633.50	720
4600 Signal bell		8	1		78	53.50		131.50	168
4800 Trouble buzzer or manual station		8	1		82.50	53.50		136	173
5600 Strobe and horn		5.30	1.509		151	80.50		231.50	291
5800 Fire alarm horn		6.70	1.194		60.50	63.50		124	165
6000 Door holder, electro-magnetic		4	2		102	107		209	277
6200 Combination holder and closer		3.20	2.500		122	133		255	340
6600 Drill switch		8	1		365	53.50		418.50	490
6800 Master box		2.70	2.963		6,350	158		6,508	7,225
7000 Break glass station		8	1		55	53.50		108.50	143
7800 Remote annunciator, 8 zone lamp	▼	1.80	4.444		207	237		444	590
8000 12 zone lamp	2 Elec	2.60	6.154		330	330		660	875
8200 16 zone lamp	"	2.20	7.273	▼	415	390		805	1,050

28 31 43 – Fire Detection Sensors

28 31 43.50 Fire and Heat Detectors

	Crew	Daily Output	Labor-Hours	Unit	Material	2014 Bare Costs Labor	Equipment	Total	Total Incl O&P
0010 **FIRE & HEAT DETECTORS**									
5000 Detector, rate of rise	1 Elec	8	1	Ea.	50.50	53.50		104	138
5100 Fixed temperature	"	8	1	"	50.50	53.50		104	138

28 31 46 – Smoke Detection Sensors

28 31 46.50 Smoke Detectors

	Crew	Daily Output	Labor-Hours	Unit	Material	2014 Bare Costs Labor	Equipment	Total	Total Incl O&P
0010 **SMOKE DETECTORS**									
5200 Smoke detector, ceiling type	1 Elec	6.20	1.290	Ea.	109	69		178	227
5400 Duct type	"	3.20	2.500	"	325	133		458	560

28 39 10.10 Mass Notification System	Crew	Daily Output	Labor-Hours	Unit	Material	2014 Bare Costs Labor	Equipment	Total	Total Incl O&P
0010 **MASS NOTIFICATION SYSTEM**									
0100　Wireless command center, 10,000 devices	2 Elec	1.33	12.030	Ea.	3,575	640		4,215	4,925
0200　　Option, email notification					1,750			1,750	1,925
0210　　　Remote device supervision & monitor					2,425			2,425	2,650
0300　Antenna VHF or UHF, for medium range	1 Elec	4	2		128	107		235	305
0310　　For high-power transmitter		2	4		665	213		878	1,050
0400　Transmitter, 25 watt		4	2		2,000	107		2,107	2,375
0410　　40 watt		2.66	3.008		2,675	160		2,835	3,200
0420　　100 watt		1.33	6.015		6,700	320		7,020	7,875
0500　Wireless receiver/control module for speaker		8	1		262	53.50		315.50	370
0600　Desktop paging controller, stand alone		4	2		365	107		472	570

Estimating Tips

31 05 00 Common Work Results for Earthwork

- Estimating the actual cost of performing earthwork requires careful consideration of the variables involved. This includes items such as type of soil, whether water will be encountered, dewatering, whether banks need bracing, disposal of excavated earth, and length of haul to fill or spoil sites, etc. If the project has large quantities of cut or fill, consider raising or lowering the site to reduce costs, while paying close attention to the effect on site drainage and utilities.

- If the project has large quantities of fill, creating a borrow pit on the site can significantly lower the costs.

- It is very important to consider what time of year the project is scheduled for completion. Bad weather can create large cost overruns from dewatering, site repair, and lost productivity from cold weather.

Reference Numbers

Reference numbers are shown in shaded boxes at the beginning of some major classifications. These numbers refer to related items in the Reference Section. The reference information may be an estimating procedure, an alternate pricing method, or technical information.

Note: Not all subdivisions listed here necessarily appear in this publication.

Division 31 - Earthwork

31 05 Common Work Results for Earthwork

31 05 13 – Soils for Earthwork

31 05 13.10 Borrow		Crew	Daily Output	Labor-Hours	Unit	Material	2014 Bare Costs Labor	Equipment	Total	Total Incl O&P
0010	**BORROW**									
0020	Spread, 200 H.P. dozer, no compaction, 2 mi. RT haul									
0200	Common borrow	B-15	600	.047	C.Y.	12.35	1.90	4.52	18.77	21.50
0700	Screened loam		600	.047		28	1.90	4.52	34.42	38.50
0800	Topsoil, weed free	↓	600	.047		24.50	1.90	4.52	30.92	35
0900	For 5 mile haul, add	B-34B	200	.040	↓		1.50	3.46	4.96	6.25

31 05 16 – Aggregates for Earthwork

31 05 16.10 Borrow		Crew	Daily Output	Labor-Hours	Unit	Material	2014 Bare Costs Labor	Equipment	Total	Total Incl O&P
0010	**BORROW**									
0020	Spread, with 200 H.P. dozer, no compaction, 2 mi. RT haul									
0100	Bank run gravel	B-15	600	.047	L.C.Y.	22	1.90	4.52	28.42	32
0300	Crushed stone (1.40 tons per CY) , 1-1/2"		600	.047		28.50	1.90	4.52	34.92	39
0320	3/4"		600	.047		28.50	1.90	4.52	34.92	39
0340	1/2"		600	.047		27	1.90	4.52	33.42	37.50
0360	3/8"		600	.047		25.50	1.90	4.52	31.92	36.50
0400	Sand, washed, concrete		600	.047		42	1.90	4.52	48.42	54
0500	Dead or bank sand		600	.047		17.55	1.90	4.52	23.97	27.50
0600	Select structural fill		600	.047		21	1.90	4.52	27.42	31
0900	For 5 mile haul, add	B-34B	200	.040	↓		1.50	3.46	4.96	6.25

31 06 Schedules for Earthwork

31 06 60 – Schedules for Special Foundations and Load Bearing Elements

31 06 60.14 Piling Special Costs		Crew	Daily Output	Labor-Hours	Unit	Material	2014 Bare Costs Labor	Equipment	Total	Total Incl O&P
0010	**PILING SPECIAL COSTS**									
0011	Piling special costs, pile caps, see Section 03 30 53.40									
0500	Cutoffs, concrete piles, plain	1 Pile	5.50	1.455	Ea.		64.50		64.50	106
0600	With steel thin shell, add		38	.211			9.35		9.35	15.30
0700	Steel pile or "H" piles		19	.421			18.70		18.70	30.50
0800	Wood piles	↓	38	.211	↓		9.35		9.35	15.30
1000	Testing, any type piles, test load is twice the design load									
1050	50 ton design load, 100 ton test				Ea.				14,000	15,500
1100	100 ton design load, 200 ton test								20,000	22,000
1200	200 ton design load, 400 ton test				↓				28,000	31,000

31 06 60.15 Mobilization		Crew	Daily Output	Labor-Hours	Unit	Material	2014 Bare Costs Labor	Equipment	Total	Total Incl O&P
0010	**MOBILIZATION**									
0020	Set up & remove, air compressor, 600 CFM	A-5	3.30	5.455	Ea.		200	20.50	220.50	355
0100	1200 CFM	"	2.20	8.182			300	30.50	330.50	525
0200	Crane, with pile leads and pile hammer, 75 ton	B-19	.60	106			4,900	3,075	7,975	11,300
0300	150 ton	"	.36	177	↓		8,175	5,125	13,300	18,800

31 14 Earth Stripping and Stockpiling

31 14 13 – Soil Stripping and Stockpiling

31 14 13.23 Topsoil Stripping and Stockpiling

		Crew	Daily Output	Labor-Hours	Unit	Material	2014 Bare Costs Labor	Equipment	Total	Total Incl O&P
0010	**TOPSOIL STRIPPING AND STOCKPILING**									
1500	Loam or topsoil, remove/stockpile on site									
1510	By hand, 6" deep, 50' haul, less than 100 S.Y.	B-1	100	.240	S.Y.		8.95		8.95	14.70
1520	By skid steer, 6" deep, 100' haul, 101-500 S.Y.	B-62	500	.048			1.93	.35	2.28	3.50
1530	100' haul, 501-900 S.Y.	"	900	.027			1.07	.19	1.26	1.94
1540	200' haul, 901-1100 S.Y.	B-63	1000	.040			1.55	.17	1.72	2.71
1550	By dozer, 200' haul, 1101-4000 S.Y.	B-10B	4000	.003	↓		.13	.33	.46	.58

31 23 Excavation and Fill

31 23 16 – Excavation

31 23 16.13 Excavating, Trench

		Crew	Daily Output	Labor-Hours	Unit	Material	2014 Bare Costs Labor	Equipment	Total	Total Incl O&P
0010	**EXCAVATING, TRENCH**									
0011	Or continuous footing									
0020	Common earth with no sheeting or dewatering included									
1400	By hand with pick and shovel 2' to 6' deep, light soil	1 Clab	8	1	B.C.Y.		36.50		36.50	60
1500	Heavy soil	"	4	2	"		73.50		73.50	120
1700	For tamping backfilled trenches, air tamp, add	A-1G	100	.080	E.C.Y.		2.93	.56	3.49	5.45
1900	Vibrating plate, add	B-18	180	.133	"		4.98	.26	5.24	8.45
2100	Trim sides and bottom for concrete pours, common earth		1500	.016	S.F.		.60	.03	.63	1.01
2300	Hardpan	↓	600	.040	"		1.49	.08	1.57	2.53
9000	Minimum labor/equipment charge	1 Clab	4	2	Job		73.50		73.50	120

31 23 16.14 Excavating, Utility Trench

		Crew	Daily Output	Labor-Hours	Unit	Material	2014 Bare Costs Labor	Equipment	Total	Total Incl O&P
0010	**EXCAVATING, UTILITY TRENCH**									
0011	Common earth									
0050	Trenching with chain trencher, 12 H.P., operator walking									
0100	4" wide trench, 12" deep	B-53	800	.010	L.F.		.47	.09	.56	.85
0150	18" deep		750	.011			.50	.10	.60	.90
0200	24" deep		700	.011			.54	.10	.64	.96
0300	6" wide trench, 12" deep		650	.012			.58	.11	.69	1.04
0350	18" deep		600	.013			.63	.12	.75	1.12
0400	24" deep		550	.015			.68	.13	.81	1.23
0450	36" deep		450	.018			.84	.16	1	1.50
0600	8" wide trench, 12" deep		475	.017			.79	.15	.94	1.42
0650	18" deep		400	.020			.94	.18	1.12	1.69
0700	24" deep		350	.023			1.08	.20	1.28	1.93
0750	36" deep		300	.027	↓		1.25	.24	1.49	2.25
0900	Minimum labor/equipment charge	↓	2	4	Job		188	35.50	223.50	335
1000	Backfill by hand including compaction, add									
1050	4" wide trench, 12" deep	A-1G	800	.010	L.F.		.37	.07	.44	.68
1100	18" deep		530	.015			.55	.11	.66	1.03
1150	24" deep		400	.020			.73	.14	.87	1.35
1300	6" wide trench, 12" deep		540	.015			.54	.10	.64	1
1350	18" deep		405	.020			.72	.14	.86	1.34
1400	24" deep		270	.030			1.09	.21	1.30	2.01
1450	36" deep		180	.044			1.63	.31	1.94	3.02
1600	8" wide trench, 12" deep		400	.020			.73	.14	.87	1.35
1650	18" deep		265	.030			1.11	.21	1.32	2.05
1700	24" deep		200	.040			1.47	.28	1.75	2.72
1750	36" deep	↓	135	.059	↓		2.17	.41	2.58	4.03
2000	Chain trencher, 40 H.P. operator riding									
2050	6" wide trench and backfill, 12" deep	B-54	1200	.007	L.F.		.31	.28	.59	.81

31 23 Excavation and Fill

31 23 16 – Excavation

31 23 16.14 Excavating, Utility Trench

		Crew	Daily Output	Labor-Hours	Unit	Material	2014 Bare Costs		Total	Total Incl O&P
							Labor	Equipment		
2100	18" deep	B-54	1000	.008	L.F.		.38	.34	.72	.97
2150	24" deep		975	.008			.39	.35	.74	.99
2200	36" deep		900	.009			.42	.38	.80	1.07
2250	48" deep		750	.011			.50	.45	.95	1.30
2300	60" deep		650	.012			.58	.52	1.10	1.49
2400	8" wide trench and backfill, 12" deep		1000	.008			.38	.34	.72	.97
2450	18" deep		950	.008			.40	.36	.76	1.02
2500	24" deep		900	.009			.42	.38	.80	1.07
2550	36" deep		800	.010			.47	.42	.89	1.22
2600	48" deep		650	.012			.58	.52	1.10	1.49
2700	12" wide trench and backfill, 12" deep		975	.008			.39	.35	.74	.99
2750	18" deep		860	.009			.44	.39	.83	1.12
2800	24" deep		800	.010			.47	.42	.89	1.22
2850	36" deep		725	.011			.52	.47	.99	1.33
3000	16" wide trench and backfill, 12" deep		835	.010			.45	.41	.86	1.16
3050	18" deep		750	.011			.50	.45	.95	1.30
3100	24" deep	▼	700	.011	▼		.54	.49	1.03	1.38
3200	Compaction with vibratory plate, add								35%	35%
5100	Hand excavate and trim for pipe bells after trench excavation									
5200	8" pipe	1 Clab	155	.052	L.F.		1.89		1.89	3.11
5300	18" pipe	"	130	.062	"		2.26		2.26	3.70
9000	Minimum labor/equipment charge	A-1G	4	2	Job		73.50	14	87.50	135

31 23 16.16 Structural Excavation for Minor Structures

		Crew	Daily Output	Labor-Hours	Unit	Material	2014 Bare Costs		Total	Total Incl O&P
							Labor	Equipment		
0010	**STRUCTURAL EXCAVATION FOR MINOR STRUCTURES**									
0015	Hand, pits to 6' deep, sandy soil	1 Clab	8	1	B.C.Y.		36.50		36.50	60
0100	Heavy soil or clay		4	2			73.50		73.50	120
0300	Pits 6' to 12' deep, sandy soil		5	1.600			58.50		58.50	96.50
0500	Heavy soil or clay		3	2.667			97.50		97.50	161
0700	Pits 12' to 18' deep, sandy soil		4	2			73.50		73.50	120
0900	Heavy soil or clay		2	4			147		147	241
1100	Hand loading trucks from stock pile, sandy soil		12	.667			24.50		24.50	40
1300	Heavy soil or clay	▼	8	1	▼		36.50		36.50	60
1500	For wet or muck hand excavation, add to above								50%	50%
6000	Machine excavation, for spread and mat footings, elevator pits,									
6001	and small building foundations									
6030	Common earth, hydraulic backhoe, 1/2 C.Y. bucket	B-12E	55	.291	B.C.Y.		12.65	8.15	20.80	29.50
6035	3/4 C.Y. bucket	B-12F	90	.178			7.70	7.35	15.05	20.50
6040	1 C.Y. bucket	B-12A	108	.148			6.45	7.55	14	18.65
6050	1-1/2 C.Y. bucket	B-12B	144	.111			4.83	7.15	11.98	15.65
6060	2 C.Y. bucket	B-12C	200	.080			3.48	5.90	9.38	12.05
6070	Sand and gravel, 3/4 C.Y. bucket	B-12F	100	.160			6.95	6.60	13.55	18.50
6080	1 C.Y. bucket	B-12A	120	.133			5.80	6.80	12.60	16.80
6090	1-1/2 C.Y. bucket	B-12B	160	.100			4.35	6.45	10.80	14.10
6100	2 C.Y. bucket	B-12C	220	.073			3.16	5.35	8.51	11
6110	Clay, till, or blasted rock, 3/4 C.Y. bucket	B-12F	80	.200			8.70	8.30	17	23
6120	1 C.Y. bucket	B-12A	95	.168			7.30	8.60	15.90	21.50
6130	1-1/2 C.Y. bucket	B-12B	130	.123			5.35	7.95	13.30	17.30
6140	2 C.Y. bucket	B-12C	175	.091			3.97	6.70	10.67	13.80
6230	Sandy clay & loam, hydraulic backhoe, 1/2 C.Y. bucket	B-12E	60	.267			11.60	7.45	19.05	27
6235	3/4 C.Y. bucket	B-12F	98	.163			7.10	6.75	13.85	18.85
6240	1 C.Y. bucket	B-12A	116	.138			6	7	13	17.40
6250	1-1/2 C.Y. bucket	B-12B	156	.103	▼		4.46	6.60	11.06	14.40

31 23 Excavation and Fill

31 23 16 – Excavation

31 23 16.16 Structural Excavation for Minor Structures

		Crew	Daily Output	Labor-Hours	Unit	Material	2014 Bare Costs Labor	Equipment	Total	Total Incl O&P
9000	Minimum labor/equipment charge	1 Clab	4	2	Job		73.50		73.50	120

31 23 16.42 Excavating, Bulk Bank Measure

			Crew	Daily Output	Labor-Hours	Unit	Material	Labor	Equipment	Total	Total Incl O&P
0010	**EXCAVATING, BULK BANK MEASURE**	R312316-40									
0011	Common earth piled										
0020	For loading onto trucks, add									15%	15%
0200	Excavator, hydraulic, crawler mtd., 1 C.Y. cap. = 100 C.Y./hr.	R312316-45	B-12A	800	.020	B.C.Y.		.87	1.02	1.89	2.52
1200	Front end loader, track mtd., 1-1/2 C.Y. cap. = 70 C.Y./hr.		B-10N	560	.021			.96	.93	1.89	2.57
1500	Wheel mounted, 3/4 C.Y. cap. = 45 C.Y./hr.		B-10R	360	.033			1.49	.82	2.31	3.29
5000	Excavating, bulk bank measure, sandy clay & loam piled										
5020	For loading onto trucks, add									15%	15%
5100	Excavator, hydraulic, crawler mtd., 1 C.Y. cap. = 120 C.Y./hr.		B-12A	960	.017	B.C.Y.		.72	.85	1.57	2.10
9000	Minimum labor/equipment charge		B-10L	2	6	Job		269	240	509	695

31 23 16.46 Excavating, Bulk, Dozer

		Crew	Daily Output	Labor-Hours	Unit	Material	Labor	Equipment	Total	Total Incl O&P
0010	**EXCAVATING, BULK, DOZER**									
0011	Open site									
2000	80 H.P., 50' haul, sand & gravel	B-10L	460	.026	B.C.Y.		1.17	1.05	2.22	3.02
2200	150' haul, sand & gravel		230	.052			2.34	2.09	4.43	6.05
2400	300' haul, sand & gravel		120	.100			4.48	4.01	8.49	11.60
3000	105 H.P., 50' haul, sand & gravel	B-10W	700	.017			.77	.85	1.62	2.16
3200	150' haul, sand & gravel		310	.039			1.74	1.91	3.65	4.88
3300	300' haul, sand & gravel		140	.086			3.84	4.23	8.07	10.80
4000	200 H.P., 50' haul, sand & gravel	B-10B	1400	.009			.38	.95	1.33	1.66
4200	150' haul, sand & gravel		595	.020			.90	2.23	3.13	3.90
4400	300' haul, sand & gravel		310	.039			1.74	4.27	6.01	7.50
5040	Clay	B-10M	1025	.012			.52	1.77	2.29	2.79
5400	300' haul, sand & gravel	"	470	.026			1.14	3.87	5.01	6.10

31 23 23 – Fill

31 23 23.13 Backfill

		Crew	Daily Output	Labor-Hours	Unit	Material	Labor	Equipment	Total	Total Incl O&P
0010	**BACKFILL**	R312323-30								
0015	By hand, no compaction, light soil	1 Clab	14	.571	L.C.Y.		21		21	34.50
0100	Heavy soil		11	.727	"		26.50		26.50	44
0300	Compaction in 6" layers, hand tamp, add to above		20.60	.388	E.C.Y.		14.25		14.25	23.50
0400	Roller compaction operator walking, add	B-10A	100	.120			5.40	1.83	7.23	10.60
0500	Air tamp, add	B-9D	190	.211			7.80	1.40	9.20	14.35
0600	Vibrating plate, add	A-1D	60	.133			4.89	.60	5.49	8.70
0800	Compaction in 12" layers, hand tamp, add to above	1 Clab	34	.235			8.60		8.60	14.15
1000	Air tamp, add	B-9	285	.140			5.20	.82	6.02	9.45
1100	Vibrating plate, add	A-1E	90	.089			3.26	.51	3.77	5.90
1200	Trench, dozer, no compaction, 60 HP	B-10L	425	.028	L.C.Y.		1.27	1.13	2.40	3.28
1300	Dozer backfilling, bulk, up to 300' haul, no compaction	B-10B	1200	.010	"		.45	1.10	1.55	1.93
1400	Air tamped, add	B-11B	80	.200	E.C.Y.		8.35	3.78	12.13	17.65
1900	Dozer backfilling, trench, up to 300' haul, no compaction	B-10B	900	.013	L.C.Y.		.60	1.47	2.07	2.58
2000	Air tamped, add	B-11B	80	.200	E.C.Y.		8.35	3.78	12.13	17.65
2350	Spreading in 8" layers, small dozer	B-10B	1060	.011	L.C.Y.		.51	1.25	1.76	2.18
2450	Compacting with vibrating plate, 8" lifts	A-1D	73	.110	E.C.Y.		4.02	.49	4.51	7.15

31 23 23.14 Backfill, Structural

		Crew	Daily Output	Labor-Hours	Unit	Material	Labor	Equipment	Total	Total Incl O&P
0010	**BACKFILL, STRUCTURAL**									
0011	Dozer or F.E. loader									
0020	From existing stockpile, no compaction									
2000	80 H.P., 50' haul, sand & gravel	B-10L	1100	.011	L.C.Y.		.49	.44	.93	1.26
2010	Sandy clay & loam		1070	.011			.50	.45	.95	1.29

31 23 Excavation and Fill

31 23 23 – Fill

31 23 23.14 Backfill, Structural

		Crew	Daily Output	Labor-Hours	Unit	Material	2014 Bare Costs Labor	2014 Bare Costs Equipment	Total	Total Incl O&P
2020	Common earth	B-10L	975	.012	L.C.Y.		.55	.49	1.04	1.42
2040	Clay		850	.014			.63	.57	1.20	1.63
2400	300' haul, sand & gravel		370	.032			1.45	1.30	2.75	3.76
2410	Sandy clay & loam		360	.033			1.49	1.34	2.83	3.86
2420	Common earth		330	.036			1.63	1.46	3.09	4.21
2440	Clay		290	.041			1.85	1.66	3.51	4.79
3000	105 H.P., 50' haul, sand & gravel	B-10W	1350	.009			.40	.44	.84	1.12
3010	Sandy clay & loam		1325	.009			.41	.45	.86	1.14
3020	Common earth		1225	.010			.44	.48	.92	1.23
3040	Clay		1100	.011			.49	.54	1.03	1.37
3300	300' haul, sand & gravel		465	.026			1.16	1.27	2.43	3.25
3310	Sandy clay & loam		455	.026			1.18	1.30	2.48	3.32
3320	Common earth		415	.029			1.30	1.43	2.73	3.65
3340	Clay		370	.032			1.45	1.60	3.05	4.09

31 23 23.16 Fill By Borrow and Utility Bedding

		Crew	Daily Output	Labor-Hours	Unit	Material	2014 Bare Costs Labor	2014 Bare Costs Equipment	Total	Total Incl O&P
0010	**FILL BY BORROW AND UTILITY BEDDING**									
0049	Utility bedding, for pipe & conduit, not incl. compaction									
0050	Crushed or screened bank run gravel	B-6	150	.160	L.C.Y.	25	6.40	2.44	33.84	40.50
0100	Crushed stone 3/4" to 1/2"		150	.160		28.50	6.40	2.44	37.34	44
0200	Sand, dead or bank		150	.160		17.55	6.40	2.44	26.39	32.50
0500	Compacting bedding in trench	A-1D	90	.089	E.C.Y.		3.26	.40	3.66	5.80
0600	If material source exceeds 2 miles, add for extra mileage.									

31 23 23.17 General Fill

		Crew	Daily Output	Labor-Hours	Unit	Material	2014 Bare Costs Labor	2014 Bare Costs Equipment	Total	Total Incl O&P
0010	**GENERAL FILL**									
0011	Spread dumped material, no compaction									
0020	By dozer, no compaction	B-10B	1000	.012	L.C.Y.		.54	1.33	1.87	2.32
0100	By hand	1 Clab	12	.667	"		24.50		24.50	40
9000	Minimum labor/equipment charge	"	4	2	Job		73.50		73.50	120

31 23 23.20 Hauling

		Crew	Daily Output	Labor-Hours	Unit	Material	2014 Bare Costs Labor	2014 Bare Costs Equipment	Total	Total Incl O&P
0010	**HAULING**									
0011	Excavated or borrow, loose cubic yards									
0012	no loading equipment, including hauling,waiting, loading/dumping									
0013	time per cycle (wait, load, travel, unload or dump & return)									
0014	8 C.Y. truck, 15 MPH ave, cycle 0.5 miles, 10 min. wait/Ld./Uld.	B-34A	320	.025	L.C.Y.		.94	1.30	2.24	2.96
0016	cycle 1 mile		272	.029			1.10	1.53	2.63	3.49
0018	cycle 2 miles		208	.038			1.44	2.01	3.45	4.56
0020	cycle 4 miles		144	.056			2.09	2.90	4.99	6.60
0022	cycle 6 miles		112	.071			2.68	3.73	6.41	8.45
0024	cycle 8 miles		88	.091			3.41	4.74	8.15	10.75
0026	20 MPH ave,cycle 0.5 mile		336	.024			.89	1.24	2.13	2.82
0028	cycle 1 mile		296	.027			1.02	1.41	2.43	3.20
0030	cycle 2 miles		240	.033			1.25	1.74	2.99	3.94
0032	cycle 4 miles		176	.045			1.71	2.37	4.08	5.40
0034	cycle 6 miles		136	.059			2.21	3.07	5.28	6.95
0036	cycle 8 miles		112	.071			2.68	3.73	6.41	8.45
0044	25 MPH ave, cycle 4 miles		192	.042			1.56	2.17	3.73	4.93
0046	cycle 6 miles		160	.050			1.88	2.61	4.49	5.90
0048	cycle 8 miles		128	.063			2.35	3.26	5.61	7.40
0050	30 MPH ave, cycle 4 miles		216	.037			1.39	1.93	3.32	4.39
0052	cycle 6 miles		176	.045			1.71	2.37	4.08	5.40
0054	cycle 8 miles		144	.056			2.09	2.90	4.99	6.60
0114	15 MPH ave, cycle 0.5 mile, 15 min. wait/Ld./Uld.		224	.036			1.34	1.86	3.20	4.23

31 23 Excavation and Fill

31 23 23 - Fill

31 23 23.20 Hauling		Crew	Daily Output	Labor-Hours	Unit	Material	2014 Bare Costs Labor	Equipment	Total	Total Incl O&P
0116	cycle 1 mile	B-34A	200	.040	L.C.Y.		1.50	2.09	3.59	4.73
0118	cycle 2 miles		168	.048			1.79	2.48	4.27	5.65
0120	cycle 4 miles		120	.067			2.50	3.48	5.98	7.90
0122	cycle 6 miles		96	.083			3.13	4.35	7.48	9.90
0124	cycle 8 miles		80	.100			3.76	5.20	8.96	11.85
0126	20 MPH ave, cycle 0.5 mile		232	.034			1.29	1.80	3.09	4.09
0128	cycle 1 mile		208	.038			1.44	2.01	3.45	4.56
0130	cycle 2 miles		184	.043			1.63	2.27	3.90	5.15
0132	cycle 4 miles		144	.056			2.09	2.90	4.99	6.60
0134	cycle 6 miles		112	.071			2.68	3.73	6.41	8.45
0136	cycle 8 miles		96	.083			3.13	4.35	7.48	9.90
0144	25 MPH ave, cycle 4 miles		152	.053			1.98	2.74	4.72	6.25
0146	cycle 6 miles		128	.063			2.35	3.26	5.61	7.40
0148	cycle 8 miles		112	.071			2.68	3.73	6.41	8.45
0150	30 MPH ave, cycle 4 miles		168	.048			1.79	2.48	4.27	5.65
0152	cycle 6 miles		144	.056			2.09	2.90	4.99	6.60
0154	cycle 8 miles		120	.067			2.50	3.48	5.98	7.90
0214	15 MPH ave, cycle 0.5 mile, 20 min wait/Ld./Uld.		176	.045			1.71	2.37	4.08	5.40
0216	cycle 1 mile		160	.050			1.88	2.61	4.49	5.90
0218	cycle 2 miles		136	.059			2.21	3.07	5.28	6.95
0220	cycle 4 miles		104	.077			2.89	4.01	6.90	9.10
0222	cycle 6 miles		88	.091			3.41	4.74	8.15	10.75
0224	cycle 8 miles		72	.111			4.17	5.80	9.97	13.15
0226	20 MPH ave, cycle 0.5 mile		176	.045			1.71	2.37	4.08	5.40
0228	cycle 1 mile		168	.048			1.79	2.48	4.27	5.65
0230	cycle 2 miles		144	.056			2.09	2.90	4.99	6.60
0232	cycle 4 miles		120	.067			2.50	3.48	5.98	7.90
0234	cycle 6 miles		96	.083			3.13	4.35	7.48	9.90
0236	cycle 8 miles		88	.091			3.41	4.74	8.15	10.75
0244	25 MPH ave, cycle 4 miles		128	.063			2.35	3.26	5.61	7.40
0246	cycle 6 miles		112	.071			2.68	3.73	6.41	8.45
0248	cycle 8 miles		96	.083			3.13	4.35	7.48	9.90
0250	30 MPH ave, cycle 4 miles		136	.059			2.21	3.07	5.28	6.95
0252	cycle 6 miles		120	.067			2.50	3.48	5.98	7.90
0254	cycle 8 miles		104	.077			2.89	4.01	6.90	9.10
0314	15 MPH ave, cycle 0.5 mile, 25 min wait/Ld./Uld.		144	.056			2.09	2.90	4.99	6.60
0316	cycle 1 mile		128	.063			2.35	3.26	5.61	7.40
0318	cycle 2 miles		112	.071			2.68	3.73	6.41	8.45
0320	cycle 4 miles		96	.083			3.13	4.35	7.48	9.90
0322	cycle 6 miles		80	.100			3.76	5.20	8.96	11.85
0324	cycle 8 miles		64	.125			4.69	6.50	11.19	14.80
0326	20 MPH ave, cycle 0.5 mile		144	.056			2.09	2.90	4.99	6.60
0328	cycle 1 mile		136	.059			2.21	3.07	5.28	6.95
0330	cycle 2 miles		120	.067			2.50	3.48	5.98	7.90
0332	cycle 4 miles		104	.077			2.89	4.01	6.90	9.10
0334	cycle 6 miles		88	.091			3.41	4.74	8.15	10.75
0336	cycle 8 miles		80	.100			3.76	5.20	8.96	11.85
0344	25 MPH ave, cycle 4 miles		112	.071			2.68	3.73	6.41	8.45
0346	cycle 6 miles		96	.083			3.13	4.35	7.48	9.90
0348	cycle 8 miles		88	.091			3.41	4.74	8.15	10.75
0350	30 MPH ave, cycle 4 miles		112	.071			2.68	3.73	6.41	8.45
0352	cycle 6 miles		104	.077			2.89	4.01	6.90	9.10
0354	cycle 8 miles		96	.083			3.13	4.35	7.48	9.90

31 23 23.20 Hauling		Crew	Daily Output	Labor-Hours	Unit	Material	2014 Bare Costs		Total	Total Incl O&P
							Labor	Equipment		
0414	15 MPH ave, cycle 0.5 mile, 30 min wait/Ld./Uld.	B-34A	120	.067	L.C.Y.		2.50	3.48	5.98	7.90
0416	cycle 1 mile		112	.071			2.68	3.73	6.41	8.45
0418	cycle 2 miles		96	.083			3.13	4.35	7.48	9.90
0420	cycle 4 miles		80	.100			3.76	5.20	8.96	11.85
0422	cycle 6 miles		72	.111			4.17	5.80	9.97	13.15
0424	cycle 8 miles		64	.125			4.69	6.50	11.19	14.80
0426	20 MPH ave, cycle 0.5 mile		120	.067			2.50	3.48	5.98	7.90
0428	cycle 1 mile		112	.071			2.68	3.73	6.41	8.45
0430	cycle 2 miles		104	.077			2.89	4.01	6.90	9.10
0432	cycle 4 miles		88	.091			3.41	4.74	8.15	10.75
0434	cycle 6 miles		80	.100			3.76	5.20	8.96	11.85
0436	cycle 8 miles		72	.111			4.17	5.80	9.97	13.15
0444	25 MPH ave, cycle 4 miles		96	.083			3.13	4.35	7.48	9.90
0446	cycle 6 miles		88	.091			3.41	4.74	8.15	10.75
0448	cycle 8 miles		80	.100			3.76	5.20	8.96	11.85
0450	30 MPH ave, cycle 4 miles		96	.083			3.13	4.35	7.48	9.90
0452	cycle 6 miles		88	.091			3.41	4.74	8.15	10.75
0454	cycle 8 miles		80	.100			3.76	5.20	8.96	11.85
0514	15 MPH ave, cycle 0.5 mile, 35 min wait/Ld./Uld.		104	.077			2.89	4.01	6.90	9.10
0516	cycle 1 mile		96	.083			3.13	4.35	7.48	9.90
0518	cycle 2 miles		88	.091			3.41	4.74	8.15	10.75
0520	cycle 4 miles		72	.111			4.17	5.80	9.97	13.15
0522	cycle 6 miles		64	.125			4.69	6.50	11.19	14.80
0524	cycle 8 miles		56	.143			5.35	7.45	12.80	16.90
0526	20 MPH ave, cycle 0.5 mile		104	.077			2.89	4.01	6.90	9.10
0528	cycle 1 mile		96	.083			3.13	4.35	7.48	9.90
0530	cycle 2 miles		96	.083			3.13	4.35	7.48	9.90
0532	cycle 4 miles		80	.100			3.76	5.20	8.96	11.85
0534	cycle 6 miles		72	.111			4.17	5.80	9.97	13.15
0536	cycle 8 miles		64	.125			4.69	6.50	11.19	14.80
0544	25 MPH ave, cycle 4 miles		88	.091			3.41	4.74	8.15	10.75
0546	cycle 6 miles		80	.100			3.76	5.20	8.96	11.85
0548	cycle 8 miles		72	.111			4.17	5.80	9.97	13.15
0550	30 MPH ave, cycle 4 miles		88	.091			3.41	4.74	8.15	10.75
0552	cycle 6 miles		80	.100			3.76	5.20	8.96	11.85
0554	cycle 8 miles		72	.111			4.17	5.80	9.97	13.15
1014	12 C.Y. truck, cycle 0.5 mile, 15 MPH ave, 15 min. wait/Ld./Uld.	B-34B	336	.024			.89	2.06	2.95	3.72
1016	cycle 1 mile		300	.027			1	2.31	3.31	4.17
1018	cycle 2 miles		252	.032			1.19	2.75	3.94	4.96
1020	cycle 4 miles		180	.044			1.67	3.85	5.52	6.95
1022	cycle 6 miles		144	.056			2.09	4.81	6.90	8.70
1024	cycle 8 miles		120	.067			2.50	5.75	8.25	10.40
1025	cycle 10 miles		96	.083			3.13	7.20	10.33	13.05
1026	20 MPH ave, cycle 0.5 mile		348	.023			.86	1.99	2.85	3.59
1028	cycle 1 mile		312	.026			.96	2.22	3.18	4.01
1030	cycle 2 miles		276	.029			1.09	2.51	3.60	4.53
1032	cycle 4 miles		216	.037			1.39	3.21	4.60	5.80
1034	cycle 6 miles		168	.048			1.79	4.12	5.91	7.45
1036	cycle 8 miles		144	.056			2.09	4.81	6.90	8.70
1038	cycle 10 miles		120	.067			2.50	5.75	8.25	10.40
1040	25 MPH ave, cycle 4 miles		228	.035			1.32	3.04	4.36	5.50
1042	cycle 6 miles		192	.042			1.56	3.61	5.17	6.50
1044	cycle 8 miles		168	.048			1.79	4.12	5.91	7.45

31 23 Excavation and Fill

31 23 23 – Fill

31 23 23.20 Hauling	Crew	Daily Output	Labor-Hours	Unit	Material	2014 Bare Costs Labor	Equipment	Total	Total Incl O&P
1046	cycle 10 miles	B-34B	144	.056	L.C.Y.		2.09	4.81	6.90	8.70
1050	30 MPH ave, cycle 4 miles		252	.032			1.19	2.75	3.94	4.96
1052	cycle 6 miles		216	.037			1.39	3.21	4.60	5.80
1054	cycle 8 miles		180	.044			1.67	3.85	5.52	6.95
1056	cycle 10 miles		156	.051			1.93	4.44	6.37	8
1060	35 MPH ave, cycle 4 miles		264	.030			1.14	2.62	3.76	4.73
1062	cycle 6 miles		228	.035			1.32	3.04	4.36	5.50
1064	cycle 8 miles		204	.039			1.47	3.39	4.86	6.10
1066	cycle 10 miles		180	.044			1.67	3.85	5.52	6.95
1068	cycle 20 miles		120	.067			2.50	5.75	8.25	10.40
1069	cycle 30 miles		84	.095			3.58	8.25	11.83	14.85
1070	cycle 40 miles		72	.111			4.17	9.60	13.77	17.40
1072	40 MPH ave, cycle 6 miles		240	.033			1.25	2.88	4.13	5.20
1074	cycle 8 miles		216	.037			1.39	3.21	4.60	5.80
1076	cycle 10 miles		192	.042			1.56	3.61	5.17	6.50
1078	cycle 20 miles		120	.067			2.50	5.75	8.25	10.40
1080	cycle 30 miles		96	.083			3.13	7.20	10.33	13.05
1082	cycle 40 miles		72	.111			4.17	9.60	13.77	17.40
1084	cycle 50 miles		60	.133			5	11.55	16.55	21
1094	45 MPH ave, cycle 8 miles		216	.037			1.39	3.21	4.60	5.80
1096	cycle 10 miles		204	.039			1.47	3.39	4.86	6.10
1098	cycle 20 miles		132	.061			2.28	5.25	7.53	9.45
1100	cycle 30 miles		108	.074			2.78	6.40	9.18	11.55
1102	cycle 40 miles		84	.095			3.58	8.25	11.83	14.85
1104	cycle 50 miles		72	.111			4.17	9.60	13.77	17.40
1106	50 MPH ave, cycle 10 miles		216	.037			1.39	3.21	4.60	5.80
1108	cycle 20 miles		144	.056			2.09	4.81	6.90	8.70
1110	cycle 30 miles		108	.074			2.78	6.40	9.18	11.55
1112	cycle 40 miles		84	.095			3.58	8.25	11.83	14.85
1114	cycle 50 miles		72	.111			4.17	9.60	13.77	17.40
1214	15 MPH ave, cycle 0.5 mile, 20 min. wait/Ld./Uld.		264	.030			1.14	2.62	3.76	4.73
1216	cycle 1 mile		240	.033			1.25	2.88	4.13	5.20
1218	cycle 2 miles		204	.039			1.47	3.39	4.86	6.10
1220	cycle 4 miles		156	.051			1.93	4.44	6.37	8
1222	cycle 6 miles		132	.061			2.28	5.25	7.53	9.45
1224	cycle 8 miles		108	.074			2.78	6.40	9.18	11.55
1225	cycle 10 miles		96	.083			3.13	7.20	10.33	13.05
1226	20 MPH ave, cycle 0.5 mile		264	.030			1.14	2.62	3.76	4.73
1228	cycle 1 mile		252	.032			1.19	2.75	3.94	4.96
1230	cycle 2 miles		216	.037			1.39	3.21	4.60	5.80
1232	cycle 4 miles		180	.044			1.67	3.85	5.52	6.95
1234	cycle 6 miles		144	.056			2.09	4.81	6.90	8.70
1236	cycle 8 miles		132	.061			2.28	5.25	7.53	9.45
1238	cycle 10 miles		108	.074			2.78	6.40	9.18	11.55
1240	25 MPH ave, cycle 4 miles		192	.042			1.56	3.61	5.17	6.50
1242	cycle 6 miles		168	.048			1.79	4.12	5.91	7.45
1244	cycle 8 miles		144	.056			2.09	4.81	6.90	8.70
1246	cycle 10 miles		132	.061			2.28	5.25	7.53	9.45
1250	30 MPH ave, cycle 4 miles		204	.039			1.47	3.39	4.86	6.10
1252	cycle 6 miles		180	.044			1.67	3.85	5.52	6.95
1254	cycle 8 miles		156	.051			1.93	4.44	6.37	8
1256	cycle 10 miles		144	.056			2.09	4.81	6.90	8.70
1260	35 MPH ave, cycle 4 miles		216	.037			1.39	3.21	4.60	5.80

31 23 23.20 Hauling		Crew	Daily Output	Labor-Hours	Unit	Material	2014 Bare Costs Labor	Equipment	Total	Total Incl O&P
1262	cycle 6 miles	B-34B	192	.042	L.C.Y.		1.56	3.61	5.17	6.50
1264	cycle 8 miles		168	.048			1.79	4.12	5.91	7.45
1266	cycle 10 miles		156	.051			1.93	4.44	6.37	8
1268	cycle 20 miles		108	.074			2.78	6.40	9.18	11.55
1269	cycle 30 miles		72	.111			4.17	9.60	13.77	17.40
1270	cycle 40 miles		60	.133			5	11.55	16.55	21
1272	40 MPH ave, cycle 6 miles		192	.042			1.56	3.61	5.17	6.50
1274	cycle 8 miles		180	.044			1.67	3.85	5.52	6.95
1276	cycle 10 miles		156	.051			1.93	4.44	6.37	8
1278	cycle 20 miles		108	.074			2.78	6.40	9.18	11.55
1280	cycle 30 miles		84	.095			3.58	8.25	11.83	14.85
1282	cycle 40 miles		72	.111			4.17	9.60	13.77	17.40
1284	cycle 50 miles		60	.133			5	11.55	16.55	21
1294	45 MPH ave, cycle 8 miles		180	.044			1.67	3.85	5.52	6.95
1296	cycle 10 miles		168	.048			1.79	4.12	5.91	7.45
1298	cycle 20 miles		120	.067			2.50	5.75	8.25	10.40
1300	cycle 30 miles		96	.083			3.13	7.20	10.33	13.05
1302	cycle 40 miles		72	.111			4.17	9.60	13.77	17.40
1304	cycle 50 miles		60	.133			5	11.55	16.55	21
1306	50 MPH ave, cycle 10 miles		180	.044			1.67	3.85	5.52	6.95
1308	cycle 20 miles		132	.061			2.28	5.25	7.53	9.45
1310	cycle 30 miles		96	.083			3.13	7.20	10.33	13.05
1312	cycle 40 miles		84	.095			3.58	8.25	11.83	14.85
1314	cycle 50 miles		72	.111			4.17	9.60	13.77	17.40
1414	15 MPH ave, cycle 0.5 mile, 25 min. wait/Ld./Uld.		204	.039			1.47	3.39	4.86	6.10
1416	cycle 1 mile		192	.042			1.56	3.61	5.17	6.50
1418	cycle 2 miles		168	.048			1.79	4.12	5.91	7.45
1420	cycle 4 miles		132	.061			2.28	5.25	7.53	9.45
1422	cycle 6 miles		120	.067			2.50	5.75	8.25	10.40
1424	cycle 8 miles		96	.083			3.13	7.20	10.33	13.05
1425	cycle 10 miles		84	.095			3.58	8.25	11.83	14.85
1426	20 MPH ave, cycle 0.5 mile		216	.037			1.39	3.21	4.60	5.80
1428	cycle 1 mile		204	.039			1.47	3.39	4.86	6.10
1430	cycle 2 miles		180	.044			1.67	3.85	5.52	6.95
1432	cycle 4 miles		156	.051			1.93	4.44	6.37	8
1434	cycle 6 miles		132	.061			2.28	5.25	7.53	9.45
1436	cycle 8 miles		120	.067			2.50	5.75	8.25	10.40
1438	cycle 10 miles		96	.083			3.13	7.20	10.33	13.05
1440	25 MPH ave, cycle 4 miles		168	.048			1.79	4.12	5.91	7.45
1442	cycle 6 miles		144	.056			2.09	4.81	6.90	8.70
1444	cycle 8 miles		132	.061			2.28	5.25	7.53	9.45
1446	cycle 10 miles		108	.074			2.78	6.40	9.18	11.55
1450	30 MPH ave, cycle 4 miles		168	.048			1.79	4.12	5.91	7.45
1452	cycle 6 miles		156	.051			1.93	4.44	6.37	8
1454	cycle 8 miles		132	.061			2.28	5.25	7.53	9.45
1456	cycle 10 miles		120	.067			2.50	5.75	8.25	10.40
1460	35 MPH ave, cycle 4 miles		180	.044			1.67	3.85	5.52	6.95
1462	cycle 6 miles		156	.051			1.93	4.44	6.37	8
1464	cycle 8 miles		144	.056			2.09	4.81	6.90	8.70
1466	cycle 10 miles		132	.061			2.28	5.25	7.53	9.45
1468	cycle 20 miles		96	.083			3.13	7.20	10.33	13.05
1469	cycle 30 miles		72	.111			4.17	9.60	13.77	17.40
1470	cycle 40 miles		60	.133			5	11.55	16.55	21

31 23 Excavation and Fill

31 23 23 – Fill

31 23 23.20 Hauling		Crew	Daily Output	Labor-Hours	Unit	Material	2014 Bare Costs Labor	Equipment	Total	Total Incl O&P
1472	40 MPH ave, cycle 6 miles	B-34B	168	.048	L.C.Y.		1.79	4.12	5.91	7.45
1474	cycle 8 miles		156	.051			1.93	4.44	6.37	8
1476	cycle 10 miles		144	.056			2.09	4.81	6.90	8.70
1478	cycle 20 miles		96	.083			3.13	7.20	10.33	13.05
1480	cycle 30 miles		84	.095			3.58	8.25	11.83	14.85
1482	cycle 40 miles		60	.133			5	11.55	16.55	21
1484	cycle 50 miles		60	.133			5	11.55	16.55	21
1494	45 MPH ave, cycle 8 miles		156	.051			1.93	4.44	6.37	8
1496	cycle 10 miles		144	.056			2.09	4.81	6.90	8.70
1498	cycle 20 miles		108	.074			2.78	6.40	9.18	11.55
1500	cycle 30 miles		84	.095			3.58	8.25	11.83	14.85
1502	cycle 40 miles		72	.111			4.17	9.60	13.77	17.40
1504	cycle 50 miles		60	.133			5	11.55	16.55	21
1506	50 MPH ave, cycle 10 miles		156	.051			1.93	4.44	6.37	8
1508	cycle 20 miles		120	.067			2.50	5.75	8.25	10.40
1510	cycle 30 miles		96	.083			3.13	7.20	10.33	13.05
1512	cycle 40 miles		72	.111			4.17	9.60	13.77	17.40
1514	cycle 50 miles		60	.133			5	11.55	16.55	21
1614	15 MPH, cycle 0.5 mile, 30 min. wait/Ld./Uld.		180	.044			1.67	3.85	5.52	6.95
1616	cycle 1 mile		168	.048			1.79	4.12	5.91	7.45
1618	cycle 2 miles		144	.056			2.09	4.81	6.90	8.70
1620	cycle 4 miles		120	.067			2.50	5.75	8.25	10.40
1622	cycle 6 miles		108	.074			2.78	6.40	9.18	11.55
1624	cycle 8 miles		84	.095			3.58	8.25	11.83	14.85
1625	cycle 10 miles		84	.095			3.58	8.25	11.83	14.85
1626	20 MPH ave, cycle 0.5 mile		180	.044			1.67	3.85	5.52	6.95
1628	cycle 1 mile		168	.048			1.79	4.12	5.91	7.45
1630	cycle 2 miles		156	.051			1.93	4.44	6.37	8
1632	cycle 4 miles		132	.061			2.28	5.25	7.53	9.45
1634	cycle 6 miles		120	.067			2.50	5.75	8.25	10.40
1636	cycle 8 miles		108	.074			2.78	6.40	9.18	11.55
1638	cycle 10 miles		96	.083			3.13	7.20	10.33	13.05
1640	25 MPH ave, cycle 4 miles		144	.056			2.09	4.81	6.90	8.70
1642	cycle 6 miles		132	.061			2.28	5.25	7.53	9.45
1644	cycle 8 miles		108	.074			2.78	6.40	9.18	11.55
1646	cycle 10 miles		108	.074			2.78	6.40	9.18	11.55
1650	30 MPH ave, cycle 4 miles		144	.056			2.09	4.81	6.90	8.70
1652	cycle 6 miles		132	.061			2.28	5.25	7.53	9.45
1654	cycle 8 miles		120	.067			2.50	5.75	8.25	10.40
1656	cycle 10 miles		108	.074			2.78	6.40	9.18	11.55
1660	35 MPH ave, cycle 4 miles		156	.051			1.93	4.44	6.37	8
1662	cycle 6 miles		144	.056			2.09	4.81	6.90	8.70
1664	cycle 8 miles		132	.061			2.28	5.25	7.53	9.45
1666	cycle 10 miles		120	.067			2.50	5.75	8.25	10.40
1668	cycle 20 miles		84	.095			3.58	8.25	11.83	14.85
1669	cycle 30 miles		72	.111			4.17	9.60	13.77	17.40
1670	cycle 40 miles		60	.133			5	11.55	16.55	21
1672	40 MPH, cycle 6 miles		144	.056			2.09	4.81	6.90	8.70
1674	cycle 8 miles		132	.061			2.28	5.25	7.53	9.45
1676	cycle 10 miles		120	.067			2.50	5.75	8.25	10.40
1678	cycle 20 miles		96	.083			3.13	7.20	10.33	13.05
1680	cycle 30 miles		72	.111			4.17	9.60	13.77	17.40
1682	cycle 40 miles		60	.133			5	11.55	16.55	21

31 23 23.20 Hauling		Crew	Daily Output	Labor-Hours	Unit	Material	2014 Bare Costs Labor	Equipment	Total	Total Incl O&P
1684	cycle 50 miles	B-34B	48	.167	L.C.Y.		6.25	14.40	20.65	26
1694	45 MPH ave, cycle 8 miles		144	.056			2.09	4.81	6.90	8.70
1696	cycle 10 miles		132	.061			2.28	5.25	7.53	9.45
1698	cycle 20 miles		96	.083			3.13	7.20	10.33	13.05
1700	cycle 30 miles		84	.095			3.58	8.25	11.83	14.85
1702	cycle 40 miles		60	.133			5	11.55	16.55	21
1704	cycle 50 miles		60	.133			5	11.55	16.55	21
1706	50 MPH ave, cycle 10 miles		132	.061			2.28	5.25	7.53	9.45
1708	cycle 20 miles		108	.074			2.78	6.40	9.18	11.55
1710	cycle 30 miles		84	.095			3.58	8.25	11.83	14.85
1712	cycle 40 miles		72	.111			4.17	9.60	13.77	17.40
1714	cycle 50 miles		60	.133			5	11.55	16.55	21
2000	Hauling, 8 C.Y. truck, small project cost per hour	B-34A	8	1	Hr.		37.50	52	89.50	119
2100	12 C.Y. Truck	B-34B	8	1			37.50	86.50	124	156
2150	16.5 C.Y. Truck	B-34C	8	1			37.50	92.50	130	163
2175	18 C.Y. 8 wheel Truck	B-34I	8	1			37.50	108	145.50	180
2200	20 C.Y. Truck	B-34D	8	1			37.50	94	131.50	165
2300	Grading at dump, or embankment if required, by dozer	B-10B	1000	.012	L.C.Y.		.54	1.33	1.87	2.32
2310	Spotter at fill or cut, if required	1 Clab	8	1	Hr.		36.50		36.50	60
9014	18 C.Y. truck, 8 wheels,15 min. wait/Ld./Uld.,15 MPH, cycle 0.5 mi.	B-34I	504	.016	L.C.Y.		.60	1.72	2.32	2.86
9016	cycle 1 mile		450	.018			.67	1.93	2.60	3.21
9018	cycle 2 miles		378	.021			.79	2.29	3.08	3.81
9020	cycle 4 miles		270	.030			1.11	3.21	4.32	5.35
9022	cycle 6 miles		216	.037			1.39	4.02	5.41	6.70
9024	cycle 8 miles		180	.044			1.67	4.82	6.49	8
9025	cycle 10 miles		144	.056			2.09	6.05	8.14	10.05
9026	20 MPH ave, cycle 0.5 mile		522	.015			.58	1.66	2.24	2.77
9028	cycle 1 mile		468	.017			.64	1.85	2.49	3.08
9030	cycle 2 miles		414	.019			.73	2.10	2.83	3.48
9032	cycle 4 miles		324	.025			.93	2.68	3.61	4.46
9034	cycle 6 miles		252	.032			1.19	3.44	4.63	5.75
9036	cycle 8 miles		216	.037			1.39	4.02	5.41	6.70
9038	cycle 10 miles		180	.044			1.67	4.82	6.49	8
9040	25 MPH ave, cycle 4 miles		342	.023			.88	2.54	3.42	4.22
9042	cycle 6 miles		288	.028			1.04	3.01	4.05	5
9044	cycle 8 miles		252	.032			1.19	3.44	4.63	5.75
9046	cycle 10 miles		216	.037			1.39	4.02	5.41	6.70
9050	30 MPH ave, cycle 4 miles		378	.021			.79	2.29	3.08	3.81
9052	cycle 6 miles		324	.025			.93	2.68	3.61	4.46
9054	cycle 8 miles		270	.030			1.11	3.21	4.32	5.35
9056	cycle 10 miles		234	.034			1.28	3.71	4.99	6.15
9060	35 MPH ave, cycle 4 miles		396	.020			.76	2.19	2.95	3.64
9062	cycle 6 miles		342	.023			.88	2.54	3.42	4.22
9064	cycle 8 miles		288	.028			1.04	3.01	4.05	5
9066	cycle 10 miles		270	.030			1.11	3.21	4.32	5.35
9068	cycle 20 miles		162	.049			1.85	5.35	7.20	8.90
9070	cycle 30 miles		126	.063			2.38	6.90	9.28	11.45
9072	cycle 40 miles		90	.089			3.34	9.65	12.99	16.05
9074	40 MPH ave, cycle 6 miles		360	.022			.83	2.41	3.24	4.01
9076	cycle 8 miles		324	.025			.93	2.68	3.61	4.46
9078	cycle 10 miles		288	.028			1.04	3.01	4.05	5
9080	cycle 20 miles		180	.044			1.67	4.82	6.49	8
9082	cycle 30 miles		144	.056			2.09	6.05	8.14	10.05

31 23 23.20 Hauling		Crew	Daily Output	Labor-Hours	Unit	Material	2014 Bare Costs Labor	Equipment	Total	Total Incl O&P
9084	cycle 40 miles	B-34I	108	.074	L.C.Y.		2.78	8.05	10.83	13.35
9086	cycle 50 miles		90	.089			3.34	9.65	12.99	16.05
9094	45 MPH ave, cycle 8 miles		324	.025			.93	2.68	3.61	4.46
9096	cycle 10 miles		306	.026			.98	2.83	3.81	4.72
9098	cycle 20 miles		198	.040			1.52	4.38	5.90	7.30
9100	cycle 30 miles		144	.056			2.09	6.05	8.14	10.05
9102	cycle 40 miles		126	.063			2.38	6.90	9.28	11.45
9104	cycle 50 miles		108	.074			2.78	8.05	10.83	13.35
9106	50 MPH ave, cycle 10 miles		324	.025			.93	2.68	3.61	4.46
9108	cycle 20 miles		216	.037			1.39	4.02	5.41	6.70
9110	cycle 30 miles		162	.049			1.85	5.35	7.20	8.90
9112	cycle 40 miles		126	.063			2.38	6.90	9.28	11.45
9114	cycle 50 miles		108	.074			2.78	8.05	10.83	13.35
9214	20 min. wait/Ld./Uld.,15 MPH, cycle 0.5 mi.		396	.020			.76	2.19	2.95	3.64
9216	cycle 1 mile		360	.022			.83	2.41	3.24	4.01
9218	cycle 2 miles		306	.026			.98	2.83	3.81	4.72
9220	cycle 4 miles		234	.034			1.28	3.71	4.99	6.15
9222	cycle 6 miles		198	.040			1.52	4.38	5.90	7.30
9224	cycle 8 miles		162	.049			1.85	5.35	7.20	8.90
9225	cycle 10 miles		144	.056			2.09	6.05	8.14	10.05
9226	20 MPH ave, cycle 0.5 mile		396	.020			.76	2.19	2.95	3.64
9228	cycle 1 mile		378	.021			.79	2.29	3.08	3.81
9230	cycle 2 miles		324	.025			.93	2.68	3.61	4.46
9232	cycle 4 miles		270	.030			1.11	3.21	4.32	5.35
9234	cycle 6 miles		216	.037			1.39	4.02	5.41	6.70
9236	cycle 8 miles		198	.040			1.52	4.38	5.90	7.30
9238	cycle 10 miles		162	.049			1.85	5.35	7.20	8.90
9240	25 MPH ave, cycle 4 miles		288	.028			1.04	3.01	4.05	5
9242	cycle 6 miles		252	.032			1.19	3.44	4.63	5.75
9244	cycle 8 miles		216	.037			1.39	4.02	5.41	6.70
9246	cycle 10 miles		198	.040			1.52	4.38	5.90	7.30
9250	30 MPH ave, cycle 4 miles		306	.026			.98	2.83	3.81	4.72
9252	cycle 6 miles		270	.030			1.11	3.21	4.32	5.35
9254	cycle 8 miles		234	.034			1.28	3.71	4.99	6.15
9256	cycle 10 miles		216	.037			1.39	4.02	5.41	6.70
9260	35 MPH ave, cycle 4 miles		324	.025			.93	2.68	3.61	4.46
9262	cycle 6 miles		288	.028			1.04	3.01	4.05	5
9264	cycle 8 miles		252	.032			1.19	3.44	4.63	5.75
9266	cycle 10 miles		234	.034			1.28	3.71	4.99	6.15
9268	cycle 20 miles		162	.049			1.85	5.35	7.20	8.90
9270	cycle 30 miles		108	.074			2.78	8.05	10.83	13.35
9272	cycle 40 miles		90	.089			3.34	9.65	12.99	16.05
9274	40 MPH ave, cycle 6 miles		288	.028			1.04	3.01	4.05	5
9276	cycle 8 miles		270	.030			1.11	3.21	4.32	5.35
9278	cycle 10 miles		234	.034			1.28	3.71	4.99	6.15
9280	cycle 20 miles		162	.049			1.85	5.35	7.20	8.90
9282	cycle 30 miles		126	.063			2.38	6.90	9.28	11.45
9284	cycle 40 miles		108	.074			2.78	8.05	10.83	13.35
9286	cycle 50 miles		90	.089			3.34	9.65	12.99	16.05
9294	45 MPH ave, cycle 8 miles		270	.030			1.11	3.21	4.32	5.35
9296	cycle 10 miles		252	.032			1.19	3.44	4.63	5.75
9298	cycle 20 miles		180	.044			1.67	4.82	6.49	8
9300	cycle 30 miles		144	.056			2.09	6.05	8.14	10.05

31 23 23.20 Hauling		Crew	Daily Output	Labor-Hours	Unit	Material	2014 Bare Costs Labor	Equipment	Total	Total Incl O&P
9302	cycle 40 miles	B-34I	108	.074	L.C.Y.		2.78	8.05	10.83	13.35
9304	cycle 50 miles		90	.089			3.34	9.65	12.99	16.05
9306	50 MPH ave, cycle 10 miles		270	.030			1.11	3.21	4.32	5.35
9308	cycle 20 miles		198	.040			1.52	4.38	5.90	7.30
9310	cycle 30 miles		144	.056			2.09	6.05	8.14	10.05
9312	cycle 40 miles		126	.063			2.38	6.90	9.28	11.45
9314	cycle 50 miles		108	.074			2.78	8.05	10.83	13.35
9414	25 min. wait/Ld./Uld.,15 MPH, cycle 0.5 mi.		306	.026			.98	2.83	3.81	4.72
9416	cycle 1 mile		288	.028			1.04	3.01	4.05	5
9418	cycle 2 miles		252	.032			1.19	3.44	4.63	5.75
9420	cycle 4 miles		198	.040			1.52	4.38	5.90	7.30
9422	cycle 6 miles		180	.044			1.67	4.82	6.49	8
9424	cycle 8 miles		144	.056			2.09	6.05	8.14	10.05
9425	cycle 10 miles		126	.063			2.38	6.90	9.28	11.45
9426	20 MPH ave, cycle 0.5 mile		324	.025			.93	2.68	3.61	4.46
9428	cycle 1 mile		306	.026			.98	2.83	3.81	4.72
9430	cycle 2 miles		270	.030			1.11	3.21	4.32	5.35
9432	cycle 4 miles		234	.034			1.28	3.71	4.99	6.15
9434	cycle 6 miles		198	.040			1.52	4.38	5.90	7.30
9436	cycle 8 miles		180	.044			1.67	4.82	6.49	8
9438	cycle 10 miles		144	.056			2.09	6.05	8.14	10.05
9440	25 MPH ave, cycle 4 miles		252	.032			1.19	3.44	4.63	5.75
9442	cycle 6 miles		216	.037			1.39	4.02	5.41	6.70
9444	cycle 8 miles		198	.040			1.52	4.38	5.90	7.30
9446	cycle 10 miles		180	.044			1.67	4.82	6.49	8
9450	30 MPH ave, cycle 4 miles		252	.032			1.19	3.44	4.63	5.75
9452	cycle 6 miles		234	.034			1.28	3.71	4.99	6.15
9454	cycle 8 miles		198	.040			1.52	4.38	5.90	7.30
9456	cycle 10 miles		180	.044			1.67	4.82	6.49	8
9460	35 MPH ave, cycle 4 miles		270	.030			1.11	3.21	4.32	5.35
9462	cycle 6 miles		234	.034			1.28	3.71	4.99	6.15
9464	cycle 8 miles		216	.037			1.39	4.02	5.41	6.70
9466	cycle 10 miles		198	.040			1.52	4.38	5.90	7.30
9468	cycle 20 miles		144	.056			2.09	6.05	8.14	10.05
9470	cycle 30 miles		108	.074			2.78	8.05	10.83	13.35
9472	cycle 40 miles		90	.089			3.34	9.65	12.99	16.05
9474	40 MPH ave, cycle 6 miles		252	.032			1.19	3.44	4.63	5.75
9476	cycle 8 miles		234	.034			1.28	3.71	4.99	6.15
9478	cycle 10 miles		216	.037			1.39	4.02	5.41	6.70
9480	cycle 20 miles		144	.056			2.09	6.05	8.14	10.05
9482	cycle 30 miles		126	.063			2.38	6.90	9.28	11.45
9484	cycle 40 miles		90	.089			3.34	9.65	12.99	16.05
9486	cycle 50 miles		90	.089			3.34	9.65	12.99	16.05
9494	45 MPH ave, cycle 8 miles		234	.034			1.28	3.71	4.99	6.15
9496	cycle 10 miles		216	.037			1.39	4.02	5.41	6.70
9498	cycle 20 miles		162	.049			1.85	5.35	7.20	8.90
9500	cycle 30 miles		126	.063			2.38	6.90	9.28	11.45
9502	cycle 40 miles		108	.074			2.78	8.05	10.83	13.35
9504	cycle 50 miles		90	.089			3.34	9.65	12.99	16.05
9506	50 MPH ave, cycle 10 miles		234	.034			1.28	3.71	4.99	6.15
9508	cycle 20 miles		180	.044			1.67	4.82	6.49	8
9510	cycle 30 miles		144	.056			2.09	6.05	8.14	10.05
9512	cycle 40 miles		108	.074			2.78	8.05	10.83	13.35

31 23 Excavation and Fill

31 23 23 – Fill

31 23 23.20 Hauling

		Crew	Daily Output	Labor-Hours	Unit	Material	2014 Bare Costs Labor	2014 Bare Costs Equipment	Total	Total Incl O&P
9514	cycle 50 miles	B-34I	90	.089	L.C.Y.		3.34	9.65	12.99	16.05
9614	30 min. wait/Ld./Uld.,15 MPH, cycle 0.5 mi.		270	.030			1.11	3.21	4.32	5.35
9616	cycle 1 mile		252	.032			1.19	3.44	4.63	5.75
9618	cycle 2 miles		216	.037			1.39	4.02	5.41	6.70
9620	cycle 4 miles		180	.044			1.67	4.82	6.49	8
9622	cycle 6 miles		162	.049			1.85	5.35	7.20	8.90
9624	cycle 8 miles		126	.063			2.38	6.90	9.28	11.45
9625	cycle 10 miles		126	.063			2.38	6.90	9.28	11.45
9626	20 MPH ave, cycle 0.5 mile		270	.030			1.11	3.21	4.32	5.35
9628	cycle 1 mile		252	.032			1.19	3.44	4.63	5.75
9630	cycle 2 miles		234	.034			1.28	3.71	4.99	6.15
9632	cycle 4 miles		198	.040			1.52	4.38	5.90	7.30
9634	cycle 6 miles		180	.044			1.67	4.82	6.49	8
9636	cycle 8 miles		162	.049			1.85	5.35	7.20	8.90
9638	cycle 10 miles		144	.056			2.09	6.05	8.14	10.05
9640	25 MPH ave, cycle 4 miles		216	.037			1.39	4.02	5.41	6.70
9642	cycle 6 miles		198	.040			1.52	4.38	5.90	7.30
9644	cycle 8 miles		180	.044			1.67	4.82	6.49	8
9646	cycle 10 miles		162	.049			1.85	5.35	7.20	8.90
9650	30 MPH ave, cycle 4 miles		216	.037			1.39	4.02	5.41	6.70
9652	cycle 6 miles		198	.040			1.52	4.38	5.90	7.30
9654	cycle 8 miles		180	.044			1.67	4.82	6.49	8
9656	cycle 10 miles		162	.049			1.85	5.35	7.20	8.90
9660	35 MPH ave, cycle 4 miles		234	.034			1.28	3.71	4.99	6.15
9662	cycle 6 miles		216	.037			1.39	4.02	5.41	6.70
9664	cycle 8 miles		198	.040			1.52	4.38	5.90	7.30
9666	cycle 10 miles		180	.044			1.67	4.82	6.49	8
9668	cycle 20 miles		126	.063			2.38	6.90	9.28	11.45
9670	cycle 30 miles		108	.074			2.78	8.05	10.83	13.35
9672	cycle 40 miles		90	.089			3.34	9.65	12.99	16.05
9674	40 MPH ave, cycle 6 miles		216	.037			1.39	4.02	5.41	6.70
9676	cycle 8 miles		198	.040			1.52	4.38	5.90	7.30
9678	cycle 10 miles		180	.044			1.67	4.82	6.49	8
9680	cycle 20 miles		144	.056			2.09	6.05	8.14	10.05
9682	cycle 30 miles		108	.074			2.78	8.05	10.83	13.35
9684	cycle 40 miles		90	.089			3.34	9.65	12.99	16.05
9686	cycle 50 miles		72	.111			4.17	12.05	16.22	20
9694	45 MPH ave, cycle 8 miles		216	.037			1.39	4.02	5.41	6.70
9696	cycle 10 miles		198	.040			1.52	4.38	5.90	7.30
9698	cycle 20 miles		144	.056			2.09	6.05	8.14	10.05
9700	cycle 30 miles		126	.063			2.38	6.90	9.28	11.45
9702	cycle 40 miles		108	.074			2.78	8.05	10.83	13.35
9704	cycle 50 miles		90	.089			3.34	9.65	12.99	16.05
9706	50 MPH ave, cycle 10 miles		198	.040			1.52	4.38	5.90	7.30
9708	cycle 20 miles		162	.049			1.85	5.35	7.20	8.90
9710	cycle 30 miles		126	.063			2.38	6.90	9.28	11.45
9712	cycle 40 miles		108	.074			2.78	8.05	10.83	13.35
9714	cycle 50 miles		90	.089			3.34	9.65	12.99	16.05

31 23 23.23 Compaction

		Crew	Daily Output	Labor-Hours	Unit	Material	2014 Bare Costs Labor	2014 Bare Costs Equipment	Total	Total Incl O&P
0010	**COMPACTION**									
5000	Riding, vibrating roller, 6" lifts, 2 passes	B-10Y	3000	.004	E.C.Y.		.18	.19	.37	.50
5020	3 passes		2300	.005			.23	.24	.47	.64

509

31 23 23.23 Compaction

		Crew	Daily Output	Labor-Hours	Unit	Material	2014 Bare Costs Labor	Equipment	Total	Total Incl O&P
5040	4 passes	B-10Y	1900	.006	E.C.Y.		.28	.29	.57	.77
5050	8" lifts, 2 passes		4100	.003			.13	.14	.27	.36
5060	12" lifts, 2 passes		5200	.002			.10	.11	.21	.29
5080	3 passes		3500	.003			.15	.16	.31	.43
5100	4 passes		2600	.005			.21	.22	.43	.57
5600	Sheepsfoot or wobbly wheel roller, 6" lifts, 2 passes	B-10G	2400	.005			.22	.51	.73	.92
5620	3 passes		1735	.007			.31	.70	1.01	1.27
5640	4 passes		1300	.009			.41	.94	1.35	1.69
5680	12" lifts, 2 passes		5200	.002			.10	.23	.33	.43
5700	3 passes		3500	.003			.15	.35	.50	.63
5720	4 passes		2600	.005			.21	.47	.68	.85
7000	Walk behind, vibrating plate 18" wide, 6" lifts, 2 passes	A-1D	200	.040			1.47	.18	1.65	2.61
7020	3 passes		185	.043			1.58	.19	1.77	2.81
7040	4 passes		140	.057			2.09	.26	2.35	3.72
7200	12" lifts, 2 passes, 21" wide	A-1E	560	.014			.52	.08	.60	.95
7220	3 passes		375	.021			.78	.12	.90	1.42
7240	4 passes		280	.029			1.05	.16	1.21	1.90
7500	Vibrating roller 24" wide, 6" lifts, 2 passes	B-10A	420	.029			1.28	.44	1.72	2.53
7520	3 passes		280	.043			1.92	.65	2.57	3.80
7540	4 passes		210	.057			2.56	.87	3.43	5.05
7600	12" lifts, 2 passes		840	.014			.64	.22	.86	1.27
7620	3 passes		560	.021			.96	.33	1.29	1.90
7640	4 passes		420	.029			1.28	.44	1.72	2.53
8000	Rammer tamper, 6" to 11", 4" lifts, 2 passes	A-1F	130	.062			2.26	.38	2.64	4.12
8050	3 passes		97	.082			3.02	.51	3.53	5.50
8100	4 passes		65	.123			4.51	.76	5.27	8.25
8200	8" lifts, 2 passes		260	.031			1.13	.19	1.32	2.06
8250	3 passes		195	.041			1.50	.25	1.75	2.75
8300	4 passes		130	.062			2.26	.38	2.64	4.12
8400	13" to 18", 4" lifts, 2 passes	A-1G	390	.021			.75	.14	.89	1.39
8450	3 passes		290	.028			1.01	.19	1.20	1.87
8500	4 passes		195	.041			1.50	.29	1.79	2.79
8600	8" lifts, 2 passes		780	.010			.38	.07	.45	.70
8650	3 passes		585	.014			.50	.10	.60	.93
8700	4 passes		390	.021			.75	.14	.89	1.39
9000	Water, 3000 gal. truck, 3 mile haul	B-45	1888	.008		1.20	.37	.49	2.06	2.45
9010	6 mile haul		1444	.011		1.20	.48	.64	2.32	2.79
9020	12 mile haul		1000	.016		1.20	.69	.92	2.81	3.44
9030	6000 gal. wagon, 3 mile haul	B-59	2000	.004		1.20	.15	.25	1.60	1.84
9040	6 mile haul	"	1600	.005		1.20	.19	.32	1.71	1.98

31 23 23.24 Compaction, Structural

		Crew	Daily Output	Labor-Hours	Unit	Material	2014 Bare Costs Labor	Equipment	Total	Total Incl O&P
0010	**COMPACTION, STRUCTURAL** R312323-30									
0020	Steel wheel tandem roller, 5 tons	B-10E	8	1.500	Hr.		67	19.90	86.90	130
0050	Air tamp, 6" to 8" lifts, common fill	B-9	250	.160	E.C.Y.		5.95	.93	6.88	10.80
0060	Select fill	"	300	.133			4.94	.78	5.72	8.95
0600	Vibratory plate, 8" lifts, common fill	A-1D	200	.040			1.47	.18	1.65	2.61
0700	Select fill	"	216	.037			1.36	.17	1.53	2.41
9000	Minimum labor/equipment charge	1 Clab	4	2	Job		73.50		73.50	120

31 25 Erosion and Sedimentation Controls

31 25 14 – Stabilization Measures for Erosion and Sedimentation Control

31 25 14.16 Rolled Erosion Control Mats and Blankets

		Crew	Daily Output	Labor-Hours	Unit	Material	2014 Bare Costs Labor	Equipment	Total	Total Incl O&P
0010	**ROLLED EROSION CONTROL MATS AND BLANKETS**									
0020	Jute mesh, 100 S.Y. per roll, 4' wide, stapled G	B-80A	2400	.010	S.Y.	1.11	.37	.14	1.62	1.97
0100	Plastic netting, stapled, 2" x 1" mesh, 20 mil G	B-1	2500	.010		.23	.36		.59	.84
0200	Polypropylene mesh, stapled, 6.5 oz./S.Y. G		2500	.010		2.33	.36		2.69	3.15
0300	Tobacco netting, or jute mesh #2, stapled G		2500	.010		.18	.36		.54	.79
1000	Silt fence, polypropylene, 3' high, ideal conditions G	2 Clab	1600	.010	L.F.	.24	.37		.61	.86
1100	Adverse conditions G	"	950	.017	"	.24	.62		.86	1.27
1200	Place and remove hay bales G	A-2	3	8	Ton	241	293	90	624	845
1250	Hay bales, staked G	"	2500	.010	L.F.	9.65	.35	.11	10.11	11.30

31 31 Soil Treatment

31 31 16 – Termite Control

31 31 16.13 Chemical Termite Control

		Crew	Daily Output	Labor-Hours	Unit	Material	2014 Bare Costs Labor	Equipment	Total	Total Incl O&P
0010	**CHEMICAL TERMITE CONTROL**									
0020	Slab and walls, residential	1 Skwk	1200	.007	SF Flr.	.37	.32		.69	.92
0100	Commercial, minimum		2496	.003		.32	.15		.47	.60
0200	Maximum		1645	.005		.48	.23		.71	.90
0390	Minimum labor/equipment charge		4	2	Job		94.50		94.50	154
0400	Insecticides for termite control, minimum		14.20	.563	Gal.	63	26.50		89.50	113
0500	Maximum		11	.727	"	108	34.50		142.50	175

31 41 Shoring

31 41 13 – Timber Shoring

31 41 13.10 Building Shoring

		Crew	Daily Output	Labor-Hours	Unit	Material	2014 Bare Costs Labor	Equipment	Total	Total Incl O&P
0010	**BUILDING SHORING**									
0020	Shoring, existing building, with timber, no salvage allowance	B-51	2.20	21.818	M.B.F.	760	805	123	1,688	2,300
1000	On cribbing with 35 ton screw jacks, per box and jack		3.60	13.333	Jack	71	495	75	641	970
1090	Minimum labor/equipment charge		2	24	Ea.		885	135	1,020	1,600
1100	Masonry openings in walls, see Section 02 41 19.16									

31 41 16 – Sheet Piling

31 41 16.10 Sheet Piling Systems

		Crew	Daily Output	Labor-Hours	Unit	Material	2014 Bare Costs Labor	Equipment	Total	Total Incl O&P
0010	**SHEET PILING SYSTEMS**									
0020	Sheet piling steel, not incl. wales, 22 psf, 15' excav., left in place	B-40	10.81	5.920	Ton	1,450	272	355	2,077	2,425
0100	Drive, extract & salvage R314116-40		6	10.667	"	505	490	635	1,630	2,050
1200	15' deep excavation, 22 psf, left in place		983	.065	S.F.	16.95	3	3.89	23.84	28
1300	Drive, extract & salvage		545	.117	"	5.65	5.40	7	18.05	22.50
2100	Rent steel sheet piling and wales, first month				Ton	305			305	335
2200	Per added month				"	30.50			30.50	33.50
3900	Wood, solid sheeting, incl. wales, braces and spacers,									
3910	drive, extract & salvage, 8' deep excavation	B-31	330	.121	S.F.	1.76	4.71	.66	7.13	10.40
4520	Left in place, 8' deep, 55 S.F./hr.		440	.091	"	3.18	3.54	.50	7.22	9.85
4990	Minimum labor/equipment charge		2	20	Job		780	110	890	1,400
5000	For treated lumber add cost of treatment to lumber									

31 43 Concrete Raising

31 43 13 - Pressure Grouting

31 43 13.13 Concrete Pressure Grouting	Crew	Daily Output	Labor-Hours	Unit	Material	2014 Bare Costs Labor	2014 Bare Costs Equipment	Total	Total Incl O&P
0010 **CONCRETE PRESSURE GROUTING**									
0020 Grouting, pressure, cement & sand, 1:1 mix, minimum	B-61	124	.323	Bag	13.95	12.60	2.81	29.36	39
0100 Maximum		51	.784	"	13.95	30.50	6.85	51.30	73
0200 Cement and sand, 1:1 mix, minimum		250	.160	C.F.	28	6.25	1.40	35.65	42
0300 Maximum		100	.400		42	15.65	3.49	61.14	75.50
0400 Epoxy cement grout, minimum		137	.292		720	11.40	2.55	733.95	815
0500 Maximum		57	.702		720	27.50	6.10	753.60	845
0700 Alternate pricing method: (Add for materials)									
0710 5 person crew and equipment	B-61	1	40	Day		1,575	350	1,925	2,925

31 46 Needle Beams

31 46 13 - Cantilever Needle Beams

31 46 13.10 Needle Beams

	Crew	Daily Output	Labor-Hours	Unit	Material	2014 Bare Costs Labor	2014 Bare Costs Equipment	Total	Total Incl O&P
0010 **NEEDLE BEAMS**									
0011 Incl. wood shoring 10' x 10' opening									
0400 Block, concrete, 8" thick	B-9	7.10	5.634	Ea.	50	209	33	292	435
0420 12" thick		6.70	5.970		58	221	35	314	470
0800 Brick, 4" thick with 8" backup block		5.70	7.018		58	260	41	359	535
1000 Brick, solid, 8" thick		6.20	6.452		50	239	37.50	326.50	490
1040 12" thick		4.90	8.163		58	300	47.50	405.50	610
1080 16" thick		4.50	8.889		74	330	52	456	680
2000 Add for additional floors of shoring	B-1	6	4		50	149		199	300
9000 Minimum labor/equipment charge	"	2	12	Job		450		450	735

31 48 Underpinning

31 48 13 - Underpinning Piers

31 48 13.10 Underpinning Foundations

	Crew	Daily Output	Labor-Hours	Unit	Material	2014 Bare Costs Labor	2014 Bare Costs Equipment	Total	Total Incl O&P
0010 **UNDERPINNING FOUNDATIONS**									
0011 Including excavation,									
0020 forming, reinforcing, concrete and equipment									
0100 5' to 16' below grade, 100 to 500 C.Y.	B-52	2.30	24.348	C.Y.	274	1,025	259	1,558	2,250
0200 Over 500 C.Y.		2.50	22.400		247	950	238	1,435	2,075
0400 16' to 25' below grade, 100 to 500 C.Y.		2	28		300	1,200	298	1,798	2,600
0500 Over 500 C.Y.		2.10	26.667		285	1,125	283	1,693	2,475
0700 26' to 40' below grade, 100 to 500 C.Y.		1.60	35		330	1,500	370	2,200	3,200
0800 Over 500 C.Y.		1.80	31.111		300	1,325	330	1,955	2,850
0900 For under 50 C.Y., add					10%	40%			

31 62 Driven Piles

31 62 13 - Concrete Piles

31 62 13.23 Prestressed Concrete Piles

31 62 13.23 Prestressed Concrete Piles	Crew	Daily Output	Labor-Hours	Unit	Material	2014 Bare Costs Labor	Equipment	Total	Total Incl O&P
0010 **PRESTRESSED CONCRETE PILES**, 200 piles									
0020 Unless specified otherwise, not incl. pile caps or mobilization									
3100 Precast, prestressed, 40' long, 10" thick, square	B-19	700	.091	V.L.F.	18.05	4.21	2.63	24.89	29.50
3200 12" thick, square		680	.094		21.50	4.33	2.71	28.54	34
3400 14" thick, square	↓	600	.107		25	4.91	3.07	32.98	39
4000 18" thick, square	B-19A	520	.123	↓	47	5.65	4.34	56.99	65.50

31 62 16 - Steel Piles

31 62 16.13 Steel Piles

31 62 16.13 Steel Piles	Crew	Daily Output	Labor-Hours	Unit	Material	2014 Bare Costs Labor	Equipment	Total	Total Incl O&P
0010 **STEEL PILES**									
0100 Step tapered, round, concrete filled									
0110 8" tip, 60 ton capacity, 30' depth	B-19	760	.084	V.L.F.	11.35	3.87	2.42	17.64	21.50
0120 60' depth		740	.086		12.85	3.98	2.49	19.32	23.50
0250 "H" Sections, 50' long, HP8 x 36	↓	640	.100		16.15	4.60	2.88	23.63	28.50
1300 HP14 X 102	B-19A	510	.125	↓	45	5.75	4.43	55.18	63.50

31 62 19 - Timber Piles

31 62 19.10 Wood Piles

31 62 19.10 Wood Piles	Crew	Daily Output	Labor-Hours	Unit	Material	2014 Bare Costs Labor	Equipment	Total	Total Incl O&P
0010 **WOOD PILES**									
0011 Friction or end bearing, not including									
0050 mobilization or demobilization									
0100 Untreated piles, up to 30' long, 12" butts, 8" points	B-19	625	.102	V.L.F.	17.40	4.71	2.95	25.06	30
0200 30' to 39' long, 12" butts, 8" points	"	700	.091	"	17.40	4.21	2.63	24.24	29
0800 Treated piles, 12 lb. per C.F.,									
0810 friction or end bearing, ASTM class B									
1000 Up to 30' long, 12" butts, 8" points	B-19	625	.102	V.L.F.	16.70	4.71	2.95	24.36	29
1100 30' to 39' long, 12" butts, 8" points		700	.091		18.20	4.21	2.63	25.04	29.50
2700 Mobilization for 10,000 L.F. pile job, add		3300	.019			.89	.56	1.45	2.05
2800 25,000 L.F. pile job, add	↓	8500	.008	↓		.35	.22	.57	.80

31 62 23 - Composite Piles

31 62 23.13 Concrete-Filled Steel Piles

31 62 23.13 Concrete-Filled Steel Piles	Crew	Daily Output	Labor-Hours	Unit	Material	2014 Bare Costs Labor	Equipment	Total	Total Incl O&P
0010 **CONCRETE-FILLED STEEL PILES** no mobilization or demobilization									
2600 Pipe piles, 50' lg. 8" diam., 29 lb. per L.F., no concrete	B-19	500	.128	V.L.F.	20.50	5.90	3.68	30.08	36.50
2700 Concrete filled		460	.139		21.50	6.40	4	31.90	39
3500 14" diameter, 46 lb. per L.F., no concrete		430	.149		35.50	6.85	4.28	46.63	55
3600 Concrete filled		355	.180		40.50	8.30	5.20	54	63.50
4100 18" diameter, 59 lb. per L.F., no concrete		355	.180		50.50	8.30	5.20	64	74.50
4200 Concrete filled	↓	310	.206	↓	56.50	9.50	5.95	71.95	84

31 63 Bored Piles

31 63 26 - Drilled Caissons

31 63 26.13 Fixed End Caisson Piles

31 63 26.13 Fixed End Caisson Piles	Crew	Daily Output	Labor-Hours	Unit	Material	2014 Bare Costs Labor	Equipment	Total	Total Incl O&P
0010 **FIXED END CAISSON PILES**									
0015 Including excavation, concrete, 50 lb. reinforcing									
0020 per C.Y., not incl. mobilization, boulder removal, disposal									
0100 Open style, machine drilled, to 50' deep, in stable ground, no R316326-60									
0110 casings or ground water, 18" diam., 0.065 C.Y./L.F.	B-43	200	.240	V.L.F.	8.05	9.70	12.75	30.50	38.50
0200 24" diameter, 0.116 C.Y./L.F.		190	.253	"	14.40	10.20	13.45	38.05	47
0210 4' bell diameter , add		20	2.400	Ea.	250	97	128	475	570
0500 48" diameter, 0.465 C.Y./L.F.		100	.480	V.L.F.	57.50	19.40	25.50	102.40	123
0510 9' bell diameter , add	↓	2	24	Ea.	1,475	970	1,275	3,720	4,575

31 63 Bored Piles

31 63 26 – Drilled Caissons

31 63 26.13 Fixed End Caisson Piles

		Crew	Daily Output	Labor-Hours	Unit	Material	2014 Bare Costs Labor	Equipment	Total	Total Incl O&P
1200	Open style, machine drilled, to 50' deep, in wet ground, pulled									
1220	pulled casing and pumping									
1400	24" diameter, 0.116 C.Y./L.F.	B-48	125	.448	V.L.F.	14.40	18.50	23.50	56.40	71.50
1410	4' bell diameter, add	"	19.80	2.828	Ea.	250	117	147	514	625
1700	48" diameter, 0.465 C.Y./L.F.	B-49	55	1.600	V.L.F.	57.50	68.50	66.50	192.50	248
1710	9' bell diameter, add	"	3.30	26.667	Ea.	1,475	1,150	1,100	3,725	4,675
2300	Open style, machine drilled, to 50' deep, in soft rocks and									
2320	medium hard shales									
2500	24" diameter, 0.116 C.Y./L.F.	B-49	30	2.933	V.L.F.	14.40	126	122	262.40	355
2510	4' bell diameter, add		10.90	8.073	Ea.	250	345	335	930	1,200
2800	48" diameter, 0.465 C.Y./L.F.		10	8.800	V.L.F.	57.50	380	365	802.50	1,075
2810	9' bell diameter, add		1.10	80	Ea.	1,100	3,425	3,325	7,850	10,400
3600	For rock excavation, sockets, add, minimum		120	.733	C.F.		31.50	30.50	62	84.50
3650	Average		95	.926			40	38.50	78.50	107
3700	Maximum		48	1.833			78.50	76	154.50	211
3900	For 50' to 100' deep, add				V.L.F.				7%	7%
4000	For 100' to 150' deep, add								25%	25%
4100	For 150' to 200' deep, add								30%	30%
4200	For casings left in place, add				Lb.	1.13			1.13	1.24
4300	For other than 50 lb. reinf. per C.Y., add or deduct				"	1.10			1.10	1.21
4400	For steel "I" beam cores, add	B-49	8.30	10.602	Ton	2,125	455	440	3,020	3,550
4500	Load and haul excess excavation, 2 miles	B-34B	178	.045	L.C.Y.		1.69	3.89	5.58	7
4600	For mobilization, 50 mile radius, rig to 36"	B-43	2	24	Ea.		970	1,275	2,245	2,975
4650	Rig to 84"	B-48	1.75	32			1,325	1,650	2,975	3,950
4700	For low headroom, add								50%	50%
4750	For difficult access, add								25%	25%

31 63 29 – Drilled Concrete Piers and Shafts

31 63 29.13 Uncased Drilled Concrete Piers

		Crew	Daily Output	Labor-Hours	Unit	Material	2014 Bare Costs Labor	Equipment	Total	Total Incl O&P
0010	**UNCASED DRILLED CONCRETE PIERS**									
0020	Unless specified otherwise, not incl. pile caps or mobilization									
0800	Cast in place friction pile, 50' long, fluted,									
0810	tapered steel, 4000 psi concrete, no reinforcing									
0900	12" diameter, 7 ga.	B-19	600	.107	V.L.F.	29.50	4.91	3.07	37.48	44
1200	18" diameter, 7 ga.	"	480	.133	"	44	6.15	3.83	53.98	62.50
1300	End bearing, fluted, constant diameter,									
1320	4000 psi concrete, no reinforcing									
1340	12" diameter, 7 ga.	B-19	600	.107	V.L.F.	30.50	4.91	3.07	38.48	45
1400	18" diameter, 7 ga.	"	480	.133	"	49	6.15	3.83	58.98	68

Estimating Tips

32 01 00 Operations and Maintenance of Exterior Improvements

- Recycling of asphalt pavement is becoming very popular and is an alternative to removal and replacement. It can be a good value engineering proposal if removed pavement can be recycled, either at the project site or at another site that is reasonably close to the project site. Sections on repair of flexible and rigid pavement are included.

32 10 00 Bases, Ballasts, and Paving

- When estimating paving, keep in mind the project schedule. Also note that prices for asphalt and concrete are generally higher in the cold seasons. Lines for pavement markings, including tactile warning systems and fence lines, are included.

32 90 00 Planting

- The timing of planting and guarantee specifications often dictate the costs for establishing tree and shrub growth and a stand of grass or ground cover. Establish the work performance schedule to coincide with the local planting season. Maintenance and growth guarantees can add from 20%–100% to the total landscaping cost and can be contractually cumbersome. The cost to replace trees and shrubs can be as high as 5% of the total cost, depending on the planting zone, soil conditions, and time of year.

Reference Numbers

Reference numbers are shown in shaded boxes at the beginning of some major classifications. These numbers refer to related items in the Reference Section. The reference information may be an estimating procedure, an alternate pricing method, or technical information.

Note: Not all subdivisions listed here necessarily appear in this publication.

Division 32 - Exterior Improvements

32 01 13 – Flexible Paving Surface Treatment

32 01 13.61 Slurry Seal (Latex Modified)

		Crew	Daily Output	Labor-Hours	Unit	Material	2014 Bare Costs Labor	Equipment	Total	Total Incl O&P
0010	**SLURRY SEAL (LATEX MODIFIED)**									
3600	Waterproofing, membrane, tar and fabric, small area	B-63	233	.172	S.Y.	13.90	6.65	.75	21.30	27
3640	Large area		1435	.028		12.80	1.08	.12	14	16
3680	Preformed rubberized asphalt, small area		100	.400		18.95	15.50	1.74	36.19	48
3720	Large area	▼	367	.109		17.25	4.22	.48	21.95	26.50
3780	Rubberized asphalt (latex) seal	B-45	5000	.003	▼	2.78	.14	.18	3.10	3.48
9000	Minimum labor/equipment charge	1 Clab	2	4	Job		147		147	241

32 01 13.62 Asphalt Surface Treatment

		Crew	Daily Output	Labor-Hours	Unit	Material	2014 Bare Costs Labor	Equipment	Total	Total Incl O&P
0010	**ASPHALT SURFACE TREATMENT**									
3000	Pavement overlay, polypropylene									
3040	6 oz. per S.Y., ideal conditions	B-63	10000	.004	S.Y.	2.16	.15	.02	2.33	2.65
3080	Adverse conditions		1000	.040		2.89	1.55	.17	4.61	5.90
3120	4 oz. per S.Y., ideal conditions		10000	.004		1.68	.15	.02	1.85	2.12
3160	Adverse conditions	▼	1000	.040		2.17	1.55	.17	3.89	5.10
3200	Tack coat, emulsion, .05 gal. per S.Y., 1000 S.Y.	B-45	2500	.006		.28	.28	.37	.93	1.16
3240	10,000 S.Y.		10000	.002		.22	.07	.09	.38	.46
3270	.10 gal. per S.Y., 1000 S.Y.		2500	.006		.53	.28	.37	1.18	1.43
3275	10,000 S.Y.		10000	.002		.42	.07	.09	.58	.67
3280	.15 gal. per S.Y., 1000 S.Y.		2500	.006		.77	.28	.37	1.42	1.70
3320	10,000 S.Y.	▼	10000	.002	▼	.62	.07	.09	.78	.89

32 01 13.64 Sand Seal

		Crew	Daily Output	Labor-Hours	Unit	Material	2014 Bare Costs Labor	Equipment	Total	Total Incl O&P
0010	**SAND SEAL**									
2080	Sand sealing, sharp sand, asphalt emulsion, small area	B-91	10000	.006	S.Y.	1.47	.28	.24	1.99	2.32
2120	Roadway or large area	"	18000	.004	"	1.26	.15	.13	1.54	1.78
3000	Sealing random cracks, min 1/2" wide, to 1-1/2", 1,000 L.F.	B-77	2800	.014	L.F.	1.50	.53	.21	2.24	2.76
3040	10,000 L.F.		4000	.010	"	1.04	.37	.15	1.56	1.92
3080	Alternate method, 1,000 L.F.		200	.200	Gal.	39.50	7.40	3.01	49.91	58.50
3120	10,000 L.F.	▼	325	.123	"	31.50	4.56	1.85	37.91	44
3200	Multi-cracks (flooding), 1 coat, small area	B-92	460	.070	S.Y.	2.32	2.58	1.39	6.29	8.35
3240	Large area		2850	.011		2.06	.42	.22	2.70	3.21
3280	2 coat, small area		230	.139		14.40	5.15	2.78	22.33	27.50
3320	Large area		1425	.022	▼	13.05	.83	.45	14.33	16.20
3360	Alternate method, small area		115	.278	Gal.	14.40	10.35	5.55	30.30	39
3400	Large area	▼	715	.045	"	13.50	1.66	.89	16.05	18.55

32 01 13.66 Fog Seal

		Crew	Daily Output	Labor-Hours	Unit	Material	2014 Bare Costs Labor	Equipment	Total	Total Incl O&P
0010	**FOG SEAL**									
0012	Sealcoating, 2 coat coal tar pitch emulsion over 10,000 S.Y.	B-45	5000	.003	S.Y.	1.29	.14	.18	1.61	1.84
0030	1000 to 10,000 S.Y.	"	3000	.005		1.29	.23	.31	1.83	2.13
0100	Under 1000 S.Y.	B-1	1050	.023		1.29	.85		2.14	2.82
0300	Petroleum resistant, over 10,000 S.Y.	B-45	5000	.003		1.29	.14	.18	1.61	1.84
0320	1000 to 10,000 S.Y.	"	3000	.005		1.29	.23	.31	1.83	2.13
0400	Under 1000 S.Y.	B-1	1050	.023		1.29	.85		2.14	2.82
0600	Non-skid pavement renewal, over 10,000 S.Y.	B-45	5000	.003		1.36	.14	.18	1.68	1.92
0620	1000 to 10,000 S.Y.	"	3000	.005		1.36	.23	.31	1.90	2.21
0700	Under 1000 S.Y.	B-1	1050	.023		1.36	.85		2.21	2.90
0800	Prepare and clean surface for above	A-2	8545	.003	▼		.10	.03	.13	.20
1000	Hand seal asphalt curbing	B-1	4420	.005	L.F.	.61	.20		.81	1
1900	Asphalt surface treatment, single course, small area									
1901	0.30 gal/S.Y. asphalt material, 20#/S.Y. aggregate	B-91	5000	.013	S.Y.	1.29	.55	.47	2.31	2.83
1910	Roadway or large area		10000	.006		1.19	.28	.24	1.71	2.01
1950	Asphalt surface treatment, dbl. course for small area		3000	.021		2.91	.92	.78	4.61	5.55
1960	Roadway or large area	▼	6000	.011	▼	2.62	.46	.39	3.47	4.05

32 01 Operation and Maintenance of Exterior Improvements

32 01 13 – Flexible Paving Surface Treatment

32 01 13.66 Fog Seal

	32 01 13.66 Fog Seal	Crew	Daily Output	Labor-Hours	Unit	Material	2014 Bare Costs Labor	2014 Bare Costs Equipment	Total	Total Incl O&P
1980	Asphalt surface treatment, single course, for shoulders	B-91	7500	.009	S.Y.	1.45	.37	.31	2.13	2.54

32 01 13.68 Slurry Seal

	32 01 13.68 Slurry Seal	Crew	Daily Output	Labor-Hours	Unit	Material	Labor	Equipment	Total	Total Incl O&P
0010	**SLURRY SEAL**									
0100	Slurry seal, type I, 8 lb. agg./S.Y., 1 coat, small or irregular area	B-90	2800	.023	S.Y.	1.84	.91	.79	3.54	4.36
0150	Roadway or large area		10000	.006		1.84	.25	.22	2.31	2.67
0200	Type II, 12 lb. aggregate/S.Y., 2 coats, small or irregular area		2000	.032		3.68	1.27	1.11	6.06	7.35
0250	Roadway or large area		8000	.008		3.68	.32	.28	4.28	4.88
0300	Type III, 20 lb. aggregate/S.Y., 2 coats, small or irregular area		1800	.036		4.34	1.41	1.23	6.98	8.45
0350	Roadway or large area		6000	.011		4.34	.42	.37	5.13	5.90
0400	Slurry seal, thermoplastic coal-tar, type I, small or irregular area		2400	.027		3.73	1.06	.93	5.72	6.85
0450	Roadway or large area		8000	.008		3.73	.32	.28	4.33	4.93
0500	Type II, small or irregular area		2400	.027		4.77	1.06	.93	6.76	8
0550	Roadway or large area		7800	.008		4.77	.33	.28	5.38	6.10

32 01 16 – Flexible Paving Rehabilitation

32 01 16.71 Cold Milling Asphalt Paving

	32 01 16.71 Cold Milling Asphalt Paving	Crew	Daily Output	Labor-Hours	Unit	Material	Labor	Equipment	Total	Total Incl O&P
0010	**COLD MILLING ASPHALT PAVING**									
5200	Cold planing & cleaning, 1" to 3" asphalt pavmt., over 25,000 S.Y.	B-71	6000	.009	S.Y.		.39	1.15	1.54	1.91
5280	5,000 S.Y. to 10,000 S.Y.	"	4000	.014	"		.59	1.73	2.32	2.85
5300	Asphalt pavement removal from conc. base, no haul									
5320	Rip, load & sweep 1" to 3"	B-70	8000	.007	S.Y.		.30	.23	.53	.73
5330	3" to 6" deep	"	5000	.011			.47	.37	.84	1.16
5340	Profile grooving, asphalt pavement load & sweep, 1" deep	B-71	12500	.004			.19	.55	.74	.92
5350	3" deep		9000	.006			.26	.77	1.03	1.27
5360	6" deep		5000	.011			.47	1.38	1.85	2.28

32 01 16.73 In Place Cold Reused Asphalt Paving

	32 01 16.73 In Place Cold Reused Asphalt Paving	Crew	Daily Output	Labor-Hours	Unit	Material	Labor	Equipment	Total	Total Incl O&P
0010	**IN PLACE COLD REUSED ASPHALT PAVING**									
5000	Reclamation, pulverizing and blending with existing base									
5040	Aggregate base, 4" thick pavement, over 15,000 S.Y.	B-73	2400	.027	S.Y.		1.19	2.16	3.35	4.28
5080	5,000 S.Y. to 15,000 S.Y.		2200	.029			1.30	2.35	3.65	4.67
5120	8" thick pavement, over 15,000 S.Y.		2200	.029			1.30	2.35	3.65	4.67
5160	5,000 S.Y. to 15,000 S.Y.		2000	.032			1.43	2.59	4.02	5.15

32 01 16.74 In Place Hot Reused Asphalt Paving

	32 01 16.74 In Place Hot Reused Asphalt Paving		Crew	Daily Output	Labor-Hours	Unit	Material	Labor	Equipment	Total	Total Incl O&P
0010	**IN PLACE HOT REUSED ASPHALT PAVING**										
5500	Recycle asphalt pavement at site										
5520	Remove, rejuvenate and spread 4" deep	G	B-72	2500	.026	S.Y.	4.59	1.10	4.60	10.29	11.85
5521	6" deep	G	"	2000	.032	"	6.75	1.38	5.75	13.88	15.90

32 01 17 – Flexible Paving Repair

32 01 17.10 Repair of Asphalt Pavement Holes

	32 01 17.10 Repair of Asphalt Pavement Holes	Crew	Daily Output	Labor-Hours	Unit	Material	Labor	Equipment	Total	Total Incl O&P
0010	**REPAIR OF ASPHALT PAVEMENT HOLES** (cold patch)									
0100	Flexible pavement repair holes, roadway, light traffic, 1 C.F. size	B-37A	24	1	Ea.	9.05	36.50	15.60	61.15	87
0150	Group of two, 1 C.F. size each		16	1.500	Set	18.05	55	23.50	96.55	136
0200	Group of three, 1 C.F. size each		12	2	"	27	73	31	131	185
0300	Medium traffic, 1 C.F. size each	B-37B	24	1.333	Ea.	9.05	49	15.60	73.65	107
0350	Group of two, 1 C.F. size each		16	2	Set	18.05	73	23.50	114.55	166
0400	Group of three, 1 C.F. size each		12	2.667	"	27	97.50	31	155.50	225
0500	Highway/heavy traffic, 1 C.F. size each	B-37C	24	1.333	Ea.	9.05	49	27	85.05	119
0550	Group of two, 1 C.F. size each		16	2	Set	18.05	73	40.50	131.55	184
0600	Group of three, 1 C.F. size each		12	2.667	"	27	97.50	54	178.50	248
0700	Add police officer and car for traffic control				Hr.	45.50			45.50	50
1000	Flexible pavement repair holes, parking lot, bag material, 1 C.F. size each	B-37D	18	.889	Ea.	64.50	32.50	8.70	105.70	134
1010	Economy bag material, 1 C.F. each		18	.889	"	43	32.50	8.70	84.20	110

32 01 17.10 Repair of Asphalt Pavement Holes

		Crew	Daily Output	Labor-Hours	Unit	Material	2014 Bare Costs Labor	2014 Bare Costs Equipment	Total	Total Incl O&P
1100	Group of two, 1 C.F. size each	B-37D	12	1.333	Set	129	49	13.10	191.10	236
1110	Group of two, economy bag, 1 C.F. size each		12	1.333		86	49	13.10	148.10	188
1200	Group of three 1 C.F. size each		10	1.600		194	58.50	15.70	268.20	325
1210	Economy bag, group of three, 1 C.F. size each	▼	10	1.600	▼	129	58.50	15.70	203.20	255
1300	Flexible pavement repair holes, parking lot, 1 C.F. single hole	A-3A	4	2	Ea.	64.50	73	42	179.50	237
1310	Economy material, 1 C.F. single hole		4	2	"	43	73	42	158	213
1400	Flexible pavement repair holes, parking lot, 1 C.F. four holes		2	4	Set	259	146	84	489	615
1410	Economy material, 1 C.F. four holes	▼	2	4	"	172	146	84	402	520
1500	Flexible pavement repair holes, large parking lot, bulk matl, 1 C.F. size	B-37A	32	.750	Ea.	9.05	27.50	11.70	48.25	68

32 01 17.20 Repair of Asphalt Pavement Patches

		Crew	Daily Output	Labor-Hours	Unit	Material	2014 Bare Costs Labor	2014 Bare Costs Equipment	Total	Total Incl O&P
0010	**REPAIR OF ASPHALT PAVEMENT PATCHES**									
0100	Flexible pavement patches, roadway, light traffic, sawcut 10-25 S.F.	B-89	12	1.333	Ea.		55.50	44	99.50	138
0150	Sawcut 26-60 S.F.		10	1.600			67	52.50	119.50	165
0200	Sawcut 61-100 S.F.		8	2			83.50	65.50	149	207
0210	Sawcut groups of small size patches		24	.667			28	22	50	68.50
0220	Large size patches	▼	16	1			42	33	75	103
0300	Flexible pavement patches, roadway, light traffic, digout 10-25 S.F.	B-6	16	1.500			60	23	83	123
0350	Digout 26-60 S.F.		12	2			80	30.50	110.50	164
0400	Digout 61-100 S.F.	▼	8	3	▼		120	45.50	165.50	245
0450	Add 8 C.Y. truck, small project debris haulaway	B-34A	8	1	Hr.		37.50	52	89.50	119
0460	Add 12 C.Y. truck, small project debris haulaway	B-34B	8	1			37.50	86.50	124	156
0480	Add flagger for non-intersection medium traffic	1 Clab	8	1			36.50		36.50	60
0490	Add flasher truck for intersection medium traffic or heavy traffic	A-2B	8	1	▼		36.50	34	70.50	96.50
0500	Flexible pavement patches, roadway, repave, cold, 15 S.F., 4" D	B-37	8	6	Ea.	43	232	19.85	294.85	450
0510	6" depth		8	6		65	232	19.85	316.85	475
0520	Repave, cold, 20 S.F., 4" depth		8	6		57.50	232	19.85	309.35	465
0530	6" depth		8	6		87	232	19.85	338.85	500
0540	Repave, cold, 25 S.F., 4" depth		8	6		71.50	232	19.85	323.35	480
0550	6" depth		8	6		108	232	19.85	359.85	520
0600	Repave, cold, 30 S.F., 4" depth		8	6		86	232	19.85	337.85	495
0610	6" depth		8	6		130	232	19.85	381.85	545
0640	Repave, cold, 40 S.F., 4" depth		8	6		114	232	19.85	365.85	530
0650	6" depth		8	6		173	232	19.85	424.85	595
0680	Repave, cold, 50 S.F., 4" depth		8	6		143	232	19.85	394.85	560
0690	6" depth		8	6		217	232	19.85	468.85	640
0720	Repave, cold, 60 S.F., 4" depth		8	6		172	232	19.85	423.85	590
0730	6" depth		8	6		260	232	19.85	511.85	690
0800	Repave, cold, 70 S.F., 4" depth		7	6.857		200	266	22.50	488.50	680
0810	6" depth		7	6.857		305	266	22.50	593.50	795
0820	Repave, cold, 75 S.F., 4" depth		7	6.857		213	266	22.50	501.50	695
0830	6" depth		7	6.857		325	266	22.50	613.50	820
0900	Repave, cold, 80 S.F., 4" depth		6	8		229	310	26.50	565.50	785
0910	6" depth		6	8		345	310	26.50	681.50	915
0940	Repave, cold, 90 S.F., 4" depth		6	8		257	310	26.50	593.50	815
0950	6" depth		6	8		390	310	26.50	726.50	965
0980	Repave, cold, 100 S.F., 4" depth		6	8		286	310	26.50	622.50	850
0990	6" depth	▼	6	8	▼	435	310	26.50	771.50	1,000
1000	Add flasher truck for paving operations in medium or heavy traffic	A-2B	8	1	Hr.		36.50	34	70.50	96.50
1100	Prime coat for repair 15-40 S.F., 25% overspray	B-37A	48	.500	Ea.	7	18.30	7.80	33.10	46.50
1150	41-60 S.F.		40	.600		14	22	9.35	45.35	61.50
1175	61-80 S.F.		32	.750		18.95	27.50	11.70	58.15	79
1200	81-100 S.F.	▼	32	.750	▼	23.50	27.50	11.70	62.70	83.50

32 01 Operation and Maintenance of Exterior Improvements

32 01 17 – Flexible Paving Repair

32 01 17.20 Repair of Asphalt Pavement Patches

		Crew	Daily Output	Labor-Hours	Unit	Material	2014 Bare Costs Labor	Equipment	Total	Total Incl O&P
1210	Groups of patches w/25% overspray	B-37A	3600	.007	S.F.	.23	.24	.10	.57	.77
1300	Flexible pavement repair patches,street repave,hot, 60 S.F., 4" D	B-37	8	6	Ea.	100	232	19.85	351.85	510
1310	6" depth		8	6		151	232	19.85	402.85	570
1320	Repave,hot, 70 S.F., 4" depth		7	6.857		116	266	22.50	404.50	590
1330	6" depth		7	6.857		176	266	22.50	464.50	655
1340	Repave,hot, 75 S.F., 4" depth		7	6.857		124	266	22.50	412.50	595
1350	6" depth		7	6.857		189	266	22.50	477.50	670
1360	Repave,hot, 80 S.F., 4" depth		6	8		133	310	26.50	469.50	680
1370	6" depth		6	8		202	310	26.50	538.50	755
1380	Repave,hot, 90 S.F., 4" depth		6	8		150	310	26.50	486.50	700
1390	6" depth		6	8		227	310	26.50	563.50	785
1400	Repave,hot, 100 S.F., 4" depth		6	8		166	310	26.50	502.50	715
1410	6" depth		6	8		252	310	26.50	588.50	810
1420	Pave hot groups of patches, 4" depth		900	.053	S.F.	1.66	2.06	.18	3.90	5.40
1430	6" depth		900	.053	"	2.52	2.06	.18	4.76	6.35
1500	Add 8 C.Y. truck for hot asphalt paving operations	B-34A	1	8	Day		300	415	715	950
1550	Add flasher truck for hot paving operations in med/heavy traffic	A-2B	8	1	Hr.		36.50	34	70.50	96.50
2000	Add police officer and car for traffic control				"	45.50			45.50	50

32 01 17.61 Sealing Cracks In Asphalt Paving

		Crew	Daily Output	Labor-Hours	Unit	Material	2014 Bare Costs Labor	Equipment	Total	Total Incl O&P
0010	**SEALING CRACKS IN ASPHALT PAVING**									
0100	Sealing cracks in asphalt paving, 1/8" wide x 1/2" depth, slow set	B-37A	2000	.012	L.F.	.17	.44	.19	.80	1.12
0110	1/4" wide x 1/2" depth		2000	.012		.20	.44	.19	.83	1.15
0130	3/8" wide x 1/2" depth		2000	.012		.22	.44	.19	.85	1.18
0140	1/2" wide x 1/2" depth		1800	.013		.25	.49	.21	.95	1.31
0150	3/4" wide x 1/2" depth		1600	.015		.31	.55	.23	1.09	1.50
0160	1" wide x 1/2" depth		1600	.015		.36	.55	.23	1.14	1.56
0165	1/8" wide x 1" depth, rapid set	B-37F	2000	.016		.25	.59	.30	1.14	1.57
0170	1/4" wide x 1" depth		2000	.016		.48	.59	.30	1.37	1.83
0175	3/8" wide x 1" depth		1800	.018		.73	.65	.34	1.72	2.24
0180	1/2" wide x 1" depth		1800	.018		.97	.65	.34	1.96	2.51
0185	5/8" wide x 1" depth		1800	.018		1.21	.65	.34	2.20	2.77
0190	3/4" wide x 1" depth		1600	.020		1.46	.73	.38	2.57	3.22
0195	1" wide x 1" depth		1600	.020		1.94	.73	.38	3.05	3.75
0200	1/8" wide x 2" depth, rapid set		2000	.016		.48	.59	.30	1.37	1.83
0210	1/4" wide x 2" depth		2000	.016		.97	.59	.30	1.86	2.37
0220	3/8" wide x 2" depth		1800	.018		1.46	.65	.34	2.45	3.04
0230	1/2" wide x 2" depth		1800	.018		1.94	.65	.34	2.93	3.57
0240	5/8" wide x 2" depth		1800	.018		2.43	.65	.34	3.42	4.11
0250	3/4" wide x 2" depth		1600	.020		2.91	.73	.38	4.02	4.82
0260	1" wide x 2" depth		1600	.020		3.88	.73	.38	4.99	5.90
0300	Add flagger for non-intersection medium traffic	1 Clab	8	1	Hr.		36.50		36.50	60
0400	Add flasher truck for intersection medium traffic or heavy traffic	A-2B	8	1	"		36.50	34	70.50	96.50

32 01 29 – Rigid Paving Repair

32 01 29.61 Partial Depth Patching of Rigid Pavement

		Crew	Daily Output	Labor-Hours	Unit	Material	2014 Bare Costs Labor	Equipment	Total	Total Incl O&P
0010	**PARTIAL DEPTH PATCHING OF RIGID PAVEMENT**									
0100	Rigid pavement repair, roadway,light traffic, 25% pitting 15 S.F.	B-37F	16	2	Ea.	27.50	73	38	138.50	192
0110	Pitting 20 S.F.		16	2		36.50	73	38	147.50	202
0120	Pitting 25 S.F.		16	2		45.50	73	38	156.50	212
0130	Pitting 30 S.F.		16	2		54.50	73	38	165.50	222
0140	Pitting 40 S.F.		16	2		73	73	38	184	242
0150	Pitting 50 S.F.		12	2.667		91	97.50	51	239.50	315
0160	Pitting 60 S.F.		12	2.667		109	97.50	51	257.50	335

32 01 29.61 Partial Depth Patching of Rigid Pavement

		Crew	Daily Output	Labor-Hours	Unit	Material	Labor	Equipment	Total	Total Incl O&P
0170	Pitting 70 S.F.	B-37F	12	2.667	Ea.	128	97.50	51	276.50	355
0180	Pitting 75 S.F.		12	2.667		137	97.50	51	285.50	365
0190	Pitting 80 S.F.		8	4		146	146	76	368	485
0200	Pitting 90 S.F.		8	4		164	146	76	386	505
0210	Pitting 100 S.F.		8	4		182	146	76	404	525
0300	Roadway, light traffic, 50% pitting 15 S.F.		12	2.667		54.50	97.50	51	203	276
0310	Pitting 20 S.F.		12	2.667		98	97.50	51	246.50	325
0320	Pitting 25 S.F.		12	2.667		91	97.50	51	239.50	315
0330	Pitting 30 S.F.		12	2.667		109	97.50	51	257.50	335
0340	Pitting 40 S.F.		12	2.667		146	97.50	51	294.50	375
0350	Pitting 50 S.F.		8	4		182	146	76	404	525
0360	Pitting 60 S.F.		8	4		219	146	76	441	565
0370	Pitting 70 S.F.		8	4		255	146	76	477	605
0380	Pitting 75 S.F.		8	4		273	146	76	495	625
0390	Pitting 80 S.F.		6	5.333		292	195	101	588	750
0400	Pitting 90 S.F.		6	5.333		330	195	101	626	790
0410	Pitting 100 S.F.		6	5.333		365	195	101	661	830
1000	Rigid pavement repair, light traffic, surface patch, 2" deep, 15 S.F.		8	4		109	146	76	331	445
1010	Surface patch, 2" deep, 20 S.F.		8	4		146	146	76	368	485
1020	Surface patch, 2" deep, 25 S.F.		8	4		182	146	76	404	525
1030	Surface patch, 2" deep, 30 S.F.		8	4		219	146	76	441	565
1040	Surface patch, 2" deep, 40 S.F.		8	4		292	146	76	514	645
1050	Surface patch, 2" deep, 50 S.F.		6	5.333		365	195	101	661	830
1060	Surface patch, 2" deep, 60 S.F.		6	5.333		440	195	101	736	910
1070	Surface patch, 2" deep, 70 S.F.		6	5.333		510	195	101	806	990
1080	Surface patch, 2" deep, 75 S.F.		6	5.333		545	195	101	841	1,025
1090	Surface patch, 2" deep, 80 S.F.		5	6.400		585	234	122	941	1,150
1100	Surface patch, 2" deep, 90 S.F.		5	6.400		655	234	122	1,011	1,250
1200	Surface patch, 2" deep, 100 S.F.		5	6.400		730	234	122	1,086	1,325
2000	Add flagger for non-intersection medium traffic	1 Clab	8	1	Hr.		36.50		36.50	60
2100	Add flasher truck for intersection medium traffic or heavy traffic	A-2B	8	1			36.50	34	70.50	96.50
2200	Add police officer and car for traffic control					45.50			45.50	50

32 01 29.70 Full Depth Patching of Rigid Pavement

		Crew	Daily Output	Labor-Hours	Unit	Material	Labor	Equipment	Total	Total Incl O&P
0010	**FULL DEPTH PATCHING OF RIGID PAVEMENT**									
0015	Pavement preparation includes sawcut, remove pavement and replace									
0020	6 inches of subbase and one layer of reinforcement									
0030	Trucking and haulaway of debris excluded									
0100	Rigid pavement replace, light traffic, prep, 15 S.F., 6" depth	B-37E	16	3.500	Ea.	21.50	139	67.50	228	325
0110	Replacement preparation 20 S.F., 6" depth		16	3.500		28.50	139	67.50	235	330
0115	25 S.F., 6" depth		16	3.500		35.50	139	67.50	242	340
0120	30 S.F., 6" depth		14	4		42.50	159	77	278.50	390
0125	35 S.F., 6" depth		14	4		50	159	77	286	400
0130	40 S.F., 6" depth		14	4		57	159	77	293	405
0135	45 S.F., 6" depth		14	4		64	159	77	300	415
0140	50 S.F., 6" depth		12	4.667		71	186	90	347	480
0145	55 S.F., 6" depth		12	4.667		78.50	186	90	354.50	485
0150	60 S.F., 6" depth		10	5.600		85.50	223	108	416.50	575
0155	65 S.F., 6" depth		10	5.600		92.50	223	108	423.50	580
0160	70 S.F., 6" depth		10	5.600		99.50	223	108	430.50	590
0165	75 S.F., 6" depth		10	5.600		107	223	108	438	595
0170	80 S.F., 6" depth		8	7		114	279	135	528	725
0175	85 S.F., 6" depth		8	7		121	279	135	535	730

32 01 29 – Rigid Paving Repair

32 01 29.70 Full Depth Patching of Rigid Pavement	Crew	Daily Output	Labor-Hours	Unit	Material	2014 Bare Costs Labor	Equipment	Total	Total Incl O&P
0180	90 S.F., 6" depth	B-37E	8	7	Ea.	128	279	135	542	740
0185	95 S.F., 6" depth		8	7		135	279	135	549	750
0190	100 S.F., 6" depth		8	7		142	279	135	556	755
0200	Pavement preparation for 8 inch rigid paving same as 6 inch									
0290	Pavement preparation for 9 inch rigid paving same as 10 inch									
0300	Rigid pavement replace, light traffic,prep, 15 S.F.,10" depth	B-37E	16	3.500	Ea.	35	139	67.50	241.50	340
0302	Pavement preparation 10 inch includes sawcut, remove pavement and									
0304	replace 6 inches of subbase and two layers of reinforcement									
0306	Trucking and haulaway of debris excluded									
0310	Replacement preparation 20 S.F., 10" depth	B-37E	16	3.500	Ea.	46.50	139	67.50	253	350
0315	25 S.F., 10" depth		16	3.500		58	139	67.50	264.50	365
0320	30 S.F., 10" depth		14	4		69.50	159	77	305.50	420
0325	35 S.F., 10" depth		14	4		54.50	159	77	290.50	405
0330	40 S.F., 10" depth		14	4		93	159	77	329	445
0335	45 S.F., 10" depth		12	4.667		105	186	90	381	515
0340	50 S.F., 10" depth		12	4.667		116	186	90	392	525
0345	55 S.F., 10" depth		12	4.667		128	186	90	404	540
0350	60 S.F., 10" depth		10	5.600		139	223	108	470	630
0355	65 S.F., 10" depth		10	5.600		151	223	108	482	645
0360	70 S.F., 10" depth		10	5.600		163	223	108	494	660
0365	75 S.F., 10" depth		8	7		174	279	135	588	790
0370	80 S.F., 10" depth		8	7		186	279	135	600	805
0375	85 S.F., 10" depth		8	7		198	279	135	612	815
0380	90 S.F., 10" depth		8	7		209	279	135	623	830
0385	95 S.F., 10" depth		8	7		221	279	135	635	840
0390	100 S.F., 10" depth		8	7		232	279	135	646	855
0500	Add 8 C.Y. truck, small project debris haulaway	B-34A	8	1	Hr.		37.50	52	89.50	119
0550	Add 12 C.Y. truck, small project debris haulaway	B-34B	8	1			37.50	86.50	124	156
0600	Add flagger for non-intersection medium traffic	1 Clab	8	1			36.50		36.50	60
0650	Add flasher truck for intersection medium traffic or heavy traffic	A-2B	8	1			36.50	34	70.50	96.50
0700	Add police officer and car for traffic control					45.50			45.50	50
0990	Concrete will replaced using quick set mix with aggregate									
1000	Rigid pavement replace, light traffic,repour,15 S.F.,6" depth	B-37F	18	1.778	Ea.	163	65	34	262	325
1010	20 S.F., 6" depth		18	1.778		217	65	34	316	385
1015	25 S.F., 6" depth		18	1.778		272	65	34	371	445
1020	30 S.F., 6" depth		16	2		325	73	38	436	520
1025	35 S.F., 6" depth		16	2		380	73	38	491	580
1030	40 S.F., 6" depth		16	2		435	73	38	546	640
1035	45 S.F., 6" depth		16	2		490	73	38	601	700
1040	50 S.F., 6" depth		16	2		545	73	38	656	755
1045	55 S.F., 6" depth		12	2.667		595	97.50	51	743.50	870
1050	60 S.F., 6" depth		12	2.667		650	97.50	51	798.50	930
1055	65 S.F., 6" depth		12	2.667		705	97.50	51	853.50	990
1060	70 S.F., 6" depth		12	2.667		760	97.50	51	908.50	1,050
1065	75 S.F., 6" depth		10	3.200		815	117	61	993	1,150
1070	80 S.F., 6" depth		10	3.200		870	117	61	1,048	1,225
1075	85 S.F., 6" depth		8	4		925	146	76	1,147	1,350
1080	90 S.F., 6" depth		8	4		980	146	76	1,202	1,400
1085	95 S.F., 6" depth		8	4		1,025	146	76	1,247	1,450
1090	100 S.F., 6" depth		8	4		1,075	146	76	1,297	1,525
1099	Concrete will be replaced using 4500 PSI Concrete ready mix									
1100	Rigid pavement replace, light traffic,repour, 15 S.F.,6" depth	A-2	12	2	Ea.	289	73	22.50	384.50	465
1110	20-50 S.F., 6" depth		12	2		289	73	22.50	384.50	465

32 01 Operation and Maintenance of Exterior Improvements

32 01 29 – Rigid Paving Repair

32 01 29.70 Full Depth Patching of Rigid Pavement		Crew	Daily Output	Labor-Hours	Unit	Material	2014 Bare Costs Labor	Equipment	Total	Total Incl O&P
1120	55-65 S.F., 6" depth	A-2	10	2.400	Ea.	320	88	27	435	525
1130	70-80 S.F., 6" depth		10	2.400		345	88	27	460	555
1140	85-100 S.F., 6" depth		8	3		405	110	34	549	660
1200	Repour 15-40 S.F.,8" depth		12	2		289	73	22.50	384.50	465
1210	45-50 S.F.,8" depth		12	2		320	73	22.50	415.50	495
1220	55-60 S.F.,8" depth		10	2.400		345	88	27	460	555
1230	65-80 S.F.,8" depth		10	2.400		405	88	27	520	620
1240	85-90 S.F.,8" depth		8	3		435	110	34	579	695
1250	95-100 S.F.,8" depth		8	3		460	110	34	604	725
1300	Repour 15-30 S.F.,10" depth		12	2		289	73	22.50	384.50	465
1310	35-40 S.F.,10" depth		12	2		320	73	22.50	415.50	495
1320	45 S.F.,10" depth		12	2		345	73	22.50	440.50	525
1330	50-65 S.F.,10" depth		10	2.400		405	88	27	520	620
1340	70 S.F.,10" depth		10	2.400		435	88	27	550	655
1350	75-80 S.F.,10" depth		10	2.400		460	88	27	575	685
1360	85-95 S.F.,10" depth		8	3		520	110	34	664	785
1370	100 S.F.,10" depth		8	3		550	110	34	694	820

32 06 Schedules for Exterior Improvements

32 06 10 – Schedules for Bases, Ballasts, and Paving

32 06 10.10 Sidewalks, Driveways and Patios

		Crew	Daily Output	Labor-Hours	Unit	Material	2014 Bare Costs Labor	Equipment	Total	Total Incl O&P
0010	**SIDEWALKS, DRIVEWAYS AND PATIOS** No base									
0020	Asphaltic concrete, 2" thick	B-37	720	.067	S.Y.	7.20	2.58	.22	10	12.35
0100	2-1/2" thick	"	660	.073	"	9.15	2.82	.24	12.21	14.90
0110	Bedding for brick or stone, mortar, 1" thick	D-1	300	.053	S.F.	.76	2.20		2.96	4.42
0120	2" thick	"	200	.080		1.90	3.30		5.20	7.45
0130	Sand, 2" thick	B-18	8000	.003		.26	.11	.01	.38	.48
0140	4" thick	"	4000	.006		.52	.22	.01	.75	.96
0300	Concrete, 3000 psi, CIP, 6 x 6 - W1.4 x W1.4 mesh,									
0310	broomed finish, no base, 4" thick	B-24	600	.040	S.F.	1.65	1.69		3.34	4.55
0350	5" thick		545	.044		2.20	1.86		4.06	5.45
0400	6" thick		510	.047		2.57	1.99		4.56	6.05
0450	For bank run gravel base, 4" thick, add	B-18	2500	.010		.51	.36	.02	.89	1.17
0520	8" thick, add	"	1600	.015		1.03	.56	.03	1.62	2.08
0550	Exposed aggregate finish, add to above, minimum	B-24	1875	.013		.10	.54		.64	.98
0600	Maximum	"	455	.053		.34	2.23		2.57	3.98
0950	Concrete tree grate, 5' square	B-6	25	.960	Ea.	420	38.50	14.60	473.10	540
0955	Tree well & cover, concrete, 3' square		25	.960		315	38.50	14.60	368.10	425
0960	Cast iron tree grate with frame, 2 piece, round, 5' diameter		25	.960		1,100	38.50	14.60	1,153.10	1,275
0980	Square, 5' side		25	.960		1,100	38.50	14.60	1,153.10	1,275
1700	Redwood, prefabricated, 4' x 4' sections	2 Carp	316	.051	S.F.	4.77	2.32		7.09	9.05
1750	Redwood planks, 1" thick, on sleepers	"	240	.067	"	4.77	3.06		7.83	10.25
2250	Stone dust, 4" thick	B-62	900	.027	S.Y.	3.89	1.07	.19	5.15	6.20
9000	Minimum labor/equipment charge	D-1	2	8	Job		330		330	535

32 06 10.20 Steps

		Crew	Daily Output	Labor-Hours	Unit	Material	2014 Bare Costs Labor	Equipment	Total	Total Incl O&P
0010	**STEPS**									
0011	Incl. excav., borrow & concrete base as required									
0100	Brick steps	B-24	35	.686	LF Riser	15	29		44	63.50
0200	Railroad ties	2 Clab	25	.640		3.55	23.50		27.05	42.50
0300	Bluestone treads, 12" x 2" or 12" x 1-1/2"	B-24	30	.800		33	33.50		66.50	90.50
0490	Minimum labor/equipment charge	D-1	2	8	Job		330		330	535

32 06 Schedules for Exterior Improvements

32 06 10 – Schedules for Bases, Ballasts, and Paving

32 06 10.20 Steps	Crew	Daily Output	Labor-Hours	Unit	Material	2014 Bare Costs Labor	Equipment	Total	Total Incl O&P
0500	Concrete, cast in place, see Section 03 30 53.40								
0600	Precast concrete, see Section 03 41 23.50								

32 11 Base Courses

32 11 23 – Aggregate Base Courses

32 11 23.23 Base Course Drainage Layers

		Crew	Daily Output	Labor-Hours	Unit	Material	2014 Bare Costs Labor	Equipment	Total	Total Incl O&P
0010	**BASE COURSE DRAINAGE LAYERS**									
0011	For roadways and large areas									
0050	Crushed 3/4" stone base, compacted, 3" deep	B-36C	5200	.008	S.Y.	2.76	.34	.79	3.89	4.45
0100	6" deep		5000	.008		5.50	.36	.82	6.68	7.50
0200	9" deep		4600	.009		8.30	.39	.89	9.58	10.70
0300	12" deep		4200	.010		11.05	.42	.98	12.45	13.90
0301	Crushed 1-1/2" stone base, compacted to 4" deep	B-36B	6000	.011		3.80	.46	.79	5.05	5.80
0302	6" deep		5400	.012		5.70	.51	.88	7.09	8.05
0303	8" deep		4500	.014		7.60	.61	1.05	9.26	10.50
0304	12" deep		3800	.017		11.40	.73	1.24	13.37	15.10
0310	Minimum labor/equipment charge	B-36	1	40	Job		1,675	1,600	3,275	4,475
0350	Bank run gravel, spread and compacted									
0370	6" deep	B-32	6000	.005	S.Y.	4.26	.24	.38	4.88	5.50
0390	9" deep		4900	.007		6.40	.30	.46	7.16	8.05
0400	12" deep		4200	.008		8.55	.35	.54	9.44	10.55
6900	For small and irregular areas, add						50%	50%		
6990	Minimum labor/equipment charge	1 Clab	3	2.667	Job		97.50		97.50	161
7000	Prepare and roll sub-base, small areas to 2500 S.Y.	B-32A	1500	.016	S.Y.		.72	.93	1.65	2.18
8000	Large areas over 2500 S.Y.	"	3500	.007			.31	.40	.71	.93
8050	For roadways	B-32	4000	.008			.37	.57	.94	1.22
9000	Minimum labor/equipment charge	1 Clab	4	2	Job		73.50		73.50	120

32 12 Flexible Paving

32 12 16 – Asphalt Paving

32 12 16.13 Plant-Mix Asphalt Paving

		Crew	Daily Output	Labor-Hours	Unit	Material	2014 Bare Costs Labor	Equipment	Total	Total Incl O&P
0010	**PLANT-MIX ASPHALT PAVING**									
0080	Binder course, 1-1/2" thick	B-25	7725	.011	S.Y.	5.55	.46	.36	6.37	7.25
0120	2" thick		6345	.014		7.40	.56	.44	8.40	9.55
0130	2-1/2" thick		5620	.016		9.25	.63	.49	10.37	11.70
0160	3" thick		4905	.018		11.10	.72	.56	12.38	14
0170	3-1/2" thick		4520	.019		12.95	.78	.61	14.34	16.20
0300	Wearing course, 1" thick	B-25B	10575	.009		3.67	.37	.28	4.32	4.95
0340	1-1/2" thick		7725	.012		6.15	.51	.39	7.05	8.05
0380	2" thick		6345	.015		8.30	.62	.47	9.39	10.60
0420	2-1/2" thick		5480	.018		10.20	.72	.55	11.47	13
0460	3" thick		4900	.020		12.20	.80	.61	13.61	15.35
0470	3-1/2" thick		4520	.021		14.30	.87	.66	15.83	17.85
0480	4" thick		4140	.023		16.35	.95	.73	18.03	20.50
0500	Open graded friction course	B-25C	5000	.010		2.04	.39	.48	2.91	3.42
0800	Alternate method of figuring paving costs									
0810	Binder course, 1-1/2" thick	B-25	630	.140	Ton	68	5.60	4.38	77.98	89
0811	2" thick		690	.128		68	5.10	4	77.10	87.50
0812	3" thick		800	.110		68	4.42	3.45	75.87	86

32 12 Flexible Paving

32 12 16 – Asphalt Paving

32 12 16.13 Plant-Mix Asphalt Paving

		Crew	Daily Output	Labor-Hours	Unit	Material	2014 Bare Costs Labor	Equipment	Total	Total Incl O&P
0813	4" thick	B-25	900	.098	Ton	68	3.93	3.07	75	85
0850	Wearing course, 1" thick	B-25B	575	.167		68	6.85	5.20	80.05	92
0851	1-1/2" thick		630	.152		68	6.25	4.76	79.01	90.50
0852	2" thick		690	.139		68	5.70	4.35	78.05	89
0853	2-1/2" thick		765	.125		68	5.15	3.92	77.07	87.50
0854	3" thick	↓	800	.120	↓	68	4.91	3.75	76.66	87
1000	Pavement replacement over trench, 2" thick	B-37	90	.533	S.Y.	7.65	20.50	1.77	29.92	44
1050	4" thick		70	.686		15.10	26.50	2.27	43.87	62.50
1080	6" thick	↓	55	.873	↓	24	34	2.89	60.89	84.50
3000	Prime coat, emulsion, .30 gal. per S.Y., 1000 S.Y.	B-45	2500	.006		1.68	.28	.37	2.33	2.70
3100	Tack coat, emulsion, .10 gal. per S.Y., 1000 S.Y.	"	2500	.006	↓	.56	.28	.37	1.21	1.47

32 12 16.14 Asphaltic Concrete Paving

		Crew	Daily Output	Labor-Hours	Unit	Material	2014 Bare Costs Labor	Equipment	Total	Total Incl O&P
0011	**ASPHALTIC CONCRETE PAVING**, parking lots & driveways									
0015	No asphalt hauling included									
0020	6" stone base, 2" binder course, 1" topping	B-25C	9000	.005	S.F.	1.74	.22	.27	2.23	2.56
0025	2" binder course, 2" topping		9000	.005		2.16	.22	.27	2.65	3.01
0030	3" binder course, 2" topping		9000	.005		2.57	.22	.27	3.06	3.47
0035	4" binder course, 2" topping		9000	.005		2.98	.22	.27	3.47	3.92
0040	1.5" binder course, 1" topping		9000	.005		1.54	.22	.27	2.03	2.33
0042	3" binder course, 1" topping		9000	.005		2.16	.22	.27	2.65	3.01
0045	3" binder course, 3" topping		9000	.005		2.98	.22	.27	3.47	3.92
0050	4" binder course, 3" topping		9000	.005		3.39	.22	.27	3.88	4.37
0055	4" binder course, 4" topping		9000	.005		3.80	.22	.27	4.29	4.82
0300	Binder course, 1-1/2" thick		35000	.001		.62	.06	.07	.75	.85
0400	2" thick		25000	.002		.80	.08	.10	.98	1.12
0500	3" thick		15000	.003		1.24	.13	.16	1.53	1.75
0600	4" thick		10800	.004		1.62	.18	.22	2.02	2.33
0800	Sand finish course, 3/4" thick		41000	.001		.32	.05	.06	.43	.49
0900	1" thick	↓	34000	.001		.39	.06	.07	.52	.60
1000	Fill pot holes, hot mix, 2" thick	B-16	4200	.008		.84	.28	.16	1.28	1.57
1100	4" thick		3500	.009		1.23	.34	.20	1.77	2.13
1120	6" thick		3100	.010		1.65	.39	.22	2.26	2.70
1140	Cold patch, 2" thick	B-51	3000	.016		.98	.59	.09	1.66	2.14
1160	4" thick		2700	.018		1.86	.66	.10	2.62	3.23
1180	6" thick	↓	1900	.025	↓	2.89	.93	.14	3.96	4.87
3000	Prime coat, emulsion, .30 gal. per S.Y., 1000 S.Y.	B-45	2500	.006	S.Y.	1.68	.28	.37	2.33	2.70
3100	Tack coat, emulsion, .10 gal. per S.Y., 1000 S.Y.	"	2500	.006	"	.56	.28	.37	1.21	1.47

32 13 Rigid Paving

32 13 13 – Concrete Paving

32 13 13.23 Concrete Paving Surface Treatment

		Crew	Daily Output	Labor-Hours	Unit	Material	2014 Bare Costs Labor	Equipment	Total	Total Incl O&P
0010	**CONCRETE PAVING SURFACE TREATMENT**									
0015	Including joints, finishing and curing									
0020	Fixed form, 12' pass, unreinforced, 6" thick	B-26	3000	.029	S.Y.	21	1.20	1.12	23.32	26.50
0100	8" thick		2750	.032		29	1.31	1.22	31.53	35.50
0400	12" thick		1800	.049		41.50	2	1.87	45.37	51
0410	Conc. pavement, w/jt.,fnsh.&curing,fix form,24' pass,unreinforced,6"T		6000	.015		20	.60	.56	21.16	23.50
0430	8" thick		5500	.016		27.50	.66	.61	28.77	31.50
0460	12" thick		3600	.024		40	1	.93	41.93	46.50
0520	Welded wire fabric, sheets for rigid paving 2.33 lb./S.Y.	2 Rodm	389	.041		1.31	2.08		3.39	4.86
0530	Reinforcing steel for rigid paving 12 lb./S.Y.	↓	666	.024	↓	6.30	1.22		7.52	8.95

32 13 Rigid Paving

32 13 13 – Concrete Paving

32 13 13.23 Concrete Paving Surface Treatment

		Crew	Daily Output	Labor-Hours	Unit	Material	Labor	Equipment	Total	Total Incl O&P
							2014 Bare Costs			
0540	Reinforcing steel for rigid paving 18 lb./S.Y.	2 Rodm	444	.036	S.Y.	9.45	1.83		11.28	13.40
0620	Slip form, 12' pass, unreinforced, 6" thick	B-26A	5600	.016		20.50	.64	.63	21.77	24.50
0624	8" thick		5300	.017		28	.68	.67	29.35	32.50
0630	12" thick		3470	.025		40.50	1.04	1.02	42.56	47.50
0632	15" thick		2890	.030		51	1.25	1.22	53.47	59.50
0640	Slip form, 24' pass, unreinforced, 6" thick		11200	.008		20	.32	.32	20.64	23
0644	8" thick		10600	.008		27	.34	.33	27.67	30.50
0650	12" thick		6940	.013		39.50	.52	.51	40.53	45
0652	15" thick		5780	.015		49.50	.62	.61	50.73	56
0700	Finishing, broom finish small areas	2 Cefi	120	.133			5.85		5.85	9.25
1000	Curing, with sprayed membrane by hand	2 Clab	1500	.011		.99	.39		1.38	1.73

32 14 Unit Paving

32 14 13 – Precast Concrete Unit Paving

32 14 13.18 Precast Concrete Plantable Pavers

		Crew	Daily Output	Labor-Hours	Unit	Material	Labor	Equipment	Total	Total Incl O&P
							2014 Bare Costs			
0010	**PRECAST CONCRETE PLANTABLE PAVERS** (50% grass)									
0300	3/4" crushed stone base for plantable pavers, 6 inch depth	B-62	1000	.024	S.Y.	5.50	.96	.17	6.63	7.80
0400	8 inch depth		900	.027		7.40	1.07	.19	8.66	10.10
0500	10 inch depth		800	.030		9.20	1.20	.22	10.62	12.30
0600	12 inch depth		700	.034		11.05	1.38	.25	12.68	14.65
0700	Hydro seeding plantable pavers	B-81A	20	.800	M.S.F.	19.35	29.50	23.50	72.35	95
0800	Apply fertilizer and seed to plantable pavers	1 Clab	8	1	"	51.50	36.50		88	117

32 14 16 – Brick Unit Paving

32 14 16.10 Brick Paving

		Crew	Daily Output	Labor-Hours	Unit	Material	Labor	Equipment	Total	Total Incl O&P
							2014 Bare Costs			
0010	**BRICK PAVING**									
0012	4" x 8" x 1-1/2", without joints (4.5 brick/S.F.)	D-1	110	.145	S.F.	2.21	6		8.21	12.20
0100	Grouted, 3/8" joint (3.9 brick/S.F.)		90	.178		2.15	7.35		9.50	14.30
0200	4" x 8" x 2-1/4", without joints (4.5 bricks/S.F.)		110	.145		2.48	6		8.48	12.50
0300	Grouted, 3/8" joint (3.9 brick/S.F.)		90	.178		2.15	7.35		9.50	14.30
0500	Bedding, asphalt, 3/4" thick	B-25	5130	.017		.68	.69	.54	1.91	2.46
0540	Course washed sand bed, 1" thick	B-18	5000	.005		.29	.18	.01	.48	.62
0580	Mortar, 1" thick	D-1	300	.053		.63	2.20		2.83	4.28
0620	2" thick		200	.080		1.27	3.30		4.57	6.75
1500	Brick on 1" thick sand bed laid flat, 4.5 per S.F.		100	.160		3.12	6.60		9.72	14.20
2000	Brick pavers, laid on edge, 7.2 per S.F.		70	.229		3.83	9.45		13.28	19.55
2500	For 4" thick concrete bed and joints, add		595	.027		1.15	1.11		2.26	3.06
2800	For steam cleaning, add	A-1H	950	.008		.09	.31	.08	.48	.70
9000	Minimum labor/equipment charge	1 Bric	2	4	Job		182		182	296

32 14 23 – Asphalt Unit Paving

32 14 23.10 Asphalt Blocks

		Crew	Daily Output	Labor-Hours	Unit	Material	Labor	Equipment	Total	Total Incl O&P
							2014 Bare Costs			
0010	**ASPHALT BLOCKS**									
0020	Rectangular, 6" x 12" x 1-1/4", w/bed & neopr. adhesive	D-1	135	.119	S.F.	9.20	4.89		14.09	18.05
0100	3" thick		130	.123		12.90	5.10		18	22.50
0300	Hexagonal tile, 8" wide, 1-1/4" thick		135	.119		9.20	4.89		14.09	18.05
0400	2" thick		130	.123		12.90	5.10		18	22.50
0500	Square, 8" x 8", 1-1/4" thick		135	.119		9.20	4.89		14.09	18.05
0600	2" thick		130	.123		12.90	5.10		18	22.50
9000	Minimum labor/equipment charge	1 Bric	2	4	Job		182		182	296

32 14 Unit Paving

32 14 40 – Stone Paving

32 14 40.10 Stone Pavers

		Crew	Daily Output	Labor-Hours	Unit	Material	2014 Bare Costs Labor	Equipment	Total	Total Incl O&P
0010	**STONE PAVERS**									
1300	Slate, natural cleft, irregular, 3/4" thick	D-1	92	.174	S.F.	9.15	7.20		16.35	21.50
1350	Random rectangular, gauged, 1/2" thick		105	.152		19.80	6.30		26.10	32
1400	Random rectangular, butt joint, gauged, 1/4" thick	↓	150	.107		21.50	4.41		25.91	30.50
1450	For sand rubbed finish, add					9.20			9.20	10.10
1550	Granite blocks, 3-1/2" x 3-1/2" x 3-1/2"	D-1	92	.174		11.60	7.20		18.80	24.50
1600	4" to 12" long, 3" to 5" wide, 3" to 5" thick	"	98	.163	↓	9.70	6.75		16.45	21.50

32 16 Curbs, Gutters, Sidewalks, and Driveways

32 16 13 – Curbs and Gutters

32 16 13.13 Cast-in-Place Concrete Curbs and Gutters

		Crew	Daily Output	Labor-Hours	Unit	Material	2014 Bare Costs Labor	Equipment	Total	Total Incl O&P
0010	**CAST-IN-PLACE CONCRETE CURBS AND GUTTERS**									
0290	Forms only, no concrete									
0300	Concrete, wood forms, 6" x 18", straight	C-2	500	.096	L.F.	2.95	4.29		7.24	10.30
0400	6" x 18", radius	"	200	.240		3.06	10.70		13.76	21
0404	Concrete, wood forms, 6" x 18", straight & concrete	C-2A	500	.096		5.70	4.26		9.96	13.25
0406	6" x 18", radius	"	200	.240		5.85	10.65		16.50	24
0415	Machine formed, 6" x 18", straight	B-69A	2000	.024		3.54	.97	.45	4.96	5.95
0416	6" x 18", radius	"	900	.053	↓	3.57	2.15	1	6.72	8.50

32 16 13.23 Precast Concrete Curbs and Gutters

		Crew	Daily Output	Labor-Hours	Unit	Material	2014 Bare Costs Labor	Equipment	Total	Total Incl O&P
0010	**PRECAST CONCRETE CURBS AND GUTTERS**									
0550	Precast, 6" x 18", straight	B-29	700	.080	L.F.	9.90	3.19	1.26	14.35	17.50
0600	6" x 18", radius	"	325	.172	"	10.40	6.85	2.71	19.96	25.50

32 16 13.33 Asphalt Curbs

		Crew	Daily Output	Labor-Hours	Unit	Material	2014 Bare Costs Labor	Equipment	Total	Total Incl O&P
0010	**ASPHALT CURBS**									
0012	Curbs, asphaltic, machine formed, 8" wide, 6" high, 40 L.F./ton	B-27	1000	.032	L.F.	1.74	1.19	.29	3.22	4.19
0100	8" wide, 8" high, 30 L.F. per ton		900	.036		2.33	1.32	.33	3.98	5.10
0150	Asphaltic berm, 12" W, 3"-6" H, 35 L.F./ton, before pavement	↓	700	.046		.04	1.70	.42	2.16	3.29
0200	12" W, 1-1/2" to 4" H, 60 L.F. per ton, laid with pavement	B-2	1050	.038	↓	.02	1.41		1.43	2.35

32 16 13.43 Stone Curbs

		Crew	Daily Output	Labor-Hours	Unit	Material	2014 Bare Costs Labor	Equipment	Total	Total Incl O&P
0010	**STONE CURBS**									
1000	Granite, split face, straight, 5" x 16"	D-13	275	.175	L.F.	12.30	7.65	1.75	21.70	28
1100	6" x 18"	"	250	.192		16.15	8.45	1.93	26.53	33.50
1300	Radius curbing, 6" x 18", over 10' radius	B-29	260	.215	↓	19.80	8.60	3.39	31.79	39.50
1400	Corners, 2' radius	"	80	.700	Ea.	66.50	28	11	105.50	131
1600	Edging, 4-1/2" x 12", straight	d-13	300	.160	L.F.	6.15	7	1.60	14.75	19.90
1800	Curb inlets, (guttermouth) straight	B-29	41	1.366	Ea.	148	54.50	21.50	224	274
2000	Indian granite (belgian block)									
2100	Jumbo, 10-1/2" x 7-1/2" x 4", grey	D-1	150	.107	L.F.	6.05	4.41		10.46	13.80
2150	Pink		150	.107		8.20	4.41		12.61	16.15
2200	Regular, 9" x 4-1/2" x 4-1/2", grey		160	.100		4.53	4.13		8.66	11.70
2250	Pink		160	.100		5.80	4.13		9.93	13.05
2300	Cubes, 4" x 4" x 4", grey		175	.091		3.30	3.78		7.08	9.80
2350	Pink		175	.091		3.58	3.78		7.36	10.10
2400	6" x 6" x 6", pink	↓	155	.103	↓	11.85	4.26		16.11	19.90
2500	Alternate pricing method for indian granite									
2550	Jumbo, 10-1/2" x 7-1/2" x 4" (30 lb.), grey				Ton	345			345	380
2600	Pink					475			475	525
2650	Regular, 9" x 4-1/2" x 4-1/2" (20 lb.), grey					320			320	350
2700	Pink				↓	405			405	445

32 16 Curbs, Gutters, Sidewalks, and Driveways

32 16 13 – Curbs and Gutters

32 16 13.43 Stone Curbs		Crew	Daily Output	Labor-Hours	Unit	Material	2014 Bare Costs Labor	Equipment	Total	Total Incl O&P
2750	Cubes, 4" x 4" x 4" (5 lb.), grey				Ton	400			400	440
2800	Pink					460			460	505
2850	6" x 6" x 6" (25 lb.), pink					460			460	505
2900	For pallets, add					22			22	24

32 17 Paving Specialties

32 17 13 – Parking Bumpers

32 17 13.13 Metal Parking Bumpers

		Crew	Daily Output	Labor-Hours	Unit	Material	2014 Bare Costs Labor	Equipment	Total	Total Incl O&P
0010	**METAL PARKING BUMPERS**									
0015	Bumper rails for garages, 12 Ga. rail, 6" wide, with steel									
0020	posts 12'-6" O.C., minimum	E-4	190	.168	L.F.	17.30	8.70	.75	26.75	36
0030	Average		165	.194		21.50	10	.86	32.36	43.50
0100	Maximum		140	.229		26	11.80	1.01	38.81	51
1300	Pipe bollards, conc. filled/paint, 8' L x 4' D hole, 6" diam.	B-6	20	1.200	Ea.	660	48	18.25	726.25	825
1400	8" diam.		15	1.600		890	64	24.50	978.50	1,100
1500	12" diam.		12	2		1,125	80	30.50	1,235.50	1,400
8900	Security bollards, SS, lighted, hyd., incl. controls, group of 3	L-7	.06	509		48,400	22,500		70,900	89,500
8910	Group of 5	"	.04	682		65,000	30,200		95,200	120,500
9000	Minimum labor/equipment charge	E-4	2	16	Job		825	71	896	1,600

32 17 13.16 Plastic Parking Bumpers

			Crew	Daily Output	Labor-Hours	Unit	Material	2014 Bare Costs Labor	Equipment	Total	Total Incl O&P
0010	**PLASTIC PARKING BUMPERS**										
1600	Bollards, recycled plastic, 5" x 5" x 5' L	G	B-6	20	1.200	Ea.	98	48	18.25	164.25	206
1610	Wheel stops, recycled plastic, yellow, 4" x 6" x 6' L	G		20	1.200		68	48	18.25	134.25	173
1620	Speed bumps, recycled plastic, yellow, 3"H x 10" W x 6' L	G		20	1.200		133	48	18.25	199.25	245
1630	3"H x 10" W x 9' L	G		20	1.200		214	48	18.25	280.25	335

32 17 13.19 Precast Concrete Parking Bumpers

		Crew	Daily Output	Labor-Hours	Unit	Material	2014 Bare Costs Labor	Equipment	Total	Total Incl O&P
0010	**PRECAST CONCRETE PARKING BUMPERS**									
1000	Wheel stops, precast concrete incl. dowels, 6" x 10" x 6'-0"	B-2	120	.333	Ea.	39.50	12.35		51.85	63.50
1100	8" x 13" x 6'-0"	"	120	.333		45.50	12.35		57.85	70.50
1540	Bollards, precast concrete, free standing, round, 15" Dia x 36" H	B-6	14	1.714		310	69	26	405	480
1550	16" Dia x 30" H		14	1.714		310	69	26	405	480
1560	18" Dia x 34" H		14	1.714		350	69	26	445	525
1570	18" Dia x 72" H		14	1.714		395	69	26	490	575
1572	26" Dia x 18" H		12	2		365	80	30.50	475.50	565
1574	26" Dia x 30" H		12	2		605	80	30.50	715.50	830
1578	26" Dia x 50" H		12	2		915	80	30.50	1,025.50	1,175
1580	Square, 22" x 32" H		12	2		450	80	30.50	560.50	660
1585	22" x 41" H		12	2		620	80	30.50	730.50	845
1590	Hexagon, 26" x 41" H		10	2.400		1,100	96.50	36.50	1,233	1,400

32 17 13.26 Wood Parking Bumpers

		Crew	Daily Output	Labor-Hours	Unit	Material	2014 Bare Costs Labor	Equipment	Total	Total Incl O&P
0010	**WOOD PARKING BUMPERS**									
0020	Parking barriers, timber w/saddles, treated type									
0100	4" x 4" for cars	B-2	520	.077	L.F.	2.79	2.85		5.64	7.75
0200	6" x 6" for trucks	"	520	.077	"	5.80	2.85		8.65	11.05

32 17 23 – Pavement Markings

32 17 23.13 Painted Pavement Markings

		Crew	Daily Output	Labor-Hours	Unit	Material	2014 Bare Costs Labor	Equipment	Total	Total Incl O&P
0010	**PAINTED PAVEMENT MARKINGS**									
0020	Acrylic waterborne, white or yellow, 4" wide, less than 3000 L.F.	B-78	20000	.002	L.F.	.15	.09	.03	.27	.35
0200	6" wide, less than 3000 L.F.		11000	.004		.23	.16	.06	.45	.57
0500	8" wide, less than 3000 L.F.		10000	.005		.30	.18	.06	.54	.69

32 17 Paving Specialties

32 17 23 – Pavement Markings

32 17 23.13 Painted Pavement Markings

		Crew	Daily Output	Labor-Hours	Unit	Material	2014 Bare Costs Labor	Equipment	Total	Total Incl O&P
0600	12" wide, less than 3000 L.F.	B-78	4000	.012	L.F.	.45	.44	.16	1.05	1.41
0620	Arrows or gore lines		2300	.021	S.F.	.21	.77	.28	1.26	1.80
0640	Temporary paint, white or yellow, less than 3000 L.F.	↓	15000	.003	L.F.	.07	.12	.04	.23	.32
0660	Removal	1 Clab	300	.027			.98		.98	1.61
0680	Temporary tape	2 Clab	1500	.011		.47	.39		.86	1.16
0710	Thermoplastic, white or yellow, 4" wide, less than 6000 L.F.	B-79	15000	.003		.30	.10	.10	.50	.61
0730	6" wide, less than 6000 L.F.		14000	.003		.45	.11	.11	.67	.79
0740	8" wide, less than 6000 L.F.		12000	.003		.60	.12	.13	.85	1
0750	12" wide, less than 6000 L.F.		6000	.007	↓	.89	.25	.26	1.40	1.66
0760	Arrows		660	.061	S.F.	.60	2.24	2.38	5.22	6.95
0770	Gore lines		2500	.016		.60	.59	.63	1.82	2.32
0780	Letters	↓	660	.061	↓	.60	2.24	2.38	5.22	6.95

32 17 23.14 Pavement Parking Markings

		Crew	Daily Output	Labor-Hours	Unit	Material	2014 Bare Costs Labor	Equipment	Total	Total Incl O&P
0010	**PAVEMENT PARKING MARKINGS**									
0790	Layout of pavement marking	A-2	25000	.001	L.F.		.04	.01	.05	.07
0800	Lines on pvmt., parking stall, paint, white, 4" wide	B-78B	400	.045	Stall	4.62	1.70	.98	7.30	8.95
0825	Parking stall, small quantities	2 Pord	80	.200		9.25	7.90		17.15	23
0830	Lines on pvmt., parking stall, thermoplastic, white, 4" wide	B-79	300	.133	↓	13	4.94	5.25	23.19	28
1000	Street letters and numbers	B-78B	1600	.011	S.F.	.70	.43	.24	1.37	1.74

32 31 Fences and Gates

32 31 13 – Chain Link Fences and Gates

32 31 13.20 Fence, Chain Link Industrial

		Crew	Daily Output	Labor-Hours	Unit	Material	2014 Bare Costs Labor	Equipment	Total	Total Incl O&P
0010	**FENCE, CHAIN LINK INDUSTRIAL**									
0011	Schedule 40, including concrete									
0020	3 strands barb wire, 2" post @ 10' O.C., set in concrete, 6' H									
0200	9 ga. wire, galv. steel, in concrete	B-80C	240	.100	L.F.	19.10	3.66	1.16	23.92	28.50
0248	Fence, add for vinyl coated fabric				S.F.	.68			.68	.75
0300	Aluminized steel	B-80C	240	.100	L.F.	19.70	3.66	1.16	24.52	29
0500	6 ga. wire, galv. steel		240	.100		20.50	3.66	1.16	25.32	30.50
0600	Aluminized steel		240	.100		29.50	3.66	1.16	34.32	40
0800	6 ga. wire, 6' high but omit barbed wire, galv. steel		250	.096		19.40	3.51	1.11	24.02	28.50
0900	Aluminized steel, in concrete		250	.096		23.50	3.51	1.11	28.12	33
0920	8' H, 6 ga. wire, 2-1/2" line post, galv. steel, in concrete		180	.133		31	4.88	1.55	37.43	43.50
0940	Aluminized steel, in concrete		180	.133	↓	37.50	4.88	1.55	43.93	51
1100	Add for corner posts, 3" diam., galv. steel, in concrete		40	.600	Ea.	91.50	22	6.95	120.45	144
1200	Aluminized steel, in concrete		40	.600		91.50	22	6.95	120.45	144
1300	Add for braces, galv. steel		80	.300		38.50	11	3.48	52.98	64.50
1350	Aluminized steel		80	.300		50	11	3.48	64.48	77
1400	Gate for 6' high fence, 1-5/8" frame, 3' wide, galv. steel		10	2.400		191	88	28	307	385
1500	Aluminized steel, in concrete	↓	10	2.400	↓	191	88	28	307	385
2000	5'-0" high fence, 9 ga., no barbed wire, 2" line post, in concrete									
2010	10' O.C., 1-5/8" top rail, in concrete									
2100	Galvanized steel, in concrete	B-80C	300	.080	L.F.	18.10	2.93	.93	21.96	25.50
2200	Aluminized steel, in concrete		300	.080	"	18.75	2.93	.93	22.61	26.50
2400	Gate, 4' wide, 5' high, 2" frame, galv. steel, in concrete		10	2.400	Ea.	176	88	28	292	370
2500	Aluminized steel, in concrete		10	2.400	"	192	88	28	308	385
3100	Overhead slide gate, chain link, 6' high, to 18' wide, in concrete		38	.632	L.F.	92.50	23	7.30	122.80	148
3110	Cantilever type, in concrete	B-80	48	.667		118	26.50	15.80	160.30	190
3120	8' high, in concrete		24	1.333		157	53	31.50	241.50	293
3130	10' high, in concrete	↓	18	1.778	↓	198	70.50	42	310.50	380

32 31 Fences and Gates

32 31 13 – Chain Link Fences and Gates

32 31 13.20 Fence, Chain Link Industrial

		Daily Output	Labor-Hours	Unit	Material	2014 Bare Costs Labor	Equipment	Total	Total Incl O&P
		Crew							
9000	Minimum labor/equipment charge	B-80	2	16	Job		635	380	1,015	1,450

32 31 13.25 Fence, Chain Link Residential

		Crew	Daily Output	Labor-Hours	Unit	Material	Labor	Equipment	Total	Total Incl O&P
0010	**FENCE, CHAIN LINK RESIDENTIAL**									
0011	Schedule 20, 11 ga. wire, 1-5/8" post									
3300	Residential, 11 ga. wire, 1-5/8" line post @ 10' O.C.									
3310	1-3/8" top rail									
3350	4' high, galvanized steel	B-80C	475	.051	L.F.	12.50	1.85	.59	14.94	17.40
3400	Aluminized		475	.051	"	14.35	1.85	.59	16.79	19.45
3600	Gate, 3' wide, 1-3/8" frame, galv. steel		10	2.400	Ea.	96.50	88	28	212.50	281
3700	Aluminized		10	2.400	"	105	88	28	221	291
3900	3' high, galvanized steel		620	.039	L.F.	89	1.42	.45	90.87	100
4000	Aluminized		620	.039	"	94	1.42	.45	95.87	107
4200	Gate, 3' wide, 1-3/8" frame, galv. steel		12	2	Ea.	97.50	73	23	193.50	253
4300	Aluminized		12	2	"	105	73	23	201	261
9000	Minimum labor/equipment charge	B-1	2	12	Job		450		450	735

32 31 13.26 Tennis Court Fences and Gates

		Crew	Daily Output	Labor-Hours	Unit	Material	Labor	Equipment	Total	Total Incl O&P
0010	**TENNIS COURT FENCES AND GATES**									
3150	Tennis courts, 11 ga. wire, 1-3/4" mesh, 2-1/2" line posts									
3170	1-5/8" top rail, 3" corner and gate posts									
3190	10' high, galvanized steel	B-80	190	.168	L.F.	26.50	6.70	3.99	37.19	44
3210	Vinyl covered 9 ga. wire		190	.168	"	30.50	6.70	3.99	41.19	48.50
3240	Corner posts for above, 3" diameter, 10' high		30	1.067	Ea.	81	42.50	25.50	149	186

32 31 13.40 Fence, Fabric and Accessories

		Crew	Daily Output	Labor-Hours	Unit	Material	Labor	Equipment	Total	Total Incl O&P
0010	**FENCE, FABRIC & ACCESSORIES**									
8000	Components only, fabric, galvanized, 4' high	B-80C	585	.041	L.F.	3.36	1.50	.48	5.34	6.70
8040	6' high		430	.056	"	5	2.04	.65	7.69	9.55
8200	Posts, line post, 4' high		34	.706	Ea.	12.70	26	8.20	46.90	65.50
8240	6' high		26	.923	"	16.15	34	10.70	60.85	85
8400	Top rails, 1-3/8" O.D.		1000	.024	L.F.	1.55	.88	.28	2.71	3.46
8440	1-5/8" O.D.		1000	.024	"	2.39	.88	.28	3.55	4.38

32 31 19 – Decorative Metal Fences and Gates

32 31 19.10 Decorative Fence

		Crew	Daily Output	Labor-Hours	Unit	Material	Labor	Equipment	Total	Total Incl O&P
0010	**DECORATIVE FENCE**									
5300	Tubular picket, steel, 6' sections, 1-9/16" posts, 4' high	B-80C	300	.080	L.F.	30.50	2.93	.93	34.36	39.50
5400	2" posts, 5' high		240	.100		34.50	3.66	1.16	39.32	45.50
5600	2" posts, 6' high		200	.120		41	4.39	1.39	46.78	54
5700	Staggered picket 1-9/16" posts, 4' high		300	.080		30.50	2.93	.93	34.36	39.50
5800	2" posts, 5' high		240	.100		34.50	3.66	1.16	39.32	45.50
5900	2" posts, 6' high		200	.120		41	4.39	1.39	46.78	54
6200	Gates, 4' high, 3' wide	B-1	10	2.400	Ea.	274	89.50		363.50	445
6300	5' high, 3' wide		10	2.400		340	89.50		429.50	520
6400	6' high, 3' wide		10	2.400		390	89.50		479.50	575
6500	4' wide		10	2.400		415	89.50		504.50	600

32 31 23 – Plastic Fences and Gates

32 31 23.20 Fence, Recycled Plastic

			Crew	Daily Output	Labor-Hours	Unit	Material	Labor	Equipment	Total	Total Incl O&P
0010	**FENCE, RECYCLED PLASTIC**										
9015	Fence rail, made from recycled plastic, various colors, 2 rail	G	B-1	150	.160	L.F.	10.20	5.95		16.15	21
9018	3 rail	G		150	.160		13.05	5.95		19	24
9020	4 rail	G		150	.160		15.85	5.95		21.80	27
9030	Fence pole, made from recycled plastic, various colors, 7'	G		96	.250	Ea.	49	9.35		58.35	69.50
9040	Stockade fence, made from recycled plastic, various colors, 4' high	G	B-80C	160	.150	L.F.	36	5.50	1.74	43.24	50.50

32 31 Fences and Gates

32 31 23 – Plastic Fences and Gates

32 31 23.20 Fence, Recycled Plastic

			Crew	Daily Output	Labor-Hours	Unit	Material	2014 Bare Costs Labor	Equipment	Total	Total Incl O&P
9050	6' high	G	B-80C	160	.150	L.F.	36.50	5.50	1.74	43.74	51
9060	6' pole	G		96	.250	Ea.	38.50	9.15	2.90	50.55	60.50
9070	9' pole	G		96	.250	"	45	9.15	2.90	57.05	67.50
9080	Picket fence, made from recycled plastic, various colors, 3' high	G		160	.150	L.F.	23	5.50	1.74	30.24	36.50
9090	4' high	G		160	.150	"	34	5.50	1.74	41.24	48
9100	3' high gate	G		8	3	Ea.	22.50	110	35	167.50	244
9110	4' high gate	G		8	3		29.50	110	35	174.50	251
9120	5' high pole	G		96	.250		37.50	9.15	2.90	49.55	59.50
9130	6' high pole	G		96	.250		45	9.15	2.90	57.05	67.50
9140	Pole cap only	G					5.85			5.85	6.40
9150	Keeper pins only	G					.39			.39	.43

32 31 26 – Wire Fences and Gates

32 31 26.10 Fences, Misc. Metal

		Crew	Daily Output	Labor-Hours	Unit	Material	2014 Bare Costs Labor	Equipment	Total	Total Incl O&P
0010	**FENCES, MISC. METAL**									
0012	Chicken wire, posts @ 4', 1" mesh, 4' high	B-80C	410	.059	L.F.	3.61	2.14	.68	6.43	8.25
0100	2" mesh, 6' high		350	.069		3.80	2.51	.79	7.10	9.15
0200	Galv. steel, 12 ga., 2" x 4" mesh, posts 5' O.C., 3' high		300	.080		2.75	2.93	.93	6.61	8.85
0300	5' high		300	.080		3.35	2.93	.93	7.21	9.50
0400	14 ga., 1" x 2" mesh, 3' high		300	.080		3.40	2.93	.93	7.26	9.55
0500	5' high		300	.080		4.55	2.93	.93	8.41	10.80
1000	Kennel fencing, 1-1/2" mesh, 6' long, 3'-6" wide, 6'-2" high	2 Clab	4	4	Ea.	500	147		647	790
1050	12' long		4	4		715	147		862	1,025
1200	Top covers, 1-1/2" mesh, 6' long		15	1.067		135	39		174	213
1250	12' long		12	1.333		190	49		239	290
4500	Security fence, prison grade, set in concrete, 12' high	B-80	25	1.280	L.F.	61	51	30.50	142.50	183
4600	16' high	"	20	1.600	"	79	63.50	38	180.50	232

32 31 29 – Wood Fences and Gates

32 31 29.20 Fence, Wood Rail

		Crew	Daily Output	Labor-Hours	Unit	Material	2014 Bare Costs Labor	Equipment	Total	Total Incl O&P
0010	**FENCE, WOOD RAIL**									
0012	Picket, No. 2 cedar, Gothic, 2 rail, 3' high	B-1	160	.150	L.F.	7.55	5.60		13.15	17.50
0050	Gate, 3'-6" wide	B-80C	9	2.667	Ea.	76.50	97.50	31	205	278
0600	Open rail, rustic, No. 1 cedar, 2 rail, 3' high		160	.150	L.F.	5.85	5.50	1.74	13.09	17.35
0650	Gate, 3' wide		9	2.667	Ea.	80	97.50	31	208.50	282
1200	Stockade, No. 2 cedar, treated wood rails, 6' high		160	.150	L.F.	8.80	5.50	1.74	16.04	20.50
1250	Gate, 3' wide		9	2.667	Ea.	95	97.50	31	223.50	299
3300	Board, shadow box, 1" x 6", treated pine, 6' high		160	.150	L.F.	12.40	5.50	1.74	19.64	24.50
3400	No. 1 cedar, 6' high		150	.160		24.50	5.85	1.85	32.20	38.50
3900	Basket weave, No. 1 cedar, 6' high		160	.150		33.50	5.50	1.74	40.74	48
3950	Gate, 3'-6" wide	B-1	8	3	Ea.	220	112		332	425
4000	Treated pine, 6' high		150	.160	L.F.	15.80	5.95		21.75	27
4200	Gate, 3'-6" wide		9	2.667	Ea.	160	99.50		259.50	340
8000	Posts only, 4' high		40	.600		11.05	22.50		33.55	49
8040	6' high		30	.800		17.25	30		47.25	68
9000	Minimum labor/equipment charge	1 Clab	2	4	Job		147		147	241

32 32 Retaining Walls

32 32 29 – Timber Retaining Walls

32 32 29.10 Landscape Timber Retaining Walls

		Crew	Daily Output	Labor-Hours	Unit	Material	2014 Bare Costs Labor	Equipment	Total	Total Incl O&P
0010	**LANDSCAPE TIMBER RETAINING WALLS**									
0100	Treated timbers, 6" x 6"	1 Clab	265	.030	L.F.	2	1.11		3.11	4.02
0110	6" x 8"	"	200	.040	"	2.62	1.47		4.09	5.30
0120	Drilling holes in timbers for fastening, 1/2"	1 Carp	450	.018	Inch		.82		.82	1.34
0130	5/8"	"	450	.018	"		.82		.82	1.34
0140	Reinforcing rods for fastening, 1/2"	1 Clab	312	.026	L.F.	.37	.94		1.31	1.94
0150	5/8"	"	312	.026	"	.57	.94		1.51	2.17
0160	Reinforcing fabric	2 Clab	2500	.006	S.Y.	1.88	.23		2.11	2.46
0170	Gravel backfill		28	.571	C.Y.	19.90	21		40.90	56.50
0180	Perforated pipe, 4" diameter with silt sock		1200	.013	L.F.	1.29	.49		1.78	2.22
0190	Galvanized 60d common nails	1 Clab	625	.013	Ea.	.16	.47		.63	.95
0200	20d common nails	"	3800	.002	"	.04	.08		.12	.17

32 32 60 – Stone Retaining Walls

32 32 60.10 Retaining Walls, Stone

		Crew	Daily Output	Labor-Hours	Unit	Material	2014 Bare Costs Labor	Equipment	Total	Total Incl O&P
0010	**RETAINING WALLS, STONE**									
0015	Including excavation, concrete footing and									
0020	stone 3' below grade. Price is exposed face area.									
0200	Decorative random stone, to 6' high, 1'-6" thick, dry set	D-1	35	.457	S.F.	30.50	18.90		49.40	64
0300	Mortar set		40	.400		33.50	16.50		50	64
0500	Cut stone, to 6' high, 1'-6" thick, dry set		35	.457		31.50	18.90		50.40	65.50
0600	Mortar set		40	.400		32.50	16.50		49	63
0800	Random stone, 6' to 10' high, 2' thick, dry set		45	.356		41	14.70		55.70	69
0900	Mortar set		50	.320		42	13.20		55.20	67.50
1100	Cut stone, 6' to 10' high, 2' thick, dry set		45	.356		40	14.70		54.70	68
1200	Mortar set		50	.320		42	13.20		55.20	67.50
9000	Minimum labor/equipment charge		2	8	Job		330		330	535

32 84 Planting Irrigation

32 84 23 – Underground Sprinklers

32 84 23.10 Sprinkler Irrigation System

		Crew	Daily Output	Labor-Hours	Unit	Material	2014 Bare Costs Labor	Equipment	Total	Total Incl O&P
0010	**SPRINKLER IRRIGATION SYSTEM**									
0011	For lawns									
0100	Golf course with fully automatic system	C-17	.05	1600	9 holes	100,000	76,500		176,500	234,500
0200	24' diam. head at 15' O.C. incl. piping, auto oper., minimum	B-20	70	.343	Head	23.50	14		37.50	48.50
0300	Maximum		40	.600		56	24.50		80.50	102
0500	60' diam. head at 40' O.C. incl. piping, auto oper., minimum		28	.857		70.50	35		105.50	135
0600	Maximum		23	1.043		190	42.50		232.50	279
0800	Residential system, custom, 1" supply		2000	.012	S.F.	.26	.49		.75	1.09
0900	1-1/2" supply		1800	.013	"	.49	.54		1.03	1.43

32 91 13.23 Structural Soil Mixing	Crew	Daily Output	Labor-Hours	Unit	Material	2014 Bare Costs Labor	2014 Bare Costs Equipment	Total	Total Incl O&P
0010 **STRUCTURAL SOIL MIXING**									
0100 Rake topsoil, site material, harley rock rake, ideal	B-6	33	.727	M.S.F.		29	11.05	40.05	59.50
0200 Adverse	"	7	3.429			138	52	190	281
0300 Screened loam, york rake and finish, ideal	B-62	24	1			40	7.25	47.25	73
0400 Adverse	"	20	1.200			48	8.70	56.70	87.50
1000 Remove topsoil & stock pile on site, 75 HP dozer, 6" deep, 50' haul	B-10L	30	.400			17.95	16.05	34	46
1050 300' haul		6.10	1.967			88	79	167	228
1100 12" deep, 50' haul		15.50	.774			34.50	31	65.50	89.50
1150 300' haul		3.10	3.871			174	155	329	450
1200 200 HP dozer, 6" deep, 50' haul	B-10B	125	.096			4.30	10.60	14.90	18.55
1250 300' haul		30.70	.391			17.50	43	60.50	75.50
1300 12" deep, 50' haul		62	.194			8.65	21.50	30.15	37.50
1350 300' haul		15.40	.779			35	86	121	151
1400 Alternate method, 75 HP dozer, 50' haul	B-10L	860	.014	C.Y.		.63	.56	1.19	1.62
1450 300' haul	"	114	.105			4.72	4.22	8.94	12.20
1500 200 HP dozer, 50' haul	B-10B	2660	.005			.20	.50	.70	.87
1600 300' haul	"	570	.021			.94	2.32	3.26	4.07
1800 Rolling topsoil, hand push roller	1 Clab	3200	.003	S.F.		.09		.09	.15
1850 Tractor drawn roller	B-66	10666	.001	"		.04	.02	.06	.09
2000 Root raking and loading, residential, no boulders	B-6	53.30	.450	M.S.F.		18.05	6.85	24.90	37
2100 With boulders		32	.750			30	11.40	41.40	61.50
2200 Municipal, no boulders		200	.120			4.81	1.83	6.64	9.80
2300 With boulders		120	.200			8	3.04	11.04	16.35
2400 Large commercial, no boulders	B-10B	400	.030			1.34	3.31	4.65	5.80
2500 With boulders	"	240	.050			2.24	5.50	7.74	9.65
3000 Scarify subsoil, residential, skid steer loader w/scarifiers, 50 HP	B-66	32	.250			11.75	8.10	19.85	27.50
3050 Municipal, skid steer loader w/scarifiers, 50 HP	"	120	.067			3.14	2.16	5.30	7.35
3100 Large commercial, 75 HP, dozer w/scarifier	B-10L	240	.050			2.24	2	4.24	5.80
3500 Screen topsoil from stockpile, vibrating screen, wet material (organic)	B-10P	200	.060	C.Y.		2.69	5.95	8.64	10.85
3550 Dry material	"	300	.040			1.79	3.97	5.76	7.25
3600 Mixing with conditioners, manure and peat	B-10R	550	.022			.98	.54	1.52	2.16
3650 Mobilization add for 2 days or less operation	B-34K	3	2.667	Job		100	320	420	520
3800 Spread conditioned topsoil, 6" deep, by hand	B-1	360	.067	S.Y.	5.45	2.49		7.94	10.10
3850 300 HP dozer	B-10M	27	.444	M.S.F.	590	19.90	67.50	677.40	755
4000 Spread soil conditioners, alum. sulfate, 1#/S.Y., hand push spreader	1 Clab	17500	.001	S.Y.	19.50	.02		19.52	21.50
4050 Tractor spreader	B-66	700	.011	M.S.F.	2,175	.54	.37	2,175.91	2,375
4100 Fertilizer, 0.2#/S.Y., push spreader	1 Clab	17500	.001	S.Y.	.49	.02		.51	.57
4150 Tractor spreader	B-66	700	.011	M.S.F.	54.50	.54	.37	55.41	61.50
4200 Ground limestone, 1#/S.Y., push spreader	1 Clab	17500	.001	S.Y.	.18	.02		.20	.23
4250 Tractor spreader	B-66	700	.011	M.S.F.	20	.54	.37	20.91	23.50
4400 Manure, 18#/S.Y., push spreader	1 Clab	2500	.003	S.Y.	7.85	.12		7.97	8.85
4450 Tractor spreader	B-66	280	.029	M.S.F.	870	1.34	.93	872.27	965
4500 Perlite, 1" deep, push spreader	1 Clab	17500	.001	S.Y.	9.25	.02		9.27	10.25
4550 Tractor spreader	B-66	700	.011	M.S.F.	1,025	.54	.37	1,025.91	1,125
4600 Vermiculite, push spreader	1 Clab	17500	.001	S.Y.	8.75	.02		8.77	9.70
4650 Tractor spreader	B-66	700	.011	M.S.F.	970	.54	.37	970.91	1,075
5000 Spread topsoil, skid steer loader and hand dress	B-62	270	.089	C.Y.	24.50	3.57	.65	28.72	33.50
5100 Articulated loader and hand dress	B-100	320	.038		24.50	1.68	3	29.18	33
5200 Articulated loader and 75HP dozer	B-10M	500	.024		24.50	1.08	3.63	29.21	32.50
5300 Road grader and hand dress	B-11L	1000	.016		24.50	.68	.71	25.89	29
6000 Tilling topsoil, 20 HP tractor, disk harrow, 2" deep	B-66	450	.018	M.S.F.		.84	.58	1.42	1.96
6050 4" deep		360	.022			1.05	.72	1.77	2.45
6100 6" deep		270	.030			1.39	.96	2.35	3.27

32 91 Planting Preparation

32 91 13 – Soil Preparation

32 91 13.23 Structural Soil Mixing

		Crew	Daily Output	Labor-Hours	Unit	Material	2014 Bare Costs Labor	Equipment	Total	Total Incl O&P
6150	26" rototiller, 2" deep	A-1J	1250	.006	S.Y.		.23	.05	.28	.44
6200	4" deep		1000	.008			.29	.06	.35	.54
6250	6" deep	↓	750	.011	↓		.39	.08	.47	.72

32 91 13.26 Planting Beds

		Crew	Daily Output	Labor-Hours	Unit	Material	2014 Bare Costs Labor	Equipment	Total	Total Incl O&P
0010	**PLANTING BEDS**									
0100	Backfill planting pit, by hand, on site topsoil	2 Clab	18	.889	C.Y.		32.50		32.50	53.50
0200	Prepared planting mix, by hand	"	24	.667			24.50		24.50	40
0300	Skid steer loader, on site topsoil	B-62	340	.071			2.83	.51	3.34	5.15
0400	Prepared planting mix	"	410	.059			2.35	.43	2.78	4.28
1000	Excavate planting pit, by hand, sandy soil	2 Clab	16	1			36.50		36.50	60
1100	Heavy soil or clay	"	8	2			73.50		73.50	120
1200	1/2 C.Y. backhoe, sandy soil	B-11C	150	.107			4.56	2.44	7	10.05
1300	Heavy soil or clay	"	115	.139			5.95	3.18	9.13	13.10
2000	Mix planting soil, incl. loam, manure, peat, by hand	2 Clab	60	.267		43	9.75		52.75	63.50
2100	Skid steer loader	B-62	150	.160	↓	43	6.40	1.16	50.56	59
3000	Pile sod, skid steer loader	"	2800	.009	S.Y.		.34	.06	.40	.63
3100	By hand	2 Clab	400	.040			1.47		1.47	2.41
4000	Remove sod, F.E. loader	B-10S	2000	.006			.27	.19	.46	.64
4100	Sod cutter	B-12K	3200	.005			.22	.31	.53	.70
4200	By hand	2 Clab	240	.067	↓		2.44		2.44	4.01

32 91 19 – Landscape Grading

32 91 19.13 Topsoil Placement and Grading

		Crew	Daily Output	Labor-Hours	Unit	Material	2014 Bare Costs Labor	Equipment	Total	Total Incl O&P
0010	**TOPSOIL PLACEMENT AND GRADING**									
0700	Furnish and place, truck dumped, screened, 4" deep	B-10S	1300	.009	S.Y.	3.49	.41	.29	4.19	4.82
0800	6" deep	↓	820	.015	"	4.46	.66	.46	5.58	6.45
0810	Minimum labor/equipment charge	↓	2	6	Ea.		269	187	456	635
0900	Fine grading and seeding, incl. lime, fertilizer & seed,									
1000	With equipment	B-14	1000	.048	S.Y.	.47	1.86	.37	2.70	3.94
2000	Minimum labor/equipment charge	1 Clab	4	2	Job		73.50		73.50	120

32 92 Turf and Grasses

32 92 19 – Seeding

32 92 19.13 Mechanical Seeding

		Crew	Daily Output	Labor-Hours	Unit	Material	2014 Bare Costs Labor	Equipment	Total	Total Incl O&P
0010	**MECHANICAL SEEDING**									
0020	Mechanical seeding, 215 lb./acre	B-66	1.50	5.333	Acre	650	251	173	1,074	1,300
0100	44 lb./M.S.Y.	"	2500	.003	S.Y.	.18	.15	.10	.43	.55
0101	$2.00/lb., 44 lb./M.S.Y.	1 Clab	13950	.001	S.F.	.02	.02		.04	.05
0300	Fine grading and seeding incl. lime, fertilizer & seed,									
0310	with equipment	B-14	1000	.048	S.Y.	.44	1.86	.37	2.67	3.91
0400	Fertilizer hand push spreader, 35 lb. per M.S.F.	1 Clab	200	.040	M.S.F.	14.95	1.47		16.42	18.80
0600	Limestone hand push spreader, 50 lb. per M.S.F.	↓	180	.044		5.70	1.63		7.33	8.95
0800	Grass seed hand push spreader, 4.5 lb. per M.S.F.	↓	180	.044	↓	20	1.63		21.63	24.50
1000	Hydro or air seeding for large areas, incl. seed and fertilizer	B-81	8900	.003	S.Y.	.43	.11	.08	.62	.74
1100	With wood fiber mulch added	"	8900	.003	"	1.76	.11	.08	1.95	2.21
1300	Seed only, over 100 lb., field seed, minimum				Lb.	.75			.75	.83
1400	Maximum					4.30			4.30	4.73
1500	Lawn seed, minimum					1.25			1.25	1.38
1600	Maximum				↓	2.45			2.45	2.70
1800	Aerial operations, seeding only, field seed	B-58	50	.480	Acre	244	19.25	62	325.25	365
1900	Lawn seed	↓	50	.480	↓	405	19.25	62	486.25	545

533

32 92 Turf and Grasses

32 92 19 – Seeding

32 92 19.13 Mechanical Seeding	Crew	Daily Output	Labor-Hours	Unit	Material	2014 Bare Costs Labor	Equipment	Total	Total Incl O&P
2100	Seed and liquid fertilizer, field seed	B-58	50	.480	Acre	735	19.25	62	816.25	905
2200	Lawn seed	↓	50	.480	↓	895	19.25	62	976.25	1,075
9000	Minimum labor/equipment charge	1 Clab	4	2	Job		73.50		73.50	120

32 92 23 – Sodding

32 92 23.10 Sodding Systems

		Crew	Daily Output	Labor-Hours	Unit	Material	Labor	Equipment	Total	Total Incl O&P
0010	**SODDING SYSTEMS**									
0020	Sodding, 1" deep, bluegrass sod, on level ground, over 8 M.S.F.	B-63	22	1.818	M.S.F.	250	70.50	7.95	328.45	400
0200	4 M.S.F.		17	2.353		265	91	10.25	366.25	450
0300	1000 S.F.		13.50	2.963		290	115	12.90	417.90	520
0500	Sloped ground, over 8 M.S.F.		6	6.667		250	258	29	537	725
0600	4 M.S.F.		5	8		265	310	35	610	835
0700	1000 S.F.		4	10		290	385	43.50	718.50	1,000
1000	Bent grass sod, on level ground, over 6 M.S.F.		20	2		253	77.50	8.70	339.20	415
1100	3 M.S.F.		18	2.222		265	86	9.70	360.70	445
1200	Sodding 1000 S.F. or less		14	2.857		293	111	12.45	416.45	520
1500	Sloped ground, over 6 M.S.F.		15	2.667		253	103	11.65	367.65	460
1600	3 M.S.F.		13.50	2.963		265	115	12.90	392.90	495
1700	1000 S.F.	↓	12	3.333	↓	293	129	14.55	436.55	550

32 93 Plants

32 93 13 – Ground Covers

32 93 13.10 Ground Cover Plants

		Crew	Daily Output	Labor-Hours	Unit	Material	Labor	Equipment	Total	Total Incl O&P
0010	**GROUND COVER PLANTS**									
0012	Plants, pachysandra, in prepared beds	B-1	15	1.600	C	79.50	59.50		139	185
0200	Vinca minor, 1 yr., bare root, in prepared beds		12	2	"	64.50	74.50		139	194
0600	Stone chips, in 50 lb. bags, Georgia marble		520	.046	Bag	4.13	1.72		5.85	7.35
0700	Onyx gemstone		260	.092		16.50	3.45		19.95	24
0800	Quartz		260	.092	↓	6.15	3.45		9.60	12.40
0900	Pea gravel, truckload lots	↓	28	.857	Ton	24	32		56	78.50

32 93 33 – Shrubs

32 93 33.10 Shrubs and Trees

		Crew	Daily Output	Labor-Hours	Unit	Material	Labor	Equipment	Total	Total Incl O&P
0010	**SHRUBS AND TREES**									
0011	Evergreen, in prepared beds, B & B									
0100	Arborvitae pyramidal, 4'-5'	B-17	30	1.067	Ea.	110	42	26	178	218
0150	Globe, 12"-15"	B-1	96	.250		21.50	9.35		30.85	39
0300	Cedar, blue, 8'-10'	B-17	18	1.778		230	70	43.50	343.50	415
0500	Hemlock, Canadian, 2-1/2'-3'	B-1	36	.667		30.50	25		55.50	74.50
0550	Holly, Savannah, 8' - 10' H		9.68	2.479		258	92.50		350.50	435
0600	Juniper, andorra, 18"-24"		80	.300		36	11.20		47.20	58
0620	Wiltoni, 15"-18"	↓	80	.300		28.50	11.20		39.70	50
0640	Skyrocket, 4-1/2'-5'	B-17	55	.582		117	23	14.25	154.25	182
0660	Blue pfitzer, 2'-2-1/2'	B-1	44	.545		42.50	20.50		63	80
0680	Ketleerie, 2-1/2'-3'		50	.480		51	17.90		68.90	85.50
0700	Pine, black, 2-1/2'-3'		50	.480		59.50	17.90		77.40	95
0720	Mugo, 18"-24"	↓	60	.400		59	14.95		73.95	89.50
0740	White, 4'-5'	B-17	75	.427		51	16.85	10.45	78.30	95
0800	Spruce, blue, 18"-24"	B-1	60	.400		66.50	14.95		81.45	97.50
0840	Norway, 4'-5'	B-17	75	.427		82	16.85	10.45	109.30	129
0900	Yew, denisforma, 12"-15"	B-1	60	.400		36	14.95		50.95	64
1000	Capitata, 18"-24"	↓	30	.800	↓	32.50	30		62.50	85

32 93 Plants

32 93 33 – Shrubs

32 93 33.10 Shrubs and Trees		Crew	Daily Output	Labor-Hours	Unit	Material	2014 Bare Costs Labor	Equipment	Total	Total Incl O&P
1100	Hicksi, 2'-2-1/2'	B-1	30	.800	Ea.	86.50	30		116.50	144

32 93 33.20 Shrubs

		Crew	Daily Output	Labor-Hours	Unit	Material	Labor	Equipment	Total	Total Incl O&P
0010	**SHRUBS**									
0011	Broadleaf Evergreen, planted in prepared beds									
0100	Andromeda, 15"-18", container	B-1	96	.250	Ea.	33	9.35		42.35	52
0200	Azalea, 15" - 18", container		96	.250		28.50	9.35		37.85	47
0300	Barberry, 9"-12", container		130	.185		17.55	6.90		24.45	30.50
0400	Boxwood, 15"-18", B&B		96	.250		42	9.35		51.35	61.50
0500	Euonymus, emerald gaiety, 12" to 15", container		115	.209		23	7.80		30.80	38.50
0600	Holly, 15"-18", B & B		96	.250		35.50	9.35		44.85	55
0900	Mount laurel, 18" - 24", B & B		80	.300		70	11.20		81.20	95.50
1000	Paxistema, 9 – 12" high		130	.185		22	6.90		28.90	35.50
1100	Rhododendron, 18"-24", container		48	.500		38	18.65		56.65	72.50
1200	Rosemary, 1 gal. container		600	.040		18	1.49		19.49	22.50
2000	Deciduous, planted in prepared beds, amelanchier, 2'-3', B & B		57	.421		120	15.70		135.70	158
2100	Azalea, 15"-18", B & B		96	.250		28.50	9.35		37.85	47
2300	Bayberry, 2'-3', B & B		57	.421		24	15.70		39.70	52
2600	Cotoneaster, 15"-18", B & B		80	.300		27	11.20		38.20	48
2800	Dogwood, 3'-4', B & B	B-17	40	.800		31.50	31.50	19.55	82.55	107
2900	Euonymus, alatus compacta, 15" to 18", container	B-1	80	.300		25.50	11.20		36.70	46.50
3200	Forsythia, 2'-3', container	"	60	.400		18.70	14.95		33.65	45
3300	Hibiscus, 3'-4', B & B	B-17	75	.427		48	16.85	10.45	75.30	91.50
3400	Honeysuckle, 3'-4', B & B	B-1	60	.400		26	14.95		40.95	53
3500	Hydrangea, 2'-3', B & B	"	57	.421		29.50	15.70		45.20	58.50
3600	Lilac, 3'-4', B & B	B-17	40	.800		27.50	31.50	19.55	78.55	103
3900	Privet, bare root, 18"-24"	B-1	80	.300		14.25	11.20		25.45	34
4100	Quince, 2'-3', B & B	"	57	.421		28	15.70		43.70	56.50
4200	Russian olive, 3'-4', B & B	B-17	75	.427		26.50	16.85	10.45	53.80	68
4400	Spirea, 3'-4', B & B	B-1	70	.343		20	12.80		32.80	43
4500	Viburnum, 3'-4', B & B	B-17	40	.800		24	31.50	19.55	75.05	99

32 93 43 – Trees

32 93 43.20 Trees

			Crew	Daily Output	Labor-Hours	Unit	Material	Labor	Equipment	Total	Total Incl O&P
0010	**TREES**										
0011	Deciduous, in prep. beds, balled & burlapped (B&B)										
0100	Ash, 2" caliper	G	B-17	8	4	Ea.	185	158	98	441	570
0200	Beech, 5'-6'	G		50	.640		185	25.50	15.65	226.15	262
0300	Birch, 6'-8', 3 stems	G		20	1.600		170	63	39	272	330
0500	Crabapple, 6'-8'	G		20	1.600		140	63	39	242	299
0600	Dogwood, 4'-5'	G		40	.800		130	31.50	19.55	181.05	216
0700	Eastern redbud 4'-5'	G		40	.800		148	31.50	19.55	199.05	235
0800	Elm, 8'-10'	G		20	1.600		260	63	39	362	430
0900	Ginkgo, 6'-7'	G		24	1.333		150	52.50	32.50	235	287
1000	Hawthorn, 8'-10', 1" caliper	G		20	1.600		163	63	39	265	325
1100	Honeylocust, 10'-12', 1-1/2" caliper	G		10	3.200		205	126	78	409	515
1300	Larch, 8'	G		32	1		125	39.50	24.50	189	229
1400	Linden, 8'-10', 1" caliper	G		20	1.600		143	63	39	245	300
1500	Magnolia, 4'-5'	G		20	1.600		100	63	39	202	255
1600	Maple, red, 8'-10', 1-1/2" caliper	G		10	3.200		200	126	78	404	510
1700	Mountain ash, 8'-10', 1" caliper	G		16	2		175	79	49	303	375
1800	Oak, 2-1/2"-3" caliper	G		6	5.333		320	211	130	661	835
2100	Planetree, 9'-11', 1-1/4" caliper	G		10	3.200		240	126	78	444	555
2200	Plum, 6'-8', 1" caliper	G		20	1.600		80	63	39	182	233

32 93 Plants

32 93 43 – Trees

32 93 43.20 Trees		Crew	Daily Output	Labor-Hours	Unit	Material	2014 Bare Costs Labor	Equipment	Total	Total Incl O&P
2300	Poplar, 9'-11', 1-1/4" caliper	G	B-17	10	3.200	Ea.	145	126	78	349	450
2500	Sumac, 2'-3'	G		75	.427		45	16.85	10.45	72.30	88.50
2700	Tulip, 5'-6'	G		40	.800		48	31.50	19.55	99.05	126
2800	Willow, 6'-8', 1" caliper	G		20	1.600		95	63	39	197	250
9000	Minimum labor/equipment charge		1 Clab	4	2	Job		73.50		73.50	120

32 94 Planting Accessories

32 94 13 – Landscape Edging

32 94 13.20 Edging

		Crew	Daily Output	Labor-Hours	Unit	Material	Labor	Equipment	Total	Total Incl O&P
0010	**EDGING**									
0050	Aluminum alloy, including stakes, 1/8" x 4", mill finish	B-1	390	.062	L.F.	2.26	2.30		4.56	6.25
0051	Black paint		390	.062		2.62	2.30		4.92	6.65
0052	Black anodized		390	.062		3.03	2.30		5.33	7.10
0100	Brick, set horizontally, 1-1/2 bricks per L.F.	D-1	370	.043		1.39	1.79		3.18	4.42
0150	Set vertically, 3 bricks per L.F.	"	135	.119		3.60	4.89		8.49	11.90
0200	Corrugated aluminum, roll, 4" wide	1 Carp	650	.012		1.95	.56		2.51	3.08
0250	6" wide	"	550	.015		2.44	.67		3.11	3.78
0600	Railroad ties, 6" x 8"	2 Carp	170	.094		3.03	4.32		7.35	10.45
0650	7" x 9"		136	.118		3.36	5.40		8.76	12.55
0750	Redwood 2" x 4"		330	.048		2.26	2.22		4.48	6.15
0800	Steel edge strips, incl. stakes, 1/4" x 5"	B-1	390	.062		3.90	2.30		6.20	8.05
0850	3/16" x 4"	"	390	.062		3.08	2.30		5.38	7.15
9000	Minimum labor/equipment charge	1 Carp	4	2	Job		91.50		91.50	151

32 94 50 – Tree Guying

32 94 50.10 Tree Guying Systems

		Crew	Daily Output	Labor-Hours	Unit	Material	Labor	Equipment	Total	Total Incl O&P
0010	**TREE GUYING SYSTEMS**									
0015	Tree guying Including stakes, guy wire and wrap									
0100	Less than 3" caliper, 2 stakes	2 Clab	35	.457	Ea.	14.20	16.75		30.95	43
0200	3" to 4" caliper, 3 stakes	"	21	.762	"	19.20	28		47.20	67
1000	Including arrowhead anchor, cable, turnbuckles and wrap									
1100	Less than 3" caliper, 3" anchors	2 Clab	20	.800	Ea.	44.50	29.50		74	97
1200	3" to 6" caliper, 4" anchors		15	1.067		38	39		77	106
1300	6" caliper, 6" anchors		12	1.333		44.50	49		93.50	130
1400	8" caliper, 8" anchors		9	1.778		128	65		193	248

32 96 Transplanting

32 96 23 – Plant and Bulb Transplanting

32 96 23.23 Planting

		Crew	Daily Output	Labor-Hours	Unit	Material	Labor	Equipment	Total	Total Incl O&P
0010	**PLANTING**									
0012	Moving shrubs on site, 12" ball	B-62	28	.857	Ea.		34.50	6.20	40.70	62.50
0100	24" ball	"	22	1.091	"		44	7.90	51.90	79.50

32 96 23.43 Moving Trees

		Crew	Daily Output	Labor-Hours	Unit	Material	Labor	Equipment	Total	Total Incl O&P
0010	**MOVING TREES**, On site									
0300	Moving trees on site, 36" ball	B-6	3.75	6.400	Ea.		257	97.50	354.50	520
0400	60" ball	"	1	24	"		965	365	1,330	1,950

32 96 43.20 Tree Removal	Crew	Daily Output	Labor-Hours	Unit	Material	2014 Bare Costs Labor	2014 Bare Costs Equipment	Total	Total Incl O&P
0010 **TREE REMOVAL**									
0100 Dig & lace, shrubs, broadleaf evergreen, 18"-24" high	B-1	55	.436	Ea.		16.30		16.30	27
0200 2'-3'	"	35	.686			25.50		25.50	42
0300 3'-4'	B-6	30	.800			32	12.20	44.20	65.50
0400 4'-5'	"	20	1.200			48	18.25	66.25	98
1000 Deciduous, 12"-15"	B-1	110	.218			8.15		8.15	13.35
1100 18"-24"		65	.369			13.80		13.80	22.50
1200 2'-3'		55	.436			16.30		16.30	27
1300 3'-4'	B-6	50	.480			19.25	7.30	26.55	39
2000 Evergreen, 18"-24"	B-1	55	.436			16.30		16.30	27
2100 2'-0" to 2'-6"		50	.480			17.90		17.90	29.50
2200 2'-6" to 3'-0"		35	.686			25.50		25.50	42
2300 3'-0" to 3'-6"		20	1.200			45		45	73.50
3000 Trees, deciduous, small, 2'-3'		55	.436			16.30		16.30	27
3100 3'-4'	B-6	50	.480			19.25	7.30	26.55	39
3200 4'-5'		35	.686			27.50	10.45	37.95	56
3300 5'-6'		30	.800			32	12.20	44.20	65.50
4000 Shade, 5'-6'		50	.480			19.25	7.30	26.55	39
4100 6'-8'		35	.686			27.50	10.45	37.95	56
4200 8'-10'		25	.960			38.50	14.60	53.10	78.50
4300 2" caliper		12	2			80	30.50	110.50	164
5000 Evergreen, 4'-5'		35	.686			27.50	10.45	37.95	56
5100 5'-6'		25	.960			38.50	14.60	53.10	78.50
5200 6'-7'		19	1.263			50.50	19.25	69.75	103
5300 7'-8'		15	1.600			64	24.50	88.50	131
5400 8'-10'		11	2.182			87.50	33	120.50	179

Division Notes

		CREW	DAILY OUTPUT	LABOR-HOURS	UNIT	BARE COSTS				TOTAL INCL O&P
						MAT.	LABOR	EQUIP.	TOTAL	

Estimating Tips

33 10 00 Water Utilities
33 30 00 Sanitary Sewerage Utilities
33 40 00 Storm Drainage Utilities

- Never assume that the water, sewer, and drainage lines will go in at the early stages of the project. Consider the site access needs before dividing the site in half with open trenches, loose pipe, and machinery obstructions. Always inspect the site to establish that the site drawings are complete. Check off all existing utilities on your drawings as you locate them. Be especially careful with underground utilities because appurtenances are sometimes buried during regrading or repaving operations. If you find any discrepancies, mark up the site plan for further research. Differing site conditions can be very costly if discovered later in the project.

- See also Section 33 01 00 for restoration of pipe where removal/replacement may be undesirable. Use of new types of piping materials can reduce the overall project cost. Owners/design engineers should consider the installing contractor as a valuable source of current information on utility products and local conditions that could lead to significant cost savings.

Reference Numbers

Reference numbers are shown in shaded boxes at the beginning of some major classifications. These numbers refer to related items in the Reference Section. The reference information may be an estimating procedure, an alternate pricing method, or technical information.

Note: Not all subdivisions listed here necessarily appear in this publication.

Division 33 - Utilities

Note: **Trade Service,** *in part, has been used as a reference source for some of the material prices used in Division 33.*

33 01 30 – Operation and Maintenance of Sewer Utilities

33 01 30.16 TV Inspection of Sewer Pipelines

		Crew	Daily Output	Labor-Hours	Unit	Material	2014 Bare Costs Labor	Equipment	Total	Total Incl O&P
0010	**TV INSPECTION OF SEWER PIPELINES**									
0100	Pipe internal cleaning & inspection, cleaning, pressure pipe systems									
0120	Pig method, lengths 1000' to 10,000'									
0140	4" diameter thru 24" diameter, minimum				L.F.				3.60	4.14
0160	Maximum				"				18	21
6000	Sewage/sanitary systems									
6100	Power rodder with header & cutters									
6110	Mobilization charge, minimum				Total				695	800
6120	Mobilization charge, maximum				"				9,125	10,600
6140	Cleaning 4"-12" diameter				L.F.				3.39	3.90
6190	14"-24" diameter								3.98	4.59
6240	30" diameter								5.80	6.65
6250	36" diameter								6.75	7.75
6260	48" diameter								7.70	8.85
6270	60" diameter								8.70	9.95
6280	72" diameter								9.65	11.10
9000	Inspection, television camera with video									
9060	up to 500 linear feet				Total				715	820

33 01 30.72 Relining Sewers

		Crew	Daily Output	Labor-Hours	Unit	Material	2014 Bare Costs Labor	Equipment	Total	Total Incl O&P
0010	**RELINING SEWERS**									
0011	With cement incl. bypass & cleaning									
0020	Less than 10,000 L.F., urban, 6" to 10"	C-17E	130	.615	L.F.	9.55	29.50	.73	39.78	59.50
0050	10" to 12"		125	.640		11.75	30.50	.76	43.01	63
0070	12" to 16"		115	.696		12.05	33	.82	45.87	68
0100	16" to 20"		95	.842		14.15	40	.99	55.14	82
0200	24" to 36"		90	.889		15.25	42.50	1.05	58.80	87
0300	48" to 72"		80	1		24.50	47.50	1.18	73.18	105
0500	Rural, 6" to 10"		180	.444		9.55	21	.52	31.07	45.50
0550	10" to 12"		175	.457		11.75	22	.54	34.29	49
0570	12" to 16"		160	.500		12.05	24	.59	36.64	53
0600	16" to 20"		135	.593		14.15	28.50	.70	43.35	62.50
0700	24" to 36"		125	.640		15.25	30.50	.76	46.51	67
0800	48" to 72"		100	.800		24.50	38	.94	63.44	89.50
1000	Greater than 10,000 L.F., urban, 6" to 10"		160	.500		9.55	24	.59	34.14	50
1050	10" to 12"		155	.516		11.75	24.50	.61	36.86	53.50
1070	12" to 16"		140	.571		12.05	27.50	.67	40.22	58.50
1100	16" to 20"		120	.667		14.15	32	.79	46.94	68.50
1200	24" to 36"		115	.696		15.25	33	.82	49.07	71.50
1300	48" to 72"		95	.842		24.50	40	.99	65.49	93
1500	Rural, 6" to 10"		215	.372		9.55	17.75	.44	27.74	40
1550	10" to 12"		210	.381		11.75	18.15	.45	30.35	43
1570	12" to 16"		185	.432		12.05	20.50	.51	33.06	47.50
1600	16" to 20"		150	.533		14.15	25.50	.63	40.28	57.50
1700	24" to 36"		140	.571		15.25	27.50	.67	43.42	62
1800	48" to 72"		120	.667		24.50	32	.79	57.29	79.50

33 05 Common Work Results for Utilities

33 05 16 – Utility Structures

33 05 16.13 Precast Concrete Utility Boxes

33 05 16.13 Precast Concrete Utility Boxes	Crew	Daily Output	Labor-Hours	Unit	Material	2014 Bare Costs Labor	Equipment	Total	Total Incl O&P
0010 **PRECAST CONCRETE UTILITY BOXES**, 6" thick									
0050 5' x 10' x 6' high, I.D.	B-13	2	28	Ea.	3,675	1,125	375	5,175	6,225
0350 Hand hole, precast concrete, 1-1/2" thick									
0400 1'-0" x 2'-0" x 1'-9", I.D., light duty	B-1	4	6	Ea.	410	224		634	820
0450 4'-6" x 3'-2" x 2'-0", O.D., heavy duty	B-6	3	8	"	1,475	320	122	1,917	2,250

33 05 23 – Trenchless Utility Installation

33 05 23.19 Microtunneling

33 05 23.19 Microtunneling	Crew	Daily Output	Labor-Hours	Unit	Material	2014 Bare Costs Labor	Equipment	Total	Total Incl O&P
0010 **MICROTUNNELING**									
0011 Not including excavation, backfill, shoring,									
0020 or dewatering, average 50'/day, slurry method									
0100 24" to 48" outside diameter, minimum				L.F.				875	965
0110 Adverse conditions, add				%				50%	50%
1000 Rent microtunneling machine, average monthly lease				Month				97,500	107,000
1010 Operating technician				Day				630	705
1100 Mobilization and demobilization, minimum				Job				41,200	45,900
1110 Maximum				"				445,500	490,500

33 05 23.20 Horizontal Boring

33 05 23.20 Horizontal Boring	Crew	Daily Output	Labor-Hours	Unit	Material	2014 Bare Costs Labor	Equipment	Total	Total Incl O&P
0010 **HORIZONTAL BORING**									
0011 Casing only, 100' minimum,									
0020 not incl. jacking pits or dewatering									
0100 Roadwork, 1/2" thick wall, 24" diameter casing	B-42	20	3.200	L.F.	121	132	68.50	321.50	425
0200 36" diameter		16	4		223	165	85.50	473.50	610
0300 48" diameter		15	4.267		310	176	91	577	730
0500 Railroad work, 24" diameter		15	4.267		121	176	91	388	525
0600 36" diameter		14	4.571		223	189	97.50	509.50	660
0700 48" diameter		12	5.333		310	220	114	644	830
0900 For ledge, add								20%	20%
1000 Small diameter boring, 3", sandy soil	B-82	900	.018		22	.74	.09	22.83	25.50
1040 Rocky soil	"	500	.032		22	1.34	.17	23.51	26.50

33 05 26 – Utility Identification

33 05 26.10 Utility Accessories

33 05 26.10 Utility Accessories		Crew	Daily Output	Labor-Hours	Unit	Material	2014 Bare Costs Labor	Equipment	Total	Total Incl O&P
0010 **UTILITY ACCESSORIES**	R312316-40									
0400 Underground tape, detectable, reinforced, alum. foil core, 2"		1 Clab	150	.053	C.L.F.	5.65	1.95		7.60	9.45
0500 6"			140	.057	"	27.50	2.09		29.59	34
9000 Minimum labor/equipment charge			4	2	Job		73.50		73.50	120

33 11 Water Utility Distribution Piping

33 11 13 – Public Water Utility Distribution Piping

33 11 13.15 Water Supply, Ductile Iron Pipe

33 11 13.15 Water Supply, Ductile Iron Pipe		Crew	Daily Output	Labor-Hours	Unit	Material	2014 Bare Costs Labor	Equipment	Total	Total Incl O&P
0010 **WATER SUPPLY, DUCTILE IRON PIPE**	R331113-80									
0020 Not including excavation or backfill										
2000 Pipe, class 50 water piping, 18' lengths										
2020 Mechanical joint, 4" diameter		B-21A	200	.200	L.F.	15.60	9.15	2.41	27.16	34.50
3000 Tyton, push-on joint, 4" diameter			400	.100		17	4.58	1.20	22.78	27.50
3020 6" diameter			333.33	.120		17.85	5.50	1.44	24.79	30
8000 Fittings, mechanical joint										
8006 90° bend, 4" diameter		B-20A	16	2	Ea.	273	89.50		362.50	445
8020 6" diameter			12.80	2.500		405	112		517	625
8200 Wye or tee, 4" diameter			10.67	2.999		440	134		574	700
8220 6" diameter			8.53	3.751		670	168		838	1,000

541

33 11 Water Utility Distribution Piping

33 11 13 – Public Water Utility Distribution Piping

33 11 13.15 Water Supply, Ductile Iron Pipe

	33 11 13.15 Water Supply, Ductile Iron Pipe	Crew	Daily Output	Labor-Hours	Unit	Material	2014 Bare Costs Labor	Equipment	Total	Total Incl O&P
8398	45° bends, 4" diameter	B-20A	16	2	Ea.	254	89.50		343.50	420
8400	6" diameter		12.80	2.500		365	112		477	585
8405	8" diameter		10.67	2.999		520	134		654	790
8450	Decreaser, 6" x 4" diameter		14.22	2.250		360	101		461	555
8460	8" x 6" diameter	▼	11.64	2.749	▼	525	123		648	775
8550	Piping, butterfly valves, cast iron									
8560	4" diameter	B-20	6	4	Ea.	715	163		878	1,050
9600	Steel sleeve with tap, 4" diameter		3	8		430	325		755	1,000
9620	6" diameter	▼	2	12	▼	470	490		960	1,325

33 12 Water Utility Distribution Equipment

33 12 13 – Water Service Connections

33 12 13.15 Tapping, Crosses and Sleeves

		Crew	Daily Output	Labor-Hours	Unit	Material	2014 Bare Costs Labor	Equipment	Total	Total Incl O&P
0010	**TAPPING, CROSSES AND SLEEVES**									
4000	Drill and tap pressurized main (labor only)									
4100	6" main, 1" to 2" service	Q-1	3	5.333	Ea.		276		276	430
4150	8" main, 1" to 2" service	"	2.75	5.818	"		300		300	470
4500	Tap and insert gate valve									
4600	8" main, 4" branch	B-21	3.20	8.750	Ea.		370	44	414	650
4650	6" branch		2.70	10.370			440	52	492	770
4800	12" main, 6" branch	▼	2.35	11.915	▼		505	59.50	564.50	885

33 21 Water Supply Wells

33 21 13 – Public Water Supply Wells

33 21 13.10 Wells and Accessories

			Crew	Daily Output	Labor-Hours	Unit	Material	2014 Bare Costs Labor	Equipment	Total	Total Incl O&P
0010	**WELLS & ACCESSORIES**	R221113-50									
0011	Domestic										
0100	Drilled, 4" to 6" diameter		B-23	120	.333	L.F.		12.35	24	36.35	47
0200	8" diameter		"	95.20	.420	"		15.55	30.50	46.05	59
1400	Remove & reset pump, minimum		B-21	4	7	Ea.		295	35	330	520
1420	Maximum		"	2	14	"		590	70	660	1,025
1500	Pumps, installed in wells to 100' deep, 4" submersible										
1510	1/2 H.P.		Q-1	3.22	4.969	Ea.	450	257		707	895
1520	3/4 H.P.			2.66	6.015		590	310		900	1,125
1600	1 H.P.		▼	2.29	6.987		680	360		1,040	1,300
1700	1-1/2 H.P.		Q-22	1.60	10		735	520	415	1,670	2,075
1800	2 H.P.			1.33	12.030		890	625	500	2,015	2,500
1900	3 H.P.			1.14	14.035		1,375	725	580	2,680	3,275
2000	5 H.P.			1.14	14.035		2,300	725	580	3,605	4,300
2050	Remove and install motor only, 4 H.P.		▼	1.14	14.035		1,100	725	580	2,405	2,975
5000	Wells to 180 ft. deep, 4" submersible, 1 HP		B-21	1.10	25.455		2,350	1,075	127	3,552	4,475
5500	2 HP			1.10	25.455		3,275	1,075	127	4,477	5,500
6000	3 HP			1	28		4,375	1,175	140	5,690	6,900
7000	5 HP		▼	.90	31.111	▼	6,025	1,325	156	7,506	8,950
9000	Minimum labor/equipment charge			1.80	15.556	Job		655	78	733	1,150

33 31 Sanitary Utility Sewerage Piping

33 31 13 – Public Sanitary Utility Sewerage Piping

33 31 13.15 Sewage Collection, Concrete Pipe

	Crew	Daily Output	Labor-Hours	Unit	Material	2014 Bare Costs Labor	Equipment	Total	Total Incl O&P
0010 **SEWAGE COLLECTION, CONCRETE PIPE**									
0020 See Section 33 41 13.60 for sewage/drainage collection, concrete pipe									

33 31 13.25 Sewage Collection, Polyvinyl Chloride Pipe

	Crew	Daily Output	Labor-Hours	Unit	Material	2014 Bare Costs Labor	Equipment	Total	Total Incl O&P
0010 **SEWAGE COLLECTION, POLYVINYL CHLORIDE PIPE**									
0020 Not including excavation or backfill									
2000 20' lengths, SDR 35, B&S, 4" diameter	B-20	375	.064	L.F.	1.46	2.62		4.08	5.90
2040 6" diameter		350	.069		3.29	2.80		6.09	8.20
2080 13' lengths , SDR 35, B&S, 8" diameter	↓	335	.072		6.95	2.93		9.88	12.40
2120 10" diameter	B-21	330	.085		11.40	3.58	.42	15.40	18.85
4000 Piping, DWV PVC, no exc./bkfill., 10' L, Sch 40, 4" diameter	B-20	375	.064		4.64	2.62		7.26	9.40
4010 6" diameter		350	.069		10.20	2.80		13	15.80
4020 8" diameter	↓	335	.072	↓	19.70	2.93		22.63	26.50

33 36 Utility Septic Tanks

33 36 13 – Utility Septic Tank and Effluent Wet Wells

33 36 13.13 Concrete Utility Septic Tank

	Crew	Daily Output	Labor-Hours	Unit	Material	2014 Bare Costs Labor	Equipment	Total	Total Incl O&P
0010 **CONCRETE UTILITY SEPTIC TANK**									
0011 Not including excavation or piping									
0015 Septic tanks, precast, 1,000 gallon	B-21	8	3.500	Ea.	1,075	148	17.50	1,240.50	1,450
0020 1,250 gallon		8	3.500		1,100	148	17.50	1,265.50	1,475
0060 1,500 gallon		7	4		1,500	169	20	1,689	1,950
0100 2,000 gallon		5	5.600		1,975	236	28	2,239	2,575
0140 2,500 gallon		5	5.600		2,500	236	28	2,764	3,150
0180 4,000 gallon	↓	4	7		5,575	295	35	5,905	6,650
0220 5,000 gal., 4 piece	B-13	3	18.667		10,400	745	249	11,394	12,900
0300 15,000 gallon, 4 piece	B-13B	1.70	32.941		21,700	1,325	670	23,695	26,800
0400 25,000 gallon, 4 piece		1.10	50.909		42,200	2,025	1,025	45,250	51,000
0500 40,000 gallon, 4 piece	↓	.80	70		54,000	2,800	1,425	58,225	65,500
0520 50,000 gallon, 5 piece	B-13C	.60	93.333		62,000	3,725	2,850	68,575	77,500
0640 75,000 gallon, cast in place	C-14C	.25	448		75,500	19,700	130	95,330	115,500
0660 100,000 gallon	"	.15	746		93,500	32,800	217	126,517	156,500
1150 Leaching field chambers, 13' x 3'-7" x 1'-4", standard	B-13	16	3.500		480	140	46.50	666.50	805
1200 Heavy duty, 8' x 4' x 1'-6"		14	4		284	159	53.50	496.50	630
1300 13' x 3'-9" x 1'-6"		12	4.667		1,125	186	62	1,373	1,625
1350 20' x 4' x 1'-6"	↓	5	11.200		1,175	445	149	1,769	2,175
1420 Leaching pit, precast concrete, 6', dia, 3' deep	B-21	4.70	5.957		885	251	30	1,166	1,425
1600 Leaching pit, 6'-6" diameter, 6' deep		5	5.600		1,025	236	28	1,289	1,550
1620 8' deep		4	7		1,200	295	35	1,530	1,850
1700 8' diameter, H-20 load, 6' deep		4	7		1,500	295	35	1,830	2,175
1720 8' deep		3	9.333		2,500	395	46.50	2,941.50	3,450
2000 Velocity reducing pit, precast conc., 6' diameter, 3' deep	↓	4.70	5.957	↓	1,600	251	30	1,881	2,200

33 36 13.19 Polyethylene Utility Septic Tank

	Crew	Daily Output	Labor-Hours	Unit	Material	2014 Bare Costs Labor	Equipment	Total	Total Incl O&P
0010 **POLYETHYLENE UTILITY SEPTIC TANK**									
0015 High density polyethylene, 1,000 gallon	B-21	8	3.500	Ea.	1,300	148	17.50	1,465.50	1,675
0020 1,250 gallon		8	3.500		1,400	148	17.50	1,565.50	1,800
0025 1,500 gallon	↓	7	4	↓	1,650	169	20	1,839	2,125

33 36 19 – Utility Septic Tank Effluent Filter

33 36 19.13 Utility Septic Tank Effluent Tube Filter

	Crew	Daily Output	Labor-Hours	Unit	Material	2014 Bare Costs Labor	Equipment	Total	Total Incl O&P
0010 **UTILITY SEPTIC TANK EFFLUENT TUBE FILTER**									
3000 Effluent filter, 4" diameter	1 Skwk	8	1	Ea.	55.50	47.50		103	138

33 36 Utility Septic Tanks

33 36 19 – Utility Septic Tank Effluent Filter

33 36 19.13 Utility Septic Tank Effluent Tube Filter	Crew	Daily Output	Labor-Hours	Unit	Material	2014 Bare Costs Labor	Equipment	Total	Total Incl O&P
3020 6" diameter	1 Skwk	7	1.143	Ea.	230	54		284	340

33 36 33 – Utility Septic Tank Drainage Field

33 36 33.13 Utility Septic Tank Tile Drainage Field

0010	**UTILITY SEPTIC TANK TILE DRAINAGE FIELD**								
0015	Distribution box, concrete, 5 outlets	2 Clab	20	.800	Ea.	78.50	29.50		108	134
0020	7 outlets		16	1		78.50	36.50		115	146
0025	9 outlets		8	2		475	73.50		548.50	645
0115	Distribution boxes, HDPE, 5 outlets		20	.800		64.50	29.50		94	119
0120	8 outlets		10	1.600		68.50	58.50		127	172
0240	Distribution boxes, Outlet Flow Leveler	1 Clab	50	.160		2.22	5.85		8.07	12.10
0300	Precast concrete, galley, 4' x 4' x 4'	B-21	16	1.750		241	74	8.75	323.75	395

33 36 50 – Drainage Field Systems

33 36 50.10 Drainage Field Excavation and Fill

0010	**DRAINAGE FIELD EXCAVATION AND FILL**								
2200	Septic tank & drainage field excavation with 3/4 c.y backhoe	B-12F	145	.110	C.Y.		4.79	4.57	9.36	12.70
2400	4' trench for disposal field, 3/4 C.Y. backhoe	"	335	.048	L.F.		2.08	1.98	4.06	5.50
2600	Gravel fill, run of bank	B-6	150	.160	C.Y.	19.90	6.40	2.44	28.74	35
2800	Crushed stone, 3/4"	"	150	.160	"	34.50	6.40	2.44	43.34	50.50

33 41 Storm Utility Drainage Piping

33 41 13 – Public Storm Utility Drainage Piping

33 41 13.40 Piping, Storm Drainage, Corrugated Metal

0010	**PIPING, STORM DRAINAGE, CORRUGATED METAL** R221113-50								
0020	Not including excavation or backfill								
2000	Corrugated metal pipe, galvanized								
2020	Bituminous coated with paved invert, 20' lengths								
2040	8" diameter, 16 ga.	B-14	330	.145	L.F.	8.70	5.65	1.11	15.46	19.95
2080	12" diameter, 16 ga.	"	210	.229	"	11.10	8.85	1.74	21.69	28.50

33 41 13.60 Sewage/Drainage Collection, Concrete Pipe

0010	**SEWAGE/DRAINAGE COLLECTION, CONCRETE PIPE**								
0020	Not including excavation or backfill								
1000	Non-reinforced pipe, extra strength, B&S or T&G joints								
1010	6" diameter	B-14	265.04	.181	L.F.	5.60	7	1.38	13.98	19.10
1020	8" diameter		224	.214		6.15	8.30	1.63	16.08	22
1040	12" diameter		200	.240		8.15	9.30	1.83	19.28	26
2000	Reinforced culvert, class 3, no gaskets								
2010	12" diameter	B-14	150	.320	L.F.	10	12.40	2.44	24.84	33.50
2020	15" diameter	"	150	.320	"	13	12.40	2.44	27.84	37

33 44 Storm Utility Water Drains

33 44 13 – Utility Area Drains

33 44 13.13 Catchbasins	Crew	Daily Output	Labor-Hours	Unit	Material	2014 Bare Costs Labor	Equipment	Total	Total Incl O&P
0010 **CATCHBASINS**									
0011 Not including footing & excavation									
1600 Frames & grates, C.I., 24" square, 500 lb.	B-6	7.80	3.077	Ea.	340	123	47	510	625
1700 26" D shape, 600 lb.	"	7	3.429	"	505	138	52	695	835
3320 Frames and covers, existing, raised for paving, 2", including									
3340 row of brick, concrete collar, up to 12" wide frame	B-6	18	1.333	Ea.	44.50	53.50	20.50	118.50	158

33 44 13.15 Remove and Replace Catch Basin Cover

	Crew	Daily Output	Labor-Hours	Unit	Material	2014 Bare Costs Labor	Equipment	Total	Total Incl O&P
0010 **REMOVE AND REPLACE CATCH BASIN COVER**									
0023 Remove catch basin cover	1 Clab	80	.100	Ea.		3.67		3.67	6
0033 Replace catch basin cover	"	80	.100	"		3.67		3.67	6

33 49 Storm Drainage Structures

33 49 13 – Storm Drainage Manholes, Frames, and Covers

33 49 13.10 Storm Drainage Manholes, Frames and Covers

	Crew	Daily Output	Labor-Hours	Unit	Material	2014 Bare Costs Labor	Equipment	Total	Total Incl O&P
0010 **STORM DRAINAGE MANHOLES, FRAMES & COVERS**									
0020 Excludes footing, excavation, backfill (See line items for frame & cover)									
0050 Brick, 4' inside diameter, 4' deep	D-1	1	16	Ea.	510	660		1,170	1,625
0100 6' deep		.70	22.857		725	945		1,670	2,325
0150 8' deep		.50	32		935	1,325		2,260	3,175
0200 For depths over 8', add		4	4	V.L.F.	83.50	165		248.50	360
1110 Precast, 4' I.D., 4' deep	B-22	4.10	7.317	Ea.	775	315	51	1,141	1,425
1120 6' deep		3	10		970	425	70	1,465	1,850
1130 8' deep		2	15		1,100	640	105	1,845	2,400
1140 For depths over 8', add		16	1.875	V.L.F.	125	80	13.15	218.15	282

33 51 Natural-Gas Distribution

33 51 13 – Natural-Gas Piping

33 51 13.10 Piping, Gas Service and Distribution, P.E.

	Crew	Daily Output	Labor-Hours	Unit	Material	2014 Bare Costs Labor	Equipment	Total	Total Incl O&P
0010 **PIPING, GAS SERVICE AND DISTRIBUTION, POLYETHYLENE**									
0020 Not including excavation or backfill									
1000 60 psi coils, compression coupling @ 100', 1/2" diameter, SDR 11	B-20A	608	.053	L.F.	.61	2.35		2.96	4.42
1010 1" diameter, SDR 11		544	.059		1.41	2.63		4.04	5.75
1040 1-1/4" diameter, SDR 11		544	.059		1.76	2.63		4.39	6.15
1100 2" diameter, SDR 11		488	.066		2.85	2.93		5.78	7.80
1160 3" diameter, SDR 11		408	.078		5.60	3.51		9.11	11.75
1500 60 PSI 40' joints with coupling, 3" diameter, SDR 11	B-21A	408	.098		5.55	4.49	1.18	11.22	14.55
1540 4" diameter, SDR 11		352	.114		12.15	5.20	1.37	18.72	23
1600 6" diameter, SDR 11		328	.122		33.50	5.60	1.47	40.57	47.50
1640 8" diameter, SDR 11		272	.147		51.50	6.75	1.77	60.02	69
9000 Minimum labor/equipment charge	B-20	2	12	Job		490		490	805

33 52 16.13 Gasoline Piping	Crew	Daily Output	Labor-Hours	Unit	Material	2014 Bare Costs Labor	Equipment	Total	Total Incl O&P
0010 **GASOLINE PIPING**									
0020 Primary containment pipe, fiberglass-reinforced									
0030 Plastic pipe 15' & 30' lengths									
0040 2" diameter	Q-6	425	.056	L.F.	5.95	3.08		9.03	11.35
0050 3" diameter		400	.060		10.40	3.28		13.68	16.50
0060 4" diameter		375	.064		13.70	3.49		17.19	20.50
0100 Fittings									
0110 Elbows, 90° & 45°, bell-ends, 2"	Q-6	24	1	Ea.	43.50	54.50		98	133
0120 3" diameter		22	1.091		55	59.50		114.50	154
0130 4" diameter		20	1.200		70	65.50		135.50	179
0200 Tees, bell ends, 2"		21	1.143		60.50	62.50		123	164
0210 3" diameter		18	1.333		64	73		137	185
0220 4" diameter		15	1.600		84	87.50		171.50	229
0230 Flanges bell ends, 2"		24	1		33.50	54.50		88	122
0240 3" diameter		22	1.091		39	59.50		98.50	136
0250 4" diameter		20	1.200		45	65.50		110.50	152
0260 Sleeve couplings, 2"		21	1.143		12.40	62.50		74.90	111
0270 3" diameter		18	1.333		17.80	73		90.80	134
0280 4" diameter		15	1.600		23	87.50		110.50	162
0290 Threaded adapters 2"		21	1.143		18	62.50		80.50	117
0300 3" diameter		18	1.333		34	73		107	152
0310 4" diameter		15	1.600		38	87.50		125.50	178
0320 Reducers, 2"		27	.889		27.50	48.50		76	106
0330 3" diameter		22	1.091		27.50	59.50		87	123
0340 4" diameter		20	1.200		37	65.50		102.50	143
1010 Gas station product line for secondary containment (double wall)									
1100 Fiberglass reinforced plastic pipe 25' lengths									
1120 Pipe, plain end, 3" diameter	Q-6	375	.064	L.F.	26.50	3.49		29.99	35
1130 4" diameter		350	.069		32	3.74		35.74	41.50
1140 5" diameter		325	.074		35.50	4.03		39.53	45.50
1150 6" diameter		300	.080		39	4.37		43.37	50
1200 Fittings									
1230 Elbows, 90° & 45°, 3" diameter	Q-6	18	1.333	Ea.	136	73		209	264
1240 4" diameter		16	1.500		167	82		249	310
1250 5" diameter		14	1.714		184	93.50		277.50	350
1260 6" diameter		12	2		204	109		313	395
1270 Tees, 3" diameter		15	1.600		166	87.50		253.50	320
1280 4" diameter		12	2		202	109		311	390
1290 5" diameter		9	2.667		315	146		461	575
1300 6" diameter		6	4		375	218		593	755
1310 Couplings, 3" diameter		18	1.333		55	73		128	175
1320 4" diameter		16	1.500		119	82		201	259
1330 5" diameter		14	1.714		214	93.50		307.50	380
1340 6" diameter		12	2		315	109		424	520
1350 Cross-over nipples, 3" diameter		18	1.333		10.60	73		83.60	126
1360 4" diameter		16	1.500		12.75	82		94.75	142
1370 5" diameter		14	1.714		15.90	93.50		109.40	164
1380 6" diameter		12	2		19.10	109		128.10	191
1400 Telescoping, reducers, concentric 4" x 3"		18	1.333		47.50	73		120.50	167
1410 5" x 4"		17	1.412		95.50	77		172.50	225
1420 6" x 5"		16	1.500		234	82		316	385

33 71 Electrical Utility Transmission and Distribution

33 71 19 – Electrical Underground Ducts and Manholes

33 71 19.17 Electric and Telephone Underground	Crew	Daily Output	Labor-Hours	Unit	Material	2014 Bare Costs Labor	Equipment	Total	Total Incl O&P
0010 **ELECTRIC AND TELEPHONE UNDERGROUND**									
0011 Not including excavation									
0200 backfill and cast in place concrete									
4200 Underground duct, banks ready for concrete fill, min. of 7.5"									
4400 between conduits, center to center									
4600 2 @ 2" diameter	2 Elec	240	.067	L.F.	1.45	3.56		5.01	7.10
4800 4 @ 2" diameter		120	.133		2.90	7.10		10	14.20
5600 4 @ 4" diameter		80	.200		6.05	10.65		16.70	23
6200 Rigid galvanized steel, 2 @ 2" diameter		180	.089		12.10	4.74		16.84	20.50
6400 4 @ 2" diameter		90	.178		24	9.50		33.50	41
7400 4 @ 4" diameter		34	.471		80	25		105	127
9990 Minimum labor/equipment charge	1 Elec	3.50	2.286	Job		122		122	189

Division Notes

	CREW	DAILY OUTPUT	LABOR-HOURS	UNIT	BARE COSTS				TOTAL INCL O&P
					MAT.	LABOR	EQUIP.	TOTAL	

Estimating Tips

34 11 00 Rail Tracks

This subdivision includes items that may involve either repair of existing, or construction of new, railroad tracks. Additional preparation work, such as the roadbed earthwork, would be found in Division 31. Additional new construction siding and turnouts are found in Subdivision 34 72. Maintenance of railroads is found under 34 01 23 Operation and Maintenance of Railways.

34 40 00 Traffic Signals

This subdivision includes traffic signal systems. Other traffic control devices such as traffic signs are found in Subdivision 10 14 53 Traffic Signage.

34 70 00 Vehicle Barriers

This subdivision includes security vehicle barriers, guide and guard rails, crash barriers, and delineators. The actual maintenance and construction of concrete and asphalt pavement is found in Division 32.

Reference Numbers

Reference numbers are shown in shaded boxes at the beginning of some major classifications. These numbers refer to related items in the Reference Section. The reference information may be an estimating procedure, an alternate pricing method, or technical information.

Note: Not all subdivisions listed here necessarily appear in this publication.

Division 34 - Transportation

34 71 Roadway Construction

34 71 13 – Vehicle Barriers

34 71 13.26 Vehicle Guide Rails	Crew	Daily Output	Labor-Hours	Unit	Material	2014 Bare Costs Labor	2014 Bare Costs Equipment	Total	Total Incl O&P
0010 VEHICLE GUIDE RAILS									
0012 Corrugated stl., galv. stl. posts, 6'-3" O.C.	B-80	850	.038	L.F.	21.50	1.50	.89	23.89	27.50
0200 End sections, galvanized, flared		50	.640	Ea.	94	25.50	15.15	134.65	162
0300 Wrap around end		50	.640	"	137	25.50	15.15	177.65	209
0400 Timber guide rail, 4" x 8" with 6" x 8" wood posts, treated	▼	960	.033	L.F.	11.80	1.32	.79	13.91	16

Estimating Tips

Products such as conveyors, material handling cranes and hoists, as well as other items specified in this division, require trained installers. The general contractor may not have any choice as to who will perform the installation or when it will be performed. Long lead times are often required for these products, making early decisions in purchasing and scheduling necessary.

The installation of this type of equipment may require the embedment of mounting hardware during construction of floors, structural walls, or interior walls/partitions. Electrical connections will require coordination with the electrical contractor.

Reference Numbers

Reference numbers are shown in shaded boxes at the beginning of some major classifications. These numbers refer to related items in the Reference Section. The reference information may be an estimating procedure, an alternate pricing method, or technical information.

Note: Not all subdivisions listed here necessarily appear in this publication.

41 22 Cranes and Hoists

41 22 13 – Cranes

41 22 13.10 Crane Rail	Crew	Daily Output	Labor-Hours	Unit	Material	2014 Bare Costs Labor	Equipment	Total	Total Incl O&P
0010 **CRANE RAIL**									
0020 Box beam bridge, no equipment included	E-4	3400	.009	Lb.	1.33	.49	.04	1.86	2.40
0210 Running track only, 104 lb. per yard, 20' piece	"	160	.200	L.F.	23	10.30	.89	34.19	45.50

41 22 13.13 Bridge Cranes

	Crew	Daily Output	Labor-Hours	Unit	Material	2014 Bare Costs Labor	Equipment	Total	Total Incl O&P
0010 **BRIDGE CRANES**									
0100 1 girder, 20' span, 3 ton	M-3	1	34	Ea.	24,100	1,900	140	26,140	29,600
0125 5 ton		1	34		26,400	1,900	140	28,440	32,200
0150 7.5 ton		1	34		31,400	1,900	140	33,440	37,700
0175 10 ton		.80	42.500		41,600	2,375	175	44,150	49,700
0200 15 ton		.80	42.500		53,500	2,375	175	56,050	63,000
0225 30' span, 3 ton		1	34		25,100	1,900	140	27,140	30,700
0250 5 ton		1	34		27,600	1,900	140	29,640	33,400
0275 7.5 ton		1	34		33,000	1,900	140	35,040	39,400
0300 10 ton		.80	42.500		43,000	2,375	175	45,550	51,000
0325 15 ton		.80	42.500		56,000	2,375	175	58,550	65,500
0350 2 girder, 40' span, 3 ton	M-4	.50	72		41,300	3,975	355	45,630	52,000
0375 5 ton		.50	72		43,300	3,975	355	47,630	54,000
0400 7.5 ton		.50	72		47,500	3,975	355	51,830	58,500
0425 10 ton		.40	90		55,500	4,975	445	60,920	69,500
0450 15 ton		.40	90		75,500	4,975	445	80,920	91,500
0475 25 ton		.30	120		89,500	6,625	595	96,720	109,000
0500 50' span, 3 ton		.50	72		47,100	3,975	355	51,430	58,500
0525 5 ton		.50	72		49,000	3,975	355	53,330	60,500
0550 7.5 ton		.50	72		52,500	3,975	355	56,830	64,000
0575 10 ton		.40	90		60,500	4,975	445	65,920	75,000
0600 15 ton		.40	90		79,000	4,975	445	84,420	95,500
0625 25 ton		.30	120		93,500	6,625	595	100,720	114,000

41 22 13.19 Jib Cranes

	Crew	Daily Output	Labor-Hours	Unit	Material	2014 Bare Costs Labor	Equipment	Total	Total Incl O&P
0010 **JIB CRANES**									
0020 Jib crane, wall cantilever, 500 lb. capacity, 8' span	2 Mill	1	16	Ea.	1,400	770		2,170	2,725
0040 12' span		1	16		1,525	770		2,295	2,875
0060 16' span		1	16		1,700	770		2,470	3,075
0080 20' span		1	16		2,150	770		2,920	3,575
0100 1000 lb. capacity, 8' span		1	16		1,500	770		2,270	2,850
0120 12' span		1	16		1,625	770		2,395	3,000
0130 16' span		1	16		2,150	770		2,920	3,575
0150 20' span		1	16		2,525	770		3,295	3,975

Assemblies Section

Table of Contents

Table of Contents (cont.)

How RSMeans Assemblies Data Works

Assemblies estimating provides a fast and reasonably accurate way to develop construction costs. An assembly is the grouping of individual work items, with appropriate quantities, to provide a cost for a major construction component in a convenient unit of measure.

An assemblies estimate is often used during early stages of design development to compare the cost impact of various design alternatives on total building cost.

Assemblies estimates are also used as an efficient tool to verify construction estimates.

Assemblies estimates do not require a completed design or detailed drawings. Instead, they are based on the general size of the structure and other known parameters of the project. The degree of accuracy of an assemblies estimate is generally within +/- 15%.

A10 Foundations

A1010 Standard Foundations

This page illustrates and describes a spread footing system including concrete, forms, reinforcing and anchor bolts. Lines within System Components give the unit price and total price on a cost each basis for this system. Prices for spread footing systems are on Line Items A1010 230 1200 thru 2300. Both material quantities and labor costs have been adjusted for the system listed.

Factors: To adjust for job conditions other than normal working situations use Lines A1010 230 2900 thru 4000.

Example: You are to install the system in an existing occupied building. Access to the site and protection to the building are mandatory. Go to Lines A1010 230 3600 and 3800 and apply these percentages to the appropriate MAT. and INST. costs.

RSMeans assemblies are identified by a **unique 12-character identifier**. The assemblies are numbered using UNIFORMAT II, ASTM Standard E1557. The first 6 characters represent this system to Level 4. The last 6 characters represent further breakdown by RSMeans in order to arrange items in understandable groups of similar tasks. Line numbers are consistent across all RSMeans publications, so a line number in any RSMeans assemblies data set will always refer to the same work.

System Components	QUANTITY	UNIT	COST EACH MAT.	COST EACH INST.	COST EACH TOTAL
Interior column footing, 3' square 1' thick, 2000 psi concrete, Including forms, reinforcing, and anchor bolts.					
Concrete, 2000 psi	.330	C.Y.	33.66		33.66
Placing concrete	.330	C.Y.		18.43	18.43
Forms, footing, 4 uses	12.000	SFCA	8.52	66.60	75.12
Reinforcing	11.000	Lb.	6.05	6.93	12.98
Anchor bolts, 3/4" diameter	2.000	Ea.	3.28	8.98	12.26
TOTAL			51.51	100.94	152.45

A1010 230	Spread Footing	COST EACH MAT.	COST EACH INST.	COST EACH TOTAL
1200	3' square x 1' thick, 2000 psi concrete	51.50	101	152.50
1300	3000 psi concrete	54	101	155
1400	4000 psi concrete	55.50	101	156.50
1600	For alternate footing systems:			
1700	4' square x 1' thick, 2000 psi concrete	85.50	143	228.50
1800	3000 psi concrete	89.50	143	232.50
1900	4000 psi concrete	92.50	143	235.50
2100	5' square x 1'-3" thick, 2000 psi concrete	160	237	397
2200	3000 psi concrete	168	237	405
2300	4000 psi concrete	174	237	411
2600				
2700				
2900	Cut & patch to match existing construction, add, minimum	2%	3%	
3000	Maximum	5%	9%	
3100	Dust protection, add, minimum	1%	2%	
3200	Maximum	4%	11%	
3300	Equipment usage curtailment, add, minimum	1%	1%	
3400	Maximum	3%	10%	
3500	Material handling & storage limitation, add, minimum	1%	1%	
3600	Maximum	6%	7%	
3700	Protection of existing work, add, minimum	2%	2%	
3800	Maximum	5%	7%	
3900	Shift work requirements, add, minimum		5%	
4000	Maximum		30%	

RSMeans assemblies **Narrative descriptions** are shown in a hierarchical structure to make them readable. In order to read a complete description, read up through the indents to the top of the section. Include everything that is above and to the left that is not contradicted by information below.

For supplemental customizable square foot estimating forms, visit: **http://www.reedconstructiondata.com/rsmeans/assemblies**

Most assemblies consist of three major elements: a graphic, the system components, and the cost data itself. The **Graphic** is a visual representation showing the typical appearance of the assembly in question, frequently accompanied by additional explanatory technical information describing the class of items. The **System Components** is a listing of the individual tasks that make up the assembly, including the quantity and unit of measure for each item, along with the cost of material and installation. The **Assemblies Data** below lists prices for other similar systems with dimensional and/or size variations.

All RSMeans assemblies costs represent the cost for the installing contractor. An allowance for profit has been added to all material, labor, and equipment rental costs.

A markup for labor burdens, including workers' compensation, fixed overhead, and business overhead, is included with installation costs.

The data published in RSMeans print books represents a "national average" cost. This data should be modified to the project location using the **City Cost Indexes** or **Location Factors** tables found in the Reference Section in the back of the book.

All RSMeans assemblies data includes a typical **Unit of Measure** used for estimating that item. For instance, while the unit of measure for the graphic shown here is Each, some A/C systems are estimated by the square foot (S.F.). The estimator needs to take special care that the unit in the data matches the unit in the takeoff. Abbreviations can be found in the Reference Section.

A10 Foundations

A1010 Standard Foundations

This page illustrates and describes a spread footing system including concrete, forms, reinforcing and anchor bolts. Lines within System Components give the unit price and total price on a cost each basis for this system. Prices for spread footing systems are on Line Items A1010 230 1200 thru 2300. Both material quantities and labor costs have been adjusted for the system listed.

Factors: To adjust for job conditions other than normal working situations use Lines A1010 230 2900 thru 4000.

Example: You are to install the system in an existing occupied building. Access to the site and protection to the building are mandatory. Go to Lines A1010 230 3600 and 3800 and apply these percentages to the appropriate MAT. and INST. costs.

System Components	QUANTITY	UNIT	COST EACH		
			MAT.	INST.	TOTAL
Interior column footing, 3' square 1' thick, 2000 psi concrete, Including forms, reinforcing, and anchor bolts.					
Concrete, 2000 psi	.330	C.Y.	33.66		33.66
Placing concrete	.330	C.Y.		18.43	18.43
Forms, footing, 4 uses	12.000	SFCA	8.52	66.60	75.12
Reinforcing	11.000	Lb.	6.05	6.93	12.98
Anchor bolts, 3/4" diameter	2.000	Ea.	3.28	8.98	12.26
TOTAL			51.51	100.94	152.45

System components are listed separately to detail what is included in the development of the total system price.

A1010 230	Spread Footing	COST EACH		
		MAT.	INST.	TOTAL
1200	3' square x 1' thick, 2000 psi concrete	51.50	101	152.50
1300	3000 psi concrete	54	101	155
1400	4000 psi concrete	55.50	101	156.50
1600	For alternate footing systems:			
1700	4' square x 1' thick, 2000 psi concrete	85.50	143	228.50
1800	3000 psi concrete	89.50	143	232.50
1900	4000 psi concrete	92.50	143	235.50
2100	5' square x 1'-3" thick, 2000 psi concrete	160	237	397
2200	3000 psi concrete	168	237	405
2300	4000 psi concrete	174	237	411
2600				
2700				
2900	Cut & patch to match existing construction, add, minimum	2%	3%	
3000	Maximum	5%	9%	
3100	Dust protection, add, minimum	1%	2%	
3200	Maximum	4%	11%	
3300	Equipment usage curtailment, add, minimum	1%	1%	
3400	Maximum	3%	10%	
3500	Material handling & storage limitation, add, minimum	1%	1%	
3600	Maximum	6%	7%	
3700	Protection of existing work, add, minimum	2%	2%	
3800	Maximum	5%	7%	
3900	Shift work requirements, add, minimum		5%	
4000	Maximum		30%	

How RSMeans Assemblies Data Works (Continued)

Sample Estimate

This sample demonstrates the elements of an estimate, including a tally of the RSMeans data lines. Published assemblies costs include all markups for labor burden and profit for the installing contractor. This estimate adds a summary of the markups applied by a general contractor on the installing contractors' work. These figures represent the total cost to the owner. The RSMeans location factor is added at the bottom of the estimate to adjust the cost of the work to a specific location

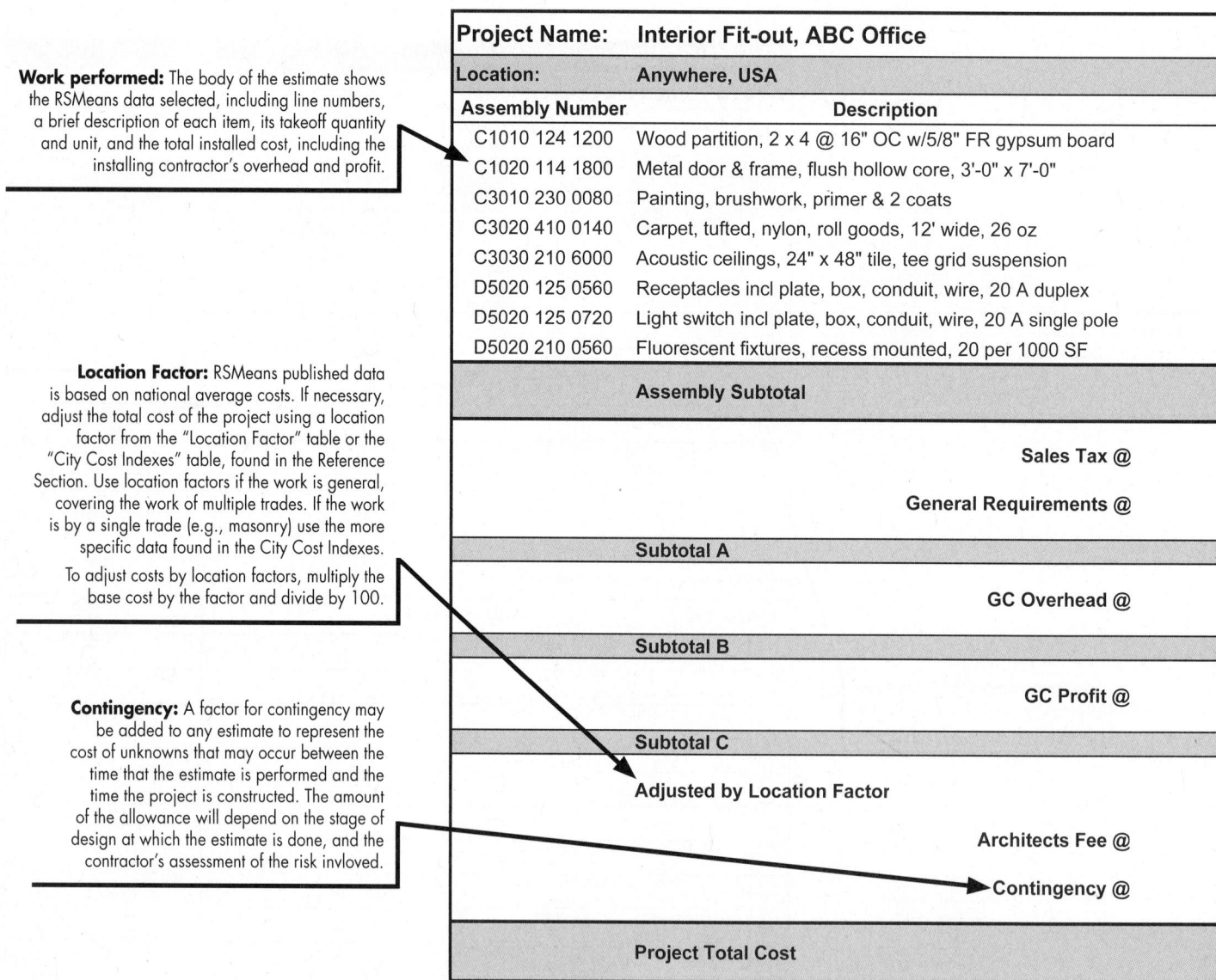

Work performed: The body of the estimate shows the RSMeans data selected, including line numbers, a brief description of each item, its takeoff quantity and unit, and the total installed cost, including the installing contractor's overhead and profit.

Location Factor: RSMeans published data is based on national average costs. If necessary, adjust the total cost of the project using a location factor from the "Location Factor" table or the "City Cost Indexes" table, found in the Reference Section. Use location factors if the work is general, covering the work of multiple trades. If the work is by a single trade (e.g., masonry) use the more specific data found in the City Cost Indexes.

To adjust costs by location factors, multiply the base cost by the factor and divide by 100.

Contingency: A factor for contingency may be added to any estimate to represent the cost of unknowns that may occur between the time that the estimate is performed and the time the project is constructed. The amount of the allowance will depend on the stage of design at which the estimate is done, and the contractor's assessment of the risk invloved.

Project Name:	Interior Fit-out, ABC Office
Location:	**Anywhere, USA**
Assembly Number	**Description**
C1010 124 1200	Wood partition, 2 x 4 @ 16" OC w/5/8" FR gypsum board
C1020 114 1800	Metal door & frame, flush hollow core, 3'-0" x 7'-0"
C3010 230 0080	Painting, brushwork, primer & 2 coats
C3020 410 0140	Carpet, tufted, nylon, roll goods, 12' wide, 26 oz
C3030 210 6000	Acoustic ceilings, 24" x 48" tile, tee grid suspension
D5020 125 0560	Receptacles incl plate, box, conduit, wire, 20 A duplex
D5020 125 0720	Light switch incl plate, box, conduit, wire, 20 A single pole
D5020 210 0560	Fluorescent fixtures, recess mounted, 20 per 1000 SF
Assembly Subtotal	
	Sales Tax @
	General Requirements @
Subtotal A	
	GC Overhead @
Subtotal B	
	GC Profit @
Subtotal C	
Adjusted by Location Factor	
	Architects Fee @
	Contingency @
Project Total Cost	

This estimate is based on an interactive spreadsheet.
A copy of this spreadsheet is located on the RSMeans website at
http://www.reedconstructiondata.com/rsmeans/extras/546011.
You are free to download it and adjust it to your methodology.

558

Date: 1/1/2014		R+R
Qty.	Unit	Subtotal
560.000	S.F.	$2,704.80
2.000	Ea.	$2,670.00
1,120.000	S.F.	$1,400.00
240.000	S.F.	$1,166.40
200.000	S.F.	$936.00
8.000	Ea.	$2,168.00
2.000	Ea.	$543.00
200.000	S.F.	$2,142.00
		$13,730.20
5 %		$ 343.26
7 %		$ 961.11
		$15,034.57
5 %		$ 751.73
		$15,786.30
5 %		$ 789.31
		$16,575.61
118.1		$ 19,575.80
8 %		$ 1,566.06
15 %		$ 2,936.37
		$ 24,078.23

Sales Tax: If the work is subject to state or local sales taxes, the amount must be added to the estimate. In a conceptual estimate it can be assumed that one half of the total represents material costs. Therefore, apply the sales tax rate to 50% of the assembly subtotal.

General Requirements: This item covers project-wide needs provided by the General Contractor. These items vary by project, but may include temporary facilities and utilities, security, testing, project cleanup, etc. In assemblies estimates a percentage is used, typically between 5% and 15% of project cost.

General Contractor Overhead: This entry represents the General Contractor's markup on all work to cover project administration costs.

General Contractor Profit: This entry represents the GC's profit on all work performed. The value included here can vary widely by project, and is influenced by the GC's perception of the project's financial risk and market conditions.

Architects Fee: If appropriate, add the design cost to the project estimate. These fees vary based on project complexity and size. Typical design and engineering fees can be found in the reference section.

A1010 Standard Foundations

This page illustrates and describes a strip footing system including concrete, forms, reinforcing, keyway and dowels. Lines within System Components give the unit price and total price per linear foot for this system. Prices for strip footing systems are on Line Items A1010 120 1400 thru 2500. Both material quantities and labor costs have been adjusted for the system listed.

Factors: To adjust for job conditions other than normal working situations use Lines A1010 120 2900 thru 4000.

Example: You are to install this footing, and due to a lack of accessibility, only hand tools can be used. Material handling is also a problem. Go to Lines A1010 120 3400 and 3600 and apply these percentages to the appropriate MAT. and INST. costs.

System Components			COST PER L.F.		
	QUANTITY	UNIT	MAT.	INST.	TOTAL
Strip footing, 2'-0" wide x 1'-0" thick, 2000 psi concrete including forms, reinforcing, keyway, and dowels.					
Concrete, 2000 psi	.074	C.Y.	7.55		7.55
Placing concrete	.074	C.Y.		1.89	1.89
Forms, footing, 4 uses	2.000	S.F.	4.46	9.44	13.90
Reinforcing	3.170	Lb.	1.74	2	3.74
Keyway, 2" x 4", 4 uses	1.000	L.F.	.22	1.14	1.36
Dowels, #4 bars, 2' long, 24" O.C.	.500	Ea.	.41	1.39	1.80
TOTAL			14.38	15.86	30.24

A1010 120	Strip Footing	COST PER L.F.		
		MAT.	INST.	TOTAL
1400	2'-0" wide x 1' thick, 2000 psi concrete	14.40	15.85	30.25
1500	3000 psi concrete	14.90	15.85	30.75
1600	4000 psi concrete	15.25	15.85	31.10
1800	For alternate footing systems:			
1900	2'-6" wide x 1' thick, 2000 psi concrete	16.80	16.85	33.65
2000	3000 psi concrete	17.45	16.85	34.30
2100	4000 psi concrete	17.90	16.85	34.75
2300	3'-0" wide x 1' thick, 2000 psi concrete	18.95	17.80	36.75
2400	3000 psi concrete	19.70	17.80	37.50
2500	4000 psi concrete	20.50	17.80	38.30
2700				
2800				
2900	Cut & patch to match existing construction, add, minimum	2%	3%	
3000	Maximum	5%	9%	
3100	Dust protection, add, minimum	1%	2%	
3200	Maximum	4%	11%	
3300	Equipment usage curtailment, add, minimum	1%	1%	
3400	Maximum	3%	10%	
3500	Material handling & storage limitation, add, minimum	1%	1%	
3600	Maximum	6%	7%	
3700	Protection of existing work, add, minimum	2%	2%	
3800	Maximum	5%	7%	
3900	Shift work requirements, add, minimum		5%	
4000	Maximum		30%	

A1010 Standard Foundations

This page illustrates and describes a spread footing system including concrete, forms, reinforcing and anchor bolts. Lines within System Components give the unit price and total price on a cost each basis for this system. Prices for spread footing systems are on Line Items A1010 230 1200 thru 2300. Both material quantities and labor costs have been adjusted for the system listed.

Factors: To adjust for job conditions other than normal working situations use Lines A1010 230 2900 thru 4000.

Example: You are to install the system in an existing occupied building. Access to the site and protection to the building are mandatory. Go to Lines A1010 230 3600 and 3800 and apply these percentages to the appropriate MAT. and INST. costs.

System Components	QUANTITY	UNIT	COST EACH		
			MAT.	INST.	TOTAL
Interior column footing, 3' square 1' thick, 2000 psi concrete, including forms, reinforcing, and anchor bolts.					
Concrete, 2000 psi	.330	C.Y.	33.66		33.66
Placing concrete	.330	C.Y.		18.43	18.43
Forms, footing, 4 uses	12.000	SFCA	8.52	66.60	75.12
Reinforcing	11.000	Lb.	6.05	6.93	12.98
Anchor bolts, 3/4" diameter	2.000	Ea.	3.28	8.98	12.26
TOTAL			51.51	100.94	152.45

A1010 230	Spread Footing	COST EACH		
		MAT.	INST.	TOTAL
1200	3' square x 1' thick, 2000 psi concrete	51.50	101	152.50
1300	3000 psi concrete	54	101	155
1400	4000 psi concrete	55.50	101	156.50
1600	For alternate footing systems:			
1700	4' square x 1' thick, 2000 psi concrete	85.50	143	228.50
1800	3000 psi concrete	89.50	143	232.50
1900	4000 psi concrete	92.50	143	235.50
2100	5' square x 1'-3" thick, 2000 psi concrete	160	237	397
2200	3000 psi concrete	168	237	405
2300	4000 psi concrete	174	237	411
2600				
2700				
2900	Cut & patch to match existing construction, add, minimum	2%	3%	
3000	Maximum	5%	9%	
3100	Dust protection, add, minimum	1%	2%	
3200	Maximum	4%	11%	
3300	Equipment usage curtailment, add, minimum	1%	1%	
3400	Maximum	3%	10%	
3500	Material handling & storage limitation, add, minimum	1%	1%	
3600	Maximum	6%	7%	
3700	Protection of existing work, add, minimum	2%	2%	
3800	Maximum	5%	7%	
3900	Shift work requirements, add, minimum		5%	
4000	Maximum		30%	

A10 Foundations

A1010 Standard Foundations

General: Footing drains can be placed either inside or outside of foundation walls depending upon the source of water to be intercepted. If the source of subsurface water is principally from grade or a subsurface stream above the bottom of the footing, outside drains should be used. For high water tables, use inside drains or both inside and outside.

The effectiveness of underdrains depends on good waterproofing. This must be carefully installed and protected during construction.

Costs below include the labor and materials for the pipe and 6" of crushed stone around pipe. Excavation and backfill are not included.

System Components	QUANTITY	UNIT	COST PER L.F. MAT.	COST PER L.F. INST.	COST PER L.F. TOTAL
Foundation underdrain, outside, PVC 4″ diameter.					
PVC pipe 4″ diam. S.D.R. 35	1.000	L.F.	1.61	4.28	5.89
Crushed stone 3/4″ to 1/2″	.070	C.Y.	2.17	.92	3.09
TOTAL			3.78	5.20	8.98

A1010 310	Foundation Underdrain	COST PER L.F. MAT.	COST PER L.F. INST.	COST PER L.F. TOTAL
1000	Foundation underdrain, outside only, PVC, 4″ diameter	3.78	5.20	8.98
1100	6″ diameter	6.40	5.80	12.20
1400	Perforated HDPE, 6″ diameter	4.41	2.25	6.66
1450	8″ diameter	6.45	2.81	9.26
1500	12″ diameter	12	6.85	18.85
1600	Corrugated metal, 16 ga. asphalt coated, 6″ diameter	10	5.40	15.40
1650	8″ diameter	12.85	5.80	18.65
1700	10″ diameter	15.85	7.50	23.35
3000	Outside and inside, PVC, 4″ diameter	7.55	10.40	17.95
3100	6″ diameter	12.80	11.55	24.35
3400	Perforated HDPE, 6″ diameter	8.80	4.49	13.29
3450	8″ diameter	12.90	5.65	18.55
3500	12″ diameter	24	13.60	37.60
3600	Corrugated metal, 16 ga., asphalt coated, 6″ diameter	20	10.85	30.85
3650	8″ diameter	25.50	11.55	37.05
3700	10″ diameter	31.50	14.95	46.45
4700	Cut & patch to match existing construction, add, minimum	2%	3%	
4800	Maximum	5%	9%	
4900	Dust protection, add, minimum	1%	2%	
5000	Maximum	4%	11%	
5100	Equipment usage curtailment, add, minimum	1%	1%	
5200	Maximum	3%	10%	
5300	Material handling & storage limitation, add, minimum	1%	1%	
5400	Maximum	6%	7%	
5500	Protection of existing work, add, minimum	2%	2%	
5600	Maximum	5%	7%	
5700	Shift work requirements, add, minimum		5%	
5800	Maximum		30%	
5900	Temporary shoring and bracing, add, minimum	2%	5%	
6000	Maximum	5%	12%	

A10 Foundations

A1030 Slab on Grade

This page illustrates and describes a slab on grade system including slab, bank run gravel, bulkhead forms, placing concrete, welded wire fabric, vapor barrier, steel trowel finish and curing paper. Lines within System Components give the unit price and total price per square foot for this system. Prices for slab on grade systems are on Line Items A1030 110 1400 thru 2600. Both material quantities and labor costs have been adjusted for the system listed.

Factors: To adjust for job conditions other than normal working situations use Lines A1030 110 2900 thru 4000.

Example: You are to install the system at a site where protection of the existing building is required. Go to Line A1030 110 3800 and apply these percentages to the appropriate MAT. and INST. costs.

System Components	QUANTITY	UNIT	COST PER S.F. MAT.	COST PER S.F. INST.	COST PER S.F. TOTAL
Ground slab, 4″ thick, 3000 psi concrete, 4″ granular base, vapor barrier, welded wire fabric, screed and steel trowel finish.					
Concrete, 4″ thick, 3000 psi concrete	.012	C.Y.	1.31		1.31
Bank run gravel, 4″ deep	.074	C.Y.	.29	.10	.39
Polyethylene vapor barrier, 10 mil.	.011	C.S.F.	.11	.18	.29
Bulkhead forms, expansion material	.100	L.F.	.03	.38	.41
Welded wire fabric, 6 x 6 - #10/10	.011	C.S.F.	.18	.42	.60
Place concrete	.012	C.Y.		.33	.33
Screed & steel trowel finish	1.000	S.F.		.96	.96
TOTAL			1.92	2.37	4.29

A1030 110	Interior Slab on Grade	COST PER S.F. MAT.	COST PER S.F. INST.	COST PER S.F. TOTAL
1400	4″ thick slab, 3000 PSI concrete, 4″ deep bank run gravel	1.92	2.37	4.29
1500	6″ deep bank run gravel	2.15	2.36	4.51
1600	12″ deep bank run gravel	2.66	2.40	5.06
1700				
1800				
1900				
2000	For alternate slab systems:			
2100	5″ thick slab, 3000 psi concrete, 6″ deep bank run gravel	2.48	2.45	4.93
2200	12″ deep bank run gravel	2.99	2.49	5.48
2300				
2400				
2500	6″ thick slab, 3000 psi concrete, 6″ deep bank run gravel	2.91	2.55	5.46
2600	12″ deep bank run gravel	3.42	2.59	6.01
2700				
2900	Cut & patch to match existing construction, add, minimum	2%	3%	
3000	Maximum	5%	9%	
3100	Dust protection, add, minimum	1%	2%	
3200	Maximum	4%	11%	
3300	Equipment usage curtailment, add, minimum	1%	1%	
3400	Maximum	3%	10%	
3500	Material handling & storage limitation, add, minimum	1%	1%	
3600	Maximum	6%	7%	
3700	Protection of existing work, add, minimum	2%	2%	
3800	Maximum	5%	7%	
3900	Shift work requirements, add, minimum		5%	
4000	Maximum		30%	

A20 Basement Construction

A2010 Basement Excavation

This page illustrates and describes continuous footing and trench excavation systems including a wheel mounted backhoe, operator, equipment rental, fuel, oil, mobilization, no hauling or backfill. Lines within System Components give the unit price and total price per linear foot for this system. Prices for alternate continuous footing and trench excavation systems are on Line Items A2010 130 1200 thru 2700. Both material quantities and labor costs have been adjusted for the system listed.

Factors: To adjust for job conditions other than normal working situations use Lines A2010 130 2900 thru 4000.

Example: You are to install the system and supply dust protection. Go to Line A2010 130 3000 and apply this percentage to the appropriate TOTAL costs.

System Components	QUANTITY	UNIT	COST PER L.F. EQUIP.	COST PER L.F. LABOR	COST PER L.F. TOTAL
Continuous footing or trench excav. w/ 3/4 C.Y. wheel mntd backhoe, including operator, equipment rental, fuel, oil and mobilization. Trench is 4' wide at bottom, 3' deep w/sides sloped 1 to 2 and 200' long. Costs are based on a production rate of 240 C.Y./day. No hauling/backfill incl.					
Equipment operator	4.000	Hr.		310	310
3/4 C.Y. backhoe, wheel mounted	.500	Day	95.70		95.70
Operating expense (fuel, oil)	4.000	Hr.	105.16		105.16
Mobilization	1.000	Ea.	294	136	430
TOTAL			494.86	446	940.86
COST PER L.F.		L.F.	2.47	2.23	4.70

A2010 130	Excavation, Footings or Trench		COST PER L.F. EQUIP.	COST PER L.F. LABOR	COST PER L.F. TOTAL
1200	For alternate trench sizes, 4' bottom with sloped sides:				
1300	2' deep, 50' long		8.20	8.90	17.10
1400	100' long		4.29	4.46	8.75
1500	300' long		1.63	1.48	3.11
1600	4' deep, 50' long		8.60	8.90	17.50
1700	100' long		4.69	4.46	9.15
1800	300' long		2.38	2.65	5.03
1900	6' deep, 50' long		9.20	8.90	18.10
2000	100' long		4.88	5.65	10.53
2100	300' long		3.66	4.58	8.24
2200	8' deep, 50' long		9.90	8.90	18.80
2300	100' long		6.95	7.55	14.50
2400	300' long		4.99	4.58	9.57
2500	10' deep, 50' long		11.90	12	23.90
2600	100' long		8.70	10.30	19
2700	300' long		6.60	9.10	15.70
2800					
2900	Dust protection, add, minimum			2%	2%
3000	Maximum			11%	11%
3100	Equipment usage curtailment, add, minimum			1%	1%
3200	Maximum			10%	10%
3300	Material handling & storage limitation, add, minimum			1%	1%
3400	Maximum			7%	7%
3500	Protection of existing work, add, minimum			2%	2%
3600	Maximum			7%	7%
3700	Shift work requirements, add, minimum			5%	5%
3800	Maximum			30%	30%
3900	Temporary shoring and bracing, add, minimum			5%	5%
4000	Maximum			12%	12%

A2010 Basement Excavation

This page illustrates and describes foundation excavation systems including a backhoe-loader, operator, equipment rental, fuel, oil, mobilization, hauling material, no backfilling. Lines within System Components give the unit price and total price per cubic yard for this system. Prices for foundation excavation systems are on Line Items A2010 140 1600 thru 2200. Both material quantities and labor costs have been adjusted for the system listed.

Factors: To adjust for job conditions other than normal working situations use Lines A2010 140 2900 thru 4000.

Example: You are to install the system with the use of temporary shoring and bracing. Go to Line A2010 140 3900 and apply these percentages to the appropriate TOTAL costs.

System Components	QUANTITY	UNIT	COST PER C.Y.		
			EQUIP.	LABOR	TOTAL
Foundation excav w/ 3/4 C.Y. backhoe-loader, incl. operator, equip rental, fuel, oil, and mobilization. Hauling of excavated material is included. Prices based on one day production of 360 C.Y. in medium soil without backfilling.					
Equipment operator	8.000	Hr.		620	620
Backhoe-loader, 3/4 C.Y.	1.000	Day	191.40		191.40
Operating expense (fuel, oil)	8.000	Hr.	210.32		210.32
Hauling, 12 C.Y. trucks, 1 mile round trip	360.000	L.C.Y.	1,087.20	698.40	1,785.60
Mobilization	1.000	Ea.	294	136	430
TOTAL			1,782.92	1,454.40	3,237.32
COST PER C.Y.		C.Y.	4.94	4.03	8.99

A2010 140	Excavation, Foundation	COST PER C.Y.		
		EQUIP.	LABOR	TOTAL
1600	100 C.Y.	6.55	6.80	13.35
1700	200 C.Y.	5.60	4.37	9.97
1800	300 C.Y.	5.15	4.12	9.27
1850	360 C.Y.	4.93	4.03	8.96
1900	400 C.Y.	4.87	3.99	8.86
2000	500 C.Y.	4.74	3.95	8.69
2100	600 C.Y.	4.60	3.89	8.49
2200	700 C.Y.	4.54	3.81	8.35
2300				
2400				
2900	Dust protection, add, minimum		2%	2%
3000	Maximum		11%	11%
3100	Equipment usage curtailment, add, minimum		1%	1%
3200	Maximum		10%	10%
3300	Material handling & storage limitation, add, minimum		1%	1%
3400	Maximum		7%	7%
3500	Protection of existing work, add, minimum		2%	2%
3600	Maximum		7%	7%
3700	Shift work requirements, add, minimum		5%	5%
3800	Maximum		30%	30%
3900	Temporary shoring and bracing, add, minimum		5%	5%
4000	Maximum		12%	12%

A2020 Basement Walls

This page illustrates and describes a concrete wall system including concrete, placing concrete, forms, reinforcing, insulation, waterproofing and anchor bolts. Lines within System Components give the unit price and total price per linear foot for this system. Prices for concrete wall systems are on Line Items A2020 120 1400 thru 2600. Both material quantities and labor costs have been adjusted for the system listed.

Factors: To adjust for job conditions other than normal working situations use Lines A2020 120 2900 thru 4000.

Example: You are to install this wall system where delivery of material is difficult. Go to Line A2020 120 3600 and apply these percentages to the appropriate MAT. and INST. costs.

System Components	QUANTITY	UNIT	COST PER L.F. MAT.	COST PER L.F. INST.	COST PER L.F. TOTAL
Cast in place concrete foundation wall, 8″ thick, 3′ high, 2500 psi concrete including forms, reinforcing, waterproofing, and anchor bolts.					
Concrete, 2500 psi, 8″ thick, 3′ high	.070	C.Y.	7.35		7.35
Forms, wall, 4 uses	6.000	S.F.	6.54	41.70	48.24
Reinforcing	6.000	Lb.	3.30	2.64	5.94
Placing concrete	.070	C.Y.		3.47	3.47
Waterproofing	3.000	S.F.	1.50	3.39	4.89
Rigid insulaton, 1″ polystyrene	3.000	S.F.	.78	2.67	3.45
Anchor bolts, 1/2″ diameter, 4′ O.C.	.250	Ea.	.46	1.13	1.59
TOTAL			19.93	55	74.93

A2020 120	Concrete Wall	COST PER L.F. MAT.	COST PER L.F. INST.	COST PER L.F. TOTAL
1400	8″ thick, 2500 psi concrete, 3′ high	19.95	55	74.95
1500	4′ high	27	73.50	100.50
1600	6′ high	40.50	109	149.50
1700	8′ high	54	146	200
1800	3500 psi concrete, 4′ high	27.50	73.50	101
1900	6′ high	41.50	109	150.50
2000	8′ high	55	146	201
2100	12″ thick, 2500 psi concrete, 4′ high	34.50	77.50	112
2200	6′ high	50	115	165
2300	8′ high	66.50	153	219.50
2400	3500 psi concrete, 4′ high	35.50	77.50	113
2500	8′ high	68.50	153	221.50
2600	10′ high	84.50	190	274.50
2700				
2900	Cut & patch to match existing construction, add, minimum	2%	3%	
3000	Maximum	5%	9%	
3100	Dust protection, add, minimum	1%	2%	
3200	Maximum	4%	11%	
3300	Equipment usage curtailment, add, minimum	1%	1%	
3400	Maximum	3%	10%	
3500	Material handling & storage limitation, add, minimum	1%	1%	
3600	Maximum	6%	7%	
3700	Protection of existing work, add, minimum	2%	2%	
3800	Maximum	5%	7%	
3900	Shift work requirements, add, minimum		5%	
4000	Maximum		30%	

A20 Basement Construction

A2020 Basement Walls

This page illustrates and describes a concrete block wall system including concrete block, masonry reinforcing, parging, waterproofing insulation and anchor bolts. Lines within System Components give the unit price and total price per linear foot for this system. Prices for concrete block wall systems are on Line Items A2020 140 1200 thru 2600. Both material quantities and labor costs have been adjusted for the system listed.

Factors: To adjust for job conditions other than normal working situations use Lines A2020 140 2900 thru 4000.

Example: You are to install the system to match an existing foundation wall. Go to Line A2020 140 3000 and apply these percentages to the appropriate MAT. and INST. costs.

System Components			COST PER L.F.		
	QUANTITY	UNIT	MAT.	INST.	TOTAL
Concrete block, 8" thick, masonry reinforcing, parged and waterproofed, insulation and anchor bolts, wall 2'-8" high.					
Concrete block, 8" x 8" x 16"	2.670	S.F.	8.62	17.22	25.84
Masonry reinforcing	2.000	L.F.	.50	.40	.90
Parging	.193	S.Y.	.76	2.63	3.39
Waterproofing	2.670	S.F.	1.34	3.02	4.36
Insulation, 1" rigid polystyrene	2.670	S.F.	.69	2.38	3.07
Anchor bolts, 1/2" diameter, 4' O.C.	.250	Ea.	.46	1.13	1.59
TOTAL			12.37	26.78	39.15

A2020 140	Concrete Block Wall	COST PER L.F.		
		MAT.	INST.	TOTAL
1200	8" thick block, 2'-8" high	12.35	26.50	38.85
1300	4' high	18.30	39.50	57.80
1400	6' high	27	59	86
1500	8' high	36	78	114
1600	Grouted solid, 4' high	23.50	53	76.50
1700	6' high	34.50	79	113.50
1800	8' high	46	105	151
2100	12" thick block, 4' high	24	57	81
2200	6' high	35.50	85	120.50
2300	8' high	47.50	113	160.50
2400	Grouted solid, 4' high	32	71.50	103.50
2500	6' high	47.50	107	154.50
2600	8' high	63.50	142	205.50
2700				
2900	Cut & patch to match existing construction, add, minimum	2%	3%	
3000	Maximum	5%	9%	
3100	Dust protection, add, minimum	1%	2%	
3200	Maximum	4%	11%	
3300	Equipment usage curtailment, add, minimum	1%	1%	
3400	Maximum	3%	10%	
3500	Material handling & storage limitation, add, minimum	1%	1%	
3600	Maximum	6%	7%	
3700	Protection of existing work, add, minimum	2%	2%	
3800	Maximum	5%	7%	
3900	Shift work requirements, add, minimum		5%	
4000	Maximum		30%	

B10 Superstructure

B1010 Floor Construction

This page illustrates and describes a reinforced concrete slab system including concrete, placing concrete, formwork, reinforcing, steel trowel finish, V.A. floor tile and acoustical spray ceiling finish. Lines within System Components give the unit price per square foot for this system. Prices for reinforced concrete slab systems are on Line Items B1010 225 1400 thru 1800. Both material quantities and labor costs have been adjusted for the system listed.

Factors: To adjust for job conditions other than normal working situations use Lines B1010 225 2700 thru 4000.

Example: You are to install the system to match an existing floor system. Go to Line B1010 225 2800 and apply these percentages to the appropriate MAT. and INST. costs.

System Components	QUANTITY	UNIT	COST PER S.F.		
			MAT.	INST.	TOTAL
Flat slab system, reinforced concrete with vinyl tile floor, sprayed acoustical ceiling finish, not including columns.					
Concrete, 4000 psi, 6″ thick	.020	C.Y.	2.28		2.28
Placing concrete	.020	C.Y.		.70	.70
Formwork, 4 use	1.000	S.F.	1.30	6.30	7.60
Edge form	.120	S.F.	.06	1.22	1.28
Reinforcing steel	3.000	Lb.	1.65	1.89	3.54
Steel trowel finish	1.000	S.F.		1.26	1.26
Vinyl floor tile	1.000	S.F.	5.50	1.06	6.56
Acoustical spray ceiling finish	1.000	S.F.	.30	.17	.47
TOTAL			11.09	12.60	23.69

B1010 225	Floor - Ceiling, Concrete Slab	COST PER S.F.		
		MAT.	INST.	TOTAL
1400	Concrete, 4000 psi, 6″ thick	11.10	12.60	23.70
1500	7″ thick	11.55	13.15	24.70
1600	8″ thick	12.25	13.80	26.05
1700	9″ thick	12.80	14.35	27.15
1800	10″ thick	13.50	15.10	28.60
1900				
2000				
2100				
2200				
2300				
2400				
2500				
2700	Cut & patch to match existing construction, add, minimum	2%	3%	
2800	Maximum	5%	9%	
2900	Dust protection, add, minimum	1%	2%	
3000	Maximum	4%	11%	
3100	Equipment usage curtailment, add, minimum	1%	1%	
3200	Maximum	3%	10%	
3300	Material handling & storage limitation, add, minimum	1%	1%	
3400	Maximum	6%	7%	
3500	Protection of existing work, add, minimum	2%	2%	
3600	Maximum	5%	7%	
3700	Shift work requirements, add, minimum		5%	
3800	Maximum		30%	
3900	Temporary shoring and bracing, add, minimum	2%	5%	
4000	Maximum	5%	12%	

B1010 Floor Construction

This page illustrates and describes a hollow core prestressed concrete panel system including hollow core slab, grout, carpet, carpet padding, and sprayed ceiling. Lines within System Components give the unit price and total price per square foot for this system. Prices for hollow core prestressed concrete panel systems are on Line Items B1010 232 1200 thru 1600. Both material and labor costs have been adjusted for the system listed.

Factors: To adjust for job conditions other than normal working situations use Lines B1010 232 2700 thru 3800.

Example: You are to install the system where dust control is a major concern. Go to Line B1010 232 2800 and apply these percentages to the appropriate MAT. and INST. costs.

System Components	QUANTITY	UNIT	COST PER S.F.		
			MAT.	INST.	TOTAL
Precast hollow core plank with carpeted floors, padding and sprayed textured ceiling.					
Hollow core plank, 4" thick with grout topping	1.000	S.F.	6.45	3.54	9.99
Nylon carpet, 26 oz. medium traffic	.110	S.Y.	4.62	.78	5.40
Carpet padding, minimum quality	.110	S.Y.	.52	.39	.91
Sprayed texture ceiling	1.000	S.F.	.04	.64	.68
TOTAL			11.63	5.35	16.98

B1010 232	Floor - Ceiling, Conc. Panel	COST PER S.F.		
		MAT.	INST.	TOTAL
1200	Hollow core concrete plank, with grout, 4" thick	11.65	5.35	17
1300	6" thick	12.10	4.84	16.94
1400	8" thick	13	4.46	17.46
1500	10" thick	13.20	4.17	17.37
1600	12" thick	13.85	3.94	17.79
1700				
1800				
1900				
2000				
2100				
2200				
2300				
2400				
2500				
2700	Dust protection, add, minimum	1%	2%	
2800	Maximum	4%	11%	
2900	Equipment usage curtailment, add, minimum	1%	1%	
3000	Maximum	3%	10%	
3100	Material handling & storage limitation, add, minimum	1%	1%	
3200	Maximum	6%	7%	
3300	Protection of existing work, add, minimum	2%	2%	
3400	Maximum	5%	7%	
3500	Shift work requirements, add, minimum		5%	
3600	Maximum		30%	
3700	Temporary shoring and bracing, add, minimum	2%	5%	
3800	Maximum	5%	12%	

B10 Superstructure

B1010 Floor Construction

This page illustrates and describes a hollow core plank system including precast hollow core plank, concrete topping, V.A. tile, concealed suspension system and ceiling tile. Lines within System Components give the unit price and total price per square foot for this system. Prices for hollow core plank systems are on Line Items B1010 233 1400 thru 1800. Both material quantities and labor costs have been adjusted for the system listed.

Factors: To adjust for job conditions other than normal working situations use Lines B1010 233 2900 thru 4000.

Example: You are to install the system where equipment usage is a problem. Go to Line B1010 233 3200 and apply these percentages to the appropriate MAT. and INST. costs.

System Components	QUANTITY	UNIT	COST PER S.F.		
			MAT.	INST.	TOTAL
Precast hollow core plank with 2" topping, vinyl composition floor tile and suspended acoustical tile ceiling.					
Hollow core concrete plank, 4" thick	1.000	S.F.	6.45	3.54	9.99
Concrete topping, 2" thick	1.000	S.F.	1.27	5.72	6.99
Vinyl composition tile, .08" thick	1.000	S.F.	1.61	1.06	2.67
Concealed Z bar suspension system, 12" module	1.000	S.F.	.86	1.16	2.02
Ceiling tile, mineral fiber, 3/4" thick	1.000	S.F.	1.96	2.01	3.97
TOTAL			12.15	13.49	25.64

B1010 233	Floor - Ceiling, Conc. Plank	COST PER S.F.		
		MAT.	INST.	TOTAL
1400	Hollow core concrete plank, 4" thick	12.15	13.50	25.65
1500	6" thick	12.60	13	25.60
1600	8" thick	13.50	12.60	26.10
1700	10" thick	13.70	12.35	26.05
1800	12" thick	14.35	12.10	26.45
1900				
2000				
2100				
2200				
2300				
2400				
2500				
2600				
2700				
2900	Dust protection, add, minimum	1%	2%	
3000	Maximum	4%	11%	
3100	Equipment usage curtailment, add, minimum	1%	1%	
3200	Maximum	3%	10%	
3300	Material handling & storage limitation, add, minimum	1%	1%	
3400	Maximum	6%	7%	
3500	Protection of existing work, add, minimum	2%	2%	
3600	Maximum	5%	7%	
3700	Shift work requirements, add, minimum		5%	
3800	Maximum		30%	
3900	Temporary shoring and bracing, add, minimum	2%	5%	
4000	Maximum	5%	12%	

B1010 Floor Construction

This page illustrates and describes a structural steel w/metal decking and concrete system including steel beams, steel decking, shear studs, concrete, placing concrete, edge form, steel trowel finish, curing, wire fabric, fireproofing, beams and decking, tile floor, and suspended ceiling. Lines within System Components give the unit price and total price per square foot for this system. Prices for alternate structural steel w/metal decking and concrete systems are on Line Items B1010 243 1900 thru 2400. Both material quantities and labor costs have been adjusted for the system listed.

Factors: To adjust for job conditions other than normal working situations use Lines B1010 243 2900 thru 4000.

Example: You are to install the system where material handling and storage are a problem. Go to Line B1010 243 3400 and apply these percentages to the appropriate MAT. and INST. costs.

System Components	QUANTITY	UNIT	COST PER S.F.		
			MAT.	INST.	TOTAL
Composite structural beams, 20 ga. 3″ deep steel decking, shear studs, 3000 psi, concrete, placing concrete, edge forms, steel trowel finish, welded wire fabric fireproofing, tile floor and suspended ceiling.					
Steel deck, 20 gage, 3″ deep, galvanized	1.000	S.F.	2.48	1.06	3.54
Structural steel framing	.004	Ton	11.70	2.81	14.51
Shear studs, 3/4″	.250	Ea.	.14	.50	.64
Concrete, 3000 psi, 5″ thick	.015	C.Y.	1.64		1.64
Place concrete	.015	C.Y.		.53	.53
Edge form	.140	L.F.	.03	.64	.67
Steel trowel finish	1.000	S.F.		1.26	1.26
Welded wire fabric 6 x 6 - #10/10	.011	C.S.F.	.18	.42	.60
Fireproofing, sprayed	1.880	S.F.	1.09	2.07	3.16
Vinyl composition floor tile	1.000	S.F.	.95	1.06	2.01
Suspended acoustical ceiling	1.000	S.F.	2.61	1.59	4.20
TOTAL			20.82	11.94	32.76

B1010 243	Floor - Ceiling, Struc. Steel	COST PER S.F.		
		MAT.	INST.	TOTAL
1900	Composite deck, galvanized, 3″ deep, 22 ga.	20.50	11.90	32.40
1950	20 ga.	21	11.95	32.95
2000	18 ga.	21.50	12	33.50
2100	16 ga.	22.50	12.05	34.55
2200	Composite deck, galvanized, 2″ deep, 22 ga.	20.50	11.70	32.20
2300	20 ga.	20.50	11.75	32.25
2400	16 ga.	22	11.90	33.90
2500				
2900	Dust protection, add, minimum	1%	2%	
3000	Maximum	4%	11%	
3100	Equipment usage curtailment, add, minimum	1%	1%	
3200	Maximum	3%	10%	
3300	Material handling & storage limitation, add, minimum	1%	1%	
3400	Maximum	6%	7%	
3500	Protection of existing work, add, minimum	2%	2%	
3600	Maximum	5%	7%	
3700	Shift work requirements, add, minimum		5%	
3800	Maximum		30%	
3900	Temporary shoring and bracing, add, minimum	2%	5%	
4000	Maximum	5%	12%	

B1010 Floor Construction

This page illustrates and describes an open web joist and steel slab-form system including open web steel joist, slab form, concrete, placing concrete, wire fabric, steel trowel finish, tile floor and plasterboard. Lines within System Components give the unit price and total price per square foot for this system. Prices for open web joists and steel slab-form systems are on Line Items B1010 245 1800 thru 2200. Both material quantities and labor costs have been adjusted for the systems listed.

Factors: To adjust for job conditions other than normal working situations use Lines B1010 245 2900 thru 4000.

Example: You are to install the system in a congested commercial area and most work will be done at night. Go to Line B1010 245 3800 and apply this percentage to the appropriate INST. cost.

System Components	QUANTITY	UNIT	COST PER S.F. MAT.	COST PER S.F. INST.	COST PER S.F. TOTAL
Open web steel joists, 24″ O.C., slab form, 3000 psi concrete, welded wire fabric, steel trowel finish, floor tile, 5/8″ drywall ceiling.					
Open web steel joists, 12″ deep, 5.2#/L.F., 24″ O.C.	2.630	Lb.	2.58	1.21	3.79
Slab form, 28 gage, 9/16″ deep, galvanized	1.000	S.F.	1.45	.80	2.25
Concrete, 3000 psi, 2-1/2″ thick	.008	C.Y.	.87		.87
Placing concrete	.008	C.Y.		.28	.28
Welded wire fabric 6 x 6 - #10/10	.011	C.S.F.	.18	.42	.60
Steel trowel finish	1.000	S.F.		1.26	1.26
Vinyl composition floor tile	1.000	S.F.	.95	1.06	2.01
Ceiling furring, 3/4″ channels, 24″ O.C.	1.000	S.F.	.22	1.21	1.43
Gypsum drywall, 5/8″ thick, finished	1.000	S.F.	.41	1.58	1.99
Paint ceiling	1.000	S.F.	.21	.67	.88
TOTAL			6.87	8.49	15.36

B1010 245	Floor - Ceiling, Steel Joists	COST PER S.F. MAT.	COST PER S.F. INST.	COST PER S.F. TOTAL
1800	Open web joists, 12″ deep, 5.2#/L.F.	6.85	8.50	15.35
1900	16″ deep, 6.6#/L.F.	7.50	8.80	16.30
2000	20″ deep, 8.4# L.F.	8.40	9.20	17.60
2100	24″ deep, 11.5# L.F.	9.95	9.90	19.85
2200	26″ deep, 12.8# L.F.	10.55	10.25	20.80
2300				
2400				
2500				
2600				
2700				
2900	Dust protection, add, minimum	1%	2%	
3000	Maximum	4%	11%	
3100	Equipment usage curtailment, add, minimum	1%	1%	
3200	Maximum	3%	10%	
3300	Material handling & storage limitation, add, minimum	1%	1%	
3400	Maximum	6%	7%	
3500	Protection of existing work, add, minimum	2%	2%	
3600	Maximum	5%	7%	
3700	Shift work requirements, add, minimum		5%	
3800	Maximum		30%	
3900	Temporary shoring and bracing, add, minimum	2%	5%	
4000	Maximum	5%	12%	

B1010 Floor Construction

Joist Hangers

Existing Girder

Fiberglass Insulation, Kraft Faced, 9" Thick

Steel Cross Bridging

12" Open Web Wood Joists, 2'-0" o.c.

3/4" CDX Plywood Sub-floor

Existing Foundation

2" x 8" Sill

Anchor Bolts, 1/2" x 8"

Open Web Wood Joists

This page illustrates and describes floor framing systems including sills, joist hangers, joists, bridging, subfloor and insulation. Lines within systems components give the unit price and total price per square foot for this system. Prices for alternate joist types are on line items B1010 262 0100 through 0700. Both material quantities and labor costs have been adjusted for the system listed.

Factors: To adjust for job conditions other than normal working situations use lines B1010 262 2700 through 4000.

Example: You are to install the system where delivery of material is difficult. Go to line B1010 262 3400 and apply these percentages to the appropriate MAT. and INST. costs.

System Components	QUANTITY	UNIT	COST PER S.F.		
			MAT.	INST.	TOTAL
Open web wood joists, sill, butt to girder, 5/8" subfloor, insul.					
Anchor bolt, hook type, with nut and washer, 1/2" x 8" long	.250	Ea.	.04	.11	.15
Joist & beam hanger, 18 ga. galvanized	.750	Ea.	.11	.27	.38
Bridging, steel, compression, for 2" x 12" joists	.010	C.Pr.	.01	.03	.04
Framing, open web wood joists, 12" deep	.001	M.L.F.	3.40	1.38	4.78
Framing, sills, 2" x 8"	.001	M.B.F.	.70	1.80	2.50
Sub-floor, plywood, CDX, 3/4" thick	1.000	S.F.	.82	.89	1.71
Insulation, fiberglass, kraft face, 9" thick x 23" wide	1.000	S.F.	.77	.45	1.22
TOTAL			5.85	4.93	10.78

B1010 262	Open Web Wood Joists	COST PER S.F.		
		MAT.	INST.	TOTAL
0100	12" open web joists, sill, butt to girder, 5/8" sub-floor	5.85	4.93	10.78
0200	14" joists	6.05	5.05	11.10
0300	16" joists	6.50	5.10	11.60
0400	18" joists	6.85	5.20	12.05
0450	Wood struc." I " joists, 24" O.C., to 24' span, 50 PSF LL, butt to girder	4.59	4.57	9.16
0500	55 PSF LL	4.88	4.63	9.51
0600	to 30'span, 45 PSF LL	5.35	4.49	9.84
0700	55 PSF LL	6.75	4.57	11.32
2700	Cut & patch to match existing construction, add, minimum	2%	3%	
2800	Maximum	5%	9%	
2900	Dust protection, add, minimum	1%	2%	
3000	Maximum	4%	11%	
3100	Equipment usage curtailment, add, minimum	1%	1%	
3200	Maximum	3%	10%	
3300	Material handling & storage limitation, add, minimum	1%	1%	
3400	Maximum	6%	7%	
3500	Protection of existing work, add, minimum	2%	2%	
3600	Maximum	5%	7%	
3700	Shift work requirements, add, minimum		5%	
3800	Maximum		30%	
3900	Temporary shoring and bracing, add, minimum	2%	5%	
4000	Maximum	5%	12%	

B1010 Floor Construction

This page illustrates and describes a wood joist floor system including wood joist, oak floor, sub-floor, bridging, sand and finish floor, furring, plasterboard, taped, finished and painted ceiling. Lines within System Components give the unit price and total price per square foot for this system. Prices for wood joist floor systems are on Line Items B1010 263 1700 thru 2300. Both material quantities and labor costs have been adjusted for the system listed.

Factors: To adjust for job conditions other than normal working situations use Lines B1010 263 2700 thru 4000.

Example: You are to install the system during off peak hours, 6 P.M. to 2 A.M. Go to Line B1010 263 3800 and apply this percentage to the appropriate INST. costs.

System Components	QUANTITY	UNIT	COST PER S.F.		
			MAT.	INST.	TOTAL
Wood joists, 2" x 8", 16" O.C.,oak floor (sanded & finished),1/2" sub floor, 1"x 3" bridging, furring, 5/8" drywall, taped, finished and painted.					
Wood joists, 2" x 8", 16" O.C.	1.000	L.F.	.94	1.10	2.04
Subfloor plywood CDX 1/2"	1.000	SF Flr.	.65	.80	1.45
Bridging 1" x 3"	.150	Pr.	.10	.70	.80
Oak flooring, No. 1 common	1.000	S.F.	4.53	3.55	8.08
Sand and finish floor	1.000	S.F.	.97	1.63	2.60
Wood furring, 1" x 3", 16" O.C.	1.000	L.F.	.42	1.72	2.14
Gypsum drywall, 5/8" thick	1.000	S.F.	.35	.67	1.02
Tape and finishing	1.000	S.F.	.05	.60	.65
Paint ceiling	1.000	S.F.	.21	.67	.88
TOTAL			8.22	11.44	19.66

B1010 263	Floor-Ceiling, Wood Joists	COST PER S.F.		
		MAT.	INST.	TOTAL
1700	16" on center, 2" x 6" joists	7.90	11.30	19.20
1750	2" x 8"	8.20	11.45	19.65
1800	2" x 10"	8.55	11.70	20.25
1900	2" x 12"	9	11.70	20.70
2000	2" x 14"	9.25	11.90	21.15
2100	12" on center, 2" x 10" joists	8.85	12	20.85
2200	2" x 12"	9.40	12.05	21.45
2300	2" x 14"	9.75	12.30	22.05
2400				
2500				
2700	Cut & patch to match existing construction, add, minimum	2%	3%	
2800	Maximum	5%	9%	
2900	Dust protection, add, minimum	1%	2%	
3000	Maximum	4%	11%	
3100	Equipment usage curtailment, add, minimum	1%	1%	
3200	Maximum	3%	10%	
3300	Material handling & storage limitation, add, minimum	1%	1%	
3400	Maximum	6%	7%	
3500	Protection of existing work, add, minimum	2%	2%	
3600	Maximum	5%	7%	
3700	Shift work requirements, add, minimum		5%	
3800	Maximum		30%	
3900	Temporary shoring and bracing, add, minimum	2%	5%	
4000	Maximum	5%	12%	

This page illustrates and describes a flat roof bar joist system including asphalt and gravel roof, lightweight concrete, metal decking, open web joists, and suspended acoustic ceiling. Lines within System Components give the unit price and total price per square foot for this system. Prices for flat roof bar joist systems are on Line Items B1020 106 1200 thru 1600. Both material quantities and labor costs have been adjusted for the system listed.

Factors: To adjust for job conditions other than normal working situations use Lines B1020 106 2700 thru 4000.

Example: You are to install the system where material handling and storage present some problem. Go to Line B1020 106 3300 and apply these percentages to the appropriate MAT. and INST. costs.

System Components	QUANTITY	UNIT	COST PER S.F.		
			MAT.	INST.	TOTAL
Three ply asphalt and gravel roof on lightweight concrete, metal decking on web joist 4' O.C., with suspended acoustic ceiling.					
Open web joist, 10" deep, 4' O.C.	1.250	Lb.	1.23	.58	1.81
Metal decking, 1-1/2" deep, 22 Ga., galvanized	1.000	S.F.	2.17	.70	2.87
Gravel roofing, 3 ply asphalt	.010	C.S.F.	1.42	1.96	3.38
Perlite roof fill, 3" thick	1.000	S.F.	2.30	.58	2.88
Suspended ceiling, 3/4" mineral fiber on "Z" bar suspension	1.000	S.F.	2.73	4.02	6.75
TOTAL			9.85	7.84	17.69

B1020 106	Steel Joist Roof & Ceiling	COST PER S.F.		
		MAT.	INST.	TOTAL
1200	Open web bar joist, 10" deep, 5#/L.F.	9.85	7.85	17.70
1300	16" deep, 5#/L.F.	10.25	8.05	18.30
1400	18" deep, 6.6#/L.F.	10.60	8.15	18.75
1500	20" deep, 9.6#/L.F.	10.95	8.35	19.30
1600	24" deep, 11.52#/L.F.	11.45	8.60	20.05
1700				
1800				
1900				
2000				
2100				
2200				
2300				
2400				
2500				
2700	Cut & patch to match existing construction, add, minimum	2%	3%	
2800	Maximum	5%	9%	
2900	Dust protection, add, minimum	1%	2%	
3000	Maximum	4%	11%	
3100	Equipment usage curtailment, add, minimum	1%	1%	
3200	Maximum	3%	10%	
3300	Material handling & storage limitation, add, minimum	1%	1%	
3400	Maximum	6%	7%	
3500	Protection of existing work, add, minimum	2%	2%	
3600	Maximum	5%	7%	
3700	Shift work requirements, add, minimum		5%	
3800	Maximum		30%	
3900	Temporary shoring and bracing, add, minimum	2%	5%	
4000	Maximum	5%	12%	

B1020 Roof Construction

This page illustrates and describes a wood frame roof system including rafters, ceiling joists, sheathing, building paper, asphalt shingles, roof trim, furring, insulation, plaster and paint. Lines within System Components give the unit price and total price per square foot for this system. Prices for wood frame roof systems are on Line Items B1020 202 1800 thru 2700. Both material quantities and labor costs have been adjusted for the system listed.

Factors: To adjust for job conditions other than normal working situations use Lines B1020 202 3300 thru 4000.

Example: You are to install the system while protecting existing work. Go to Line B1020 202 3800 and apply these percentages to the appropriate MAT. and INST. costs.

System Components	QUANTITY	UNIT	COST PER S.F.		
			MAT.	INST.	TOTAL
Wood frame roof system, 4 in 12 pitch, including rafters, sheathing, shingles, insulation, drywall, thin coat plaster, and painting.					
Rafters, 2" x 6", 16" O.C., 4 in 12 pitch	1.080	L.F.	.68	1.31	1.99
Ceiling joists, 2" x 6", 16 O.C.	1.000	L.F.	.63	.96	1.59
Sheathing, 1/2" CDX	1.080	S.F.	.70	.93	1.63
Building paper, 15# felt	.011	C.S.F.	.07	.18	.25
Asphalt shingles, 240#	.011	C.S.F.	1.17	1.24	2.41
Roof trim	.100	L.F.	.18	.26	.44
Furring, 1" x 3", 16" O.C.	1.000	L.F.	.42	1.72	2.14
Fiberglass insulation, 6" batts	1.000	S.F.	.63	.45	1.08
Gypsum board, 1/2" thick	1.000	S.F.	.33	.67	1
Thin coat plaster	1.000	S.F.	.11	.75	.86
Paint, roller, 2 coats	1.000	S.F.	.21	.67	.88
TOTAL			5.13	9.14	14.27

B1020 202	Wood Frame Roof & Ceiling	COST PER S.F.		
		MAT.	INST.	TOTAL
1800	Rafters 16" O.C., 2" x 6"	5.15	9.15	14.30
1900	2" x 8"	5.45	9.20	14.65
2000	2" x 10"	5.80	9.90	15.70
2100	2" x 12"	6.30	10.10	16.40
2200	Rafters 24" O.C., 2" x 6"	4.79	8.55	13.34
2300	2" x 8"	5.05	8.60	13.65
2400	2" x 10"	5.30	9.15	14.45
2500	2" x 12"	5.65	9.30	14.95
2600	Roof pitch, 6 in 12, add	3%	10%	
2700	8 in 12, add	5%	12%	
2800				
2900				
3000				
3100				
3300	Cut & patch to match existing construction, add, minimum	2%	3%	
3400	Maximum	5%	9%	
3500	Material handling & storage limitation, add, minimum	1%	1%	
3600	Maximum	6%	7%	
3700	Protection of existing work, add, minimum	2%	2%	
3800	Maximum	5%	7%	
3900	Shift work requirements, add, minimum		5%	
4000	Maximum		30%	

B1020 Roof Construction

5/8" Plywood Sheathing

Truss Anchors

Roof Trusses at 2'-0" o.c.

9" Fiberglass Insulation

1" x 8" Fascia Board

Wood Fabricated Roof Truss System

This page illustrates and describes a sloped roof truss framing system including trusses, truss anchors, sheathing, fascia and insulation. Lines B1020 210 1500 through 1800 are for a flat roof framing system including flat roof trusses, truss anchors, sheathing, fascia and insulation. Lines within system components give the unit price and total price per square foot for this system. Prices for alternate sizes and systems are given in line items B1020 210 0100 through 1800. Both material quantities and labor costs have been adjusted for the system listed.

Factors: To adjust for job conditions other than normal working situations use lines B1020 210 2700 through 4000.

Example: You are to install the system where crane placement and movement will be difficult. Go to line B1020 210 3200 and apply these percentages to the appropriate MAT. and INST. costs.

System Components			COST PER S.F.		
	QUANTITY	UNIT	MAT.	INST.	TOTAL
Roof truss, 2' O.C., 4/12 slope, 12' span, 5/8 sheath., fascia, insul.					
Timber connectors, rafter anchors, galv., 1 1/2" x 5 1/4"	.084	Ea.	.05	.35	.40
Plywood sheathing, CDX, 5/8" thick	1.054	S.F.	.86	.98	1.84
Truss, 2' O.C., metal plate connectors, 12' span	.042	Ea.	2	1.87	3.87
Molding, fascia trim, 1" x 8"	.167	L.F.	.30	.44	.74
Insulation, fiberglass, kraft face, 9" thick x 23" wide	1.000	S.F.	.77	.45	1.22
TOTAL			3.98	4.09	8.07

B1020 210	Roof Truss, Wood	COST PER S.F.		
		MAT.	INST.	TOTAL
0100	Roof truss, 2'O.C., 4/12p, 1'ovhg, 12'span, 5/8"sheath, fascia, insul.	3.98	4.09	8.07
0200	20' span	3.74	3.47	7.21
0300	24' span	3.60	3.25	6.85
0400	26' span	5.15	4.33	9.48
0500	28' span	3.65	3.17	6.82
0600	30' span	3.69	3.14	6.83
0700	32' span	3.69	3.08	6.77
0800	34' span	3.71	3.04	6.75
0890	60' span	5.10	3.45	8.55
0900	8/12 pitch, 20' span	4.09	3.73	7.82
1000	24' span	4.21	3.49	7.70
1100	26' span	4.06	3.42	7.48
1200	28' span	4.15	3.42	7.57
1300	32' span	4.27	3.35	7.62
1400	36' span	4.47	3.28	7.75
1500	Flat roof frame, fab.strl.joists, 2' O.C., 15'-24' span, 50 PSF LL	3.94	2.77	6.71
1600	55 PSF LL	4.23	2.83	7.06
1700	24'-30'span, 45 PSF LL	4.65	2.65	7.30
1800	55 PSF LL	6.05	2.73	8.78
1900				
2700	Cut & patch to match existing construction, add, minimum	2%	3%	
2800	Maximum	5%	9%	
2900	Dust protection, add, minimum	1%	2%	
3000	Maximum	4%	11%	
3100	Equipment usage curtailment, add, minimum	1%	1%	
3200	Maximum	3%	10%	
3300	Material handling & storage limitation, add, minimum	1%	1%	
3400	Maximum	6%	7%	

B10 Superstructure

B1020   Roof Construction

B1020 210	Roof Truss, Wood	COST PER S.F.		
		MAT.	INST.	TOTAL
3500	Protection of existing work, add, minimum	2%	2%	
3600	Maximum	5%	7%	
3700	Shift work requirements, add, minimum		5%	
3800	Maximum		30%	
3900	Temporary shoring and bracing, add, minimum	2%	5%	
4000	Maximum	5%	12%	

B2010 Exterior Walls

This page illustrates and describes a masonry concrete block system including concrete block wall, pointed, reinforcing, waterproofing, gypsum plaster on gypsum lath, and furring. Lines within System Components give the unit price and total price per square foot for this system. Prices for masonry concrete block wall systems are on Line Items B2010 108 1400 thru 2200. Both material quantities and labor costs have been adjusted for the system listed.

Factors: To adjust for job conditions other than normal working situations use Lines B2010 108 2700 thru 4000.

Example: You are to install the system and match existing construction at several locations. Go to Line B2010 108 2800 and apply these percentages to the appropriate MAT. and INST. costs.

System Components	QUANTITY	UNIT	COST PER S.F.		
			MAT.	INST.	TOTAL
Concrete block, 8″ thick, reinforced every 2 courses, waterproofing gypsum plaster over gypsum lath on 1″ x 3″ furring, interior painting & baseboard.					
Concrete block, 8″ x 8″ x 16″, reinforced	1.000	S.F.	4.58	6.60	11.18
Silicone waterproofing, 2 coats	1.000	S.F.	.78	.19	.97
Bituminous coating, 1/16″ thick	1.000	S.F.	.37	1.13	1.50
On concrete	1.000	L.F.	.46	2.32	2.78
Gypsum lath, 3/8″ thick	.110	S.Y.	.33	.66	.99
Gypsum plaster, 2 coats	.110	S.Y.	.41	2.87	3.28
Painting, 2 coats	1.000	S.F.	.14	.52	.66
Baseboard wood, 9/16″ x 2-5/8″	.100	L.F.	.16	.25	.41
Paint baseboard, primer + 1 coat enamel	.100	L.F.	.02	.06	.08
TOTAL			7.25	14.60	21.85

B2010 108	Masonry Wall, Concrete Block	COST PER S.F.		
		MAT.	INST.	TOTAL
1400	8″ thick block, regular	7.25	14.60	21.85
1500	Fluted 2 sides	8.15	17.15	25.30
1600	Deep grooved	7.65	17.15	24.80
1700	Slump block	8.55	14.90	23.45
1800	Split rib	7.95	17.15	25.10
1900				
2000	12″ thick block, regular	6.70	17.45	24.15
2100	Slump block	14.80	16.25	31.05
2200	Split rib	8.85	19.70	28.55
2300				
2700	Cut & patch to match existing construction, add, minimum	2%	3%	
2800	Maximum	5%	9%	
2900	Dust protection, add, minimum	1%	2%	
3000	Maximum	4%	11%	
3100	Equipment usage curtailment, add, minimum	1%	1%	
3200	Maximum	3%	10%	
3300	Material handling & storage limitation, add, minimum	1%	1%	
3400	Maximum	6%	7%	
3500	Protection of existing work, add, minimum	2%	2%	
3600	Maximum	5%	7%	
3700	Shift work requirements, add, minimum		5%	
3800	Maximum		30%	
3900	Temporary shoring and bracing, add, minimum	2%	5%	
4000	Maximum	5%	12%	

B2010 Exterior Walls

This page illustrates and describes a masonry wall, brick-stone system including brick, concrete block, durawall, insulation, plasterboard, taped and finished, furring, baseboard and painting interior. Lines within System Components give the unit price and total price per square foot for this system. Prices for masonry wall, brick-stone systems are on Line Item B2010 131 1400 thru 2500. Both material quantities and labor costs have been adjusted for the system listed.

Factors: To adjust for job conditions other than normal working situations use Lines B2010 131 3100 thru 4200.

Example: You are to install the system without damaging the existing work. Go to Line B2010 131 3900 and apply these percentages to the appropriate MAT. and INST. costs.

System Components	QUANTITY	UNIT	COST PER S.F.		
			MAT.	INST.	TOTAL
Face brick, 4"thick, concrete block back-up, reinforce every second course, 3/4"insulation, furring, 1/2"drywall, taped, finish, and painted, baseboard.					
Face brick, 4" brick	1.000	S.F.	4.40	12.45	16.85
Concrete back-up block, reinforced 8" thick	1.000	S.F.	2.88	6.95	9.83
3/4" rigid polystyrene insulation	1.000	S.F.	.57	.75	1.32
Furring, 1" x 3", wood, 16" O.C.	1.000	L.F.	.46	1.22	1.68
Drywall, 1/2" thick	1.000	S.F.	.33	.60	.93
Taping & finishing	1.000	S.F.	.05	.60	.65
Painting, 2 coats	1.000	S.F.	.21	.67	.88
Baseboard, wood, 9/16" x 2-5/8"	.100	L.F.	.16	.25	.41
Paint baseboard, primer + 1 coat enamel	.100	L.F.	.02	.06	.08
TOTAL			9.08	23.55	32.63

B2010 131		Masonry Wall, Brick - Stone	COST PER S.F.		
			MAT.	INST.	TOTAL
1400		Face brick, standard, red, 4" x 2-2/3" x 8" (6.75/S.F.)	9.10	23.50	32.60
1500		Norman, 4" x 2-2/3" x 12" (4.5 per S.F.)	11.10	19.65	30.75
1600		Roman, 4" x 2" x 12" (6.0 per S.F.)	13.20	22	35.20
1700		Engineer, 4" x 3-1/5" x 8" (5.63 per S.F.)	8.50	21.50	30
1800		S.C.R., 6" x 2-2/3" x 12" (4.5 per S.F.)	11.90	19.95	31.85
1900		Jumbo, 6" x 4" x 12" (3.0 per S.F.)	9.65	17.40	27.05
2000		Norwegian, 6" x 3-1/5" x 12" (3.75 per S.F.)	9.80	18.40	28.20
2100					
2200					
2300		Stone, veneer, fieldstone, 6" thick	11.50	20	31.50
2400		Marble, 2" thick	48.50	35	83.50
2500		Limestone, 2" thick	43	21.50	64.50
3100		Cut & patch to match existing construction, add, minimum	2%	3%	
3200		Maximum	5%	9%	
3300		Dust protection, add, minimum	1%	2%	
3400		Maximum	4%	11%	
3500		Equipment usage curtailment, add, minimum	1%	1%	
3600		Maximum	3%	10%	
3700		Material handling & storage limitation, add, minimum	1%	1%	
3800		Maximum	6%	7%	
3900		Protection of existing work, add, minimum	2%	2%	
4000		Maximum	5%	7%	
4100		Shift work requirements, add, minimum		5%	
4200		Maximum		30%	

B2010 Exterior Walls

This page illustrates and describes a parapet wall system including wall, coping, flashing and cant strip. Lines within System Components give the unit price and cost per lineal foot for this system. Prices for parapet wall systems are on Lines B2010 142 1300 thru 2400. Both material quantities and labor costs have been adjusted for the system listed.

Factors: To adjust for job conditions other than normal working situations, use Lines B2010 142 2900 thru 4000.

Example: You are to install the system without damaging the adjacent property. Go to Line B2010 142 3600 and apply these percentages to the appropriate MAT. and INST. costs.

System Components			COST PER L.F.		
	QUANTITY	UNIT	MAT.	INST.	TOTAL
Concrete block parapet, incl. reinf., coping, flashing & cant strip, 2'high.					
8" concrete block	2.000	S.F.	9.16	13.20	22.36
Masonry reinforcing	1.000	L.F.	.25	.20	.45
Coping, precast	1.000	L.F.	20.50	15.35	35.85
Roof cant	1.000	L.F.	2.48	1.74	4.22
16 oz.	1.000	L.F.	6.40	2.68	9.08
Cap flashing	1.000	L.F.	7.65	4.91	12.56
TOTAL			46.44	38.08	84.52

B2010 142	Parapet Wall	COST PER L.F.		
		MAT.	INST.	TOTAL
1300	Concrete block, 8" thick	46.50	38	84.50
1400	12" thick	55	49.50	104.50
1500	Split rib block, 8" thick	48	43	91
1600	12" thick	53.50	51	104.50
1700	Brick, common brick, 8" wall	55	65.50	120.50
1800	12" wall	64	82.50	146.50
1900	4" brick, 4" backup block	50	62.50	112.50
2000	8" backup block	51.50	64.50	116
2100	Stucco on masonry	46.50	43	89.50
2200	On wood frame	21.50	34.50	56
2300	Wood, T 1-11 siding	32	41.50	73.50
2400	Boards, 1" x 6" cedar	38.50	46	84.50
2500				
2600				
2900	Dust protection, add, minimum	1%	2%	
3000	Maximum	4%	11%	
3100	Equipment usage curtailment, add, minimum	1%	1%	
3200	Maximum	3%	10%	
3300	Material handling & storage limitation, add, minimum	1%	1%	
3400	Maximum	6%	7%	
3500	Protection of existing work, add, minimum	2%	2%	
3600	Maximum	5%	7%	
3700	Shift work requirements, add, minimum		5%	
3800	Maximum		30%	
3900	Temporary shoring and bracing, add, minimum	2%	5%	
4000	Maximum	5%	12%	

B2010 Exterior Walls

This page illustrates and describes a masonry cleaning and restoration system, including staging, cleaning, repointing. Lines within System Components give the unit price and cost per square foot for this system. Prices for systems are on Lines B2010 143 1300 thru 2500. Both material quantities and labor costs have been adjusted for the system listed.

Factors: To adjust for conditions other than normal working situations, use Lines B2010 143 2900 thru 4200.

Example: You are to clean a wall and be concerned about dust control. Go to line B2010 143 3100 and apply these percentages to the appropriate MAT. and INST. costs.

System Components			COST PER S.F.		
	QUANTITY	UNIT	MAT.	INST.	TOTAL
Repoint existing building, brick, common bond, high pressure cleaning, water only, soft old mortar.					
Scaffolding, steel tubular, bldg ext wall face, labor only, 1 to 5 stories	.010	C.S.F.		2.26	2.26
Cleaning masonry, high pressure wash, water only, avg soil, bio staining	1.100	S.F.		1.63	1.63
Repoint, brick common bond	1.000	S.F.	.56	6.15	6.71
TOTAL			.56	10.04	10.60

B2010 143	Masonry Restoration - Cleaning	COST PER S.F.		
		MAT.	INST.	TOTAL
1300	Brick, common bond	.56	10	10.56
1400	Flemish bond	.59	10.45	11.04
1500	English bond	.59	11.05	11.64
1700	Stone, 2' x 2' blocks	.75	7.55	8.30
1800	2' x 4' blocks	.56	6.65	7.21
2000	Add to above prices for alternate cleaning systems:			
2100	Chemical brush and wash	.05	.67	.72
2200	High pressure chemical and water	.07	.56	.63
2300	Sandblasting, wet system	.41	1.61	2.02
2400	Dry system	.39	.95	1.34
2500	Steam cleaning		.46	.46
2600				
2900	Cut & patch to match existing construction, add, minimum	2%	3%	
3000	Maximum	5%	9%	
3100	Dust protection, add, minimum	1%	2%	
3200	Maximum	4%	11%	
3300	Equipment usage curtailment, add, minimum	1%	1%	
3400	Maximum	3%	10%	
3500	Material handling & storage limitation, add, minimum	1%	1%	
3600	Maximum	6%	7%	
3900	Protection of existing work, add, minimum	2%	2%	
4000	Maximum	5%	7%	
4100	Shift work requirements, add, minimum		5%	
4200	Maximum		30%	

B2010 Exterior Walls

This page illustrates and describes a wood frame exterior wall system including wood studs, sheathing, felt, insulation, plasterboard, taped and finished, baseboard and painted interior. Lines within System Components give the unit price and total price per square foot for this system. Prices for wood frame exterior wall systems are on Line Items B2010 150 1600 thru 2700. Both material quantities and labor costs have been adjusted for the system listed.

Factors: To adjust for job conditions other than normal working situations use Lines B2010 150 3100 thru 4200.

Example: You are to install the system with need for complete temporary bracing. Go to Line B2010 150 4200 and apply these percentages to the appropriate MAT. and INST. costs.

System Components	QUANTITY	UNIT	COST PER S.F.		
			MAT.	INST.	TOTAL
Wood stud wall, cedar shingle siding, building paper, plywood sheathing, insulation, 5/8″ drywall, taped, finished and painted, baseboard.					
2″ x 4″ wood studs, 16″ O.C.	.100	L.F.	.44	1.21	1.65
1/2″ CDX sheathing	1.000	S.F.	.65	.86	1.51
18″ No. 1 red cedar shingles, 7-1/2″ exposure	.008	C.S.F.	1.47	2.14	3.61
15# felt paper	.010	C.S.F.	.06	.16	.22
3-1/2″ fiberglass insulation	1.000	S.F.	.48	.45	.93
5/8″ drywall	1.000	S.F.	.35	.60	.95
Drywall finishing adder	1.000	S.F.	.05	.60	.65
Baseboard trim, stock pine, 9/16″ x 3-1/2″, painted	.100	L.F.	.16	.25	.41
Paint baseboard, primer + 1 coat enamel	.100	L.F.	.02	.06	.08
Paint, 2 coats, interior	1.000	S.F.	.21	.67	.88
TOTAL			3.89	7	10.89

B2010 150	Wood Frame Exterior Wall	COST PER S.F.		
		MAT.	INST.	TOTAL
1600	Cedar shingle siding, painted	3.89	7	10.89
1700	Aluminum siding, horizontal clapboard	5	7.20	12.20
1800	Cedar bevel siding, 1/2″ x 6″, vertical , painted	6.95	6.90	13.85
1900	Redwood siding 1″ x 4″ to 1″ x 6″ vertical, T & G	6.95	7.60	14.55
2000	Board and batten	7.20	6.30	13.50
2100	Ship lap siding	7.30	6.70	14
2200	Plywood, grooved (T1-11) fir	4.15	6.65	10.80
2300	Redwood	5.10	6.65	11.75
2400	Southern yellow pine	3.73	6.65	10.38
2500	Masonry on stud wall, stucco, wire and plaster	3.21	10.55	13.76
2600	Stone veneer	9.25	13.80	23.05
2700	Brick veneer, brick $275 per M	6.80	17.30	24.10
3100	Cut & patch to match existing construction, add, minimum	2%	3%	
3200	Maximum	5%	9%	
3300	Dust protection, add, minimum	1%	2%	
3400	Maximum	4%	11%	
3500	Material handling & storage limitation, add, minimum	1%	1%	
3600	Maximum	6%	7%	
3700	Protection of existing work, add, minimum	2%	2%	
3800	Maximum	5%	7%	
3900	Shift work requirements, add, minimum		5%	
4000	Maximum		30%	
4100	Temporary shoring and bracing, add, minimum	2%	5%	
4200	Maximum	5%	12%	

B2010 Exterior Walls

B2010 190	Selective Price Sheet	COST PER S.F.		
		MAT.	INST.	TOTAL
0100	Exterior surface, masonry, concrete block, standard 4" thick	1.74	6.35	8.09
0200	6" thick	2.30	6.85	9.15
0300	8" thick	2.61	7.30	9.91
0400	12" thick	4.04	9.45	13.49
0500	Split rib, 4" thick	3.98	7.95	11.93
0600	8" thick	5.30	9.15	14.45
0700	Brick running bond, standard size, 6.75/S.F.	4.40	12.45	16.85
0800	Buff, 6.75/S.F.	4.65	12.45	17.10
0900	Stucco, on frame	.80	5.75	6.55
1000	On masonry	.31	4.53	4.84
1100	Metal, aluminum, horizontal, plain	2.60	2.34	4.94
1200	Insulated	2.83	2.34	5.17
1300	Vertical, plain	2.01	2.34	4.35
1400	Insulated	2.10	2.44	4.54
1500	Wood, beveled siding, "A" grade cedar, 1/2" x 6"	4.55	2.04	6.59
1600	1/2" x 8"	6.50	1.83	8.33
1700	Shingles, 16" #1 red, 7-1/2" exposure	1.94	2.94	4.88
1800	18" perfections, 7-1/2" exposure	2.27	2.46	4.73
1900	Handsplit, 10" exposure	2.78	2.41	5.19
2000	White cedar, 7-1/2" exposure	1.36	3	4.36
2100	Vertical, board & batten, redwood	4.52	2.74	7.26
2200	White pine	2.41	1.83	4.24
2300	T. & G. boards, redwood, 1" x 4"	2.79	2.74	5.53
2400	1' x 8"	4.51	1.83	6.34
2500				
2600	Interior surface, drywall, taped & finished, standard, 1/2"	.38	1.25	1.63
2700	5/8" thick	.41	1.25	1.66
2800	Fire resistant, 1/2" thick	.41	1.25	1.66
2900	5/8" thick	.43	1.25	1.68
3000	Moisture resistant, 1/2" thick	.47	1.25	1.72
3100	5/8" thick	.55	1.25	1.80
3200	Core board, 1" thick	.81	2.51	3.32
3300	Plaster, gypsum, 2 coats	.41	2.89	3.30
3400	3 coats	.59	3.47	4.06
3500	Perlite or vermiculite, 2 coats	.46	3.30	3.76
3600	3 coats	.77	4.13	4.90
3700	Gypsum lath, standard, 3/8" thick	.33	.67	1
3800	1/2" thick	.30	.71	1.01
3900	Fire resistant, 3/8" thick	.30	.81	1.11
4000	1/2" thick	.33	.87	1.20
4100	Metal lath, diamond, 2.5 lb.	.52	.67	1.19
4200	Rib, 3.4 lb.	.54	.81	1.35
4300	Framing metal studs including top and bottom			
4400	Runners, walls 10' high			
4500	24" O.C., non load bearing 20 gauge, 2-1/2" wide	.35	1	1.35
4600	3-5/8" wide	.38	1.02	1.40
4700	4" wide	.46	1.02	1.48
4800	6" wide	.58	1.04	1.62
4900	Load bearing 18 gauge, 2-1/2" wide	.66	1.13	1.79
5000	3-5/8" wide	.78	1.15	1.93
5100	4" wide	.88	1.46	2.34
5200	6" wide	1.04	1.20	2.24
5300	16" O.C., non load bearing 20 gauge, 2-1/2" wide	.48	1.55	2.03
5400	3-5/8" wide	.52	1.57	2.09
5500	4" wide	.63	1.59	2.22
5600	6" wide	.79	1.61	2.40
5700	Load bearing 18 gauge, 2-1/2" wide	.89	1.57	2.46
5800	3-5/8" wide	1.05	1.59	2.64

B2010 Exterior Walls

B2010 190	Selective Price Sheet	COST PER S.F.		
		MAT.	INST.	TOTAL
5900	4" wide	1.11	1.63	2.74
6000	6" wide	1.40	1.65	3.05
6100	Framing wood studs incl. double top plate and			
6200	Single bottom plate, walls 10' high			
6300	24" O.C., 2" x 4"	.33	.97	1.30
6400	2" x 6"	.50	1.05	1.55
6500	16" O.C., 2" x 4"	.44	1.21	1.65
6600	2" x 6"	.66	1.34	2
6700	Sheathing, boards, 1" x 6"	1.92	1.86	3.78
6800	1" x 8"	2.09	1.58	3.67
6900	Plywood, 3/8" thick	.55	1	1.55
7000	1/2" thick	.65	1.07	1.72
7100	5/8" thick	.82	1.15	1.97
7200	3/4" thick	.97	1.24	2.21
7300	Wood fiber, 5/8" thick	.84	1	1.84
7400	Gypsum weatherproof, 1/2" thick	.48	1.07	1.55
7500	Insulation, fiberglass batts, 3-1/2" thick, R13	.41	.86	1.27
7600	6" thick, R19	.53	1	1.53
7700	Poured 4" thick, fiberglass wool, R4/inch	.59	3.01	3.60
7800	Mineral wool, R3/inch	.43	3.01	3.44
7900	Polystyrene, R4/inch	2.75	3.01	5.76
8000	Perlite or vermiculite, R2.7/inch	5.95	3.01	8.96
8100	Rigid, fiberglass, R4.3/inch, 1" thick	.57	.60	1.17
8200	R8.7/inch, 2" thick	1.16	.68	1.84

B20 Exterior Enclosure

B2020 Exterior Windows

B2020 108 — Vinyl Clad Windows

	MATERIAL	TYPE	GLAZING	SIZE	DETAIL	MAT.	INST.	TOTAL
1000	Vinyl clad	casement	insul. glass	1'-4" x 4'-0"		425	139	564
1010				2'-0" x 3'-0"		360	139	499
1020				2'-0" x 4'-0"		415	146	561
1030				2'-0" x 5'-0"		465	154	619
1040				2'-0" x 6'-0"		485	154	639
1050				2'-4" x 4'-0"		465	154	619
1060				2'-6" x 5'-0"		570	150	720
1070				3'-0" x 5'-0"		795	154	949
1080				4'-0" x 3'-0"		870	154	1,024
1090				4'-0" x 4'-0"		750	154	904
1100				4'-8" x 4'-0"		825	154	979
1110				4'-8" x 5'-0"		930	179	1,109
1120				4'-8" x 6'-0"		1,025	179	1,204
1130				6'-0" x 4'-0"		950	179	1,129
1140				6'-0" x 5'-0"		1,050	179	1,229
3000		double-hung	insul. glass	2'-0" x 4'-0"		445	134	579
3050				2'-0" x 5'-0"		505	134	639
3100				2'-4" x 4'-0"		460	139	599
3150				2'-4" x 4'-8"		460	139	599
3200				2'-4" x 6'-0"		520	139	659
3250				2'-6" x 4'-0"		460	139	599
3300				2'-8" x 4'-0"		685	179	864
3350				2'-8" x 5'-0"		540	154	694
3375				2'-8" x 6'-0"		550	154	704
3400				3'-0 x 3'-6"		435	139	574
3450				3'-0 x 4'-0"		500	146	646
3500				3'-0 x 4'-8"		535	146	681
3550				3'-0 x 5'-0"		550	154	704
3600				3'-0 x 6'-0"		495	154	649
3700				4'-0 x 5'-0"		680	165	845
3800				4'-0 x 6'-0"		830	165	995

B2020 Exterior Windows

This page illustrates and describes an aluminum window system including double hung aluminum window, exterior and interior trim, hardware and insulating glass. Lines within System Components give the unit price and total price on a cost each basis for this system. Prices for aluminum window systems are on Line Items B2020 110 1000 thru 2400. Both material quantities and labor costs have been adjusted for the system listed.

Factors: To adjust for job conditions other than normal working situations use Lines B2020 110 3100 thru 4000.

Example: You are to install the system and cut and patch to match existing construction. Go to Line B2020 110 3200 and apply these percentages to the appropriate MAT. and INST. costs.

System Components	QUANTITY	UNIT	COST EACH		
			MAT.	INST.	TOTAL
Double hung aluminum window, 2'-4" x 2'-6" exterior and interior trim, hardware glazed with insulating glass.					
Double hung aluminum window, 2'-4" x 2' 6"	1.000	Ea.	250.69	43.73	294.42
Exterior and interior trim	1.000	Set	40.50	46.50	87
Hardware	1.000	Set	4.73	25	29.73
Insulating glass	5.830	S.F.	81.91	33.23	115.14
TOTAL			377.83	148.46	526.29

B2020 110	Windows - Aluminum	COST EACH		
		MAT.	INST.	TOTAL
1000	Aluminum, double hung, 2'-4" x 2'-6"	380	148	528
1100	2'-8" x 4'-6"	735	244	979
1200	3'- 4" x 5'-6"	1,125	365	1,490
1300	Casement, 3'-6" x 2'-4"	505	179	684
1400	4'-6" x 2'-4"	645	224	869
1500	5'-6" x 2'-4"	800	294	1,094
1600	Projected window, 2'-1" x 3'-0"	375	154	529
1700	3'-5" x 3'-0"	590	221	811
1800	4'-0" x 4'-0"	915	335	1,250
1900	Horizontal sliding 3'-0" x 3'-0"	385	190	575
2000	3'-6" x 4'-0"	580	270	850
2100	5'-0" x 6'-0"	1,200	520	1,720
2200	Picture window, 3'-8" x 3'-1"	430	220	650
2300	4'-4" x 4'-5"	705	340	1,045
2400	5'-8" x 4'-9"	990	480	1,470
2500				
2600				
2700				
2800				
2900				
3100	Cut & patch to match existing construction, add, minimum	2%	3%	
3200	Maximum	5%	9%	
3300	Dust protection, add, minimum	1%	2%	
3400	Maximum	4%	11%	
3500	Material handling & storage limitation, add, minimum	1%	1%	
3600	Maximum	6%	7%	
3700	Protection of existing work, add, minimum	2%	2%	
3800	Maximum	5%	7%	
3900	Shift work requirements, add, minimum		5%	
4000	Maximum		30%	

B2020 Exterior Windows

This page illustrates and describes a wood window system including wood picture window, exterior and interior trim, hardware and insulating glass. Lines within System Components give the unit price and total price on a cost each basis for this system. Prices for wood window systems are on Line Items B2020 112 1200 thru 2900. Both material quantities and labor costs have been adjusted for the system listed.

Factors: To adjust for job conditions other than normal working situations use Lines B2020 112 3100 thru 4000.

Example: You are to install the above system where dust control is vital. Go to Line B2020 112 3400 and apply these percentages to the appropriate MAT. and INST. costs.

System Components	QUANTITY	UNIT	COST EACH MAT.	COST EACH INST.	COST EACH TOTAL
Wood picture window 4'-0" x 4'-6", exterior and interior trim, hardware, glazed with insulating glass.					
4'-0" x 4'-6" wood picture window with insulating glass	1.000	Ea.	585	110	695
Exterior and interior trim	1.000	Set	69	100	169
Hardware	1.000	Set	4.73	25	29.73
TOTAL			658.73	235	893.73

B2020 112	Windows - Wood	COST EACH MAT.	COST EACH INST.	COST EACH TOTAL
1200	Picture window, 4'-0" x 4'-6"	660	235	895
1300	5'-0" x 4'-0"	740	235	975
1400	6'-0" x 4'-6"	775	246	1,021
1500	Bow, bay window, 8'-0" x 5'-0", standard	2,575	246	2,821
1600	Deluxe	1,900	246	2,146
1700	Bow, bay window, 12'-0" x 6'-0" standard	3,300	325	3,625
1800	Deluxe	2,650	325	2,975
1900	Double hung, 3'-0" x 4'-0"	375	153	528
2000	4'-0" x 4'-6"	455	201	656
2100	Casement 2'-0" x 3'-0"	330	132	462
2200	2 leaf, 4'-0" x 4'-0"	865	220	1,085
2300	3 leaf, 6'-0" x 6'-0"	1,650	350	2,000
2400	Awning, 2'-10" x 1'-10"	345	132	477
2500	3'-6" x 2'-4"	430	153	583
2600	4'-0" x 3'-0"	615	201	816
2700	Horizontal sliding 3'-0" x 2'-0"	385	132	517
2800	4'-0" x 3'-6"	455	153	608
2900	6'-0" x 5'-0"	655	201	856
3100	Cut & patch to match existing construction, add, minimum	2%	3%	
3200	Maximum	5%	9%	
3300	Dust protection, add, minimum	1%	2%	
3400	Maximum	4%	11%	
3500	Material handling & storage limitation, add, minimum	1%	1%	
3600	Maximum	6%	7%	
3700	Protection of existing work, add, minimum	2%	2%	
3800	Maximum	5%	7%	
3900	Shift work requirements, add, minimum		5%	
4000	Maximum		30%	

B20 Exterior Enclosure

B2020 Exterior Windows

This page illustrates and describes storm window and door systems based on a cost each price. Prices for storm window and door systems are on Line Items B2020 116 0400 thru 2400. Both material quantities and labor costs have been adjusted for the system listed.

Factors: To adjust for job conditions other than normal working situations use Lines B2020 116 3100 thru 4000 and apply these percentages to the appropriate MAT and INST. costs.

Example: You are to install the system and protect all existing construction. Go to Line B2020 116 3800 and apply these percentages to the appropriate MAT. and INST. costs.

| B2020 116 | Storm Windows & Doors | COST EACH | | |
		MAT.	INST.	TOTAL
0350	Storm Window and door systems, single glazed			
0400	Window, custom aluminum anodized, 2'-0" x 3'-5"	99	40	139
0500	2'-6" x 5'-0"	121	43	164
0600	4'-0" x 6'-0"	249	48	297
0700	White painted aluminum, 2'-0" x 3'-5"	110	40	150
0800	2'-6" x 5'-0"	176	43	219
0900	4'-0" x 6'-0"	300	48	348
1000	Average quality aluminum, anodized, 2'-0" x 3'-5"	94.50	40	134.50
1100	2'-6" x 5'-0"	125	43	168
1200	4'-0" x 6'-0"	139	48	187
1300	White painted aluminum, 2'-0" x 3'-5"	93.50	40	133.50
1400	2'-6" x 5'-0"	101	43	144
1500	4'-0" x 6'-0"	110	48	158
1600	Mill finish, 2'-0" x 3'-5"	84.50	40	124.50
1700	2'-6" x 5'-0"	94.50	43	137.50
1800	4'-0" x 6'-0"	110	48	158
1900				
2000	Door, aluminum anodized 3'-0" x 6'-8"	179	86	265
2100	White painted aluminum, 3'-0" x 6'-8"	335	86	421
2200	Mill finish, 3'-0" x 6'-8"	284	86	370
2300				
2400	Wood, storm and screen, painted	340	134	474
2500				
2600				
2700				
2800				
3100	Cut & patch to match existing construction, add, minimum	2%	3%	
3200	Maximum	5%	9%	
3300	Dust protection, add, minimum	1%	2%	
3400	Maximum	4%	11%	
3500	Material handling & storage limitation, add, minimum	1%	1%	
3600	Maximum	6%	7%	
3700	Protection of existing work, add, minimum	2%	2%	
3800	Maximum	5%	7%	
3900	Shift work requirements, add, minimum		5%	
4000	Maximum		30%	

B2020 Exterior Windows

This page illustrates and describes a window wall system including aluminum tube framing, caulking, and glass. Lines within System Components give the unit price and total price per square foot for this system. Prices for window wall systems are on Line Items B2020 124 1300 thru 2600. Both material quantities and labor costs have been adjusted for the system listed.

Factors: To adjust for job conditions other than normal working situations use Lines B2020 124 3100 thru 4000.

Example: You are to install the system with need for complete dust protection. Go to Line B2020 124 3400 and apply these percentages to the appropriate MAT. and INST. costs.

System Components	QUANTITY	UNIT	COST PER S.F. MAT.	COST PER S.F. INST.	COST PER S.F. TOTAL
Window wall, including aluminum header, sill, mullions, caulking and glass.					
Header, mill finish, 1-3/4" x 4-1/2" deep	.167	L.F.	3.34	2.30	5.64
Sill, mill finish, 1-3/4" x 4-1/2" deep	.167	L.F.	3.33	2.25	5.58
Vertical mullion, 1-3/4" x 4-1/2" deep, 6' O.C.	.191	L.F.	8.41	5.60	14.01
Caulking	.381	L.F.	.08	.78	.86
Glass, 1/4" plate	1.000	S.F.	6.35	9.50	15.85
TOTAL			21.51	20.43	41.94

B2020 124	Aluminum Frame, Window Wall	MAT.	INST.	TOTAL
1300	Mill finish, 1-3/4" x 4-1/2" deep, 1/4" plate glass	21.50	20.50	42
1400	2" x 4-1/2" deep, insulating glass	24	23.50	47.50
1500	Thermo-break, 2-1/4" x 4-1/2" deep, insulating glass	25	24	49
1600	Bronze finish, 1-3/4" x 4-1/2" deep, 1/4" plate glass	24	22	46
1700	2" x 4-1/2" deep, insulating glass	26	25.50	51.50
1800	Thermo-break, 2-1/4" x 4-1/2" deep, insulating glass	27.50	26	53.50
2000	Black finish, 1-3/4" x 4-1/2" deep, 1/4" plate glass	25.50	23	48.50
2100	2" x 4-1/2" deep, insulating glass	27.50	26.50	54
2200	Thermo-break, 2-1/4" x 4-1/2" deep, insulating glass	29	27	56
2300				
2400	Stainless steel, 1-3/4" x 4-1/2" deep, 1/4" plate glass	33	28	61
2500	2" x 4-1/2" deep, insulating glass	33.50	32	65.50
2600	Thermo-break, 2-1/4" x 4-1/2" deep, insulating glass	35.50	32.50	68
2700				
3100	Cut & patch to match existing construction, add, minimum	2%	3%	
3200	Maximum	5%	9%	
3300	Dust protection, add, minimum	1%	2%	
3400	Maximum	4%	11%	
3500	Material handling, & storage limitation, add, minimum	1%	1%	
3600	Maximum	6%	7%	
3700	Protection of existing work, add, minimum	2%	2%	
3800	Maximum	5%	7%	
3900	Shift work requirements, add, minimum		5%	
4000	Maximum		30%	

B2030 Exterior Doors

This page illustrates and describes a commercial metal door system, including a single aluminum and glass door, narrow stiles, jamb, hardware weatherstripping, panic hardware and closer. Lines within System Components give the unit price and total price on a cost each basis for this system. Prices for commercial metal door systems are on Line Items B2030 125 1200 thru 2500. Both material quantities and labor costs have been adjusted for the system listed.

Factors: To adjust for job conditions other than normal working situations, use Lines B2030 125 3100 thru 4000.

Example: You are to install the system and cut and patch to match existing construction. Go to Line B2030 125 3200 and apply these percentages to the appropriate MAT. and INST. costs.

System Components	QUANTITY	UNIT	COST EACH		
			MAT.	INST.	TOTAL
Single aluminum and glass door, 3'-0"x7'-0", with narrow stiles, ext. jamb, weatherstripping, 1/2" tempered insul. glass, panic hardware, and closer.					
Aluminum door, 3'-0" x 7'-0" x 1-3/4", narrow stiles	1.000	Ea.	975	750	1,725
Tempered insulating glass, 1/2" thick	20.000	S.F.	530	420	950
Panic hardware	1.000	Set	505	100	605
Surface mount regular arm	1.000	Ea.	138	92.50	230.50
TOTAL			2,148	1,362.50	3,510.50

B2030 125	Doors, Metal - Commercial	COST EACH		
		MAT.	INST.	TOTAL
1200	Single aluminum and glass, 3'-0" x 7'-0"	2,150	1,375	3,525
1300	With transom, 3'-0" x 10'-0"	2,800	1,625	4,425
1400	Anodized aluminum and glass, 3'-0" x 7'-0"	2,500	1,625	4,125
1500	With transom, 3'-0" x 10'-0"	3,300	1,900	5,200
1600	Steel, deluxe, hollow metal 3'-0" x 7'-0"	1,650	515	2,165
1700	With transom 3'-0" x 10'-0"	2,175	585	2,760
1800	Fire door, "A" label, 3'-0" x 7'-0"	1,800	515	2,315
1900	Double, aluminum and glass, 6'-0" x 7'-0"	3,425	2,325	5,750
2000	With transom, 6'-0" x 10'-0"	4,300	2,875	7,175
2100	Anodized aluminum and glass 6'-0" x 7'-0"	3,875	2,725	6,600
2200	With transom, 6'-0" x 10'-0"	4,925	3,375	8,300
2300	Steel, deluxe, hollow metal, 6'-0" x 7'-0"	2,900	905	3,805
2400	With transom, 6'-0" x 10'-0"	3,975	1,050	5,025
2500	Fire door, "A" label, 6'-0" x 7'-0"	3,100	895	3,995
2800				
2900				
3100	Cut & patch to match existing construction, add, minimum	2%	3%	
3200	Maximum	5%	9%	
3300	Dust protection, add, minimum	1%	2%	
3400	Maximum	4%	11%	
3500	Material handling & storage limitation, add, minimum	1%	1%	
3600	Maximum	6%	7%	
3700	Protection of existing work, add, minimum	2%	2%	
3800	Maximum	5%	7%	
3900	Shift work requirements, add, minimum		5%	
4000	Maximum		30%	

B2030 Exterior Doors

This page illustrates and describes sliding door systems including a sliding door, frame, interior and exterior trim with exterior staining. Lines within System Components give the unit price and total price on a cost each basis for this system. Prices for sliding door systems are on Line Items B2030 150 1000 thru 2400. Both material quantities and labor costs have been adjusted for the system listed.

Factors: To adjust for job conditions other than normal working situations use Lines B2030 150 2700 thru 4000.

Example: You are to install the system with temporary shoring and bracing. Go to Line B2030 150 3900 and apply these percentages to the appropriate MAT. and INST. costs.

System Components	QUANTITY	UNIT	COST EACH		
			MAT.	INST.	TOTAL
Sliding wood door, 6'-0" x 6'-8", with wood frame, interior and exterior trim and exterior staining.					
Sliding wood door, standard, 6'-0" x 6'-8", insulated glass	1.000	Ea.	1,275	300	1,575
Interior & exterior trim	1.000	Set	33.40	48.20	81.60
Stain door	1.000	Ea.	2.17	30	32.17
Stain trim	1.000	Ea.	3	12.60	15.60
TOTAL			1,313.57	390.80	1,704.37

B2030 150	Doors, Sliding - Patio	COST EACH		
		MAT.	INST.	TOTAL
1000	Wood, standard, 6'-0" x 6'-8", insulated glass	1,325	390	1,715
1100	8'-0" x 6'-8"	1,700	495	2,195
1200	12'-0" x 6'-8"	2,750	605	3,355
1300	Vinyl coated, 6'-0" x 6'-8"	1,625	390	2,015
1400	8'-0" x 6'-8"	2,050	495	2,545
1500	12'-0" x 6'-8"	3,350	605	3,955
1700	Aluminum, standard, 6'-0" x 6'-8", insulated glass	1,050	420	1,470
1800	8'-0" x 6'-8"	1,625	535	2,160
1900	12'-0" x 6'-8"	1,750	635	2,385
2000	Anodized, 6'-0" x 6'-8"	1,775	420	2,195
2100	8'-0" x 6'-8"	1,900	535	2,435
2200	12'-0" x 6'-8"	3,350	635	3,985
2300				
2400	Deduct for single glazing	81		81
2500				
2700	Cut & patch to match existing construction, add, minimum	2%	3%	
2800	Maximum	5%	9%	
2900	Dust protection, add, minimum	1%	2%	
3000	Maximum	4%	11%	
3100	Equipment usage curtailment, add, minimum	1%	1%	
3200	Maximum	3%	10%	
3300	Material handling & storage limitation, add, minimum	1%	1%	
3400	Maximum	6%	7%	
3500	Protection of existing, work, add, minimum	2%	2%	
3600	Maximum	5%	7%	
3700	Shift work requirements, add, minimum		5%	
3800	Maximum		30%	
3900	Temporary shoring and bracing, add, minimum	2%	5%	
4000	Maximum	5%	12%	

B2030 Exterior Doors

This page illustrates and describes residential door systems including a door, frame, trim, hardware, weatherstripping, stained and finished. Lines within System Components give the unit price and total price on a cost each basis for this system. Prices for residential door systems are on Line Items B2030 240 1500 thru 2200. Both material quantities and labor costs have been adjusted for the system listed.

Factors: To adjust for job conditions other than normal working situations use Lines B2030 240 3100 thru 4000.

Example: You are to install the system with a material handling and storage limitation. Go to Line B2030 240 3600 and apply these percentages to the appropriate MAT. and INST. costs.

System Components	QUANTITY	UNIT	COST EACH MAT.	COST EACH INST.	COST EACH TOTAL
Single solid wood colonial door, 3′ x 6′-8″ with wood frame and trim, stained and finished, including hardware and weatherstripping.					
Solid wood colonial door, fir 3′ x 6′-8″ x 1-3/4″, hinges	1.000	Ea.	490	80.50	570.50
Hinges, ball bearing	1.000	Ea.	37		37
Exterior frame, with trim	1.000	Set	147.90	54.74	202.64
Interior trim	1.000	Set	28	50	78
Lockset	1.000	Set	55	43	98
Sill, oak 8″ deep	3.500	Ea.	65.80	42.18	107.98
Weatherstripping	1.000	Set	25.50	79.50	105
Stained and finished	1.000	Ea.	4.64	63.50	68.14
TOTAL			853.84	413.42	1,267.26

B2030 240	Doors, Residential - Exterior	COST EACH MAT.	COST EACH INST.	COST EACH TOTAL
1400	Single doors, 3′ x 6′-8″			
1500	Solid colonial door, fir	855	415	1,270
1600	Hollow metal exterior door, plain	825	385	1,210
1700	Solid core wood door, plain	495	395	890
1800				
1900	Double doors, 6′ x 6′-8″			
2000	Solid colonial double doors, fir	1,425	550	1,975
2100	Hollow metal exterior doors, plain	1,375	515	1,890
2200	Hollow core wood doors, plain	710	530	1,240
2300				
2800				
2900				
3100	Cut & patch to match existing construction, add, minimum	2%	3%	
3200	Maximum	5%	9%	
3300	Dust protection, add, minimum	1%	2%	
3400	Maximum	4%	11%	
3500	Material handling & storage limitation, add, minimum	1%	1%	
3600	Maximum	6%	7%	
3700	Protection of existing work, add, minimum	2%	2%	
3800	Maximum	5%	7%	
3900	Shift work requirements, add, minimum		5%	
4000	Maximum		30%	

B2030 Exterior Doors

This page illustrates and describes overhead door systems including an overhead door, track, hardware, trim, and electric door opener. Lines within System Components give the unit price and total price on a cost each basis for this system. Prices for overhead door systems are on Line Items B2030 410 1200 thru 2300. Both material quantities and labor costs have been adjusted for the system listed.

Factors: To adjust for job conditions other than normal working situations use Lines B2030 410 3100 thru 4000.

Example: You are to install the system and match existing construction. Go to Line B2030 410 3200 and apply these percentages to the appropriate MAT. and INST. costs.

System Components	QUANTITY	UNIT	COST EACH		
			MAT.	INST.	TOTAL
Wood overhead door, commercial sectional, including track, door, hardware and trim, electrically operated.					
Commercial, heavy duty wood door, 8' x 8' x 1-3/4" thick	1.000	Ea.	1,125	605	1,730
Frame, 2 x 8, pressure treated	1.000	Set	26.64	76.08	102.72
Wood trim	1.000	Set	37.92	60.24	98.16
Painting, two coats	1.000	Ea.	20.16	203.04	223.20
Electric trolley operator	1.000	Ea.	1,025	300	1,325
TOTAL			2,234.72	1,244.36	3,479.08

B2030 410	Doors, Overhead	COST EACH		
		MAT.	INST.	TOTAL
1200	Commercial, wood, 1-3/4" thick, 8' x 8'	2,225	1,250	3,475
1300	12' x 12'	3,400	1,750	5,150
1400	14' x 14'	4,750	2,050	6,800
1500	Fiberglass & aluminum 12' x 12'	4,150	1,775	5,925
1600	20' x 20'	8,825	4,525	13,350
1700	Residential, wood, 9' x 7'	1,075	475	1,550
1800	16' x 7'	1,900	705	2,605
1900	Hardboard faced, 9' x 7'	725	475	1,200
2000	16' x 7'	1,450	705	2,155
2100	Fiberglass & aluminum, 9' x 7'	1,100	550	1,650
2200	16' x 7'	1,825	705	2,530
2300	For residential electric opener, add	675	75.50	750.50
2400				
2500				
2600				
2700				
2800				
2900				
3100	Cut & patch to match existing construction, add, minumum	2%	3%	
3200	Maximum	5%	9%	
3300	Dust protection, add, minimum	1%	2%	
3400	Maximum	4%	11%	
3500	Material handling & storage limitation, add, minimum	1%	1%	
3600	Maximum	6%	7%	
3700	Protection of existing work, add, minimum	2%	2%	
3800	Maximum	5%	7%	
3900	Shift work requirements, add, minimum		5%	
4000	Maximum		30%	

B2030 Exterior Doors

B2030 810	Selective Price Sheet	COST EACH		
		MAT.	INST.	TOTAL
0100	Door closer, rack and pinion	207	100	307
0200	Backcheck and adjustable power	207	100	307
0300	Regular, hinge face mount, all sizes, regular arm	207	100	307
0400	Hold open arm	220	100	320
0500	Top jamb mount, all sizes, regular arm	207	100	307
0600	Hold open arm	220	100	320
0700	Stop face mount, all sizes, regular arm	207	100	307
0800	Hold open arm	220	100	320
0900	Fusible link, hinge face mount, all sizes, regular arm	246	100	346
1000	Hold open arm	259	100	359
1100	Top jamb mount, all sizes, regular arm	246	100	346
1200	Hold open arm	259	100	359
1300	Stop face mount, all sizes, regular arm	246	100	346
1400	Hold open arm	259	100	359
1500				
1600				
1700	Door stops			
1800				
1900	Holder & bumper, floor or wall	37.50	18.85	56.35
2000	Wall bumper	12.85	18.85	31.70
2100	Floor bumper	8.90	18.85	27.75
2200	Plunger type, door mounted	30.50	18.85	49.35
2300	Hinges, full mortise, material only, per pair			
2400	Low frequency, 4-1/2" x 4-1/2", steel base, USP	24.50		24.50
2500	Brass base, US10	58.50		58.50
2600	Stainless steel base, US32	82		82
2700	Average frequency, 4-1/2" x 4-1/2", steel base, USP	40		40
2800	Brass base, US10	64.50		64.50
2900	Stainless steel base, US32	81.50		81.50
3000	High frequency, 4-1/2" x 4-1/2", steel base, USP	69		69
3100	Brass base, US10	81		81
3200	Stainless steel base, US32	114		114
3300	Kick plate			
3400				
3500	6" high, for 3'-0" door, aluminum	31.50	40	71.50
3600	Bronze	61.50	40	101.50
3700	Panic device			
3800				
3900	For rim locks, single door, exit	505	100	605
4000	Outside key and pull	630	121	751
4100	Bar and vertical rod, exit only	955	121	1,076
4200	Outside key and pull	1,025	151	1,176
4300	Lockset			
4400				
4500	Heavy duty, cylindrical, passage doors	138	50	188
4600	Classroom	495	75.50	570.50
4700	Bedroom, bathroom, and inner office doors	171	50	221
4800	Apartment, office, and corridor doors	320	60.50	380.50
4900	Standard duty, cylindrical, exit doors	118	60.50	178.50
5100	Passage doors	82.50	50	132.50
5200	Public restroom, classroom, & office doors	226	75.50	301.50
5300	Deadlock, mortise, heavy duty	220	67	287
5400	Double cylinder	220	67	287
5500	Entrance lock, cylinder, deadlocking latch	193	67	260
5600	Deadbolt	193	75.50	268.50
5700	Commercial, mortise, wrought knob, keyed, minimum	208	75.50	283.50
5800	Maximum	545	86	631
5900	Cast knob, keyed, minimum	286	67	353

B20 Exterior Enclosure

B2030 Exterior Doors

B2030 810	Selective Price Sheet	COST EACH		
		MAT.	INST.	TOTAL
6000	Maximum	580	67	647
6100	Push-pull			
6200				
6300	Aluminum	12.25	50	62.25
6400	Bronze	27.50	50	77.50
6500	Door pull, designer style, minimum	97.50	50	147.50
6600	Maximum	405	75.50	480.50
6700	Threshold			
6800				
6900	3'-0" long door saddles, aluminum, minimum	8.95	12.55	21.50
7000	Maximum	53.50	50	103.50
7100	Bronze, minimum	45.50	10.05	55.55
7200	Maximum	173	50	223
7300	Rubber, 1/2" thick, 5-1/2" wide	44	30	74
7400	2-3/4" wide	41.50	30	71.50
7500	Weatherstripping, per set			
7600				
7700	Doors, wood frame, interlocking for 3' x 7' door, zinc	48.50	201	249.50
7800	Bronze	61.50	201	262.50
7900	Wood frame, spring type for 3' x 7' door, bronze	25.50	79.50	105
8000	Metal frame, spring type for 3' x 7' door, bronze	51	201	252
8100	For stainless steel, spring type, add	133%		
8200				
8300	Metal frame, extruded sections, 3' x 7' door, aluminum	31	201	232
8400	Bronze	90	201	291

B3010 Roof Coverings

B3010 160	Selective Price Sheet	COST PER S.F.		
		MAT.	INST.	TOTAL
0100	Roofing, built-up, asphalt roll roof, 3 ply organic/mineral surface	.82	1.60	2.42
0200	3 plies glass fiber felt type iv, 1 ply mineral surface	1.38	1.73	3.11
0300	Cold applied, 3 ply		.56	.56
0400	Coal tar pitch, 4 ply tarred felt	2.57	2.05	4.62
0500	Mopped, 3 ply glass fiber	2.12	2.26	4.38
0600	4 ply organic felt	2.57	2.05	4.62
0700	Elastomeric, hypalon, neoprene unreinforced	1.43	3.79	5.22
0800	Polyester reinforced	1.56	4.48	6.04
0900	Neoprene, 5 coats 60 mils	4.75	13.20	17.95
1000	Over 10,000 S.F.	4.75	6.85	11.60
1600				
1700	Asphalt, strip, 210-235#/sq.	.89	1.03	1.92
1800	235-240#/sq.	1.06	1.13	2.19
1900	Class A laminated	1.16	1.25	2.41
2000	Class C laminated	1.16	1.41	2.57
2100	Slate, buckingham, 3/16" thick	5.25	3.25	8.50
2200	Black, 1/4" thick	5.25	3.25	8.50
2300	Wood, shingles, 16" no. 1, 5" exp.	2.91	2.41	5.32
2400	Red cedar, 18" perfections	2.50	2.19	4.69
2500	Shakes, 24", 10" exposure	2.78	2.41	5.19
2600	18", 8-1/2" exposure	1.97	3	4.97
2700	Insulation, ceiling batts, fiberglass, 3-1/2" thick, R13	.34	.45	.79
2800	6" thick, R19	.46	.45	.91
2900	9" thick, R30	.77	.52	1.29
3000	12" thick, R38	.98	.52	1.50
3100	Mineral, 3-1/2" thick, R13	.66	.38	1.04
3200	Fiber, 6" thick, R19	1.04	.38	1.42
3300	Roof deck, fiberboard, 1" thick, R2.78	.57	.77	1.34
3400	Mineral, 2" thick, R5.26	1.17	.77	1.94
3500	Perlite boards, 3/4" thick, R2.08	.39	.77	1.16
3600	2" thick, R5.26	1.09	.85	1.94
3700	Polystyrene extruded, R5.26, 1" thick,	.58	.52	1.10
3800	2" thick R10	.76	.58	1.34
3900	40 PSI compressive strength, 1" thick R5	.56	.52	1.08
4000	Tapered for drainage	.80	.54	1.34
4300	Ceiling, plaster, gypsum, 2 coats	.41	3.30	3.71
4400	3 coats	.59	3.89	4.48
4500	Perlite or vermiculite, 2 coats	.46	3.83	4.29
4600	3 coats	.77	4.83	5.60
4700	Gypsum lath, plain 3/8" thick	.33	.67	1
4800	1/2" thick	.30	.71	1.01
4900	Firestop, 3/8" thick	.30	.81	1.11
5000	1/2" thick	.33	.87	1.20
5100	Metal lath, rib, 2.75 lb.	.40	.75	1.15
5200	3.40 lb.	.54	.81	1.35
5300	Diamond, 2.50 lb.	.52	.75	1.27
5400	3.40 lb.	.52	.94	1.46
5500	Drywall, taped and finished standard, 1/2" thick	.38	1.58	1.96
5600	5/8" thick	.41	1.58	1.99
5700	Fire resistant, 1/2" thick	.41	1.58	1.99
5800	5/8" thick	.43	1.58	2.01
5900	Water resist., 1/2" thick	.47	1.58	2.05
6000	5/8" thick	.55	1.58	2.13
6100	Finish, instead of taping			
6200	For thin coat plaster, add	.11	.75	.86
6300	Finish textured spray, add	.04	.64	.68
6500	Tile, stapled glued, mineral fiber plastic coated, 5/8" thick	2.06	2.01	4.07
6600	3/4" thick	1.96	2.01	3.97

B3010 Roof Coverings

B3010 160	Selective Price Sheet	COST PER S.F.		
		MAT.	INST.	TOTAL
6700	Wood fiber, 1/2" thick	1.20	1.51	2.71
6800	3/4" thick	1.31	1.51	2.82
6900	Suspended, fiberglass film faced, 5/8" thick	1.12	.96	2.08
7000	3" thick	2.09	1.34	3.43
7100	Mineral fiber 5/8" thick, standard face	.79	.89	1.68
7200	Aluminum faced	3.21	1	4.21
7500	Ceiling suspension systems, for tile, "T" bar, class "A", 2' x 4' grid	.77	.75	1.52
7600	2' x 2' grid	1	.93	1.93
7700	Concealed "Z" bar, 12" module	.86	1.16	2.02
7800				
7900	Plaster/drywall, 3/4" channels, steel furring, 16" O.C.	.34	1.76	2.10
8000	24" O.C.	.22	1.21	1.43
8100	1-1/2" channels, 16" O.C.	.46	1.96	2.42
8200	24" O.C.	.30	1.31	1.61
8300	Ceiling framing, 2" x 4" studs, 16" O.C.	.32	1.01	1.33
8400	24" O.C.	.21	.67	.88

B30 Roofing

B3020   Roof Openings

This page illustrates and describes a roof hatch system. Lines within System Components give the unit price and total cost each for this system. Prices for systems are on Lines B3020 230 1400 thru 2400. Both material quantities and labor costs have been adjusted for the system listed.

Factors: To adjust for job conditions other than normal working situtations use Lines B3020 230 2900 thru 4000.

Example: You are to install the system and cut and patch to match existing construction. Use line B3020 230 3000 and apply these percentages to the appropriate MAT. and INST. costs.

System Components	QUANTITY	UNIT	COST EACH MAT.	COST EACH INST.	COST EACH TOTAL
Roof hatch, 2'-6" x 3'-0", aluminum, curb and cover included.					
through steel construction.					
Roof hatch, 2'-6" x 3'-0", aluminum	1.000	Ea.	1,175	234	1,409
Cutout decking	11.000	L.F.	3.85	27.28	31.13
Frame opening	44.000	L.F.	38.28	404.36	442.64
Flashing, 16 oz. copper	16.000	S.F.	122.40	78.56	200.96
Cant strip, 4 x 4, foamglass	12.000	L.F.	29.76	20.88	50.64
TOTAL			1,369.29	765.08	2,134.37

B3020 230	Roof Hatches, Skylights	COST EACH MAT.	COST EACH INST.	COST EACH TOTAL
1400	Roof hatch, aluminum, curb and cover, 2'-6" x 3'-0"	1,375	765	2,140
1500	2'-6" x 4'-6"	1,250	935	2,185
1600	2'-6" x 8'-0"	2,325	1,350	3,675
1700	Skylight, plexiglass dome, with curb mounting, 30" x 32"	725	725	1,450
1800	30" x 45"	780	910	1,690
1900	40" x 45"	935	1,225	2,160
2000	Smoke hatch, unlabeled, 2'-6" x 3'-0"	1,675	820	2,495
2100	2'-6" x 4'-6"	1,500	1,000	2,500
2200	2'-6" x 8'-0"	2,525	1,375	3,900
2300				
2400	For steel ladder, add per vertical linear foot	40.50	37.50	78
2500				
2600				
2700				
2900	Cut & patch to match existing construction, add, minimum	2%	3%	
3000	Maximum	5%	9%	
3100	Dust protection, add, minimum	1%	2%	
3200	Maximum	4%	11%	
3300	Equipment usage curtailment, add, minimum	1%	1%	
3400	Maximum	3%	10%	
3500	Material handling & storage limitation, add, minimum	1%	1%	
3600	Maximum	6%	7%	
3700	Protection of existing work, add, minimum	2%	2%	
3800	Maximum	5%	7%	
3900	Shift work requirements, add, minimum		5%	
4000	Maximum		30%	

B3020 240	Selective Price Sheet	COST PER L.F.		
		MAT.	INST.	TOTAL
0100	Downspouts per L.F., aluminum, enameled .024" thick, 2" x 3"	2.26	3.83	6.09
0200	3" x 4"	3.17	4.93	8.10
0300	Round .025" thick, 3" diam.	1.73	3.63	5.36
0400	4" diam.	2.56	4.93	7.49
0500	Copper, round 16 oz. stock, 2" diam.	9.40	3.63	13.03
0600	3" diam.	9.25	3.63	12.88
0700	4" diam.	11.60	4.76	16.36
0800	5" diam.	20	5.30	25.30
0900	Rectangular, 2" x 3"	14.65	3.63	18.28
1000	3" x 4"	18.60	4.76	23.36
1100	Lead coated copper, round, 2" diam.	27.50	3.63	31.13
1200	3" diam.	23.50	3.63	27.13
1300	4" diam.	24.50	4.76	29.26
1400	5" diam.	26.50	5.30	31.80
1500	Rectangular, 2" x 3"	26.50	3.63	30.13
1600	3" x 4"	36.50	4.76	41.26
1700	Steel galvanized, round 28 gauge, 3" diam.	2.29	3.63	5.92
1800	4" diam.	2.87	4.76	7.63
1900	5" diam.	3.81	5.30	9.11
2000	6" diam.	4.62	6.55	11.17
2100	Rectangular, 2" x 3"	3.33	3.63	6.96
2200	3" x 4"	3.37	4.76	8.13
2300	Elbows, aluminum, round, 3" diam.	3.01	6.90	9.91
2400	4" diam.	6.35	6.90	13.25
2500	Rectangular, 2" x 3"	1.05	6.90	7.95
2600	3" x 4"	3.85	6.90	10.75
2700	Copper, round 16 oz., 2" diam.	10.40	6.90	17.30
2800	3" diam.	9.90	6.90	16.80
2900	4" diam.	14.50	6.90	21.40
3100	Rectangular, 2" x 3"	9.90	6.90	16.80
3200	3" x 4"	15	6.90	21.90
3300	Drip edge per L.F., aluminum, 5" wide	.44	1.51	1.95
3400	8" wide	.76	1.51	2.27
3500	28" wide	4.24	6.05	10.29
3600				
3700	Steel galvanized, 5" wide	.58	1.51	2.09
3800	8" wide	.76	1.51	2.27
3900				
4000				
4100				
4200				
4300	Flashing 12" wide per S.F., aluminum, mill finish, .013" thick	.87	3.89	4.76
4400	.019" thick	1.27	3.89	5.16
4500	.040" thick	2.54	3.89	6.43
4600	.050" thick	2.67	3.89	6.56
4700	Copper, mill finish, 16 oz.	7.65	4.91	12.56
4800	20 oz.	10.85	5.15	16
4900	24 oz.	13.35	5.40	18.75
5000	32 oz.	17.80	5.65	23.45
5100	Lead, 2.5 lb./S.F., 12" wide	5.50	4.18	9.68
5200	Over 12" wide	4.39	4.18	8.57
5900	Polyvinyl chloride, black, .010" thick	.23	1.98	2.21
6000	.020" thick	.31	1.98	2.29
6100	.030" thick	.39	1.98	2.37
6200	.056" thick	.94	1.98	2.92
6300	Steel, galvanized, 20 gauge	1.38	4.34	5.72
6400	30 gauge	.64	3.53	4.17
6500	Stainless, 32 gauge, .010" thick	3.30	3.64	6.94

B3020 Roof Openings

B3020 240	Selective Price Sheet	COST PER L.F.		
		MAT.	INST.	TOTAL
6600	28 gauge, .015" thick	4.39	3.64	8.03
6700	26 gauge, .018" thick	4.68	3.64	8.32
6800	24 gauge, .025" thick	5.25	3.64	8.89
6900	Gutters per L.F., aluminum, 5" box, .027" thick	2.97	5.70	8.67
7000	.032" thick	3.51	5.50	9.01
7100	Copper, half round, 4" wide	11.55	5.50	17.05
7200	6" wide	15.40	5.85	21.25
7300	Steel, 26 gauge galvanized, 5" wide	2.40	5.50	7.90
7400	6" wide	2.94	5.50	8.44
7500	Wood, treated hem-fir, 3" x 4"	13.65	6.05	19.70
7600	4" x 5"	21.50	6.05	27.55
7700	Reglet per L.F., aluminum, .025" thick	2.02	2.68	4.70
7800	Copper, 10 oz.	6.40	2.68	9.08
7900	Steel, galvanized, 24 gauge	1.41	2.68	4.09
8000	Stainless, .020" thick	4	2.68	6.68
8100	Counter flashing 12" wide per L.F., aluminum, .032" thick	2.52	4.60	7.12
8200	Aluminum, .025" thick	2.52	4.60	7.12
8300	Steel, galvanized, 24 gauge	1.42	4.60	6.02
8400	Stainless, .020" thick	6.25	4.60	10.85

C10 Interior Construction

C1010   Partitions

This page illustrates and describes a concrete block wall system including concrete block, horizontal reinforcing alternate courses, mortar, and tooled joints both sides. Lines within System Components give the unit price and total price per square foot for this system. Prices for concrete block wall systems are on Line Items C1010 106 0800 thru 2100. Both material quantities and labor costs have been adjusted for the system listed.

Factors: To adjust for job conditions other than normal working situations use Lines C1010 106 2900 thru 4000.

Example: You are to install the system and protect all existing work. Go to Line C1010 106 3600 and apply these percentages to the appropriate MAT. and INST. costs.

System Components	QUANTITY	UNIT	COST PER S.F.		
			MAT.	INST.	TOTAL
Concrete block partition, including horizontal reinforcing every second course, mortar, tooled joints both sides.					
8" x 16" concrete block, normal weight, 4" thick	1.000	S.F.	1.74	6.35	8.09
Horizontal reinforcing every second course	.750	L.F.	.19	.15	.34
TOTAL			1.93	6.50	8.43

C1010 106	Partitions, Concrete Block	COST PER S.F.		
		MAT.	INST.	TOTAL
0800	8" x 16" concrete block, normal weight, 4" thick	1.93	6.50	8.43
0900	6" thick	2.49	7	9.49
1000	8" thick	2.80	7.45	10.25
1100	10" thick	3.34	7.75	11.09
1200	12" thick	4.23	9.60	13.83
1300	8" x 16" concrete block, lightweight, 4" thick	2.08	6.35	8.43
1400	6" thick	2.88	6.85	9.73
1500	8" thick	3.47	7.25	10.72
1600	10" thick	4.16	7.55	11.71
1700	12" thick	4.38	9.35	13.73
1800	8" x 16" glazed concrete block, 4" thick	11	8.10	19.10
1900	8" thick	12.65	9	21.65
2000	Structural facing tile, 6T series, glazed 2 sides, 4" thick	17.50	14.20	31.70
2100	6" thick	23.50	14.95	38.45
2200				
2300				
2400				
2500				
2600				
2900	Cut & patch to match existing construction, add, minimum	2%	3%	
3000	Maximum	5%	9%	
3100	Dust protection, add, minimum	1%	2%	
3200	Maximum	4%	11%	
3300	Material handling & storage limitation, add, minimum	1%	1%	
3400	Maximum	6%	7%	
3500	Protection of existing work, add, minimum	2%	2%	
3600	Maximum	5%	7%	
3700	Shift work requirements, add, minimum		5%	
3800	Maximum		30%	
3900	Temporary shoring and bracing, add, minimum	2%	5%	
4000	Maximum	5%	12%	

C1010 Partitions

This page illustrates and describes a wood stud partition system including wood studs with plates, gypsum plasterboard – taped and finished, insulation, baseboard and painting. Lines within System Components give the unit price and total price per square foot for this system. Prices for wood stud partition systems are on Line Items C1010 132 1300 thru 2700. Both material quantities and labor costs have been adjusted for the system listed.

Factors: To adjust for job conditions other than normal working situations use Lines C1010 132 2900 thru 4000.

Example: You are to install the system where material handling and storage present a serious problem. Go to Line C1010 132 3400 and apply these percentages to the appropriate MAT. and INST. costs.

System Components	QUANTITY	UNIT	COST PER S.F. MAT.	COST PER S.F. INST.	COST PER S.F. TOTAL
Wood stud wall, 2″x4″, 16″ O.C., dbl. top plate, sngl bot. plate, 5/8″ dwl.					
taped, finished and painted on 2 faces, insulation, baseboard, wall 8′ high.					
Wood studs, 2″ x 4″, 16″ O.C., 8′ high	1.000	S.F.	.47	1.51	1.98
Gypsum drywall, 5/8″ thick	2.000	S.F.	.70	1.20	1.90
Taping and finishing	2.000	S.F.	.10	1.20	1.30
Insulation, 3-1/2″ fiberglass batts	1.000	S.F.	.48	.45	.93
Baseboard	.200	L.F.	.40	.63	1.03
Paint baseboard, primer + 2 coats	.200	L.F.	.05	.37	.42
Painting, roller, 2 coats	2.000	S.F.	.42	1.34	1.76
TOTAL			2.62	6.70	9.32

C1010 132	Partitions, Wood Stud	MAT.	INST.	TOTAL
1300	2″ x 3″ studs, 8′ high, 16″ O.C.	2.59	6.60	9.19
1400	24″ O.C.	2.49	6.35	8.84
1500	10′ high, 16″ O.C.	2.57	6.35	8.92
1600	24″ O.C.	2.47	6.10	8.57
1650	2″ x 4″ studs, 8′ high, 16″ O.C.	2.62	6.70	9.32
1700	24″ O.C.	2.52	6.40	8.92
1800	10′ high, 16″ O.C.	2.59	6.40	8.99
1900	24″ O.C.	2.48	6.15	8.63
2000	12′ high, 16″ O.C.	2.55	6.40	8.95
2100	24″ O.C.	2.45	6.15	8.60
2200	2″ x 6″ studs, 8′ high, 16″ O.C.	2.86	6.85	9.71
2300	24″ O.C.	2.70	6.50	9.20
2400	10′ high, 16″ O.C.	2.81	6.55	9.36
2500	24″ O.C.	2.65	6.25	8.90
2600	12′ high, 16″ O.C.	2.75	6.55	9.30
2700	24″ O.C.	2.60	6.25	8.85
2900	Cut & patch to match existing construction, add, minimum	2%	3%	
3000	Maximum	5%	9%	
3100	Dust protection, add, minimum	1%	2%	
3200	Maximum	4%	11%	
3300	Material handling & storage limitation, add, minimum	1%	1%	
3400	Maximum	6%	7%	
3500	Protection of existing work, add, minimum	2%	2%	
3600	Maximum	5%	7%	
3700	Shift work requirements, add, minimum		5%	
3800	Maximum		30%	
3900	Temporary shoring and bracing, add, minimum	2%	5%	
4000	Maximum	5%	12%	

C1010 Partitions

This page illustrates and describes a non-load bearing metal stud partition system including metal studs with runners, gypsum plasterboard, taped and finished, insulation, baseboard and painting. Lines within System Components give the unit price and total price per square foot for this system. Prices for non-load bearing metal stud partition systems are on Line Items C1010 134 1300 thru 2300. Both material quantities and labor costs have been adjusted for the system listed.

Factors: To adjust for job conditions other than normal working situations use Lines C1010 134 2900 thru 4000.

Example: You are to install the system and cut and patch to match existing construction. Go to Line C1010 134 3000 and apply these percentages to the appropriate MAT. and INST. costs.

System Components	QUANTITY	UNIT	COST PER S.F. MAT.	COST PER S.F. INST.	COST PER S.F. TOTAL
Non-load bearing metal studs, including top & bottom runners, 5/8″ drywall, taped, finished and painted 2 faces, insulation, painted baseboard.					
Metal studs, 25 ga., 3-5/8″ wide, 24″ O.C.	1.000	S.F.	.30	.81	1.11
Gypsum drywall, 5/8″ thick	2.000	S.F.	.70	1.20	1.90
Taping & finishing	2.000	S.F.	.10	1.20	1.30
Insulation, 3-1/2″ fiberglass batts	1.000	S.F.	.48	.45	.93
Baseboard	.200	L.F.	.32	.50	.82
Paint baseboard, primer + 2 coats	.200	L.F.	.04	.30	.34
Painting, roller work, 2 coats	2.000	S.F.	.42	1.34	1.76
TOTAL			**2.36**	**5.80**	**8.16**

C1010 134	Partitions, Metal Stud, NLB	COST PER S.F. MAT.	COST PER S.F. INST.	COST PER S.F. TOTAL
1300	Non-load bearing, 25 ga., 24″ O.C., 2-1/2″ wide	2.31	5.80	8.11
1350	3-5/8″ wide	2.36	5.80	8.16
1400	6″ wide	2.47	5.80	8.27
1500	16″ O.C., 2-1/2″ wide	2.37	6	8.37
1600	3-5/8″ wide	2.44	6	8.44
1700	6″ wide	2.57	6.05	8.62
1800	20 ga., 24″ O.C., 2-1/2″ wide	2.41	6	8.41
1900	3-5/8″ wide	2.52	6	8.52
2000	6″ wide	2.64	6.05	8.69
2100	16″ O.C., 2-1/2″ wide	2.50	6.25	8.75
2200	3-5/8″ wide	2.64	6.25	8.89
2300	6″ wide	2.79	6.30	9.09
2400				
2500				
2600				
2700				
2900	Cut & patch to match existing construction, add, minimum	2%	3%	
3000	Maximum	5%	9%	
3100	Dust protection, add, minimum	1%	2%	
3200	Maximum	4%	11%	
3300	Material handling & storage limitation, add, minimum	1%	1%	
3400	Maximum	6%	7%	
3500	Protection of existing work, add, minimum	2%	2%	
3600	Maximum	5%	7%	
3700	Shift work requirements, add, minimum		5%	
3800	Maximum		30%	
3900	Temporary shoring and bracing, add, minimum	2%	5%	
4000	Maximum	5%	12%	

C1010 Partitions

This page illustrates and describes a drywall system including gypsum plasterboard, taped and finished, metal studs with runners, insulation, baseboard and painting. Lines within System Components give the unit price and total price per square foot for this system. Prices for drywall systems are on Line Items C1010 136 1200 thru 1900. Both material quantities and labor costs have been adjusted for the system listed.

Factors: To adjust for job conditions other than normal working situations use Lines C1010 136 2900 thru 4000.

Example: You are to install the system and control dust in the work area. Go to Line C1010 136 3100 and apply these percentages to the appropriate MAT. and INST. costs.

System Components	QUANTITY	UNIT	COST PER S.F.		
			MAT.	INST.	TOTAL
Gypsum drywall, taped, finished and painted 2 faces, galvanized metal studs,					
including top & bottom runners, insulation, painted baseboard, wall 10'high.					
Gypsum drywall, 5/8" thick, standard	2.000	S.F.	.70	1.20	1.90
Taping and finishing	2.000	S.F.	.10	1.20	1.30
Metal studs, 20 ga., 3-5/8" wide, 24" O.C.	1.000	S.F.	.38	1.02	1.40
Insulation, 3-1/2" fiberglass batts	1.000	S.F.	.48	.45	.93
Baseboard	.200	L.F.	.32	.50	.82
Paint baseboard, primer + 2 coats	.200	L.F.	.03	.13	.16
Painting, roller 2 coats	2.000	S.F.	.28	1.26	1.54
TOTAL			2.29	5.76	8.05

C1010 136	Partitions, Drywall	COST PER S.F.		
		MAT.	INST.	TOTAL
1200	Gypsum drywall, 5/8" thick, standard	2.29	5.75	8.04
1300	Fire resistant	2.25	5.55	7.80
1400	Water resistant	2.51	5.55	8.06
1500	1/2" thick, standard	2.17	5.55	7.72
1600	Fire resistant	2.21	5.55	7.76
1700	Water resistant	2.35	5.55	7.90
1800	3/8" thick, vinyl faced, standard	2.57	7.05	9.62
1900	5/8" thick, vinyl faced, fire resistant	3.47	7.05	10.52
2000				
2100				
2200				
2300				
2400				
2500				
2600				
2700				
2900	Cut & patch to match existing construction, add, minimum	2%	3%	
3000	Maximum	5%	9%	
3100	Dust protection, add, minimum	1%	2%	
3200	Maximum	4%	11%	
3300	Material handling & storage limitation, add, minimum	1%	1%	
3400	Maximum	6%	7%	
3500	Protection of existing work, add, minimum	2%	2%	
3600	Maximum	5%	7%	
3700	Shift work requirements, add, minimum		5%	
3800	Maximum		30%	
3900	Temporary shoring and bracing, add, minimum	2%	5%	
4000	Maximum	5%	12%	

C10 Interior Construction

C1010 Partitions

This page illustrates and describes a load bearing metal stud wall system including metal studs, sheetrock–taped and finished, insulation, baseboard and painting. Lines within System Components give the unit price and total price per square foot for this system. Prices for load bearing metal stud wall systems are on Line Items C1010 138 1500 thru 2500. Both material quantities and labor costs have been adjusted for the system listed.

Factors: To adjust for job conditions other than normal working situations use Lines C1010 138 2900 thru 4000.

Example: You are to install the system using temporary shoring and bracing. Go to Line C1010 138 3900 and apply these percentages to the appropriate MAT. and INST. costs.

System Components	QUANTITY	UNIT	COST PER S.F. MAT.	COST PER S.F. INST.	COST PER S.F. TOTAL
Load bearing, 18 ga., 3-5/8″, galvanized metal studs, 24″ O.C.,including top and bottom runners, 1/2″ drywall, taped, finished and painted 2 faces, 3″ insulation, and painted baseboard, wall 10′ high.					
Metal studs, 24″ O.C., 18 ga., 3-5/8″ wide, galvanized	1.000	S.F.	.78	1.15	1.93
Gypsum drywall 1/2″ thick	2.000	S.F.	.66	1.20	1.86
Taping and finishing	2.000	S.F.	.10	1.20	1.30
Insulation, 3-1/2″ fiberglass batts	1.000	S.F.	.48	.45	.93
Baseboard	.200	L.F.	.32	.50	.82
Paint baseboard, primer + 2 coats	.200	L.F.	.04	.30	.34
Painting, roller 2 coats	2.000	S.F.	.42	1.34	1.76
TOTAL			2.80	6.14	8.94

C1010 138	Partitions, Metal Stud, LB	COST PER S.F. MAT.	COST PER S.F. INST.	COST PER S.F. TOTAL
1500	Load bearing, 18 ga., 24″ O.C., 2-1/2″ wide	2.68	6.10	8.78
1550	3-5/8″ wide	2.80	6.15	8.95
1600	6″ wide	3.06	6.20	9.26
1700	16″ O.C. 2-1/2″ wide	2.84	6.40	9.24
1800	3-5/8″ wide	2.99	6.45	9.44
1900	6″ wide	3.31	6.50	9.81
2000	16 ga., 24″ O.C., 2-1/2″ wide	2.79	6.30	9.09
2100	3-5/8″ wide	2.93	6.30	9.23
2200	6″ wide	3.22	6.35	9.57
2300	16″ O.C., 2-1/2″ wide	2.98	6.60	9.58
2400	3-5/8″ wide	3.16	6.65	9.81
2500	6″ wide	3.52	6.70	10.22
2600				
2700				
2900	Cut & patch to match existing construction, add, minimum	2%	3%	
3000	Maximum	5%	9%	
3100	Dust protection, add, minumum	1%	2%	
3200	Maximum	4%	11%	
3300	Material handling & storage limitation, add, minimum	1%	1%	
3400	Maximum	6%	7%	
3500	Protection of existing work, add, minimum	2%	2%	
3600	Maximum	5%	7%	
3700	Shift work requirements, add, minimum		5%	
3800	Maximum		30%	
3900	Temporary shoring and bracing, add, minimum	2%	5%	
4000	Maximum	5%	12%	

612

C1010 Partitions

This page illustrates and describes a plaster and lath system including gypsum plaster, gypsum lath, wood studs with plates, insulation, baseboard and painting. Lines within System Components give the unit price and price per square foot for this system. Prices for plaster and lath systems are on Line Items C1010 148 1400 thru 2500. Both material quantities and labor costs have been adjusted for the system listed.

Factors: To adjust for job conditions other than normal working situations use Lines C1010 148 2900 thru 4000.

Example: You are to install the system during evening hours only. Go to Line C1010 148 3800 and apply this percentage to the appropriate INST. costs.

System Components	QUANTITY	UNIT	COST PER S.F.		
			MAT.	INST.	TOTAL
Gypsum plaster, 2 coats, over 3/8″ lath, 2 faces, 2″ x 4″ wood stud partition, 24″O.C. incl. double top plate, single bottom plate, 3-1/2″ insulation, baseboard and painting.					
Gypsum plaster, 2 coats	.220	S.Y.	.82	5.72	6.54
Lath, gypsum, 3/8″ thick	.220	S.Y.	.65	1.32	1.97
Wood studs, 2″ x 4″, 24″ O.C.	1.000	S.F.	.33	.97	1.30
Insulation, 3-1/2″ fiberglass batts	1.000	S.F.	.48	.45	.93
Baseboard, 9/16″ x 3-1/2″	.200	L.F.	.32	.50	.82
Paint baseboard, primer + 2 coats	.200	L.F.	.03	.13	.16
Paint, 2 coats	2.000	S.F.	.42	1.34	1.76
TOTAL			3.05	10.43	13.48

C1010 148	Partitions, Plaster & Lath	COST PER S.F.		
		MAT.	INST.	TOTAL
1400	Gypsum plaster, 2 coats	3.05	10.45	13.50
1500	3 coats	3.40	11.60	15
1600	Perlite plaster, 2 coats	3.15	11.25	14.40
1700	3 coats	3.76	12.85	16.61
1800				
1900				
2000	For alternate lath systems:			
2100	Gypsum lath, 1/2″ thick	3.09	11.35	14.44
2200	Foil back, 3/8″ thick	3.28	11.45	14.73
2300	1/2″ thick	3.35	11.55	14.90
2400	Metal lath, 2.5 Lb. diamond	3.53	11.25	14.78
2500	3.4 Lb. diamond	3.54	11.45	14.99
2600				
2700				
2900	Cut & patch to match existing construction, add, minimum	2%	3%	
3000	Maximum	5%	9%	
3100	Dust protection, add, minimum	1%	2%	
3200	Maximum	4%	11%	
3300	Material handling & storage limitation, add, minimum	1%	1%	
3400	Maximum	6%	7%	
3500	Protection of existing work, add, minimum	2%	2%	
3600	Maximum	5%	7%	
3700	Shift work requirements, add, minimum		5%	
3800	Maximum		30%	
3900	Temporary shoring and bracing, add, minimum	2%	5%	
4000	Maximum	5%	12%	

C10 Interior Construction

C1010 Partitions

C1010 170	Selective Price Sheet	COST PER S.F.		
		MAT.	INST.	TOTAL
0100	Studs			
0200				
0300	24" O.C. metal, 10' high wall, including			
0400	Top and bottom runners			
0500	Non load bearing, galvanized 25 Ga., 1-5/8" wide	.21	.79	1
0600	2-1/2" wide	.25	.80	1.05
0700	3-5/8" wide	.30	.81	1.11
0800	4" wide	.32	.81	1.13
0900	6" wide	.41	.83	1.24
1000				
1100	Galvanized 20 Ga., 2-1/2" wide	.35	1	1.35
1200	3-5/8" wide	.38	1.02	1.40
1300	4" wide	.46	1.02	1.48
1400	6" wide	.58	1.04	1.62
1500	Load bearing, painted 18 Ga., 2-1/2" wide	.66	1.13	1.79
1600	3-5/8" wide	.78	1.15	1.93
1700	4" wide	.70	1.17	1.87
1800	6" wide	1.04	1.20	2.24
1900	Galvanized 18 Ga., 2-1/2" wide	.66	1.13	1.79
2000	3-5/8" wide	.78	1.15	1.93
2100	4" wide	.70	1.17	1.87
2200	6" wide	1.04	1.20	2.24
2300	Galvanized 16 Ga., 2-1/2" wide	.77	1.29	2.06
2400	3-5/8" wide	.91	1.31	2.22
2500	4" wide	.96	1.34	2.30
2600	6" wide	1.20	1.37	2.57
2700				
2800				
2900	24" O.C. wood, 10' high wall, including			
3000	Double top plate and shoe			
3100	2" x 4"	.39	1.14	1.53
3200	2" x 6"	.58	1.22	1.80
3300				
3400				
3500	Furring, 24" O.C. 10' high wall, metal, 3/4" channels	.22	1.21	1.43
3600	1-1/2" channels	.30	1.31	1.61
3700	Wood, on wood, 1" x 2" strips	.13	.55	.68
3800	1" x 3" strips	.21	.55	.76
3900	On masonry, 1" x 2" strips	.15	.61	.76
4000	1" x 3" strips	.23	.61	.84
4100	On concrete, 1" x 2" strips	.15	1.16	1.31
4200	1" x 3" strips	.23	1.16	1.39
4300	Studs			
4400				
4500	16" O.C., metal, 10' high wall, including			
4600	Top and bottom runners			
4700	Non load bearing, galvanized 25 Ga., 1-5/8" wide	.28	1.22	1.50
4800	2-1/2" wide	.33	1.23	1.56
4900	3-5/8" wide	.40	1.26	1.66
5000	4" wide	.44	1.27	1.71
5100	6" wide	.55	1.28	1.83
5200				
5300	Galvanized 20 Ga., 2-1/2" wide	.48	1.55	2.03
5400	3-5/8" wide	.52	1.57	2.09
5500	4" wide	.63	1.59	2.22
5600	6" wide	.79	1.61	2.40

C10 Interior Construction

C1010 Partitions

C1010 170	Selective Price Sheet	COST PER S.F.		
		MAT.	INST.	TOTAL
5700	Load bearing, painted 18 Ga., 2-1/2" wide	.89	1.57	2.46
5800	3-5/8" wide	1.05	1.59	2.64
5900	4" wide	1.11	1.63	2.74
6000	6" wide	1.40	1.65	3.05
6100	Galvanized 18 Ga., 2-1/2" wide	.89	1.57	2.46
6200	3-5/8" wide	1.05	1.59	2.64
6300	4" wide	1.11	1.63	2.74
6400	6" wide	1.40	1.65	3.05
6500	Galvanized 16 Ga., 2-1/2" wide	1.05	1.78	2.83
6600	3-5/8" wide	1.26	1.83	3.09
6700	4" wide	1.32	1.86	3.18
6800	6" wide	1.65	1.89	3.54
6900				
7000				
7100	16" O.C., wood, 10' high wall, including			
7200	Double top plate and shoe			
7300	2" x 4"	.48	1.31	1.79
7400	2" x 6"	.58	1.18	1.76
7500				
7600				
7700	Furring, 16" O.C. 10' high wall, metal, 3/4" channels	.34	1.76	2.10
7800	1-1/2" channels	.46	1.96	2.42
7900	Wood, on wood, 1" x 2" strips	.20	.83	1.03
8000	1" x 3" strips	.32	.83	1.15
8100	On masonry, 1" x 2" strips	.22	.92	1.14
8200	1" x 3" strips	.35	.92	1.27
8300	On concrete, 1" x 2" strips	.22	1.74	1.96
8400	1" x 3" strips	.35	1.74	2.09

C10 Interior Construction

C1010 Partitions

C1010 180	Selective Price Sheet, Drywall & Plaster	COST PER S.F.		
		MAT.	INST.	TOTAL
0100	Lath, gypsum perforated			
0200				
0300	Lath, gypsum, perforated, regular, 3/8" thick	.33	.67	1
0400	1/2" thick	.30	.81	1.11
0500	Fire resistant, 3/8" thick	.30	.81	1.11
0600	1/2" thick	.33	.87	1.20
0700	Foil back, 3/8" thick	.40	.75	1.15
0800	1/2" thick	.43	.81	1.24
0900				
1000	Metal lath			
1100	Metal lath, diamond, painted, 2.5 lb.	.52	.67	1.19
1200	3.4 lb.	.52	.75	1.27
1300	Rib painted, 2.75 lb	.40	.75	1.15
1400	3.40 lb	.54	.81	1.35
1500				
1600				
1700	Plaster, gypsum, 2 coats	.41	2.89	3.30
1800	3 coats	.59	3.47	4.06
1900	Perlite/vermiculite, 2 coats	.46	3.30	3.76
2000	3 coats	.77	4.13	4.90
2100	Bondcrete, 1 coat	.44	1.52	1.96
2200				
2500				
2600				
2700	Drywall, standard, 3/8" thick, no finish included	.34	.60	.94
2800	1/2" thick, no finish included	.33	.60	.93
2900	Taped and finished	.38	1.25	1.63
3000	5/8" thick, no finish included	.35	.60	.95
3100	Taped and finished	.41	1.25	1.66
3200	Fire resistant, 1/2" thick, no finish included	.35	.60	.95
3300	Taped and finished	.41	1.25	1.66
3400	5/8" thick, no finish included	.37	.60	.97
3500	Taped and finished	.43	1.25	1.68
3600	Water resistant, 1/2" thick, no finish included	.42	.60	1.02
3700	Taped and finished	.47	1.25	1.72
3800	5/8" thick, no finish included	.50	.60	1.10
3900	Taped and finished	.55	1.25	1.80
4000	Finish, instead of taping			
4100	For thin coat plaster, add	.11	.75	.86
4200	Finish, textured spray, add	.04	.64	.68

C10 Interior Construction

C1010 Partitions

This page illustrates and describes a movable office partition system including demountable office partitions of various styles and sizes based on a cost per square foot basis. Prices for movable office partition systems are on Line Items C1010 210 0300 thru 3600.

C1010 210	Partitions, Movable Office	COST PER S.F.		
		MAT.	INST.	TOTAL
0250	Office partition, demountable, no deduction for door opening, add for doors			
0300	Air wall, cork finish, semi acoustic, 1-5/8" thick, minimum	41.50	3.71	45.21
0400	Maximum	46	6.35	52.35
0500	Acoustic, 2" thick, minimum	39.50	3.95	43.45
0600	Maximum	60	5.35	65.35
0700				
0800				
0900	In-plant modular office system, w/prehung steel door			
1000	3" thick honeycomb core panels			
1100	12' x 12', 2 wall	9.05	.51	9.56
1200	4 wall	24	1.52	25.52
1300				
1400				
1500	Gypsum, demountable, 3" to 3-3/4" thick x 9' high, vinyl clad	7.20	2.78	9.98
1600	Fabric clad	18	3.05	21.05
1700	1.75 system, vinyl clad hardboard, paper honeycomb core panel			
1800	1-3/4" to 2-1/2" thick x 9' high	12.10	2.78	14.88
1900	Unitized gypsum panel, 2" to 2-1/2" thick x 9' high, vinyl clad	15.55	2.78	18.33
2000	Fabric clad	25.50	3.05	28.55
2100				
2200				
2300	Unitized mineral fiber panel system, 2-1/4" thick x 9' high			
2400	Vinyl clad mineral fiber	15.45	2.78	18.23
2500	Fabric clad mineral fiber	23	3.05	26.05
2600				
2700	Movable steel walls, modular system			
2800	Unitized panels, 48" wide x 9' high			
2900	Baked enamel, pre-finished	17.55	2.22	19.77
3000	Fabric clad	25.50	2.39	27.89
3100	For acoustical partitions, add, minimum	2.54		2.54
3200	Maximum	11.85		11.85
3300				
3400				
3500	Note: For door prices, see Div. 08			
3600	For door hardware prices, see Div. 08			
3700				
3800				
3900				
4000				

C1020 Interior Doors

This page illustrates and describes flush interior door systems including hollow core door, jamb, header and trim with hardware. Lines within System Components give the unit price and total price on a cost each basis for this system. Prices for flush interior door systems are on Line items C1020 106 1000 thru 2400. Both material quantities and labor costs have been adjusted for the system listed.

Factors: To adjust for job conditions other than normal working situations use Lines C1020 106 2700 thru 3800.

Example: You are to install the system in an area where dust protection is vital. Go to Line C1020 106 3000 and apply these percentages to the appropriate MAT. and INST. costs.

System Components			COST EACH		
	QUANTITY	UNIT	MAT.	INST.	TOTAL
Single hollow core door, include jamb, header, trim and hardware, painted.					
Hollow core Lauan, 1-3/8" thick, 2'-0" x 6'-8", painted	1.000	Ea.	38.50	67	105.50
Paint door and frame, 1 coat	1.000	Ea.	2.17	30	32.17
Wood jamb, 4-9/16" deep	1.000	Set	109.60	51.52	161.12
Trim, casing	1.000	Set	53.44	77.12	130.56
Hardware, hinges	1.000	Set	24.50		24.50
Hardware, lockset	1.000	Set	33	37.50	70.50
TOTAL			261.21	263.14	524.35

C1020 106	Doors, Interior Flush, Wood	COST EACH		
		MAT.	INST.	TOTAL
1000	Lauan (Mahogany) hollow core, 1-3/8" x 2'-0" x 6'-8"	261	263	524
1100	2'-6" x 6'-8"	270	267	537
1200	2'-8" x 6'-8"	275	270	545
1300	3'-0" x 6'-8"	283	280	563
1500	Birch, hollow core, 1-3/8" x 2'-0" x 6'-8"	269	263	532
1600	2'-6" x 6'-8"	283	267	550
1700	2'-8" x 6'-8"	287	270	557
1800	3'-0" x 6'-8"	294	280	574
1900	Solid core, pre-hung, 1-3/8" x 2'-6" x 6'-8"	515	271	786
2000	2'-8" x 6'-8"	450	274	724
2100	3'-0" x 6'-8"	550	285	835
2200				
2400	For metal frame instead of wood, add	50%	20%	
2600				
2700	Cut & patch to match existing construction, add, minimum	2%	3%	
2800	Maximum	5%	9%	
2900	Dust protection, add, minimum	1%	2%	
3000	Maximum	4%	11%	
3100	Equipment usage curtailment, add, minimum	1%	1%	
3200	Maximum	3%	10%	
3300	Material handling & storage limitation, add, minimum	1%	1%	
3400	Maximum	6%	7%	
3500	Protection of existing work, add, minimum	2%	2%	
3600	Maximum	5%	7%	
3700	Shift work requirements, add, minimum		5%	
3800	Maximum		30%	
3900				

C1020 Interior Doors

This page illustrates and describes interior, solid and louvered door systems including a pine panel door, wood jambs, header, and trim with hardware. Lines within System Components give the unit price and total price on a cost each basis for this system. Prices for interior, solid and louvered systems are on Line Items C1020 108 1100 thru 2400. Both material quantities and labor costs have been adjusted for the system listed.

Factors: To adjust for job conditions other than normal working situations use Lines C1020 108 2900 thru 4000.

Example: You are to install the system during night hours only. Go to Line C1020 108 4000 and apply these percentages to the appropriate INST. costs.

System Components	QUANTITY	UNIT	COST EACH MAT.	COST EACH INST.	COST EACH TOTAL
Single interior door, including jamb, header, trim and hardware, painted.					
Solid pine panel door, 1-3/8" thick, 2'-0" x 6'-8"	1.000	Ea.	168	67	235
Paint door and frame, 1 coat	1.000	Ea.	2.17	30	32.17
Wooden jamb, 4-5/8" deep	1.000	Set	109.60	51.52	161.12
Trim, casing	1.000	Set	53.44	77.12	130.56
Hardware, hinges	1.000	Set	24.50		24.50
Hardware, lockset	1.000	Set	33	37.50	70.50
TOTAL			390.71	263.14	653.85

C1020 108	Doors, Interior Solid & Louvered		COST EACH MAT.	COST EACH INST.	COST EACH TOTAL
1000					
1100	Solid pine, painted raised panel, 1-3/8" x 2'-0" x 6'-8"		390	263	653
1200	2'-6" x 6'-8"		430	267	697
1300	2'-8" x 6'-8"		435	270	705
1400	3'-0" x 6'-8"		460	280	740
1500					
1600	Louvered pine, painted 1'-6" x 6'-8"		355	260	615
1700	2'-0" x 6'-8"		370	267	637
1800	2'-6" x 6'-8"		395	270	665
1900	3'-0" x 6'-8"		430	280	710
2200	For prehung door, deduct		5%	30%	
2300					
2400	For metal frame instead of wood, add		50%	20%	
2500					
2900	Cut & patch to match existing construction, add, minimum		2%	3%	
3000	Maximum		5%	9%	
3100	Dust protection, add, minimum		1%	2%	
3200	Maximum		4%	11%	
3300	Equipment usage curtailment, add, minimum		1%	1%	
3400	Maximum		3%	10%	
3500	Material handling & storage limitation, add, minimum		1%	1%	
3600	Maximum		6%	7%	
3700	Protection of existing work, add, minimum		2%	2%	
3800	Maximum		5%	7%	
3900	Shift work requirements, add, minimum			5%	
4000	Maximum			30%	

C1020 Interior Doors

This page illustrates and describes interior metal door systems including a metal door, metal frame and hardware. Lines within System Components give the unit price and total price on a cost each for this system. Prices for interior metal door systems are on Line Items C1020 110 1000 thru 2000. Both material quantities and labor costs have been adjusted for the system listed.

Factors: To adjust for job conditions other than normal working situations use Lines C1020 110 2900 thru 4000.

Example: You are to install the system while protecting existing construction. Go to Line C1020 110 3700 and apply these percentages to the appropriate MAT. and INST. costs.

System Components				COST EACH		
	QUANTITY	UNIT	MAT.	INST.	TOTAL
Single metal door, including frame and hardware.					
Hollow metal door, 1-3/8" thick, 2'-6" x 6'-8", painted	1.000	Ea.	545	80.50	625.50
Metal frame, 6-1/4" deep	1.000	Set	186	75.50	261.50
Paint door and frame, 1 coat	1.000	Ea.	2.17	30	32.17
Hardware, hinges	1.000	Set	94.50		94.50
Hardware, passage lockset	1.000	Set	33	37.50	70.50
TOTAL			860.67	223.50	1,084.17

C1020 110	Doors, Interior Flush, Metal	COST EACH		
		MAT.	INST.	TOTAL
1000	Hollow metal doors, 1-3/8" thick, 2'-6" x 6'-8"	860	224	1,084
1100	1-3/8" thick, 2'-8" x 6'-8"	865	224	1,089
1200	3'-0" x 7'-0"	850	234	1,084
1300				
1400	Interior fire door, 1-3/8" thick, 2'-6" x 6'-8"	1,075	224	1,299
1500	2'-8" x 6'-8"	1,075	224	1,299
1600	3'-0" x 7'-0"	1,050	234	1,284
1700				
1800	Add to fire doors:			
1900	Baked enamel finish	30%	15%	
2000	Galvanizing	20%		
2200				
2300				
2400				
2900	Cut & patch to match existing construction, add, minimum	2%	3%	
3000	Maximum	5%	9%	
3100	Dust protection, add, minimum	1%	2%	
3200	Maximum	4%	11%	
3300	Equipment usage curtailment, add, minimum	1%	1%	
3400	Maximum	3%	10%	
3500	Material handling & storage limitation, add, minimum	1%	1%	
3600	Maximum	6%	7%	
3700	Protection of existing work, add, minimum	2%	2%	
3800	Maximum	5%	7%	
3900	Shift work requirements, add, minimum		5%	
4000	Maximum		30%	

C1020 Interior Doors

This page illustrates and describes an interior closet door system including an interior closet door, painted, with trim and hardware. Prices for interior closet door systems are on Line Items C1020 112 0500 thru 2200. Both material quantities and labor costs have been adjusted for the system listed.

Factors: To adjust for job conditions other than normal working situations use Lines C1020 112 2900 thru 4000.

Example: You are to install the system and match the existing construction. Go to Line C1020 112 2900 and apply these percentages to the appropriate MAT. and INST. costs.

C1020 112	Doors, Closet	COST PER SET		
		MAT.	INST.	TOTAL
0350	Interior closet door painted, including frame, trim and hardware, prehung.			
0400	Bi-fold doors			
0500	Pine paneled, 3'-0" x 6'-8"	450	218	668
0600	6'-0" x 6'-8"	610	294	904
0700	Birch, hollow core, 3'-0" x 6'-8"	239	237	476
0800	6'-0" x 6'-8"	340	320	660
0900	Lauan, hollow core, 3'-0" x 6'-8"	223	218	441
1000	6'-0" x 6'-8"	315	294	609
1100	Louvered pine, 3'-0" x 6'-8"	370	218	588
1200	6'-0" x 6'-8"	490	294	784
1300				
1400	Sliding, bi-passing closet doors			
1500	Pine paneled, 4'-0" x 6'-8"	720	231	951
1600	6'-0" x 6'-8"	840	294	1,134
1700	Birch, hollow core, 4'-0" x 6'-8"	400	231	631
1800	6'-0" x 6'-8"	460	294	754
1900	Lauan, hollow core, 4'-0" x 6'-8"	345	231	576
2000	6'-0" x 6'-8"	400	294	694
2100	Louvered pine, 4'-0" x 6'-8"	605	231	836
2200	6'-0" x 6'-8"	755	294	1,049
2300				
2400				
2500				
2600				
2700				
2800				
2900	Cut & patch to match existing construction, add, minimum	2%	3%	
3000	Maximum	5%	9%	
3100	Dust protection, add, minimum	1%	2%	
3200	Maximum	4%	11%	
3300	Equipment usage curtailment, add, minimum	1%	1%	
3400	Maximum	3%	10%	
3500	Material handling & storage limitation, add, minimum	1%	1%	
3600	Maximum	6%	7%	
3700	Protection of existing work, add, minimum	2%	2%	
3800	Maximum	5%	7%	
3900	Shift work requirements, add, minimum		5%	
4000	Maximum		30%	

C2010 Stair Construction

This page illustrates and describes a stair system based on a cost per flight price. Prices for various stair systems are on Line Items C2010 130 0700 thru 3200. Both material quantities and labor costs have been adjusted for the system listed.

Factors: To adjust for job conditions other than normal working situations use Lines C2010 130 3500 thru 4200.

Example: You are to install the system during evenings only. Go to Line C2010 130 4200 and apply this percentage to the appropriate MAT. and INST. costs.

System Components	QUANTITY	UNIT	COST PER FLIGHT		
			MAT.	INST.	TOTAL
Below are various stair systems based on cost per flight of stairs, no side walls. Stairs are 4'-0" wide, railings are included unless otherwise noted.					

C2010 130	Stairs	COST PER FLIGHT		
		MAT.	INST.	TOTAL
0700	Concrete, cast in place, no nosings, no railings, 12 risers	286	2,075	2,361
0800	24 risers	570	4,125	4,695
0900	Add for 1 intermediate landing	155	570	725
1000	Concrete, cast in place, with nosings, no railings, 12 risers	1,175	2,275	3,450
1100	24 risers	2,325	4,550	6,875
1200	Add for 1 intermediate landing	228	590	818
1300	Steel, grating tread, safety nosing, 12 risers	4,750	1,200	5,950
1400	24 risers	9,500	2,400	11,900
1500	Add for intermediate landing	1,175	320	1,495
1600	Steel, cement fill pan tread, 12 risers	7,250	1,200	8,450
1700	24 risers	14,500	2,400	16,900
1800	Add for intermediate landing	1,175	320	1,495
1900	Spiral, industrial, 4' - 6" diameter, 12 risers	7,150	850	8,000
2000	24 risers	14,300	1,700	16,000
2100	Wood, box stairs, oak treads, 12 risers	2,325	680	3,005
2200	24 risers	4,650	1,350	6,000
2300	Add for 1 intermediate landing	205	154	359
2400	Wood, basement stairs, no risers, 12 steps	785	276	1,061
2500	24 steps	1,575	550	2,125
2600	Add for 1 intermediate landing	41	29.50	70.50
2700	Wood, open, rough sawn cedar, 12 steps	2,650	550	3,200
2800	24 steps	5,275	1,100	6,375
2900	Add for 1 intermediate landing	22	30.50	52.50
3000	Wood, residential, oak treads, 12 risers	2,300	3,025	5,325
3100	24 risers	4,625	6,050	10,675
3200	Add for 1 intermediate landing	185	140	325
3500	Dust protection, add, minimum	1%	2%	
3600	Maximum	4%	11%	
3700	Material handling & storage limitation, add, minimum	1%	1%	
3800	Maximum	6%	7%	
3900	Protection of existing work, add, minimum	2%	2%	
4000	Maximum	5%	7%	
4100	Shift work requirements, add, minimum		5%	
4200	Maximum		30%	

C3010 Wall Finishes

C3010 210	Selective Price Sheet	COST PER S.F.		
		MAT.	INST.	TOTAL
0100	Painting, on plaster or drywall, brushwork, primer and 1 ct.	.14	.75	.89
0200	Primer and 2 ct.	.21	1.19	1.40
0300	Rollerwork, primer and 1 ct.	.14	.63	.77
0400	Primer and 2 ct.	.21	1.01	1.22
0500	Woodwork incl. puttying, brushwork, primer and 1 ct.	.14	1.13	1.27
0600	Primer and 2 ct.	.21	1.49	1.70
0700	Wood trim to 6" wide, enamel, primer and 1 ct.	.15	.63	.78
0800	Primer and 2 ct.	.22	.81	1.03
0900	Cabinets and casework, enamel, primer and 1 ct.	.15	1.27	1.42
1000	Primer and 2 ct.	.22	1.56	1.78
1100	On masonry or concrete, latex, brushwork, primer and 1 ct.	.31	1.06	1.37
1200	Primer and 2 ct.	.41	1.52	1.93
1300	For block filler, add	.24	1.30	1.54
1400				
1500	Varnish, wood trim, sealer 1 ct., sanding, puttying, quality work	.14	2.29	2.43
1600	Medium work	.11	1.78	1.89
1700	Without sanding	.17	.27	.44
1800				
1900	Wall coverings, wall paper, at low price per double roll, avg workmanship	.47	.80	1.27
2000	At medium price per double roll, average workmanship	1.08	.95	2.03
2100	At high price per double roll, quality workmanship	2.13	1.17	3.30
2200				
2300	Grass cloths with lining paper, minimum	.73	1.28	2.01
2400	Maximum	2.93	1.46	4.39
2500	Vinyl, fabric backed, light weight	1.02	.80	1.82
2600	Medium weight	.99	1.06	2.05
2700	Heavy weight	1.63	1.17	2.80
2800				
2900	Cork tiles, 12" x 12", 3/16" thick	5.55	2.13	7.68
3000	5/16" thick	3.25	2.17	5.42
3100	Granular surface, 12" x 36", 1/2" thick	1.42	1.33	2.75
3200	1" thick	1.83	1.38	3.21
3300	Aluminum foil	1.14	1.86	3
3400				
3500	Tile, ceramic, adhesive set, 4-1/4" x 4-1/4"	2.48	4.99	7.47
3600	6" x 6"	3.43	5.40	8.83
3700	Decorated, 4-1/4" x 4-1/4", minimum	3.50	3.51	7.01
3800	Maximum	54.50	5.25	59.75
3900	For epoxy grout, add	.45	1.18	1.63
4000	Pregrouted sheets	5.55	3.95	9.50
4100	Glass mosaics, 3/4" tile on 12" sheets, minimum	18.10	13	31.10
4200	Color group 8	59.50	14.80	74.30
4300	Metal, tile pattern, 4' x 4' sheet, 24 ga., nailed			
4400	Stainless steel	30	2.35	32.35
4500	Aluminized steel	16.25	2.35	18.60
4600				
4700	Brick, interior veneer, 4" face brick, running bond, minimum	4.33	12.75	17.08
4800	Maximum	4.33	12.75	17.08
4900	Simulated, urethane pieces, set in mastic	9.05	4.02	13.07
5000	Fiberglass panels	8.85	3.01	11.86
5100	Wall coating, on drywall, thin coat, plain	.11	.75	.86
5200	Stipple	.11	.75	.86
5300	Textured spray	.04	.64	.68
5400				
5500	Paneling not incl. furring or trim, hardboard, tempered, 1/8" thick	.43	2.41	2.84
5600	1/4" thick	.69	2.41	3.10
5700	Plastic faced, 1/8" thick	.69	2.41	3.10
5800	1/4" thick	.95	2.41	3.36

C30 Interior Finishes

C3010 Wall Finishes

C3010 210	Selective Price Sheet	COST PER S.F.		
		MAT.	INST.	TOTAL
5900	Woodgrained, 1/4" thick, minimum	.73	2.41	3.14
6000	Maximum	1.49	2.84	4.33
6100	Plywood, 4' x 8' shts. 1/4" thick, prefin., birch faced, min.	.45	2.41	2.86
6200	Maximum	1.38	3.44	4.82
6300	Walnut, minimum	2.27	2.41	4.68
6400	Maximum	5.85	3.01	8.86
6500	Mahogany, African	3.19	3.01	6.20
6600	Philippine	.66	2.41	3.07
6700	Chestnut	5.35	3.22	8.57
6800	Pecan	2.31	3.01	5.32
6900	Rosewood	3.19	3.77	6.96
7000	Teak	3.19	3.01	6.20
7100	Aromatic cedar, plywood	2.33	3.01	5.34
7200	Particle board	1.13	3.01	4.14
7300	Wood board, 3/4" thick, knotty pine	2.10	4.02	6.12
7400	Rough sawn cedar	3.40	4.02	7.42
7500	Redwood, clear	5.45	4.02	9.47
7600	Aromatic cedar	2.22	4.38	6.60

C3020 Floor Finishes

C3020 430	Selective Price Sheet	COST PER S.F.		
		MAT.	INST.	TOTAL
0100	Flooring, carpet, acrylic, 26 oz. light traffic	3.66	.78	4.44
0200	35 oz. heavy traffic	6.85	.78	7.63
0300	Nylon anti-static, 15 oz. light traffic	2.39	1.03	3.42
0400	22 oz. medium traffic	4.83	.78	5.61
0500	26 oz. heavy traffic	6.35	.84	7.19
0600	28 oz. heavy traffic	6.90	.84	7.74
0700	Tile, foamed back, needle punch	4.75	.93	5.68
0800	Tufted loop	3.41	.93	4.34
0900	Wool, 36 oz. medium traffic	16	.84	16.84
1000	42 oz. heavy traffic	16.55	.84	17.39
1100	Composition, epoxy, with colored chips, minimum	3.03	4.54	7.57
1200	Maximum	4.37	6.25	10.62
1300	Trowelled, minimum	3.85	5.50	9.35
1400	Maximum	5.80	6.40	12.20
1500	Terrazzo, 1/4" thick, chemical resistant, minimum	6.50	6.40	12.90
1600	Maximum	9.90	8.55	18.45
1700	Resilient, asphalt tile, 1/8" thick	1.31	1.32	2.63
1800	Conductive flooring, rubber, 1/8" thick	7.25	1.68	8.93
1900	Cork tile 1/8" thick, standard finish	7.70	1.68	9.38
2000	Urethane finish	10.45	1.68	12.13
2100	PVC sheet goods for gyms, 1/4" thick	10.55	6.60	17.15
2200	3/8" thick	12.10	8.80	20.90
2300	Vinyl composition 12" x 12" tile, plain, 1/16" thick	.95	1.06	2.01
2400	1/8" thick	2.49	1.06	3.55
2500	Vinyl tile, 12" x 12" x 1/8" thick, minimum	5.50	1.06	6.56
2600	Maximum	14.30	1.06	15.36
2700	Vinyl sheet goods, backed, .093" thick	4.51	2.30	6.81
2900	Slate, random rectangular, 1/4" thick	23.50	7.15	30.65
3000	1/2" thick	22	10.20	32.20
3100	Natural cleft, irregular, 3/4" thick	10.05	11.65	21.70
3200	For sand rubbed finish, add	10.10		10.10
3300	Terrazzo, cast in place, bonded 1-3/4" thick, gray cement	3.61	17.10	20.71
3400	White cement	4.02	17.10	21.12
3500	Not bonded 3" thick, gray cement	4.49	18.30	22.79
3600	White cement	5.25	18.30	23.55
3700	Precast, 12" x 12" x 1" thick	21.50	17.90	39.40
3800	1-1/4" thick	22.50	17.90	40.40
3900	16" x 16" x 1-1/4" thick	24.50	21.50	46
4000	1-1/2" thick	22.50	24	46.50
4100	Marble travertine, standard, 12" x 12" x 3/4" thick	14.60	15.80	30.40
4200				
4300	Tile, ceramic, natural clay, thin set	4.56	5.20	9.76
4400	Porcelain, thin set	6.55	4.99	11.54
4500	Specialty, decorator finish	11.45	5.20	16.65
4600				
4700	Quarry, red, mud set, 4" x 4" x 1/2" thick	7.75	7.90	15.65
4800	6" x 6" x 1/2" thick	8.05	6.75	14.80
4900	Brown, imported, 6" x 6" x 3/4" thick	8.60	7.90	16.50
5000	8" x 8" x 1" thick	9.40	8.60	18
5100	Slate, Vermont, thin set, 6" x 6" x 1/4" thick	7.70	5.25	12.95
5200				
5300	Wood, maple strip, 25/32" x 2-1/4", finished, select	6.50	3.82	10.32
5400	2nd and better	4.89	3.82	8.71
5500	Oak, 25/32" x 2-1/4" finished, clear	3.45	3.82	7.27
5600	No. 1 common	4.70	3.82	8.52
5700	Parquet, standard, 5/16", finished, minimum	4.72	4.04	8.76
5800	Maximum	7.85	6.30	14.15
5900	Custom, finished, minimum	17.25	6.05	23.30

C30 Interior Finishes

C3020 Floor Finishes

C3020 430	Selective Price Sheet	COST PER S.F.		
		MAT.	INST.	TOTAL
6000	Maximum	23	12.05	35.05
6100	Prefinished, oak, 2-1/4" wide	5.15	3.55	8.70
6200	Ranch plank	7.85	4.16	12.01
6300	Sleepers on concrete, treated, 24" O.C., 1" x 2"	.23	.40	.63
6400	1" x 3"	.42	.51	.93
6500	2" x 4"	.51	.71	1.22
6600	2" x 6"	.81	.82	1.63
6700	Refinish old floors, minimum	.97	1.20	2.17
6800	Maximum	1.44	3.70	5.14
6900	Subflooring, plywood, CDX, 1/2" thick	.65	.80	1.45
7000	5/8" thick	.82	.89	1.71
7100	3/4" thick	.97	.96	1.93
7200				
7300	1" x 10" boards, S4S, laid regular	2.14	1.10	3.24
7400	Laid diagonal	2.14	1.34	3.48
7500	1" x 8" boards, S4S, laid regular	2.09	1.21	3.30
7600	Laid diagonal	2.09	1.42	3.51
7700	Underlayment, plywood, underlayment grade, 3/8" thick	1.02	.80	1.82
7800	1/2" thick	1.17	.83	2
7900	5/8" thick	1.30	.86	2.16
8000	3/4" thick	1.54	.93	2.47
8100	Particle board, 3/8" thick	.44	.80	1.24
8200	1/2" thick	.46	.83	1.29
8300	5/8" thick	.57	.86	1.43
8400	3/4" thick	.68	.93	1.61

C3030 Ceiling Finishes

This page illustrates suspended acoustical board systems including acoustic ceiling board, hangers, and T bar suspension. Lines within System Components give the unit price and total price per square foot for this system. Prices for suspended acoustical board systems are on Line Items C3030 210 1000 thru 2400. Both material quantities and labor costs have been adjusted for the system listed.

Factors: To adjust for job conditions other than normal working situations use Lines C3030 210 2900 thru 4000.

Example: You are to install the system and protect existing construction. Go to Line C3030 210 3800 and apply these percentages to the appropriate MAT. and INST. costs.

System Components	QUANTITY	UNIT	COST PER S.F.		
			MAT.	INST.	TOTAL
Suspended acoustical ceiling board installed on exposed grid system.					
Fiberglass boards, film faced, 2' x 4', 5/8" thick	1.000	S.F.	1.12	.96	2.08
Hangers, #12 wire	1.000	S.F.	.02	.58	.60
T bar suspension system, 2' x 4' grid	1.000	S.F.	.77	.75	1.52
TOTAL			1.91	2.29	4.20

C3030 210	Ceiling, Suspended Acoustical	COST PER S.F.		
		MAT.	INST.	TOTAL
1000	2' x 4' grid, fiberglass board, film faced, 5/8" thick	1.91	2.29	4.20
1100	Mineral fiber board, aluminum faced	4.02	2.26	6.28
1200	Standard faced	1.58	2.22	3.80
1300	Plastic faced	2	2.84	4.84
1400	Fiberglass, film faced, 3" thick, R11	2.88	2.67	5.55
1500	Grass cloth faced, 3/4" thick	3	2.54	5.54
1600	1" thick	3.80	2.57	6.37
1700	1-1/2" thick, nubby face	3.54	2.60	6.14
2200				
2300				
2400	Add for 2' x 2' grid system	.20	.19	.39
2500				
2600				
2700				
2900	Cut & patch to match existing construction, add, minimum	2%	3%	
3000	Maximum	5%	9%	
3100	Dust protection, add, minimum	1%	2%	
3200	Maximum	4%	11%	
3300	Equipment usage curtailment, add, minimum	1%	1%	
3400	Maximum	3%	10%	
3500	Material handling & storage limitation, add, minimum	1%	1%	
3600	Maximum	6%	7%	
3700	Protection of existing work, add, minimum	2%	2%	
3800	Maximum	5%	7%	
3900	Shift work requirements, add, minimum		5%	
4000	Maximum		30%	

C3030 Ceiling Finishes

This page illustrates and describes suspended gypsum board systems including gypsum board, metal furring, taping, finished and painted. Lines within System Components give the unit price and total price per square foot for this system. Prices for suspended gypsum board systems are on Line Items C3030 220 1400 thru 1700. Both material quantities and labor costs have been adjusted for the system listed.

Factors: To adjust for job conditions other than normal working situations use Lines C3030 220 2900 thru 4000.

Example: You are to install the system and control dust in the working area. Go to Line C3030 220 3200 and apply these percentages to the appropriate MAT. and INST. costs.

System Components	QUANTITY	UNIT	COST PER S.F.		
			MAT.	INST.	TOTAL
Suspended ceiling gypsum board, 4′ x 8′ x 5/8″ thick, on metal furring, taped, finished and painted.					
Gypsum drywall, 4′ x 8′, 5/8″ thick, screwed	1.000	S.F.	.35	.67	1.02
Main runners, 1-1/2″ C.R.C., 4′ O.C.	.500	S.F.	.15	.66	.81
25 ga., channels, 2′ O.C.	1.000	S.F.	.22	1.21	1.43
Taped and finished	1.000	S.F.	.05	.60	.65
Paint, 2 coats, roller work	1.000	S.F.	.21	.67	.88
TOTAL			.98	3.81	4.79

C3030 220	Ceilings, Suspended Gypsum Board	COST PER S.F.		
		MAT.	INST.	TOTAL
1400	4′ x 8′ x 5/8″, gypsum drywall, 2 coats paint	.98	3.81	4.79
1500	Thin coat plaster, 2 coats paint	.83	3.29	4.12
1600	Spray-on sand finish, no paint	.76	3.18	3.94
1700	12″ x 12″ x 3/4″ acoustical wood fiber tile	2.03	4.05	6.08
1800				
1900				
2000				
2100				
2200				
2300				
2400				
2500				
2600				
2700				
2900	Cut & patch to match existing construction, add, minimum	2%	3%	
3000	Maximum	5%	9%	
3100	Dust protection, add, minimum	1%	2%	
3200	Maximum	4%	11%	
3300	Equipment usage curtailment, add, minimum	1%	1%	
3400	Maximum	3%	10%	
3500	Material handling & storage limitation, add, minimum	1%	1%	
3600	Maximum	6%	7%	
3700	Protection of existing work, add, minimum	2%	2%	
3800	Maximum	5%	7%	
3900	Shift work requirements, add, minimum		5%	
4000	Maximum		30%	

C3030 Ceiling Finishes

This page illustrates and describes suspended plaster and lath systems including gypsum plaster, lath, furring and runners with ceiling painted. Lines within System Components give the unit price and total price per square foot for this system. Prices for suspended plaster and lath systems are on Line Items C3030 230 1200 thru 2300. Both material quantities and labor costs have been adjusted for the system listed.

Factors: To adjust for job conditions other than normal working situations use Lines C3030 230 2900 thru 4000.

Example: You are to install the system to match existing construction. Go to Line C3030 230 2900 and apply these percentages to the appropriate MAT. and INST. costs.

System Components	QUANTITY	UNIT	COST PER S.F.		
			MAT.	INST.	TOTAL
Gypsum plaster, 3 coats, on 3.4# rib lath, on 3/4″ C.R.C. furring on 1-1/2″ main runners, ceiling painted.					
Gypsum plaster, 3 coats	.110	S.Y.	.58	3.85	4.43
3.4# rib lath	.110	S.Y.	.53	.80	1.33
Main runners, 1-1/2″ C.R.C. 24″ O.C.	.333	S.F.	.30	1.31	1.61
Furring 3/4″ C.R.C. 16″ O.C.	1.000	S.F.	.34	1.76	2.10
Painting, 2 coats, roller work	1.000	S.F.	.21	.67	.88
TOTAL			1.96	8.39	10.35

C3030 230	Ceiling, Suspended Plaster	COST PER S.F.		
		MAT.	INST.	TOTAL
1200	Gypsum plaster, 3 coats, on 3.4# rib lath	1.96	8.35	10.31
1300	On 2.5# diamond lath	1.94	8.30	10.24
1400	On 3/8″ gypsum lath	1.76	8.30	10.06
1500	2 coats, on 3.4# rib lath	1.72	8.35	10.07
1600	On 2.5# diamond lath	1.77	7.75	9.52
1700	On 3/8″ gypsum lath	1.59	7.75	9.34
1800	Perlite plaster, 3 coats, on 3.4# rib lath	2.14	9.35	11.49
1900	On 2.5# diamond lath	2.12	9.30	11.42
2000	On 3/8″ gypsum lath	1.94	9.30	11.24
2100	2 coats, on 3.4# rib lath	1.84	8.30	10.14
2200	On 2.5# diamond lath	1.82	8.25	10.07
2300	On 3/8″ gypsum lath	1.64	8.25	9.89
2400				
2500				
2600				
2700				
2900	Cut & patch to match existing construction, add, minimum	2%	3%	
3000	Maximum	5%	9%	
3100	Dust protection, add, minimum	1%	2%	
3200	Maximum	4%	11%	
3300	Equipment usage curtailment, add, minimum	1%	1%	
3400	Maximum	3%	10%	
3500	Material handling & storage limitation, add, minimum	1%	1%	
3600	Maximum	6%	7%	
3700	Protection of existing work, add, minimum	2%	2%	
3800	Maximum	5%	7%	
3900	Shift work requirements, add, minimum		5%	
4000	Maximum		30%	

C3030 Ceiling Finishes

C3030 250	Selective Price Sheet	COST PER S.F.		
		MAT.	INST.	TOTAL
0100	Ceiling, plaster, gypsum, 2 coats	.41	3.30	3.71
0200	3 coats	.59	3.89	4.48
0300	Perlite or vermiculite, 2 coats	.46	3.83	4.29
0400	3 coats	.77	4.83	5.60
0500	Gypsum lath, plain, 3/8″ thick	.33	.67	1
0600	1/2″ thick	.30	.71	1.01
0700	Firestop, 3/8″ thick	.30	.81	1.11
0800	1/2″ thick	.33	.87	1.20
0900	Metal lath, rib, 2.75 lb.	.40	.75	1.15
1000	3.40 lb.	.54	.81	1.35
1100	Diamond, 2.50 lb.	.52	.75	1.27
1200	3.40 lb.	.52	.94	1.46
1500	Drywall, standard, 1/2″ thick, no finish included	.33	.67	1
1600	Taped and finished	.38	1.58	1.96
1700	5/8″ thick, no finish included	.35	.67	1.02
1800	Taped and finished	.41	1.58	1.99
1900	Fire resistant, 1/2″ thick, no finish included	.35	.67	1.02
2000	Taped and finished	.41	1.58	1.99
2100	5/8″ thick, no finish included	.37	.67	1.04
2200	Taped and finished	.43	1.58	2.01
2300	Water resistant, 1/2″ thick, no finish included	.42	.67	1.09
2400	Taped and finished	.47	1.58	2.05
2500	5/8″ thick, no finish included	.50	.67	1.17
2600	Taped and finished	.55	1.58	2.13
2700	Finish, instead of taping			
2800	For thin coat plaster, add	.11	.75	.86
2900	Finish, textured spray, add	.04	.64	.68
3000				
3100				
3200				
3300	Tile, stapled or glued, mineral fiber plastic coated, 5/8″ thick	2.06	2.01	4.07
3400	3/4″ thick	1.96	2.01	3.97
3500	Wood fiber, 1/2″ thick	1.20	1.51	2.71
3600	3/4″ thick	1.31	1.51	2.82
3700	Suspended, fiberglass, film faced, 5/8″ thick	1.12	.96	2.08
3800	3″ thick	2.09	1.34	3.43
3900	Mineral fiber, 5/8″ thick, standard	.79	.89	1.68
4000	Aluminum	3.21	1	4.21
4100	Wood fiber, reveal edge, 1″ thick			
4200	3″ thick			
4300	Framing, metal furring, 3/4″ channels, 12″ O.C.	.37	2.43	2.80
4400	16″ O.C.	.34	1.76	2.10
4500	24″ O.C.	.22	1.21	1.43
4600				
4700	1-1/2″ channels, 12″ O.C.	.51	2.68	3.19
4800	16″ O.C.	.46	1.96	2.42
4900	24″ O.C.	.30	1.31	1.61
5000				
5100				
5200				
5300	Ceiling suspension systems, for tile,			
5400	Concealed ″Z″ bar, 12″ module	.86	1.16	2.02
5500	Class A, ″T″ bar 2′-0″ x 4′-0″ grid	.77	.75	1.52
5600	2′-0″ x 2′-0″ grid	1	.93	1.93
5700	Carrier channels for lighting fixtures, add	.22	1.31	1.53
5800				
5900				
6000				

C30 Interior Finishes

C3030 Ceiling Finishes

C3030 250	Selective Price Sheet	COST PER S.F.		
		MAT.	INST.	TOTAL
6100	Wood, furring 1" x 3", on wood, 12" O.C.	.42	1.72	2.14
6200	16" O.C..	.32	1.29	1.61
6300	24" O.C.	.21	.86	1.07
6400				
6500	On concrete, 12" O.C.	.46	2.87	3.33
6600	16" O.C.	.35	2.15	2.50
6700	24" O.C.	.23	1.44	1.67
6800				
6900	Joists, 2" x 4", 12" O.C.	.54	1.24	1.78
7000	16" O.C.	.45	1.04	1.49
7100	24" O.C.	.37	.84	1.21
7200	32" O.C.	.28	.64	.92
7300	2" x 6", 12" O.C.	.82	1.25	2.07
7400	16" O.C.	.68	1.04	1.72
7500	24" O.C.	.54	.83	1.37
7600	32" O.C.	.40	.61	1.01

This page illustrates and describes oil hydraulic elevator systems. Prices for various oil hydraulic elevator systems are on Line Items D1010 130 0400 thru 2000. Both material quantities and labor costs have been adjusted for the system listed.

Factors: To adjust for job conditions other than normal working situations use Lines D1010 130 3100 thru 4000.

Example: You are to install the system with limited equipment usage. Go to Line D1010 130 3400 and apply this percentage to the appropriate TOTAL costs.

D1010 130	Oil Hydraulic Elevators	COST EACH		
		MAT.	INST.	TOTAL
0310	Oil-hydraulic elevator systems			
0320	Including piston and piston shaft			
0330				
0400	1500 Lb. passenger, 2 floors	42,500	18,300	60,800
0500	3 floors	54,500	28,300	82,800
0600	4 floors	85,000	39,800	124,800
0700	5 floors	96,500	49,600	146,100
0800	6 floors	107,000	59,000	166,000
0900				
1000	2500 Lb. passenger, 2 floors	45,500	18,300	63,800
1100	3 floors	57,500	28,300	85,800
1200	4 floors	84,000	39,800	123,800
1300	5 floors	95,000	49,600	144,600
1400	6 floors	110,000	59,000	169,000
1500				
1600	4000 Lb. passenger, 2 floors	51,000	18,300	69,300
1700	3 floors	65,000	28,300	93,300
1800	4 floors	94,000	39,800	133,800
1900	5 floors	105,000	49,600	154,600
2000	6 floors	115,500	59,000	174,500
2100				
2200				
2300				
2400				
2500				
2600				
2700				
2800				
2900				
3000				
3100	Dust protection, add, minimum	1%	2%	
3200	Maximum	4%	11%	
3300	Equipment usage curtailment, add, minimum	1%	1%	
3400	Maximum	3%	10%	
3500	Material handling & storage limitation, add, minimum	1%	1%	
3600	Maximum	6%	7%	
3700	Protection of existing work, add, minimum	2%	2%	
3800	Maximum	5%	7%	
3900	Shift work requirements, add, minimum		5%	
4000	Maximum		30%	

D2010 Plumbing Fixtures

This page illustrates and describes a women's public restroom system including a water closet, lavatory, accessories, and service piping. Lines within System Components give the unit price and total price on a cost each basis for this system. Prices for women's public restroom systems are on Line Items D2010 956 1300 thru 1700. Both material quantities and labor costs have been adjusted for the system listed.

Factors: To adjust for job conditions other than normal working situations use Lines D2010 956 2900 thru 4000.

Example: You are to install the system and protect surrounding area from dust. Go to Line D2010 956 3100 and apply these percentages to the MAT. and INST. costs.

System Components	QUANTITY	UNIT	COST EACH MAT.	COST EACH INST.	COST EACH TOTAL
Public women's restroom incl. water closet, lavatory, accessories and necessary service piping to install this system in one wall.					
Water closet, wall mounted, one piece	1.000	Ea.	830	223	1,053
Rough-in waste and vent for water closet	1.000	Set	980	505	1,485
Lavatory, 20" x 18" P.E. cast iron with accessories	1.000	Ea.	305	162	467
Rough-in waste and vent for lavatory	1.000	Set	520	780	1,300
Toilet partition, painted metal between walls, floor mounted	1.000	Ea.	415	201	616
For handicap unit, add	1.000	Ea.	410		410
Grab bar, 36" long	1.000	Ea.	85	60	145
Mirror, 18" x 24", with stainless steel shelf	1.000	Ea.	205	30	235
Napkin/tampon dispenser, recessed	1.000	Ea.	575	40	615
Soap Dispenser, chrome, surface mounted, liquid	1.000	Ea.	51	30	81
Toilet tissue dispenser, surface mounted, stainless steel	1.000	Ea.	19.60	20	39.60
Towel dispenser, surface mounted, stainless steel	1.000	Ea.	49	37.50	86.50
TOTAL			4,444.60	2,088.50	6,533.10

D2010 956	Plumbing - Public Restroom	COST EACH MAT.	COST EACH INST.	COST EACH TOTAL
1200				
1300	Public women's restroom, one water closet, one lavatory	4,450	2,100	6,550
1400	Two water closets, two lavatories	8,225	3,975	12,200
1500				
1600	For each additional water closet over 2, add	2,475	920	3,395
1700	For each additional lavatory over 2, add	1,075	1,000	2,075
1800				
1900				
2400	NOTE: PLUMBING APPROXIMATIONS			
2500	WATER CONTROL: water meter, backflow preventer,			
2600	Shock absorbers, vacuum breakers, mixer....10 to 15% of fixtures			
2700	PIPE AND FITTINGS: .... 30 to 60% of fixtures			
2800				
2900	Cut & patch to match existing construction, add, minimum	2%	3%	
3000	Maximum	5%	9%	
3100	Dust protection, add, minimum	1%	2%	
3200	Maximum	4%	11%	
3300	Equipment usage curtailment, add, minimum	1%	1%	
3400	Maximum	3%	10%	
3500	Material handling & storage limitation, add, minimum	1%	1%	

D20 Plumbing

D2010 Plumbing Fixtures

D2010 956	Plumbing - Public Restroom	COST EACH		
		MAT.	INST.	TOTAL
3600	Maximum	6%	7%	
3700	Protection of existing work, add, minimum	2%	2%	
3800	Maximum	5%	7%	
3900	Shift work requirements, add, minimum		5%	
4000	Maximum		30%	

D2010 Plumbing Fixtures

This page illustrates and describes a men's public restroom system including a water closet, urinal, lavatory, accessories and service piping. Lines within System Components give the unit price and total price on a cost each basis for this system. Prices for men's public restroom systems are on Line Items D2010 957 1700 thru 2200. Both material quantities and labor costs have been adjusted for the system listed.

Factors: To adjust for job conditions other than normal working situations use Lines D2010 957 2900 thru 4000.

Example: You are to install the system and match existing construction. Go to Line D2010 957 3000 and apply these percentages to the appropriate MAT. and INST. costs.

System Components	QUANTITY	UNIT	COST EACH		
			MAT.	INST.	TOTAL
Public men's restroom incl. water closet, urinal, lavatory, accessories,					
and necessary service piping to install this system in one wall.					
Water closet, wall mounted, one piece	1.000	Ea.	830	223	1,053
Rough-in waste & vent for water closet	1.000	Set	980	505	1,485
Urinal, wall hung	1.000	Ea.	350	430	780
Rough-in waste & vent for urinal	1.000	Set	630	455	1,085
Lavatory, 20" x 18", P.E. cast iron with accessories	1.000	Ea.	305	162	467
Rough-in waste & vent for lavatory	1.000	Set	520	780	1,300
Partition, painted mtl., between walls, floor mntd.	1.000	Ea.	415	201	616
For handicap unit, add	1.000	Ea.	410		410
Grab bars	1.000	Ea.	85	60	145
Urinal screen, powder coated steel, wall mounted	1.000	Ea.	168	121	289
Mirror, 18" x 24" with stainless steel shelf	1.000	Ea.	205	30	235
Soap dispenser, surface mounted, liquid	1.000	Ea.	51	30	81
Toilet tissue dispenser, surface mounted, stainless steel	1.000	Ea.	19.60	20	39.60
Towel dispenser, surface mounted, stainless steel	1.000	Ea.	49	37.50	86.50
TOTAL			5,017.60	3,054.50	8,072.10

D2010 957	Plumbing - Public Restroom	COST EACH		
		MAT.	INST.	TOTAL
1600				
1700	Public men's restroom, one water closet, one urinal, one lavatory	5,025	3,050	8,075
1800	Two water closets, two urinals, two lavatories	9,950	5,950	15,900
1900				
2000	For each additional water closet over 2, add	2,475	920	3,395
2100	For each additional urinal over 2, add	1,150	1,000	2,150
2200	For each additional lavatory over 2, add	1,075	1,000	2,075
2300				
2400	NOTE: PLUMBING APPROXIMATIONS			
2500	WATER CONTROL: water meter, backflow preventer,			
2600	Shock absorbers, vacuum breakers, mixer....10 to 15% of fixtures			
2700	PIPE AND FITTINGS: .... 30 to 60% of fixtures			
2800				
2900	Cut & patch to match existing construction, add, minimum	2%	3%	
3000	Maximum	5%	9%	
3100	Dust protection, add, minimum	1%	2%	
3200	Maximum	4%	11%	
3300	Equipment usage curtailment, add, minimum	1%	1%	

D2010 Plumbing Fixtures

D2010 957	Plumbing - Public Restroom	COST EACH		
		MAT.	INST.	TOTAL
3400	Maximum	3%	10%	
3500	Material handling, & storage limitation, add, minimum	1%	1%	
3600	Maximum	6%	7%	
3700	Protection of existing work, add, minimum	2%	2%	
3800	Maximum	5%	7%	
3900	Shift work requirements, add, minimum		5%	
4000	Maximum		30%	

D2010 Plumbing Fixtures

This page illustrates and describes a two fixture lavatory system including a water closet, lavatory, accessories and all service piping. Lines within System Components give the unit price and total price on a cost each basis for this system. Prices for two fixture lavatory systems are on Line Items D2010 958 1800 and 1900. Both material quantities and labor costs have been adjusted for the system listed.

Factors: To adjust for job conditions other than normal working situations use Lines D2010 958 2900 thru 4000.

Example: You are to install the system while controlling dust in the work area. Go to Line D2010 958 3200 and apply these percentages to the appropriate MAT. and INST. costs.

System Components	QUANTITY	UNIT	COST EACH		
			MAT.	INST.	TOTAL
Two fixture bathroom incl. water closet, lavatory, accessories and necessary service piping to install this system in 2 walls.					
Water closet, floor mounted, 2 piece, close coupled	1.000	Ea.	256	244	500
Rough in waste & vent for water closet	1.000	Set	365	425	790
Lavatory, 20" x 18", P.E. cast iron with accessories	1.000	Ea.	305	162	467
Rough in waste & vent for lavatory	1.000	Set	520	780	1,300
Additional service piping					
1/2" copper pipe with sweat solder joints	10.000	L.F.	37.10	88.50	125.60
2" black schedule 40 steel pipe with threaded couplings	12.000	L.F.	118.20	240	358.20
4" cast iron soil pipe with lead and oakum joints	7.000	L.F.	129.85	164.50	294.35
Accessories					
Toilet tissue dispenser, chrome, single roll	1.000	Ea.	19.60	20	39.60
18" long stainless steel towel bar	1.000	Ea.	46	26	72
Medicine cabinet with mirror, 20" x 16", unlighted	1.000	Ea.	105	43	148
TOTAL			1,901.75	2,193	4,094.75

D2010 958	Plumbing - Two Fixture Bathroom	COST EACH		
		MAT.	INST.	TOTAL
1800	Water closet, lavatory & accessories, in 2 walls with all service piping	1,900	2,200	4,100
1900	Above system installed in 1 wall	1,775	1,900	3,675
2000				
2400	NOTE: PLUMBING APPROXIMATIONS			
2500	WATER CONTROL: water meter, backflow preventer,			
2600	Shock absorbers, vacuum breakers, mixer....10 to 15% of fixtures			
2700	PIPE AND FITTINGS: .... 30 to 60% of fixtures			
2800				
2900	Cut & patch to match existing construction, add, minimum	2%	3%	
3000	Maximum	5%	9%	
3100	Dust protection, add, minimum	1%	2%	
3200	Maximum	4%	11%	
3300	Equipment usage curtailment, add, minimum	1%	1%	
3400	Maximum	3%	10%	
3500	Material handling & storage limitation, add, minimum	1%	1%	
3600	Maximum	6%	7%	
3700	Protection of existing work, add, minimum	2%	2%	
3800	Maximum	5%	7%	
3900	Shift work requirements, add, minimum		5%	
4000	Maximum		30%	

D20 Plumbing

D2010 Plumbing Fixtures

This page illustrates and describes a three fixture bathroom system including a water closet, tub, lavatory, accessories and service piping. Lines within System Components give the unit price and total price on a cost each basis for this system. Prices for a three fixture bathroom system is on Line Item D2010 959 1700. Both material quantities and labor costs have been adjusted for the system listed.

Factors: To adjust for job conditions other than normal working situations use Lines D2010 959 2900 thru 4000.

Example: You are to install the system and protect all existing work. Go to Line D2010 959 3800 and apply these percentages to the appropriate MAT. and INST. costs.

System Components	QUANTITY	UNIT	COST EACH		
			MAT.	INST.	TOTAL
Three fixture bathroom incl. water closet, bathtub, lavatory, accessories, and necessary service piping to install this system in 1 wall.					
Two piece, close coupled	1.000	Ea.	256	244	500
For rough-in, supply, waste and vent	.930	Set	339.45	395.25	734.70
Bath tub, P.E. cast iron, 5' long, with accessories	1.000	Ea.	1,225	294	1,519
Rough-in, supply, waste and vent, for all above tubs, add	.950	Set	508.25	593.75	1,102
Lavatory, 20" x 18" P.E. cast iron with accessories	1.000	Ea.	305	162	467
Rough-in, supply, waste and vent for above lavatories	1.000	Set	520	780	1,300
Accessories					
Toilet tissue dispenser, surface mounted, SS, single roll	1.000	Ea.	19.60	20	39.60
Towel bar, stainless steel, 18" long	2.000	Ea.	92	52	144
Medicine cabinets with mirror, sst. frame, 16" x 22", unlighted	1.000	Ea.	105	43	148
TOTAL			3,370.30	2,584	5,954.30

D2010 959	Plumbing - Three Fixture Bathroom	COST EACH		
		MAT.	INST.	TOTAL
1600				
1700	Water closet, lavatory, bathtub, in 1 wall with all service piping	3,375	2,575	5,950
2400	NOTE: PLUMBING APPROXIMATIONS			
2500	WATER CONTROL: water meter, backflow preventer,			
2600	Shock absorbers, vacuum breakers, mixer....10 to 15% of fixtures			
2700	PIPE AND FITTINGS: .... 30 to 60% of fixtures			
2800				
2900	Cut & patch to match existing construction, add, minimum	2%	3%	
3000	Maximum	5%	9%	
3100	Dust protection, add, minimum	1%	2%	
3200	Maximum	4%	11%	
3300	Equipment usage curtailment, add, minimum	1%	1%	
3400	Maximum	3%	10%	
3500	Material handling & storage limitation, add, minimum	1%	1%	
3600	Maximum	6%	7%	
3700	Protection of existing work, add, minimum	2%	2%	
3800	Maximum	5%	7%	
3900	Shift work requirements, add, minimum		5%	
4000	Maximum		30%	

640

D2010 Plumbing Fixtures

This page illustrates and describes a three fixture bathroom system including a water closet, tub, lavatory, accessories, and service piping. Lines within System Components give the unit price and total price on a cost each basis for this system. Prices for a three fixture bathroom system are on Line Item D2010 960 1900 thru 2000. Both material quantities and labor costs have been adjusted for the system listed.

Factors: To adjust for job conditions other than normal working situations use Lines D2010 960 2900 thru 4000.

Example: You are to install the system and protect the surrounding area from dust. Go to Line D2010 960 3100 and apply these percentages to the appropriate MAT. and INST. costs.

System Components	QUANTITY	UNIT	COST EACH		
			MAT.	INST.	TOTAL
Three fixture bathroom incl. water closet, bathtub, lavatory, accessories, and necessary service piping to install this system in 2 walls.					
Water closet, floor mounted, 2 piece, close coupled	1.000	Ea.	256	244	500
Rough-in waste & vent for water closet	1.000	Set	365	425	790
Bathtub, P.E. cast iron, 5' long with accessories	1.000	Ea.	1,225	294	1,519
Rough-in waste & vent for bathtub	1.000	Set	535	625	1,160
Lavatory, 20" x 18" P.E. cast iron with accessories	1.000	Ea.	305	162	467
Rough-in waste & vent for lavatory	1.000	Set	520	780	1,300
Additional service piping					
1-1/4" copper DWV type tubing, sweat solder joints	6.000	L.F.	65.40	71.70	137.10
2" black schedule 40 steel pipe with threaded couplings	12.000	L.F.	118.20	240	358.20
Accessories					
Toilet tissue dispenser, chrome, single roll	1.000	Ea.	19.60	20	39.60
18" long stainless steel towel bar	2.000	Ea.	92	52	144
Medicine cabinet with mirror, 20" x 16", unlighted	1.000	Ea.	105	43	148
TOTAL			3,606.20	2,956.70	6,562.90

D2010 960	Plumbing - Three Fixture Bathroom	COST EACH		
		MAT.	INST.	TOTAL
1900	Water closet, lavatory, bathtub, in 2 walls with all service piping	3,600	2,950	6,550
2000	Above system with corner contour tub, P.E. cast iron	5,275	2,950	8,225
2300				
2400	NOTE: PLUMBING APPROXIMATIONS			
2500	WATER CONTROL: water meter, backflow preventer,			
2600	Shock absorbers, vacuum breakers, mixer....10 to 15% of fixtures			
2700	PIPE AND FITTINGS: .... 30 to 60% of fixtures			
2800				
2900	Cut & patch to match existing construction, add, minimum	2%	3%	
3000	Maximum	5%	9%	
3100	Dust protection, add, minimum	1%	2%	
3200	Maximum	4%	11%	
3300	Equipment usage curtailment, add, minimum	1%	1%	
3400	Maximum	3%	10%	
3500	Material handling & storage limitation, add, minimum	1%	1%	
3600	Maximum	6%	7%	
3700	Protection of existing work, add, minimum	2%	2%	
3800	Maximum	5%	7%	
3900	Shift work requirements, add, minimum		5%	
4000	Maximum		30%	

D20 Plumbing

D2010 Plumbing Fixtures

This page illustrates and describes a three fixture bathroom system including a water closet, shower, lavatory, accessories, and service piping, Lines within System Components give the unit price and total price on a cost each basis for this system. Prices for three fixture bathroom systems are on Line Items D2010 961 2100 thru 2200. Both material quantities and labor costs have been adjusted for the system listed.

Factors: To adjust for job conditions other than normal working situations use Lines D2010 961 2900 thru 4000.

Example: You are to install the system and protect existing construction. Go to Line D2010 961 3700 and apply these percentages to the appropriate MAT. and INST. costs.

System Components	QUANTITY	UNIT	COST EACH MAT.	COST EACH INST.	COST EACH TOTAL
Three fixture bathroom incl. water closet, shower, lavatory, accessories, and necessary service piping to install this system in 2 walls.					
Water closet, floor mounted, 2 piece, close coupled	1.000	Ea.	256	244	500
Rough-in waste & vent for water closet	1.000	Set	365	425	790
32" shower, enameled stall, molded stone receptor	1.000	Ea.	1,275	259	1,534
Rough-in waste & vent for shower	1.000	Set	590	630	1,220
Lavatory, 20" x 18" P.E. cast iron with accessories	1.000	Ea.	305	162	467
Rough-in waste & vent for lavatory	1.000	Set	520	780	1,300
Additional service piping					
1-1/4" Copper DWV type tubing, sweat solder joints	4.000	L.F.	43.60	47.80	91.40
2" black schedule 40 steel pipe with threaded couplings	6.000	L.F.	59.10	120	179.10
4" cast iron soil with lead and oakum joints	7.000	L.F.	129.85	164.50	294.35
Accessories					
Toilet tissue dispenser, chrome, single roll	1.000	Ea.	19.60	20	39.60
18" long stainless steel towel bar	2.000	Ea.	92	52	144
Medicine cabinet with mirror, 20" x 16", unlighted	1.000	Ea.	105	43	148
TOTAL			3,760.15	2,947.30	6,707.45

D2010 961	Plumbing - Three Fixture Bathroom	COST EACH MAT.	COST EACH INST.	COST EACH TOTAL
2100	Water closet, 32" shower, lavavatory, in 2 walls with all service piping	3,750	2,950	6,700
2200	Above system with 36" corner angle shower	4,375	2,950	7,325
2300				
2400	NOTE: PLUMBING APPROXIMATIONS			
2500	WATER CONTROL: water meter, backflow preventer,			
2600	Shock absorbers, vacuum breakers, mixer....10 to 15% of fixtures			
2700	PIPE AND FITTINGS: .... 30 to 60% of fixtures			
2800				
2900	Cut & patch to match existing construction, add, minimum	2%	3%	
3000	Maximum	5%	9%	
3100	Dust protection, add, minimum	1%	2%	
3200	Maximum	4%	11%	
3300	Equipment usage curtailment, add, minimum	1%	1%	
3400	Maximum	3%	10%	
3500	Material handling & storage limitation, add, minimum	1%	1%	
3600	Maximum	6%	7%	
3700	Protection of existing work, add, minimum	2%	2%	
3800	Maximum	5%	7%	
3900	Shift work requirements, add, minimum		5%	
4000	Maximum		30%	

D20 Plumbing

D2010 Plumbing Fixtures

This page illustrates and describes a four fixture bathroom system including a water closet, shower, bathtub, lavatory, accessories, and service piping. Lines within System Components give the unit price and total price on a cost each basis for this system. Prices for four fixture bathroom systems are on Line Items D2010 962 1800 thru 1900. Both material quantities and labor costs have been adjusted for the system listed.

Factors: To adjust for job conditions other than normal working situations use Lines D2010 962 2900 thru 4000.

Example: You are to install the system during weekends and evenings. Go to Line D2010 962 4000 and apply these percentages to the appropriate MAT. and INST. costs.

System Components	QUANTITY	UNIT	COST EACH MAT.	COST EACH INST.	COST EACH TOTAL
Four fixture bathroom incl. water closet, shower, bathtub, lavatory accessories and necessary service piping to install this system in 2 walls.					
Water closet, floor mounted, 2 piece, close coupled	1.000	Ea.	256	244	500
Rough-in waste & vent for water closet	1.000	Set	365	425	790
32" shower, enameled steel stall, molded stone receptor	1.000	Ea.	1,275	259	1,534
Rough-in waste & vent for shower	1.000	Set	590	630	1,220
Bathtub, P.E. cast iron, 5' long with accessories	1.000	Ea.	1,225	294	1,519
Rough-in waste & vent for bathtub	1.000	Set	535	625	1,160
Lavatory, 20" x 18" P.E. cast iron with accessories	1.000	Ea.	305	162	467
Rough-in waste & vent for lavatory	1.000	Set	520	780	1,300
Accessories					
Toilet tissue dispenser, chrome, single roll	1.000	Ea.	19.60	20	39.60
18" long stainless steel towel bar	2.000	Ea.	92	52	144
Medicine cabinet with mirror, 20" x 16" unlighted	1.000	Ea.	105	43	148
TOTAL			5,287.60	3,534	8,821.60

D2010 962	Plumbing - Four Fixture Bathroom	MAT.	INST.	TOTAL
1800	Water closet, 32" shower, bathtub, lavavatory, in 2 walls	5,300	3,525	8,825
1900	Above system with 36" corner angle shower, plumbing in 3 walls	6,075	3,875	9,950
2000				
2300				
2400	NOTE: PLUMBING APPROXIMATIONS			
2500	WATER CONTROL: water meter, backflow preventer,			
2600	Shock absorbers, vacuum breakers, mixer....10 to 15% of fixtures			
2700	PIPE AND FITTINGS: .... 30 to 60% of fixtures			
2800				
2900	Cut & patch to match existing construction, add, minimum	2%	3%	
3000	Maximum	5%	9%	
3100	Dust protection, add, minimum	1%	2%	
3200	Maximum	4%	11%	
3300	Equipment usage curtailment, add, minimum	1%	1%	
3400	Maximum	3%	10%	
3500	Material handling & storage limitation, add, minimum	1%	1%	
3600	Maximum	6%	7%	
3700	Protection of existing work, add, minimum	2%	2%	
3800	Maximum	5%	7%	
3900	Shift work requirements, add, minimum		5%	
4000	Maximum		30%	

D20 Plumbing

D2010 Plumbing Fixtures

This page illustrates and describes a five fixture bathroom system including a water closet, shower, bathtub, lavatories, accessories, and service piping. Lines within System Components give the unit price and total price on a cost each basis for this system. Prices for five fixture bathroom systems are on Line Items D2010 963 1800 thru 1900. Both material quantities and labor costs have been adjusted for the system listed.

Factors: To adjust for job conditions other than normal working situations use Lines D2010 963 2900 thru 4000.

Example: You are to install and match any existing construction. Go to Line D2010 963 2900 and apply these percentages to the appropriate MAT. and INST. costs.

System Components	QUANTITY	UNIT	COST EACH		
			MAT.	INST.	TOTAL
Five fixture bathroom incl. water closet, shower, bathtub, 2 lavatories, accessories and necessary service piping to install this system in 1 wall.					
Water closet, floor mounted, 2 piece, close coupled	1.000	Ea.	256	244	500
Rough-in waste & vent for water closet	1.000	Set	365	425	790
36" corner angle shower, enameled steel stall, molded stone receptor	1.000	Ea.	1,900	269	2,169
Rough-in waste & vent for shower	1.000	Set	590	630	1,220
Bathtub, P.E. cast iron, 5' long with accessories	1.000	Ea.	1,225	294	1,519
Rough-in waste & vent for bathtub	1.000	Set	535	625	1,160
Countertop, plastic laminate, with backsplash	2.000	Ea.	170	80	250
Vanity base, 2 doors, 24" wide	2.000	Ea.	380	110	490
Lavatories, 20" x 18" cabinet mntd, PECI	2.000	Ea.	720	404	1,124
Rough-in waste & vent for lavatories	1.600	Set	728	896	1,624
Accessories					
Toilet tissue dispenser, chrome, single roll	1.000	Ea.	19.60	20	39.60
18" long stainless steel towel bars	2.000	Ea.	92	52	144
Medicine cabinet with mirror, 20" x 16", unlighted	2.000	Ea.	210	86	296
TOTAL			7,190.60	4,135	11,325.60

D2010 963	Plumbing - Five Fixture Bathroom	COST EACH		
		MAT.	INST.	TOTAL
1800	Water closet, shower, bathtub, 2 lavatories, on 1 wall	7,200	4,125	11,325
1900	Above system installed in 2 walls with all necessary service piping	7,250	4,275	11,525
2000				
2100				
2200				
2300				
2400	NOTE: PLUMBING APPROXIMATIONS			
2500	WATER CONTROL: water meter, backflow preventer,			
2600	Shock absorbers, vacuum breakers, mixer....10 to 15% of fixtures			
2700	PIPE AND FITTINGS: .... 30 to 60% of fixtures			
2800				
2900	Cut & patch to match existing construction, add, minimum	2%	3%	
3000	Maximum	5%	9%	
3100	Dust protection, add, minimum	1%	2%	
3200	Maximum	4%	11%	
3300	Equipment usage curtailment, add, minimum	1%	1%	
3400	Maximum	3%	10%	
3500	Material handling & storage limitation, add, minimum	1%	1%	

D2010 Plumbing Fixtures

D2010 963	Plumbing - Five Fixture Bathroom	COST EACH		
		MAT.	INST.	TOTAL
3600	Maximum	6%	7%	
3700	Protection of existing work, add, minimum	2%	2%	
3800	Maximum	5%	7%	
3900	Shift work requirements, add, minimum		5%	
4000	Maximum		30%	

D3010 Energy Supply

This page illustrates and describes an oil fired hot water baseboard system including an oil fired boiler, fin tube radiation and all fittings and piping. Lines within System Components give the unit price and total price per square foot for this system. Prices for oil fired hot water baseboard systems are on Line Items D3010 540 1600 thru 2100. Both material quantities and labor costs have been adjusted for the system listed.

Factors: To adjust for job conditions other than normal working situations use Lines D3010 540 2900 thru 4000.

Example: You are to install the system while protecting all existing work. Go to Line D3010 540 3700 and apply these percentages to the appropriate MAT. and INST. costs.

System Components			COST PER S.F.		
	QUANTITY	UNIT	MAT.	INST.	TOTAL
Oil fired hot water baseboard system including boiler, fin tube radiation, and all necessary fittings and piping.					
Area to 800 S.F.					
Boiler, cast iron, w/oil piping, 97 MBH	1.000	Ea.	2,437.50	1,593.75	4,031.25
Copper piping	130.000	L.F.	1,605.50	1,612	3,217.50
Fin tube radiation	68.000	L.F.	550.80	1,530	2,080.80
Circulator	1.000	Ea.	600	216	816
Oil tank	1.000	Ea.	540	263	803
Expansion tank, ASME	1.000	Ea.	785	94	879
TOTAL			6,518.80	5,308.75	11,827.55
COST PER S.F.		S.F.	8.15	6.64	14.79

D3010 540	Heating - Oil Fired Hot Water	COST PER S.F.		
		MAT.	INST.	TOTAL
1600	Cast iron boiler, area to 800 S.F.	8.16	6.63	14.79
1700	To 1000 S.F.	7.10	5.70	12.80
1800	To 1200 S.F.	6.15	5.20	11.35
1900	To 1600 S.F.	7.25	5.15	12.40
2000	To 2000 S.F.	6.10	4.61	10.71
2100	To 3000 S.F.	4.49	3.86	8.35
2200				
2300				
2700				
2800				
2900	Cut & patch to match existing construction, add, minimum	2%	3%	
3000	Maximum	5%	9%	
3100	Dust protection, add, minimum	1%	2%	
3200	Maximum	4%	11%	
3300	Equipment usage curtailment, add, minimum	1%	1%	
3400	Maximum	3%	10%	
3500	Material handling & storage limitation, add, minimum	1%	1%	
3600	Maximum	6%	7%	
3700	Protection of existing work, add, minimum	2%	2%	
3800	Maximum	5%	7%	
3900	Shift work requirements, add, minimum		5%	
4000	Maximum		30%	

D3010 Energy Supply

This page illustrates and describes a gas fired hot water baseboard system including a gas fired boiler, fin tube radiation, fittings and piping. Lines within System Components give the unit price and total price per square foot for this system. Prices for gas fired hot water baseboard systems are on Line Items D3010 550 1400 thru 1900. Both material quantities and labor costs have been adjusted for the system listed.

Factors: To adjust for job conditions other than normal working situations use Lines D3010 550 2900 thru 4000.

Example: You are to install the system with minimal equipment usage. Go to Line D3010 550 3400 and apply these percentages to the appropriate MAT. and INST. costs.

System Components	QUANTITY	UNIT	COST PER S.F.		
			MAT.	INST.	TOTAL
Gas fired hot water baseboard system including boiler, fin tube radiation, all necessary fittings and piping.					
Area to 800 S.F.					
Cast iron boiler, insulating jacket, gas piping, 80 MBH	1.000	Ea.	2,968.75	2,375	5,343.75
Copper piping	130.000	L.F.	1,605.50	1,612	3,217.50
Fin tube radiation	68.000	L.F.	550.80	1,530	2,080.80
Circulator, flange connection	1.000	Ea.	600	216	816
Expansion tank, ASME	1.000	Ea.	785	94	879
TOTAL			6,510.05	5,827	12,337.05
COST PER S.F.		S.F.	8.14	7.28	15.42

D3010 550	Heating - Gas Fired Hot Water	COST PER S.F.		
		MAT.	INST.	TOTAL
1400	Cast iron boiler, area to 800 S.F.	8.13	7.28	15.41
1500	To 1000 S.F.	6.85	6.40	13.25
1600	To 1200 S.F.	5.90	5.75	11.65
1700	To 1600 S.F.	7.10	5.60	12.70
1800	To 2000 S.F.	6.05	5.05	11.10
1900	To 3000 S.F.	4.72	4.39	9.11
2000				
2100				
2900	Cut & patch to match existing construction, add, minimum	2%	3%	
3000	Maximum	5%	9%	
3100	Dust protection, add, minimum	1%	2%	
3200	Maximum	4%	11%	
3300	Equipment usage curtailment, add, minimum	1%	1%	
3400	Maximum	3%	10%	
3500	Material handling & storage limitation, add, minimum	1%	1%	
3600	Maximum	6%	7%	
3700	Protection of existing work, add, minimum	2%	2%	
3800	Maximum	5%	7%	
3900	Shift work requirements, add, minimum		5%	
4000	Maximum		30%	

D3010 Energy Supply

This page illustrates and describes a wood burning stove system including a free standing stove, preformed hearth, masonry chimney, and necessary piping and fittings. Lines within System Components give the unit price and total price on a cost each basis for this system. Prices for wood burning stove systems are on Line Items D3010 991 1400 thru 2000. Both material quantities and labor costs have been adjusted for the system listed.

Factors: To adjust for job conditions other than normal working situations use Lines D3010 991 2900 thru 4000.

Example: You are to install the system and protect existing construction. Go to Line D3010 991 3500 and apply these percentages to the appropriate MAT., and INST. costs.

System Components		QUANTITY	UNIT	COST EACH		
				MAT.	INST.	TOTAL
Cast iron, free standing,wood burning stove with preformed hearth, masonry chimney, and all necessary piping and fittings to install in chimney.						
	Cast iron wood burning stove, stove pipe	1.000	Ea.	1,075	925	2,000
	Wall panel or hearth, non-combustible	1.000	Ea.	1,045	170.05	1,215.05
	16" x 16" brick chimney, 8" x 8" flue	20.000	V.L.F.	687.50	1,475	2,162.50
	Concrete in place, chimney foundations	.500	C.Y.	81	125.56	206.56
	TOTAL			2,888.50	2,695.61	5,584.11

D3010 991	Wood Burning Stoves		COST EACH		
			MAT.	INST.	TOTAL
1400	Cast iron, free standing with preformed hearth		2,900	2,700	5,600
1500					
1600	Installed in existing fireplace		1,625	1,025	2,650
1700					
1800	Installed with insulated metal chimney				
1900	System including ceiling package,				
2000	Metal chimney to 10 L.F.		3,400	1,425	4,825
2100					
2200					
2300					
2400					
2500					
2600					
2700					
2900	Dust protection, add, minimum		1%	2%	
3000	Maximum		4%	11%	
3100	Equipment usage curtailment, add, minimum		1%	1%	
3200	Maximum		3%	10%	
3300	Material handling & storage limitation, add, minimum		1%	1%	
3400	Maximum		6%	7%	
3500	Protection of existing work, add, minimum		2%	2%	
3600	Maximum		5%	7%	
3700	Shift work requirements, add, minimum			5%	
3800	Maximum			30%	
3900	Temporary shoring and bracing, add, minimum		2%	5%	
4000	Maximum		5%	12%	

D3010 Energy Supply

This page illustrates and describes masonry fireplace systems including a brick fireplace, footing, foundation, hearth, firebox, chimney and flue. Lines within System Components give the unit price and total price on a cost each basis for this system. Prices for masonry fireplace systems are on Line Items D3010 992 1200 thru 1500. Both material quantities and labor costs have been adjusted for the system listed.

Factors: To adjust for job conditions other than normal working situations use Lines D3010 992 2700 thru 4000.

Example: You are to install the system with some temporary shoring and bracing. Go to Line D3010 992 3900 and apply these percentages to the appropriate MAT. and INST. costs.

System Components	QUANTITY	UNIT	COST EACH MAT.	COST EACH INST.	COST EACH TOTAL
Brick masonry fireplace, including footing, foundation, hearth, firebox, chimney and flue, chimney 12' above firebox.					
Footing, 4' x 7' x 12" thick, 3000 psi concrete	1.040	C.Y.	188.24	300.85	489.09
Foundation, 12" concrete block	180.000	S.F.	842.40	1,935	2,777.40
Fireplace, brick faced, 6'-0" wide x 5'-0" high	1.000	Ea.	605	2,675	3,280
Hearth	1.000	Ea.	225	535	760
Chimney, 20" x 20", one 12" x 12" flue, 12 V.L.F.	12.000	V.L.F.	654	942	1,596
Mantle, wood	7.000	L.F.	63.70	117.25	180.95
TOTAL			2,578.34	6,505.10	9,083.44

D3010 992	Masonry Fireplace	COST EACH MAT.	COST EACH INST.	COST EACH TOTAL
1200	Chimney, 20" x 20", one 12" x 12" flue, 12 V.L.F.	2,575	6,500	9,075
1300	18 V.L.F.	2,900	6,975	9,875
1400	24 V.L.F.	3,225	7,450	10,675
1500	Fieldstone face instead of brick	2,850	6,500	9,350
1600				
1700				
1800				
1900				
2000				
2100				
2200				
2300				
2700	Cut & patch to match existing construction, add, minimum	2%	3%	
2800	Maximum	5%	9%	
2900	Dust protection, add, minimum	1%	2%	
3000	Maximum	4%	11%	
3100	Equipment usage curtailment, add, minimum	1%	1%	
3200	Maximum	3%	10%	
3300	Material handling & storage limitation, add, minimum	1%	1%	
3400	Maximum	6%	7%	
3500	Protection of existing work, add, minimum	2%	2%	
3600	Maximum	5%	7%	
3700	Shift work requirements, add, minimum		5%	
3800	Maximum		30%	
3900	Temporary shoring and bracing, add, minimum	2%	5%	
4000	Maximum	5%	12%	

D3020 Heat Generating Systems

This page illustrates and describes an oil fired forced air system including an oil fired furnace, ductwork, registers and hookups. Lines within System Components give the unit price and total price per square foot for this system. Prices for oil fired forced air systems are on Line Items D3020 122 1600 thru 2800. Both material quantities and labor costs have been adjusted for the system listed.

Factors: To adjust for job conditions other than normal working situations use Lines D3020 122 3100 thru 4200.

Example: You are to install the system during evenings and weekends. Go to Line D3020 122 4200 and apply this percentage to the appropriate INST. cost.

System Components			COST PER S.F.		
	QUANTITY	UNIT	MAT.	INST.	TOTAL
Oil fired hot air heating system including furnace, ductwork, registers and all necessary hookups.					
Area to 800 S.F., heat only					
Furnace, oil, atomizing gun type burner, w/oil piping	1.000	Ea.	2,125	431.25	2,556.25
Oil tank, steel, 275 gallon	1.000	Ea.	540	263	803
Duct, galvanized, steel	312.000	Lb.	227.76	2,558.40	2,786.16
Insulation, blanket type, duct work	270.000	S.F.	264.60	912.60	1,177.20
Flexible duct, 6" diameter, insulated	100.000	L.F.	323	478	801
Registers, baseboard, gravity, 12" x 6"	8.000	Ea.	50.40	240	290.40
Return, damper, 36" x 18"	1.000	Ea.	80	69	149
TOTAL			3,610.76	4,952.25	8,563.01
COST PER S.F.		S.F.	4.51	6.19	10.70

D3020 122	Heating-Cooling, Oil, Forced Air	COST PER S.F.		
		MAT.	INST.	TOTAL
1600	Oil fired, area to 800 S.F.	4.50	6.19	10.69
1700	To 1000 S.F.	3.62	5	8.62
1800	To 1200 S.F.	3.16	4.43	7.59
1900	To 1600 S.F.	2.59	3.69	6.28
2000	To 2000 S.F.	2.65	4.75	7.40
2100	To 3000 S.F.	2.07	3.79	5.86
2200	For combined heating and cooling systems:			
2300	Oil fired, heating and cooling, area to 800 S.F.	6.70	7.35	14.05
2400	To 1000 S.F.	5.40	6	11.40
2500	To 1200 S.F.	4.64	5.25	9.89
2600	To 1600 S.F.	3.78	4.34	8.12
2700	To 2000 S.F.	3.69	5.35	9.04
2800	To 3000 S.F.	2.79	4.21	7
3100	Cut & patch to match existing construction, add, minimum	2%	3%	
3200	Maximum	5%	9%	
3300	Dust protection, add, minimum	1%	2%	
3400	Maximum	4%	11%	
3500	Equipment usage curtailment, add, minimum	1%	1%	
3600	Maximum	3%	10%	
3700	Material handling & storage limitation, add, minimum	1%	1%	
3800	Maximum	6%	7%	
3900	Protection of existing work, add, minimum	2%	2%	
4000	Maximum	5%	7%	
4100	Shift work requirements, add, minimum		5%	
4200	Maximum		30%	

D30 HVAC

D3020 Heat Generating Systems

This page illustrates and describes a gas fired forced air system including a gas fired furnace, ductwork, registers and hookups. Lines within System Components give the unit price and total price per square foot for this system. Prices for gas fired forced air systems are on Line Items D3020 124 1400 thru 2600. Both material quantities and labor costs have been adjusted for the system listed.

Factors: To adjust for job conditions other than normal working situations use Lines D3020 124 2900 thru 4000.

Example: You are to install the system with material handling and storage limitations. Go to Line D3020 124 3500 and apply these percentages to the appropriate MAT. and INST. costs.

System Components	QUANTITY	UNIT	COST PER S.F.		
			MAT.	INST.	TOTAL
Gas fired hot air heating system including furnace, ductwork, registers and all necessary hookups.					
Area to 800 S.F., heat only					
Furnace, gas, AGA certified, direct drive, w/gas piping, 44 MBH	1.000	Ea.	737.50	387.50	1,125
Duct, galvanized steel	312.000	Lb.	227.76	2,558.40	2,786.16
Insulation, blanket type, ductwork	270.000	S.F.	264.60	912.60	1,177.20
Flexible duct, 6″ diameter, insulated	100.000	L.F.	323	478	801
Registers, baseboard, gravity, 12″ x 6″	8.000	Ea.	50.40	240	290.40
Return, damper, 36″ x 18″	1.000	Ea.	80	69	149
TOTAL			1,683.26	4,628.76	6,328.76
COST PER S.F.		S.F.	2.10	5.81	7.91

D3020 124	Heating-Cooling, Gas, Forced Air	COST PER S.F.		
		MAT.	INST.	TOTAL
1400	Gas fired, area to 800 S.F.	2.09	5.81	7.90
1500	To 1000 S.F.	1.69	4.73	6.42
1600	To 1200 S.F.	1.55	4.18	5.73
1700	To 1600 S.F.	1.51	3.93	5.44
1800	To 2000 S.F.	1.55	4.64	6.19
1900	To 3000 S.F.	1.21	3.70	4.91
2000	For combined heating and cooling systems:			
2100	Gas fired, heating and cooling, area to 800 S.F.	4.30	7	11.30
2200	To 1000 S.F.	3.46	5.70	9.16
2300	To 1200 S.F.	3.03	4.99	8.02
2400	To 1600 S.F.	2.70	4.57	7.27
2500	To 2000 S.F.	2.58	5.20	7.78
2600	To 3000 S.F.	1.93	4.11	6.04
2900	Cut & patch to match existing construction, add, minimum	2%	3%	
3000	Maximum	5%	9%	
3100	Dust protection, add, minimum	1%	2%	
3200	Maximum	4%	11%	
3300	Equipment usage curtailment, add, minimum	1%	1%	
3400	Maximum	3%	10%	
3500	Material handling & storage limitation, add, minimum	1%	1%	
3600	Maximum	6%	7%	
3700	Protection of existing work, add, minimum	2%	2%	
3800	Maximum	5%	7%	
3900	Shift work requirements, add, minimum		5%	
4000	Maximum		30%	

D3020 Heat Generating Systems

Expansion Tank

Supply Piping

Gas Supply

Pressure Relief Valve

Return Piping

Circulating Pump

Cast Iron Boiler, Hot Water, Gas Fired

This page illustrates and describes boilers including expansion tank, circulating pump and all service piping. Lines within Systems Components give the material and installation price on a cost each basis for the components. Prices for boiler systems are on Line Items D3020 130 1010 thru D3020 138 1040. Material quantities and labor costs have been adjusted for the system listed.

Factors: To adjust for job conditions other than normal working situations use Line D3020 138 2700 thru 4000.

System Components	QUANTITY	UNIT	COST EACH		
			MAT.	INST.	TOTAL
Cast iron boiler, including piping, chimney and accessories.					
Boilers, gas fired, std controls, CI, insulated, HW, gross output 100 MBH	1.000	Ea.	2,525	2,050	4,575
Pipe, black steel, Sch 40, threaded, W/coupling & hangers, 10' OC, 3/4" dia	20.000	L.F.	78.53	265.50	344.03
Pipe, black steel, Sch 40, threaded, W/coupling & hangers, 10' OC, 1" dia.	20.000	L.F.	109.65	291.33	400.98
Elbow, 90°, black, straight, 3/4" dia.	9.000	Ea.	36.63	463.50	500.13
Elbow, 90°, black, straight, 1" dia.	6.000	Ea.	42.30	333	375.30
Tee, black, straight, 3/4" dia.	2.000	Ea.	12.90	160	172.90
Tee, black, straight, 1" dia.	2.000	Ea.	22.10	180	202.10
Tee, black, reducing, 1" dia.	2.000	Ea.	35.50	180	215.50
Pipe cap, black, 3/4" dia.	1.000	Ea.	4.61	22.50	27.11
Union, black with brass seat, 3/4" dia.	2.000	Ea.	34.20	111	145.20
Union, black with brass seat, 1" dia.	2.000	Ea.	45	120	165
Pipe nipples, black, 3/4" dia.	5.000	Ea.	8.73	29.50	38.23
Pipe nipples, black, 1" dia.	3.000	Ea.	7.65	20.33	27.98
Valves, bronze, gate, N.R.S., threaded, class 150, 3/4" size	2.000	Ea.	185	72	257
Valves, bronze, gate, N.R.S., threaded, class 150, 1" size	2.000	Ea.	232	76	308
Gas cock, brass, 3/4" size	1.000	Ea.	17.05	32.50	49.55
Thermometer, stem type, 9" case, 8" stem, 3/4" NPT	2.000	Ea.	454	52	506
Tank, steel, liquid expansion, ASME, painted, 15 gallon capacity	1.000	Ea.	700	77.50	777.50
Pump, circulating, bronze, flange connection, 3/4" to 1-1/2" size, 1/8 HP	1.000	Ea.	1,025	216	1,241
Vent chimney, all fuel, pressure tight, double wall, SS, 6" dia.	20.000	L.F.	1,230	410	1,640
Vent chimney, elbow, 90° fixed, 6" dia.	2.000	Ea.	860	83	943
Vent chimney, Tee, 6" dia.	2.000	Ea.	504	104	608
Vent chimney, ventilated roof thimble, 6" dia.	1.000	Ea.	263	48	311
Vent chimney, flat roof flashing, 6" dia.	1.000	Ea.	113	41.50	154.50
Vent chimney, stack cap, 6" diameter	1.000	Ea.	310	27	337
Insulation, fiberglass pipe covering, 1" wall, 1" IPS	20.000	L.F.	22.80	108	130.80
TOTAL			8,878.65	5,574.16	14,452.81

D3020 130	Boiler, Cast Iron, Hot Water, Gas	COST EACH		
		MAT.	INST.	TOTAL
1000	For alternate boilers:			
1010	Boiler, cast iron, gas, hot water, 100 MBH	8,875	5,575	14,450
1020	200 MBH	10,400	6,375	16,775
1030	320 MBH	10,400	6,950	17,350
1040	440 MBH	14,200	8,975	23,175
1050	544 MBH	23,400	14,000	37,400
1060	765 MBH	28,300	15,100	43,400
1070	1088 MBH	31,500	16,100	47,600

D30 HVAC

D3020 Heat Generating Systems

D3020 130	Boiler, Cast Iron, Hot Water, Gas	COST EACH		
		MAT.	INST.	TOTAL
1080	1530 MBH	36,500	21,200	57,700
1090	2312 MBH	42,800	25,000	67,800

D3020 134	Boiler, Cast Iron, Steam, Gas	COST EACH		
		MAT.	INST.	TOTAL
1010	Boiler, cast iron, gas, steam, 100 MBH	7,475	5,425	12,900
1020	200 MBH	15,100	10,200	25,300
1030	320 MBH	16,700	11,400	28,100
1040	544 MBH	24,900	17,900	42,800
1050	765 MBH	28,100	18,600	46,700
1060	1275 MBH	33,400	20,400	53,800
1070	2675 MBH	51,000	29,800	80,800

D3020 136	Boiler, Cast Iron, Hot Water, Gas/Oil	COST EACH		
		MAT.	INST.	TOTAL
1010	Boiler, cast iron, gas & oil, hot water, 584 MBH	29,800	15,600	45,400
1020	876 MBH	37,900	16,700	54,600
1030	1168 MBH	43,400	18,900	62,300
1040	1460 MBH	49,800	22,700	72,500
1050	2044 MBH	51,500	23,400	74,900
1060	2628 MBH	75,500	28,500	104,000

D3020 138	Boiler, Cast Iron, Steam, Gas/Oil	COST EACH		
		MAT.	INST.	TOTAL
1010	Boiler, cast iron, gas & oil, steam, 810 MBH	32,000	20,200	52,200
1020	1360 MBH	37,400	21,600	59,000
1030	2040 MBH	46,200	27,600	73,800
1040	2700 MBH	49,600	30,700	80,300
2700	Cut & patch to match existing construction, add, minimum	2%	3%	
2800	Maximum	5%	9%	
2900	Dust protection, add, minimum	1%	2%	
3000	Maximum	4%	11%	
3100	Equipment usage curtailment, add, minimum	1%	1%	
3200	Maximum	3%	10%	
3300	Material handling & storage limitation, add, minimum	1%	1%	
3400	Maximum	6%	7%	
3500	Protection of existing work, add, minimum	2%	2%	
3600	Maximum	5%	7%	
3700	Shift work requirements, add, minimum		5%	
3800	Maximum		30%	
3900	Temporary shoring and bracing, add, minimum	2%	5%	
4000	Maximum	5%	12%	

D3020 Heat Generating Systems

Base Mounted End–Suction Pump

This page illustrates and describes end suction base mounted circulating pumps, including strainer and piping. Lines within system components give the material and installation price on a cost each basis for the components. Prices for circulating pumps are on Line items D3020 330 1010 thru 1050. Material quantities and labor costs have been adjusting for the system listed.

Factors: To adjust for job conditions other than normal working situations uses Lines D3020 330 2700 thru 4000.

System Components	QUANTITY	UNIT	COST EACH		
			MAT.	INST.	TOTAL
Circulator pump, end suction, including pipe, valves, fittings and guages.					
Pump, circulating, CI, base mounted, 2-1/2" size, 3 HP, to 150 GPM	1.000	Ea.	8,100	720	8,820
Pipe, black steel, Sch. 40, on yoke & roll hangers, 10' O.C., 2-1/2" dia	12.000	L.F.	166.80	345.48	512.28
Elbow, 90°, weld joint, steel, 2-1/2" pipe size	1.000	Ea.	30.50	169.60	200.10
Flange, weld neck, 150 LB, 2-1/2" pipe size	8.000	Ea.	280	678.40	958.40
Valve, iron body, gate, 125 lb., N.R.S., flanged, 2-1/2" size	1.000	Ea.	770	259	1,029
Strainer, Y type, iron body, flanged, 125 lb., 2-1/2" pipe size	1.000	Ea.	127	263	390
Multipurpose valve, CI body, 2" size	1.000	Ea.	505	91.50	596.50
Expansion joint, flanged spool, 6" F to F, 2-1/2" dia	2.000	Ea.	588	212	800
T-O-L, weld joint, socket, 1/4" pipe size, nozzle	2.000	Ea.	15.60	117.28	132.88
T-O-L, weld joint, socket, 1/2" pipe size, nozzle	2.000	Ea.	15.60	123.52	139.12
Control gauges, pressure or vacuum, 3-1/2" diameter dial	2.000	Ea.	79	46	125
Pressure/temperature relief plug, 316 SS, 3/4" OD, 7-1/2" insertion	2.000	Ea.	151	46	197
Insulation, fiberglass pipe covering, 1-1/2" wall, 2-1/2" IPS	12.000	L.F.	32.16	78.60	110.76
Pump control system	1.000	Ea.	1,350	660	2,010
Pump balancing	1.000	Ea.		320	320
TOTAL			12,210.66	4,130.38	16,341.04

D3020 330	Circulating Pump Systems, End Suction	COST EACH		
		MAT.	INST.	TOTAL
1000	For alternate pump sizes:			
1010	Pump, base mtd with motor, end-suction, 2-1/2" size, 3 HP, to 150 GPM	12,200	4,150	16,350
1020	3" size, 5 HP, to 225 GPM	14,300	4,725	19,025
1030	4" size, 7-1/2 HP, to 350 GPM	17,800	5,700	23,500
1040	5" size, 15 HP, to 1000 GPM	25,800	8,625	34,425
1050	6" size, 25 HP, to 1550 GPM	34,400	10,400	44,800
2700	Cut & patch to match existing construction, add, minimum	2%	3%	
2800	Maximum	5%	9%	
2900	Dust protection, add, minimum	1%	2%	
3000	Maximum	4%	11%	
3100	Equipment usage curtailment, add, minimum	1%	1%	
3200	Maximum	3%	10%	
3300	Material handling & storage limitation, add, minimum	1%	1%	
3400	Maximum	6%	7%	
3500	Protection of existing work, add, minimum	2%	2%	
3600	Maximum	5%	7%	

D30 HVAC

D3020 Heat Generating Systems

D3020 330	Circulating Pump Systems, End Suction	COST EACH		
		MAT.	INST.	TOTAL
3700	Shift work requirements, add, minimum		5%	
3800	Maximum		30%	
3900	Temporary shoring and bracing, add, minimum	2%	5%	
4000	Maximum	5%	12%	

D3040 Distribution Systems

Galvanized Steel Duct

Fiberglass Duct Insulation

Flexible Fiberglass Duct

Horizontal Fan Coil Air Conditioning System

This page illustrates and describes fan coil air conditioners including duct work, duct installation, piping and diffusers. Lines within Systems Components give the material and installation price on a cost each basis for the components. Prices for fan coil A/C unit systems are on Line Items D3040 118 1010 thru D3040 126 1120. Material quantities and labor costs have been adjusted for the system listed.

Factors: To adjust for job conditions other than normal working situations use Lines D3040 126 2700 thru 4000.

System Components

	QUANTITY	UNIT	MAT.	INST.	TOTAL
Fan coil A/C system, horizontal, with housing, controls, 2 pipe, 1/2 ton.					
Fan coil A/C, horizontal housing, filters, chilled water, 1/2 ton cooling	1.000	Ea.	1,325	164	1,489
Pipe, black steel, Sch 40, threaded, W/cplgs & hangers, 10' OC, 3/4" dia.	20.000	L.F.	75.04	253.70	328.74
Elbow, 90°, black, straight, 3/4" dia.	6.000	Ea.	24.42	309	333.42
Tee, black, straight, 3/4" dia.	2.000	Ea.	12.90	160	172.90
Union, black with brass seat, 3/4" dia.	2.000	Ea.	34.20	111	145.20
Pipe nipples, 3/4" diam	3.000	Ea.	5.24	17.70	22.94
Valves, bronze, gate, N.R.S., threaded, class 150, 3/4" size	2.000	Ea.	185	72	257
Circuit setter, balance valve, bronze body, threaded, 3/4" pipe size	1.000	Ea.	87	36.50	123.50
Insulation, fiberglass pipe covering, 1" wall, 3/4" IPS	20.000	L.F.	21.40	103	124.40
Ductwork, 12" x 8" fabricated, galvanized steel, 12 LF	55.000	Lb.	40.15	451	491.15
Insulation, ductwork, blanket type, fiberglass, 1" thk, 1-1/2 LB density	40.000	S.F.	39.20	135.20	174.40
Diffusers, aluminum, OB damper, ceiling, perf, 24"x24" panel size, 6"x6"	2.000	Ea.	332	86	418
Ductwork, flexible, fiberglass fabric, insulated, 1"thk, PE jacket, 6" dia	16.000	L.F.	51.68	76.48	128.16
Round volume control damper 6" dia.	2.000	Ea.	55	63	118
Fan coil unit balancing	1.000	Ea.		89.50	89.50
Re-heat coil balancing	1.000	Ea.		135	135
Diffuser/register, high, balancing	2.000	Ea.		248	248
TOTAL			2,288.23	2,511.08	4,799.31

D3040 118	Fan Coil A/C Unit, Two Pipe	MAT.	INST.	TOTAL
1000	For alternate A/C units:			
1010	Fan coil A/C system, cabinet mounted, controls, 2 pipe, 1/2 Ton	1,325	1,350	2,675
1020	1 Ton	1,625	1,525	3,150
1030	1-1/2 Ton	1,725	1,550	3,275
1040	2 Ton	2,725	1,875	4,600
1050	3 Ton	3,425	1,950	5,375

D3040 120	Fan Coil A/C Unit, Two Pipe, Electric Heat	MAT.	INST.	TOTAL
1010	Fan coil A/C system, cabinet mntd, elect. ht, controls, 2 pipe, 1/2 Ton	1,875	1,350	3,225
1020	1 Ton	2,275	1,525	3,800
1030	1-1/2 Ton	2,650	1,550	4,200
1040	2 Ton	4,075	1,900	5,975
1050	3 Ton	6,850	1,950	8,800

D3040 Distribution Systems

D3040 122	Fan Coil A/C Unit, Four Pipe	COST EACH		
		MAT.	INST.	TOTAL
1010	Fan coil A/C system, cabinet mounted, controls, 4 pipe, 1/2 Ton	2,150	2,625	4,775
1020	1 Ton	2,475	2,800	5,275
1030	1-1/2 Ton	2,625	2,825	5,450
1040	2 Ton	3,175	2,925	6,100
1050	3 Ton	4,325	3,150	7,475

D3040 124	Fan Coil A/C, Horizontal, Duct Mount, 2 Pipe	COST EACH		
		MAT.	INST.	TOTAL
1010	Fan coil A/C system, horizontal w/housing, controls, 2 pipe, 1/2 Ton	2,300	2,500	4,800
1020	1 Ton	3,000	3,650	6,650
1030	1-1/2 Ton	3,750	4,725	8,475
1040	2 Ton	4,950	5,675	10,625
1050	3 Ton	5,975	7,500	13,475
1060	3-1/2 Ton	6,250	7,775	14,025
1070	4 Ton	6,375	8,825	15,200
1080	5 Ton	7,575	11,200	18,775
1090	6 Ton	7,675	12,000	19,675
1100	7 Ton	7,700	12,500	20,200
1110	8 Ton	7,700	12,700	20,400
1120	10 Ton	9,125	13,200	22,325

D3040 126	Fan Coil A/C, Horiz., Duct Mount, 2 Pipe, Elec. Ht.	COST EACH		
		MAT.	INST.	TOTAL
1010	Fan coil A/C system, horiz. hsng, elect. ht, ctrls, 2 pipe, 1/2 Ton	2,575	2,500	5,075
1020	1 Ton	3,350	3,650	7,000
1030	1-1/2 Ton	4,000	4,725	8,725
1040	2 Ton	5,400	5,675	11,075
1050	3 Ton	8,575	7,750	16,325
1060	3-1/2 Ton	9,625	7,775	17,400
1070	4 Ton	10,800	8,825	19,625
1080	5 Ton	13,100	11,200	24,300
1090	6 Ton	13,200	12,000	25,200
1100	7 Ton	13,100	12,700	25,800
1110	8 Ton	13,800	13,300	27,100
1120	10 Ton	14,600	12,500	27,100
2700	Cut & patch to match existing construction, add, minimum	2%	3%	
2800	Maximum	5%	9%	
2900	Dust protection, add, minimum	1%	2%	
3000	Maximum	4%	11%	
3100	Equipment usage curtailment, add, minimum	1%	1%	
3200	Maximum	3%	10%	
3300	Material handling & storage limitation, add, minimum	1%	1%	
3400	Maximum	6%	7%	
3500	Protection of existing work, add, minimum	2%	2%	
3600	Maximum	5%	7%	
3700	Shift work requirements, add, minimum		5%	
3800	Maximum		30%	
3900	Temporary shoring and bracing, add, minimum	2%	5%	
4000	Maximum	5%	12%	

D3040 Distribution Systems

Plate Heat Exchanger

Shell and Tube Heat Exchanger

This page illustrates and describes plate and shell and tube type heat exchangers including pressure gauge and exchanger control system. Lines within Systems Components give the material and installation price on a cost each basis for the components. Prices for heat exchanger systems are on Line Items D3040 610 1010 thru D3040 620 1040. Material quantities and labor costs have been adjusted for the system listed.

Factors To adjust for job conditions other then normal working situations use Lines D3040 620 2700 thru 4000.

System Components	QUANTITY	UNIT	COST EACH		
			MAT.	INST.	TOTAL
Shell and tube type heat exchanger					
with related valves and piping.					
Heat exchanger, 4 pass, 3/4" O.D. copper tubes, by steam at 10 psi, 40 GPM	1.000	Ea.	5,525	330	5,855
Pipe, black steel, Sch 40, threaded, W/couplings & hangers, 10' OC, 2" dia.	40.000	L.F.	497.43	1,010	1,507.43
Elbow, 90°, straight, 2" dia.	16.000	Ea.	424	1,152	1,576
Reducer, black steel, concentric, 2" dia.	2.000	Ea.	60	123	183
Valves, bronze, gate, rising stem, threaded, class 150, 2" size	6.000	Ea.	1,554	393	1,947
Valves, bronze, globe, class 150, rising stem, threaded, 2" size	2.000	Ea.	1,350	131	1,481
Strainers, Y type, bronze body, screwed, 125 lb, 2" pipe size	2.000	Ea.	256	112	368
Valve, electric motor actuated, brass, 2 way, screwed, 1-1/2" pipe size	1.000	Ea.	705	55	760
Union, black with brass seat, 2" dia.	8.000	Ea.	372	608	980
Tee, black, straight, 2" dia.	9.000	Ea.	301.50	1,062	1,363.50
Tee, black, reducing run and outlet, 2" dia.	4.000	Ea.	244	472	716
Pipe nipple, black, 2" dia.	21.000	Ea.	4.93	10	14.93
Thermometers, stem type, 9" case, 8" stem, 3/4" NPT	2.000	Ea.	454	52	506
Gauges, pressure or vacuum, 3-1/2" diameter dial	2.000	Ea.	79	46	125
Insulation, fiberglass pipe covering, 1" wall, 2" IPS	40.000	L.F.	58	236	294
Heat exchanger control system	1.000	Ea.	2,850	2,300	5,150
Coil balancing	1.000	Ea.		135	135
TOTAL			14,734.86	8,227	22,961.86

D3040 610	Heat Exchanger, Plate Type	COST EACH		
		MAT.	INST.	TOTAL
1000	For alternate heat exchangers:			
1010	Plate heat exchanger, 400 GPM	55,500	16,600	72,100
1020	800 GPM	88,500	21,100	109,600
1030	1200 GPM	133,500	28,600	162,100
1040	1800 GPM	180,000	35,700	215,700

D3040 620	Heat Exchanger, Shell & Tube	COST EACH		
		MAT.	INST.	TOTAL
1010	Shell & tube heat exchanger, 40 GPM	14,700	8,225	22,925
1020	96 GPM	26,100	14,600	40,700
1030	240 GPM	47,800	19,800	67,600
1040	600 GPM	92,500	27,800	120,300
2700	Cut & patch to match existing construction, add, minimum	2%	3%	
2800	Maximum	5%	9%	

D30 HVAC

D3040 Distribution Systems

| D3040 620 | Heat Exchanger, Shell & Tube | COST EACH | | |
		MAT.	INST.	TOTAL
2900	Dust protection, add, minimum	1%	2%	
3000	Maximum	4%	11%	
3100	Equipment usage curtailment, add, minimum	1%	1%	
3200	Maximum	3%	10%	
3300	Material handling & storage limitation, add, minimum	1%	1%	
3400	Maximum	6%	7%	
3500	Protection of existing work, add, minimum	2%	2%	
3600	Maximum	5%	7%	
3700	Shift work requirements, add, minimum		5%	
3800	Maximum		30%	
3900	Temporary shoring and bracing, add, minimum	2%	5%	
4000	Maximum	5%	12%	

D3050 Terminal & Package Units

Weather Cap Roof Vent

Roof Flashing

Vent Pipe

90° Elbow

Tee

Tee Cap

Gas Cock

Gas Unit Heater

Hydronic Unit Heater

This page illustrates and describes unit heaters including piping and vents. Lines within Systems Components give the material and installation price on a cost each basis for this system. Prices for unit heater systems are on Line items D3050 120 1010 thru D3050 140 1040. Material quantities and labor costs have been adjusted for the system listed.

Factors: To adjust for job conditions other than normal working situations use Lines D3050 140 2700 thru 4000.

System Components	QUANTITY	UNIT	COST EACH		
			MAT.	INST.	TOTAL
Unit heaters complete with piping, thermostats and chimney as required.					
Space heater, propeller fan, 20 MBH output	1.000	Ea.	1,125	155	1,280
Pipe, black steel, Sch 40, threaded, W/coupling & hangers, 10' OC, 3/4" dia	20.000	L.F.	73.29	247.80	321.09
Elbow, 90°, black steel, straight, 1/2" dia.	3.000	Ea.	10.11	144	154.11
Elbow, 90°, black steel, straight, 3/4" dia.	3.000	Ea.	12.21	154.50	166.71
Tee, black steel, reducing, 3/4" dia.	1.000	Ea.	11.10	80	91.10
Union, black with brass seat, 3/4" dia.	1.000	Ea.	17.10	55.50	72.60
Pipe nipples, black, 1/2" dia	2.000	Ea.	6	22.80	28.80
Pipe nipples, black, 3/4" dia	2.000	Ea.	3.49	11.80	15.29
Pipe cap, black, 3/4" dia.	1.000	Ea.	4.61	22.50	27.11
Gas cock, brass, 3/4" size	1.000	Ea.	17.05	32.50	49.55
Thermostat, 1 set back, electric, timed	1.000	Ea.	39.50	91.50	131
Wiring, thermostat hook-up,25' of #18-3	1.000	Ea.	10.55	27.50	38.05
Vent chimney, prefab metal, U.L. listed, gas, double wall, galv. st, 4" dia	12.000	L.F.	95.40	219	314.40
Vent chimney, gas, double wall, galv. steel, elbow 90°, 4" dia.	2.000	Ea.	59	73	132
Vent chimney, gas, double wall, galv. steel, Tee, 4" dia.	1.000	Ea.	42.50	48	90.50
Vent chimney, gas, double wall, galv. steel, T cap, 4" dia.	1.000	Ea.	2.79	29.50	32.29
Vent chimney, gas, double wall, galv. steel, roof flashing, 4" dia.	1.000	Ea.	10.90	36.50	47.40
Vent chimney, gas, double wall, galv. steel, top, 4" dia.	1.000	Ea.	15.10	28	43.10
TOTAL			1,555.70	1,479.40	3,035.10

D3050 120	Unit Heaters, Gas	COST EACH		
		MAT.	INST.	TOTAL
1000	For alternate unit heaters:			
1010	Space heater, suspended, gas fired, propeller fan, 20 MBH	1,550	1,475	3,025
1020	60 MBH	1,800	1,550	3,350
1030	100 MBH	2,225	1,625	3,850
1040	160 MBH	2,700	1,800	4,500
1050	200 MBH	3,450	2,000	5,450
1060	280 MBH	4,050	2,125	6,175
1070	320 MBH	5,650	2,400	8,050

D3050 Terminal & Package Units

D3050 130	Unit Heaters, Hydronic	COST EACH		
		MAT.	INST.	TOTAL
1010	Space heater, suspended, horiz. mount, HW, prop. fan, 20 MBH	2,050	1,600	3,650
1020	60 MBH	2,800	1,800	4,600
1030	100 MBH	3,400	1,950	5,350
1040	150 MBH	3,850	2,150	6,000
1050	200 MBH	4,350	2,425	6,775
1060	300 MBH	5,150	2,850	8,000

D3050 140	Cabinet Unit Heaters, Hydronic	COST EACH		
		MAT.	INST.	TOTAL
1010	Unit heater, cabinet type, horizontal blower, hot water, 20 MBH	2,375	1,550	3,925
1020	60 MBH	3,450	1,725	5,175
1030	100 MBH	3,900	1,900	5,800
1040	120 MBH	3,975	1,950	5,925
2700	Cut & patch to match existing construction, add, minimum	2%	3%	
2800	Maximum	5%	9%	
2900	Dust protection, add, minimum	1%	2%	
3000	Maximum	4%	11%	
3100	Equipment usage curtailment, add, minimum	1%	1%	
3200	Maximum	3%	10%	
3300	Material handling & storage limitation, add, minimum	1%	1%	
3400	Maximum	6%	7%	
3500	Protection of existing work, add, minimum	2%	2%	
3600	Maximum	5%	7%	
3700	Shift work requirements, add, minimum		5%	
3800	Maximum		30%	
3900	Temporary shoring and bracing, add, minimum	2%	5%	
4000	Maximum	5%	12%	

D3050 Terminal & Package Units

Rooftop Air Conditioner Unit

Gas Cock

Roof Curb

Gas Piping

This page illustrates and describes packaged air conditioners including rooftop DX unit, pipes and fittings. Lines within Systems Components give the material and installation price on a cost each basis for the components. Prices for A/C systems are on Line Items D3050 175 1010 thru D3050 180 1060. Material quantities and labor costs have been adjusted for the system listed.

Factors: To adjust for job conditions other than normal working situations use Lines D3050 180 2700 thru 4000.

System Components	QUANTITY	UNIT	COST EACH MAT.	COST EACH INST.	COST EACH TOTAL
Packaged rooftop DX unit, gas, with related piping and valves.					
Roof top A/C, curb, economizer, sgl zone, elec cool, gas ht, 5 ton, 112 MBH	1.000	Ea.	5,800	2,350	8,150
Pipe, black steel, Sch 40, threaded, W/cplgs & hangers, 10' OC, 1" dia	20.000	L.F.	107.10	284.55	391.65
Elbow, 90°, black, straight, 3/4" dia.	3.000	Ea.	12.21	154.50	166.71
Elbow, 90°, black, straight, 1" dia.	3.000	Ea.	21.15	166.50	187.65
Tee, black, reducing, 1" dia.	1.000	Ea.	17.75	90	107.75
Union, black with brass seat, 1" dia.	1.000	Ea.	22.50	60	82.50
Pipe nipple, black, 3/4" dia	2.000	Ea.	6.98	23.60	30.58
Pipe nipple, black, 1" dia	2.000	Ea.	5.10	13.55	18.65
Cap, black, 1" dia.	1.000	Ea.	5.60	24	29.60
Gas cock, brass, 1" size	1.000	Ea.	34	38	72
Control system, pneumatic, Rooftop A/C unit	1.000	Ea.	2,950	2,575	5,525
Rooftop unit heat/cool balancing	1.000	Ea.		485	485
TOTAL			8,982.39	6,264.70	15,247.09

D3050 175	Rooftop Air Conditioner, Const. Volume	COST EACH MAT.	COST EACH INST.	COST EACH TOTAL
1000	For alternate A/C systems:			
1010	A/C, Rooftop, DX cool, gas heat, curb, economizer, fltrs, 5 Ton	8,975	6,275	15,250
1020	7-1/2 Ton	12,100	6,525	18,625
1030	12-1/2 Ton	19,700	7,150	26,850
1040	18 Ton	22,900	7,825	30,725
1050	25 Ton	33,800	8,925	42,725
1060	40 Ton	43,900	11,900	55,800

D3050 180	Rooftop Air Conditioner, Variable Air Volume	COST EACH MAT.	COST EACH INST.	COST EACH TOTAL
1010	A/C, Rooftop, DX cool, gas heat, curb, ecmizr, fltrs, VAV, 12-1/2 Ton	22,300	7,650	29,950
1020	18 Ton	26,000	8,425	34,425
1030	25 Ton	37,400	9,675	47,075
1040	40 Ton	50,500	13,100	63,600
1050	60 Ton	72,000	17,900	89,900
1060	80 Ton	113,000	22,400	135,400
2700	Cut & patch to match existing construction, add, minimum	2%	3%	
2800	Maximum	5%	9%	
2900	Dust protection, add, minimum	1%	2%	
3000	Maximum	4%	11%	

D3050 Terminal & Package Units

D3050 180	Rooftop Air Conditioner, Variable Air Volume	COST EACH		
		MAT.	INST.	TOTAL
3100	Equipment usage curtailment, add, minimum	1%	1%	
3200	Maximum	3%	10%	
3300	Material handling & storage limitation, add, minimum	1%	1%	
3400	Maximum	6%	7%	
3500	Protection of existing work, add, minimum	2%	2%	
3600	Maximum	5%	7%	
3700	Shift work requirements, add, minimum		5%	
3800	Maximum		30%	
3900	Temporary shoring and bracing, add, minimum	2%	5%	
4000	Maximum	5%	12%	

D3050 Terminal & Package Units

Condenser Supply Water Piping

Condenser Return Water Piping

Self—Contained Air Conditioner Unit, Water Cooled

This page illustrates and describes packaged electrical air conditioning units including multizone control and related piping. Lines within Systems Components give the material and installation price on a cost each basis for the components. Prices for packaged electrical A/C unit systems are on Line Items D3050 210 1010 thru D3050 225 1060. Material quantities and labor costs have been adjusted for the system listed.

Factors: To adjust for job conditions other than normal working situations use Lines D3050 225 2700 thru 4000.

System Components	QUANTITY	UNIT	COST EACH		
			MAT.	INST.	TOTAL
Packaged water cooled electric air conditioning unit with related piping and valves.					
Self-contained, water cooled, elect. heat, not inc tower, 5 ton, const vol	1.000	Ea.	9,350	1,700	11,050
Pipe, black steel, Sch 40, threaded, W/cplg & hangers, 10' OC, 1-1/4" dia.	20.000	L.F.	135.45	312.83	448.28
Elbow, 90°, black, straight, 1-1/4" dia.	6.000	Ea.	69.90	354	423.90
Tee, black, straight, 1-1/4" dia.	2.000	Ea.	35.90	185	220.90
Tee, black, reducing, 1-1/4" dia.	2.000	Ea.	63	185	248
Thermometers, stem type, 9" case, 8" stem, 3/4" NPT	2.000	Ea.	454	52	506
Union, black with brass seat, 1-1/4" dia.	2.000	Ea.	64	123	187
Pipe nipple, black, 1-1/4" dia	3.000	Ea.	9.45	21.83	31.28
Valves, bronze, gate, N.R.S., threaded, class 150, 1-1/4" size	2.000	Ea.	316	96	412
Circuit setter, bal valve, bronze body, threaded, 1-1/4" pipe size	1.000	Ea.	165	48.50	213.50
Insulation, fiberglass pipe covering, 1" wall, 1-1/4" IPS	20.000	L.F.	24.80	113	137.80
Control system, pneumatic, A/C Unit with heat	1.000	Ea.	2,950	2,575	5,525
Re-heat coil balancing	1.000	Ea.		135	135
Rooftop unit heat/cool balancing	1.000	Ea.		485	485
TOTAL			13,637.50	6,386.16	20,023.66

D3050 210	AC Unit, Package, Elec. Ht., Water Cooled	COST EACH		
		MAT.	INST.	TOTAL
1000	For alternate A/C systems:			
1010	A/C, Self contained, single pkg., water cooled, elect. heat, 5 Ton	13,600	6,375	19,975
1020	10 Ton	21,000	7,850	28,850
1030	20 Ton	31,000	10,000	41,000
1040	30 Ton	47,900	10,800	58,700
1050	40 Ton	61,000	12,000	73,000
1060	50 Ton	80,000	14,400	94,400

D3050 215	AC Unit, Package, Elec. Ht., Water Cooled, VAV	COST EACH		
		MAT.	INST.	TOTAL
1010	A/C, Self contained, single pkg., water cooled, elect. ht, VAV, 10 Ton	23,200	7,850	31,050
1020	20 Ton	34,600	10,000	44,600
1030	30 Ton	53,500	10,800	64,300
1040	40 Ton	67,500	12,000	79,500
1050	50 Ton	88,500	14,400	102,900
1060	60 Ton	100,500	17,400	117,900

D30 HVAC

D3050 Terminal & Package Units

D3050 220	AC Unit, Package, Hot Water Coil, Water Cooled	COST EACH		
		MAT.	INST.	TOTAL
1010	A/C, Self contn'd, single pkg., water cool, H/W ht, const. vol, 5 Ton	12,000	8,875	20,875
1020	10 Ton	17,300	10,600	27,900
1030	20 Ton	43,000	13,100	56,100
1040	30 Ton	56,000	16,700	72,700
1050	40 Ton	69,000	20,300	89,300
1060	50 Ton	84,500	24,900	109,400

D3050 225	AC Unit, Package, HW Coil, Water Cooled, VAV	COST EACH		
		MAT.	INST.	TOTAL
1010	A/C, Self contn'd, single pkg., water cool, H/W ht, VAV, 10 Ton	19,500	9,925	29,425
1020	20 Ton	30,800	12,800	43,600
1030	30 Ton	46,300	15,900	62,200
1040	40 Ton	61,000	17,400	78,400
1050	50 Ton	78,000	20,500	98,500
1060	60 Ton	91,500	22,300	113,800
2700	Cut & patch to match existing construction, add, minimum	2%	3%	
2800	Maximum	5%	9%	
2900	Dust protection, add, minimum	1%	2%	
3000	Maximum	4%	11%	
3100	Equipment usage curtailment, add, minimum	1%	1%	
3200	Maximum	3%	10%	
3300	Material handling & storage limitation, add, minimum	1%	1%	
3400	Maximum	6%	7%	
3500	Protection of existing work, add, minimum	2%	2%	
3600	Maximum	5%	7%	
3700	Shift work requirements, add, minimum		5%	
3800	Maximum		30%	
3900	Temporary shoring and bracing, add, minimum	2%	5%	
4000	Maximum	5%	12%	

D3050 Terminal & Package Units

Thru—Wall Heat Pump   Thru—Wall Air Conditioner

This page illustrates and describes thru-wall air conditioning and heat pump units. Lines within Systems Components give the material and installation price on a cost each basis for the components. Prices for thru-wall unit systems are on Line Items D3050 255 1010 thru D3050 260 1050. Material quantities and labor costs have been adjusted for the system listed.

Factors: To adjust for job conditions other than normal working conditions use Lines D3050 260 2700 thru 4000.

System Components	QUANTITY	UNIT	COST EACH		
			MAT.	INST.	TOTAL
Electric thru-wall air conditioning unit.					
A/C unit, thru-wall, electric heat., cabinet, louver, 1/2 ton	1.000	Ea.	855	219	1,074
TOTAL			855	219	1,074

D3050 255	Thru-Wall A/C Unit	COST EACH		
		MAT.	INST.	TOTAL
1000	For alternate A/C units:			
1010	A/C Unit, thru-the-wall, supplemental elect. heat, cabinet, louver, 1/2 Ton	855	219	1,074
1020	3/4 Ton	935	263	1,198
1030	1 Ton	1,000	330	1,330
1040	1-1/2 Ton	2,100	550	2,650
1050	2 Ton	2,125	690	2,815

D3050 260	Thru-Wall Heat Pump	COST EACH		
		MAT.	INST.	TOTAL
1010	Heat pump, thru-the-wall, cabinet, louver, 1/2 Ton	2,600	164	2,764
1020	3/4 Ton	2,750	219	2,969
1030	1 Ton	3,150	330	3,480
1040	Supplemental. elect. heat, 1-1/2 Ton	3,025	850	3,875
1050	2 Ton	3,250	875	4,125
2700	Cut & patch to match existing construction, add, minimum	2%	3%	
2800	Maximum	5%	9%	
2900	Dust protection, add, minimum	1%	2%	
3000	Maximum	4%	11%	
3100	Equipment usage curtailment, add, minimum	1%	1%	
3200	Maximum	3%	10%	
3300	Material handling & storage limitation, add, minimum	1%	1%	
3400	Maximum	6%	7%	
3500	Protection of existing work, add, minimum	2%	2%	
3600	Maximum	5%	7%	
3700	Shift work requirements, add, minimum		5%	
3800	Maximum		30%	
3900	Temporary shoring and bracing, add, minimum	2%	5%	
4000	Maximum	5%	12%	

D4010 Sprinklers

This page illustrates and describes a dry type fire sprinkler system. Lines within System Components give the unit cost of a system for a 2,000 square foot building. Lines D4010 320 1700 thru 2400 give the square foot costs for alternate systems. Both material quantities and labor costs have been adjusted for the system listed.

Factors: To adjust for conditions other than normal working conditions, use Lines D4010 320 2900 thru 4000.

System Components	QUANTITY	UNIT	COST EACH		
			MAT.	INST.	TOTAL
Pre-action fire sprinkler system, ordinary hazard, open area to 2000 S.F. on one floor.					
Air compressor	1.000	Ea.	810	530	1,340
4″ OS & Y valve	1.000	Ea.	805	430	1,235
Pipe riser 4″ diameter	10.000	L.F.	235	366.40	601.40
Sprinkler head supply piping, 1″	163.000	L.F.	382.50	1,016.25	1,398.75
Sprinkler head supply piping, 1-1/4″	163.000	L.F.	346.50	800.25	1,146.75
Sprinkler head supply piping, 2-1/2″	163.000	L.F.	587.10	988	1,575.10
Pipe fittings, 1″	8.000	Ea.	88.40	720	808.40
Pipe fittings, 1-1/4″	8.000	Ea.	143.60	740	883.60
Pipe fittings, 2-1/2″	4.000	Ea.	328	576	904
Pipe fittings, 4″	2.000	Ea.	584	650	1,234
Detectors	2.000	Ea.	1,500	87	1,587
Sprinkler heads	16.000	Ea.	164	696	860
Fire department connection	1.000	Ea.	545	249	794
TOTAL			6,519.10	7,848.90	14,368

D4010 320	Fire Sprinkler Systems, Dry	COST PER S.F.		
		MAT.	INST.	TOTAL
1700	Ordinary hazard, one floor, area to 2000 S.F./floor	3.24	3.94	7.18
1800	For each additional floor, add per floor	1.41	3.29	4.70
1900	Area to 3200 S.F./ floor	2.60	3.90	6.50
2000	For each additional floor, add per floor	1.46	3.49	4.95
2100	Area to 5000 S.F./ floor	2.93	3.96	6.89
2200	For each additional floor, add per floor	1.90	3.68	5.58
2300	Area to 8000 S.F./ floor	2.24	3.33	5.57
2400	For each additional floor, add per floor	1.50	3.15	4.65
2500				
2600				
2700				
2800				
2900	Cut & patch to match existing construction, add, minimum	2%	3%	
3000	Maximum	5%	9%	
3100	Dust protection, add, minimum	1%	2%	
3200	Maximum	4%	11%	
3300	Equipment usage curtailment, add, minimum	1%	1%	
3400	Maximum	3%	10%	

D40 Fire Protection

D4010 Sprinklers

D4010 320	Fire Sprinkler Systems, Dry	COST PER S.F.		
		MAT.	INST.	TOTAL
3500	Material handling & storage limitation, add, minimum	1%	1%	
3600	Maximum	6%	7%	
3700	Protection of existing work, add, minimum	2%	2%	
3800	Maximum	5%	7%	
3900	Shift work requirements, add, minimum		5%	
4000	Maximum		30%	

D4010 Sprinklers

This page illustrates and describes a wet type fire sprinkler system. Lines within System Components give the unit cost of a system for a 2,000 square foot building. Lines D4010 420 1900 thru 2600 give the square foot costs for alternate systems. Both material quantities and labor costs have been adjusted for the system listed.

Factors: To adjust for conditions other than normal working conditions, use Lines D4010 420 2900 thru 4000.

System Components	QUANTITY	UNIT	COST EACH MAT.	COST EACH INST.	COST EACH TOTAL
Wet pipe fire sprinkler system, ordinary hazard, open area to 2000 S.F. on one floor.					
4" OS & Y valve	1.000	Ea.	805	430	1,235
Wet pipe alarm valve	1.000	Ea.	1,775	625	2,400
Water motor alarm	1.000	Ea.	430	173	603
3" check valve	1.000	Ea.	365	415	780
Pipe riser, 4" diameter	10.000	L.F.	235	366.40	601.40
Water gauges and trim	1.000	Set	3,000	1,250	4,250
Electric fire horn	1.000	Ea.	66.50	98.50	165
Sprinkler head supply piping, 1" diameter	168.000	L.F.	382.50	1,016.25	1,398.75
Sprinkler head supply piping, 1-1/2" diameter	168.000	L.F.	404.25	888.25	1,292.50
Sprinkler head supply piping, 2-1/2" diameter	168.000	L.F.	587.10	988	1,575.10
Pipe fittings, 1"	8.000	Ea.	88.40	720	808.40
Pipe fittings, 1-1/2"	8.000	Ea.	180	796	976
Pipe fittings, 2-1/2"	4.000	Ea.	328	576	904
Pipe fittings, 4"	2.000	Ea.	584	650	1,234
Sprinkler heads	16.000	Ea.	164	696	860
Fire department connection	1.000	Ea.	545	249	794
TOTAL			9,939.75	9,937.40	19,877.15

D4010 420	Fire Sprinkler Systems, Wet	COST PER S.F. MAT.	COST PER S.F. INST.	COST PER S.F. TOTAL
1900	Ordinary hazard, one floor, area to 2000 S.F./floor	4.95	4.99	9.94
2000	For each additional floor, add per floor	1.46	3.36	4.82
2100	Area to 3200 S.F./floor	3.63	4.50	8.13
2200	For each additional floor, add per floor	1.46	3.49	4.95
2300	Area to 5000 S.F./ floor	3.30	4.33	7.63
2400	For each additional floor, add per floor	1.90	3.68	5.58
2500	Area to 8000 S.F./ floor	2.38	3.55	5.93
2600	For each additional floor, add per floor	1.61	3.34	4.95
2700				
2900	Cut & patch to match existing construction, add minimum	2%	3%	
3000	Maximum	5%	9%	
3100	Dust protection, add, minimum	1%	2%	
3200	Maximum	4%	11%	
3300	Equipment usage curtailment, add, minimum	1%	1%	
3400	Maximum	3%	10%	
3500	Material handling & storage limitation, add, minimum	1%	1%	
3600	Maximum	6%	7%	

D5010 Electrical Service/Distribution

This page illustrates and describes commercial service systems including a meter socket, service head and cable, entrance switch, steel conduit, copper wire, panel board, ground rod, wire, and conduit. Lines within System Components give the unit price and total price on a cost each basis for this system. Prices for commercial service systems are on Line Items D5010 210 1500 thru 1700. Both material quantities and labor costs have been adjusted for the system listed.

Factors: To adjust for job conditions other than normal working situations use Lines D5010 210 2900 thru 4000.

Example: You are to install the system with maximum equipment usage curtailment. Go to Line D5010 210 3400 and apply these percentages to the appropriate MAT. and INST. costs.

System Components	QUANTITY	UNIT	COST EACH MAT.	COST EACH INST.	COST EACH TOTAL
Commercial electric service including service breakers, metering 120/208 Volt, 3 phase, 4 wire, feeder, and panel board.					
100 Amp Service					
Meter socket	1.000	Ea.	46	206	252
Service head	.200	C.L.F.	56.40	132	188.40
Service entrance switch	1.000	Ea.	276	350	626
Rigid steel conduit	20.000	L.F.	82.20	203	285.20
600 volt copper wire #3	1.000	C.L.F.	139	132	271
Panel board, 24 circuits, 20 Amp breakers	1.000	Ea.	995	1,100	2,095
Ground rod	1.000	Ea.	22.50	120	142.50
TOTAL			1,617.10	2,243	3,860.10

D5010 210	Commercial Service - 3 Phase	COST EACH MAT.	COST EACH INST.	COST EACH TOTAL
1500	120/208 Volt, 3 phase, 4 wire service, 60 Amp	1,100	1,750	2,850
1550	100 Amp	1,625	2,250	3,875
1600	200 Amp	3,250	3,950	7,200
1700	400 Amp	7,050	4,950	12,000
1800				
1900				
2000				
2100				
2200				
2300				
2400				
2500				
2900	Cut & patch to match existing construction, add, minimum	2%	3%	
3000	Maximum	5%	9%	
3100	Dust protection, add, minimum	1%	2%	
3200	Maximum	4%	11%	
3300	Equipment usage curtailment, add, minimum	1%	1%	
3400	Maximum	3%	10%	
3500	Material handling & storage limitation, add, minimum	1%	1%	
3600	Maximum	6%	7%	
3700	Protection of existing work, add, minimum	2%	2%	
3800	Maximum	5%	7%	
3900	Shift work requirements, add, minimum		5%	
4000	Maximum		30%	

D5010 Electrical Service/Distribution

This page illustrates and describes a residential, single phase system including a weather cap, service entrance cable, meter socket, entrance switch, ground rod, ground cable, EMT, and panelboard. Lines within System Components give the unit price and total price on a cost each basis for this system. Prices for a residential, single phase system are also given. Both material quantities and labor costs have been adjusted for the system listed.

Factors: To adjust for job conditions other than normal working situations use Lines D5010 220 2900 thru 4000.

Example: You are to install the system with a minimum equipment usage curtailment. Go to Line D5010 220 3300 and apply these percentages to the appropriate MAT. and INST. costs.

System Components	QUANTITY	UNIT	COST EACH		
			MAT.	INST.	TOTAL
100 Amp Service, single phase					
Weathercap	1.000	Ea.	11.35	55	66.35
Service entrance cable	.200	C.L.F.	56.40	132	188.40
Meter socket	1.000	Ea.	46	206	252
Entrance disconnect switch	1.000	Ea.	276	350	626
Ground rod, with clamp	1.000	Ea.	25	138	163
Ground cable	.100	C.L.F.	16.10	41.50	57.60
Panelboard, 12 circuit	1.000	Ea.	267	550	817
TOTAL			697.85	1,472.50	2,170.35
200 Amp Service , single phase					
Weathercap	1.000	Ea.	31.50	82.50	114
Service entrance cable	.200	C.L.F.	144	189	333
Meter socket	1.000	Ea.	98.50	350	448.50
Entrance disconnect switch	1.000	Ea.	590	510	1,100
Ground rod, with clamp	1.000	Ea.	43	150	193
Ground cable	.100	C.L.F.	34.50	22.80	57.30
3/4" EMT	10.000	L.F.	9.40	51	60.40
Panelboard, 24 circuit	1.000	Ea.	585	860	1,445
TOTAL			1,535.90	2,215.30	3,751.20

D5010 220	Residential Service - Single Phase	COST EACH		
		MAT.	INST.	TOTAL
2800				
2810	100 Amp Service, single phase	700	1,475	2,175
2820	200 Amp Service, single phase	1,525	2,225	3,750
2900	Cut & patch to match existing construction, add, minimum	2%	3%	
3000	Maximum	5%	9%	
3100	Dust protection, add, minimum	1%	2%	
3200	Maximum	4%	11%	
3300	Equipment usage curtailment, add, minimum	1%	1%	
3400	Maximum	3%	10%	
3500	Material handling & storage limitation, add, minimum	1%	1%	
3600	Maximum	6%	7%	
3700	Protection of existing work, add, minimum	2%	2%	
3800	Maximum	5%	7%	
3900	Shift work requirements, add, minimum		5%	
4000	Maximum		30%	

671

D5020 Lighting and Branch Wiring

D5020 180	Selective Price Sheet	COST EACH		
		MAT.	INST.	TOTAL
0100	Using non-metallic sheathed, cable, air conditioning receptacle	23	66	89
0200	Disposal wiring	19.85	73.50	93.35
0300	Dryer circuit	42.50	120	162.50
0400	Duplex receptacle	23	51	74
0500	Fire alarm or smoke detector	100	66	166
0600	Furnace circuit & switch	30.50	110	140.50
0700	Ground fault receptacle	61	82.50	143.50
0800	Heater circuit	27.50	82.50	110
0900	Lighting wiring	28	41.50	69.50
1000	Range circuit	86	165	251
1100	Switches single pole	23.50	41.50	65
1200	3-way	26	55	81
1300	Water heater circuit	33	132	165
1400	Weatherproof receptacle	138	110	248
1500	Using BX cable, air conditioning receptacle	32.50	79.50	112
1600	Disposal wiring	28.50	88	116.50
1700	Dryer circuit	48	144	192
1800	Duplex receptacle	32.50	61	93.50
1900	Fire alarm or smoke detector	100	66	166
2000	Furnace circuit & switch	42.50	132	174.50
2100	Ground fault receptacle	70.50	100	170.50
2200	Heater circuit	32.50	100	132.50
2300	Lighting wiring	33.50	49.50	83
2400	Range circuit	121	200	321
2500	Switches, single pole	33	49.50	82.50
2600	3-way	34	66	100
2700	Water heater circuit	48	157	205
2800	Weatherproof receptacle	144	132	276
2900	Using EMT conduit, air conditioning receptacle	43.50	98.50	142
3000	Disposal wiring	41.50	110	151.50
3100	Dryer circuit	55	178	233
3200	Duplex receptacle	43.50	76	119.50
3300	Fire alarm or smoke detector	116	98.50	214.50
3400	Furnace circuit & switch	49.50	165	214.50
3500	Ground fault receptacle	91.50	122	213.50
3600	Heater circuit	43	122	165
3700	Lighting wiring	41	61.50	102.50
3800	Range circuit	97	245	342
3900	Switches, single pole	44	61.50	105.50
4000	3-way	39	82.50	121.50
4100	Water heater circuit	48.50	194	242.50
4200	Weatherproof receptacle	155	165	320
4300	Using aluminum conduit, air conditioning receptacle	50	132	182
4400	Disposal wiring	48	147	195
4500	Dryer circuit	72.50	236	308.50
4600	Duplex receptacle	47.50	102	149.50
4700	Fire alarm or smoke detector	128	132	260
4800	Furnace circuit & switch	59.50	220	279.50
4900	Ground fault receptacle	96	165	261
5000	Heater circuit	48.50	165	213.50
5100	Lighting wiring	56.50	82.50	139
5200	Range circuit	119	330	449
5300	Switches, single pole	57.50	82.50	140
5400	3-way	53	110	163
5500	Water heater circuit	62	264	326
5600	Weatherproof receptacle	177	220	397
5700	Using galvanized steel conduit	52	141	193
5800	Disposal wiring	44	157	201

D50 Electrical

D5020 Lighting and Branch Wiring

D5020 180	Selective Price Sheet	COST EACH		
		MAT.	INST.	TOTAL
5900	Dryer circuit	76.50	254	330.50
6000	Duplex receptacle	52	108	160
6100	Fire alarm or smoke detector	125	141	266
6200	Furnace circuit & switch	56	236	292
6300	Ground fault receptacle	97.50	174	271.50
6400	Heater circuit	50	174	224
6500	Lighting wiring	56	88	144
6600	Range circuit	121	350	471
6700	Switches, single pole	59.50	88	147.50
6800	3-way	54.50	114	168.50
6900	Water heater circuit	61.50	275	336.50
7000	Weatherproof receptacle	171	236	407
7100				
7200				
7300				
7400				
7500				
7600				
7700				
7800				
7900				
8000				
8100				
8200				
8300				
8400				

D5020 Lighting and Branch Wiring

This page illustrates and describes fluorescent lighting systems including a fixture, lamp, outlet box and wiring. Lines within System Components give the unit price and total price on a cost each basis for this system. Prices for fluorescent lighting systems are on Line Items D5020 248 1200 thru 1500. Both material quantities and labor costs have been adjusted for the system listed.

Factors: To adjust for job conditions other than normal working situations use Lines D5020 248 2900 thru 4000.

Example: You are to install the system during evening hours. Go to Line D5020 248 3900 and apply this percentage to the appropriate INST. cost.

System Components			COST EACH		
	QUANTITY	UNIT	MAT.	INST.	TOTAL
Fluorescent lighting, including fixture, lamp, outlet box and wiring.					
Recessed lighting fixture, on suspended system	1.000	Ea.	63.50	141	204.50
Outlet box	1.000	Ea.	2.31	36.50	38.81
#12 wire	.660	C.L.F.	9.83	39.60	49.43
Conduit, EMT, 1/2" conduit	20.000	L.F.	12.40	77.60	90
TOTAL			88.04	294.70	382.74

D5020 248	Lighting, Fluorescent	COST EACH		
		MAT.	INST.	TOTAL
1200	Recessed lighting fixture, on suspended system	88	295	383
1300	Surface mounted, 2' x 4', acrylic prismatic diffuser	114	310	424
1400	Strip fixture, 8' long, two 8' lamps	87.50	291	378.50
1500	Pendant mounted, industrial, 8' long, with reflectors	132	335	467
1600				
1700				
1800				
1900				
2000				
2100				
2200				
2300				
2900	Cut & patch to match existing construction, add, minimum	2%	3%	
3000	Maximum	5%	9%	
3100	Dust protection, add, minimum	1%	2%	
3200	Maximum	4%	11%	
3300	Equipment usage curtailment, add, minimum	1%	1%	
3400	Maximum	3%	10%	
3500	Material handling & storage limitation, add, minimum	1%	1%	
3600	Maximum	6%	7%	
3700	Protection of existing work, add, minimum	2%	2%	
3800	Maximum	5%	7%	
3900	Shift work requirements, add, minimum		5%	
4000	Maximum		30%	

D5020 Lighting and Branch Wiring

This page illustrates and describes incandescent lighting systems including a fixture, lamp, outlet box, conduit and wiring. Lines within System Components give the unit price and total price on a cost each basis for this system. Prices for an alternate incandescent lighting system are also given. Both material quantities and labor costs have been adjusted for the system listed.

Factors: To adjust for conditions other than normal working situations use Lines D5020 250 2900 thru 4000.

Example: You are to install the system and cut and match existing construction. Go to Line D5020 250 3000 and apply this percentage to the appropriate INST. costs.

System Components		QUANTITY	UNIT	COST EACH		
				MAT.	INST.	TOTAL
Incandescent light fixture, including lamp, outlet box, conduit and wiring.						
Recessed wide reflector with flat glass lens		1.000	Ea.	106	98.50	204.50
Outlet box		1.000	Ea.	2.31	36.50	38.81
Armored cable, 3 wire		.200	C.L.F.	18.40	60	78.40
	TOTAL			126.71	195	321.71
Recessed flood light fixture, including lamp, outlet box, conduit & wire						
Recessed, R-40 flood lamp with refractor		1.000	Ea.	113	82.50	195.50
150 watt R-40 flood lamp		.010	Ea.	6.75	5.10	11.85
Outlet box		1.000	Ea.	2.31	36.50	38.81
Outlet box cover		1.000	Ea.	1.53	10.30	11.83
Romex, 12-2 with ground		.200	C.L.F.	8.50	60	68.50
Conduit, 1/2" EMT		20.000	L.F.	12.40	77.60	90
	TOTAL			144.49	272	416.49

D5020 250	Lighting, Incandescent	COST EACH		
		MAT.	INST.	TOTAL
2810	Incandescent light fixture, including lamp, outlet box, conduit and wiring.	127	195	322
2820	Recessed flood light fixture, including lamp, outlet box, conduit & wire	144	272	416
2900	Cut & patch to match existing construction, add, minimum	2%	3%	
3000	Maximum	5%	9%	
3100	Dust protection, add, minimum	1%	2%	
3200	Maximum	4%	11%	
3300	Equipment usage curtailment, add, minimum	1%	1%	
3400	Maximum	3%	10%	
3500	Material handling & storage limitation, add, minimum	1%	1%	
3600	Maximum	6%	7%	
3700	Protection of existing work, add, minimum	2%	2%	
3800	Maximum	5%	7%	
3900	Shift work requirements, add, minimum		5%	
4000	Maximum		30%	

D50 Electrical

D5020　Lighting and Branch Wiring

This page illustrates and describes high intensity lighting systems including a lamp, EMT conduit, EMT "T" fitting with cover, and wire. Lines within System Components give the unit price and total price on a cost each basis for this system. Prices for high intensity lighting systems are on Line Items D5020 252 1100 thru 1800. Both material quantities and labor costs have been adjusted for the system listed.

Factors: To adjust for job conditions other than normal working situations use Lines D5020 252 2900 thru 4000.

Example: You are to install the system and protect existing construction. Go to Line D5020 252 3700 and apply these percentages to the appropriate MAT. and INST. costs.

System Components	QUANTITY	UNIT	COST EACH MAT.	COST EACH INST.	COST EACH TOTAL
High intensity lighting system consisting of 400 watt metal halide fixture and lamp with 1/2″ EMT conduit and fittings using #12 wire, high bay.					
Single unit, 400 watt	1.000	Ea.	450	287	737
Electric metallic tubing (EMT), 1/2″ diameter	30.000	Ea.	18.60	116.40	135
1/2″ EMT "T" fitting with cover	1.000	Ea.	10.20	41.50	51.70
Wire, 600 volt, type THWN-THHN, copper, solid, #12	.600	Ea.	8.94	36	44.94
TOTAL			487.74	480.90	968.64

D5020 252	Lighting, High Intensity	COST EACH MAT.	COST EACH INST.	COST EACH TOTAL
1100	High bay: 400 watt, metal halide fixture and lamp	490	480	970
1200	High pressure sodium and lamp	455	480	935
1400	1000 watt, metal halide	685	525	1,210
1500	High pressure sodium	635	525	1,160
1700	Low bay: 250 watt, metal halide	435	400	835
1800	150 watt, high pressure sodium	395	400	795
1900				
2000				
2100				
2200				
2300				
2400				
2500				
2600				
2700				
2900	Cut & patch to match existing construction, add, minimum	2%	3%	
3000	Maximum	5%	9%	
3100	Dust protection, add, minimum	1%	2%	
3200	Maximum	4%	11%	
3300	Equipment usage curtailment, add, minimum	1%	1%	
3400	Maximum	3%	10%	
3500	Material handling & storage limitation, add, minimum	1%	1%	
3600	Maximum	6%	7%	
3700	Protection of existing work, add, minimum	2%	2%	
3800	Maximum	5%	7%	
3900	Shift work requirements, add, minimum		5%	
4000	Maximum		30%	

D5090 Other Electrical Systems

This page illustrates and describes baseboard heat systems including a thermostat, outlet box, breaker, and feed. Lines within System Components give the unit price and total price on a cost each basis for this system. Prices for baseboard heat systems are on Line Items D5090 530 1500 thru 1800. Both material quantities and labor costs have been adjusted for the system listed.

Factors: To adjust for job conditions other than normal working situations use Lines D5090 530 2900 thru 4000.

Example: You are to install the system during evenings and weekends only. Go to Line D5090 530 4000 and apply this percentage to the appropriate INST. cost.

System Components	QUANTITY	UNIT	COST EACH		
			MAT.	INST.	TOTAL
Baseboard heat including thermostat, outlet box, breaker and feed.					
Electric baseboard heater, 4' long	1.000	Ea.	45	98.50	143.50
Thermostat, integral	1.000	Ea.	33	41.50	74.50
Romex, 12-3 with ground	.400	C.L.F.	23.80	132	155.80
Panel board breaker, 20 Amp	1.000	Ea.	35	82.50	117.50
Outlet box	1.000	Ea.	2.31	36.50	38.81
TOTAL			139.11	391	530.11

D5090 530	Heat, Baseboard	COST EACH		
		MAT.	INST.	TOTAL
1400	Heat, electric baseboard			
1500	2' long	127	375	502
1550	4' long	139	390	529
1600	6' long	156	425	581
1700	8' long	170	460	630
1800	10' long	305	495	800
1900				
2000				
2100				
2200				
2300				
2400				
2500				
2600				
2700				
2900	Cut & patch to match existing construction, add, minimum	2%	3%	
3000	Maximum	5%	9%	
3100	Dust protection, add, minimum	1%	2%	
3200	Maximum	4%	11%	
3300	Equipment usage curtailment, add, minimum	1%	1%	
3400	Maximum	3%	10%	
3500	Material handling & storage limitation, add, minimum	1%	1%	
3600	Maximum	6%	7%	
3700	Protection of existing work, add, minimum	2%	2%	
3800	Maximum	5%	7%	
3900	Shift work requirements, add, minimum		5%	
4000	Maximum		30%	

E10 Equipment

E1090 Other Equipment

This page illustrates and describes kitchen systems including top and bottom cabinets, custom laminated plastic top, single bowl sink, and appliances. Lines within System Components give the unit price and total price on a cost each basis for this system. Prices for kitchen systems are on Line Items E1090 310 1400 thru 1600. Both material quantities and labor costs have been adjusted for the system listed.

Factors: To adjust for job conditions other than normal working situations use Lines E1090 310 2900 thru 4000.

Example: You are to install the system and protect the work area from dust. Go to Line E1090 310 3200 and apply these percentages to the appropriate MAT. and INST. costs.

System Components	QUANTITY	UNIT	COST EACH MAT.	COST EACH INST.	COST EACH TOTAL
Kitchen cabinets including wall and base cabinets, custom laminated plastic top, sink & appliances, no plumbing or electrical rough-in included.					
Prefinished wood cabinets, average quality, wall and base	20.000	L.F.	3,700	800	4,500
Custom laminated plastic counter top	20.000	L.F.	367	400	767
Stainless steel sink, 22" x 25"	1.000	Ea.	725	231	956
Faucet, top mount	1.000	Ea.	67.50	72	139.50
Dishwasher, built-in	1.000	Ea.	258	345	603
Compactor, built-in	1.000	Ea.	705	121	826
Range hood, vented, 30" wide	1.000	Ea.	76.50	256	332.50
TOTAL			5,899	2,225	8,124

E1090 310	Kitchens	COST EACH MAT.	COST EACH INST.	COST EACH TOTAL
1400	Prefinished wood cabinets, average quality	5,900	2,225	8,125
1500	Prefinished wood cabinets, high quality	11,000	2,550	13,550
1600	Custom cabinets, built in place, high quality	14,400	2,925	17,325
1700				
1800				
1900				
2000				
2100				
2200	NOTE: No plumbing or electric rough-ins are included in the above			
2300	Prices, for plumbing see Division 22, for electric see Division 26.			
2400				
2500				
2600				
2700				
2900	Cut & patch to match existing construction, add, minimum	2%	3%	
3000	Maximum	5%	9%	
3100	Dust protection, add, minimum	1%	2%	
3200	Maximum	4%	11%	
3300	Equipment usage curtailment, add, minimum	1%	1%	
3400	Maximum	3%	10%	
3500	Material handling & storage limitation, add, minimum	1%	1%	
3600	Maximum	6%	7%	
3700	Protection of existing work, add, minimum	2%	2%	
3800	Maximum	5%	7%	
3900	Shift work requirements, add, minimum		5%	
4000	Maximum		30%	

E1090 Other Equipment

E1090 315	Selective Price Sheet	COST EACH		
		MAT.	INST.	TOTAL
0100	Cabinets standard wood, base, one drawer one door, 12" wide	279	48.50	327.50
0200	15" wide	291	50	341
0300	18" wide	315	51.50	366.50
0400	21" wide	325	53	378
0500	24" wide	385	54	439
0600				
0700	Two drawers two doors, 27" wide	415	55	470
0800	30" wide	450	56.50	506.50
0900	33" wide	465	57.50	522.50
1000	36" wide	480	59.50	539.50
1100	42" wide	510	61	571
1200	48" wide	545	64	609
1300	Drawer base (4 drawers), 12" wide	293	48.50	341.50
1400	15" wide	298	50	348
1500	18" wide	330	51.50	381.50
1600	24" wide	360	54	414
1700	Sink or range base, 30" wide	370	56.50	426.50
1800	33" wide	400	57.50	457.50
1900	36" wide	415	59.50	474.50
2000	42" wide	440	61	501
2100	Corner base, 36" wide	660	67	727
2200	Lazy Susan with revolving door	885	73	958
2300	Cabinets standard wood, wall two doors, 12" high, 30" wide	250	48.50	298.50
2400	36" wide	297	50	347
2500	15" high, 30" high	254	50	304
2600	36" wide	305	53	358
2700	24" high, 30" wide	340	51.50	391.50
2800	36" wide	375	53	428
2900	30" high, 30" wide	380	62.50	442.50
3000	36" wide	430	64	494
3100	42" wide	465	65	530
3200	48" wide	530	65.50	595.50
3300	One door, 30" high, 12" wide	227	55	282
3400	15" wide	254	56.50	310.50
3500	18" wide	279	57.50	336.50
3600	24" wide	325	59.50	384.50
3700	Corner, 30" high, 24" wide	375	67	442
3800	36" wide	450	73	523
3900	Broom, 84" high, 24" deep, 18" wide	685	121	806
4000	Oven, 84" high, 24" deep, 27" wide	1,050	151	1,201
4100	Valance board, 4' long	57	12.15	69.15
4200	6' long	86	18.25	104.25
4300	Counter tops, laminated plastic, stock 25" wide w/backsplash, min.	18.35	20	38.35
4400	Maximum	37	24	61
4500	Custom, 7/8" thick, no splash	32.50	20	52.50
4600	Cove splash	31.50	20	51.50
4700	1-1/4" thick, no splash	38	21.50	59.50
4800	Square splash	45.50	21.50	67
4900	Post formed	11	20	31
5000				
5100	Maple laminated 1-1/2" thick, no splash	81.50	21.50	103
5200	Square splash	97	21.50	118.50
5300				
5400				
5500	Appliances, range, free standing, minimum	480	96.50	576.50
5600	Maximum	2,200	241	2,441
5700	Built-in, minimum	740	110	850
5800	Maximum	1,475	605	2,080

E1090   Other Equipment

E1090 315	Selective Price Sheet	COST EACH		
		MAT.	INST.	TOTAL
5900	Counter top range 4 burner, maximum	320	110	430
6000	Maximum	1,425	220	1,645
6100	Compactor, built-in, minimum	705	121	826
6200	Maximum	1,100	201	1,301
6300	Dishwasher, built-in, minimum	258	345	603
6400	Maximum	470	690	1,160
6500	Garbage disposer, sink-pipe, minimum	95	138	233
6600	Maximum	239	138	377
6700	Range hood, 30" wide, 2 speed, minimum	76.50	256	332.50
6800	Maximum	845	425	1,270
6900	Refrigerator, no frost, 12 cu. ft.	460	96.50	556.50
7000	20 cu. ft.	485	161	646
7100	Plumb. not incl. rough-ins, sinks porc. C.I., single bowl, 21" x 24"	300	231	531
7200	21" x 30"	630	231	861
7300	Double bowl, 20" x 32"	375	269	644
7400				
7500	Stainless steel, single bowl, 19" x 18"	650	231	881
7600	22" x 25"	725	231	956
7700				
7800				
7900				
8000				
8100				
8200				
8300				
8400				

G1030 Site Earthwork

This page illustrates and describes utility trench excavation with backfill systems including a trench, backfill, excavated material, utility pipe or ductwork not included. Lines within System Components give the unit price and total price on a linear foot basis for this system. Prices for utility trench excavation with backfill systems are on Line Items G1030 810 1100 thru 2500. Both material quantities

and labor costs have been adjusted for the system listed.

Factors: To adjust for job conditions other than normal working situations use Lines G1030 810 3100 thru 4000.

Example: You are to install the system and protect existing construction. Go to Line G1030 810 3600 and apply these percentages to the appropriate TOTAL cost.

System Components	QUANTITY	UNIT	COST PER L.F. MAT.	COST PER L.F. INST.	COST PER L.F. TOTAL
Cont. utility trench excav. with 3/8 C.Y. wheel mtd. backhoe, backfilling with excav. mat. and comp. in 12″ lifts. Trench is 2′ wide by 4′ dp. Cost of utility piping or ductwork is not incl. Cost based on an excavation production rate of 150 C.Y. daily no hauling included.					
Machine excavate trench, 2′ wide by 4′ deep	.296	C.Y.	.79	2.18	2.97
Dozer backfill with excavated material	.296	C.Y.	.37	.60	.97
Compact in 12″ lifts, vibrating plate	.296	C.Y.	.08	2.41	2.49
TOTAL			1.24	5.19	6.43

G1030 810	Excavation, Utility Trench	COST PER L.F. MAT.	COST PER L.F. INST.	COST PER L.F. TOTAL
1100	2′ wide x 2′ deep	.63	2.60	3.23
1200	3′ deep	.93	3.89	4.82
1250	4′ deep	1.24	5.20	6.45
1300	With sloping sides, 2′ wide x 5′ deep	3.50	14.60	18.10
1400	6′ deep	4.68	19.50	24
1500	7′ deep	6	25	31
1600	8′ deep	7.50	31	38.50
1700	9′ deep	9.15	38	47
1800	10′ deep	10.90	45.50	56.50
2000	For hauling excavated material up to 2 miles & backfilling w/ gravel			
2100	Gravel, 2′ wide by 2′ deep, add	4.07	3.69	7.76
2200	4′ deep, add	8.15	7.40	15.55
2300	6′ deep, add	30.50	27.50	58
2400	8′ deep, add	49	44.50	93.50
2500	10′ deep, add	71.50	65	136.50
2600				
2700				
2800	For shallow, hand excavated trenches, no backfill, to 6′ dp, light soil		60	60
2900	Heavy soil		120	120
3000				
3100	Equipment usage curtailment, add, minimum	1%	1%	
3200	Maximum	3%	10%	
3300	Material handling & storage limitation, add, minimum	1%	1%	
3400	Maximum	6%	7%	
3500	Protection of existing work, add, minimum	2%	2%	
3600	Maximum	5%	7%	
3700	Shift work requirements, add, minimum		5%	
3800	Maximum		30%	
3900	Temporary shoring and bracing, add, minimum	2%	5%	
4000	Maximum	5%	12%	

G20 Site Improvements

G2010 Roadways

This page illustrates and describes driveway systems including concrete slab, gravel base, broom finish, compaction, and joists. Lines within System Components give the unit price and total price on a cost each basis for this system. Prices for driveway systems are on Line Items G2010 240 1200 thru 2700. Both material quantities and labor costs have been adjusted for the system listed.

Factors: To adjust for job conditions other than normal working situations use Lines G2010 240 2900 thru 4000.

Example: You are to install the system and match existing construction. Go to Line G2010 240 3000 and apply these percentages to the appropriate MAT. and INST. costs.

System Components	QUANTITY	UNIT	COST EACH		
			MAT.	INST.	TOTAL
Complete driveway, 10' x 30', 4" concrete slab, 3000 psi, on 6" crushed stone base, concrete broom finished and cured with 10' x 10' joints.					
Grade and compact subgrade	33.000	S.Y.		71.94	71.94
Place and compact 6" crushed stone base	33.000	S.Y.	199.65	48.51	248.16
Place and remove edgeforms (4 use)	80.000	L.F.	27.20	305.60	332.80
Concrete for slab, 3000 psi	4.000	C.Y.	436		436
Place concrete, 4" thick slab, direct chute	4.000	C.Y.		110.64	110.64
Screed, float and broom finish slab	4.000	C.Y.		258	258
Spray on membrane curing compound	3.000	S.F.	36.15	30.45	66.60
Saw cut 3" deep joints	60.000	L.F.	9.60	100.80	110.40
TOTAL			708.60	925.94	1,634.54

G2010 240	Driveways	COST EACH		
		MAT.	INST.	TOTAL
1200	Concrete: 10' x 30' with 4" concrete on 6" crushed stone	710	925	1,635
1300	With 6" concrete	925	985	1,910
1400	20' x 30' with 4" concrete	1,425	1,775	3,200
1500	With 6" concrete	1,850	1,875	3,725
1600	10' wide, for each additional 10' length over 30', 4" thick, add	227	298	525
1700	6" thick, add	310	320	630
1800	20' wide, for each additional 10' length over 30', 4" thick, add	450	570	1,020
1900	6" thick, add	590	605	1,195
2000	Asphalt: 10' x 30' with 2" binder, 1" topping on 6" cr. st., sealed	650	680	1,330
2100	3" binder, 1" topping	780	695	1,475
2200	20' x 30' with 2" binder, 1" topping	1,300	935	2,235
2300	3" binding, 1" topping	1,575	965	2,540
2400	10' wide for each add'l. 10' length over 30', 2" b + 1" t, add	216	84.50	300.50
2500	3" binder, 1" topping	261	89	350
2600	20' wide for each add'l. 10' length over 30', 2" b + 1" t, add	435	169	604
2700	3" binder, 1" topping	520	178	698
2800				
2900	Cut & patch to match existing construction, add, minimum	2%	3%	
3000	Maximum	5%	9%	
3100	Dust protection, add, minimum	1%	2%	
3200	Maximum	4%	11%	
3300	Equipment usage curtailment, add, minimum	1%	1%	
3400	Maximum	3%	10%	
3500	Material handling & storage limitation, add, minimum	1%	1%	
3600	Maximum	6%	7%	
3700	Protection of existing work, add, minimum	2%	2%	
3800	Maximum	5%	7%	
3900	Shift work requirements, add, minimum		5%	
4000	Maximum		30%	

G2020 Parking Lots

This page illustrates and describes asphalt parking lot systems including asphalt binder, topping, crushed stone base, painted parking stripes and concrete parking blocks. Lines within System Components give the unit price and total price per square yard for this system. Prices for asphalt parking lot systems are on Line Items G2020 230 1400 thru 2500. Both material quantities and labor costs have been adjusted for the system listed.

Factors: To adjust for job conditions other than normal working situations use Lines G2020 230 2900 thru 4000.

Example: You are to install the system and match existing construction. Go to Line G2020 230 2900 and apply these percentages to the appropriate MAT. and INST. costs.

System Components	QUANTITY	UNIT	COST PER S.Y. MAT.	COST PER S.Y. INST.	COST PER S.Y. TOTAL
Parking lot consisting of 2″ asphalt binder and 1″ topping on 6″ crushed stone base with painted parking stripes and concrete parking blocks.					
Fine grade and compact subgrade	1.000	S.Y.		2.18	2.18
6″ crushed stone base, stone	.320	Ton	6.05	1.47	7.52
2″ asphalt binder	1.000	S.Y.	8.15	1.38	9.53
1″ asphalt topping	1.000	S.Y.	4.04	.91	4.95
Paint parking stripes	.500	L.F.	.08	.10	.18
6″ x 10″ x 6′ precast concrete parking blocks	.020	Ea.	.86	.41	1.27
Mobilization of equipment	.005	Ea.		2.15	2.15
TOTAL			19.18	8.60	27.78

G2020 230	Parking Lots, Asphalt	COST PER S.Y. MAT.	COST PER S.Y. INST.	COST PER S.Y. TOTAL
1400	2″ binder plus 1″ topping on 6″ crushed stone	19.20	8.60	27.80
1500	9″ crushed stone	22	8.75	30.75
1600	12″ crushed stone	25.50	8.90	34.40
1700	On bank run gravel, 6″ deep	17.80	7.95	25.75
1800	9″ deep	20	8.10	28.10
1900	12″ deep	22.50	8.30	30.80
2000	3″ binder plus 1″ topping on 6″ crushed stone	23	9	32
2100	9″ deep crushed stone	26.50	9.15	35.65
2200	12″ deep crushed stone	29.50	9.30	38.80
2300	On bank run gravel, 6″ deep	22	8.35	30.35
2400	9″ deep	24	8.55	32.55
2500	12″ deep	26.50	8.70	35.20
2600				
2700				
2900	Cut & patch to match existing construction, add, minimum	2%	3%	
3000	Maximum	5%	9%	
3100	Dust protection, add, minimum	1%	2%	
3200	Maximum	4%	11%	
3300	Equipment usage curtailment, add, minimum	1%	1%	
3400	Maximum	3%	10%	
3500	Material handling & storage limitation, add, minimum	1%	1%	
3600	Maximum	6%	7%	
3700	Protection of existing work, add, minimum	2%	2%	
3800	Maximum	5%	7%	
3900	Shift work requirements, add, minimum		5%	
4000	Maximum		30%	

G2020 Parking Lots

This page illustrates and describes concrete parking lot systems including a concrete slab, unreinforced, crushed stone, broom finished, cured, joints, painted parking stripes, and parking blocks. Lines within System Components give the unit price and total price per square yard for this system. Prices for concrete parking lot systems are on Line Items G2020 240 1500 thru 2500. All materials have been adjusted according to the system listed.

Factors: To adjust for job conditions other than normal working situations use Lines G2020 240 2900 thru 4000.

Example: You are to install the system and protect existing construction. Go to Line G2020 240 3800 and apply these percentages to the appropriate MAT. and INST. costs.

System Components			COST PER S.Y.		
	QUANTITY	UNIT	MAT.	INST.	TOTAL
Parking lot, 4″ slab, 3000 psi concrete on 6″ crushed stone base with 12′ x 12′ joints, painted parking strips, conc. parking blocks.					
Grade and compact subgrade	1.000	S.Y.		2.18	2.18
6″ crushed stone base, stone	.320	Ton	6.05	1.47	7.52
Place and remove edge forms, 4 use	.250	L.F.	.09	.96	1.05
Concrete for slab, 3000 psi	1.000	S.F.	11.99		11.99
Place concrete, 4″ thick slab, direct chute	1.000	S.F.		3.04	3.04
Spray on membrane curing compound	1.000	S.F.	1.09	.64	1.73
Saw cut 3″ deep joints	2.250	L.F.	.36	3.78	4.14
Paint parking stripes	.500	L.F.	.08	.10	.18
6″ x 10″ x 6′ precast concrete parking blocks	.020	Ea.	.86	.41	1.27
TOTAL			20.52	12.58	33.10

G2020 240	Parking Lots, Concrete	COST PER S.Y.		
		MAT.	INST.	TOTAL
1500	4″ concrete slab, 3000 psi on 3″ crushed stone	17.50	12.50	30
1550	6″ crushed stone	20.50	12.60	33.10
1600	9″ crushed stone	23.50	12.75	36.25
1700	On bank run gravel, 6″ deep	19.15	11.90	31.05
1800	9″ deep	21.50	12.10	33.60
1900	On compacted subgrade only	14.45	11.10	25.55
2000	6″ concrete slab, 3000 psi on 3″ crushed stone	23.50	14	37.50
2100	6″ crushed stone	26.50	14.05	40.55
2200	9″ crushed stone	29.50	14.15	43.65
2300	On bank run gravel, 6″ deep	25	13.40	38.40
2400	9″ deep	27.50	13.55	41.05
2500	On compacted subgrade only	26.50	14.05	40.55
2600				
2700				
2900	Cut & patch to match existing construction, add, minimum	2%	3%	
3000	Maximum	5%	9%	
3100	Dust protection, add, minimum	1%	2%	
3200	Maximum	4%	11%	
3300	Equipment usage curtailment, add, minimum	1%	1%	
3400	Maximum	3%	10%	
3500	Material handling & storage limitation, add, minimum	1%	1%	
3600	Maximum	6%	7%	
3700	Protection of existing work, add, minimum	2%	2%	
3800	Maximum	5%	7%	
3900	Shift work requirements, add, minimum		5%	
4000	Maximum		30%	

G2030 Pedestrian Paving

This page illustrates and describes sidewalk systems including concrete, welded wire and broom finish. Lines within System Components give unit price and total price per square foot for this system. Prices for sidewalk systems are on Line Items G2030 105 1700 thru 1900. Both material quantities and labor costs have been adjusted for the system listed.

Factors: To adjust for job conditions other than normal working situations use Lines G2030 105 2900 thru 4000.

Example: You are to install the system and match existing construction. Go to Line G2030 105 2900 and apply these percentages to the appropriate MAT. and INST. costs.

System Components	QUANTITY	UNIT	COST PER S.F. MAT.	COST PER S.F. INST.	COST PER S.F. TOTAL
4" thick concrete sidewalk with welded wire fabric, 3000 psi air entrained concrete, broom finish.					
Gravel fill, 4" deep	.012	C.Y.	.29	.10	.39
Compact fill	.012	C.Y.		.03	.03
Hand grade	1.000	S.F.		2.17	2.17
Edge form	.250	L.F.	.09	.96	1.05
Welded wire fabric	.011	S.F.	.18	.42	.60
Concrete, 3000 psi air entrained	.012	C.Y.	1.31		1.31
Place concrete	.012	C.Y.		.33	.33
Broom finish	1.000	S.F.		.86	.86
TOTAL			1.87	4.87	6.74

G2030 105	Sidewalks	COST PER S.F. MAT.	COST PER S.F. INST.	COST PER S.F. TOTAL
1700	Asphalt (bituminous), 2" thick	1.16	2.79	3.95
1750	4" thick	1.87	4.87	6.74
1800	Brick, on sand, bed, 4.5 brick per S.F.	3.43	10.75	14.18
1900	Flagstone, slate, 1" thick, rectangular	10.60	11.65	22.25
2000				
2100				
2200				
2300				
2400				
2500				
2600				
2700				
2900	Cut & patch to match existing construction, add, minimum	2%	3%	
3000	Maximum	5%	9%	
3100	Dust protection, add, minimum	1%	2%	
3200	Maximum	4%	11%	
3300	Equipment usage curtailment, add, minimum	1%	1%	
3400	Maximum	3%	10%	
3500	Material handling & storage limitation, add, minimum	1%	1%	
3600	Maximum	6%	7%	
3700	Protection of existing work, add, minimum	2%	2%	
3800	Maximum	5%	7%	
3900	Shift work requirements, add, minimum		5%	
4000	Maximum		30%	

G20 Site Improvements

G2050 Landscaping

This page describes landscaping—lawn establishment systems including loam, lime, fertilizer, side and top mulching. Lines within system components give the unit price and total price per square yard for this system. Prices for landscaping—lawn establishment systems are on Line Items G2050 420 1000 thru 1200. Both material quantities and labor costs have been adjusted for the system listed.

Factors: To adjust for job conditions other than normal working situations use Lines G2050 420 2900 thru 4000.

Example: You are to install the system and provide dust protection. Go to Line G2050 420 3200 and apply these percentages to the appropriate MAT. and INST. costs.

System Components	QUANTITY	UNIT	COST PER S.Y.		
			MAT.	INST.	TOTAL
Establishing lawns with loam, lime, fertilizer, seed and top mulching on rough graded areas.					
Furnish and place loam 4" deep	.110	C.Y.	3.84	.98	4.82
Fine grade, lime, fertilize and seed	1.000	S.Y.	.51	3.43	3.94
Hay mulch, 1 bale/M.S.F.	1.000	S.Y.	.20	.59	.79
Rolling with hand roller	1.000	S.Y.		1.06	1.06
TOTAL			4.55	6.06	10.61

G2050 420	Landscaping - Lawn Establishment	COST PER S.Y.		
		MAT.	INST.	TOTAL
1000	Establishing lawns with loam, lime, fertilizer, seed and hay mulch	4.55	6.05	10.60
1100	Above system with jute mesh in place of hay mulch	5.55	6.20	11.75
1200	Above system with sod in place of seed	6.55	2.14	8.69
1300				
1400				
1500				
1600				
1700				
1800				
1900				
2000				
2100				
2200				
2300				
2400				
2500				
2600				
2700				
2900	Cut & patch to match existing construction, add, minimum	2%	3%	
3000	Maximum	5%	9%	
3100	Dust protection, add, minimum	1%	2%	
3200	Maximum	4%	11%	
3300	Equipment usage curtailment, add, minimum	1%	1%	
3400	Maximum	3%	10%	
3500	Material handling & storage limitation, add, minimum	1%	1%	
3600	Maximum	6%	7%	
3700	Protection of existing work, add, minimum	2%	2%	
3800	Maximum	5%	7%	
3900	Shift work requirements, add, minimum		5%	
4000	Maximum		30%	

G2050 Landscaping

G2050 510	Selective Price Sheet	COST PER UNIT		
		MAT.	INST.	TOTAL
0100	Shrubs and trees, Evergreen, in prepared beds			
0200				
0300	Arborvitae pyramidal, 4'-5'	121	97	218
0400	Globe, 12"-15"	23.50	15.35	38.85
0500	Cedar, blue, 8'-10'	252	162	414
0600	Hemlock, Canadian, 2-1/2'-3'	33.50	41	74.50
0700	Juniper, andora, 18"-24"	39.50	18.40	57.90
0800	Wiltoni, 15"-18"	31.50	18.40	49.90
0900	Skyrocket, 4-1/2'-5'	129	52.50	181.50
1000	Blue pfitzer, 2'-2-1/2'	46.50	33.50	80
1100	Ketleerie, 2-1/2'-3'	56	29.50	85.50
1200	Pine, black, 2-1/2'-3'	65.50	29.50	95
1300	Mugo, 18"-24"	65	24.50	89.50
1400	White, 4'-5'	56	39	95
1500	Spruce, blue, 18"-24"	73	24.50	97.50
1600	Norway, 4'-5'	90	39	129
1700	Yew, denisforma, 12"-15"	39.50	24.50	64
1800	Capitata, 18"-24"	36	49	85
1900	Hicksi, 2'-2-1/2'	95	49	144
2000				
2100	Trees, Deciduous, in prepared beds			
2200				
2300	Beech, 5'-6'	204	58	262
2400	Dogwood, 4'-5'	143	72.50	215.50
2500	Elm, 8'-10'	286	145	431
2600	Magnolia, 4'-5'	110	145	255
2700	Maple, red, 8'-10', 1-1/2" caliper	220	291	511
2800	Oak, 2-1/2"-3" caliper	350	485	835
2900	Willow, 6'-8', 1" caliper	105	145	250
3000				
3100	Shrubs, Broadleaf Evergreen, in prepared beds			
3200				
3300	Andromeda, 15"-18", container	36.50	15.35	51.85
3400	Azalea, 15"-18", container	31.50	15.35	46.85
3500	Barberry, 9"-12", container	19.30	11.30	30.60
3600	Boxwood, 15"-18", B & B	46	15.35	61.35
3700	Euonymus, emerald gaiety, 12"-15", container	25.50	12.80	38.30
3800	Holly, 15"-18", B & B	39.50	15.35	54.85
3900	Mount laurel, 18"-24", B & B	77	18.40	95.40
4000	Privet, 18"-24", B & B	24	11.30	35.30
4100	Rhododendron, 18"-24", container	42	30.50	72.50
4200	Rosemary, 1 gal. container	19.80	2.45	22.25
4300	Deciduous, amalanchier, 2'-3', B & B	132	26	158
4400	Azalea, 15"-18", B & B	31.50	15.35	46.85
4500	Bayberry, 2'-3', B & B	26	26	52
4600	Cotoneaster, 15"-18", B & B	29.50	18.40	47.90
4700	Dogwood, 3'-4', B & B	34.50	72.50	107
4800	Euonymus, alatus compacta, 15"-18", container	28	18.40	46.40
4900	Forsythia, 2'-3', container	20.50	24.50	45
5000	Honeysuckle, 3'-4', B & B	28.50	24.50	53
5100	Hydrangea, 2'-3', B & B	32.50	26	58.50
5200	Lilac, 3'-4', B & B	30	72.50	102.50
5300	Quince, 2'-3', B & B	30.50	26	56.50
5400				
5500	Ground Cover			
5600				
5700	Plants, Pachysandra, prepared beds, per hundred	87	98	185
5800	Vinca minor or English ivy, per hundred	71	123	194

G20 Site Improvements

G2050 Landscaping

G2050 510	Selective Price Sheet	COST PER UNIT		
		MAT.	INST.	TOTAL
5900	Plant bed prep. 18" dp., mach., per square foot	2.64	.44	3.08
6000	By hand, per square foot	2.64	3.11	5.75
6100	Stone chips, Georgia marble, 50# bags, per bag	4.54	2.83	7.37
6200	Onyx gemstone, per bag	18.15	5.65	23.80
6300	Quartz, per bag	6.75	5.65	12.40
6400	Pea gravel, truck load lots, per cubic yard	26	52.50	78.50
6500	Mulch, polyethylene mulch, per square yard	.48	.48	.96
6600	Wood chips, 2" deep, per square yard	1.60	2.19	3.79
6700	Peat moss, 1" deep, per square yard	2.89	.54	3.43
6800	Erosion control per square yard, Jute mesh stapled	1.22	.75	1.97
6900	Plastic netting, stapled	.25	.59	.84
7000	Polypropylene mesh, stapled	2.56	.59	3.15
7100	Tobacco netting, stapled	.20	.59	.79
7200	Lawns per square yard, seeding incl. fine grade, limestone, fert. and seed	.51	3.43	3.94
7300	Sodding, incl. fine grade, level ground	2.48	1.12	3.60
7500	Edging, per linear foot, Redwood, untreated, 1" x 4"	1.28	2.41	3.69
7600	2" x 4"	2.49	3.65	6.14
7700	Stl. edge strips, 1/4" x 5" inc. stakes	4.29	3.65	7.94
7800	3/16" x 4"	2.59	3.65	6.24
7900	Brick edging, set on edge	3.05	7.95	11
8000	Set flat	1.52	2.90	4.42
8100				
8200				
8300				
8400				

G30 Site Mechanical Utilities

G3020 Sanitary Sewer

This page illustrates and describes drainage and utilities – septic system including a tank, distribution box, excavation, piping, crushed stone and backfill. Lines within System Components give the unit price and total price on a cost each basis for this system. Prices for drainage and utilities – septic systems are on Line Items G3020 610 1600 thru 2000. Both material quantities and labor costs have been adjusted for the system listed.

Factors: To adjust for job conditions other than normal working situations use Lines G3020 610 3100 thru 4000.

Example: You are to install the system with a material handling limitation. Go to Line G3020 610 3500 and apply these percentages to the appropriate MAT. and INST. costs.

System Components	QUANTITY	UNIT	COST EACH		
			MAT.	INST.	TOTAL
Septic system including tank, distribution box, excavation, piping, crushed stone and backfill for a 1000 S.F. leaching field.					
Precast concrete septic tank, 1000 gal. capacity	1.000	Ea.	1,200	260.25	1,460.25
Concrete distribution box	1.000	Ea.	86	60	146
Sch. 40 sewer pipe, PVC, 4″ diameter	25.000	L.F.	273.70	727.60	1,001.30
Sch. 40 sewer pipe fittings, PVC, 4″ diameter	8.000	Ea.	118.80	616	734.80
Excavation for septic tank	120.000	C.Y.		228.60	228.60
Excavation for disposal field	120.000	C.Y.		556.51	556.51
Crushed stone backfill	76.000	C.Y.	1,672	994.08	2,666.08
Backfill with excavated material	26.000	C.Y.		50.18	50.18
Asphalt felt paper, 15#	6.000	Sq.	35.70	97.80	133.50
TOTAL			3,386.20	3,591.02	6,977.22

G3020 610	Septic Systems	COST EACH		
		MAT.	INST.	TOTAL
1600	1000 gal. tank with 1000 S.F. field	3,375	3,600	6,975
1700	1000 gal. tank with 2000 S.F. field	4,775	5,300	10,075
1800	With leaching pits	3,350	2,100	5,450
1900	2000 gal. tank with 2000 S.F. field	5,725	5,475	11,200
2000	With leaching pits	4,375	2,700	7,075
2100				
2200				
2300				
2400				
2500				
2600				
2700				
2800				
2900				
3100	Dust protection, add, minimum	1%	2%	
3200	Maximum	4%	11%	
3300	Equipment usage curtailment, add, minimum	1%	1%	
3400	Maximum	3%	10%	
3500	Material handling & storage limitation, add, minimum	1%	1%	
3600	Maximum	6%	7%	
3700	Protection of existing work, add, minimum	2%	2%	
3800	Maximum	5%	7%	
3900	Shift work requirements, add, minimum		5%	
4000	Maximum		30%	

692

G3060 Fuel Distribution

<- 2" Vent Cap

3" Fill Box

Manway Extension

Supply

Return

Hold Down Straps

Pea Gravel Backfill

Concrete Slab w/ Reinforcing Steel

Fiberglass Underground Fuel Storage Tank, Single Wall

This page illustrates and describes fiberglass tanks including hold down slab, reinforcing steel and peastone gravel. Lines within Systems Components give the material and installation price on a cost each basis for the components. Prices for fiberglass tank systems are on Line Items G3060 310 1010 through 1100. Material quantities and labor costs have been adjusted for the system listed.

Factors: To adjust for job conditions other than normal working situations use Lines G3060 310 2700 thru 4000.

System Components	QUANTITY	UNIT	COST EACH		
			MAT.	INST.	TOTAL
Double wall underground fiberglass storage tanks including, excavation, hold down slab, backfill, manway extension and related piping.					
Excavating trench, no sheeting or dewatering, 6'-10 ' D, 3/4 CY hyd backhoe	18.000	Ea.		147.78	147.78
Corrosion resistance wrap & coat, small diam. pipe, 1" diam., add	120.000	Ea.	218.40		218.40
Fiberglass-reinforced elbows 90 & 45 degree, 2 inch	7.000	Ea.	332.50	595	927.50
Fiberglass-reinforced threaded adapters, 2 inch	2.000	Ea.	39.60	195	234.60
Remote tank gauging system, 30', 5" pointer travel	1.000	Ea.	5,400	365	5,765
Corrosion resistance wrap & coat, small diam. pipe. 4 " diam. add	30.000	Ea.	83.40		83.40
Pea gravel	9.000	Ea.	747	472.50	1,219.50
Reinforcing in hold down pad, #3 to #7	120.000	Ea.	66	75.60	141.60
Tank leak detector system, 8 channel, external monitoring	1.000	Ea.	1,000		1,000
Tubbing copper, type L, 3/4" diam.	120.000	Ea.	678	1,134	1,812
Elbow 90 degree ,wrought cu x cu 3/4 " diam.	4.000	Ea.	30.40	152	182.40
Pipe, black steel welded, sch 40, 3" diam.	30.000	Ea.	508.50	942.30	1,450.80
Elbow 90 degree, steel welded butt joint, 3 " diam.	3.000	Ea.	96	581.10	677.10
Fiberglass-reinforced plastic pipe, 2 inch	156.000	Ea.	1,021.80	750.36	1,772.16
Fiberglass-reinforced plastic pipe, 3 inch	36.000	Ea.	1,062	196.20	1,258.20
Fiberglass-reinforced elbows 90 & 45 degree, 3 inch	3.000	Ea.	450	342	792
Tank leak detection system, probes, well monitoring, liquid phase detection	2.000	Ea.	1,040		1,040
Double wall fiberglass annular space	1.000	Ea.	350		350
Flange, weld neck, 150 lb, 3 " pipe size	1.000	Ea.	38.50	96.84	135.34
Vent protector/breather, 2" diam.	1.000	Ea.	33.50	23	56.50
Corrosion resistance wrap & coat, small diam. pipe, 2" diam., add	36.000	Ea.	71.64		71.64
Concrete hold down pad, 6' x 5' x 8" thick	30.000	Ea.	86.70	48.30	135
600 gallon capacity, underground storage tank, double wall fiberglass	1.000	Ea.	7,525	545	8,070
Tank, for hold-downs 500-4000 gal., add	1.000	Ea.	470	174	644
Foot valve, single poppet, 3/4" diam.	1.000	Ea.	78.50	40.50	119
Fuel fill box, locking inner cover, 3" diam.	1.000	Ea.	133	146	279
Fuel oil specialties, valve,ball chk, globe type fusible, 3/4" diam.	2.000	Ea.	154	73	227
TOTAL			21,714.44	7,095.48	28,809.92

G3060 310	Fiberglass Fuel Tank, Double Wall	COST EACH		
		MAT.	INST.	TOTAL
1010	Storage tank, fuel, underground, double wall fiberglass, 600 Gal.	21,700	7,100	28,800
1020	2500 Gal.	33,400	9,775	43,175
1030	4000 Gal.	38,700	12,100	50,800
1040	6000 Gal.	45,000	13,700	58,700
1050	8000 Gal.	52,000	16,500	68,500
1060	10,000 Gal.	58,500	19,000	77,500

G3060 Fuel Distribution

G3060 310	Fiberglass Fuel Tank, Double Wall	COST EACH		
		MAT.	INST.	TOTAL
1070	15,000 Gal.	80,000	21,900	101,900
1080	20,000 Gal.	100,500	26,500	127,000
1090	25,000 Gal.	127,500	30,700	158,200
1100	30,000 Gal.	146,000	32,600	178,600
2700	Cut & patch to match existing construction, add, minimum	2%	3%	
2800	Maximum	5%	9%	
2900	Dust protection, add, minimum	1%	2%	
3000	Maximum	4%	11%	
3100	Equipment usage curtailment, add, minimum	1%	1%	
3200	Maximum	3%	10%	
3300	Material handling & storage limitation, add, minimum	1%	1%	
3400	Maximum	6%	7%	
3500	Protection of existing work, add, minimum	2%	2%	
3600	Maximum	5%	7%	
3700	Shift work requirements, add, minimum		5%	
3800	Maximum		30%	
3900	Temporary shoring and bracing, add, minimum	2%	5%	
4000	Maximum	5%	12%	

G3060 Fuel Distribution

Steel Underground Fuel Storage Tank, Double Wall

System Components	QUANTITY	UNIT	COST EACH		
			MAT.	INST.	TOTAL
Double wall underground steel storage tank including, excavation, hold down slab, backfill, manway extension and related piping.					
Fiberglass-reinforced plastic pipe, 2 inch	156.000	Ea.	1,021.80	750.36	1,772.16
Fiberglass-reinforced plastic pipe, 3 inch	36.000	Ea.	1,062	196.20	1,258.20
Fiberglass-reinforced elbows 90 & 45 degree, 3 inch	3.000	Ea.	450	342	792
Tank leak detection system, probes, well monitoring, liquid phase detection	2.000	Ea.	1,040		1,040
Flange, weld neck, 150 lb, 3" pipe size	1.000	Ea.	38.50	96.84	135.34
Vent protector/breather, 2" diam.	1.000	Ea.	33.50	23	56.50
Concrete hold down pad, 6' x 5' x 8" thick	30.000	Ea.	86.70	48.30	135
Tanks, for hold-downs, 500-2000 gal, add	1.000	Ea.	201	174	375
Double wall steel tank annular space	1.000	Ea.	365		365
Foot valve, single poppet, 3/4" diam.	1.000	Ea.	78.50	40.50	119
Fuel fill box, locking inner cover, 3" diam.	1.000	Ea.	133	146	279
Fuel oil specialties, valve, ball chk, globe type fusible, 3/4" diam.	2.000	Ea.	154	73	227
Pea gravel	9.000	Ea.	747	472.50	1,219.50
Reinforcing in hold down pad, #3 to #7	120.000	Ea.	66	75.60	141.60
Tank, for manways, add	1.000	Ea.	2,000		2,000
Tank leak detector system, 8 channel, external monitoring	1.000	Ea.	1,000		1,000
Tubbing copper, type L, 3/4" diam.	120.000	Ea.	678	1,134	1,812
Elbow 90 degree, wrought cu x cu 3/4" diam.	8.000	Ea.	60.80	304	364.80
Pipe, black steel welded, sch 40, 3" diam.	30.000	Ea.	508.50	942.30	1,450.80
Elbow 90 degree, steel welded butt joint, 3" diam.	3.000	Ea.	96	581.10	677.10
Excavating trench, no sheeting or dewatering, 6'-10' D, 3/4 CY hyd backhoe	18.000	Ea.		147.78	147.78
Fiberglass-reinforced elbows 90 & 45 degree, 2 inch	7.000	Ea.	332.50	595	927.50
Fiberglass-reinforced threaded adapters, 2 inch	2.000	Ea.	39.60	195	234.60
500 gallon capacity, underground storage tank, double wall steel	1.000	Ea.	6,150	550	6,700
Remote tank gauging system, 30', 5" pointer travel	1.000	Ea.	5,400	365	5,765
TOTAL			21,742.40	7,252.48	28,994.88

G3060 320	Steel Fuel Tank, Double Wall	COST EACH		
		MAT.	INST.	TOTAL
1010	Storage tank, fuel, underground, double wall steel, 500 Gal.	21,700	7,250	28,950
1020	2000 Gal.	28,600	9,475	38,075
1030	4000 Gal.	38,600	12,300	50,900
1040	6000 Gal.	50,000	13,500	63,500
1050	8000 Gal.	56,000	16,800	72,800
1060	10,000 Gal.	62,000	19,300	81,300

G3060 Fuel Distribution

G3060 320	Steel Fuel Tank, Double Wall	COST EACH		
		MAT.	INST.	TOTAL
1070	15,000 Gal.	69,500	22,400	91,900
1080	20,000 Gal.	80,000	26,900	106,900
1090	25,000 Gal.	126,500	30,700	157,200
1100	30,000 Gal.	145,000	32,700	177,700
1110	40,000 Gal.	181,500	41,200	222,700
1120	50,000 Gal.	219,000	49,300	268,300

G3060 325	Steel Tank, Above Ground, Single Wall	COST EACH		
		MAT.	INST.	TOTAL
1010	Storage tank, fuel, above ground, single wall steel, 550 Gal.	13,500	5,050	18,550
1020	2000 Gal.	20,400	5,150	25,550
1030	5000 Gal.	32,600	7,925	40,525
1040	10,000 Gal.	46,700	8,450	55,150
1050	15,000 Gal.	56,500	8,675	65,175
1060	20,000 Gal.	70,000	8,975	78,975
1070	25,000 Gal.	79,500	9,200	88,700
1080	30,000 Gal.	93,000	9,575	102,575

G3060 330	Steel Tank, Above Ground, Double Wall	COST EACH		
		MAT.	INST.	TOTAL
1010	Storage tank, fuel, above ground, double wall steel, 500 Gal.	14,000	5,100	19,100
1020	2000 Gal.	22,200	5,225	27,425
1030	4000 Gal.	31,100	5,325	36,425
1040	6000 Gal.	36,500	8,200	44,700
1050	8000 Gal.	43,400	8,450	51,850
1060	10,000 Gal.	46,900	8,600	55,500
1070	15,000 Gal.	64,000	8,900	72,900
1080	20,000 Gal.	71,000	9,200	80,200
1090	25,000 Gal.	83,500	9,475	92,975
1100	30,000 Gal.	90,000	9,825	99,825
2700	Cut & patch to match existing construction, add, minimum	2%	3%	
2800	Maximum	5%	9%	
2900	Dust protection, add, minimum	1%	2%	
3000	Maximum	4%	11%	
3100	Equipment usage curtailment, add, minimum	1%	1%	
3200	Maximum	3%	10%	
3300	Material handling & storage limitation, add, minimum	1%	1%	
3400	Maximum	6%	7%	
3500	Protection of existing work, add, minimum	2%	2%	
3600	Maximum	5%	7%	
3700	Shift work requirements, add, minimum		5%	
3800	Maximum		30%	
3900	Temporary shoring and bracing, add, minimum	2%	5%	
4000	Maximum	5%	12%	

G4020 Site Lighting

This page illustrates and describes light poles for parking or walkway area lighting. Included are aluminum or steel light poles, single or multiple fixture bracket arms, excavation, concrete footing, backfill and compaction. Lines within system components give the unit price and total price on a cost per each basis. Prices for systems are shown on lines G4020 210 0200 through 1440. Both material quantities and labor costs have been adjusted for the system listed.

Factors: To adjust for job conditions other than normal working situations use lines G4020 210 2700 through 3600.

Example: You are to install the system where you must be careful not to damage existing walks or parking areas. Go to line G4020 210 3300 and apply these percentages to the appropriate MAT. and INST. costs.

System Components			COST EACH		
	QUANTITY	UNIT	MAT.	INST.	TOTAL
Light poles, aluminum, 20' high, 1 arm bracket.					
Aluminum light pole, 20', no concrete base	1.000	Ea.	1,025	618	1,643
Bracket arm for Aluminum light pole	1.000	Ea.	131	82.50	213.50
Excavation by hand, pits to 6' deep, heavy soil or clay	2.368	C.Y.		284.16	284.16
Footing, concrete incl forms, reinforcing, spread, under 1 C.Y.	.465	C.Y.	84.17	134.52	218.69
Backfill by hand	1.903	C.Y.		83.73	83.73
Compaction vibrating plate	1.903	C.Y.		11.25	11.25
TOTAL			1,240.17	1,214.16	2,454.33

G4020 210	Light Pole (Installed)	COST EACH		
		MAT.	INST.	TOTAL
0200	Light pole, aluminum, 20' high, 1 arm bracket	1,250	1,200	2,450
0240	2 arm brackets	1,375	1,200	2,575
0280	3 arm brackets	1,500	1,250	2,750
0320	4 arm brackets	1,650	1,250	2,900
0360	30' high, 1 arm bracket	2,150	1,525	3,675
0400	2 arm brackets	2,300	1,525	3,825
0440	3 arm brackets	2,425	1,575	4,000
0480	4 arm brackets	2,550	1,575	4,125
0680	40' high, 1 arm bracket	2,650	2,050	4,700
0720	2 arm brackets	2,800	2,050	4,850
0760	3 arm brackets	2,925	2,100	5,025
0800	4 arm brackets	3,050	2,100	5,150
0840	Steel, 20' high, 1 arm bracket	1,475	1,275	2,750
0880	2 arm brackets	1,600	1,275	2,875
0920	3 arm brackets	1,625	1,325	2,950
0960	4 arm brackets	1,750	1,325	3,075
1000	30' high, 1 arm bracket	1,725	1,650	3,375
1040	2 arm brackets	1,825	1,650	3,475
1080	3 arm brackets	1,850	1,675	3,525
1120	4 arm brackets	2,000	1,675	3,675
1320	40' high, 1 arm bracket	2,250	2,225	4,475
1360	2 arm brackets	2,350	2,225	4,575
1400	3 arm brackets	2,375	2,275	4,650
1440	4 arm brackets	2,500	2,275	4,775
2700	Cut & patch to match existing construction, add, minimum	2%	3%	
2800	Maximum	5%	9%	
2900	Equipment usage curtailment, add, minimum	1%	1%	
3000	Maximum	3%	10%	

G4020 Site Lighting

G4020 210	Light Pole (Installed)	COST EACH		
		MAT.	INST.	TOTAL
3100	Material handling & storage limitation, add, minimum	1%	1%	
3200	Maximum	6%	7%	
3300	Protection of existing work, add, minimum	2%	2%	
3400	Maximum	5%	7%	
3500	Shift work requirements, add, minimum		5%	
3600	Maximum		30%	

Reference Section

All the reference information is in one section, making it easy to find what you need to know . . . and easy to use the book on a daily basis. This section is visually identified by a vertical gray bar on the page edges.

In this Reference Section, we've included Equipment Rental Costs, a listing of rental and operating costs; Crew Listings, a full listing of all crews and equipment, and their costs; Historical Cost Indexes for cost comparisons over time; City Cost Indexes and Location Factors for adjusting costs to the region you are in; Reference Tables, where you will find explanations, estimating information and procedures, or technical data; Change Orders, information on pricing changes to contract documents; Square Foot Costs that allow you to make a rough estimate for the overall cost of a project; and an explanation of all the Abbreviations in the book.

Table of Contents

Estimating Tips

- This section contains the average costs to rent and operate hundreds of pieces of construction equipment. This is useful information when estimating the time and material requirements of any particular operation in order to establish a unit or total cost. Equipment costs include not only rental, but also operating costs for equipment under normal use.

Rental Costs

- Equipment rental rates are obtained from industry sources throughout North America–contractors, suppliers, dealers, manufacturers, and distributors.
- Rental rates vary throughout the country, with larger cities generally having lower rates. Lease plans for new equipment are available for periods in excess of six months, with a percentage of payments applying toward purchase.
- Monthly rental rates vary from 2% to 5% of the purchase price of the equipment depending on the anticipated life of the equipment and its wearing parts.
- Weekly rental rates are about 1/3 the monthly rates, and daily rental rates are about 1/3 the weekly rate.
- Rental rates can also be treated as reimbursement costs for contractor-owned equipment. Owned equipment costs include depreciation, loan payments, interest, taxes, insurance, storage, and major repairs.

Operating Costs

- The operating costs include parts and labor for routine servicing, such as repair and replacement of pumps, filters and worn lines. Normal operating expendables, such as fuel, lubricants, tires and electricity (where applicable), are also included.
- Extraordinary operating expendables with highly variable wear patterns, such as diamond bits and blades, are excluded. These costs can be found as material costs in the Unit Price section.
- The hourly operating costs listed do not include the operator's wages.

Equipment Cost/Day

- Any power equipment required by a crew is shown in the Crew Listings with a daily cost.
- The daily cost of equipment needed by a crew is based on dividing the weekly rental rate by 5 (number of working days in the week), and then adding the hourly operating cost times 8 (the number of hours in a day). This "Equipment Cost/Day" is shown in the far right column of the Equipment Rental pages.
- If equipment is needed for only one or two days, it is best to develop your own cost by including components for daily rent and hourly operating cost. This is important when the listed Crew for a task does not contain the equipment needed, such as a crane for lifting mechanical heating/cooling equipment up onto a roof.
- If the quantity of work is less than the crew's Daily Output shown for a Unit Price line item that includes a bare unit equipment cost, it is recommended to estimate one day's rental cost and operating cost for equipment shown in the Crew Listing for that line item.

Mobilization/ Demobilization

- The cost to move construction equipment from an equipment yard or rental company to the jobsite and back again is not included in equipment rental costs listed in the Reference section, nor in the bare equipment cost of any Unit Price line item, nor in any equipment costs shown in the Crew listings.
- Mobilization (to the site) and demobilization (from the site) costs can be found in the Unit Price section.
- If a piece of equipment is already at the jobsite, it is not appropriate to utilize mobil./demob. costs again in an estimate.

01 54 33 | Equipment Rental

		UNIT	HOURLY OPER. COST	RENT PER DAY	RENT PER WEEK	RENT PER MONTH	EQUIPMENT COST/DAY	
10	0010	**CONCRETE EQUIPMENT RENTAL** without operators							**10**
	0200	Bucket, concrete lightweight, 1/2 C.Y. R015433 -10	Ea.	.80	23	69	207	20.20	
	0300	1 C.Y.		.85	27	81	243	23	
	0400	1-1/2 C.Y.		1.10	36.50	110	330	30.80	
	0500	2 C.Y.		1.20	43.50	130	390	35.60	
	0580	8 C.Y.		5.95	252	755	2,275	198.60	
	0600	Cart, concrete, self-propelled, operator walking, 10 C.F.		3.40	55	165	495	60.20	
	0700	Operator riding, 18 C.F.		5.65	93.50	280	840	101.20	
	0800	Conveyer for concrete, portable, gas, 16" wide, 26' long		13.50	122	365	1,100	181	
	0900	46' long		13.90	147	440	1,325	199.20	
	1000	56' long		14.05	155	465	1,400	205.40	
	1100	Core drill, electric, 2-1/2 H.P., 1" to 8" bit diameter		1.50	57	171	515	46.20	
	1150	11 H.P., 8" to 18" cores		5.90	115	345	1,025	116.20	
	1200	Finisher, concrete floor, gas, riding trowel, 96" wide		14.05	142	425	1,275	197.40	
	1300	Gas, walk-behind, 3 blade, 36" trowel		2.35	20	60	180	30.80	
	1400	4 blade, 48" trowel		4.70	26.50	80	240	53.60	
	1500	Float, hand-operated (Bull float) 48" wide		.08	13.35	40	120	8.65	
	1570	Curb builder, 14 H.P., gas, single screw		14.65	250	750	2,250	267.20	
	1590	Double screw		15.30	287	860	2,575	294.40	
	1600	Floor grinder, concrete and terrazzo, electric, 22" path		2.19	134	402	1,200	97.90	
	1700	Edger, concrete, electric, 7" path		1.02	51.50	155	465	39.15	
	1750	Vacuum pick-up system for floor grinders, wet/dry		1.47	81.50	245	735	60.75	
	1800	Mixer, powered, mortar and concrete, gas, 6 C.F., 18 H.P.		9.20	117	350	1,050	143.60	
	1900	10 C.F., 25 H.P.		11.60	140	420	1,250	176.80	
	2000	16 C.F.		11.95	162	485	1,450	192.60	
	2100	Concrete, stationary, tilt drum, 2 C.Y.		6.80	228	685	2,050	191.40	
	2120	Pump, concrete, truck mounted 4" line 80' boom		24.55	855	2,570	7,700	710.40	
	2140	5" line, 110' boom		31.75	1,125	3,400	10,200	934	
	2160	Mud jack, 50 C.F. per hr.		7.35	127	380	1,150	134.80	
	2180	225 C.F. per hr.		9.65	145	435	1,300	164.20	
	2190	Shotcrete pump rig, 12 C.Y./hr.		15.10	220	660	1,975	252.80	
	2200	35 C.Y./hr.		17.80	237	710	2,125	284.40	
	2600	Saw, concrete, manual, gas, 18 H.P.		7.25	43.50	130	390	84	
	2650	Self-propelled, gas, 30 H.P.		14.40	100	300	900	175.20	
	2675	V-groove crack chaser, manual, gas, 6 H.P.		2.55	17.35	52	156	30.80	
	2700	Vibrators, concrete, electric, 60 cycle, 2 H.P.		.43	8.65	26	78	8.65	
	2800	3 H.P.		.61	11.65	35	105	11.90	
	2900	Gas engine, 5 H.P.		2.20	16	48	144	27.20	
	3000	8 H.P.		3.00	15	45	135	33	
	3050	Vibrating screed, gas engine, 8 H.P.		2.78	68.50	205	615	63.25	
	3120	Concrete transit mixer, 6 x 4, 250 H.P., 8 C.Y., rear discharge		62.50	565	1,690	5,075	838	
	3200	Front discharge		73.60	690	2,065	6,200	1,002	
	3300	6 x 6, 285 H.P., 12 C.Y., rear discharge		72.65	650	1,950	5,850	971.20	
	3400	Front discharge		75.95	695	2,085	6,250	1,025	
20	0010	**EARTHWORK EQUIPMENT RENTAL** without operators							**20**
	0040	Aggregate spreader, push type 8' to 12' wide R015433 -10	Ea.	3.25	25.50	76	228	41.20	
	0045	Tailgate type, 8' wide		3.10	32.50	98	294	44.40	
	0055	Earth auger, truck-mounted, for fence & sign posts, utility poles		19.75	445	1,335	4,000	425	
	0060	For borings and monitoring wells		47.30	680	2,040	6,125	786.40	
	0070	Portable, trailer mounted		3.15	32.50	98	294	44.80	
	0075	Truck-mounted, for caissons, water wells		100.90	2,900	8,720	26,200	2,551	
	0080	Horizontal boring machine, 12" to 36" diameter, 45 H.P.		24.60	193	580	1,750	312.80	
	0090	12" to 48" diameter, 65 H.P.		34.85	335	1,005	3,025	479.80	
	0095	Auger, for fence posts, gas engine, hand held		.55	6	18	54	8	
	0100	Excavator, diesel hydraulic, crawler mounted, 1/2 C.Y. cap.		25.00	415	1,240	3,725	448	
	0120	5/8 C.Y. capacity		33.05	550	1,650	4,950	594.40	
	0140	3/4 C.Y. capacity		36.00	625	1,870	5,600	662	
	0150	1 C.Y. capacity		50.60	685	2,050	6,150	814.80	

01 54 33 | Equipment Rental

		UNIT	HOURLY OPER. COST	RENT PER DAY	RENT PER WEEK	RENT PER MONTH	EQUIPMENT COST/DAY	
20								**20**
0200	1-1/2 C.Y. capacity	Ea.	60.80	910	2,725	8,175	1,031	
0300	2 C.Y. capacity		68.50	1,050	3,135	9,400	1,175	
0320	2-1/2 C.Y. capacity		104.75	1,325	3,995	12,000	1,637	
0325	3-1/2 C.Y. capacity		147.35	2,100	6,315	18,900	2,442	
0330	4-1/2 C.Y. capacity		176.65	2,725	8,150	24,500	3,043	
0335	6 C.Y. capacity		224.40	2,875	8,640	25,900	3,523	
0340	7 C.Y. capacity		226.60	2,975	8,915	26,700	3,596	
0342	Excavator attachments, bucket thumbs		3.20	245	735	2,200	172.60	
0345	Grapples		2.75	193	580	1,750	138	
0347	Hydraulic hammer for boom mounting, 5000 ft lb.		14.30	425	1,280	3,850	370.40	
0349	11,000 ft lb.		23.20	750	2,250	6,750	635.60	
0350	Gradall type, truck mounted, 3 ton @ 15' radius, 5/8 C.Y.		43.45	890	2,670	8,000	881.60	
0370	1 C.Y. capacity		47.65	1,050	3,120	9,350	1,005	
0400	Backhoe-loader, 40 to 45 H.P., 5/8 C.Y. capacity		14.95	233	700	2,100	259.60	
0450	45 H.P. to 60 H.P., 3/4 C.Y. capacity		23.90	290	870	2,600	365.20	
0460	80 H.P., 1-1/4 C.Y. capacity		26.20	315	940	2,825	397.60	
0470	112 H.P., 1-1/2 C.Y. capacity		41.65	645	1,935	5,800	720.20	
0482	Backhoe-loader attachment, compactor, 20,000 lb.		5.75	142	425	1,275	131	
0485	Hydraulic hammer, 750 ft lb.		3.25	96.50	290	870	84	
0486	Hydraulic hammer, 1200 ft lb.		6.30	217	650	1,950	180.40	
0500	Brush chipper, gas engine, 6" cutter head, 35 H.P.		11.95	107	320	960	159.60	
0550	Diesel engine, 12" cutter head, 130 H.P.		28.20	285	855	2,575	396.60	
0600	15" cutter head, 165 H.P.		33.90	330	985	2,950	468.20	
0750	Bucket, clamshell, general purpose, 3/8 C.Y.		1.25	38.50	115	345	33	
0800	1/2 C.Y.		1.35	45	135	405	37.80	
0850	3/4 C.Y.		1.50	53.50	160	480	44	
0900	1 C.Y.		1.55	58.50	175	525	47.40	
0950	1-1/2 C.Y.		2.55	80	240	720	68.40	
1000	2 C.Y.		2.65	88.50	265	795	74.20	
1010	Bucket, dragline, medium duty, 1/2 C.Y.		.75	23.50	70	210	20	
1020	3/4 C.Y.		.75	24.50	74	222	20.80	
1030	1 C.Y.		.80	26	78	234	22	
1040	1-1/2 C.Y.		1.20	40	120	360	33.60	
1050	2 C.Y.		1.25	45	135	405	37	
1070	3 C.Y.		1.95	61.50	185	555	52.60	
1200	Compactor, manually guided 2-drum vibratory smooth roller, 7.5 H.P.		7.35	207	620	1,850	182.80	
1250	Rammer/tamper, gas, 8"		2.70	46.50	140	420	49.60	
1260	15"		3.00	53.50	160	480	56	
1300	Vibratory plate, gas, 18" plate, 3000 lb. blow		2.65	24.50	73	219	35.80	
1350	21" plate, 5000 lb. blow		3.30	32.50	98	294	46	
1370	Curb builder/extruder, 14 H.P., gas, single screw		14.65	250	750	2,250	267.20	
1390	Double screw		15.30	287	860	2,575	294.40	
1500	Disc harrow attachment, for tractor		.43	72.50	217	650	46.85	
1810	Feller buncher, shearing & accumulating trees, 100 H.P.		42.50	650	1,945	5,825	729	
1860	Grader, self-propelled, 25,000 lb.		39.55	595	1,780	5,350	672.40	
1910	30,000 lb.		43.25	600	1,805	5,425	707	
1920	40,000 lb.		64.65	1,000	3,015	9,050	1,120	
1930	55,000 lb.		84.65	1,600	4,800	14,400	1,637	
1950	Hammer, pavement breaker, self-propelled, diesel, 1000 to 1250 lb.		30.25	355	1,060	3,175	454	
2000	1300 to 1500 lb.		45.38	705	2,120	6,350	787.05	
2050	Pile driving hammer, steam or air, 4150 ft lb. @ 225 bpm		10.35	475	1,425	4,275	367.80	
2100	8750 ft lb. @ 145 bpm		12.35	660	1,980	5,950	494.80	
2150	15,000 ft lb. @ 60 bpm		13.95	795	2,380	7,150	587.60	
2200	24,450 ft lb. @ 111 bpm		14.95	880	2,640	7,925	647.60	
2250	Leads, 60' high for pile driving hammers up to 20,000 ft lb.		3.30	80.50	242	725	74.80	
2300	90' high for hammers over 20,000 ft lb.		4.95	141	424	1,275	124.40	
2350	Diesel type hammer, 22,400 ft lb.		26.93	535	1,610	4,825	537.45	
2400	41,300 ft lb.		36.30	585	1,760	5,275	642.40	

01 54 33 | Equipment Rental

		UNIT	HOURLY OPER. COST	RENT PER DAY	RENT PER WEEK	RENT PER MONTH	EQUIPMENT COST/DAY
2450	141,000 ft lb.	Ea.	55.55	1,050	3,160	9,475	1,076
2500	Vib. elec. hammer/extractor, 200 kW diesel generator, 34 H.P.		56.25	635	1,910	5,725	832
2550	80 H.P.		103.45	930	2,785	8,350	1,385
2600	150 H.P.		196.65	1,775	5,335	16,000	2,640
2800	Log chipper, up to 22" diameter, 600 H.P.		64.95	630	1,895	5,675	898.60
2850	Logger, for skidding & stacking logs, 150 H.P.		53.45	820	2,460	7,375	919.60
2860	Mulcher, diesel powered, trailer mounted		24.70	213	640	1,925	325.60
2900	Rake, spring tooth, with tractor		18.31	335	1,007	3,025	347.90
3000	Roller, vibratory, tandem, smooth drum, 20 H.P.		8.75	148	445	1,325	159
3050	35 H.P.		11.25	253	760	2,275	242
3100	Towed type vibratory compactor, smooth drum, 50 H.P.		26.25	335	1,010	3,025	412
3150	Sheepsfoot, 50 H.P.		27.60	370	1,115	3,350	443.80
3170	Landfill compactor, 220 H.P.		91.85	1,500	4,485	13,500	1,632
3200	Pneumatic tire roller, 80 H.P.		17.00	355	1,065	3,200	349
3250	120 H.P.		25.45	605	1,815	5,450	566.60
3300	Sheepsfoot vibratory roller, 240 H.P.		69.65	1,100	3,305	9,925	1,218
3320	340 H.P.		101.85	1,600	4,830	14,500	1,781
3350	Smooth drum vibratory roller, 75 H.P.		25.15	595	1,790	5,375	559.20
3400	125 H.P.		32.85	715	2,150	6,450	692.80
3410	Rotary mower, brush, 60", with tractor		22.65	305	915	2,750	364.20
3420	Rototiller, walk-behind, gas, 5 H.P.		2.23	66	198	595	57.45
3422	8 H.P.		3.30	91.50	275	825	81.40
3440	Scrapers, towed type, 7 C.Y. capacity		5.70	110	330	990	111.60
3450	10 C.Y. capacity		6.45	150	450	1,350	141.60
3500	15 C.Y. capacity		6.85	173	520	1,550	158.80
3525	Self-propelled, single engine, 14 C.Y. capacity		113.60	1,525	4,600	13,800	1,829
3550	Dual engine, 21 C.Y. capacity		174.50	2,000	6,015	18,000	2,599
3600	31 C.Y. capacity		232.10	2,850	8,545	25,600	3,566
3640	44 C.Y. capacity		287.55	3,650	10,960	32,900	4,492
3650	Elevating type, single engine, 11 C.Y. capacity		71.20	1,025	3,050	9,150	1,180
3700	22 C.Y. capacity		138.15	2,225	6,690	20,100	2,443
3710	Screening plant 110 H.P. w/5' x 10' screen		31.63	435	1,300	3,900	513.05
3720	5' x 16' screen		34.85	540	1,615	4,850	601.80
3850	Shovel, crawler-mounted, front-loading, 7 C.Y. capacity		246.75	2,900	8,700	26,100	3,714
3855	12 C.Y. capacity		354.50	3,950	11,840	35,500	5,204
3860	Shovel/backhoe bucket, 1/2 C.Y.		2.45	66.50	200	600	59.60
3870	3/4 C.Y.		2.50	73.50	220	660	64
3880	1 C.Y.		2.60	83.50	250	750	70.80
3890	1-1/2 C.Y.		2.75	96.50	290	870	80
3910	3 C.Y.		3.10	130	390	1,175	102.80
3950	Stump chipper, 18" deep, 30 H.P.		7.06	176	528	1,575	162.10
4110	Dozer, crawler, torque converter, diesel 80 H.P.		29.75	405	1,215	3,650	481
4150	105 H.P.		36.10	505	1,515	4,550	591.80
4200	140 H.P.		52.10	780	2,335	7,000	883.80
4260	200 H.P.		77.35	1,175	3,530	10,600	1,325
4310	300 H.P.		100.55	1,700	5,065	15,200	1,817
4360	410 H.P.		135.65	2,200	6,620	19,900	2,409
4370	500 H.P.		174.30	2,875	8,610	25,800	3,116
4380	700 H.P.		261.35	4,000	11,970	35,900	4,485
4400	Loader, crawler, torque conv., diesel, 1-1/2 C.Y., 80 H.P.		31.35	455	1,360	4,075	522.80
4450	1-1/2 to 1-3/4 C.Y., 95 H.P.		34.15	585	1,760	5,275	625.20
4510	1-3/4 to 2-1/4 C.Y., 130 H.P.		54.60	870	2,615	7,850	959.80
4530	2-1/2 to 3-1/4 C.Y., 190 H.P.		67.00	1,100	3,275	9,825	1,191
4560	3-1/2 to 5 C.Y., 275 H.P.		86.10	1,400	4,215	12,600	1,532
4610	Front end loader, 4WD, articulated frame, diesel, 1 to 1-1/4 C.Y., 70 H.P.		19.90	227	680	2,050	295.20
4620	1-1/2 to 1-3/4 C.Y., 95 H.P.		25.30	285	855	2,575	373.40
4650	1-3/4 to 2 C.Y., 130 H.P.		29.45	365	1,100	3,300	455.60
4710	2-1/2 to 3-1/2 C.Y., 145 H.P.		33.35	425	1,280	3,850	522.80

01 54 33 | Equipment Rental

		UNIT	HOURLY OPER. COST	RENT PER DAY	RENT PER WEEK	RENT PER MONTH	EQUIPMENT COST/DAY	
20	4730	3 to 4-1/2 C.Y., 185 H.P.	Ea.	42.85	550	1,655	4,975	673.80	**20**
	4760	5-1/4 to 5-3/4 C.Y., 270 H.P.		67.80	845	2,535	7,600	1,049	
	4810	7 to 9 C.Y., 475 H.P.		116.25	1,775	5,295	15,900	1,989	
	4870	9 - 11 C.Y., 620 H.P.		155.75	2,425	7,285	21,900	2,703	
	4880	Skid steer loader, wheeled, 10 C.F., 30 H.P. gas		10.90	145	435	1,300	174.20	
	4890	1 C.Y., 78 H.P., diesel		20.35	243	730	2,200	308.80	
	4892	Skid-steer attachment, auger		.50	83.50	251	755	54.20	
	4893	Backhoe		.66	111	332	995	71.70	
	4894	Broom		.74	124	372	1,125	80.30	
	4895	Forks		.23	38.50	115	345	24.85	
	4896	Grapple		.56	92.50	278	835	60.10	
	4897	Concrete hammer		1.06	177	531	1,600	114.70	
	4898	Tree spade		1.03	172	515	1,550	111.25	
	4899	Trencher		.67	112	335	1,000	72.35	
	4900	Trencher, chain, boom type, gas, operator walking, 12 H.P.		5.40	46.50	140	420	71.20	
	4910	Operator riding, 40 H.P.		20.55	292	875	2,625	339.40	
	5000	Wheel type, diesel, 4' deep, 12" wide		87.50	845	2,530	7,600	1,206	
	5100	6' deep, 20" wide		93.25	1,925	5,760	17,300	1,898	
	5150	Chain type, diesel, 5' deep, 8" wide		38.85	560	1,685	5,050	647.80	
	5200	Diesel, 8' deep, 16" wide		156.45	3,550	10,620	31,900	3,376	
	5202	Rock trencher, wheel type, 6" wide x 18" deep		21.50	330	985	2,950	369	
	5206	Chain type, 18" wide x 7' deep		112.60	2,825	8,445	25,300	2,590	
	5210	Tree spade, self-propelled		14.00	267	800	2,400	272	
	5250	Truck, dump, 2-axle, 12 ton, 8 C.Y. payload, 220 H.P.		35.15	227	680	2,050	417.20	
	5300	Three axle dump, 16 ton, 12 C.Y. payload, 400 H.P.		62.40	320	965	2,900	692.20	
	5310	Four axle dump, 25 ton, 18 C.Y. payload, 450 H.P.		73.20	470	1,410	4,225	867.60	
	5350	Dump trailer only, rear dump, 16-1/2 C.Y.		5.40	138	415	1,250	126.20	
	5400	20 C.Y.		5.85	157	470	1,400	140.80	
	5450	Flatbed, single axle, 1-1/2 ton rating		28.65	68.50	205	615	270.20	
	5500	3 ton rating		34.25	98.50	295	885	333	
	5550	Off highway rear dump, 25 ton capacity		74.55	1,200	3,590	10,800	1,314	
	5600	35 ton capacity		83.10	1,350	4,025	12,100	1,470	
	5610	50 ton capacity		103.40	1,600	4,800	14,400	1,787	
	5620	65 ton capacity		106.30	1,575	4,735	14,200	1,797	
	5630	100 ton capacity		154.35	2,775	8,315	24,900	2,898	
	6000	Vibratory plow, 25 H.P., walking		9.25	60	180	540	110	
40	0010	**GENERAL EQUIPMENT RENTAL** without operators							**40**
	0150	Aerial lift, scissor type, to 15' high, 1000 lb. cap., electric	Ea.	3.10	51.50	155	465	55.80	
	0160	To 25' high, 2000 lb. capacity		3.55	66.50	200	600	68.40	
	0170	Telescoping boom to 40' high, 500 lb. capacity, diesel		17.00	315	945	2,825	325	
	0180	To 45' high, 500 lb. capacity		18.85	355	1,070	3,200	364.80	
	0190	To 60' high, 600 lb. capacity		21.25	475	1,430	4,300	456	
	0195	Air compressor, portable, 6.5 CFM, electric		.56	12.65	38	114	12.10	
	0196	Gasoline		.79	19	57	171	17.70	
	0200	Towed type, gas engine, 60 CFM		13.55	48.50	145	435	137.40	
	0300	160 CFM		15.80	51.50	155	465	157.40	
	0400	Diesel engine, rotary screw, 250 CFM		17.05	110	330	990	202.40	
	0500	365 CFM		23.10	133	400	1,200	264.80	
	0550	450 CFM		29.35	167	500	1,500	334.80	
	0600	600 CFM		51.70	232	695	2,075	552.60	
	0700	750 CFM		51.90	240	720	2,150	559.20	
	0800	For silenced models, small sizes, add to rent		3%	5%	5%	5%		
	0900	Large sizes, add to rent		5%	7%	7%	7%		
	0930	Air tools, breaker, pavement, 60 lb.	Ea.	.50	9.65	29	87	9.80	
	0940	80 lb.		.50	10.35	31	93	10.20	
	0950	Drills, hand (jackhammer) 65 lb.		.60	17.35	52	156	15.20	
	0960	Track or wagon, swing boom, 4" drifter		63.45	885	2,660	7,975	1,040	
	0970	5" drifter		75.50	1,075	3,255	9,775	1,255	

Note: Line 0150 shows reference R015433 -10.

01 54 33 | Equipment Rental

		UNIT	HOURLY OPER. COST	RENT PER DAY	RENT PER WEEK	RENT PER MONTH	EQUIPMENT COST/DAY	
40	0975	Track mounted quarry drill, 6" diameter drill	Ea.	129.75	1,600	4,830	14,500	2,004	40
	0980	Dust control per drill		.97	24	72	216	22.15	
	0990	Hammer, chipping, 12 lb.		.55	26	78	234	20	
	1000	Hose, air with couplings, 50' long, 3/4" diameter		.03	5	15	45	3.25	
	1100	1" diameter		.04	6.35	19	57	4.10	
	1200	1-1/2" diameter		.05	9	27	81	5.80	
	1300	2" diameter		.07	12	36	108	7.75	
	1400	2-1/2" diameter		.11	19	57	171	12.30	
	1410	3" diameter		.14	23	69	207	14.90	
	1450	Drill, steel, 7/8" x 2'		.05	8.65	26	78	5.60	
	1460	7/8" x 6'		.05	9	27	81	5.80	
	1520	Moil points		.02	3.33	10	30	2.15	
	1525	Pneumatic nailer w/accessories		.47	31	93	279	22.35	
	1530	Sheeting driver for 60 lb. breaker		.03	5.65	17	51	3.65	
	1540	For 90 lb. breaker		.11	7.35	22	66	5.30	
	1550	Spade, 25 lb.		.45	7	21	63	7.80	
	1560	Tamper, single, 35 lb.		.55	36.50	109	325	26.20	
	1570	Triple, 140 lb.		.82	54.50	164	490	39.35	
	1580	Wrenches, impact, air powered, up to 3/4" bolt		.40	12.65	38	114	10.80	
	1590	Up to 1-1/4" bolt		.50	23.50	70	210	18	
	1600	Barricades, barrels, reflectorized, 1 to 99 barrels		.03	4.60	13.80	41.50	3	
	1610	100 to 200 barrels		.02	3.53	10.60	32	2.30	
	1620	Barrels with flashers, 1 to 99 barrels		.03	5.25	15.80	47.50	3.40	
	1630	100 to 200 barrels		.03	4.20	12.60	38	2.75	
	1640	Barrels with steady burn type C lights		.04	7	21	63	4.50	
	1650	Illuminated board, trailer mounted, with generator		3.55	130	390	1,175	106.40	
	1670	Portable barricade, stock, with flashers, 1 to 6 units		.03	5.25	15.80	47.50	3.40	
	1680	25 to 50 units		.03	4.90	14.70	44	3.20	
	1685	Butt fusion machine, wheeled, 1.5 HP electric, 2" - 8" diameter pipe		2.62	167	500	1,500	120.95	
	1690	Tracked, 20 HP diesel, 4"-12" diameter pipe		11.10	490	1,465	4,400	381.80	
	1695	83 HP diesel, 8" - 24" diameter pipe		30.30	975	2,930	8,800	828.40	
	1700	Carts, brick, hand powered, 1000 lb. capacity		.44	72.50	218	655	47.10	
	1800	Gas engine, 1500 lb., 7-1/2' lift		4.10	115	345	1,025	101.80	
	1822	Dehumidifier, medium, 6 lb./hr., 150 CFM		.99	62	186	560	45.10	
	1824	Large, 18 lb./hr., 600 CFM		2.01	126	378	1,125	91.70	
	1830	Distributor, asphalt, trailer mounted, 2000 gal., 38 H.P. diesel		10.15	330	985	2,950	278.20	
	1840	3000 gal., 38 H.P. diesel		11.65	360	1,075	3,225	308.20	
	1850	Drill, rotary hammer, electric		1.00	26.50	80	240	24	
	1860	Carbide bit, 1-1/2" diameter, add to electric rotary hammer		.02	3.61	10.84	32.50	2.35	
	1865	Rotary, crawler, 250 H.P.		150.45	2,100	6,285	18,900	2,461	
	1870	Emulsion sprayer, 65 gal., 5 H.P. gas engine		2.90	98	294	880	82	
	1880	200 gal., 5 H.P. engine		7.85	163	490	1,475	160.80	
	1900	Floor auto-scrubbing machine, walk-behind, 28" path		4.52	293	880	2,650	212.15	
	1930	Floodlight, mercury vapor, or quartz, on tripod, 1000 watt		.41	19.35	58	174	14.90	
	1940	2000 watt		.78	39	117	350	29.65	
	1950	Floodlights, trailer mounted with generator, 1 - 300 watt light		3.65	71.50	215	645	72.20	
	1960	2 - 1000 watt lights		4.90	98.50	295	885	98.20	
	2000	4 - 300 watt lights		4.60	93.50	280	840	92.80	
	2005	Foam spray rig, incl. box trailer, compressor, generator, proportioner		36.53	490	1,465	4,400	585.25	
	2020	Forklift, straight mast, 12' lift, 5000 lb., 2 wheel drive, gas		25.35	203	610	1,825	324.80	
	2040	21' lift, 5000 lb., 4 wheel drive, diesel		21.15	242	725	2,175	314.20	
	2050	For rough terrain, 42' lift, 35' reach, 9000 lb., 110 H.P.		29.95	485	1,460	4,375	531.60	
	2060	For plant, 4 ton capacity, 80 H.P., 2 wheel drive, gas		15.50	93.50	280	840	180	
	2080	10 ton capacity, 120 H.P., 2 wheel drive, diesel		24.30	162	485	1,450	291.40	
	2100	Generator, electric, gas engine, 1.5 kW to 3 kW		3.95	11.35	34	102	38.40	
	2200	5 kW		5.10	15.35	46	138	50	
	2300	10 kW		9.65	36.50	110	330	99.20	
	2400	25 kW		11.00	86.50	260	780	140	

01 54 33 | Equipment Rental

		UNIT	HOURLY OPER. COST	RENT PER DAY	RENT PER WEEK	RENT PER MONTH	EQUIPMENT COST/DAY	
40	2500	Diesel engine, 20 kW	Ea.	12.55	68.50	205	615	141.40	40
	2600	50 kW		24.35	103	310	930	256.80	
	2700	100 kW		45.15	130	390	1,175	439.20	
	2800	250 kW		88.85	237	710	2,125	852.80	
	2850	Hammer, hydraulic, for mounting on boom, to 500 ft lb.		2.55	75	225	675	65.40	
	2860	1000 ft lb.		4.35	127	380	1,150	110.80	
	2900	Heaters, space, oil or electric, 50 MBH		1.93	7.65	23	69	20.05	
	3000	100 MBH		3.61	10.65	32	96	35.30	
	3100	300 MBH		10.58	38.50	115	345	107.65	
	3150	500 MBH		17.40	45	135	405	166.20	
	3200	Hose, water, suction with coupling, 20' long, 2" diameter		.02	3	9	27	1.95	
	3210	3" diameter		.03	4.33	13	39	2.85	
	3220	4" diameter		.03	5	15	45	3.25	
	3230	6" diameter		.11	17.65	53	159	11.50	
	3240	8" diameter		.20	33.50	100	300	21.60	
	3250	Discharge hose with coupling, 50' long, 2" diameter		.01	1.33	4	12	.90	
	3260	3" diameter		.01	2.33	7	21	1.50	
	3270	4" diameter		.02	3.67	11	33	2.35	
	3280	6" diameter		.06	9.35	28	84	6.10	
	3290	8" diameter		.20	33.50	100	300	21.60	
	3295	Insulation blower		.77	6	18	54	9.75	
	3300	Ladders, extension type, 16' to 36' long		.14	22.50	68	204	14.70	
	3400	40' to 60' long		.19	31	93	279	20.10	
	3405	Lance for cutting concrete		2.52	89	267	800	73.55	
	3407	Lawn mower, rotary, 22", 5 H.P.		2.10	59	177	530	52.20	
	3408	48" self propelled		2.92	75	225	675	68.35	
	3410	Level, electronic, automatic, with tripod and leveling rod		1.49	99	297	890	71.30	
	3430	Laser type, for pipe and sewer line and grade		.73	48.50	145	435	34.85	
	3440	Rotating beam for interior control		.97	64	192	575	46.15	
	3460	Builder's optical transit, with tripod and rod		.10	16.65	50	150	10.80	
	3500	Light towers, towable, with diesel generator, 2000 watt		4.60	93.50	280	840	92.80	
	3600	4000 watt		4.90	98.50	295	885	98.20	
	3700	Mixer, powered, plaster and mortar, 6 C.F., 7 H.P.		2.90	19	57	171	34.60	
	3800	10 C.F., 9 H.P.		3.05	30.50	91	273	42.60	
	3850	Nailer, pneumatic		.47	31	93	279	22.35	
	3900	Paint sprayers complete, 8 CFM		.94	62.50	187	560	44.90	
	4000	17 CFM		1.57	104	313	940	75.15	
	4020	Pavers, bituminous, rubber tires, 8' wide, 50 H.P., diesel		31.85	500	1,500	4,500	554.80	
	4030	10' wide, 150 H.P.		107.95	1,825	5,460	16,400	1,956	
	4050	Crawler, 8' wide, 100 H.P., diesel		90.45	1,825	5,500	16,500	1,824	
	4060	10' wide, 150 H.P.		115.10	2,250	6,715	20,100	2,264	
	4070	Concrete paver, 12' to 24' wide, 250 H.P.		102.05	1,525	4,600	13,800	1,736	
	4080	Placer-spreader-trimmer, 24' wide, 300 H.P.		147.05	2,475	7,405	22,200	2,657	
	4100	Pump, centrifugal gas pump, 1-1/2" diam., 65 GPM		3.95	50	150	450	61.60	
	4200	2" diameter, 130 GPM		5.30	55	165	495	75.40	
	4300	3" diameter, 250 GPM		5.60	56.50	170	510	78.80	
	4400	6" diameter, 1500 GPM		29.35	177	530	1,600	340.80	
	4500	Submersible electric pump, 1-1/4" diameter, 55 GPM		.38	16.65	50	150	13.05	
	4600	1-1/2" diameter, 83 GPM		.42	19	57	171	14.75	
	4700	2" diameter, 120 GPM		1.43	23.50	71	213	25.65	
	4800	3" diameter, 300 GPM		2.55	41.50	125	375	45.40	
	4900	4" diameter, 560 GPM		10.65	160	480	1,450	181.20	
	5000	6" diameter, 1590 GPM		15.75	215	645	1,925	255	
	5100	Diaphragm pump, gas, single, 1-1/2" diameter		1.18	50.50	152	455	39.85	
	5200	2" diameter		4.25	63.50	190	570	72	
	5300	3" diameter		4.25	63.50	190	570	72	
	5400	Double, 4" diameter		6.35	108	325	975	115.80	
	5450	Pressure washer 5 GPM, 3000 psi		4.80	51.50	155	465	69.40	

01 54 33 | Equipment Rental

		UNIT	HOURLY OPER. COST	RENT PER DAY	RENT PER WEEK	RENT PER MONTH	EQUIPMENT COST/DAY	
5460	7 GPM, 3000 psi	Ea.	6.25	60	180	540	86	40
5500	Trash pump, self-priming, gas, 2" diameter		4.50	21.50	64	192	48.80	
5600	Diesel, 4" diameter		9.30	90	270	810	128.40	
5650	Diesel, 6" diameter		25.55	150	450	1,350	294.40	
5655	Grout Pump		26.80	260	780	2,350	370.40	
5700	Salamanders, L.P. gas fired, 100,000 Btu		3.81	13.65	41	123	38.70	
5705	50,000 Btu		2.39	10.35	31	93	25.30	
5720	Sandblaster, portable, open top, 3 C.F. capacity		.55	26.50	80	240	20.40	
5730	6 C.F. capacity		.95	40	120	360	31.60	
5740	Accessories for above		.13	21.50	64	192	13.85	
5750	Sander, floor		.71	17	51	153	15.90	
5760	Edger		.57	18.35	55	165	15.55	
5800	Saw, chain, gas engine, 18" long		2.25	22	66	198	31.20	
5900	Hydraulic powered, 36" long		.75	65	195	585	45	
5950	60" long		.75	66.50	200	600	46	
6000	Masonry, table mounted, 14" diameter, 5 H.P.		1.31	56.50	170	510	44.50	
6050	Portable cut-off, 8 H.P.		2.40	33.50	100	300	39.20	
6100	Circular, hand held, electric, 7-1/4" diameter		.22	4.67	14	42	4.55	
6200	12" diameter		.22	8	24	72	6.55	
6250	Wall saw, w/hydraulic power, 10 H.P.		10.45	60	180	540	119.60	
6275	Shot blaster, walk-behind, 20" wide		4.80	293	880	2,650	214.40	
6280	Sidewalk broom, walk-behind		2.32	70	210	630	60.55	
6300	Steam cleaner, 100 gallons per hour		3.70	76.50	230	690	75.60	
6310	200 gallons per hour		5.25	95	285	855	99	
6340	Tar Kettle/Pot, 400 gallons		10.50	76.50	230	690	130	
6350	Torch, cutting, acetylene-oxygen, 150' hose, excludes gases		.30	15	45	135	11.40	
6360	Hourly operating cost includes tips and gas		19.00				152	
6410	Toilet, portable chemical		.12	20.50	62	186	13.35	
6420	Recycle flush type		.15	24.50	74	222	16	
6430	Toilet, fresh water flush, garden hose,		.18	29.50	89	267	19.25	
6440	Hoisted, non-flush, for high rise		.15	24.50	73	219	15.80	
6465	Tractor, farm with attachment		21.90	277	830	2,500	341.20	
6500	Trailers, platform, flush deck, 2 axle, 25 ton capacity		5.45	117	350	1,050	113.60	
6600	40 ton capacity		7.00	160	480	1,450	152	
6700	3 axle, 50 ton capacity		7.55	177	530	1,600	166.40	
6800	75 ton capacity		9.35	232	695	2,075	213.80	
6810	Trailer mounted cable reel for high voltage line work		5.35	255	764	2,300	195.60	
6820	Trailer mounted cable tensioning rig		10.64	505	1,520	4,550	389.10	
6830	Cable pulling rig		71.33	2,825	8,510	25,500	2,273	
6900	Water tank trailer, engine driven discharge, 5000 gallons		6.95	143	430	1,300	141.60	
6925	10,000 gallons		9.50	198	595	1,775	195	
6950	Water truck, off highway, 6000 gallons		89.80	775	2,330	7,000	1,184	
7010	Tram car for high voltage line work, powered, 2 conductor		6.27	138	415	1,250	133.15	
7020	Transit (builder's level) with tripod		.10	16.65	50	150	10.80	
7030	Trench box, 3000 lb., 6' x 8'		.56	93.50	280	840	60.50	
7040	7200 lb., 6' x 20'		.78	130	389	1,175	84.05	
7050	8000 lb., 8' x 16'		1.08	180	540	1,625	116.65	
7060	9500 lb., 8' x 20'		1.21	201	603	1,800	130.30	
7065	11,000 lb., 8' x 24'		1.27	211	633	1,900	136.75	
7070	12,000 lb., 10' x 20'		1.36	227	680	2,050	146.90	
7100	Truck, pickup, 3/4 ton, 2 wheel drive		15.25	58.50	175	525	157	
7200	4 wheel drive		15.55	73.50	220	660	168.40	
7250	Crew carrier, 9 passenger		21.60	86.50	260	780	224.80	
7290	Flat bed truck, 20,000 lb. GVW		22.30	125	375	1,125	253.40	
7300	Tractor, 4 x 2, 220 H.P.		31.05	197	590	1,775	366.40	
7410	330 H.P.		46.05	272	815	2,450	531.40	
7500	6 x 4, 380 H.P.		52.85	315	950	2,850	612.80	
7600	450 H.P.		64.05	385	1,150	3,450	742.40	

01 54 33 | Equipment Rental

		UNIT	HOURLY OPER. COST	RENT PER DAY	RENT PER WEEK	RENT PER MONTH	EQUIPMENT COST/DAY	
40	7610	Tractor, with A frame, boom and winch, 225 H.P.	Ea.	33.95	272	815	2,450	434.60	**40**
	7620	Vacuum truck, hazardous material, 2500 gallons		12.00	292	875	2,625	271	
	7625	5,000 gallons		14.27	410	1,230	3,700	360.15	
	7650	Vacuum, HEPA, 16 gallon, wet/dry		.83	18	54	162	17.45	
	7655	55 gallon, wet/dry		.77	27	81	243	22.35	
	7660	Water tank, portable		.16	26.50	80	240	17.30	
	7690	Sewer/catch basin vacuum, 14 C.Y., 1500 gallons		18.61	615	1,850	5,550	518.90	
	7700	Welder, electric, 200 amp		3.64	16.35	49	147	38.90	
	7800	300 amp		5.41	20	60	180	55.30	
	7900	Gas engine, 200 amp		13.90	23.50	70	210	125.20	
	8000	300 amp		15.90	24.50	74	222	142	
	8100	Wheelbarrow, any size		.08	13	39	117	8.45	
	8200	Wrecking ball, 4000 lb.		2.30	68.50	205	615	59.40	
50	0010	**HIGHWAY EQUIPMENT RENTAL** without operators							**50**
	0050	Asphalt batch plant, portable drum mixer, 100 ton/hr.	Ea.	79.15	1,450	4,320	13,000	1,497	
	0060	200 ton/hr.		90.32	1,525	4,590	13,800	1,641	
	0070	300 ton/hr.		107.39	1,800	5,390	16,200	1,937	
	0100	Backhoe attachment, long stick, up to 185 H.P., 10.5' long		.35	23	69	207	16.60	
	0140	Up to 250 H.P., 12' long		.37	24.50	74	222	17.75	
	0180	Over 250 H.P., 15' long		.52	34.50	103	310	24.75	
	0200	Special dipper arm, up to 100 H.P., 32' long		1.06	70.50	211	635	50.70	
	0240	Over 100 H.P., 33' long		1.32	87.50	263	790	63.15	
	0280	Catch basin/sewer cleaning truck, 3 ton, 9 C.Y., 1000 gal.		46.25	390	1,170	3,500	604	
	0300	Concrete batch plant, portable, electric, 200 C.Y./hr.		22.08	510	1,525	4,575	481.65	
	0520	Grader/dozer attachment, ripper/scarifier, rear mounted, up to 135 H.P.		3.45	65	195	585	66.60	
	0540	Up to 180 H.P.		4.05	81.50	245	735	81.40	
	0580	Up to 250 H.P.		4.45	93.50	280	840	91.60	
	0700	Pvmt. removal bucket, for hyd. excavator, up to 90 H.P.		1.90	51.50	155	465	46.20	
	0740	Up to 200 H.P.		2.10	73.50	220	660	60.80	
	0780	Over 200 H.P.		2.25	85	255	765	69	
	0900	Aggregate spreader, self-propelled, 187 H.P.		53.75	685	2,055	6,175	841	
	1000	Chemical spreader, 3 C.Y.		3.40	43.50	130	390	53.20	
	1900	Hammermill, traveling, 250 H.P.		77.73	2,050	6,120	18,400	1,846	
	2000	Horizontal borer, 3" diameter, 13 H.P. gas driven		6.25	55	165	495	83	
	2150	Horizontal directional drill, 20,000 lb. thrust, 78 H.P. diesel		31.55	675	2,030	6,100	658.40	
	2160	30,000 lb. thrust, 115 H.P.		39.40	1,025	3,105	9,325	936.20	
	2170	50,000 lb. thrust, 170 H.P.		56.45	1,325	3,970	11,900	1,246	
	2190	Mud trailer for HDD, 1500 gallons, 175 H.P., gas		35.35	153	460	1,375	374.80	
	2200	Hydromulcher, diesel, 3000 gallon, for truck mounting		24.05	247	740	2,225	340.40	
	2300	Gas, 600 gallon		9.20	98.50	295	885	132.60	
	2400	Joint & crack cleaner, walk behind, 25 H.P.		4.35	50	150	450	64.80	
	2500	Filler, trailer mounted, 400 gallons, 20 H.P.		9.60	212	635	1,900	203.80	
	3000	Paint striper, self-propelled, 40 gallon, 22 H.P.		7.60	157	470	1,400	154.80	
	3100	120 gallon, 120 H.P.		24.80	400	1,195	3,575	437.40	
	3200	Post drivers, 6" I-Beam frame, for truck mounting		19.65	380	1,145	3,425	386.20	
	3400	Road sweeper, self-propelled, 8' wide, 90 H.P.		40.30	570	1,715	5,150	665.40	
	3450	Road sweeper, vacuum assisted, 4 C.Y., 220 gallons		77.55	625	1,870	5,600	994.40	
	4000	Road mixer, self-propelled, 130 H.P.		47.80	775	2,320	6,950	846.40	
	4100	310 H.P.		84.40	2,100	6,335	19,000	1,942	
	4220	Cold mix paver, incl. pug mill and bitumen tank, 165 H.P.		98.80	2,325	6,965	20,900	2,183	
	4240	Pavement brush, towed		3.20	93.50	280	840	81.60	
	4250	Paver, asphalt, wheel or crawler, 130 H.P., diesel		98.45	2,300	6,905	20,700	2,169	
	4300	Paver, road widener, gas 1' to 6', 67 H.P.		49.40	905	2,715	8,150	938.20	
	4400	Diesel, 2' to 14', 88 H.P.		63.70	1,050	3,170	9,500	1,144	
	4600	Slipform pavers, curb and gutter, 2 track, 75 H.P.		52.00	805	2,410	7,225	898	
	4700	4 track, 165 H.P.		41.65	730	2,185	6,550	770.20	
	4800	Median barrier, 215 H.P.		54.00	890	2,670	8,000	966	

R015433 -10

01 54 33 | Equipment Rental

			UNIT	HOURLY OPER. COST	RENT PER DAY	RENT PER WEEK	RENT PER MONTH	EQUIPMENT COST/DAY	
50	4901	Trailer, low bed, 75 ton capacity	Ea.	10.10	232	695	2,075	219.80	50
	5000	Road planer, walk behind, 10" cutting width, 10 H.P.		4.00	33.50	100	300	52	
	5100	Self-propelled, 12" cutting width, 64 H.P.		11.45	113	340	1,025	159.60	
	5120	Traffic line remover, metal ball blaster, truck mounted, 115 H.P.		48.75	750	2,245	6,725	839	
	5140	Grinder, truck mounted, 115 H.P.		55.45	810	2,435	7,300	930.60	
	5160	Walk-behind, 11 H.P.		4.55	53.50	160	480	68.40	
	5200	Pavement profiler, 4' to 6' wide, 450 H.P.		258.10	3,350	10,045	30,100	4,074	
	5300	8' to 10' wide, 750 H.P.		405.10	4,400	13,180	39,500	5,877	
	5400	Roadway plate, steel, 1" x 8' x 20'		.08	13	39	117	8.45	
	5600	Stabilizer, self-propelled, 150 H.P.		50.10	610	1,835	5,500	767.80	
	5700	310 H.P.		100.25	1,700	5,125	15,400	1,827	
	5800	Striper, truck mounted, 120 gallon paint, 460 H.P.		71.05	485	1,460	4,375	860.40	
	5900	Thermal paint heating kettle, 115 gallons		5.95	25.50	77	231	63	
	6000	Tar kettle, 330 gallon, trailer mounted		8.70	58.50	175	525	104.60	
	7000	Tunnel locomotive, diesel, 8 to 12 ton		32.40	585	1,760	5,275	611.20	
	7005	Electric, 10 ton		26.55	670	2,010	6,025	614.40	
	7010	Muck cars, 1/2 C.Y. capacity		2.05	24.50	74	222	31.20	
	7020	1 C.Y. capacity		2.30	32.50	98	294	38	
	7030	2 C.Y. capacity		2.45	36.50	110	330	41.60	
	7040	Side dump, 2 C.Y. capacity		2.65	45	135	405	48.20	
	7050	3 C.Y. capacity		3.55	51.50	155	465	59.40	
	7060	5 C.Y. capacity		5.10	65	195	585	79.80	
	7100	Ventilating blower for tunnel, 7-1/2 H.P.		2.05	51.50	155	465	47.40	
	7110	10 H.P.		2.22	53.50	160	480	49.75	
	7120	20 H.P.		3.43	69.50	208	625	69.05	
	7140	40 H.P.		5.59	98.50	295	885	103.70	
	7160	60 H.P.		8.54	152	455	1,375	159.30	
	7175	75 H.P.		11.25	207	620	1,850	214	
	7180	200 H.P.		22.56	305	910	2,725	362.50	
	7800	Windrow loader, elevating		55.95	1,325	3,960	11,900	1,240	
60	0010	**LIFTING AND HOISTING EQUIPMENT RENTAL** without operators							60
	0120	Aerial lift truck, 2 person, to 80'	Ea.	26.75	715	2,145	6,425	643	
	0140	Boom work platform, 40' snorkel		16.10	277	830	2,500	294.80	
	0150	Crane, flatbed mounted, 3 ton capacity		16.55	193	580	1,750	248.40	
	0200	Crane, climbing, 106' jib, 6000 lb. capacity, 410 fpm		37.76	1,625	4,860	14,600	1,274	
	0300	101' jib, 10,250 lb. capacity, 270 fpm		44.26	2,050	6,160	18,500	1,586	
	0500	Tower, static, 130' high, 106' jib, 6200 lb. capacity at 400 fpm		41.56	1,875	5,620	16,900	1,456	
	0600	Crawler mounted, lattice boom, 1/2 C.Y., 15 tons at 12' radius		37.52	640	1,920	5,750	684.15	
	0700	3/4 C.Y., 20 tons at 12' radius		50.03	800	2,400	7,200	880.25	
	0800	1 C.Y., 25 tons at 12' radius		66.70	1,075	3,195	9,575	1,173	
	0900	1-1/2 C.Y., 40 tons at 12' radius		66.70	1,075	3,225	9,675	1,179	
	1000	2 C.Y., 50 tons at 12' radius		70.70	1,250	3,765	11,300	1,319	
	1100	3 C.Y., 75 tons at 12' radius		75.65	1,475	4,435	13,300	1,492	
	1200	100 ton capacity, 60' boom		85.65	1,700	5,090	15,300	1,703	
	1300	165 ton capacity, 60' boom		109.15	2,000	5,980	17,900	2,069	
	1400	200 ton capacity, 70' boom		132.10	2,500	7,480	22,400	2,553	
	1500	350 ton capacity, 80' boom		184.60	3,725	11,210	33,600	3,719	
	1600	Truck mounted, lattice boom, 6 x 4, 20 tons at 10' radius		37.31	1,100	3,310	9,925	960.50	
	1700	25 tons at 10' radius		40.35	1,200	3,610	10,800	1,045	
	1800	8 x 4, 30 tons at 10' radius		43.85	1,275	3,840	11,500	1,119	
	1900	40 tons at 12' radius		46.92	1,325	4,010	12,000	1,177	
	2000	60 tons at 15' radius		53.24	1,425	4,240	12,700	1,274	
	2050	82 tons at 15' radius		60.06	1,525	4,540	13,600	1,388	
	2100	90 tons at 15' radius		67.57	1,650	4,940	14,800	1,529	
	2200	115 tons at 15' radius		76.34	1,850	5,520	16,600	1,715	
	2300	150 tons at 18' radius		84.40	1,950	5,815	17,400	1,838	
	2350	165 tons at 18' radius		90.25	2,050	6,160	18,500	1,954	
	2400	Truck mounted, hydraulic, 12 ton capacity		43.00	530	1,595	4,775	663	

R015433 -10

R015433 -15

R312316 -45

01 54 33 | Equipment Rental

		UNIT	HOURLY OPER. COST	RENT PER DAY	RENT PER WEEK	RENT PER MONTH	EQUIPMENT COST/DAY	
60	2500	25 ton capacity	Ea.	45.35	640	1,915	5,750	745.80	60
	2550	33 ton capacity		45.90	655	1,960	5,875	759.20	
	2560	40 ton capacity		59.35	765	2,290	6,875	932.80	
	2600	55 ton capacity		77.50	860	2,585	7,750	1,137	
	2700	80 ton capacity		101.35	1,400	4,205	12,600	1,652	
	2720	100 ton capacity		94.95	1,450	4,325	13,000	1,625	
	2740	120 ton capacity		109.95	1,550	4,665	14,000	1,813	
	2760	150 ton capacity		128.55	2,050	6,135	18,400	2,255	
	2800	Self-propelled, 4 x 4, with telescoping boom, 5 ton		17.75	230	690	2,075	280	
	2900	12-1/2 ton capacity		32.65	365	1,100	3,300	481.20	
	3000	15 ton capacity		33.35	385	1,160	3,475	498.80	
	3050	20 ton capacity		36.30	450	1,350	4,050	560.40	
	3100	25 ton capacity		37.90	505	1,520	4,550	607.20	
	3150	40 ton capacity		46.50	570	1,705	5,125	713	
	3200	Derricks, guy, 20 ton capacity, 60' boom, 75' mast		27.18	395	1,190	3,575	455.45	
	3300	100' boom, 115' mast		42.63	685	2,050	6,150	751.05	
	3400	Stiffleg, 20 ton capacity, 70' boom, 37' mast		29.70	515	1,550	4,650	547.60	
	3500	100' boom, 47' mast		45.64	825	2,480	7,450	861.10	
	3550	Helicopter, small, lift to 1250 lb. maximum, w/pilot		100.87	3,200	9,610	28,800	2,729	
	3600	Hoists, chain type, overhead, manual, 3/4 ton		.10	.33	1	3	1	
	3900	10 ton		.75	6	18	54	9.60	
	4000	Hoist and tower, 5000 lb. cap., portable electric, 40' high		4.77	228	685	2,050	175.15	
	4100	For each added 10' section, add		.11	18	54	162	11.70	
	4200	Hoist and single tubular tower, 5000 lb. electric, 100' high		6.47	320	957	2,875	243.15	
	4300	For each added 6'-6" section, add		.19	31	93	279	20.10	
	4400	Hoist and double tubular tower, 5000 lb., 100' high		6.95	350	1,054	3,150	266.40	
	4500	For each added 6'-6" section, add		.21	34.50	103	310	22.30	
	4550	Hoist and tower, mast type, 6000 lb., 100' high		7.48	365	1,093	3,275	278.45	
	4570	For each added 10' section, add		.13	21.50	64	192	13.85	
	4600	Hoist and tower, personnel, electric, 2000 lb., 100' @ 125 fpm		15.90	970	2,910	8,725	709.20	
	4700	3000 lb., 100' @ 200 fpm		18.13	1,100	3,290	9,875	803.05	
	4800	3000 lb., 150' @ 300 fpm		20.13	1,225	3,690	11,100	899.05	
	4900	4000 lb., 100' @ 300 fpm		20.82	1,250	3,760	11,300	918.55	
	5000	6000 lb., 100' @ 275 fpm		22.44	1,325	3,950	11,900	969.50	
	5100	For added heights up to 500', add	L.F.	.01	1.67	5	15	1.10	
	5200	Jacks, hydraulic, 20 ton	Ea.	.05	2	6	18	1.60	
	5500	100 ton		.40	11.65	35	105	10.20	
	6100	Jacks, hydraulic, climbing w/50' jackrods, control console, 30 ton cap.		1.97	131	394	1,175	94.55	
	6150	For each added 10' jackrod section, add		.05	3.33	10	30	2.40	
	6300	50 ton capacity		3.17	211	633	1,900	151.95	
	6350	For each added 10' jackrod section, add		.06	4	12	36	2.90	
	6500	125 ton capacity		8.30	555	1,660	4,975	398.40	
	6550	For each added 10' jackrod section, add		.57	37.50	113	340	27.15	
	6600	Cable jack, 10 ton capacity with 200' cable		1.65	110	329	985	79	
	6650	For each added 50' of cable, add		.20	13	39	117	9.40	
70	0010	**WELLPOINT EQUIPMENT RENTAL** without operators							70
	0020	Based on 2 months rental							
	0100	Combination jetting & wellpoint pump, 60 H.P. diesel	Ea.	18.14	325	976	2,925	340.30	
	0200	High pressure gas jet pump, 200 H.P., 300 psi	"	43.54	278	834	2,500	515.10	
	0300	Discharge pipe, 8" diameter	L.F.	.01	.53	1.59	4.77	.40	
	0350	12" diameter		.01	.78	2.33	7	.55	
	0400	Header pipe, flows up to 150 GPM, 4" diameter		.01	.48	1.44	4.32	.35	
	0500	400 GPM, 6" diameter		.01	.56	1.69	5.05	.40	
	0600	800 GPM, 8" diameter		.01	.78	2.33	7	.55	
	0700	1500 GPM, 10" diameter		.01	.82	2.46	7.40	.55	
	0800	2500 GPM, 12" diameter		.02	1.55	4.65	13.95	1.10	
	0900	4500 GPM, 16" diameter		.03	1.98	5.95	17.85	1.45	

Cell (row 70, 0010) note: R015433 -10

01 54 33 | Equipment Rental

			UNIT	HOURLY OPER. COST	RENT PER DAY	RENT PER WEEK	RENT PER MONTH	EQUIPMENT COST/DAY	
70	0950	For quick coupling aluminum and plastic pipe, add	L.F.	.03	2.05	6.16	18.50	1.45	70
	1100	Wellpoint, 25' long, with fittings & riser pipe, 1-1/2" or 2" diameter		.06	4.10	12.29	37	2.95	
	1200	Wellpoint pump, diesel powered, 4" suction, 20 H.P.		7.71	188	563	1,700	174.30	
	1300	6" suction, 30 H.P.		10.54	233	698	2,100	223.90	
	1400	8" suction, 40 H.P.		14.24	320	957	2,875	305.30	
	1500	10" suction, 75 H.P.		21.97	375	1,119	3,350	399.55	
	1600	12" suction, 100 H.P.		31.24	590	1,770	5,300	603.90	
	1700	12" suction, 175 H.P.		46.78	655	1,970	5,900	768.25	
80	0010	**MARINE EQUIPMENT RENTAL** without operators R015433 -10	Ea.						80
	0200	Barge, 400 Ton, 30' wide x 90' long		17.50	1,075	3,205	9,625	781	
	0240	800 Ton, 45' wide x 90' long		21.20	1,300	3,900	11,700	949.60	
	2000	Tugboat, diesel, 100 H.P.		38.95	217	650	1,950	441.60	
	2040	250 H.P.		81.55	395	1,185	3,550	889.40	
	2080	380 H.P.		160.00	1,175	3,545	10,600	1,989	
	3000	Small work boat, gas, 16-foot, 50 H.P.		19.15	60	180	540	189.20	
	4000	Large, diesel, 48-foot, 200 H.P.		90.80	1,250	3,745	11,200	1,475	

Crews

Crew A-1	Hr.	Daily	Hr.	Daily	Bare Costs	Incl. O&P
1 Building Laborer	$36.65	$293.20	$60.20	$481.60	$36.65	$60.20
1 Concrete Saw, Gas Manual		84.00		92.40	10.50	11.55
8 L.H., Daily Totals		$377.20		$574.00	$47.15	$71.75

Crew A-1A	Hr.	Daily	Hr.	Daily	Bare Costs	Incl. O&P
1 Skilled Worker	$47.30	$378.40	$77.05	$616.40	$47.30	$77.05
1 Shot Blaster, 20"		214.40		235.84	26.80	29.48
8 L.H., Daily Totals		$592.80		$852.24	$74.10	$106.53

Crew A-1B	Hr.	Daily	Hr.	Daily	Bare Costs	Incl. O&P
1 Building Laborer	$36.65	$293.20	$60.20	$481.60	$36.65	$60.20
1 Concrete Saw		175.20		192.72	21.90	24.09
8 L.H., Daily Totals		$468.40		$674.32	$58.55	$84.29

Crew A-1C	Hr.	Daily	Hr.	Daily	Bare Costs	Incl. O&P
1 Building Laborer	$36.65	$293.20	$60.20	$481.60	$36.65	$60.20
1 Chain Saw, Gas, 18"		31.20		34.32	3.90	4.29
8 L.H., Daily Totals		$324.40		$515.92	$40.55	$64.49

Crew A-1D	Hr.	Daily	Hr.	Daily	Bare Costs	Incl. O&P
1 Building Laborer	$36.65	$293.20	$60.20	$481.60	$36.65	$60.20
1 Vibrating Plate, Gas, 18"		35.80		39.38	4.47	4.92
8 L.H., Daily Totals		$329.00		$520.98	$41.13	$65.12

Crew A-1E	Hr.	Daily	Hr.	Daily	Bare Costs	Incl. O&P
1 Building Laborer	$36.65	$293.20	$60.20	$481.60	$36.65	$60.20
1 Vibrating Plate, Gas, 21"		46.00		50.60	5.75	6.33
8 L.H., Daily Totals		$339.20		$532.20	$42.40	$66.53

Crew A-1F	Hr.	Daily	Hr.	Daily	Bare Costs	Incl. O&P
1 Building Laborer	$36.65	$293.20	$60.20	$481.60	$36.65	$60.20
1 Rammer/Tamper, Gas, 8"		49.60		54.56	6.20	6.82
8 L.H., Daily Totals		$342.80		$536.16	$42.85	$67.02

Crew A-1G	Hr.	Daily	Hr.	Daily	Bare Costs	Incl. O&P
1 Building Laborer	$36.65	$293.20	$60.20	$481.60	$36.65	$60.20
1 Rammer/Tamper, Gas, 15"		56.00		61.60	7.00	7.70
8 L.H., Daily Totals		$349.20		$543.20	$43.65	$67.90

Crew A-1H	Hr.	Daily	Hr.	Daily	Bare Costs	Incl. O&P
1 Building Laborer	$36.65	$293.20	$60.20	$481.60	$36.65	$60.20
1 Exterior Steam Cleaner		75.60		83.16	9.45	10.40
8 L.H., Daily Totals		$368.80		$564.76	$46.10	$70.59

Crew A-1J	Hr.	Daily	Hr.	Daily	Bare Costs	Incl. O&P
1 Building Laborer	$36.65	$293.20	$60.20	$481.60	$36.65	$60.20
1 Cultivator, Walk-Behind, 5 H.P.		57.45		63.20	7.18	7.90
8 L.H., Daily Totals		$350.65		$544.79	$43.83	$68.10

Crew A-1K	Hr.	Daily	Hr.	Daily	Bare Costs	Incl. O&P
1 Building Laborer	$36.65	$293.20	$60.20	$481.60	$36.65	$60.20
1 Cultivator, Walk-Behind, 8 H.P.		81.40		89.54	10.18	11.19
8 L.H., Daily Totals		$374.60		$571.14	$46.83	$71.39

Crew A-1M	Hr.	Daily	Hr.	Daily	Bare Costs	Incl. O&P
1 Building Laborer	$36.65	$293.20	$60.20	$481.60	$36.65	$60.20
1 Snow Blower, Walk-Behind		60.55		66.61	7.57	8.33
8 L.H., Daily Totals		$353.75		$548.21	$44.22	$68.53

Crew A-2	Hr.	Daily	Hr.	Daily	Bare Costs	Incl. O&P
2 Laborers	$36.65	$586.40	$60.20	$963.20	$36.60	$59.92
1 Truck Driver (light)	36.50	292.00	59.35	474.80		
1 Flatbed Truck, Gas, 1.5 Ton		270.20		297.22	11.26	12.38
24 L.H., Daily Totals		$1148.60		$1735.22	$47.86	$72.30

Crew A-2A	Hr.	Daily	Hr.	Daily	Bare Costs	Incl. O&P
2 Laborers	$36.65	$586.40	$60.20	$963.20	$36.60	$59.92
1 Truck Driver (light)	36.50	292.00	59.35	474.80		
1 Flatbed Truck, Gas, 1.5 Ton		270.20		297.22		
1 Concrete Saw		175.20		192.72	18.56	20.41
24 L.H., Daily Totals		$1323.80		$1927.94	$55.16	$80.33

Crew A-2B	Hr.	Daily	Hr.	Daily	Bare Costs	Incl. O&P
1 Truck Driver (light)	$36.50	$292.00	$59.35	$474.80	$36.50	$59.35
1 Flatbed Truck, Gas, 1.5 Ton		270.20		297.22	33.77	37.15
8 L.H., Daily Totals		$562.20		$772.02	$70.28	$96.50

Crew A-3A	Hr.	Daily	Hr.	Daily	Bare Costs	Incl. O&P
1 Truck Driver (light)	$36.50	$292.00	$59.35	$474.80	$36.50	$59.35
1 Pickup Truck, 4 x 4, 3/4 Ton		168.40		185.24	21.05	23.16
8 L.H., Daily Totals		$460.40		$660.04	$57.55	$82.50

Crew A-3B	Hr.	Daily	Hr.	Daily	Bare Costs	Incl. O&P
1 Equip. Oper. (medium)	$48.90	$391.20	$77.55	$620.40	$43.23	$69.30
1 Truck Driver (heavy)	37.55	300.40	61.05	488.40		
1 Dump Truck, 12 C.Y., 400 H.P.		692.20		761.42		
1 F.E. Loader, W.M., 2.5 C.Y.		522.80		575.08	75.94	83.53
16 L.H., Daily Totals		$1906.60		$2445.30	$119.16	$152.83

Crew A-3C	Hr.	Daily	Hr.	Daily	Bare Costs	Incl. O&P
1 Equip. Oper. (light)	$47.05	$376.40	$74.60	$596.80	$47.05	$74.60
1 Loader, Skid Steer, 78 H.P.		308.80		339.68	38.60	42.46
8 L.H., Daily Totals		$685.20		$936.48	$85.65	$117.06

Crew A-3D	Hr.	Daily	Hr.	Daily	Bare Costs	Incl. O&P
1 Truck Driver (light)	$36.50	$292.00	$59.35	$474.80	$36.50	$59.35
1 Pickup Truck, 4 x 4, 3/4 Ton		168.40		185.24		
1 Flatbed Trailer, 25 Ton		113.60		124.96	35.25	38.77
8 L.H., Daily Totals		$574.00		$785.00	$71.75	$98.13

Crew A-3E	Hr.	Daily	Hr.	Daily	Bare Costs	Incl. O&P
1 Equip. Oper. (crane)	$50.25	$402.00	$79.70	$637.60	$43.90	$70.38
1 Truck Driver (heavy)	37.55	300.40	61.05	488.40		
1 Pickup Truck, 4 x 4, 3/4 Ton		168.40		185.24	10.53	11.58
16 L.H., Daily Totals		$870.80		$1311.24	$54.42	$81.95

Crew A-3F	Hr.	Daily	Hr.	Daily	Bare Costs	Incl. O&P
1 Equip. Oper. (crane)	$50.25	$402.00	$79.70	$637.60	$43.90	$70.38
1 Truck Driver (heavy)	37.55	300.40	61.05	488.40		
1 Pickup Truck, 4 x 4, 3/4 Ton		168.40		185.24		
1 Truck Tractor, 6x4, 380 H.P.		612.80		674.08		
1 Lowbed Trailer, 75 Ton		219.80		241.78	62.56	68.82
16 L.H., Daily Totals		$1703.40		$2227.10	$106.46	$139.19

Crew A-3G

Crew No.	Bare Costs Hr.	Bare Costs Daily	Incl. Subs O&P Hr.	Incl. Subs O&P Daily	Cost Per Labor-Hour Bare Costs	Cost Per Labor-Hour Incl. O&P
1 Equip. Oper. (crane)	$50.25	$402.00	$79.70	$637.60	$43.90	$70.38
1 Truck Driver (heavy)	37.55	300.40	61.05	488.40		
1 Pickup Truck, 4 x 4, 3/4 Ton		168.40		185.24		
1 Truck Tractor, 6x4, 450 H.P.		742.40		816.64		
1 Lowbed Trailer, 75 Ton		219.80		241.78	70.66	77.73
16 L.H., Daily Totals		$1833.00		$2369.66	$114.56	$148.10

Crew A-3H

Crew No.	Bare Costs Hr.	Bare Costs Daily	Incl. Subs O&P Hr.	Incl. Subs O&P Daily	Bare Costs	Incl. O&P
1 Equip. Oper. (crane)	$50.25	$402.00	$79.70	$637.60	$50.25	$79.70
1 Hyd. Crane, 12 Ton (Daily)		874.00		961.40	109.25	120.18
8 L.H., Daily Totals		$1276.00		$1599.00	$159.50	$199.88

Crew A-3I

Crew No.	Bare Costs Hr.	Bare Costs Daily	Incl. Subs O&P Hr.	Incl. Subs O&P Daily	Bare Costs	Incl. O&P
1 Equip. Oper. (crane)	$50.25	$402.00	$79.70	$637.60	$50.25	$79.70
1 Hyd. Crane, 25 Ton (Daily)		1003.00		1103.30	125.38	137.91
8 L.H., Daily Totals		$1405.00		$1740.90	$175.63	$217.61

Crew A-3J

Crew No.	Bare Costs Hr.	Bare Costs Daily	Incl. Subs O&P Hr.	Incl. Subs O&P Daily	Bare Costs	Incl. O&P
1 Equip. Oper. (crane)	$50.25	$402.00	$79.70	$637.60	$50.25	$79.70
1 Hyd. Crane, 40 Ton (Daily)		1240.00		1364.00	155.00	170.50
8 L.H., Daily Totals		$1642.00		$2001.60	$205.25	$250.20

Crew A-3K

Crew No.	Bare Costs Hr.	Bare Costs Daily	Incl. Subs O&P Hr.	Incl. Subs O&P Daily	Bare Costs	Incl. O&P
1 Equip. Oper. (crane)	$50.25	$402.00	$79.70	$637.60	$46.90	$74.38
1 Equip. Oper. (oiler)	43.55	348.40	69.05	552.40		
1 Hyd. Crane, 55 Ton (Daily)		1480.00		1628.00		
1 P/U Truck, 3/4 Ton (Daily)		182.00		200.20	103.88	114.26
16 L.H., Daily Totals		$2412.40		$3018.20	$150.78	$188.64

Crew A-3L

Crew No.	Bare Costs Hr.	Bare Costs Daily	Incl. Subs O&P Hr.	Incl. Subs O&P Daily	Bare Costs	Incl. O&P
1 Equip. Oper. (crane)	$50.25	$402.00	$79.70	$637.60	$46.90	$74.38
1 Equip. Oper. (oiler)	43.55	348.40	69.05	552.40		
1 Hyd. Crane, 80 Ton (Daily)		2211.00		2432.10		
1 P/U Truck, 3/4 Ton (Daily)		182.00		200.20	149.56	164.52
16 L.H., Daily Totals		$3143.40		$3822.30	$196.46	$238.89

Crew A-3M

Crew No.	Bare Costs Hr.	Bare Costs Daily	Incl. Subs O&P Hr.	Incl. Subs O&P Daily	Bare Costs	Incl. O&P
1 Equip. Oper. (crane)	$50.25	$402.00	$79.70	$637.60	$46.90	$74.38
1 Equip. Oper. (oiler)	43.55	348.40	69.05	552.40		
1 Hyd. Crane, 100 Ton (Daily)		2200.00		2420.00		
1 P/U Truck, 3/4 Ton (Daily)		182.00		200.20	148.88	163.76
16 L.H., Daily Totals		$3132.40		$3810.20	$195.78	$238.14

Crew A-3N

Crew No.	Bare Costs Hr.	Bare Costs Daily	Incl. Subs O&P Hr.	Incl. Subs O&P Daily	Bare Costs	Incl. O&P
1 Equip. Oper. (crane)	$50.25	$402.00	$79.70	$637.60	$50.25	$79.70
1 Tower Cane (monthly)		1100.00		1210.00	137.50	151.25
8 L.H., Daily Totals		$1502.00		$1847.60	$187.75	$230.95

Crew A-3P

Crew No.	Bare Costs Hr.	Bare Costs Daily	Incl. Subs O&P Hr.	Incl. Subs O&P Daily	Bare Costs	Incl. O&P
1 Equip. Oper. (light)	$47.05	$376.40	$74.60	$596.80	$47.05	$74.60
1 A.T. Forklift, 42' lift		531.60		584.76	66.45	73.09
8 L.H., Daily Totals		$908.00		$1181.56	$113.50	$147.69

Crew A-4

Crew No.	Bare Costs Hr.	Bare Costs Daily	Incl. Subs O&P Hr.	Incl. Subs O&P Daily	Bare Costs	Incl. O&P
2 Carpenters	$45.85	$733.60	$75.35	$1205.60	$43.75	$71.38
1 Painter, Ordinary	39.55	316.40	63.45	507.60		
24 L.H., Daily Totals		$1050.00		$1713.20	$43.75	$71.38

Crew A-5

Crew No.	Bare Costs Hr.	Bare Costs Daily	Incl. Subs O&P Hr.	Incl. Subs O&P Daily	Bare Costs	Incl. O&P
2 Laborers	$36.65	$586.40	$60.20	$963.20	$36.63	$60.11
.25 Truck Driver (light)	36.50	73.00	59.35	118.70		
.25 Flatbed Truck, Gas, 1.5 Ton		67.55		74.31	3.75	4.13
18 L.H., Daily Totals		$726.95		$1156.20	$40.39	$64.23

Crew A-6

Crew No.	Bare Costs Hr.	Bare Costs Daily	Incl. Subs O&P Hr.	Incl. Subs O&P Daily	Bare Costs	Incl. O&P
1 Instrument Man	$47.30	$378.40	$77.05	$616.40	$45.67	$74.22
1 Rodman/Chainman	44.05	352.40	71.40	571.20		
1 Level, Electronic		71.30		78.43	4.46	4.90
16 L.H., Daily Totals		$802.10		$1266.03	$50.13	$79.13

Crew A-7

Crew No.	Bare Costs Hr.	Bare Costs Daily	Incl. Subs O&P Hr.	Incl. Subs O&P Daily	Bare Costs	Incl. O&P
1 Chief of Party	$59.90	$479.20	$95.10	$760.80	$50.42	$81.18
1 Instrument Man	47.30	378.40	77.05	616.40		
1 Rodman/Chainman	44.05	352.40	71.40	571.20		
1 Level, Electronic		71.30		78.43	2.97	3.27
24 L.H., Daily Totals		$1281.30		$2026.83	$53.39	$84.45

Crew A-8

Crew No.	Bare Costs Hr.	Bare Costs Daily	Incl. Subs O&P Hr.	Incl. Subs O&P Daily	Bare Costs	Incl. O&P
1 Chief of Party	$59.90	$479.20	$95.10	$760.80	$48.83	$78.74
1 Instrument Man	47.30	378.40	77.05	616.40		
2 Rodmen/Chainmen	44.05	704.80	71.40	1142.40		
1 Level, Electronic		71.30		78.43	2.23	2.45
32 L.H., Daily Totals		$1633.70		$2598.03	$51.05	$81.19

Crew A-9

Crew No.	Bare Costs Hr.	Bare Costs Daily	Incl. Subs O&P Hr.	Incl. Subs O&P Daily	Bare Costs	Incl. O&P
1 Asbestos Foreman	$51.65	$413.20	$82.95	$663.60	$51.21	$82.25
7 Asbestos Workers	51.15	2864.40	82.15	4600.40		
64 L.H., Daily Totals		$3277.60		$5264.00	$51.21	$82.25

Crew A-10A

Crew No.	Bare Costs Hr.	Bare Costs Daily	Incl. Subs O&P Hr.	Incl. Subs O&P Daily	Bare Costs	Incl. O&P
1 Asbestos Foreman	$51.65	$413.20	$82.95	$663.60	$51.32	$82.42
2 Asbestos Workers	51.15	818.40	82.15	1314.40		
24 L.H., Daily Totals		$1231.60		$1978.00	$51.32	$82.42

Crew A-10B

Crew No.	Bare Costs Hr.	Bare Costs Daily	Incl. Subs O&P Hr.	Incl. Subs O&P Daily	Bare Costs	Incl. O&P
1 Asbestos Foreman	$51.65	$413.20	$82.95	$663.60	$51.27	$82.35
3 Asbestos Workers	51.15	1227.60	82.15	1971.60		
32 L.H., Daily Totals		$1640.80		$2635.20	$51.27	$82.35

Crew A-10C

Crew No.	Bare Costs Hr.	Bare Costs Daily	Incl. Subs O&P Hr.	Incl. Subs O&P Daily	Bare Costs	Incl. O&P
3 Asbestos Workers	$51.15	$1227.60	$82.15	$1971.60	$51.15	$82.15
1 Flatbed Truck, Gas, 1.5 Ton		270.20		297.22	11.26	12.38
24 L.H., Daily Totals		$1497.80		$2268.82	$62.41	$94.53

Crew A-10D

Crew No.	Bare Costs Hr.	Bare Costs Daily	Incl. Subs O&P Hr.	Incl. Subs O&P Daily	Bare Costs	Incl. O&P
2 Asbestos Workers	$51.15	$818.40	$82.15	$1314.40	$49.02	$78.26
1 Equip. Oper. (crane)	50.25	402.00	79.70	637.60		
1 Equip. Oper. (oiler)	43.55	348.40	69.05	552.40		
1 Hydraulic Crane, 33 Ton		759.20		835.12	23.73	26.10
32 L.H., Daily Totals		$2328.00		$3339.52	$72.75	$104.36

Crew A-11

Crew No.	Bare Costs Hr.	Bare Costs Daily	Incl. Subs O&P Hr.	Incl. Subs O&P Daily	Bare Costs	Incl. O&P
1 Asbestos Foreman	$51.65	$413.20	$82.95	$663.60	$51.21	$82.25
7 Asbestos Workers	51.15	2864.40	82.15	4600.40		
2 Chip. Hammers, 12 Lb., Elec.		40.00		44.00	.63	.69
64 L.H., Daily Totals		$3317.60		$5308.00	$51.84	$82.94

Crew No.	Bare Costs Hr.	Bare Costs Daily	Incl. Subs O&P Hr.	Incl. Subs O&P Daily	Cost Per Labor-Hour Bare Costs	Cost Per Labor-Hour Incl. O&P
Crew A-12	Hr.	Daily	Hr.	Daily	Bare Costs	Incl. O&P
1 Asbestos Foreman	$51.65	$413.20	$82.95	$663.60	$51.21	$82.25
7 Asbestos Workers	51.15	2864.40	82.15	4600.40		
1 Trk-Mtd Vac, 14 CY, 1500 Gal.		518.90		570.79		
1 Flatbed Truck, 20,000 GVW		253.40		278.74	12.07	13.27
64 L.H., Daily Totals		$4049.90		$6113.53	$63.28	$95.52

Crew No.	Bare Costs Hr.	Bare Costs Daily	Incl. Subs O&P Hr.	Incl. Subs O&P Daily	Cost Per Labor-Hour Bare Costs	Cost Per Labor-Hour Incl. O&P
Crew A-13	Hr.	Daily	Hr.	Daily	Bare Costs	Incl. O&P
1 Equip. Oper. (light)	$47.05	$376.40	$74.60	$596.80	$47.05	$74.60
1 Trk-Mtd Vac, 14 CY, 1500 Gal.		518.90		570.79		
1 Flatbed Truck, 20,000 GVW		253.40		278.74	96.54	106.19
8 L.H., Daily Totals		$1148.70		$1446.33	$143.59	$180.79

Crew No.	Bare Costs Hr.	Bare Costs Daily	Incl. Subs O&P Hr.	Incl. Subs O&P Daily	Cost Per Labor-Hour Bare Costs	Cost Per Labor-Hour Incl. O&P
Crew B-1	Hr.	Daily	Hr.	Daily	Bare Costs	Incl. O&P
1 Labor Foreman (outside)	$38.65	$309.20	$63.50	$508.00	$37.32	$61.30
2 Laborers	36.65	586.40	60.20	963.20		
24 L.H., Daily Totals		$895.60		$1471.20	$37.32	$61.30

Crew No.	Bare Costs Hr.	Bare Costs Daily	Incl. Subs O&P Hr.	Incl. Subs O&P Daily	Cost Per Labor-Hour Bare Costs	Cost Per Labor-Hour Incl. O&P
Crew B-1A	Hr.	Daily	Hr.	Daily	Bare Costs	Incl. O&P
1 Labor Foreman (outside)	$38.65	$309.20	$63.50	$508.00	$37.32	$61.30
2 Laborers	36.65	586.40	60.20	963.20		
2 Cutting Torches		22.80		25.08		
2 Sets of Gases		304.00		334.40	13.62	14.98
24 L.H., Daily Totals		$1222.40		$1830.68	$50.93	$76.28

Crew No.	Bare Costs Hr.	Bare Costs Daily	Incl. Subs O&P Hr.	Incl. Subs O&P Daily	Cost Per Labor-Hour Bare Costs	Cost Per Labor-Hour Incl. O&P
Crew B-1B	Hr.	Daily	Hr.	Daily	Bare Costs	Incl. O&P
1 Labor Foreman (outside)	$38.65	$309.20	$63.50	$508.00	$40.55	$65.90
2 Laborers	36.65	586.40	60.20	963.20		
1 Equip. Oper. (crane)	50.25	402.00	79.70	637.60		
2 Cutting Torches		22.80		25.08		
2 Sets of Gases		304.00		334.40		
1 Hyd. Crane, 12 Ton		663.00		729.30	30.93	34.02
32 L.H., Daily Totals		$2287.40		$3197.58	$71.48	$99.92

Crew No.	Bare Costs Hr.	Bare Costs Daily	Incl. Subs O&P Hr.	Incl. Subs O&P Daily	Cost Per Labor-Hour Bare Costs	Cost Per Labor-Hour Incl. O&P
Crew B-1C	Hr.	Daily	Hr.	Daily	Bare Costs	Incl. O&P
1 Labor Foreman (outside)	$38.65	$309.20	$63.50	$508.00	$37.32	$61.30
2 Laborers	36.65	586.40	60.20	963.20		
1 Aerial Lift Truck, 60' Boom		456.00		501.60	19.00	20.90
24 L.H., Daily Totals		$1351.60		$1972.80	$56.32	$82.20

Crew No.	Bare Costs Hr.	Bare Costs Daily	Incl. Subs O&P Hr.	Incl. Subs O&P Daily	Cost Per Labor-Hour Bare Costs	Cost Per Labor-Hour Incl. O&P
Crew B-1D	Hr.	Daily	Hr.	Daily	Bare Costs	Incl. O&P
2 Laborers	$36.65	$586.40	$60.20	$963.20	$36.65	$60.20
1 Small Work Boat, Gas, 50 H.P.		189.20		208.12		
1 Pressure Washer, 7 GPM		86.00		94.60	17.20	18.92
16 L.H., Daily Totals		$861.60		$1265.92	$53.85	$79.12

Crew No.	Bare Costs Hr.	Bare Costs Daily	Incl. Subs O&P Hr.	Incl. Subs O&P Daily	Cost Per Labor-Hour Bare Costs	Cost Per Labor-Hour Incl. O&P
Crew B-1E	Hr.	Daily	Hr.	Daily	Bare Costs	Incl. O&P
1 Labor Foreman (outside)	$38.65	$309.20	$63.50	$508.00	$37.15	$61.02
3 Laborers	36.65	879.60	60.20	1444.80		
1 Work Boat, Diesel, 200 H.P.		1475.00		1622.50		
2 Pressure Washer, 7 GPM		172.00		189.20	51.47	56.62
32 L.H., Daily Totals		$2835.80		$3764.50	$88.62	$117.64

Crew No.	Bare Costs Hr.	Bare Costs Daily	Incl. Subs O&P Hr.	Incl. Subs O&P Daily	Cost Per Labor-Hour Bare Costs	Cost Per Labor-Hour Incl. O&P
Crew B-1F	Hr.	Daily	Hr.	Daily	Bare Costs	Incl. O&P
2 Skilled Workers	$47.30	$756.80	$77.05	$1232.80	$43.75	$71.43
1 Laborer	36.65	293.20	60.20	481.60		
1 Small Work Boat, Gas, 50 H.P.		189.20		208.12		
1 Pressure Washer, 7 GPM		86.00		94.60	11.47	12.61
24 L.H., Daily Totals		$1325.20		$2017.12	$55.22	$84.05

Crew No.	Bare Costs Hr.	Bare Costs Daily	Incl. Subs O&P Hr.	Incl. Subs O&P Daily	Cost Per Labor-Hour Bare Costs	Cost Per Labor-Hour Incl. O&P
Crew B-1G	Hr.	Daily	Hr.	Daily	Bare Costs	Incl. O&P
2 Laborers	$36.65	$586.40	$60.20	$963.20	$36.65	$60.20
1 Small Work Boat, Gas, 50 H.P.		189.20		208.12	11.82	13.01
16 L.H., Daily Totals		$775.60		$1171.32	$48.48	$73.21

Crew No.	Bare Costs Hr.	Bare Costs Daily	Incl. Subs O&P Hr.	Incl. Subs O&P Daily	Cost Per Labor-Hour Bare Costs	Cost Per Labor-Hour Incl. O&P
Crew B-1H	Hr.	Daily	Hr.	Daily	Bare Costs	Incl. O&P
2 Skilled Workers	$47.30	$756.80	$77.05	$1232.80	$43.75	$71.43
1 Laborer	36.65	293.20	60.20	481.60		
1 Small Work Boat, Gas, 50 H.P.		189.20		208.12	7.88	8.67
24 L.H., Daily Totals		$1239.20		$1922.52	$51.63	$80.11

Crew No.	Bare Costs Hr.	Bare Costs Daily	Incl. Subs O&P Hr.	Incl. Subs O&P Daily	Cost Per Labor-Hour Bare Costs	Cost Per Labor-Hour Incl. O&P
Crew B-1J	Hr.	Daily	Hr.	Daily	Bare Costs	Incl. O&P
1 Labor Foreman (inside)	$37.15	$297.20	$61.05	$488.40	$36.90	$60.63
1 Laborer	36.65	293.20	60.20	481.60		
16 L.H., Daily Totals		$590.40		$970.00	$36.90	$60.63

Crew No.	Bare Costs Hr.	Bare Costs Daily	Incl. Subs O&P Hr.	Incl. Subs O&P Daily	Cost Per Labor-Hour Bare Costs	Cost Per Labor-Hour Incl. O&P
Crew B-1K	Hr.	Daily	Hr.	Daily	Bare Costs	Incl. O&P
1 Carpenter Foreman (inside)	$46.35	$370.80	$76.15	$609.20	$46.10	$75.75
1 Carpenter	45.85	366.80	75.35	602.80		
16 L.H., Daily Totals		$737.60		$1212.00	$46.10	$75.75

Crew No.	Bare Costs Hr.	Bare Costs Daily	Incl. Subs O&P Hr.	Incl. Subs O&P Daily	Cost Per Labor-Hour Bare Costs	Cost Per Labor-Hour Incl. O&P
Crew B-2	Hr.	Daily	Hr.	Daily	Bare Costs	Incl. O&P
1 Labor Foreman (outside)	$38.65	$309.20	$63.50	$508.00	$37.05	$60.86
4 Laborers	36.65	1172.80	60.20	1926.40		
40 L.H., Daily Totals		$1482.00		$2434.40	$37.05	$60.86

Crew No.	Bare Costs Hr.	Bare Costs Daily	Incl. Subs O&P Hr.	Incl. Subs O&P Daily	Cost Per Labor-Hour Bare Costs	Cost Per Labor-Hour Incl. O&P
Crew B-2A	Hr.	Daily	Hr.	Daily	Bare Costs	Incl. O&P
1 Labor Foreman (outside)	$38.65	$309.20	$63.50	$508.00	$37.32	$61.30
2 Laborers	36.65	586.40	60.20	963.20		
1 Aerial Lift Truck, 60' Boom		456.00		501.60	19.00	20.90
24 L.H., Daily Totals		$1351.60		$1972.80	$56.32	$82.20

Crew No.	Bare Costs Hr.	Bare Costs Daily	Incl. Subs O&P Hr.	Incl. Subs O&P Daily	Cost Per Labor-Hour Bare Costs	Cost Per Labor-Hour Incl. O&P
Crew B-3	Hr.	Daily	Hr.	Daily	Bare Costs	Incl. O&P
1 Labor Foreman (outside)	$38.65	$309.20	$63.50	$508.00	$39.33	$63.92
2 Laborers	36.65	586.40	60.20	963.20		
1 Equip. Oper. (medium)	48.90	391.20	77.55	620.40		
2 Truck Drivers (heavy)	37.55	600.80	61.05	976.80		
1 Crawler Loader, 3 C.Y.		1191.00		1310.10		
2 Dump Trucks, 12 C.Y., 400 H.P.		1384.40		1522.84	53.65	59.02
48 L.H., Daily Totals		$4463.00		$5901.34	$92.98	$122.94

Crew No.	Bare Costs Hr.	Bare Costs Daily	Incl. Subs O&P Hr.	Incl. Subs O&P Daily	Cost Per Labor-Hour Bare Costs	Cost Per Labor-Hour Incl. O&P
Crew B-3A	Hr.	Daily	Hr.	Daily	Bare Costs	Incl. O&P
4 Laborers	$36.65	$1172.80	$60.20	$1926.40	$39.10	$63.67
1 Equip. Oper. (medium)	48.90	391.20	77.55	620.40		
1 Hyd. Excavator, 1.5 C.Y.		1031.00		1134.10	25.77	28.35
40 L.H., Daily Totals		$2595.00		$3680.90	$64.88	$92.02

Crew No.	Bare Costs Hr.	Bare Costs Daily	Incl. Subs O&P Hr.	Incl. Subs O&P Daily	Cost Per Labor-Hour Bare Costs	Cost Per Labor-Hour Incl. O&P
Crew B-3B	Hr.	Daily	Hr.	Daily	Bare Costs	Incl. O&P
2 Laborers	$36.65	$586.40	$60.20	$963.20	$39.94	$64.75
1 Equip. Oper. (medium)	48.90	391.20	77.55	620.40		
1 Truck Driver (heavy)	37.55	300.40	61.05	488.40		
1 Backhoe Loader, 80 H.P.		397.60		437.36		
1 Dump Truck, 12 C.Y., 400 H.P.		692.20		761.42	34.06	37.46
32 L.H., Daily Totals		$2367.80		$3270.78	$73.99	$102.21

Crew No.	Bare Costs Hr.	Bare Costs Daily	Incl. Subs O&P Hr.	Incl. Subs O&P Daily	Cost Per Labor-Hour Bare Costs	Cost Per Labor-Hour Incl. O&P
Crew B-3C	Hr.	Daily	Hr.	Daily	Bare Costs	Incl. O&P
3 Laborers	$36.65	$879.60	$60.20	$1444.80	$39.71	$64.54
1 Equip. Oper. (medium)	48.90	391.20	77.55	620.40		
1 Crawler Loader, 4 C.Y.		1532.00		1685.20	47.88	52.66
32 L.H., Daily Totals		$2802.80		$3750.40	$87.59	$117.20

Crew B-4

Crew No.	Bare Costs Hr.	Daily	Incl. Subs O&P Hr.	Daily	Cost Per Labor-Hour Bare Costs	Incl. O&P
1 Labor Foreman (outside)	$38.65	$309.20	$63.50	$508.00	$37.13	$60.89
4 Laborers	36.65	1172.80	60.20	1926.40		
1 Truck Driver (heavy)	37.55	300.40	61.05	488.40		
1 Truck Tractor, 220 H.P.		366.40		403.04		
1 Flatbed Trailer, 40 Ton		152.00		167.20	10.80	11.88
48 L.H., Daily Totals		$2300.80		$3493.04	$47.93	$72.77

Crew B-5

Crew No.	Bare Costs Hr.	Daily	Incl. Subs O&P Hr.	Daily	Cost Per Labor-Hour Bare Costs	Incl. O&P
1 Labor Foreman (outside)	$38.65	$309.20	$63.50	$508.00	$40.44	$65.63
4 Laborers	36.65	1172.80	60.20	1926.40		
2 Equip. Oper. (medium)	48.90	782.40	77.55	1240.80		
1 Air Compressor, 250 cfm		202.40		222.64		
2 Breakers, Pavement, 60 lb.		19.60		21.56		
2 -50' Air Hoses, 1.5"		11.60		12.76		
1 Crawler Loader, 3 C.Y.		1191.00		1310.10	25.44	27.98
56 L.H., Daily Totals		$3689.00		$5242.26	$65.88	$93.61

Crew B-5D

Crew No.	Bare Costs Hr.	Daily	Incl. Subs O&P Hr.	Daily	Cost Per Labor-Hour Bare Costs	Incl. O&P
1 Labor Foreman (outside)	$38.65	$309.20	$63.50	$508.00	$40.08	$65.06
4 Laborers	36.65	1172.80	60.20	1926.40		
2 Equip. Oper. (medium)	48.90	782.40	77.55	1240.80		
1 Truck Driver (heavy)	37.55	300.40	61.05	488.40		
1 Air Compressor, 250 cfm		202.40		222.64		
2 Breakers, Pavement, 60 lb.		19.60		21.56		
2 -50' Air Hoses, 1.5"		11.60		12.76		
1 Crawler Loader, 3 C.Y.		1191.00		1310.10		
1 Dump Truck, 12 C.Y., 400 H.P.		692.20		761.42	33.08	36.38
64 L.H., Daily Totals		$4681.60		$6492.08	$73.15	$101.44

Crew B-6

Crew No.	Bare Costs Hr.	Daily	Incl. Subs O&P Hr.	Daily	Cost Per Labor-Hour Bare Costs	Incl. O&P
2 Laborers	$36.65	$586.40	$60.20	$963.20	$40.12	$65.00
1 Equip. Oper. (light)	47.05	376.40	74.60	596.80		
1 Backhoe Loader, 48 H.P.		365.20		401.72	15.22	16.74
24 L.H., Daily Totals		$1328.00		$1961.72	$55.33	$81.74

Crew B-6B

Crew No.	Bare Costs Hr.	Daily	Incl. Subs O&P Hr.	Daily	Cost Per Labor-Hour Bare Costs	Incl. O&P
2 Labor Foremen (outside)	$38.65	$618.40	$63.50	$1016.00	$37.32	$61.30
4 Laborers	36.65	1172.80	60.20	1926.40		
1 S.P. Crane, 4x4, 5 Ton		280.00		308.00		
1 Flatbed Truck, Gas, 1.5 Ton		270.20		297.22		
1 Butt Fusion Mach., 4"-12" diam.		381.80		419.98	19.42	21.36
48 L.H., Daily Totals		$2723.20		$3967.60	$56.73	$82.66

Crew B-6C

Crew No.	Bare Costs Hr.	Daily	Incl. Subs O&P Hr.	Daily	Cost Per Labor-Hour Bare Costs	Incl. O&P
2 Labor Foremen (outside)	$38.65	$618.40	$63.50	$1016.00	$37.32	$61.30
4 Laborers	36.65	1172.80	60.20	1926.40		
1 S.P. Crane, 4x4, 12 Ton		481.20		529.32		
1 Flatbed Truck, Gas, 3 Ton		333.00		366.30		
1 Butt Fusion Mach., 8"-24" diam.		828.40		911.24	34.22	37.64
48 L.H., Daily Totals		$3433.80		$4749.26	$71.54	$98.94

Crew B-7

Crew No.	Bare Costs Hr.	Daily	Incl. Subs O&P Hr.	Daily	Cost Per Labor-Hour Bare Costs	Incl. O&P
1 Labor Foreman (outside)	$38.65	$309.20	$63.50	$508.00	$39.02	$63.64
4 Laborers	36.65	1172.80	60.20	1926.40		
1 Equip. Oper. (medium)	48.90	391.20	77.55	620.40		
1 Brush Chipper, 12", 130 H.P.		396.60		436.26		
1 Crawler Loader, 3 C.Y.		1191.00		1310.10		
2 Chain Saws, Gas, 36" Long		90.00		99.00	34.95	38.45
48 L.H., Daily Totals		$3550.80		$4900.16	$73.97	$102.09

Crew B-7A

Crew No.	Bare Costs Hr.	Daily	Incl. Subs O&P Hr.	Daily	Cost Per Labor-Hour Bare Costs	Incl. O&P
2 Laborers	$36.65	$586.40	$60.20	$963.20	$40.12	$65.00
1 Equip. Oper. (light)	47.05	376.40	74.60	596.80		
1 Rake w/Tractor		347.90		382.69		
2 Chain Saw, Gas, 18"		62.40		68.64	17.10	18.81
24 L.H., Daily Totals		$1373.10		$2011.33	$57.21	$83.81

Crew B-7B

Crew No.	Bare Costs Hr.	Daily	Incl. Subs O&P Hr.	Daily	Cost Per Labor-Hour Bare Costs	Incl. O&P
1 Labor Foreman (outside)	$38.65	$309.20	$63.50	$508.00	$38.81	$63.27
4 Laborers	36.65	1172.80	60.20	1926.40		
1 Equip. Oper. (medium)	48.90	391.20	77.55	620.40		
1 Truck Driver (heavy)	37.55	300.40	61.05	488.40		
1 Brush Chipper, 12", 130 H.P.		396.60		436.26		
1 Crawler Loader, 3 C.Y.		1191.00		1310.10		
2 Chain Saws, Gas, 36" Long		90.00		99.00		
1 Dump Truck, 8 C.Y., 220 H.P.		417.20		458.92	37.41	41.15
56 L.H., Daily Totals		$4268.40		$5847.48	$76.22	$104.42

Crew B-7C

Crew No.	Bare Costs Hr.	Daily	Incl. Subs O&P Hr.	Daily	Cost Per Labor-Hour Bare Costs	Incl. O&P
1 Labor Foreman (outside)	$38.65	$309.20	$63.50	$508.00	$38.81	$63.27
4 Laborers	36.65	1172.80	60.20	1926.40		
1 Equip. Oper. (medium)	48.90	391.20	77.55	620.40		
1 Truck Driver (heavy)	37.55	300.40	61.05	488.40		
1 Brush Chipper, 12", 130 H.P.		396.60		436.26		
1 Crawler Loader, 3 C.Y.		1191.00		1310.10		
2 Chain Saws, Gas, 36" Long		90.00		99.00		
1 Dump Truck, 12 C.Y., 400 H.P.		692.20		761.42	42.32	46.55
56 L.H., Daily Totals		$4543.40		$6149.98	$81.13	$109.82

Crew B-8

Crew No.	Bare Costs Hr.	Daily	Incl. Subs O&P Hr.	Daily	Cost Per Labor-Hour Bare Costs	Incl. O&P
1 Labor Foreman (outside)	$38.65	$309.20	$63.50	$508.00	$41.05	$66.27
2 Laborers	36.65	586.40	60.20	963.20		
2 Equip. Oper. (medium)	48.90	782.40	77.55	1240.80		
1 Equip. Oper. (oiler)	43.55	348.40	69.05	552.40		
2 Truck Drivers (heavy)	37.55	600.80	61.05	976.80		
1 Hyd. Crane, 25 Ton		745.80		820.38		
1 Crawler Loader, 3 C.Y.		1191.00		1310.10		
2 Dump Trucks, 12 C.Y., 400 H.P.		1384.40		1522.84	51.89	57.08
64 L.H., Daily Totals		$5948.40		$7894.52	$92.94	$123.35

Crew B-9

Crew No.	Bare Costs Hr.	Daily	Incl. Subs O&P Hr.	Daily	Cost Per Labor-Hour Bare Costs	Incl. O&P
1 Labor Foreman (outside)	$38.65	$309.20	$63.50	$508.00	$37.05	$60.86
4 Laborers	36.65	1172.80	60.20	1926.40		
1 Air Compressor, 250 cfm		202.40		222.64		
2 Breakers, Pavement, 60 lb.		19.60		21.56		
2 -50' Air Hoses, 1.5"		11.60		12.76	5.84	6.42
40 L.H., Daily Totals		$1715.60		$2691.36	$42.89	$67.28

Crew B-9A

Crew No.	Bare Costs Hr.	Daily	Incl. Subs O&P Hr.	Daily	Cost Per Labor-Hour Bare Costs	Incl. O&P
2 Laborers	$36.65	$586.40	$60.20	$963.20	$36.95	$60.48
1 Truck Driver (heavy)	37.55	300.40	61.05	488.40		
1 Water Tank Trailer, 5000 Gal.		141.60		155.76		
1 Truck Tractor, 220 H.P.		366.40		403.04		
2 -50' Discharge Hoses, 3"		3.00		3.30	21.29	23.42
24 L.H., Daily Totals		$1397.80		$2013.70	$58.24	$83.90

Crew B-9B

Crew B-9B	Bare Costs Hr.	Daily	Incl. Subs O&P Hr.	Daily	Cost Per L.H. Bare Costs	Incl. O&P
2 Laborers	$36.65	$586.40	$60.20	$963.20	$36.95	$60.48
1 Truck Driver (heavy)	37.55	300.40	61.05	488.40		
2 -50' Discharge Hoses, 3"		3.00		3.30		
1 Water Tank Trailer, 5000 Gal.		141.60		155.76		
1 Truck Tractor, 220 H.P.		366.40		403.04		
1 Pressure Washer		69.40		76.34	24.18	26.60
24 L.H., Daily Totals		$1467.20		$2090.04	$61.13	$87.08

Crew B-9D

Crew B-9D	Hr.	Daily	Hr.	Daily	Bare Costs	Incl. O&P
1 Labor Foreman (outside)	$38.65	$309.20	$63.50	$508.00	$37.05	$60.86
4 Common Laborers	36.65	1172.80	60.20	1926.40		
1 Air Compressor, 250 cfm		202.40		222.64		
2 -50' Air Hoses, 1.5"		11.60		12.76		
2 Air Powered Tampers		52.40		57.64	6.66	7.33
40 L.H., Daily Totals		$1748.40		$2727.44	$43.71	$68.19

Crew B-10

Crew B-10	Hr.	Daily	Hr.	Daily	Bare Costs	Incl. O&P
1 Equip. Oper. (medium)	$48.90	$391.20	$77.55	$620.40	$44.82	$71.77
.5 Laborer	36.65	146.60	60.20	240.80		
12 L.H., Daily Totals		$537.80		$861.20	$44.82	$71.77

Crew B-10A

Crew B-10A	Hr.	Daily	Hr.	Daily	Bare Costs	Incl. O&P
1 Equip. Oper. (medium)	$48.90	$391.20	$77.55	$620.40	$44.82	$71.77
.5 Laborer	36.65	146.60	60.20	240.80		
1 Roller, 2-Drum, W.B., 7.5 H.P.		182.80		201.08	15.23	16.76
12 L.H., Daily Totals		$720.60		$1062.28	$60.05	$88.52

Crew B-10B

Crew B-10B	Hr.	Daily	Hr.	Daily	Bare Costs	Incl. O&P
1 Equip. Oper. (medium)	$48.90	$391.20	$77.55	$620.40	$44.82	$71.77
.5 Laborer	36.65	146.60	60.20	240.80		
1 Dozer, 200 H.P.		1325.00		1457.50	110.42	121.46
12 L.H., Daily Totals		$1862.80		$2318.70	$155.23	$193.22

Crew B-10C

Crew B-10C	Hr.	Daily	Hr.	Daily	Bare Costs	Incl. O&P
1 Equip. Oper. (medium)	$48.90	$391.20	$77.55	$620.40	$44.82	$71.77
.5 Laborer	36.65	146.60	60.20	240.80		
1 Dozer, 200 H.P.		1325.00		1457.50		
1 Vibratory Roller, Towed, 23 Ton		412.00		453.20	144.75	159.22
12 L.H., Daily Totals		$2274.80		$2771.90	$189.57	$230.99

Crew B-10D

Crew B-10D	Hr.	Daily	Hr.	Daily	Bare Costs	Incl. O&P
1 Equip. Oper. (medium)	$48.90	$391.20	$77.55	$620.40	$44.82	$71.77
.5 Laborer	36.65	146.60	60.20	240.80		
1 Dozer, 200 H.P.		1325.00		1457.50		
1 Sheepsft. Roller, Towed		443.80		488.18	147.40	162.14
12 L.H., Daily Totals		$2306.60		$2806.88	$192.22	$233.91

Crew B-10E

Crew B-10E	Hr.	Daily	Hr.	Daily	Bare Costs	Incl. O&P
1 Equip. Oper. (medium)	$48.90	$391.20	$77.55	$620.40	$44.82	$71.77
.5 Laborer	36.65	146.60	60.20	240.80		
1 Tandem Roller, 5 Ton		159.00		174.90	13.25	14.57
12 L.H., Daily Totals		$696.80		$1036.10	$58.07	$86.34

Crew B-10F

Crew B-10F	Hr.	Daily	Hr.	Daily	Bare Costs	Incl. O&P
1 Equip. Oper. (medium)	$48.90	$391.20	$77.55	$620.40	$44.82	$71.77
.5 Laborer	36.65	146.60	60.20	240.80		
1 Tandem Roller, 10 Ton		242.00		266.20	20.17	22.18
12 L.H., Daily Totals		$779.80		$1127.40	$64.98	$93.95

Crew B-10G

Crew B-10G	Hr.	Daily	Hr.	Daily	Bare Costs	Incl. O&P
1 Equip. Oper. (medium)	$48.90	$391.20	$77.55	$620.40	$44.82	$71.77
.5 Laborer	36.65	146.60	60.20	240.80		
1 Sheepsfoot Roller, 240 H.P.		1218.00		1339.80	101.50	111.65
12 L.H., Daily Totals		$1755.80		$2201.00	$146.32	$183.42

Crew B-10H

Crew B-10H	Hr.	Daily	Hr.	Daily	Bare Costs	Incl. O&P
1 Equip. Oper. (medium)	$48.90	$391.20	$77.55	$620.40	$44.82	$71.77
.5 Laborer	36.65	146.60	60.20	240.80		
1 Diaphragm Water Pump, 2"		72.00		79.20		
1 -20' Suction Hose, 2"		1.95		2.15		
2 -50' Discharge Hoses, 2"		1.80		1.98	6.31	6.94
12 L.H., Daily Totals		$613.55		$944.52	$51.13	$78.71

Crew B-10I

Crew B-10I	Hr.	Daily	Hr.	Daily	Bare Costs	Incl. O&P
1 Equip. Oper. (medium)	$48.90	$391.20	$77.55	$620.40	$44.82	$71.77
.5 Laborer	36.65	146.60	60.20	240.80		
1 Diaphragm Water Pump, 4"		115.80		127.38		
1 -20' Suction Hose, 4"		3.25		3.58		
2 -50' Discharge Hoses, 4"		4.70		5.17	10.31	11.34
12 L.H., Daily Totals		$661.55		$997.33	$55.13	$83.11

Crew B-10J

Crew B-10J	Hr.	Daily	Hr.	Daily	Bare Costs	Incl. O&P
1 Equip. Oper. (medium)	$48.90	$391.20	$77.55	$620.40	$44.82	$71.77
.5 Laborer	36.65	146.60	60.20	240.80		
1 Centrifugal Water Pump, 3"		78.80		86.68		
1 -20' Suction Hose, 3"		2.85		3.13		
2 -50' Discharge Hoses, 3"		3.00		3.30	7.05	7.76
12 L.H., Daily Totals		$622.45		$954.32	$51.87	$79.53

Crew B-10K

Crew B-10K	Hr.	Daily	Hr.	Daily	Bare Costs	Incl. O&P
1 Equip. Oper. (medium)	$48.90	$391.20	$77.55	$620.40	$44.82	$71.77
.5 Laborer	36.65	146.60	60.20	240.80		
1 Centr. Water Pump, 6"		340.80		374.88		
1 -20' Suction Hose, 6"		11.50		12.65		
2 -50' Discharge Hoses, 6"		12.20		13.42	30.38	33.41
12 L.H., Daily Totals		$902.30		$1262.15	$75.19	$105.18

Crew B-10L

Crew B-10L	Hr.	Daily	Hr.	Daily	Bare Costs	Incl. O&P
1 Equip. Oper. (medium)	$48.90	$391.20	$77.55	$620.40	$44.82	$71.77
.5 Laborer	36.65	146.60	60.20	240.80		
1 Dozer, 80 H.P.		481.00		529.10	40.08	44.09
12 L.H., Daily Totals		$1018.80		$1390.30	$84.90	$115.86

Crew B-10M

Crew B-10M	Hr.	Daily	Hr.	Daily	Bare Costs	Incl. O&P
1 Equip. Oper. (medium)	$48.90	$391.20	$77.55	$620.40	$44.82	$71.77
.5 Laborer	36.65	146.60	60.20	240.80		
1 Dozer, 300 H.P.		1817.00		1998.70	151.42	166.56
12 L.H., Daily Totals		$2354.80		$2859.90	$196.23	$238.32

Crew B-10N

Crew B-10N	Hr.	Daily	Hr.	Daily	Bare Costs	Incl. O&P
1 Equip. Oper. (medium)	$48.90	$391.20	$77.55	$620.40	$44.82	$71.77
.5 Laborer	36.65	146.60	60.20	240.80		
1 F.E. Loader, T.M., 1.5 C.Y.		522.80		575.08	43.57	47.92
12 L.H., Daily Totals		$1060.60		$1436.28	$88.38	$119.69

Crew B-100

Crew B-100	Hr.	Daily	Hr.	Daily	Bare Costs	Incl. O&P
1 Equip. Oper. (medium)	$48.90	$391.20	$77.55	$620.40	$44.82	$71.77
.5 Laborer	36.65	146.60	60.20	240.80		
1 F.E. Loader, T.M., 2.25 C.Y.		959.80		1055.78	79.98	87.98
12 L.H., Daily Totals		$1497.60		$1916.98	$124.80	$159.75

Crew No.	Bare Costs		Incl. Subs O&P		Cost Per Labor-Hour	
Crew B-10P	Hr.	Daily	Hr.	Daily	Bare Costs	Incl. O&P
1 Equip. Oper. (medium)	$48.90	$391.20	$77.55	$620.40	$44.82	$71.77
.5 Laborer	36.65	146.60	60.20	240.80		
1 Crawler Loader, 3 C.Y.		1191.00		1310.10	99.25	109.18
12 L.H., Daily Totals		$1728.80		$2171.30	$144.07	$180.94
Crew B-10Q	Hr.	Daily	Hr.	Daily	Bare Costs	Incl. O&P
1 Equip. Oper. (medium)	$48.90	$391.20	$77.55	$620.40	$44.82	$71.77
.5 Laborer	36.65	146.60	60.20	240.80		
1 Crawler Loader, 4 C.Y.		1532.00		1685.20	127.67	140.43
12 L.H., Daily Totals		$2069.80		$2546.40	$172.48	$212.20
Crew B-10R	Hr.	Daily	Hr.	Daily	Bare Costs	Incl. O&P
1 Equip. Oper. (medium)	$48.90	$391.20	$77.55	$620.40	$44.82	$71.77
.5 Laborer	36.65	146.60	60.20	240.80		
1 F.E. Loader, W.M., 1 C.Y.		295.20		324.72	24.60	27.06
12 L.H., Daily Totals		$833.00		$1185.92	$69.42	$98.83
Crew B-10S	Hr.	Daily	Hr.	Daily	Bare Costs	Incl. O&P
1 Equip. Oper. (medium)	$48.90	$391.20	$77.55	$620.40	$44.82	$71.77
.5 Laborer	36.65	146.60	60.20	240.80		
1 F.E. Loader, W.M., 1.5 C.Y.		373.40		410.74	31.12	34.23
12 L.H., Daily Totals		$911.20		$1271.94	$75.93	$106.00
Crew B-10T	Hr.	Daily	Hr.	Daily	Bare Costs	Incl. O&P
1 Equip. Oper. (medium)	$48.90	$391.20	$77.55	$620.40	$44.82	$71.77
.5 Laborer	36.65	146.60	60.20	240.80		
1 F.E. Loader, W.M.,2.5 C.Y.		522.80		575.08	43.57	47.92
12 L.H., Daily Totals		$1060.60		$1436.28	$88.38	$119.69
Crew B-10U	Hr.	Daily	Hr.	Daily	Bare Costs	Incl. O&P
1 Equip. Oper. (medium)	$48.90	$391.20	$77.55	$620.40	$44.82	$71.77
.5 Laborer	36.65	146.60	60.20	240.80		
1 F.E. Loader, W.M., 5.5 C.Y.		1049.00		1153.90	87.42	96.16
12 L.H., Daily Totals		$1586.80		$2015.10	$132.23	$167.93
Crew B-10V	Hr.	Daily	Hr.	Daily	Bare Costs	Incl. O&P
1 Equip. Oper. (medium)	$48.90	$391.20	$77.55	$620.40	$44.82	$71.77
.5 Laborer	36.65	146.60	60.20	240.80		
1 Dozer, 700 H.P.		4485.00		4933.50	373.75	411.13
12 L.H., Daily Totals		$5022.80		$5794.70	$418.57	$482.89
Crew B-10W	Hr.	Daily	Hr.	Daily	Bare Costs	Incl. O&P
1 Equip. Oper. (medium)	$48.90	$391.20	$77.55	$620.40	$44.82	$71.77
.5 Laborer	36.65	146.60	60.20	240.80		
1 Dozer, 105 H.P.		591.80		650.98	49.32	54.25
12 L.H., Daily Totals		$1129.60		$1512.18	$94.13	$126.02
Crew B-10X	Hr.	Daily	Hr.	Daily	Bare Costs	Incl. O&P
1 Equip. Oper. (medium)	$48.90	$391.20	$77.55	$620.40	$44.82	$71.77
.5 Laborer	36.65	146.60	60.20	240.80		
1 Dozer, 410 H.P.		2409.00		2649.90	200.75	220.82
12 L.H., Daily Totals		$2946.80		$3511.10	$245.57	$292.59
Crew B-10Y	Hr.	Daily	Hr.	Daily	Bare Costs	Incl. O&P
1 Equip. Oper. (medium)	$48.90	$391.20	$77.55	$620.40	$44.82	$71.77
.5 Laborer	36.65	146.60	60.20	240.80		
1 Vibr. Roller, Towed, 12 Ton		559.20		615.12	46.60	51.26
12 L.H., Daily Totals		$1097.00		$1476.32	$91.42	$123.03

Crew No.	Bare Costs		Incl. Subs O&P		Cost Per Labor-Hour	
Crew B-11A	Hr.	Daily	Hr.	Daily	Bare Costs	Incl. O&P
1 Equipment Oper. (med.)	$48.90	$391.20	$77.55	$620.40	$42.77	$68.88
1 Laborer	36.65	293.20	60.20	481.60		
1 Dozer, 200 H.P.		1325.00		1457.50	82.81	91.09
16 L.H., Daily Totals		$2009.40		$2559.50	$125.59	$159.97
Crew B-11B	Hr.	Daily	Hr.	Daily	Bare Costs	Incl. O&P
1 Equipment Oper. (light)	$47.05	$376.40	$74.60	$596.80	$41.85	$67.40
1 Laborer	36.65	293.20	60.20	481.60		
1 Air Powered Tamper		26.20		28.82		
1 Air Compressor, 365 cfm		264.80		291.28		
2 -50' Air Hoses, 1.5"		11.60		12.76	18.91	20.80
16 L.H., Daily Totals		$972.20		$1411.26	$60.76	$88.20
Crew B-11C	Hr.	Daily	Hr.	Daily	Bare Costs	Incl. O&P
1 Equipment Oper. (med.)	$48.90	$391.20	$77.55	$620.40	$42.77	$68.88
1 Laborer	36.65	293.20	60.20	481.60		
1 Backhoe Loader, 48 H.P.		365.20		401.72	22.82	25.11
16 L.H., Daily Totals		$1049.60		$1503.72	$65.60	$93.98
Crew B-11K	Hr.	Daily	Hr.	Daily	Bare Costs	Incl. O&P
1 Equipment Oper. (med.)	$48.90	$391.20	$77.55	$620.40	$42.77	$68.88
1 Laborer	36.65	293.20	60.20	481.60		
1 Trencher, Chain Type, 8' D		3376.00		3713.60	211.00	232.10
16 L.H., Daily Totals		$4060.40		$4815.60	$253.78	$300.98
Crew B-11L	Hr.	Daily	Hr.	Daily	Bare Costs	Incl. O&P
1 Equipment Oper. (med.)	$48.90	$391.20	$77.55	$620.40	$42.77	$68.88
1 Laborer	36.65	293.20	60.20	481.60		
1 Grader, 30,000 Lbs.		707.00		777.70	44.19	48.61
16 L.H., Daily Totals		$1391.40		$1879.70	$86.96	$117.48
Crew B-11M	Hr.	Daily	Hr.	Daily	Bare Costs	Incl. O&P
1 Equipment Oper. (med.)	$48.90	$391.20	$77.55	$620.40	$42.77	$68.88
1 Laborer	36.65	293.20	60.20	481.60		
1 Backhoe Loader, 80 H.P.		397.60		437.36	24.85	27.34
16 L.H., Daily Totals		$1082.00		$1539.36	$67.63	$96.21
Crew B-11S	Hr.	Daily	Hr.	Daily	Bare Costs	Incl. O&P
1 Equipment Operator (med.)	$48.90	$391.20	$77.55	$620.40	$44.82	$71.77
.5 Laborer	36.65	146.60	60.20	240.80		
1 Dozer, 300 H.P.		1817.00		1998.70		
1 Ripper, Beam & 1 Shank		81.40		89.54	158.20	174.02
12 L.H., Daily Totals		$2436.20		$2949.44	$203.02	$245.79
Crew B-11T	Hr.	Daily	Hr.	Daily	Bare Costs	Incl. O&P
1 Equipment Operator (med.)	$48.90	$391.20	$77.55	$620.40	$44.82	$71.77
.5 Laborer	36.65	146.60	60.20	240.80		
1 Dozer, 410 H.P.		2409.00		2649.90		
1 Ripper, Beam & 2 Shanks		91.60		100.76	208.38	229.22
12 L.H., Daily Totals		$3038.40		$3611.86	$253.20	$300.99
Crew B-11W	Hr.	Daily	Hr.	Daily	Bare Costs	Incl. O&P
1 Equipment Operator (med.)	$48.90	$391.20	$77.55	$620.40	$38.42	$62.35
1 Common Laborer	36.65	293.20	60.20	481.60		
10 Truck Drivers (heavy)	37.55	3004.00	61.05	4884.00		
1 Dozer, 200 H.P.		1325.00		1457.50		
1 Vibratory Roller, Towed, 23 Ton		412.00		453.20		
10 Dump Trucks, 8 C.Y., 220 H.P.		4172.00		4589.20	61.55	67.71
96 L.H., Daily Totals		$9597.40		$12485.90	$99.97	$130.06

Crew B-11Y

Crew No.	Bare Costs Hr.	Daily	Incl. Subs O&P Hr.	Daily	Cost Per Labor-Hour Bare Costs	Incl. O&P
1 Labor Foreman (outside)	$38.65	$309.20	$63.50	$508.00	$40.96	$66.35
5 Common Laborers	36.65	1466.00	60.20	2408.00		
3 Equipment Operators (med.)	48.90	1173.60	77.55	1861.20		
1 Dozer, 80 H.P.		481.00		529.10		
2 Roller, 2-Drum, W.B., 7.5 H.P.		365.60		402.16		
4 Vibrating Plate, Gas, 21"		184.00		202.40	14.31	15.75
72 L.H., Daily Totals		$3979.40		$5910.86	$55.27	$82.10

Crew B-12A

Crew No.	Bare Costs Hr.	Daily	Incl. Subs O&P Hr.	Daily	Cost Per Labor-Hour Bare Costs	Incl. O&P
1 Equip. Oper. (crane)	$50.25	$402.00	$79.70	$637.60	$43.45	$69.95
1 Laborer	36.65	293.20	60.20	481.60		
1 Hyd. Excavator, 1 C.Y.		814.80		896.28	50.92	56.02
16 L.H., Daily Totals		$1510.00		$2015.48	$94.38	$125.97

Crew B-12B

Crew No.	Bare Costs Hr.	Daily	Incl. Subs O&P Hr.	Daily	Cost Per Labor-Hour Bare Costs	Incl. O&P
1 Equip. Oper. (crane)	$50.25	$402.00	$79.70	$637.60	$43.45	$69.95
1 Laborer	36.65	293.20	60.20	481.60		
1 Hyd. Excavator, 1.5 C.Y.		1031.00		1134.10	64.44	70.88
16 L.H., Daily Totals		$1726.20		$2253.30	$107.89	$140.83

Crew B-12C

Crew No.	Bare Costs Hr.	Daily	Incl. Subs O&P Hr.	Daily	Cost Per Labor-Hour Bare Costs	Incl. O&P
1 Equip. Oper. (crane)	$50.25	$402.00	$79.70	$637.60	$43.45	$69.95
1 Laborer	36.65	293.20	60.20	481.60		
1 Hyd. Excavator, 2 C.Y.		1175.00		1292.50	73.44	80.78
16 L.H., Daily Totals		$1870.20		$2411.70	$116.89	$150.73

Crew B-12D

Crew No.	Bare Costs Hr.	Daily	Incl. Subs O&P Hr.	Daily	Cost Per Labor-Hour Bare Costs	Incl. O&P
1 Equip. Oper. (crane)	$50.25	$402.00	$79.70	$637.60	$43.45	$69.95
1 Laborer	36.65	293.20	60.20	481.60		
1 Hyd. Excavator, 3.5 C.Y.		2442.00		2686.20	152.63	167.89
16 L.H., Daily Totals		$3137.20		$3805.40	$196.07	$237.84

Crew B-12E

Crew No.	Bare Costs Hr.	Daily	Incl. Subs O&P Hr.	Daily	Cost Per Labor-Hour Bare Costs	Incl. O&P
1 Equip. Oper. (crane)	$50.25	$402.00	$79.70	$637.60	$43.45	$69.95
1 Laborer	36.65	293.20	60.20	481.60		
1 Hyd. Excavator, .5 C.Y.		448.00		492.80	28.00	30.80
16 L.H., Daily Totals		$1143.20		$1612.00	$71.45	$100.75

Crew B-12F

Crew No.	Bare Costs Hr.	Daily	Incl. Subs O&P Hr.	Daily	Cost Per Labor-Hour Bare Costs	Incl. O&P
1 Equip. Oper. (crane)	$50.25	$402.00	$79.70	$637.60	$43.45	$69.95
1 Laborer	36.65	293.20	60.20	481.60		
1 Hyd. Excavator, .75 C.Y.		662.00		728.20	41.38	45.51
16 L.H., Daily Totals		$1357.20		$1847.40	$84.83	$115.46

Crew B-12G

Crew No.	Bare Costs Hr.	Daily	Incl. Subs O&P Hr.	Daily	Cost Per Labor-Hour Bare Costs	Incl. O&P
1 Equip. Oper. (crane)	$50.25	$402.00	$79.70	$637.60	$43.45	$69.95
1 Laborer	36.65	293.20	60.20	481.60		
1 Crawler Crane, 15 Ton		684.15		752.57		
1 Clamshell Bucket, .5 C.Y.		37.80		41.58	45.12	49.63
16 L.H., Daily Totals		$1417.15		$1913.35	$88.57	$119.58

Crew B-12H

Crew No.	Bare Costs Hr.	Daily	Incl. Subs O&P Hr.	Daily	Cost Per Labor-Hour Bare Costs	Incl. O&P
1 Equip. Oper. (crane)	$50.25	$402.00	$79.70	$637.60	$43.45	$69.95
1 Laborer	36.65	293.20	60.20	481.60		
1 Crawler Crane, 25 Ton		1173.00		1290.30		
1 Clamshell Bucket, 1 C.Y.		47.40		52.14	76.28	83.90
16 L.H., Daily Totals		$1915.60		$2461.64	$119.72	$153.85

Crew B-12I

Crew No.	Bare Costs Hr.	Daily	Incl. Subs O&P Hr.	Daily	Cost Per Labor-Hour Bare Costs	Incl. O&P
1 Equip. Oper. (crane)	$50.25	$402.00	$79.70	$637.60	$43.45	$69.95
1 Laborer	36.65	293.20	60.20	481.60		
1 Crawler Crane, 20 Ton		880.25		968.27		
1 Dragline Bucket, .75 C.Y.		20.80		22.88	56.32	61.95
16 L.H., Daily Totals		$1596.25		$2110.36	$99.77	$131.90

Crew B-12J

Crew No.	Bare Costs Hr.	Daily	Incl. Subs O&P Hr.	Daily	Cost Per Labor-Hour Bare Costs	Incl. O&P
1 Equip. Oper. (crane)	$50.25	$402.00	$79.70	$637.60	$43.45	$69.95
1 Laborer	36.65	293.20	60.20	481.60		
1 Gradall, 5/8 C.Y.		881.60		969.76	55.10	60.61
16 L.H., Daily Totals		$1576.80		$2088.96	$98.55	$130.56

Crew B-12K

Crew No.	Bare Costs Hr.	Daily	Incl. Subs O&P Hr.	Daily	Cost Per Labor-Hour Bare Costs	Incl. O&P
1 Equip. Oper. (crane)	$50.25	$402.00	$79.70	$637.60	$43.45	$69.95
1 Laborer	36.65	293.20	60.20	481.60		
1 Gradall, 3 Ton, 1 C.Y.		1005.00		1105.50	62.81	69.09
16 L.H., Daily Totals		$1700.20		$2224.70	$106.26	$139.04

Crew B-12L

Crew No.	Bare Costs Hr.	Daily	Incl. Subs O&P Hr.	Daily	Cost Per Labor-Hour Bare Costs	Incl. O&P
1 Equip. Oper. (crane)	$50.25	$402.00	$79.70	$637.60	$43.45	$69.95
1 Laborer	36.65	293.20	60.20	481.60		
1 Crawler Crane, 15 Ton		684.15		752.57		
1 F.E. Attachment, .5 C.Y.		59.60		65.56	46.48	51.13
16 L.H., Daily Totals		$1438.95		$1937.33	$89.93	$121.08

Crew B-12M

Crew No.	Bare Costs Hr.	Daily	Incl. Subs O&P Hr.	Daily	Cost Per Labor-Hour Bare Costs	Incl. O&P
1 Equip. Oper. (crane)	$50.25	$402.00	$79.70	$637.60	$43.45	$69.95
1 Laborer	36.65	293.20	60.20	481.60		
1 Crawler Crane, 20 Ton		880.25		968.27		
1 F.E. Attachment, .75 C.Y.		64.00		70.40	59.02	64.92
16 L.H., Daily Totals		$1639.45		$2157.88	$102.47	$134.87

Crew B-12N

Crew No.	Bare Costs Hr.	Daily	Incl. Subs O&P Hr.	Daily	Cost Per Labor-Hour Bare Costs	Incl. O&P
1 Equip. Oper. (crane)	$50.25	$402.00	$79.70	$637.60	$43.45	$69.95
1 Laborer	36.65	293.20	60.20	481.60		
1 Crawler Crane, 25 Ton		1173.00		1290.30		
1 F.E. Attachment, 1 C.Y.		70.80		77.88	77.74	85.51
16 L.H., Daily Totals		$1939.00		$2487.38	$121.19	$155.46

Crew B-12O

Crew No.	Bare Costs Hr.	Daily	Incl. Subs O&P Hr.	Daily	Cost Per Labor-Hour Bare Costs	Incl. O&P
1 Equip. Oper. (crane)	$50.25	$402.00	$79.70	$637.60	$43.45	$69.95
1 Laborer	36.65	293.20	60.20	481.60		
1 Crawler Crane, 40 Ton		1179.00		1296.90		
1 F.E. Attachment, 1.5 C.Y.		80.00		88.00	78.69	86.56
16 L.H., Daily Totals		$1954.20		$2504.10	$122.14	$156.51

Crew B-12P

Crew No.	Bare Costs Hr.	Daily	Incl. Subs O&P Hr.	Daily	Cost Per Labor-Hour Bare Costs	Incl. O&P
1 Equip. Oper. (crane)	$50.25	$402.00	$79.70	$637.60	$43.45	$69.95
1 Laborer	36.65	293.20	60.20	481.60		
1 Crawler Crane, 40 Ton		1179.00		1296.90		
1 Dragline Bucket, 1.5 C.Y.		33.60		36.96	75.79	83.37
16 L.H., Daily Totals		$1907.80		$2453.06	$119.24	$153.32

Crew B-12Q

Crew No.	Bare Costs Hr.	Daily	Incl. Subs O&P Hr.	Daily	Cost Per Labor-Hour Bare Costs	Incl. O&P
1 Equip. Oper. (crane)	$50.25	$402.00	$79.70	$637.60	$43.45	$69.95
1 Laborer	36.65	293.20	60.20	481.60		
1 Hyd. Excavator, 5/8 C.Y.		594.40		653.84	37.15	40.87
16 L.H., Daily Totals		$1289.60		$1773.04	$80.60	$110.82

Crew B-12S

	Bare Costs Hr.	Bare Costs Daily	Incl. Subs O&P Hr.	Incl. Subs O&P Daily	Cost Per Labor-Hour Bare Costs	Cost Per Labor-Hour Incl. O&P
1 Equip. Oper. (crane)	$50.25	$402.00	$79.70	$637.60	$43.45	$69.95
1 Laborer	36.65	293.20	60.20	481.60		
1 Hyd. Excavator, 2.5 C.Y.		1637.00		1800.70	102.31	112.54
16 L.H., Daily Totals		$2332.20		$2919.90	$145.76	$182.49

Crew B-12T

	Bare Costs Hr.	Bare Costs Daily	Incl. Subs O&P Hr.	Incl. Subs O&P Daily	Cost Per Labor-Hour Bare Costs	Cost Per Labor-Hour Incl. O&P
1 Equip. Oper. (crane)	$50.25	$402.00	$79.70	$637.60	$43.45	$69.95
1 Laborer	36.65	293.20	60.20	481.60		
1 Crawler Crane, 75 Ton		1492.00		1641.20		
1 F.E. Attachment, 3 C.Y.		102.80		113.08	99.67	109.64
16 L.H., Daily Totals		$2290.00		$2873.48	$143.13	$179.59

Crew B-12V

	Bare Costs Hr.	Bare Costs Daily	Incl. Subs O&P Hr.	Incl. Subs O&P Daily	Cost Per Labor-Hour Bare Costs	Cost Per Labor-Hour Incl. O&P
1 Equip. Oper. (crane)	$50.25	$402.00	$79.70	$637.60	$43.45	$69.95
1 Laborer	36.65	293.20	60.20	481.60		
1 Crawler Crane, 75 Ton		1492.00		1641.20		
1 Dragline Bucket, 3 C.Y.		52.60		57.86	96.54	106.19
16 L.H., Daily Totals		$2239.80		$2818.26	$139.99	$176.14

Crew B-12Y

	Bare Costs Hr.	Bare Costs Daily	Incl. Subs O&P Hr.	Incl. Subs O&P Daily	Cost Per Labor-Hour Bare Costs	Cost Per Labor-Hour Incl. O&P
1 Equip. Oper. (crane)	$50.25	$402.00	$79.70	$637.60	$41.18	$66.70
2 Laborers	36.65	586.40	60.20	963.20		
1 Hyd. Excavator, 3.5 C.Y.		2442.00		2686.20	101.75	111.93
24 L.H., Daily Totals		$3430.40		$4287.00	$142.93	$178.63

Crew B-12Z

	Bare Costs Hr.	Bare Costs Daily	Incl. Subs O&P Hr.	Incl. Subs O&P Daily	Cost Per Labor-Hour Bare Costs	Cost Per Labor-Hour Incl. O&P
1 Equip. Oper. (crane)	$50.25	$402.00	$79.70	$637.60	$41.18	$66.70
2 Laborers	36.65	586.40	60.20	963.20		
1 Hyd. Excavator, 2.5 C.Y.		1637.00		1800.70	68.21	75.03
24 L.H., Daily Totals		$2625.40		$3401.50	$109.39	$141.73

Crew B-13

	Bare Costs Hr.	Bare Costs Daily	Incl. Subs O&P Hr.	Incl. Subs O&P Daily	Cost Per Labor-Hour Bare Costs	Cost Per Labor-Hour Incl. O&P
1 Labor Foreman (outside)	$38.65	$309.20	$63.50	$508.00	$39.86	$64.72
4 Laborers	36.65	1172.80	60.20	1926.40		
1 Equip. Oper. (crane)	50.25	402.00	79.70	637.60		
1 Equip. Oper. (oiler)	43.55	348.40	69.05	552.40		
1 Hyd. Crane, 25 Ton		745.80		820.38	13.32	14.65
56 L.H., Daily Totals		$2978.20		$4444.78	$53.18	$79.37

Crew B-13A

	Bare Costs Hr.	Bare Costs Daily	Incl. Subs O&P Hr.	Incl. Subs O&P Daily	Cost Per Labor-Hour Bare Costs	Cost Per Labor-Hour Incl. O&P
1 Labor Foreman (outside)	$38.65	$309.20	$63.50	$508.00	$40.69	$65.87
2 Laborers	36.65	586.40	60.20	963.20		
2 Equipment Operators (med.)	48.90	782.40	77.55	1240.80		
2 Truck Drivers (heavy)	37.55	600.80	61.05	976.80		
1 Crawler Crane, 75 Ton		1492.00		1641.20		
1 Crawler Loader, 4 C.Y.		1532.00		1685.20		
2 Dump Trucks, 8 C.Y., 220 H.P.		834.40		917.84	68.90	75.79
56 L.H., Daily Totals		$6137.20		$7933.04	$109.59	$141.66

Crew B-13B

	Bare Costs Hr.	Bare Costs Daily	Incl. Subs O&P Hr.	Incl. Subs O&P Daily	Cost Per Labor-Hour Bare Costs	Cost Per Labor-Hour Incl. O&P
1 Labor Foreman (outside)	$38.65	$309.20	$63.50	$508.00	$39.86	$64.72
4 Laborers	36.65	1172.80	60.20	1926.40		
1 Equip. Oper. (crane)	50.25	402.00	79.70	637.60		
1 Equip. Oper. (oiler)	43.55	348.40	69.05	552.40		
1 Hyd. Crane, 55 Ton		1137.00		1250.70	20.30	22.33
56 L.H., Daily Totals		$3369.40		$4875.10	$60.17	$87.06

Crew B-13C

	Bare Costs Hr.	Bare Costs Daily	Incl. Subs O&P Hr.	Incl. Subs O&P Daily	Cost Per Labor-Hour Bare Costs	Cost Per Labor-Hour Incl. O&P
1 Labor Foreman (outside)	$38.65	$309.20	$63.50	$508.00	$39.86	$64.72
4 Laborers	36.65	1172.80	60.20	1926.40		
1 Equip. Oper. (crane)	50.25	402.00	79.70	637.60		
1 Equip. Oper. (oiler)	43.55	348.40	69.05	552.40		
1 Crawler Crane, 100 Ton		1703.00		1873.30	30.41	33.45
56 L.H., Daily Totals		$3935.40		$5497.70	$70.28	$98.17

Crew B-13D

	Bare Costs Hr.	Bare Costs Daily	Incl. Subs O&P Hr.	Incl. Subs O&P Daily	Cost Per Labor-Hour Bare Costs	Cost Per Labor-Hour Incl. O&P
1 Laborer	$36.65	$293.20	$60.20	$481.60	$43.45	$69.95
1 Equip. Oper. (crane)	50.25	402.00	79.70	637.60		
1 Hyd. Excavator, 1 C.Y.		814.80		896.28		
1 Trench Box		84.05		92.45	56.18	61.80
16 L.H., Daily Totals		$1594.05		$2107.93	$99.63	$131.75

Crew B-13E

	Bare Costs Hr.	Bare Costs Daily	Incl. Subs O&P Hr.	Incl. Subs O&P Daily	Cost Per Labor-Hour Bare Costs	Cost Per Labor-Hour Incl. O&P
1 Laborer	$36.65	$293.20	$60.20	$481.60	$43.45	$69.95
1 Equip. Oper. (crane)	50.25	402.00	79.70	637.60		
1 Hyd. Excavator, 1.5 C.Y.		1031.00		1134.10		
1 Trench Box		84.05		92.45	69.69	76.66
16 L.H., Daily Totals		$1810.25		$2345.76	$113.14	$146.61

Crew B-13F

	Bare Costs Hr.	Bare Costs Daily	Incl. Subs O&P Hr.	Incl. Subs O&P Daily	Cost Per Labor-Hour Bare Costs	Cost Per Labor-Hour Incl. O&P
1 Laborer	$36.65	$293.20	$60.20	$481.60	$43.45	$69.95
1 Equip. Oper. (crane)	50.25	402.00	79.70	637.60		
1 Hyd. Excavator, 3.5 C.Y.		2442.00		2686.20		
1 Trench Box		84.05		92.45	157.88	173.67
16 L.H., Daily Totals		$3221.25		$3897.86	$201.33	$243.62

Crew B-13G

	Bare Costs Hr.	Bare Costs Daily	Incl. Subs O&P Hr.	Incl. Subs O&P Daily	Cost Per Labor-Hour Bare Costs	Cost Per Labor-Hour Incl. O&P
1 Laborer	$36.65	$293.20	$60.20	$481.60	$43.45	$69.95
1 Equip. Oper. (crane)	50.25	402.00	79.70	637.60		
1 Hyd. Excavator, .75 C.Y.		662.00		728.20		
1 Trench Box		84.05		92.45	46.63	51.29
16 L.H., Daily Totals		$1441.25		$1939.86	$90.08	$121.24

Crew B-13H

	Bare Costs Hr.	Bare Costs Daily	Incl. Subs O&P Hr.	Incl. Subs O&P Daily	Cost Per Labor-Hour Bare Costs	Cost Per Labor-Hour Incl. O&P
1 Laborer	$36.65	$293.20	$60.20	$481.60	$43.45	$69.95
1 Equip. Oper. (crane)	50.25	402.00	79.70	637.60		
1 Gradall, 5/8 C.Y.		881.60		969.76		
1 Trench Box		84.05		92.45	60.35	66.39
16 L.H., Daily Totals		$1660.85		$2181.42	$103.80	$136.34

Crew B-13I

	Bare Costs Hr.	Bare Costs Daily	Incl. Subs O&P Hr.	Incl. Subs O&P Daily	Cost Per Labor-Hour Bare Costs	Cost Per Labor-Hour Incl. O&P
1 Laborer	$36.65	$293.20	$60.20	$481.60	$43.45	$69.95
1 Equip. Oper. (crane)	50.25	402.00	79.70	637.60		
1 Gradall, 3 Ton, 1 C.Y.		1005.00		1105.50		
1 Trench Box		84.05		92.45	68.07	74.87
16 L.H., Daily Totals		$1784.25		$2317.16	$111.52	$144.82

Crew B-13J

	Bare Costs Hr.	Bare Costs Daily	Incl. Subs O&P Hr.	Incl. Subs O&P Daily	Cost Per Labor-Hour Bare Costs	Cost Per Labor-Hour Incl. O&P
1 Laborer	$36.65	$293.20	$60.20	$481.60	$43.45	$69.95
1 Equip. Oper. (crane)	50.25	402.00	79.70	637.60		
1 Hyd. Excavator, 2.5 C.Y.		1637.00		1800.70		
1 Trench Box		84.05		92.45	107.57	118.32
16 L.H., Daily Totals		$2416.25		$3012.36	$151.02	$188.27

Crews

Crew No.	Bare Costs		Incl. Subs O&P		Cost Per Labor-Hour	

Crew B-14	Hr.	Daily	Hr.	Daily	Bare Costs	Incl. O&P
1 Labor Foreman (outside)	$38.65	$309.20	$63.50	$508.00	$38.72	$63.15
4 Laborers	36.65	1172.80	60.20	1926.40		
1 Equip. Oper. (light)	47.05	376.40	74.60	596.80		
1 Backhoe Loader, 48 H.P.		365.20		401.72	7.61	8.37
48 L.H., Daily Totals		$2223.60		$3432.92	$46.33	$71.52

Crew B-14A	Hr.	Daily	Hr.	Daily	Bare Costs	Incl. O&P
1 Equip. Oper. (crane)	$50.25	$402.00	$79.70	$637.60	$45.72	$73.20
.5 Laborer	36.65	146.60	60.20	240.80		
1 Hyd. Excavator, 4.5 C.Y.		3043.00		3347.30	253.58	278.94
12 L.H., Daily Totals		$3591.60		$4225.70	$299.30	$352.14

Crew B-14B	Hr.	Daily	Hr.	Daily	Bare Costs	Incl. O&P
1 Equip. Oper. (crane)	$50.25	$402.00	$79.70	$637.60	$45.72	$73.20
.5 Laborer	36.65	146.60	60.20	240.80		
1 Hyd. Excavator, 6 C.Y.		3523.00		3875.30	293.58	322.94
12 L.H., Daily Totals		$4071.60		$4753.70	$339.30	$396.14

Crew B-14C	Hr.	Daily	Hr.	Daily	Bare Costs	Incl. O&P
1 Equip. Oper. (crane)	$50.25	$402.00	$79.70	$637.60	$45.72	$73.20
.5 Laborer	36.65	146.60	60.20	240.80		
1 Hyd. Excavator, 7 C.Y.		3596.00		3955.60	299.67	329.63
12 L.H., Daily Totals		$4144.60		$4834.00	$345.38	$402.83

Crew B-14F	Hr.	Daily	Hr.	Daily	Bare Costs	Incl. O&P
1 Equip. Oper. (crane)	$50.25	$402.00	$79.70	$637.60	$45.72	$73.20
.5 Laborer	36.65	146.60	60.20	240.80		
1 Hyd. Shovel, 7 C.Y.		3714.00		4085.40	309.50	340.45
12 L.H., Daily Totals		$4262.60		$4963.80	$355.22	$413.65

Crew B-14G	Hr.	Daily	Hr.	Daily	Bare Costs	Incl. O&P
1 Equip. Oper. (crane)	$50.25	$402.00	$79.70	$637.60	$45.72	$73.20
.5 Laborer	36.65	146.60	60.20	240.80		
1 Hyd. Shovel, 12 C.Y.		5204.00		5724.40	433.67	477.03
12 L.H., Daily Totals		$5752.60		$6602.80	$479.38	$550.23

Crew B-14J	Hr.	Daily	Hr.	Daily	Bare Costs	Incl. O&P
1 Equip. Oper. (medium)	$48.90	$391.20	$77.55	$620.40	$44.82	$71.77
.5 Laborer	36.65	146.60	60.20	240.80		
1 F.E. Loader, 8 C.Y.		1989.00		2187.90	165.75	182.32
12 L.H., Daily Totals		$2526.80		$3049.10	$210.57	$254.09

Crew B-14K	Hr.	Daily	Hr.	Daily	Bare Costs	Incl. O&P
1 Equip. Oper. (medium)	$48.90	$391.20	$77.55	$620.40	$44.82	$71.77
.5 Laborer	36.65	146.60	60.20	240.80		
1 F.E. Loader, 10 C.Y.		2703.00		2973.30	225.25	247.78
12 L.H., Daily Totals		$3240.80		$3834.50	$270.07	$319.54

Crew B-15	Hr.	Daily	Hr.	Daily	Bare Costs	Incl. O&P
1 Equipment Oper. (med.)	$48.90	$391.20	$77.55	$620.40	$40.66	$65.64
.5 Laborer	36.65	146.60	60.20	240.80		
2 Truck Drivers (heavy)	37.55	600.80	61.05	976.80		
2 Dump Trucks, 12 C.Y., 400 H.P.		1384.40		1522.84		
1 Dozer, 200 H.P.		1325.00		1457.50	96.76	106.44
28 L.H., Daily Totals		$3848.00		$4818.34	$137.43	$172.08

Crew B-16	Hr.	Daily	Hr.	Daily	Bare Costs	Incl. O&P
1 Labor Foreman (outside)	$38.65	$309.20	$63.50	$508.00	$37.38	$61.24
2 Laborers	36.65	586.40	60.20	963.20		
1 Truck Driver (heavy)	37.55	300.40	61.05	488.40		
1 Dump Truck, 12 C.Y., 400 H.P.		692.20		761.42	21.63	23.79
32 L.H., Daily Totals		$1888.20		$2721.02	$59.01	$85.03

Crew B-17	Hr.	Daily	Hr.	Daily	Bare Costs	Incl. O&P
2 Laborers	$36.65	$586.40	$60.20	$963.20	$39.48	$64.01
1 Equip. Oper. (light)	47.05	376.40	74.60	596.80		
1 Truck Driver (heavy)	37.55	300.40	61.05	488.40		
1 Backhoe Loader, 48 H.P.		365.20		401.72		
1 Dump Truck, 8 C.Y., 220 H.P.		417.20		458.92	24.45	26.90
32 L.H., Daily Totals		$2045.60		$2909.04	$63.92	$90.91

Crew B-17A	Hr.	Daily	Hr.	Daily	Bare Costs	Incl. O&P
2 Labor Foremen (outside)	$38.65	$618.40	$63.50	$1016.00	$39.38	$64.56
6 Laborers	36.65	1759.20	60.20	2889.60		
1 Skilled Worker Foreman (out)	49.30	394.40	80.30	642.40		
1 Skilled Worker	47.30	378.40	77.05	616.40		
80 L.H., Daily Totals		$3150.40		$5164.40	$39.38	$64.56

Crew B-17B	Hr.	Daily	Hr.	Daily	Bare Costs	Incl. O&P
2 Laborers	$36.65	$586.40	$60.20	$963.20	$39.48	$64.01
1 Equip. Oper. (light)	47.05	376.40	74.60	596.80		
1 Truck Driver (heavy)	37.55	300.40	61.05	488.40		
1 Backhoe Loader, 48 H.P.		365.20		401.72		
1 Dump Truck, 12 C.Y., 400 H.P.		692.20		761.42	33.04	36.35
32 L.H., Daily Totals		$2320.60		$3211.54	$72.52	$100.36

Crew B-18	Hr.	Daily	Hr.	Daily	Bare Costs	Incl. O&P
1 Labor Foreman (outside)	$38.65	$309.20	$63.50	$508.00	$37.32	$61.30
2 Laborers	36.65	586.40	60.20	963.20		
1 Vibrating Plate, Gas, 21"		46.00		50.60	1.92	2.11
24 L.H., Daily Totals		$941.60		$1521.80	$39.23	$63.41

Crew B-19	Hr.	Daily	Hr.	Daily	Bare Costs	Incl. O&P
1 Pile Driver Foreman (outside)	$46.40	$371.20	$75.90	$607.20	$46.01	$74.37
4 Pile Drivers	44.40	1420.80	72.65	2324.80		
2 Equip. Oper. (crane)	50.25	804.00	79.70	1275.20		
1 Equip. Oper. (oiler)	43.55	348.40	69.05	552.40		
1 Crawler Crane, 40 Ton		1179.00		1296.90		
1 Lead, 90' High		124.40		136.84		
1 Hammer, Diesel, 22k ft-lb		537.45		591.20	28.76	31.64
64 L.H., Daily Totals		$4785.25		$6784.53	$74.77	$106.01

Crew B-19A	Hr.	Daily	Hr.	Daily	Bare Costs	Incl. O&P
1 Pile Driver Foreman (outside)	$46.40	$371.20	$75.90	$607.20	$46.01	$74.37
4 Pile Drivers	44.40	1420.80	72.65	2324.80		
2 Equip. Oper. (crane)	50.25	804.00	79.70	1275.20		
1 Equip. Oper. (oiler)	43.55	348.40	69.05	552.40		
1 Crawler Crane, 75 Ton		1492.00		1641.20		
1 Lead, 90' high		124.40		136.84		
1 Hammer, Diesel, 41k ft-lb		642.40		706.64	35.29	38.82
64 L.H., Daily Totals		$5203.20		$7244.28	$81.30	$113.19

Crew B-19B

Crew No.	Bare Costs Hr.	Bare Costs Daily	Incl. Subs O&P Hr.	Incl. Subs O&P Daily	Cost Per Labor-Hour Bare Costs	Cost Per Labor-Hour Incl. O&P
1 Pile Driver Foreman (outside)	$46.40	$371.20	$75.90	$607.20	$46.01	$74.37
4 Pile Drivers	44.40	1420.80	72.65	2324.80		
2 Equip. Oper. (crane)	50.25	804.00	79.70	1275.20		
1 Equip. Oper. (oiler)	43.55	348.40	69.05	552.40		
1 Crawler Crane, 40 Ton		1179.00		1296.90		
1 Lead, 90' High		124.40		136.84		
1 Hammer, Diesel, 22k ft-lb		537.45		591.20		
1 Barge, 400 Ton		781.00		859.10	40.97	45.06
64 L.H., Daily Totals		$5566.25		$7643.64	$86.97	$119.43

Crew B-19C

Crew No.	Bare Costs Hr.	Bare Costs Daily	Incl. Subs O&P Hr.	Incl. Subs O&P Daily	Cost Per Labor-Hour Bare Costs	Cost Per Labor-Hour Incl. O&P
1 Pile Driver Foreman (outside)	$46.40	$371.20	$75.90	$607.20	$46.01	$74.37
4 Pile Drivers	44.40	1420.80	72.65	2324.80		
2 Equip. Oper. (crane)	50.25	804.00	79.70	1275.20		
1 Equip. Oper. (oiler)	43.55	348.40	69.05	552.40		
1 Crawler Crane, 75 Ton		1492.00		1641.20		
1 Lead, 90' High		124.40		136.84		
1 Hammer, Diesel, 41k ft-lb		642.40		706.64		
1 Barge, 400 Ton		781.00		859.10	47.50	52.25
64 L.H., Daily Totals		$5984.20		$8103.38	$93.50	$126.62

Crew B-20

Crew No.	Bare Costs Hr.	Bare Costs Daily	Incl. Subs O&P Hr.	Incl. Subs O&P Daily	Cost Per Labor-Hour Bare Costs	Cost Per Labor-Hour Incl. O&P
1 Labor Foreman (outside)	$38.65	$309.20	$63.50	$508.00	$40.87	$66.92
1 Skilled Worker	47.30	378.40	77.05	616.40		
1 Laborer	36.65	293.20	60.20	481.60		
24 L.H., Daily Totals		$980.80		$1606.00	$40.87	$66.92

Crew B-20A

Crew No.	Bare Costs Hr.	Bare Costs Daily	Incl. Subs O&P Hr.	Incl. Subs O&P Daily	Cost Per Labor-Hour Bare Costs	Cost Per Labor-Hour Incl. O&P
1 Labor Foreman (outside)	$38.65	$309.20	$63.50	$508.00	$44.73	$71.34
1 Laborer	36.65	293.20	60.20	481.60		
1 Plumber	57.55	460.40	89.80	718.40		
1 Plumber Apprentice	46.05	368.40	71.85	574.80		
32 L.H., Daily Totals		$1431.20		$2282.80	$44.73	$71.34

Crew B-21

Crew No.	Bare Costs Hr.	Bare Costs Daily	Incl. Subs O&P Hr.	Incl. Subs O&P Daily	Cost Per Labor-Hour Bare Costs	Cost Per Labor-Hour Incl. O&P
1 Labor Foreman (outside)	$38.65	$309.20	$63.50	$508.00	$42.21	$68.74
1 Skilled Worker	47.30	378.40	77.05	616.40		
1 Laborer	36.65	293.20	60.20	481.60		
.5 Equip. Oper. (crane)	50.25	201.00	79.70	318.80		
.5 S.P. Crane, 4x4, 5 Ton		140.00		154.00	5.00	5.50
28 L.H., Daily Totals		$1321.80		$2078.80	$47.21	$74.24

Crew B-21A

Crew No.	Bare Costs Hr.	Bare Costs Daily	Incl. Subs O&P Hr.	Incl. Subs O&P Daily	Cost Per Labor-Hour Bare Costs	Cost Per Labor-Hour Incl. O&P
1 Labor Foreman (outside)	$38.65	$309.20	$63.50	$508.00	$45.83	$73.01
1 Laborer	36.65	293.20	60.20	481.60		
1 Plumber	57.55	460.40	89.80	718.40		
1 Plumber Apprentice	46.05	368.40	71.85	574.80		
1 Equip. Oper. (crane)	50.25	402.00	79.70	637.60		
1 S.P. Crane, 4x4, 12 Ton		481.20		529.32	12.03	13.23
40 L.H., Daily Totals		$2314.40		$3449.72	$57.86	$86.24

Crew B-21B

Crew No.	Bare Costs Hr.	Bare Costs Daily	Incl. Subs O&P Hr.	Incl. Subs O&P Daily	Cost Per Labor-Hour Bare Costs	Cost Per Labor-Hour Incl. O&P
1 Labor Foreman (outside)	$38.65	$309.20	$63.50	$508.00	$39.77	$64.76
3 Laborers	36.65	879.60	60.20	1444.80		
1 Equip. Oper. (crane)	50.25	402.00	79.70	637.60		
1 Hyd. Crane, 12 Ton		663.00		729.30	16.57	18.23
40 L.H., Daily Totals		$2253.80		$3319.70	$56.34	$82.99

Crew B-21C

Crew No.	Bare Costs Hr.	Bare Costs Daily	Incl. Subs O&P Hr.	Incl. Subs O&P Daily	Cost Per Labor-Hour Bare Costs	Cost Per Labor-Hour Incl. O&P
1 Labor Foreman (outside)	$38.65	$309.20	$63.50	$508.00	$39.86	$64.72
4 Laborers	36.65	1172.80	60.20	1926.40		
1 Equip. Oper. (crane)	50.25	402.00	79.70	637.60		
1 Equip. Oper. (oiler)	43.55	348.40	69.05	552.40		
2 Cutting Torches		22.80		25.08		
2 Sets of Gases		304.00		334.40		
1 Lattice Boom Crane, 90 Ton		1529.00		1681.90	33.14	36.45
56 L.H., Daily Totals		$4088.20		$5665.78	$73.00	$101.17

Crew B-22

Crew No.	Bare Costs Hr.	Bare Costs Daily	Incl. Subs O&P Hr.	Incl. Subs O&P Daily	Cost Per Labor-Hour Bare Costs	Cost Per Labor-Hour Incl. O&P
1 Labor Foreman (outside)	$38.65	$309.20	$63.50	$508.00	$42.74	$69.47
1 Skilled Worker	47.30	378.40	77.05	616.40		
1 Laborer	36.65	293.20	60.20	481.60		
.75 Equip. Oper. (crane)	50.25	301.50	79.70	478.20		
.75 S.P. Crane, 4x4, 5 Ton		210.00		231.00	7.00	7.70
30 L.H., Daily Totals		$1492.30		$2315.20	$49.74	$77.17

Crew B-22A

Crew No.	Bare Costs Hr.	Bare Costs Daily	Incl. Subs O&P Hr.	Incl. Subs O&P Daily	Cost Per Labor-Hour Bare Costs	Cost Per Labor-Hour Incl. O&P
1 Labor Foreman (outside)	$38.65	$309.20	$63.50	$508.00	$41.90	$68.13
1 Skilled Worker	47.30	378.40	77.05	616.40		
2 Laborers	36.65	586.40	60.20	963.20		
1 Equipment Operator, Crane	50.25	402.00	79.70	637.60		
1 S.P. Crane, 4x4, 5 Ton		280.00		308.00		
1 Butt Fusion Mach., 4"-12" diam.		381.80		419.98	16.55	18.20
40 L.H., Daily Totals		$2337.80		$3453.18	$58.45	$86.33

Crew B-22B

Crew No.	Bare Costs Hr.	Bare Costs Daily	Incl. Subs O&P Hr.	Incl. Subs O&P Daily	Cost Per Labor-Hour Bare Costs	Cost Per Labor-Hour Incl. O&P
1 Labor Foreman (outside)	$38.65	$309.20	$63.50	$508.00	$41.90	$68.13
1 Skilled Worker	47.30	378.40	77.05	616.40		
2 Laborers	36.65	586.40	60.20	963.20		
1 Equip. Oper. (crane)	50.25	402.00	79.70	637.60		
1 S.P. Crane, 4x4, 5 Ton		280.00		308.00		
1 Butt Fusion Mach., 8"-24" diam.		828.40		911.24	27.71	30.48
40 L.H., Daily Totals		$2784.40		$3944.44	$69.61	$98.61

Crew B-22C

Crew No.	Bare Costs Hr.	Bare Costs Daily	Incl. Subs O&P Hr.	Incl. Subs O&P Daily	Cost Per Labor-Hour Bare Costs	Cost Per Labor-Hour Incl. O&P
1 Skilled Worker	$47.30	$378.40	$77.05	$616.40	$41.98	$68.63
1 Laborer	36.65	293.20	60.20	481.60		
1 Butt Fusion Mach., 2"-8" diam.		120.95		133.04	7.56	8.32
16 L.H., Daily Totals		$792.55		$1231.05	$49.53	$76.94

Crew B-23

Crew No.	Bare Costs Hr.	Bare Costs Daily	Incl. Subs O&P Hr.	Incl. Subs O&P Daily	Cost Per Labor-Hour Bare Costs	Cost Per Labor-Hour Incl. O&P
1 Labor Foreman (outside)	$38.65	$309.20	$63.50	$508.00	$37.05	$60.86
4 Laborers	36.65	1172.80	60.20	1926.40		
1 Drill Rig, Truck-Mounted		2551.00		2806.10		
1 Flatbed Truck, Gas, 3 Ton		333.00		366.30	72.10	79.31
40 L.H., Daily Totals		$4366.00		$5606.80	$109.15	$140.17

Crew B-23A

Crew No.	Bare Costs Hr.	Bare Costs Daily	Incl. Subs O&P Hr.	Incl. Subs O&P Daily	Cost Per Labor-Hour Bare Costs	Cost Per Labor-Hour Incl. O&P
1 Labor Foreman (outside)	$38.65	$309.20	$63.50	$508.00	$41.40	$67.08
1 Laborer	36.65	293.20	60.20	481.60		
1 Equip. Oper. (medium)	48.90	391.20	77.55	620.40		
1 Drill Rig, Truck-Mounted		2551.00		2806.10		
1 Pickup Truck, 3/4 Ton		157.00		172.70	112.83	124.12
24 L.H., Daily Totals		$3701.60		$4588.80	$154.23	$191.20

Crews

Crew No.	Bare Costs		Incl. Subs O&P		Cost Per Labor-Hour	

Crew B-23B

Crew B-23B	Hr.	Daily	Hr.	Daily	Bare Costs	Incl. O&P
1 Labor Foreman (outside)	$38.65	$309.20	$63.50	$508.00	$41.40	$67.08
1 Laborer	36.65	293.20	60.20	481.60		
1 Equip. Oper. (medium)	48.90	391.20	77.55	620.40		
1 Drill Rig, Truck-Mounted		2551.00		2806.10		
1 Pickup Truck, 3/4 Ton		157.00		172.70		
1 Centr. Water Pump, 6"		340.80		374.88	127.03	139.74
24 L.H., Daily Totals		$4042.40		$4963.68	$168.43	$206.82

Crew B-24

Crew B-24	Hr.	Daily	Hr.	Daily	Bare Costs	Incl. O&P
1 Cement Finisher	$44.05	$352.40	$69.50	$556.00	$42.18	$68.35
1 Laborer	36.65	293.20	60.20	481.60		
1 Carpenter	45.85	366.80	75.35	602.80		
24 L.H., Daily Totals		$1012.40		$1640.40	$42.18	$68.35

Crew B-25

Crew B-25	Hr.	Daily	Hr.	Daily	Bare Costs	Incl. O&P
1 Labor Foreman (outside)	$38.65	$309.20	$63.50	$508.00	$40.17	$65.23
7 Laborers	36.65	2052.40	60.20	3371.20		
3 Equip. Oper. (medium)	48.90	1173.60	77.55	1861.20		
1 Asphalt Paver, 130 H.P.		2169.00		2385.90		
1 Tandem Roller, 10 Ton		242.00		266.20		
1 Roller, Pneum. Whl., 12 Ton		349.00		383.90	31.36	34.50
88 L.H., Daily Totals		$6295.20		$8776.40	$71.54	$99.73

Crew B-25B

Crew B-25B	Hr.	Daily	Hr.	Daily	Bare Costs	Incl. O&P
1 Labor Foreman (outside)	$38.65	$309.20	$63.50	$508.00	$40.90	$66.26
7 Laborers	36.65	2052.40	60.20	3371.20		
4 Equip. Oper. (medium)	48.90	1564.80	77.55	2481.60		
1 Asphalt Paver, 130 H.P.		2169.00		2385.90		
2 Tandem Rollers, 10 Ton		484.00		532.40		
1 Roller, Pneum. Whl., 12 Ton		349.00		383.90	31.27	34.40
96 L.H., Daily Totals		$6928.40		$9663.00	$72.17	$100.66

Crew B-25C

Crew B-25C	Hr.	Daily	Hr.	Daily	Bare Costs	Incl. O&P
1 Labor Foreman (outside)	$38.65	$309.20	$63.50	$508.00	$41.07	$66.53
3 Laborers	36.65	879.60	60.20	1444.80		
2 Equip. Oper. (medium)	48.90	782.40	77.55	1240.80		
1 Asphalt Paver, 130 H.P.		2169.00		2385.90		
1 Tandem Roller, 10 Ton		242.00		266.20	50.23	55.25
48 L.H., Daily Totals		$4382.20		$5845.70	$91.30	$121.79

Crew B-25D

Crew B-25D	Hr.	Daily	Hr.	Daily	Bare Costs	Incl. O&P
1 Labor Foreman (outside)	$38.65	$309.20	$63.50	$508.00	$41.15	$66.64
3 Laborers	36.65	879.60	60.20	1444.80		
2.125 Equip. Oper. (medium)	48.90	831.30	77.55	1318.35		
.125 Truck Driver (heavy)	37.55	37.55	61.05	61.05		
.125 Truck Tractor, 6x4, 380 H.P.		76.60		84.26		
.125 Dist. Tanker, 3000 Gallon		38.52		42.38		
1 Asphalt Paver, 130 H.P.		2169.00		2385.90		
1 Tandem Roller, 10 Ton		242.00		266.20	50.52	55.57
50 L.H., Daily Totals		$4583.77		$6110.94	$91.68	$122.22

Crew B-25E

Crew B-25E	Hr.	Daily	Hr.	Daily	Bare Costs	Incl. O&P
1 Labor Foreman (outside)	$38.65	$309.20	$63.50	$508.00	$41.23	$66.75
3 Laborers	36.65	879.60	60.20	1444.80		
2.250 Equip. Oper. (medium)	48.90	880.20	77.55	1395.90		
.25 Truck Driver (heavy)	37.55	75.10	61.05	122.10		
.25 Truck Tractor, 6x4, 380 H.P.		153.20		168.52		
.25 Dist. Tanker, 3000 Gallon		77.05		84.75		
1 Asphalt Paver, 130 H.P.		2169.00		2385.90		
1 Tandem Roller, 10 Ton		242.00		266.20	50.79	55.87
52 L.H., Daily Totals		$4785.35		$6376.18	$92.03	$122.62

Crew B-26

Crew B-26	Hr.	Daily	Hr.	Daily	Bare Costs	Incl. O&P
1 Labor Foreman (outside)	$38.65	$309.20	$63.50	$508.00	$41.00	$66.58
6 Laborers	36.65	1759.20	60.20	2889.60		
2 Equip. Oper. (medium)	48.90	782.40	77.55	1240.80		
1 Rodman (reinf.)	50.65	405.20	83.10	664.80		
1 Cement Finisher	44.05	352.40	69.50	556.00		
1 Grader, 30,000 Lbs.		707.00		777.70		
1 Paving Mach. & Equip.		2657.00		2922.70	38.23	42.05
88 L.H., Daily Totals		$6972.40		$9559.60	$79.23	$108.63

Crew B-26A

Crew B-26A	Hr.	Daily	Hr.	Daily	Bare Costs	Incl. O&P
1 Labor Foreman (outside)	$38.65	$309.20	$63.50	$508.00	$41.00	$66.58
6 Laborers	36.65	1759.20	60.20	2889.60		
2 Equip. Oper. (medium)	48.90	782.40	77.55	1240.80		
1 Rodman (reinf.)	50.65	405.20	83.10	664.80		
1 Cement Finisher	44.05	352.40	69.50	556.00		
1 Grader, 30,000 Lbs.		707.00		777.70		
1 Paving Mach. & Equip.		2657.00		2922.70		
1 Concrete Saw		175.20		192.72	40.22	44.24
88 L.H., Daily Totals		$7147.60		$9752.32	$81.22	$110.82

Crew B-26B

Crew B-26B	Hr.	Daily	Hr.	Daily	Bare Costs	Incl. O&P
1 Labor Foreman (outside)	$38.65	$309.20	$63.50	$508.00	$41.66	$67.50
6 Laborers	36.65	1759.20	60.20	2889.60		
3 Equip. Oper. (medium)	48.90	1173.60	77.55	1861.20		
1 Rodman (reinf.)	50.65	405.20	83.10	664.80		
1 Cement Finisher	44.05	352.40	69.50	556.00		
1 Grader, 30,000 Lbs.		707.00		777.70		
1 Paving Mach. & Equip.		2657.00		2922.70		
1 Concrete Pump, 110' Boom		934.00		1027.40	44.77	49.25
96 L.H., Daily Totals		$8297.60		$11207.40	$86.43	$116.74

Crew B-26C

Crew B-26C	Hr.	Daily	Hr.	Daily	Bare Costs	Incl. O&P
1 Labor Foreman (outside)	$38.65	$309.20	$63.50	$508.00	$40.22	$65.48
6 Laborers	36.65	1759.20	60.20	2889.60		
1 Equip. Oper. (medium)	48.90	391.20	77.55	620.40		
1 Rodman (reinf.)	50.65	405.20	83.10	664.80		
1 Cement Finisher	44.05	352.40	69.50	556.00		
1 Paving Mach. & Equip.		2657.00		2922.70		
1 Concrete Saw		175.20		192.72	35.40	38.94
80 L.H., Daily Totals		$6049.40		$8354.22	$75.62	$104.43

Crew B-27

Crew B-27	Hr.	Daily	Hr.	Daily	Bare Costs	Incl. O&P
1 Labor Foreman (outside)	$38.65	$309.20	$63.50	$508.00	$37.15	$61.02
3 Laborers	36.65	879.60	60.20	1444.80		
1 Berm Machine		294.40		323.84	9.20	10.12
32 L.H., Daily Totals		$1483.20		$2276.64	$46.35	$71.14

Crew B-28

Crew B-28	Hr.	Daily	Hr.	Daily	Bare Costs	Incl. O&P
2 Carpenters	$45.85	$733.60	$75.35	$1205.60	$42.78	$70.30
1 Laborer	36.65	293.20	60.20	481.60		
24 L.H., Daily Totals		$1026.80		$1687.20	$42.78	$70.30

Crew B-29

Crew B-29	Hr.	Daily	Hr.	Daily	Bare Costs	Incl. O&P
1 Labor Foreman (outside)	$38.65	$309.20	$63.50	$508.00	$39.86	$64.72
4 Laborers	36.65	1172.80	60.20	1926.40		
1 Equip. Oper. (crane)	50.25	402.00	79.70	637.60		
1 Equip. Oper. (oiler)	43.55	348.40	69.05	552.40		
1 Gradall, 5/8 C.Y.		881.60		969.76	15.74	17.32
56 L.H., Daily Totals		$3114.00		$4594.16	$55.61	$82.04

Crew B-30

Crew B-30	Bare Costs Hr.	Daily	Incl. Subs O&P Hr.	Daily	Cost Per Labor-Hour Bare Costs	Incl. O&P
1 Equip. Oper. (medium)	$48.90	$391.20	$77.55	$620.40	$41.33	$66.55
2 Truck Drivers (heavy)	37.55	600.80	61.05	976.80		
1 Hyd. Excavator, 1.5 C.Y.		1031.00		1134.10		
2 Dump Trucks, 12 C.Y., 400 H.P.		1384.40		1522.84	100.64	110.71
24 L.H., Daily Totals		$3407.40		$4254.14	$141.97	$177.26

Crew B-31

Crew B-31	Bare Costs Hr.	Daily	Incl. Subs O&P Hr.	Daily	Cost Per Labor-Hour Bare Costs	Incl. O&P
1 Labor Foreman (outside)	$38.65	$309.20	$63.50	$508.00	$38.89	$63.89
3 Laborers	36.65	879.60	60.20	1444.80		
1 Carpenter	45.85	366.80	75.35	602.80		
1 Air Compressor, 250 cfm		202.40		222.64		
1 Sheeting Driver		5.30		5.83		
2 -50' Air Hoses, 1.5"		11.60		12.76	5.48	6.03
40 L.H., Daily Totals		$1774.90		$2796.83	$44.37	$69.92

Crew B-32

Crew B-32	Bare Costs Hr.	Daily	Incl. Subs O&P Hr.	Daily	Cost Per Labor-Hour Bare Costs	Incl. O&P
1 Laborer	$36.65	$293.20	$60.20	$481.60	$45.84	$73.21
3 Equip. Oper. (medium)	48.90	1173.60	77.55	1861.20		
1 Grader, 30,000 Lbs.		707.00		777.70		
1 Tandem Roller, 10 Ton		242.00		266.20		
1 Dozer, 200 H.P.		1325.00		1457.50	71.06	78.17
32 L.H., Daily Totals		$3740.80		$4844.20	$116.90	$151.38

Crew B-32A

Crew B-32A	Bare Costs Hr.	Daily	Incl. Subs O&P Hr.	Daily	Cost Per Labor-Hour Bare Costs	Incl. O&P
1 Laborer	$36.65	$293.20	$60.20	$481.60	$44.82	$71.77
2 Equip. Oper. (medium)	48.90	782.40	77.55	1240.80		
1 Grader, 30,000 Lbs.		707.00		777.70		
1 Roller, Vibratory, 25 Ton		692.80		762.08	58.33	64.16
24 L.H., Daily Totals		$2475.40		$3262.18	$103.14	$135.92

Crew B-32B

Crew B-32B	Bare Costs Hr.	Daily	Incl. Subs O&P Hr.	Daily	Cost Per Labor-Hour Bare Costs	Incl. O&P
1 Laborer	$36.65	$293.20	$60.20	$481.60	$44.82	$71.77
2 Equip. Oper. (medium)	48.90	782.40	77.55	1240.80		
1 Dozer, 200 H.P.		1325.00		1457.50		
1 Roller, Vibratory, 25 Ton		692.80		762.08	84.08	92.48
24 L.H., Daily Totals		$3093.40		$3941.98	$128.89	$164.25

Crew B-32C

Crew B-32C	Bare Costs Hr.	Daily	Incl. Subs O&P Hr.	Daily	Cost Per Labor-Hour Bare Costs	Incl. O&P
1 Labor Foreman (outside)	$38.65	$309.20	$63.50	$508.00	$43.11	$69.42
2 Laborers	36.65	586.40	60.20	963.20		
3 Equip. Oper. (medium)	48.90	1173.60	77.55	1861.20		
1 Grader, 30,000 Lbs.		707.00		777.70		
1 Tandem Roller, 10 Ton		242.00		266.20		
1 Dozer, 200 H.P.		1325.00		1457.50	47.38	52.11
48 L.H., Daily Totals		$4343.20		$5833.80	$90.48	$121.54

Crew B-33A

Crew B-33A	Bare Costs Hr.	Daily	Incl. Subs O&P Hr.	Daily	Cost Per Labor-Hour Bare Costs	Incl. O&P
1 Equip. Oper. (medium)	$48.90	$391.20	$77.55	$620.40	$45.40	$72.59
.5 Laborer	36.65	146.60	60.20	240.80		
.25 Equip. Oper. (medium)	48.90	97.80	77.55	155.10		
1 Scraper, Towed, 7 C.Y.		111.60		122.76		
1.25 Dozers, 300 H.P.		2271.25		2498.38	170.20	187.22
14 L.H., Daily Totals		$3018.45		$3637.43	$215.60	$259.82

Crew B-33B

Crew B-33B	Bare Costs Hr.	Daily	Incl. Subs O&P Hr.	Daily	Cost Per Labor-Hour Bare Costs	Incl. O&P
1 Equip. Oper. (medium)	$48.90	$391.20	$77.55	$620.40	$45.40	$72.59
.5 Laborer	36.65	146.60	60.20	240.80		
.25 Equip. Oper. (medium)	48.90	97.80	77.55	155.10		
1 Scraper, Towed, 10 C.Y.		141.60		155.76		
1.25 Dozers, 300 H.P.		2271.25		2498.38	172.35	189.58
14 L.H., Daily Totals		$3048.45		$3670.43	$217.75	$262.17

Crew B-33C

Crew B-33C	Bare Costs Hr.	Daily	Incl. Subs O&P Hr.	Daily	Cost Per Labor-Hour Bare Costs	Incl. O&P
1 Equip. Oper. (medium)	$48.90	$391.20	$77.55	$620.40	$45.40	$72.59
.5 Laborer	36.65	146.60	60.20	240.80		
.25 Equip. Oper. (medium)	48.90	97.80	77.55	155.10		
1 Scraper, Towed, 15 C.Y.		158.80		174.68		
1.25 Dozers, 300 H.P.		2271.25		2498.38	173.57	190.93
14 L.H., Daily Totals		$3065.65		$3689.36	$218.97	$263.53

Crew B-33D

Crew B-33D	Bare Costs Hr.	Daily	Incl. Subs O&P Hr.	Daily	Cost Per Labor-Hour Bare Costs	Incl. O&P
1 Equip. Oper. (medium)	$48.90	$391.20	$77.55	$620.40	$45.40	$72.59
.5 Laborer	36.65	146.60	60.20	240.80		
.25 Equip. Oper. (medium)	48.90	97.80	77.55	155.10		
1 S.P. Scraper, 14 C.Y.		1829.00		2011.90		
.25 Dozer, 300 H.P.		454.25		499.68	163.09	179.40
14 L.H., Daily Totals		$2918.85		$3527.88	$208.49	$251.99

Crew B-33E

Crew B-33E	Bare Costs Hr.	Daily	Incl. Subs O&P Hr.	Daily	Cost Per Labor-Hour Bare Costs	Incl. O&P
1 Equip. Oper. (medium)	$48.90	$391.20	$77.55	$620.40	$45.40	$72.59
.5 Laborer	36.65	146.60	60.20	240.80		
.25 Equip. Oper. (medium)	48.90	97.80	77.55	155.10		
1 S.P. Scraper, 21 C.Y.		2599.00		2858.90		
.25 Dozer, 300 H.P.		454.25		499.68	218.09	239.90
14 L.H., Daily Totals		$3688.85		$4374.88	$263.49	$312.49

Crew B-33F

Crew B-33F	Bare Costs Hr.	Daily	Incl. Subs O&P Hr.	Daily	Cost Per Labor-Hour Bare Costs	Incl. O&P
1 Equip. Oper. (medium)	$48.90	$391.20	$77.55	$620.40	$45.40	$72.59
.5 Laborer	36.65	146.60	60.20	240.80		
.25 Equip. Oper. (medium)	48.90	97.80	77.55	155.10		
1 Elev. Scraper, 11 C.Y.		1180.00		1298.00		
.25 Dozer, 300 H.P.		454.25		499.68	116.73	128.41
14 L.H., Daily Totals		$2269.85		$2813.97	$162.13	$201.00

Crew B-33G

Crew B-33G	Bare Costs Hr.	Daily	Incl. Subs O&P Hr.	Daily	Cost Per Labor-Hour Bare Costs	Incl. O&P
1 Equip. Oper. (medium)	$48.90	$391.20	$77.55	$620.40	$45.40	$72.59
.5 Laborer	36.65	146.60	60.20	240.80		
.25 Equip. Oper. (medium)	48.90	97.80	77.55	155.10		
1 Elev. Scraper, 22 C.Y.		2443.00		2687.30		
.25 Dozer, 300 H.P.		454.25		499.68	206.95	227.64
14 L.H., Daily Totals		$3532.85		$4203.27	$252.35	$300.23

Crew B-33K

Crew B-33K	Bare Costs Hr.	Daily	Incl. Subs O&P Hr.	Daily	Cost Per Labor-Hour Bare Costs	Incl. O&P
1 Equipment Operator (med.)	$48.90	$391.20	$77.55	$620.40	$45.40	$72.59
.25 Equipment Operator (med.)	48.90	97.80	77.55	155.10		
.5 Laborer	36.65	146.60	60.20	240.80		
1 S.P. Scraper, 31 C.Y.		3566.00		3922.60		
.25 Dozer, 410 H.P.		602.25		662.48	297.73	327.51
14 L.H., Daily Totals		$4803.85		$5601.38	$343.13	$400.10

Crew B-34A

Crew B-34A	Bare Costs Hr.	Daily	Incl. Subs O&P Hr.	Daily	Cost Per Labor-Hour Bare Costs	Incl. O&P
1 Truck Driver (heavy)	$37.55	$300.40	$61.05	$488.40	$37.55	$61.05
1 Dump Truck, 8 C.Y., 220 H.P.		417.20		458.92	52.15	57.37
8 L.H., Daily Totals		$717.60		$947.32	$89.70	$118.42

Crew B-34B

Crew B-34B	Bare Costs Hr.	Daily	Incl. Subs O&P Hr.	Daily	Cost Per Labor-Hour Bare Costs	Incl. O&P
1 Truck Driver (heavy)	$37.55	$300.40	$61.05	$488.40	$37.55	$61.05
1 Dump Truck, 12 C.Y., 400 H.P.		692.20		761.42	86.53	95.18
8 L.H., Daily Totals		$992.60		$1249.82	$124.08	$156.23

Crews

Crew No.	Bare Costs Hr.	Daily	Incl. Subs O&P Hr.	Daily	Bare Costs	Incl. O&P
Crew B-34C						
1 Truck Driver (heavy)	$37.55	$300.40	$61.05	$488.40	$37.55	$61.05
1 Truck Tractor, 6x4, 380 H.P.		612.80		674.08		
1 Dump Trailer, 16.5 C.Y.		126.20		138.82	92.38	101.61
8 L.H., Daily Totals		$1039.40		$1301.30	$129.93	$162.66
Crew B-34D						
1 Truck Driver (heavy)	$37.55	$300.40	$61.05	$488.40	$37.55	$61.05
1 Truck Tractor, 6x4, 380 H.P.		612.80		674.08		
1 Dump Trailer, 20 C.Y.		140.80		154.88	94.20	103.62
8 L.H., Daily Totals		$1054.00		$1317.36	$131.75	$164.67
Crew B-34E						
1 Truck Driver (heavy)	$37.55	$300.40	$61.05	$488.40	$37.55	$61.05
1 Dump Truck, Off Hwy., 25 Ton		1314.00		1445.40	164.25	180.68
8 L.H., Daily Totals		$1614.40		$1933.80	$201.80	$241.72
Crew B-34F						
1 Truck Driver (heavy)	$37.55	$300.40	$61.05	$488.40	$37.55	$61.05
1 Dump Truck, Off Hwy., 35 Ton		1470.00		1617.00	183.75	202.13
8 L.H., Daily Totals		$1770.40		$2105.40	$221.30	$263.18
Crew B-34G						
1 Truck Driver (heavy)	$37.55	$300.40	$61.05	$488.40	$37.55	$61.05
1 Dump Truck, Off Hwy., 50 Ton		1787.00		1965.70	223.38	245.71
8 L.H., Daily Totals		$2087.40		$2454.10	$260.93	$306.76
Crew B-34H						
1 Truck Driver (heavy)	$37.55	$300.40	$61.05	$488.40	$37.55	$61.05
1 Dump Truck, Off Hwy., 65 Ton		1797.00		1976.70	224.63	247.09
8 L.H., Daily Totals		$2097.40		$2465.10	$262.18	$308.14
Crew B-34I						
1 Truck Driver (heavy)	$37.55	$300.40	$61.05	$488.40	$37.55	$61.05
1 Dump Truck, 18 C.Y., 450 H.P.		867.60		954.36	108.45	119.30
8 L.H., Daily Totals		$1168.00		$1442.76	$146.00	$180.35
Crew B-34J						
1 Truck Driver (heavy)	$37.55	$300.40	$61.05	$488.40	$37.55	$61.05
1 Dump Truck, Off Hwy., 100 Ton		2898.00		3187.80	362.25	398.48
8 L.H., Daily Totals		$3198.40		$3676.20	$399.80	$459.52
Crew B-34K						
1 Truck Driver (heavy)	$37.55	$300.40	$61.05	$488.40	$37.55	$61.05
1 Truck Tractor, 6x4, 450 H.P.		742.40		816.64		
1 Lowbed Trailer, 75 Ton		219.80		241.78	120.28	132.30
8 L.H., Daily Totals		$1262.60		$1546.82	$157.82	$193.35
Crew B-34L						
1 Equip. Oper. (light)	$47.05	$376.40	$74.60	$596.80	$47.05	$74.60
1 Flatbed Truck, Gas, 1.5 Ton		270.20		297.22	33.77	37.15
8 L.H., Daily Totals		$646.60		$894.02	$80.83	$111.75
Crew B-34M						
1 Equip. Oper. (light)	$47.05	$376.40	$74.60	$596.80	$47.05	$74.60
1 Flatbed Truck, Gas, 3 Ton		333.00		366.30	41.63	45.79
8 L.H., Daily Totals		$709.40		$963.10	$88.67	$120.39
Crew B-34N						
1 Truck Driver (heavy)	$37.55	$300.40	$61.05	$488.40	$37.55	$61.05
1 Dump Truck, 8 C.Y., 220 H.P.		417.20		458.92		
1 Flatbed Trailer, 40 Ton		152.00		167.20	71.15	78.27
8 L.H., Daily Totals		$869.60		$1114.52	$108.70	$139.32
Crew B-34P						
1 Pipe Fitter	$58.50	$468.00	$91.25	$730.00	$47.97	$76.05
1 Truck Driver (light)	36.50	292.00	59.35	474.80		
1 Equip. Oper. (medium)	48.90	391.20	77.55	620.40		
1 Flatbed Truck, Gas, 3 Ton		333.00		366.30		
1 Backhoe Loader, 48 H.P.		365.20		401.72	29.09	32.00
24 L.H., Daily Totals		$1849.40		$2593.22	$77.06	$108.05
Crew B-34Q						
1 Pipe Fitter	$58.50	$468.00	$91.25	$730.00	$48.42	$76.77
1 Truck Driver (light)	36.50	292.00	59.35	474.80		
1 Equip. Oper. (crane)	50.25	402.00	79.70	637.60		
1 Flatbed Trailer, 25 Ton		113.60		124.96		
1 Dump Truck, 8 C.Y., 220 H.P.		417.20		458.92		
1 Hyd. Crane, 25 Ton		745.80		820.38	53.19	58.51
24 L.H., Daily Totals		$2438.60		$3246.66	$101.61	$135.28
Crew B-34R						
1 Pipe Fitter	$58.50	$468.00	$91.25	$730.00	$48.42	$76.77
1 Truck Driver (light)	36.50	292.00	59.35	474.80		
1 Equip. Oper. (crane)	50.25	402.00	79.70	637.60		
1 Flatbed Trailer, 25 Ton		113.60		124.96		
1 Dump Truck, 8 C.Y., 220 H.P.		417.20		458.92		
1 Hyd. Crane, 25 Ton		745.80		820.38		
1 Hyd. Excavator, 1 C.Y.		814.80		896.28	87.14	95.86
24 L.H., Daily Totals		$3253.40		$4142.94	$135.56	$172.62
Crew B-34S						
2 Pipe Fitters	$58.50	$936.00	$91.25	$1460.00	$51.20	$80.81
1 Truck Driver (heavy)	37.55	300.40	61.05	488.40		
1 Equip. Oper. (crane)	50.25	402.00	79.70	637.60		
1 Flatbed Trailer, 40 Ton		152.00		167.20		
1 Truck Tractor, 6x4, 380 H.P.		612.80		674.08		
1 Hyd. Crane, 80 Ton		1652.00		1817.20		
1 Hyd. Excavator, 2 C.Y.		1175.00		1292.50	112.24	123.47
32 L.H., Daily Totals		$5230.20		$6536.98	$163.44	$204.28
Crew B-34T						
2 Pipe Fitters	$58.50	$936.00	$91.25	$1460.00	$51.20	$80.81
1 Truck Driver (heavy)	37.55	300.40	61.05	488.40		
1 Equip. Oper. (crane)	50.25	402.00	79.70	637.60		
1 Flatbed Trailer, 40 Ton		152.00		167.20		
1 Truck Tractor, 6x4, 380 H.P.		612.80		674.08		
1 Hyd. Crane, 80 Ton		1652.00		1817.20	75.53	83.08
32 L.H., Daily Totals		$4055.20		$5244.48	$126.72	$163.89
Crew B-35						
1 Labor Foreman (outside)	$38.65	$309.20	$63.50	$508.00	$45.66	$73.22
1 Skilled Worker	47.30	378.40	77.05	616.40		
1 Welder (plumber)	57.55	460.40	89.80	718.40		
1 Laborer	36.65	293.20	60.20	481.60		
1 Equip. Oper. (crane)	50.25	402.00	79.70	637.60		
1 Equip. Oper. (oiler)	43.55	348.40	69.05	552.40		
1 Welder, Electric, 300 amp		55.30		60.83		
1 Hyd. Excavator, .75 C.Y.		662.00		728.20	14.94	16.44
48 L.H., Daily Totals		$2908.90		$4303.43	$60.60	$89.65

725

Crew No.	Bare Costs		Incl. Subs O&P		Cost Per Labor-Hour	
Crew B-35A	Hr.	Daily	Hr.	Daily	Bare Costs	Incl. O&P
1 Labor Foreman (outside)	$38.65	$309.20	$63.50	$508.00	$44.37	$71.36
2 Laborers	36.65	586.40	60.20	963.20		
1 Skilled Worker	47.30	378.40	77.05	616.40		
1 Welder (plumber)	57.55	460.40	89.80	718.40		
1 Equip. Oper. (crane)	50.25	402.00	79.70	637.60		
1 Equip. Oper. (oiler)	43.55	348.40	69.05	552.40		
1 Welder, Gas Engine, 300 amp		142.00		156.20		
1 Crawler Crane, 75 Ton		1492.00		1641.20	29.18	32.10
56 L.H., Daily Totals		$4118.80		$5793.40	$73.55	$103.45

Crew No.	Bare Costs		Incl. Subs O&P		Cost Per Labor-Hour	
Crew B-36	Hr.	Daily	Hr.	Daily	Bare Costs	Incl. O&P
1 Labor Foreman (outside)	$38.65	$309.20	$63.50	$508.00	$41.95	$67.80
2 Laborers	36.65	586.40	60.20	963.20		
2 Equip. Oper. (medium)	48.90	782.40	77.55	1240.80		
1 Dozer, 200 H.P.		1325.00		1457.50		
1 Aggregate Spreader		41.20		45.32		
1 Tandem Roller, 10 Ton		242.00		266.20	40.20	44.23
40 L.H., Daily Totals		$3286.20		$4481.02	$82.16	$112.03

Crew No.	Bare Costs		Incl. Subs O&P		Cost Per Labor-Hour	
Crew B-36A	Hr.	Daily	Hr.	Daily	Bare Costs	Incl. O&P
1 Labor Foreman (outside)	$38.65	$309.20	$63.50	$508.00	$43.94	$70.59
2 Laborers	36.65	586.40	60.20	963.20		
4 Equip. Oper. (medium)	48.90	1564.80	77.55	2481.60		
1 Dozer, 200 H.P.		1325.00		1457.50		
1 Aggregate Spreader		41.20		45.32		
1 Tandem Roller, 10 Ton		242.00		266.20		
1 Roller, Pneum. Whl., 12 Ton		349.00		383.90	34.95	38.45
56 L.H., Daily Totals		$4417.60		$6105.72	$78.89	$109.03

Crew No.	Bare Costs		Incl. Subs O&P		Cost Per Labor-Hour	
Crew B-36B	Hr.	Daily	Hr.	Daily	Bare Costs	Incl. O&P
1 Labor Foreman (outside)	$38.65	$309.20	$63.50	$508.00	$43.14	$69.39
2 Laborers	36.65	586.40	60.20	963.20		
4 Equip. Oper. (medium)	48.90	1564.80	77.55	2481.60		
1 Truck Driver (heavy)	37.55	300.40	61.05	488.40		
1 Grader, 30,000 Lbs.		707.00		777.70		
1 F.E. Loader, Crl, 1.5 C.Y.		625.20		687.72		
1 Dozer, 300 H.P.		1817.00		1998.70		
1 Roller, Vibratory, 25 Ton		692.80		762.08		
1 Truck Tractor, 6x4, 450 H.P.		742.40		816.64		
1 Water Tank Trailer, 5000 Gal.		141.60		155.76	73.84	81.23
64 L.H., Daily Totals		$7486.80		$9639.80	$116.98	$150.62

Crew No.	Bare Costs		Incl. Subs O&P		Cost Per Labor-Hour	
Crew B-36C	Hr.	Daily	Hr.	Daily	Bare Costs	Incl. O&P
1 Labor Foreman (outside)	$38.65	$309.20	$63.50	$508.00	$44.58	$71.44
3 Equip. Oper. (medium)	48.90	1173.60	77.55	1861.20		
1 Truck Driver (heavy)	37.55	300.40	61.05	488.40		
1 Grader, 30,000 Lbs.		707.00		777.70		
1 Dozer, 300 H.P.		1817.00		1998.70		
1 Roller, Vibratory, 25 Ton		692.80		762.08		
1 Truck Tractor, 6x4, 450 H.P.		742.40		816.64		
1 Water Tank Trailer, 5000 Gal.		141.60		155.76	102.52	112.77
40 L.H., Daily Totals		$5884.00		$7368.48	$147.10	$184.21

Crew No.	Bare Costs		Incl. Subs O&P		Cost Per Labor-Hour	
Crew B-37	Hr.	Daily	Hr.	Daily	Bare Costs	Incl. O&P
1 Labor Foreman (outside)	$38.65	$309.20	$63.50	$508.00	$38.72	$63.15
4 Laborers	36.65	1172.80	60.20	1926.40		
1 Equip. Oper. (light)	47.05	376.40	74.60	596.80		
1 Tandem Roller, 5 Ton		159.00		174.90	3.31	3.64
48 L.H., Daily Totals		$2017.40		$3206.10	$42.03	$66.79

Crew No.	Bare Costs		Incl. Subs O&P		Cost Per Labor-Hour	
Crew B-37A	Hr.	Daily	Hr.	Daily	Bare Costs	Incl. O&P
2 Laborers	$36.65	$586.40	$60.20	$963.20	$36.60	$59.92
1 Truck Driver (light)	36.50	292.00	59.35	474.80		
1 Flatbed Truck, Gas, 1.5 Ton		270.20		297.22		
1 Tar Kettle, T.M.		104.60		115.06	15.62	17.18
24 L.H., Daily Totals		$1253.20		$1850.28	$52.22	$77.09

Crew No.	Bare Costs		Incl. Subs O&P		Cost Per Labor-Hour	
Crew B-37B	Hr.	Daily	Hr.	Daily	Bare Costs	Incl. O&P
3 Laborers	$36.65	$879.60	$60.20	$1444.80	$36.61	$59.99
1 Truck Driver (light)	36.50	292.00	59.35	474.80		
1 Flatbed Truck, Gas, 1.5 Ton		270.20		297.22		
1 Tar Kettle, T.M.		104.60		115.06	11.71	12.88
32 L.H., Daily Totals		$1546.40		$2331.88	$48.33	$72.87

Crew No.	Bare Costs		Incl. Subs O&P		Cost Per Labor-Hour	
Crew B-37C	Hr.	Daily	Hr.	Daily	Bare Costs	Incl. O&P
2 Laborers	$36.65	$586.40	$60.20	$963.20	$36.58	$59.77
2 Truck Drivers (light)	36.50	584.00	59.35	949.60		
2 Flatbed Trucks, Gas, 1.5 Ton		540.40		594.44		
1 Tar Kettle, T.M.		104.60		115.06	20.16	22.17
32 L.H., Daily Totals		$1815.40		$2622.30	$56.73	$81.95

Crew No.	Bare Costs		Incl. Subs O&P		Cost Per Labor-Hour	
Crew B-37D	Hr.	Daily	Hr.	Daily	Bare Costs	Incl. O&P
1 Laborer	$36.65	$293.20	$60.20	$481.60	$36.58	$59.77
1 Truck Driver (light)	36.50	292.00	59.35	474.80		
1 Pickup Truck, 3/4 Ton		157.00		172.70	9.81	10.79
16 L.H., Daily Totals		$742.20		$1129.10	$46.39	$70.57

Crew No.	Bare Costs		Incl. Subs O&P		Cost Per Labor-Hour	
Crew B-37E	Hr.	Daily	Hr.	Daily	Bare Costs	Incl. O&P
3 Laborers	$36.65	$879.60	$60.20	$1444.80	$39.84	$64.49
1 Equip. Oper. (light)	47.05	376.40	74.60	596.80		
1 Equip. Oper. (medium)	48.90	391.20	77.55	620.40		
2 Truck Drivers (light)	36.50	584.00	59.35	949.60		
4 Barrels w/ Flasher		13.60		14.96		
1 Concrete Saw		175.20		192.72		
1 Rotary Hammer Drill		24.00		26.40		
1 Hammer Drill Bit		2.35		2.59		
1 Loader, Skid Steer, 30 H.P.		174.20		191.62		
1 Conc. Hammer Attach.		114.70		126.17		
1 Vibrating Plate, Gas, 18"		35.80		39.38		
2 Flatbed Trucks, Gas, 1.5 Ton		540.40		594.44	19.29	21.22
56 L.H., Daily Totals		$3311.45		$4799.88	$59.13	$85.71

Crew No.	Bare Costs		Incl. Subs O&P		Cost Per Labor-Hour	
Crew B-37F	Hr.	Daily	Hr.	Daily	Bare Costs	Incl. O&P
3 Laborers	$36.65	$879.60	$60.20	$1444.80	$36.61	$59.99
1 Truck Driver (light)	36.50	292.00	59.35	474.80		
4 Barrels w/ Flasher		13.60		14.96		
1 Concrete Mixer, 10 C.F.		176.80		194.48		
1 Air Compressor, 60 cfm		137.40		151.14		
1 -50' Air Hose, 3/4"		3.25		3.58		
1 Spade (Chipper)		7.80		8.58		
1 Flatbed Truck, Gas, 1.5 Ton		270.20		297.22	19.03	20.94
32 L.H., Daily Totals		$1780.65		$2589.55	$55.65	$80.92

Crew No.	Bare Costs		Incl. Subs O&P		Cost Per Labor-Hour	
Crew B-37G	Hr.	Daily	Hr.	Daily	Bare Costs	Incl. O&P
1 Labor Foreman (outside)	$38.65	$309.20	$63.50	$508.00	$38.72	$63.15
4 Laborers	36.65	1172.80	60.20	1926.40		
1 Equip. Oper. (light)	47.05	376.40	74.60	596.80		
1 Berm Machine		294.40		323.84		
1 Tandem Roller, 5 Ton		159.00		174.90	9.45	10.39
48 L.H., Daily Totals		$2311.80		$3529.94	$48.16	$73.54

Crew No.	Bare Costs		Incl. Subs O&P		Cost Per Labor-Hour	

Crew B-37H	Hr.	Daily	Hr.	Daily	Bare Costs	Incl. O&P
1 Labor Foreman (outside)	$38.65	$309.20	$63.50	$508.00	$38.72	$63.15
4 Laborers	36.65	1172.80	60.20	1926.40		
1 Equip. Oper. (light)	47.05	376.40	74.60	596.80		
1 Tandem Roller, 5 Ton		159.00		174.90		
1 Flatbed Trucks, Gas, 1.5 Ton		270.20		297.22		
1 Tar Kettle, T.M.		104.60		115.06	11.12	12.23
48 L.H., Daily Totals		$2392.20		$3618.38	$49.84	$75.38

Crew B-37I	Hr.	Daily	Hr.	Daily	Bare Costs	Incl. O&P
3 Laborers	$36.65	$879.60	$60.20	$1444.80	$39.84	$64.49
1 Equip. Oper. (light)	47.05	376.40	74.60	596.80		
1 Equip. Oper. (medium)	48.90	391.20	77.55	620.40		
2 Truck Drivers (light)	36.50	584.00	59.35	949.60		
4 Barrels w/ Flasher		13.60		14.96		
1 Concrete Saw		175.20		192.72		
1 Rotary Hammer Drill		24.00		26.40		
1 Hammer Drill Bit		2.35		2.59		
1 Air Compressor, 60 cfm		137.40		151.14		
1 -50' Air Hose, 3/4"		3.25		3.58		
1 Spade (Chipper)		7.80		8.58		
1 Loader, Skid Steer, 30 H.P.		174.20		191.62		
1 Conc. Hammer Attach.		114.70		126.17		
1 Concrete Mixer, 10 C.F.		176.80		194.48		
1 Vibrating Plate, Gas, 18"		35.80		39.38		
2 Flatbed Trucks, Gas, 1.5 Ton		540.40		594.44	25.10	27.61
56 L.H., Daily Totals		$3636.70		$5157.65	$64.94	$92.10

Crew B-37J	Hr.	Daily	Hr.	Daily	Bare Costs	Incl. O&P
1 Labor Foreman (outside)	$38.65	$309.20	$63.50	$508.00	$38.72	$63.15
4 Laborers	36.65	1172.80	60.20	1926.40		
1 Equip. Oper. (light)	47.05	376.40	74.60	596.80		
1 Air Compressor, 60 cfm		137.40		151.14		
1 -50' Air Hose, 3/4"		3.25		3.58		
2 Concrete Mixer, 10 C.F.		353.60		388.96		
2 Flatbed Trucks, Gas, 1.5 Ton		540.40		594.44		
1 Shot Blaster, 20"		214.40		235.84	26.02	28.62
48 L.H., Daily Totals		$3107.45		$4405.15	$64.74	$91.77

Crew B-37K	Hr.	Daily	Hr.	Daily	Bare Costs	Incl. O&P
1 Labor Foreman (outside)	$38.65	$309.20	$63.50	$508.00	$38.72	$63.15
4 Laborers	36.65	1172.80	60.20	1926.40		
1 Equip. Oper. (light)	47.05	376.40	74.60	596.80		
1 Air Compressor, 60 cfm		137.40		151.14		
1 -50' Air Hose, 3/4"		3.25		3.58		
2 Flatbed Trucks, Gas, 1.5 Ton		540.40		594.44		
1 Shot Blaster, 20"		214.40		235.84	18.66	20.52
48 L.H., Daily Totals		$2753.85		$4016.20	$57.37	$83.67

Crew B-38	Hr.	Daily	Hr.	Daily	Bare Costs	Incl. O&P
1 Labor Foreman (outside)	$38.65	$309.20	$63.50	$508.00	$41.58	$67.21
2 Laborers	36.65	586.40	60.20	963.20		
1 Equip. Oper. (light)	47.05	376.40	74.60	596.80		
1 Equip. Oper. (medium)	48.90	391.20	77.55	620.40		
1 Backhoe Loader, 48 H.P.		365.20		401.72		
1 Hyd. Hammer, (1200 lb.)		180.40		198.44		
1 F.E. Loader, W.M., 4 C.Y.		673.80		741.18		
1 Pvmt. Rem. Bucket		60.80		66.88	32.01	35.21
40 L.H., Daily Totals		$2943.40		$4096.62	$73.58	$102.42

Crew B-39	Hr.	Daily	Hr.	Daily	Bare Costs	Incl. O&P
1 Labor Foreman (outside)	$38.65	$309.20	$63.50	$508.00	$38.72	$63.15
4 Laborers	36.65	1172.80	60.20	1926.40		
1 Equip. Oper. (light)	47.05	376.40	74.60	596.80		
1 Air Compressor, 250 cfm		202.40		222.64		
2 Breakers, Pavement, 60 lb.		19.60		21.56		
2 -50' Air Hoses, 1.5"		11.60		12.76	4.87	5.35
48 L.H., Daily Totals		$2092.00		$3288.16	$43.58	$68.50

Crew B-40	Hr.	Daily	Hr.	Daily	Bare Costs	Incl. O&P
1 Pile Driver Foreman (outside)	$46.40	$371.20	$75.90	$607.20	$46.01	$74.37
4 Pile Drivers	44.40	1420.80	72.65	2324.80		
2 Equip. Oper. (crane)	50.25	804.00	79.70	1275.20		
1 Equip. Oper. (oiler)	43.55	348.40	69.05	552.40		
1 Crawler Crane, 40 Ton		1179.00		1296.90		
1 Vibratory Hammer & Gen.		2640.00		2904.00	59.67	65.64
64 L.H., Daily Totals		$6763.40		$8960.50	$105.68	$140.01

Crew B-40B	Hr.	Daily	Hr.	Daily	Bare Costs	Incl. O&P
1 Labor Foreman (outside)	$38.65	$309.20	$63.50	$508.00	$40.40	$65.47
3 Laborers	36.65	879.60	60.20	1444.80		
1 Equip. Oper. (crane)	50.25	402.00	79.70	637.60		
1 Equip. Oper. (oiler)	43.55	348.40	69.05	552.40		
1 Lattice Boom Crane, 40 Ton		1177.00		1294.70	24.52	26.97
48 L.H., Daily Totals		$3116.20		$4437.50	$64.92	$92.45

Crew B-41	Hr.	Daily	Hr.	Daily	Bare Costs	Incl. O&P
1 Labor Foreman (outside)	$38.65	$309.20	$63.50	$508.00	$37.95	$62.09
4 Laborers	36.65	1172.80	60.20	1926.40		
.25 Equip. Oper. (crane)	50.25	100.50	79.70	159.40		
.25 Equip. Oper. (oiler)	43.55	87.10	69.05	138.10		
.25 Crawler Crane, 40 Ton		294.75		324.23	6.70	7.37
44 L.H., Daily Totals		$1964.35		$3056.13	$44.64	$69.46

Crew B-42	Hr.	Daily	Hr.	Daily	Bare Costs	Incl. O&P
1 Labor Foreman (outside)	$38.65	$309.20	$63.50	$508.00	$41.27	$68.35
4 Laborers	36.65	1172.80	60.20	1926.40		
1 Equip. Oper. (crane)	50.25	402.00	79.70	637.60		
1 Equip. Oper. (oiler)	43.55	348.40	69.05	552.40		
1 Welder	51.10	408.80	93.75	750.00		
1 Hyd. Crane, 25 Ton		745.80		820.38		
1 Welder, Gas Engine, 300 amp		142.00		156.20		
1 Horz. Boring Csg. Mch.		479.80		527.78	21.37	23.51
64 L.H., Daily Totals		$4008.80		$5878.76	$62.64	$91.86

Crew B-43	Hr.	Daily	Hr.	Daily	Bare Costs	Incl. O&P
1 Labor Foreman (outside)	$38.65	$309.20	$63.50	$508.00	$40.40	$65.47
3 Laborers	36.65	879.60	60.20	1444.80		
1 Equip. Oper. (crane)	50.25	402.00	79.70	637.60		
1 Equip. Oper. (oiler)	43.55	348.40	69.05	552.40		
1 Drill Rig, Truck-Mounted		2551.00		2806.10	53.15	58.46
48 L.H., Daily Totals		$4490.20		$5948.90	$93.55	$123.94

Crew B-44	Hr.	Daily	Hr.	Daily	Bare Costs	Incl. O&P
1 Pile Driver Foreman (outside)	$46.40	$371.20	$75.90	$607.20	$45.14	$73.26
4 Pile Drivers	44.40	1420.80	72.65	2324.80		
2 Equip. Oper. (crane)	50.25	804.00	79.70	1275.20		
1 Laborer	36.65	293.20	60.20	481.60		
1 Crawler Crane, 40 Ton		1179.00		1296.90		
1 Lead, 60' High		74.80		82.28		
1 Hammer, Diesel, 15K ft.-lbs.		587.60		646.36	28.77	31.65
64 L.H., Daily Totals		$4730.60		$6714.34	$73.92	$104.91

Crew No.	Bare Costs		Incl. Subs O&P		Cost Per Labor-Hour	
	Hr.	Daily	Hr.	Daily	Bare Costs	Incl. O&P
Crew B-45					$43.23	$69.30
1 Equip. Oper. (medium)	$48.90	$391.20	$77.55	$620.40		
1 Truck Driver (heavy)	37.55	300.40	61.05	488.40		
1 Dist. Tanker, 3000 Gallon		308.20		339.02		
1 Truck Tractor, 6x4, 380 H.P.		612.80		674.08	57.56	63.32
16 L.H., Daily Totals		$1612.60		$2121.90	$100.79	$132.62
Crew B-46					$40.86	$66.97
1 Pile Driver Foreman (outside)	$46.40	$371.20	$75.90	$607.20		
2 Pile Drivers	44.40	710.40	72.65	1162.40		
3 Laborers	36.65	879.60	60.20	1444.80		
1 Chain Saw, Gas, 36" Long		45.00		49.50	.94	1.03
48 L.H., Daily Totals		$2006.20		$3263.90	$41.80	$68.00
Crew B-47					$40.78	$66.10
1 Blast Foreman (outside)	$38.65	$309.20	$63.50	$508.00		
1 Driller	36.65	293.20	60.20	481.60		
1 Equip. Oper. (light)	47.05	376.40	74.60	596.80		
1 Air Track Drill, 4"		1040.00		1144.00		
1 Air Compressor, 600 cfm		552.60		607.86		
2 -50' Air Hoses, 3"		29.80		32.78	67.60	74.36
24 L.H., Daily Totals		$2601.20		$3371.04	$108.38	$140.46
Crew B-47A					$44.15	$70.75
1 Drilling Foreman (outside)	$38.65	$309.20	$63.50	$508.00		
1 Equip. Oper. (heavy)	50.25	402.00	79.70	637.60		
1 Equip. Oper. (oiler)	43.55	348.40	69.05	552.40		
1 Air Track Drill, 5"		1255.00		1380.50	52.29	57.52
24 L.H., Daily Totals		$2314.60		$3078.50	$96.44	$128.27
Crew B-47C					$41.85	$67.40
1 Laborer	$36.65	$293.20	$60.20	$481.60		
1 Equip. Oper. (light)	47.05	376.40	74.60	596.80		
1 Air Compressor, 750 cfm		559.20		615.12		
2 -50' Air Hoses, 3"		29.80		32.78		
1 Air Track Drill, 4"		1040.00		1144.00	101.81	111.99
16 L.H., Daily Totals		$2298.60		$2870.30	$143.66	$179.39
Crew B-47E					$37.15	$61.02
1 Labor Foreman (outside)	$38.65	$309.20	$63.50	$508.00		
3 Laborers	36.65	879.60	60.20	1444.80		
1 Flatbed Truck, Gas, 3 Ton		333.00		366.30	10.41	11.45
32 L.H., Daily Totals		$1521.80		$2319.10	$47.56	$72.47
Crew B-47G					$39.75	$64.63
1 Labor Foreman (outside)	$38.65	$309.20	$63.50	$508.00		
2 Laborers	36.65	586.40	60.20	963.20		
1 Equip. Oper. (light)	47.05	376.40	74.60	596.80		
1 Air Track Drill, 4"		1040.00		1144.00		
1 Air Compressor, 600 cfm		552.60		607.86		
2 -50' Air Hoses, 3"		29.80		32.78		
1 Gunite Pump Rig		370.40		407.44	62.27	68.50
32 L.H., Daily Totals		$3264.80		$4260.08	$102.03	$133.13
Crew B-47H					$47.80	$77.86
1 Skilled Worker Foreman (out)	$49.30	$394.40	$80.30	$642.40		
3 Skilled Workers	47.30	1135.20	77.05	1849.20		
1 Flatbed Truck, Gas, 3 Ton		333.00		366.30	10.41	11.45
32 L.H., Daily Totals		$1862.60		$2857.90	$58.21	$89.31

Crew No.	Bare Costs		Incl. Subs O&P		Cost Per Labor-Hour	
	Hr.	Daily	Hr.	Daily	Bare Costs	Incl. O&P
Crew B-48					$41.35	$66.78
1 Labor Foreman (outside)	$38.65	$309.20	$63.50	$508.00		
3 Laborers	36.65	879.60	60.20	1444.80		
1 Equip. Oper. (crane)	50.25	402.00	79.70	637.60		
1 Equip. Oper. (oiler)	43.55	348.40	69.05	552.40		
1 Equip. Oper. (light)	47.05	376.40	74.60	596.80		
1 Centr. Water Pump, 6"		340.80		374.88		
1 -20' Suction Hose, 6"		11.50		12.65		
1 -50' Discharge Hose, 6"		6.10		6.71		
1 Drill Rig, Truck-Mounted		2551.00		2806.10	51.95	57.15
56 L.H., Daily Totals		$5225.00		$6939.94	$93.30	$123.93
Crew B-49					$42.91	$69.23
1 Labor Foreman (outside)	$38.65	$309.20	$63.50	$508.00		
3 Laborers	36.65	879.60	60.20	1444.80		
2 Equip. Oper. (crane)	50.25	804.00	79.70	1275.20		
2 Equip. Oper. (oilers)	43.55	696.80	69.05	1104.80		
1 Equip. Oper. (light)	47.05	376.40	74.60	596.80		
2 Pile Drivers	44.40	710.40	72.65	1162.40		
1 Hyd. Crane, 25 Ton		745.80		820.38		
1 Centr. Water Pump, 6"		340.80		374.88		
1 -20' Suction Hose, 6"		11.50		12.65		
1 -50' Discharge Hose, 6"		6.10		6.71		
1 Drill Rig, Truck-Mounted		2551.00		2806.10	41.54	45.69
88 L.H., Daily Totals		$7431.60		$10112.72	$84.45	$114.92
Crew B-50					$43.80	$71.20
2 Pile Driver Foremen (outside)	$46.40	$742.40	$75.90	$1214.40		
6 Pile Drivers	44.40	2131.20	72.65	3487.20		
2 Equip. Oper. (crane)	50.25	804.00	79.70	1275.20		
1 Equip. Oper. (oiler)	43.55	348.40	69.05	552.40		
3 Laborers	36.65	879.60	60.20	1444.80		
1 Crawler Crane, 40 Ton		1179.00		1296.90		
1 Lead, 60' High		74.80		82.28		
1 Hammer, Diesel, 15K ft.-lbs.		587.60		646.36		
1 Air Compressor, 600 cfm		552.60		607.86		
2 -50' Air Hoses, 3"		29.80		32.78		
1 Chain Saw, Gas, 36" Long		45.00		49.50	22.04	24.25
112 L.H., Daily Totals		$7374.40		$10689.68	$65.84	$95.44
Crew B-51					$36.96	$60.61
1 Labor Foreman (outside)	$38.65	$309.20	$63.50	$508.00		
4 Laborers	36.65	1172.80	60.20	1926.40		
1 Truck Driver (light)	36.50	292.00	59.35	474.80		
1 Flatbed Truck, Gas, 1.5 Ton		270.20		297.22	5.63	6.19
48 L.H., Daily Totals		$2044.20		$3206.42	$42.59	$66.80
Crew B-52					$42.50	$69.20
1 Carpenter Foreman (outside)	$47.85	$382.80	$78.60	$628.80		
1 Carpenter	45.85	366.80	75.35	602.80		
3 Laborers	36.65	879.60	60.20	1444.80		
1 Cement Finisher	44.05	352.40	69.50	556.00		
.5 Rodman (reinf.)	50.65	202.60	83.10	332.40		
.5 Equip. Oper. (medium)	48.90	195.60	77.55	310.20		
.5 Crawler Loader, 3 C.Y.		595.50		655.05	10.63	11.70
56 L.H., Daily Totals		$2975.30		$4530.05	$53.13	$80.89
Crew B-53					$47.05	$74.60
1 Equip. Oper. (light)	$47.05	$376.40	$74.60	$596.80		
1 Trencher, Chain, 12 H.P.		71.20		78.32	8.90	9.79
8 L.H., Daily Totals		$447.60		$675.12	$55.95	$84.39

Crews

Crew B-54

Crew B-54	Hr.	Daily	Hr.	Daily	Bare Costs	Incl. O&P
1 Equip. Oper. (light)	$47.05	$376.40	$74.60	$596.80	$47.05	$74.60
1 Trencher, Chain, 40 H.P.		339.40		373.34	42.42	46.67
8 L.H., Daily Totals		$715.80		$970.14	$89.47	$121.27

Crew B-54A

Crew B-54A	Hr.	Daily	Hr.	Daily	Bare Costs	Incl. O&P
.17 Labor Foreman (outside)	$38.65	$52.56	$63.50	$86.36	$47.41	$75.51
1 Equipment Operator (med.)	48.90	391.20	77.55	620.40		
1 Wheel Trencher, 67 H.P.		1206.00		1326.60	128.85	141.73
9.36 L.H., Daily Totals		$1649.76		$2033.36	$176.26	$217.24

Crew B-54B

Crew B-54B	Hr.	Daily	Hr.	Daily	Bare Costs	Incl. O&P
.25 Labor Foreman (outside)	$38.65	$77.30	$63.50	$127.00	$46.85	$74.74
1 Equipment Operator (med.)	48.90	391.20	77.55	620.40		
1 Wheel Trencher, 150 H.P.		1898.00		2087.80	189.80	208.78
10 L.H., Daily Totals		$2366.50		$2835.20	$236.65	$283.52

Crew B-54D

Crew B-54D	Hr.	Daily	Hr.	Daily	Bare Costs	Incl. O&P
1 Laborer	$36.65	$293.20	$60.20	$481.60	$42.77	$68.88
1 Equipment Operator (med.)	48.90	391.20	77.55	620.40		
1 Rock Trencher, 6" Width		369.00		405.90	23.06	25.37
16 L.H., Daily Totals		$1053.40		$1507.90	$65.84	$94.24

Crew B-54E

Crew B-54E	Hr.	Daily	Hr.	Daily	Bare Costs	Incl. O&P
1 Laborer	$36.65	$293.20	$60.20	$481.60	$42.77	$68.88
1 Equipment Operator (med.)	48.90	391.20	77.55	620.40		
1 Rock Trencher, 18" Width		2590.00		2849.00	161.88	178.06
16 L.H., Daily Totals		$3274.40		$3951.00	$204.65	$246.94

Crew B-55

Crew B-55	Hr.	Daily	Hr.	Daily	Bare Costs	Incl. O&P
2 Laborers	$36.65	$586.40	$60.20	$963.20	$36.60	$59.92
1 Truck Driver (light)	36.50	292.00	59.35	474.80		
1 Truck-Mounted Earth Auger		786.40		865.04		
1 Flatbed Truck, Gas, 3 Ton		333.00		366.30	46.64	51.31
24 L.H., Daily Totals		$1997.80		$2669.34	$83.24	$111.22

Crew B-56

Crew B-56	Hr.	Daily	Hr.	Daily	Bare Costs	Incl. O&P
1 Laborer	$36.65	$293.20	$60.20	$481.60	$41.85	$67.40
1 Equip. Oper. (light)	47.05	376.40	74.60	596.80		
1 Air Track Drill, 4"		1040.00		1144.00		
1 Air Compressor, 600 cfm		552.60		607.86		
1 -50' Air Hose, 3"		14.90		16.39	100.47	110.52
16 L.H., Daily Totals		$2277.10		$2846.65	$142.32	$177.92

Crew B-57

Crew B-57	Hr.	Daily	Hr.	Daily	Bare Costs	Incl. O&P
1 Labor Foreman (outside)	$38.65	$309.20	$63.50	$508.00	$42.13	$67.88
2 Laborers	36.65	586.40	60.20	963.20		
1 Equip. Oper. (crane)	50.25	402.00	79.70	637.60		
1 Equip. Oper. (light)	47.05	376.40	74.60	596.80		
1 Equip. Oper. (oiler)	43.55	348.40	69.05	552.40		
1 Crawler Crane, 25 Ton		1173.00		1290.30		
1 Clamshell Bucket, 1 C.Y.		47.40		52.14		
1 Centr. Water Pump, 6"		340.80		374.88		
1 -20' Suction Hose, 6"		11.50		12.65		
20 -50' Discharge Hoses, 6"		122.00		134.20	35.31	38.84
48 L.H., Daily Totals		$3717.10		$5122.17	$77.44	$106.71

Crew B-58

Crew B-58	Hr.	Daily	Hr.	Daily	Bare Costs	Incl. O&P
2 Laborers	$36.65	$586.40	$60.20	$963.20	$40.12	$65.00
1 Equip. Oper. (light)	47.05	376.40	74.60	596.80		
1 Backhoe Loader, 48 H.P.		365.20		401.72		
1 Small Helicopter, w/ Pilot		2729.00		3001.90	128.93	141.82
24 L.H., Daily Totals		$4057.00		$4963.62	$169.04	$206.82

Crew B-59

Crew B-59	Hr.	Daily	Hr.	Daily	Bare Costs	Incl. O&P
1 Truck Driver (heavy)	$37.55	$300.40	$61.05	$488.40	$37.55	$61.05
1 Truck Tractor, 220 H.P.		366.40		403.04		
1 Water Tank Trailer, 5000 Gal.		141.60		155.76	63.50	69.85
8 L.H., Daily Totals		$808.40		$1047.20	$101.05	$130.90

Crew B-59A

Crew B-59A	Hr.	Daily	Hr.	Daily	Bare Costs	Incl. O&P
2 Laborers	$36.65	$586.40	$60.20	$963.20	$36.95	$60.48
1 Truck Driver (heavy)	37.55	300.40	61.05	488.40		
1 Water Tank Trailer, 5000 Gal.		141.60		155.76		
1 Truck Tractor, 220 H.P.		366.40		403.04	21.17	23.28
24 L.H., Daily Totals		$1394.80		$2010.40	$58.12	$83.77

Crew B-60

Crew B-60	Hr.	Daily	Hr.	Daily	Bare Costs	Incl. O&P
1 Labor Foreman (outside)	$38.65	$309.20	$63.50	$508.00	$42.84	$68.84
2 Laborers	36.65	586.40	60.20	963.20		
1 Equip. Oper. (crane)	50.25	402.00	79.70	637.60		
2 Equip. Oper. (light)	47.05	752.80	74.60	1193.60		
1 Equip. Oper. (oiler)	43.55	348.40	69.05	552.40		
1 Crawler Crane, 40 Ton		1179.00		1296.90		
1 Lead, 60' High		74.80		82.28		
1 Hammer, Diesel, 15K ft.-lbs.		587.60		646.36		
1 Backhoe Loader, 48 H.P.		365.20		401.72	39.40	43.34
56 L.H., Daily Totals		$4605.40		$6282.06	$82.24	$112.18

Crew B-61

Crew B-61	Hr.	Daily	Hr.	Daily	Bare Costs	Incl. O&P
1 Labor Foreman (outside)	$38.65	$309.20	$63.50	$508.00	$39.13	$63.74
3 Laborers	36.65	879.60	60.20	1444.80		
1 Equip. Oper. (light)	47.05	376.40	74.60	596.80		
1 Cement Mixer, 2 C.Y.		191.40		210.54		
1 Air Compressor, 160 cfm		157.40		173.14	8.72	9.59
40 L.H., Daily Totals		$1914.00		$2933.28	$47.85	$73.33

Crew B-62

Crew B-62	Hr.	Daily	Hr.	Daily	Bare Costs	Incl. O&P
2 Laborers	$36.65	$586.40	$60.20	$963.20	$40.12	$65.00
1 Equip. Oper. (light)	47.05	376.40	74.60	596.80		
1 Loader, Skid Steer, 30 H.P.		174.20		191.62	7.26	7.98
24 L.H., Daily Totals		$1137.00		$1751.62	$47.38	$72.98

Crew B-63

Crew B-63	Hr.	Daily	Hr.	Daily	Bare Costs	Incl. O&P
4 Laborers	$36.65	$1172.80	$60.20	$1926.40	$38.73	$63.08
1 Equip. Oper. (light)	47.05	376.40	74.60	596.80		
1 Loader, Skid Steer, 30 H.P.		174.20		191.62	4.36	4.79
40 L.H., Daily Totals		$1723.40		$2714.82	$43.09	$67.87

Crew B-63B

Crew B-63B	Hr.	Daily	Hr.	Daily	Bare Costs	Incl. O&P
1 Labor Foreman (inside)	$37.15	$297.20	$61.05	$488.40	$39.38	$64.01
2 Laborers	36.65	586.40	60.20	963.20		
1 Equip. Oper. (light)	47.05	376.40	74.60	596.80		
1 Loader, Skid Steer, 78 H.P.		308.80		339.68	9.65	10.62
32 L.H., Daily Totals		$1568.80		$2388.08	$49.02	$74.63

Crew B-64

Crew No.	Bare Costs Hr.	Daily	Incl. Subs O&P Hr.	Daily	Bare Costs	Incl. O&P
1 Laborer	$36.65	$293.20	$60.20	$481.60	$36.58	$59.77
1 Truck Driver (light)	36.50	292.00	59.35	474.80		
1 Power Mulcher (small)		159.60		175.56		
1 Flatbed Truck, Gas, 1.5 Ton		270.20		297.22	26.86	29.55
16 L.H., Daily Totals		$1015.00		$1429.18	$63.44	$89.32

Crew B-65

Crew No.	Bare Costs Hr.	Daily	Incl. Subs O&P Hr.	Daily	Bare Costs	Incl. O&P
1 Laborer	$36.65	$293.20	$60.20	$481.60	$36.58	$59.77
1 Truck Driver (light)	36.50	292.00	59.35	474.80		
1 Power Mulcher (Large)		325.60		358.16		
1 Flatbed Truck, Gas, 1.5 Ton		270.20		297.22	37.24	40.96
16 L.H., Daily Totals		$1181.00		$1611.78	$73.81	$100.74

Crew B-66

Crew No.	Bare Costs Hr.	Daily	Incl. Subs O&P Hr.	Daily	Bare Costs	Incl. O&P
1 Equip. Oper. (light)	$47.05	$376.40	$74.60	$596.80	$47.05	$74.60
1 Loader-Backhoe, 40 H.P.		259.60		285.56	32.45	35.70
8 L.H., Daily Totals		$636.00		$882.36	$79.50	$110.30

Crew B-67

Crew No.	Bare Costs Hr.	Daily	Incl. Subs O&P Hr.	Daily	Bare Costs	Incl. O&P
1 Millwright	$48.10	$384.80	$75.65	$605.20	$47.58	$75.13
1 Equip. Oper. (light)	47.05	376.40	74.60	596.80		
1 Forklift, R/T, 4,000 Lb.		314.20		345.62	19.64	21.60
16 L.H., Daily Totals		$1075.40		$1547.62	$67.21	$96.73

Crew B-67B

Crew No.	Bare Costs Hr.	Daily	Incl. Subs O&P Hr.	Daily	Bare Costs	Incl. O&P
1 Millwright Foreman (inside)	$48.60	$388.80	$76.45	$611.60	$48.35	$76.05
1 Millwright	48.10	384.80	75.65	605.20		
16 L.H., Daily Totals		$773.60		$1216.80	$48.35	$76.05

Crew B-68

Crew No.	Bare Costs Hr.	Daily	Incl. Subs O&P Hr.	Daily	Bare Costs	Incl. O&P
2 Millwrights	$48.10	$769.60	$75.65	$1210.40	$47.75	$75.30
1 Equip. Oper. (light)	47.05	376.40	74.60	596.80		
1 Forklift, R/T, 4,000 Lb.		314.20		345.62	13.09	14.40
24 L.H., Daily Totals		$1460.20		$2152.82	$60.84	$89.70

Crew B-68A

Crew No.	Bare Costs Hr.	Daily	Incl. Subs O&P Hr.	Daily	Bare Costs	Incl. O&P
1 Millwright Foreman (inside)	$48.60	$388.80	$76.45	$611.60	$48.27	$75.92
2 Millwrights	48.10	769.60	75.65	1210.40		
1 Forklift, 8,000 Lb.		180.00		198.00	7.50	8.25
24 L.H., Daily Totals		$1338.40		$2020.00	$55.77	$84.17

Crew B-68B

Crew No.	Bare Costs Hr.	Daily	Incl. Subs O&P Hr.	Daily	Bare Costs	Incl. O&P
1 Millwright Foreman (inside)	$48.60	$388.80	$76.45	$611.60	$52.37	$81.78
2 Millwrights	48.10	769.60	75.65	1210.40		
2 Electricians	53.35	853.60	82.55	1320.80		
2 Plumbers	57.55	920.80	89.80	1436.80		
1 Forklift, 5,000 Lb.		324.80		357.28	5.80	6.38
56 L.H., Daily Totals		$3257.60		$4936.88	$58.17	$88.16

Crew B-68C

Crew No.	Bare Costs Hr.	Daily	Incl. Subs O&P Hr.	Daily	Bare Costs	Incl. O&P
1 Millwright Foreman (inside)	$48.60	$388.80	$76.45	$611.60	$51.90	$81.11
1 Millwright	48.10	384.80	75.65	605.20		
1 Electrician	53.35	426.80	82.55	660.40		
1 Plumber	57.55	460.40	89.80	718.40		
1 Forklift, 5,000 Lb.		324.80		357.28	10.15	11.16
32 L.H., Daily Totals		$1985.60		$2952.88	$62.05	$92.28

Crew B-68D

Crew No.	Bare Costs Hr.	Daily	Incl. Subs O&P Hr.	Daily	Bare Costs	Incl. O&P
1 Labor Foreman (inside)	$37.15	$297.20	$61.05	$488.40	$40.28	$65.28
1 Laborer	36.65	293.20	60.20	481.60		
1 Equip. Oper. (light)	47.05	376.40	74.60	596.80		
1 Forklift, 5,000 Lb.		324.80		357.28	13.53	14.89
24 L.H., Daily Totals		$1291.60		$1924.08	$53.82	$80.17

Crew B-68E

Crew No.	Bare Costs Hr.	Daily	Incl. Subs O&P Hr.	Daily	Bare Costs	Incl. O&P
1 Struc. Steel Foreman (inside)	$51.60	$412.80	$94.70	$757.60	$51.20	$93.94
3 Struc. Steel Workers	51.10	1226.40	93.75	2250.00		
1 Welder	51.10	408.80	93.75	750.00		
1 Forklift, 8,000 Lb.		180.00		198.00	4.50	4.95
40 L.H., Daily Totals		$2228.00		$3955.60	$55.70	$98.89

Crew B-68F

Crew No.	Bare Costs Hr.	Daily	Incl. Subs O&P Hr.	Daily	Bare Costs	Incl. O&P
1 Skilled Worker Foreman (out)	$49.30	$394.40	$80.30	$642.40	$47.97	$78.13
2 Skilled Workers	47.30	756.80	77.05	1232.80		
1 Forklift, 5,000 Lb.		324.80		357.28	13.53	14.89
24 L.H., Daily Totals		$1476.00		$2232.48	$61.50	$93.02

Crew B-69

Crew No.	Bare Costs Hr.	Daily	Incl. Subs O&P Hr.	Daily	Bare Costs	Incl. O&P
1 Labor Foreman (outside)	$38.65	$309.20	$63.50	$508.00	$40.40	$65.47
3 Laborers	36.65	879.60	60.20	1444.80		
1 Equip. Oper. (crane)	50.25	402.00	79.70	637.60		
1 Equip. Oper. (oiler)	43.55	348.40	69.05	552.40		
1 Hyd. Crane, 80 Ton		1652.00		1817.20	34.42	37.86
48 L.H., Daily Totals		$3591.20		$4960.00	$74.82	$103.33

Crew B-69A

Crew No.	Bare Costs Hr.	Daily	Incl. Subs O&P Hr.	Daily	Bare Costs	Incl. O&P
1 Labor Foreman (outside)	$38.65	$309.20	$63.50	$508.00	$40.26	$65.19
3 Laborers	36.65	879.60	60.20	1444.80		
1 Equip. Oper. (medium)	48.90	391.20	77.55	620.40		
1 Concrete Finisher	44.05	352.40	69.50	556.00		
1 Curb/Gutter Paver, 2-Track		898.00		987.80	18.71	20.58
48 L.H., Daily Totals		$2830.40		$4117.00	$58.97	$85.77

Crew B-69B

Crew No.	Bare Costs Hr.	Daily	Incl. Subs O&P Hr.	Daily	Bare Costs	Incl. O&P
1 Labor Foreman (outside)	$38.65	$309.20	$63.50	$508.00	$40.26	$65.19
3 Laborers	36.65	879.60	60.20	1444.80		
1 Equip. Oper. (medium)	48.90	391.20	77.55	620.40		
1 Cement Finisher	44.05	352.40	69.50	556.00		
1 Curb/Gutter Paver, 4-Track		770.20		847.22	16.05	17.65
48 L.H., Daily Totals		$2702.60		$3976.42	$56.30	$82.84

Crew B-70

Crew No.	Bare Costs Hr.	Daily	Incl. Subs O&P Hr.	Daily	Bare Costs	Incl. O&P
1 Labor Foreman (outside)	$38.65	$309.20	$63.50	$508.00	$42.19	$68.11
3 Laborers	36.65	879.60	60.20	1444.80		
3 Equip. Oper. (medium)	48.90	1173.60	77.55	1861.20		
1 Grader, 30,000 Lbs.		707.00		777.70		
1 Ripper, Beam & 1 Shank		81.40		89.54		
1 Road Sweeper, S.P., 8' wide		665.40		731.94		
1 F.E. Loader, W.M., 1.5 C.Y.		373.40		410.74	32.63	35.89
56 L.H., Daily Totals		$4189.60		$5823.92	$74.81	$104.00

Crew B-71

Crew No.	Bare Costs Hr.	Daily	Incl. Subs O&P Hr.	Daily	Bare Costs	Incl. O&P
1 Labor Foreman (outside)	$38.65	$309.20	$63.50	$508.00	$42.19	$68.11
3 Laborers	36.65	879.60	60.20	1444.80		
3 Equip. Oper. (medium)	48.90	1173.60	77.55	1861.20		
1 Pvmt. Profiler, 750 H.P.		5877.00		6464.70		
1 Road Sweeper, S.P., 8' wide		665.40		731.94		
1 F.E. Loader, W.M., 1.5 C.Y.		373.40		410.74	123.50	135.85
56 L.H., Daily Totals		$9278.20		$11421.38	$165.68	$203.95

Crews

Crew No.	Bare Costs		Incl. Subs O&P		Cost Per Labor-Hour	

Crew B-72	Hr.	Daily	Hr.	Daily	Bare Costs	Incl. O&P
1 Labor Foreman (outside)	$38.65	$309.20	$63.50	$508.00	$43.02	$69.29
3 Laborers	36.65	879.60	60.20	1444.80		
4 Equip. Oper. (medium)	48.90	1564.80	77.55	2481.60		
1 Pvmt. Profiler, 750 H.P.		5877.00		6464.70		
1 Hammermill, 250 H.P.		1846.00		2030.60		
1 Windrow Loader		1240.00		1364.00		
1 Mix Paver 165 H.P.		2183.00		2401.30		
1 Roller, Pneum. Whl., 12 Ton		349.00		383.90	179.61	197.57
64 L.H., Daily Totals		$14248.60		$17078.90	$222.63	$266.86

Crew B-73	Hr.	Daily	Hr.	Daily	Bare Costs	Incl. O&P
1 Labor Foreman (outside)	$38.65	$309.20	$63.50	$508.00	$44.56	$71.46
2 Laborers	36.65	586.40	60.20	963.20		
5 Equip. Oper. (medium)	48.90	1956.00	77.55	3102.00		
1 Road Mixer, 310 H.P.		1942.00		2136.20		
1 Tandem Roller, 10 Ton		242.00		266.20		
1 Hammermill, 250 H.P.		1846.00		2030.60		
1 Grader, 30,000 Lbs.		707.00		777.70		
.5 F.E. Loader, W.M., 1.5 C.Y.		186.70		205.37		
.5 Truck Tractor, 220 H.P.		183.20		201.52		
.5 Water Tank Trailer, 5000 Gal.		70.80		77.88	80.90	88.99
64 L.H., Daily Totals		$8029.30		$10268.67	$125.46	$160.45

Crew B-74	Hr.	Daily	Hr.	Daily	Bare Costs	Incl. O&P
1 Labor Foreman (outside)	$38.65	$309.20	$63.50	$508.00	$43.25	$69.50
1 Laborer	36.65	293.20	60.20	481.60		
4 Equip. Oper. (medium)	48.90	1564.80	77.55	2481.60		
2 Truck Drivers (heavy)	37.55	600.80	61.05	976.80		
1 Grader, 30,000 Lbs.		707.00		777.70		
1 Ripper, Beam & 1 Shank		81.40		89.54		
2 Stabilizers, 310 H.P.		3654.00		4019.40		
1 Flatbed Truck, Gas, 3 Ton		333.00		366.30		
1 Chem. Spreader, Towed		53.20		58.52		
1 Roller, Vibratory, 25 Ton		692.80		762.08		
1 Water Tank Trailer, 5000 Gal.		141.60		155.76		
1 Truck Tractor, 220 H.P.		366.40		403.04	94.21	103.63
64 L.H., Daily Totals		$8797.40		$11080.34	$137.46	$173.13

Crew B-75	Hr.	Daily	Hr.	Daily	Bare Costs	Incl. O&P
1 Labor Foreman (outside)	$38.65	$309.20	$63.50	$508.00	$44.06	$70.71
1 Laborer	36.65	293.20	60.20	481.60		
4 Equip. Oper. (medium)	48.90	1564.80	77.55	2481.60		
1 Truck Driver (heavy)	37.55	300.40	61.05	488.40		
1 Grader, 30,000 Lbs.		707.00		777.70		
1 Ripper, Beam & 1 Shank		81.40		89.54		
2 Stabilizers, 310 H.P.		3654.00		4019.40		
1 Dist. Tanker, 3000 Gallon		308.20		339.02		
1 Truck Tractor, 6x4, 380 H.P.		612.80		674.08		
1 Roller, Vibratory, 25 Ton		692.80		762.08	108.15	118.96
56 L.H., Daily Totals		$8523.80		$10621.42	$152.21	$189.67

Crew B-76	Hr.	Daily	Hr.	Daily	Bare Costs	Incl. O&P
1 Dock Builder Foreman (outside)	$46.40	$371.20	$75.90	$607.20	$45.83	$74.18
5 Dock Builders	44.40	1776.00	72.65	2906.00		
2 Equip. Oper. (crane)	50.25	804.00	79.70	1275.20		
1 Equip. Oper. (oiler)	43.55	348.40	69.05	552.40		
1 Crawler Crane, 50 Ton		1319.00		1450.90		
1 Barge, 400 Ton		781.00		859.10		
1 Hammer, Diesel, 15K ft.-lbs.		587.60		646.36		
1 Lead, 60' High		74.80		82.28		
1 Air Compressor, 600 cfm		552.60		607.86		
2 -50' Air Hoses, 3"		29.80		32.78	46.46	51.10
72 L.H., Daily Totals		$6644.40		$9020.08	$92.28	$125.28

Crew B-76A	Hr.	Daily	Hr.	Daily	Bare Costs	Incl. O&P
1 Labor Foreman (outside)	$38.65	$309.20	$63.50	$508.00	$39.46	$64.16
5 Laborers	36.65	1466.00	60.20	2408.00		
1 Equip. Oper. (crane)	50.25	402.00	79.70	637.60		
1 Equip. Oper. (oiler)	43.55	348.40	69.05	552.40		
1 Crawler Crane, 50 Ton		1319.00		1450.90		
1 Barge, 400 Ton		781.00		859.10	32.81	36.09
64 L.H., Daily Totals		$4625.60		$6416.00	$72.28	$100.25

Crew B-77	Hr.	Daily	Hr.	Daily	Bare Costs	Incl. O&P
1 Labor Foreman (outside)	$38.65	$309.20	$63.50	$508.00	$37.02	$60.69
3 Laborers	36.65	879.60	60.20	1444.80		
1 Truck Driver (light)	36.50	292.00	59.35	474.80		
1 Crack Cleaner, 25 H.P.		64.80		71.28		
1 Crack Filler, Trailer Mtd.		203.80		224.18		
1 Flatbed Truck, Gas, 3 Ton		333.00		366.30	15.04	16.54
40 L.H., Daily Totals		$2082.40		$3089.36	$52.06	$77.23

Crew B-78	Hr.	Daily	Hr.	Daily	Bare Costs	Incl. O&P
1 Labor Foreman (outside)	$38.65	$309.20	$63.50	$508.00	$36.96	$60.61
4 Laborers	36.65	1172.80	60.20	1926.40		
1 Truck Driver (light)	36.50	292.00	59.35	474.80		
1 Paint Striper, S.P., 40 Gallon		154.80		170.28		
1 Flatbed Truck, Gas, 3 Ton		333.00		366.30		
1 Pickup Truck, 3/4 Ton		157.00		172.70	13.43	14.78
48 L.H., Daily Totals		$2418.80		$3618.48	$50.39	$75.39

Crew B-78A	Hr.	Daily	Hr.	Daily	Bare Costs	Incl. O&P
1 Equip. Oper. (light)	$47.05	$376.40	$74.60	$596.80	$47.05	$74.60
1 Line Rem. (Metal Balls) 115 H.P.		839.00		922.90	104.88	115.36
8 L.H., Daily Totals		$1215.40		$1519.70	$151.93	$189.96

Crew B-78B	Hr.	Daily	Hr.	Daily	Bare Costs	Incl. O&P
2 Laborers	$36.65	$586.40	$60.20	$963.20	$37.81	$61.80
.25 Equip. Oper. (light)	47.05	94.10	74.60	149.20		
1 Pickup Truck, 3/4 Ton		157.00		172.70		
1 Line Rem.,11 H.P.,Walk Behind		68.40		75.24		
.25 Road Sweeper, S.P., 8' wide		166.35		182.99	21.76	23.94
18 L.H., Daily Totals		$1072.25		$1543.33	$59.57	$85.74

Crew B-78C	Hr.	Daily	Hr.	Daily	Bare Costs	Incl. O&P
1 Labor Foreman (outside)	$38.65	$309.20	$63.50	$508.00	$36.96	$60.61
4 Laborers	36.65	1172.80	60.20	1926.40		
1 Truck Driver (light)	36.50	292.00	59.35	474.80		
1 Paint Striper, T.M., 120 Gal.		860.40		946.44		
1 Flatbed Truck, Gas, 3 Ton		333.00		366.30		
1 Pickup Truck, 3/4 Ton		157.00		172.70	28.13	30.95
48 L.H., Daily Totals		$3124.40		$4394.64	$65.09	$91.56

Crew B-78D	Hr.	Daily	Hr.	Daily	Bare Costs	Incl. O&P
2 Labor Foremen (outside)	$38.65	$618.40	$63.50	$1016.00	$37.03	$60.77
7 Laborers	36.65	2052.40	60.20	3371.20		
1 Truck Driver (light)	36.50	292.00	59.35	474.80		
1 Paint Striper, T.M., 120 Gal.		860.40		946.44		
1 Flatbed Truck, Gas, 3 Ton		333.00		366.30		
3 Pickup Trucks, 3/4 Ton		471.00		518.10		
1 Air Compressor, 60 cfm		137.40		151.14		
1 -50' Air Hose, 3/4"		3.25		3.58		
1 Breakers, Pavement, 60 lb.		9.80		10.78	22.69	24.95
80 L.H., Daily Totals		$4777.65		$6858.34	$59.72	$85.73

Crew B-78E	Hr.	Daily	Hr.	Daily	Bare Costs	Incl. O&P
2 Labor Foremen (outside)	$38.65	$618.40	$63.50	$1016.00	$36.97	$60.68
9 Laborers	36.65	2638.80	60.20	4334.40		
1 Truck Driver (light)	36.50	292.00	59.35	474.80		
1 Paint Striper, T.M., 120 Gal.		860.40		946.44		
1 Flatbed Truck, Gas, 3 Ton		333.00		366.30		
4 Pickup Trucks, 3/4 Ton		628.00		690.80		
2 Air Compressor, 60 cfm		274.80		302.28		
2 -50' Air Hose, 3/4"		6.50		7.15		
2 Breakers, Pavement, 60 lb.		19.60		21.56	22.11	24.32
96 L.H., Daily Totals		$5671.50		$8159.73	$59.08	$85.00

Crew B-78F	Hr.	Daily	Hr.	Daily	Bare Costs	Incl. O&P
2 Labor Foremen (outside)	$38.65	$618.40	$63.50	$1016.00	$36.92	$60.61
11 Laborers	36.65	3225.20	60.20	5297.60		
1 Truck Driver (light)	36.50	292.00	59.35	474.80		
1 Paint Striper, T.M., 120 Gal.		860.40		946.44		
1 Flatbed Truck, Gas, 3 Ton		333.00		366.30		
7 Pickup Trucks, 3/4 Ton		1099.00		1208.90		
3 Air Compressor, 60 cfm		412.20		453.42		
3 -50' Air Hose, 3/4"		9.75		10.73		
3 Breakers, Pavement, 60 lb.		29.40		32.34	24.50	26.95
112 L.H., Daily Totals		$6879.35		$9806.52	$61.42	$87.56

Crew B-79	Hr.	Daily	Hr.	Daily	Bare Costs	Incl. O&P
1 Labor Foreman (outside)	$38.65	$309.20	$63.50	$508.00	$37.02	$60.69
3 Laborers	36.65	879.60	60.20	1444.80		
1 Truck Driver (light)	36.50	292.00	59.35	474.80		
1 Paint Striper, T.M., 120 Gal.		860.40		946.44		
1 Heating Kettle, 115 Gallon		63.00		69.30		
1 Flatbed Truck, Gas, 3 Ton		333.00		366.30		
2 Pickup Trucks, 3/4 Ton		314.00		345.40	39.26	43.19
40 L.H., Daily Totals		$3051.20		$4155.04	$76.28	$103.88

Crew B-79A	Hr.	Daily	Hr.	Daily	Bare Costs	Incl. O&P
1.5 Equip. Oper. (light)	$47.05	$564.60	$74.60	$895.20	$47.05	$74.60
.5 Line Remov. (Grinder) 115 H.P.		465.30		511.83		
1 Line Rem. (Metal Balls) 115 H.P.		839.00		922.90	108.69	119.56
12 L.H., Daily Totals		$1868.90		$2329.93	$155.74	$194.16

Crew B-79B	Hr.	Daily	Hr.	Daily	Bare Costs	Incl. O&P
1 Laborer	$36.65	$293.20	$60.20	$481.60	$36.65	$60.20
1 Set of Gases		152.00		167.20	19.00	20.90
8 L.H., Daily Totals		$445.20		$648.80	$55.65	$81.10

Crew B-79C	Hr.	Daily	Hr.	Daily	Bare Costs	Incl. O&P
1 Labor Foreman (outside)	$38.65	$309.20	$63.50	$508.00	$36.91	$60.55
5 Laborers	36.65	1466.00	60.20	2408.00		
1 Truck Driver (light)	36.50	292.00	59.35	474.80		
1 Paint Striper, T.M., 120 Gal.		860.40		946.44		
1 Heating Kettle, 115 Gallon		63.00		69.30		
1 Flatbed Truck, Gas, 3 Ton		333.00		366.30		
3 Pickup Trucks, 3/4 Ton		471.00		518.10		
1 Air Compressor, 60 cfm		137.40		151.14		
1 -50' Air Hose, 3/4"		3.25		3.58		
1 Breakers, Pavement, 60 lb.		9.80		10.78	33.53	36.89
56 L.H., Daily Totals		$3945.05		$5456.44	$70.45	$97.44

Crew B-79D	Hr.	Daily	Hr.	Daily	Bare Costs	Incl. O&P
2 Labor Foremen (outside)	$38.65	$618.40	$63.50	$1016.00	$37.13	$60.92
5 Laborers	36.65	1466.00	60.20	2408.00		
1 Truck Driver (light)	36.50	292.00	59.35	474.80		
1 Paint Striper, T.M., 120 Gal.		860.40		946.44		
1 Heating Kettle, 115 Gallon		63.00		69.30		
1 Flatbed Truck, Gas, 3 Ton		333.00		366.30		
4 Pickup Trucks, 3/4 Ton		628.00		690.80		
1 Air Compressor, 60 cfm		137.40		151.14		
1 -50' Air Hose, 3/4"		3.25		3.58		
1 Breakers, Pavement, 60 lb.		9.80		10.78	31.79	34.97
64 L.H., Daily Totals		$4411.25		$6137.14	$68.93	$95.89

Crew B-79E	Hr.	Daily	Hr.	Daily	Bare Costs	Incl. O&P
2 Labor Foremen (outside)	$38.65	$618.40	$63.50	$1016.00	$37.03	$60.77
7 Laborers	36.65	2052.40	60.20	3371.20		
1 Truck Driver (light)	36.50	292.00	59.35	474.80		
1 Paint Striper, T.M., 120 Gal.		860.40		946.44		
1 Heating Kettle, 115 Gallon		63.00		69.30		
1 Flatbed Truck, Gas, 3 Ton		333.00		366.30		
5 Pickup Trucks, 3/4 Ton		785.00		863.50		
2 Air Compressors, 60 cfm		274.80		302.28		
2 -50' Air Hoses, 3/4"		6.50		7.15		
2 Breakers, Pavement, 60 lb.		19.60		21.56	29.28	32.21
80 L.H., Daily Totals		$5305.10		$7438.53	$66.31	$92.98

Crew B-80	Hr.	Daily	Hr.	Daily	Bare Costs	Incl. O&P
1 Labor Foreman (outside)	$38.65	$309.20	$63.50	$508.00	$39.71	$64.41
1 Laborer	36.65	293.20	60.20	481.60		
1 Truck Driver (light)	36.50	292.00	59.35	474.80		
1 Equip. Oper. (light)	47.05	376.40	74.60	596.80		
1 Flatbed Truck, Gas, 3 Ton		333.00		366.30		
1 Earth Auger, Truck-Mtd.		425.00		467.50	23.69	26.06
32 L.H., Daily Totals		$2028.80		$2895.00	$63.40	$90.47

Crew B-80A	Hr.	Daily	Hr.	Daily	Bare Costs	Incl. O&P
3 Laborers	$36.65	$879.60	$60.20	$1444.80	$36.65	$60.20
1 Flatbed Truck, Gas, 3 Ton		333.00		366.30	13.88	15.26
24 L.H., Daily Totals		$1212.60		$1811.10	$50.52	$75.46

Crew B-80B	Hr.	Daily	Hr.	Daily	Bare Costs	Incl. O&P
3 Laborers	$36.65	$879.60	$60.20	$1444.80	$39.25	$63.80
1 Equip. Oper. (light)	47.05	376.40	74.60	596.80		
1 Crane, Flatbed Mounted, 3 Ton		248.40		273.24	7.76	8.54
32 L.H., Daily Totals		$1504.40		$2314.84	$47.01	$72.34

Crew B-80C

Crew No.	Hr.	Daily	Hr.	Daily	Bare Costs	Incl. O&P
2 Laborers	$36.65	$586.40	$60.20	$963.20	$36.60	$59.92
1 Truck Driver (light)	36.50	292.00	59.35	474.80		
1 Flatbed Truck, Gas, 1.5 Ton		270.20		297.22		
1 Manual Fence Post Auger, Gas		8.00		8.80	11.59	12.75
24 L.H., Daily Totals		$1156.60		$1744.02	$48.19	$72.67

Crew B-81

Crew No.	Hr.	Daily	Hr.	Daily	Bare Costs	Incl. O&P
1 Laborer	$36.65	$293.20	$60.20	$481.60	$41.03	$66.27
1 Equip. Oper. (medium)	48.90	391.20	77.55	620.40		
1 Truck Driver (heavy)	37.55	300.40	61.05	488.40		
1 Hydromulcher, T.M., 3000 Gal.		340.40		374.44		
1 Truck Tractor, 220 H.P.		366.40		403.04	29.45	32.40
24 L.H., Daily Totals		$1691.60		$2367.88	$70.48	$98.66

Crew B-81A

Crew No.	Hr.	Daily	Hr.	Daily	Bare Costs	Incl. O&P
1 Laborer	$36.65	$293.20	$60.20	$481.60	$36.58	$59.77
1 Truck Driver (light)	36.50	292.00	59.35	474.80		
1 Hydromulcher, T.M., 600 Gal.		132.60		145.86		
1 Flatbed Truck, Gas, 3 Ton		333.00		366.30	29.10	32.01
16 L.H., Daily Totals		$1050.80		$1468.56	$65.67	$91.78

Crew B-82

Crew No.	Hr.	Daily	Hr.	Daily	Bare Costs	Incl. O&P
1 Laborer	$36.65	$293.20	$60.20	$481.60	$41.85	$67.40
1 Equip. Oper. (light)	47.05	376.40	74.60	596.80		
1 Horiz. Borer, 6 H.P.		83.00		91.30	5.19	5.71
16 L.H., Daily Totals		$752.60		$1169.70	$47.04	$73.11

Crew B-82A

Crew No.	Hr.	Daily	Hr.	Daily	Bare Costs	Incl. O&P
1 Laborer	$36.65	$293.20	$60.20	$481.60	$41.85	$67.40
1 Equip. Oper. (light)	47.05	376.40	74.60	596.80		
1 Flatbed Truck, Gas, 3 Ton		333.00		366.30		
1 Flatbed Trailer, 25 Ton		113.60		124.96		
1 Horiz. Dir. Drill, 20k lb. Thrust		658.40		724.24	69.06	75.97
16 L.H., Daily Totals		$1774.60		$2293.90	$110.91	$143.37

Crew B-82B

Crew No.	Hr.	Daily	Hr.	Daily	Bare Costs	Incl. O&P
2 Laborers	$36.65	$586.40	$60.20	$963.20	$40.12	$65.00
1 Equip. Oper. (light)	47.05	376.40	74.60	596.80		
1 Flatbed Truck, Gas, 3 Ton		333.00		366.30		
1 Flatbed Trailer, 25 Ton		113.60		124.96		
1 Horiz. Dir. Drill, 30k lb. Thrust		936.20		1029.82	57.62	63.38
24 L.H., Daily Totals		$2345.60		$3081.08	$97.73	$128.38

Crew B-82C

Crew No.	Hr.	Daily	Hr.	Daily	Bare Costs	Incl. O&P
2 Laborers	$36.65	$586.40	$60.20	$963.20	$40.12	$65.00
1 Equip. Oper. (light)	47.05	376.40	74.60	596.80		
1 Flatbed Truck, Gas, 3 Ton		333.00		366.30		
1 Flatbed Trailer, 25 Ton		113.60		124.96		
1 Horiz. Dir. Drill, 50k lb. Thrust		1246.00		1370.60	70.53	77.58
24 L.H., Daily Totals		$2655.40		$3421.86	$110.64	$142.58

Crew B-82D

Crew No.	Hr.	Daily	Hr.	Daily	Bare Costs	Incl. O&P
1 Equip. Oper. (light)	$47.05	$376.40	$74.60	$596.80	$47.05	$74.60
1 Mud Trailer for HDD, 1500 Gal.		374.80		412.28	46.85	51.53
8 L.H., Daily Totals		$751.20		$1009.08	$93.90	$126.14

Crew B-83

Crew No.	Hr.	Daily	Hr.	Daily	Bare Costs	Incl. O&P
1 Tugboat Captain	$48.90	$391.20	$77.55	$620.40	$42.77	$68.88
1 Tugboat Hand	36.65	293.20	60.20	481.60		
1 Tugboat, 250 H.P.		889.40		978.34	55.59	61.15
16 L.H., Daily Totals		$1573.80		$2080.34	$98.36	$130.02

Crew B-84

Crew No.	Hr.	Daily	Hr.	Daily	Bare Costs	Incl. O&P
1 Equip. Oper. (medium)	$48.90	$391.20	$77.55	$620.40	$48.90	$77.55
1 Rotary Mower/Tractor		364.20		400.62	45.52	50.08
8 L.H., Daily Totals		$755.40		$1021.02	$94.42	$127.63

Crew B-85

Crew No.	Hr.	Daily	Hr.	Daily	Bare Costs	Incl. O&P
3 Laborers	$36.65	$879.60	$60.20	$1444.80	$39.28	$63.84
1 Equip. Oper. (medium)	48.90	391.20	77.55	620.40		
1 Truck Driver (heavy)	37.55	300.40	61.05	488.40		
1 Aerial Lift Truck, 80'		643.00		707.30		
1 Brush Chipper, 12", 130 H.P.		396.60		436.26		
1 Pruning Saw, Rotary		6.55		7.21	26.15	28.77
40 L.H., Daily Totals		$2617.35		$3704.36	$65.43	$92.61

Crew B-86

Crew No.	Hr.	Daily	Hr.	Daily	Bare Costs	Incl. O&P
1 Equip. Oper. (medium)	$48.90	$391.20	$77.55	$620.40	$48.90	$77.55
1 Stump Chipper, S.P.		162.10		178.31	20.26	22.29
8 L.H., Daily Totals		$553.30		$798.71	$69.16	$99.84

Crew B-86A

Crew No.	Hr.	Daily	Hr.	Daily	Bare Costs	Incl. O&P
1 Equip. Oper. (medium)	$48.90	$391.20	$77.55	$620.40	$48.90	$77.55
1 Grader, 30,000 Lbs.		707.00		777.70	88.38	97.21
8 L.H., Daily Totals		$1098.20		$1398.10	$137.28	$174.76

Crew B-86B

Crew No.	Hr.	Daily	Hr.	Daily	Bare Costs	Incl. O&P
1 Equip. Oper. (medium)	$48.90	$391.20	$77.55	$620.40	$48.90	$77.55
1 Dozer, 200 H.P.		1325.00		1457.50	165.63	182.19
8 L.H., Daily Totals		$1716.20		$2077.90	$214.53	$259.74

Crew B-87

Crew No.	Hr.	Daily	Hr.	Daily	Bare Costs	Incl. O&P
1 Laborer	$36.65	$293.20	$60.20	$481.60	$46.45	$74.08
4 Equip. Oper. (medium)	48.90	1564.80	77.55	2481.60		
2 Feller Bunchers, 100 H.P.		1458.00		1603.80		
1 Log Chipper, 22" Tree		898.60		988.46		
1 Dozer, 105 H.P.		591.80		650.98		
1 Chain Saw, Gas, 36" Long		45.00		49.50	74.83	82.32
40 L.H., Daily Totals		$4851.40		$6255.94	$121.29	$156.40

Crew B-88

Crew No.	Hr.	Daily	Hr.	Daily	Bare Costs	Incl. O&P
1 Laborer	$36.65	$293.20	$60.20	$481.60	$47.15	$75.07
6 Equip. Oper. (medium)	48.90	2347.20	77.55	3722.40		
2 Feller Bunchers, 100 H.P.		1458.00		1603.80		
1 Log Chipper, 22" Tree		898.60		988.46		
2 Log Skidders, 50 H.P.		1839.20		2023.12		
1 Dozer, 105 H.P.		591.80		650.98		
1 Chain Saw, Gas, 36" Long		45.00		49.50	86.30	94.93
56 L.H., Daily Totals		$7473.00		$9519.86	$133.45	$170.00

Crew B-89

Crew No.	Hr.	Daily	Hr.	Daily	Bare Costs	Incl. O&P
1 Equip. Oper. (light)	$47.05	$376.40	$74.60	$596.80	$41.77	$66.97
1 Truck Driver (light)	36.50	292.00	59.35	474.80		
1 Flatbed Truck, Gas, 3 Ton		333.00		366.30		
1 Concrete Saw		175.20		192.72		
1 Water Tank, 65 Gal.		17.30		19.03	32.84	36.13
16 L.H., Daily Totals		$1193.90		$1649.65	$74.62	$103.10

Crew No.	Bare Costs		Incl. Subs O&P		Cost Per Labor-Hour	
Crew B-89A	Hr.	Daily	Hr.	Daily	Bare Costs	Incl. O&P
1 Skilled Worker	$47.30	$378.40	$77.05	$616.40	$41.98	$68.63
1 Laborer	36.65	293.20	60.20	481.60		
1 Core Drill (Large)		116.20		127.82	7.26	7.99
16 L.H., Daily Totals		$787.80		$1225.82	$49.24	$76.61

Crew B-89B	Hr.	Daily	Hr.	Daily	Bare Costs	Incl. O&P
1 Equip. Oper. (light)	$47.05	$376.40	$74.60	$596.80	$41.77	$66.97
1 Truck Driver (light)	36.50	292.00	59.35	474.80		
1 Wall Saw, Hydraulic, 10 H.P.		119.60		131.56		
1 Generator, Diesel, 100 kW		439.20		483.12		
1 Water Tank, 65 Gal.		17.30		19.03		
1 Flatbed Truck, Gas, 3 Ton		333.00		366.30	56.82	62.50
16 L.H., Daily Totals		$1577.50		$2071.61	$98.59	$129.48

Crew B-90	Hr.	Daily	Hr.	Daily	Bare Costs	Incl. O&P
1 Labor Foreman (outside)	$38.65	$309.20	$63.50	$508.00	$39.73	$64.42
3 Laborers	36.65	879.60	60.20	1444.80		
2 Equip. Oper. (light)	47.05	752.80	74.60	1193.60		
2 Truck Drivers (heavy)	37.55	600.80	61.05	976.80		
1 Road Mixer, 310 H.P.		1942.00		2136.20		
1 Dist. Truck, 2000 Gal.		278.20		306.02	34.69	38.16
64 L.H., Daily Totals		$4762.60		$6565.42	$74.42	$102.58

Crew B-90A	Hr.	Daily	Hr.	Daily	Bare Costs	Incl. O&P
1 Labor Foreman (outside)	$38.65	$309.20	$63.50	$508.00	$43.94	$70.59
2 Laborers	36.65	586.40	60.20	963.20		
4 Equip. Oper. (medium)	48.90	1564.80	77.55	2481.60		
2 Graders, 30,000 Lbs.		1414.00		1555.40		
1 Tandem Roller, 10 Ton		242.00		266.20		
1 Roller, Pneum. Whl. 12 Ton		349.00		383.90	35.80	39.38
56 L.H., Daily Totals		$4465.40		$6158.30	$79.74	$109.97

Crew R-90B	Hr.	Daily	Hr.	Daily	Bare Costs	Incl. O&P
1 Labor Foreman (outside)	$38.65	$309.20	$63.50	$508.00	$43.11	$69.42
2 Laborers	36.65	586.40	60.20	963.20		
3 Equip. Oper. (medium)	48.90	1173.60	77.55	1861.20		
1 Roller, Pneum. Whl. 12 Ton		349.00		383.90		
1 Road Mixer, 310 H.P.		1942.00		2136.20	47.73	52.50
48 L.H., Daily Totals		$4360.20		$5852.50	$90.84	$121.93

Crew B-90C	Hr.	Daily	Hr.	Daily	Bare Costs	Incl. O&P
1 Labor Foreman (outside)	$38.65	$309.20	$63.50	$508.00	$40.42	$65.46
4 Laborers	36.65	1172.80	60.20	1926.40		
3 Equip. Oper. (medium)	48.90	1173.60	77.55	1861.20		
3 Truck Drivers (heavy)	37.55	901.20	61.05	1465.20		
3 Road Mixers, 310 H.P.		5826.00		6408.60	66.20	72.83
88 L.H., Daily Totals		$9382.80		$12169.40	$106.62	$138.29

Crew B-90D	Hr.	Daily	Hr.	Daily	Bare Costs	Incl. O&P
1 Labor Foreman (outside)	$38.65	$309.20	$63.50	$508.00	$39.84	$64.65
6 Laborers	36.65	1759.20	60.20	2889.60		
3 Equip. Oper. (medium)	48.90	1173.60	77.55	1861.20		
3 Truck Drivers (heavy)	37.55	901.20	61.05	1465.20		
3 Road Mixers, 310 H.P.		5826.00		6408.60	56.02	61.62
104 L.H., Daily Totals		$9969.20		$13132.60	$95.86	$126.28

Crew B-90E	Hr.	Daily	Hr.	Daily	Bare Costs	Incl. O&P
1 Labor Foreman (outside)	$38.65	$309.20	$63.50	$508.00	$41.06	$66.44
4 Laborers	36.65	1172.80	60.20	1926.40		
3 Equip. Oper. (medium)	48.90	1173.60	77.55	1861.20		
1 Truck Driver (heavy)	37.55	300.40	61.05	488.40		
1 Road Mixers, 310 H.P.		1942.00		2136.20	26.97	29.67
72 L.H., Daily Totals		$4898.00		$6920.20	$68.03	$96.11

Crew B-91	Hr.	Daily	Hr.	Daily	Bare Costs	Incl. O&P
1 Labor Foreman (outside)	$38.65	$309.20	$63.50	$508.00	$43.14	$69.39
2 Laborers	36.65	586.40	60.20	963.20		
4 Equip. Oper. (medium)	48.90	1564.80	77.55	2481.60		
1 Truck Driver (heavy)	37.55	300.40	61.05	488.40		
1 Dist. Tanker, 3000 Gallon		308.20		339.02		
1 Truck Tractor, 6x4, 380 H.P.		612.80		674.08		
1 Aggreg. Spreader, S.P.		841.00		925.10		
1 Roller, Pneum. Whl., 12 Ton		349.00		383.90		
1 Tandem Roller, 10 Ton		242.00		266.20	36.77	40.44
64 L.H., Daily Totals		$5113.80		$7029.50	$79.90	$109.84

Crew B-91B	Hr.	Daily	Hr.	Daily	Bare Costs	Incl. O&P
1 Laborer	$36.65	$293.20	$60.20	$481.60	$42.77	$68.88
1 Equipment Oper. (med.)	48.90	391.20	77.55	620.40		
1 Road Sweeper, Vac. Assist.		994.40		1093.84	62.15	68.36
16 L.H., Daily Totals		$1678.80		$2195.84	$104.93	$137.24

Crew B-91C	Hr.	Daily	Hr.	Daily	Bare Costs	Incl. O&P
1 Laborer	$36.65	$293.20	$60.20	$481.60	$36.58	$59.77
1 Truck Driver (light)	36.50	292.00	59.35	474.80		
1 Catch Basin Cleaning Truck		604.00		664.40	37.75	41.52
16 L.H., Daily Totals		$1189.20		$1620.80	$74.33	$101.30

Crew B-91D	Hr.	Daily	Hr.	Daily	Bare Costs	Incl. O&P
1 Labor Foreman (outside)	$38.65	$309.20	$63.50	$508.00	$41.65	$67.26
5 Laborers	36.65	1466.00	60.20	2408.00		
5 Equip. Oper. (medium)	48.90	1956.00	77.55	3102.00		
2 Truck Drivers (heavy)	37.55	600.80	61.05	976.80		
1 Aggreg. Spreader, S.P.		841.00		925.10		
2 Truck Tractor, 6x4, 380 H.P.		1225.60		1348.16		
2 Dist. Tanker, 3000 Gallon		616.40		678.04		
2 Pavement Brush, Towed		163.20		179.52		
2 Roller, Pneum. Whl., 12 Ton		698.00		767.80	34.08	37.49
104 L.H., Daily Totals		$7876.20		$10893.42	$75.73	$104.74

Crew B-92	Hr.	Daily	Hr.	Daily	Bare Costs	Incl. O&P
1 Labor Foreman (outside)	$38.65	$309.20	$63.50	$508.00	$37.15	$61.02
3 Laborers	36.65	879.60	60.20	1444.80		
1 Crack Cleaner, 25 H.P.		64.80		71.28		
1 Air Compressor, 60 cfm		137.40		151.14		
1 Tar Kettle, T.M.		104.60		115.06		
1 Flatbed Truck, Gas, 3 Ton		333.00		366.30	19.99	21.99
32 L.H., Daily Totals		$1828.60		$2656.58	$57.14	$83.02

Crew B-93	Hr.	Daily	Hr.	Daily	Bare Costs	Incl. O&P
1 Equip. Oper. (medium)	$48.90	$391.20	$77.55	$620.40	$48.90	$77.55
1 Feller Buncher, 100 H.P.		729.00		801.90	91.13	100.24
8 L.H., Daily Totals		$1120.20		$1422.30	$140.03	$177.79

Crew No.	Bare Costs		Incl. Subs O&P		Cost Per Labor-Hour	
	Hr.	Daily	Hr.	Daily	Bare Costs	Incl. O&P
Crew B-94A	Hr.	Daily	Hr.	Daily	Bare Costs	Incl. O&P
1 Laborer	$36.65	$293.20	$60.20	$481.60	$36.65	$60.20
1 Diaphragm Water Pump, 2"		72.00		79.20		
1 -20' Suction Hose, 2"		1.95		2.15		
2 -50' Discharge Hoses, 2"		1.80		1.98	9.47	10.42
8 L.H., Daily Totals		$368.95		$564.92	$46.12	$70.62
Crew B-94B	Hr.	Daily	Hr.	Daily	Bare Costs	Incl. O&P
1 Laborer	$36.65	$293.20	$60.20	$481.60	$36.65	$60.20
1 Diaphragm Water Pump, 4"		115.80		127.38		
1 -20' Suction Hose, 4"		3.25		3.58		
2 -50' Discharge Hoses, 4"		4.70		5.17	15.47	17.02
8 L.H., Daily Totals		$416.95		$617.73	$52.12	$77.22
Crew B-94C	Hr.	Daily	Hr.	Daily	Bare Costs	Incl. O&P
1 Laborer	$36.65	$293.20	$60.20	$481.60	$36.65	$60.20
1 Centrifugal Water Pump, 3"		78.80		86.68		
1 -20' Suction Hose, 3"		2.85		3.13		
2 -50' Discharge Hoses, 3"		3.00		3.30	10.58	11.64
8 L.H., Daily Totals		$377.85		$574.72	$47.23	$71.84
Crew B-94D	Hr.	Daily	Hr.	Daily	Bare Costs	Incl. O&P
1 Laborer	$36.65	$293.20	$60.20	$481.60	$36.65	$60.20
1 Centr. Water Pump, 6"		340.80		374.88		
1 -20' Suction Hose, 6"		11.50		12.65		
2 -50' Discharge Hoses, 6"		12.20		13.42	45.56	50.12
8 L.H., Daily Totals		$657.70		$882.55	$82.21	$110.32
Crew C-1	Hr.	Daily	Hr.	Daily	Bare Costs	Incl. O&P
3 Carpenters	$45.85	$1100.40	$75.35	$1808.40	$43.55	$71.56
1 Laborer	36.65	293.20	60.20	481.60		
32 L.H., Daily Totals		$1393.60		$2290.00	$43.55	$71.56
Crew C-2	Hr.	Daily	Hr.	Daily	Bare Costs	Incl. O&P
1 Carpenter Foreman (outside)	$47.85	$382.80	$78.60	$628.80	$44.65	$73.37
4 Carpenters	45.85	1467.20	75.35	2411.20		
1 Laborer	36.65	293.20	60.20	481.60		
48 L.H., Daily Totals		$2143.20		$3521.60	$44.65	$73.37
Crew C-2A	Hr.	Daily	Hr.	Daily	Bare Costs	Incl. O&P
1 Carpenter Foreman (outside)	$47.85	$382.80	$78.60	$628.80	$44.35	$72.39
3 Carpenters	45.85	1100.40	75.35	1808.40		
1 Cement Finisher	44.05	352.40	69.50	556.00		
1 Laborer	36.65	293.20	60.20	481.60		
48 L.H., Daily Totals		$2128.80		$3474.80	$44.35	$72.39
Crew C-3	Hr.	Daily	Hr.	Daily	Bare Costs	Incl. O&P
1 Rodman Foreman (outside)	$52.65	$421.20	$86.40	$691.20	$46.95	$76.72
4 Rodmen (reinf.)	50.65	1620.80	83.10	2659.20		
1 Equip. Oper. (light)	47.05	376.40	74.60	596.80		
2 Laborers	36.65	586.40	60.20	963.20		
3 Stressing Equipment		30.60		33.66		
.5 Grouting Equipment		82.10		90.31	1.76	1.94
64 L.H., Daily Totals		$3117.50		$5034.37	$48.71	$78.66
Crew C-4	Hr.	Daily	Hr.	Daily	Bare Costs	Incl. O&P
1 Rodman Foreman (outside)	$52.65	$421.20	$86.40	$691.20	$51.15	$83.92
3 Rodmen (reinf.)	50.65	1215.60	83.10	1994.40		
3 Stressing Equipment		30.60		33.66	.96	1.05
32 L.H., Daily Totals		$1667.40		$2719.26	$52.11	$84.98
Crew C-4A	Hr.	Daily	Hr.	Daily	Bare Costs	Incl. O&P
2 Rodmen (reinf.)	$50.65	$810.40	$83.10	$1329.60	$50.65	$83.10
4 Stressing Equipment		40.80		44.88	2.55	2.81
16 L.H., Daily Totals		$851.20		$1374.48	$53.20	$85.91
Crew C-5	Hr.	Daily	Hr.	Daily	Bare Costs	Incl. O&P
1 Rodman Foreman (outside)	$52.65	$421.20	$86.40	$691.20	$49.86	$81.08
4 Rodmen (reinf.)	50.65	1620.80	83.10	2659.20		
1 Equip. Oper. (crane)	50.25	402.00	79.70	637.60		
1 Equip. Oper. (oiler)	43.55	348.40	69.05	552.40		
1 Hyd. Crane, 25 Ton		745.80		820.38	13.32	14.65
56 L.H., Daily Totals		$3538.20		$5360.78	$63.18	$95.73
Crew C-6	Hr.	Daily	Hr.	Daily	Bare Costs	Incl. O&P
1 Labor Foreman (outside)	$38.65	$309.20	$63.50	$508.00	$38.22	$62.30
4 Laborers	36.65	1172.80	60.20	1926.40		
1 Cement Finisher	44.05	352.40	69.50	556.00		
2 Gas Engine Vibrators		66.00		72.60	1.38	1.51
48 L.H., Daily Totals		$1900.40		$3063.00	$39.59	$63.81
Crew C-7	Hr.	Daily	Hr.	Daily	Bare Costs	Incl. O&P
1 Labor Foreman (outside)	$38.65	$309.20	$63.50	$508.00	$39.82	$64.51
5 Laborers	36.65	1466.00	60.20	2408.00		
1 Cement Finisher	44.05	352.40	69.50	556.00		
1 Equip. Oper. (medium)	48.90	391.20	77.55	620.40		
1 Equip. Oper. (oiler)	43.55	348.40	69.05	552.40		
2 Gas Engine Vibrators		66.00		72.60		
1 Concrete Bucket, 1 C.Y.		23.00		25.30		
1 Hyd. Crane, 55 Ton		1137.00		1250.70	17.03	18.73
72 L.H., Daily Totals		$4093.20		$5993.40	$56.85	$83.24
Crew C-8	Hr.	Daily	Hr.	Daily	Bare Costs	Incl. O&P
1 Labor Foreman (outside)	$38.65	$309.20	$63.50	$508.00	$40.80	$65.81
3 Laborers	36.65	879.60	60.20	1444.80		
2 Cement Finishers	44.05	704.80	69.50	1112.00		
1 Equip. Oper. (medium)	48.90	391.20	77.55	620.40		
1 Concrete Pump (Small)		710.40		781.44	12.69	13.95
56 L.H., Daily Totals		$2995.20		$4466.64	$53.49	$79.76
Crew C-8A	Hr.	Daily	Hr.	Daily	Bare Costs	Incl. O&P
1 Labor Foreman (outside)	$38.65	$309.20	$63.50	$508.00	$39.45	$63.85
3 Laborers	36.65	879.60	60.20	1444.80		
2 Cement Finishers	44.05	704.80	69.50	1112.00		
48 L.H., Daily Totals		$1893.60		$3064.80	$39.45	$63.85
Crew C-8B	Hr.	Daily	Hr.	Daily	Bare Costs	Incl. O&P
1 Labor Foreman (outside)	$38.65	$309.20	$63.50	$508.00	$39.50	$64.33
3 Laborers	36.65	879.60	60.20	1444.80		
1 Equip. Oper. (medium)	48.90	391.20	77.55	620.40		
1 Vibrating Power Screed		63.25		69.58		
1 Roller, Vibratory, 25 Ton		692.80		762.08		
1 Dozer, 200 H.P.		1325.00		1457.50	52.03	57.23
40 L.H., Daily Totals		$3661.05		$4862.35	$91.53	$121.56

Crew No.	Bare Costs Hr.	Daily	Incl. Subs O&P Hr.	Daily	Cost Per Labor-Hour Bare Costs	Incl. O&P
Crew C-8C	**Hr.**	**Daily**	**Hr.**	**Daily**	**Bare Costs**	**Incl. O&P**
1 Labor Foreman (outside)	$38.65	$309.20	$63.50	$508.00	$40.26	$65.19
3 Laborers	36.65	879.60	60.20	1444.80		
1 Cement Finisher	44.05	352.40	69.50	556.00		
1 Equip. Oper. (medium)	48.90	391.20	77.55	620.40		
1 Shotcrete Rig, 12 C.Y./hr		252.80		278.08		
1 Air Compressor, 160 cfm		157.40		173.14		
4 -50' Air Hoses, 1"		16.40		18.04		
4 -50' Air Hoses, 2"		31.00		34.10	9.53	10.49
48 L.H., Daily Totals		$2390.00		$3632.56	$49.79	$75.68
Crew C-8D	**Hr.**	**Daily**	**Hr.**	**Daily**	**Bare Costs**	**Incl. O&P**
1 Labor Foreman (outside)	$38.65	$309.20	$63.50	$508.00	$41.60	$66.95
1 Laborer	36.65	293.20	60.20	481.60		
1 Cement Finisher	44.05	352.40	69.50	556.00		
1 Equipment Oper. (light)	47.05	376.40	74.60	596.80		
1 Air Compressor, 250 cfm		202.40		222.64		
2 -50' Air Hoses, 1"		8.20		9.02	6.58	7.24
32 L.H., Daily Totals		$1541.80		$2374.06	$48.18	$74.19
Crew C-8E	**Hr.**	**Daily**	**Hr.**	**Daily**	**Bare Costs**	**Incl. O&P**
1 Labor Foreman (outside)	$38.65	$309.20	$63.50	$508.00	$39.95	$64.70
3 Laborers	36.65	879.60	60.20	1444.80		
1 Cement Finisher	44.05	352.40	69.50	556.00		
1 Equipment Oper. (light)	47.05	376.40	74.60	596.80		
1 Shotcrete Rig, 35 C.Y./hr		284.40		312.84		
1 Air Compressor, 250 cfm		202.40		222.64		
4 -50' Air Hoses, 1"		16.40		18.04		
4 -50' Air Hoses, 2"		31.00		34.10	11.13	12.24
48 L.H., Daily Totals		$2451.80		$3693.22	$51.08	$76.94
Crew C-10	**Hr.**	**Daily**	**Hr.**	**Daily**	**Bare Costs**	**Incl. O&P**
1 Laborer	$36.65	$293.20	$60.20	$481.60	$41.58	$66.40
2 Cement Finishers	44.05	704.80	69.50	1112.00		
24 L.H., Daily Totals		$998.00		$1593.60	$41.58	$66.40
Crew C-10B	**Hr.**	**Daily**	**Hr.**	**Daily**	**Bare Costs**	**Incl. O&P**
3 Laborers	$36.65	$879.60	$60.20	$1444.80	$39.61	$63.92
2 Cement Finishers	44.05	704.80	69.50	1112.00		
1 Concrete Mixer, 10 C.F.		176.80		194.48		
2 Trowels, 48" Walk-Behind		107.20		117.92	7.10	7.81
40 L.H., Daily Totals		$1868.40		$2869.20	$46.71	$71.73
Crew C-10C	**Hr.**	**Daily**	**Hr.**	**Daily**	**Bare Costs**	**Incl. O&P**
1 Laborer	$36.65	$293.20	$60.20	$481.60	$41.58	$66.40
2 Cement Finishers	44.05	704.80	69.50	1112.00		
1 Trowel, 48" Walk-Behind		53.60		58.96	2.23	2.46
24 L.H., Daily Totals		$1051.60		$1652.56	$43.82	$68.86
Crew C-10D	**Hr.**	**Daily**	**Hr.**	**Daily**	**Bare Costs**	**Incl. O&P**
1 Laborer	$36.65	$293.20	$60.20	$481.60	$41.58	$66.40
2 Cement Finishers	44.05	704.80	69.50	1112.00		
1 Vibrating Power Screed		63.25		69.58		
1 Trowel, 48" Walk-Behind		53.60		58.96	4.87	5.36
24 L.H., Daily Totals		$1114.85		$1722.14	$46.45	$71.76
Crew C-10E	**Hr.**	**Daily**	**Hr.**	**Daily**	**Bare Costs**	**Incl. O&P**
1 Laborer	$36.65	$293.20	$60.20	$481.60	$41.58	$66.40
2 Cement Finishers	44.05	704.80	69.50	1112.00		
1 Vibrating Power Screed		63.25		69.58		
1 Cement Trowel, 96" Ride-On		197.40		217.14	10.86	11.95
24 L.H., Daily Totals		$1258.65		$1880.32	$52.44	$78.35

Crew No.	Bare Costs Hr.	Daily	Incl. Subs O&P Hr.	Daily	Cost Per Labor-Hour Bare Costs	Incl. O&P
Crew C-10F	**Hr.**	**Daily**	**Hr.**	**Daily**	**Bare Costs**	**Incl. O&P**
1 Laborer	$36.65	$293.20	$60.20	$481.60	$41.58	$66.40
2 Cement Finishers	44.05	704.80	69.50	1112.00		
1 Aerial Lift Truck, 60' Boom		456.00		501.60	19.00	20.90
24 L.H., Daily Totals		$1454.00		$2095.20	$60.58	$87.30
Crew C-11	**Hr.**	**Daily**	**Hr.**	**Daily**	**Bare Costs**	**Incl. O&P**
1 Struc. Steel Foreman (outside)	$53.10	$424.80	$97.45	$779.60	$50.39	$89.86
6 Struc. Steel Workers	51.10	2452.80	93.75	4500.00		
1 Equip. Oper. (crane)	50.25	402.00	79.70	637.60		
1 Equip. Oper. (oiler)	43.55	348.40	69.05	552.40		
1 Lattice Boom Crane, 150 Ton		1838.00		2021.80	25.53	28.08
72 L.H., Daily Totals		$5466.00		$8491.40	$75.92	$117.94
Crew C-12	**Hr.**	**Daily**	**Hr.**	**Daily**	**Bare Costs**	**Incl. O&P**
1 Carpenter Foreman (outside)	$47.85	$382.80	$78.60	$628.80	$45.38	$74.09
3 Carpenters	45.85	1100.40	75.35	1808.40		
1 Laborer	36.65	293.20	60.20	481.60		
1 Equip. Oper. (crane)	50.25	402.00	79.70	637.60		
1 Hyd. Crane, 12 Ton		663.00		729.30	13.81	15.19
48 L.H., Daily Totals		$2841.40		$4285.70	$59.20	$89.29
Crew C-13	**Hr.**	**Daily**	**Hr.**	**Daily**	**Bare Costs**	**Incl. O&P**
1 Struc. Steel Worker	$51.10	$408.80	$93.75	$750.00	$49.35	$87.62
1 Welder	51.10	408.80	93.75	750.00		
1 Carpenter	45.85	366.80	75.35	602.80		
1 Welder, Gas Engine, 300 amp		142.00		156.20	5.92	6.51
24 L.H., Daily Totals		$1326.40		$2259.00	$55.27	$94.13
Crew C-14	**Hr.**	**Daily**	**Hr.**	**Daily**	**Bare Costs**	**Incl. O&P**
1 Carpenter Foreman (outside)	$47.85	$382.80	$78.60	$628.80	$44.90	$73.13
5 Carpenters	45.85	1834.00	75.35	3014.00		
4 Laborers	36.65	1172.80	60.20	1926.40		
4 Rodmen (reinf.)	50.65	1620.80	83.10	2659.20		
2 Cement Finishers	44.05	704.80	69.50	1112.00		
1 Equip. Oper. (crane)	50.25	402.00	79.70	637.60		
1 Equip. Oper. (oiler)	43.55	348.40	69.05	552.40		
1 Hyd. Crane, 80 Ton		1652.00		1817.20	11.47	12.62
144 L.H., Daily Totals		$8117.60		$12347.60	$56.37	$85.75
Crew C-14A	**Hr.**	**Daily**	**Hr.**	**Daily**	**Bare Costs**	**Incl. O&P**
1 Carpenter Foreman (outside)	$47.85	$382.80	$78.60	$628.80	$46.01	$75.36
16 Carpenters	45.85	5868.80	75.35	9644.80		
4 Rodmen (reinf.)	50.65	1620.80	83.10	2659.20		
2 Laborers	36.65	586.40	60.20	963.20		
1 Cement Finisher	44.05	352.40	69.50	556.00		
1 Equip. Oper. (medium)	48.90	391.20	77.55	620.40		
1 Gas Engine Vibrator		33.00		36.30		
1 Concrete Pump (Small)		710.40		781.44	3.72	4.09
200 L.H., Daily Totals		$9945.80		$15890.14	$49.73	$79.45
Crew C-14B	**Hr.**	**Daily**	**Hr.**	**Daily**	**Bare Costs**	**Incl. O&P**
1 Carpenter Foreman (outside)	$47.85	$382.80	$78.60	$628.80	$45.94	$75.14
16 Carpenters	45.85	5868.80	75.35	9644.80		
4 Rodmen (reinf.)	50.65	1620.80	83.10	2659.20		
2 Laborers	36.65	586.40	60.20	963.20		
2 Cement Finishers	44.05	704.80	69.50	1112.00		
1 Equip. Oper. (medium)	48.90	391.20	77.55	620.40		
1 Gas Engine Vibrator		33.00		36.30		
1 Concrete Pump (Small)		710.40		781.44	3.57	3.93
208 L.H., Daily Totals		$10298.20		$16446.14	$49.51	$79.07

Crew No.	Bare Costs		Incl. Subs O&P		Cost Per Labor-Hour	

Crew C-14C	Hr.	Daily	Hr.	Daily	Bare Costs	Incl. O&P
1 Carpenter Foreman (outside)	$47.85	$382.80	$78.60	$628.80	$43.92	$71.94
6 Carpenters	45.85	2200.80	75.35	3616.80		
2 Rodmen (reinf.)	50.65	810.40	83.10	1329.60		
4 Laborers	36.65	1172.80	60.20	1926.40		
1 Cement Finisher	44.05	352.40	69.50	556.00		
1 Gas Engine Vibrator		33.00		36.30	.29	.32
112 L.H., Daily Totals		$4952.20		$8093.90	$44.22	$72.27

Crew C-14D	Hr.	Daily	Hr.	Daily	Bare Costs	Incl. O&P
1 Carpenter Foreman (outside)	$47.85	$382.80	$78.60	$628.80	$45.63	$74.74
18 Carpenters	45.85	6602.40	75.35	10850.40		
2 Rodmen (reinf.)	50.65	810.40	83.10	1329.60		
2 Laborers	36.65	586.40	60.20	963.20		
1 Cement Finisher	44.05	352.40	69.50	556.00		
1 Equip. Oper. (medium)	48.90	391.20	77.55	620.40		
1 Gas Engine Vibrator		33.00		36.30		
1 Concrete Pump (Small)		710.40		781.44	3.72	4.09
200 L.H., Daily Totals		$9869.00		$15766.14	$49.34	$78.83

Crew C-14E	Hr.	Daily	Hr.	Daily	Bare Costs	Incl. O&P
1 Carpenter Foreman (outside)	$47.85	$382.80	$78.60	$628.80	$45.10	$73.80
2 Carpenters	45.85	733.60	75.35	1205.60		
4 Rodmen (reinf.)	50.65	1620.80	83.10	2659.20		
3 Laborers	36.65	879.60	60.20	1444.80		
1 Cement Finisher	44.05	352.40	69.50	556.00		
1 Gas Engine Vibrator		33.00		36.30	.38	.41
88 L.H., Daily Totals		$4002.20		$6530.70	$45.48	$74.21

Crew C-14F	Hr.	Daily	Hr.	Daily	Bare Costs	Incl. O&P
1 Labor Foreman (outside)	$38.65	$309.20	$63.50	$508.00	$41.81	$66.77
2 Laborers	36.65	586.40	60.20	963.20		
6 Cement Finishers	44.05	2114.40	69.50	3336.00		
1 Gas Engine Vibrator		33.00		36.30	.46	.50
72 L.H., Daily Totals		$3043.00		$4843.50	$42.26	$67.27

Crew C-14G	Hr.	Daily	Hr.	Daily	Bare Costs	Incl. O&P
1 Labor Foreman (outside)	$38.65	$309.20	$63.50	$508.00	$41.16	$65.99
2 Laborers	36.65	586.40	60.20	963.20		
4 Cement Finishers	44.05	1409.60	69.50	2224.00		
1 Gas Engine Vibrator		33.00		36.30	.59	.65
56 L.H., Daily Totals		$2338.20		$3731.50	$41.75	$66.63

Crew C-14H	Hr.	Daily	Hr.	Daily	Bare Costs	Incl. O&P
1 Carpenter Foreman (outside)	$47.85	$382.80	$78.60	$628.80	$45.15	$73.68
2 Carpenters	45.85	733.60	75.35	1205.60		
1 Rodman (reinf.)	50.65	405.20	83.10	664.80		
1 Laborer	36.65	293.20	60.20	481.60		
1 Cement Finisher	44.05	352.40	69.50	556.00		
1 Gas Engine Vibrator		33.00		36.30	.69	.76
48 L.H., Daily Totals		$2200.20		$3573.10	$45.84	$74.44

Crew C-14L	Hr.	Daily	Hr.	Daily	Bare Costs	Incl. O&P
1 Carpenter Foreman (outside)	$47.85	$382.80	$78.60	$628.80	$42.80	$70.08
6 Carpenters	45.85	2200.80	75.35	3616.80		
4 Laborers	36.65	1172.80	60.20	1926.40		
1 Cement Finisher	44.05	352.40	69.50	556.00		
1 Gas Engine Vibrator		33.00		36.30	.34	.38
96 L.H., Daily Totals		$4141.80		$6764.30	$43.14	$70.46

Crew C-14M	Hr.	Daily	Hr.	Daily	Bare Costs	Incl. O&P
1 Carpenter Foreman (outside)	$47.85	$382.80	$78.60	$628.80	$44.56	$72.48
2 Carpenters	45.85	733.60	75.35	1205.60		
1 Rodman (reinf.)	50.65	405.20	83.10	664.80		
2 Laborers	36.65	586.40	60.20	963.20		
1 Cement Finisher	44.05	352.40	69.50	556.00		
1 Equip. Oper. (medium)	48.90	391.20	77.55	620.40		
1 Gas Engine Vibrator		33.00		36.30		
1 Concrete Pump (Small)		710.40		781.44	11.62	12.78
64 L.H., Daily Totals		$3595.00		$5456.54	$56.17	$85.26

Crew C-15	Hr.	Daily	Hr.	Daily	Bare Costs	Incl. O&P
1 Carpenter Foreman (outside)	$47.85	$382.80	$78.60	$628.80	$43.14	$70.22
2 Carpenters	45.85	733.60	75.35	1205.60		
3 Laborers	36.65	879.60	60.20	1444.80		
2 Cement Finishers	44.05	704.80	69.50	1112.00		
1 Rodman (reinf.)	50.65	405.20	83.10	664.80		
72 L.H., Daily Totals		$3106.00		$5056.00	$43.14	$70.22

Crew C-16	Hr.	Daily	Hr.	Daily	Bare Costs	Incl. O&P
1 Labor Foreman (outside)	$38.65	$309.20	$63.50	$508.00	$40.80	$65.81
3 Laborers	36.65	879.60	60.20	1444.80		
2 Cement Finishers	44.05	704.80	69.50	1112.00		
1 Equip. Oper. (medium)	48.90	391.20	77.55	620.40		
1 Gunite Pump Rig		370.40		407.44		
2 -50' Air Hoses, 3/4"		6.50		7.15		
2 -50' Air Hoses, 2"		15.50		17.05	7.01	7.71
56 L.H., Daily Totals		$2677.20		$4116.84	$47.81	$73.52

Crew C-16A	Hr.	Daily	Hr.	Daily	Bare Costs	Incl. O&P
1 Laborer	$36.65	$293.20	$60.20	$481.60	$43.41	$69.19
2 Cement Finishers	44.05	704.80	69.50	1112.00		
1 Equip. Oper. (medium)	48.90	391.20	77.55	620.40		
1 Gunite Pump Rig		370.40		407.44		
2 -50' Air Hoses, 3/4"		6.50		7.15		
2 -50' Air Hoses, 2"		15.50		17.05		
1 Aerial Lift Truck, 60' Boom		456.00		501.60	26.51	29.16
32 L.H., Daily Totals		$2237.60		$3147.24	$69.92	$98.35

Crew C-17	Hr.	Daily	Hr.	Daily	Bare Costs	Incl. O&P
2 Skilled Worker Foremen (out)	$49.30	$788.80	$80.30	$1284.80	$47.70	$77.70
8 Skilled Workers	47.30	3027.20	77.05	4931.20		
80 L.H., Daily Totals		$3816.00		$6216.00	$47.70	$77.70

Crew C-17A	Hr.	Daily	Hr.	Daily	Bare Costs	Incl. O&P
2 Skilled Worker Foremen (out)	$49.30	$788.80	$80.30	$1284.80	$47.73	$77.72
8 Skilled Workers	47.30	3027.20	77.05	4931.20		
.125 Equip. Oper. (crane)	50.25	50.25	79.70	79.70		
.125 Hyd. Crane, 80 Ton		206.50		227.15	2.55	2.80
81 L.H., Daily Totals		$4072.75		$6522.85	$50.28	$80.53

Crew C-17B	Hr.	Daily	Hr.	Daily	Bare Costs	Incl. O&P
2 Skilled Worker Foremen (out)	$49.30	$788.80	$80.30	$1284.80	$47.76	$77.75
8 Skilled Workers	47.30	3027.20	77.05	4931.20		
.25 Equip. Oper. (crane)	50.25	100.50	79.70	159.40		
.25 Hyd. Crane, 80 Ton		413.00		454.30		
.25 Trowel, 48" Walk-Behind		13.40		14.74	5.20	5.72
82 L.H., Daily Totals		$4342.90		$6844.44	$52.96	$83.47

Crew No.	Bare Costs Hr.	Daily	Incl. Subs O&P Hr.	Daily	Cost Per Labor-Hour Bare Costs	Incl. O&P
Crew C-17C	Hr.	Daily	Hr.	Daily	Bare Costs	Incl. O&P
2 Skilled Worker Foremen (out)	$49.30	$788.80	$80.30	$1284.80	$47.79	$77.77
8 Skilled Workers	47.30	3027.20	77.05	4931.20		
.375 Equip. Oper. (crane)	50.25	150.75	79.70	239.10		
.375 Hyd. Crane, 80 Ton		619.50		681.45	7.46	8.21
83 L.H., Daily Totals		$4586.25		$7136.55	$55.26	$85.98
Crew C-17D	Hr.	Daily	Hr.	Daily	Bare Costs	Incl. O&P
2 Skilled Worker Foremen (out)	$49.30	$788.80	$80.30	$1284.80	$47.82	$77.80
8 Skilled Workers	47.30	3027.20	77.05	4931.20		
.5 Equip. Oper. (crane)	50.25	201.00	79.70	318.80		
.5 Hyd. Crane, 80 Ton		826.00		908.60	9.83	10.82
84 L.H., Daily Totals		$4843.00		$7443.40	$57.65	$88.61
Crew C-17E	Hr.	Daily	Hr.	Daily	Bare Costs	Incl. O&P
2 Skilled Worker Foremen (out)	$49.30	$788.80	$80.30	$1284.80	$47.70	$77.70
8 Skilled Workers	47.30	3027.20	77.05	4931.20		
1 Hyd. Jack with Rods		94.55		104.01	1.18	1.30
80 L.H., Daily Totals		$3910.55		$6320.01	$48.88	$79.00
Crew C-18	Hr.	Daily	Hr.	Daily	Bare Costs	Incl. O&P
.125 Labor Foreman (outside)	$38.65	$38.65	$63.50	$63.50	$36.87	$60.57
1 Laborer	36.65	293.20	60.20	481.60		
1 Concrete Cart, 10 C.F.		60.20		66.22	6.69	7.36
9 L.H., Daily Totals		$392.05		$611.32	$43.56	$67.92
Crew C-19	Hr.	Daily	Hr.	Daily	Bare Costs	Incl. O&P
.125 Labor Foreman (outside)	$38.65	$38.65	$63.50	$63.50	$36.87	$60.57
1 Laborer	36.65	293.20	60.20	481.60		
1 Concrete Cart, 18 C.F.		101.20		111.32	11.24	12.37
9 L.H., Daily Totals		$433.05		$656.42	$48.12	$72.94
Crew C-20	Hr.	Daily	Hr.	Daily	Bare Costs	Incl. O&P
1 Labor Foreman (outside)	$38.65	$309.20	$63.50	$508.00	$39.36	$63.94
5 Laborers	36.65	1466.00	60.20	2408.00		
1 Cement Finisher	44.05	352.40	69.50	556.00		
1 Equip. Oper. (medium)	48.90	391.20	77.55	620.40		
2 Gas Engine Vibrators		66.00		72.60		
1 Concrete Pump (Small)		710.40		781.44	12.13	13.34
64 L.H., Daily Totals		$3295.20		$4946.44	$51.49	$77.29
Crew C-21	Hr.	Daily	Hr.	Daily	Bare Costs	Incl. O&P
1 Labor Foreman (outside)	$38.65	$309.20	$63.50	$508.00	$39.36	$63.94
5 Laborers	36.65	1466.00	60.20	2408.00		
1 Cement Finisher	44.05	352.40	69.50	556.00		
1 Equip. Oper. (medium)	48.90	391.20	77.55	620.40		
2 Gas Engine Vibrators		66.00		72.60		
1 Concrete Conveyer		205.40		225.94	4.24	4.66
64 L.H., Daily Totals		$2790.20		$4390.94	$43.60	$68.61
Crew C-22	Hr.	Daily	Hr.	Daily	Bare Costs	Incl. O&P
1 Rodman Foreman (outside)	$52.65	$421.20	$86.40	$691.20	$50.85	$83.31
4 Rodmen (reinf.)	50.65	1620.80	83.10	2659.20		
.125 Equip. Oper. (crane)	50.25	50.25	79.70	79.70		
.125 Equip. Oper. (oiler)	43.55	43.55	69.05	69.05		
.125 Hyd. Crane, 25 Ton		93.22		102.55	2.22	2.44
42 L.H., Daily Totals		$2229.03		$3601.70	$53.07	$85.75

Crew No.	Bare Costs Hr.	Daily	Incl. Subs O&P Hr.	Daily	Cost Per Labor-Hour Bare Costs	Incl. O&P
Crew C-23	Hr.	Daily	Hr.	Daily	Bare Costs	Incl. O&P
2 Skilled Worker Foremen (out)	$49.30	$788.80	$80.30	$1284.80	$47.62	$77.17
6 Skilled Workers	47.30	2270.40	77.05	3698.40		
1 Equip. Oper. (crane)	50.25	402.00	79.70	637.60		
1 Equip. Oper. (oiler)	43.55	348.40	69.05	552.40		
1 Lattice Boom Crane, 90 Ton		1529.00		1681.90	19.11	21.02
80 L.H., Daily Totals		$5338.60		$7855.10	$66.73	$98.19
Crew C-24	Hr.	Daily	Hr.	Daily	Bare Costs	Incl. O&P
2 Skilled Worker Foremen (out)	$49.30	$788.80	$80.30	$1284.80	$47.62	$77.17
6 Skilled Workers	47.30	2270.40	77.05	3698.40		
1 Equip. Oper. (crane)	50.25	402.00	79.70	637.60		
1 Equip. Oper. (oiler)	43.55	348.40	69.05	552.40		
1 Lattice Boom Crane, 150 Ton		1838.00		2021.80	22.98	25.27
80 L.H., Daily Totals		$5647.60		$8195.00	$70.59	$102.44
Crew C-25	Hr.	Daily	Hr.	Daily	Bare Costs	Incl. O&P
2 Rodmen (reinf.)	$50.65	$810.40	$83.10	$1329.60	$39.90	$67.83
2 Rodmen Helpers	29.15	466.40	52.55	840.80		
32 L.H., Daily Totals		$1276.80		$2170.40	$39.90	$67.83
Crew C-27	Hr.	Daily	Hr.	Daily	Bare Costs	Incl. O&P
2 Cement Finishers	$44.05	$704.80	$69.50	$1112.00	$44.05	$69.50
1 Concrete Saw		175.20		192.72	10.95	12.05
16 L.H., Daily Totals		$880.00		$1304.72	$55.00	$81.55
Crew C-28	Hr.	Daily	Hr.	Daily	Bare Costs	Incl. O&P
1 Cement Finisher	$44.05	$352.40	$69.50	$556.00	$44.05	$69.50
1 Portable Air Compressor, Gas		17.70		19.47	2.21	2.43
8 L.H., Daily Totals		$370.10		$575.47	$46.26	$71.93
Crew C-29	Hr.	Daily	Hr.	Daily	Bare Costs	Incl. O&P
1 Laborer	$36.65	$293.20	$60.20	$481.60	$36.65	$60.20
1 Pressure Washer		69.40		76.34	8.68	9.54
8 L.H., Daily Totals		$362.60		$557.94	$45.33	$69.74
Crew C-30	Hr.	Daily	Hr.	Daily	Bare Costs	Incl. O&P
1 Laborer	$36.65	$293.20	$60.20	$481.60	$36.65	$60.20
1 Concrete Mixer, 10 C.F.		176.80		194.48	22.10	24.31
8 L.H., Daily Totals		$470.00		$676.08	$58.75	$84.51
Crew C-31	Hr.	Daily	Hr.	Daily	Bare Costs	Incl. O&P
1 Cement Finisher	$44.05	$352.40	$69.50	$556.00	$44.05	$69.50
1 Grout Pump		370.40		407.44	46.30	50.93
8 L.H., Daily Totals		$722.80		$963.44	$90.35	$120.43
Crew C-32	Hr.	Daily	Hr.	Daily	Bare Costs	Incl. O&P
1 Cement Finisher	$44.05	$352.40	$69.50	$556.00	$40.35	$64.85
1 Laborer	36.65	293.20	60.20	481.60		
1 Crack Chaser Saw, Gas, 6 H.P.		30.80		33.88		
1 Vacuum Pick-Up System		60.75		66.83	5.72	6.29
16 L.H., Daily Totals		$737.15		$1138.31	$46.07	$71.14
Crew D-1	Hr.	Daily	Hr.	Daily	Bare Costs	Incl. O&P
1 Bricklayer	$45.60	$364.80	$74.05	$592.40	$41.30	$67.08
1 Bricklayer Helper	37.00	296.00	60.10	480.80		
16 L.H., Daily Totals		$660.80		$1073.20	$41.30	$67.08

Crew No.	Bare Costs		Incl. Subs O&P		Cost Per Labor-Hour	
Crew D-2	Hr.	Daily	Hr.	Daily	Bare Costs	Incl. O&P
3 Bricklayers	$45.60	$1094.40	$74.05	$1777.20	$42.50	$69.10
2 Bricklayer Helpers	37.00	592.00	60.10	961.60		
.5 Carpenter	45.85	183.40	75.35	301.40		
44 L.H., Daily Totals		$1869.80		$3040.20	$42.50	$69.10
Crew D-3	Hr.	Daily	Hr.	Daily	Bare Costs	Incl. O&P
3 Bricklayers	$45.60	$1094.40	$74.05	$1777.20	$42.34	$68.80
2 Bricklayer Helpers	37.00	592.00	60.10	961.60		
.25 Carpenter	45.85	91.70	75.35	150.70		
42 L.H., Daily Totals		$1778.10		$2889.50	$42.34	$68.80
Crew D-4	Hr.	Daily	Hr.	Daily	Bare Costs	Incl. O&P
1 Bricklayer	$45.60	$364.80	$74.05	$592.40	$41.66	$67.21
2 Bricklayer Helpers	37.00	592.00	60.10	961.60		
1 Equip. Oper. (light)	47.05	376.40	74.60	596.80		
1 Grout Pump, 50 C.F./hr.		134.80		148.28	4.21	4.63
32 L.H., Daily Totals		$1468.00		$2299.08	$45.88	$71.85
Crew D-5	Hr.	Daily	Hr.	Daily	Bare Costs	Incl. O&P
1 Bricklayer	$45.60	$364.80	$74.05	$592.40	$45.60	$74.05
8 L.H., Daily Totals		$364.80		$592.40	$45.60	$74.05
Crew D-6	Hr.	Daily	Hr.	Daily	Bare Costs	Incl. O&P
3 Bricklayers	$45.60	$1094.40	$74.05	$1777.20	$41.48	$67.41
3 Bricklayer Helpers	37.00	888.00	60.10	1442.40		
.25 Carpenter	45.85	91.70	75.35	150.70		
50 L.H., Daily Totals		$2074.10		$3370.30	$41.48	$67.41
Crew D-7	Hr.	Daily	Hr.	Daily	Bare Costs	Incl. O&P
1 Tile Layer	$41.95	$335.60	$66.05	$528.40	$37.60	$59.20
1 Tile Layer Helper	33.25	266.00	52.35	418.80		
16 L.H., Daily Totals		$601.60		$947.20	$37.60	$59.20
Crew D-8	Hr.	Daily	Hr.	Daily	Bare Costs	Incl. O&P
3 Bricklayers	$45.60	$1094.40	$74.05	$1777.20	$42.16	$68.47
2 Bricklayer Helpers	37.00	592.00	60.10	961.60		
40 L.H., Daily Totals		$1686.40		$2738.80	$42.16	$68.47
Crew D-9	Hr.	Daily	Hr.	Daily	Bare Costs	Incl. O&P
3 Bricklayers	$45.60	$1094.40	$74.05	$1777.20	$41.30	$67.08
3 Bricklayer Helpers	37.00	888.00	60.10	1442.40		
48 L.H., Daily Totals		$1982.40		$3219.60	$41.30	$67.08
Crew D-10	Hr.	Daily	Hr.	Daily	Bare Costs	Incl. O&P
1 Bricklayer Foreman (outside)	$47.60	$380.80	$77.30	$618.40	$45.11	$72.79
1 Bricklayer	45.60	364.80	74.05	592.40		
1 Bricklayer Helper	37.00	296.00	60.10	480.80		
1 Equip. Oper. (crane)	50.25	402.00	79.70	637.60		
1 S.P. Crane, 4x4, 12 Ton		481.20		529.32	15.04	16.54
32 L.H., Daily Totals		$1924.80		$2858.52	$60.15	$89.33
Crew D-11	Hr.	Daily	Hr.	Daily	Bare Costs	Incl. O&P
1 Bricklayer Foreman (outside)	$47.60	$380.80	$77.30	$618.40	$43.40	$70.48
1 Bricklayer	45.60	364.80	74.05	592.40		
1 Bricklayer Helper	37.00	296.00	60.10	480.80		
24 L.H., Daily Totals		$1041.60		$1691.60	$43.40	$70.48

Crew No.	Bare Costs		Incl. Subs O&P		Cost Per Labor-Hour	
Crew D-12	Hr.	Daily	Hr.	Daily	Bare Costs	Incl. O&P
1 Bricklayer Foreman (outside)	$47.60	$380.80	$77.30	$618.40	$41.80	$67.89
1 Bricklayer	45.60	364.80	74.05	592.40		
2 Bricklayer Helpers	37.00	592.00	60.10	961.60		
32 L.H., Daily Totals		$1337.60		$2172.40	$41.80	$67.89
Crew D-13	Hr.	Daily	Hr.	Daily	Bare Costs	Incl. O&P
1 Bricklayer Foreman (outside)	$47.60	$380.80	$77.30	$618.40	$43.88	$71.10
1 Bricklayer	45.60	364.80	74.05	592.40		
2 Bricklayer Helpers	37.00	592.00	60.10	961.60		
1 Carpenter	45.85	366.80	75.35	602.80		
1 Equip. Oper. (crane)	50.25	402.00	79.70	637.60		
1 S.P. Crane, 4x4, 12 Ton		481.20		529.32	10.03	11.03
48 L.H., Daily Totals		$2587.60		$3942.12	$53.91	$82.13
Crew E-1	Hr.	Daily	Hr.	Daily	Bare Costs	Incl. O&P
1 Welder Foreman (outside)	$53.10	$424.80	$97.45	$779.60	$50.42	$88.60
1 Welder	51.10	408.80	93.75	750.00		
1 Equip. Oper. (light)	47.05	376.40	74.60	596.80		
1 Welder, Gas Engine, 300 amp		142.00		156.20	5.92	6.51
24 L.H., Daily Totals		$1352.00		$2282.60	$56.33	$95.11
Crew E-2	Hr.	Daily	Hr.	Daily	Bare Costs	Incl. O&P
1 Struc. Steel Foreman (outside)	$53.10	$424.80	$97.45	$779.60	$50.19	$88.74
4 Struc. Steel Workers	51.10	1635.20	93.75	3000.00		
1 Equip. Oper. (crane)	50.25	402.00	79.70	637.60		
1 Equip. Oper. (oiler)	43.55	348.40	69.05	552.40		
1 Lattice Boom Crane, 90 Ton		1529.00		1681.90	27.30	30.03
56 L.H., Daily Totals		$4339.40		$6651.50	$77.49	$118.78
Crew E-3	Hr.	Daily	Hr.	Daily	Bare Costs	Incl. O&P
1 Struc. Steel Foreman (outside)	$53.10	$424.80	$97.45	$779.60	$51.77	$94.98
1 Struc. Steel Worker	51.10	408.80	93.75	750.00		
1 Welder	51.10	408.80	93.75	750.00		
1 Welder, Gas Engine, 300 amp		142.00		156.20	5.92	6.51
24 L.H., Daily Totals		$1384.40		$2435.80	$57.68	$101.49
Crew E-3A	Hr.	Daily	Hr.	Daily	Bare Costs	Incl. O&P
1 Struc. Steel Foreman (outside)	$53.10	$424.80	$97.45	$779.60	$51.77	$94.98
1 Struc. Steel Worker	51.10	408.80	93.75	750.00		
1 Welder	51.10	408.80	93.75	750.00		
1 Welder, Gas Engine, 300 amp		142.00		156.20		
1 Aerial Lift Truck, 40' Boom		325.00		357.50	19.46	21.40
24 L.H., Daily Totals		$1709.40		$2793.30	$71.22	$116.39
Crew E-4	Hr.	Daily	Hr.	Daily	Bare Costs	Incl. O&P
1 Struc. Steel Foreman (outside)	$53.10	$424.80	$97.45	$779.60	$51.60	$94.67
3 Struc. Steel Workers	51.10	1226.40	93.75	2250.00		
1 Welder, Gas Engine, 300 amp		142.00		156.20	4.44	4.88
32 L.H., Daily Totals		$1793.20		$3185.80	$56.04	$99.56
Crew E-5	Hr.	Daily	Hr.	Daily	Bare Costs	Incl. O&P
2 Struc. Steel Foremen (outside)	$53.10	$849.60	$97.45	$1559.20	$50.66	$90.61
5 Struc. Steel Workers	51.10	2044.00	93.75	3750.00		
1 Equip. Oper. (crane)	50.25	402.00	79.70	637.60		
1 Welder	51.10	408.80	93.75	750.00		
1 Equip. Oper. (oiler)	43.55	348.40	69.05	552.40		
1 Lattice Boom Crane, 90 Ton		1529.00		1681.90		
1 Welder, Gas Engine, 300 amp		142.00		156.20	20.89	22.98
80 L.H., Daily Totals		$5723.80		$9087.30	$71.55	$113.59

Crew No.	Bare Costs		Incl. Subs O&P		Cost Per Labor-Hour	

Crew E-6

Crew E-6	Hr.	Daily	Hr.	Daily	Bare Costs	Incl. O&P
3 Struc. Steel Foremen (outside)	$53.10	$1274.40	$97.45	$2338.80	$50.70	$90.83
9 Struc. Steel Workers	51.10	3679.20	93.75	6750.00		
1 Equip. Oper. (crane)	50.25	402.00	79.70	637.60		
1 Welder	51.10	408.80	93.75	750.00		
1 Equip. Oper. (oiler)	43.55	348.40	69.05	552.40		
1 Equip. Oper. (light)	47.05	376.40	74.60	596.80		
1 Lattice Boom Crane, 90 Ton		1529.00		1681.90		
1 Welder, Gas Engine, 300 amp		142.00		156.20		
1 Air Compressor, 160 cfm		157.40		173.14		
2 Impact Wrenches		36.00		39.60	14.57	16.02
128 L.H., Daily Totals		$8353.60		$13676.44	$65.26	$106.85

Crew E-7	Hr.	Daily	Hr.	Daily	Bare Costs	Incl. O&P
1 Struc. Steel Foreman (outside)	$53.10	$424.80	$97.45	$779.60	$50.66	$90.61
4 Struc. Steel Workers	51.10	1635.20	93.75	3000.00		
1 Equip. Oper. (crane)	50.25	402.00	79.70	637.60		
1 Equip. Oper. (oiler)	43.55	348.40	69.05	552.40		
1 Welder Foreman (outside)	53.10	424.80	97.45	779.60		
2 Welders	51.10	817.60	93.75	1500.00		
1 Lattice Boom Crane, 90 Ton		1529.00		1681.90		
2 Welder, Gas Engine, 300 amp		284.00		312.40	22.66	24.93
80 L.H., Daily Totals		$5865.80		$9243.50	$73.32	$115.54

Crew E-8	Hr.	Daily	Hr.	Daily	Bare Costs	Incl. O&P
1 Struc. Steel Foreman (outside)	$53.10	$424.80	$97.45	$779.60	$50.45	$89.87
4 Struc. Steel Workers	51.10	1635.20	93.75	3000.00		
1 Welder Foreman (outside)	53.10	424.80	97.45	779.60		
4 Welders	51.10	1635.20	93.75	3000.00		
1 Equip. Oper. (crane)	50.25	402.00	79.70	637.60		
1 Equip. Oper. (oiler)	43.55	348.40	69.05	552.40		
1 Equip. Oper. (light)	47.05	376.40	74.60	596.80		
1 Lattice Boom Crane, 90 Ton		1529.00		1681.90		
4 Welder, Gas Engine, 300 amp		568.00		624.80	20.16	22.18
104 L.H., Daily Totals		$7343.80		$11652.70	$70.61	$112.05

Crew E-9	Hr.	Daily	Hr.	Daily	Bare Costs	Incl. O&P
2 Struc. Steel Foremen (outside)	$53.10	$849.60	$97.45	$1559.20	$50.70	$90.83
5 Struc. Steel Workers	51.10	2044.00	93.75	3750.00		
1 Welder Foreman (outside)	53.10	424.80	97.45	779.60		
5 Welders	51.10	2044.00	93.75	3750.00		
1 Equip. Oper. (crane)	50.25	402.00	79.70	637.60		
1 Equip. Oper. (oiler)	43.55	348.40	69.05	552.40		
1 Equip. Oper. (light)	47.05	376.40	74.60	596.80		
1 Lattice Boom Crane, 90 Ton		1529.00		1681.90		
5 Welder, Gas Engine, 300 amp		710.00		781.00	17.49	19.24
128 L.H., Daily Totals		$8728.20		$14088.50	$68.19	$110.07

Crew E-10	Hr.	Daily	Hr.	Daily	Bare Costs	Incl. O&P
1 Welder Foreman (outside)	$53.10	$424.80	$97.45	$779.60	$52.10	$95.60
1 Welder	51.10	408.80	93.75	750.00		
1 Welder, Gas Engine, 300 amp		142.00		156.20		
1 Flatbed Truck, Gas, 3 Ton		333.00		366.30	29.69	32.66
16 L.H., Daily Totals		$1308.60		$2052.10	$81.79	$128.26

Crew E-11	Hr.	Daily	Hr.	Daily	Bare Costs	Incl. O&P
2 Painters, Struc. Steel	$40.50	$648.00	$77.10	$1233.60	$41.17	$72.25
1 Building Laborer	36.65	293.20	60.20	481.60		
1 Equip. Oper. (light)	47.05	376.40	74.60	596.80		
1 Air Compressor, 250 cfm		202.40		222.64		
1 Sandblaster, Portable, 3 C.F.		20.40		22.44		
1 Set Sand Blasting Accessories		13.85		15.23	7.40	8.13
32 L.H., Daily Totals		$1554.25		$2572.32	$48.57	$80.38

Crew E-11A	Hr.	Daily	Hr.	Daily	Bare Costs	Incl. O&P
2 Painters, Struc. Steel	$40.50	$648.00	$77.10	$1233.60	$41.17	$72.25
1 Building Laborer	36.65	293.20	60.20	481.60		
1 Equip. Oper. (light)	47.05	376.40	74.60	596.80		
1 Air Compressor, 250 cfm		202.40		222.64		
1 Sandblaster, Portable, 3 C.F.		20.40		22.44		
1 Set Sand Blasting Accessories		13.85		15.23		
1 Aerial Lift Truck, 60' Boom		456.00		501.60	21.65	23.81
32 L.H., Daily Totals		$2010.25		$3073.92	$62.82	$96.06

Crew E-11B	Hr.	Daily	Hr.	Daily	Bare Costs	Incl. O&P
2 Painters, Struc. Steel	$40.50	$648.00	$77.10	$1233.60	$39.22	$71.47
1 Building Laborer	36.65	293.20	60.20	481.60		
2 Paint Sprayer, 8 C.F.M.		89.80		98.78		
1 Aerial Lift Truck, 60' Boom		456.00		501.60	22.74	25.02
24 L.H., Daily Totals		$1487.00		$2315.58	$61.96	$96.48

Crew E-12	Hr.	Daily	Hr.	Daily	Bare Costs	Incl. O&P
1 Welder Foreman (outside)	$53.10	$424.80	$97.45	$779.60	$50.08	$86.03
1 Equip. Oper. (light)	47.05	376.40	74.60	596.80		
1 Welder, Gas Engine, 300 amp		142.00		156.20	8.88	9.76
16 L.H., Daily Totals		$943.20		$1532.60	$58.95	$95.79

Crew E-13	Hr.	Daily	Hr.	Daily	Bare Costs	Incl. O&P
1 Welder Foreman (outside)	$53.10	$424.80	$97.45	$779.60	$51.08	$89.83
.5 Equip. Oper. (light)	47.05	188.20	74.60	298.40		
1 Welder, Gas Engine, 300 amp		142.00		156.20	11.83	13.02
12 L.H., Daily Totals		$755.00		$1234.20	$62.92	$102.85

Crew E-14	Hr.	Daily	Hr.	Daily	Bare Costs	Incl. O&P
1 Welder Foreman (outside)	$53.10	$424.80	$97.45	$779.60	$53.10	$97.45
1 Welder, Gas Engine, 300 amp		142.00		156.20	17.75	19.52
8 L.H., Daily Totals		$566.80		$935.80	$70.85	$116.97

Crew E-16	Hr.	Daily	Hr.	Daily	Bare Costs	Incl. O&P
1 Welder Foreman (outside)	$53.10	$424.80	$97.45	$779.60	$52.10	$95.60
1 Welder	51.10	408.80	93.75	750.00		
1 Welder, Gas Engine, 300 amp		142.00		156.20	8.88	9.76
16 L.H., Daily Totals		$975.60		$1685.80	$60.98	$105.36

Crew E-17	Hr.	Daily	Hr.	Daily	Bare Costs	Incl. O&P
1 Struc. Steel Foreman (outside)	$53.10	$424.80	$97.45	$779.60	$52.10	$95.60
1 Structural Steel Worker	51.10	408.80	93.75	750.00		
16 L.H., Daily Totals		$833.60		$1529.60	$52.10	$95.60

Crew E-18	Hr.	Daily	Hr.	Daily	Bare Costs	Incl. O&P
1 Struc. Steel Foreman (outside)	$53.10	$424.80	$97.45	$779.60	$51.06	$91.25
3 Structural Steel Workers	51.10	1226.40	93.75	2250.00		
1 Equipment Operator (med.)	48.90	391.20	77.55	620.40		
1 Lattice Boom Crane, 20 Ton		960.50		1056.55	24.01	26.41
40 L.H., Daily Totals		$3002.90		$4706.55	$75.07	$117.66

Crew E-19	Hr.	Daily	Hr.	Daily	Bare Costs	Incl. O&P
1 Struc. Steel Foreman (outside)	$53.10	$424.80	$97.45	$779.60	$50.42	$88.60
1 Structural Steel Worker	51.10	408.80	93.75	750.00		
1 Equip. Oper. (light)	47.05	376.40	74.60	596.80		
1 Lattice Boom Crane, 20 Ton		960.50		1056.55	40.02	44.02
24 L.H., Daily Totals		$2170.50		$3182.95	$90.44	$132.62

Crews

Crew No.	Bare Costs Hr.	Daily	Incl. Subs O&P Hr.	Daily	Cost Per Labor-Hour Bare Costs	Incl. O&P
Crew E-20	**Hr.**	**Daily**	**Hr.**	**Daily**	**Bare Costs**	**Incl. O&P**
1 Struc. Steel Foreman (outside)	$53.10	$424.80	$97.45	$779.60	$50.30	$89.37
5 Structural Steel Workers	51.10	2044.00	93.75	3750.00		
1 Equip. Oper. (crane)	50.25	402.00	79.70	637.60		
1 Equip. Oper. (oiler)	43.55	348.40	69.05	552.40		
1 Lattice Boom Crane, 40 Ton		1177.00		1294.70	18.39	20.23
64 L.H., Daily Totals		$4396.20		$7014.30	$68.69	$109.60

Crew No.	**Hr.**	**Daily**	**Hr.**	**Daily**	**Bare Costs**	**Incl. O&P**
Crew E-22						
1 Skilled Worker Foreman (out)	$49.30	$394.40	$80.30	$642.40	$47.97	$78.13
2 Skilled Workers	47.30	756.80	77.05	1232.80		
24 L.H., Daily Totals		$1151.20		$1875.20	$47.97	$78.13

Crew No.	**Hr.**	**Daily**	**Hr.**	**Daily**	**Bare Costs**	**Incl. O&P**
Crew E-24						
3 Structural Steel Workers	$51.10	$1226.40	$93.75	$2250.00	$50.55	$89.70
1 Equipment Operator (med.)	48.90	391.20	77.55	620.40		
1 Hyd. Crane, 25 Ton		745.80		820.38	23.31	25.64
32 L.H., Daily Totals		$2363.40		$3690.78	$73.86	$115.34

Crew No.	**Hr.**	**Daily**	**Hr.**	**Daily**	**Bare Costs**	**Incl. O&P**
Crew E-25						
1 Welder Foreman (outside)	$53.10	$424.80	$97.45	$779.60	$53.10	$97.45
1 Cutting Torch		11.40		12.54	1.43	1.57
8 L.H., Daily Totals		$436.20		$792.14	$54.52	$99.02

Crew No.	**Hr.**	**Daily**	**Hr.**	**Daily**	**Bare Costs**	**Incl. O&P**
Crew F-3						
4 Carpenters	$45.85	$1467.20	$75.35	$2411.20	$46.73	$76.22
1 Equip. Oper. (crane)	50.25	402.00	79.70	637.60		
1 Hyd. Crane, 12 Ton		663.00		729.30	16.57	18.23
40 L.H., Daily Totals		$2532.20		$3778.10	$63.31	$94.45

Crew No.	**Hr.**	**Daily**	**Hr.**	**Daily**	**Bare Costs**	**Incl. O&P**
Crew F-4						
4 Carpenters	$45.85	$1467.20	$75.35	$2411.20	$46.20	$75.03
1 Equip. Oper. (crane)	50.25	402.00	79.70	637.60		
1 Equip. Oper. (oiler)	43.55	348.40	69.05	552.40		
1 Hyd. Crane, 55 Ton		1137.00		1250.70	23.69	26.06
48 L.H., Daily Totals		$3354.60		$4851.90	$69.89	$101.08

Crew No.	**Hr.**	**Daily**	**Hr.**	**Daily**	**Bare Costs**	**Incl. O&P**
Crew F-5						
1 Carpenter Foreman (outside)	$47.85	$382.80	$78.60	$628.80	$46.35	$76.16
3 Carpenters	45.85	1100.40	75.35	1808.40		
32 L.H., Daily Totals		$1483.20		$2437.20	$46.35	$76.16

Crew No.	**Hr.**	**Daily**	**Hr.**	**Daily**	**Bare Costs**	**Incl. O&P**
Crew F-6						
2 Carpenters	$45.85	$733.60	$75.35	$1205.60	$43.05	$70.16
2 Building Laborers	36.65	586.40	60.20	963.20		
1 Equip. Oper. (crane)	50.25	402.00	79.70	637.60		
1 Hyd. Crane, 12 Ton		663.00		729.30	16.57	18.23
40 L.H., Daily Totals		$2385.00		$3535.70	$59.63	$88.39

Crew No.	**Hr.**	**Daily**	**Hr.**	**Daily**	**Bare Costs**	**Incl. O&P**
Crew F-7						
2 Carpenters	$45.85	$733.60	$75.35	$1205.60	$41.25	$67.78
2 Building Laborers	36.65	586.40	60.20	963.20		
32 L.H., Daily Totals		$1320.00		$2168.80	$41.25	$67.78

Crew No.	Bare Costs Hr.	Daily	Incl. Subs O&P Hr.	Daily	Cost Per Labor-Hour Bare Costs	Incl. O&P
Crew G-1	**Hr.**	**Daily**	**Hr.**	**Daily**	**Bare Costs**	**Incl. O&P**
1 Roofer Foreman (outside)	$41.15	$329.20	$74.15	$593.20	$36.58	$65.92
4 Roofers Composition	39.15	1252.80	70.55	2257.60		
2 Roofer Helpers	29.15	466.40	52.55	840.80		
1 Application Equipment		199.20		219.12		
1 Tar Kettle/Pot		130.00		143.00		
1 Crew Truck		224.80		247.28	9.89	10.88
56 L.H., Daily Totals		$2602.40		$4301.00	$46.47	$76.80

Crew No.	**Hr.**	**Daily**	**Hr.**	**Daily**	**Bare Costs**	**Incl. O&P**
Crew G-2						
1 Plasterer	$41.95	$335.60	$67.35	$538.80	$38.60	$62.42
1 Plasterer Helper	37.20	297.60	59.70	477.60		
1 Building Laborer	36.65	293.20	60.20	481.60		
1 Grout Pump, 50 C.F./hr.		134.80		148.28	5.62	6.18
24 L.H., Daily Totals		$1061.20		$1646.28	$44.22	$68.59

Crew No.	**Hr.**	**Daily**	**Hr.**	**Daily**	**Bare Costs**	**Incl. O&P**
Crew G-2A						
1 Roofer Composition	$39.15	$313.20	$70.55	$564.40	$34.98	$61.10
1 Roofer Helper	29.15	233.20	52.55	420.40		
1 Building Laborer	36.65	293.20	60.20	481.60		
1 Foam Spray Rig, Trailer-Mtd.		585.25		643.77		
1 Pickup Truck, 3/4 Ton		157.00		172.70	30.93	34.02
24 L.H., Daily Totals		$1581.85		$2282.88	$65.91	$95.12

Crew No.	**Hr.**	**Daily**	**Hr.**	**Daily**	**Bare Costs**	**Incl. O&P**
Crew G-3						
2 Sheet Metal Workers	$54.70	$875.20	$86.25	$1380.00	$45.67	$73.22
2 Building Laborers	36.65	586.40	60.20	963.20		
32 L.H., Daily Totals		$1461.60		$2343.20	$45.67	$73.22

Crew No.	**Hr.**	**Daily**	**Hr.**	**Daily**	**Bare Costs**	**Incl. O&P**
Crew G-4						
1 Labor Foreman (outside)	$38.65	$309.20	$63.50	$508.00	$37.32	$61.30
2 Building Laborers	36.65	586.40	60.20	963.20		
1 Flatbed Truck, Gas, 1.5 Ton		270.20		297.22		
1 Air Compressor, 160 cfm		157.40		173.14	17.82	19.60
24 L.H., Daily Totals		$1323.20		$1941.56	$55.13	$80.90

Crew No.	**Hr.**	**Daily**	**Hr.**	**Daily**	**Bare Costs**	**Incl. O&P**
Crew G-5						
1 Roofer Foreman (outside)	$41.15	$329.20	$74.15	$593.20	$35.55	$64.07
2 Roofers Composition	39.15	626.40	70.55	1128.80		
2 Roofer Helpers	29.15	466.40	52.55	840.80		
1 Application Equipment		199.20		219.12	4.98	5.48
40 L.H., Daily Totals		$1621.20		$2781.92	$40.53	$69.55

Crew No.	**Hr.**	**Daily**	**Hr.**	**Daily**	**Bare Costs**	**Incl. O&P**
Crew G-6A						
2 Roofers Composition	$39.15	$626.40	$70.55	$1128.80	$39.15	$70.55
1 Small Compressor, Electric		12.10		13.31		
2 Pneumatic Nailers		44.70		49.17	3.55	3.90
16 L.H., Daily Totals		$683.20		$1191.28	$42.70	$74.45

Crew No.	**Hr.**	**Daily**	**Hr.**	**Daily**	**Bare Costs**	**Incl. O&P**
Crew G-7						
1 Carpenter	$45.85	$366.80	$75.35	$602.80	$45.85	$75.35
1 Small Compressor, Electric		12.10		13.31		
1 Pneumatic Nailer		22.35		24.59	4.31	4.74
8 L.H., Daily Totals		$401.25		$640.70	$50.16	$80.09

Crew No.	**Hr.**	**Daily**	**Hr.**	**Daily**	**Bare Costs**	**Incl. O&P**
Crew H-1						
2 Glaziers	$44.05	$704.80	$71.40	$1142.40	$47.58	$82.58
2 Struc. Steel Workers	51.10	817.60	93.75	1500.00		
32 L.H., Daily Totals		$1522.40		$2642.40	$47.58	$82.58

741

Crews

Crew H-2	Bare Costs Hr.	Daily	Incl. Subs O&P Hr.	Daily	Bare Costs	Incl. O&P
2 Glaziers	$44.05	$704.80	$71.40	$1142.40	$41.58	$67.67
1 Building Laborer	36.65	293.20	60.20	481.60		
24 L.H., Daily Totals		$998.00		$1624.00	$41.58	$67.67

Crew H-3	Hr.	Daily	Hr.	Daily	Bare Costs	Incl. O&P
1 Glazier	$44.05	$352.40	$71.40	$571.20	$39.35	$64.28
1 Helper	34.65	277.20	57.15	457.20		
16 L.H., Daily Totals		$629.60		$1028.40	$39.35	$64.28

Crew H-4	Hr.	Daily	Hr.	Daily	Bare Costs	Incl. O&P
1 Carpenter	$45.85	$366.80	$75.35	$602.80	$42.87	$69.51
1 Carpenter Helper	34.65	277.20	57.15	457.20		
.5 Electrician	53.35	213.40	82.55	330.20		
20 L.H., Daily Totals		$857.40		$1390.20	$42.87	$69.51

Crew J-1	Hr.	Daily	Hr.	Daily	Bare Costs	Incl. O&P
3 Plasterers	$41.95	$1006.80	$67.35	$1616.40	$40.05	$64.29
2 Plasterer Helpers	37.20	595.20	59.70	955.20		
1 Mixing Machine, 6 C.F.		143.60		157.96	3.59	3.95
40 L.H., Daily Totals		$1745.60		$2729.56	$43.64	$68.24

Crew J-2	Hr.	Daily	Hr.	Daily	Bare Costs	Incl. O&P
3 Plasterers	$41.95	$1006.80	$67.35	$1616.40	$40.14	$64.20
2 Plasterer Helpers	37.20	595.20	59.70	955.20		
1 Lather	40.60	324.80	63.75	510.00		
1 Mixing Machine, 6 C.F.		143.60		157.96	2.99	3.29
48 L.H., Daily Totals		$2070.40		$3239.56	$43.13	$67.49

Crew J-3	Hr.	Daily	Hr.	Daily	Bare Costs	Incl. O&P
1 Terrazzo Worker	$41.65	$333.20	$65.55	$524.40	$38.23	$60.17
1 Terrazzo Helper	34.80	278.40	54.80	438.40		
1 Floor Grinder, 22" Path		97.90		107.69		
1 Terrazzo Mixer		192.60		211.86	18.16	19.97
16 L.H., Daily Totals		$902.10		$1282.35	$56.38	$80.15

Crew J-4	Hr.	Daily	Hr.	Daily	Bare Costs	Incl. O&P
2 Cement Finishers	$44.05	$704.80	$69.50	$1112.00	$41.58	$66.40
1 Laborer	36.65	293.20	60.20	481.60		
1 Floor Grinder, 22" Path		97.90		107.69		
1 Floor Edger, 7" Path		39.15		43.06		
1 Vacuum Pick-Up System		60.75		66.83	8.24	9.07
24 L.H., Daily Totals		$1195.80		$1811.18	$49.83	$75.47

Crew J-4A	Hr.	Daily	Hr.	Daily	Bare Costs	Incl. O&P
2 Cement Finishers	$44.05	$704.80	$69.50	$1112.00	$40.35	$64.85
2 Laborers	36.65	586.40	60.20	963.20		
1 Floor Grinder, 22" Path		97.90		107.69		
1 Floor Edger, 7" Path		39.15		43.06		
1 Vacuum Pick-Up System		60.75		66.83		
1 Floor Auto Scrubber		212.15		233.37	12.81	14.09
32 L.H., Daily Totals		$1701.15		$2526.15	$53.16	$78.94

Crew J-4B	Hr.	Daily	Hr.	Daily	Bare Costs	Incl. O&P
1 Laborer	$36.65	$293.20	$60.20	$481.60	$36.65	$60.20
1 Floor Auto Scrubber		212.15		233.37	26.52	29.17
8 L.H., Daily Totals		$505.35		$714.97	$63.17	$89.37

Crew J-6	Hr.	Daily	Hr.	Daily	Bare Costs	Incl. O&P
2 Painters	$39.55	$632.80	$63.45	$1015.20	$40.70	$65.42
1 Building Laborer	36.65	293.20	60.20	481.60		
1 Equip. Oper. (light)	47.05	376.40	74.60	596.80		
1 Air Compressor, 250 cfm		202.40		222.64		
1 Sandblaster, Portable, 3 C.F.		20.40		22.44		
1 Set Sand Blasting Accessories		13.85		15.23	7.40	8.13
32 L.H., Daily Totals		$1539.05		$2353.92	$48.10	$73.56

Crew J-7	Hr.	Daily	Hr.	Daily	Bare Costs	Incl. O&P
2 Painters	$39.55	$632.80	$63.45	$1015.20	$39.55	$63.45
1 Floor Belt Sander		15.90		17.49		
1 Floor Sanding Edger		15.55		17.11	1.97	2.16
16 L.H., Daily Totals		$664.25		$1049.80	$41.52	$65.61

Crew K-1	Hr.	Daily	Hr.	Daily	Bare Costs	Incl. O&P
1 Carpenter	$45.85	$366.80	$75.35	$602.80	$41.17	$67.35
1 Truck Driver (light)	36.50	292.00	59.35	474.80		
1 Flatbed Truck, Gas, 3 Ton		333.00		366.30	20.81	22.89
16 L.H., Daily Totals		$991.80		$1443.90	$61.99	$90.24

Crew K-2	Hr.	Daily	Hr.	Daily	Bare Costs	Incl. O&P
1 Struc. Steel Foreman (outside)	$53.10	$424.80	$97.45	$779.60	$46.90	$83.52
1 Struc. Steel Worker	51.10	408.80	93.75	750.00		
1 Truck Driver (light)	36.50	292.00	59.35	474.80		
1 Flatbed Truck, Gas, 3 Ton		333.00		366.30	13.88	15.26
24 L.H., Daily Totals		$1458.60		$2370.70	$60.77	$98.78

Crew L-1	Hr.	Daily	Hr.	Daily	Bare Costs	Incl. O&P
1 Electrician	$53.35	$426.80	$82.55	$660.40	$55.45	$86.17
1 Plumber	57.55	460.40	89.80	718.40		
16 L.H., Daily Totals		$887.20		$1378.80	$55.45	$86.17

Crew L-2	Hr.	Daily	Hr.	Daily	Bare Costs	Incl. O&P
1 Carpenter	$45.85	$366.80	$75.35	$602.80	$40.25	$66.25
1 Carpenter Helper	34.65	277.20	57.15	457.20		
16 L.H., Daily Totals		$644.00		$1060.00	$40.25	$66.25

Crew L-3	Hr.	Daily	Hr.	Daily	Bare Costs	Incl. O&P
1 Carpenter	$45.85	$366.80	$75.35	$602.80	$49.94	$79.88
.5 Electrician	53.35	213.40	82.55	330.20		
.5 Sheet Metal Worker	54.70	218.80	86.25	345.00		
16 L.H., Daily Totals		$799.00		$1278.00	$49.94	$79.88

Crew L-3A	Hr.	Daily	Hr.	Daily	Bare Costs	Incl. O&P
1 Carpenter Foreman (outside)	$47.85	$382.80	$78.60	$628.80	$50.13	$81.15
.5 Sheet Metal Worker	54.70	218.80	86.25	345.00		
12 L.H., Daily Totals		$601.60		$973.80	$50.13	$81.15

Crew L-4	Hr.	Daily	Hr.	Daily	Bare Costs	Incl. O&P
2 Skilled Workers	$47.30	$756.80	$77.05	$1232.80	$43.08	$70.42
1 Helper	34.65	277.20	57.15	457.20		
24 L.H., Daily Totals		$1034.00		$1690.00	$43.08	$70.42

Crew L-5	Hr.	Daily	Hr.	Daily	Bare Costs	Incl. O&P
1 Struc. Steel Foreman (outside)	$53.10	$424.80	$97.45	$779.60	$51.26	$92.27
5 Struc. Steel Workers	51.10	2044.00	93.75	3750.00		
1 Equip. Oper. (crane)	50.25	402.00	79.70	637.60		
1 Hyd. Crane, 25 Ton		745.80		820.38	13.32	14.65
56 L.H., Daily Totals		$3616.60		$5987.58	$64.58	$106.92

Crew No.	Bare Costs Hr.	Daily	Incl. Subs O&P Hr.	Daily	Cost Per Labor-Hour Bare Costs	Incl. O&P
Crew L-5A	Hr.	Daily	Hr.	Daily	Bare Costs	Incl. O&P
1 Struc. Steel Foreman (outside)	$53.10	$424.80	$97.45	$779.60	$51.39	$91.16
2 Structural Steel Workers	51.10	817.60	93.75	1500.00		
1 Equip. Oper. (crane)	50.25	402.00	79.70	637.60		
1 S.P. Crane, 4x4, 25 Ton		607.20		667.92	18.98	20.87
32 L.H., Daily Totals		$2251.60		$3585.12	$70.36	$112.04

Crew No.	Bare Costs Hr.	Daily	Incl. Subs O&P Hr.	Daily	Cost Per Labor-Hour Bare Costs	Incl. O&P
Crew L-5B	Hr.	Daily	Hr.	Daily	Bare Costs	Incl. O&P
1 Struc. Steel Foreman (outside)	$53.10	$424.80	$97.45	$779.60	$52.53	$86.81
2 Structural Steel Workers	51.10	817.60	93.75	1500.00		
2 Electricians	53.35	853.60	82.55	1320.80		
2 Steamfitters/Pipefitters	58.50	936.00	91.25	1460.00		
1 Equip. Oper. (crane)	50.25	402.00	79.70	637.60		
1 Equip. Oper. (oiler)	43.55	348.40	69.05	552.40		
1 Hyd. Crane, 80 Ton		1652.00		1817.20	22.94	25.24
72 L.H., Daily Totals		$5434.40		$8067.60	$75.48	$112.05

Crew No.	Bare Costs Hr.	Daily	Incl. Subs O&P Hr.	Daily	Cost Per Labor-Hour Bare Costs	Incl. O&P
Crew L-6	Hr.	Daily	Hr.	Daily	Bare Costs	Incl. O&P
1 Plumber	$57.55	$460.40	$89.80	$718.40	$56.15	$87.38
.5 Electrician	53.35	213.40	82.55	330.20		
12 L.H., Daily Totals		$673.80		$1048.60	$56.15	$87.38

Crew No.	Bare Costs Hr.	Daily	Incl. Subs O&P Hr.	Daily	Cost Per Labor-Hour Bare Costs	Incl. O&P
Crew L-7	Hr.	Daily	Hr.	Daily	Bare Costs	Incl. O&P
2 Carpenters	$45.85	$733.60	$75.35	$1205.60	$44.29	$72.05
1 Building Laborer	36.65	293.20	60.20	481.60		
.5 Electrician	53.35	213.40	82.55	330.20		
28 L.H., Daily Totals		$1240.20		$2017.40	$44.29	$72.05

Crew No.	Bare Costs Hr.	Daily	Incl. Subs O&P Hr.	Daily	Cost Per Labor-Hour Bare Costs	Incl. O&P
Crew L-8	Hr.	Daily	Hr.	Daily	Bare Costs	Incl. O&P
2 Carpenters	$45.85	$733.60	$75.35	$1205.60	$48.19	$78.24
.5 Plumber	57.55	230.20	89.80	359.20		
20 L.H., Daily Totals		$963.80		$1564.80	$48.19	$78.24

Crew No.	Bare Costs Hr.	Daily	Incl. Subs O&P Hr.	Daily	Cost Per Labor-Hour Bare Costs	Incl. O&P
Crew L-9	Hr.	Daily	Hr.	Daily	Bare Costs	Incl. O&P
1 Labor Foreman (inside)	$37.15	$297.20	$61.05	$488.40	$41.83	$70.33
2 Building Laborers	36.65	586.40	60.20	963.20		
1 Struc. Steel Worker	51.10	408.80	93.75	750.00		
.5 Electrician	53.35	213.40	82.55	330.20		
36 L.H., Daily Totals		$1505.80		$2531.80	$41.83	$70.33

Crew No.	Bare Costs Hr.	Daily	Incl. Subs O&P Hr.	Daily	Cost Per Labor-Hour Bare Costs	Incl. O&P
Crew L-10	Hr.	Daily	Hr.	Daily	Bare Costs	Incl. O&P
1 Struc. Steel Foreman (outside)	$53.10	$424.80	$97.45	$779.60	$51.48	$90.30
1 Structural Steel Worker	51.10	408.80	93.75	750.00		
1 Equip. Oper. (crane)	50.25	402.00	79.70	637.60		
1 Hyd. Crane, 12 Ton		663.00		729.30	27.63	30.39
24 L.H., Daily Totals		$1898.60		$2896.50	$79.11	$120.69

Crew No.	Bare Costs Hr.	Daily	Incl. Subs O&P Hr.	Daily	Cost Per Labor-Hour Bare Costs	Incl. O&P
Crew L-11	Hr.	Daily	Hr.	Daily	Bare Costs	Incl. O&P
2 Wreckers	$36.65	$586.40	$65.25	$1044.00	$42.65	$71.20
1 Equip. Oper. (crane)	50.25	402.00	79.70	637.60		
1 Equip. Oper. (light)	47.05	376.40	74.60	596.80		
1 Hyd. Excavator, 2.5 C.Y.		1637.00		1800.70		
1 Loader, Skid Steer, 78 H.P.		308.80		339.68	60.81	66.89
32 L.H., Daily Totals		$3310.60		$4418.78	$103.46	$138.09

Crew No.	Bare Costs Hr.	Daily	Incl. Subs O&P Hr.	Daily	Cost Per Labor-Hour Bare Costs	Incl. O&P
Crew M-1	Hr.	Daily	Hr.	Daily	Bare Costs	Incl. O&P
3 Elevator Constructors	$74.15	$1779.60	$114.65	$2751.60	$70.44	$108.91
1 Elevator Apprentice	59.30	474.40	91.70	733.60		
5 Hand Tools		48.00		52.80	1.50	1.65
32 L.H., Daily Totals		$2302.00		$3538.00	$71.94	$110.56

Crew No.	Bare Costs Hr.	Daily	Incl. Subs O&P Hr.	Daily	Cost Per Labor-Hour Bare Costs	Incl. O&P
Crew M-3	Hr.	Daily	Hr.	Daily	Bare Costs	Incl. O&P
1 Electrician Foreman (outside)	$55.35	$442.80	$85.65	$685.20	$55.92	$87.43
1 Common Laborer	36.65	293.20	60.20	481.60		
.25 Equipment Operator (med.)	48.90	97.80	77.55	155.10		
1 Elevator Constructor	74.15	593.20	114.65	917.20		
1 Elevator Apprentice	59.30	474.40	91.70	733.60		
.25 S.P. Crane, 4x4, 20 Ton		140.10		154.11	4.12	4.53
34 L.H., Daily Totals		$2041.50		$3126.81	$60.04	$91.97

Crew No.	Bare Costs Hr.	Daily	Incl. Subs O&P Hr.	Daily	Cost Per Labor-Hour Bare Costs	Incl. O&P
Crew M-4	Hr.	Daily	Hr.	Daily	Bare Costs	Incl. O&P
1 Electrician Foreman (outside)	$55.35	$442.80	$85.65	$685.20	$55.31	$86.53
1 Common Laborer	36.65	293.20	60.20	481.60		
.25 Equipment Operator, Crane	50.25	100.50	79.70	159.40		
.25 Equip. Oper. (oiler)	43.55	87.10	69.05	138.10		
1 Elevator Constructor	74.15	593.20	114.65	917.20		
1 Elevator Apprentice	59.30	474.40	91.70	733.60		
.25 S.P. Crane, 4x4, 40 Ton		178.25		196.07	4.95	5.45
36 L.H., Daily Totals		$2169.45		$3311.18	$60.26	$91.98

Crew No.	Bare Costs Hr.	Daily	Incl. Subs O&P Hr.	Daily	Cost Per Labor-Hour Bare Costs	Incl. O&P
Crew Q-1	Hr.	Daily	Hr.	Daily	Bare Costs	Incl. O&P
1 Plumber	$57.55	$460.40	$89.80	$718.40	$51.80	$80.83
1 Plumber Apprentice	46.05	368.40	71.85	574.80		
16 L.H., Daily Totals		$828.80		$1293.20	$51.80	$80.83

Crew No.	Bare Costs Hr.	Daily	Incl. Subs O&P Hr.	Daily	Cost Per Labor-Hour Bare Costs	Incl. O&P
Crew Q-1A	Hr.	Daily	Hr.	Daily	Bare Costs	Incl. O&P
.25 Plumber Foreman (outside)	$59.55	$119.10	$92.90	$185.80	$57.95	$90.42
1 Plumber	57.55	460.40	89.80	718.40		
10 L.H., Daily Totals		$579.50		$904.20	$57.95	$90.42

Crew No.	Bare Costs Hr.	Daily	Incl. Subs O&P Hr.	Daily	Cost Per Labor-Hour Bare Costs	Incl. O&P
Crew Q-1C	Hr.	Daily	Hr.	Daily	Bare Costs	Incl. O&P
1 Plumber	$57.55	$460.40	$89.80	$718.40	$50.83	$79.73
1 Plumber Apprentice	46.05	368.40	71.85	574.80		
1 Equip. Oper. (medium)	48.90	391.20	77.55	620.40		
1 Trencher, Chain Type, 8' D		3376.00		3713.60	140.67	154.73
24 L.H., Daily Totals		$4596.00		$5627.20	$191.50	$234.47

Crew No.	Bare Costs Hr.	Daily	Incl. Subs O&P Hr.	Daily	Cost Per Labor-Hour Bare Costs	Incl. O&P
Crew Q-2	Hr.	Daily	Hr.	Daily	Bare Costs	Incl. O&P
2 Plumbers	$57.55	$920.80	$89.80	$1436.80	$53.72	$83.82
1 Plumber Apprentice	46.05	368.40	71.85	574.80	53.72	83.82
24 L.H., Daily Totals		$1289.20		$2011.60	$53.72	$83.82

Crew No.	Bare Costs Hr.	Daily	Incl. Subs O&P Hr.	Daily	Cost Per Labor-Hour Bare Costs	Incl. O&P
Crew Q-3	Hr.	Daily	Hr.	Daily	Bare Costs	Incl. O&P
1 Plumber Foreman (inside)	$58.05	$464.40	$90.55	$724.40	$54.80	$85.50
2 Plumbers	57.55	920.80	89.80	1436.80		
1 Plumber Apprentice	46.05	368.40	71.85	574.80		
32 L.H., Daily Totals		$1753.60		$2736.00	$54.80	$85.50

Crew No.	Bare Costs Hr.	Daily	Incl. Subs O&P Hr.	Daily	Cost Per Labor-Hour Bare Costs	Incl. O&P
Crew Q-4	Hr.	Daily	Hr.	Daily	Bare Costs	Incl. O&P
1 Plumber Foreman (inside)	$58.05	$464.40	$90.55	$724.40	$54.80	$85.50
1 Plumber	57.55	460.40	89.80	718.40		
1 Welder (plumber)	57.55	460.40	89.80	718.40		
1 Plumber Apprentice	46.05	368.40	71.85	574.80		
1 Welder, Electric, 300 amp		55.30		60.83	1.73	1.90
32 L.H., Daily Totals		$1808.90		$2796.83	$56.53	$87.40

Crew No.	Bare Costs Hr.	Daily	Incl. Subs O&P Hr.	Daily	Cost Per Labor-Hour Bare Costs	Incl. O&P
Crew Q-5	Hr.	Daily	Hr.	Daily	Bare Costs	Incl. O&P
1 Steamfitter	$58.50	$468.00	$91.25	$730.00	$52.65	$82.13
1 Steamfitter Apprentice	46.80	374.40	73.00	584.00		
16 L.H., Daily Totals		$842.40		$1314.00	$52.65	$82.13

Crew No.	Bare Costs Hr.	Daily	Incl. Subs O&P Hr.	Daily	Cost Per Labor-Hour Bare Costs	Incl. O&P
Crew Q-6	Hr.	Daily	Hr.	Daily	Bare Costs	Incl. O&P
2 Steamfitters	$58.50	$936.00	$91.25	$1460.00	$54.60	$85.17
1 Steamfitter Apprentice	46.80	374.40	73.00	584.00	54.60	85.17
24 L.H., Daily Totals		$1310.40		$2044.00	$54.60	$85.17
Crew Q-7	Hr.	Daily	Hr.	Daily	Bare Costs	Incl. O&P
1 Steamfitter Foreman (inside)	$59.00	$472.00	$92.05	$736.40	$55.70	$86.89
2 Steamfitters	58.50	936.00	91.25	1460.00		
1 Steamfitter Apprentice	46.80	374.40	73.00	584.00		
32 L.H., Daily Totals		$1782.40		$2780.40	$55.70	$86.89
Crew Q-8	Hr.	Daily	Hr.	Daily	Bare Costs	Incl. O&P
1 Steamfitter Foreman (inside)	$59.00	$472.00	$92.05	$736.40	$55.70	$86.89
1 Steamfitter	58.50	468.00	91.25	730.00		
1 Welder (steamfitter)	58.50	468.00	91.25	730.00		
1 Steamfitter Apprentice	46.80	374.40	73.00	584.00		
1 Welder, Electric, 300 amp		55.30		60.83	1.73	1.90
32 L.H., Daily Totals		$1837.70		$2841.23	$57.43	$88.79
Crew Q-9	Hr.	Daily	Hr.	Daily	Bare Costs	Incl. O&P
1 Sheet Metal Worker	$54.70	$437.60	$86.25	$690.00	$49.23	$77.63
1 Sheet Metal Apprentice	43.75	350.00	69.00	552.00		
16 L.H., Daily Totals		$787.60		$1242.00	$49.23	$77.63
Crew Q-10	Hr.	Daily	Hr.	Daily	Bare Costs	Incl. O&P
2 Sheet Metal Workers	$54.70	$875.20	$86.25	$1380.00	$51.05	$80.50
1 Sheet Metal Apprentice	43.75	350.00	69.00	552.00		
24 L.H., Daily Totals		$1225.20		$1932.00	$51.05	$80.50
Crew Q-11	Hr.	Daily	Hr.	Daily	Bare Costs	Incl. O&P
1 Sheet Metal Foreman (inside)	$55.20	$441.60	$87.05	$696.40	$52.09	$82.14
2 Sheet Metal Workers	54.70	875.20	86.25	1380.00		
1 Sheet Metal Apprentice	43.75	350.00	69.00	552.00		
32 L.H., Daily Totals		$1666.80		$2628.40	$52.09	$82.14
Crew Q-12	Hr.	Daily	Hr.	Daily	Bare Costs	Incl. O&P
1 Sprinkler Installer	$55.40	$443.20	$86.50	$692.00	$49.85	$77.83
1 Sprinkler Apprentice	44.30	354.40	69.15	553.20		
16 L.H., Daily Totals		$797.60		$1245.20	$49.85	$77.83
Crew Q-13	Hr.	Daily	Hr.	Daily	Bare Costs	Incl. O&P
1 Sprinkler Foreman (inside)	$55.90	$447.20	$87.25	$698.00	$52.75	$82.35
2 Sprinkler Installers	55.40	886.40	86.50	1384.00		
1 Sprinkler Apprentice	44.30	354.40	69.15	553.20		
32 L.H., Daily Totals		$1688.00		$2635.20	$52.75	$82.35
Crew Q-14	Hr.	Daily	Hr.	Daily	Bare Costs	Incl. O&P
1 Asbestos Worker	$51.15	$409.20	$82.15	$657.20	$46.02	$73.92
1 Asbestos Apprentice	40.90	327.20	65.70	525.60		
16 L.H., Daily Totals		$736.40		$1182.80	$46.02	$73.92
Crew Q-15	Hr.	Daily	Hr.	Daily	Bare Costs	Incl. O&P
1 Plumber	$57.55	$460.40	$89.80	$718.40	$51.80	$80.83
1 Plumber Apprentice	46.05	368.40	71.85	574.80		
1 Welder, Electric, 300 amp		55.30		60.83	3.46	3.80
16 L.H., Daily Totals		$884.10		$1354.03	$55.26	$84.63

Crew No.	Bare Costs Hr.	Daily	Incl. Subs O&P Hr.	Daily	Cost Per Labor-Hour Bare Costs	Incl. O&P
Crew Q-16	Hr.	Daily	Hr.	Daily	Bare Costs	Incl. O&P
2 Plumbers	$57.55	$920.80	$89.80	$1436.80	$53.72	$83.82
1 Plumber Apprentice	46.05	368.40	71.85	574.80		
1 Welder, Electric, 300 amp		55.30		60.83	2.30	2.53
24 L.H., Daily Totals		$1344.50		$2072.43	$56.02	$86.35
Crew Q-17	Hr.	Daily	Hr.	Daily	Bare Costs	Incl. O&P
1 Steamfitter	$58.50	$468.00	$91.25	$730.00	$52.65	$82.13
1 Steamfitter Apprentice	46.80	374.40	73.00	584.00		
1 Welder, Electric, 300 amp		55.30		60.83	3.46	3.80
16 L.H., Daily Totals		$897.70		$1374.83	$56.11	$85.93
Crew Q-17A	Hr.	Daily	Hr.	Daily	Bare Costs	Incl. O&P
1 Steamfitter	$58.50	$468.00	$91.25	$730.00	$51.85	$81.32
1 Steamfitter Apprentice	46.80	374.40	73.00	584.00		
1 Equip. Oper. (crane)	50.25	402.00	79.70	637.60		
1 Hyd. Crane, 12 Ton		663.00		729.30		
1 Welder, Electric, 300 amp		55.30		60.83	29.93	32.92
24 L.H., Daily Totals		$1962.70		$2741.73	$81.78	$114.24
Crew Q-18	Hr.	Daily	Hr.	Daily	Bare Costs	Incl. O&P
2 Steamfitters	$58.50	$936.00	$91.25	$1460.00	$54.60	$85.17
1 Steamfitter Apprentice	46.80	374.40	73.00	584.00		
1 Welder, Electric, 300 amp		55.30		60.83	2.30	2.53
24 L.H., Daily Totals		$1365.70		$2104.83	$56.90	$87.70
Crew Q-19	Hr.	Daily	Hr.	Daily	Bare Costs	Incl. O&P
1 Steamfitter	$58.50	$468.00	$91.25	$730.00	$52.88	$82.27
1 Steamfitter Apprentice	46.80	374.40	73.00	584.00		
1 Electrician	53.35	426.80	82.55	660.40		
24 L.H., Daily Totals		$1269.20		$1974.40	$52.88	$82.27
Crew Q-20	Hr.	Daily	Hr.	Daily	Bare Costs	Incl. O&P
1 Sheet Metal Worker	$54.70	$437.60	$86.25	$690.00	$50.05	$78.61
1 Sheet Metal Apprentice	43.75	350.00	69.00	552.00		
.5 Electrician	53.35	213.40	82.55	330.20		
20 L.H., Daily Totals		$1001.00		$1572.20	$50.05	$78.61
Crew Q-21	Hr.	Daily	Hr.	Daily	Bare Costs	Incl. O&P
2 Steamfitters	$58.50	$936.00	$91.25	$1460.00	$54.29	$84.51
1 Steamfitter Apprentice	46.80	374.40	73.00	584.00		
1 Electrician	53.35	426.80	82.55	660.40		
32 L.H., Daily Totals		$1737.20		$2704.40	$54.29	$84.51
Crew Q-22	Hr.	Daily	Hr.	Daily	Bare Costs	Incl. O&P
1 Plumber	$57.55	$460.40	$89.80	$718.40	$51.80	$80.83
1 Plumber Apprentice	46.05	368.40	71.85	574.80		
1 Hyd. Crane, 12 Ton		663.00		729.30	41.44	45.58
16 L.H., Daily Totals		$1491.80		$2022.50	$93.24	$126.41
Crew Q-22A	Hr.	Daily	Hr.	Daily	Bare Costs	Incl. O&P
1 Plumber	$57.55	$460.40	$89.80	$718.40	$47.63	$75.39
1 Plumber Apprentice	46.05	368.40	71.85	574.80		
1 Laborer	36.65	293.20	60.20	481.60		
1 Equip. Oper. (crane)	50.25	402.00	79.70	637.60		
1 Hyd. Crane, 12 Ton		663.00		729.30	20.72	22.79
32 L.H., Daily Totals		$2187.00		$3141.70	$68.34	$98.18

Crews

Crew No.	Bare Costs		Incl. Subs O&P		Cost Per Labor-Hour	
Crew Q-23	Hr.	Daily	Hr.	Daily	Bare Costs	Incl. O&P
1 Plumber Foreman (outside)	$59.55	$476.40	$92.90	$743.20	$55.33	$86.75
1 Plumber	57.55	460.40	89.80	718.40		
1 Equip. Oper. (medium)	48.90	391.20	77.55	620.40		
1 Lattice Boom Crane, 20 Ton		960.50		1056.55	40.02	44.02
24 L.H., Daily Totals		$2288.50		$3138.55	$95.35	$130.77
Crew R-1	Hr.	Daily	Hr.	Daily	Bare Costs	Incl. O&P
1 Electrician Foreman	$53.85	$430.80	$83.30	$666.40	$47.20	$74.21
3 Electricians	53.35	1280.40	82.55	1981.20		
2 Helpers	34.65	554.40	57.15	914.40		
48 L.H., Daily Totals		$2265.60		$3562.00	$47.20	$74.21
Crew R-1A	Hr.	Daily	Hr.	Daily	Bare Costs	Incl. O&P
1 Electrician	$53.35	$426.80	$82.55	$660.40	$44.00	$69.85
1 Helper	34.65	277.20	57.15	457.20		
16 L.H., Daily Totals		$704.00		$1117.60	$44.00	$69.85
Crew R-2	Hr.	Daily	Hr.	Daily	Bare Costs	Incl. O&P
1 Electrician Foreman	$53.85	$430.80	$83.30	$666.40	$47.64	$74.99
3 Electricians	53.35	1280.40	82.55	1981.20		
2 Helpers	34.65	554.40	57.15	914.40		
1 Equip. Oper. (crane)	50.25	402.00	79.70	637.60		
1 S.P. Crane, 4x4, 5 Ton		280.00		308.00	5.00	5.50
56 L.H., Daily Totals		$2947.60		$4507.60	$52.64	$80.49
Crew R-3	Hr.	Daily	Hr.	Daily	Bare Costs	Incl. O&P
1 Electrician Foreman	$53.85	$430.80	$83.30	$666.40	$52.93	$82.28
1 Electrician	53.35	426.80	82.55	660.40		
.5 Equip. Oper. (crane)	50.25	201.00	79.70	318.80		
.5 S.P. Crane, 4x4, 5 Ton		140.00		154.00	7.00	7.70
20 L.H., Daily Totals		$1198.60		$1799.60	$59.93	$89.98
Crew R-4	Hr.	Daily	Hr.	Daily	Bare Costs	Incl. O&P
1 Struc. Steel Foreman (outside)	$53.10	$424.80	$97.45	$779.60	$51.95	$92.25
3 Struc. Steel Workers	51.10	1226.40	93.75	2250.00		
1 Electrician	53.35	426.80	82.55	660.40		
1 Welder, Gas Engine, 300 amp		142.00		156.20	3.55	3.90
40 L.H., Daily Totals		$2220.00		$3846.20	$55.50	$96.16
Crew R-5	Hr.	Daily	Hr.	Daily	Bare Costs	Incl. O&P
1 Electrician Foreman	$53.85	$430.80	$83.30	$666.40	$46.60	$73.38
4 Electrician Linemen	53.35	1707.20	82.55	2641.60		
2 Electrician Operators	53.35	853.60	82.55	1320.80		
4 Electrician Groundmen	34.65	1108.80	57.15	1828.80		
1 Crew Truck		224.80		247.28		
1 Flatbed Truck, 20,000 GVW		253.40		278.74		
1 Pickup Truck, 3/4 Ton		157.00		172.70		
.2 Hyd. Crane, 55 Ton		227.40		250.14		
.2 Hyd. Crane, 12 Ton		132.60		145.86		
.2 Earth Auger, Truck-Mtd.		85.00		93.50		
1 Tractor w/Winch		434.60		478.06	17.21	18.93
88 L.H., Daily Totals		$5615.20		$8123.88	$63.81	$92.32

Crew No.	Bare Costs		Incl. Subs O&P		Cost Per Labor-Hour	
Crew R-6	Hr.	Daily	Hr.	Daily	Bare Costs	Incl. O&P
1 Electrician Foreman	$53.85	$430.80	$83.30	$666.40	$46.60	$73.38
4 Electrician Linemen	53.35	1707.20	82.55	2641.60		
2 Electrician Operators	53.35	853.60	82.55	1320.80		
4 Electrician Groundmen	34.65	1108.80	57.15	1828.80		
1 Crew Truck		224.80		247.28		
1 Flatbed Truck, 20,000 GVW		253.40		278.74		
1 Pickup Truck, 3/4 Ton		157.00		172.70		
.2 Hyd. Crane, 55 Ton		227.40		250.14		
.2 Hyd. Crane, 12 Ton		132.60		145.86		
.2 Earth Auger, Truck-Mtd.		85.00		93.50		
1 Tractor w/Winch		434.60		478.06		
3 Cable Trailers		586.80		645.48		
.5 Tensioning Rig		194.55		214.01		
.5 Cable Pulling Rig		1136.50		1250.15	39.01	42.91
88 L.H., Daily Totals		$7533.05		$10233.51	$85.60	$116.29
Crew R-7	Hr.	Daily	Hr.	Daily	Bare Costs	Incl. O&P
1 Electrician Foreman	$53.85	$430.80	$83.30	$666.40	$37.85	$61.51
5 Electrician Groundmen	34.65	1386.00	57.15	2286.00		
1 Crew Truck		224.80		247.28	4.68	5.15
48 L.H., Daily Totals		$2041.60		$3199.68	$42.53	$66.66
Crew R-8	Hr.	Daily	Hr.	Daily	Bare Costs	Incl. O&P
1 Electrician Foreman	$53.85	$430.80	$83.30	$666.40	$47.20	$74.21
3 Electrician Linemen	53.35	1280.40	82.55	1981.20		
2 Electrician Groundmen	34.65	554.40	57.15	914.40		
1 Pickup Truck, 3/4 Ton		157.00		172.70		
1 Crew Truck		224.80		247.28	7.95	8.75
48 L.H., Daily Totals		$2647.40		$3981.98	$55.15	$82.96
Crew R-9	Hr.	Daily	Hr.	Daily	Bare Costs	Incl. O&P
1 Electrician Foreman	$53.85	$430.80	$83.30	$666.40	$44.06	$69.94
1 Electrician Lineman	53.35	426.80	82.55	660.40		
2 Electrician Operators	53.35	853.60	82.55	1320.80		
4 Electrician Groundmen	34.65	1108.80	57.15	1828.80		
1 Pickup Truck, 3/4 Ton		157.00		172.70		
1 Crew Truck		224.80		247.28	5.97	6.56
64 L.H., Daily Totals		$3201.80		$4896.38	$50.03	$76.51
Crew R-10	Hr.	Daily	Hr.	Daily	Bare Costs	Incl. O&P
1 Electrician Foreman	$53.85	$430.80	$83.30	$666.40	$50.32	$78.44
4 Electrician Linemen	53.35	1707.20	82.55	2641.60		
1 Electrician Groundman	34.65	277.20	57.15	457.20		
1 Crew Truck		224.80		247.28		
3 Tram Cars		399.45		439.39	13.01	14.31
48 L.H., Daily Totals		$3039.45		$4451.88	$63.32	$92.75
Crew R-11	Hr.	Daily	Hr.	Daily	Bare Costs	Incl. O&P
1 Electrician Foreman	$53.85	$430.80	$83.30	$666.40	$50.59	$79.06
4 Electricians	53.35	1707.20	82.55	2641.60		
1 Equip. Oper. (crane)	50.25	402.00	79.70	637.60		
1 Common Laborer	36.65	293.20	60.20	481.60		
1 Crew Truck		224.80		247.28		
1 Hyd. Crane, 12 Ton		663.00		729.30	15.85	17.44
56 L.H., Daily Totals		$3721.00		$5403.78	$66.45	$96.50

Crew No.	Bare Costs		Incl. Subs O & P		Cost Per Labor-Hour	

Crew R-12	Hr.	Daily	Hr.	Daily	Bare Costs	Incl. O&P
1 Carpenter Foreman (inside)	$46.35	$370.80	$76.15	$609.20	$43.30	$71.79
4 Carpenters	45.85	1467.20	75.35	2411.20		
4 Common Laborers	36.65	1172.80	60.20	1926.40		
1 Equip. Oper. (medium)	48.90	391.20	77.55	620.40		
1 Steel Worker	51.10	408.80	93.75	750.00		
1 Dozer, 200 H.P.		1325.00		1457.50		
1 Pickup Truck, 3/4 Ton		157.00		172.70	16.84	18.52
88 L.H., Daily Totals		$5292.80		$7947.40	$60.15	$90.31

Crew R-13	Hr.	Daily	Hr.	Daily	Bare Costs	Incl. O&P
1 Electrician Foreman	$53.85	$430.80	$83.30	$666.40	$51.43	$79.99
3 Electricians	53.35	1280.40	82.55	1981.20		
.25 Equip. Oper. (crane)	50.25	100.50	79.70	159.40		
1 Equipment Oiler	43.55	348.40	69.05	552.40		
.25 Hydraulic Crane, 33 Ton		189.80		208.78	4.52	4.97
42 L.H., Daily Totals		$2349.90		$3568.18	$55.95	$84.96

Crew R-15	Hr.	Daily	Hr.	Daily	Bare Costs	Incl. O&P
1 Electrician Foreman	$53.85	$430.80	$83.30	$666.40	$52.38	$81.35
4 Electricians	53.35	1707.20	82.55	2641.60		
1 Equipment Oper. (light)	47.05	376.40	74.60	596.80		
1 Aerial Lift Truck, 40' Boom		325.00		357.50	6.77	7.45
48 L.H., Daily Totals		$2839.40		$4262.30	$59.15	$88.80

Crew R-18	Hr.	Daily	Hr.	Daily	Bare Costs	Incl. O&P
.25 Electrician Foreman	$53.85	$107.70	$83.30	$166.60	$41.88	$66.98
1 Electrician	53.35	426.80	82.55	660.40		
2 Helpers	34.65	554.40	57.15	914.40		
26 L.H., Daily Totals		$1088.90		$1741.40	$41.88	$66.98

Crew R-19	Hr.	Daily	Hr.	Daily	Bare Costs	Incl. O&P
.5 Electrician Foreman	$53.85	$215.40	$83.30	$333.20	$53.45	$82.70
2 Electricians	53.35	853.60	82.55	1320.80		
20 L.H., Daily Totals		$1069.00		$1654.00	$53.45	$82.70

Crew R-21	Hr.	Daily	Hr.	Daily	Bare Costs	Incl. O&P
1 Electrician Foreman	$53.85	$430.80	$83.30	$666.40	$53.36	$82.61
3 Electricians	53.35	1280.40	82.55	1981.20		
.1 Equip. Oper. (medium)	48.90	39.12	77.55	62.04		
.1 S.P. Crane, 4x4, 25 Ton		60.72		66.79	1.85	2.04
32.8 L.H., Daily Totals		$1811.04		$2776.43	$55.21	$84.65

Crew R-22	Hr.	Daily	Hr.	Daily	Bare Costs	Incl. O&P
.66 Electrician Foreman	$53.85	$284.33	$83.30	$439.82	$45.40	$71.75
2 Electricians	53.35	853.60	82.55	1320.80		
2 Helpers	34.65	554.40	57.15	914.40		
37.28 L.H., Daily Totals		$1692.33		$2675.02	$45.40	$71.75

Crew R-30	Hr.	Daily	Hr.	Daily	Bare Costs	Incl. O&P
.25 Electrician Foreman (outside)	$55.35	$110.70	$85.65	$171.30	$43.23	$69.03
1 Electrician	53.35	426.80	82.55	660.40		
2 Laborers, (Semi-Skilled)	36.65	586.40	60.20	963.20		
26 L.H., Daily Totals		$1123.90		$1794.90	$43.23	$69.03

Crew R-31	Hr.	Daily	Hr.	Daily	Bare Costs	Incl. O&P
1 Electrician	$53.35	$426.80	$82.55	$660.40	$53.35	$82.55
1 Core Drill, Electric, 2.5 H.P.		46.20		50.82	5.78	6.35
8 L.H., Daily Totals		$473.00		$711.22	$59.13	$88.90

Historical Cost Indexes

The table below lists both the RSMeans® historical cost index based on Jan. 1, 1993 = 100 as well as the computed value of an index based on Jan. 1, 2014 costs. Since the Jan. 1, 2014 figure is estimated, space is left to write in the actual index figures as they become available through either the quarterly *RSMeans Construction Cost Indexes* or as printed in the *Engineering News-Record*. To compute the actual index based on Jan. 1, 2014 = 100, divide the historical cost index for a particular year by the actual Jan. 1, 2014 construction cost index. Space has been left to advance the index figures as the year progresses.

Year	Historical Cost Index Jan. 1, 1993 = 100 Est.	Historical Cost Index Jan. 1, 1993 = 100 Actual	Current Index Based on Jan. 1, 2014 = 100 Est.	Current Index Based on Jan. 1, 2014 = 100 Actual
Oct 2014*				
July 2014*				
April 2014*				
Jan 2014*	202.7		100.0	100.0
July 2013		201.2	99.3	
2012		194.6	96.0	
2011		191.2	94.3	
2010		183.5	90.5	
2009		180.1	88.9	
2008		180.4	89.0	
2007		169.4	83.6	
2006		162.0	79.9	
2005		151.6	74.8	
2004		143.7	70.9	
2003		132.0	65.1	
2002		128.7	63.5	
2001		125.1	61.7	
2000		120.9	59.6	

Year	Historical Cost Index Jan. 1, 1993 = 100 Actual	Current Index Based on Jan. 1, 2014 = 100 Est.	Current Index Based on Jan. 1, 2014 = 100 Actual
July 1999	117.6	58.0	
1998	115.1	56.8	
1997	112.8	55.6	
1996	110.2	54.4	
1995	107.6	53.1	
1994	104.4	51.5	
1993	101.7	50.2	
1992	99.4	49.1	
1991	96.8	47.8	
1990	94.3	46.5	
1989	92.1	45.5	
1988	89.9	44.3	
1987	87.7	43.3	
1986	84.2	41.6	
1985	82.6	40.8	
1984	82.0	40.4	
1983	80.2	39.5	
1982	76.1	37.6	

Year	Historical Cost Index Jan. 1, 1993 = 100 Actual	Current Index Based on Jan. 1, 2014 = 100 Est.	Current Index Based on Jan. 1, 2014 = 100 Actual
July 1981	70.0	34.5	
1980	62.9	31.0	
1979	57.8	28.5	
1978	53.5	26.4	
1977	49.5	24.4	
1976	46.9	23.1	
1975	44.8	22.1	
1974	41.4	20.4	
1973	37.7	18.6	
1972	34.8	17.2	
1971	32.1	15.8	
1970	28.7	14.2	
1969	26.9	13.3	
1968	24.9	12.3	
1967	23.5	11.6	
1966	22.7	11.2	
1965	21.7	10.7	
1964	21.2	10.5	

Adjustments to Costs

The "Historical Cost Index" can be used to convert national average building costs at a particular time to the approximate building costs for some other time.

Example:

Estimate and compare construction costs for different years in the same city.

To estimate the national average construction cost of a building in 1970, knowing that it cost $900,000 in 2014:

INDEX in 1970 = 28.7

INDEX in 2014 = 202.7

Note: The city cost indexes for Canada can be used to convert U.S. national averages to local costs in Canadian dollars.

*Historical Cost Index updates and other resources are provided on the following website.
http://www.reedconstructiondata.com/rsmeans/chgnotice/456321

Time Adjustment Using the Historical Cost Indexes:

$$\frac{\text{Index for Year A}}{\text{Index for Year B}} \times \text{Cost in Year B} = \text{Cost in Year A}$$

$$\frac{\text{INDEX 1970}}{\text{INDEX 2014}} \times \text{Cost 2014} = \text{Cost 1970}$$

$$\frac{28.7}{202.7} \times \$900{,}000 = .142 \times \$900{,}000 = \$128{,}000$$

The construction cost of the building in 1970 is $128,000.

How to Use the City Cost Indexes

What you should know before you begin

RSMeans City Cost Indexes (CCI) are an extremely useful tool to use when you want to compare costs from city to city and region to region.

This publication contains average construction cost indexes for 731 U.S. and Canadian cities covering over 930 three-digit zip code locations, as listed directly under each city.

Keep in mind that a City Cost Index number is a percentage ratio of a specific city's cost to the national average cost of the same item at a stated time period.

In other words, these index figures represent relative construction factors (or, if you prefer, multipliers) for Material and Installation costs, as well as the weighted average for Total In Place costs for each CSI MasterFormat division. Installation costs include both labor and equipment rental costs. When estimating equipment rental rates only, for a specific location, use 01 54 33 EQUIPMENT RENTAL COSTS in the Reference Section at the back of the book.

The 30 City Average Index is the average of 30 major U.S. cities and serves as a National Average.

Index figures for both material and installation are based on the 30 major city average of 100 and represent the cost relationship as of July 1, 2013. The index for each division is computed from representative material and labor quantities for that division. The weighted average for each city is a weighted total of the components listed above it, but does not include relative productivity between trades or cities.

As changes occur in local material prices, labor rates, and equipment rental rates (including fuel costs), the impact of these changes should be accurately measured by the change in the City Cost Index for each particular city (as compared to the 30 City Average).

Therefore, if you know (or have estimated) building costs in one city today, you can easily convert those costs to expected building costs in another city.

In addition, by using the Historical Cost Index, you can easily convert National Average building costs at a particular time to the approximate building costs for some other time. The City Cost Indexes can then be applied to calculate the costs for a particular city.

Quick Calculations

Location Adjustment Using the City Cost Indexes:

$$\frac{\text{Index for City A}}{\text{Index for City B}} \times \text{Cost in City B} = \text{Cost in City A}$$

Time Adjustment for the National Average Using the Historical Cost Index:

$$\frac{\text{Index for Year A}}{\text{Index for Year B}} \times \text{Cost in Year B} = \text{Cost in Year A}$$

Adjustment from the National Average:

$$\frac{\text{Index for City A}}{100} \times \text{National Average Cost} = \text{Cost in City A}$$

Since each of the other RSMeans publications contains many different items, any *one* item multiplied by the particular city index may give incorrect results. However, the larger the number of items compiled, the closer the results should be to actual costs for that particular city.

The City Cost Indexes for Canadian cities are calculated using Canadian material and equipment prices and labor rates, in Canadian dollars. Therefore, indexes for Canadian cities can be used to convert U.S. National Average prices to local costs in Canadian dollars.

How to use this section

1. Compare costs from city to city.

In using the RSMeans Indexes, remember that an index number is not a fixed number but a ratio: It's a percentage ratio of a building component's cost at any stated time to the National Average cost of that same component at the same time period. Put in the form of an equation:

$$\frac{\text{Specific City Cost}}{\text{National Average Cost}} \times 100 = \text{City Index Number}$$

Therefore, when making cost comparisons between cities, do not subtract one city's index number from the index number of another city and read the result as a percentage difference. Instead, divide one city's index number by that of the other city. The resulting number may then be used as a multiplier to calculate cost differences from city to city.

The formula used to find cost differences between cities for the purpose of comparison is as follows:

$$\frac{\text{City A Index}}{\text{City B Index}} \times \text{City B Cost (Known)} = \text{City A Cost (Unknown)}$$

In addition, you can use RSMeans CCI to calculate and compare costs division by division between cities using the same basic formula. (Just be sure that you're comparing similar divisions.)

2. Compare a specific city's construction costs with the National Average.

When you're studying construction location feasibility, it's advisable to compare a prospective project's cost index with an index of the National Average cost.

For example, divide the weighted average index of construction costs of a specific city by that of the 30 City Average, which = 100.

$$\frac{\text{City Index}}{100} = \% \text{ of National Average}$$

As a result, you get a ratio that indicates the relative cost of construction in that city in comparison with the National Average.

3. Convert U.S. National Average to actual costs in Canadian City.

$$\frac{\text{Index for Canadian City}}{100} \times \text{National Average Cost} = \text{Cost in Canadian City in \$ CAN}$$

4. Adjust construction cost data based on a National Average.

When you use a source of construction cost data which is based on a National Average (such as RSMeans cost data publications), it is necessary to adjust those costs to a specific location.

$$\frac{\text{City Index}}{100} \times \frac{\text{``Book'' Cost Based on}}{\text{National Average Costs}} = \frac{\text{City Cost}}{\text{(Unknown)}}$$

5. When applying the City Cost Indexes to demolition projects, use the appropriate division installation index. For example, for removal of existing doors and windows, use Division 8 (Openings) index.

What you might like to know about how we developed the Indexes

The information presented in the CCI is organized according to the Construction Specifications Institute (CSI) MasterFormat 2012 classification system.

To create a reliable index, RSMeans researched the building type most often constructed in the United States and Canada. Because it was concluded that no one type of building completely represented the building construction industry, nine different types of buildings were combined to create a composite model.

The exact material, labor, and equipment quantities are based on detailed analyses of these nine building types, and then each quantity is weighted in proportion to expected usage. These various material items, labor hours, and equipment rental rates are thus combined to form a composite building representing as closely as possible the actual usage of materials, labor, and equipment used in the North American building construction industry.

The following structures were chosen to make up that composite model:

1. Factory, 1 story
2. Office, 2–4 story
3. Store, Retail
4. Town Hall, 2–3 story
5. High School, 2–3 story
6. Hospital, 4–8 story
7. Garage, Parking
8. Apartment, 1–3 story
9. Hotel/Motel, 2–3 story

For the purposes of ensuring the timeliness of the data, the components of the index for the composite model have been streamlined. They currently consist of:

- specific quantities of 66 commonly used construction materials;
- specific labor-hours for 21 building construction trades; and
- specific days of equipment rental for 6 types of construction equipment (normally used to install the 66 material items by the 21 trades.) Fuel costs and routine maintenance costs are included in the equipment cost.

A sophisticated computer program handles the updating of all costs for each city on a quarterly basis. Material and equipment price quotations are gathered quarterly from 731 cities in the United States and Canada. These prices and the latest negotiated labor wage rates for 21 different building trades are used to compile the quarterly update of the City Cost Index.

The 30 major U.S. cities used to calculate the National Average are:

Atlanta, GA	Memphis, TN
Baltimore, MD	Milwaukee, WI
Boston, MA	Minneapolis, MN
Buffalo, NY	Nashville, TN
Chicago, IL	New Orleans, LA
Cincinnati, OH	New York, NY
Cleveland, OH	Philadelphia, PA
Columbus, OH	Phoenix, AZ
Dallas, TX	Pittsburgh, PA
Denver, CO	St. Louis, MO
Detroit, MI	San Antonio, TX
Houston, TX	San Diego, CA
Indianapolis, IN	San Francisco, CA
Kansas City, MO	Seattle, WA
Los Angeles, CA	Washington, DC

What the CCI does not indicate

The weighted average for each city is a total of the divisional components weighted to reflect typical usage, but it does not include the productivity variations between trades or cities.

In addition, the CCI does not take into consideration factors such as the following:

- managerial efficiency
- competitive conditions
- automation
- restrictive union practices
- unique local requirements
- regional variations due to specific building codes

City Cost Indexes

Table 1

	DIVISION	UNITED STATES 30 CITY AVERAGE			ANNISTON 362			BIRMINGHAM 350 - 352			BUTLER 369			DECATUR 356			DOTHAN 363		
		MAT.	INST.	TOTAL	MAT.	INST.	TOTAL	MAT.	INST.	TOTAL	MAT.	INST.	TOTAL	MAT.	INST.	TOTAL	MAT.	INST.	TOTAL
015433	CONTRACTOR EQUIPMENT		100.0	100.0		101.6	101.6		101.7	101.7		98.8	98.8		101.6	101.6		98.8	98.8
0241, 31 - 34	SITE & INFRASTRUCTURE, DEMOLITION	100.0	100.0	100.0	87.7	94.3	92.3	88.8	94.9	93.1	101.0	88.3	92.1	81.3	92.8	89.3	98.7	88.3	91.4
0310	Concrete Forming & Accessories	100.0	100.0	100.0	92.7	48.2	54.3	93.3	70.2	73.4	89.0	43.6	49.8	94.7	46.4	53.0	97.9	43.0	50.5
0320	Concrete Reinforcing	100.0	100.0	100.0	87.0	87.4	87.2	92.9	87.8	90.4	92.0	47.4	69.7	87.0	79.5	83.3	92.0	46.8	69.4
0330	Cast-in-Place Concrete	100.0	100.0	100.0	102.0	50.5	80.6	99.7	74.7	89.3	99.4	55.7	81.3	93.7	65.1	81.9	99.4	47.0	77.7
03	CONCRETE	100.0	100.0	100.0	99.8	57.9	79.1	95.1	76.1	85.7	100.6	50.4	75.8	91.4	60.7	76.3	100.0	47.0	73.9
04	MASONRY	100.0	100.0	100.0	90.5	67.9	76.5	89.9	76.2	81.4	95.3	49.4	66.9	88.4	52.1	66.0	96.6	40.4	61.8
05	METALS	100.0	100.0	100.0	96.9	92.5	95.5	97.0	94.7	96.3	95.8	78.1	90.4	99.0	87.7	95.5	95.9	76.9	90.0
06	WOOD, PLASTICS & COMPOSITES	100.0	100.0	100.0	92.7	43.7	65.1	96.3	68.3	80.5	87.3	43.4	62.5	98.0	43.9	67.5	99.6	43.4	67.9
07	THERMAL & MOISTURE PROTECTION	100.0	100.0	100.0	100.1	53.8	81.3	95.9	81.4	90.0	100.1	57.6	82.9	93.1	59.3	79.4	100.1	49.9	79.7
08	OPENINGS	100.0	100.0	100.0	93.9	50.9	83.8	95.8	72.3	90.3	94.0	45.2	82.4	98.8	51.6	87.6	94.0	45.2	82.5
0920	Plaster & Gypsum Board	100.0	100.0	100.0	87.5	42.4	56.8	97.0	67.8	77.1	84.9	42.0	55.7	98.1	42.6	60.4	95.3	42.0	59.1
0950, 0980	Ceilings & Acoustic Treatment	100.0	100.0	100.0	87.8	42.4	57.6	98.4	67.8	78.0	87.8	42.0	57.3	95.7	42.6	60.4	87.8	42.0	57.3
0960	Flooring	100.0	100.0	100.0	104.1	41.0	85.2	109.0	76.2	99.2	109.2	57.0	93.6	106.0	51.5	89.7	114.9	28.0	88.9
0970, 0990	Wall Finishes & Painting/Coating	100.0	100.0	100.0	91.4	32.1	55.8	93.5	56.8	71.4	91.4	54.5	69.2	89.3	68.2	76.7	91.4	54.5	69.2
09	FINISHES	100.0	100.0	100.0	92.7	44.0	65.6	99.4	69.3	82.6	95.9	46.7	68.5	95.9	48.8	69.7	98.7	41.0	66.6
COVERS	DIVS. 10 - 14, 25, 28, 41, 43, 44, 46	100.0	100.0	100.0	100.0	70.1	94.0	100.0	87.4	97.5	100.0	42.5	88.5	100.0	44.4	88.9	100.0	42.6	88.5
21, 22, 23	FIRE SUPPRESSION, PLUMBING & HVAC	100.0	100.0	100.0	99.9	56.6	82.6	100.0	62.8	85.1	97.3	34.0	71.9	100.0	41.7	76.6	97.3	33.9	71.9
26, 27, 3370	ELECTRICAL, COMMUNICATIONS & UTIL.	100.0	100.0	100.0	90.7	58.7	74.0	99.7	62.8	80.4	92.6	41.2	65.7	94.5	66.5	79.9	91.5	58.8	74.4
MF2010	WEIGHTED AVERAGE	100.0	100.0	100.0	96.5	63.0	81.9	97.5	74.1	87.3	96.8	50.5	76.6	96.6	59.1	80.3	96.9	50.5	76.7

ALABAMA

	DIVISION	EVERGREEN 364			GADSDEN 359			HUNTSVILLE 357 - 358			JASPER 355			MOBILE 365 - 366			MONTGOMERY 360 - 361		
		MAT.	INST.	TOTAL	MAT.	INST.	TOTAL	MAT.	INST.	TOTAL	MAT.	INST.	TOTAL	MAT.	INST.	TOTAL	MAT.	INST.	TOTAL
015433	CONTRACTOR EQUIPMENT		98.8	98.8		101.6	101.6		101.6	101.6		101.6	101.6		98.8	98.8		98.8	98.8
0241, 31 - 34	SITE & INFRASTRUCTURE, DEMOLITION	101.5	88.6	92.4	86.7	93.8	91.7	81.1	93.8	90.0	86.3	93.6	91.4	94.0	89.3	90.7	94.0	89.2	90.6
0310	Concrete Forming & Accessories	85.6	45.2	50.8	87.0	43.3	49.3	94.7	71.1	74.3	92.2	35.3	43.0	97.1	55.0	60.7	96.9	45.0	52.1
0320	Concrete Reinforcing	92.0	47.4	69.7	92.2	87.7	90.0	87.0	80.5	83.8	87.0	86.5	86.8	89.8	79.4	84.6	94.9	87.1	91.0
0330	Cast-in-Place Concrete	99.5	58.3	82.4	93.8	66.7	82.5	91.3	69.6	82.3	103.9	44.8	79.3	104.3	67.4	88.9	105.4	57.4	85.5
03	CONCRETE	100.9	52.0	76.8	95.7	61.4	78.8	90.3	73.3	81.9	98.9	50.1	74.8	97.0	65.3	81.4	98.3	58.9	78.8
04	MASONRY	95.4	54.1	69.8	86.7	62.3	71.6	89.7	67.7	76.1	84.2	42.0	58.1	93.8	55.1	69.9	90.4	50.5	65.7
05	METALS	95.9	78.1	90.4	96.9	94.0	96.0	99.0	90.5	96.4	96.9	91.1	95.1	97.9	90.6	95.6	97.0	92.8	95.7
06	WOOD, PLASTICS & COMPOSITES	83.6	43.4	60.9	87.8	39.6	60.6	98.0	74.3	84.6	94.8	32.3	59.6	98.2	54.1	73.3	97.7	43.4	67.0
07	THERMAL & MOISTURE PROTECTION	100.1	57.9	83.0	93.1	72.4	84.7	93.0	78.5	87.1	93.2	46.1	74.1	99.8	71.3	88.2	100.2	67.8	87.0
08	OPENINGS	94.0	45.2	82.4	95.4	49.8	84.6	98.8	68.2	91.5	95.3	48.7	84.3	97.2	58.6	88.1	98.3	54.0	87.8
0920	Plaster & Gypsum Board	84.2	42.0	55.5	89.8	38.2	54.7	98.1	73.9	81.7	94.2	30.7	51.0	92.1	53.1	65.5	91.5	42.0	57.8
0950, 0980	Ceilings & Acoustic Treatment	87.8	42.0	57.3	92.1	38.2	56.2	97.6	73.9	81.9	92.1	30.7	51.2	93.3	53.1	66.5	95.9	42.0	60.0
0960	Flooring	107.0	57.0	92.1	102.0	76.2	94.3	106.0	76.2	97.1	104.3	41.0	85.3	114.6	59.5	98.1	110.8	59.5	95.5
0970, 0990	Wall Finishes & Painting/Coating	91.4	54.5	69.2	89.3	62.0	72.9	89.3	59.7	71.5	89.3	39.4	59.3	95.0	55.4	71.2	91.2	54.5	69.1
09	FINISHES	95.3	47.9	68.9	93.3	49.4	68.8	96.4	71.1	82.3	94.5	35.2	61.5	99.0	54.7	74.3	99.0	47.1	70.1
COVERS	DIVS. 10 - 14, 25, 28, 41, 43, 44, 46	100.0	44.1	88.8	100.0	79.5	95.9	100.0	85.3	97.0	100.0	40.8	88.1	100.0	83.9	96.8	100.0	79.4	95.9
21, 22, 23	FIRE SUPPRESSION, PLUMBING & HVAC	97.3	36.3	72.9	102.0	36.9	75.9	100.0	52.9	81.1	102.0	53.8	82.6	100.0	61.5	84.5	100.1	34.8	73.9
26, 27, 3370	ELECTRICAL, COMMUNICATIONS & UTIL.	90.1	41.2	64.6	94.5	62.8	78.0	95.7	66.5	80.4	94.1	62.8	77.7	93.4	58.5	75.2	93.9	62.3	77.4
MF2010	WEIGHTED AVERAGE	96.5	51.9	77.1	96.7	60.8	81.1	96.7	70.8	85.4	97.0	56.7	79.4	97.8	65.9	83.9	97.9	58.1	80.5

ALABAMA / ALASKA

	DIVISION	PHENIX CITY 368			SELMA 367			TUSCALOOSA 354			ANCHORAGE 995 - 996			FAIRBANKS 997			JUNEAU 998		
		MAT.	INST.	TOTAL	MAT.	INST.	TOTAL	MAT.	INST.	TOTAL	MAT.	INST.	TOTAL	MAT.	INST.	TOTAL	MAT.	INST.	TOTAL
015433	CONTRACTOR EQUIPMENT		98.8	98.8		98.8	98.8		101.6	101.6		113.5	113.5		113.5	113.5		113.5	113.5
0241, 31 - 34	SITE & INFRASTRUCTURE, DEMOLITION	105.2	89.3	94.0	98.6	89.1	92.0	81.6	94.0	90.3	125.5	128.7	127.8	116.4	128.8	125.1	132.0	128.8	129.8
0310	Concrete Forming & Accessories	92.6	39.9	47.1	90.3	43.5	49.9	94.6	48.8	55.1	127.8	119.0	120.2	133.0	118.7	120.7	129.2	118.9	120.3
0320	Concrete Reinforcing	91.9	63.3	77.7	92.0	86.2	89.1	87.0	87.7	87.3	148.0	111.5	129.8	142.1	111.5	126.8	122.7	111.5	117.1
0330	Cast-in-Place Concrete	99.5	57.9	82.2	99.4	47.2	77.8	95.1	68.5	84.1	131.0	117.4	125.3	129.2	117.7	124.4	136.1	117.4	128.3
03	CONCRETE	103.6	52.4	78.3	99.4	54.5	77.3	92.1	64.5	78.5	143.0	116.3	129.8	126.5	116.3	121.4	139.9	116.2	128.2
04	MASONRY	95.3	41.8	62.2	98.7	39.3	62.0	88.6	65.5	74.3	180.9	122.2	144.6	182.2	122.2	145.1	167.6	122.2	139.5
05	METALS	95.8	83.5	92.0	95.8	90.3	94.1	98.2	94.1	96.9	114.6	102.5	110.9	118.8	102.6	113.8	117.6	102.4	112.9
06	WOOD, PLASTICS & COMPOSITES	92.5	36.3	60.8	89.3	43.4	63.4	98.0	45.4	68.3	117.1	117.9	117.6	125.0	117.4	120.7	119.8	117.9	118.7
07	THERMAL & MOISTURE PROTECTION	100.4	64.9	86.0	100.0	53.0	80.9	93.1	74.4	85.5	169.9	115.5	147.8	169.2	116.6	147.9	163.4	115.5	143.9
08	OPENINGS	93.9	44.6	82.3	93.9	54.0	84.5	98.8	59.8	89.6	119.7	115.2	118.7	116.2	115.2	116.0	116.6	115.2	116.3
0920	Plaster & Gypsum Board	89.0	34.7	52.1	86.8	42.0	56.3	98.1	44.2	61.4	126.3	118.3	120.9	148.9	117.8	127.7	131.2	118.3	122.4
0950, 0980	Ceilings & Acoustic Treatment	87.8	34.7	52.5	87.8	42.0	57.3	97.6	44.2	62.1	126.5	118.3	121.0	121.7	117.8	119.1	123.5	118.3	120.0
0960	Flooring	111.3	59.5	95.8	109.8	29.0	85.6	106.0	76.2	97.1	150.1	128.3	143.6	140.7	128.3	137.0	142.1	128.3	138.0
0970, 0990	Wall Finishes & Painting/Coating	91.4	54.5	69.2	91.4	54.5	69.2	89.3	46.9	63.8	146.5	113.3	126.5	143.9	121.9	130.7	143.3	113.3	125.2
09	FINISHES	97.5	43.2	67.2	96.0	41.2	65.5	96.3	52.0	71.6	143.1	120.5	130.5	139.4	121.2	129.2	139.6	120.5	129.0
COVERS	DIVS. 10 - 14, 25, 28, 41, 43, 44, 46	100.0	79.0	95.8	100.0	42.5	88.5	100.0	81.3	96.2	100.0	112.5	102.5	100.0	112.5	102.5	100.0	112.5	102.5
21, 22, 23	FIRE SUPPRESSION, PLUMBING & HVAC	97.3	35.1	72.4	97.3	34.3	72.1	100.0	34.6	73.8	100.2	104.3	101.9	100.2	106.7	102.8	100.1	100.6	100.3
26, 27, 3370	ELECTRICAL, COMMUNICATIONS & UTIL.	92.1	71.2	81.2	91.2	41.2	65.1	95.1	62.8	78.2	120.5	115.6	118.0	134.7	115.6	124.7	125.5	115.6	120.3
MF2010	WEIGHTED AVERAGE	97.3	55.7	79.2	96.7	50.8	76.7	96.7	62.0	81.6	121.3	114.3	118.3	120.7	115.0	118.2	120.6	113.5	117.5

DIVISION		ALASKA KETCHIKAN 999			ARIZONA CHAMBERS 865			ARIZONA FLAGSTAFF 860			ARIZONA GLOBE 855			ARIZONA KINGMAN 864			ARIZONA MESA/TEMPE 852		
		MAT.	INST.	TOTAL	MAT.	INST.	TOTAL	MAT.	INST.	TOTAL	MAT.	INST.	TOTAL	MAT.	INST.	TOTAL	MAT.	INST.	TOTAL
015433	CONTRACTOR EQUIPMENT		113.5	113.5		92.6	92.6		92.6	92.6		94.2	94.2		92.6	92.6		94.2	94.2
0241, 31 - 34	SITE & INFRASTRUCTURE, DEMOLITION	170.9	128.8	141.3	67.2	96.6	87.9	84.8	96.8	93.3	100.7	98.4	99.1	67.2	96.8	88.0	91.4	98.6	96.4
0310	Concrete Forming & Accessories	124.5	118.9	119.7	98.2	59.2	64.5	103.7	66.4	71.5	96.3	59.3	64.3	96.5	66.4	70.5	99.3	69.6	73.6
0320	Concrete Reinforcing	111.6	111.5	111.5	100.0	83.5	91.7	99.8	83.5	91.7	110.1	83.5	96.8	100.1	83.5	91.8	110.8	83.5	97.2
0330	Cast-in-Place Concrete	261.0	117.4	201.4	90.3	73.5	83.3	90.4	73.8	83.5	93.8	73.6	85.4	90.0	73.8	83.3	94.6	73.9	86.0
03	CONCRETE	214.6	116.2	166.0	96.5	68.9	82.8	116.1	72.2	94.4	109.8	68.9	89.7	96.1	72.2	84.3	101.7	73.7	87.8
04	MASONRY	191.0	122.2	148.4	90.6	62.7	73.3	90.7	62.8	73.4	110.3	62.7	80.9	90.6	62.8	73.4	110.6	62.8	81.0
05	METALS	119.0	102.4	113.9	95.1	75.0	88.9	95.6	75.7	89.5	92.4	75.5	87.2	95.7	75.8	89.6	92.7	76.4	87.7
06	WOOD, PLASTICS & COMPOSITES	115.7	117.9	117.0	96.1	56.3	73.6	102.2	65.7	81.6	90.0	56.4	71.0	91.6	65.7	77.0	93.4	69.9	80.2
07	THERMAL & MOISTURE PROTECTION	172.3	115.5	149.2	95.1	65.1	82.9	96.7	68.2	85.1	99.3	64.6	85.2	95.0	65.7	83.1	98.6	66.6	85.6
08	OPENINGS	118.1	115.2	117.4	108.1	65.7	98.1	108.2	70.8	99.4	102.2	65.8	93.6	108.3	70.8	99.4	102.3	73.2	95.4
0920	Plaster & Gypsum Board	137.4	118.3	124.4	85.6	55.0	64.8	89.1	64.7	72.5	94.2	55.0	67.5	79.1	64.7	69.3	96.4	69.0	77.7
0950, 0980	Ceilings & Acoustic Treatment	114.7	118.3	117.1	107.8	55.0	72.7	108.7	64.7	79.4	96.4	55.0	68.8	108.7	64.7	79.4	96.4	69.0	78.1
0960	Flooring	140.7	128.3	137.0	92.1	40.3	76.6	94.1	40.4	78.1	100.0	40.3	82.1	91.1	54.7	80.2	101.1	50.4	86.0
0970, 0990	Wall Finishes & Painting/Coating	143.9	113.3	125.5	97.8	56.3	72.9	97.8	56.3	72.9	108.9	56.3	77.3	97.8	56.3	72.9	108.9	56.3	77.3
09	FINISHES	140.7	120.5	129.5	95.7	54.0	72.4	98.8	59.6	76.9	97.6	54.1	73.4	94.7	62.0	76.5	97.1	64.0	78.7
COVERS	DIVS. 10 - 14, 25, 28, 41, 43, 44, 46	100.0	112.5	102.5	100.0	82.3	96.5	100.0	83.3	96.7	100.0	82.5	96.5	100.0	83.3	96.7	100.0	84.0	96.8
21, 22, 23	FIRE SUPPRESSION, PLUMBING & HVAC	98.4	100.6	99.3	97.0	78.9	89.7	100.2	80.0	92.1	95.2	78.9	88.7	97.0	80.0	90.2	101.7	79.0	91.6
26, 27, 3370	ELECTRICAL, COMMUNICATIONS & UTIL.	134.6	115.6	124.7	102.2	72.6	86.7	101.1	65.8	82.7	98.7	65.8	81.6	102.2	65.8	83.2	95.3	65.8	79.9
MF2010	WEIGHTED AVERAGE	132.0	115.8	124.0	97.3	71.9	86.3	101.0	72.9	88.8	99.0	71.2	86.9	97.3	73.2	86.8	98.8	73.8	87.9

DIVISION		ARIZONA PHOENIX 850,853			ARIZONA PRESCOTT 863			ARIZONA SHOW LOW 859			ARIZONA TUCSON 856 - 857			ARKANSAS BATESVILLE 725			ARKANSAS CAMDEN 717		
		MAT.	INST.	TOTAL	MAT.	INST.	TOTAL	MAT.	INST.	TOTAL	MAT.	INST.	TOTAL	MAT.	INST.	TOTAL	MAT.	INST.	TOTAL
015433	CONTRACTOR EQUIPMENT		94.7	94.7		92.6	92.6		94.2	94.2		94.2	94.2		89.0	89.0		89.0	89.0
0241, 31 - 34	SITE & INFRASTRUCTURE, DEMOLITION	91.9	98.8	96.7	73.5	96.6	89.7	102.8	98.4	99.7	87.1	98.6	95.1	73.4	84.9	81.5	73.3	84.5	81.2
0310	Concrete Forming & Accessories	100.2	69.7	73.9	99.8	53.5	59.8	103.2	69.3	74.0	99.8	69.5	73.6	85.2	45.9	51.3	83.9	31.4	38.6
0320	Concrete Reinforcing	109.0	83.7	96.3	99.8	83.5	91.6	110.8	83.5	97.2	91.8	83.5	87.6	86.7	65.8	76.3	88.2	65.7	76.9
0330	Cast-in-Place Concrete	94.7	74.0	86.1	90.3	73.5	83.3	93.9	73.6	85.5	97.4	73.9	87.6	81.1	46.1	66.6	81.2	39.0	64.5
03	CONCRETE	101.3	73.8	87.7	101.7	66.3	84.2	112.1	73.4	93.0	99.7	73.6	86.8	85.2	50.5	68.0	86.9	41.5	64.5
04	MASONRY	98.0	64.6	77.3	90.7	62.7	73.4	110.4	62.7	80.9	95.9	62.8	75.4	98.7	41.5	63.3	111.6	31.9	62.3
05	METALS	94.2	77.2	88.9	95.6	74.7	89.2	92.2	75.7	87.1	93.5	76.3	88.2	98.0	66.9	88.4	97.3	66.5	87.8
06	WOOD, PLASTICS & COMPOSITES	94.4	69.9	80.6	97.5	48.5	69.9	98.0	69.9	82.1	93.7	69.9	80.3	86.3	46.5	63.9	89.8	30.4	56.3
07	THERMAL & MOISTURE PROTECTION	98.2	68.7	86.2	95.5	64.2	82.8	99.5	66.5	86.1	99.6	65.8	85.9	100.2	44.8	77.7	96.1	36.4	71.9
08	OPENINGS	104.2	73.2	96.9	108.2	61.5	97.2	101.3	73.2	94.7	98.3	73.2	92.4	94.6	46.0	83.1	93.5	40.6	81.0
0920	Plaster & Gypsum Board	98.5	69.0	78.4	85.7	47.0	59.4	98.6	69.0	78.4	101.9	69.0	79.5	81.0	45.4	56.7	80.2	28.7	45.2
0950, 0980	Ceilings & Acoustic Treatment	103.5	69.0	80.5	106.9	47.0	67.1	96.4	69.0	78.1	97.3	69.0	78.4	90.6	45.4	60.5	86.2	28.7	47.9
0960	Flooring	101.4	52.7	86.8	92.9	40.3	77.1	102.5	45.9	85.5	91.9	45.0	77.9	104.6	60.1	91.3	111.2	40.3	90.0
0970, 0990	Wall Finishes & Painting/Coating	108.9	62.0	80.7	97.8	56.3	72.9	108.9	56.3	77.3	110.1	56.3	77.8	99.8	42.0	65.1	99.5	50.8	70.2
09	FINISHES	99.1	65.0	80.1	96.2	49.4	70.1	99.2	63.0	79.0	95.4	62.9	77.3	89.4	47.8	66.4	92.1	34.2	59.8
COVERS	DIVS. 10 - 14, 25, 28, 41, 43, 44, 46	100.0	84.0	96.8	100.0	81.4	96.3	100.0	84.0	96.8	100.0	84.0	96.8	100.0	40.6	88.1	100.0	36.5	87.3
21, 22, 23	FIRE SUPPRESSION, PLUMBING & HVAC	100.0	80.0	92.0	100.2	78.9	91.7	95.2	79.0	88.7	100.1	79.0	91.6	95.3	52.1	77.9	95.3	53.5	78.5
26, 27, 3370	ELECTRICAL, COMMUNICATIONS & UTIL.	102.2	68.3	84.5	100.7	65.8	82.5	95.7	65.8	80.1	97.6	65.8	81.0	95.0	64.0	78.8	91.5	62.0	76.1
MF2010	WEIGHTED AVERAGE	99.4	74.8	88.7	98.9	69.7	86.2	99.1	73.5	88.0	97.6	73.6	87.1	94.2	55.1	77.2	94.5	50.4	75.3

DIVISION		ARKANSAS FAYETTEVILLE 727			ARKANSAS FORT SMITH 729			ARKANSAS HARRISON 726			ARKANSAS HOT SPRINGS 719			ARKANSAS JONESBORO 724			ARKANSAS LITTLE ROCK 720 - 722		
		MAT.	INST.	TOTAL	MAT.	INST.	TOTAL	MAT.	INST.	TOTAL	MAT.	INST.	TOTAL	MAT.	INST.	TOTAL	MAT.	INST.	TOTAL
015433	CONTRACTOR EQUIPMENT		89.0	89.0		89.0	89.0		89.0	89.0		89.0	89.0		107.5	107.5		89.0	89.0
0241, 31 - 34	SITE & INFRASTRUCTURE, DEMOLITION	72.8	86.4	82.4	77.7	86.3	83.8	77.9	84.9	82.8	76.4	85.9	83.0	96.9	100.3	99.3	87.9	86.3	86.8
0310	Concrete Forming & Accessories	80.6	39.4	45.1	100.2	57.7	63.5	89.7	45.8	51.8	81.2	36.5	42.6	88.7	49.2	54.6	95.3	60.4	65.2
0320	Concrete Reinforcing	86.7	71.6	79.2	87.7	72.3	80.0	86.3	65.7	76.0	86.5	65.8	76.2	83.9	64.8	74.4	92.7	66.5	79.6
0330	Cast-in-Place Concrete	81.1	50.2	68.3	92.8	70.4	83.5	90.0	44.2	71.0	83.0	39.5	64.9	88.3	55.9	74.9	91.5	70.5	82.8
03	CONCRETE	84.9	50.1	67.7	93.1	65.3	79.4	92.6	49.8	71.4	90.7	44.0	67.6	89.8	55.9	73.1	94.7	65.4	80.2
04	MASONRY	89.1	42.1	60.0	94.1	50.0	66.8	99.0	39.7	62.3	83.9	34.1	53.1	90.5	42.6	60.9	93.9	50.0	66.7
05	METALS	98.0	69.3	89.1	100.3	71.1	91.3	99.1	66.6	89.1	97.3	66.9	87.9	94.6	78.8	89.7	100.5	69.2	90.8
06	WOOD, PLASTICS & COMPOSITES	81.9	36.3	56.2	103.9	60.4	79.4	92.3	46.5	66.5	86.8	36.5	58.4	90.1	49.4	67.1	96.3	63.9	78.1
07	THERMAL & MOISTURE PROTECTION	101.0	46.2	78.8	101.4	54.5	82.4	100.5	43.5	77.4	96.3	38.6	72.9	105.2	50.0	82.8	97.7	54.9	80.3
08	OPENINGS	94.6	45.8	83.0	95.4	57.1	86.4	95.4	46.7	83.9	93.5	42.4	81.4	97.4	53.5	87.0	96.2	58.9	87.4
0920	Plaster & Gypsum Board	78.7	34.9	48.9	86.6	59.7	68.3	85.5	45.4	58.2	78.8	35.1	49.0	95.4	48.0	63.1	92.1	63.3	72.5
0950, 0980	Ceilings & Acoustic Treatment	90.6	34.9	53.5	92.4	59.7	70.6	92.4	45.4	61.1	86.2	35.1	52.2	93.8	48.0	63.3	95.8	63.3	74.2
0960	Flooring	102.0	60.1	89.5	111.0	61.9	96.3	106.9	60.1	92.9	110.0	60.1	95.1	74.5	54.4	68.5	109.1	61.9	95.0
0970, 0990	Wall Finishes & Painting/Coating	99.8	30.0	57.8	99.8	55.0	72.8	99.8	42.0	65.1	99.5	50.8	70.2	88.3	49.4	64.9	100.9	56.4	74.2
09	FINISHES	88.9	40.9	62.2	93.0	58.4	73.8	91.8	47.8	67.3	91.8	41.3	63.7	86.5	49.6	66.0	95.9	60.7	76.3
COVERS	DIVS. 10 - 14, 25, 28, 41, 43, 44, 46	100.0	50.0	90.0	100.0	76.8	95.4	100.0	50.5	90.1	100.0	37.5	87.5	100.0	46.3	89.3	100.0	77.2	95.4
21, 22, 23	FIRE SUPPRESSION, PLUMBING & HVAC	95.3	50.6	77.4	100.2	50.1	80.1	95.3	49.8	77.0	95.3	49.1	76.8	100.4	52.9	81.4	100.0	56.4	82.5
26, 27, 3370	ELECTRICAL, COMMUNICATIONS & UTIL.	88.8	52.4	69.8	92.3	66.1	78.6	93.5	38.0	64.5	93.5	69.4	81.0	99.0	64.0	80.7	99.3	69.5	83.7
MF2010	WEIGHTED AVERAGE	93.0	52.9	75.6	96.8	61.7	81.5	95.5	51.1	76.1	93.8	52.3	75.8	96.3	59.4	80.2	98.0	63.8	83.1

ARKANSAS / CALIFORNIA

	DIVISION	PINE BLUFF 716			RUSSELLVILLE 728			TEXARKANA 718			WEST MEMPHIS 723			ALHAMBRA 917 - 918			ANAHEIM 928		
		MAT.	INST.	TOTAL	MAT.	INST.	TOTAL	MAT.	INST.	TOTAL	MAT.	INST.	TOTAL	MAT.	INST.	TOTAL	MAT.	INST.	TOTAL
015433	CONTRACTOR EQUIPMENT		89.0	89.0		89.0	89.0		89.7	89.7		107.5	107.5		98.9	98.9		100.0	100.0
0241, 31 - 34	SITE & INFRASTRUCTURE, DEMOLITION	78.5	86.3	84.0	74.5	84.9	81.8	90.2	86.9	87.9	103.2	100.3	101.2	96.4	109.7	105.7	96.5	107.7	104.4
0310	Concrete Forming & Accessories	80.9	60.3	63.2	85.9	56.0	60.1	87.6	41.0	47.4	94.4	49.5	55.6	115.1	116.9	116.6	105.5	123.1	120.7
0320	Concrete Reinforcing	88.1	66.5	77.3	87.3	65.6	76.5	87.7	65.8	76.8	83.9	64.9	74.4	107.4	114.9	111.1	93.2	114.8	103.9
0330	Cast-in-Place Concrete	83.0	70.4	77.8	85.0	46.0	68.8	90.5	44.0	71.2	92.6	56.0	77.4	94.7	119.1	104.8	91.3	121.7	104.0
03	CONCRETE	91.5	65.4	78.6	88.4	54.9	71.9	89.1	47.6	68.6	97.3	56.0	76.9	104.0	116.4	110.1	103.1	120.0	111.4
04	MASONRY	120.2	50.0	76.8	93.3	38.0	59.1	98.1	33.7	58.2	76.8	42.6	55.7	122.3	118.6	120.0	77.4	116.2	101.4
05	METALS	98.0	69.1	89.1	98.0	66.5	88.3	90.8	67.0	83.5	93.6	79.1	89.2	84.0	99.9	88.9	103.1	100.2	102.2
06	WOOD, PLASTICS & COMPOSITES	86.3	63.9	73.7	87.7	60.4	72.3	95.2	43.0	65.7	96.3	49.4	69.9	96.6	113.1	105.9	98.5	121.4	111.4
07	THERMAL & MOISTURE PROTECTION	96.4	54.9	79.6	101.2	44.7	78.3	97.1	45.3	76.1	105.6	50.0	83.1	95.2	117.2	104.2	97.9	121.3	107.4
08	OPENINGS	93.5	58.9	85.3	94.6	56.2	85.5	98.3	46.7	86.1	97.4	53.5	87.0	89.8	115.5	95.9	100.3	120.2	105.0
0920	Plaster & Gypsum Board	78.4	63.3	68.1	81.0	59.7	66.5	82.2	41.7	54.6	98.0	48.0	64.0	102.1	113.7	110.0	100.6	122.0	115.2
0950, 0980	Ceilings & Acoustic Treatment	86.2	63.3	71.0	90.6	59.7	70.0	89.7	41.7	57.8	91.8	48.0	62.7	102.5	113.7	109.9	106.7	122.0	116.9
0960	Flooring	109.7	61.9	95.4	104.3	60.1	91.1	111.9	51.9	94.0	76.7	54.4	70.0	93.0	109.2	97.8	105.1	114.1	107.8
0970, 0990	Wall Finishes & Painting/Coating	99.5	56.4	73.6	99.8	35.7	61.3	99.5	31.0	58.3	88.3	50.8	65.8	101.7	108.4	105.7	100.4	106.2	103.9
09	FINISHES	91.8	60.7	74.5	90.0	55.3	70.7	94.3	41.3	64.7	87.7	49.8	66.6	98.0	114.0	106.9	102.0	119.6	111.8
COVERS	DIVS. 10 - 14, 25, 28, 41, 43, 44, 46	100.0	77.2	95.4	100.0	42.1	88.4	100.0	33.5	86.7	100.0	46.4	89.3	100.0	110.1	102.0	100.0	111.3	102.3
21, 22, 23	FIRE SUPPRESSION, PLUMBING & HVAC	100.2	52.4	81.1	95.3	51.9	77.9	100.2	54.6	81.9	95.5	66.5	83.9	95.1	113.7	102.6	100.0	118.0	107.2
26, 27, 3370	ELECTRICAL, COMMUNICATIONS & UTIL.	91.6	69.5	80.1	92.2	45.7	68.0	93.4	36.8	63.9	100.6	65.8	82.4	120.2	119.9	120.0	91.4	105.9	99.0
MF2010	WEIGHTED AVERAGE	96.9	62.9	82.1	94.1	54.4	76.8	95.7	49.9	75.7	95.6	62.7	81.2	98.2	113.9	105.0	98.9	114.1	105.6

CALIFORNIA

	DIVISION	BAKERSFIELD 932 - 933			BERKELEY 947			EUREKA 955			FRESNO 936 - 938			INGLEWOOD 903 - 905			LONG BEACH 906 - 908		
		MAT.	INST.	TOTAL	MAT.	INST.	TOTAL	MAT.	INST.	TOTAL	MAT.	INST.	TOTAL	MAT.	INST.	TOTAL	MAT.	INST.	TOTAL
015433	CONTRACTOR EQUIPMENT		97.9	97.9		98.5	98.5		97.6	97.6		97.9	97.9		95.7	95.7		95.7	95.7
0241, 31 - 34	SITE & INFRASTRUCTURE, DEMOLITION	97.5	105.3	103.0	119.7	106.0	110.1	108.5	101.6	103.7	99.4	104.8	103.2	92.6	102.2	99.3	99.8	102.2	101.5
0310	Concrete Forming & Accessories	104.6	122.7	120.2	118.3	148.0	143.9	114.9	130.6	128.4	103.9	131.7	127.9	113.1	116.9	116.4	108.0	116.9	115.7
0320	Concrete Reinforcing	108.4	114.7	111.5	92.5	116.2	104.3	101.9	115.4	108.6	84.7	115.4	100.0	108.6	114.9	111.7	107.6	114.9	111.2
0330	Cast-in-Place Concrete	92.1	120.7	104.0	127.8	122.0	125.4	99.1	116.3	106.2	97.5	117.3	105.7	87.6	120.2	101.1	99.7	120.2	108.2
03	CONCRETE	101.1	119.4	110.1	110.4	131.2	120.6	114.4	121.4	117.8	101.5	122.4	111.8	95.7	116.8	106.1	105.0	116.8	110.8
04	MASONRY	93.2	115.7	107.1	119.2	131.9	127.0	99.4	123.4	114.3	96.3	121.3	111.7	75.8	118.7	102.4	84.5	118.7	105.7
05	METALS	105.8	99.4	103.8	106.5	100.3	104.6	102.9	97.8	101.3	105.9	100.4	104.2	93.8	100.6	95.9	93.7	100.6	95.8
06	WOOD, PLASTICS & COMPOSITES	93.8	121.5	109.4	110.4	154.0	135.0	112.3	135.9	125.6	105.3	135.9	122.5	106.0	113.2	110.1	99.5	113.2	107.2
07	THERMAL & MOISTURE PROTECTION	104.0	111.9	107.2	103.2	135.9	116.5	101.9	116.0	107.6	94.0	113.6	101.9	100.9	118.5	108.1	101.1	118.5	108.2
08	OPENINGS	96.5	116.2	101.2	96.8	140.5	107.1	99.8	112.7	102.8	96.7	124.0	103.1	91.0	115.5	96.8	91.0	115.5	96.8
0920	Plaster & Gypsum Board	98.9	122.0	114.7	102.8	155.2	138.4	106.0	136.9	127.0	97.5	136.9	124.3	103.9	113.7	110.5	99.8	113.7	109.2
0950, 0980	Ceilings & Acoustic Treatment	109.6	122.0	117.9	104.1	155.2	138.1	112.1	136.9	128.6	106.3	136.9	126.5	101.7	113.7	109.7	101.7	113.7	109.7
0960	Flooring	104.9	109.2	106.2	108.7	126.4	114.0	109.3	118.7	112.1	110.4	135.9	118.0	98.9	109.2	102.0	96.5	109.2	100.3
0970, 0990	Wall Finishes & Painting/Coating	100.8	104.2	102.8	102.7	142.1	126.4	102.0	47.2	69.1	115.0	108.6	111.1	102.1	108.4	105.9	102.1	108.4	105.9
09	FINISHES	102.9	118.7	111.7	103.9	145.5	127.1	107.9	122.2	115.9	104.3	131.9	119.7	101.4	114.1	108.4	100.6	114.1	108.1
COVERS	DIVS. 10 - 14, 25, 28, 41, 43, 44, 46	100.0	111.3	102.3	100.0	125.1	105.0	100.0	121.4	104.3	100.0	121.4	104.3	100.0	110.2	102.0	100.0	110.2	102.0
21, 22, 23	FIRE SUPPRESSION, PLUMBING & HVAC	100.1	108.3	103.4	95.2	144.7	115.0	95.1	99.1	96.7	100.2	109.6	104.0	94.7	113.7	102.4	94.7	113.7	102.4
26, 27, 3370	ELECTRICAL, COMMUNICATIONS & UTIL.	102.0	102.3	102.2	109.2	142.6	126.6	98.8	112.6	106.0	91.7	102.9	97.6	105.5	119.9	113.0	105.2	119.9	112.9
MF2010	WEIGHTED AVERAGE	100.8	110.6	105.1	103.4	133.1	116.4	101.6	111.6	106.0	100.0	114.5	106.3	95.7	113.4	103.4	97.1	113.4	104.2

CALIFORNIA

	DIVISION	LOS ANGELES 900 - 902			MARYSVILLE 959			MODESTO 953			MOJAVE 935			OAKLAND 946			OXNARD 930		
		MAT.	INST.	TOTAL	MAT.	INST.	TOTAL	MAT.	INST.	TOTAL	MAT.	INST.	TOTAL	MAT.	INST.	TOTAL	MAT.	INST.	TOTAL
015433	CONTRACTOR EQUIPMENT		99.2	99.2		97.6	97.6		97.6	97.6		97.9	97.9		98.5	98.5		96.8	96.8
0241, 31 - 34	SITE & INFRASTRUCTURE, DEMOLITION	100.3	105.7	104.1	104.8	104.5	104.6	99.6	104.5	103.0	93.1	105.3	101.7	126.2	106.0	112.0	99.7	103.4	102.3
0310	Concrete Forming & Accessories	109.9	123.2	121.4	105.0	131.8	128.2	101.3	131.8	127.7	116.3	113.5	113.9	107.2	148.0	142.4	107.7	123.1	121.0
0320	Concrete Reinforcing	109.4	115.0	112.2	101.9	115.3	108.6	105.5	115.5	110.5	102.0	114.6	108.3	94.6	116.2	105.4	100.1	114.8	107.4
0330	Cast-in-Place Concrete	94.6	120.9	105.5	110.7	117.6	113.6	99.1	117.6	106.8	84.4	120.7	99.4	121.2	122.0	121.5	98.2	121.0	107.6
03	CONCRETE	100.9	119.9	110.3	115.1	122.6	118.8	105.9	122.6	114.1	93.9	115.4	104.5	109.9	131.2	120.4	102.1	119.8	110.8
04	MASONRY	90.0	119.9	108.5	100.3	118.2	111.4	99.3	122.3	113.5	94.7	115.7	107.7	126.6	131.9	129.9	97.5	116.5	109.3
05	METALS	100.6	102.0	101.0	102.4	101.1	102.0	99.6	101.4	100.2	102.6	99.3	101.6	100.8	100.3	100.7	100.7	100.0	100.5
06	WOOD, PLASTICS & COMPOSITES	105.7	121.4	114.5	99.5	135.9	120.0	95.3	135.9	118.2	105.0	109.2	107.4	98.4	154.0	129.8	99.6	121.5	111.9
07	THERMAL & MOISTURE PROTECTION	100.3	121.1	108.7	101.4	119.3	108.6	101.0	118.5	108.1	100.1	110.2	104.2	101.2	135.9	115.3	103.3	119.4	109.8
08	OPENINGS	97.8	120.2	103.1	99.1	124.7	105.2	98.0	124.7	104.3	92.1	109.5	96.2	96.8	140.5	107.2	94.5	120.2	100.6
0920	Plaster & Gypsum Board	103.5	122.0	116.1	98.3	136.9	124.5	101.0	136.9	125.4	108.9	109.4	109.2	97.4	155.2	136.7	101.8	122.0	115.6
0950, 0980	Ceilings & Acoustic Treatment	111.6	122.0	118.5	111.2	136.9	128.3	106.7	136.9	126.8	107.4	109.4	108.7	107.0	155.2	139.1	109.9	122.0	118.0
0960	Flooring	96.8	114.1	101.9	105.2	111.3	107.0	105.6	113.5	107.9	110.4	109.2	110.0	104.4	126.4	111.0	102.9	114.1	106.2
0970, 0990	Wall Finishes & Painting/Coating	101.1	108.4	105.5	102.0	118.3	111.8	102.0	118.3	111.8	100.5	104.2	102.7	102.7	142.1	126.4	100.5	101.2	100.9
09	FINISHES	102.9	119.8	112.3	105.0	128.9	118.3	102.3	129.2	118.1	104.6	111.3	108.3	103.1	145.5	126.7	102.3	119.1	111.6
COVERS	DIVS. 10 - 14, 25, 28, 41, 43, 44, 46	100.0	111.3	102.3	100.0	121.4	104.3	100.0	121.4	104.3	100.0	110.0	102.0	100.0	125.1	105.0	100.0	111.5	102.3
21, 22, 23	FIRE SUPPRESSION, PLUMBING & HVAC	100.0	118.0	107.2	95.1	109.8	101.0	100.0	108.8	103.5	95.2	108.3	100.4	100.1	144.7	118.0	100.1	118.0	107.3
26, 27, 3370	ELECTRICAL, COMMUNICATIONS & UTIL.	103.6	120.6	112.5	95.4	109.9	103.0	97.9	106.5	102.4	90.5	102.3	96.6	108.3	142.6	126.2	96.2	109.9	103.3
MF2010	WEIGHTED AVERAGE	100.1	116.5	107.3	100.8	115.1	107.0	100.4	114.9	106.7	96.8	108.6	101.9	103.9	133.1	116.6	99.6	114.2	105.9

CALIFORNIA

DIVISION		PALM SPRINGS 922			PALO ALTO 943			PASADENA 910 - 912			REDDING 960			RICHMOND 948			RIVERSIDE 925		
		MAT.	INST.	TOTAL	MAT.	INST.	TOTAL	MAT.	INST.	TOTAL	MAT.	INST.	TOTAL	MAT.	INST.	TOTAL	MAT.	INST.	TOTAL
015433	CONTRACTOR EQUIPMENT		98.8	98.8		98.5	98.5		98.9	98.9		97.6	97.6		98.5	98.5		98.8	98.8
0241, 31 - 34	SITE & INFRASTRUCTURE, DEMOLITION	88.2	105.7	100.5	115.6	106.0	108.8	93.4	109.7	104.8	109.5	104.5	106.0	125.4	106.0	111.8	95.0	105.7	102.5
0310	Concrete Forming & Accessories	102.1	116.9	114.9	105.4	144.5	139.2	104.9	116.9	115.2	105.0	129.6	126.2	120.9	147.8	144.2	102.1	120.7	
0320	Concrete Reinforcing	107.1	114.7	110.9	92.5	115.9	104.2	108.3	114.9	111.6	104.7	115.3	110.0	92.5	116.0	104.2	104.1	114.7	109.4
0330	Cast-in-Place Concrete	87.1	121.6	101.4	108.1	122.0	113.8	89.9	119.1	102.0	110.9	117.6	113.7	124.3	122.0	123.4	94.7	121.7	105.9
03	CONCRETE	97.7	117.2	107.3	99.3	129.6	114.2	99.4	116.4	107.8	115.2	121.5	118.3	112.0	131.0	121.4	103.8	120.0	111.8
04	MASONRY	74.9	115.9	100.3	101.7	127.8	117.8	106.8	118.6	114.1	110.3	118.2	115.2	119.0	127.8	124.4	75.9	115.9	100.7
05	METALS	103.8	99.9	102.6	98.3	99.8	98.8	84.1	99.9	88.9	100.5	101.1	100.7	98.4	99.8	98.8	103.4	100.1	102.4
06	WOOD, PLASTICS & COMPOSITES	93.2	113.3	104.5	95.8	149.6	126.1	83.3	113.1	100.1	97.8	132.8	117.5	114.2	154.0	136.7	98.5	121.4	111.4
07	THERMAL & MOISTURE PROTECTION	97.6	119.0	106.3	100.8	133.4	114.0	95.0	117.2	104.0	108.6	118.9	112.8	101.4	134.2	114.7	98.1	121.2	107.5
08	OPENINGS	96.6	115.5	101.1	96.8	137.5	106.5	89.8	115.5	95.9	102.0	123.0	107.0	96.9	139.9	107.1	99.1	120.2	104.1
0920	Plaster & Gypsum Board	95.5	113.7	107.9	95.6	150.6	133.0	95.0	113.7	107.7	104.5	133.7	124.4	104.9	155.2	139.1	99.9	122.0	115.0
0950, 0980	Ceilings & Acoustic Treatment	104.1	113.7	110.5	105.0	150.6	135.4	102.5	113.7	109.9	131.8	133.7	133.1	105.0	155.2	138.4	111.0	122.0	118.4
0960	Flooring	107.7	109.2	108.1	103.4	126.4	110.3	88.9	109.2	95.0	105.4	111.3	107.2	110.3	126.4	115.1	109.1	114.1	110.6
0970, 0990	Wall Finishes & Painting/Coating	98.7	113.7	107.7	102.7	142.1	126.4	101.7	108.4	105.7	104.1	118.3	112.6	102.7	142.1	126.4	98.7	106.2	103.2
09	FINISHES	100.7	114.7	108.5	101.4	142.9	124.5	95.7	114.0	105.9	110.9	127.1	119.9	105.4	145.5	127.7	103.5	119.6	112.5
COVERS	DIVS. 10 - 14, 25, 28, 41, 43, 44, 46	100.0	110.4	102.1	100.0	124.7	104.9	100.0	110.1	102.0	100.0	121.1	104.2	100.0	125.1	105.0	100.0	111.3	102.3
21, 22, 23	FIRE SUPPRESSION, PLUMBING & HVAC	95.1	113.6	102.5	95.2	143.3	114.5	95.1	113.7	102.6	100.1	109.8	104.0	95.2	144.7	115.0	100.0	118.0	107.2
26, 27, 3370	ELECTRICAL, COMMUNICATIONS & UTIL.	95.0	106.0	100.8	108.1	153.8	132.0	116.8	119.9	118.4	97.8	109.9	104.1	108.8	132.4	121.1	91.6	106.0	99.1
MF2010	WEIGHTED AVERAGE	96.7	111.6	103.2	99.5	133.1	114.2	96.3	113.9	104.0	103.6	114.6	108.4	102.5	131.2	115.0	98.9	114.0	105.5

CALIFORNIA

DIVISION		SACRAMENTO 942,956 - 958			SALINAS 939			SAN BERNARDINO 923 - 924			SAN DIEGO 919 - 921			SAN FRANCISCO 940 - 941			SAN JOSE 951		
		MAT.	INST.	TOTAL	MAT.	INST.	TOTAL	MAT.	INST.	TOTAL	MAT.	INST.	TOTAL	MAT.	INST.	TOTAL	MAT.	INST.	TOTAL
015433	CONTRACTOR EQUIPMENT		98.0	98.0		97.9	97.9		98.8	98.8		99.0	99.0		108.8	108.8		98.5	98.5
0241, 31 - 34	SITE & INFRASTRUCTURE, DEMOLITION	101.0	111.5	108.3	112.3	105.1	107.2	75.1	105.7	96.6	99.7	103.3	102.2	128.6	111.8	116.8	132.0	99.7	109.3
0310	Concrete Forming & Accessories	105.6	132.4	128.7	110.9	132.8	129.8	109.5	116.9	115.9	103.8	112.0	110.9	106.9	149.0	143.2	107.4	147.9	142.3
0320	Concrete Reinforcing	87.6	115.6	101.6	100.6	115.9	108.3	104.1	114.7	109.4	104.9	114.7	109.8	107.8	116.6	112.2	92.8	116.2	104.5
0330	Cast-in-Place Concrete	102.5	118.4	109.1	97.0	117.9	105.7	65.5	121.6	88.8	98.5	108.7	102.7	124.3	123.5	124.0	115.1	121.6	117.8
03	CONCRETE	99.8	122.7	111.1	112.4	123.2	117.7	77.7	117.2	97.2	104.6	110.7	107.6	113.5	132.7	123.0	111.8	131.4	121.5
04	MASONRY	103.4	122.3	115.1	94.4	127.4	114.8	82.4	115.9	103.1	97.1	114.2	107.7	127.2	136.2	132.8	126.8	131.9	130.0
05	METALS	96.4	95.7	96.2	105.3	102.5	104.4	103.3	99.9	102.3	99.6	101.3	100.1	107.1	110.1	108.0	97.8	107.1	100.6
06	WOOD, PLASTICS & COMPOSITES	92.3	136.1	117.0	104.4	136.1	122.3	102.3	113.3	108.5	97.0	108.8	103.6	98.4	154.2	129.9	107.5	153.8	133.6
07	THERMAL & MOISTURE PROTECTION	108.5	121.1	113.6	100.6	125.9	110.9	96.8	119.0	105.8	99.7	106.6	102.5	102.9	139.0	117.6	97.4	138.4	114.1
08	OPENINGS	110.7	124.8	114.1	95.6	130.7	103.9	96.6	115.5	101.1	96.8	111.4	100.3	101.4	140.6	110.7	89.5	140.3	101.5
0920	Plaster & Gypsum Board	92.5	136.9	122.7	102.9	137.1	126.2	101.7	113.7	109.9	102.3	108.9	106.8	99.8	155.2	137.5	96.2	155.2	136.3
0950, 0980	Ceilings & Acoustic Treatment	105.0	136.9	126.2	107.4	137.1	127.2	106.7	113.7	111.4	109.6	108.9	109.1	114.8	155.2	141.7	104.8	155.2	138.3
0960	Flooring	103.3	119.7	108.2	105.1	123.3	110.6	111.0	109.2	110.4	96.2	114.1	101.5	104.4	126.4	111.0	98.7	126.4	107.0
0970, 0990	Wall Finishes & Painting/Coating	100.3	118.3	111.1	101.6	142.1	126.0	98.7	106.2	103.2	98.3	106.4	103.2	102.7	152.6	132.7	102.3	142.1	126.2
09	FINISHES	99.8	130.4	116.9	104.2	133.7	120.6	101.8	113.9	108.6	101.0	111.3	106.7	105.2	146.8	128.4	102.7	145.3	126.4
COVERS	DIVS. 10 - 14, 25, 28, 41, 43, 44, 46	100.0	121.9	104.4	100.0	121.5	104.3	100.0	110.2	102.1	100.0	109.1	101.8	100.0	125.6	105.1	100.0	124.7	105.0
21, 22, 23	FIRE SUPPRESSION, PLUMBING & HVAC	100.0	121.9	108.7	95.2	115.3	103.2	95.1	113.8	102.6	100.0	116.3	106.5	100.0	171.6	128.7	100.0	143.3	117.3
26, 27, 3370	ELECTRICAL, COMMUNICATIONS & UTIL.	103.4	111.3	107.5	91.7	122.8	107.9	95.0	103.7	99.6	102.2	98.9	100.5	108.3	161.4	136.1	101.0	153.8	128.6
MF2010	WEIGHTED AVERAGE	101.2	118.6	108.8	100.2	120.3	108.9	94.6	111.2	101.9	100.2	109.1	104.1	106.1	143.8	122.5	102.2	134.6	116.3

CALIFORNIA

DIVISION		SAN LUIS OBISPO 934			SAN MATEO 944			SAN RAFAEL 949			SANTA ANA 926 - 927			SANTA BARBARA 931			SANTA CRUZ 950		
		MAT.	INST.	TOTAL	MAT.	INST.	TOTAL	MAT.	INST.	TOTAL	MAT.	INST.	TOTAL	MAT.	INST.	TOTAL	MAT.	INST.	TOTAL
015433	CONTRACTOR EQUIPMENT		97.9	97.9		98.5	98.5		98.5	98.5		98.8	98.8		97.9	97.9		98.5	98.5
0241, 31 - 34	SITE & INFRASTRUCTURE, DEMOLITION	104.7	105.3	105.1	122.8	106.0	111.0	113.7	111.6	112.2	86.7	105.7	100.0	99.6	105.3	103.6	131.6	99.5	109.0
0310	Concrete Forming & Accessories	118.0	116.9	117.0	111.2	147.9	142.9	115.2	147.8	143.4	109.7	116.9	115.9	108.6	123.1	121.1	107.5	133.0	129.5
0320	Concrete Reinforcing	102.0	114.8	108.4	92.5	116.1	104.3	93.1	116.1	104.6	107.6	114.7	111.2	100.1	114.8	107.4	115.0	115.9	115.5
0330	Cast-in-Place Concrete	104.2	120.8	111.1	120.4	122.0	121.0	140.1	121.2	132.2	83.6	121.6	99.4	97.8	120.9	107.4	114.3	119.8	116.6
03	CONCRETE	110.1	116.9	113.4	108.4	131.1	119.6	129.7	130.6	130.2	95.2	117.2	106.1	102.0	119.7	110.7	115.0	124.1	119.5
04	MASONRY	96.1	117.4	109.3	118.7	130.8	126.2	98.0	130.8	118.3	72.6	116.2	99.6	94.9	117.4	108.8	130.4	127.5	128.6
05	METALS	103.2	99.7	102.1	98.2	100.1	98.8	99.6	97.8	99.1	103.4	99.9	102.3	101.1	100.0	100.8	105.1	105.8	105.3
06	WOOD, PLASTICS & COMPOSITES	107.5	113.4	110.8	103.5	154.0	132.0	100.4	153.8	130.5	103.9	113.3	109.2	99.6	121.5	111.9	107.5	136.2	123.7
07	THERMAL & MOISTURE PROTECTION	100.8	117.5	107.6	101.2	136.2	115.4	105.2	132.9	116.5	97.9	119.1	106.5	100.2	119.0	107.9	97.4	128.5	110.0
08	OPENINGS	93.9	111.8	98.1	96.8	139.9	107.0	108.2	139.8	115.7	96.0	115.5	100.6	95.2	120.2	101.1	90.7	130.8	100.2
0920	Plaster & Gypsum Board	110.4	113.7	112.6	100.8	155.2	137.8	102.5	155.2	138.4	102.4	113.7	110.1	101.8	122.0	115.6	103.7	137.1	126.4
0950, 0980	Ceilings & Acoustic Treatment	107.4	113.7	111.6	105.0	155.2	138.4	113.0	155.2	141.1	106.7	113.7	111.4	109.9	122.0	118.0	108.5	137.1	127.5
0960	Flooring	111.3	109.2	110.7	106.0	126.4	112.1	115.1	121.3	117.0	111.5	109.2	110.8	104.4	109.2	105.8	102.8	123.3	108.9
0970, 0990	Wall Finishes & Painting/Coating	100.5	101.1	100.9	102.7	142.1	126.4	99.0	142.1	124.9	98.7	106.2	103.2	100.5	101.2	100.9	102.5	142.1	126.3
09	FINISHES	106.1	112.6	109.7	103.4	145.5	126.8	105.8	144.4	127.3	103.3	113.9	109.2	102.9	118.2	111.4	105.7	133.8	121.3
COVERS	DIVS. 10 - 14, 25, 28, 41, 43, 44, 46	100.0	120.4	104.1	100.0	122.5	105.0	100.0	124.5	104.9	100.0	110.4	102.1	100.0	111.5	102.3	100.0	121.8	104.4
21, 22, 23	FIRE SUPPRESSION, PLUMBING & HVAC	95.2	113.8	102.6	95.2	142.8	114.3	95.1	164.7	123.0	95.1	113.8	102.6	100.1	118.0	107.3	100.0	115.3	106.1
26, 27, 3370	ELECTRICAL, COMMUNICATIONS & UTIL.	90.5	106.0	98.6	108.1	143.6	126.7	105.1	116.4	111.0	95.0	105.9	100.7	89.4	111.8	101.1	99.9	122.8	111.9
MF2010	WEIGHTED AVERAGE	99.3	111.6	104.7	101.7	132.7	115.2	104.2	133.6	117.0	96.5	111.6	103.1	98.9	114.6	105.7	104.1	120.4	111.2

DIVISION		CALIFORNIA															COLORADO		
		SANTA ROSA			STOCKTON			SUSANVILLE			VALLEJO			VAN NUYS			ALAMOSA		
		954			952			961			945			913 - 916			811		
		MAT.	INST.	TOTAL	MAT.	INST.	TOTAL	MAT.	INST.	TOTAL	MAT.	INST.	TOTAL	MAT.	INST.	TOTAL	MAT.	INST.	TOTAL
015433	CONTRACTOR EQUIPMENT		98.2	98.2		97.6	97.6		97.6	97.6		98.5	98.5		98.9	98.9		93.8	93.8
0241, 31 - 34	SITE & INFRASTRUCTURE, DEMOLITION	100.1	104.5	103.2	99.4	104.5	102.9	115.9	104.5	107.9	100.5	111.4	108.2	109.9	109.7	109.7	132.1	89.0	101.9
0310	Concrete Forming & Accessories	103.1	146.8	140.8	105.3	131.8	128.2	106.2	129.6	126.4	105.6	146.5	140.9	110.9	116.9	116.1	105.2	69.0	73.9
0320	Concrete Reinforcing	102.7	116.4	109.6	105.5	115.5	110.5	104.7	115.3	110.0	94.3	116.3	105.3	108.3	114.9	111.6	108.0	78.4	93.2
0330	Cast-in-Place Concrete	108.7	119.2	113.1	96.6	117.6	105.3	100.9	117.6	107.8	111.6	119.6	114.9	94.8	119.1	104.9	100.6	79.3	91.8
03	CONCRETE	114.9	130.0	122.4	104.9	122.6	113.6	117.6	121.5	119.5	105.2	129.5	117.2	113.8	116.4	115.1	115.5	74.6	95.3
04	MASONRY	98.6	133.7	120.3	99.2	122.3	113.5	108.3	118.2	114.4	74.6	132.4	110.4	122.3	118.6	120.0	123.2	72.7	92.0
05	METALS	103.7	104.3	103.9	99.8	101.4	100.3	99.6	101.1	100.1	99.6	97.6	99.0	83.2	99.9	88.3	97.2	81.1	92.2
06	WOOD, PLASTICS & COMPOSITES	94.6	153.6	127.9	100.8	135.9	120.6	99.5	132.8	118.3	89.8	153.8	125.9	91.6	113.1	103.8	93.8	69.0	79.8
07	THERMAL & MOISTURE PROTECTION	98.3	134.5	113.0	101.1	118.5	108.2	109.2	118.9	113.2	103.0	134.0	115.6	95.8	117.2	104.5	105.1	78.4	94.2
08	OPENINGS	97.4	140.2	107.6	98.0	124.7	104.3	101.9	123.0	106.9	110.0	140.3	117.2	89.7	115.5	95.8	98.4	75.3	92.9
0920	Plaster & Gypsum Board	97.2	155.2	136.7	101.0	136.9	125.4	105.4	133.7	124.7	97.3	155.2	136.7	99.9	113.7	109.3	75.8	67.9	70.4
0950, 0980	Ceilings & Acoustic Treatment	106.7	155.2	139.0	113.7	136.9	129.1	123.9	133.7	130.4	115.0	155.2	141.8	99.8	113.7	109.1	104.2	67.9	80.1
0960	Flooring	108.1	117.0	110.8	105.6	113.5	107.9	105.9	111.3	107.5	111.2	126.4	115.7	91.1	109.2	96.5	112.4	55.8	95.5
0970, 0990	Wall Finishes & Painting/Coating	98.7	142.1	124.8	102.0	118.3	111.8	104.1	118.3	112.6	99.9	142.1	125.3	101.7	108.4	105.7	113.0	24.1	59.6
09	FINISHES	102.6	143.0	125.1	105.5	129.2	118.7	110.4	127.1	119.7	102.8	144.7	126.1	97.7	114.0	106.8	104.9	61.2	80.5
COVERS	DIVS. 10 - 14, 25, 28, 41, 43, 44, 46	100.0	123.2	104.7	100.0	121.4	104.3	100.0	121.1	104.2	100.0	123.7	104.7	100.0	110.1	102.0	100.0	89.1	97.8
21, 22, 23	FIRE SUPPRESSION, PLUMBING & HVAC	95.1	163.4	122.5	100.0	108.8	103.5	95.2	109.8	101.0	100.0	128.8	111.6	95.1	113.7	102.6	95.2	72.6	86.1
26, 27, 3370	ELECTRICAL, COMMUNICATIONS & UTIL.	95.4	116.6	106.4	97.9	110.9	104.7	98.1	109.9	104.3	100.6	125.1	113.4	116.8	119.9	118.4	96.8	74.2	85.0
MF2010	WEIGHTED AVERAGE	100.3	133.4	114.7	100.5	115.5	107.0	102.6	114.6	107.8	100.6	127.2	112.2	99.1	113.9	105.5	102.0	74.6	90.1

DIVISION		COLORADO																	
		BOULDER			COLORADO SPRINGS			DENVER			DURANGO			FORT COLLINS			FORT MORGAN		
		803			808 - 809			800 - 802			813			805			807		
		MAT.	INST.	TOTAL	MAT.	INST.	TOTAL	MAT.	INST.	TOTAL	MAT.	INST.	TOTAL	MAT.	INST.	TOTAL	MAT.	INST.	TOTAL
015433	CONTRACTOR EQUIPMENT		94.9	94.9		93.4	93.4		97.7	97.7		93.8	93.8		94.9	94.9		94.9	94.9
0241, 31 - 34	SITE & INFRASTRUCTURE, DEMOLITION	92.4	95.1	94.3	94.5	93.1	93.5	93.7	101.2	99.0	125.8	89.0	100.0	104.3	94.7	97.5	95.3	94.6	94.8
0310	Concrete Forming & Accessories	102.0	81.7	84.4	92.9	77.4	79.5	98.5	77.7	80.5	111.4	69.2	74.9	99.3	76.4	79.5	102.5	76.6	80.2
0320	Concrete Reinforcing	102.0	78.5	90.3	101.2	82.7	92.0	101.2	82.7	92.0	108.0	78.4	93.2	102.1	78.6	90.3	102.2	78.4	90.3
0330	Cast-in-Place Concrete	102.4	79.8	93.0	105.2	82.9	95.9	99.6	82.6	92.5	115.7	79.4	100.6	115.6	78.6	100.2	100.5	78.6	91.4
03	CONCRETE	104.7	80.6	92.8	108.1	80.6	94.6	102.4	80.6	91.7	117.8	74.8	96.5	115.3	77.8	96.8	103.2	77.8	90.7
04	MASONRY	93.1	73.2	80.8	94.1	73.0	81.0	96.1	73.3	82.0	110.9	72.4	87.1	110.4	76.9	89.7	107.5	72.9	86.1
05	METALS	97.7	84.4	93.6	100.8	86.5	96.4	103.4	86.7	98.2	97.2	81.2	92.2	98.9	81.3	93.5	97.5	81.1	92.4
06	WOOD, PLASTICS & COMPOSITES	93.3	84.9	88.6	83.8	79.1	81.2	91.0	79.0	84.3	102.6	69.0	83.7	90.8	79.0	84.1	93.3	79.0	85.2
07	THERMAL & MOISTURE PROTECTION	104.4	80.5	94.7	105.3	80.3	95.1	103.7	74.6	91.9	105.0	78.3	94.2	104.8	72.2	91.6	104.4	79.9	94.4
08	OPENINGS	101.5	83.9	97.3	105.8	82.0	100.2	106.5	81.9	100.7	105.3	75.3	98.2	101.4	80.7	96.5	101.4	80.7	96.5
0920	Plaster & Gypsum Board	104.0	84.6	90.8	86.1	78.6	81.0	99.6	78.6	85.3	88.1	67.9	74.3	98.0	78.6	84.8	104.0	78.6	86.7
0950, 0980	Ceilings & Acoustic Treatment	98.0	84.6	89.1	105.1	78.6	87.4	108.2	78.6	88.5	104.2	67.9	80.1	98.0	78.6	85.0	98.0	78.6	85.0
0960	Flooring	103.7	85.3	98.2	95.8	69.5	87.9	100.5	86.3	96.3	116.8	55.8	98.5	100.4	55.8	87.1	104.1	55.8	89.7
0970, 0990	Wall Finishes & Painting/Coating	100.8	68.0	81.1	100.5	41.4	65.0	100.4	77.3	86.7	113.0	24.1	59.6	100.8	41.1	64.9	100.8	54.7	73.1
09	FINISHES	102.6	81.2	90.7	99.4	72.0	84.2	103.1	79.0	89.7	106.9	61.2	81.5	101.4	68.9	83.3	102.6	70.4	84.7
COVERS	DIVS. 10 - 14, 25, 28, 41, 43, 44, 46	100.0	90.0	98.0	100.0	89.7	97.9	100.0	89.4	97.9	100.0	89.1	97.8	100.0	89.4	97.9	100.0	89.4	97.9
21, 22, 23	FIRE SUPPRESSION, PLUMBING & HVAC	95.2	77.6	88.1	100.2	72.7	89.2	100.0	79.9	91.9	95.2	84.9	91.0	100.1	77.5	91.0	95.2	77.5	88.1
26, 27, 3370	ELECTRICAL, COMMUNICATIONS & UTIL.	96.9	85.2	90.8	100.5	83.0	91.4	102.1	85.2	93.3	96.2	71.1	83.1	96.9	85.1	90.7	97.2	85.1	90.9
MF2010	WEIGHTED AVERAGE	98.6	82.0	91.3	101.3	79.3	91.7	101.6	82.6	93.3	102.4	76.8	91.2	102.1	79.6	92.3	99.1	79.6	90.6

DIVISION		COLORADO																	
		GLENWOOD SPRINGS			GOLDEN			GRAND JUNCTION			GREELEY			MONTROSE			PUEBLO		
		816			804			815			806			814			810		
		MAT.	INST.	TOTAL	MAT.	INST.	TOTAL	MAT.	INST.	TOTAL	MAT.	INST.	TOTAL	MAT.	INST.	TOTAL	MAT.	INST.	TOTAL
015433	CONTRACTOR EQUIPMENT		96.5	96.5		94.9	94.9		96.5	96.5		94.9	94.9		95.1	95.1		93.8	93.8
0241, 31 - 34	SITE & INFRASTRUCTURE, DEMOLITION	140.8	95.9	109.3	104.4	94.9	97.7	125.5	95.5	104.5	91.7	94.1	93.4	134.6	92.1	104.8	117.7	91.5	99.3
0310	Concrete Forming & Accessories	102.3	76.7	80.2	95.2	76.5	79.1	110.1	76.2	80.8	97.5	80.2	82.5	101.8	76.4	79.9	107.3	77.8	81.8
0320	Concrete Reinforcing	106.9	78.4	92.7	102.2	78.4	90.3	107.3	78.3	92.8	102.0	77.0	89.5	106.8	78.3	92.6	103.3	82.7	93.1
0330	Cast-in-Place Concrete	100.6	78.8	91.5	100.5	78.6	91.4	111.4	78.1	97.5	96.6	58.5	80.8	100.6	78.7	91.5	99.9	83.7	93.2
03	CONCRETE	120.6	77.9	99.6	113.8	77.8	96.0	114.1	77.4	96.0	99.9	72.2	86.3	111.6	77.7	94.9	104.3	81.1	92.8
04	MASONRY	97.5	72.9	82.3	110.3	72.9	87.2	129.6	72.7	94.4	104.6	49.7	70.6	103.9	72.7	84.6	94.1	73.2	81.2
05	METALS	96.9	81.8	92.2	97.7	81.2	92.6	98.4	80.5	92.9	98.9	78.5	92.6	96.0	80.8	91.3	100.0	87.4	96.1
06	WOOD, PLASTICS & COMPOSITES	89.1	79.1	83.4	86.2	79.0	82.1	100.4	79.1	88.4	88.4	84.9	86.4	90.2	79.2	84.0	96.3	79.4	86.8
07	THERMAL & MOISTURE PROTECTION	105.0	79.5	94.6	105.3	74.2	92.7	104.1	68.8	89.8	104.3	65.0	88.3	105.1	79.5	94.7	103.6	80.0	94.0
08	OPENINGS	104.3	80.8	98.7	101.4	80.7	96.5	105.0	80.8	99.3	101.4	83.9	97.3	105.5	80.8	99.7	100.1	82.1	95.9
0920	Plaster & Gypsum Board	111.5	78.6	89.1	95.8	78.6	84.1	123.4	78.6	92.9	96.5	84.6	88.4	75.0	78.6	77.4	80.2	78.6	79.1
0950, 0980	Ceilings & Acoustic Treatment	103.4	78.6	86.9	98.0	78.6	85.0	103.4	78.6	86.9	98.0	84.6	89.1	104.2	78.6	87.2	113.1	78.6	90.1
0960	Flooring	111.7	51.4	93.7	98.3	55.8	85.6	116.2	55.8	98.1	99.5	55.8	86.4	114.6	46.2	94.2	113.4	86.3	105.3
0970, 0990	Wall Finishes & Painting/Coating	112.9	54.7	77.9	100.8	68.0	81.1	112.9	68.0	85.9	100.8	25.6	55.6	113.0	24.1	59.6	113.0	38.4	68.1
09	FINISHES	109.9	69.8	87.5	101.3	72.6	85.3	110.8	72.0	89.2	100.1	70.7	83.7	105.4	65.3	83.1	105.8	74.9	88.6
COVERS	DIVS. 10 - 14, 25, 28, 41, 43, 44, 46	100.0	89.5	97.9	100.0	89.4	97.9	100.0	89.5	97.9	100.0	90.0	98.0	100.0	89.8	98.0	100.0	90.3	98.1
21, 22, 23	FIRE SUPPRESSION, PLUMBING & HVAC	95.2	84.8	91.0	95.2	77.0	87.9	100.0	84.3	93.7	100.1	77.5	91.0	95.2	84.8	91.0	100.0	72.8	89.1
26, 27, 3370	ELECTRICAL, COMMUNICATIONS & UTIL.	93.5	71.1	81.8	97.2	85.1	90.9	95.9	55.1	74.6	96.9	85.1	90.7	95.9	57.7	76.0	96.9	74.3	85.1
MF2010	WEIGHTED AVERAGE	102.2	79.3	92.2	100.6	79.6	91.4	104.4	76.7	92.4	99.7	76.1	89.4	101.2	76.5	90.5	100.9	78.6	91.2

754

City Cost Indexes

		COLORADO			CONNECTICUT														
DIVISION		SALIDA			BRIDGEPORT			BRISTOL			HARTFORD			MERIDEN			NEW BRITAIN		
		812			066			060			061			064			060		
		MAT.	INST.	TOTAL	MAT.	INST.	TOTAL	MAT.	INST.	TOTAL	MAT.	INST.	TOTAL	MAT.	INST.	TOTAL	MAT.	INST.	TOTAL
015433	CONTRACTOR EQUIPMENT		95.1	95.1		100.6	100.6		100.6	100.6		100.6	100.6		101.1	101.1		100.6	100.6
0241, 31 - 34	SITE & INFRASTRUCTURE, DEMOLITION	125.5	92.4	102.3	111.7	104.0	106.3	110.9	104.0	106.1	106.0	104.0	104.6	108.9	104.7	105.9	111.1	104.0	106.1
0310	Concrete Forming & Accessories	110.0	76.4	81.0	98.2	123.8	120.3	98.2	123.7	120.3	95.1	123.7	119.8	97.9	123.7	120.2	98.6	123.7	120.3
0320	Concrete Reinforcing	106.6	78.3	92.5	110.0	129.3	119.7	110.0	129.3	119.7	109.5	129.3	119.4	110.0	129.3	119.7	110.0	129.3	119.7
0330	Cast-in-Place Concrete	115.2	78.7	100.1	103.7	127.5	113.6	97.2	127.4	109.8	99.0	127.4	110.8	93.5	127.4	107.6	98.8	127.4	110.7
03	CONCRETE	112.8	77.7	95.5	105.3	125.8	115.4	102.2	125.7	113.8	102.8	125.8	114.1	100.5	125.7	112.9	103.0	125.7	114.2
04	MASONRY	131.2	72.7	95.0	98.1	134.8	120.8	90.8	134.8	118.0	94.7	134.8	119.5	90.4	134.8	117.9	92.1	134.8	118.6
05	METALS	95.7	80.8	91.1	102.0	125.1	109.1	102.0	125.1	109.1	107.8	125.1	113.1	99.5	125.1	107.4	98.6	125.1	106.8
06	WOOD, PLASTICS & COMPOSITES	97.4	79.2	87.2	99.1	122.9	112.5	99.1	122.9	112.5	92.6	122.9	109.7	99.1	122.9	112.5	99.1	122.9	112.5
07	THERMAL & MOISTURE PROTECTION	104.1	79.5	94.1	100.3	129.2	112.0	100.4	126.9	111.2	104.8	126.9	113.8	100.4	126.9	111.2	100.4	126.9	111.2
08	OPENINGS	98.5	80.8	94.3	107.0	132.2	113.0	107.0	132.2	113.0	106.1	132.2	112.2	109.4	132.2	114.8	107.0	132.2	113.0
0920	Plaster & Gypsum Board	75.4	78.6	77.5	99.9	123.0	115.6	99.9	123.0	115.6	95.4	123.0	114.2	101.5	123.0	116.1	99.9	123.0	115.6
0950, 0980	Ceilings & Acoustic Treatment	104.2	78.6	87.2	97.9	123.0	114.6	97.9	123.0	114.6	101.3	123.0	115.7	102.1	123.0	116.0	97.9	123.0	114.6
0960	Flooring	119.1	46.2	97.3	99.3	133.6	109.6	99.3	133.6	109.6	97.8	133.6	108.5	99.3	133.6	109.6	99.3	133.6	109.6
0970, 0990	Wall Finishes & Painting/Coating	113.0	24.1	59.6	96.4	122.3	112.0	96.4	122.3	112.0	97.3	122.3	112.3	96.4	122.3	112.0	96.4	122.3	112.0
09	FINISHES	105.6	65.3	83.2	100.8	125.1	114.3	100.8	125.1	114.3	99.7	125.1	113.8	101.9	125.1	114.8	100.8	125.1	114.3
COVERS	DIVS. 10 - 14, 25, 28, 41, 43, 44, 46	100.0	89.9	98.0	100.0	110.4	102.1	100.0	110.5	102.1	100.0	110.5	102.1	100.0	110.5	102.1	100.0	110.5	102.1
21, 22, 23	FIRE SUPPRESSION, PLUMBING & HVAC	95.2	72.6	86.1	100.0	116.0	106.4	100.0	116.0	106.4	100.0	116.0	106.4	95.1	116.0	103.5	100.0	116.0	106.4
26, 27, 3370	ELECTRICAL, COMMUNICATIONS & UTIL.	96.1	74.2	84.7	99.2	108.7	104.2	99.2	111.3	105.5	98.6	112.3	105.7	99.2	111.3	105.5	99.3	111.3	105.6
MF2010	WEIGHTED AVERAGE	101.7	76.2	90.6	101.8	120.2	109.8	101.1	120.4	109.4	102.0	120.6	110.1	99.6	120.5	108.7	100.8	120.4	109.3

		CONNECTICUT																	
DIVISION		NEW HAVEN			NEW LONDON			NORWALK			STAMFORD			WATERBURY			WILLIMANTIC		
		065			063			068			069			067			062		
		MAT.	INST.	TOTAL	MAT.	INST.	TOTAL	MAT.	INST.	TOTAL	MAT.	INST.	TOTAL	MAT.	INST.	TOTAL	MAT.	INST.	TOTAL
015433	CONTRACTOR EQUIPMENT		101.1	101.1		101.1	101.1		100.6	100.6		100.6	100.6		100.6	100.6		100.6	100.6
0241, 31 - 34	SITE & INFRASTRUCTURE, DEMOLITION	110.9	104.7	106.5	103.1	104.7	104.2	111.5	104.0	106.2	112.2	104.0	106.4	111.4	104.0	106.2	111.6	104.0	106.3
0310	Concrete Forming & Accessories	98.0	123.7	120.2	97.9	123.7	120.2	98.2	124.2	120.6	98.2	124.2	120.7	98.2	123.7	120.2	98.2	123.7	120.2
0320	Concrete Reinforcing	110.0	129.3	119.7	86.3	129.3	107.7	110.0	129.4	119.7	110.0	129.4	119.7	110.0	129.3	119.7	110.0	129.3	119.7
0330	Cast-in-Place Concrete	100.5	127.4	111.7	85.7	127.4	103.0	102.0	128.9	113.2	103.7	128.9	114.2	103.7	127.4	113.6	96.9	127.4	109.6
03	CONCRETE	117.2	125.7	121.4	90.2	125.7	107.7	104.5	126.5	115.3	105.3	126.5	115.8	105.3	125.7	115.4	102.1	125.7	113.7
04	MASONRY	91.0	134.8	118.1	89.4	134.8	117.5	90.6	134.8	118.0	91.3	134.8	118.2	91.3	134.8	118.2	90.6	134.8	118.0
05	METALS	98.8	125.1	106.9	98.5	125.1	106.7	102.0	125.5	109.3	102.0	125.6	109.3	102.0	125.0	109.1	101.8	125.0	108.9
06	WOOD, PLASTICS & COMPOSITES	99.1	122.9	112.5	99.1	122.9	112.5	99.1	122.9	112.5	99.1	122.9	112.5	99.1	122.9	112.5	99.1	122.9	112.5
07	THERMAL & MOISTURE PROTECTION	100.5	126.7	111.1	100.4	126.9	111.1	100.4	129.4	112.2	100.4	129.4	112.2	100.4	126.7	111.1	100.6	125.7	110.8
08	OPENINGS	107.0	132.2	113.0	109.9	132.2	115.2	107.0	132.2	113.0	107.0	132.2	113.0	107.0	132.2	113.0	110.0	132.2	115.2
0920	Plaster & Gypsum Board	99.9	123.0	115.6	99.9	123.0	115.6	99.9	123.0	115.6	99.9	123.0	115.6	99.9	123.0	115.6	99.9	123.0	115.6
0950, 0980	Ceilings & Acoustic Treatment	97.9	123.0	114.6	95.9	123.0	113.9	97.9	123.0	114.6	97.9	123.0	114.6	97.9	123.0	114.6	95.9	123.0	113.9
0960	Flooring	99.3	133.6	109.6	99.3	133.6	109.6	99.3	133.6	109.6	99.3	133.6	109.6	99.3	135.7	110.2	99.3	135.7	110.2
0970, 0990	Wall Finishes & Painting/Coating	96.4	122.3	112.0	96.4	122.3	112.0	96.4	122.3	112.0	96.4	122.3	112.0	96.4	122.3	112.0	96.4	122.3	112.0
09	FINISHES	100.8	125.1	114.4	99.8	125.1	113.9	100.8	125.1	114.4	100.9	125.1	114.4	100.7	125.1	114.3	100.5	125.4	114.4
COVERS	DIVS. 10 - 14, 25, 28, 41, 43, 44, 46	100.0	110.5	102.1	100.0	110.5	102.1	100.0	110.6	102.1	100.0	110.7	102.1	100.0	110.4	102.1	100.0	110.5	102.1
21, 22, 23	FIRE SUPPRESSION, PLUMBING & HVAC	100.0	116.0	106.4	95.1	116.0	103.5	100.0	116.1	106.4	100.0	116.1	106.4	100.0	116.0	106.4	100.0	116.0	106.4
26, 27, 3370	ELECTRICAL, COMMUNICATIONS & UTIL.	99.2	111.3	105.5	95.9	111.3	103.9	99.2	156.4	129.1	99.2	163.8	132.9	98.7	108.7	103.9	99.2	112.2	106.0
MF2010	WEIGHTED AVERAGE	102.2	120.5	110.2	97.7	120.5	107.6	101.4	126.9	112.5	101.5	127.9	113.0	101.4	120.1	109.6	101.4	120.6	109.7

		D.C.			DELAWARE									FLORIDA					
DIVISION		WASHINGTON			DOVER			NEWARK			WILMINGTON			DAYTONA BEACH			FORT LAUDERDALE		
		200 - 205			199			197			198			321			333		
		MAT.	INST.	TOTAL	MAT.	INST.	TOTAL	MAT.	INST.	TOTAL	MAT.	INST.	TOTAL	MAT.	INST.	TOTAL	MAT.	INST.	TOTAL
015433	CONTRACTOR EQUIPMENT		104.4	104.4		117.0	117.0		117.0	117.0		117.2	117.2		98.8	98.8		91.7	91.7
0241, 31 - 34	SITE & INFRASTRUCTURE, DEMOLITION	106.8	94.0	97.8	99.7	112.3	108.6	99.1	112.3	108.4	92.4	112.6	106.6	107.0	90.4	95.4	93.6	78.3	82.9
0310	Concrete Forming & Accessories	99.5	79.2	81.9	97.1	101.5	100.9	97.2	101.5	100.9	98.3	101.5	101.1	97.3	69.7	73.5	95.5	70.1	73.6
0320	Concrete Reinforcing	109.0	91.3	100.2	98.5	105.2	101.9	93.8	105.2	99.5	96.4	105.2	100.8	92.8	79.0	85.9	89.8	74.4	82.1
0330	Cast-in-Place Concrete	121.4	88.1	107.5	99.1	100.6	99.7	84.4	100.6	91.1	88.9	100.6	93.8	86.6	72.0	80.5	90.9	78.4	85.7
03	CONCRETE	109.6	85.8	97.9	99.9	102.8	101.3	92.1	102.8	97.4	94.8	102.8	98.7	88.2	73.4	80.9	90.7	75.0	82.9
04	MASONRY	95.9	80.0	86.1	103.3	97.2	99.5	99.9	97.2	98.2	103.6	97.2	99.6	92.3	66.8	76.5	89.9	69.4	77.3
05	METALS	100.1	113.3	102.3	103.1	117.0	107.4	103.7	117.0	107.8	102.9	117.0	107.3	96.4	92.8	95.3	95.5	91.5	94.2
06	WOOD, PLASTICS & COMPOSITES	103.5	77.2	88.7	95.0	101.1	98.4	97.6	101.1	99.6	98.2	101.1	99.8	99.7	70.8	83.4	96.0	68.7	80.6
07	THERMAL & MOISTURE PROTECTION	102.4	86.0	95.8	101.9	110.2	105.3	104.2	110.2	106.7	102.2	110.2	105.5	99.6	74.9	89.6	96.9	82.3	91.0
08	OPENINGS	100.3	87.6	97.3	94.3	110.5	98.1	93.4	110.5	97.4	96.6	110.5	99.9	98.9	69.1	91.8	96.9	67.1	89.9
0920	Plaster & Gypsum Board	105.8	76.5	85.9	105.9	101.0	102.6	103.4	101.0	101.8	104.8	101.0	102.2	95.1	70.3	78.3	98.5	68.2	77.9
0950, 0980	Ceilings & Acoustic Treatment	107.8	76.5	87.0	104.2	101.0	102.0	95.0	101.0	99.0	102.2	101.0	101.4	90.7	70.3	77.2	91.3	68.2	75.9
0960	Flooring	104.7	95.3	101.9	99.1	109.0	102.1	95.5	109.0	99.6	101.4	109.0	103.7	115.2	74.9	103.2	115.4	70.6	102.0
0970, 0990	Wall Finishes & Painting/Coating	104.6	84.0	92.2	97.3	105.3	102.1	99.5	105.3	103.0	97.3	105.3	102.1	99.4	75.7	85.2	96.5	71.7	81.6
09	FINISHES	101.6	81.7	90.5	101.4	102.8	102.2	97.4	102.8	100.4	102.0	102.8	102.4	100.8	70.9	84.1	99.4	69.6	82.8
COVERS	DIVS. 10 - 14, 25, 28, 41, 43, 44, 46	100.0	98.4	99.7	100.0	89.7	97.9	100.0	89.7	97.9	100.0	89.7	97.9	100.0	83.5	96.7	100.0	86.5	97.3
21, 22, 23	FIRE SUPPRESSION, PLUMBING & HVAC	100.1	92.9	97.2	100.0	115.8	106.3	100.2	115.8	106.5	100.2	115.8	106.4	100.0	77.8	91.1	100.0	68.0	87.2
26, 27, 3370	ELECTRICAL, COMMUNICATIONS & UTIL.	102.7	102.6	102.6	95.2	109.0	102.4	97.7	109.0	103.6	96.6	109.0	103.1	94.4	56.2	74.5	92.6	72.7	82.2
MF2010	WEIGHTED AVERAGE	101.6	91.6	97.2	99.7	108.1	103.3	98.8	108.1	102.8	99.4	108.1	103.2	97.4	74.4	87.3	96.4	73.9	86.6

755

FLORIDA

DIVISION		FORT MYERS 339,341			GAINESVILLE 326,344			JACKSONVILLE 320,322			LAKELAND 338			MELBOURNE 329			MIAMI 330 - 332,340		
		MAT.	INST.	TOTAL	MAT.	INST.	TOTAL	MAT.	INST.	TOTAL	MAT.	INST.	TOTAL	MAT.	INST.	TOTAL	MAT.	INST.	TOTAL
015433	CONTRACTOR EQUIPMENT		98.8	98.8		98.8	98.8		98.8	98.8		98.8	98.8		98.8	98.8		91.7	91.7
0241, 31 - 34	SITE & INFRASTRUCTURE, DEMOLITION	104.3	89.5	93.9	115.4	89.5	97.2	107.0	89.8	94.9	106.2	89.9	94.7	113.9	89.7	96.9	96.7	78.1	83.6
0310	Concrete Forming & Accessories	91.1	76.6	78.6	92.3	55.5	60.5	97.1	55.9	61.5	87.4	77.1	78.5	93.5	71.4	74.4	100.7	70.5	74.6
0320	Concrete Reinforcing	90.8	95.7	93.3	98.5	66.9	82.7	92.8	67.0	79.9	93.1	96.6	94.8	93.9	79.0	86.5	95.9	74.5	85.2
0330	Cast-in-Place Concrete	94.8	69.4	84.3	99.4	63.6	84.5	87.4	69.5	80.0	97.0	70.8	86.1	104.3	74.3	91.9	91.7	79.4	86.6
03	CONCRETE	91.3	78.6	85.1	98.7	62.0	80.6	88.6	64.2	76.6	93.0	79.5	86.3	99.0	75.0	87.1	92.4	75.5	84.0
04	MASONRY	84.1	62.9	71.0	106.7	62.3	79.2	92.3	62.3	73.7	100.3	77.1	85.9	91.2	71.0	78.7	90.3	73.2	79.7
05	METALS	97.6	98.6	97.9	95.3	86.6	92.7	95.0	87.0	92.5	97.5	99.5	98.1	104.4	93.0	100.9	95.9	90.3	94.1
06	WOOD, PLASTICS & COMPOSITES	92.5	79.2	85.0	93.2	53.0	70.5	99.7	53.0	73.4	87.5	79.2	82.8	94.9	70.8	81.3	103.4	68.7	83.8
07	THERMAL & MOISTURE PROTECTION	96.8	81.3	90.5	99.9	62.5	84.7	99.8	63.1	84.9	96.7	86.0	92.4	100.0	77.3	90.8	98.1	76.5	89.4
08	OPENINGS	97.9	76.2	92.8	97.1	54.0	86.9	98.9	57.2	89.0	97.9	76.9	92.9	98.1	72.4	92.0	99.1	67.0	91.5
0920	Plaster & Gypsum Board	93.9	79.0	83.8	90.8	51.9	64.4	95.1	51.9	65.8	90.5	79.0	82.7	90.8	70.3	76.9	96.2	68.2	77.1
0950, 0980	Ceilings & Acoustic Treatment	85.8	79.0	81.3	86.1	51.9	63.4	90.7	51.9	64.9	85.8	79.0	81.3	88.1	70.3	76.3	95.9	68.2	77.4
0960	Flooring	112.1	56.1	95.4	112.6	43.9	92.1	115.2	65.7	100.4	109.8	57.6	94.2	112.8	74.9	101.5	118.5	74.3	105.3
0970, 0990	Wall Finishes & Painting/Coating	101.6	62.1	77.8	99.4	62.1	77.0	99.4	66.3	79.5	101.6	62.1	77.8	99.4	93.9	96.1	93.5	71.7	80.4
09	FINISHES	98.9	71.5	83.6	99.4	52.9	73.5	100.9	57.7	76.8	97.9	71.8	83.3	99.6	73.9	85.3	101.9	70.8	84.5
COVERS	DIVS. 10 - 14, 25, 28, 41, 43, 44, 46	100.0	74.6	94.9	100.0	81.9	96.4	100.0	81.4	96.3	100.0	74.6	94.9	100.0	84.9	97.0	100.0	87.1	97.4
21, 22, 23	FIRE SUPPRESSION, PLUMBING & HVAC	97.4	65.7	84.7	98.8	65.5	85.5	100.0	65.5	86.2	97.4	82.5	91.5	100.0	79.9	92.0	100.0	67.9	87.1
26, 27, 3370	ELECTRICAL, COMMUNICATIONS & UTIL.	94.7	64.3	78.9	94.7	73.5	83.6	94.1	63.7	78.2	92.8	63.1	77.3	95.7	69.5	82.0	96.6	75.5	85.6
MF2010	WEIGHTED AVERAGE	96.4	74.1	86.7	98.7	68.0	85.3	97.2	67.7	84.3	97.1	79.3	89.4	99.9	77.9	90.3	97.7	74.6	87.6

FLORIDA

DIVISION		ORLANDO 327 - 328,347			PANAMA CITY 324			PENSACOLA 325			SARASOTA 342			ST. PETERSBURG 337			TALLAHASSEE 323		
		MAT.	INST.	TOTAL	MAT.	INST.	TOTAL	MAT.	INST.	TOTAL	MAT.	INST.	TOTAL	MAT.	INST.	TOTAL	MAT.	INST.	TOTAL
015433	CONTRACTOR EQUIPMENT		98.8	98.8		98.8	98.8		98.8	98.8		98.8	98.8		98.8	98.8		98.8	98.8
0241, 31 - 34	SITE & INFRASTRUCTURE, DEMOLITION	108.9	89.6	95.4	119.4	88.6	97.8	118.9	89.1	98.0	111.3	89.6	96.1	107.8	89.3	94.8	105.5	88.9	93.8
0310	Concrete Forming & Accessories	99.8	73.7	77.3	96.4	44.9	52.0	94.4	53.0	58.6	96.2	76.7	79.4	95.0	52.2	58.1	100.4	45.1	52.7
0320	Concrete Reinforcing	95.9	76.2	86.1	97.0	74.9	85.9	99.4	75.4	87.4	92.8	96.5	94.6	93.1	88.8	91.0	102.5	66.8	84.6
0330	Cast-in-Place Concrete	107.4	71.8	92.6	91.9	57.7	77.7	113.4	67.0	94.2	104.0	70.6	90.1	98.0	65.5	84.5	93.5	57.3	78.5
03	CONCRETE	99.0	74.6	86.9	96.8	56.7	77.0	106.3	63.6	85.2	97.2	79.2	88.3	94.6	65.2	80.1	94.3	55.2	75.0
04	MASONRY	97.1	66.8	78.4	97.0	48.1	66.7	114.9	54.5	78.1	92.6	77.1	83.0	138.8	49.9	83.8	93.8	54.8	69.6
05	METALS	95.2	91.3	94.0	96.2	88.2	93.7	97.3	89.6	94.9	99.8	99.1	99.6	98.4	94.6	97.2	93.2	86.2	91.1
06	WOOD, PLASTICS & COMPOSITES	99.3	76.9	86.7	98.5	42.7	67.0	96.1	52.7	71.6	99.4	79.2	88.0	97.4	51.3	71.4	98.3	42.3	66.7
07	THERMAL & MOISTURE PROTECTION	98.9	75.5	89.4	100.1	57.5	82.8	100.0	63.4	85.1	98.4	86.0	93.4	96.9	58.7	81.4	105.5	72.7	92.2
08	OPENINGS	100.0	70.9	93.1	96.8	47.6	85.1	96.7	58.3	87.6	99.6	76.0	94.0	97.9	62.4	89.5	102.0	48.5	89.3
0920	Plaster & Gypsum Board	99.8	76.7	84.0	93.7	41.4	58.1	94.8	51.7	65.5	95.7	79.0	84.3	96.5	50.2	65.0	105.5	40.9	61.6
0950, 0980	Ceilings & Acoustic Treatment	99.6	76.7	84.3	88.1	41.4	57.0	88.1	51.7	63.9	91.3	79.0	83.1	87.8	50.2	62.7	99.5	40.9	60.5
0960	Flooring	112.1	74.9	101.0	114.8	43.8	93.5	110.4	64.1	96.6	117.1	58.9	99.7	114.2	56.2	96.8	112.1	63.1	97.4
0970, 0990	Wall Finishes & Painting/Coating	96.2	71.7	81.5	99.4	66.3	79.5	99.4	66.3	79.5	102.2	62.1	78.1	101.6	62.1	77.8	96.4	66.3	78.3
09	FINISHES	103.1	74.1	86.9	101.3	45.8	70.4	99.8	55.7	75.3	102.6	72.0	85.6	100.4	52.9	74.0	103.5	49.3	73.3
COVERS	DIVS. 10 - 14, 25, 28, 41, 43, 44, 46	100.0	84.2	96.8	100.0	47.4	89.5	100.0	47.5	89.5	100.0	74.6	94.9	100.0	57.3	91.4	100.0	67.6	93.5
21, 22, 23	FIRE SUPPRESSION, PLUMBING & HVAC	100.0	57.8	83.1	100.0	53.4	81.3	100.0	53.6	81.4	99.9	64.1	85.5	100.0	59.7	83.9	100.0	39.8	75.9
26, 27, 3370	ELECTRICAL, COMMUNICATIONS & UTIL.	98.9	61.4	79.3	93.1	60.7	76.2	97.0	56.8	76.0	95.7	63.0	78.6	92.8	63.0	77.3	99.2	60.8	79.1
MF2010	WEIGHTED AVERAGE	99.3	71.4	87.1	98.5	59.1	81.3	100.8	62.4	84.1	99.3	75.3	88.8	100.2	64.7	84.7	98.7	58.0	81.0

FLORIDA / GEORGIA

DIVISION		TAMPA 335 - 336,346			WEST PALM BEACH 334,349			ALBANY 317,398			ATHENS 306			ATLANTA 300 - 303,399			AUGUSTA 308 - 309		
		MAT.	INST.	TOTAL	MAT.	INST.	TOTAL	MAT.	INST.	TOTAL	MAT.	INST.	TOTAL	MAT.	INST.	TOTAL	MAT.	INST.	TOTAL
015433	CONTRACTOR EQUIPMENT		98.8	98.8		91.7	91.7		92.5	92.5		93.8	93.8		94.3	94.3		93.8	93.8
0241, 31 - 34	SITE & INFRASTRUCTURE, DEMOLITION	108.3	89.8	95.3	90.5	78.4	82.0	96.0	79.8	84.6	93.9	93.2	93.4	90.8	94.7	93.5	87.9	92.9	91.4
0310	Concrete Forming & Accessories	98.0	77.3	80.1	99.2	69.7	73.7	90.9	44.5	50.9	90.6	47.0	52.9	94.1	75.0	77.6	91.6	67.0	70.4
0320	Concrete Reinforcing	89.8	96.6	93.2	92.3	74.2	83.3	89.6	81.4	85.5	98.6	80.4	89.5	97.9	82.4	90.2	99.0	74.1	86.6
0330	Cast-in-Place Concrete	95.8	70.9	85.5	86.4	75.5	81.9	92.4	55.3	77.0	107.4	56.5	86.3	107.4	71.1	92.3	101.4	50.6	80.3
03	CONCRETE	93.2	79.6	86.5	87.8	73.7	80.9	91.0	56.7	74.1	103.8	57.3	80.8	101.3	75.1	88.4	96.8	63.0	80.1
04	MASONRY	90.9	77.1	82.4	89.5	67.7	76.0	93.8	49.9	66.6	77.7	54.7	63.5	90.9	66.9	76.1	91.2	44.0	62.0
05	METALS	97.4	99.7	98.1	94.6	90.9	93.5	96.6	86.4	93.5	90.8	74.6	85.8	91.6	77.9	87.4	90.5	72.7	85.0
06	WOOD, PLASTICS & COMPOSITES	101.7	79.2	89.0	101.3	68.7	82.9	93.0	38.9	62.5	90.3	41.9	63.0	94.4	77.5	84.9	91.7	72.6	80.9
07	THERMAL & MOISTURE PROTECTION	97.1	86.0	92.6	96.7	71.4	86.4	96.5	61.4	82.3	93.6	53.8	77.5	93.5	73.0	85.2	93.3	58.1	79.0
08	OPENINGS	99.1	79.2	94.4	96.2	67.1	89.3	98.8	45.0	86.0	90.4	46.9	80.1	95.8	73.4	90.5	90.4	63.7	84.1
0920	Plaster & Gypsum Board	99.2	79.0	85.5	103.2	68.2	79.4	100.1	37.4	57.5	96.9	40.4	58.4	99.1	77.2	84.2	98.0	72.1	80.4
0950, 0980	Ceilings & Acoustic Treatment	91.3	79.0	83.1	85.8	68.2	74.1	93.5	37.4	56.2	94.1	40.4	58.4	94.1	77.2	82.8	95.1	72.1	79.8
0960	Flooring	115.4	57.6	98.1	117.4	67.7	102.5	116.2	48.7	96.0	94.5	54.9	82.7	95.8	66.4	87.0	94.8	47.4	80.6
0970, 0990	Wall Finishes & Painting/Coating	101.6	62.1	77.8	96.5	71.7	81.6	97.6	53.9	71.3	96.1	46.9	66.6	96.1	85.9	89.9	96.1	46.9	66.6
09	FINISHES	102.0	71.8	85.2	99.1	69.0	82.4	101.6	44.2	69.6	93.5	46.8	67.5	93.8	74.8	83.2	93.3	61.9	75.8
COVERS	DIVS. 10 - 14, 25, 28, 41, 43, 44, 46	100.0	84.9	96.7	100.0	86.5	97.3	100.0	80.3	95.9	100.0	79.4	95.9	100.0	85.7	97.1	100.0	80.6	96.1
21, 22, 23	FIRE SUPPRESSION, PLUMBING & HVAC	100.0	82.6	93.0	97.4	64.0	84.0	100.0	69.5	87.7	95.1	71.1	85.5	100.0	71.9	88.7	100.0	62.6	85.0
26, 27, 3370	ELECTRICAL, COMMUNICATIONS & UTIL.	92.6	63.1	77.2	93.8	72.7	82.8	96.1	60.1	77.3	99.5	71.2	84.7	98.8	72.7	85.2	100.1	63.2	80.9
MF2010	WEIGHTED AVERAGE	97.9	79.8	90.0	95.3	72.3	85.3	97.5	62.5	82.3	94.7	65.1	81.8	96.8	75.3	87.5	95.6	64.8	82.2

GEORGIA

DIVISION		COLUMBUS 318 - 319 MAT.	INST.	TOTAL	DALTON 307 MAT.	INST.	TOTAL	GAINESVILLE 305 MAT.	INST.	TOTAL	MACON 310 - 312 MAT.	INST.	TOTAL	SAVANNAH 313 - 314 MAT.	INST.	TOTAL	STATESBORO 304 MAT.	INST.	TOTAL
015433	CONTRACTOR EQUIPMENT		92.5	92.5		105.5	105.5		93.8	93.8		102.8	102.8		93.5	93.5		93.2	93.2
0241, 31 - 34	SITE & INFRASTRUCTURE, DEMOLITION	95.9	79.9	84.6	94.2	97.5	96.5	93.7	93.2	93.3	96.6	94.8	95.3	97.6	81.2	86.1	95.0	77.6	82.7
0310	Concrete Forming & Accessories	90.8	55.6	60.4	83.8	47.8	52.7	93.8	43.9	50.7	90.3	53.1	58.2	92.5	51.0	56.7	78.7	52.6	56.2
0320	Concrete Reinforcing	89.8	81.8	85.8	98.1	76.3	87.2	98.4	80.3	89.4	91.0	81.5	86.2	96.8	74.2	85.5	97.7	43.1	70.4
0330	Cast-in-Place Concrete	92.1	54.8	76.6	104.3	51.0	82.2	112.8	53.8	88.3	90.9	66.7	80.8	100.2	55.8	81.8	107.1	60.7	87.9
03	CONCRETE	90.8	61.5	76.4	102.9	55.8	79.7	105.7	54.9	80.6	90.4	64.4	77.6	95.9	58.4	77.4	103.2	55.3	79.5
04	MASONRY	93.7	56.2	70.5	78.8	37.3	53.2	86.3	55.1	67.0	105.6	45.3	68.3	90.3	51.4	66.2	80.2	41.3	56.1
05	METALS	96.1	87.5	93.5	91.6	84.3	89.3	90.0	73.8	85.0	92.2	87.1	90.6	93.3	83.8	90.3	95.0	74.0	88.5
06	WOOD, PLASTICS & COMPOSITES	93.0	53.3	70.6	74.1	48.5	59.7	94.2	38.8	62.9	101.2	52.4	73.7	105.9	47.0	72.7	67.6	55.1	60.6
07	THERMAL & MOISTURE PROTECTION	96.5	64.6	83.5	95.6	52.5	78.1	93.6	55.8	78.2	94.9	63.2	82.1	95.6	57.4	80.1	94.2	52.1	77.1
08	OPENINGS	98.8	60.2	89.6	91.2	50.7	81.6	90.4	40.9	78.7	97.6	53.7	87.2	103.0	49.6	90.4	92.2	41.6	80.2
0920	Plaster & Gypsum Board	100.1	52.3	67.6	84.0	47.3	59.0	99.1	37.2	57.0	105.5	51.3	68.6	98.1	45.8	62.5	84.1	54.1	63.7
0950, 0980	Ceilings & Acoustic Treatment	93.5	52.3	66.1	106.9	47.3	67.2	94.1	37.2	56.2	88.4	51.3	63.7	101.5	45.8	64.4	102.2	54.1	70.2
0960	Flooring	116.2	51.3	96.8	94.7	47.8	80.7	95.7	47.4	81.3	91.7	48.7	78.8	113.7	47.2	93.8	112.7	45.7	92.7
0970, 0990	Wall Finishes & Painting/Coating	97.6	67.9	79.7	87.3	61.1	71.5	96.1	46.9	66.6	99.8	53.9	72.2	96.0	59.5	74.1	94.0	40.1	61.6
09	FINISHES	101.5	54.7	75.4	101.7	48.1	71.9	94.0	42.6	65.3	89.7	51.0	68.2	101.7	49.9	72.9	104.7	50.1	74.3
COVERS	DIVS. 10 - 14, 25, 28, 41, 43, 44, 46	100.0	81.9	96.4	100.0	23.4	84.6	100.0	40.5	88.1	100.0	80.3	96.1	100.0	80.0	96.0	100.0	44.7	88.9
21, 22, 23	FIRE SUPPRESSION, PLUMBING & HVAC	100.0	64.7	85.8	95.2	58.2	80.4	95.1	71.0	85.5	100.0	68.2	87.2	100.0	62.9	85.2	95.7	58.0	80.5
26, 27, 3370	ELECTRICAL, COMMUNICATIONS & UTIL.	96.2	71.3	83.2	109.8	69.3	88.7	99.5	71.2	84.7	95.2	62.7	78.2	101.0	58.7	78.9	99.6	58.7	78.3
MF2010	WEIGHTED AVERAGE	97.4	66.6	84.0	96.4	60.1	80.6	95.2	62.8	81.1	96.2	65.9	83.0	98.4	62.0	82.6	96.5	56.9	79.2

GEORGIA / HAWAII / IDAHO

DIVISION		VALDOSTA 316 MAT.	INST.	TOTAL	WAYCROSS 315 MAT.	INST.	TOTAL	HILO 967 MAT.	INST.	TOTAL	HONOLULU 968 MAT.	INST.	TOTAL	STATES & POSS., GUAM 969 MAT.	INST.	TOTAL	BOISE 836 - 837 MAT.	INST.	TOTAL
015433	CONTRACTOR EQUIPMENT		92.5	92.5		92.5	92.5		98.6	98.6		98.6	98.6		162.1	162.1		97.9	97.9
0241, 31 - 34	SITE & INFRASTRUCTURE, DEMOLITION	104.6	79.9	87.3	101.5	78.6	85.4	126.9	106.4	112.5	136.4	106.4	115.3	165.7	103.6	122.1	82.4	97.1	92.7
0310	Concrete Forming & Accessories	81.4	45.0	50.0	83.1	66.3	68.6	108.1	135.3	131.5	119.2	135.3	133.1	110.3	64.7	70.9	100.7	79.2	82.2
0320	Concrete Reinforcing	91.7	78.8	85.3	91.7	75.0	83.3	109.0	121.6	115.3	116.9	121.6	119.2	188.7	31.1	110.0	101.9	81.2	91.6
0330	Cast-in-Place Concrete	90.5	56.5	76.4	102.2	49.0	80.1	186.3	126.3	161.4	153.8	126.3	142.4	161.5	106.6	138.7	91.1	89.4	90.4
03	CONCRETE	95.4	56.9	76.4	98.7	62.8	81.0	148.2	128.4	138.4	141.5	128.4	135.0	149.6	73.5	112.0	100.7	83.2	92.1
04	MASONRY	99.3	51.0	69.4	100.0	39.9	62.8	127.9	128.5	128.3	128.1	128.5	128.4	182.7	44.3	97.1	118.9	82.4	96.3
05	METALS	95.7	85.4	92.5	94.8	79.3	90.0	107.6	107.9	107.7	120.8	107.9	116.8	138.8	76.3	119.5	101.1	81.2	95.0
06	WOOD, PLASTICS & COMPOSITES	81.0	38.5	57.0	82.8	74.1	77.9	101.3	137.9	122.0	119.2	137.9	129.7	113.8	68.6	88.3	88.9	77.7	82.6
07	THERMAL & MOISTURE PROTECTION	96.7	63.3	83.1	96.5	51.2	78.1	108.0	124.8	114.8	123.3	124.8	123.9	124.5	67.7	101.5	99.1	72.5	89.4
08	OPENINGS	94.7	43.5	82.6	94.7	59.2	86.3	99.7	132.7	107.5	108.8	132.7	114.4	104.3	55.2	92.6	99.1	72.5	92.8
0920	Plaster & Gypsum Board	92.0	37.1	54.6	92.4	73.7	79.7	107.7	138.9	128.9	143.9	138.9	140.5	213.3	56.8	106.8	84.9	76.9	79.5
0950, 0980	Ceilings & Acoustic Treatment	90.8	37.1	55.1	88.9	73.7	78.8	121.3	138.9	133.0	132.4	138.9	136.7	240.6	56.8	118.3	107.2	76.9	87.0
0960	Flooring	110.1	48.7	91.7	111.2	30.4	87.1	125.5	138.2	129.3	144.2	138.2	142.4	147.9	47.2	117.8	95.5	85.2	92.4
0970, 0990	Wall Finishes & Painting/Coating	97.6	53.3	70.9	97.6	46.9	67.1	99.1	145.5	127.0	107.4	145.5	130.3	104.1	36.7	63.6	102.9	40.3	65.3
09	FINISHES	99.0	44.5	68.7	98.6	58.7	76.4	115.6	138.1	128.1	130.3	138.1	134.6	192.9	60.0	118.8	97.8	76.5	85.9
COVERS	DIVS. 10 - 14, 25, 28, 41, 43, 44, 46	100.0	79.1	95.8	100.0	52.9	90.6	100.0	116.4	103.3	100.0	116.4	103.3	100.0	76.3	95.3	100.0	89.8	98.0
21, 22, 23	FIRE SUPPRESSION, PLUMBING & HVAC	100.0	71.4	88.5	96.8	58.3	81.4	100.1	109.4	103.8	100.2	109.4	103.8	102.1	38.1	76.4	100.0	72.5	90.9
26, 27, 3370	ELECTRICAL, COMMUNICATIONS & UTIL.	94.2	57.6	75.1	98.7	58.7	77.8	105.2	124.0	115.0	106.5	124.0	115.7	151.3	42.2	94.3	96.6	74.6	85.1
MF2010	WEIGHTED AVERAGE	97.5	62.6	82.3	97.3	60.7	81.3	110.4	121.0	115.0	114.9	121.0	117.6	131.2	58.9	99.7	99.8	79.4	90.9

IDAHO / ILLINOIS

DIVISION		COEUR D'ALENE 838 MAT.	INST.	TOTAL	IDAHO FALLS 834 MAT.	INST.	TOTAL	LEWISTON 835 MAT.	INST.	TOTAL	POCATELLO 832 MAT.	INST.	TOTAL	TWIN FALLS 833 MAT.	INST.	TOTAL	BLOOMINGTON 617 MAT.	INST.	TOTAL
015433	CONTRACTOR EQUIPMENT		92.5	92.5		97.9	97.9		92.5	92.5		97.9	97.9		97.9	97.9		101.4	101.4
0241, 31 - 34	SITE & INFRASTRUCTURE, DEMOLITION	79.9	92.3	88.6	80.3	96.9	91.9	86.3	93.1	91.1	83.1	97.1	92.9	89.4	98.0	95.5	96.3	97.8	97.3
0310	Concrete Forming & Accessories	113.8	82.2	86.5	94.9	79.0	81.1	118.9	83.1	88.0	100.9	78.9	81.9	101.8	56.0	62.3	85.5	119.2	114.6
0320	Concrete Reinforcing	109.5	96.9	103.2	103.9	81.0	92.4	109.5	97.1	103.3	102.3	81.2	91.8	104.2	81.0	92.6	95.8	111.2	103.5
0330	Cast-in-Place Concrete	98.5	86.4	93.5	86.8	75.0	81.9	102.3	86.8	95.9	93.7	89.2	91.8	96.1	64.4	82.9	98.7	113.8	104.9
03	CONCRETE	107.5	86.3	97.1	92.9	78.0	85.6	111.1	86.9	99.2	99.9	83.0	91.5	107.5	64.2	86.1	97.2	115.8	106.4
04	MASONRY	120.4	85.3	98.7	114.1	82.4	94.5	120.8	85.3	98.8	116.6	82.4	95.4	119.0	82.4	96.4	113.4	118.3	116.4
05	METALS	95.2	87.1	92.7	108.9	79.6	99.9	94.6	88.0	92.6	109.0	80.9	100.3	109.0	79.5	99.9	97.3	113.3	102.2
06	WOOD, PLASTICS & COMPOSITES	92.7	81.8	86.5	83.0	79.4	80.9	97.9	81.8	88.8	88.9	77.7	82.6	89.8	48.3	66.4	88.1	118.1	105.0
07	THERMAL & MOISTURE PROTECTION	147.5	81.5	120.7	94.6	71.7	85.3	147.7	81.5	120.8	95.0	73.9	86.4	95.7	75.2	87.4	100.3	113.3	105.6
08	OPENINGS	117.8	73.5	107.4	102.8	68.6	94.7	117.8	76.1	107.9	99.8	67.5	92.1	102.8	49.6	90.2	93.1	106.6	96.3
0920	Plaster & Gypsum Board	152.1	81.2	103.9	75.3	78.7	77.6	153.2	81.2	104.3	77.6	76.9	77.1	78.5	46.7	56.8	90.3	118.6	109.5
0950, 0980	Ceilings & Acoustic Treatment	138.9	81.2	100.5	105.1	78.7	87.5	138.9	81.2	100.5	113.1	76.9	89.0	107.8	46.7	67.1	94.3	118.6	110.5
0960	Flooring	137.5	46.7	110.3	95.7	43.9	80.2	140.2	92.5	126.0	98.7	85.2	94.6	99.7	43.9	83.0	98.0	120.9	104.8
0970, 0990	Wall Finishes & Painting/Coating	122.3	66.3	88.7	102.9	41.2	65.8	122.3	66.3	88.7	102.8	42.0	66.2	102.9	38.1	63.9	95.3	127.8	114.8
09	FINISHES	166.2	74.0	114.8	95.5	69.5	81.0	167.3	83.0	120.4	98.9	76.7	86.5	98.9	50.8	72.1	97.4	121.1	110.6
COVERS	DIVS. 10 - 14, 25, 28, 41, 43, 44, 46	100.0	89.7	97.9	100.0	48.9	89.8	100.0	89.7	97.9	100.0	89.8	98.0	100.0	45.4	89.1	100.0	103.9	100.8
21, 22, 23	FIRE SUPPRESSION, PLUMBING & HVAC	99.5	84.3	93.4	101.0	72.3	89.5	100.7	87.2	95.3	100.0	72.4	88.9	100.0	70.8	88.3	95.0	107.8	100.1
26, 27, 3370	ELECTRICAL, COMMUNICATIONS & UTIL.	88.7	79.4	83.9	88.7	70.9	79.4	86.7	80.8	83.6	94.1	70.9	82.0	90.2	61.6	75.2	93.5	96.8	95.3
MF2010	WEIGHTED AVERAGE	107.6	83.3	97.0	99.6	75.5	89.1	108.3	85.5	98.4	100.8	78.4	91.1	101.9	68.5	87.4	96.9	109.9	102.6

757

City Cost Indexes

ILLINOIS

DIVISION		CARBONDALE 629 MAT.	INST.	TOTAL	CENTRALIA 628 MAT.	INST.	TOTAL	CHAMPAIGN 618-619 MAT.	INST.	TOTAL	CHICAGO 606-608 MAT.	INST.	TOTAL	DECATUR 625 MAT.	INST.	TOTAL	EAST ST. LOUIS 620-622 MAT.	INST.	TOTAL
015433	CONTRACTOR EQUIPMENT		107.7	107.7		107.7	107.7		102.1	102.1		93.9	93.9		102.1	102.1		107.7	107.7
0241, 31 - 34	SITE & INFRASTRUCTURE, DEMOLITION	100.2	98.6	99.0	100.5	99.2	99.6	105.2	98.4	100.4	105.3	95.4	98.4	92.2	98.6	96.7	102.6	99.2	100.2
0310	Concrete Forming & Accessories	95.5	107.9	106.2	97.4	114.8	112.4	91.6	117.1	113.7	96.6	159.8	151.1	97.7	116.9	114.2	92.8	115.0	112.0
0320	Concrete Reinforcing	89.8	100.4	95.1	89.8	113.3	101.5	95.8	105.1	100.5	95.5	163.2	129.3	87.9	105.9	96.9	89.7	113.4	101.5
0330	Cast-in-Place Concrete	91.8	101.1	95.7	92.3	118.5	103.2	114.4	109.2	112.2	103.4	149.6	122.6	100.2	111.9	105.1	93.8	118.5	104.1
03	CONCRETE	87.0	104.8	95.8	87.5	116.3	101.7	109.6	112.1	110.8	99.2	155.5	127.0	97.5	113.1	105.2	88.4	116.5	102.3
04	MASONRY	79.4	107.7	96.9	79.5	117.4	103.0	136.2	118.4	125.2	101.8	158.0	136.6	75.9	115.5	100.4	79.7	117.4	103.0
05	METALS	94.3	113.7	100.3	94.4	120.8	102.5	97.3	108.7	100.8	95.0	135.9	107.6	97.9	109.6	101.5	95.4	121.0	103.3
06	WOOD, PLASTICS & COMPOSITES	106.0	106.1	106.1	108.7	112.3	110.7	90.6	116.5	107.1	98.2	159.6	132.8	106.2	116.5	112.0	103.2	112.3	108.3
07	THERMAL & MOISTURE PROTECTION	98.0	101.6	99.5	98.0	112.3	103.8	100.9	114.5	106.5	99.2	147.5	118.8	104.0	109.6	106.3	98.0	111.9	103.6
08	OPENINGS	88.3	110.5	93.6	88.4	117.3	95.2	93.7	112.1	98.1	101.3	162.6	115.8	99.3	112.4	102.4	88.4	117.3	95.3
0920	Plaster & Gypsum Board	95.7	106.2	102.9	96.8	112.6	107.6	92.5	116.9	109.1	89.7	161.3	138.4	98.4	116.9	111.0	94.6	112.6	106.9
0950, 0980	Ceilings & Acoustic Treatment	96.2	106.2	102.9	96.2	112.6	107.1	94.3	116.9	109.4	101.5	161.3	141.3	102.4	116.9	112.1	96.2	112.6	107.1
0960	Flooring	121.3	122.4	121.6	122.3	117.9	120.9	100.7	122.4	107.1	93.1	150.7	110.3	108.6	118.8	111.7	120.2	117.9	119.5
0970, 0990	Wall Finishes & Painting/Coating	104.5	99.5	101.5	104.5	105.2	104.9	95.3	111.1	104.8	93.8	156.1	131.2	96.1	108.4	103.5	104.5	105.2	104.9
09	FINISHES	102.4	108.9	106.0	102.8	114.4	109.3	99.3	118.0	109.7	98.7	158.7	132.1	102.9	117.3	110.9	102.0	114.5	109.0
COVERS	DIVS. 10 - 14, 25, 28, 41, 43, 44, 46	100.0	104.1	100.8	100.0	106.5	101.3	100.0	103.1	100.6	100.0	125.0	105.0	100.0	103.0	100.6	100.0	106.5	101.3
21, 22, 23	FIRE SUPPRESSION, PLUMBING & HVAC	95.0	104.3	98.7	95.0	94.4	94.8	95.0	105.3	99.1	99.9	136.1	114.4	100.0	98.9	99.5	99.9	98.4	99.3
26, 27, 3370	ELECTRICAL, COMMUNICATIONS & UTIL.	94.0	106.7	100.6	95.5	104.3	100.1	96.8	94.5	95.6	96.1	137.1	117.5	98.4	91.3	94.7	95.0	104.3	99.9
MF2010	WEIGHTED AVERAGE	93.9	106.2	99.2	94.1	108.4	100.4	100.2	108.0	103.6	98.9	141.9	117.6	98.2	105.9	101.6	95.5	109.3	101.5

ILLINOIS

DIVISION		EFFINGHAM 624 MAT.	INST.	TOTAL	GALESBURG 614 MAT.	INST.	TOTAL	JOLIET 604 MAT.	INST.	TOTAL	KANKAKEE 609 MAT.	INST.	TOTAL	LA SALLE 613 MAT.	INST.	TOTAL	NORTH SUBURBAN 600-603 MAT.	INST.	TOTAL
015433	CONTRACTOR EQUIPMENT		102.1	102.1		101.4	101.4		92.0	92.0		92.0	92.0		101.4	101.4		92.0	92.0
0241, 31 - 34	SITE & INFRASTRUCTURE, DEMOLITION	97.5	98.2	98.0	98.7	97.7	98.0	105.2	94.7	97.8	98.9	93.9	95.4	98.1	98.4	98.3	104.4	93.7	96.8
0310	Concrete Forming & Accessories	102.2	115.5	113.7	91.5	119.0	115.3	98.4	163.3	154.4	92.4	141.3	134.6	105.1	125.1	122.4	97.8	153.4	145.8
0320	Concrete Reinforcing	90.7	101.0	95.9	95.4	111.1	103.2	95.5	155.7	125.6	96.3	146.5	121.4	95.5	143.7	119.6	95.5	157.3	126.4
0330	Cast-in-Place Concrete	99.9	107.3	103.0	101.6	107.9	104.2	103.3	149.4	122.4	96.4	132.5	111.4	101.5	123.6	110.7	103.4	143.5	120.0
03	CONCRETE	98.4	109.9	104.1	100.1	113.7	106.8	99.3	155.5	127.1	93.7	138.2	115.6	100.9	127.9	114.3	99.3	149.4	124.0
04	MASONRY	83.8	107.6	98.5	113.5	119.7	117.4	105.0	151.1	133.5	101.3	139.8	125.1	113.5	125.6	121.0	101.8	146.6	129.5
05	METALS	95.1	106.1	98.5	97.3	112.8	102.1	92.9	130.6	104.6	92.9	124.7	102.7	97.4	130.3	107.5	94.1	130.1	105.2
06	WOOD, PLASTICS & COMPOSITES	108.8	116.5	113.1	94.8	118.2	108.0	99.7	164.8	136.4	92.8	140.7	119.8	110.0	123.5	117.6	98.2	154.1	129.7
07	THERMAL & MOISTURE PROTECTION	103.6	107.6	105.2	100.5	109.9	104.3	99.1	144.5	117.5	98.4	135.6	113.5	100.6	119.4	108.2	99.5	140.8	116.3
08	OPENINGS	93.8	111.2	97.9	93.1	112.2	97.6	99.0	163.5	114.2	91.9	147.0	105.0	93.1	128.3	101.5	99.0	157.1	112.8
0920	Plaster & Gypsum Board	98.3	116.9	111.0	92.5	118.7	110.3	86.7	166.8	141.2	84.1	142.0	123.5	99.2	124.2	116.2	89.7	155.8	134.6
0950, 0980	Ceilings & Acoustic Treatment	96.2	116.9	110.0	94.3	118.7	110.5	101.5	166.8	144.9	101.5	142.0	128.4	94.3	124.2	114.2	101.5	155.8	137.6
0960	Flooring	109.7	122.4	113.5	100.6	120.9	106.7	92.7	142.9	107.7	90.1	134.3	103.3	106.5	124.8	112.0	93.1	142.9	108.0
0970, 0990	Wall Finishes & Painting/Coating	96.1	104.2	101.0	95.3	96.0	95.7	92.0	151.4	127.7	92.0	127.8	113.5	95.3	127.8	114.8	93.8	151.4	128.4
09	FINISHES	101.9	116.8	110.2	98.6	117.8	109.3	98.1	160.0	132.6	96.6	137.1	119.2	101.2	124.7	114.3	98.7	152.5	128.7
COVERS	DIVS. 10 - 14, 25, 28, 41, 43, 44, 46	100.0	71.7	94.3	100.0	103.8	100.8	100.0	125.4	105.1	100.0	117.6	103.5	100.0	104.4	100.9	100.0	120.4	104.1
21, 22, 23	FIRE SUPPRESSION, PLUMBING & HVAC	95.1	103.5	98.4	95.0	105.7	99.3	100.0	132.7	113.1	95.1	126.6	107.7	95.0	124.8	107.0	99.9	130.9	112.3
26, 27, 3370	ELECTRICAL, COMMUNICATIONS & UTIL.	96.0	106.6	101.6	94.5	87.3	90.7	95.4	141.2	119.3	90.1	140.4	116.4	91.6	140.4	117.1	95.2	131.5	114.2
MF2010	WEIGHTED AVERAGE	96.3	106.3	100.6	97.6	107.6	102.0	98.4	140.7	116.8	94.8	130.8	110.5	97.7	125.1	109.6	98.5	135.9	114.8

ILLINOIS

DIVISION		PEORIA 615-616 MAT.	INST.	TOTAL	QUINCY 623 MAT.	INST.	TOTAL	ROCK ISLAND 612 MAT.	INST.	TOTAL	ROCKFORD 610-611 MAT.	INST.	TOTAL	SOUTH SUBURBAN 605 MAT.	INST.	TOTAL	SPRINGFIELD 626-627 MAT.	INST.	TOTAL
015433	CONTRACTOR EQUIPMENT		101.4	101.4		102.1	102.1		101.4	101.4		101.4	101.4		92.0	92.0		102.1	102.1
0241, 31 - 34	SITE & INFRASTRUCTURE, DEMOLITION	99.2	97.8	98.2	96.3	98.1	97.6	96.8	96.8	96.8	98.5	98.8	98.7	104.4	93.7	96.8	99.2	98.6	98.8
0310	Concrete Forming & Accessories	94.5	119.9	116.4	100.0	113.8	111.9	93.2	101.3	100.2	98.9	130.1	125.8	97.8	153.4	145.8	98.1	117.3	114.6
0320	Concrete Reinforcing	92.9	111.2	102.0	90.4	105.6	98.0	95.4	104.2	99.8	87.8	138.2	113.0	95.5	157.3	126.4	92.8	106.1	99.4
0330	Cast-in-Place Concrete	98.5	116.0	105.8	100.0	104.2	101.8	99.4	98.4	99.0	100.9	126.4	111.5	103.4	143.5	120.0	95.2	108.5	100.7
03	CONCRETE	97.3	116.9	106.9	98.0	109.0	103.4	98.1	101.2	99.6	97.8	130.1	113.7	99.3	149.4	124.0	95.6	112.1	103.7
04	MASONRY	113.5	120.0	117.5	104.2	104.6	104.4	113.4	96.2	102.7	88.8	134.3	117.0	101.8	146.6	129.5	86.1	119.0	106.5
05	METALS	100.0	113.6	104.2	95.1	108.4	99.2	97.3	108.3	100.7	100.0	127.8	108.6	94.1	130.1	105.2	95.5	109.7	99.9
06	WOOD, PLASTICS & COMPOSITES	102.5	118.2	111.4	106.1	116.5	112.0	96.4	100.6	98.8	102.5	127.6	116.8	98.2	154.1	129.7	103.0	116.5	110.6
07	THERMAL & MOISTURE PROTECTION	101.2	113.8	106.3	103.6	104.1	103.8	100.4	98.5	99.7	103.5	128.4	113.6	99.5	140.8	116.3	105.2	112.8	108.3
08	OPENINGS	99.2	116.7	103.4	94.6	112.4	98.8	93.1	101.0	95.0	99.2	132.5	107.1	99.0	157.1	112.8	101.3	112.4	103.9
0920	Plaster & Gypsum Board	96.3	118.7	111.5	96.8	116.9	110.5	92.5	100.5	97.9	96.3	128.5	118.2	89.7	155.8	134.6	97.1	116.9	110.6
0950, 0980	Ceilings & Acoustic Treatment	100.5	118.7	112.6	96.2	116.9	110.0	94.3	100.5	98.4	100.5	128.5	119.2	101.5	155.8	137.6	106.6	116.9	113.5
0960	Flooring	103.8	120.9	108.9	108.6	110.1	109.1	101.7	107.5	103.4	103.8	124.8	110.1	93.1	142.9	108.0	113.1	109.8	112.1
0970, 0990	Wall Finishes & Painting/Coating	95.3	127.8	114.8	96.1	105.1	101.5	95.3	95.3	95.3	95.3	135.3	119.3	93.8	151.4	128.4	94.6	105.1	100.9
09	FINISHES	101.4	121.4	112.6	101.3	113.6	108.2	98.8	101.9	100.6	101.4	129.8	117.2	98.7	152.5	128.7	106.1	115.4	111.3
COVERS	DIVS. 10 - 14, 25, 28, 41, 43, 44, 46	100.0	104.3	100.9	100.0	72.7	94.5	100.0	97.2	99.4	100.0	111.6	102.3	100.0	120.4	104.1	100.0	103.3	100.7
21, 22, 23	FIRE SUPPRESSION, PLUMBING & HVAC	99.9	105.8	102.3	95.1	100.8	97.4	95.0	99.8	96.9	100.0	114.9	106.0	99.9	130.9	112.3	99.9	103.4	101.3
26, 27, 3370	ELECTRICAL, COMMUNICATIONS & UTIL.	95.5	97.4	96.5	93.2	81.3	87.0	86.5	95.7	91.3	95.8	127.0	112.1	95.2	131.5	114.2	101.0	92.8	96.8
MF2010	WEIGHTED AVERAGE	99.9	110.4	104.5	96.9	101.6	99.0	96.6	99.8	98.0	98.9	123.5	109.6	98.5	135.9	114.8	99.0	107.2	102.5

INDIANA

DIVISION		ANDERSON 460 MAT.	INST.	TOTAL	BLOOMINGTON 474 MAT.	INST.	TOTAL	COLUMBUS 472 MAT.	INST.	TOTAL	EVANSVILLE 476-477 MAT.	INST.	TOTAL	FORT WAYNE 467-468 MAT.	INST.	TOTAL	GARY 463-464 MAT.	INST.	TOTAL
015433	CONTRACTOR EQUIPMENT		96.7	96.7		87.2	87.2		87.2	87.2		116.1	116.1		96.7	96.7		96.7	96.7
0241, 31 - 34	SITE & INFRASTRUCTURE, DEMOLITION	90.5	96.0	94.4	82.7	94.8	91.2	79.4	94.6	90.1	87.8	123.5	112.9	91.5	96.0	94.6	91.0	99.2	96.8
0310	Concrete Forming & Accessories	98.8	80.8	83.3	101.9	81.1	83.9	95.9	78.9	81.2	95.4	81.9	83.7	97.1	75.4	78.3	98.9	115.2	113.0
0320	Concrete Reinforcing	98.0	83.7	90.9	87.1	83.4	85.2	87.5	83.4	85.4	95.4	76.7	86.1	98.0	76.8	87.4	98.0	110.1	104.0
0330	Cast-in-Place Concrete	104.8	78.1	93.7	100.8	78.0	91.3	100.4	72.5	88.8	96.3	87.7	92.8	111.3	83.7	99.9	109.5	112.4	110.7
03	CONCRETE	96.3	80.9	88.7	102.3	80.3	91.4	101.6	77.3	89.6	102.7	83.1	93.0	99.3	79.1	89.3	98.5	113.1	105.7
04	MASONRY	84.8	79.7	81.7	90.5	76.4	81.8	90.4	76.2	81.6	86.4	83.3	84.5	88.2	77.3	81.4	86.1	112.8	102.7
05	METALS	92.9	89.8	92.0	95.9	78.7	90.6	95.9	78.0	90.4	89.2	84.4	87.8	92.9	86.4	90.9	92.9	108.0	97.6
06	WOOD, PLASTICS & COMPOSITES	108.2	80.8	92.8	118.0	81.1	93.2	112.5	78.3	93.2	97.4	80.8	88.0	107.9	74.8	89.2	105.7	115.0	110.9
07	THERMAL & MOISTURE PROTECTION	105.4	77.1	93.9	95.3	79.7	88.9	94.9	79.4	88.6	99.3	84.7	93.4	105.2	79.0	94.6	104.0	109.0	106.0
08	OPENINGS	95.0	81.9	91.9	105.0	82.0	99.6	100.8	80.5	96.0	98.3	79.8	93.9	95.0	74.7	90.2	95.0	119.4	100.8
0920	Plaster & Gypsum Board	94.3	80.6	85.0	98.1	81.2	86.6	94.7	78.3	83.6	93.1	79.6	83.9	93.5	74.4	80.5	87.6	115.8	106.8
0950, 0980	Ceilings & Acoustic Treatment	89.6	80.6	83.7	83.9	81.2	82.1	83.9	78.3	80.2	88.8	79.6	82.7	89.6	74.4	79.5	89.6	115.8	107.1
0960	Flooring	99.9	86.6	96.0	105.8	76.4	97.0	101.4	76.4	93.9	100.8	82.2	95.2	99.9	80.2	94.0	99.9	123.6	107.0
0970, 0990	Wall Finishes & Painting/Coating	97.3	70.9	81.4	89.6	83.0	85.7	89.6	83.0	85.7	94.7	86.7	89.9	97.3	74.4	83.5	97.3	126.6	114.9
09	FINISHES	95.0	80.9	87.1	96.2	80.4	87.4	94.5	78.7	85.7	95.2	82.4	88.1	94.8	76.1	84.4	94.0	118.3	107.5
COVERS	DIVS. 10 - 14, 25, 28, 41, 43, 44, 46	100.0	91.5	98.3	100.0	89.1	97.8	100.0	88.7	97.7	100.0	94.1	98.8	100.0	89.5	97.9	100.0	105.3	101.1
21, 22, 23	FIRE SUPPRESSION, PLUMBING & HVAC	100.0	75.8	90.3	99.8	79.0	91.4	94.9	79.0	88.5	100.0	80.2	92.0	100.0	72.4	88.9	100.0	105.9	102.3
26, 27, 3370	ELECTRICAL, COMMUNICATIONS & UTIL.	85.9	88.4	87.2	98.2	83.5	90.5	97.3	85.2	91.0	94.5	86.3	90.2	86.6	78.4	82.3	97.7	110.2	104.2
MF2010	WEIGHTED AVERAGE	95.5	83.1	90.1	98.7	81.5	91.2	96.6	80.9	89.7	96.5	86.6	92.1	96.0	79.2	88.7	96.8	110.1	102.6

INDIANA

DIVISION		INDIANAPOLIS 461-462 MAT.	INST.	TOTAL	KOKOMO 469 MAT.	INST.	TOTAL	LAFAYETTE 479 MAT.	INST.	TOTAL	LAWRENCEBURG 470 MAT.	INST.	TOTAL	MUNCIE 473 MAT.	INST.	TOTAL	NEW ALBANY 471 MAT.	INST.	TOTAL
015433	CONTRACTOR EQUIPMENT		93.3	93.3		96.7	96.7		87.2	87.2		105.0	105.0		95.7	95.7		95.1	95.1
0241, 31 - 34	SITE & INFRASTRUCTURE, DEMOLITION	90.3	99.3	96.6	87.1	95.8	93.2	80.2	94.5	90.3	78.0	111.0	101.2	82.5	95.0	91.3	75.3	97.4	90.8
0310	Concrete Forming & Accessories	98.0	85.1	86.8	102.4	77.8	81.2	93.5	82.8	84.3	92.4	77.2	79.3	93.5	80.5	82.3	90.2	75.1	77.2
0320	Concrete Reinforcing	100.0	85.4	92.7	88.7	83.7	86.2	87.1	83.6	85.4	86.3	76.6	81.5	96.3	83.6	90.0	87.7	79.6	83.6
0330	Cast-in-Place Concrete	103.3	84.7	95.6	103.7	81.0	94.3	100.9	80.7	92.5	94.4	76.6	87.0	105.9	77.7	94.2	97.4	75.7	88.4
03	CONCRETE	99.5	84.8	92.3	93.1	80.5	86.9	101.8	81.9	92.0	95.0	77.4	86.3	101.1	80.6	91.0	100.2	76.5	88.5
04	MASONRY	90.3	81.3	84.7	84.4	80.0	81.7	95.5	79.8	85.8	75.6	76.0	75.9	92.4	79.8	84.6	82.3	69.5	74.4
05	METALS	93.6	81.7	89.9	89.5	89.3	89.4	94.3	78.6	89.5	91.1	85.2	89.3	97.7	89.9	95.3	93.0	82.7	89.8
06	WOOD, PLASTICS & COMPOSITES	105.3	85.3	94.0	111.6	76.6	91.9	109.5	83.2	94.7	95.8	77.0	85.2	111.4	80.6	94.0	97.9	76.0	85.5
07	THERMAL & MOISTURE PROTECTION	100.9	82.6	93.5	105.0	77.1	93.7	94.9	81.5	89.5	99.2	78.3	90.7	97.9	78.0	89.8	86.8	71.4	80.6
08	OPENINGS	103.1	84.8	98.6	90.0	79.6	87.5	99.2	83.1	95.4	100.4	76.8	94.8	98.5	81.7	94.5	97.9	78.2	93.2
0920	Plaster & Gypsum Board	88.5	85.1	86.2	99.8	76.3	83.8	91.8	83.3	86.0	72.6	76.8	75.5	93.1	80.6	84.6	91.2	75.6	80.6
0950, 0980	Ceilings & Acoustic Treatment	91.3	85.1	87.2	89.6	76.3	80.8	79.4	83.3	82.0	93.2	76.8	82.3	84.8	80.6	82.0	88.8	75.6	80.0
0960	Flooring	101.7	86.6	97.2	103.6	89.9	99.5	100.4	88.1	96.8	74.8	86.6	78.3	100.7	86.6	96.5	98.3	64.0	88.1
0970, 0990	Wall Finishes & Painting/Coating	99.5	83.0	89.6	97.3	73.3	82.9	89.6	95.1	92.9	90.6	73.2	80.1	89.6	70.9	78.4	94.7	84.5	88.6
09	FINISHES	95.4	85.4	89.8	96.6	79.3	87.0	92.9	85.2	88.6	85.8	78.9	82.0	94.0	80.7	86.6	94.5	74.3	83.2
COVERS	DIVS. 10 - 14, 25, 28, 41, 43, 44, 46	100.0	93.0	98.6	100.0	89.1	97.8	100.0	91.3	98.3	100.0	44.9	89.0	100.0	90.9	98.2	100.0	44.3	88.8
21, 22, 23	FIRE SUPPRESSION, PLUMBING & HVAC	99.9	80.1	92.0	95.1	79.2	88.7	94.9	80.2	89.0	95.6	75.7	87.6	99.8	75.8	90.2	95.1	76.9	87.8
26, 27, 3370	ELECTRICAL, COMMUNICATIONS & UTIL.	100.7	88.3	94.2	90.4	78.8	84.4	96.8	82.6	89.4	92.3	75.3	83.4	90.2	80.3	85.0	92.8	77.6	84.9
MF2010	WEIGHTED AVERAGE	98.3	85.1	92.6	93.3	82.0	88.4	96.3	82.9	90.5	93.3	79.3	87.2	97.3	81.8	90.6	94.4	77.0	86.8

INDIANA / IOWA

DIVISION		SOUTH BEND 465-466 MAT.	INST.	TOTAL	TERRE HAUTE 478 MAT.	INST.	TOTAL	WASHINGTON 475 MAT.	INST.	TOTAL	BURLINGTON 526 MAT.	INST.	TOTAL	CARROLL 514 MAT.	INST.	TOTAL	CEDAR RAPIDS 522-524 MAT.	INST.	TOTAL
015433	CONTRACTOR EQUIPMENT		105.0	105.0		116.1	116.1		116.1	116.1		100.2	100.2		100.2	100.2		96.8	96.8
0241, 31 - 34	SITE & INFRASTRUCTURE, DEMOLITION	92.9	95.9	95.0	89.7	124.2	113.9	89.2	121.5	111.9	96.5	97.3	97.1	85.8	97.3	93.9	98.5	96.0	96.8
0310	Concrete Forming & Accessories	102.6	79.8	82.9	96.3	78.1	80.6	97.1	80.6	82.9	97.3	77.3	80.1	85.2	51.6	56.2	103.2	81.0	84.1
0320	Concrete Reinforcing	101.1	79.1	90.1	95.4	83.8	89.6	88.2	50.3	69.3	94.3	85.4	89.9	95.1	81.1	88.1	95.1	86.8	90.9
0330	Cast-in-Place Concrete	96.3	80.7	89.8	93.3	87.0	90.7	101.5	86.6	95.3	109.6	56.3	87.5	109.6	61.0	89.4	109.9	81.3	98.0
03	CONCRETE	90.8	81.3	86.1	105.6	82.6	94.2	111.1	77.1	94.3	101.7	72.5	87.3	100.5	61.7	81.3	101.8	82.8	92.4
04	MASONRY	90.7	79.1	83.5	93.6	80.5	85.5	86.4	82.3	83.9	97.2	66.0	77.9	99.0	73.5	83.2	102.8	77.5	87.1
05	METALS	93.0	99.8	95.1	89.9	88.1	89.4	84.7	69.6	80.0	87.0	94.9	89.4	87.0	90.4	88.1	89.3	93.8	90.7
06	WOOD, PLASTICS & COMPOSITES	105.0	79.2	90.4	99.5	76.4	86.5	100.0	80.7	89.1	95.3	78.4	85.7	81.8	45.9	61.6	101.8	80.5	89.8
07	THERMAL & MOISTURE PROTECTION	97.5	81.9	91.2	99.4	81.9	92.3	99.5	84.4	93.4	103.8	75.6	92.4	104.1	70.5	90.5	104.7	79.9	94.6
08	OPENINGS	91.0	78.9	88.1	98.9	79.4	94.3	95.6	69.2	89.3	92.4	72.1	87.6	96.6	54.7	86.7	97.6	81.7	93.8
0920	Plaster & Gypsum Board	87.0	78.9	81.5	93.1	75.0	80.8	93.0	79.5	83.8	100.7	77.7	85.1	95.9	44.3	60.8	105.3	80.1	88.2
0950, 0980	Ceilings & Acoustic Treatment	93.4	78.9	83.8	88.8	75.0	79.6	82.5	79.5	80.5	110.6	77.7	88.7	110.6	44.3	66.5	114.1	80.1	91.5
0960	Flooring	97.4	89.9	95.1	100.8	86.6	96.6	101.7	77.8	94.6	111.2	38.5	89.5	105.6	33.8	84.2	127.9	79.7	113.5
0970, 0990	Wall Finishes & Painting/Coating	87.6	87.4	87.5	94.7	83.7	88.1	94.7	85.2	89.0	99.0	80.2	87.7	99.0	79.9	87.5	100.4	73.7	84.3
09	FINISHES	95.3	82.4	88.1	95.2	79.9	86.6	94.3	81.4	87.1	107.2	70.4	86.7	103.3	49.4	73.3	113.2	80.0	94.7
COVERS	DIVS. 10 - 14, 25, 28, 41, 43, 44, 46	100.0	90.7	98.1	100.0	93.2	98.6	100.0	94.0	98.8	100.0	89.2	97.8	100.0	66.9	93.4	100.0	90.2	98.0
21, 22, 23	FIRE SUPPRESSION, PLUMBING & HVAC	99.9	77.4	90.9	100.0	80.4	92.1	95.1	79.3	88.7	95.3	76.9	87.9	95.3	74.2	86.8	100.2	80.7	92.4
26, 27, 3370	ELECTRICAL, COMMUNICATIONS & UTIL.	97.6	86.6	91.9	92.6	83.6	87.9	93.1	86.3	89.5	100.7	69.3	84.3	101.4	81.3	90.9	98.2	81.3	89.3
MF2010	WEIGHTED AVERAGE	95.7	84.2	90.7	97.2	85.8	92.2	95.0	83.3	89.9	96.6	76.9	88.0	96.4	72.2	85.9	99.4	83.4	92.4

IOWA

DIVISION		COUNCIL BLUFFS 515			CRESTON 508			DAVENPORT 527 - 528			DECORAH 521			DES MOINES 500 - 503,509			DUBUQUE 520		
		MAT.	INST.	TOTAL	MAT.	INST.	TOTAL	MAT.	INST.	TOTAL	MAT.	INST.	TOTAL	MAT.	INST.	TOTAL	MAT.	INST.	TOTAL
015433	CONTRACTOR EQUIPMENT		96.3	96.3		100.2	100.2		100.2	100.2		100.2	100.2		101.8	101.8		95.7	95.7
0241, 31 - 34	SITE & INFRASTRUCTURE, DEMOLITION	103.6	92.3	95.7	86.7	96.4	93.5	96.8	99.3	98.6	95.1	96.3	95.9	95.5	99.7	98.5	96.4	93.3	94.2
0310	Concrete Forming & Accessories	84.6	70.7	72.6	84.5	67.2	69.6	102.5	91.2	92.7	94.9	46.5	53.1	103.2	78.9	82.2	85.9	73.8	75.4
0320	Concrete Reinforcing	97.0	79.3	88.2	93.3	81.2	87.3	95.1	100.0	97.5	94.3	79.0	86.7	102.7	81.4	92.0	93.7	86.6	90.2
0330	Cast-in-Place Concrete	114.3	75.1	98.0	102.1	65.4	86.9	105.9	91.7	100.0	106.7	59.3	87.0	89.8	88.0	89.1	107.6	100.4	104.6
03	CONCRETE	104.1	74.7	89.6	96.9	70.2	83.7	99.9	93.5	96.7	99.6	58.4	79.3	95.0	83.2	89.2	98.6	86.2	92.4
04	MASONRY	104.5	75.9	86.8	96.9	81.4	87.3	100.0	85.5	91.1	117.7	72.7	89.8	90.7	80.4	84.3	103.7	73.7	85.1
05	METALS	94.3	90.2	93.1	89.4	90.6	89.8	89.3	103.9	93.8	87.1	87.7	87.3	95.2	92.9	94.5	88.0	93.5	89.7
06	WOOD, PLASTICS & COMPOSITES	80.6	69.7	74.4	79.1	63.1	70.1	101.9	90.3	95.3	92.3	37.9	61.6	98.8	77.4	86.8	82.2	71.7	76.3
07	THERMAL & MOISTURE PROTECTION	104.2	68.4	89.6	106.2	78.8	95.1	104.2	87.4	97.4	104.0	54.7	84.0	100.6	79.5	92.0	104.4	71.3	90.9
08	OPENINGS	96.6	75.5	91.6	106.6	64.4	96.6	97.6	91.4	96.1	95.2	49.8	84.5	101.9	82.8	97.4	96.6	79.3	92.5
0920	Plaster & Gypsum Board	95.9	69.0	77.6	94.1	62.0	72.2	105.3	90.0	94.9	99.6	36.0	56.4	91.9	76.8	81.6	95.9	71.1	79.0
0950, 0980	Ceilings & Acoustic Treatment	110.6	69.0	82.9	111.5	62.0	78.5	114.1	90.0	98.1	110.6	36.0	61.0	115.0	76.8	89.6	110.6	71.1	84.3
0960	Flooring	104.3	82.1	97.6	104.2	33.8	83.2	113.5	98.7	109.1	111.1	48.0	92.2	109.4	87.6	102.9	118.8	77.6	106.5
0970, 0990	Wall Finishes & Painting/Coating	95.3	66.9	78.2	95.8	79.9	86.3	99.0	97.6	98.1	99.0	33.6	59.7	91.2	79.9	84.4	99.4	65.1	78.8
09	FINISHES	104.1	72.0	86.2	102.4	61.5	79.6	109.1	93.2	100.2	106.9	43.6	71.6	105.5	80.4	91.5	108.4	72.9	88.6
COVERS	DIVS. 10 - 14, 25, 28, 41, 43, 44, 46	100.0	88.9	97.8	100.0	71.4	94.3	100.0	93.1	98.6	100.0	85.2	97.0	100.0	90.3	98.1	100.0	88.6	97.7
21, 22, 23	FIRE SUPPRESSION, PLUMBING & HVAC	100.2	75.8	90.4	95.3	80.3	89.2	100.2	93.2	97.4	95.3	74.5	86.9	100.0	79.8	91.9	100.2	75.4	90.2
26, 27, 3370	ELECTRICAL, COMMUNICATIONS & UTIL.	103.7	81.6	92.1	94.8	81.3	87.8	95.5	91.2	93.2	98.1	45.4	70.6	106.9	81.3	93.6	102.2	78.4	89.8
MF2010	WEIGHTED AVERAGE	100.2	78.8	90.9	96.7	77.9	88.5	98.4	93.4	96.2	97.4	65.6	83.5	99.4	83.9	92.7	98.5	80.4	90.6

IOWA

DIVISION		FORT DODGE 505			MASON CITY 504			OTTUMWA 525			SHENANDOAH 516			SIBLEY 512			SIOUX CITY 510 - 511		
		MAT.	INST.	TOTAL	MAT.	INST.	TOTAL	MAT.	INST.	TOTAL	MAT.	INST.	TOTAL	MAT.	INST.	TOTAL	MAT.	INST.	TOTAL
015433	CONTRACTOR EQUIPMENT		100.2	100.2		100.2	100.2		95.7	95.7		96.3	96.3		100.2	100.2		100.2	100.2
0241, 31 - 34	SITE & INFRASTRUCTURE, DEMOLITION	94.6	95.0	94.9	94.6	96.2	95.8	96.8	91.4	93.0	102.0	91.4	94.6	106.0	95.0	98.3	107.6	95.8	99.3
0310	Concrete Forming & Accessories	85.1	46.0	51.3	89.6	46.4	52.3	92.9	71.9	74.8	86.2	57.8	61.7	86.6	38.7	45.3	103.2	67.9	72.7
0320	Concrete Reinforcing	93.3	67.4	80.4	93.2	80.6	86.9	94.3	85.6	90.0	97.0	68.6	82.8	97.0	67.3	82.2	95.1	78.2	86.7
0330	Cast-in-Place Concrete	95.8	45.0	74.7	95.8	58.7	80.4	110.3	54.8	87.3	110.5	61.1	90.0	108.3	45.7	82.3	109.0	56.7	87.3
03	CONCRETE	92.6	51.1	72.1	92.9	58.5	75.9	101.2	69.4	85.5	101.5	62.1	82.1	100.5	48.1	74.6	101.2	66.9	84.3
04	MASONRY	95.9	38.5	60.4	108.7	69.4	84.4	100.3	57.1	73.6	104.0	75.9	86.6	122.1	38.8	70.6	97.2	55.6	71.4
05	METALS	89.5	81.9	87.2	89.5	88.8	89.3	86.9	92.0	88.5	93.3	84.3	90.5	87.2	81.4	85.4	89.3	88.2	89.0
06	WOOD, PLASTICS & COMPOSITES	79.6	46.2	60.8	83.9	37.9	58.0	89.4	78.2	83.1	82.2	54.0	66.3	83.1	36.7	56.9	101.8	68.2	82.9
07	THERMAL & MOISTURE PROTECTION	105.6	58.5	86.5	105.2	64.6	88.7	104.6	65.2	88.6	103.5	66.6	88.5	103.8	49.2	81.6	104.3	64.9	88.3
08	OPENINGS	100.8	50.1	88.8	93.3	50.2	83.1	96.6	76.2	91.8	88.1	55.5	80.4	93.4	44.9	81.9	97.6	66.9	90.3
0920	Plaster & Gypsum Board	94.1	44.6	60.4	94.1	36.0	54.6	97.0	77.7	83.9	95.9	52.8	66.6	95.9	34.7	54.3	105.3	67.2	79.4
0950, 0980	Ceilings & Acoustic Treatment	111.5	44.6	67.0	111.5	36.0	61.3	110.6	77.7	88.7	110.6	52.8	72.1	110.6	34.7	60.1	114.1	67.2	82.9
0960	Flooring	105.8	48.0	88.5	107.9	48.0	90.0	121.8	51.1	100.6	104.9	34.9	84.0	106.4	34.6	85.0	113.6	54.7	96.0
0970, 0990	Wall Finishes & Painting/Coating	95.8	63.1	76.1	95.8	30.7	56.7	99.4	79.9	87.7	95.3	66.9	78.2	99.0	63.1	77.4	99.0	63.1	77.4
09	FINISHES	104.4	47.1	72.5	105.0	42.9	70.4	109.5	69.2	87.0	104.2	53.4	75.9	106.7	38.9	68.9	110.7	64.8	85.1
COVERS	DIVS. 10 - 14, 25, 28, 41, 43, 44, 46	100.0	79.8	96.0	100.0	84.8	97.0	100.0	84.2	96.8	100.0	67.9	93.6	100.0	78.9	95.8	100.0	86.9	97.4
21, 22, 23	FIRE SUPPRESSION, PLUMBING & HVAC	95.3	65.8	83.4	95.3	71.9	85.9	95.3	71.3	85.7	95.3	75.1	87.2	95.3	69.5	84.9	100.2	76.3	90.6
26, 27, 3370	ELECTRICAL, COMMUNICATIONS & UTIL.	101.9	42.9	71.1	100.9	57.0	77.9	100.5	67.8	83.4	98.1	80.6	89.0	98.1	42.4	69.1	98.2	74.7	85.9
MF2010	WEIGHTED AVERAGE	96.6	58.8	80.2	96.5	66.6	83.5	97.3	73.0	86.7	97.1	72.1	86.2	97.7	57.5	80.2	99.1	73.6	88.0

		IOWA						KANSAS											
DIVISION		SPENCER 513			WATERLOO 506 - 507			BELLEVILLE 669			COLBY 677			DODGE CITY 678			EMPORIA 668		
		MAT.	INST.	TOTAL	MAT.	INST.	TOTAL	MAT.	INST.	TOTAL	MAT.	INST.	TOTAL	MAT.	INST.	TOTAL	MAT.	INST.	TOTAL
015433	CONTRACTOR EQUIPMENT		100.2	100.2		100.2	100.2		103.1	103.1		103.1	103.1		103.1	103.1		101.4	101.4
0241, 31 - 34	SITE & INFRASTRUCTURE, DEMOLITION	106.1	95.0	98.3	99.5	96.1	97.1	111.0	94.7	99.5	109.4	94.8	99.1	111.9	94.5	99.7	102.8	92.2	95.3
0310	Concrete Forming & Accessories	92.8	38.7	46.1	101.6	48.1	55.4	95.0	55.3	60.7	102.2	59.6	65.4	95.3	59.5	64.4	86.5	66.7	69.4
0320	Concrete Reinforcing	97.0	67.3	82.2	94.0	86.5	90.2	99.6	56.1	77.9	101.2	56.1	78.7	98.8	56.1	77.5	98.2	56.7	77.5
0330	Cast-in-Place Concrete	108.3	45.7	82.3	102.6	55.0	82.9	118.9	56.9	93.2	114.3	57.0	90.6	116.4	56.7	91.6	114.9	54.8	90.0
03	CONCRETE	100.9	48.1	74.9	98.4	59.1	79.0	117.7	57.4	88.0	114.9	59.3	87.5	116.2	59.1	88.0	110.0	61.8	86.2
04	MASONRY	122.1	38.8	70.6	96.6	73.0	82.0	94.9	59.8	73.2	96.9	59.8	73.9	104.4	60.0	76.9	100.5	68.4	80.7
05	METALS	87.1	81.4	85.4	91.8	92.8	92.1	97.8	78.4	91.9	98.2	78.7	92.2	99.7	77.8	92.9	97.6	79.9	92.1
06	WOOD, PLASTICS & COMPOSITES	89.3	36.7	59.6	98.6	37.9	64.4	96.4	53.3	72.1	103.9	59.2	78.7	95.3	59.2	74.9	87.7	68.2	76.7
07	THERMAL & MOISTURE PROTECTION	104.6	49.2	82.1	105.4	71.4	91.6	98.4	62.3	83.7	101.9	62.9	86.1	101.9	62.3	85.8	97.0	77.4	89.1
08	OPENINGS	104.3	44.9	90.2	94.2	53.5	84.5	96.4	49.4	85.3	99.5	52.6	88.4	99.5	52.6	88.4	94.4	57.5	85.6
0920	Plaster & Gypsum Board	97.0	34.7	54.7	103.9	36.0	57.7	98.0	51.8	66.6	100.7	57.9	71.6	94.8	57.9	69.7	95.1	67.1	76.0
0950, 0980	Ceilings & Acoustic Treatment	110.6	34.7	60.1	115.0	36.0	62.5	91.6	51.8	65.1	94.3	57.9	70.1	94.3	57.9	70.1	91.6	67.1	75.3
0960	Flooring	109.1	34.6	86.8	113.3	76.9	102.4	106.4	39.9	86.5	105.7	39.9	86.0	102.2	39.9	83.6	101.8	37.1	82.4
0970, 0990	Wall Finishes & Painting/Coating	99.0	63.1	77.4	95.8	79.4	86.0	97.4	39.8	62.8	97.4	39.8	62.8	97.4	39.8	62.8	97.4	39.8	62.8
09	FINISHES	107.6	38.9	69.3	108.8	54.4	78.5	101.3	50.4	72.9	101.5	53.9	75.0	99.8	53.9	74.2	98.6	58.6	76.3
COVERS	DIVS. 10 - 14, 25, 28, 41, 43, 44, 46	100.0	78.9	95.8	100.0	85.3	97.1	100.0	41.8	88.3	100.0	42.5	88.5	100.0	42.5	88.5	100.0	41.5	88.3
21, 22, 23	FIRE SUPPRESSION, PLUMBING & HVAC	95.3	69.5	84.9	100.2	80.0	92.1	95.1	73.1	86.3	95.1	68.7	84.5	100.0	68.7	87.4	95.1	73.4	86.4
26, 27, 3370	ELECTRICAL, COMMUNICATIONS & UTIL.	99.9	42.4	69.9	97.0	57.0	76.1	93.3	66.0	79.1	97.9	66.0	81.3	94.7	73.4	83.6	90.8	73.1	81.5
MF2010	WEIGHTED AVERAGE	99.2	57.5	81.0	98.3	70.9	86.4	99.4	65.6	84.7	100.2	65.6	85.1	101.7	66.5	86.4	97.8	70.0	85.7

KANSAS

	DIVISION	FORT SCOTT 667			HAYS 676			HUTCHINSON 675			INDEPENDENCE 673			KANSAS CITY 660 - 662			LIBERAL 679		
		MAT.	INST.	TOTAL	MAT.	INST.	TOTAL	MAT.	INST.	TOTAL	MAT.	INST.	TOTAL	MAT.	INST.	TOTAL	MAT.	INST.	TOTAL
015433	CONTRACTOR EQUIPMENT		102.3	102.3		103.1	103.1		103.1	103.1		103.1	103.1		99.7	99.7		103.1	103.1
0241, 31 - 34	SITE & INFRASTRUCTURE, DEMOLITION	99.4	93.0	94.9	115.5	94.8	100.9	93.4	94.6	94.3	113.1	94.6	100.1	93.5	92.9	93.1	115.2	94.6	100.7
0310	Concrete Forming & Accessories	102.6	78.6	81.9	99.7	59.6	65.1	89.9	59.5	63.6	110.8	67.8	73.7	99.3	96.3	96.7	95.8	59.5	64.5
0320	Concrete Reinforcing	97.5	96.3	96.9	98.8	56.1	77.5	98.8	56.1	77.5	98.2	63.0	80.6	94.6	97.8	96.2	100.2	56.1	78.2
0330	Cast-in-Place Concrete	106.6	55.7	85.5	90.2	57.0	76.5	83.6	54.2	71.4	116.8	54.5	91.0	91.4	99.3	94.7	90.3	54.2	75.3
03	CONCRETE	105.2	74.6	90.1	106.7	59.3	83.3	89.1	58.3	73.9	117.4	63.3	90.7	97.3	97.9	97.6	108.9	58.3	83.9
04	MASONRY	101.0	61.4	76.5	104.3	59.8	76.8	96.4	59.6	73.6	94.0	65.7	76.5	103.6	99.5	101.1	102.4	75.6	75.9
05	METALS	97.5	94.4	96.5	97.8	78.7	91.9	97.6	77.7	91.5	97.5	81.3	92.5	104.9	100.6	103.5	98.1	77.7	91.8
06	WOOD, PLASTICS & COMPOSITES	106.5	85.4	94.6	100.6	59.2	77.2	89.9	59.2	72.6	114.7	69.6	89.3	102.4	96.7	99.1	95.9	59.2	75.2
07	THERMAL & MOISTURE PROTECTION	97.8	82.8	91.7	102.1	62.9	86.2	100.9	62.2	85.2	101.9	82.4	94.0	97.5	99.8	98.4	102.3	62.2	86.0
08	OPENINGS	94.4	80.1	91.0	99.4	52.6	88.3	99.4	52.6	88.3	97.2	59.8	88.4	95.6	90.5	94.4	99.5	52.6	88.4
0920	Plaster & Gypsum Board	100.6	84.9	89.9	98.1	57.9	70.7	93.6	57.9	69.3	107.8	68.6	81.1	93.5	96.5	95.5	95.5	57.9	69.9
0950, 0980	Ceilings & Acoustic Treatment	91.6	84.9	87.2	94.3	57.9	70.1	94.3	57.9	70.1	94.3	68.6	77.2	91.6	96.5	94.9	94.3	57.9	70.1
0960	Flooring	117.6	40.1	94.4	104.7	39.9	85.3	99.5	39.9	81.7	109.9	39.9	89.0	93.5	100.5	95.6	102.4	39.9	83.7
0970, 0990	Wall Finishes & Painting/Coating	99.2	39.8	63.5	97.4	39.8	62.8	97.4	39.8	62.8	97.4	39.8	62.8	105.6	69.2	83.7	97.4	39.8	62.8
09	FINISHES	114.0	68.4	84.2	101.4	53.9	74.9	97.3	53.9	73.1	103.8	60.0	79.4	98.5	93.1	94.3	100.7	53.9	74.6
COVERS	DIVS. 10 - 14, 25, 28, 41, 43, 44, 46	100.0	47.4	89.5	100.0	42.5	88.5	100.0	42.5	88.5	100.0	43.7	88.7	100.0	63.5	92.7	100.0	42.5	88.5
21, 22, 23	FIRE SUPPRESSION, PLUMBING & HVAC	95.1	69.3	84.7	95.1	68.7	84.5	95.1	68.7	84.5	95.1	71.1	85.5	99.9	96.8	98.6	95.1	68.7	84.5
26, 27, 3370	ELECTRICAL, COMMUNICATIONS & UTIL.	90.1	73.1	81.2	96.8	66.0	80.7	91.7	66.0	78.3	94.0	73.1	83.0	95.5	97.3	96.4	94.7	73.4	83.6
MF2010	WEIGHTED AVERAGE	97.7	74.3	87.5	99.6	65.6	84.8	95.8	65.4	82.5	99.9	70.3	87.0	99.4	95.7	97.7	99.5	66.4	85.1

	DIVISION	KANSAS SALINA 674			TOPEKA 664 - 666			WICHITA 670 - 672			KENTUCKY ASHLAND 411 - 412			BOWLING GREEN 421 - 422			CAMPTON 413 - 414		
		MAT.	INST.	TOTAL	MAT.	INST.	TOTAL	MAT.	INST.	TOTAL	MAT.	INST.	TOTAL	MAT.	INST.	TOTAL	MAT.	INST.	TOTAL
015433	CONTRACTOR EQUIPMENT		103.1	103.1		101.4	101.4		103.1	103.1		98.0	98.0		95.1	95.1		101.5	101.5
0241, 31 - 34	SITE & INFRASTRUCTURE, DEMOLITION	102.2	94.8	97.0	97.9	91.2	93.2	98.7	93.3	94.9	108.9	87.0	93.5	75.6	97.7	91.1	83.8	98.8	94.3
0310	Concrete Forming & Accessories	91.8	55.7	60.6	97.2	41.8	49.4	97.8	51.7	58.0	89.0	105.7	103.4	86.5	84.0	84.4	90.4	84.6	85.4
0320	Concrete Reinforcing	98.2	62.6	80.4	97.7	97.2	97.5	97.5	75.8	86.7	89.1	106.1	97.6	86.4	89.5	88.0	87.3	105.0	96.1
0330	Cast-in-Place Concrete	101.0	54.7	81.8	96.1	46.5	75.6	94.7	52.7	77.3	88.7	102.9	94.6	88.0	97.5	91.9	98.1	75.2	88.6
03	CONCRETE	103.0	58.0	80.8	98.3	55.4	77.1	97.6	57.8	78.0	96.1	105.2	100.6	94.4	89.7	92.1	98.2	85.2	91.8
04	MASONRY	118.4	59.8	82.1	97.6	56.9	72.4	94.9	51.1	67.8	92.2	105.1	100.2	94.0	81.6	86.3	91.6	70.2	78.4
05	METALS	99.5	81.5	93.9	101.6	96.4	100.0	101.6	83.7	96.1	92.1	109.8	97.6	93.7	86.9	91.6	93.0	93.7	93.2
06	WOOD, PLASTICS & COMPOSITES	91.5	53.3	70.0	95.4	38.1	63.1	95.3	52.5	71.2	79.0	105.4	93.9	92.3	83.9	87.5	90.8	91.1	90.9
07	THERMAL & MOISTURE PROTECTION	101.4	62.6	85.7	100.6	69.1	87.8	100.0	57.6	82.8	91.3	99.3	94.5	86.7	82.1	84.8	99.6	69.4	87.3
08	OPENINGS	99.4	49.7	87.6	98.6	55.3	88.4	101.6	56.6	91.0	97.0	99.3	97.5	97.9	79.4	93.5	99.3	89.8	97.1
0920	Plaster & Gypsum Board	93.6	51.8	65.2	97.6	36.1	55.8	92.4	51.0	64.2	61.2	105.6	91.4	86.4	83.7	84.6	86.4	90.2	89.0
0950, 0980	Ceilings & Acoustic Treatment	94.3	51.8	66.0	97.6	36.1	56.7	99.4	51.0	67.2	83.8	105.6	98.3	88.8	83.7	85.4	88.8	90.2	89.7
0960	Flooring	100.7	63.1	89.5	106.9	75.0	97.3	108.3	64.1	95.1	80.1	104.2	87.3	96.5	87.6	93.9	98.6	42.0	81.7
0970, 0990	Wall Finishes & Painting/Coating	97.4	39.8	62.8	99.2	53.7	71.9	96.3	49.0	67.9	96.9	103.4	100.8	94.7	74.3	82.4	94.7	66.8	77.9
09	FINISHES	98.5	54.8	74.2	103.1	47.0	71.8	102.7	53.5	75.3	82.5	105.7	95.4	93.1	84.0	88.0	93.9	75.7	83.8
COVERS	DIVS. 10 - 14, 25, 28, 41, 43, 44, 46	100.0	54.2	90.8	100.0	48.4	89.7	100.0	51.1	90.2	100.0	96.3	99.3	100.0	59.8	91.9	100.0	57.3	91.4
21, 22, 23	FIRE SUPPRESSION, PLUMBING & HVAC	100.0	68.7	87.5	100.0	69.0	87.5	99.8	64.3	85.6	95.0	92.9	94.1	100.0	84.3	93.7	95.1	81.5	89.7
26, 27, 3370	ELECTRICAL, COMMUNICATIONS & UTIL.	94.5	73.3	83.4	94.2	73.1	83.2	99.0	73.3	85.6	90.7	99.6	95.4	93.3	82.1	87.4	90.6	67.7	78.6
MF2010	WEIGHTED AVERAGE	100.4	67.0	85.9	99.4	66.5	85.1	99.9	65.1	84.8	94.0	100.1	96.6	95.5	84.8	90.8	95.1	80.2	88.6

KENTUCKY

	DIVISION	CORBIN 407 - 409			COVINGTON 410			ELIZABETHTOWN 427			FRANKFORT 406			HAZARD 417 - 418			HENDERSON 424		
		MAT.	INST.	TOTAL	MAT.	INST.	TOTAL	MAT.	INST.	TOTAL	MAT.	INST.	TOTAL	MAT.	INST.	TOTAL	MAT.	INST.	TOTAL
015433	CONTRACTOR EQUIPMENT		101.5	101.5		105.0	105.0		95.1	95.1		101.5	101.5		101.5	101.5		116.1	116.1
0241, 31 - 34	SITE & INFRASTRUCTURE, DEMOLITION	83.0	98.5	93.9	79.4	112.3	102.5	70.4	97.8	89.6	87.1	99.7	95.9	81.8	100.1	94.6	78.4	124.1	110.5
0310	Concrete Forming & Accessories	88.9	72.3	74.6	86.0	92.9	92.0	81.6	82.4	82.3	99.5	73.4	77.0	87.1	85.4	85.6	93.4	83.5	84.8
0320	Concrete Reinforcing	87.0	72.1	79.5	85.9	94.0	90.0	86.9	93.8	90.3	99.8	93.7	96.8	87.7	105.0	96.3	86.6	87.6	87.1
0330	Cast-in-Place Concrete	92.2	59.9	78.8	93.9	99.6	96.3	79.6	74.6	77.5	87.2	70.6	80.3	94.4	84.2	90.2	77.8	92.5	83.9
03	CONCRETE	92.6	68.4	80.7	96.5	95.5	96.0	86.6	82.0	84.3	93.0	76.6	84.9	95.0	88.7	91.9	91.6	87.4	89.5
04	MASONRY	89.8	63.0	73.2	105.4	103.3	104.1	78.5	76.8	77.4	87.2	80.8	83.3	89.3	72.8	79.1	97.8	94.5	95.8
05	METALS	93.4	79.8	89.2	91.0	91.7	91.2	92.8	88.8	91.6	95.8	89.5	93.9	93.0	93.7	93.2	84.4	88.6	85.7
06	WOOD, PLASTICS & COMPOSITES	88.5	77.7	82.4	88.7	86.0	87.2	87.4	83.9	85.4	105.5	70.3	85.6	87.7	91.1	89.6	95.1	80.8	87.1
07	THERMAL & MOISTURE PROTECTION	98.8	65.6	85.3	99.4	95.4	97.8	86.4	78.8	83.3	98.8	77.1	90.0	99.5	71.3	88.1	99.0	93.6	96.8
08	OPENINGS	99.3	67.2	91.7	101.3	85.7	97.6	97.9	85.3	94.9	102.1	78.2	96.4	99.7	80.3	95.1	96.0	81.8	92.7
0920	Plaster & Gypsum Board	90.6	76.4	80.9	69.4	86.1	80.8	85.6	83.7	84.3	100.9	68.8	79.0	85.6	90.2	88.7	89.7	79.7	82.9
0950, 0980	Ceilings & Acoustic Treatment	86.1	76.4	79.6	92.3	86.1	88.2	88.8	83.7	85.4	96.8	68.8	78.1	88.8	90.2	89.7	88.5	79.7	80.6
0960	Flooring	100.6	42.0	83.1	72.7	86.2	76.7	94.1	87.6	92.2	108.0	55.4	92.3	97.1	42.7	80.9	100.1	87.6	96.4
0970, 0990	Wall Finishes & Painting/Coating	94.2	50.5	67.9	90.6	84.1	86.7	94.7	77.8	84.6	93.9	81.5	86.5	94.7	66.8	77.9	94.7	98.1	96.7
09	FINISHES	93.9	65.0	77.8	84.8	90.5	87.9	92.0	82.5	86.7	101.6	70.3	84.2	93.2	76.5	83.9	92.6	85.7	88.8
COVERS	DIVS. 10 - 14, 25, 28, 41, 43, 44, 46	100.0	49.7	89.9	100.0	102.8	100.6	100.0	86.6	97.3	100.0	67.2	93.4	100.0	58.1	91.6	100.0	67.1	93.4
21, 22, 23	FIRE SUPPRESSION, PLUMBING & HVAC	95.1	72.9	86.2	95.6	90.6	93.6	95.4	81.9	90.0	100.1	84.1	93.7	95.1	82.4	90.0	95.4	79.3	88.9
26, 27, 3370	ELECTRICAL, COMMUNICATIONS & UTIL.	90.5	82.1	86.1	94.6	79.6	86.8	90.4	82.1	86.1	99.0	89.2	93.9	90.6	59.7	74.5	92.7	82.2	87.2
MF2010	WEIGHTED AVERAGE	94.4	73.3	85.2	95.2	93.2	94.3	92.2	83.7	88.5	97.9	82.4	91.1	94.6	79.9	88.2	93.0	87.9	90.8

KENTUCKY

DIVISION		LEXINGTON 403 - 405			LOUISVILLE 400 - 402			OWENSBORO 423			PADUCAH 420			PIKEVILLE 415 - 416			SOMERSET 425 - 426		
		MAT.	INST.	TOTAL	MAT.	INST.	TOTAL	MAT.	INST.	TOTAL	MAT.	INST.	TOTAL	MAT.	INST.	TOTAL	MAT.	INST.	TOTAL
015433	CONTRACTOR EQUIPMENT		101.5	101.5		95.1	95.1		116.1	116.1		116.1	116.1		98.0	98.0		101.5	101.5
0241, 31 - 34	SITE & INFRASTRUCTURE, DEMOLITION	85.0	100.9	96.2	75.7	97.8	91.3	87.9	124.1	113.3	80.9	123.6	110.9	119.6	86.0	96.0	75.1	99.3	92.1
0310	Concrete Forming & Accessories	101.5	74.3	78.0	100.6	83.0	85.4	91.8	83.4	84.5	89.9	81.8	82.9	97.7	90.9	91.9	88.0	77.6	79.0
0320	Concrete Reinforcing	95.5	93.5	94.5	97.1	93.8	95.4	86.6	90.2	88.4	87.1	89.0	88.0	89.6	105.9	97.7	86.9	93.7	90.3
0330	Cast-in-Place Concrete	94.3	93.9	94.2	95.8	75.4	87.4	90.7	96.1	92.9	82.9	88.3	85.1	97.5	98.7	98.0	77.8	100.3	87.1
03	CONCRETE	95.8	84.9	90.5	96.7	82.5	89.7	103.4	89.1	96.4	96.0	85.5	90.8	109.6	97.1	103.5	81.8	88.6	85.2
04	MASONRY	88.4	73.4	79.1	88.9	78.2	82.3	90.5	92.6	91.8	93.5	90.0	91.3	90.0	98.5	95.2	84.7	78.1	80.6
05	METALS	95.8	89.9	93.9	97.6	88.9	94.9	85.9	90.2	87.2	83.0	88.4	84.6	92.0	108.5	97.1	92.9	89.3	91.8
06	WOOD, PLASTICS & COMPOSITES	105.1	70.3	85.5	103.1	83.9	92.3	93.0	80.8	86.1	90.6	80.9	85.2	88.6	90.4	89.6	88.3	77.7	82.3
07	THERMAL & MOISTURE PROTECTION	99.1	85.7	93.6	97.9	79.5	90.4	99.3	93.9	97.1	99.0	80.9	91.7	91.9	81.5	87.7	99.0	71.8	87.9
08	OPENINGS	99.5	75.3	93.8	99.0	85.3	95.8	96.0	83.9	93.1	95.2	79.4	91.5	97.7	88.4	95.5	98.7	79.6	94.2
0920	Plaster & Gypsum Board	100.6	68.8	79.0	93.2	83.7	86.7	88.2	79.7	82.4	87.1	79.8	82.1	64.5	90.2	82.0	85.6	76.4	79.4
0950, 0980	Ceilings & Acoustic Treatment	90.5	68.8	76.1	94.3	83.7	87.2	82.5	79.7	80.6	82.5	79.8	80.7	83.8	90.2	88.0	88.8	76.4	80.5
0960	Flooring	105.0	71.6	95.0	102.9	87.6	98.3	99.5	87.6	96.0	98.5	60.4	87.1	83.8	104.2	89.9	97.4	42.0	80.8
0970, 0990	Wall Finishes & Painting/Coating	94.2	82.8	87.3	93.9	77.8	84.2	94.7	98.1	96.7	94.7	81.4	86.7	96.9	83.0	88.5	94.7	77.8	84.6
09	FINISHES	97.5	73.6	84.2	97.9	83.5	89.9	92.9	85.2	88.6	92.1	77.8	84.1	84.9	93.0	89.4	92.6	70.9	80.5
COVERS	DIVS. 10 - 14, 25, 28, 41, 43, 44, 46	100.0	88.4	97.7	100.0	87.1	97.4	100.0	100.9	100.2	100.0	63.4	92.7	100.0	57.8	91.5	100.0	60.0	92.0
21, 22, 23	FIRE SUPPRESSION, PLUMBING & HVAC	100.0	80.6	92.2	100.0	82.6	93.0	100.0	78.4	91.3	95.4	82.9	90.4	95.0	89.0	92.6	95.4	79.1	88.8
26, 27, 3370	ELECTRICAL, COMMUNICATIONS & UTIL.	93.4	82.1	87.5	100.0	82.1	90.6	92.7	82.2	87.3	95.1	81.8	88.2	93.7	75.1	84.0	91.0	82.1	86.4
MF2010	WEIGHTED AVERAGE	97.0	82.4	90.7	97.8	84.2	91.9	95.6	88.9	92.7	93.2	86.2	90.2	96.2	90.0	93.5	92.7	81.5	87.8

LOUISIANA

DIVISION		ALEXANDRIA 713 - 714			BATON ROUGE 707 - 708			HAMMOND 704			LAFAYETTE 705			LAKE CHARLES 706			MONROE 712		
		MAT.	INST.	TOTAL	MAT.	INST.	TOTAL	MAT.	INST.	TOTAL	MAT.	INST.	TOTAL	MAT.	INST.	TOTAL	MAT.	INST.	TOTAL
015433	CONTRACTOR EQUIPMENT		89.7	89.7		89.3	89.3		89.9	89.9		89.9	89.9		89.3	89.3		89.7	89.7
0241, 31 - 34	SITE & INFRASTRUCTURE, DEMOLITION	96.3	86.7	89.5	96.0	86.0	89.0	99.1	86.9	90.5	100.1	87.0	90.9	100.8	85.9	90.3	96.3	85.9	89.0
0310	Concrete Forming & Accessories	83.0	44.2	49.5	94.1	61.7	66.1	78.1	46.9	51.2	95.2	54.9	60.4	96.1	57.5	62.8	82.5	43.9	49.2
0320	Concrete Reinforcing	89.4	56.0	72.7	95.1	59.0	77.1	93.3	59.4	76.4	94.6	59.0	76.8	94.6	59.2	76.9	88.4	55.6	72.0
0330	Cast-in-Place Concrete	94.6	50.3	76.2	91.8	58.7	78.0	93.9	43.9	73.2	93.5	47.6	74.4	98.4	67.4	85.5	94.6	56.7	78.8
03	CONCRETE	94.7	49.7	72.5	95.9	60.7	78.5	93.3	49.1	71.5	94.4	53.8	74.4	96.7	61.8	79.5	94.5	51.5	73.3
04	MASONRY	116.0	54.2	77.8	97.6	54.7	71.0	99.0	51.8	69.8	99.0	53.0	70.5	98.3	59.5	74.3	110.9	48.4	72.2
05	METALS	89.5	71.1	83.9	106.0	70.1	94.9	97.6	69.5	88.9	96.7	70.0	88.5	96.7	70.5	88.7	89.5	68.5	83.0
06	WOOD, PLASTICS & COMPOSITES	89.8	42.7	63.2	98.5	65.3	79.8	84.8	48.1	64.1	106.3	57.0	78.5	104.4	59.1	78.8	89.1	43.2	63.2
07	THERMAL & MOISTURE PROTECTION	97.5	54.1	79.9	95.8	62.4	82.2	96.9	57.0	80.7	97.4	60.8	82.5	96.5	59.5	81.5	97.5	54.7	80.1
08	OPENINGS	99.8	45.8	87.0	98.6	60.0	89.5	92.7	52.5	83.2	96.3	53.9	86.3	96.3	55.7	86.7	99.7	48.8	87.7
0920	Plaster & Gypsum Board	79.0	41.4	53.4	99.4	64.6	75.7	100.1	46.8	63.8	109.6	56.0	73.2	109.6	58.1	74.6	78.6	41.9	53.6
0950, 0980	Ceilings & Acoustic Treatment	87.1	41.4	56.7	103.1	64.6	77.4	98.7	46.8	64.2	97.0	56.0	69.7	98.0	58.1	71.5	87.1	41.9	57.0
0960	Flooring	110.0	66.9	97.1	106.0	66.9	94.3	98.6	66.9	89.1	106.8	66.9	94.9	106.8	74.3	97.1	109.5	58.1	94.2
0970, 0990	Wall Finishes & Painting/Coating	99.5	65.8	79.2	96.1	47.3	66.8	103.4	49.3	70.9	103.4	59.2	76.8	103.4	51.0	71.9	99.5	49.1	69.2
09	FINISHES	93.2	50.0	69.1	100.6	61.6	78.9	97.8	50.9	71.7	101.1	57.5	76.8	101.3	59.9	78.2	93.0	46.5	67.1
COVERS	DIVS. 10 - 14, 25, 28, 41, 43, 44, 46	100.0	51.4	90.3	100.0	80.9	96.2	100.0	46.6	89.3	100.0	79.4	95.9	100.0	80.4	96.1	100.0	47.0	89.4
21, 22, 23	FIRE SUPPRESSION, PLUMBING & HVAC	100.2	56.5	82.7	100.0	59.5	83.8	95.2	43.7	74.5	100.1	60.7	84.3	100.1	61.7	84.7	100.2	54.1	81.7
26, 27, 3370	ELECTRICAL, COMMUNICATIONS & UTIL.	90.5	58.2	73.6	103.0	60.8	81.0	98.2	57.3	76.8	99.5	66.6	82.3	98.9	66.6	82.0	92.2	59.6	75.2
MF2010	WEIGHTED AVERAGE	96.8	57.8	79.8	100.4	63.6	84.4	96.3	54.9	78.3	98.5	62.7	82.9	98.6	65.0	84.0	96.7	56.4	79.2

LOUISIANA / MAINE

DIVISION		NEW ORLEANS 700 - 701			SHREVEPORT 710 - 711			THIBODAUX 703			AUGUSTA 043			BANGOR 044			BATH 045		
		MAT.	INST.	TOTAL	MAT.	INST.	TOTAL	MAT.	INST.	TOTAL	MAT.	INST.	TOTAL	MAT.	INST.	TOTAL	MAT.	INST.	TOTAL
015433	CONTRACTOR EQUIPMENT		90.2	90.2		89.7	89.7		89.9	89.9		100.6	100.6		100.6	100.6		100.6	100.6
0241, 31 - 34	SITE & INFRASTRUCTURE, DEMOLITION	105.2	88.4	93.4	100.8	86.0	90.4	101.4	87.0	91.3	89.2	100.8	97.3	91.0	101.0	98.0	88.9	100.8	97.2
0310	Concrete Forming & Accessories	97.7	66.5	70.8	98.8	44.7	52.2	90.1	64.3	67.8	99.2	97.0	97.3	93.6	98.8	98.1	89.7	97.2	96.2
0320	Concrete Reinforcing	96.7	60.1	78.4	92.6	56.1	74.4	93.3	59.2	76.3	96.4	110.1	103.2	90.1	111.5	100.8	89.2	111.2	100.2
0330	Cast-in-Place Concrete	99.7	70.1	87.4	99.4	53.4	80.3	100.9	51.3	80.3	97.9	60.3	82.3	80.2	113.0	93.8	80.2	60.3	72.0
03	CONCRETE	97.8	67.1	82.6	99.6	50.9	75.6	98.4	59.3	79.1	104.6	86.2	95.5	94.4	105.3	99.8	94.5	86.4	90.5
04	MASONRY	101.8	60.7	76.4	102.0	51.0	70.4	124.8	49.3	78.1	96.8	64.8	77.0	106.0	103.9	104.7	112.3	85.8	95.9
05	METALS	109.5	73.0	98.3	93.3	69.2	85.9	97.6	69.4	88.9	97.8	88.0	94.8	88.7	90.4	89.2	87.2	89.6	87.9
06	WOOD, PLASTICS & COMPOSITES	99.7	67.9	81.8	101.7	43.7	69.0	92.9	69.7	79.8	98.6	107.7	103.7	95.1	98.7	97.1	89.7	107.7	99.9
07	THERMAL & MOISTURE PROTECTION	96.1	69.0	85.1	97.1	52.2	78.9	96.7	54.6	79.6	104.3	66.8	89.1	100.2	86.0	94.5	100.2	73.2	89.2
08	OPENINGS	96.2	66.4	89.2	98.8	46.4	86.4	97.1	64.2	89.3	104.2	90.0	100.8	102.5	85.0	98.4	102.5	90.0	99.5
0920	Plaster & Gypsum Board	108.2	67.2	80.3	90.0	42.5	57.7	102.7	69.1	79.8	100.8	107.4	105.2	98.8	98.0	98.2	95.1	107.4	103.4
0950, 0980	Ceilings & Acoustic Treatment	98.7	67.2	77.8	91.3	42.5	58.8	98.7	69.1	79.0	101.5	107.4	105.4	91.6	98.0	95.9	89.6	107.4	101.4
0960	Flooring	105.3	66.9	93.8	113.4	62.4	98.1	104.3	44.9	86.5	103.1	56.3	89.1	98.9	113.0	103.1	97.3	56.3	85.0
0970, 0990	Wall Finishes & Painting/Coating	108.8	65.5	82.8	95.1	47.4	66.5	104.7	50.6	72.2	101.0	64.7	79.2	95.3	45.1	65.1	95.3	45.1	65.1
09	FINISHES	102.4	66.6	82.4	98.2	47.4	69.9	100.1	60.1	77.8	101.4	87.7	93.8	98.6	96.9	97.3	97.1	85.6	90.7
COVERS	DIVS. 10 - 14, 25, 28, 41, 43, 44, 46	100.0	83.2	96.6	100.0	77.3	95.5	100.0	81.3	96.3	100.0	103.3	100.7	100.0	110.0	102.0	100.0	103.3	100.7
21, 22, 23	FIRE SUPPRESSION, PLUMBING & HVAC	100.0	65.8	86.3	100.0	58.9	83.5	95.2	61.7	81.7	99.9	65.6	86.2	100.1	75.9	90.4	95.2	65.7	83.4
26, 27, 3370	ELECTRICAL, COMMUNICATIONS & UTIL.	103.2	72.9	87.4	97.7	67.2	81.8	96.7	72.8	84.2	99.3	80.0	89.2	98.5	77.2	87.4	96.4	80.0	87.9
MF2010	WEIGHTED AVERAGE	101.5	69.8	87.7	98.4	59.6	81.5	98.7	64.9	84.0	100.3	80.8	91.8	97.6	90.8	94.7	96.1	83.0	90.4

MAINE

DIVISION		HOULTON 047 MAT.	INST.	TOTAL	KITTERY 039 MAT.	INST.	TOTAL	LEWISTON 042 MAT.	INST.	TOTAL	MACHIAS 046 MAT.	INST.	TOTAL	PORTLAND 040-041 MAT.	INST.	TOTAL	ROCKLAND 048 MAT.	INST.	TOTAL
015433	CONTRACTOR EQUIPMENT		100.6	100.6		100.6	100.6		100.6	100.6		100.6	100.6		100.6	100.6		100.6	100.6
0241, 31 - 34	SITE & INFRASTRUCTURE, DEMOLITION	90.7	101.8	98.5	85.6	100.8	96.3	88.2	101.0	97.2	90.1	101.8	98.3	86.9	101.0	96.8	86.3	101.8	97.2
0310	Concrete Forming & Accessories	97.1	103.6	102.7	90.4	97.7	96.7	98.9	98.9	98.9	94.4	103.5	102.3	95.8	98.9	98.4	95.4	103.5	102.4
0320	Concrete Reinforcing	90.1	109.9	100.0	84.5	111.3	97.8	110.8	111.5	111.1	90.1	109.9	100.0	107.5	111.5	109.5	90.1	109.9	100.0
0330	Cast-in-Place Concrete	80.3	72.6	77.1	81.4	61.2	73.0	81.9	113.0	94.8	80.2	72.0	76.8	95.5	113.0	102.7	81.9	72.0	77.8
03	CONCRETE	95.5	93.3	94.4	90.1	87.0	88.6	95.1	105.3	100.1	94.9	93.1	94.0	100.8	105.3	103.0	92.2	93.1	92.6
04	MASONRY	91.0	76.3	81.9	101.0	86.8	92.2	91.7	103.9	99.2	91.0	76.3	81.9	101.3	103.9	102.9	85.9	76.3	80.0
05	METALS	87.4	87.9	87.5	87.1	89.8	87.9	91.7	90.4	91.3	87.4	87.9	87.6	99.4	90.4	96.6	87.3	87.9	87.5
06	WOOD, PLASTICS & COMPOSITES	99.1	107.7	104.0	88.7	107.7	99.4	101.2	98.7	99.8	96.1	107.7	102.6	96.1	98.7	97.5	96.9	107.7	103.0
07	THERMAL & MOISTURE PROTECTION	100.3	74.0	89.6	103.2	72.5	90.7	100.1	86.0	94.4	100.3	73.0	89.2	101.4	86.0	95.2	100.0	73.0	89.1
08	OPENINGS	102.6	88.2	99.2	102.7	90.0	99.6	105.6	85.0	100.7	102.6	88.2	99.2	105.7	85.0	100.8	102.5	88.2	99.1
0920	Plaster & Gypsum Board	101.0	107.4	105.3	94.7	107.4	103.3	104.5	98.0	100.1	99.5	107.4	104.8	101.0	98.0	99.0	99.5	107.4	104.8
0950, 0980	Ceilings & Acoustic Treatment	89.6	107.4	101.4	90.6	107.4	101.8	101.4	98.0	99.1	89.6	107.4	101.4	104.4	98.0	100.1	89.6	107.4	101.4
0960	Flooring	100.1	52.7	85.9	97.5	58.7	85.9	101.6	113.0	105.0	99.3	52.7	85.4	101.9	113.0	105.2	99.6	52.7	85.6
0970, 0990	Wall Finishes & Painting/Coating	95.3	140.1	122.2	95.4	39.3	61.7	95.3	45.1	65.1	95.3	140.1	122.2	93.4	45.1	64.4	95.3	140.1	122.2
09	FINISHES	98.8	99.7	99.3	96.2	85.6	90.3	101.8	96.3	98.7	98.3	99.7	99.1	102.5	96.3	99.0	98.0	99.7	98.9
COVERS	DIVS. 10 - 14, 25, 28, 41, 43, 44, 46	100.0	108.9	101.8	100.0	103.6	100.7	100.0	110.0	102.0	100.0	108.9	101.8	100.0	110.0	102.0	100.0	108.9	101.8
21, 22, 23	FIRE SUPPRESSION, PLUMBING & HVAC	95.2	74.1	86.8	95.2	77.3	88.0	100.1	75.9	90.4	95.2	74.1	86.8	100.0	75.9	90.3	95.2	74.1	86.8
26, 27, 3370	ELECTRICAL, COMMUNICATIONS & UTIL.	100.6	80.0	89.9	98.0	80.0	88.6	100.6	80.1	89.9	100.6	80.0	89.9	103.3	80.1	91.2	100.5	80.0	89.8
MF2010	WEIGHTED AVERAGE	95.9	86.6	91.8	95.1	85.7	91.0	98.3	91.2	95.2	95.7	86.5	91.7	100.8	91.2	96.6	95.0	86.5	91.3

MAINE / MARYLAND

DIVISION		WATERVILLE 049 MAT.	INST.	TOTAL	ANNAPOLIS 214 MAT.	INST.	TOTAL	BALTIMORE 210-212 MAT.	INST.	TOTAL	COLLEGE PARK 207-208 MAT.	INST.	TOTAL	CUMBERLAND 215 MAT.	INST.	TOTAL	EASTON 216 MAT.	INST.	TOTAL
015433	CONTRACTOR EQUIPMENT		100.6	100.6		99.3	99.3		102.8	102.8		104.3	104.3		99.3	99.3		99.3	99.3
0241, 31 - 34	SITE & INFRASTRUCTURE, DEMOLITION	90.8	100.8	97.8	98.2	90.9	93.1	99.8	94.8	96.3	103.7	94.1	96.9	91.4	90.9	91.1	98.2	88.0	91.3
0310	Concrete Forming & Accessories	89.2	97.0	96.0	98.1	70.3	74.1	100.3	72.6	76.4	86.2	71.2	73.2	91.6	80.8	82.3	89.5	71.7	74.2
0320	Concrete Reinforcing	90.1	110.1	100.1	104.0	82.1	93.0	104.5	82.1	93.3	109.0	80.5	94.7	87.7	74.6	81.2	87.0	80.6	83.8
0330	Cast-in-Place Concrete	80.3	60.3	72.0	110.8	77.1	96.8	111.3	77.9	97.4	122.5	78.0	104.0	93.6	85.7	90.3	104.0	49.2	81.2
03	CONCRETE	96.0	86.2	91.1	103.7	75.9	90.0	104.2	77.2	90.9	109.4	76.6	93.2	89.4	82.2	85.9	97.0	66.6	82.0
04	MASONRY	100.7	64.8	78.5	96.1	72.9	81.7	98.4	72.9	82.6	108.4	69.4	84.3	94.6	84.4	88.3	108.1	43.7	68.2
05	METALS	87.3	88.0	87.5	104.7	93.8	101.3	101.5	94.3	99.3	87.0	97.5	90.2	99.2	91.2	96.7	99.4	88.1	95.9
06	WOOD, PLASTICS & COMPOSITES	89.2	107.7	99.6	97.6	70.6	82.4	97.3	73.7	84.0	87.6	70.8	78.1	86.3	79.8	82.6	84.1	79.1	81.3
07	THERMAL & MOISTURE PROTECTION	100.3	66.8	86.7	101.1	79.6	92.4	99.1	80.2	91.4	102.6	78.5	92.9	99.5	80.4	91.7	99.6	60.4	83.7
08	OPENINGS	102.6	90.0	99.6	99.3	78.1	94.3	97.7	79.8	93.5	94.7	75.2	90.1	96.0	78.7	91.9	94.4	72.9	89.3
0920	Plaster & Gypsum Board	95.1	107.4	103.4	100.5	70.0	79.7	103.4	73.0	82.8	97.1	70.0	78.6	100.7	79.5	86.3	100.3	78.8	85.7
0950, 0980	Ceilings & Acoustic Treatment	89.6	107.4	101.4	100.6	70.0	80.2	98.1	73.0	81.4	98.1	70.0	79.4	100.1	79.5	86.4	100.1	78.8	85.9
0960	Flooring	97.0	56.3	84.8	100.7	78.6	94.1	100.0	78.6	93.6	97.9	80.5	92.7	96.2	92.5	95.1	95.4	52.6	82.6
0970, 0990	Wall Finishes & Painting/Coating	95.3	64.7	76.9	91.7	80.9	85.2	94.6	80.9	86.4	104.6	77.5	88.3	94.4	75.0	82.7	94.4	77.5	84.3
09	FINISHES	97.2	87.7	91.9	97.2	72.1	83.2	99.9	73.9	85.4	96.3	72.8	83.2	97.6	82.3	89.1	97.8	70.5	82.6
COVERS	DIVS. 10 - 14, 25, 28, 41, 43, 44, 46	100.0	103.3	100.7	100.0	85.6	97.1	100.0	86.3	97.3	100.0	83.8	96.8	100.0	90.2	98.0	100.0	77.2	95.4
21, 22, 23	FIRE SUPPRESSION, PLUMBING & HVAC	95.2	65.6	83.3	100.0	81.7	92.6	100.0	81.7	92.7	95.3	85.0	91.2	95.1	73.0	86.2	95.1	68.6	84.5
26, 27, 3370	ELECTRICAL, COMMUNICATIONS & UTIL.	100.6	80.0	89.8	96.7	91.7	94.1	101.4	91.7	96.3	102.2	99.8	100.9	96.6	81.6	88.8	96.1	64.4	79.5
MF2010	WEIGHTED AVERAGE	96.2	80.8	89.5	100.3	81.8	92.3	100.5	82.8	92.8	97.6	83.9	91.7	96.0	81.9	89.9	97.4	69.3	85.3

MARYLAND / MASSACHUSETTS

DIVISION		ELKTON 219 MAT.	INST.	TOTAL	HAGERSTOWN 217 MAT.	INST.	TOTAL	SALISBURY 218 MAT.	INST.	TOTAL	SILVER SPRING 209 MAT.	INST.	TOTAL	WALDORF 206 MAT.	INST.	TOTAL	BOSTON 020-022, 024 MAT.	INST.	TOTAL
015433	CONTRACTOR EQUIPMENT		99.3	99.3		99.3	99.3		99.3	99.3		97.2	97.2		97.2	97.2		106.3	106.3
0241, 31 - 34	SITE & INFRASTRUCTURE, DEMOLITION	85.8	88.7	87.8	89.8	91.6	91.0	98.1	88.0	91.0	91.3	87.5	88.6	98.0	87.1	90.3	100.8	108.2	106.0
0310	Concrete Forming & Accessories	95.5	82.6	84.4	90.6	76.3	78.3	103.5	52.9	59.8	94.8	71.4	74.6	102.4	69.6	74.1	100.9	142.0	136.4
0320	Concrete Reinforcing	87.0	101.6	94.3	87.7	74.6	81.2	87.0	65.6	76.3	107.6	80.4	94.0	108.3	80.4	94.4	108.7	157.1	132.8
0330	Cast-in-Place Concrete	84.2	76.5	81.0	89.2	85.7	87.8	104.0	47.9	80.7	125.4	79.8	106.5	140.5	76.9	114.1	104.6	152.2	124.5
03	CONCRETE	82.6	84.7	83.7	86.0	80.2	83.1	97.9	55.0	76.7	108.0	77.1	92.7	118.7	75.3	97.3	108.3	147.2	127.5
04	MASONRY	94.1	59.7	73.0	100.3	84.4	90.4	107.7	48.1	70.9	107.3	72.7	85.9	92.7	67.6	77.2	108.6	162.1	141.7
05	METALS	99.5	99.2	99.4	99.3	91.3	96.8	99.5	82.4	94.2	91.2	93.9	92.1	91.2	93.8	92.0	100.8	132.1	110.5
06	WOOD, PLASTICS & COMPOSITES	91.3	88.8	89.9	85.4	73.5	78.7	101.5	56.3	76.0	94.5	70.1	80.7	102.3	70.1	84.1	100.3	141.7	123.6
07	THERMAL & MOISTURE PROTECTION	99.2	75.1	89.4	99.2	78.6	90.8	99.8	65.2	85.7	105.6	84.4	97.0	106.1	82.2	96.4	104.0	151.9	123.5
08	OPENINGS	94.4	81.4	91.3	94.4	74.5	89.6	94.6	62.8	87.1	86.8	74.7	84.0	87.5	74.7	84.5	99.2	144.4	109.9
0920	Plaster & Gypsum Board	103.6	88.8	93.6	100.3	73.0	81.8	110.0	55.3	72.8	102.9	70.0	80.5	106.2	70.0	81.6	104.2	142.4	130.2
0950, 0980	Ceilings & Acoustic Treatment	100.1	88.8	92.6	101.0	73.0	82.4	100.1	55.3	70.3	107.8	70.0	82.6	107.8	70.0	82.6	101.8	142.4	128.8
0960	Flooring	97.6	59.5	86.2	95.8	92.5	94.8	101.0	65.9	90.5	104.0	80.5	97.0	107.5	80.5	99.4	98.6	183.1	123.9
0970, 0990	Wall Finishes & Painting/Coating	94.4	77.5	84.3	94.4	77.5	84.3	94.4	77.5	84.3	111.6	77.5	91.1	111.6	77.5	91.1	98.6	150.8	130.0
09	FINISHES	98.0	78.4	87.1	97.5	78.9	87.1	100.7	57.3	76.5	96.8	72.3	83.2	98.5	71.7	83.6	102.1	151.0	129.3
COVERS	DIVS. 10 - 14, 25, 28, 41, 43, 44, 46	100.0	61.4	92.3	100.0	89.5	97.9	100.0	39.7	87.9	100.0	83.1	96.6	100.0	81.4	96.3	100.0	118.6	103.7
21, 22, 23	FIRE SUPPRESSION, PLUMBING & HVAC	95.1	79.3	88.8	100.0	81.4	92.5	95.1	61.2	81.5	95.3	86.3	91.7	95.3	83.7	90.6	100.1	127.0	110.9
26, 27, 3370	ELECTRICAL, COMMUNICATIONS & UTIL.	97.9	91.7	94.6	96.4	81.6	88.7	94.8	68.7	81.2	99.4	99.8	99.6	96.6	99.8	98.3	100.9	138.6	120.6
MF2010	WEIGHTED AVERAGE	95.1	81.9	89.4	96.9	82.8	90.7	97.8	63.3	82.8	96.9	83.8	91.2	97.5	82.2	90.9	101.8	138.1	117.6

MASSACHUSETTS

DIVISION		BROCKTON 023			BUZZARDS BAY 025			FALL RIVER 027			FITCHBURG 014			FRAMINGHAM 017			GREENFIELD 013		
		MAT.	INST.	TOTAL	MAT.	INST.	TOTAL	MAT.	INST.	TOTAL	MAT.	INST.	TOTAL	MAT.	INST.	TOTAL	MAT.	INST.	TOTAL
015433	CONTRACTOR EQUIPMENT		102.4	102.4		102.4	102.4		103.3	103.3		100.6	100.6		101.8	101.8		100.6	100.6
0241, 31 - 34	SITE & INFRASTRUCTURE, DEMOLITION	95.7	104.8	102.1	85.8	104.8	99.1	94.8	104.9	101.9	85.8	104.7	99.1	82.5	104.5	97.9	89.6	103.2	99.2
0310	Concrete Forming & Accessories	102.6	131.5	127.5	100.2	131.4	127.1	102.6	131.7	127.7	94.8	126.0	121.7	102.0	131.2	127.2	93.2	112.1	109.5
0320	Concrete Reinforcing	106.8	157.0	131.9	85.6	165.2	125.4	106.8	165.2	136.0	85.4	156.0	120.6	85.3	156.7	121.0	88.6	126.0	107.3
0330	Cast-in-Place Concrete	98.6	152.4	120.9	82.0	152.4	111.2	95.4	152.9	119.3	85.7	148.3	111.7	85.8	140.8	108.6	88.2	129.2	105.2
03	CONCRETE	104.8	142.5	123.4	88.7	144.0	115.9	103.3	144.3	123.5	86.8	138.3	112.2	89.7	138.4	113.7	90.6	119.9	105.1
04	MASONRY	102.4	159.6	137.8	95.0	159.6	134.9	103.3	159.5	138.1	93.0	155.2	131.5	98.6	155.3	133.7	96.9	133.2	119.4
05	METALS	99.4	129.7	108.8	94.4	132.9	106.3	99.4	133.3	109.9	95.6	126.2	105.0	95.6	129.0	105.9	97.8	109.2	101.3
06	WOOD, PLASTICS & COMPOSITES	102.0	129.4	117.5	98.9	129.4	116.1	102.0	129.6	117.6	95.7	122.7	111.0	102.2	129.1	117.4	93.5	109.8	102.7
07	THERMAL & MOISTURE PROTECTION	101.7	148.3	120.6	101.0	146.7	119.5	101.6	145.9	119.6	100.8	140.1	116.8	100.9	145.2	118.8	100.9	121.2	109.1
08	OPENINGS	98.1	137.7	107.4	94.0	135.4	103.8	98.1	135.5	106.9	104.5	133.9	111.5	94.7	137.6	104.8	104.5	114.7	106.9
0920	Plaster & Gypsum Board	95.4	129.7	118.7	91.1	129.7	117.3	95.4	129.7	118.7	97.3	122.8	114.6	99.9	129.7	120.1	98.0	109.4	105.8
0950, 0980	Ceilings & Acoustic Treatment	100.9	129.7	120.1	90.0	129.7	116.4	100.9	129.7	120.1	90.6	122.8	112.0	90.6	129.7	116.6	99.5	109.4	106.1
0960	Flooring	100.4	183.1	125.1	98.9	183.1	124.1	99.8	183.1	124.7	98.2	183.1	123.6	99.6	183.1	124.5	97.5	149.9	113.2
0970, 0990	Wall Finishes & Painting/Coating	96.0	135.1	119.5	96.0	135.1	119.5	96.0	135.1	119.5	95.1	135.1	119.2	96.1	135.1	119.6	95.1	108.5	103.1
09	FINISHES	100.0	141.4	121.0	96.0	141.4	121.3	99.9	141.6	123.1	96.1	137.4	119.1	96.7	141.2	121.5	98.3	118.7	109.7
COVERS	DIVS. 10 - 14, 25, 28, 41, 43, 44, 46	100.0	116.4	103.3	100.0	116.4	103.3	100.0	117.0	103.4	100.0	102.5	100.5	100.0	115.9	103.2	100.0	105.1	101.0
21, 22, 23	FIRE SUPPRESSION, PLUMBING & HVAC	100.1	111.2	104.5	95.2	111.2	101.6	100.1	111.3	104.6	95.8	113.6	103.0	95.8	120.4	105.7	95.8	100.8	97.8
26, 27, 3370	ELECTRICAL, COMMUNICATIONS & UTIL.	100.7	100.7	100.7	97.6	100.7	99.2	100.6	100.7	100.6	100.4	104.2	102.4	96.7	129.2	113.7	100.4	92.8	96.4
MF2010	WEIGHTED AVERAGE	100.4	126.3	111.7	94.9	126.7	108.8	100.2	126.8	111.8	96.3	124.6	108.6	95.5	131.0	111.0	97.5	110.2	103.0

MASSACHUSETTS

DIVISION		HYANNIS 026			LAWRENCE 019			LOWELL 018			NEW BEDFORD 027			PITTSFIELD 012			SPRINGFIELD 010 - 011		
		MAT.	INST.	TOTAL	MAT.	INST.	TOTAL	MAT.	INST.	TOTAL	MAT.	INST.	TOTAL	MAT.	INST.	TOTAL	MAT.	INST.	TOTAL
015433	CONTRACTOR EQUIPMENT		102.4	102.4		102.4	102.4		100.6	100.6		103.3	103.3		100.6	100.6		100.6	100.6
0241, 31 - 34	SITE & INFRASTRUCTURE, DEMOLITION	91.9	104.8	101.0	94.5	104.8	101.7	93.7	104.7	101.5	93.4	104.9	101.5	94.7	103.1	100.6	94.2	103.2	100.5
0310	Concrete Forming & Accessories	94.6	131.4	126.3	103.2	131.7	127.8	100.0	131.5	127.2	102.6	131.7	127.7	99.9	111.5	109.9	100.2	111.7	110.1
0320	Concrete Reinforcing	85.6	165.2	125.4	105.6	146.6	126.0	106.5	146.3	126.4	106.8	165.2	136.0	87.9	126.0	106.9	106.5	126.0	116.2
0330	Cast-in-Place Concrete	90.0	152.4	115.9	99.2	149.8	120.2	90.2	149.7	114.9	84.1	152.9	112.6	98.4	128.3	110.8	93.9	128.5	108.3
03	CONCRETE	95.0	144.0	119.2	104.9	139.8	122.1	96.3	139.5	117.6	97.9	144.3	120.8	97.2	119.3	108.1	98.0	119.4	108.6
04	MASONRY	101.4	159.6	137.4	103.3	159.6	138.1	92.4	155.2	131.3	101.3	159.5	137.3	93.0	131.5	116.8	92.7	131.9	117.0
05	METALS	95.9	132.9	107.3	98.2	125.8	106.7	98.1	123.0	105.8	99.4	133.3	109.9	98.0	109.2	101.4	100.6	109.2	103.2
06	WOOD, PLASTICS & COMPOSITES	91.9	129.4	113.1	102.7	129.4	117.7	101.9	129.4	117.4	102.0	129.6	117.6	101.9	109.8	106.4	101.9	109.8	106.4
07	THERMAL & MOISTURE PROTECTION	101.2	146.7	119.7	101.3	147.9	120.2	101.2	145.8	119.3	101.6	145.9	119.6	101.2	120.4	109.0	101.2	120.6	109.1
08	OPENINGS	94.6	135.4	104.3	98.4	134.9	107.1	105.7	134.9	112.6	98.1	135.5	106.9	105.7	114.7	107.8	105.7	114.7	107.8
0920	Plaster & Gypsum Board	86.7	129.7	115.9	102.8	129.7	121.1	102.8	129.7	121.1	95.4	129.7	118.7	102.8	109.4	107.3	102.8	109.4	107.3
0950, 0980	Ceilings & Acoustic Treatment	92.9	129.7	117.4	101.5	129.7	120.2	101.5	129.7	120.2	100.9	129.7	120.1	101.5	109.4	106.8	101.5	109.4	106.8
0960	Flooring	96.8	183.1	122.6	100.2	183.1	125.0	100.2	183.1	125.0	99.8	183.1	124.7	100.4	149.9	115.2	99.9	149.9	114.8
0970, 0990	Wall Finishes & Painting/Coating	96.0	135.1	119.5	95.2	135.1	119.2	95.1	135.1	119.2	96.0	135.1	119.5	95.1	108.5	103.1	96.5	108.5	103.7
09	FINISHES	95.8	141.4	121.2	100.4	141.4	123.2	100.3	141.4	123.2	99.7	141.6	123.0	100.4	118.3	110.4	100.3	118.4	110.4
COVERS	DIVS. 10 - 14, 25, 28, 41, 43, 44, 46	100.0	116.4	103.3	100.0	116.5	103.3	100.0	116.5	103.3	100.0	117.0	103.4	100.0	104.5	100.9	100.0	104.6	100.9
21, 22, 23	FIRE SUPPRESSION, PLUMBING & HVAC	100.1	111.2	104.5	100.0	120.4	108.2	100.0	118.1	107.3	100.1	111.3	104.6	100.0	100.0	100.0	100.0	100.2	100.1
26, 27, 3370	ELECTRICAL, COMMUNICATIONS & UTIL.	98.1	100.7	99.4	99.4	129.2	115.0	99.9	129.2	115.2	101.5	100.7	101.1	99.9	92.8	96.2	99.9	92.8	96.2
MF2010	WEIGHTED AVERAGE	97.6	126.7	110.3	100.1	131.3	113.7	99.4	130.1	112.8	99.6	126.8	111.4	99.6	109.6	103.9	100.0	109.8	104.3

DIVISION		MASSACHUSETTS WORCESTER 015 - 016			MICHIGAN ANN ARBOR 481			BATTLE CREEK 490			BAY CITY 487			DEARBORN 481			DETROIT 482		
		MAT.	INST.	TOTAL	MAT.	INST.	TOTAL	MAT.	INST.	TOTAL	MAT.	INST.	TOTAL	MAT.	INST.	TOTAL	MAT.	INST.	TOTAL
015433	CONTRACTOR EQUIPMENT		100.6	100.6		110.7	110.7		102.6	102.6		110.7	110.7		110.7	110.7		98.7	98.7
0241, 31 - 34	SITE & INFRASTRUCTURE, DEMOLITION	94.1	104.7	101.5	78.7	97.2	91.6	89.4	87.9	88.4	70.2	96.4	88.6	78.4	97.4	91.7	92.0	99.0	96.9
0310	Concrete Forming & Accessories	100.5	126.1	122.6	97.8	111.4	109.6	97.5	87.1	88.5	97.9	89.0	90.2	97.7	116.2	113.6	99.5	116.2	113.9
0320	Concrete Reinforcing	106.5	155.2	130.8	95.7	123.7	109.7	92.2	96.0	94.1	95.7	122.8	109.3	95.7	123.8	109.8	97.2	123.8	110.5
0330	Cast-in-Place Concrete	93.3	148.3	116.2	86.2	109.5	95.9	95.1	100.0	97.1	82.5	92.0	86.5	84.3	112.5	96.0	91.4	112.5	100.1
03	CONCRETE	97.8	138.2	117.7	92.7	113.2	102.8	96.0	92.6	94.3	91.0	97.0	94.0	91.8	116.4	103.9	95.5	115.2	105.2
04	MASONRY	92.2	155.2	131.2	97.2	108.2	104.0	99.1	86.5	91.3	96.8	87.3	90.9	97.1	113.6	107.3	95.5	113.6	106.7
05	METALS	100.6	126.0	108.4	93.7	118.2	101.2	95.8	88.6	93.6	94.3	115.0	100.7	93.7	118.5	101.4	96.3	101.2	97.8
06	WOOD, PLASTICS & COMPOSITES	102.4	122.7	113.9	94.9	112.4	104.8	100.3	86.3	92.4	94.9	88.7	91.4	94.9	116.9	107.3	97.2	116.9	108.3
07	THERMAL & MOISTURE PROTECTION	101.2	140.1	117.0	100.0	108.5	103.4	96.7	85.5	92.1	97.8	94.2	96.3	98.5	113.5	104.6	97.3	113.5	103.9
08	OPENINGS	105.7	133.7	112.3	97.7	110.0	100.6	94.2	82.7	91.5	97.7	94.8	97.0	97.7	112.4	101.1	100.0	112.1	102.8
0920	Plaster & Gypsum Board	102.8	122.8	116.4	106.2	111.8	110.0	93.0	82.0	85.6	106.2	87.3	93.4	106.2	116.4	113.2	109.0	116.4	114.0
0950, 0980	Ceilings & Acoustic Treatment	101.5	122.8	115.7	93.1	111.8	105.5	96.5	82.0	86.9	94.1	87.3	89.6	93.1	116.4	108.6	96.8	116.4	109.8
0960	Flooring	100.2	183.1	125.0	96.1	117.6	102.5	103.7	92.6	100.7	96.1	81.9	91.8	95.7	116.0	101.8	97.1	116.0	102.7
0970, 0990	Wall Finishes & Painting/Coating	95.1	135.1	119.2	86.5	100.8	95.1	97.2	81.8	87.9	86.5	83.7	84.9	86.5	99.0	94.0	88.5	99.0	94.8
09	FINISHES	100.3	137.4	121.0	94.3	111.7	104.0	97.7	87.5	92.0	94.1	86.5	89.9	94.2	114.8	105.7	96.8	114.8	106.8
COVERS	DIVS. 10 - 14, 25, 28, 41, 43, 44, 46	100.0	108.6	101.7	100.0	106.1	101.2	100.0	98.2	99.6	100.0	92.6	98.5	100.0	107.7	101.5	100.0	107.7	101.5
21, 22, 23	FIRE SUPPRESSION, PLUMBING & HVAC	100.0	113.1	105.3	100.0	99.9	100.0	100.0	87.7	95.1	100.0	84.6	93.8	100.0	108.8	103.5	100.0	109.0	103.6
26, 27, 3370	ELECTRICAL, COMMUNICATIONS & UTIL.	99.9	104.2	102.1	96.0	110.0	103.4	90.3	80.4	85.1	95.0	91.1	92.9	96.0	105.2	100.8	97.2	105.1	101.3
MF2010	WEIGHTED AVERAGE	100.0	124.6	110.7	96.4	107.9	101.4	96.8	87.4	92.7	95.8	92.5	94.4	96.2	110.9	102.6	97.9	109.3	102.8

MICHIGAN

DIVISION		FLINT 484-485 MAT.	INST.	TOTAL	GAYLORD 497 MAT.	INST.	TOTAL	GRAND RAPIDS 493,495 MAT.	INST.	TOTAL	IRON MOUNTAIN 498-499 MAT.	INST.	TOTAL	JACKSON 492 MAT.	INST.	TOTAL	KALAMAZOO 491 MAT.	INST.	TOTAL
015433	CONTRACTOR EQUIPMENT		110.7	110.7		105.1	105.1		102.6	102.6		94.2	94.2		105.1	105.1		102.6	102.6
0241, 31 - 34	SITE & INFRASTRUCTURE, DEMOLITION	68.2	96.5	88.1	83.4	85.7	85.0	89.5	88.0	88.4	92.1	94.1	93.5	105.8	88.0	93.3	89.7	87.9	88.4
0310	Concrete Forming & Accessories	100.6	91.4	92.7	95.4	77.7	80.1	97.0	84.7	86.4	87.5	86.1	86.3	92.4	88.3	88.9	97.5	86.8	88.2
0320	Concrete Reinforcing	95.7	123.2	109.5	85.9	109.3	97.6	98.6	95.9	97.2	85.7	95.4	90.6	83.5	123.1	103.3	92.2	93.6	92.9
0330	Cast-in-Place Concrete	86.8	94.7	90.1	94.9	87.8	92.0	100.1	97.6	99.1	112.3	87.2	101.9	94.8	93.8	94.4	97.0	99.8	98.2
03	CONCRETE	93.2	99.1	96.1	92.4	88.2	90.3	99.3	90.7	95.1	101.8	88.4	95.2	87.2	97.3	92.2	99.4	92.0	95.8
04	MASONRY	97.3	96.8	97.0	109.6	80.5	91.6	96.1	86.6	90.2	95.6	87.6	90.7	89.7	92.8	91.7	97.8	86.5	90.8
05	METALS	93.7	115.7	100.5	97.2	111.7	101.6	93.0	88.2	91.5	96.6	91.1	94.9	97.3	113.6	102.4	95.8	87.5	93.3
06	WOOD, PLASTICS & COMPOSITES	98.2	89.9	93.5	92.8	76.9	83.8	101.5	83.1	91.1	87.5	86.1	86.7	91.5	86.6	88.7	100.3	86.3	92.4
07	THERMAL & MOISTURE PROTECTION	97.8	97.9	97.9	95.1	76.2	87.4	99.5	77.4	90.5	98.6	83.1	92.3	94.5	94.5	94.5	96.7	85.5	92.1
08	OPENINGS	97.7	95.5	97.1	94.8	76.0	90.3	100.6	85.6	97.0	101.3	77.3	95.7	93.8	93.9	93.8	94.2	82.1	91.3
0920	Plaster & Gypsum Board	107.7	88.6	94.7	92.8	74.9	80.6	94.9	78.8	83.9	53.7	86.1	75.7	91.0	84.9	86.9	93.0	82.0	85.6
0950, 0980	Ceilings & Acoustic Treatment	93.1	88.6	90.1	95.7	74.9	81.9	105.1	78.8	87.6	94.6	86.1	88.9	95.7	84.9	88.5	96.5	82.0	86.9
0960	Flooring	96.1	94.9	95.7	95.7	93.9	95.1	103.6	84.3	97.8	119.6	95.6	112.4	94.4	84.3	91.4	103.7	77.1	95.8
0970, 0990	Wall Finishes & Painting/Coating	86.5	87.3	87.0	93.1	83.7	87.5	98.9	80.0	87.6	111.4	71.8	87.6	93.1	98.8	96.5	97.2	81.8	87.9
09	FINISHES	93.6	90.7	92.0	97.5	79.8	87.7	101.7	83.8	91.7	99.7	86.4	92.3	98.6	88.0	92.7	97.7	84.2	90.2
COVERS	DIVS. 10 - 14, 25, 28, 41, 43, 44, 46	100.0	93.9	98.8	100.0	90.7	98.1	100.0	98.2	99.6	100.0	89.5	97.9	100.0	93.7	98.7	100.0	98.2	99.6
21, 22, 23	FIRE SUPPRESSION, PLUMBING & HVAC	100.0	90.6	96.2	95.5	80.1	89.3	100.0	83.8	93.5	95.4	86.0	91.6	95.5	88.8	92.8	100.0	81.6	92.6
26, 27, 3370	ELECTRICAL, COMMUNICATIONS & UTIL.	96.0	98.3	97.2	88.4	78.9	83.4	95.2	72.3	83.3	94.5	86.3	90.2	92.2	110.0	101.5	90.2	83.7	86.8
MF2010	WEIGHTED AVERAGE	96.1	96.8	96.4	95.5	84.4	90.7	98.1	84.5	92.2	97.5	87.4	93.1	95.0	95.9	95.4	97.1	85.9	92.2

MICHIGAN / MINNESOTA

DIVISION		LANSING 488-489 MAT.	INST.	TOTAL	MUSKEGON 494 MAT.	INST.	TOTAL	ROYAL OAK 480,483 MAT.	INST.	TOTAL	SAGINAW 486 MAT.	INST.	TOTAL	TRAVERSE CITY 496 MAT.	INST.	TOTAL	BEMIDJI 566 MAT.	INST.	TOTAL
015433	CONTRACTOR EQUIPMENT		110.7	110.7		102.6	102.6		96.2	96.2		110.7	110.7		94.2	94.2		99.0	99.0
0241, 31 - 34	SITE & INFRASTRUCTURE, DEMOLITION	90.5	96.6	94.8	87.5	87.9	87.8	83.0	96.8	92.7	71.2	96.4	88.9	78.4	93.6	89.0	94.0	98.3	97.0
0310	Concrete Forming & Accessories	98.0	89.2	90.4	97.9	85.6	87.3	93.6	112.7	110.1	97.8	88.8	90.0	87.5	75.7	77.3	88.7	91.4	91.0
0320	Concrete Reinforcing	99.0	123.0	111.0	92.8	96.1	94.5	86.8	123.8	105.2	95.7	122.8	109.3	87.0	92.9	90.0	97.0	108.0	102.5
0330	Cast-in-Place Concrete	100.5	92.9	97.3	94.8	95.8	95.2	75.5	108.3	89.1	85.2	91.9	88.0	87.6	80.0	84.5	104.1	104.2	104.1
03	CONCRETE	100.0	97.4	98.7	94.3	90.6	92.5	79.9	112.2	95.8	92.2	96.9	94.5	83.9	80.8	82.4	96.9	100.0	98.4
04	MASONRY	95.3	93.3	94.1	96.3	89.4	92.0	92.0	112.1	104.5	98.7	87.3	91.6	93.7	82.3	86.7	97.2	104.8	101.9
05	METALS	91.4	115.1	98.7	93.6	88.5	92.0	96.8	99.4	97.6	93.8	114.8	100.3	96.5	89.7	94.4	90.2	121.0	99.7
06	WOOD, PLASTICS & COMPOSITES	96.4	88.0	91.6	96.5	85.2	90.1	90.4	113.1	103.2	91.2	88.7	89.8	87.5	75.2	80.6	71.5	87.5	80.6
07	THERMAL & MOISTURE PROTECTION	98.6	90.6	95.3	95.8	80.4	89.5	96.5	112.3	102.9	98.6	94.2	96.9	97.8	72.8	87.6	105.6	97.1	102.1
08	OPENINGS	98.7	94.4	97.7	93.4	86.5	91.8	97.6	110.4	100.6	95.6	94.8	95.4	101.3	71.4	94.3	97.5	109.2	100.2
0920	Plaster & Gypsum Board	92.2	86.6	88.4	74.3	80.9	78.8	103.2	112.5	109.5	106.2	87.3	93.4	53.7	74.9	68.1	100.6	87.4	91.6
0950, 0980	Ceilings & Acoustic Treatment	96.8	86.6	90.0	97.4	80.9	86.4	92.3	112.5	105.8	93.1	87.3	89.3	94.6	74.9	81.5	137.1	87.4	104.0
0960	Flooring	102.8	84.3	97.2	102.5	84.3	97.1	93.7	116.0	100.4	96.1	81.9	91.8	119.6	93.9	111.9	107.8	123.0	112.3
0970, 0990	Wall Finishes & Painting/Coating	96.3	81.5	87.4	95.6	80.0	86.3	87.9	98.8	94.5	86.5	83.7	84.9	111.4	45.6	71.9	95.3	97.9	96.9
09	FINISHES	98.2	87.0	91.9	94.3	84.0	88.6	93.3	112.2	103.8	93.9	86.5	89.8	98.6	74.3	85.1	111.3	97.1	103.4
COVERS	DIVS. 10 - 14, 25, 28, 41, 43, 44, 46	100.0	93.3	98.7	100.0	98.0	99.6	100.0	104.6	100.9	100.0	92.6	98.5	100.0	86.8	97.4	100.0	99.3	99.9
21, 22, 23	FIRE SUPPRESSION, PLUMBING & HVAC	99.9	88.9	95.5	99.9	83.1	93.1	95.4	108.0	100.5	100.0	84.2	93.7	95.4	79.4	89.0	95.5	84.8	91.2
26, 27, 3370	ELECTRICAL, COMMUNICATIONS & UTIL.	99.2	91.4	95.1	90.7	77.2	83.6	98.3	104.5	101.5	93.5	91.1	92.3	89.9	78.9	84.2	104.4	105.2	104.8
MF2010	WEIGHTED AVERAGE	97.7	94.1	96.1	95.6	85.5	91.2	94.2	107.5	100.0	92.4	92.4	94.2	94.6	81.0	88.6	97.7	99.5	98.5

MINNESOTA

DIVISION		BRAINERD 564 MAT.	INST.	TOTAL	DETROIT LAKES 565 MAT.	INST.	TOTAL	DULUTH 556-558 MAT.	INST.	TOTAL	MANKATO 560 MAT.	INST.	TOTAL	MINNEAPOLIS 553-555 MAT.	INST.	TOTAL	ROCHESTER 559 MAT.	INST.	TOTAL
015433	CONTRACTOR EQUIPMENT		101.6	101.6		99.0	99.0		100.4	100.4		101.6	101.6		103.8	103.8		100.4	100.4
0241, 31 - 34	SITE & INFRASTRUCTURE, DEMOLITION	94.2	103.0	100.4	92.2	98.6	96.7	96.3	100.4	99.2	91.1	103.7	99.9	97.9	105.6	103.3	97.0	100.0	99.1
0310	Concrete Forming & Accessories	90.6	93.6	93.2	85.7	93.5	92.5	100.4	112.2	110.6	98.4	101.1	100.7	101.2	127.4	123.8	102.8	106.6	106.1
0320	Concrete Reinforcing	95.9	108.2	102.0	97.0	108.0	102.5	102.6	108.5	105.5	95.8	118.2	107.0	97.2	118.5	107.8	94.8	118.2	106.5
0330	Cast-in-Place Concrete	113.1	108.2	111.1	101.1	107.5	103.7	107.4	107.0	107.2	104.2	109.0	106.2	110.5	117.3	113.3	109.0	100.9	105.6
03	CONCRETE	100.8	102.4	101.6	94.5	102.1	98.2	101.3	110.3	105.7	96.5	107.9	102.1	103.4	122.6	112.9	100.7	107.7	104.1
04	MASONRY	119.6	113.5	115.8	119.9	110.8	114.2	104.6	117.0	112.3	108.6	110.5	109.8	114.7	125.3	121.3	107.0	112.5	110.4
05	METALS	91.3	121.0	100.5	90.2	120.9	99.7	93.4	123.1	102.6	91.2	126.7	102.1	98.6	130.0	108.3	95.2	128.4	105.4
06	WOOD, PLASTICS & COMPOSITES	89.5	87.3	88.3	68.5	87.5	79.3	103.6	111.9	108.3	99.0	98.7	98.8	109.0	126.0	118.6	109.0	105.2	106.9
07	THERMAL & MOISTURE PROTECTION	104.7	109.9	106.8	105.4	110.1	107.3	100.1	116.9	106.9	105.0	100.6	103.2	102.1	128.6	112.9	103.5	102.0	102.9
08	OPENINGS	84.8	109.0	90.5	97.4	109.2	100.2	98.3	118.2	103.0	89.1	117.7	95.9	94.9	133.8	104.1	93.5	122.5	100.4
0920	Plaster & Gypsum Board	84.6	87.4	86.5	99.5	87.4	91.3	91.1	112.6	105.8	89.5	99.1	96.0	99.3	127.0	118.2	99.5	105.8	103.8
0950, 0980	Ceilings & Acoustic Treatment	66.7	87.4	80.5	137.1	87.4	104.0	98.7	112.6	108.0	66.7	99.1	88.3	98.5	127.0	117.5	95.0	105.8	102.2
0960	Flooring	106.7	123.0	111.6	106.6	123.0	111.5	107.1	124.3	112.3	108.3	123.0	112.7	98.3	123.0	105.7	103.2	123.0	109.1
0970, 0990	Wall Finishes & Painting/Coating	89.6	97.9	94.6	95.3	97.9	96.9	91.0	111.3	103.2	101.0	105.3	103.6	96.5	128.1	115.5	91.3	105.3	99.7
09	FINISHES	93.1	98.5	96.1	110.7	98.6	104.0	101.4	114.7	108.8	94.8	105.3	100.7	100.5	127.2	115.4	99.4	109.5	105.0
COVERS	DIVS. 10 - 14, 25, 28, 41, 43, 44, 46	100.0	100.9	100.2	100.0	101.2	100.2	100.0	100.1	100.0	100.0	101.1	100.2	100.0	109.1	101.8	100.0	102.6	100.5
21, 22, 23	FIRE SUPPRESSION, PLUMBING & HVAC	94.8	87.8	92.0	95.5	87.6	92.3	99.9	97.2	98.8	94.8	88.5	92.3	99.9	116.9	106.7	100.0	96.0	98.4
26, 27, 3370	ELECTRICAL, COMMUNICATIONS & UTIL.	101.9	104.9	103.4	104.1	69.1	85.8	98.4	104.9	101.8	108.8	89.2	98.5	101.8	109.0	105.6	98.2	89.2	93.5
MF2010	WEIGHTED AVERAGE	96.3	102.3	98.9	98.3	96.7	97.6	99.0	108.6	103.2	96.6	102.4	99.1	100.6	119.9	109.0	98.8	104.9	101.5

765

		MINNESOTA																MISSISSIPPI		
		SAINT PAUL			ST. CLOUD			THIEF RIVER FALLS			WILLMAR			WINDOM			BILOXI		
	DIVISION	550 - 551			563			567			562			561			395		
		MAT.	INST.	TOTAL	MAT.	INST.	TOTAL	MAT.	INST.	TOTAL	MAT.	INST.	TOTAL	MAT.	INST.	TOTAL	MAT.	INST.	TOTAL
015433	CONTRACTOR EQUIPMENT		100.4	100.4		101.6	101.6		99.0	99.0		101.6	101.6		101.6	101.6		99.3	99.3
0241, 31 - 34	SITE & INFRASTRUCTURE, DEMOLITION	99.1	101.1	100.5	89.7	105.1	100.5	92.9	98.2	96.7	89.1	102.8	98.7	83.3	101.7	96.3	98.8	89.6	92.3
0310	Concrete Forming & Accessories	102.0	124.9	121.8	87.7	120.4	116.0	89.4	90.8	90.6	87.5	93.1	92.3	92.0	86.8	87.5	95.6	54.1	59.8
0320	Concrete Reinforcing	98.5	118.5	108.5	95.9	118.4	107.1	97.4	107.9	102.7	95.6	118.0	106.8	95.6	117.1	106.4	95.8	58.4	77.1
0330	Cast-in-Place Concrete	120.2	116.7	118.7	99.9	115.8	106.5	103.2	89.5	97.5	101.4	86.9	95.4	87.7	67.8	79.4	108.7	54.8	86.3
03	CONCRETE	110.6	121.3	115.9	92.3	118.9	105.4	95.6	94.6	95.1	92.2	96.7	94.4	83.2	87.2	85.2	100.0	56.8	78.7
04	MASONRY	115.6	125.3	121.6	105.3	122.1	115.7	97.2	104.8	101.9	109.7	113.5	112.0	119.4	91.2	102.0	90.3	45.1	62.4
05	METALS	94.1	129.8	105.1	92.0	128.0	103.1	90.3	120.3	99.6	91.1	125.8	101.8	91.0	123.5	101.0	91.9	82.4	89.0
06	WOOD, PLASTICS & COMPOSITES	102.8	122.7	114.0	86.8	117.6	104.2	72.5	87.5	81.0	86.6	87.5	87.1	90.8	84.8	87.4	102.3	57.4	77.0
07	THERMAL & MOISTURE PROTECTION	101.8	128.1	112.5	104.8	120.1	111.0	106.5	100.0	103.9	104.6	110.8	107.1	104.6	91.0	99.1	97.0	55.4	80.1
08	OPENINGS	97.1	132.0	105.3	89.1	129.2	98.6	97.5	109.2	100.2	86.7	93.5	88.3	90.2	92.0	90.6	97.2	58.6	88.0
0920	Plaster & Gypsum Board	87.3	123.8	112.1	84.6	118.6	107.7	100.2	87.4	91.5	84.6	87.6	86.7	84.6	84.8	84.7	104.4	56.5	71.8
0950, 0980	Ceilings & Acoustic Treatment	98.5	123.8	115.4	66.7	118.6	101.2	137.1	87.4	104.0	66.7	87.6	80.6	66.7	84.8	78.7	95.9	56.5	69.7
0960	Flooring	99.5	123.0	106.5	103.3	123.0	109.2	107.5	123.0	112.1	105.1	123.0	110.4	107.3	123.0	112.0	114.4	56.1	97.0
0970, 0990	Wall Finishes & Painting/Coating	99.9	127.1	116.3	101.0	128.1	117.3	95.3	97.9	96.9	95.3	97.9	96.9	95.3	105.3	101.3	94.7	44.4	64.5
09	FINISHES	99.5	125.1	113.8	92.6	121.9	108.9	111.1	97.1	103.3	92.7	96.2	94.6	92.8	93.2	93.0	100.8	53.6	74.5
COVERS	DIVS. 10 - 14, 25, 28, 41, 43, 44, 46	100.0	108.5	101.7	100.0	107.2	101.4	100.0	99.2	99.8	100.0	100.8	100.2	100.0	95.6	99.1	100.0	56.9	91.4
21, 22, 23	FIRE SUPPRESSION, PLUMBING & HVAC	99.9	114.9	105.9	99.7	116.3	106.3	95.5	84.5	91.1	94.8	108.4	100.2	94.8	85.3	91.0	100.0	50.1	80.0
26, 27, 3370	ELECTRICAL, COMMUNICATIONS & UTIL.	95.2	111.4	103.7	101.9	111.4	106.9	101.4	69.1	84.6	101.9	87.2	94.2	108.8	89.1	98.5	98.5	57.6	77.1
MF2010	WEIGHTED AVERAGE	100.2	118.8	108.3	96.3	117.8	105.7	97.3	93.8	95.7	94.9	103.0	98.4	95.3	93.3	94.4	97.7	59.1	80.9

		MISSISSIPPI																		
		CLARKSDALE			COLUMBUS			GREENVILLE			GREENWOOD			JACKSON			LAUREL		
	DIVISION	386			397			387			389			390 - 392			394		
		MAT.	INST.	TOTAL	MAT.	INST.	TOTAL	MAT.	INST.	TOTAL	MAT.	INST.	TOTAL	MAT.	INST.	TOTAL	MAT.	INST.	TOTAL
015433	CONTRACTOR EQUIPMENT		99.3	99.3		99.3	99.3		99.3	99.3		99.3	99.3		99.3	99.3		99.3	99.3
0241, 31 - 34	SITE & INFRASTRUCTURE, DEMOLITION	95.6	89.4	91.2	97.1	89.6	91.9	101.3	89.6	93.1	98.3	89.1	91.8	95.9	89.6	91.5	102.9	89.5	93.5
0310	Concrete Forming & Accessories	85.3	50.4	55.2	84.4	54.6	58.8	82.0	55.2	67.5	94.3	50.4	56.4	94.6	58.9	63.8	84.4	54.2	58.3
0320	Concrete Reinforcing	100.0	42.9	71.5	102.7	43.9	73.3	100.6	62.2	81.4	100.0	54.2	77.1	101.2	57.5	79.4	103.3	40.3	71.9
0330	Cast-in-Place Concrete	103.0	54.4	82.8	110.8	59.5	89.5	106.0	56.5	85.5	110.7	54.1	87.2	98.9	57.8	81.8	108.4	56.1	86.7
03	CONCRETE	95.9	52.1	74.3	101.6	54.9	78.6	101.1	63.0	82.3	102.1	53.9	78.3	96.1	59.7	78.2	104.0	53.9	79.3
04	MASONRY	93.5	45.8	64.0	114.7	52.5	76.2	138.0	50.3	83.8	94.1	45.6	64.1	95.7	50.3	67.6	110.9	49.0	72.6
05	METALS	90.5	74.9	85.7	88.9	75.8	84.9	91.5	84.1	89.3	90.5	76.4	86.2	98.5	82.3	93.5	89.0	74.8	84.6
06	WOOD, PLASTICS & COMPOSITES	85.6	52.4	66.9	87.2	53.4	68.1	82.2	69.7	75.1	98.7	52.4	72.6	99.6	61.0	77.8	88.3	55.9	70.0
07	THERMAL & MOISTURE PROTECTION	95.9	48.0	76.5	97.0	52.3	78.8	96.2	61.0	81.9	96.3	47.9	76.6	97.1	60.3	82.1	97.1	54.0	79.6
08	OPENINGS	96.8	50.6	85.8	96.5	50.7	85.7	96.8	62.9	88.8	96.8	51.9	86.2	101.0	56.8	90.5	93.5	51.5	83.6
0920	Plaster & Gypsum Board	87.7	51.4	63.0	92.7	52.4	65.3	87.3	69.2	75.0	98.9	51.4	66.6	97.4	60.2	72.1	92.7	54.9	67.0
0950, 0980	Ceilings & Acoustic Treatment	87.8	51.4	63.6	90.3	52.4	65.1	89.7	69.2	76.1	87.8	51.4	63.6	98.4	60.2	73.0	90.3	54.9	66.8
0960	Flooring	111.6	53.8	94.3	108.2	60.3	93.9	109.9	53.8	93.1	117.1	53.8	98.2	111.9	56.1	95.2	106.8	53.8	91.0
0970, 0990	Wall Finishes & Painting/Coating	97.4	47.1	67.2	94.7	54.1	70.3	97.4	67.3	79.3	97.4	47.1	67.2	91.7	67.3	77.0	94.7	62.2	75.2
09	FINISHES	96.5	51.0	71.1	96.3	54.4	73.0	97.0	64.3	78.8	99.9	51.0	72.7	100.6	59.6	77.8	96.4	55.5	73.6
COVERS	DIVS. 10 - 14, 25, 28, 41, 43, 44, 46	100.0	57.2	91.4	100.0	58.4	91.7	100.0	60.0	92.0	100.0	57.2	91.4	100.0	59.1	91.8	100.0	38.5	87.7
21, 22, 23	FIRE SUPPRESSION, PLUMBING & HVAC	97.9	42.2	75.6	97.3	38.3	73.7	100.0	48.6	79.4	97.9	40.2	74.7	100.0	58.3	83.3	97.4	46.8	77.1
26, 27, 3370	ELECTRICAL, COMMUNICATIONS & UTIL.	95.6	47.5	70.5	95.7	50.3	72.0	95.6	64.2	79.2	95.6	44.5	68.9	100.1	64.2	81.3	97.3	58.3	77.0
MF2010	WEIGHTED AVERAGE	95.8	53.8	77.5	97.1	54.3	78.8	99.4	63.1	83.6	97.0	53.3	78.0	99.1	63.3	83.6	97.2	57.1	79.7

		MISSISSIPPI									MISSOURI								
		MCCOMB			MERIDIAN			TUPELO			BOWLING GREEN			CAPE GIRARDEAU			CHILLICOTHE		
	DIVISION	396			393			388			633			637			646		
		MAT.	INST.	TOTAL	MAT.	INST.	TOTAL	MAT.	INST.	TOTAL	MAT.	INST.	TOTAL	MAT.	INST.	TOTAL	MAT.	INST.	TOTAL
015433	CONTRACTOR EQUIPMENT		99.3	99.3		99.3	99.3		99.3	99.3		106.6	106.6		106.6	106.6		102.1	102.1
0241, 31 - 34	SITE & INFRASTRUCTURE, DEMOLITION	90.3	89.2	89.6	94.3	89.9	91.2	93.1	89.3	90.4	90.1	95.1	93.6	91.7	95.0	94.1	105.0	94.6	97.7
0310	Concrete Forming & Accessories	84.4	52.2	56.6	81.7	64.8	67.1	82.5	52.5	56.6	94.2	88.8	89.5	87.3	75.1	76.8	89.9	95.2	94.5
0320	Concrete Reinforcing	103.9	42.3	73.1	102.7	57.5	80.1	97.9	54.2	76.1	103.2	100.8	102.0	104.5	88.8	96.7	97.4	110.0	103.7
0330	Cast-in-Place Concrete	96.2	53.8	78.7	102.9	60.1	85.2	103.0	55.8	83.4	92.6	85.4	89.6	91.6	87.3	89.8	97.9	87.8	93.7
03	CONCRETE	91.6	52.5	72.3	95.8	63.2	79.7	95.4	55.4	75.7	95.0	91.0	93.5	95.0	83.4	89.3	102.1	95.9	99.1
04	MASONRY	116.2	45.1	72.2	90.0	54.5	68.0	127.9	48.7	78.9	122.1	97.9	107.1	118.5	79.0	94.1	103.6	100.6	101.7
05	METALS	89.1	73.1	84.2	90.0	82.5	87.7	90.4	76.6	86.2	96.1	113.8	101.6	97.2	107.3	100.3	96.9	110.5	101.1
06	WOOD, PLASTICS & COMPOSITES	87.2	55.3	69.2	84.6	66.7	74.5	82.8	53.4	66.2	95.3	88.0	91.2	88.1	71.5	78.7	96.0	95.4	95.7
07	THERMAL & MOISTURE PROTECTION	96.6	47.2	76.6	96.8	62.6	82.9	95.9	53.8	78.8	103.2	98.8	101.4	103.1	83.5	95.1	97.8	97.0	97.4
08	OPENINGS	96.6	52.2	86.1	96.5	65.5	89.2	96.8	51.8	86.1	97.0	98.5	97.3	97.0	75.5	91.9	96.0	98.1	96.5
0920	Plaster & Gypsum Board	92.7	54.3	66.6	92.7	66.1	74.6	87.3	52.4	63.6	97.9	87.6	90.9	96.4	70.6	78.8	97.4	95.1	95.8
0950, 0980	Ceilings & Acoustic Treatment	90.3	54.3	66.4	92.3	66.1	74.8	87.8	52.4	64.2	97.1	87.6	90.8	97.1	70.6	79.5	92.2	95.1	94.1
0960	Flooring	108.2	53.8	91.9	104.7	77.8	84.5	110.1	53.8	93.3	98.4	98.5	98.4	95.2	85.6	92.3	96.0	104.4	98.5
0970, 0990	Wall Finishes & Painting/Coating	94.7	43.2	63.8	94.7	77.8	84.5	97.4	60.0	74.9	102.3	102.8	102.6	102.3	74.8	85.8	96.2	91.3	93.3
09	FINISHES	95.7	52.1	71.4	96.0	65.2	78.8	96.0	53.8	72.5	100.8	91.2	95.4	99.6	75.4	86.1	99.9	96.4	97.9
COVERS	DIVS. 10 - 14, 25, 28, 41, 43, 44, 46	100.0	60.7	92.1	100.0	61.1	92.2	100.0	58.4	91.7	100.0	90.2	98.0	100.0	92.3	98.5	100.0	90.9	98.2
21, 22, 23	FIRE SUPPRESSION, PLUMBING & HVAC	97.3	35.3	72.5	100.0	60.4	84.1	98.1	44.2	76.5	95.0	97.7	96.1	99.9	96.6	98.6	95.2	99.2	96.8
26, 27, 3370	ELECTRICAL, COMMUNICATIONS & UTIL.	94.1	50.6	71.4	97.3	58.2	76.9	95.4	50.4	71.9	98.0	80.8	89.1	98.0	103.9	101.1	93.7	80.5	86.8
MF2010	WEIGHTED AVERAGE	95.7	52.9	77.1	96.2	65.3	82.7	97.3	56.1	79.4	98.1	94.7	96.6	99.1	90.6	95.4	97.7	96.2	97.1

City Cost Indexes

MISSOURI

DIVISION		COLUMBIA 652			FLAT RIVER 636			HANNIBAL 634			HARRISONVILLE 647			JEFFERSON CITY 650 - 651			JOPLIN 648		
		MAT.	INST.	TOTAL	MAT.	INST.	TOTAL	MAT.	INST.	TOTAL	MAT.	INST.	TOTAL	MAT.	INST.	TOTAL	MAT.	INST.	TOTAL
015433	CONTRACTOR EQUIPMENT		107.7	107.7		106.6	106.6		106.6	106.6		102.1	102.1		107.7	107.7		105.8	105.8
0241, 31 - 34	SITE & INFRASTRUCTURE, DEMOLITION	100.0	96.6	97.6	92.8	95.2	94.5	88.0	95.1	93.0	96.1	95.6	95.8	99.2	96.6	97.4	105.6	99.4	101.3
0310	Concrete Forming & Accessories	85.5	80.0	80.7	100.1	86.2	88.1	92.4	79.3	81.1	87.3	100.9	99.1	95.6	80.0	82.1	101.6	73.7	77.5
0320	Concrete Reinforcing	98.1	116.3	107.2	104.5	108.0	106.3	102.7	100.8	101.7	97.0	110.1	103.5	100.4	113.1	106.7	100.6	101.7	101.1
0330	Cast-in-Place Concrete	89.8	87.1	88.7	95.6	94.2	95.0	87.6	85.2	86.6	100.3	106.1	102.7	95.3	87.1	91.9	106.0	79.2	94.9
03	CONCRETE	86.8	90.6	88.7	98.8	94.2	96.6	92.2	86.8	89.5	98.5	104.8	101.6	91.9	90.0	91.0	101.7	81.7	91.8
04	MASONRY	133.2	88.7	105.7	119.0	80.5	95.2	113.5	97.9	103.8	98.3	105.3	102.6	97.0	88.7	91.9	96.6	86.8	90.5
05	METALS	97.1	119.7	104.1	96.0	115.8	102.1	96.1	113.5	101.5	97.3	111.5	101.7	96.6	118.4	103.3	100.0	102.2	100.7
06	WOOD, PLASTICS & COMPOSITES	95.4	76.3	84.6	103.2	84.5	92.7	93.3	75.5	83.2	92.5	99.8	96.6	102.0	76.3	87.5	107.5	71.8	87.4
07	THERMAL & MOISTURE PROTECTION	95.5	88.1	92.5	103.4	93.8	99.5	103.0	96.9	100.5	97.1	105.8	100.6	100.8	88.1	95.7	97.1	79.6	90.0
08	OPENINGS	94.7	93.3	94.4	96.9	98.8	97.4	97.0	84.3	94.0	96.1	102.9	97.7	94.2	92.5	93.8	97.2	78.2	92.7
0920	Plaster & Gypsum Board	85.3	75.5	78.7	103.8	84.1	90.4	96.7	74.7	81.8	92.5	99.6	97.3	89.2	75.5	79.9	103.5	70.7	81.2
0950, 0980	Ceilings & Acoustic Treatment	97.9	75.5	83.0	97.1	84.1	88.4	97.1	74.7	82.2	92.2	99.6	97.1	102.1	75.5	84.4	93.0	70.7	78.2
0960	Flooring	109.7	97.5	106.1	101.3	85.6	96.6	97.7	98.5	98.0	91.7	104.4	95.5	116.0	97.5	110.5	121.0	76.3	107.6
0970, 0990	Wall Finishes & Painting/Coating	102.4	78.8	88.2	102.3	80.0	88.9	102.3	102.8	102.6	101.1	105.3	103.6	99.6	78.8	87.1	95.8	76.5	84.2
09	FINISHES	97.5	81.6	88.6	102.5	84.1	92.3	100.2	83.8	91.1	97.5	101.7	99.9	101.7	81.6	90.5	106.1	74.5	88.4
COVERS	DIVS. 10 - 14, 25, 28, 41, 43, 44, 46	100.0	95.6	99.1	100.0	94.3	98.8	100.0	88.8	97.8	100.0	93.1	98.6	100.0	95.6	99.1	100.0	89.6	97.9
21, 22, 23	FIRE SUPPRESSION, PLUMBING & HVAC	99.9	97.8	99.0	95.0	97.6	96.1	95.0	97.6	96.1	95.1	100.5	97.2	99.9	98.7	99.4	100.1	72.7	89.1
26, 27, 3370	ELECTRICAL, COMMUNICATIONS & UTIL.	98.4	86.6	92.2	102.4	104.0	103.2	96.8	82.9	89.6	100.4	99.7	100.1	104.3	86.6	95.1	91.5	69.7	80.1
MF2010	WEIGHTED AVERAGE	98.6	93.5	96.4	99.0	95.8	97.6	97.1	92.6	95.1	97.3	102.2	99.5	98.4	93.4	96.2	99.5	81.0	91.5

MISSOURI

DIVISION		KANSAS CITY 640 - 641			KIRKSVILLE 635			POPLAR BLUFF 639			ROLLA 654 - 655			SEDALIA 653			SIKESTON 638		
		MAT.	INST.	TOTAL	MAT.	INST.	TOTAL	MAT.	INST.	TOTAL	MAT.	INST.	TOTAL	MAT.	INST.	TOTAL	MAT.	INST.	TOTAL
015433	CONTRACTOR EQUIPMENT		103.4	103.4		99.0	99.0		101.3	101.3		107.7	107.7		99.7	99.7		101.3	101.3
0241, 31 - 34	SITE & INFRASTRUCTURE, DEMOLITION	98.2	98.0	98.0	90.9	91.2	91.1	78.4	95.0	90.1	99.0	96.6	97.3	94.9	92.5	93.2	81.7	95.1	91.1
0310	Concrete Forming & Accessories	100.3	107.8	106.8	85.2	79.3	80.1	85.3	75.0	76.4	92.7	94.0	93.8	90.1	79.3	80.8	86.4	75.0	76.5
0320	Concrete Reinforcing	95.5	117.1	106.3	103.4	101.9	102.6	106.5	97.6	102.0	98.6	97.7	98.2	97.1	109.4	103.2	105.9	101.4	103.6
0330	Cast-in-Place Concrete	98.6	107.8	102.4	95.5	85.1	91.2	73.5	87.8	79.5	91.8	96.4	93.7	95.9	84.5	91.2	78.6	87.8	82.4
03	CONCRETE	97.8	109.7	103.7	110.2	86.4	98.5	86.0 *	84.6	85.3	88.6	96.5	92.5	101.1	87.6	94.4	89.6	85.3	87.5
04	MASONRY	100.4	109.1	105.8	125.6	88.7	102.8	117.1	79.1	93.6	109.4	89.4	97.0	115.2	86.6	97.5	116.8	79.1	93.5
05	METALS	107.7	114.9	109.9	95.7	105.2	98.6	96.3	102.9	98.3	96.5	111.9	101.3	95.1	109.3	99.5	96.6	104.4	99.0
06	WOOD, PLASTICS & COMPOSITES	106.7	107.5	107.1	81.1	76.3	78.4	80.3	71.5	75.3	103.0	94.9	98.5	95.4	76.3	84.6	81.9	71.5	76.0
07	THERMAL & MOISTURE PROTECTION	97.2	108.6	101.8	109.8	89.1	101.4	108.3	85.3	99.0	108.5	85.3	98.5	101.8	93.7	98.5	108.5	83.9	98.5
08	OPENINGS	103.5	109.8	105.0	102.0	85.6	98.1	103.0	77.9	97.1	94.7	90.4	93.7	99.0	87.3	96.2	103.0	78.9	97.3
0920	Plaster & Gypsum Board	100.2	107.5	105.1	91.8	75.5	80.7	92.3	70.6	77.5	87.2	94.7	92.3	80.4	75.5	77.1	94.1	70.6	78.1
0950, 0980	Ceilings & Acoustic Treatment	99.3	107.5	104.7	95.3	75.5	82.1	97.1	70.6	79.5	97.9	94.7	95.8	97.9	75.5	83.0	97.1	70.6	79.5
0960	Flooring	96.6	109.3	100.4	76.5	97.5	82.8	90.2	83.5	88.2	113.0	97.5	108.3	86.4	97.5	89.7	90.6	83.5	88.5
0970, 0990	Wall Finishes & Painting/Coating	101.1	112.6	108.0	97.6	80.4	87.2	97.1	74.8	83.7	102.4	102.8	102.7	102.4	102.4	102.4	97.1	74.8	83.7
09	FINISHES	101.4	108.5	105.4	100.0	81.7	89.8	99.6	75.1	85.9	98.8	95.5	96.9	95.7	83.7	89.0	100.3	75.1	86.2
COVERS	DIVS. 10 - 14, 25, 28, 41, 43, 44, 46	100.0	101.3	100.3	100.0	89.0	97.8	100.0	92.4	98.5	100.0	91.4	98.3	100.0	91.5	98.3	100.0	92.4	98.5
21, 22, 23	FIRE SUPPRESSION, PLUMBING & HVAC	100.0	106.7	102.7	95.1	97.1	95.9	95.1	96.0	95.4	95.0	98.0	96.2	94.9	93.8	94.5	95.1	96.1	95.5
26, 27, 3370	ELECTRICAL, COMMUNICATIONS & UTIL.	102.0	100.1	101.0	97.0	82.9	89.6	97.2	103.9	100.7	96.6	86.6	91.4	98.2	99.7	99.0	96.3	103.9	100.3
MF2010	WEIGHTED AVERAGE	101.6	106.7	103.8	100.3	90.0	95.8	97.0	90.3	94.1	96.3	95.6	96.0	98.1	92.6	95.7	97.5	90.6	94.5

MISSOURI / MONTANA

DIVISION		SPRINGFIELD 656 - 658			ST. JOSEPH 644 - 645			ST. LOUIS 630 - 631			BILLINGS 590 - 591			BUTTE 597			GREAT FALLS 594		
		MAT.	INST.	TOTAL	MAT.	INST.	TOTAL	MAT.	INST.	TOTAL	MAT.	INST.	TOTAL	MAT.	INST.	TOTAL	MAT.	INST.	TOTAL
015433	CONTRACTOR EQUIPMENT		102.3	102.3		102.1	102.1		107.6	107.6		99.3	99.3		99.0	99.0		99.0	99.0
0241, 31 - 34	SITE & INFRASTRUCTURE, DEMOLITION	97.2	94.4	95.2	99.8	93.7	95.5	91.9	98.4	96.5	95.9	97.1	96.8	103.3	96.9	98.8	107.1	96.9	100.0
0310	Concrete Forming & Accessories	98.2	74.7	77.9	100.2	91.1	92.3	100.2	103.6	103.1	101.3	71.6	75.7	88.4	73.3	75.4	101.1	71.6	75.6
0320	Concrete Reinforcing	94.3	116.0	105.1	94.4	109.8	102.1	95.5	114.0	104.7	93.9	82.8	88.3	101.9	82.9	92.4	94.0	82.8	88.4
0330	Cast-in-Place Concrete	97.5	78.8	89.7	98.5	103.6	100.6	91.6	105.0	97.2	120.2	68.9	98.9	132.3	70.3	106.6	139.8	65.0	108.7
03	CONCRETE	97.7	84.6	91.2	97.5	99.5	98.5	94.5	106.8	100.5	106.9	73.6	90.5	110.6	74.9	93.0	115.9	72.2	94.3
04	MASONRY	89.5	87.2	88.1	100.1	96.7	98.0	99.7	112.5	107.6	117.9	75.0	91.4	113.3	77.9	91.4	117.5	76.7	92.3
05	METALS	101.2	107.5	103.1	103.7	110.7	105.9	101.9	120.5	107.7	107.5	91.0	102.4	100.6	91.1	97.7	103.8	91.1	99.9
06	WOOD, PLASTICS & COMPOSITES	103.4	72.8	86.1	107.5	89.7	97.4	103.1	100.8	101.8	99.5	70.0	82.8	86.6	72.5	78.6	100.7	70.0	83.4
07	THERMAL & MOISTURE PROTECTION	99.9	81.1	92.2	97.7	97.4	97.5	103.2	107.6	105.0	108.1	71.2	93.1	108.0	72.5	93.6	108.5	69.8	92.8
08	OPENINGS	101.6	81.2	96.8	101.7	98.3	100.9	97.2	110.5	100.4	93.9	68.7	88.0	92.3	71.3	87.3	95.0	68.1	88.6
0920	Plaster & Gypsum Board	88.3	71.9	77.1	104.8	89.1	94.1	104.7	100.8	102.1	99.9	69.3	79.1	100.3	71.9	81.0	100.7	69.3	82.2
0950, 0980	Ceilings & Acoustic Treatment	97.9	71.9	80.6	98.4	89.1	92.2	102.4	100.8	101.3	99.8	69.3	79.5	107.0	71.9	83.6	108.8	69.3	82.3
0960	Flooring	110.5	76.3	100.3	99.8	104.4	101.2	101.1	99.4	100.6	106.0	71.5	95.7	103.9	75.5	95.4	111.0	75.5	100.4
0970, 0990	Wall Finishes & Painting/Coating	96.2	76.5	84.4	96.2	88.6	91.6	102.3	106.5	104.8	99.0	88.5	92.7	97.2	52.3	70.2	97.2	88.5	92.0
09	FINISHES	101.0	75.1	86.6	102.5	92.7	97.0	103.7	102.5	103.0	102.7	73.0	86.2	103.4	71.2	85.5	107.4	73.7	88.6
COVERS	DIVS. 10 - 14, 25, 28, 41, 43, 44, 46	100.0	93.0	98.6	100.0	96.9	99.4	100.0	102.3	100.5	100.0	96.1	99.2	100.0	96.4	99.3	100.0	96.1	99.2
21, 22, 23	FIRE SUPPRESSION, PLUMBING & HVAC	99.9	73.0	89.1	100.1	89.5	95.8	100.0	107.6	103.0	100.1	74.9	90.0	100.2	70.7	88.4	100.2	72.2	89.0
26, 27, 3370	ELECTRICAL, COMMUNICATIONS & UTIL.	102.9	70.3	85.9	100.5	80.5	90.1	100.5	107.1	103.9	96.8	73.9	84.8	104.4	72.2	87.6	96.9	72.2	84.0
MF2010	WEIGHTED AVERAGE	99.9	82.1	92.1	100.7	93.9	97.8	99.6	107.6	103.1	102.2	77.9	91.6	102.0	77.2	91.2	103.4	77.1	92.0

767

MONTANA

DIVISION		HAVRE 595 MAT.	INST.	TOTAL	HELENA 596 MAT.	INST.	TOTAL	KALISPELL 599 MAT.	INST.	TOTAL	MILES CITY 593 MAT.	INST.	TOTAL	MISSOULA 598 MAT.	INST.	TOTAL	WOLF POINT 592 MAT.	INST.	TOTAL
015433	CONTRACTOR EQUIPMENT		99.0	99.0		99.0	99.0		99.0	99.0		99.0	99.0		99.0	99.0		99.0	99.0
0241, 31 - 34	SITE & INFRASTRUCTURE, DEMOLITION	111.0	96.7	100.9	100.1	96.6	97.7	93.4	96.8	95.8	99.9	96.3	97.4	85.8	96.6	93.4	118.0	96.4	102.9
0310	Concrete Forming & Accessories	81.6	69.1	70.8	104.4	66.7	71.9	91.6	71.5	74.3	99.6	67.6	72.0	91.6	71.5	74.2	92.2	67.8	71.2
0320	Concrete Reinforcing	102.7	82.8	92.8	106.8	82.8	94.8	104.6	83.4	94.0	102.3	82.8	92.6	103.6	83.4	93.5	103.7	82.8	93.3
0330	Cast-in-Place Concrete	142.5	61.8	109.0	106.9	64.3	89.2	114.9	64.0	93.8	125.8	61.6	99.1	97.5	66.2	84.5	140.8	62.0	108.1
03	CONCRETE	119.1	70.0	94.9	104.5	69.8	87.3	100.0	72.0	86.2	107.4	69.3	88.6	88.0	72.7	80.4	123.0	69.6	96.6
04	MASONRY	114.2	71.1	87.5	110.7	77.1	89.9	112.2	78.3	91.2	119.4	66.5	86.7	135.6	77.9	99.9	120.5	67.2	87.5
05	METALS	96.8	90.9	95.0	97.1	90.0	98.7	96.6	91.4	95.0	95.9	91.1	94.4	97.2	91.3	95.4	96.0	91.1	94.5
06	WOOD, PLASTICS & COMPOSITES	78.4	70.0	73.7	103.7	63.8	81.2	89.9	70.0	78.7	97.8	70.0	82.1	89.9	70.0	78.7	89.5	70.0	78.5
07	THERMAL & MOISTURE PROTECTION	108.3	69.4	92.5	105.4	72.2	91.9	107.7	74.3	94.1	108.0	66.8	91.3	107.4	80.6	96.5	108.7	67.1	91.8
08	OPENINGS	92.4	68.1	86.6	96.2	66.3	89.2	92.3	68.3	86.6	91.8	68.0	86.2	92.3	68.0	86.6	91.9	67.8	86.2
0920	Plaster & Gypsum Board	96.2	69.3	77.9	97.9	62.9	74.1	100.3	69.3	79.2	109.0	69.3	82.0	100.3	69.3	79.2	104.2	69.3	80.4
0950, 0980	Ceilings & Acoustic Treatment	107.0	69.3	81.9	109.7	62.9	78.5	107.0	69.3	81.9	106.1	69.3	81.6	107.0	69.3	81.9	106.1	69.3	81.6
0960	Flooring	101.3	75.5	93.6	106.1	60.2	92.4	105.7	75.5	96.7	110.7	71.5	99.0	105.7	75.5	96.7	107.1	71.5	96.5
0970, 0990	Wall Finishes & Painting/Coating	97.2	49.7	68.7	93.5	48.2	66.3	97.2	48.2	67.8	97.2	48.2	67.8	97.2	63.3	76.8	97.2	49.7	68.7
09	FINISHES	102.8	67.9	83.4	104.7	63.0	81.5	103.3	69.4	84.4	106.2	65.9	83.8	102.7	71.0	85.1	105.9	66.2	83.8
COVERS	DIVS. 10 - 14, 25, 28, 41, 43, 44, 46	100.0	72.6	94.5	100.0	95.6	99.1	100.0	96.2	99.2	100.0	92.6	98.5	100.0	96.1	99.2	100.0	92.9	98.6
21, 22, 23	FIRE SUPPRESSION, PLUMBING & HVAC	95.3	69.3	84.9	100.1	70.9	88.4	95.3	70.3	85.3	95.3	69.7	85.0	100.2	69.9	88.0	95.3	70.0	85.2
26, 27, 3370	ELECTRICAL, COMMUNICATIONS & UTIL.	96.9	72.7	84.3	103.8	72.7	87.6	101.2	71.0	85.4	96.9	77.4	86.7	102.2	69.3	85.0	96.9	77.4	86.7
MF2010	WEIGHTED AVERAGE	100.6	74.2	89.1	102.0	75.1	90.2	98.4	76.3	88.8	99.5	74.7	88.7	99.4	76.4	89.4	101.7	74.9	90.0

NEBRASKA

DIVISION		ALLIANCE 693 MAT.	INST.	TOTAL	COLUMBUS 686 MAT.	INST.	TOTAL	GRAND ISLAND 688 MAT.	INST.	TOTAL	HASTINGS 689 MAT.	INST.	TOTAL	LINCOLN 683 - 685 MAT.	INST.	TOTAL	MCCOOK 690 MAT.	INST.	TOTAL
015433	CONTRACTOR EQUIPMENT		97.5	97.5		101.4	101.4		101.4	101.4		101.4	101.4		101.4	101.4		101.4	101.4
0241, 31 - 34	SITE & INFRASTRUCTURE, DEMOLITION	98.8	98.4	98.6	99.1	92.0	94.1	103.8	92.8	96.1	102.6	92.0	95.2	93.6	92.8	93.0	102.1	91.9	95.0
0310	Concrete Forming & Accessories	88.3	57.7	61.9	95.9	68.1	71.9	95.4	74.0	76.9	98.5	73.6	77.0	97.5	68.9	72.8	93.9	57.3	62.3
0320	Concrete Reinforcing	110.1	85.0	97.6	101.7	76.9	89.3	101.1	76.8	89.0	101.1	77.5	89.3	99.2	76.3	87.7	103.1	76.5	89.8
0330	Cast-in-Place Concrete	109.4	61.3	89.4	114.9	61.3	92.6	121.6	68.6	99.6	121.6	64.6	97.9	99.8	71.0	87.9	117.6	60.6	94.0
03	CONCRETE	120.2	64.5	92.7	106.9	68.2	87.8	111.7	73.4	92.8	111.9	71.9	92.1	98.0	71.9	85.1	109.5	63.1	86.6
04	MASONRY	109.7	74.9	88.2	112.6	79.0	91.8	105.7	77.4	88.2	114.2	89.5	98.9	95.9	68.4	78.9	105.5	74.7	86.5
05	METALS	101.2	79.1	94.4	91.9	85.2	89.8	93.6	87.0	91.5	94.4	86.5	91.9	95.6	86.2	92.7	96.0	84.2	92.4
06	WOOD, PLASTICS & COMPOSITES	88.3	53.4	68.6	99.7	67.2	81.4	99.0	73.9	84.8	102.7	73.9	86.4	98.3	67.2	80.7	97.1	53.4	72.5
07	THERMAL & MOISTURE PROTECTION	106.4	69.5	91.4	104.4	70.7	90.7	104.5	74.2	92.2	104.5	85.4	96.8	100.4	70.1	88.1	100.8	67.4	87.2
08	OPENINGS	92.8	59.4	84.9	94.1	66.7	87.6	94.2	70.9	88.7	94.2	70.3	88.5	103.2	63.5	93.8	93.2	57.5	84.7
0920	Plaster & Gypsum Board	81.0	51.9	61.2	88.7	66.1	73.3	88.0	73.0	77.8	89.9	73.0	78.4	90.1	66.1	73.8	92.5	51.9	64.9
0950, 0980	Ceilings & Acoustic Treatment	98.5	51.9	67.5	93.3	66.1	75.2	93.3	73.0	79.8	93.3	73.0	79.8	99.3	66.1	77.2	94.3	51.9	66.1
0960	Flooring	104.5	83.6	98.2	102.5	102.2	102.4	102.3	109.2	104.4	103.4	102.2	103.1	107.6	85.1	100.9	101.6	83.6	96.2
0970, 0990	Wall Finishes & Painting/Coating	174.1	56.0	103.1	91.9	65.1	75.8	91.9	69.1	78.2	91.9	65.1	75.8	100.0	79.6	87.7	95.3	48.8	67.3
09	FINISHES	102.8	60.8	79.4	98.5	72.9	84.3	98.7	78.8	87.6	99.2	76.9	86.8	102.3	72.7	85.8	99.6	59.9	77.5
COVERS	DIVS. 10 - 14, 25, 28, 41, 43, 44, 46	100.0	67.0	93.4	100.0	88.3	97.7	100.0	89.3	97.9	100.0	89.1	97.8	100.0	88.6	97.7	100.0	66.3	93.2
21, 22, 23	FIRE SUPPRESSION, PLUMBING & HVAC	95.3	72.0	85.9	95.1	77.1	87.9	100.0	78.5	91.4	95.1	77.2	87.9	99.9	78.5	91.3	95.0	77.1	87.8
26, 27, 3370	ELECTRICAL, COMMUNICATIONS & UTIL.	91.7	71.0	80.9	92.0	82.4	87.0	90.7	65.9	77.8	90.1	85.6	87.7	103.2	65.9	83.7	93.9	71.0	81.9
MF2010	WEIGHTED AVERAGE	100.4	71.6	87.9	97.5	77.9	88.9	99.1	77.8	89.9	98.5	81.2	90.9	99.5	75.3	89.0	98.1	72.1	86.8

NEBRASKA / NEVADA

DIVISION		NORFOLK 687 MAT.	INST.	TOTAL	NORTH PLATTE 691 MAT.	INST.	TOTAL	OMAHA 680 - 681 MAT.	INST.	TOTAL	VALENTINE 692 MAT.	INST.	TOTAL	CARSON CITY 897 MAT.	INST.	TOTAL	ELKO 898 MAT.	INST.	TOTAL
015433	CONTRACTOR EQUIPMENT		92.7	92.7		101.4	101.4		92.7	92.7		95.6	95.6		97.9	97.9		97.9	97.9
0241, 31 - 34	SITE & INFRASTRUCTURE, DEMOLITION	82.3	91.1	88.5	103.4	92.0	95.4	86.4	91.8	90.2	86.4	95.9	93.1	78.7	99.6	93.4	61.9	98.4	87.5
0310	Concrete Forming & Accessories	82.4	72.7	74.0	96.3	73.1	76.3	93.5	72.9	75.7	84.5	57.1	60.8	105.3	94.6	96.1	111.2	83.2	87.0
0320	Concrete Reinforcing	101.8	66.6	84.3	102.5	77.4	90.0	104.1	76.9	90.5	103.1	66.3	84.8	107.5	118.0	112.7	106.9	113.9	110.4
0330	Cast-in-Place Concrete	116.1	63.8	94.4	117.6	65.9	96.2	92.6	77.1	86.2	104.3	58.6	85.3	104.1	86.2	96.7	98.7	80.9	91.3
03	CONCRETE	105.7	68.7	87.5	109.6	72.1	91.1	94.6	75.4	85.1	107.0	60.0	83.8	104.1	96.0	100.1	98.6	88.3	93.5
04	MASONRY	118.7	78.7	93.9	93.2	89.5	90.9	98.9	79.9	87.1	105.3	74.8	86.4	116.6	89.3	99.7	114.9	73.1	89.0
05	METALS	95.2	74.1	88.7	95.1	86.1	92.3	95.4	79.5	90.5	107.3	74.1	97.1	90.1	104.0	94.4	92.8	99.5	94.8
06	WOOD, PLASTICS & COMPOSITES	82.8	73.4	77.5	99.1	73.9	84.9	91.2	72.1	80.5	82.8	52.9	65.9	91.6	96.6	94.4	99.4	83.7	90.6
07	THERMAL & MOISTURE PROTECTION	104.4	74.9	92.4	100.8	84.1	94.0	100.0	79.8	91.8	101.6	69.1	88.4	102.7	91.2	98.0	99.0	76.6	89.9
08	OPENINGS	95.9	67.7	89.2	92.5	70.3	87.3	101.4	71.9	94.4	95.0	56.5	85.9	99.6	109.4	101.9	100.6	87.3	97.4
0920	Plaster & Gypsum Board	88.7	73.0	78.0	92.5	73.0	79.3	99.5	71.7	80.6	94.7	51.9	65.6	91.3	96.4	94.8	93.3	83.1	86.4
0950, 0980	Ceilings & Acoustic Treatment	106.9	73.0	84.4	94.3	73.0	80.1	112.8	71.7	85.5	113.1	51.9	72.4	101.8	96.4	98.2	102.3	83.1	89.5
0960	Flooring	131.7	102.2	122.9	102.5	102.2	102.4	129.9	83.4	116.0	133.3	81.3	117.7	100.8	109.9	103.6	103.7	52.1	88.2
0970, 0990	Wall Finishes & Painting/Coating	164.9	65.1	104.9	95.3	65.1	77.1	148.8	68.2	100.4	171.4	67.5	108.9	102.7	82.5	90.6	104.2	97.9	100.4
09	FINISHES	120.0	76.9	96.0	99.9	76.9	87.1	119.6	74.0	94.2	123.7	61.1	88.8	100.4	96.2	98.1	99.4	78.9	88.0
COVERS	DIVS. 10 - 14, 25, 28, 41, 43, 44, 46	100.0	87.9	97.6	100.0	68.6	93.7	100.0	88.1	97.6	100.0	64.3	92.8	100.0	92.0	98.4	100.0	64.5	92.9
21, 22, 23	FIRE SUPPRESSION, PLUMBING & HVAC	94.9	76.9	87.7	99.9	77.1	90.8	99.8	78.0	91.1	94.7	76.9	87.6	100.0	81.4	92.6	97.7	81.2	91.1
26, 27, 3370	ELECTRICAL, COMMUNICATIONS & UTIL.	90.9	82.4	86.5	92.0	78.9	85.2	97.9	82.4	89.8	89.0	88.6	88.8	100.4	97.4	98.8	98.1	97.3	97.7
MF2010	WEIGHTED AVERAGE	99.2	77.5	89.8	98.5	79.6	90.2	99.6	79.3	90.7	100.6	73.6	88.9	99.1	93.8	96.8	97.6	86.1	92.6

NEVADA / NEW HAMPSHIRE

DIVISION		ELY 893 MAT.	INST.	TOTAL	LAS VEGAS 889 - 891 MAT.	INST.	TOTAL	RENO 894 - 895 MAT.	INST.	TOTAL	CHARLESTON 036 MAT.	INST.	TOTAL	CLAREMONT 037 MAT.	INST.	TOTAL	CONCORD 032 - 033 MAT.	INST.	TOTAL
015433	CONTRACTOR EQUIPMENT		97.9	97.9		97.9	97.9		97.9	97.9		100.6	100.6		100.6	100.6		100.6	100.6
0241, 31 - 34	SITE & INFRASTRUCTURE, DEMOLITION	67.0	99.9	90.1	69.7	101.6	92.1	67.0	99.6	89.9	87.4	99.2	95.7	81.2	99.2	93.9	94.5	101.4	99.3
0310	Concrete Forming & Accessories	104.2	105.9	105.6	105.4	111.0	110.3	100.5	94.5	95.3	88.1	82.9	83.6	93.8	82.9	84.4	95.9	94.3	94.5
0320	Concrete Reinforcing	105.7	115.2	110.4	97.5	121.8	109.6	99.9	121.4	110.6	84.5	95.2	89.8	84.5	95.2	89.8	92.9	95.8	94.4
0330	Cast-in-Place Concrete	105.9	106.7	106.2	102.6	107.5	104.6	112.0	86.2	101.3	97.4	72.1	86.9	89.5	72.1	82.3	111.5	92.2	103.5
03	CONCRETE	106.6	107.6	107.1	101.8	111.4	106.6	106.3	96.6	101.5	99.5	81.6	90.6	91.5	81.6	86.6	106.0	93.7	100.0
04	MASONRY	119.0	104.2	109.9	108.1	102.8	104.8	114.2	89.3	98.8	87.8	82.3	84.4	87.3	82.3	84.2	97.6	102.1	100.4
05	METALS	92.7	104.8	96.4	99.8	109.3	102.7	94.2	105.3	97.6	95.2	90.6	93.8	95.2	90.6	93.8	101.2	94.0	99.0
06	WOOD, PLASTICS & COMPOSITES	90.3	106.3	99.3	89.2	110.4	101.2	85.2	96.6	91.6	86.9	92.3	90.0	93.3	92.3	92.7	94.8	93.3	93.9
07	THERMAL & MOISTURE PROTECTION	99.6	95.9	98.1	112.5	102.0	108.2	99.1	91.2	95.9	102.8	72.0	90.3	102.7	72.0	90.2	104.9	91.4	99.4
08	OPENINGS	100.5	99.6	100.3	99.6	117.9	104.0	98.6	104.2	99.9	102.6	78.0	96.8	103.8	78.0	97.7	104.1	88.4	100.4
0920	Plaster & Gypsum Board	90.0	106.4	101.1	87.8	110.7	103.4	82.0	96.4	91.8	94.7	91.4	92.5	95.8	91.4	92.8	98.4	92.4	94.4
0950, 0980	Ceilings & Acoustic Treatment	102.3	106.4	105.0	111.1	110.7	110.8	107.6	96.4	100.1	90.6	91.4	91.2	90.6	91.4	91.2	95.9	92.4	93.6
0960	Flooring	101.5	58.2	88.6	93.3	109.9	98.3	98.8	109.9	102.1	96.3	32.7	77.3	98.2	32.7	78.6	97.1	112.2	101.6
0970, 0990	Wall Finishes & Painting/Coating	104.2	123.6	115.9	107.2	123.6	117.0	104.2	82.5	91.2	95.4	46.7	66.2	95.4	46.9	66.3	95.1	97.5	96.5
09	FINISHES	98.9	99.4	99.2	98.4	112.2	106.1	98.0	96.2	97.0	94.9	71.3	81.8	95.1	71.3	81.9	95.9	98.0	97.0
COVERS	DIVS. 10 - 14, 25, 28, 41, 43, 44, 46	100.0	65.0	93.0	100.0	106.3	101.3	100.0	92.0	98.4	100.0	90.0	98.0	100.0	90.0	98.0	100.0	104.8	101.0
21, 22, 23	FIRE SUPPRESSION, PLUMBING & HVAC	97.7	106.7	101.3	100.2	105.1	102.1	100.0	81.5	92.6	95.2	40.4	73.2	95.2	40.5	73.3	99.9	86.1	94.4
26, 27, 3370	ELECTRICAL, COMMUNICATIONS & UTIL.	98.4	109.7	104.3	102.7	120.6	112.0	98.8	97.4	98.0	99.6	54.1	75.8	99.6	54.1	75.8	99.6	80.4	89.6
MF2010	WEIGHTED AVERAGE	98.7	103.4	100.8	100.2	109.4	104.2	99.0	93.8	96.7	96.9	70.1	85.2	96.0	70.1	84.7	100.8	92.3	97.1

NEW HAMPSHIRE / NEW JERSEY

DIVISION		KEENE 034 MAT.	INST.	TOTAL	LITTLETON 035 MAT.	INST.	TOTAL	MANCHESTER 031 MAT.	INST.	TOTAL	NASHUA 030 MAT.	INST.	TOTAL	PORTSMOUTH 038 MAT.	INST.	TOTAL	ATLANTIC CITY 082,084 MAT.	INST.	TOTAL
015433	CONTRACTOR EQUIPMENT		100.6	100.6		100.6	100.6		100.6	100.6		100.6	100.6		100.6	100.6		98.8	98.8
0241, 31 - 34	SITE & INFRASTRUCTURE, DEMOLITION	95.2	99.5	98.2	81.3	99.5	94.1	93.6	101.4	99.1	96.5	101.4	100.0	90.1	101.5	98.1	98.0	104.4	102.5
0310	Concrete Forming & Accessories	92.6	84.9	85.9	103.4	84.9	87.4	98.4	94.8	95.3	100.3	94.8	95.5	89.4	95.1	94.3	110.1	128.4	125.9
0320	Concrete Reinforcing	84.5	95.3	89.9	85.2	95.3	90.3	106.7	95.8	101.3	105.5	95.8	100.7	84.5	95.9	90.2	79.1	121.6	100.3
0330	Cast-in-Place Concrete	97.9	74.4	88.1	87.9	74.4	82.3	111.9	115.3	113.3	92.6	115.3	102.0	87.9	115.4	99.3	84.2	132.2	104.1
03	CONCRETE	99.2	83.2	91.3	91.0	83.3	87.2	108.6	101.9	105.3	99.5	101.9	100.6	91.0	102.1	96.4	92.9	127.3	109.9
04	MASONRY	91.7	85.9	88.1	96.9	85.9	90.1	94.9	102.1	99.4	91.4	102.1	98.0	87.7	102.1	96.6	99.2	125.4	115.4
05	METALS	95.8	91.2	94.4	95.9	91.2	94.4	103.8	94.5	100.9	100.8	94.5	98.8	97.3	95.1	96.6	95.6	106.5	99.0
06	WOOD, PLASTICS & COMPOSITES	91.6	92.3	92.0	102.9	92.3	96.9	95.1	93.3	94.1	101.4	93.3	96.8	88.2	93.3	91.1	115.6	130.2	123.9
07	THERMAL & MOISTURE PROTECTION	103.2	75.0	91.8	102.8	73.5	90.9	106.9	94.9	102.0	103.6	94.9	100.1	103.3	115.6	108.3	104.6	123.2	112.2
08	OPENINGS	101.1	82.9	96.8	104.8	78.7	98.6	106.9	88.4	102.6	105.8	88.4	101.6	106.5	85.1	101.4	102.3	125.4	107.7
0920	Plaster & Gypsum Board	95.1	91.4	92.6	108.4	91.4	96.9	98.7	92.4	94.4	103.8	92.4	96.1	94.7	92.4	93.2	107.3	130.5	123.1
0950, 0980	Ceilings & Acoustic Treatment	90.6	91.4	91.2	90.6	91.4	91.2	98.6	92.4	94.5	101.4	92.4	95.4	91.6	92.4	92.2	88.9	130.5	116.6
0960	Flooring	97.9	53.6	84.7	106.2	32.7	84.2	98.2	112.2	102.4	100.9	112.2	104.2	96.5	112.2	101.2	102.2	150.6	116.6
0970, 0990	Wall Finishes & Painting/Coating	95.4	46.7	66.2	95.4	61.2	74.9	98.2	97.5	97.8	95.4	97.5	96.7	95.4	97.5	96.7	93.0	117.3	107.6
09	FINISHES	96.7	76.2	85.3	99.0	73.8	85.0	98.5	98.0	98.2	101.0	98.0	99.3	95.9	98.0	97.1	99.4	132.5	117.8
COVERS	DIVS. 10 - 14, 25, 28, 41, 43, 44, 46	100.0	91.2	98.2	100.0	99.2	99.8	100.0	104.8	101.0	100.0	104.8	101.0	100.0	104.8	101.0	100.0	105.1	102.1
21, 22, 23	FIRE SUPPRESSION, PLUMBING & HVAC	95.2	44.2	74.7	95.2	65.2	83.2	99.9	86.2	94.4	100.1	86.2	94.5	100.1	86.2	94.5	99.6	119.6	107.6
26, 27, 3370	ELECTRICAL, COMMUNICATIONS & UTIL.	99.6	64.7	81.4	100.8	57.3	78.1	101.6	80.4	90.6	102.2	80.4	90.8	100.1	80.4	89.8	92.7	141.4	118.1
MF2010	WEIGHTED AVERAGE	97.4	74.0	87.2	97.1	77.2	88.4	102.1	93.6	98.4	100.6	93.6	97.6	98.2	94.2	96.4	98.1	123.5	109.2

NEW JERSEY

DIVISION		CAMDEN 081 MAT.	INST.	TOTAL	DOVER 078 MAT.	INST.	TOTAL	ELIZABETH 072 MAT.	INST.	TOTAL	HACKENSACK 076 MAT.	INST.	TOTAL	JERSEY CITY 073 MAT.	INST.	TOTAL	LONG BRANCH 077 MAT.	INST.	TOTAL
015433	CONTRACTOR EQUIPMENT		98.8	98.8		100.6	100.6		100.6	100.6		100.6	100.6		98.8	98.8		98.4	98.4
0241, 31 - 34	SITE & INFRASTRUCTURE, DEMOLITION	99.1	104.7	103.0	108.2	105.4	106.3	112.7	105.4	107.6	108.9	105.5	106.5	98.0	105.4	103.2	102.6	105.3	104.5
0310	Concrete Forming & Accessories	101.7	128.4	124.7	97.4	129.0	124.7	109.3	129.0	126.3	97.4	128.9	124.6	101.1	129.0	125.2	101.7	128.7	125.0
0320	Concrete Reinforcing	103.8	121.8	112.8	80.0	128.6	104.3	80.0	128.6	104.3	80.0	128.6	104.3	103.8	128.6	116.2	80.0	128.6	104.3
0330	Cast-in-Place Concrete	81.6	132.1	102.6	102.2	127.3	112.6	87.8	127.3	104.2	99.9	127.3	111.3	79.8	127.4	99.5	88.7	132.1	106.7
03	CONCRETE	94.1	127.3	110.4	99.7	127.4	113.3	95.3	127.4	111.1	97.8	127.3	112.4	93.2	127.2	110.0	97.1	128.7	112.7
04	MASONRY	89.7	125.4	111.8	87.3	125.9	111.2	101.2	125.9	116.5	90.8	125.9	112.5	80.8	125.9	108.7	94.4	125.4	113.6
05	METALS	100.7	106.6	102.5	95.6	113.6	101.2	97.1	113.6	102.2	95.7	113.4	101.2	100.8	111.2	104.0	95.7	111.1	100.5
06	WOOD, PLASTICS & COMPOSITES	104.2	130.2	118.9	101.5	130.2	117.7	117.1	130.2	124.5	101.5	130.2	117.7	102.3	130.2	118.0	103.4	130.1	118.5
07	THERMAL & MOISTURE PROTECTION	104.5	122.7	111.9	101.5	130.6	113.4	101.7	130.6	113.5	101.3	123.3	110.3	101.1	130.6	113.1	101.2	123.4	110.3
08	OPENINGS	104.6	125.4	109.5	108.8	127.9	113.4	106.9	127.9	111.9	106.2	127.9	111.4	104.5	127.9	110.0	100.7	127.9	107.1
0920	Plaster & Gypsum Board	102.8	130.5	121.6	99.9	130.5	120.7	107.7	130.5	123.2	99.9	130.5	120.7	103.2	130.5	121.8	101.7	130.5	121.3
0950, 0980	Ceilings & Acoustic Treatment	99.7	130.5	120.2	88.6	130.5	116.5	90.6	130.5	117.2	88.6	130.5	116.5	99.5	130.5	120.1	88.6	130.5	116.5
0960	Flooring	98.7	150.6	114.2	96.8	172.3	119.4	101.2	172.3	122.5	96.8	172.3	119.4	97.7	172.3	120.0	97.9	172.3	120.1
0970, 0990	Wall Finishes & Painting/Coating	93.0	117.3	107.6	94.6	119.3	109.4	94.6	119.3	109.4	94.6	119.3	109.4	94.7	119.3	109.5	94.7	117.3	108.3
09	FINISHES	100.0	132.5	118.1	97.1	135.5	118.5	100.4	135.5	119.9	96.9	135.5	118.4	99.8	135.5	119.7	97.9	136.0	119.2
COVERS	DIVS. 10 - 14, 25, 28, 41, 43, 44, 46	100.0	110.5	102.1	100.0	113.6	102.7	100.0	113.6	102.7	100.0	113.6	102.7	100.0	113.6	102.7	100.0	110.4	102.1
21, 22, 23	FIRE SUPPRESSION, PLUMBING & HVAC	100.0	119.7	107.9	99.6	123.4	109.1	100.0	122.8	109.1	99.6	123.3	109.1	100.0	123.4	109.3	99.6	122.6	108.8
26, 27, 3370	ELECTRICAL, COMMUNICATIONS & UTIL.	97.9	141.4	120.6	90.9	137.6	115.3	91.5	137.6	115.6	90.9	139.7	116.4	95.5	139.7	118.6	90.6	131.5	111.9
MF2010	WEIGHTED AVERAGE	99.4	123.6	109.9	98.7	125.4	110.3	99.5	125.3	110.7	98.4	125.5	110.2	98.5	125.5	110.2	97.8	124.1	109.2

769

NEW JERSEY

DIVISION		NEW BRUNSWICK 088-089 MAT.	INST.	TOTAL	NEWARK 070-071 MAT.	INST.	TOTAL	PATERSON 074-075 MAT.	INST.	TOTAL	POINT PLEASANT 087 MAT.	INST.	TOTAL	SUMMIT 079 MAT.	INST.	TOTAL	TRENTON 085-086 MAT.	INST.	TOTAL
015433	CONTRACTOR EQUIPMENT		98.4	98.4		100.6	100.6		100.6	100.6		98.4	98.4		100.6	100.6		98.4	98.4
0241, 31 - 34	SITE & INFRASTRUCTURE, DEMOLITION	111.8	105.3	107.3	114.4	105.4	108.1	110.9	105.5	107.1	113.5	105.3	107.7	110.1	105.4	106.8	96.6	105.3	102.7
0310	Concrete Forming & Accessories	104.6	128.9	125.6	97.2	129.0	124.6	99.4	128.9	124.8	99.3	120.3	117.4	100.2	129.0	125.0	99.9	128.6	124.6
0320	Concrete Reinforcing	80.0	128.6	104.3	103.3	128.6	116.0	103.8	128.6	116.2	80.0	128.5	104.2	80.0	128.6	104.3	103.3	115.7	109.5
0330	Cast-in-Place Concrete	103.9	132.3	115.7	109.6	127.3	117.0	101.6	127.3	112.3	103.9	128.4	114.1	84.9	127.3	102.5	99.5	132.0	113.0
03	CONCRETE	109.8	128.9	119.3	106.9	127.4	117.0	103.4	127.3	115.2	109.5	123.7	116.5	92.3	127.4	109.6	102.3	126.3	114.1
04	MASONRY	96.6	125.9	114.7	93.4	125.9	113.5	87.8	125.9	111.4	86.4	124.6	110.0	89.3	125.9	112.0	92.1	125.4	112.7
05	METALS	95.7	111.2	100.4	102.8	113.6	106.1	95.7	113.5	101.2	95.7	110.7	100.3	95.6	113.6	101.1	100.4	105.7	102.0
06	WOOD, PLASTICS & COMPOSITES	108.9	130.1	120.9	99.0	130.2	116.6	104.1	130.2	118.8	101.6	119.1	111.5	105.3	130.2	119.3	101.4	130.1	117.6
07	THERMAL & MOISTURE PROTECTION	104.8	129.9	115.0	102.0	130.6	113.6	101.6	123.3	110.4	104.8	122.1	111.8	101.9	130.6	113.6	104.2	123.1	111.9
08	OPENINGS	97.2	127.9	104.5	107.5	127.9	112.3	111.6	127.9	115.4	99.1	122.2	104.6	113.6	127.9	117.0	106.7	124.4	110.9
0920	Plaster & Gypsum Board	103.9	130.5	122.0	99.9	130.5	120.7	103.2	130.5	121.8	99.4	119.1	112.8	101.7	130.5	121.3	99.9	130.5	120.7
0950, 0980	Ceilings & Acoustic Treatment	88.9	130.5	116.6	102.4	130.5	121.1	99.5	130.5	120.1	88.9	119.1	109.0	88.6	130.5	116.5	101.4	130.5	120.8
0960	Flooring	100.0	172.3	121.6	98.5	172.3	120.6	97.7	172.3	120.0	97.8	150.6	113.6	98.0	172.3	120.2	99.3	172.3	121.1
0970, 0990	Wall Finishes & Painting/Coating	93.0	119.3	108.8	96.0	119.3	110.0	94.6	119.3	109.4	93.0	117.3	107.6	94.6	119.3	109.4	98.3	117.3	109.7
09	FINISHES	99.7	135.4	119.6	98.6	135.5	119.1	100.0	135.5	119.8	98.5	125.9	113.7	98.0	135.5	118.9	100.1	136.0	120.1
COVERS	DIVS. 10 - 14, 25, 28, 41, 43, 44, 46	100.0	113.4	102.7	100.0	113.6	102.7	100.0	113.6	102.7	100.0	104.2	100.8	100.0	113.6	102.7	100.0	110.4	102.1
21, 22, 23	FIRE SUPPRESSION, PLUMBING & HVAC	99.6	122.9	108.9	100.0	122.8	109.1	100.0	123.4	109.4	99.6	122.5	108.7	99.6	122.8	108.9	100.0	122.5	109.0
26, 27, 3370	ELECTRICAL, COMMUNICATIONS & UTIL.	93.4	137.6	116.5	99.2	139.7	120.3	95.5	137.6	117.5	92.7	131.5	112.9	91.5	137.6	115.6	101.4	138.7	120.8
MF2010	WEIGHTED AVERAGE	99.7	125.2	110.8	101.9	125.6	112.2	100.2	125.2	111.1	99.2	121.4	108.8	98.7	125.3	110.3	100.8	124.0	110.9

DIVISION		NEW JERSEY VINELAND 080,083 MAT.	INST.	TOTAL	NEW MEXICO ALBUQUERQUE 870-872 MAT.	INST.	TOTAL	CARRIZOZO 883 MAT.	INST.	TOTAL	CLOVIS 881 MAT.	INST.	TOTAL	FARMINGTON 874 MAT.	INST.	TOTAL	GALLUP 873 MAT.	INST.	TOTAL
015433	CONTRACTOR EQUIPMENT		98.8	98.8		109.6	109.6		109.6	109.6		109.6	109.6		109.6	109.6		109.6	109.6
0241, 31 - 34	SITE & INFRASTRUCTURE, DEMOLITION	102.7	104.7	104.1	82.2	104.1	97.4	102.9	104.1	103.7	91.2	104.1	100.2	88.4	104.1	99.4	96.0	104.1	101.7
0310	Concrete Forming & Accessories	96.8	128.4	124.1	101.4	65.0	70.0	99.2	65.0	69.7	99.1	64.9	69.6	101.4	65.0	70.0	101.5	65.0	70.0
0320	Concrete Reinforcing	79.1	118.5	98.7	100.5	71.1	85.8	109.9	71.1	90.5	111.2	71.1	91.2	109.9	71.1	90.5	105.2	71.1	88.2
0330	Cast-in-Place Concrete	90.7	132.2	107.9	96.9	71.2	86.2	95.4	71.2	85.3	95.3	71.1	85.3	97.8	71.2	86.8	92.1	71.2	83.4
03	CONCRETE	97.6	126.7	111.9	101.9	69.4	85.9	119.1	69.4	94.6	107.6	69.3	88.7	105.7	69.4	87.8	112.5	69.4	91.2
04	MASONRY	87.9	125.4	111.1	99.5	60.6	75.4	101.6	60.6	76.2	101.7	60.6	76.2	106.3	60.6	78.0	95.4	60.6	73.8
05	METALS	95.6	106.0	98.8	103.8	87.9	98.9	98.4	87.9	95.2	98.1	87.8	94.9	101.4	87.9	97.2	100.6	87.9	96.6
06	WOOD, PLASTICS & COMPOSITES	98.5	130.2	116.4	92.8	65.5	77.4	88.9	65.5	75.7	88.9	65.5	75.7	92.9	65.5	77.4	92.9	65.5	77.4
07	THERMAL & MOISTURE PROTECTION	104.4	123.2	112.1	99.4	71.8	88.2	100.7	71.8	89.0	99.6	71.8	88.3	99.6	71.8	88.3	100.5	71.8	88.8
08	OPENINGS	98.6	125.0	104.9	101.4	68.5	93.6	98.6	68.5	91.5	98.8	68.5	91.6	104.0	68.5	95.6	104.1	68.5	95.7
0920	Plaster & Gypsum Board	98.0	130.5	120.1	88.3	64.1	71.8	75.4	64.1	67.7	75.4	64.1	67.7	81.6	64.1	69.7	81.6	64.1	69.7
0950, 0980	Ceilings & Acoustic Treatment	88.9	130.5	116.6	106.3	64.1	78.2	104.2	64.1	77.5	104.2	64.1	77.5	103.1	64.1	77.2	103.1	64.1	77.2
0960	Flooring	97.1	150.6	113.1	100.2	67.2	90.3	100.2	67.2	90.4	100.2	67.2	90.4	101.7	67.2	91.4	101.7	67.2	91.4
0970, 0990	Wall Finishes & Painting/Coating	93.0	117.3	107.6	109.1	68.1	84.4	102.9	68.1	82.0	102.9	68.1	82.0	102.9	68.1	82.0	102.9	68.1	82.0
09	FINISHES	97.2	132.5	116.8	98.3	65.5	80.0	99.0	65.5	80.3	97.6	65.5	79.7	96.9	65.5	79.4	98.1	65.5	79.9
COVERS	DIVS. 10 - 14, 25, 28, 41, 43, 44, 46	100.0	110.5	102.1	100.0	76.3	95.2	100.0	76.3	95.2	100.0	76.3	95.2	100.0	76.3	95.2	100.0	76.3	95.2
21, 22, 23	FIRE SUPPRESSION, PLUMBING & HVAC	99.6	119.6	107.6	100.2	70.7	88.4	97.2	70.7	86.6	97.2	70.5	86.5	100.1	70.7	88.3	97.1	70.7	86.6
26, 27, 3370	ELECTRICAL, COMMUNICATIONS & UTIL.	92.7	141.4	118.1	88.5	72.9	80.4	90.6	72.9	81.4	88.1	72.9	80.2	86.8	72.9	79.6	86.0	72.9	79.2
MF2010	WEIGHTED AVERAGE	97.5	123.4	108.8	99.2	73.6	88.0	100.1	73.6	88.5	98.1	73.5	87.4	99.7	73.6	88.3	99.3	73.6	88.1

NEW MEXICO

DIVISION		LAS CRUCES 880 MAT.	INST.	TOTAL	LAS VEGAS 877 MAT.	INST.	TOTAL	ROSWELL 882 MAT.	INST.	TOTAL	SANTA FE 875 MAT.	INST.	TOTAL	SOCORRO 878 MAT.	INST.	TOTAL	TRUTH/CONSEQUENCES 879 MAT.	INST.	TOTAL
015433	CONTRACTOR EQUIPMENT		86.0	86.0		109.6	109.6		109.6	109.6		109.6	109.6		109.6	109.6		86.1	86.1
0241, 31 - 34	SITE & INFRASTRUCTURE, DEMOLITION	91.6	83.8	86.1	87.8	104.1	99.2	93.3	104.1	100.9	92.9	104.1	100.7	84.3	104.1	98.2	101.9	83.8	89.2
0310	Concrete Forming & Accessories	95.6	63.8	68.2	101.4	65.0	70.0	99.2	65.0	69.7	100.1	65.0	69.8	101.5	65.0	70.0	98.7	63.8	68.6
0320	Concrete Reinforcing	107.3	71.0	89.1	106.9	71.1	89.0	111.2	71.1	91.2	106.0	71.1	88.6	109.1	71.1	90.1	102.8	71.0	86.9
0330	Cast-in-Place Concrete	89.9	63.7	79.0	95.2	71.2	85.3	95.4	71.2	85.3	103.2	71.2	89.9	93.2	71.2	84.1	102.1	63.7	86.1
03	CONCRETE	86.1	65.9	76.1	103.1	69.4	86.4	108.3	69.4	89.1	105.6	69.4	87.7	102.0	69.4	85.9	95.1	65.9	80.7
04	MASONRY	97.5	60.2	74.4	95.6	60.6	73.9	112.2	60.6	80.3	99.5	60.6	75.4	95.5	60.6	73.9	93.1	60.2	72.8
05	METALS	97.1	81.3	92.2	100.3	87.9	96.4	99.3	87.9	95.8	97.7	87.9	94.7	100.6	87.9	96.6	100.1	81.4	94.3
06	WOOD, PLASTICS & COMPOSITES	78.8	64.4	70.7	92.9	65.5	77.4	88.9	65.5	75.7	94.6	65.5	78.2	92.9	65.5	77.4	84.6	64.4	73.2
07	THERMAL & MOISTURE PROTECTION	86.2	67.2	78.5	99.2	71.8	88.1	99.7	71.8	88.4	101.7	71.8	89.5	99.1	71.8	88.0	86.9	67.2	78.9
08	OPENINGS	91.5	67.9	85.9	100.3	68.5	92.8	98.6	68.5	91.5	102.4	68.5	94.4	100.1	68.5	92.7	93.3	67.9	87.3
0920	Plaster & Gypsum Board	74.2	64.1	67.3	81.6	64.1	69.7	75.4	64.1	67.7	91.6	64.1	72.9	81.6	64.1	69.7	83.4	64.1	70.3
0950, 0980	Ceilings & Acoustic Treatment	91.4	64.1	73.2	103.1	64.1	77.2	104.2	64.1	77.5	103.6	64.1	77.3	103.1	64.1	77.2	90.4	64.1	72.9
0960	Flooring	129.3	67.2	110.7	101.7	67.2	91.4	100.2	67.2	90.4	108.8	67.2	96.4	101.7	67.2	91.4	132.2	67.2	112.7
0970, 0990	Wall Finishes & Painting/Coating	90.1	68.1	76.8	102.9	68.1	82.0	102.9	68.1	82.0	107.7	68.1	83.9	102.9	68.1	82.0	93.7	68.1	78.3
09	FINISHES	107.1	64.6	83.4	96.8	65.5	79.3	97.7	65.5	79.8	101.9	65.5	81.6	96.7	65.5	79.3	109.0	64.6	84.3
COVERS	DIVS. 10 - 14, 25, 28, 41, 43, 44, 46	100.0	73.6	94.7	100.0	76.3	95.2	100.0	76.3	95.2	100.0	76.3	95.2	100.0	76.3	95.2	100.0	73.6	94.7
21, 22, 23	FIRE SUPPRESSION, PLUMBING & HVAC	100.4	70.5	88.4	97.1	70.7	86.6	100.0	70.7	88.3	100.1	70.7	88.3	97.1	70.7	86.6	97.0	70.5	86.4
26, 27, 3370	ELECTRICAL, COMMUNICATIONS & UTIL.	89.9	72.9	81.0	88.5	72.9	80.4	89.6	72.9	80.9	100.8	72.9	86.3	86.5	72.9	79.4	90.1	72.9	81.1
MF2010	WEIGHTED AVERAGE	95.8	70.4	84.7	97.7	73.6	87.2	99.8	73.6	88.4	100.5	73.6	88.8	97.3	73.6	87.0	97.0	70.4	85.4

City Cost Indexes

NEW MEXICO / NEW YORK

DIVISION		TUCUMCARI 884 MAT.	INST.	TOTAL	ALBANY 120-122 MAT.	INST.	TOTAL	BINGHAMTON 137-139 MAT.	INST.	TOTAL	BRONX 104 MAT.	INST.	TOTAL	BROOKLYN 112 MAT.	INST.	TOTAL	BUFFALO 140-142 MAT.	INST.	TOTAL
015433	CONTRACTOR EQUIPMENT		109.6	109.6		113.5	113.5		114.4	114.4		112.8	112.8		114.1	114.1		97.0	97.0
0241, 31-34	SITE & INFRASTRUCTURE, DEMOLITION	90.8	104.1	100.1	75.0	107.1	97.5	92.8	94.3	93.9	110.9	123.1	119.5	117.0	128.4	125.0	98.8	98.3	98.4
0310	Concrete Forming & Accessories	99.1	64.9	69.6	100.7	96.1	96.7	102.2	83.3	85.9	103.3	171.7	162.3	108.6	171.2	162.6	97.4	115.5	113.1
0320	Concrete Reinforcing	109.0	71.1	90.1	105.6	106.3	106.0	93.5	96.4	94.9	96.7	184.6	140.6	94.9	184.6	139.7	102.1	103.0	102.5
0330	Cast-in-Place Concrete	95.3	71.1	85.3	88.1	100.9	93.4	100.9	127.9	112.1	94.6	173.8	127.5	103.0	172.0	131.7	105.5	119.2	111.2
03	CONCRETE	106.7	69.3	88.3	101.0	100.3	100.6	96.2	102.7	99.4	96.5	173.2	134.4	108.3	172.0	139.7	104.6	113.7	109.1
04	MASONRY	112.9	60.6	80.5	90.9	100.6	96.7	105.8	126.6	118.7	94.3	176.4	145.1	116.4	176.4	153.5	107.3	119.6	114.9
05	METALS	98.1	87.8	94.9	101.3	109.5	103.9	96.0	118.2	102.9	100.8	149.3	115.8	104.4	140.3	115.4	99.5	95.6	98.3
06	WOOD, PLASTICS & COMPOSITES	88.9	65.5	75.7	97.7	93.6	95.4	107.3	79.3	91.5	100.1	171.4	140.4	109.3	171.1	144.1	98.7	115.2	108.0
07	THERMAL & MOISTURE PROTECTION	99.5	71.8	88.3	99.4	96.7	98.3	106.9	96.3	102.6	108.5	163.2	130.7	108.9	162.7	130.8	101.5	110.4	105.1
08	OPENINGS	98.5	68.5	91.4	99.9	92.0	98.0	90.7	81.6	88.5	87.0	172.2	107.1	88.0	166.5	106.6	91.8	103.3	94.6
0920	Plaster & Gypsum Board	75.4	64.1	67.7	105.0	93.1	96.9	111.6	78.2	88.9	105.4	173.3	151.6	106.9	173.3	152.1	103.2	115.4	111.5
0950, 0980	Ceilings & Acoustic Treatment	104.2	64.1	77.5	95.9	93.1	94.0	94.6	78.2	83.7	82.8	173.3	143.0	90.2	173.3	145.5	101.6	115.4	110.8
0960	Flooring	100.2	67.2	90.4	97.0	105.2	99.4	106.2	93.1	102.3	96.6	185.6	123.2	113.2	185.6	134.8	101.0	120.1	106.7
0970, 0990	Wall Finishes & Painting/Coating	102.9	68.1	82.0	96.8	89.4	92.4	93.3	95.3	94.5	97.9	148.0	128.0	124.2	148.0	138.5	102.4	112.5	108.5
09	FINISHES	97.6	65.5	79.7	97.8	96.7	97.2	96.7	84.9	90.1	95.3	172.0	138.1	111.3	171.8	145.0	101.0	116.9	109.9
COVERS	DIVS. 10-14, 25, 28, 41, 43, 44, 46	100.0	76.3	95.2	100.0	96.0	99.2	100.0	93.5	98.7	100.0	132.7	106.6	100.0	132.0	106.4	100.0	106.1	101.2
21, 22, 23	FIRE SUPPRESSION, PLUMBING & HVAC	97.2	70.5	86.5	100.0	98.8	99.5	100.4	87.3	95.1	100.2	164.7	126.1	99.8	164.4	125.7	100.0	97.1	98.8
26, 27, 3370	ELECTRICAL, COMMUNICATIONS & UTIL.	90.6	72.9	81.4	96.0	99.3	97.7	98.9	107.9	103.6	96.1	175.0	137.3	98.7	175.0	138.5	97.5	101.9	99.8
MF2010	WEIGHTED AVERAGE	98.8	73.5	87.8	98.6	100.2	99.3	98.1	99.4	98.6	98.0	163.9	126.7	102.6	162.9	128.9	99.7	105.8	102.4

NEW YORK

DIVISION		ELMIRA 148-149 MAT.	INST.	TOTAL	FAR ROCKAWAY 116 MAT.	INST.	TOTAL	FLUSHING 113 MAT.	INST.	TOTAL	GLENS FALLS 128 MAT.	INST.	TOTAL	HICKSVILLE 115,117,118 MAT.	INST.	TOTAL	JAMAICA 114 MAT.	INST.	TOTAL
015433	CONTRACTOR EQUIPMENT		116.0	116.0		114.1	114.1		114.1	114.1		113.5	113.5		114.1	114.1		114.1	114.1
0241, 31-34	SITE & INFRASTRUCTURE, DEMOLITION	93.3	94.3	94.0	120.2	128.4	125.9	120.2	128.4	126.0	65.2	106.7	94.3	110.1	127.3	122.2	114.5	128.4	124.3
0310	Concrete Forming & Accessories	83.9	86.3	86.0	94.9	171.2	160.8	98.7	171.2	161.3	87.1	86.9	86.9	91.5	144.5	137.3	98.7	171.2	161.3
0320	Concrete Reinforcing	100.5	90.6	95.6	94.9	184.6	139.7	96.5	184.6	140.5	97.0	94.1	95.5	94.9	184.4	139.6	94.9	184.6	139.7
0330	Cast-in-Place Concrete	94.7	96.4	95.4	111.4	172.0	136.6	111.4	172.0	136.6	81.7	96.9	88.0	94.7	165.6	124.1	103.0	172.0	131.7
03	CONCRETE	95.0	92.3	93.7	114.3	172.0	142.8	114.9	172.0	143.1	89.9	92.6	91.3	100.1	157.8	128.6	107.6	172.0	139.4
04	MASONRY	101.4	93.7	96.6	119.7	176.4	154.8	113.9	176.4	152.6	90.1	93.2	92.0	110.5	166.0	144.9	118.1	176.4	154.2
05	METALS	95.4	114.7	101.3	104.4	140.3	115.5	104.4	140.3	115.5	94.8	105.1	98.0	105.9	138.2	115.8	104.4	140.3	115.5
06	WOOD, PLASTICS & COMPOSITES	86.3	84.9	85.5	92.2	171.1	136.7	97.1	171.1	138.8	86.1	84.9	85.4	88.7	141.5	118.5	97.1	171.1	138.8
07	THERMAL & MOISTURE PROTECTION	102.2	84.1	94.8	108.8	162.7	130.7	108.9	162.7	130.7	93.0	92.8	92.9	108.5	154.3	127.1	108.7	162.7	130.6
08	OPENINGS	92.4	83.8	90.3	86.7	166.5	105.6	86.7	166.5	105.6	91.3	84.5	89.7	86.7	150.3	101.8	86.7	166.5	105.6
0920	Plaster & Gypsum Board	100.2	84.2	89.3	95.1	173.3	148.3	97.8	173.3	149.1	95.2	84.2	87.7	94.8	142.7	127.4	97.8	173.3	149.1
0950, 0980	Ceilings & Acoustic Treatment	93.4	84.2	87.2	78.7	173.3	141.6	78.7	173.3	141.6	85.9	84.2	84.8	77.7	142.7	121.0	78.7	173.3	141.6
0960	Flooring	92.9	93.1	93.0	108.5	185.6	131.6	110.0	185.6	132.6	86.1	105.2	91.8	107.6	145.3	118.9	110.0	185.6	132.6
0970, 0990	Wall Finishes & Painting/Coating	101.7	87.6	93.2	124.2	148.0	138.5	124.2	148.0	138.5	94.1	89.3	91.2	124.2	148.0	138.5	124.2	148.0	138.5
09	FINISHES	96.1	87.4	91.3	106.4	171.8	142.8	107.1	171.8	143.1	89.1	89.8	89.5	104.9	143.7	126.5	106.6	171.8	142.9
COVERS	DIVS. 10-14, 25, 28, 41, 43, 44, 46	100.0	93.4	98.7	100.0	132.0	106.4	100.0	132.0	106.4	100.0	92.7	98.5	100.0	125.1	105.0	100.0	132.0	106.4
21, 22, 23	FIRE SUPPRESSION, PLUMBING & HVAC	95.3	87.8	92.3	94.9	164.4	122.8	94.9	164.4	122.8	95.4	92.0	94.0	99.8	151.8	120.6	94.9	164.4	122.8
26, 27, 3370	ELECTRICAL, COMMUNICATIONS & UTIL.	95.5	96.9	96.2	106.1	175.0	142.1	106.1	175.0	142.1	91.1	99.3	95.4	98.0	135.8	117.7	96.9	175.0	137.7
MF2010	WEIGHTED AVERAGE	95.9	93.1	94.7	102.4	162.9	128.7	102.3	162.9	128.7	92.6	95.0	93.6	100.7	146.6	120.7	100.6	162.9	127.7

NEW YORK

DIVISION		JAMESTOWN 147 MAT.	INST.	TOTAL	KINGSTON 124 MAT.	INST.	TOTAL	LONG ISLAND CITY 111 MAT.	INST.	TOTAL	MONTICELLO 127 MAT.	INST.	TOTAL	MOUNT VERNON 105 MAT.	INST.	TOTAL	NEW ROCHELLE 108 MAT.	INST.	TOTAL
015433	CONTRACTOR EQUIPMENT		94.0	94.0		114.1	114.1		114.1	114.1		114.1	114.1		112.8	112.8		112.8	112.8
0241, 31-34	SITE & INFRASTRUCTURE, DEMOLITION	94.5	93.8	94.0	122.1	124.3	123.7	118.1	128.4	125.3	117.5	124.2	122.2	117.9	118.8	118.6	117.1	118.8	118.3
0310	Concrete Forming & Accessories	83.9	81.2	81.6	88.7	106.0	103.6	103.1	171.2	161.9	95.7	105.0	103.7	93.5	128.5	123.7	108.6	128.5	125.8
0320	Concrete Reinforcing	100.7	98.6	99.6	97.4	140.6	119.0	94.9	184.6	139.7	96.6	140.4	118.5	95.2	183.2	139.2	95.3	183.2	139.2
0330	Cast-in-Place Concrete	98.3	91.3	95.4	110.4	131.3	119.1	106.3	172.0	133.6	103.4	126.8	113.1	105.7	128.9	115.3	105.7	128.9	115.3
03	CONCRETE	98.0	88.0	93.0	112.5	120.8	116.6	110.7	172.0	140.9	107.2	118.8	112.9	105.9	137.8	121.6	105.4	137.8	121.4
04	MASONRY	109.1	91.1	98.0	104.0	136.8	124.3	113.3	176.4	152.3	98.0	131.0	118.4	100.0	126.1	116.2	100.0	126.1	116.2
05	METALS	92.7	90.9	92.2	103.3	116.5	107.4	104.4	140.3	115.4	103.3	116.1	107.2	100.6	134.6	111.1	100.9	134.6	111.3
06	WOOD, PLASTICS & COMPOSITES	84.8	78.6	81.3	87.3	98.6	93.7	103.3	171.1	141.5	95.2	98.6	97.1	89.3	131.7	113.2	107.6	131.7	121.2
07	THERMAL & MOISTURE PROTECTION	101.6	84.0	94.5	114.3	136.3	123.3	108.8	162.7	130.7	114.0	134.0	122.1	109.4	135.8	120.1	109.4	135.8	120.2
08	OPENINGS	92.2	82.5	89.9	92.8	117.5	98.7	86.7	166.5	105.6	88.5	117.5	95.4	87.0	145.0	100.7	87.0	145.0	100.7
0920	Plaster & Gypsum Board	93.2	77.7	82.6	97.2	98.6	98.1	102.6	173.3	150.7	99.5	98.6	98.9	100.1	132.3	122.0	112.8	132.3	126.1
0950, 0980	Ceilings & Acoustic Treatment	90.7	77.7	82.0	74.3	98.6	90.5	78.7	173.3	141.6	74.3	98.6	90.5	81.1	132.3	115.2	81.1	132.3	115.2
0960	Flooring	95.9	89.7	94.1	103.1	73.8	94.4	111.4	185.6	133.6	105.4	73.8	95.9	89.0	180.7	116.4	95.2	180.7	120.8
0970, 0990	Wall Finishes & Painting/Coating	103.0	91.3	96.0	125.9	113.8	118.6	124.2	148.0	138.5	125.9	113.8	118.6	96.1	148.0	127.3	96.1	148.0	127.3
09	FINISHES	95.6	83.0	88.6	103.7	98.4	100.7	107.9	171.8	143.5	104.2	97.8	100.7	92.8	139.7	118.9	96.0	139.7	120.3
COVERS	DIVS. 10-14, 25, 28, 41, 43, 44, 46	100.0	94.8	99.0	100.0	109.7	101.9	100.0	132.0	106.4	100.0	108.9	101.8	100.0	117.8	103.6	100.0	117.8	103.6
21, 22, 23	FIRE SUPPRESSION, PLUMBING & HVAC	95.2	84.6	91.0	95.3	121.1	105.6	99.8	164.4	125.7	95.3	117.9	104.4	95.4	118.6	104.7	95.4	118.6	104.7
26, 27, 3370	ELECTRICAL, COMMUNICATIONS & UTIL.	94.3	90.4	92.3	92.7	113.7	103.6	97.5	175.0	137.9	92.7	113.7	103.6	94.4	158.9	128.1	94.4	158.9	128.1
MF2010	WEIGHTED AVERAGE	96.0	87.8	92.4	100.7	118.3	108.4	102.2	162.9	128.6	99.4	116.5	106.8	97.9	133.3	113.3	98.2	133.3	113.5

771

NEW YORK

DIVISION		NEW YORK 100-102 MAT.	INST.	TOTAL	NIAGARA FALLS 143 MAT.	INST.	TOTAL	PLATTSBURGH 129 MAT.	INST.	TOTAL	POUGHKEEPSIE 125-126 MAT.	INST.	TOTAL	QUEENS 110 MAT.	INST.	TOTAL	RIVERHEAD 119 MAT.	INST.	TOTAL
015433	CONTRACTOR EQUIPMENT		113.2	113.2		94.0	94.0		99.2	99.2		114.1	114.1		114.1	114.1		114.1	114.1
0241, 31-34	SITE & INFRASTRUCTURE, DEMOLITION	119.6	123.8	122.5	96.6	95.4	95.8	89.9	102.7	98.9	118.3	124.0	122.3	113.4	128.4	123.9	111.3	127.3	122.5
0310	Concrete Forming & Accessories	107.7	179.3	169.5	83.9	113.2	109.2	91.9	83.8	84.9	88.7	148.2	140.0	91.7	171.2	160.3	96.0	144.5	137.9
0320	Concrete Reinforcing	102.4	184.7	143.5	99.3	99.3	99.3	101.3	93.6	97.5	97.4	140.9	119.1	96.5	184.6	140.5	96.7	184.4	140.5
0330	Cast-in-Place Concrete	106.4	179.2	136.7	101.6	118.7	108.7	100.1	92.7	97.0	106.9	127.3	115.4	97.9	172.0	128.7	96.3	165.6	125.0
03	CONCRETE	106.7	178.5	142.1	100.2	111.7	105.9	104.1	88.4	96.3	109.6	138.2	123.7	103.3	172.0	137.2	100.8	157.8	128.9
04	MASONRY	104.1	178.4	150.0	117.3	118.8	118.2	85.9	87.3	86.8	97.8	128.1	116.6	107.8	176.4	150.2	115.8	166.0	146.9
05	METALS	114.1	149.5	125.0	95.4	92.3	94.5	99.2	85.5	95.0	103.3	118.5	108.0	104.4	140.3	115.4	106.3	138.2	116.1
06	WOOD, PLASTICS & COMPOSITES	104.6	180.6	147.5	84.7	110.9	99.5	94.1	81.9	87.2	87.3	158.2	127.3	88.8	171.1	135.3	94.0	141.5	120.8
07	THERMAL & MOISTURE PROTECTION	108.5	165.3	131.5	101.7	108.0	104.3	108.4	89.8	100.9	114.3	138.8	124.2	108.5	162.7	130.5	109.2	154.3	127.5
08	OPENINGS	92.6	177.5	112.7	92.2	100.2	94.1	98.8	80.1	94.4	92.8	149.1	106.2	86.7	166.5	105.6	86.7	150.3	101.8
0920	Plaster & Gypsum Board	112.2	182.7	160.2	93.2	111.0	105.3	119.4	80.6	93.0	97.2	160.0	139.9	94.8	173.3	148.2	96.1	142.7	127.8
0950, 0980	Ceilings & Acoustic Treatment	101.5	182.7	155.5	90.7	111.0	104.2	100.8	80.6	87.4	74.3	160.0	131.3	78.7	173.3	141.6	78.5	142.7	121.3
0960	Flooring	97.6	185.6	123.9	95.9	113.8	101.3	109.9	105.2	108.5	103.1	148.0	116.6	107.6	185.6	130.9	108.5	145.3	119.5
0970, 0990	Wall Finishes & Painting/Coating	97.9	156.4	133.1	103.0	109.7	107.0	123.3	76.4	95.1	125.9	113.8	118.6	124.2	148.0	138.5	124.2	148.0	138.5
09	FINISHES	101.2	178.9	144.5	95.1	113.6	105.7	109.0	86.4	92.9	103.5	146.3	127.3	105.3	171.8	142.3	105.5	143.7	126.8
COVERS	DIVS. 10 - 14, 25, 28, 41, 43, 44, 46	100.0	137.1	107.4	100.0	104.7	100.9	100.0	48.9	89.8	100.0	113.3	102.7	100.0	132.0	106.4	100.0	125.1	105.0
21, 22, 23	FIRE SUPPRESSION, PLUMBING & HVAC	100.1	165.7	126.4	95.2	97.1	95.9	95.3	92.0	94.0	95.3	117.9	104.4	99.8	164.4	125.7	100.0	151.8	120.7
26, 27, 3370	ELECTRICAL, COMMUNICATIONS & UTIL.	104.2	175.0	141.1	92.9	99.3	96.3	89.2	90.4	89.8	92.7	113.7	103.6	98.0	175.0	138.2	99.7	135.8	118.5
MF2010	WEIGHTED AVERAGE	103.8	166.4	131.1	96.9	103.9	100.0	97.3	88.4	93.4	100.0	127.5	112.0	100.8	162.9	127.8	101.4	146.6	121.1

NEW YORK

DIVISION		ROCHESTER 144-146 MAT.	INST.	TOTAL	SCHENECTADY 123 MAT.	INST.	TOTAL	STATEN ISLAND 103 MAT.	INST.	TOTAL	SUFFERN 109 MAT.	INST.	TOTAL	SYRACUSE 130-132 MAT.	INST.	TOTAL	UTICA 133-135 MAT.	INST.	TOTAL
015433	CONTRACTOR EQUIPMENT		116.4	116.4		113.5	113.5		112.8	112.8		112.8	112.8		113.5	113.5		113.5	113.5
0241, 31-34	SITE & INFRASTRUCTURE, DEMOLITION	77.8	109.6	100.2	74.9	107.1	97.5	122.7	123.1	123.0	113.8	119.1	117.5	91.8	106.6	102.2	70.8	104.5	94.4
0310	Concrete Forming & Accessories	104.8	92.4	94.1	103.1	96.1	97.1	93.0	171.7	160.9	102.1	131.2	127.2	101.1	91.2	92.5	102.4	82.2	85.0
0320	Concrete Reinforcing	101.9	90.7	96.3	96.0	106.3	101.2	96.7	184.6	140.6	95.3	140.9	118.1	94.4	94.8	94.6	94.4	91.9	93.2
0330	Cast-in-Place Concrete	97.6	98.9	98.1	98.6	100.9	99.5	105.7	173.8	134.0	102.5	134.8	115.9	93.8	105.4	98.6	85.8	98.3	91.0
03	CONCRETE	107.3	95.2	101.3	104.5	100.3	102.4	107.6	173.2	140.0	102.4	133.3	117.6	99.5	97.5	98.6	97.8	90.6	94.2
04	MASONRY	100.2	98.6	99.2	88.1	100.3	95.7	106.7	176.4	149.8	99.4	138.2	123.4	98.1	106.3	103.2	90.0	97.7	94.8
05	METALS	101.4	104.5	102.3	98.8	109.5	102.1	98.7	149.3	114.3	98.7	118.1	104.7	99.5	105.0	101.2	97.5	103.8	99.5
06	WOOD, PLASTICS & COMPOSITES	103.8	90.6	96.4	106.0	93.6	99.0	87.8	171.4	135.0	99.7	131.7	117.7	103.7	87.6	94.6	103.7	79.4	90.0
07	THERMAL & MOISTURE PROTECTION	100.5	98.0	99.5	94.2	96.7	95.3	108.8	163.2	130.9	109.3	140.9	122.1	102.5	97.9	100.6	90.9	94.4	92.3
08	OPENINGS	96.7	86.9	94.4	96.9	92.0	95.7	87.0	172.2	107.1	87.0	135.5	98.5	92.5	80.4	89.6	95.2	79.2	91.4
0920	Plaster & Gypsum Board	111.1	90.3	96.9	106.6	93.1	97.4	100.2	173.3	149.9	104.6	132.3	123.5	101.9	87.0	91.7	101.9	78.6	86.0
0950, 0980	Ceilings & Acoustic Treatment	99.4	90.3	93.3	92.0	93.1	92.8	82.8	173.3	143.0	81.1	132.3	115.2	94.6	87.0	89.5	94.6	78.6	83.9
0960	Flooring	92.3	104.9	96.1	92.6	105.2	96.3	92.9	185.6	120.6	92.0	145.3	107.9	93.6	94.9	94.0	90.9	95.0	92.1
0970, 0990	Wall Finishes & Painting/Coating	102.9	97.4	99.6	94.1	89.4	91.3	97.9	148.0	128.0	96.1	121.7	111.5	98.3	97.0	97.5	90.8	97.0	94.5
09	FINISHES	103.1	95.2	98.7	94.5	96.7	95.8	94.7	172.0	137.8	93.8	130.2	114.1	96.0	92.1	93.8	94.1	85.4	89.2
COVERS	DIVS. 10 - 14, 25, 28, 41, 43, 44, 46	100.0	97.0	99.4	100.0	96.0	99.2	100.0	132.7	106.6	100.0	121.8	104.4	100.0	96.3	99.3	100.0	91.9	98.4
21, 22, 23	FIRE SUPPRESSION, PLUMBING & HVAC	100.0	87.9	95.1	100.2	98.8	99.6	100.2	164.7	126.1	95.4	119.6	105.1	100.2	91.2	96.6	100.2	88.8	95.6
26, 27, 3370	ELECTRICAL, COMMUNICATIONS & UTIL.	99.2	94.3	96.7	95.5	99.3	97.5	96.1	175.0	137.3	102.3	121.5	112.3	99.1	97.7	98.4	97.3	97.7	97.5
MF2010	WEIGHTED AVERAGE	100.3	95.6	98.3	97.8	100.2	98.8	99.7	163.9	127.6	98.0	126.2	110.3	98.5	97.0	97.9	96.7	93.2	95.1

NEW YORK / NORTH CAROLINA

DIVISION		WATERTOWN 136 MAT.	INST.	TOTAL	WHITE PLAINS 106 MAT.	INST.	TOTAL	YONKERS 107 MAT.	INST.	TOTAL	ASHEVILLE 287-288 MAT.	INST.	TOTAL	CHARLOTTE 281-282 MAT.	INST.	TOTAL	DURHAM 277 MAT.	INST.	TOTAL
015433	CONTRACTOR EQUIPMENT		113.5	113.5		112.8	112.8		112.8	112.8		95.6	95.6		95.6	95.6		100.8	100.8
0241, 31-34	SITE & INFRASTRUCTURE, DEMOLITION	78.1	106.1	97.8	110.6	118.8	116.4	119.1	118.8	118.9	102.4	76.6	84.3	106.0	76.7	85.4	102.6	85.3	90.4
0310	Concrete Forming & Accessories	87.5	87.4	87.4	107.1	128.5	125.6	107.4	128.5	125.7	95.4	42.1	49.4	98.6	43.7	51.2	100.0	45.1	52.7
0320	Concrete Reinforcing	95.0	94.1	94.5	99.1	183.2	139.2	99.1	183.2	141.1	94.4	63.0	78.7	100.3	58.3	79.3	94.8	57.6	76.2
0330	Cast-in-Place Concrete	99.8	91.8	96.5	93.8	128.9	108.4	105.0	128.9	114.9	110.7	51.9	86.3	115.3	50.4	88.4	104.1	47.6	80.7
03	CONCRETE	110.2	91.2	100.8	96.1	137.8	116.7	105.6	137.9	121.5	102.3	51.2	77.1	104.9	50.5	78.1	98.8	50.1	74.8
04	MASONRY	91.0	100.2	96.7	98.9	126.1	115.7	103.6	126.1	117.5	81.7	44.5	58.7	88.9	52.1	66.1	85.5	38.6	56.4
05	METALS	97.6	104.8	99.8	100.3	134.6	110.9	109.9	134.6	117.5	94.2	82.7	90.7	95.0	81.3	90.8	108.6	80.2	99.9
06	WOOD, PLASTICS & COMPOSITES	85.0	86.3	85.8	105.6	131.7	120.3	105.4	131.7	120.3	96.4	41.2	65.2	101.6	42.8	68.4	99.5	45.7	69.1
07	THERMAL & MOISTURE PROTECTION	91.2	94.9	92.7	109.2	135.8	120.0	109.5	135.8	120.2	103.8	44.5	79.7	98.5	47.5	77.8	106.6	46.6	82.2
08	OPENINGS	95.2	83.2	92.4	87.0	145.0	100.7	90.0	145.3	103.1	94.7	44.6	82.9	99.9	45.5	87.1	97.8	47.7	85.9
0920	Plaster & Gypsum Board	92.2	85.7	87.7	107.6	132.3	124.4	111.8	132.3	125.8	97.5	39.2	57.8	97.8	40.9	59.1	108.8	43.8	64.6
0950, 0980	Ceilings & Acoustic Treatment	94.6	85.7	88.6	81.1	132.3	115.2	99.7	132.3	121.4	91.6	39.2	56.7	96.0	40.9	59.3	95.1	43.8	61.0
0960	Flooring	84.8	95.0	87.9	93.8	180.7	119.8	93.4	180.7	119.5	101.5	43.5	84.1	101.1	44.2	84.1	106.2	43.5	87.4
0970, 0990	Wall Finishes & Painting/Coating	90.8	91.4	91.2	96.1	148.0	127.3	96.1	148.0	127.3	107.1	41.1	67.4	107.3	50.4	73.1	103.4	38.2	64.2
09	FINISHES	91.7	88.8	90.1	94.3	139.7	119.5	99.4	139.7	121.8	96.8	41.5	66.0	97.0	43.8	67.4	100.2	43.8	68.8
COVERS	DIVS. 10 - 14, 25, 28, 41, 43, 44, 46	100.0	93.8	98.8	100.0	117.8	103.6	100.0	120.5	104.1	100.0	78.2	95.6	100.0	78.6	95.7	100.0	73.8	94.8
21, 22, 23	FIRE SUPPRESSION, PLUMBING & HVAC	100.2	81.5	92.7	100.4	118.6	107.7	100.4	118.6	107.7	100.4	53.5	81.6	100.0	55.3	82.1	100.3	53.1	81.4
26, 27, 3370	ELECTRICAL, COMMUNICATIONS & UTIL.	99.1	90.5	94.6	94.4	158.9	128.1	102.4	158.9	131.9	96.8	57.0	76.0	95.7	59.9	77.1	94.4	45.6	68.9
MF2010	WEIGHTED AVERAGE	98.1	91.9	95.4	98.0	133.3	113.4	102.5	133.4	116.0	97.6	55.9	79.4	98.7	57.6	80.8	100.2	54.4	80.2

NORTH CAROLINA

DIVISION		ELIZABETH CITY 279			FAYETTEVILLE 283			GASTONIA 280			GREENSBORO 270,272 - 274			HICKORY 286			KINSTON 285		
		MAT.	INST.	TOTAL	MAT.	INST.	TOTAL	MAT.	INST.	TOTAL	MAT.	INST.	TOTAL	MAT.	INST.	TOTAL	MAT.	INST.	TOTAL
015433	CONTRACTOR EQUIPMENT		105.0	105.0		100.8	100.8		95.6	95.6		100.8	100.8		100.8	100.8		100.8	100.8
0241, 31 - 34	SITE & INFRASTRUCTURE, DEMOLITION	107.1	87.0	93.0	101.6	85.2	90.1	102.2	76.6	84.3	102.5	85.3	90.4	101.3	85.1	90.0	100.4	85.2	89.7
0310	Concrete Forming & Accessories	85.5	43.3	49.1	95.0	60.4	65.1	101.9	39.5	48.0	99.7	45.4	52.8	91.6	37.9	45.2	87.9	43.0	49.2
0320	Concrete Reinforcing	92.8	47.3	70.1	98.0	57.7	77.9	94.8	58.3	76.6	93.7	57.8	75.8	94.4	57.9	76.1	93.9	47.2	70.6
0330	Cast-in-Place Concrete	104.3	47.4	80.7	116.1	48.9	88.2	108.2	53.4	85.5	103.4	48.2	80.5	110.7	48.7	84.9	106.9	45.4	81.3
03	CONCRETE	98.8	47.3	73.4	104.4	57.3	81.2	100.9	49.7	75.6	98.3	50.4	74.7	102.0	47.3	75.6	98.9	46.4	73.0
04	MASONRY	97.5	48.8	67.4	84.7	39.6	56.8	85.8	51.7	64.7	82.9	42.1	57.6	72.2	44.4	55.0	77.5	49.0	59.8
05	METALS	96.1	76.9	90.2	113.2	80.4	103.1	94.9	81.2	90.7	101.9	80.4	95.3	94.3	79.9	89.9	93.2	76.0	87.9
06	WOOD, PLASTICS & COMPOSITES	82.0	44.5	60.9	95.9	66.6	79.4	105.5	37.4	67.1	99.2	45.9	69.1	90.9	36.0	59.9	87.7	43.9	63.0
07	THERMAL & MOISTURE PROTECTION	105.9	44.1	80.8	103.7	46.6	80.5	104.0	46.0	80.5	106.3	43.7	80.9	104.1	42.5	79.1	103.9	43.7	79.5
08	OPENINGS	95.0	39.3	81.8	94.8	59.1	86.4	98.4	42.0	85.1	97.8	47.8	86.0	94.8	37.6	81.2	94.9	44.2	82.9
0920	Plaster & Gypsum Board	100.1	42.0	60.6	102.8	65.4	77.3	105.1	35.3	57.6	110.5	44.0	65.3	97.5	33.9	54.2	97.6	42.0	59.8
0950, 0980	Ceilings & Acoustic Treatment	95.1	42.0	59.7	92.5	65.4	74.5	95.2	35.3	55.3	95.1	44.0	61.1	91.6	33.9	53.2	95.2	42.0	59.8
0960	Flooring	98.3	23.6	76.0	101.7	43.5	84.3	104.8	43.5	86.5	106.2	40.4	86.5	101.4	33.5	81.1	98.7	23.0	76.1
0970, 0990	Wall Finishes & Painting/Coating	103.4	42.9	67.0	107.1	33.9	63.1	107.1	41.1	67.4	103.4	32.3	60.7	107.1	41.1	67.4	107.1	40.1	66.8
09	FINISHES	97.1	39.5	65.0	97.7	55.5	74.2	99.5	39.4	66.0	100.5	42.8	68.3	96.9	36.2	63.1	96.8	38.8	64.5
COVERS	DIVS. 10 - 14, 25, 28, 41, 43, 44, 46	100.0	72.2	94.4	100.0	76.0	95.2	100.0	77.9	95.6	100.0	77.8	95.6	100.0	77.6	95.5	100.0	73.4	94.7
21, 22, 23	FIRE SUPPRESSION, PLUMBING & HVAC	95.3	52.2	78.0	100.3	52.8	81.3	100.4	53.5	81.6	100.2	53.3	81.4	95.5	53.3	78.6	95.5	52.3	78.2
26, 27, 3370	ELECTRICAL, COMMUNICATIONS & UTIL.	94.1	35.3	63.4	95.6	51.9	72.8	96.2	58.7	76.6	93.4	57.0	74.4	94.2	58.7	75.7	94.0	47.2	69.6
MF2010	WEIGHTED AVERAGE	96.9	52.2	77.4	100.9	58.5	82.5	98.4	56.1	80.0	98.8	56.3	80.3	95.6	54.9	77.9	95.3	53.7	77.2

NORTH CAROLINA / NORTH DAKOTA

DIVISION		MURPHY 289			RALEIGH 275 - 276			ROCKY MOUNT 278			WILMINGTON 284			WINSTON-SALEM 271			BISMARCK 585		
		MAT.	INST.	TOTAL	MAT.	INST.	TOTAL	MAT.	INST.	TOTAL	MAT.	INST.	TOTAL	MAT.	INST.	TOTAL	MAT.	INST.	TOTAL
015433	CONTRACTOR EQUIPMENT		95.6	95.6		100.8	100.8		100.8	100.8		95.6	95.6		100.8	100.8		99.0	99.0
0241, 31 - 34	SITE & INFRASTRUCTURE, DEMOLITION	103.6	76.5	84.3	103.7	85.3	90.8	105.0	85.3	91.2	103.6	76.8	84.8	102.8	85.3	90.5	100.7	97.6	98.5
0310	Concrete Forming & Accessories	102.6	40.2	48.7	98.7	47.6	54.6	92.1	45.2	51.6	96.8	49.9	56.3	101.6	49.0	56.2	103.6	41.3	49.8
0320	Concrete Reinforcing	93.9	46.9	70.4	100.0	57.8	78.9	92.8	57.6	75.2	95.1	57.6	76.4	93.7	57.6	75.7	105.6	83.2	94.4
0330	Cast-in-Place Concrete	114.5	45.0	85.7	109.3	52.0	85.5	102.0	48.3	79.7	110.3	50.2	85.3	105.9	50.6	83.0	109.5	48.4	84.1
03	CONCRETE	105.3	45.0	75.5	102.0	52.8	77.7	99.5	50.3	75.2	102.2	53.1	77.9	99.6	52.8	76.5	103.6	53.0	78.6
04	MASONRY	74.5	41.9	54.4	88.1	42.9	60.2	76.2	40.2	53.9	72.4	42.4	53.9	83.0	39.3	56.0	110.9	57.4	77.8
05	METALS	92.1	75.3	87.0	94.8	80.4	90.4	95.3	79.6	90.5	93.9	80.2	89.7	99.4	80.2	93.5	97.7	85.4	93.9
06	WOOD, PLASTICS & COMPOSITES	106.2	40.5	69.2	97.9	48.6	70.1	89.5	45.7	64.8	98.8	50.1	71.3	99.2	50.4	71.7	87.3	35.6	58.1
07	THERMAL & MOISTURE PROTECTION	104.0	41.6	78.6	100.6	47.9	79.2	106.3	41.6	80.1	103.8	47.9	81.1	106.3	44.3	81.2	109.3	50.8	85.6
08	OPENINGS	94.7	39.8	81.7	97.0	48.5	85.5	94.3	42.9	82.1	94.9	51.7	84.6	97.8	50.3	86.5	100.9	47.9	88.4
0920	Plaster & Gypsum Board	104.2	38.5	59.5	102.5	46.8	64.6	102.1	43.8	62.5	100.3	48.3	65.0	110.5	48.7	68.5	94.3	33.8	53.1
0950, 0980	Ceilings & Acoustic Treatment	91.6	38.5	56.3	95.9	46.8	63.2	92.4	43.8	60.1	92.5	48.3	63.1	95.1	48.7	64.2	136.9	33.8	68.3
0960	Flooring	105.2	24.5	81.1	103.4	43.5	85.4	101.8	22.2	78.0	102.3	45.3	85.2	106.2	43.5	87.4	109.8	73.4	98.9
0970, 0990	Wall Finishes & Painting/Coating	107.1	40.2	66.9	102.1	37.7	63.4	103.4	39.3	64.9	107.1	39.5	66.5	103.4	37.5	63.8	94.1	30.0	55.6
09	FINISHES	99.0	36.8	64.3	99.7	45.7	69.6	97.9	40.2	65.8	97.6	47.8	69.9	100.5	46.7	70.5	111.7	43.8	73.9
COVERS	DIVS. 10 - 14, 25, 28, 41, 43, 44, 46	100.0	77.5	95.5	100.0	74.5	94.9	100.0	74.4	94.9	100.0	75.7	95.1	100.0	79.3	95.9	100.0	84.8	97.0
21, 22, 23	FIRE SUPPRESSION, PLUMBING & HVAC	95.5	52.0	78.0	100.0	53.6	81.4	95.3	53.9	78.7	100.4	55.1	82.2	100.2	53.5	81.5	100.2	61.3	84.6
26, 27, 3370	ELECTRICAL, COMMUNICATIONS & UTIL.	97.8	30.0	62.4	96.5	41.3	67.7	96.1	40.6	67.1	97.0	51.9	73.4	93.4	57.0	74.4	102.2	73.3	87.1
MF2010	WEIGHTED AVERAGE	96.4	49.2	75.8	98.2	55.1	79.4	96.0	53.2	77.4	97.2	56.6	79.5	98.5	57.1	80.5	102.0	64.0	85.5

NORTH DAKOTA

DIVISION		DEVILS LAKE 583			DICKINSON 586			FARGO 580 - 581			GRAND FORKS 582			JAMESTOWN 584			MINOT 587		
		MAT.	INST.	TOTAL	MAT.	INST.	TOTAL	MAT.	INST.	TOTAL	MAT.	INST.	TOTAL	MAT.	INST.	TOTAL	MAT.	INST.	TOTAL
015433	CONTRACTOR EQUIPMENT		99.0	99.0		99.0	99.0		99.0	99.0		99.0	99.0		99.0	99.0		99.0	99.0
0241, 31 - 34	SITE & INFRASTRUCTURE, DEMOLITION	103.3	95.2	97.6	111.5	93.7	99.0	98.4	97.7	97.9	107.3	93.7	97.8	102.3	93.7	96.3	104.8	97.6	99.8
0310	Concrete Forming & Accessories	102.6	36.0	45.1	91.7	34.9	42.7	102.5	42.2	50.5	95.6	34.8	43.1	93.2	34.6	42.6	91.4	66.0	69.5
0320	Concrete Reinforcing	101.9	83.5	92.7	102.8	41.0	71.9	94.5	83.3	88.9	100.3	83.3	91.8	102.5	48.3	75.4	103.8	83.6	93.7
0330	Cast-in-Place Concrete	122.9	47.0	91.4	111.2	45.2	83.8	100.9	50.3	79.9	111.2	45.1	83.8	121.4	45.0	89.7	111.2	47.5	84.7
03	CONCRETE	110.8	50.2	80.9	110.1	41.0	76.0	104.7	54.0	79.7	107.3	48.7	78.4	109.3	42.2	76.2	105.8	63.7	85.0
04	MASONRY	111.7	64.4	82.4	113.4	59.2	79.8	97.9	57.4	72.9	106.2	63.8	80.0	123.8	33.4	67.8	105.6	64.2	80.0
05	METALS	95.1	84.6	91.9	95.1	64.1	85.5	99.0	86.0	95.0	95.1	79.3	90.2	95.1	65.1	85.8	95.4	86.3	92.6
06	WOOD, PLASTICS & COMPOSITES	88.7	32.8	57.1	76.6	32.8	51.9	86.8	36.1	58.2	80.8	32.8	53.7	78.5	32.8	52.7	76.4	68.7	72.0
07	THERMAL & MOISTURE PROTECTION	106.7	49.4	83.4	107.1	47.3	82.8	108.7	51.8	85.6	106.9	49.4	83.5	106.6	41.5	80.1	106.6	56.0	86.1
08	OPENINGS	96.6	40.8	83.4	96.5	30.9	81.0	98.8	48.2	86.8	96.6	40.8	83.4	96.6	33.0	81.5	96.7	66.0	89.4
0920	Plaster & Gypsum Board	115.2	30.9	57.9	105.2	30.9	54.7	91.5	34.3	52.6	106.7	30.9	55.1	106.3	30.9	55.0	105.2	67.9	79.8
0950, 0980	Ceilings & Acoustic Treatment	142.1	30.9	68.1	142.1	30.9	68.1	138.7	34.3	69.2	142.1	30.9	68.1	142.1	30.9	68.1	142.1	67.9	92.7
0960	Flooring	117.0	36.5	92.9	110.5	36.5	88.4	109.8	73.4	98.9	112.4	36.5	89.7	111.2	36.5	88.9	110.3	86.4	103.1
0970, 0990	Wall Finishes & Painting/Coating	94.9	23.0	51.7	94.9	23.0	51.7	91.0	72.2	79.7	94.9	28.9	55.2	94.9	23.0	51.7	94.9	25.2	53.0
09	FINISHES	117.6	32.9	70.4	115.3	32.9	69.4	112.3	48.8	76.9	115.5	33.6	69.9	114.7	32.9	69.1	114.5	65.4	87.1
COVERS	DIVS. 10 - 14, 25, 28, 41, 43, 44, 46	100.0	33.3	86.6	100.0	33.5	86.7	100.0	84.9	97.0	100.0	33.4	86.7	100.0	82.8	96.6	100.0	88.5	97.7
21, 22, 23	FIRE SUPPRESSION, PLUMBING & HVAC	95.5	74.6	87.1	95.5	67.1	84.1	100.1	77.6	91.1	100.4	33.9	73.8	95.5	35.8	71.5	100.4	61.4	84.7
26, 27, 3370	ELECTRICAL, COMMUNICATIONS & UTIL.	99.3	36.7	66.6	109.1	74.2	90.9	104.8	67.7	85.5	103.3	54.8	78.0	99.3	36.6	66.6	106.9	77.5	91.5
MF2010	WEIGHTED AVERAGE	101.0	58.6	82.5	101.9	57.9	82.7	101.7	67.6	86.9	101.8	51.6	79.9	101.0	45.1	76.7	101.8	71.0	88.4

NORTH DAKOTA / OHIO

DIVISION		WILLISTON 588			AKRON 442 - 443			ATHENS 457			CANTON 446 - 447			CHILLICOTHE 456			CINCINNATI 451 - 452		
		MAT.	INST.	TOTAL	MAT.	INST.	TOTAL	MAT.	INST.	TOTAL	MAT.	INST.	TOTAL	MAT.	INST.	TOTAL	MAT.	INST.	TOTAL
015433	CONTRACTOR EQUIPMENT		99.0	99.0		95.3	95.3		90.7	90.7		95.3	95.3		100.3	100.3		100.0	100.0
0241, 31 - 34	SITE & INFRASTRUCTURE, DEMOLITION	105.3	93.7	97.2	96.8	102.4	100.7	111.6	92.6	98.3	96.9	102.0	100.4	96.5	104.0	101.8	93.6	103.5	100.5
0310	Concrete Forming & Accessories	97.3	34.9	43.5	100.2	92.2	93.3	94.1	85.8	86.9	100.2	82.3	84.7	96.2	92.1	92.6	98.1	80.6	83.0
0320	Concrete Reinforcing	104.8	41.0	72.9	93.9	93.3	93.6	90.1	86.6	88.4	93.9	76.5	85.2	87.0	81.0	84.0	92.2	81.7	87.0
0330	Cast-in-Place Concrete	111.2	45.2	83.8	92.4	97.4	94.5	111.9	92.2	103.7	93.3	95.2	94.1	101.6	96.1	99.3	93.6	93.6	93.6
03	CONCRETE	107.3	41.0	74.6	92.9	93.5	93.2	106.4	87.6	97.2	93.4	85.3	89.4	100.8	91.3	96.1	95.3	85.5	90.4
04	MASONRY	100.0	59.2	74.7	92.1	94.1	93.3	82.7	89.5	87.0	92.8	84.6	87.7	90.1	96.7	94.2	89.8	85.5	87.1
05	METALS	95.2	64.2	85.7	94.8	82.2	90.9	101.6	78.6	94.5	94.8	75.1	88.7	93.7	84.9	91.0	95.9	84.6	92.4
06	WOOD, PLASTICS & COMPOSITES	82.2	32.8	54.3	99.1	91.4	94.7	83.4	86.8	85.3	99.5	80.8	88.9	96.0	90.6	92.9	98.5	78.5	87.2
07	THERMAL & MOISTURE PROTECTION	106.8	47.3	82.7	111.2	95.8	104.9	99.7	91.9	96.6	112.3	91.6	103.9	101.2	94.3	98.4	99.5	89.9	95.6
08	OPENINGS	96.7	30.9	81.1	115.2	92.5	109.8	99.9	83.6	96.1	108.5	77.2	101.1	91.9	84.0	90.0	99.9	78.9	94.9
0920	Plaster & Gypsum Board	106.7	30.9	55.1	102.0	90.8	94.4	93.9	86.1	88.6	103.1	79.9	87.3	96.6	90.5	92.5	98.3	78.1	84.6
0950, 0980	Ceilings & Acoustic Treatment	142.1	30.9	68.1	98.7	90.8	93.5	102.0	86.1	91.5	98.7	79.9	86.2	96.3	90.5	92.5	97.2	78.1	84.5
0960	Flooring	113.2	36.5	90.3	98.6	92.5	96.7	124.5	100.8	117.4	98.7	82.0	93.7	101.5	100.8	101.3	102.5	90.0	98.7
0970, 0990	Wall Finishes & Painting/Coating	94.9	32.2	57.2	91.7	103.9	101.2	104.9	93.1	97.8	97.1	82.8	88.5	102.2	89.8	94.7	102.2	84.8	91.7
09	FINISHES	115.6	34.0	70.1	100.1	93.3	96.4	102.9	90.1	95.8	100.4	81.8	90.0	100.4	93.7	96.6	100.8	82.2	90.4
COVERS	DIVS. 10 - 14, 25, 28, 41, 43, 44, 46	100.0	33.5	86.7	100.0	95.3	99.1	100.0	53.3	90.6	100.0	93.1	98.6	100.0	93.1	98.6	100.0	91.4	98.3
21, 22, 23	FIRE SUPPRESSION, PLUMBING & HVAC	95.5	67.1	84.1	100.0	94.3	97.7	95.2	52.4	78.0	100.0	82.5	93.0	95.6	94.0	94.9	100.0	81.3	92.5
26, 27, 3370	ELECTRICAL, COMMUNICATIONS & UTIL.	103.7	74.2	88.3	99.3	92.8	95.9	97.8	98.9	98.3	98.5	87.8	92.9	97.3	85.4	91.1	96.1	79.7	87.6
MF2010	WEIGHTED AVERAGE	100.3	58.0	81.9	99.8	93.4	97.0	99.1	80.6	91.1	99.2	85.0	93.0	96.4	92.2	94.5	97.8	84.8	92.1

OHIO

DIVISION		CLEVELAND 441			COLUMBUS 430 - 432			DAYTON 453 - 454			HAMILTON 450			LIMA 458			LORAIN 440		
		MAT.	INST.	TOTAL	MAT.	INST.	TOTAL	MAT.	INST.	TOTAL	MAT.	INST.	TOTAL	MAT.	INST.	TOTAL	MAT.	INST.	TOTAL
015433	CONTRACTOR EQUIPMENT		95.6	95.6		94.9	94.9		95.3	95.3		100.3	100.3		93.1	93.1		95.3	95.3
0241, 31 - 34	SITE & INFRASTRUCTURE, DEMOLITION	96.7	102.9	101.1	95.2	99.3	98.1	92.4	103.4	100.1	92.3	103.6	100.2	105.2	92.5	96.3	96.3	101.3	99.8
0310	Concrete Forming & Accessories	100.3	97.9	98.2	99.1	85.9	87.7	98.1	79.0	81.6	98.1	80.1	82.5	94.0	84.3	85.6	100.3	85.3	87.3
0320	Concrete Reinforcing	94.3	93.7	94.0	101.6	81.7	91.7	92.2	80.6	86.4	92.2	81.7	87.0	90.1	79.1	84.6	93.9	93.6	93.7
0330	Cast-in-Place Concrete	90.7	105.5	96.8	90.6	95.9	92.8	87.0	86.0	86.6	93.3	92.8	93.1	102.8	97.2	100.5	88.0	103.5	94.4
03	CONCRETE	92.2	99.0	95.5	95.8	88.3	92.1	92.2	81.5	86.9	95.1	85.0	90.1	99.3	87.6	93.5	90.8	92.6	91.7
04	MASONRY	96.6	105.1	101.9	97.9	94.8	96.0	89.3	81.7	84.6	89.6	84.0	86.1	112.9	81.7	93.6	88.8	98.5	94.8
05	METALS	96.3	85.2	92.9	95.9	80.5	91.2	95.2	77.8	89.8	95.2	85.1	92.1	101.6	80.4	95.1	95.4	83.3	91.6
06	WOOD, PLASTICS & COMPOSITES	98.2	94.8	96.2	97.5	83.7	89.7	99.7	77.3	87.1	98.5	78.5	87.2	83.3	84.0	83.7	99.1	82.0	89.4
07	THERMAL & MOISTURE PROTECTION	109.8	108.1	109.1	101.8	95.7	99.3	104.5	86.4	97.2	101.3	88.7	96.2	99.3	92.5	96.5	112.7	101.1	107.7
08	OPENINGS	104.5	94.3	102.1	103.0	80.4	97.7	99.3	78.0	94.2	96.9	78.9	92.6	99.9	78.3	94.8	108.5	87.4	103.5
0920	Plaster & Gypsum Board	101.2	94.3	96.5	97.6	83.2	87.8	98.3	76.8	83.7	98.3	78.1	84.6	93.9	83.2	86.6	102.0	81.2	87.8
0950, 0980	Ceilings & Acoustic Treatment	97.0	94.3	95.2	100.4	83.2	89.0	98.2	76.8	84.0	97.2	78.1	84.5	101.0	83.2	89.2	98.7	81.2	87.1
0960	Flooring	98.4	105.1	100.4	94.7	87.9	92.6	105.2	80.7	97.9	102.5	90.0	98.7	123.6	88.3	113.1	98.7	105.1	100.6
0970, 0990	Wall Finishes & Painting/Coating	97.1	105.2	102.0	100.9	93.3	96.3	102.2	85.2	92.0	102.2	84.8	91.7	104.9	83.8	92.2	97.1	105.2	102.0
09	FINISHES	99.7	99.6	99.6	97.5	86.6	91.4	101.7	79.5	89.3	100.7	81.9	90.2	101.9	84.7	92.3	100.2	90.4	94.7
COVERS	DIVS. 10 - 14, 25, 28, 41, 43, 44, 46	100.0	102.1	100.4	100.0	93.8	98.8	100.0	90.9	98.2	100.0	90.9	98.2	100.0	94.1	98.8	100.0	98.3	99.7
21, 22, 23	FIRE SUPPRESSION, PLUMBING & HVAC	100.0	99.8	99.9	100.0	92.3	96.9	100.8	81.7	93.1	100.5	80.5	92.5	95.2	84.7	91.0	100.0	85.2	94.0
26, 27, 3370	ELECTRICAL, COMMUNICATIONS & UTIL.	98.8	106.2	102.6	97.1	88.1	92.4	94.7	82.7	88.4	95.1	81.0	87.8	98.1	78.4	87.8	98.7	86.7	92.4
MF2010	WEIGHTED AVERAGE	98.9	100.0	99.4	98.6	89.7	94.7	97.5	83.2	91.3	97.4	84.5	91.8	99.6	84.4	93.0	98.8	90.4	95.2

OHIO

DIVISION		MANSFIELD 448 - 449			MARION 433			SPRINGFIELD 455			STEUBENVILLE 439			TOLEDO 434 - 436			YOUNGSTOWN 444 - 445		
		MAT.	INST.	TOTAL	MAT.	INST.	TOTAL	MAT.	INST.	TOTAL	MAT.	INST.	TOTAL	MAT.	INST.	TOTAL	MAT.	INST.	TOTAL
015433	CONTRACTOR EQUIPMENT		95.3	95.3		94.5	94.5		95.3	95.3		99.3	99.3		97.3	97.3		95.3	95.3
0241, 31 - 34	SITE & INFRASTRUCTURE, DEMOLITION	92.7	102.2	99.3	91.1	97.8	95.8	92.7	102.1	99.3	134.7	107.7	115.8	94.4	99.8	98.2	96.7	103.0	101.1
0310	Concrete Forming & Accessories	90.3	83.5	84.4	95.7	81.3	83.3	98.1	83.3	85.4	97.6	87.9	89.2	99.0	92.5	93.4	100.2	85.9	87.9
0320	Concrete Reinforcing	85.4	75.6	80.5	93.7	81.5	87.6	92.2	78.9	85.6	91.1	85.9	88.5	101.6	87.2	94.4	93.9	86.1	90.0
0330	Cast-in-Place Concrete	85.6	94.5	89.3	82.8	92.9	87.0	89.4	85.9	87.9	89.9	94.7	91.9	90.6	100.2	94.6	91.5	97.1	93.9
03	CONCRETE	85.6	85.4	85.5	88.0	85.1	86.5	93.3	83.1	88.3	91.7	89.3	90.5	95.8	93.9	94.9	92.5	89.3	90.9
04	MASONRY	91.2	93.7	92.7	100.0	92.4	95.3	89.5	81.7	84.6	86.5	93.8	91.0	106.6	96.8	100.6	92.4	91.1	91.6
05	METALS	95.6	75.5	89.4	95.0	78.1	89.8	95.1	77.0	89.5	91.6	79.9	87.9	95.7	86.9	93.0	94.8	79.3	90.0
06	WOOD, PLASTICS & COMPOSITES	86.8	82.0	84.1	93.5	81.7	86.9	101.1	83.4	91.1	89.3	86.1	87.5	97.5	91.5	94.1	99.1	84.1	90.6
07	THERMAL & MOISTURE PROTECTION	111.6	93.6	104.3	101.4	82.0	93.5	104.4	87.0	97.4	113.5	96.6	106.6	103.4	100.9	102.4	112.4	92.8	104.4
08	OPENINGS	108.8	76.7	101.2	97.1	77.6	92.5	97.4	78.6	92.9	97.5	82.9	94.0	100.4	88.8	97.6	108.5	84.2	102.7
0920	Plaster & Gypsum Board	95.2	81.2	85.7	95.4	81.2	85.7	98.3	83.2	88.0	95.5	85.1	88.4	97.6	91.2	93.2	102.0	83.3	89.3
0950, 0980	Ceilings & Acoustic Treatment	99.6	81.2	87.4	100.4	81.2	87.4	98.2	83.2	88.2	97.3	85.1	89.2	100.4	91.2	94.3	98.7	83.3	88.5
0960	Flooring	94.6	104.7	97.6	93.5	71.0	86.8	105.2	80.7	97.9	122.7	99.8	115.9	93.9	101.5	96.2	98.7	92.1	96.7
0970, 0990	Wall Finishes & Painting/Coating	97.1	88.5	91.9	100.9	48.5	69.4	102.2	85.2	92.0	114.2	102.6	107.2	100.9	102.1	101.6	97.1	92.6	94.4
09	FINISHES	98.0	87.7	92.3	96.4	76.1	85.1	101.7	83.1	91.4	114.3	91.2	101.4	97.2	94.8	95.9	100.3	87.3	93.0
COVERS	DIVS. 10 - 14, 25, 28, 41, 43, 44, 46	100.0	93.2	98.6	100.0	54.9	91.0	100.0	91.6	98.3	100.0	95.2	99.0	100.0	96.3	99.3	100.0	94.0	98.8
21, 22, 23	FIRE SUPPRESSION, PLUMBING & HVAC	95.1	83.4	90.4	95.2	89.7	93.0	100.8	81.7	93.1	95.5	91.9	94.0	100.1	99.2	99.7	100.0	88.4	95.3
26, 27, 3370	ELECTRICAL, COMMUNICATIONS & UTIL.	96.2	77.7	86.5	91.2	77.7	84.1	94.7	85.6	90.0	86.4	112.7	100.1	97.2	101.6	99.5	98.7	82.9	90.5
MF2010	WEIGHTED AVERAGE	96.6	85.6	91.8	95.0	83.7	90.1	97.5	84.2	91.7	96.8	94.5	95.8	98.7	96.4	97.7	99.1	88.3	94.4

		OHIO			OKLAHOMA														
DIVISION		ZANESVILLE			ARDMORE			CLINTON			DURANT			ENID			GUYMON		
		437 - 438			734			736			747			737			739		
		MAT.	INST.	TOTAL	MAT.	INST.	TOTAL	MAT.	INST.	TOTAL	MAT.	INST.	TOTAL	MAT.	INST.	TOTAL	MAT.	INST.	TOTAL
015433	CONTRACTOR EQUIPMENT		94.5	94.5		82.5	82.5		81.6	81.6		81.6	81.6		81.6	81.6		81.6	81.6
0241, 31 - 34	SITE & INFRASTRUCTURE, DEMOLITION	93.9	99.5	97.9	94.7	91.4	92.4	96.1	90.0	91.8	92.5	89.7	90.6	97.6	90.0	92.2	99.9	89.7	92.7
0310	Concrete Forming & Accessories	92.8	82.6	84.0	94.4	41.3	48.6	92.9	47.7	53.9	85.7	45.1	50.6	96.6	34.8	43.3	100.3	45.9	53.3
0320	Concrete Reinforcing	93.1	85.3	89.2	87.6	80.2	83.9	88.1	80.2	84.2	92.3	80.6	86.4	87.5	80.2	83.9	88.1	80.2	84.1
0330	Cast-in-Place Concrete	87.2	93.3	89.8	99.3	44.2	76.4	95.9	45.9	75.2	92.1	43.5	71.9	95.9	47.2	75.7	96.0	43.9	74.3
03	CONCRETE	91.5	86.5	89.0	97.5	50.0	74.1	97.1	53.5	75.6	92.9	51.5	72.5	97.7	48.2	73.3	100.7	51.9	76.7
04	MASONRY	96.8	83.4	88.5	93.4	58.1	71.5	118.8	58.1	81.2	92.4	63.4	74.5	100.6	58.1	74.3	95.9	54.6	70.3
05	METALS	96.4	80.3	91.4	93.3	70.6	86.3	93.4	70.6	86.4	91.4	71.3	85.2	94.8	70.5	87.3	93.9	70.3	86.6
06	WOOD, PLASTICS & COMPOSITES	89.6	81.7	85.2	100.7	38.7	65.7	99.7	47.3	70.1	89.5	44.0	63.8	103.6	30.0	62.0	107.5	47.0	73.4
07	THERMAL & MOISTURE PROTECTION	101.5	91.1	97.3	106.1	61.0	87.8	106.1	62.0	88.2	99.9	62.3	84.6	106.2	60.3	87.6	106.5	58.4	87.0
08	OPENINGS	97.1	80.2	93.1	93.9	49.6	83.4	93.9	54.0	84.4	93.9	52.7	84.1	93.9	44.4	82.1	94.0	49.8	83.5
0920	Plaster & Gypsum Board	92.8	81.2	84.9	84.3	37.5	52.4	84.0	46.3	58.3	79.1	42.9	54.5	85.1	28.4	46.5	85.7	46.0	58.7
0950, 0980	Ceilings & Acoustic Treatment	100.4	81.2	87.6	86.2	37.5	53.8	86.2	46.3	59.7	85.4	42.9	57.1	86.2	28.4	47.8	88.9	46.0	60.4
0960	Flooring	92.0	86.9	90.5	110.5	43.9	90.6	109.4	41.9	89.2	106.9	63.1	93.8	111.2	41.9	90.5	112.9	24.8	86.5
0970, 0990	Wall Finishes & Painting/Coating	100.9	76.0	85.9	96.5	52.4	70.0	96.5	52.4	70.0	100.1	52.4	71.4	96.5	52.4	70.0	96.5	33.8	58.8
09	FINISHES	95.9	82.2	88.3	93.8	41.0	64.4	93.6	45.8	67.0	91.8	47.7	67.2	94.3	35.4	61.5	95.8	39.7	64.6
COVERS	DIVS. 10 - 14, 25, 28, 41, 43, 44, 46	100.0	90.0	98.0	100.0	78.0	95.6	100.0	79.0	95.8	100.0	78.3	95.7	100.0	77.1	95.4	100.0	77.8	95.5
21, 22, 23	FIRE SUPPRESSION, PLUMBING & HVAC	95.2	89.7	93.0	95.4	66.3	83.7	95.4	66.3	83.7	95.4	65.8	83.5	100.3	66.3	86.6	95.4	64.2	82.9
26, 27, 3370	ELECTRICAL, COMMUNICATIONS & UTIL.	91.5	78.2	84.6	89.7	70.4	79.6	90.7	70.4	80.1	94.7	70.4	82.0	90.7	70.4	80.1	92.3	63.0	77.0
MF2010	WEIGHTED AVERAGE	95.5	85.6	91.2	95.2	62.3	80.9	96.5	63.6	82.2	94.3	64.0	81.1	97.2	60.9	81.4	96.3	60.5	80.7

		OKLAHOMA																	
DIVISION		LAWTON			MCALESTER			MIAMI			MUSKOGEE			OKLAHOMA CITY			PONCA CITY		
		735			745			743			744			730 - 731			746		
		MAT.	INST.	TOTAL	MAT.	INST.	TOTAL	MAT.	INST.	TOTAL	MAT.	INST.	TOTAL	MAT.	INST.	TOTAL	MAT.	INST.	TOTAL
015433	CONTRACTOR EQUIPMENT		82.5	82.5		81.6	81.6		89.7	89.7		89.7	89.7		82.7	82.7		81.6	81.6
0241, 31 - 34	SITE & INFRASTRUCTURE, DEMOLITION	94.3	91.4	92.2	86.3	89.9	88.9	87.8	87.2	87.4	88.0	87.0	87.3	93.7	91.8	92.3	93.0	89.9	90.8
0310	Concrete Forming & Accessories	100.2	45.3	52.8	83.6	44.6	49.9	96.8	67.7	71.7	101.3	34.1	43.3	98.2	55.5	61.3	92.2	47.3	53.4
0320	Concrete Reinforcing	87.7	80.2	84.0	91.9	80.2	86.1	90.5	80.3	85.4	91.3	79.7	85.5	92.8	80.2	86.5	91.3	80.3	85.8
0330	Cast-in-Place Concrete	92.8	47.3	73.9	80.8	46.0	66.3	84.6	48.3	69.6	85.7	46.6	69.4	94.5	47.7	75.1	94.6	45.5	74.2
03	CONCRETE	93.8	52.9	73.6	83.4	52.1	68.0	88.2	64.0	76.2	90.0	48.3	69.4	97.3	57.5	77.7	95.0	53.1	74.3
04	MASONRY	95.9	58.1	72.5	110.7	57.1	77.5	95.2	57.2	71.7	113.0	46.0	71.5	98.7	57.4	73.1	87.8	57.1	68.8
05	METALS	98.5	70.6	89.9	91.3	70.5	84.9	91.3	82.8	88.6	92.7	81.0	89.1	92.0	70.7	85.4	91.3	70.8	84.9
06	WOOD, PLASTICS & COMPOSITES	106.4	44.1	71.3	86.9	44.0	62.7	102.4	74.6	86.7	107.0	31.4	64.3	100.3	58.2	76.5	97.6	47.0	69.1
07	THERMAL & MOISTURE PROTECTION	106.1	61.7	88.1	99.6	61.0	83.9	99.9	64.9	85.7	100.0	49.5	79.5	98.8	62.8	84.2	100.1	66.7	86.5
08	OPENINGS	95.4	52.1	85.1	93.9	52.5	84.1	93.9	69.3	88.1	93.9	42.8	81.8	94.8	59.7	86.5	93.9	53.8	84.4
0920	Plaster & Gypsum Board	87.1	43.0	57.1	77.9	42.9	54.1	85.0	74.3	77.7	87.2	29.7	48.1	92.9	57.5	68.8	83.5	46.0	58.0
0950, 0980	Ceilings & Acoustic Treatment	94.2	43.0	60.1	85.4	42.9	57.1	85.4	74.3	78.0	94.3	29.7	51.3	97.5	57.5	70.9	85.4	46.0	59.2
0960	Flooring	113.1	41.9	91.8	105.8	41.9	86.7	112.8	63.1	97.9	115.3	40.5	92.9	109.5	41.9	89.3	109.9	41.9	89.6
0970, 0990	Wall Finishes & Painting/Coating	96.5	52.4	70.0	100.1	38.6	63.1	100.1	79.1	87.5	100.1	34.9	60.9	97.9	52.4	70.6	100.1	52.4	71.4
09	FINISHES	96.4	43.8	67.1	90.8	42.0	63.6	93.7	68.8	79.8	96.7	33.7	61.6	98.6	52.0	72.6	93.4	45.3	66.6
COVERS	DIVS. 10 - 14, 25, 28, 41, 43, 44, 46	100.0	78.6	95.7	100.0	78.3	95.6	100.0	82.1	96.4	100.0	76.5	95.3	100.0	80.0	96.0	100.0	78.6	95.7
21, 22, 23	FIRE SUPPRESSION, PLUMBING & HVAC	100.3	66.3	86.7	95.4	61.5	81.8	95.4	61.8	81.9	100.3	60.5	84.3	100.0	66.0	86.4	95.4	61.7	81.9
26, 27, 3370	ELECTRICAL, COMMUNICATIONS & UTIL.	92.3	70.4	80.9	93.1	66.1	79.0	94.6	66.1	79.7	92.7	53.7	72.3	97.3	70.4	83.3	92.7	70.0	80.8
MF2010	WEIGHTED AVERAGE	97.5	63.3	82.6	93.7	61.1	79.5	94.0	68.3	82.8	96.6	56.3	79.0	97.3	65.4	83.4	94.3	62.5	80.5

		OKLAHOMA												OREGON					
DIVISION		POTEAU			SHAWNEE			TULSA			WOODWARD			BEND			EUGENE		
		749			748			740 - 741			738			977			974		
		MAT.	INST.	TOTAL	MAT.	INST.	TOTAL	MAT.	INST.	TOTAL	MAT.	INST.	TOTAL	MAT.	INST.	TOTAL	MAT.	INST.	TOTAL
015433	CONTRACTOR EQUIPMENT		89.0	89.0		81.6	81.6		89.7	89.7		81.6	81.6		97.9	97.9		97.9	97.9
0241, 31 - 34	SITE & INFRASTRUCTURE, DEMOLITION	74.3	85.9	82.4	96.0	89.9	91.7	94.2	87.4	89.4	96.3	90.0	91.9	106.8	102.8	103.9	96.9	102.7	101.0
0310	Concrete Forming & Accessories	90.0	41.9	48.5	85.5	44.7	50.3	101.4	41.1	49.4	93.1	47.8	54.0	111.2	100.6	102.0	107.6	100.4	101.4
0320	Concrete Reinforcing	92.4	80.3	86.3	91.3	80.2	85.8	91.6	80.2	85.9	87.5	80.3	83.9	95.7	101.5	98.6	99.7	101.5	100.6
0330	Cast-in-Place Concrete	84.6	45.7	68.5	97.6	43.7	75.2	93.3	47.0	74.1	95.9	46.1	75.2	94.2	104.1	98.3	91.2	104.0	96.5
03	CONCRETE	90.6	51.6	71.3	96.6	51.4	74.3	95.3	51.7	73.8	97.4	53.6	75.8	104.8	101.6	103.2	96.3	101.5	98.9
04	MASONRY	95.5	57.2	71.8	111.9	57.1	78.0	96.1	61.0	74.4	89.5	58.1	70.1	98.7	104.5	102.3	96.0	104.5	101.3
05	METALS	91.3	82.4	88.5	91.2	70.4	84.8	95.9	82.0	91.6	93.5	71.0	86.5	90.7	96.6	92.5	91.4	96.4	93.0
06	WOOD, PLASTICS & COMPOSITES	94.3	40.0	63.7	89.3	44.0	63.7	106.2	37.5	67.4	99.8	47.0	70.0	103.3	100.3	101.6	98.8	100.3	99.6
07	THERMAL & MOISTURE PROTECTION	100.0	61.0	84.2	100.0	60.3	83.9	100.0	62.6	84.8	106.2	67.1	90.3	104.6	96.3	101.2	103.9	93.4	99.6
08	OPENINGS	93.9	50.5	83.6	93.9	52.5	84.1	95.4	48.1	84.2	93.9	53.8	84.4	93.8	103.8	96.2	94.2	103.8	96.5
0920	Plaster & Gypsum Board	82.0	38.7	52.5	79.1	42.9	54.5	87.2	36.0	52.4	84.6	46.0	58.4	103.7	100.2	101.3	101.1	100.2	100.5
0950, 0980	Ceilings & Acoustic Treatment	85.4	38.7	54.3	85.4	42.9	57.1	94.3	36.0	55.5	88.9	46.0	60.4	92.3	100.2	97.5	93.3	100.2	97.9
0960	Flooring	109.3	63.1	95.4	106.9	33.3	84.9	114.0	43.6	92.9	109.4	43.9	89.8	107.6	105.3	106.9	106.1	105.3	105.9
0970, 0990	Wall Finishes & Painting/Coating	100.1	52.4	71.4	100.1	34.9	60.9	100.1	41.4	64.8	96.5	52.4	70.0	104.6	72.3	85.2	104.6	72.3	85.2
09	FINISHES	91.5	45.3	65.8	92.1	40.1	63.1	96.5	39.7	64.9	94.4	45.9	67.4	103.3	98.1	100.4	101.7	98.1	99.7
COVERS	DIVS. 10 - 14, 25, 28, 41, 43, 44, 46	100.0	78.1	95.6	100.0	78.3	95.7	100.0	79.3	95.8	100.0	79.0	95.8	100.0	101.9	100.4	100.0	101.9	100.4
21, 22, 23	FIRE SUPPRESSION, PLUMBING & HVAC	95.4	61.7	81.9	95.4	65.8	83.5	100.3	63.5	85.5	95.4	66.3	83.7	95.1	102.6	98.1	100.0	102.6	101.0
26, 27, 3370	ELECTRICAL, COMMUNICATIONS & UTIL.	92.8	66.1	78.9	94.8	70.4	82.1	94.7	66.1	79.8	92.2	70.4	80.8	95.8	96.3	96.1	94.5	96.3	95.4
MF2010	WEIGHTED AVERAGE	93.5	62.1	79.8	95.7	62.2	81.1	97.4	62.2	82.1	95.3	63.8	81.6	97.3	100.5	98.7	97.1	100.4	98.5

OREGON

DIVISION		KLAMATH FALLS 976			MEDFORD 975			PENDLETON 978			PORTLAND 970 - 972			SALEM 973			VALE 979		
		MAT.	INST.	TOTAL	MAT.	INST.	TOTAL	MAT.	INST.	TOTAL	MAT.	INST.	TOTAL	MAT.	INST.	TOTAL	MAT.	INST.	TOTAL
015433	CONTRACTOR EQUIPMENT		97.9	97.9		97.9	97.9		95.4	95.4		97.9	97.9		97.9	97.9		95.4	95.4
0241, 31 - 34	SITE & INFRASTRUCTURE, DEMOLITION	110.8	102.7	105.1	104.5	102.7	103.3	103.2	96.4	98.4	99.4	102.8	101.7	92.9	102.8	99.8	91.4	96.3	94.9
0310	Concrete Forming & Accessories	104.1	100.3	100.9	103.2	100.3	100.7	104.4	100.7	101.2	108.8	100.6	101.7	107.1	100.6	101.5	110.9	99.7	101.2
0320	Concrete Reinforcing	95.7	101.5	98.6	97.3	101.5	99.4	95.1	101.5	98.3	100.5	101.5	101.0	106.1	101.5	103.8	92.7	101.4	97.0
0330	Cast-in-Place Concrete	94.2	104.0	98.3	94.2	104.0	98.3	95.0	105.4	99.3	93.7	104.1	98.0	88.4	104.1	94.9	74.9	105.0	87.4
03	CONCRETE	107.6	101.5	104.6	102.2	101.5	101.8	88.4	102.1	95.2	97.7	101.6	99.7	96.0	101.6	98.8	74.7	101.5	88.0
04	MASONRY	110.8	104.5	106.9	93.1	104.5	100.2	101.7	104.6	103.5	96.5	104.5	101.5	103.3	104.5	104.1	100.2	104.6	102.9
05	METALS	90.7	96.3	92.5	91.0	96.3	92.6	97.1	97.1	97.1	92.4	96.6	93.7	97.8	96.6	97.4	97.0	96.0	96.7
06	WOOD, PLASTICS & COMPOSITES	93.8	100.3	97.5	92.6	100.3	97.0	95.9	100.4	98.4	99.8	100.3	100.1	96.7	100.3	98.7	104.8	100.4	102.3
07	THERMAL & MOISTURE PROTECTION	104.7	94.8	100.7	104.4	94.8	100.5	97.4	95.4	96.6	103.8	98.1	101.5	101.7	96.3	99.5	96.9	94.8	96.1
08	OPENINGS	93.9	103.8	96.2	96.3	103.8	98.1	89.5	103.9	92.9	92.2	103.8	95.0	95.9	103.8	97.8	89.4	95.8	90.9
0920	Plaster & Gypsum Board	98.2	100.2	99.6	97.5	100.2	99.3	85.2	100.2	95.4	100.9	100.2	100.4	97.3	100.2	99.3	91.9	100.2	97.5
0950, 0980	Ceilings & Acoustic Treatment	100.3	100.2	100.2	107.3	100.2	102.6	64.6	100.2	88.3	95.3	100.2	98.5	100.7	100.2	100.4	64.6	100.2	88.3
0960	Flooring	105.0	105.3	105.1	104.4	105.3	104.7	72.5	105.3	82.3	103.6	105.3	104.1	104.3	105.3	104.6	74.2	105.3	83.5
0970, 0990	Wall Finishes & Painting/Coating	104.6	59.4	77.4	104.6	59.4	77.4	96.1	66.9	78.5	104.3	66.9	81.8	102.8	72.3	84.5	96.1	72.3	81.8
09	FINISHES	104.0	96.7	99.9	104.4	96.7	100.1	71.8	97.6	86.2	101.4	97.5	99.2	100.5	98.1	99.2	72.3	98.2	86.7
COVERS	DIVS. 10 - 14, 25, 28, 41, 43, 44, 46	100.0	101.8	100.4	100.0	101.8	100.4	100.0	92.2	98.4	100.0	101.9	100.4	100.0	101.9	100.4	100.0	102.1	100.4
21, 22, 23	FIRE SUPPRESSION, PLUMBING & HVAC	95.1	102.6	98.1	100.0	102.6	101.0	96.9	115.3	104.3	100.0	102.6	101.0	100.0	102.6	101.1	96.9	71.5	86.7
26, 27, 3370	ELECTRICAL, COMMUNICATIONS & UTIL.	94.6	81.3	87.6	97.9	81.3	89.2	87.3	96.5	92.1	94.7	103.2	99.1	102.1	96.3	99.1	87.3	73.9	80.3
MF2010	WEIGHTED AVERAGE	98.2	98.2	98.2	98.4	98.2	98.3	93.1	102.5	97.2	97.2	101.4	99.1	99.0	100.5	99.7	91.3	89.8	90.7

PENNSYLVANIA

DIVISION		ALLENTOWN 181			ALTOONA 166			BEDFORD 155			BRADFORD 167			BUTLER 160			CHAMBERSBURG 172		
		MAT.	INST.	TOTAL	MAT.	INST.	TOTAL	MAT.	INST.	TOTAL	MAT.	INST.	TOTAL	MAT.	INST.	TOTAL	MAT.	INST.	TOTAL
015433	CONTRACTOR EQUIPMENT		113.5	113.5		113.5	113.5		110.5	110.5		113.5	113.5		113.5	113.5		112.7	112.7
0241, 31 - 34	SITE & INFRASTRUCTURE, DEMOLITION	90.7	105.4	101.0	94.2	105.5	102.1	103.7	102.2	102.7	89.5	104.8	100.3	85.7	106.9	100.6	85.1	102.7	97.4
0310	Concrete Forming & Accessories	100.5	114.2	112.3	85.7	80.4	81.1	85.2	82.7	83.0	87.9	82.5	83.2	87.2	95.7	94.5	89.5	81.8	82.9
0320	Concrete Reinforcing	94.4	111.5	103.0	91.5	106.0	98.7	89.7	83.5	86.6	93.5	106.4	99.9	92.2	112.5	102.3	88.7	106.3	97.5
0330	Cast-in-Place Concrete	85.0	101.5	91.8	94.7	87.5	91.7	109.6	71.2	93.6	90.4	92.9	91.5	83.7	98.1	89.6	94.9	71.0	85.0
03	CONCRETE	94.3	110.0	102.1	89.5	89.1	89.3	103.4	80.2	91.9	96.0	92.0	94.0	81.7	100.8	91.1	103.3	84.1	93.8
04	MASONRY	94.2	102.2	99.2	96.9	65.6	77.5	114.6	88.5	98.5	94.0	88.5	90.6	98.9	98.5	98.7	94.7	88.9	91.1
05	METALS	99.9	123.1	107.0	93.7	118.3	101.3	97.5	105.6	100.0	97.8	118.2	104.1	93.4	123.4	102.7	99.5	116.5	104.7
06	WOOD, PLASTICS & COMPOSITES	103.0	117.3	111.1	81.2	82.7	82.0	83.7	82.6	83.1	87.6	80.3	83.5	82.6	94.8	89.5	92.5	82.7	87.0
07	THERMAL & MOISTURE PROTECTION	102.5	120.4	109.7	101.8	92.0	97.8	104.0	88.6	97.8	102.4	92.3	98.3	101.5	100.5	101.1	102.8	74.0	91.1
08	OPENINGS	92.5	116.3	98.1	86.4	90.1	87.3	92.1	83.6	90.1	92.6	92.3	92.5	86.4	105.7	91.0	89.7	84.8	88.6
0920	Plaster & Gypsum Board	99.7	117.6	111.8	91.1	81.9	84.8	91.6	81.9	85.0	91.9	79.4	83.4	91.1	94.4	93.3	99.4	81.9	87.5
0950, 0980	Ceilings & Acoustic Treatment	85.7	117.6	106.9	90.1	81.9	84.6	95.7	81.9	86.5	88.4	79.4	82.4	91.1	94.4	93.3	90.3	81.9	84.7
0960	Flooring	93.6	97.6	94.8	87.4	99.3	91.0	96.9	89.8	94.7	88.5	105.8	93.6	88.2	82.5	86.5	93.7	47.0	79.7
0970, 0990	Wall Finishes & Painting/Coating	98.3	72.1	82.5	94.6	108.9	103.2	104.7	83.3	91.9	98.3	92.6	94.9	94.6	108.9	103.2	101.9	83.3	90.7
09	FINISHES	93.8	107.1	101.2	92.2	85.9	88.7	98.3	82.6	89.6	91.9	85.7	88.5	92.1	93.5	92.9	93.9	75.4	83.6
COVERS	DIVS. 10 - 14, 25, 28, 41, 43, 44, 46	100.0	104.5	100.9	100.0	95.3	99.1	100.0	98.6	99.7	100.0	99.3	99.9	100.0	102.3	100.5	100.0	95.2	99.0
21, 22, 23	FIRE SUPPRESSION, PLUMBING & HVAC	100.2	110.6	104.4	99.8	84.3	93.6	95.0	89.1	92.7	95.4	90.9	93.6	95.0	93.9	94.5	95.4	89.0	92.8
26, 27, 3370	ELECTRICAL, COMMUNICATIONS & UTIL.	98.2	98.9	98.6	88.3	111.1	100.2	93.7	111.1	102.8	91.7	111.1	101.8	88.9	110.1	100.0	89.4	88.3	88.9
MF2010	WEIGHTED AVERAGE	97.6	108.8	102.4	94.3	92.7	93.6	98.0	92.6	95.7	95.3	96.8	96.0	92.1	102.2	96.5	96.0	89.7	93.2

PENNSYLVANIA

DIVISION		DOYLESTOWN 189			DUBOIS 158			ERIE 164 - 165			GREENSBURG 156			HARRISBURG 170 - 171			HAZLETON 182		
		MAT.	INST.	TOTAL	MAT.	INST.	TOTAL	MAT.	INST.	TOTAL	MAT.	INST.	TOTAL	MAT.	INST.	TOTAL	MAT.	INST.	TOTAL
015433	CONTRACTOR EQUIPMENT		94.6	94.6		110.5	110.5		113.5	113.5		113.5	113.5		110.5	110.5		112.7	112.7		113.5	113.5
0241, 31 - 34	SITE & INFRASTRUCTURE, DEMOLITION	103.5	91.4	95.1	108.7	102.5	104.4	91.1	105.9	101.5	99.8	104.7	103.2	85.2	104.5	98.7	84.1	105.7	99.3
0310	Concrete Forming & Accessories	84.7	129.1	123.0	84.7	83.9	84.0	99.9	88.3	89.9	91.5	95.5	95.1	99.8	89.4	90.8	82.3	90.2	89.1
0320	Concrete Reinforcing	91.3	135.0	113.1	89.1	106.7	97.9	93.5	106.5	100.0	89.1	112.5	100.8	98.1	106.7	102.4	91.7	110.5	101.0
0330	Cast-in-Place Concrete	80.3	87.6	83.4	105.7	93.5	100.6	93.1	82.6	88.7	101.7	97.5	100.0	97.1	96.8	97.0	80.3	92.7	85.5
03	CONCRETE	90.0	115.6	102.6	104.8	92.8	98.9	88.6	90.0	89.7	98.4	100.5	99.4	99.2	96.5	97.9	87.0	96.1	91.5
04	MASONRY	97.2	127.9	116.2	114.6	89.6	99.2	86.7	92.8	90.5	125.3	98.5	108.7	95.0	90.6	92.3	106.2	96.5	100.2
05	METALS	97.4	125.6	106.1	97.5	117.6	103.7	93.9	117.0	101.0	97.5	121.9	105.0	106.1	120.3	110.5	99.6	121.4	106.3
06	WOOD, PLASTICS & COMPOSITES	83.1	131.5	110.4	82.6	82.4	82.5	99.2	86.7	92.1	90.5	94.7	92.9	100.1	88.7	93.7	81.6	88.6	85.6
07	THERMAL & MOISTURE PROTECTION	100.6	132.8	113.7	104.3	95.5	100.7	102.3	93.4	98.7	103.9	100.1	102.4	106.2	112.2	108.6	102.0	107.6	104.2
08	OPENINGS	94.7	140.0	105.4	92.1	93.5	92.4	86.6	93.0	88.1	92.1	105.7	95.3	95.8	95.4	95.7	93.0	94.5	93.4
0920	Plaster & Gypsum Board	89.6	132.2	118.6	90.5	81.7	84.5	99.7	86.0	90.4	92.9	94.4	93.9	103.4	88.1	93.0	90.0	88.0	88.7
0950, 0980	Ceilings & Acoustic Treatment	84.9	132.2	116.4	95.7	81.7	86.4	85.7	86.0	85.9	94.8	94.4	94.5	99.4	88.1	91.9	86.7	88.0	87.6
0960	Flooring	78.6	136.8	96.0	96.7	105.8	99.4	92.3	93.5	92.7	99.8	69.3	90.7	98.7	93.4	97.1	86.2	96.3	89.2
0970, 0990	Wall Finishes & Painting/Coating	97.8	70.5	81.4	104.7	108.9	107.2	103.3	92.6	96.9	104.7	108.9	107.2	102.3	91.5	95.8	98.3	105.6	102.7
09	FINISHES	85.1	123.5	106.5	98.6	89.3	93.4	94.3	89.2	91.5	98.7	91.9	94.9	98.8	89.9	93.8	90.2	91.0	90.6
COVERS	DIVS. 10 - 14, 25, 28, 41, 43, 44, 46	100.0	71.9	94.4	100.0	98.6	99.7	100.0	100.9	100.2	100.0	102.1	100.4	100.0	96.4	99.3	100.0	99.1	99.8
21, 22, 23	FIRE SUPPRESSION, PLUMBING & HVAC	95.0	125.4	107.2	95.0	89.5	92.8	99.8	93.1	97.1	95.0	92.8	94.1	100.0	90.7	96.3	95.4	98.8	96.7
26, 27, 3370	ELECTRICAL, COMMUNICATIONS & UTIL.	91.1	126.9	109.8	94.3	111.1	103.1	90.1	87.4	88.7	94.3	111.1	103.1	96.8	88.4	92.4	92.6	91.5	92.0
MF2010	WEIGHTED AVERAGE	94.6	120.8	106.0	98.4	97.1	97.8	94.1	95.0	94.5	98.0	101.6	99.5	99.6	95.9	98.0	95.0	98.8	96.7

PENNSYLVANIA

DIVISION		INDIANA 157			JOHNSTOWN 159			KITTANNING 162			LANCASTER 175 - 176			LEHIGH VALLEY 180			MONTROSE 188		
		MAT.	INST.	TOTAL	MAT.	INST.	TOTAL	MAT.	INST.	TOTAL	MAT.	INST.	TOTAL	MAT.	INST.	TOTAL	MAT.	INST.	TOTAL
015433	CONTRACTOR EQUIPMENT		110.5	110.5		110.5	110.5		113.5	113.5		112.7	112.7		113.5	113.5		113.5	113.5
0241, 31 - 34	SITE & INFRASTRUCTURE, DEMOLITION	97.9	103.3	101.7	104.2	103.9	104.0	88.2	106.8	101.3	77.7	104.4	96.5	87.9	105.1	99.9	86.6	103.4	98.4
0310	Concrete Forming & Accessories	85.8	86.3	86.2	84.7	84.2	84.3	87.2	95.8	94.6	91.6	88.9	89.3	94.2	113.6	110.9	83.3	88.5	87.8
0320	Concrete Reinforcing	88.4	112.6	100.5	89.7	112.2	100.9	92.2	112.6	102.4	88.4	106.6	97.5	91.7	111.4	101.5	96.0	108.4	102.2
0330	Cast-in-Place Concrete	99.7	97.3	98.7	110.6	92.9	103.2	86.9	98.0	91.5	80.8	97.7	87.8	86.9	100.9	92.7	85.2	90.9	87.6
03	CONCRETE	95.9	96.3	96.1	104.2	93.7	99.0	84.1	100.8	92.4	90.9	96.5	93.7	93.3	109.4	101.2	92.0	94.1	93.1
04	MASONRY	110.3	100.2	104.1	111.1	88.0	96.8	101.7	100.2	100.8	99.9	90.8	94.3	94.2	101.7	98.8	94.1	96.0	95.3
05	METALS	97.6	121.5	105.0	97.5	120.1	104.5	93.5	123.4	102.7	99.5	119.7	105.7	99.5	121.7	106.4	97.9	115.3	103.2
06	WOOD, PLASTICS & COMPOSITES	84.5	82.4	83.3	82.6	82.6	82.6	82.6	94.8	89.5	95.2	88.7	91.5	94.4	117.3	107.3	82.4	88.3	85.8
07	THERMAL & MOISTURE PROTECTION	103.8	97.9	101.4	104.0	93.7	99.8	101.6	100.9	101.3	102.4	98.5	100.8	102.3	103.6	102.8	102.0	92.4	98.1
08	OPENINGS	92.1	95.2	92.8	92.1	91.8	92.0	86.4	102.0	90.1	89.7	99.3	92.0	93.0	116.3	98.5	89.8	93.8	90.8
0920	Plaster & Gypsum Board	92.0	81.7	85.0	90.3	81.9	84.6	91.1	94.4	93.3	101.3	88.1	92.3	93.0	117.6	109.7	90.4	87.7	88.6
0950, 0980	Ceilings & Acoustic Treatment	95.7	81.7	86.4	94.8	81.9	86.2	91.1	94.4	93.3	90.3	88.1	88.8	86.7	117.6	107.2	88.4	87.7	88.0
0960	Flooring	97.4	105.8	99.9	96.7	100.0	97.7	88.2	105.8	93.5	94.5	93.4	94.2	90.9	97.6	92.9	86.7	58.9	78.4
0970, 0990	Wall Finishes & Painting/Coating	104.7	108.9	107.2	104.7	108.9	107.2	94.6	108.9	103.2	101.9	58.4	75.7	98.3	67.9	80.0	98.3	105.6	102.7
09	FINISHES	98.0	90.2	93.7	97.9	88.7	92.8	92.3	97.5	95.2	93.9	86.2	89.6	92.2	105.5	99.6	91.0	84.8	87.5
COVERS	DIVS. 10 - 14, 25, 28, 41, 43, 44, 46	100.0	100.7	100.1	100.0	98.8	99.8	100.0	102.3	100.5	100.0	96.3	99.3	100.0	104.1	100.8	100.0	99.1	99.8
21, 22, 23	FIRE SUPPRESSION, PLUMBING & HVAC	95.0	92.7	94.1	95.0	89.8	92.9	95.0	96.1	95.4	95.4	90.8	93.5	95.4	110.3	101.4	95.4	98.0	96.4
26, 27, 3370	ELECTRICAL, COMMUNICATIONS & UTIL.	94.3	111.1	103.1	94.3	111.1	103.1	88.3	111.1	100.2	90.9	45.1	67.0	92.6	133.5	113.9	91.7	97.2	94.5
MF2010	WEIGHTED AVERAGE	96.9	100.1	98.3	97.9	97.3	97.7	92.5	103.4	97.3	94.8	89.3	92.4	95.4	112.5	102.9	94.4	97.1	95.6

PENNSYLVANIA

DIVISION		NEW CASTLE 161			NORRISTOWN 194			OIL CITY 163			PHILADELPHIA 190 - 191			PITTSBURGH 150 - 152			POTTSVILLE 179		
		MAT.	INST.	TOTAL	MAT.	INST.	TOTAL	MAT.	INST.	TOTAL	MAT.	INST.	TOTAL	MAT.	INST.	TOTAL	MAT.	INST.	TOTAL
015433	CONTRACTOR EQUIPMENT		113.5	113.5		98.0	98.0		113.5	113.5		97.5	97.5		111.8	111.8		112.7	112.7
0241, 31 - 34	SITE & INFRASTRUCTURE, DEMOLITION	86.1	106.9	100.7	92.4	99.8	97.6	84.7	105.0	99.0	99.9	99.2	99.4	103.4	106.7	105.7	80.4	104.6	97.4
0310	Concrete Forming & Accessories	87.2	97.4	96.0	83.5	130.8	124.3	87.2	83.5	84.0	98.7	139.9	134.3	99.0	98.7	98.7	83.2	90.0	89.1
0320	Concrete Reinforcing	91.0	93.3	92.2	92.5	142.2	117.3	92.2	93.1	92.6	100.5	142.2	121.3	90.1	112.9	101.5	87.7	103.8	95.7
0330	Cast-in-Place Concrete	84.4	96.9	89.6	79.7	127.5	99.6	82.0	96.5	88.1	94.8	131.7	110.1	105.7	97.7	102.4	86.0	97.9	91.0
03	CONCRETE	82.0	97.6	89.7	86.9	131.4	108.9	80.5	91.2	85.7	98.2	136.9	117.3	101.7	102.0	101.9	94.6	96.6	95.6
04	MASONRY	98.1	98.5	98.4	106.5	125.7	118.4	98.2	95.2	96.3	95.5	130.2	117.0	103.3	103.3	103.3	94.5	92.9	93.5
05	METALS	93.5	114.0	99.8	99.4	130.9	109.1	93.5	112.1	99.2	100.7	131.2	110.1	98.9	122.9	106.3	99.7	118.9	105.6
06	WOOD, PLASTICS & COMPOSITES	82.6	98.1	91.4	81.5	131.4	109.7	82.6	80.3	81.3	97.2	141.5	122.2	100.5	98.0	99.1	84.9	88.6	87.0
07	THERMAL & MOISTURE PROTECTION	101.5	97.0	99.7	103.9	132.6	115.6	101.4	94.9	98.8	102.7	135.7	116.1	104.1	102.0	103.3	102.5	107.1	104.3
08	OPENINGS	86.4	98.0	89.2	88.6	142.0	101.2	86.4	80.7	85.1	94.4	147.5	106.9	95.5	107.5	98.3	89.8	92.5	90.4
0920	Plaster & Gypsum Board	91.1	97.8	95.7	88.2	132.2	118.1	91.1	79.4	83.2	97.2	142.6	128.1	99.8	97.8	98.5	95.7	88.0	90.5
0950, 0980	Ceilings & Acoustic Treatment	91.1	97.8	95.6	90.5	132.2	118.3	91.1	79.4	83.3	91.6	142.6	125.6	95.7	97.8	97.1	90.3	88.0	88.8
0960	Flooring	88.2	58.5	79.4	91.6	139.5	105.9	88.2	105.8	93.5	98.5	139.5	110.7	102.8	108.0	104.3	91.1	93.4	91.8
0970, 0990	Wall Finishes & Painting/Coating	94.6	108.9	103.2	100.8	147.4	128.8	94.6	108.9	103.2	105.9	154.0	134.8	104.7	121.2	114.6	101.9	105.6	104.1
09	FINISHES	92.1	91.2	91.6	92.9	133.9	115.7	92.0	88.3	89.9	98.2	141.6	122.4	100.9	102.1	101.6	92.4	91.9	92.1
COVERS	DIVS. 10 - 14, 25, 28, 41, 43, 44, 46	100.0	102.6	100.5	100.0	111.7	102.3	100.0	100.4	100.1	100.0	120.5	104.1	100.0	102.5	100.5	100.0	96.7	99.3
21, 22, 23	FIRE SUPPRESSION, PLUMBING & HVAC	95.0	93.5	94.4	95.2	125.8	107.4	95.0	92.6	94.0	100.0	130.5	112.2	99.9	101.2	100.4	95.4	98.2	96.5
26, 27, 3370	ELECTRICAL, COMMUNICATIONS & UTIL.	88.9	88.7	88.8	92.0	148.7	121.6	90.8	110.1	100.9	98.6	148.7	124.7	96.7	111.1	104.2	89.0	91.1	90.1
MF2010	WEIGHTED AVERAGE	92.1	97.2	94.4	94.9	129.5	110.0	92.1	97.0	94.3	98.9	133.4	113.9	99.7	105.8	102.3	94.7	98.0	96.1

PENNSYLVANIA

DIVISION		READING 195 - 196			SCRANTON 184 - 185			STATE COLLEGE 168			STROUDSBURG 183			SUNBURY 178			UNIONTOWN 154		
		MAT.	INST.	TOTAL	MAT.	INST.	TOTAL	MAT.	INST.	TOTAL	MAT.	INST.	TOTAL	MAT.	INST.	TOTAL	MAT.	INST.	TOTAL
015433	CONTRACTOR EQUIPMENT		117.0	117.0		113.5	113.5		112.7	112.7		113.5	113.5		113.5	113.5		110.5	110.5
0241, 31 - 34	SITE & INFRASTRUCTURE, DEMOLITION	96.9	111.5	107.1	91.1	105.9	101.5	81.6	104.2	97.5	85.6	103.5	98.2	90.9	105.6	101.2	98.5	104.7	102.8
0310	Concrete Forming & Accessories	99.0	90.5	91.7	100.7	90.1	91.5	85.4	80.1	80.9	88.7	89.5	89.4	95.8	88.9	89.9	79.0	95.7	93.4
0320	Concrete Reinforcing	93.8	103.9	98.8	94.4	108.7	101.6	92.7	106.7	99.7	94.7	115.2	104.9	90.1	106.7	98.4	89.1	112.5	100.8
0330	Cast-in-Place Concrete	71.5	98.2	82.6	88.7	92.9	90.5	85.6	66.6	77.7	83.6	73.4	79.4	94.0	96.5	95.0	89.1	97.5	93.0
03	CONCRETE	86.2	96.9	91.5	96.1	95.8	96.0	96.3	81.9	89.2	90.8	89.8	90.3	98.2	96.2	97.2	95.5	100.6	98.0
04	MASONRY	96.3	94.0	94.9	94.6	96.5	95.8	99.5	79.2	87.0	91.8	101.3	97.7	93.9	90.4	91.7	127.7	98.5	109.6
05	METALS	99.7	119.2	105.7	101.9	121.2	107.9	97.6	119.0	104.2	99.6	117.8	105.2	99.4	120.0	105.8	97.3	122.0	104.9
06	WOOD, PLASTICS & COMPOSITES	100.3	88.5	93.7	103.0	88.2	94.7	89.7	82.7	85.7	88.6	88.3	88.4	93.2	88.6	90.6	76.4	94.7	86.7
07	THERMAL & MOISTURE PROTECTION	104.3	113.6	108.1	102.4	96.3	99.9	101.6	92.1	97.7	102.1	85.8	95.5	103.5	105.8	104.4	103.7	100.2	102.3
08	OPENINGS	93.1	98.3	94.3	92.5	93.7	92.8	89.6	90.1	89.7	93.0	89.1	92.1	89.9	93.4	90.7	92.0	105.7	95.3
0920	Plaster & Gypsum Board	100.4	88.0	92.0	101.9	87.6	92.2	93.1	81.9	85.5	91.4	87.7	88.9	95.2	88.0	90.3	88.4	94.4	92.5
0950, 0980	Ceilings & Acoustic Treatment	81.5	88.0	85.8	94.6	87.6	89.9	85.8	81.9	83.2	84.9	87.7	86.8	86.8	88.0	87.6	94.4	94.4	94.5
0960	Flooring	95.5	93.4	94.9	93.6	108.9	98.2	91.4	99.3	93.8	89.0	52.3	78.0	91.8	89.3	91.0	94.4	105.8	97.8
0970, 0990	Wall Finishes & Painting/Coating	99.5	105.6	103.1	98.3	105.6	102.7	98.3	108.9	104.7	98.3	66.0	78.9	101.9	105.6	104.1	104.7	108.9	107.2
09	FINISHES	94.0	91.5	92.6	96.0	94.6	95.2	91.2	85.9	88.3	90.9	80.3	85.0	93.1	90.6	91.7	96.5	97.3	96.9
COVERS	DIVS. 10 - 14, 25, 28, 41, 43, 44, 46	100.0	99.0	99.8	100.0	99.1	99.8	100.0	91.8	98.4	100.0	63.5	92.7	100.0	95.9	99.2	100.0	102.1	100.4
21, 22, 23	FIRE SUPPRESSION, PLUMBING & HVAC	100.2	107.3	103.0	100.2	98.8	99.6	95.4	84.6	91.1	95.4	100.5	97.4	95.4	90.4	93.4	95.0	92.8	94.1
26, 27, 3370	ELECTRICAL, COMMUNICATIONS & UTIL.	98.7	91.1	94.7	98.2	97.2	97.7	90.8	111.1	101.4	92.6	142.5	118.6	89.3	93.0	91.2	91.3	111.1	101.6
MF2010	WEIGHTED AVERAGE	97.1	101.1	98.8	98.3	99.7	98.9	94.9	93.0	94.1	94.9	102.0	98.0	95.5	96.3	95.8	97.1	102.2	99.4

City Cost Indexes

PENNSYLVANIA

DIVISION		WASHINGTON 153			WELLSBORO 169			WESTCHESTER 193			WILKES-BARRE 186 - 187			WILLIAMSPORT 177			YORK 173 - 174		
		MAT.	INST.	TOTAL	MAT.	INST.	TOTAL	MAT.	INST.	TOTAL	MAT.	INST.	TOTAL	MAT.	INST.	TOTAL	MAT.	INST.	TOTAL
015433	CONTRACTOR EQUIPMENT		110.5	110.5		113.5	113.5		98.0	98.0		113.5	113.5		113.5	113.5		112.7	112.7
0241, 31 - 34	SITE & INFRASTRUCTURE, DEMOLITION	98.6	104.7	102.9	93.1	103.3	100.3	98.0	97.2	97.4	83.7	105.7	99.2	82.7	104.2	97.8	81.1	104.5	97.5
0310	Concrete Forming & Accessories	85.9	95.8	94.5	87.3	87.1	87.1	90.1	129.3	123.9	91.3	90.4	90.5	92.3	61.5	65.7	86.6	89.5	89.1
0320	Concrete Reinforcing	89.1	112.6	100.9	92.7	108.3	100.5	91.7	109.7	100.7	93.5	110.5	102.0	89.4	66.6	78.0	90.1	106.7	98.4
0330	Cast-in-Place Concrete	99.7	97.6	98.8	89.7	88.8	89.3	88.2	126.7	104.2	80.3	92.6	85.4	79.6	74.3	77.4	86.4	97.9	91.2
03	CONCRETE	96.0	100.6	98.3	98.5	92.8	95.7	94.3	124.4	109.1	87.9	96.2	92.0	86.0	68.8	77.5	95.8	96.9	96.4
04	MASONRY	109.8	100.2	103.9	100.2	90.4	94.2	101.2	125.7	116.3	106.6	96.1	100.1	86.4	94.2	91.2	94.9	90.8	92.4
05	METALS	97.2	122.3	105.0	97.7	115.4	103.1	99.4	114.9	104.2	97.8	121.8	105.2	99.5	100.2	99.7	101.1	120.3	107.0
06	WOOD, PLASTICS & COMPOSITES	84.6	94.7	90.3	87.1	88.6	87.9	88.8	131.4	112.8	91.0	88.6	89.7	89.6	52.2	68.5	88.7	88.7	88.7
07	THERMAL & MOISTURE PROTECTION	103.8	100.6	102.5	102.6	90.3	97.6	104.3	131.7	115.4	102.0	107.4	104.2	103.0	103.3	103.1	102.5	112.2	106.5
08	OPENINGS	92.0	105.7	95.3	92.5	94.0	92.9	88.6	125.7	97.4	89.8	100.4	92.3	89.9	54.8	81.6	89.8	95.4	91.1
0920	Plaster & Gypsum Board	91.8	94.4	93.5	91.3	88.0	89.1	90.0	132.2	118.7	92.3	88.0	89.4	95.7	50.5	64.9	96.8	88.1	90.9
0950, 0980	Ceilings & Acoustic Treatment	94.8	94.4	94.5	85.8	88.0	87.3	90.5	132.2	118.3	88.4	88.0	88.2	90.3	50.5	63.8	89.3	88.1	88.5
0960	Flooring	97.5	105.8	100.0	88.2	51.7	77.3	94.4	139.5	107.9	89.6	96.3	91.7	90.8	50.6	78.8	92.3	93.4	92.6
0970, 0990	Wall Finishes & Painting/Coating	104.7	106.8	106.0	98.3	105.6	102.7	100.8	147.4	128.8	98.3	105.6	102.7	101.9	105.6	104.1	101.9	91.5	95.6
09	FINISHES	97.8	97.3	97.6	91.6	82.6	86.6	94.4	131.9	115.3	91.9	92.3	92.1	92.9	63.1	76.3	92.7	89.9	91.1
COVERS	DIVS. 10 - 14, 25, 28, 41, 43, 44, 46	100.0	102.1	100.4	100.0	95.8	99.2	100.0	115.5	103.1	100.0	99.0	99.8	100.0	93.2	98.6	100.0	96.5	99.3
21, 22, 23	FIRE SUPPRESSION, PLUMBING & HVAC	95.0	96.0	95.4	95.4	89.6	93.0	95.2	125.5	107.3	95.4	98.7	96.7	95.4	91.4	93.8	100.2	90.8	96.4
26, 27, 3370	ELECTRICAL, COMMUNICATIONS & UTIL.	93.7	111.1	102.8	91.7	83.3	87.3	91.9	117.6	105.3	92.6	91.5	92.0	89.8	47.7	67.8	90.9	88.4	89.6
MF2010	WEIGHTED AVERAGE	96.7	103.2	99.5	95.9	92.3	94.3	95.8	121.7	107.1	94.7	99.2	96.7	93.6	79.3	87.4	96.5	96.0	96.3

PUERTO RICO / RHODE ISLAND / SOUTH CAROLINA

DIVISION		PUERTO RICO SAN JUAN 009			RHODE ISLAND NEWPORT 028			PROVIDENCE 029			SOUTH CAROLINA AIKEN 298			BEAUFORT 299			CHARLESTON 294		
		MAT.	INST.	TOTAL	MAT.	INST.	TOTAL	MAT.	INST.	TOTAL	MAT.	INST.	TOTAL	MAT.	INST.	TOTAL	MAT.	INST.	TOTAL
015433	CONTRACTOR EQUIPMENT		90.2	90.2		102.1	102.1		102.1	102.1		100.5	100.5		100.5	100.5		100.5	100.5
0241, 31 - 34	SITE & INFRASTRUCTURE, DEMOLITION	132.3	90.5	103.0	90.6	104.2	100.2	92.0	104.2	100.6	118.8	87.1	96.5	113.9	85.3	93.8	97.9	86.0	89.5
0310	Concrete Forming & Accessories	93.7	18.1	28.4	102.6	120.6	118.1	103.9	120.6	118.3	98.6	68.9	73.0	97.5	38.8	46.8	96.5	64.4	68.8
0320	Concrete Reinforcing	191.6	13.1	102.5	106.8	153.9	130.3	103.4	153.9	128.6	94.8	67.3	81.0	93.9	26.6	60.3	93.7	61.2	77.5
0330	Cast-in-Place Concrete	103.7	31.2	73.6	80.3	124.1	98.5	96.9	124.1	108.2	80.9	70.8	76.7	80.9	47.8	67.2	94.9	50.2	76.3
03	CONCRETE	110.5	22.7	67.2	96.1	127.4	111.6	103.6	127.4	115.3	101.3	70.4	86.0	98.6	41.7	70.5	94.1	60.2	77.3
04	MASONRY	83.6	17.2	42.5	96.4	128.9	116.5	100.6	128.9	118.1	73.9	62.5	66.8	87.4	33.8	54.3	88.6	41.6	59.6
05	METALS	117.2	34.9	91.8	99.4	126.8	107.8	106.5	126.8	112.8	92.9	85.1	90.5	92.9	69.3	85.6	94.8	81.6	90.7
06	WOOD, PLASTICS & COMPOSITES	97.0	17.9	52.4	101.9	119.8	112.0	104.2	119.8	113.0	99.2	70.1	82.8	97.6	38.7	64.3	96.4	70.0	81.5
07	THERMAL & MOISTURE PROTECTION	129.7	21.3	85.7	101.5	120.4	109.2	102.3	120.4	109.6	105.3	67.7	90.0	105.0	39.6	78.5	104.2	48.2	81.5
08	OPENINGS	150.1	15.1	118.2	98.1	128.0	105.1	100.9	128.0	107.3	92.5	66.3	86.3	92.6	37.5	79.5	96.0	64.8	88.6
0920	Plaster & Gypsum Board	154.5	15.3	59.8	94.7	119.8	111.8	97.0	119.8	112.5	104.6	69.1	80.4	108.1	36.6	59.4	109.8	68.9	82.0
0950, 0980	Ceilings & Acoustic Treatment	230.8	15.3	87.4	95.3	119.8	111.6	95.2	119.8	111.6	96.0	69.1	78.1	99.5	36.6	57.7	99.5	68.9	79.1
0960	Flooring	225.0	13.4	161.7	99.8	140.3	111.9	100.4	140.3	112.4	104.8	69.7	94.3	106.1	52.1	90.0	105.8	59.3	91.9
0970, 0990	Wall Finishes & Painting/Coating	203.3	17.2	91.4	96.0	124.2	112.9	94.4	124.2	112.3	105.7	71.9	85.4	105.7	35.4	63.5	105.7	68.3	83.2
09	FINISHES	214.4	17.4	104.6	98.6	124.7	113.2	98.0	124.7	112.9	102.4	69.5	84.0	103.5	40.7	68.5	101.6	64.9	81.2
COVERS	DIVS. 10 - 14, 25, 28, 41, 43, 44, 46	100.0	16.5	83.3	100.0	105.8	101.2	100.0	105.8	101.2	100.0	73.6	94.7	100.0	72.1	94.4	100.0	70.7	94.1
21, 22, 23	FIRE SUPPRESSION, PLUMBING & HVAC	102.8	14.7	67.3	100.1	108.4	103.4	99.9	108.4	103.3	95.5	64.5	83.0	95.5	37.3	72.1	100.4	54.9	82.1
26, 27, 3370	ELECTRICAL, COMMUNICATIONS & UTIL.	126.9	13.5	67.7	101.5	104.0	101.9	102.5	100.4	101.4	96.8	67.4	81.5	100.7	34.4	66.1	99.0	90.9	94.8
MF2010	WEIGHTED AVERAGE	122.1	24.6	79.7	99.0	116.6	106.6	101.5	116.6	108.1	96.4	70.4	85.1	97.1	45.7	74.7	97.7	66.4	84.1

SOUTH CAROLINA / SOUTH DAKOTA

DIVISION		COLUMBIA 290 - 292			FLORENCE 295			GREENVILLE 296			ROCK HILL 297			SPARTANBURG 293			SOUTH DAKOTA ABERDEEN 574		
		MAT.	INST.	TOTAL	MAT.	INST.	TOTAL	MAT.	INST.	TOTAL	MAT.	INST.	TOTAL	MAT.	INST.	TOTAL	MAT.	INST.	TOTAL
015433	CONTRACTOR EQUIPMENT		100.5	100.5		100.5	100.5		100.5	100.5		100.5	100.5		100.5	100.5		99.0	99.0
0241, 31 - 34	SITE & INFRASTRUCTURE, DEMOLITION	98.0	85.9	89.5	107.9	86.0	92.5	102.9	85.6	90.7	100.4	84.6	89.3	102.7	85.6	90.7	94.3	94.5	94.4
0310	Concrete Forming & Accessories	95.4	46.1	52.9	84.6	46.3	51.5	96.0	46.1	52.9	94.5	39.6	47.1	99.0	46.2	53.5	98.9	37.5	45.9
0320	Concrete Reinforcing	96.8	61.0	78.9	93.3	61.2	77.3	93.2	45.9	69.6	94.1	45.6	69.8	93.2	58.9	76.1	100.5	39.3	69.9
0330	Cast-in-Place Concrete	97.9	50.7	78.3	80.9	50.0	68.1	80.9	49.9	68.0	80.9	44.5	65.8	80.9	50.0	68.1	110.5	44.5	83.1
03	CONCRETE	95.9	52.2	74.3	93.3	52.0	72.9	92.2	49.1	70.9	90.3	44.2	67.5	92.4	51.6	72.3	103.7	41.7	73.1
04	MASONRY	85.5	38.3	56.3	74.0	41.6	54.0	72.0	41.6	53.2	94.1	35.2	57.7	74.0	41.6	54.0	104.8	55.8	74.5
05	METALS	92.1	80.8	88.6	93.7	81.2	89.8	93.7	75.7	88.1	92.9	72.4	86.6	93.7	80.4	89.6	98.4	65.2	88.2
06	WOOD, PLASTICS & COMPOSITES	100.4	45.8	69.6	82.1	45.8	61.6	96.0	45.8	67.7	94.3	39.8	63.5	100.3	45.8	69.6	96.3	36.8	62.8
07	THERMAL & MOISTURE PROTECTION	100.0	44.2	77.4	104.5	45.7	80.6	104.4	45.7	80.6	104.3	40.5	78.4	104.5	45.7	80.6	104.3	48.8	81.8
08	OPENINGS	97.5	51.7	86.7	92.6	51.7	82.9	92.5	48.1	82.0	92.6	40.3	80.2	92.5	51.1	82.7	93.9	37.6	80.6
0920	Plaster & Gypsum Board	102.7	44.0	62.8	97.4	44.0	61.0	103.1	44.0	62.9	102.4	37.7	58.4	106.1	44.0	63.8	106.1	35.1	57.8
0950, 0980	Ceilings & Acoustic Treatment	101.2	44.0	63.1	96.9	44.0	61.7	96.0	44.0	61.4	96.0	37.7	57.2	96.0	44.0	61.4	108.2	35.1	59.6
0960	Flooring	99.7	44.4	83.1	98.4	44.4	82.3	103.7	58.2	90.1	102.9	45.3	85.7	105.0	58.2	91.0	111.1	51.2	93.2
0970, 0990	Wall Finishes & Painting/Coating	102.4	68.3	81.9	105.7	68.3	83.2	105.7	68.3	83.2	105.7	40.0	66.2	105.7	68.3	83.2	95.6	37.9	60.9
09	FINISHES	99.7	47.7	70.7	98.5	48.1	70.4	100.2	50.4	72.5	99.6	40.2	66.5	101.0	50.4	72.8	106.0	39.7	69.1
COVERS	DIVS. 10 - 14, 25, 28, 41, 43, 44, 46	100.0	67.9	93.6	100.0	67.9	93.6	100.0	67.9	93.6	100.0	66.2	93.2	100.0	67.9	93.6	100.0	41.7	88.3
21, 22, 23	FIRE SUPPRESSION, PLUMBING & HVAC	100.0	53.2	81.2	100.4	53.3	81.5	100.0	53.1	81.4	95.5	45.2	75.3	100.4	53.3	81.5	100.2	40.6	76.3
26, 27, 3370	ELECTRICAL, COMMUNICATIONS & UTIL.	99.0	61.1	79.3	96.8	61.1	78.2	99.0	58.0	77.6	99.0	57.9	77.6	99.0	58.0	77.6	99.2	52.4	74.7
MF2010	WEIGHTED AVERAGE	97.2	57.3	79.8	96.2	57.8	79.4	96.2	56.5	78.9	95.6	51.2	76.3	96.4	57.4	79.5	100.1	50.6	78.6

City Cost Indexes

SOUTH DAKOTA

DIVISION		MITCHELL 573			MOBRIDGE 576			PIERRE 575			RAPID CITY 577			SIOUX FALLS 570 - 571			WATERTOWN 572		
		MAT.	INST.	TOTAL	MAT.	INST.	TOTAL	MAT.	INST.	TOTAL	MAT.	INST.	TOTAL	MAT.	INST.	TOTAL	MAT.	INST.	TOTAL
015433	CONTRACTOR EQUIPMENT		99.0	99.0		99.0	99.0		99.0	99.0		99.0	99.0		100.0	100.0		99.0	99.0
0241, 31 - 34	SITE & INFRASTRUCTURE, DEMOLITION	91.2	94.5	93.5	91.2	94.5	93.5	93.0	94.6	94.1	92.8	94.6	94.1	92.4	96.2	95.1	91.1	94.5	93.5
0310	Concrete Forming & Accessories	98.1	37.8	46.1	88.8	37.7	44.7	101.3	39.3	47.8	106.7	37.5	47.0	104.1	41.4	50.0	85.4	37.5	44.1
0320	Concrete Reinforcing	99.9	47.8	73.9	102.5	39.3	70.9	104.3	71.5	87.9	94.0	71.6	82.8	101.7	71.5	86.6	97.1	39.4	68.3
0330	Cast-in-Place Concrete	107.4	43.3	80.8	107.4	44.5	81.3	96.8	43.2	74.6	106.5	43.8	80.5	102.8	44.0	78.4	107.4	47.0	82.3
03	CONCRETE	101.3	42.9	72.5	101.1	41.8	71.8	97.3	48.1	73.0	100.6	47.6	74.4	99.2	49.3	74.6	100.0	42.6	71.7
04	MASONRY	93.9	54.2	69.4	102.5	55.8	73.6	103.2	54.4	73.0	102.6	57.4	74.6	97.5	54.6	70.9	127.0	58.5	84.6
05	METALS	97.4	65.4	87.6	97.5	65.2	87.5	99.7	80.1	93.6	100.2	80.7	94.2	101.4	80.3	94.9	97.4	65.8	87.7
06	WOOD, PLASTICS & COMPOSITES	95.2	37.4	62.6	83.9	37.1	57.5	98.2	37.6	64.0	100.1	34.1	62.9	96.2	40.2	64.6	80.3	36.8	55.8
07	THERMAL & MOISTURE PROTECTION	104.1	46.8	80.9	104.2	48.8	81.7	105.1	47.1	81.5	104.7	49.0	82.1	109.3	49.4	85.0	104.0	49.5	81.9
08	OPENINGS	92.7	38.2	79.8	95.1	37.2	81.4	101.6	47.3	88.7	97.5	45.4	85.2	98.9	48.7	87.0	92.7	37.3	79.6
0920	Plaster & Gypsum Board	104.5	35.7	57.7	97.2	35.4	55.1	97.2	35.9	55.5	105.6	32.3	55.8	97.3	38.6	57.4	95.2	35.1	54.3
0950, 0980	Ceilings & Acoustic Treatment	104.6	35.7	58.7	108.2	35.4	59.7	106.4	35.9	59.5	110.8	32.3	58.6	107.3	38.6	61.6	104.6	35.1	58.4
0960	Flooring	110.7	51.2	93.0	106.4	51.2	89.9	110.5	36.5	88.4	110.4	80.1	101.4	105.9	76.3	97.1	105.1	51.2	89.0
0970, 0990	Wall Finishes & Painting/Coating	95.6	41.5	63.1	95.6	42.6	63.7	99.1	45.5	66.9	95.6	45.5	65.5	93.9	45.5	64.8	95.6	37.9	60.9
09	FINISHES	104.8	40.4	68.9	103.3	40.3	68.2	105.5	38.2	68.0	106.3	44.9	72.1	103.8	47.5	72.4	101.9	39.7	67.2
COVERS	DIVS. 10 - 14, 25, 28, 41, 43, 44, 46	100.0	38.7	87.7	100.0	41.7	88.3	100.0	77.9	95.6	100.0	77.8	95.6	100.0	78.3	95.7	100.0	41.7	88.3
21, 22, 23	FIRE SUPPRESSION, PLUMBING & HVAC	95.3	40.3	73.2	95.3	40.8	73.4	100.0	64.6	85.8	100.2	65.1	86.1	100.1	39.4	75.8	95.3	40.8	73.4
26, 27, 3370	ELECTRICAL, COMMUNICATIONS & UTIL.	97.5	45.0	70.1	99.2	45.9	71.4	104.6	52.4	77.4	95.7	52.5	73.1	97.4	76.9	86.7	96.7	45.9	70.2
MF2010	WEIGHTED AVERAGE	97.5	49.5	76.6	98.1	49.8	77.1	100.8	59.2	82.7	100.0	60.3	82.7	100.0	58.8	82.1	98.5	50.2	77.5

TENNESSEE

DIVISION		CHATTANOOGA 373 - 374			COLUMBIA 384			COOKEVILLE 385			JACKSON 383			JOHNSON CITY 376			KNOXVILLE 377 - 379		
		MAT.	INST.	TOTAL	MAT.	INST.	TOTAL	MAT.	INST.	TOTAL	MAT.	INST.	TOTAL	MAT.	INST.	TOTAL	MAT.	INST.	TOTAL
015433	CONTRACTOR EQUIPMENT		104.8	104.8		98.8	98.8		98.8	98.8		104.9	104.9		98.7	98.7		98.7	98.7
0241, 31 - 34	SITE & INFRASTRUCTURE, DEMOLITION	103.4	99.6	100.7	86.7	88.1	87.7	92.0	87.6	88.9	95.1	97.9	97.1	110.7	88.4	95.1	89.5	88.9	89.1
0310	Concrete Forming & Accessories	97.9	56.6	62.3	82.3	63.5	66.1	82.5	36.3	42.6	89.0	46.0	51.9	84.6	39.4	45.6	96.4	42.4	49.8
0320	Concrete Reinforcing	89.9	63.2	76.6	87.7	63.2	75.4	87.7	63.2	75.4	87.6	64.0	75.8	90.5	62.1	76.3	89.9	62.2	76.1
0330	Cast-in-Place Concrete	100.0	60.4	83.5	91.8	52.4	75.5	104.0	44.3	79.2	101.6	50.1	80.2	80.4	61.0	72.4	93.9	48.8	75.2
03	CONCRETE	93.8	60.8	77.5	93.6	61.2	77.6	103.2	46.3	75.1	94.7	52.7	74.0	100.2	53.2	77.0	91.2	50.3	71.1
04	MASONRY	108.3	49.7	72.1	118.0	55.5	79.3	112.3	44.5	70.4	118.2	48.0	74.8	123.3	45.6	75.2	85.2	53.0	65.3
05	METALS	97.7	87.4	94.5	91.5	87.6	90.3	91.6	87.5	90.3	93.8	87.6	91.9	94.9	86.4	92.3	98.3	86.7	94.7
06	WOOD, PLASTICS & COMPOSITES	107.1	58.6	79.8	73.0	65.9	69.0	73.2	34.4	51.3	88.9	46.4	65.0	79.1	37.8	55.8	93.4	37.8	62.0
07	THERMAL & MOISTURE PROTECTION	100.1	57.6	82.8	93.7	60.2	80.1	94.1	46.5	74.8	96.0	55.0	79.3	95.2	53.5	78.3	93.3	58.2	79.0
08	OPENINGS	101.7	57.1	91.2	92.5	59.3	84.6	92.5	43.2	80.8	100.1	52.9	88.9	98.0	46.2	85.7	95.3	46.2	83.7
0920	Plaster & Gypsum Board	82.0	57.8	65.6	85.1	65.3	71.6	85.1	32.8	49.5	86.8	45.2	58.5	99.3	36.3	56.5	106.9	36.3	58.9
0950, 0980	Ceilings & Acoustic Treatment	97.1	57.8	71.0	81.5	65.3	70.7	81.5	32.8	49.1	90.3	45.2	60.3	93.3	36.3	55.4	94.2	36.3	55.7
0960	Flooring	98.2	57.7	86.1	94.5	20.9	72.5	94.5	59.7	84.1	91.6	41.5	76.6	97.2	41.4	80.5	101.3	56.8	88.0
0970, 0990	Wall Finishes & Painting/Coating	97.0	53.9	71.1	87.7	34.1	55.5	87.7	37.3	57.4	89.2	50.6	66.0	94.3	43.0	63.5	94.3	49.6	67.4
09	FINISHES	94.5	56.6	73.4	92.3	53.2	70.5	92.8	39.3	63.0	91.9	44.7	65.6	99.1	38.9	65.6	92.1	44.6	65.6
COVERS	DIVS. 10 - 14, 25, 28, 41, 43, 44, 46	100.0	42.4	88.5	100.0	49.2	89.8	100.0	42.1	88.4	100.0	44.2	88.8	100.0	44.3	88.8	100.0	46.8	89.3
21, 22, 23	FIRE SUPPRESSION, PLUMBING & HVAC	100.2	61.9	84.9	97.4	79.8	90.3	97.4	74.2	88.1	100.1	69.5	87.8	100.0	60.4	84.1	100.0	65.7	86.2
26, 27, 3370	ELECTRICAL, COMMUNICATIONS & UTIL.	101.9	69.8	85.1	92.6	58.8	75.0	94.4	63.1	78.0	99.5	59.9	78.8	91.9	47.4	68.7	97.8	57.3	76.6
MF2010	WEIGHTED AVERAGE	99.5	65.5	84.7	95.3	67.5	83.2	96.4	60.4	80.7	98.3	62.5	82.7	99.2	56.7	80.7	96.2	60.5	80.6

TENNESSEE / TEXAS

DIVISION		MCKENZIE 382			MEMPHIS 375,380 - 381			NASHVILLE 370 - 372			ABILENE 795 - 796			AMARILLO 790 - 791			AUSTIN 786 - 787		
		MAT.	INST.	TOTAL	MAT.	INST.	TOTAL	MAT.	INST.	TOTAL	MAT.	INST.	TOTAL	MAT.	INST.	TOTAL	MAT.	INST.	TOTAL
015433	CONTRACTOR EQUIPMENT		98.8	98.8		103.2	103.2		105.2	105.2		89.7	89.7		89.7	89.7		89.0	89.0
0241, 31 - 34	SITE & INFRASTRUCTURE, DEMOLITION	91.7	87.7	88.9	93.0	94.6	94.1	97.7	100.3	99.6	94.0	86.7	88.8	92.7	87.7	89.2	95.8	86.8	89.5
0310	Concrete Forming & Accessories	90.1	39.0	46.0	95.4	64.7	68.9	99.3	65.7	70.3	100.3	38.9	47.3	101.2	52.5	59.2	96.9	54.3	60.2
0320	Concrete Reinforcing	87.8	63.9	75.9	95.5	64.5	80.0	97.2	63.6	80.4	89.4	51.7	70.6	93.2	51.7	72.5	91.1	49.4	70.2
0330	Cast-in-Place Concrete	101.8	58.3	83.7	92.4	61.9	79.8	89.4	66.0	79.7	100.1	47.4	78.2	92.5	53.9	76.5	93.3	61.7	80.2
03	CONCRETE	101.9	52.4	77.5	91.6	65.2	78.6	90.6	66.9	78.9	98.3	45.5	72.2	97.5	53.7	75.9	92.7	56.7	74.9
04	MASONRY	116.5	47.0	73.5	100.1	63.2	77.3	91.0	59.3	71.4	98.7	56.9	72.9	100.5	57.7	74.0	99.5	45.8	66.3
05	METALS	91.6	87.8	90.4	99.0	89.3	96.0	99.5	88.7	96.2	100.6	68.5	90.7	96.1	68.9	87.7	97.3	64.8	87.3
06	WOOD, PLASTICS & COMPOSITES	82.1	37.1	56.7	96.4	66.6	79.6	106.2	66.5	83.8	104.2	37.3	66.4	98.2	54.7	73.7	93.4	58.1	73.5
07	THERMAL & MOISTURE PROTECTION	94.1	49.5	76.0	95.5	64.0	82.7	97.1	61.7	82.7	101.2	49.6	80.2	101.8	53.5	82.2	101.1	49.6	80.2
08	OPENINGS	92.5	45.1	81.3	101.3	64.6	92.6	101.5	64.7	92.8	92.8	41.0	80.5	94.3	52.8	84.5	101.9	55.1	90.8
0920	Plaster & Gypsum Board	88.0	35.6	52.4	92.8	65.9	74.5	95.0	65.9	75.2	86.2	35.8	51.9	92.4	53.8	66.2	88.6	57.3	67.3
0950, 0980	Ceilings & Acoustic Treatment	81.5	35.6	51.0	95.4	65.9	75.8	92.1	65.9	74.6	93.3	35.8	55.1	102.3	53.8	70.0	94.3	57.3	71.4
0960	Flooring	97.2	40.1	80.1	98.9	36.7	80.3	97.4	65.4	87.9	113.4	77.9	102.8	108.3	77.9	99.2	105.5	40.2	86.0
0970, 0990	Wall Finishes & Painting/Coating	87.7	50.6	65.4	91.9	56.0	70.3	95.3	73.6	82.2	98.8	50.2	69.6	98.9	49.5	69.2	102.8	40.8	65.6
09	FINISHES	93.9	39.1	63.3	96.5	58.4	75.3	94.8	66.4	79.0	96.2	46.4	68.5	99.3	56.9	75.6	100.1	50.3	72.4
COVERS	DIVS. 10 - 14, 25, 28, 41, 43, 44, 46	100.0	28.2	85.6	100.0	82.1	96.4	100.0	82.6	96.5	100.0	76.1	95.2	100.0	67.7	93.5	100.0	78.3	95.7
21, 22, 23	FIRE SUPPRESSION, PLUMBING & HVAC	97.4	69.8	86.3	100.0	74.9	90.0	100.0	83.2	93.3	100.3	46.0	78.5	100.1	50.8	80.3	100.1	56.1	82.5
26, 27, 3370	ELECTRICAL, COMMUNICATIONS & UTIL.	94.1	64.4	78.6	100.9	64.9	82.1	97.6	63.1	79.6	94.9	48.7	70.7	98.7	64.6	80.9	97.0	62.1	78.8
MF2010	WEIGHTED AVERAGE	96.6	60.4	80.9	98.5	71.3	86.7	97.9	74.1	87.5	98.3	53.6	78.8	98.2	60.0	81.6	98.6	59.1	81.4

TEXAS

DIVISION		BEAUMONT 776 - 777			BROWNWOOD 768			BRYAN 778			CHILDRESS 792			CORPUS CHRISTI 783 - 784			DALLAS 752 - 753		
		MAT.	INST.	TOTAL	MAT.	INST.	TOTAL	MAT.	INST.	TOTAL	MAT.	INST.	TOTAL	MAT.	INST.	TOTAL	MAT.	INST.	TOTAL
015433	CONTRACTOR EQUIPMENT		91.2	91.2		89.7	89.7		91.2	91.2		89.7	89.7		96.2	96.2		99.1	99.1
0241, 31 - 34	SITE & INFRASTRUCTURE, DEMOLITION	89.0	87.6	88.0	100.5	86.1	90.4	80.7	90.3	87.5	103.1	87.0	91.8	138.3	82.8	99.3	107.7	88.2	94.0
0310	Concrete Forming & Accessories	106.7	48.4	56.4	97.7	33.0	41.8	84.5	45.5	50.8	98.7	61.9	66.9	98.8	39.8	47.9	97.5	64.1	68.7
0320	Concrete Reinforcing	89.0	41.5	65.3	91.7	50.7	71.3	91.3	49.5	70.4	89.5	51.0	70.3	84.6	47.2	65.9	99.1	52.8	76.0
0330	Cast-in-Place Concrete	86.8	51.7	72.2	105.3	42.7	79.3	69.6	65.7	68.0	102.7	49.4	80.6	109.1	46.9	83.3	96.4	54.8	79.1
03	CONCRETE	96.2	49.3	73.1	105.2	40.8	73.4	80.7	54.5	67.8	107.8	56.2	82.3	99.0	45.5	72.6	99.6	60.1	80.1
04	MASONRY	99.8	57.3	73.5	130.0	48.3	79.5	137.2	56.3	87.2	102.9	49.8	70.0	88.6	51.4	65.6	101.9	56.5	73.8
05	METALS	95.2	64.6	85.8	97.3	62.8	86.6	94.8	70.5	87.3	98.1	65.7	88.1	92.7	75.0	87.2	100.6	79.6	94.1
06	WOOD, PLASTICS & COMPOSITES	114.0	48.4	77.0	101.5	29.2	60.7	79.0	39.6	56.8	103.5	67.5	83.2	116.8	38.2	72.4	102.3	67.6	82.7
07	THERMAL & MOISTURE PROTECTION	103.5	55.5	84.0	100.1	44.1	77.4	95.4	56.2	79.5	101.7	48.8	80.3	102.3	48.4	80.4	92.1	62.5	80.1
08	OPENINGS	94.4	45.2	82.8	91.6	37.0	78.7	97.4	45.9	85.2	90.0	56.6	82.1	106.7	39.5	90.8	103.9	58.4	93.2
0920	Plaster & Gypsum Board	97.4	47.3	63.4	87.8	27.5	46.8	84.7	38.3	53.1	85.8	66.9	73.0	93.9	36.7	54.9	96.7	66.9	76.4
0950, 0980	Ceilings & Acoustic Treatment	95.5	47.3	63.5	91.7	27.5	49.0	89.0	38.3	55.3	91.5	66.9	75.2	91.5	36.7	55.0	103.4	66.9	79.1
0960	Flooring	109.1	74.3	98.7	109.2	45.5	90.1	84.2	62.9	77.9	111.6	41.6	90.7	115.4	64.2	100.1	107.8	48.6	90.1
0970, 0990	Wall Finishes & Painting/Coating	96.1	48.6	67.6	96.3	29.8	56.3	92.6	62.5	74.5	98.8	38.6	62.7	115.0	57.7	80.6	105.5	51.5	73.1
09	FINISHES	90.2	52.7	69.4	95.3	34.0	61.2	79.5	48.8	62.4	96.4	56.8	74.4	103.7	45.6	71.3	100.4	60.4	78.1
COVERS	DIVS. 10 - 14, 25, 28, 41, 43, 44, 46	100.0	79.4	95.9	100.0	37.3	87.4	100.0	79.8	96.0	100.0	70.0	94.0	100.0	78.3	95.7	100.0	82.0	96.4
21, 22, 23	FIRE SUPPRESSION, PLUMBING & HVAC	100.2	59.7	83.9	95.3	49.1	76.8	95.3	65.9	83.5	95.4	52.3	78.1	100.2	40.0	76.0	100.0	62.1	84.8
26, 27, 3370	ELECTRICAL, COMMUNICATIONS & UTIL.	92.1	70.8	81.0	93.2	43.7	67.4	90.2	67.7	78.4	94.9	43.4	68.0	91.8	61.4	76.0	95.7	65.2	79.7
MF2010	WEIGHTED AVERAGE	96.7	61.2	81.2	98.5	48.4	76.7	94.1	63.0	80.5	97.9	56.9	80.0	99.7	53.7	79.6	100.1	65.8	85.2

TEXAS

DIVISION		DEL RIO 788			DENTON 762			EASTLAND 764			EL PASO 798 - 799,885			FORT WORTH 760 - 761			GALVESTON 775		
		MAT.	INST.	TOTAL	MAT.	INST.	TOTAL	MAT.	INST.	TOTAL	MAT.	INST.	TOTAL	MAT.	INST.	TOTAL	MAT.	INST.	TOTAL
015433	CONTRACTOR EQUIPMENT		89.0	89.0		95.7	95.7		89.7	89.7		89.8	89.8		89.7	89.7		100.1	100.1
0241, 31 - 34	SITE & INFRASTRUCTURE, DEMOLITION	119.1	85.4	95.4	100.5	79.3	85.6	103.1	86.0	91.1	95.1	86.1	88.8	97.4	87.1	90.1	108.0	88.1	94.1
0310	Concrete Forming & Accessories	95.3	36.5	44.6	104.6	32.3	42.2	98.5	35.8	44.4	97.2	43.8	51.1	96.9	63.5	68.1	94.2	65.6	69.5
0320	Concrete Reinforcing	85.2	46.7	66.0	93.0	51.0	72.1	92.0	50.7	71.3	97.5	45.8	71.7	97.3	52.7	75.0	90.8	62.8	76.8
0330	Cast-in-Place Concrete	117.4	42.8	86.4	81.5	44.4	66.1	111.3	43.3	83.1	96.6	41.3	73.7	98.6	50.7	78.7	92.3	66.9	81.8
03	CONCRETE	119.8	41.7	81.3	82.8	42.0	62.7	110.0	42.4	76.6	99.9	44.3	72.5	100.7	57.7	79.5	97.2	67.1	82.3
04	MASONRY	103.6	50.0	70.4	138.8	47.1	82.1	99.9	48.2	67.9	96.5	46.9	65.8	98.4	56.4	72.4	95.9	56.4	71.5
05	METALS	92.5	60.8	82.7	96.9	75.5	90.3	97.1	63.2	86.6	95.3	62.6	85.2	98.8	68.5	89.5	96.3	88.8	94.0
06	WOOD, PLASTICS & COMPOSITES	97.0	34.6	61.8	112.9	31.9	67.2	108.3	32.8	65.7	99.9	45.8	69.4	99.5	67.5	81.4	96.4	66.4	79.4
07	THERMAL & MOISTURE PROTECTION	99.2	43.6	76.6	98.3	44.1	76.3	100.5	44.2	77.6	98.9	54.5	80.9	98.4	52.6	79.8	94.5	65.3	82.6
08	OPENINGS	99.3	33.9	83.9	107.8	37.5	91.1	72.9	39.0	64.9	91.2	43.9	80.0	98.7	58.3	89.2	101.8	64.0	92.9
0920	Plaster & Gypsum Board	89.7	33.0	51.2	92.3	30.2	50.0	87.8	31.2	49.3	93.7	44.6	60.3	92.0	66.9	74.9	92.0	65.7	74.1
0950, 0980	Ceilings & Acoustic Treatment	87.8	33.0	51.4	96.2	30.2	52.2	91.7	31.2	51.4	95.9	44.6	61.7	102.3	66.9	78.8	91.6	65.7	74.4
0960	Flooring	97.3	34.7	78.6	102.5	43.5	84.8	141.2	45.5	112.6	114.0	63.5	98.9	137.1	41.4	108.5	98.1	62.9	87.6
0970, 0990	Wall Finishes & Painting/Coating	101.3	38.4	63.5	106.2	29.6	60.2	97.8	30.5	57.4	93.2	34.9	58.2	95.2	51.1	68.7	104.3	47.0	69.9
09	FINISHES	95.8	36.0	62.5	92.0	33.5	59.4	104.8	36.3	66.6	99.2	46.5	69.9	107.4	58.8	80.3	88.8	63.0	74.4
COVERS	DIVS. 10 - 14, 25, 28, 41, 43, 44, 46	100.0	37.1	87.4	100.0	36.0	87.2	100.0	38.4	87.7	100.0	77.3	95.4	100.0	81.7	96.3	100.0	84.3	96.9
21, 22, 23	FIRE SUPPRESSION, PLUMBING & HVAC	95.2	46.9	75.8	95.3	37.9	72.3	95.3	49.4	76.9	100.0	34.2	73.6	100.0	57.7	83.1	95.2	66.0	83.5
26, 27, 3370	ELECTRICAL, COMMUNICATIONS & UTIL.	94.0	30.1	60.6	95.6	43.8	68.6	93.1	43.8	67.3	92.7	54.9	73.0	94.5	62.4	77.8	91.7	69.5	80.1
MF2010	WEIGHTED AVERAGE	99.4	46.2	76.3	98.2	46.6	75.7	96.5	49.1	75.9	97.2	50.6	76.9	99.6	62.5	83.5	96.3	69.7	84.7

TEXAS

DIVISION		GIDDINGS 789			GREENVILLE 754			HOUSTON 770 - 772			HUNTSVILLE 773			LAREDO 780			LONGVIEW 756		
		MAT.	INST.	TOTAL	MAT.	INST.	TOTAL	MAT.	INST.	TOTAL	MAT.	INST.	TOTAL	MAT.	INST.	TOTAL	MAT.	INST.	TOTAL
015433	CONTRACTOR EQUIPMENT		89.0	89.0		96.7	96.7		100.0	100.0		91.2	91.2		89.0	89.0		91.5	91.5
0241, 31 - 34	SITE & INFRASTRUCTURE, DEMOLITION	105.0	85.4	91.3	101.0	83.5	88.7	106.7	87.9	93.5	95.8	87.9	90.3	99.1	86.8	90.5	97.3	90.3	92.4
0310	Concrete Forming & Accessories	93.0	55.5	60.7	89.1	27.3	35.7	96.3	65.8	69.9	91.8	55.4	60.4	95.3	40.0	47.5	85.5	28.1	35.9
0320	Concrete Reinforcing	85.8	46.8	66.3	99.6	24.9	62.3	90.6	63.3	77.0	91.5	50.5	71.0	85.2	47.6	66.4	98.4	22.7	60.6
0330	Cast-in-Place Concrete	99.5	42.9	76.0	87.8	37.7	67.0	89.5	66.9	80.1	95.6	48.2	75.9	84.1	59.3	73.8	102.1	35.0	74.2
03	CONCRETE	96.5	50.2	73.7	92.2	32.6	62.8	94.9	67.2	81.3	103.8	52.8	78.7	91.4	49.1	70.6	108.4	30.8	70.1
04	MASONRY	111.8	50.0	73.5	159.0	46.1	89.1	95.8	66.6	77.7	135.8	51.6	83.7	97.3	58.6	73.3	154.6	42.0	85.0
05	METALS	92.0	61.8	82.6	97.9	63.6	87.3	99.2	89.7	96.3	94.7	66.3	85.9	95.0	64.0	85.5	91.2	50.5	78.7
06	WOOD, PLASTICS & COMPOSITES	96.0	59.4	75.4	92.3	26.3	55.1	98.8	66.4	80.5	88.3	58.2	71.3	97.0	38.1	63.7	86.2	28.4	53.6
07	THERMAL & MOISTURE PROTECTION	99.9	47.7	78.7	92.2	39.5	70.8	94.1	68.1	83.6	96.3	48.2	76.8	98.2	51.9	79.4	93.5	34.9	69.7
08	OPENINGS	98.5	49.0	86.7	102.1	26.0	84.1	104.4	64.0	94.8	97.4	48.5	85.8	99.2	39.4	85.0	91.7	26.0	76.1
0920	Plaster & Gypsum Board	88.6	58.7	68.3	90.4	24.5	45.5	94.5	65.7	74.9	89.5	57.4	67.7	90.8	36.7	54.0	88.7	26.8	46.6
0950, 0980	Ceilings & Acoustic Treatment	87.8	58.7	68.4	99.0	24.5	49.4	97.0	65.7	76.2	89.0	57.4	67.9	92.2	36.7	55.2	95.4	26.8	49.7
0960	Flooring	97.8	34.7	79.0	103.7	47.8	87.0	99.1	62.9	88.3	87.4	34.7	71.7	97.1	64.2	87.3	108.1	35.1	86.2
0970, 0990	Wall Finishes & Painting/Coating	101.3	30.5	58.8	105.5	25.1	57.2	104.3	62.5	79.2	92.6	31.3	55.8	101.3	54.4	73.1	95.1	29.3	55.6
09	FINISHES	94.7	50.2	69.9	96.9	30.4	59.8	96.0	64.7	78.5	81.9	49.9	64.1	95.2	45.1	67.3	101.0	29.4	61.1
COVERS	DIVS. 10 - 14, 25, 28, 41, 43, 44, 46	100.0	42.9	88.6	100.0	34.4	86.9	100.0	84.3	96.9	100.0	43.3	88.6	100.0	76.3	95.2	100.0	21.9	84.4
21, 22, 23	FIRE SUPPRESSION, PLUMBING & HVAC	95.3	62.5	82.1	95.2	43.5	74.4	100.0	66.1	86.4	95.3	63.3	82.5	100.1	38.8	75.5	95.1	27.5	68.0
26, 27, 3370	ELECTRICAL, COMMUNICATIONS & UTIL.	90.8	43.4	66.1	92.3	27.1	58.3	93.7	67.8	80.2	90.2	43.4	65.8	94.2	59.9	76.3	92.7	53.2	72.0
MF2010	WEIGHTED AVERAGE	96.4	55.6	78.6	99.4	42.2	74.5	98.7	70.9	86.6	97.2	56.9	79.6	97.1	53.7	78.2	99.0	40.5	73.5

TEXAS

DIVISION		LUBBOCK 793 - 794			LUFKIN 759			MCALLEN 785			MCKINNEY 750			MIDLAND 797			ODESSA 797		
		MAT.	INST.	TOTAL	MAT.	INST.	TOTAL	MAT.	INST.	TOTAL	MAT.	INST.	TOTAL	MAT.	INST.	TOTAL	MAT.	INST.	TOTAL
015433	CONTRACTOR EQUIPMENT		98.2	98.2		91.5	91.5		96.4	96.4		96.7	96.7		98.2	98.2		89.7	89.7
0241, 31 - 34	SITE & INFRASTRUCTURE, DEMOLITION	116.1	85.0	94.3	92.5	91.8	92.0	142.5	82.9	100.6	97.4	83.6	87.7	118.7	85.0	95.1	94.2	87.0	89.1
0310	Concrete Forming & Accessories	99.1	51.0	57.6	88.6	56.8	61.2	99.9	35.8	44.6	88.2	36.3	43.4	103.0	51.0	58.2	100.2	50.9	57.7
0320	Concrete Reinforcing	90.5	51.7	71.1	100.2	62.4	81.3	84.8	47.1	66.0	99.6	51.1	75.4	91.4	50.9	71.2	89.4	50.9	70.2
0330	Cast-in-Place Concrete	100.3	48.4	78.8	91.3	44.7	72.0	118.5	45.3	88.1	82.4	45.2	66.9	106.6	48.6	82.5	100.1	47.5	78.3
03	CONCRETE	96.9	52.0	74.7	100.8	54.3	77.8	106.6	43.1	75.3	87.6	44.0	66.0	101.6	51.9	77.1	98.3	50.7	74.8
04	MASONRY	98.1	55.7	71.8	118.7	52.3	77.6	103.2	51.4	71.1	171.0	48.4	95.1	114.8	42.0	69.7	98.7	42.0	63.6
05	METALS	104.1	80.1	96.7	98.0	69.1	89.1	92.4	74.5	86.9	97.8	74.4	90.6	102.4	79.0	95.2	99.9	67.1	89.8
06	WOOD, PLASTICS & COMPOSITES	104.1	54.9	76.3	94.3	59.4	74.6	115.4	33.6	69.2	91.0	36.4	60.2	109.1	54.9	78.5	104.2	54.7	76.3
07	THERMAL & MOISTURE PROTECTION	90.8	52.7	75.3	93.3	48.0	74.9	102.6	45.0	79.2	92.0	45.9	73.3	91.0	47.4	73.3	101.2	46.6	79.0
08	OPENINGS	103.6	49.4	90.8	69.6	53.4	65.8	103.4	36.8	87.6	102.0	39.8	87.3	102.5	49.1	89.9	92.8	49.0	82.4
0920	Plaster & Gypsum Board	86.7	53.8	64.3	87.7	58.7	68.0	94.9	31.9	52.0	89.6	34.8	52.4	88.3	53.8	64.8	86.2	53.8	64.2
0950, 0980	Ceilings & Acoustic Treatment	95.1	53.8	67.6	88.3	58.7	68.6	92.2	31.9	52.1	99.0	34.8	56.3	92.4	53.8	66.7	93.3	53.8	67.0
0960	Flooring	107.0	39.3	86.7	143.4	38.2	112.0	114.9	65.0	100.0	103.3	35.6	83.1	108.2	48.6	90.4	113.4	48.6	94.0
0970, 0990	Wall Finishes & Painting/Coating	110.2	49.5	73.7	95.1	37.8	60.6	115.0	28.9	63.2	105.5	41.2	66.9	110.2	49.5	73.7	98.8	49.5	69.2
09	FINISHES	98.8	48.8	70.9	109.1	52.0	77.3	104.3	39.8	68.4	96.4	36.7	63.1	99.2	50.7	72.1	96.2	50.6	70.8
COVERS	DIVS. 10 - 14, 25, 28, 41, 43, 44, 46	100.0	77.8	95.6	100.0	70.8	94.2	100.0	76.0	95.2	100.0	39.7	87.9	100.0	78.6	95.7	100.0	78.3	95.6
21, 22, 23	FIRE SUPPRESSION, PLUMBING & HVAC	99.8	45.2	77.9	95.1	63.5	82.4	95.3	30.8	69.4	95.2	41.4	73.6	94.9	45.3	75.0	100.3	45.3	78.2
26, 27, 3370	ELECTRICAL, COMMUNICATIONS & UTIL.	93.6	49.6	70.6	94.0	43.4	67.6	91.6	34.2	61.6	92.4	45.2	67.8	93.5	40.4	65.8	95.0	40.3	66.4
MF2010	WEIGHTED AVERAGE	100.0	56.3	81.0	95.9	59.1	79.9	99.7	46.6	76.6	99.3	48.9	77.3	99.9	53.6	79.7	98.2	52.5	78.3

TEXAS

DIVISION		PALESTINE 758			SAN ANGELO 769			SAN ANTONIO 781 - 782			TEMPLE 765			TEXARKANA 755			TYLER 757		
		MAT.	INST.	TOTAL	MAT.	INST.	TOTAL	MAT.	INST.	TOTAL	MAT.	INST.	TOTAL	MAT.	INST.	TOTAL	MAT.	INST.	TOTAL
015433	CONTRACTOR EQUIPMENT		91.5	91.5		89.7	89.7		91.5	91.5		89.7	89.7		91.5	91.5		91.5	91.5
0241, 31 - 34	SITE & INFRASTRUCTURE, DEMOLITION	98.6	91.1	93.3	97.0	88.1	90.8	101.8	91.4	94.5	86.0	85.9	85.9	87.0	91.1	89.9	96.6	91.5	93.1
0310	Concrete Forming & Accessories	80.1	55.8	59.1	98.0	36.5	44.9	94.5	54.8	60.3	101.3	39.7	48.1	95.4	34.0	42.4	90.3	33.1	40.9
0320	Concrete Reinforcing	97.7	50.7	74.2	91.6	50.9	71.3	91.8	49.1	70.5	91.8	47.4	69.6	97.6	52.4	75.0	98.4	53.0	75.7
0330	Cast-in-Place Concrete	83.5	42.6	66.5	99.3	46.6	77.4	84.5	65.4	76.6	81.4	48.4	67.7	84.1	43.4	67.2	100.2	42.5	76.3
03	CONCRETE	102.9	50.9	77.2	100.4	43.9	72.5	92.6	58.3	75.7	86.0	45.2	65.9	93.6	42.0	68.1	108.0	41.4	75.1
04	MASONRY	113.5	48.5	73.3	126.6	41.6	74.0	98.9	66.5	78.8	137.9	48.4	82.5	175.4	44.7	94.5	164.8	54.4	96.5
05	METALS	97.7	62.7	86.9	97.4	66.5	87.9	96.1	68.7	87.6	97.1	62.8	86.5	91.1	66.9	83.6	97.6	68.0	88.5
06	WOOD, PLASTICS & COMPOSITES	84.7	59.4	70.4	101.8	36.1	64.7	96.7	52.8	71.9	111.0	39.4	70.6	98.1	32.3	61.0	96.0	30.5	59.0
07	THERMAL & MOISTURE PROTECTION	93.7	46.4	74.5	100.0	42.1	76.5	95.9	64.3	83.1	99.6	45.0	77.4	93.2	47.2	74.5	93.6	53.2	77.2
08	OPENINGS	69.5	50.7	65.1	91.7	38.8	79.2	99.9	51.7	88.5	69.6	41.8	63.0	91.7	37.9	78.9	69.5	36.9	61.9
0920	Plaster & Gypsum Board	84.4	58.7	66.9	87.8	34.6	51.6	88.8	51.8	63.6	87.8	38.0	53.9	93.2	30.7	50.7	87.7	28.9	47.7
0950, 0980	Ceilings & Acoustic Treatment	88.3	58.7	68.6	91.7	34.6	53.7	91.2	51.8	65.0	91.7	38.0	56.0	95.4	30.7	52.4	88.3	28.9	48.7
0960	Flooring	135.3	58.9	112.5	109.2	34.7	86.9	97.6	64.3	87.6	143.4	41.7	113.0	115.6	59.4	98.7	145.3	37.0	112.9
0970, 0990	Wall Finishes & Painting/Coating	95.1	30.5	56.3	96.3	49.5	68.2	98.5	54.4	72.0	97.8	38.5	62.2	95.1	39.4	61.6	95.1	39.4	61.6
09	FINISHES	106.9	54.4	77.7	95.0	36.4	62.4	94.8	55.4	72.8	104.1	39.6	68.2	103.1	38.1	66.9	109.9	32.6	66.9
COVERS	DIVS. 10 - 14, 25, 28, 41, 43, 44, 46	100.0	40.7	88.1	100.0	75.0	95.0	100.0	80.6	96.1	100.0	36.8	87.3	100.0	74.9	95.0	100.0	74.7	94.9
21, 22, 23	FIRE SUPPRESSION, PLUMBING & HVAC	95.1	58.5	80.4	95.3	44.6	75.0	100.0	64.5	85.8	95.3	48.2	76.4	95.1	32.9	70.2	95.1	57.7	80.1
26, 27, 3370	ELECTRICAL, COMMUNICATIONS & UTIL.	90.1	43.4	65.7	97.2	45.8	70.4	94.3	60.0	76.4	94.3	64.9	79.0	93.8	61.1	76.8	92.7	55.0	73.0
MF2010	WEIGHTED AVERAGE	95.4	55.8	78.2	98.2	49.5	77.0	97.5	64.5	83.1	95.0	52.7	76.6	98.4	49.7	77.2	98.9	54.6	79.6

DIVISION		VICTORIA 779 (TEXAS)			WACO 766 - 767 (TEXAS)			WAXAHACHIE 751 (TEXAS)			WHARTON 774 (TEXAS)			WICHITA FALLS 763 (TEXAS)			LOGAN 843 (UTAH)		
		MAT.	INST.	TOTAL	MAT.	INST.	TOTAL	MAT.	INST.	TOTAL	MAT.	INST.	TOTAL	MAT.	INST.	TOTAL	MAT.	INST.	TOTAL
015433	CONTRACTOR EQUIPMENT		99.0	99.0		89.7	89.7		96.7	96.7		100.1	100.1		89.7	89.7		97.2	97.2
0241, 31 - 34	SITE & INFRASTRUCTURE, DEMOLITION	112.7	82.3	91.4	94.2	87.0	89.2	99.0	84.4	88.8	118.4	85.5	95.3	94.9	86.7	89.1	93.4	96.2	95.4
0310	Concrete Forming & Accessories	94.0	35.1	43.2	99.9	39.6	47.9	88.2	59.5	63.5	88.7	36.7	43.9	99.9	37.2	45.8	104.8	58.1	64.5
0320	Concrete Reinforcing	87.2	30.3	58.8	91.5	49.4	70.5	99.6	51.1	75.4	90.7	50.2	70.5	91.5	51.7	71.6	102.3	80.2	91.3
0330	Cast-in-Place Concrete	103.6	41.0	77.7	88.1	65.8	78.8	86.9	41.7	68.1	106.5	51.2	83.5	94.1	44.7	73.6	86.9	72.8	81.0
03	CONCRETE	104.5	38.5	71.9	93.0	51.7	72.6	91.3	53.2	72.5	108.8	46.4	78.0	95.8	43.8	70.1	107.9	67.9	88.2
04	MASONRY	112.4	34.1	64.0	98.3	53.7	70.7	159.7	48.5	90.9	97.0	44.6	64.6	98.8	56.9	72.9	103.9	59.7	76.5
05	METALS	94.9	70.3	87.3	99.4	67.0	89.4	97.9	77.0	91.4	96.3	78.5	90.8	99.4	68.5	89.8	101.0	78.2	94.0
06	WOOD, PLASTICS & COMPOSITES	99.9	35.9	63.8	109.2	35.1	67.4	91.0	67.5	77.8	89.4	32.6	57.3	109.2	35.0	67.3	81.5	56.2	67.2
07	THERMAL & MOISTURE PROTECTION	98.4	39.5	74.5	100.5	46.9	78.8	92.1	46.3	73.5	94.8	49.3	76.3	100.5	50.5	80.2	97.9	61.8	83.3
08	OPENINGS	101.7	35.2	85.9	81.5	42.5	72.2	102.1	56.8	91.3	101.8	37.4	86.6	81.5	40.3	71.7	94.3	57.1	85.5
0920	Plaster & Gypsum Board	89.3	34.3	51.9	88.3	33.6	51.1	90.1	66.9	74.3	86.8	30.9	48.8	88.3	33.4	51.0	75.6	54.8	61.4
0950, 0980	Ceilings & Acoustic Treatment	92.5	34.3	53.8	93.5	33.6	53.6	100.7	66.9	78.2	91.6	30.9	51.2	93.5	33.4	53.5	105.1	54.8	71.6
0960	Flooring	97.8	38.2	80.0	142.3	45.1	113.3	103.3	38.2	83.8	96.1	45.5	80.9	143.5	77.9	123.9	100.2	48.6	84.8
0970, 0990	Wall Finishes & Painting/Coating	104.5	37.8	64.4	97.8	49.8	69.0	105.5	37.8	64.8	104.3	31.3	60.5	100.5	49.5	69.9	102.9	62.0	78.3
09	FINISHES	87.0	36.0	58.6	104.7	40.2	68.8	97.1	54.8	73.5	88.3	36.7	59.5	105.3	45.0	71.7	98.5	56.0	74.8
COVERS	DIVS. 10 - 14, 25, 28, 41, 43, 44, 46	100.0	36.6	87.3	100.0	78.2	95.6	100.0	40.6	88.1	100.0	38.7	87.7	100.0	65.2	93.0	100.0	54.1	90.8
21, 22, 23	FIRE SUPPRESSION, PLUMBING & HVAC	95.3	31.2	69.6	100.2	54.2	81.8	95.2	40.5	73.2	95.2	63.4	82.5	100.2	48.4	79.5	100.0	69.0	87.6
26, 27, 3370	ELECTRICAL, COMMUNICATIONS & UTIL.	96.5	39.7	66.9	97.4	65.1	80.5	92.4	65.2	78.2	95.3	43.8	68.4	99.1	61.0	79.2	95.4	74.3	84.4
MF2010	WEIGHTED AVERAGE	98.2	42.7	74.1	97.2	57.3	79.8	99.3	56.4	80.6	98.1	53.8	78.8	97.8	55.0	79.2	99.7	68.8	86.2

UTAH / VERMONT

DIVISION		OGDEN 842,844 MAT.	INST.	TOTAL	PRICE 845 MAT.	INST.	TOTAL	PROVO 846-847 MAT.	INST.	TOTAL	SALT LAKE CITY 840-841 MAT.	INST.	TOTAL	BELLOWS FALLS 051 MAT.	INST.	TOTAL	BENNINGTON 052 MAT.	INST.	TOTAL
015433	CONTRACTOR EQUIPMENT		97.2	97.2		96.3	96.3		96.3	96.3		97.2	97.2		100.6	100.6		100.6	100.6
0241, 31 - 34	SITE & INFRASTRUCTURE, DEMOLITION	82.2	96.2	92.1	90.8	94.6	93.5	89.8	94.6	93.2	81.8	96.2	91.9	82.6	100.1	94.9	82.0	100.1	94.7
0310	Concrete Forming & Accessories	104.8	58.1	64.5	107.1	49.4	57.3	106.3	58.0	64.6	107.3	58.0	64.7	100.2	87.5	89.3	97.8	109.1	107.6
0320	Concrete Reinforcing	102.0	80.2	91.1	109.8	80.1	95.0	110.7	80.2	95.5	104.3	80.2	92.3	83.0	87.3	85.2	83.0	87.3	85.2
0330	Cast-in-Place Concrete	88.2	72.8	81.8	87.0	60.0	75.8	87.0	72.7	81.1	96.4	72.7	86.6	89.5	113.1	99.3	89.5	113.1	99.3
03	CONCRETE	97.5	67.9	82.9	109.3	59.6	84.8	107.8	67.8	88.1	116.9	67.8	92.6	93.5	96.2	94.8	93.3	105.8	99.5
04	MASONRY	97.8	59.7	74.2	109.1	59.7	78.5	109.3	59.7	78.6	111.0	59.7	79.3	94.6	96.9	96.0	102.1	96.9	98.9
05	METALS	101.5	78.2	94.3	98.3	77.6	91.9	99.3	78.0	92.7	106.1	78.0	97.4	95.6	89.3	93.6	95.5	89.2	93.6
06	WOOD, PLASTICS & COMPOSITES	81.5	56.2	67.2	84.4	45.3	62.3	82.9	56.2	67.8	83.2	56.2	68.0	102.2	85.5	92.8	99.2	115.1	108.1
07	THERMAL & MOISTURE PROTECTION	96.9	61.8	82.6	99.5	59.4	83.3	99.5	61.8	84.2	103.8	61.8	86.8	98.0	84.8	92.7	98.0	83.1	92.0
08	OPENINGS	94.3	57.1	85.5	98.3	50.1	86.9	98.3	57.1	88.5	96.1	57.1	86.9	103.5	88.1	99.9	103.5	104.2	103.7
0920	Plaster & Gypsum Board	75.6	54.8	61.4	77.9	43.5	54.5	76.0	54.8	61.6	83.0	54.8	63.8	99.8	84.4	89.3	97.9	114.9	109.5
0950, 0980	Ceilings & Acoustic Treatment	105.1	54.8	71.6	105.1	43.5	64.2	105.1	54.8	71.6	99.2	54.8	69.6	92.3	84.4	87.1	92.3	114.9	107.3
0960	Flooring	98.0	48.6	83.3	101.2	36.1	81.8	100.9	48.6	85.3	102.2	48.6	86.2	101.6	106.5	103.1	100.8	106.5	102.5
0970, 0990	Wall Finishes & Painting/Coating	102.9	62.0	78.3	102.9	38.3	64.1	102.9	49.0	70.5	106.5	49.0	71.9	95.7	106.8	102.3	95.7	106.8	102.3
09	FINISHES	96.5	56.0	74.0	99.5	44.5	68.9	99.1	54.6	74.3	98.2	54.6	73.9	97.2	92.6	94.6	96.7	110.1	104.2
COVERS	DIVS. 10 - 14, 25, 28, 41, 43, 44, 46	100.0	54.1	90.8	100.0	47.0	89.4	100.0	54.0	90.8	100.0	54.0	90.8	100.0	100.3	100.1	100.0	103.5	100.7
21, 22, 23	FIRE SUPPRESSION, PLUMBING & HVAC	100.0	69.0	87.6	97.5	68.6	85.9	100.0	69.0	87.6	100.1	69.0	87.6	95.2	98.5	96.5	95.2	98.4	96.5
26, 27, 3370	ELECTRICAL, COMMUNICATIONS & UTIL.	95.7	74.3	84.5	101.2	74.3	87.1	96.2	61.2	77.9	98.6	61.2	79.1	98.6	91.5	94.9	98.6	62.6	79.8
MF2010	WEIGHTED AVERAGE	97.9	68.8	85.2	100.1	65.3	84.9	100.1	66.7	85.6	102.2	66.8	86.8	96.6	94.7	95.8	96.9	95.3	96.2

VERMONT

DIVISION		BRATTLEBORO 053 MAT.	INST.	TOTAL	BURLINGTON 054 MAT.	INST.	TOTAL	GUILDHALL 059 MAT.	INST.	TOTAL	MONTPELIER 056 MAT.	INST.	TOTAL	RUTLAND 057 MAT.	INST.	TOTAL	ST. JOHNSBURY 058 MAT.	INST.	TOTAL
015433	CONTRACTOR EQUIPMENT		100.6	100.6		100.6	100.6		100.6	100.6		100.6	100.6		100.6	100.6		100.6	100.6
0241, 31 - 34	SITE & INFRASTRUCTURE, DEMOLITION	83.4	100.1	95.1	86.2	100.0	95.9	81.7	98.7	93.6	86.6	99.8	95.8	85.9	99.8	95.6	81.7	98.7	93.6
0310	Concrete Forming & Accessories	100.5	87.4	89.2	98.0	89.6	90.8	98.1	80.1	82.6	101.8	86.1	88.2	100.8	89.6	91.1	96.5	80.1	82.4
0320	Concrete Reinforcing	82.2	87.3	84.7	105.7	87.2	96.4	83.8	87.2	85.5	89.0	87.2	88.1	103.7	87.2	95.5	82.2	87.2	84.7
0330	Cast-in-Place Concrete	92.3	113.1	100.9	102.6	112.0	106.5	86.8	103.2	93.6	105.0	111.9	107.9	87.7	111.9	97.8	86.8	103.2	93.6
03	CONCRETE	95.5	96.2	95.9	104.0	96.7	100.4	91.0	89.5	90.3	102.8	95.2	99.0	96.9	96.7	96.8	90.7	89.5	90.1
04	MASONRY	101.1	96.9	98.5	104.8	95.4	99.0	101.3	79.6	87.8	100.1	95.4	97.2	85.8	95.4	91.7	124.9	79.6	96.9
05	METALS	95.5	89.2	93.6	104.0	88.4	99.2	95.6	88.3	93.3	100.2	88.3	96.5	101.0	88.4	97.1	95.6	88.3	93.3
06	WOOD, PLASTICS & COMPOSITES	102.6	85.5	92.9	98.3	90.3	93.8	98.5	85.5	91.2	96.4	85.5	90.3	102.7	90.3	95.7	93.6	85.5	89.0
07	THERMAL & MOISTURE PROTECTION	98.1	80.0	90.8	104.3	82.5	95.4	97.9	72.6	87.6	105.0	82.0	95.6	98.2	82.5	91.8	97.8	72.6	87.6
08	OPENINGS	103.5	88.1	99.9	107.5	86.4	102.5	103.5	83.8	98.8	103.8	83.8	99.1	106.6	86.4	101.8	103.5	83.8	98.8
0920	Plaster & Gypsum Board	99.8	84.4	89.3	100.5	89.3	92.9	106.1	84.4	91.3	105.4	84.4	91.1	100.5	89.3	92.9	108.0	84.4	91.9
0950, 0980	Ceilings & Acoustic Treatment	92.3	84.4	87.1	96.0	89.3	91.6	92.3	84.4	87.1	102.5	84.4	90.5	97.0	89.3	91.9	92.3	84.4	87.1
0960	Flooring	101.7	106.5	103.2	103.1	106.5	104.1	104.6	106.5	105.2	104.0	106.5	104.8	101.6	106.5	103.1	107.7	106.5	107.3
0970, 0990	Wall Finishes & Painting/Coating	95.7	106.8	102.3	100.4	85.3	91.4	95.7	85.3	89.4	100.5	85.3	91.4	95.7	85.3	89.4	95.7	85.3	89.4
09	FINISHES	97.3	92.6	94.7	99.1	92.7	95.5	98.8	85.9	91.6	101.0	89.8	94.8	98.4	92.7	95.2	99.9	85.9	92.1
COVERS	DIVS. 10 - 14, 25, 28, 41, 43, 44, 46	100.0	100.3	100.1	100.0	100.2	100.0	100.0	94.3	98.9	100.0	99.7	99.9	100.0	100.2	100.0	100.0	94.3	98.9
21, 22, 23	FIRE SUPPRESSION, PLUMBING & HVAC	95.2	98.4	96.5	99.9	73.3	89.3	95.2	65.3	83.2	95.0	73.3	86.3	100.1	73.3	89.3	95.2	65.3	83.2
26, 27, 3370	ELECTRICAL, COMMUNICATIONS & UTIL.	98.6	91.5	94.9	98.0	62.6	79.5	98.6	62.6	79.8	98.0	62.6	79.5	98.6	62.6	79.8	98.6	62.6	79.8
MF2010	WEIGHTED AVERAGE	97.2	94.5	96.0	101.5	85.1	94.4	96.8	79.2	89.1	99.2	84.3	92.7	99.2	85.1	93.0	97.9	79.2	89.8

VERMONT / VIRGINIA

DIVISION		WHITE RIVER JCT. 050 MAT.	INST.	TOTAL	ALEXANDRIA 223 MAT.	INST.	TOTAL	ARLINGTON 222 MAT.	INST.	TOTAL	BRISTOL 242 MAT.	INST.	TOTAL	CHARLOTTESVILLE 229 MAT.	INST.	TOTAL	CULPEPER 227 MAT.	INST.	TOTAL
015433	CONTRACTOR EQUIPMENT		100.6	100.6		102.1	102.1		100.8	100.8		100.8	100.8		105.1	105.1		100.8	100.8
0241, 31 - 34	SITE & INFRASTRUCTURE, DEMOLITION	85.7	98.8	94.9	113.5	89.3	96.5	123.7	87.3	98.2	107.8	85.7	92.3	112.6	87.7	95.1	111.2	87.2	94.3
0310	Concrete Forming & Accessories	95.0	80.7	82.7	93.3	73.6	76.3	92.5	73.0	75.7	88.4	43.4	49.6	86.8	49.6	54.7	83.9	72.3	73.9
0320	Concrete Reinforcing	83.0	87.2	85.1	85.0	87.0	86.0	95.9	87.0	91.5	95.9	67.3	81.6	95.3	73.0	84.2	95.9	86.9	91.4
0330	Cast-in-Place Concrete	92.3	104.1	97.2	107.5	82.2	97.0	104.6	81.4	95.0	104.1	49.1	81.3	108.3	56.1	86.6	107.1	68.8	91.2
03	CONCRETE	97.3	90.1	94.2	101.2	80.1	92.8	105.6	79.6	92.8	102.1	51.7	77.2	102.8	57.9	80.7	100.1	74.9	87.6
04	MASONRY	112.6	81.2	93.1	86.0	72.9	77.8	99.1	71.3	81.9	89.1	52.3	66.3	112.3	54.2	76.3	100.9	71.2	82.5
05	METALS	95.6	88.3	93.3	102.5	97.0	100.8	101.1	97.4	99.9	99.9	85.8	95.6	100.2	90.6	97.2	100.3	95.4	98.8
06	WOOD, PLASTICS & COMPOSITES	95.9	85.5	90.0	98.1	71.9	83.3	94.4	71.9	81.7	86.6	40.9	60.8	85.1	46.6	63.4	83.7	71.9	77.1
07	THERMAL & MOISTURE PROTECTION	98.2	73.3	88.1	103.2	82.4	94.7	105.1	81.2	95.4	104.7	61.3	87.1	104.3	69.0	90.0	104.5	78.7	94.0
08	OPENINGS	103.5	83.8	98.8	96.4	75.6	91.5	94.6	75.6	90.1	97.4	46.8	85.5	95.7	52.7	85.5	96.0	75.6	91.2
0920	Plaster & Gypsum Board	96.5	84.4	88.3	108.4	70.9	82.9	104.4	70.9	81.6	100.1	38.9	58.4	100.1	44.1	62.0	100.3	70.9	80.3
0950, 0980	Ceilings & Acoustic Treatment	92.3	84.4	87.1	97.7	70.9	79.9	95.1	70.9	79.0	94.2	38.9	57.4	94.2	44.1	60.8	95.1	70.9	79.0
0960	Flooring	99.7	106.5	101.8	106.7	84.5	100.0	105.2	82.7	98.5	101.9	67.7	91.7	100.6	67.7	90.7	100.6	82.7	95.2
0970, 0990	Wall Finishes & Painting/Coating	95.7	85.3	89.4	120.5	79.9	96.1	120.5	79.9	96.1	106.3	55.5	75.7	106.3	77.7	89.1	120.5	77.7	94.8
09	FINISHES	96.5	86.3	90.8	102.9	75.5	87.6	102.6	74.7	87.0	99.2	48.2	70.8	98.8	54.6	74.2	99.6	74.3	85.5
COVERS	DIVS. 10 - 14, 25, 28, 41, 43, 44, 46	100.0	94.9	99.0	100.0	88.5	97.7	100.0	86.0	97.2	100.0	69.5	93.9	100.0	78.0	95.6	100.0	86.0	97.2
21, 22, 23	FIRE SUPPRESSION, PLUMBING & HVAC	95.2	66.1	83.5	100.3	87.7	95.2	100.3	86.8	94.9	95.4	51.6	77.8	95.4	68.7	84.7	95.4	73.2	86.5
26, 27, 3370	ELECTRICAL, COMMUNICATIONS & UTIL.	98.6	62.6	79.8	95.8	99.2	97.6	93.4	99.2	96.5	95.5	36.2	64.6	95.4	70.8	82.6	98.0	99.2	98.6
MF2010	WEIGHTED AVERAGE	97.9	79.7	90.0	99.8	85.4	93.5	100.6	84.7	93.6	98.1	55.6	79.6	99.2	67.3	85.3	98.6	80.8	90.9

VIRGINIA

DIVISION		FAIRFAX 220 - 221			FARMVILLE 239			FREDERICKSBURG 224 - 225			GRUNDY 246			HARRISONBURG 228			LYNCHBURG 245		
		MAT.	INST.	TOTAL	MAT.	INST.	TOTAL	MAT.	INST.	TOTAL	MAT.	INST.	TOTAL	MAT.	INST.	TOTAL	MAT.	INST.	TOTAL
015433	CONTRACTOR EQUIPMENT		100.8	100.8		105.1	105.1		100.8	100.8		100.8	100.8		100.8	100.8		100.8	100.8
0241, 31 - 34	SITE & INFRASTRUCTURE, DEMOLITION	122.4	87.3	97.8	107.2	87.2	93.2	110.8	87.2	94.2	105.6	84.4	90.7	119.4	85.9	95.9	106.5	85.9	92.1
0310	Concrete Forming & Accessories	86.8	72.8	74.7	100.4	44.6	52.3	86.8	70.8	73.0	91.5	37.2	44.6	82.9	43.5	48.9	88.4	61.6	65.3
0320	Concrete Reinforcing	95.9	87.0	91.5	94.7	51.5	73.1	96.7	86.9	91.8	94.6	52.0	73.3	95.9	66.9	81.5	95.3	67.3	81.3
0330	Cast-in-Place Concrete	104.6	81.3	94.9	106.8	54.1	85.0	106.2	64.7	89.0	104.1	48.1	80.9	104.6	58.8	85.6	104.1	58.4	85.2
03	CONCRETE	105.3	79.4	92.5	101.4	50.9	76.5	99.8	72.8	86.5	100.9	45.3	73.5	103.2	54.9	79.3	100.8	63.0	82.1
04	MASONRY	99.0	71.3	81.8	95.6	45.6	64.7	99.9	71.2	82.1	90.9	48.1	64.4	97.4	51.2	68.8	104.9	54.1	73.5
05	METALS	100.4	97.0	99.3	100.0	78.2	93.3	100.3	96.2	99.0	99.9	71.0	91.0	100.2	85.1	95.6	100.1	86.3	95.9
06	WOOD, PLASTICS & COMPOSITES	86.6	71.9	78.3	101.9	45.0	69.8	86.6	69.6	77.0	89.6	35.8	59.3	82.7	39.8	58.5	86.6	64.0	73.9
07	THERMAL & MOISTURE PROTECTION	105.0	73.9	92.4	105.3	50.2	83.0	104.5	79.1	94.2	104.7	46.1	80.9	104.9	64.5	88.5	104.5	65.1	88.5
08	OPENINGS	94.6	75.6	90.1	94.9	44.0	82.9	95.7	74.0	90.6	97.4	35.2	82.7	96.0	50.6	85.3	96.0	59.4	87.3
0920	Plaster & Gypsum Board	100.3	70.9	80.3	109.3	42.5	63.8	100.3	68.5	78.7	100.1	33.7	54.9	100.1	37.8	57.7	100.1	62.7	74.7
0950, 0980	Ceilings & Acoustic Treatment	95.1	70.9	79.0	92.5	42.5	59.2	95.1	68.5	77.4	94.2	33.7	53.9	94.2	37.8	56.7	94.2	62.7	73.3
0960	Flooring	102.2	82.7	96.4	108.6	61.4	94.5	102.2	82.7	96.4	103.2	34.3	82.6	100.3	75.3	92.9	101.9	67.7	91.7
0970, 0990	Wall Finishes & Painting/Coating	120.5	79.9	96.1	107.7	39.6	66.7	120.5	77.7	94.8	106.3	35.9	64.0	120.5	55.5	81.4	106.3	55.5	75.7
09	FINISHES	101.2	74.7	86.4	101.8	47.0	71.3	100.1	72.9	86.0	99.3	35.9	64.0	100.0	48.9	71.5	99.0	61.5	78.1
COVERS	DIVS. 10 - 14, 25, 28, 41, 43, 44, 46	100.0	86.0	97.2	100.0	46.8	89.3	100.0	81.9	96.4	100.0	44.8	88.9	100.0	69.3	93.8	100.0	72.7	94.5
21, 22, 23	FIRE SUPPRESSION, PLUMBING & HVAC	95.4	86.8	91.9	95.3	44.3	74.9	95.4	86.5	91.8	95.4	63.5	82.6	95.4	67.1	84.1	95.4	68.4	84.6
26, 27, 3370	ELECTRICAL, COMMUNICATIONS & UTIL.	96.6	99.2	98.0	90.4	49.4	69.0	93.6	99.2	96.6	95.5	45.7	69.5	95.7	98.7	97.3	96.6	53.9	74.3
MF2010	WEIGHTED AVERAGE	99.3	84.4	92.8	97.8	53.3	78.5	98.2	83.0	91.6	98.0	53.4	78.6	98.8	68.1	85.5	98.6	66.1	84.5

VIRGINIA

DIVISION		NEWPORT NEWS 236			NORFOLK 233 - 235			PETERSBURG 238			PORTSMOUTH 237			PULASKI 243			RICHMOND 230 - 232		
		MAT.	INST.	TOTAL	MAT.	INST.	TOTAL	MAT.	INST.	TOTAL	MAT.	INST.	TOTAL	MAT.	INST.	TOTAL	MAT.	INST.	TOTAL
015433	CONTRACTOR EQUIPMENT		105.1	105.1		105.7	105.7		105.1	105.1		105.0	105.0		100.8	100.8		105.0	105.0
0241, 31 - 34	SITE & INFRASTRUCTURE, DEMOLITION	106.2	88.4	93.7	105.7	89.4	94.3	109.7	88.6	94.9	104.7	88.2	93.1	104.9	85.1	91.0	103.5	88.6	93.0
0310	Concrete Forming & Accessories	99.7	65.4	70.1	99.5	65.6	70.2	93.0	58.3	63.1	88.9	54.2	58.9	91.5	39.5	46.6	100.7	58.3	64.1
0320	Concrete Reinforcing	94.4	72.8	83.6	99.5	72.8	86.2	94.1	73.2	83.6	94.1	72.8	83.4	94.6	66.7	80.7	100.7	73.2	87.0
0330	Cast-in-Place Concrete	103.8	66.8	88.5	111.9	66.9	93.2	110.3	54.2	87.0	102.8	66.7	87.8	104.1	48.9	81.2	98.8	54.2	80.3
03	CONCRETE	98.6	68.6	83.8	103.3	68.7	86.2	103.6	61.2	82.7	97.3	63.5	80.7	100.9	49.6	75.6	97.3	61.2	79.5
04	MASONRY	90.6	54.9	68.5	99.1	54.9	71.7	103.3	53.6	72.5	96.0	54.9	70.6	85.9	49.1	63.1	92.1	53.5	68.2
05	METALS	102.2	90.4	98.6	102.0	90.5	98.4	100.1	91.1	97.3	101.2	89.7	97.7	100.0	83.8	95.0	106.2	91.1	101.5
06	WOOD, PLASTICS & COMPOSITES	100.6	67.7	82.0	97.0	67.7	80.5	91.4	59.8	73.6	87.6	52.6	67.8	89.6	37.6	60.3	101.6	59.8	78.0
07	THERMAL & MOISTURE PROTECTION	105.3	69.7	90.8	101.9	69.7	88.8	105.3	69.6	90.8	105.3	67.0	89.7	104.7	51.0	82.9	103.7	69.6	89.8
08	OPENINGS	95.3	63.3	87.7	94.2	63.3	86.9	94.6	59.9	86.4	95.4	55.0	85.8	97.5	43.2	84.6	99.0	59.9	89.8
0920	Plaster & Gypsum Board	110.2	65.8	80.0	106.3	65.8	78.8	101.7	57.7	71.8	102.0	50.2	66.8	100.1	35.5	56.1	104.7	57.7	72.8
0950, 0980	Ceilings & Acoustic Treatment	96.1	65.8	75.9	97.7	65.8	76.5	93.4	57.7	69.7	96.1	50.2	65.6	94.2	35.5	55.1	100.4	57.7	72.0
0960	Flooring	108.6	67.7	96.4	103.5	67.7	92.8	104.7	72.5	95.1	101.7	67.7	91.5	103.2	67.7	92.6	109.4	72.5	98.4
0970, 0990	Wall Finishes & Painting/Coating	107.7	42.9	68.8	105.8	77.7	88.9	107.7	77.7	89.7	107.7	77.7	89.7	106.3	55.5	75.7	107.0	77.7	89.4
09	FINISHES	102.5	63.5	80.8	100.7	67.4	82.2	100.1	62.5	79.1	99.5	57.9	76.3	99.3	44.7	68.9	104.4	62.5	81.1
COVERS	DIVS. 10 - 14, 25, 28, 41, 43, 44, 46	100.0	75.4	95.1	100.0	75.4	95.1	100.0	78.2	95.6	100.0	73.7	94.7	100.0	45.0	89.0	100.0	78.2	95.6
21, 22, 23	FIRE SUPPRESSION, PLUMBING & HVAC	100.2	64.1	85.7	100.0	64.7	85.8	95.3	66.9	83.9	100.2	64.7	86.0	95.4	63.4	82.5	100.0	66.9	86.7
26, 27, 3370	ELECTRICAL, COMMUNICATIONS & UTIL.	93.1	60.3	76.0	96.9	59.7	77.4	93.3	70.8	81.5	91.4	59.7	74.9	95.5	55.7	74.7	96.2	70.8	83.0
MF2010	WEIGHTED AVERAGE	99.2	68.2	85.7	100.0	68.8	86.4	98.6	68.9	85.6	98.6	66.1	84.5	97.7	58.3	80.6	100.4	68.9	86.7

DIVISION		VIRGINIA									WASHINGTON								
		ROANOKE 240 - 241			STAUNTON 244			WINCHESTER 226			CLARKSTON 994			EVERETT 982			OLYMPIA 985		
		MAT.	INST.	TOTAL	MAT.	INST.	TOTAL	MAT.	INST.	TOTAL	MAT.	INST.	TOTAL	MAT.	INST.	TOTAL	MAT.	INST.	TOTAL
015433	CONTRACTOR EQUIPMENT		100.8	100.8		105.1	105.1		100.8	100.8		90.4	90.4		102.1	102.1		102.1	102.1
0241, 31 - 34	SITE & INFRASTRUCTURE, DEMOLITION	105.2	85.9	91.7	109.1	87.3	93.8	118.1	87.2	96.4	97.1	90.0	92.1	89.4	110.3	104.1	90.2	110.4	104.4
0310	Concrete Forming & Accessories	97.9	61.8	66.8	91.1	51.1	56.6	85.2	70.8	72.8	114.8	68.8	75.1	114.9	99.6	101.7	103.1	99.8	100.2
0320	Concrete Reinforcing	95.6	67.4	81.5	95.3	50.5	72.9	95.3	86.3	90.8	105.7	87.4	96.6	110.2	100.2	105.2	116.1	100.2	108.2
0330	Cast-in-Place Concrete	118.3	58.5	93.5	108.3	52.0	84.9	104.6	64.7	88.1	97.0	83.2	91.3	99.8	103.8	101.5	89.2	105.4	96.0
03	CONCRETE	105.5	63.1	84.6	102.3	53.0	78.0	102.6	72.7	87.9	110.7	77.4	94.3	98.7	100.7	99.7	96.9	101.3	99.1
04	MASONRY	92.1	54.1	68.6	100.6	52.3	70.7	95.1	60.0	73.3	97.2	80.7	87.0	111.9	99.0	103.9	103.1	99.9	101.1
05	METALS	102.2	86.5	97.4	100.2	81.7	94.5	100.3	94.8	98.6	88.1	81.2	86.0	104.3	91.7	100.4	104.2	91.6	100.3
06	WOOD, PLASTICS & COMPOSITES	99.0	64.0	79.3	89.6	51.0	67.8	85.1	69.6	76.4	103.3	65.2	81.8	112.1	99.3	104.9	94.6	99.3	97.2
07	THERMAL & MOISTURE PROTECTION	104.3	67.2	89.3	104.3	53.0	83.5	105.0	76.2	93.3	142.7	76.9	116.0	100.5	100.5	100.5	101.6	97.8	100.1
08	OPENINGS	96.4	59.4	87.6	96.0	49.2	84.9	97.5	74.7	92.1	106.7	69.7	98.0	101.9	99.8	101.4	103.5	99.8	102.6
0920	Plaster & Gypsum Board	108.4	62.7	77.3	100.1	48.6	65.1	100.3	68.5	78.7	130.6	64.0	85.3	110.7	99.2	102.9	103.1	99.2	100.5
0950, 0980	Ceilings & Acoustic Treatment	97.7	62.7	74.5	94.2	48.6	63.9	95.1	68.5	77.4	97.9	64.0	75.3	99.9	99.2	99.5	106.3	99.2	101.6
0960	Flooring	106.7	67.7	95.0	102.7	40.2	84.0	101.6	82.7	96.0	98.3	48.0	83.2	117.9	93.3	110.6	109.2	93.4	104.5
0970, 0990	Wall Finishes & Painting/Coating	106.3	55.5	75.7	106.3	35.3	63.6	120.5	89.1	101.6	106.4	59.8	78.4	104.8	90.1	96.0	110.3	90.1	98.1
09	FINISHES	101.8	62.4	79.8	99.2	47.6	70.4	100.5	74.2	85.9	114.8	62.6	85.7	109.0	97.1	102.4	104.6	97.4	100.6
COVERS	DIVS. 10 - 14, 25, 28, 41, 43, 44, 46	100.0	72.7	94.5	100.0	72.6	94.5	100.0	85.7	97.1	100.0	77.3	95.5	100.0	99.6	99.9	100.0	100.1	100.0
21, 22, 23	FIRE SUPPRESSION, PLUMBING & HVAC	100.3	65.8	86.5	95.4	60.1	81.2	95.4	86.8	91.9	95.4	84.7	91.1	100.1	100.3	100.2	100.0	100.8	100.3
26, 27, 3370	ELECTRICAL, COMMUNICATIONS & UTIL.	95.5	55.7	74.7	94.3	74.6	84.0	94.1	99.2	96.8	94.9	94.4	94.6	103.0	98.5	100.7	101.0	99.7	100.3
MF2010	WEIGHTED AVERAGE	100.2	66.0	85.3	98.4	62.7	82.9	98.7	82.1	91.5	100.6	80.7	92.0	102.1	99.6	101.0	101.0	100.0	100.6

DIVISION		WASHINGTON																	
		RICHLAND 993			SEATTLE 980-981,987			SPOKANE 990-992			TACOMA 983-984			VANCOUVER 986			WENATCHEE 988		
		MAT.	INST.	TOTAL	MAT.	INST.	TOTAL	MAT.	INST.	TOTAL	MAT.	INST.	TOTAL	MAT.	INST.	TOTAL	MAT.	INST.	TOTAL
015433	CONTRACTOR EQUIPMENT		90.4	90.4		102.0	102.0		90.4	90.4		102.1	102.1		97.1	97.1		102.1	102.1
0241, 31 - 34	SITE & INFRASTRUCTURE, DEMOLITION	99.6	90.8	93.4	94.5	108.6	104.4	98.7	90.8	93.2	92.4	110.4	105.0	102.3	98.1	99.3	101.4	109.2	106.9
0310	Concrete Forming & Accessories	114.9	78.4	83.4	106.9	100.3	101.2	119.8	78.0	83.7	105.5	99.9	100.6	106.2	92.1	94.0	107.2	77.5	81.6
0320	Concrete Reinforcing	101.4	87.6	94.5	112.2	100.3	106.3	102.1	87.6	94.9	109.0	100.2	104.6	109.9	100.0	104.9	109.8	89.3	99.6
0330	Cast-in-Place Concrete	97.2	85.5	92.4	103.6	105.6	104.5	101.0	85.3	94.5	102.6	105.4	103.8	114.6	99.5	108.3	104.8	77.4	93.4
03	CONCRETE	110.3	82.6	96.6	102.0	101.7	101.8	112.6	82.3	97.6	100.5	101.3	100.9	110.5	95.9	103.3	108.4	79.8	94.3
04	MASONRY	99.3	83.2	89.3	109.2	99.9	103.4	99.9	83.8	89.9	106.7	99.9	102.5	107.3	96.7	100.7	109.1	91.5	98.2
05	METALS	88.5	83.1	87.1	104.5	93.4	101.1	90.8	83.7	88.6	106.0	91.6	101.6	103.4	92.1	99.9	103.5	86.1	98.1
06	WOOD, PLASTICS & COMPOSITES	103.4	75.7	87.8	106.9	100.3	100.6	112.1	75.7	91.6	101.3	99.3	100.2	93.1	91.9	92.5	102.9	75.9	87.6
07	THERMAL & MOISTURE PROTECTION	144.1	79.7	117.9	97.6	100.9	99.0	140.6	79.1	115.6	100.2	98.7	99.6	100.6	92.5	97.3	100.8	82.2	93.3
08	OPENINGS	109.2	71.2	100.2	105.2	99.8	103.9	109.7	71.7	100.7	102.7	99.8	102.0	98.5	94.4	97.5	102.2	71.5	94.9
0920	Plaster & Gypsum Board	130.6	74.8	92.6	106.9	99.2	101.7	121.5	74.8	89.7	111.5	99.2	103.1	109.4	91.9	97.5	114.0	75.1	87.5
0950, 0980	Ceilings & Acoustic Treatment	104.8	74.8	84.8	101.8	99.2	100.1	99.8	74.8	83.2	103.5	99.2	100.6	98.4	91.9	94.1	95.3	75.1	81.8
0960	Flooring	98.7	81.6	93.5	110.9	101.0	108.0	98.2	86.9	94.8	111.4	93.4	106.0	118.1	104.0	113.9	114.1	63.8	99.1
0970, 0990	Wall Finishes & Painting/Coating	106.4	66.2	82.2	104.2	90.1	95.7	106.6	72.4	86.0	104.8	90.1	96.0	107.2	68.4	83.9	104.8	66.2	81.6
09	FINISHES	116.6	76.7	94.4	108.1	98.9	102.9	114.3	78.5	94.3	108.2	97.4	102.2	105.6	91.9	98.0	108.5	72.9	88.7
COVERS	DIVS. 10 - 14, 25, 28, 41, 43, 44, 46	100.0	87.2	97.4	100.0	100.1	100.0	100.0	87.1	97.4	100.0	100.1	100.0	100.0	62.0	92.4	100.0	78.5	95.7
21, 22, 23	FIRE SUPPRESSION, PLUMBING & HVAC	100.3	109.7	104.1	100.0	117.1	106.8	100.2	85.9	94.5	100.1	100.8	100.4	100.2	88.6	95.5	95.2	87.9	92.3
26, 27, 3370	ELECTRICAL, COMMUNICATIONS & UTIL.	92.1	94.4	93.3	102.4	107.0	104.8	90.5	79.1	84.5	102.8	99.7	101.2	107.5	101.0	104.1	103.7	98.5	101.0
MF2010	WEIGHTED AVERAGE	102.2	89.6	96.7	102.5	104.8	103.5	102.5	82.7	93.8	102.3	100.0	101.3	103.1	93.2	98.8	102.0	87.1	95.5

DIVISION		WASHINGTON			WEST VIRGINIA														
		YAKIMA 989			BECKLEY 258 - 259			BLUEFIELD 247 - 248			BUCKHANNON 262			CHARLESTON 250 - 253			CLARKSBURG 263 - 264		
		MAT.	INST.	TOTAL	MAT.	INST.	TOTAL	MAT.	INST.	TOTAL	MAT.	INST.	TOTAL	MAT.	INST.	TOTAL	MAT.	INST.	TOTAL
015433	CONTRACTOR EQUIPMENT		102.1	102.1		100.8	100.8		100.8	100.8		100.8	100.8		100.8	100.8		100.8	100.8
0241, 31 - 34	SITE & INFRASTRUCTURE, DEMOLITION	94.7	109.8	105.3	97.9	89.2	91.8	99.6	89.2	92.3	105.8	89.2	94.1	99.0	90.0	92.7	106.3	89.2	94.3
0310	Concrete Forming & Accessories	106.0	99.2	100.3	86.3	92.0	91.2	88.3	91.9	91.4	87.7	92.2	91.6	99.6	93.4	94.2	85.3	92.1	91.1
0320	Concrete Reinforcing	109.5	88.8	99.2	92.3	89.4	90.9	94.2	84.9	89.6	94.8	85.0	89.9	100.6	89.5	95.1	94.8	84.4	89.6
0330	Cast-in-Place Concrete	109.6	84.4	99.2	102.0	102.1	102.0	101.9	102.1	102.0	101.6	100.3	101.0	100.6	102.7	101.4	111.3	98.4	105.9
03	CONCRETE	105.1	90.0	97.7	96.5	95.5	96.0	96.9	94.7	95.8	99.7	94.2	97.0	98.1	96.4	97.2	103.7	93.4	98.6
04	MASONRY	100.4	81.6	88.8	90.8	93.4	92.4	87.5	93.4	91.1	97.4	92.3	94.2	89.2	95.3	93.0	100.7	92.3	95.5
05	METALS	104.2	85.7	98.5	101.2	98.2	100.3	100.2	96.5	99.1	100.4	97.3	99.4	99.8	98.9	99.5	100.4	96.9	99.3
06	WOOD, PLASTICS & COMPOSITES	101.7	99.3	100.4	85.1	92.8	89.4	88.6	92.8	91.0	87.9	92.8	90.6	101.1	92.8	96.4	84.4	92.8	89.1
07	THERMAL & MOISTURE PROTECTION	100.3	81.6	92.7	107.1	89.4	99.9	104.4	89.4	98.4	104.7	90.0	98.7	103.6	90.2	98.2	104.6	88.9	98.3
08	OPENINGS	102.2	81.0	97.2	96.1	85.0	93.5	97.9	83.9	94.6	97.9	83.9	94.6	98.1	85.0	95.0	97.9	85.1	94.9
0920	Plaster & Gypsum Board	111.1	99.2	103.0	93.2	92.4	92.7	99.3	92.4	94.6	99.7	92.4	94.7	97.5	92.4	94.0	97.5	92.4	94.0
0950, 0980	Ceilings & Acoustic Treatment	97.3	99.2	98.6	93.4	92.4	92.7	92.4	92.4	92.4	94.2	92.4	93.0	102.2	92.4	95.7	94.2	92.4	93.0
0960	Flooring	112.4	59.1	96.4	100.5	114.1	104.6	99.8	114.1	104.1	99.5	114.1	103.9	104.4	114.1	107.3	98.6	114.1	103.2
0970, 0990	Wall Finishes & Painting/Coating	104.8	72.4	85.3	107.1	93.5	98.9	106.3	93.5	98.6	106.3	93.8	98.8	106.6	93.5	98.7	106.3	93.8	98.8
09	FINISHES	107.2	86.5	95.7	97.8	96.9	97.3	97.5	96.9	97.2	98.4	96.7	97.4	102.4	97.4	99.6	97.7	96.7	97.1
COVERS	DIVS. 10 - 14, 25, 28, 41, 43, 44, 46	100.0	97.3	99.5	100.0	56.6	91.3	100.0	56.6	91.3	100.0	96.7	99.3	100.0	97.7	99.5	100.0	96.7	99.3
21, 22, 23	FIRE SUPPRESSION, PLUMBING & HVAC	100.1	109.1	103.7	95.5	91.5	93.9	95.4	91.5	93.8	95.4	92.3	94.2	100.1	92.9	97.2	95.4	92.2	94.1
26, 27, 3370	ELECTRICAL, COMMUNICATIONS & UTIL.	105.9	94.4	99.9	91.2	91.9	91.6	94.4	91.9	93.1	95.8	96.8	96.3	96.3	91.9	94.0	95.8	96.8	96.3
MF2010	WEIGHTED AVERAGE	102.5	94.4	99.0	96.9	92.0	94.8	97.1	91.7	94.7	98.2	93.6	96.2	99.0	94.1	96.9	98.8	93.5	96.5

DIVISION		WEST VIRGINIA																	
		GASSAWAY 266			HUNTINGTON 255 - 257			LEWISBURG 249			MARTINSBURG 254			MORGANTOWN 265			PARKERSBURG 261		
		MAT.	INST.	TOTAL	MAT.	INST.	TOTAL	MAT.	INST.	TOTAL	MAT.	INST.	TOTAL	MAT.	INST.	TOTAL	MAT.	INST.	TOTAL
015433	CONTRACTOR EQUIPMENT		100.8	100.8		100.8	100.8		100.8	100.8		100.8	100.8		100.8	100.8		100.8	100.8
0241, 31 - 34	SITE & INFRASTRUCTURE, DEMOLITION	103.2	89.2	93.3	102.4	90.4	94.0	115.3	89.2	97.0	101.4	89.7	93.2	100.6	89.8	93.0	108.8	89.9	95.5
0310	Concrete Forming & Accessories	87.2	92.2	91.5	98.2	96.0	96.3	85.6	91.8	91.0	86.3	82.4	83.0	85.6	91.8	91.0	89.8	90.0	90.0
0320	Concrete Reinforcing	94.8	85.0	89.9	93.7	90.6	92.2	94.8	84.9	89.9	92.3	83.0	87.6	94.8	84.3	89.6	94.2	84.8	89.5
0330	Cast-in-Place Concrete	106.3	101.0	104.1	111.1	103.5	108.0	101.9	102.1	102.0	106.8	96.0	102.3	101.5	100.1	101.0	103.8	97.1	101.0
03	CONCRETE	100.2	94.4	97.3	101.8	98.0	99.9	105.8	94.6	100.3	99.9	88.0	94.1	96.6	93.8	95.3	101.6	92.1	96.9
04	MASONRY	101.5	92.3	95.8	89.8	99.9	96.0	90.3	93.4	92.2	91.7	85.6	87.9	117.9	92.3	102.0	78.3	90.7	86.0
05	METALS	100.3	97.2	99.4	103.6	99.5	102.3	100.3	96.5	99.1	101.6	94.9	99.5	100.4	96.7	99.3	101.0	96.8	99.7
06	WOOD, PLASTICS & COMPOSITES	87.0	92.8	90.2	97.2	95.4	96.2	84.7	92.8	89.3	85.1	81.3	82.9	84.7	92.8	89.3	88.0	88.8	88.4
07	THERMAL & MOISTURE PROTECTION	104.4	90.0	98.6	107.3	91.4	100.8	105.2	89.4	98.8	107.4	78.2	95.5	104.5	88.9	98.2	104.4	89.6	98.4
08	OPENINGS	96.1	83.9	93.2	95.4	86.6	93.4	97.9	83.9	94.6	98.1	73.9	92.4	99.1	85.1	95.8	96.9	81.8	93.3
0920	Plaster & Gypsum Board	99.0	92.4	94.5	102.1	95.1	97.4	97.5	92.4	94.0	93.9	80.5	84.8	97.5	92.4	94.0	100.1	88.3	92.0
0950, 0980	Ceilings & Acoustic Treatment	94.2	92.4	93.0	96.1	95.1	95.4	94.2	92.4	93.0	96.1	80.5	85.7	94.2	92.4	93.0	94.2	88.3	90.3
0960	Flooring	99.3	114.1	103.8	107.9	120.3	111.6	98.7	114.1	103.3	100.5	114.1	104.6	98.7	114.1	103.3	102.4	114.1	105.9
0970, 0990	Wall Finishes & Painting/Coating	106.3	93.5	98.6	107.1	93.5	98.9	106.3	77.0	88.7	107.1	42.2	68.1	106.3	93.8	98.8	106.3	93.5	98.6
09	FINISHES	97.9	96.6	97.2	101.7	100.5	101.0	98.8	95.1	96.7	98.7	82.3	89.6	97.3	96.7	96.9	99.3	94.8	96.8
COVERS	DIVS. 10 - 14, 25, 28, 41, 43, 44, 46	100.0	96.7	99.3	100.0	98.6	99.7	100.0	56.6	91.3	100.0	95.4	99.1	100.0	65.4	93.1	100.0	97.1	99.4
21, 22, 23	FIRE SUPPRESSION, PLUMBING & HVAC	95.4	91.4	93.8	100.4	89.3	95.9	95.4	91.5	93.8	95.5	86.7	91.9	95.4	92.2	94.1	100.2	88.1	95.4
26, 27, 3370	ELECTRICAL, COMMUNICATIONS & UTIL.	95.8	91.9	93.8	94.9	96.1	95.5	91.8	91.9	91.8	96.9	82.8	89.6	96.0	96.8	96.4	96.0	92.8	94.3
MF2010	WEIGHTED AVERAGE	98.2	92.8	95.8	99.8	95.2	97.8	98.4	91.4	95.4	98.3	86.1	93.0	98.8	92.6	96.1	98.9	91.4	95.6

DIVISION		WEST VIRGINIA									WISCONSIN								
		PETERSBURG			ROMNEY			WHEELING			BELOIT			EAU CLAIRE			GREEN BAY		
		268			267			260			535			547			541 - 543		
		MAT.	INST.	TOTAL	MAT.	INST.	TOTAL	MAT.	INST.	TOTAL	MAT.	INST.	TOTAL	MAT.	INST.	TOTAL	MAT.	INST.	TOTAL
015433	CONTRACTOR EQUIPMENT		100.8	100.8		100.8	100.8		100.8	100.8		102.6	102.6		101.2	101.2		99.0	99.0
0241, 31 - 34	SITE & INFRASTRUCTURE, DEMOLITION	99.9	89.8	92.8	102.6	89.8	93.6	109.5	89.9	95.7	95.8	108.6	104.8	94.6	103.6	100.9	98.2	99.6	99.2
0310	Concrete Forming & Accessories	88.7	91.6	91.2	84.8	91.6	90.7	91.5	92.6	92.4	100.1	102.1	101.9	99.7	101.3	101.1	107.8	100.5	101.5
0320	Concrete Reinforcing	94.2	84.9	89.6	94.8	76.3	85.6	93.6	84.3	89.0	96.6	117.1	106.9	93.7	100.9	97.3	91.9	93.2	92.6
0330	Cast-in-Place Concrete	101.5	96.3	99.4	106.3	96.3	102.1	103.8	100.9	102.6	103.7	101.9	102.9	102.1	99.5	101.0	105.6	100.9	103.7
03	CONCRETE	96.8	92.5	94.7	100.0	91.0	95.5	101.6	94.4	98.1	99.9	104.9	102.3	98.8	100.7	99.7	101.9	99.5	100.7
04	MASONRY	92.9	92.3	92.5	90.7	92.3	91.7	100.2	91.7	94.9	98.5	104.8	102.4	89.8	102.7	97.8	120.3	101.9	108.9
05	METALS	100.5	96.6	99.3	100.5	93.7	98.4	101.2	96.9	99.9	94.2	108.4	98.6	93.1	102.7	96.0	95.4	99.1	96.5
06	WOOD, PLASTICS & COMPOSITES	88.9	92.8	91.1	83.8	92.8	88.9	89.6	92.8	91.4	98.2	101.6	100.1	105.2	101.6	103.2	110.0	101.6	105.3
07	THERMAL & MOISTURE PROTECTION	104.5	84.5	96.4	104.6	81.2	95.1	104.7	89.5	98.5	103.4	97.9	101.2	103.2	88.1	97.1	105.0	87.1	97.7
08	OPENINGS	99.1	83.9	95.5	99.0	82.0	95.0	97.6	85.1	94.7	103.6	110.2	105.1	101.0	98.1	100.3	97.4	97.8	97.5
0920	Plaster & Gypsum Board	99.7	92.4	94.7	97.1	92.4	93.9	100.1	92.4	94.8	92.8	101.9	99.0	101.4	101.9	101.8	96.6	101.9	100.2
0950, 0980	Ceilings & Acoustic Treatment	94.2	92.4	93.0	94.2	92.4	93.0	94.2	92.4	93.0	92.5	101.9	98.8	101.7	101.9	101.9	92.7	101.9	98.9
0960	Flooring	100.3	114.1	104.5	98.5	114.1	103.2	103.2	114.1	106.4	101.9	120.3	107.4	94.2	116.2	100.8	113.3	116.2	114.2
0970, 0990	Wall Finishes & Painting/Coating	106.3	93.8	98.8	106.3	93.8	98.8	106.3	93.8	98.8	91.8	99.3	96.3	88.0	88.3	88.2	98.1	85.0	90.2
09	FINISHES	98.1	96.7	97.3	97.4	96.7	97.0	99.5	96.9	98.1	99.7	105.1	102.7	99.2	103.2	101.4	103.3	102.6	102.9
COVERS	DIVS. 10 - 14, 25, 28, 41, 43, 44, 46	100.0	65.3	93.1	100.0	96.7	99.3	100.0	97.1	99.4	100.0	98.2	99.6	100.0	98.5	99.7	100.0	98.1	99.6
21, 22, 23	FIRE SUPPRESSION, PLUMBING & HVAC	95.4	91.2	93.7	95.4	90.8	93.6	100.3	92.8	97.3	100.0	100.0	100.0	100.1	87.5	95.1	100.4	84.3	93.9
26, 27, 3370	ELECTRICAL, COMMUNICATIONS & UTIL.	99.2	82.9	90.7	98.5	82.9	90.3	93.1	96.8	95.0	102.8	87.3	94.7	103.9	86.9	95.0	98.2	82.9	90.2
MF2010	WEIGHTED AVERAGE	98.0	90.1	94.6	98.2	90.4	94.8	99.8	93.8	97.2	99.6	101.9	100.6	98.7	96.4	97.7	100.5	94.1	97.7

DIVISION		WISCONSIN																	
		KENOSHA			LA CROSSE			LANCASTER			MADISON			MILWAUKEE			NEW RICHMOND		
		531			546			538			537			530,532			540		
		MAT.	INST.	TOTAL	MAT.	INST.	TOTAL	MAT.	INST.	TOTAL	MAT.	INST.	TOTAL	MAT.	INST.	TOTAL	MAT.	INST.	TOTAL
015433	CONTRACTOR EQUIPMENT		100.5	100.5		101.2	101.2		102.6	102.6		102.6	102.6		90.8	90.8		101.6	101.6
0241, 31 - 34	SITE & INFRASTRUCTURE, DEMOLITION	101.8	105.5	104.4	88.5	103.6	99.1	95.0	108.5	104.4	91.3	108.6	103.4	98.0	98.7	98.5	91.7	104.0	100.3
0310	Concrete Forming & Accessories	106.8	102.5	103.1	86.7	100.8	98.9	99.5	99.7	99.7	103.7	101.7	102.0	102.2	120.1	117.6	95.2	102.8	101.8
0320	Concrete Reinforcing	96.4	98.6	97.5	93.4	92.9	93.1	97.9	92.8	95.4	102.3	93.1	97.7	100.5	98.9	99.7	91.0	100.7	95.9
0330	Cast-in-Place Concrete	112.8	106.0	109.9	91.8	97.0	94.0	103.0	101.0	102.2	94.3	101.8	97.4	102.3	110.6	105.7	106.3	83.6	96.9
03	CONCRETE	104.6	103.0	103.8	90.1	98.1	94.1	99.6	98.9	99.2	97.1	100.1	98.6	100.3	111.9	106.0	96.6	95.9	96.3
04	MASONRY	95.9	115.5	108.1	89.0	102.7	97.5	98.6	104.9	102.5	99.4	104.8	102.8	102.2	120.5	113.5	115.4	102.8	107.6
05	METALS	95.0	101.6	97.0	93.0	98.9	94.8	91.8	96.1	93.1	93.5	98.1	94.9	98.1	94.9	97.1	93.2	101.5	95.8
06	WOOD, PLASTICS & COMPOSITES	101.8	98.7	100.1	90.2	101.6	96.7	97.5	101.6	99.8	97.0	101.6	99.6	101.1	121.3	112.5	94.0	104.9	100.2
07	THERMAL & MOISTURE PROTECTION	103.4	108.4	105.4	102.7	87.2	96.4	103.1	83.5	95.2	106.5	94.0	101.4	99.9	113.0	105.2	104.9	93.8	100.4
08	OPENINGS	97.6	102.8	98.9	101.0	86.7	97.6	99.2	87.5	96.4	105.1	101.6	104.3	106.2	115.1	108.3	86.9	99.9	90.0
0920	Plaster & Gypsum Board	83.2	99.0	93.9	95.9	101.9	100.0	91.5	101.9	98.6	94.2	101.9	99.5	99.9	122.1	115.0	85.5	105.5	99.1
0950, 0980	Ceilings & Acoustic Treatment	92.5	99.0	96.8	100.8	101.9	101.6	87.2	101.9	97.0	102.4	101.9	102.1	96.1	122.1	113.4	65.8	105.5	92.2
0960	Flooring	120.9	112.4	118.4	88.3	116.2	96.7	101.6	112.6	104.9	103.5	112.6	106.2	101.6	116.1	105.9	106.5	116.2	109.4
0970, 0990	Wall Finishes & Painting/Coating	101.5	115.2	109.7	88.0	75.5	80.5	91.8	67.8	77.4	89.8	99.3	95.5	93.2	125.6	112.7	101.0	88.3	93.4
09	FINISHES	104.6	105.5	105.1	96.1	101.9	99.3	98.3	98.4	98.3	101.0	103.9	102.6	102.5	121.0	112.8	93.7	103.3	99.0
COVERS	DIVS. 10 - 14, 25, 28, 41, 43, 44, 46	100.0	101.6	100.3	100.0	98.5	99.7	100.0	50.6	90.1	100.0	98.2	99.6	100.0	104.8	101.0	100.0	98.4	99.7
21, 22, 23	FIRE SUPPRESSION, PLUMBING & HVAC	100.2	96.9	98.9	100.1	87.4	95.0	95.1	87.2	92.0	100.0	96.3	98.5	100.0	102.5	101.0	94.8	86.8	91.6
26, 27, 3370	ELECTRICAL, COMMUNICATIONS & UTIL.	103.4	99.6	101.4	104.2	87.1	95.3	102.6	87.1	94.5	103.6	94.3	98.8	102.9	101.9	102.4	102.0	87.1	94.3
MF2010	WEIGHTED AVERAGE	100.2	102.9	101.4	97.2	95.0	96.3	97.4	93.5	95.7	99.5	99.8	99.6	100.9	107.9	104.0	96.2	95.9	96.1

DIVISION		WISCONSIN																	
		OSHKOSH			PORTAGE			RACINE			RHINELANDER			SUPERIOR			WAUSAU		
		549			539			534			545			548			544		
		MAT.	INST.	TOTAL	MAT.	INST.	TOTAL	MAT.	INST.	TOTAL	MAT.	INST.	TOTAL	MAT.	INST.	TOTAL	MAT.	INST.	TOTAL
015433	CONTRACTOR EQUIPMENT		99.0	99.0		102.6	102.6		102.6	102.6		99.0	99.0		101.6	101.6		99.0	99.0
0241, 31 - 34	SITE & INFRASTRUCTURE, DEMOLITION	90.0	99.6	96.7	85.8	108.4	101.6	95.6	109.3	105.2	102.1	99.6	100.3	88.6	104.0	99.4	85.9	99.6	95.5
0310	Concrete Forming & Accessories	91.0	99.9	98.7	92.1	100.7	99.5	100.4	102.5	102.2	88.4	99.9	98.3	93.4	94.0	94.0	90.3	100.5	99.1
0320	Concrete Reinforcing	92.0	93.1	92.6	98.0	93.0	95.5	96.6	98.6	97.6	92.2	92.2	92.2	91.0	92.7	91.8	92.2	92.9	92.5
0330	Cast-in-Place Concrete	97.9	100.8	99.1	88.5	103.0	94.5	101.7	105.7	103.3	111.0	101.0	106.9	100.1	100.0	100.1	91.3	100.9	95.3
03	CONCRETE	91.7	99.1	95.3	87.5	100.1	93.7	98.9	102.9	100.9	103.6	99.0	101.3	91.2	96.1	93.6	86.8	99.4	93.0
04	MASONRY	102.5	102.2	102.3	97.5	104.8	102.1	98.6	115.5	109.0	118.7	102.7	108.8	114.7	106.3	109.5	102.1	101.9	102.0
05	METALS	93.4	98.4	94.9	92.5	97.1	93.9	95.9	101.5	97.6	93.3	97.8	94.7	94.1	99.4	95.7	93.2	98.9	94.9
06	WOOD, PLASTICS & COMPOSITES	89.8	101.6	96.5	88.4	101.6	95.8	98.4	98.7	98.6	87.4	101.6	95.4	92.4	92.2	92.3	89.3	101.6	96.3
07	THERMAL & MOISTURE PROTECTION	104.2	87.2	97.3	102.6	93.8	99.0	103.4	107.9	105.2	105.0	85.2	96.9	104.5	94.3	100.4	104.1	85.8	96.6
08	OPENINGS	93.4	97.8	94.5	99.3	94.2	98.1	103.6	102.8	103.4	93.5	88.8	92.4	86.4	92.5	87.8	93.6	97.7	94.6
0920	Plaster & Gypsum Board	83.9	101.9	96.2	85.4	101.9	96.7	92.8	99.0	97.0	83.9	101.9	96.2	85.4	92.4	90.2	83.9	101.9	96.2
0950, 0980	Ceilings & Acoustic Treatment	92.7	101.9	98.9	89.9	101.9	97.9	92.5	99.0	96.8	92.7	101.9	98.9	66.7	92.4	83.8	92.7	101.9	98.9
0960	Flooring	105.1	116.2	108.4	98.2	120.3	104.8	101.9	112.4	105.0	104.3	116.2	107.9	107.8	124.7	112.9	104.9	116.2	108.3
0970, 0990	Wall Finishes & Painting/Coating	95.3	85.0	89.1	91.8	67.8	77.4	91.8	115.3	105.9	95.3	61.7	75.1	89.6	103.7	98.1	95.3	85.0	89.1
09	FINISHES	98.4	100.9	99.8	96.4	100.5	98.7	99.7	105.5	103.0	99.3	99.1	99.2	93.1	100.7	97.3	98.1	102.6	100.6
COVERS	DIVS. 10 - 14, 25, 28, 41, 43, 44, 46	100.0	66.1	93.2	100.0	64.8	92.9	100.0	101.6	100.3	100.0	56.4	91.3	100.0	96.7	99.3	100.0	98.1	99.6
21, 22, 23	FIRE SUPPRESSION, PLUMBING & HVAC	95.5	83.4	90.6	95.1	96.1	95.5	100.0	96.9	98.8	95.5	87.0	92.1	94.8	90.4	93.0	95.5	86.3	91.8
26, 27, 3370	ELECTRICAL, COMMUNICATIONS & UTIL.	102.6	81.0	91.3	106.8	94.3	100.3	102.6	95.2	98.7	101.9	82.6	91.8	107.2	99.3	103.1	103.8	82.6	92.7
MF2010	WEIGHTED AVERAGE	96.3	92.4	94.6	96.1	97.9	96.9	99.7	102.6	101.0	98.7	92.4	95.9	96.1	97.6	96.7	95.7	94.4	95.2

City Cost Indexes

WYOMING

DIVISION		CASPER 826 MAT.	INST.	TOTAL	CHEYENNE 820 MAT.	INST.	TOTAL	NEWCASTLE 827 MAT.	INST.	TOTAL	RAWLINS 823 MAT.	INST.	TOTAL	RIVERTON 825 MAT.	INST.	TOTAL	ROCK SPRINGS 829-831 MAT.	INST.	TOTAL
015433	CONTRACTOR EQUIPMENT		97.9	97.9		97.9	97.9		97.9	97.9		97.9	97.9		97.9	97.9		97.9	97.9
0241, 31 - 34	SITE & INFRASTRUCTURE, DEMOLITION	97.2	95.2	95.8	90.1	95.2	93.7	82.0	94.8	91.0	95.8	94.8	95.1	89.3	94.8	93.2	85.8	94.7	92.1
0310	Concrete Forming & Accessories	104.4	43.5	51.9	106.6	54.7	61.8	97.1	63.5	68.1	101.3	63.5	68.6	96.0	63.0	67.5	103.5	62.9	68.4
0320	Concrete Reinforcing	108.6	70.5	89.6	100.8	71.3	86.1	108.4	71.7	90.1	108.1	71.7	89.9	109.1	71.4	90.2	109.1	71.4	90.3
0330	Cast-in-Place Concrete	98.6	72.6	87.8	91.1	72.7	83.5	92.0	62.1	79.6	92.1	62.1	79.6	92.0	52.6	75.7	92.0	52.3	75.5
03	CONCRETE	103.0	59.4	81.5	100.1	64.6	82.6	100.6	64.8	82.9	114.3	64.8	89.9	108.9	61.3	85.4	101.1	61.2	81.4
04	MASONRY	100.0	34.5	59.5	95.8	47.6	65.9	92.6	55.7	69.7	92.6	55.7	69.7	92.6	49.9	66.1	147.5	48.7	86.4
05	METALS	98.1	71.0	89.7	101.5	72.4	92.5	96.6	72.4	89.2	96.7	72.4	89.2	96.8	71.6	89.0	97.5	71.9	89.6
06	WOOD, PLASTICS & COMPOSITES	96.3	41.0	65.1	95.6	55.6	73.0	85.6	68.4	75.9	89.6	68.4	77.6	84.5	68.4	75.5	93.6	68.4	79.4
07	THERMAL & MOISTURE PROTECTION	105.2	49.4	82.5	99.7	54.4	81.3	101.2	55.9	82.8	102.7	55.9	83.7	102.1	59.7	84.9	101.3	59.3	84.2
08	OPENINGS	102.1	48.9	89.5	102.3	56.9	91.6	106.2	60.8	95.5	105.9	60.8	95.2	106.1	60.8	95.3	106.5	60.8	95.7
0920	Plaster & Gypsum Board	93.1	39.1	56.3	84.6	54.2	63.9	80.3	67.4	71.5	80.7	67.4	71.6	80.3	67.4	71.5	90.0	67.4	74.6
0950, 0980	Ceilings & Acoustic Treatment	108.9	39.1	62.4	100.3	54.2	69.6	102.3	67.4	79.0	102.3	67.4	79.0	102.3	67.4	79.0	102.3	67.4	79.0
0960	Flooring	109.6	33.6	86.8	107.4	54.0	91.5	101.0	52.6	86.5	103.8	52.6	88.5	100.6	52.6	86.2	105.9	52.6	89.9
0970, 0990	Wall Finishes & Painting/Coating	100.0	44.0	66.3	106.9	44.0	69.1	102.6	56.6	74.9	102.6	56.6	74.9	102.6	56.6	74.9	102.6	56.6	74.9
09	FINISHES	106.4	40.1	69.5	103.2	52.8	75.1	97.9	60.6	77.1	100.2	60.6	78.2	98.7	60.6	77.5	100.6	60.3	78.2
COVERS	DIVS. 10 - 14, 25, 28, 41, 43, 44, 46	100.0	88.9	97.8	100.0	90.6	98.1	100.0	91.5	98.3	100.0	91.5	98.3	100.0	58.0	91.6	100.0	82.7	96.5
21, 22, 23	FIRE SUPPRESSION, PLUMBING & HVAC	100.0	65.4	86.1	100.0	65.5	86.2	97.5	64.8	84.3	97.5	64.8	84.3	97.5	64.7	84.3	100.0	64.2	85.6
26, 27, 3370	ELECTRICAL, COMMUNICATIONS & UTIL.	96.0	65.6	80.1	99.1	70.2	84.0	96.8	70.6	83.2	96.8	70.6	83.2	96.8	64.4	79.9	95.0	64.4	79.0
MF2010	WEIGHTED AVERAGE	100.4	60.7	83.1	100.1	65.7	85.2	98.2	67.8	84.9	100.2	67.8	86.1	99.3	64.9	84.3	101.8	65.4	85.9

WYOMING / CANADA

DIVISION		SHERIDAN 828 MAT.	INST.	TOTAL	WHEATLAND 822 MAT.	INST.	TOTAL	WORLAND 824 MAT.	INST.	TOTAL	YELLOWSTONE NAT'L PA 821 MAT.	INST.	TOTAL	BARRIE, ONTARIO MAT.	INST.	TOTAL	BATHURST, NEW BRUNSWICK MAT.	INST.	TOTAL
015433	CONTRACTOR EQUIPMENT		97.9	97.9		97.9	97.9		97.9	97.9		97.9	97.9		101.6	101.6		101.9	101.9
0241, 31 - 34	SITE & INFRASTRUCTURE, DEMOLITION	89.8	95.2	93.6	86.4	94.8	92.3	83.9	94.7	91.5	84.0	94.9	91.7	115.3	101.0	105.3	98.4	97.3	97.6
0310	Concrete Forming & Accessories	104.3	51.6	58.8	99.1	51.1	57.7	99.2	62.7	67.7	99.2	64.0	68.8	125.1	91.5	96.1	103.7	65.1	70.4
0320	Concrete Reinforcing	109.1	71.8	90.4	108.4	71.7	90.1	109.1	71.1	90.1	111.0	71.1	91.1	174.2	86.5	130.4	139.2	58.3	98.8
0330	Cast-in-Place Concrete	95.1	72.7	85.8	96.0	61.8	81.8	92.0	52.2	75.5	92.0	54.2	76.3	166.0	90.4	134.6	136.1	62.8	105.7
03	CONCRETE	108.8	63.3	86.3	105.4	59.2	82.6	100.8	61.0	81.2	101.1	62.3	81.9	151.0	90.3	121.1	130.9	63.7	97.7
04	MASONRY	92.6	57.2	70.8	92.9	55.2	69.6	92.6	44.9	63.1	92.6	48.5	65.3	165.2	99.8	124.7	165.6	66.1	104.0
05	METALS	100.3	72.9	91.7	96.6	72.2	89.1	96.8	71.2	88.9	97.4	71.2	89.3	108.2	91.4	103.0	104.4	72.6	94.6
06	WOOD, PLASTICS & COMPOSITES	97.0	51.6	71.4	87.5	52.1	67.5	87.5	68.4	76.8	87.5	68.4	76.8	120.6	90.1	103.4	97.8	65.4	79.5
07	THERMAL & MOISTURE PROTECTION	102.4	56.5	83.7	101.5	55.0	82.6	101.3	56.0	82.9	100.8	57.5	83.2	112.4	91.0	103.7	104.6	63.6	87.9
08	OPENINGS	106.8	52.5	93.9	104.8	54.7	93.0	106.4	60.8	95.6	99.8	60.8	90.6	92.5	88.6	91.5	89.2	57.2	81.6
0920	Plaster & Gypsum Board	105.6	50.0	67.8	80.3	50.5	60.0	80.3	67.4	71.5	80.5	67.4	71.6	151.2	89.8	109.4	151.8	64.2	92.2
0950, 0980	Ceilings & Acoustic Treatment	105.2	50.0	68.5	102.3	50.5	67.8	102.3	67.4	79.0	103.1	67.4	79.3	95.2	89.8	91.6	100.9	64.2	76.5
0960	Flooring	105.0	52.6	89.3	102.5	51.7	87.3	102.5	52.6	87.6	102.5	52.6	87.6	130.7	100.7	121.7	117.8	48.0	96.9
0970, 0990	Wall Finishes & Painting/Coating	105.1	44.0	68.4	102.6	35.2	62.1	102.6	56.6	74.9	102.6	56.6	74.9	111.9	91.8	99.8	108.4	52.7	74.9
09	FINISHES	106.2	49.7	74.7	98.6	48.3	70.6	98.3	60.5	77.2	98.5	61.4	77.8	117.3	93.5	104.0	113.4	60.9	84.2
COVERS	DIVS. 10 - 14, 25, 28, 41, 43, 44, 46	100.0	90.1	98.0	100.0	82.0	96.4	100.0	57.8	91.5	100.0	59.0	91.8	139.2	76.2	126.6	131.1	66.9	118.3
21, 22, 23	FIRE SUPPRESSION, PLUMBING & HVAC	97.5	65.5	84.6	97.5	64.5	84.2	97.5	64.4	84.2	97.5	66.2	84.9	102.2	101.5	101.9	102.5	71.3	90.0
26, 27, 3370	ELECTRICAL, COMMUNICATIONS & UTIL.	99.5	64.5	81.2	96.8	70.2	82.9	96.8	64.4	79.9	95.7	64.4	79.4	116.5	92.6	104.0	114.2	63.3	87.6
MF2010	WEIGHTED AVERAGE	100.9	65.2	85.4	98.7	64.6	83.9	98.3	64.1	83.4	97.7	65.2	83.5	117.3	94.9	107.5	112.1	68.6	93.1

CANADA

DIVISION		BRANDON, MANITOBA MAT.	INST.	TOTAL	BRANTFORD, ONTARIO MAT.	INST.	TOTAL	BRIDGEWATER, NOVA SCOTIA MAT.	INST.	TOTAL	CALGARY, ALBERTA MAT.	INST.	TOTAL	CAP-DE-LA-MADELEINE, QUEBEC MAT.	INST.	TOTAL	CHARLESBOURG, QUEBEC MAT.	INST.	TOTAL
015433	CONTRACTOR EQUIPMENT		103.9	103.9		101.6	101.6		101.5	101.5		106.4	106.4		102.5	102.5		102.5	102.5
0241, 31 - 34	SITE & INFRASTRUCTURE, DEMOLITION	117.9	99.9	105.3	114.9	101.3	105.4	99.9	98.9	99.2	124.6	105.7	111.3	95.9	100.6	99.2	95.9	100.6	99.2
0310	Concrete Forming & Accessories	126.8	74.1	81.3	124.9	99.1	102.6	97.1	73.2	76.5	127.7	96.8	101.0	130.3	90.0	95.5	130.3	90.0	95.5
0320	Concrete Reinforcing	189.5	54.9	122.3	167.9	85.2	126.6	142.9	48.2	95.6	130.9	74.1	102.5	142.9	81.4	112.2	142.9	81.4	112.2
0330	Cast-in-Place Concrete	146.1	77.7	117.7	162.0	112.0	141.3	166.5	73.2	127.8	201.5	106.2	162.0	130.8	99.3	117.7	130.8	99.3	117.7
03	CONCRETE	138.9	72.4	106.1	147.1	100.9	124.3	144.7	69.3	107.5	167.1	95.9	132.0	128.7	91.7	110.5	128.7	91.7	110.5
04	MASONRY	186.5	68.8	113.7	167.9	104.4	128.6	163.2	73.2	107.5	203.4	90.7	133.7	163.7	88.6	117.2	163.7	88.6	117.2
05	METALS	117.8	77.8	105.5	105.5	92.2	101.4	104.6	75.3	95.6	130.4	89.2	117.7	103.8	88.8	99.2	103.8	88.8	99.2
06	WOOD, PLASTICS & COMPOSITES	124.4	75.1	96.6	119.8	97.9	107.4	89.2	72.6	79.9	107.8	96.5	101.4	131.6	89.9	108.1	131.6	89.9	108.1
07	THERMAL & MOISTURE PROTECTION	109.1	73.3	94.6	112.6	96.6	106.1	107.5	71.4	92.9	121.9	94.1	110.6	106.2	91.8	100.3	106.2	91.8	100.3
08	OPENINGS	97.0	66.3	89.7	93.6	94.9	93.9	86.6	66.4	81.8	94.2	86.1	92.3	94.7	83.0	91.9	94.7	83.0	91.9
0920	Plaster & Gypsum Board	129.5	73.9	91.7	142.7	97.8	112.1	141.8	71.7	94.1	140.9	95.9	110.3	172.3	89.4	115.9	172.3	89.4	115.9
0950, 0980	Ceilings & Acoustic Treatment	102.5	73.9	83.5	97.4	97.8	97.6	97.4	71.7	80.3	145.9	95.9	112.6	97.4	89.4	92.1	97.4	89.4	92.1
0960	Flooring	136.3	71.5	116.9	130.5	100.7	121.6	113.1	68.5	99.8	133.3	94.3	121.7	130.5	101.4	121.8	130.5	101.4	121.8
0970, 0990	Wall Finishes & Painting/Coating	113.1	60.0	81.2	109.0	100.8	104.1	109.0	65.5	82.9	114.2	112.4	113.1	109.0	93.7	99.8	109.0	93.7	99.8
09	FINISHES	118.8	72.5	93.0	115.6	100.1	107.0	109.7	71.8	88.7	129.1	98.5	112.0	118.9	92.8	104.4	118.9	92.8	104.4
COVERS	DIVS. 10 - 14, 25, 28, 41, 43, 44, 46	131.1	69.1	118.7	131.1	78.4	120.6	131.1	68.2	118.5	131.1	98.4	124.6	131.1	87.3	122.4	131.1	87.3	122.4
21, 22, 23	FIRE SUPPRESSION, PLUMBING & HVAC	102.5	85.9	95.9	102.5	104.5	103.3	102.5	86.3	96.0	101.3	92.2	97.6	102.9	93.0	98.9	102.9	93.0	98.9
26, 27, 3370	ELECTRICAL, COMMUNICATIONS & UTIL.	120.0	71.3	94.6	112.9	92.1	102.0	118.7	65.9	91.1	114.2	100.8	107.2	112.6	74.3	92.6	112.6	74.3	92.6
MF2010	WEIGHTED AVERAGE	118.7	77.3	100.7	115.5	98.8	108.2	113.4	76.1	97.2	124.7	95.4	111.9	112.8	89.4	102.6	112.8	89.4	102.6

CANADA

DIVISION		CHARLOTTETOWN, PRINCE EDWARD ISLAND			CHICOUTIMI, QUEBEC			CORNER BROOK, NEWFOUNDLAND			CORNWALL, ONTARIO			DALHOUSIE, NEW BRUNSWICK			DARTMOUTH, NOVA SCOTIA		
		MAT.	INST.	TOTAL	MAT.	INST.	TOTAL	MAT.	INST.	TOTAL	MAT.	INST.	TOTAL	MAT.	INST.	TOTAL	MAT.	INST.	TOTAL
015433	CONTRACTOR EQUIPMENT		101.5	101.5		102.5	102.5		103.1	103.1		101.6	101.6		101.9	101.9		101.5	101.5
0241, 31 - 34	SITE & INFRASTRUCTURE, DEMOLITION	115.8	96.4	102.2	96.1	99.7	98.6	120.7	97.9	104.7	113.0	100.8	104.5	97.6	97.3	97.4	111.0	98.9	102.5
0310	Concrete Forming & Accessories	105.6	59.5	65.8	131.4	92.8	98.1	106.9	63.0	69.0	122.8	91.6	95.9	103.2	65.3	70.5	98.9	73.2	76.8
0320	Concrete Reinforcing	146.3	48.3	97.3	105.0	96.4	100.7	173.8	50.1	112.0	167.9	84.9	126.5	144.1	58.4	101.3	181.7	48.2	115.0
0330	Cast-in-Place Concrete	164.6	62.0	122.0	128.2	99.2	116.1	170.1	71.7	129.2	145.7	102.2	127.7	137.6	62.8	106.6	164.2	73.2	126.4
03	CONCRETE	153.1	59.1	106.7	120.1	95.6	108.0	167.6	64.5	116.8	139.3	94.1	117.0	135.2	63.8	100.0	152.9	69.3	111.6
04	MASONRY	182.6	63.7	109.0	167.4	94.1	122.0	183.2	65.3	110.2	166.7	95.7	122.7	158.4	66.1	101.3	196.5	73.2	120.2
05	METALS	127.0	68.6	108.9	104.2	92.3	100.6	118.3	74.0	104.6	105.5	90.8	101.0	101.7	72.8	92.8	118.3	75.3	105.0
06	WOOD, PLASTICS & COMPOSITES	88.5	59.1	71.9	132.6	93.2	110.4	104.3	62.1	80.5	118.6	91.0	103.0	97.7	65.4	79.5	94.6	72.6	82.2
07	THERMAL & MOISTURE PROTECTION	119.5	61.7	96.1	105.0	95.9	101.3	112.7	63.2	92.6	112.4	91.1	103.8	110.8	63.6	91.6	110.4	71.4	94.6
08	OPENINGS	93.4	51.1	83.4	93.8	80.5	90.6	102.9	58.5	92.4	94.7	88.2	93.1	90.3	57.2	82.4	88.3	66.4	83.1
0920	Plaster & Gypsum Board	144.0	57.7	85.3	176.1	92.8	119.4	160.5	60.8	92.7	208.0	90.7	128.2	148.2	64.2	91.1	156.0	71.7	98.6
0950, 0980	Ceilings & Acoustic Treatment	121.3	57.7	79.0	100.1	92.8	95.2	103.4	60.8	75.0	100.9	90.7	94.1	100.2	64.2	76.3	110.5	71.7	84.7
0960	Flooring	116.1	64.0	100.5	132.3	101.4	123.0	122.1	58.3	103.0	130.5	99.2	121.1	116.3	73.4	103.5	118.0	68.5	103.2
0970, 0990	Wall Finishes & Painting/Coating	112.9	43.9	71.4	108.4	105.7	106.7	113.0	63.1	83.0	109.0	93.9	99.9	109.9	52.7	75.5	113.0	65.5	84.4
09	FINISHES	118.9	59.1	85.6	120.3	96.5	107.0	119.5	62.2	87.6	125.3	93.6	107.6	112.7	65.9	86.6	118.0	71.8	92.3
COVERS	DIVS. 10 - 14, 25, 28, 41, 43, 44, 46	131.1	66.4	118.2	131.1	88.0	122.5	131.1	67.2	118.3	131.1	75.8	120.1	131.1	66.9	118.3	131.1	68.2	118.5
21, 22, 23	FIRE SUPPRESSION, PLUMBING & HVAC	102.7	65.2	87.7	102.5	93.7	99.0	102.5	73.4	90.8	102.9	102.3	102.6	102.5	71.3	90.0	102.5	86.3	96.0
26, 27, 3370	ELECTRICAL, COMMUNICATIONS & UTIL.	111.9	53.6	81.5	111.0	86.5	98.2	117.4	59.7	87.2	113.9	93.1	103.0	115.3	59.8	86.3	122.2	65.9	92.8
MF2010	WEIGHTED AVERAGE	120.5	64.0	95.9	111.9	93.1	103.7	122.2	69.0	99.0	115.5	95.1	106.7	112.1	68.8	93.2	119.7	76.1	100.7

CANADA

DIVISION		EDMONTON, ALBERTA			FORT MCMURRAY, ALBERTA			FREDERICTON, NEW BRUNSWICK			GATINEAU, QUEBEC			GRANBY, QUEBEC			HALIFAX, NOVA SCOTIA		
		MAT.	INST.	TOTAL	MAT.	INST.	TOTAL	MAT.	INST.	TOTAL	MAT.	INST.	TOTAL	MAT.	INST.	TOTAL	MAT.	INST.	TOTAL
015433	CONTRACTOR EQUIPMENT		106.4	106.4		103.7	103.7		101.9	101.9		102.5	102.5		102.5	102.5		101.5	101.5
0241, 31 - 34	SITE & INFRASTRUCTURE, DEMOLITION	146.0	105.7	117.7	120.4	101.9	107.4	100.8	97.3	98.3	95.7	100.5	99.1	96.2	100.5	99.2	105.2	98.8	100.7
0310	Concrete Forming & Accessories	127.2	96.8	101.0	123.0	94.3	98.2	122.7	65.6	73.5	130.3	89.8	95.4	130.3	89.8	95.3	104.9	78.3	81.9
0320	Concrete Reinforcing	140.3	74.1	107.2	155.3	74.1	114.7	136.1	58.5	97.4	151.1	81.3	116.3	151.1	81.3	116.3	147.6	62.8	105.3
0330	Cast-in-Place Concrete	201.0	106.2	161.7	215.2	104.8	169.4	134.8	62.9	104.9	129.0	99.3	116.7	133.3	99.2	119.2	165.6	81.0	130.5
03	CONCRETE	168.4	95.9	132.6	170.0	94.3	132.7	133.1	64.0	99.0	129.2	91.7	110.7	131.2	91.6	111.7	146.0	76.9	111.9
04	MASONRY	193.2	90.7	129.8	207.6	89.6	134.6	192.4	67.6	115.2	163.6	88.6	117.2	163.9	88.6	117.3	193.7	83.4	125.5
05	METALS	130.4	89.2	117.7	130.8	89.0	117.9	123.0	73.3	107.7	103.8	88.7	99.2	103.8	88.6	99.1	130.3	81.6	115.3
06	WOOD, PLASTICS & COMPOSITES	108.6	96.5	101.8	113.7	93.8	102.5	112.9	65.4	86.1	131.6	89.9	108.1	131.6	89.9	108.1	88.7	77.4	82.3
07	THERMAL & MOISTURE PROTECTION	127.2	94.1	113.8	120.1	92.6	108.9	117.3	64.6	95.9	106.2	91.8	100.3	106.2	90.2	99.7	118.6	77.9	102.1
08	OPENINGS	94.4	86.1	92.4	94.7	84.6	92.3	89.3	56.1	81.5	94.7	78.2	90.8	94.7	78.2	90.8	86.5	72.0	83.1
0920	Plaster & Gypsum Board	145.5	95.9	111.8	140.9	93.3	108.5	153.7	64.2	92.8	140.5	89.4	105.8	143.0	89.4	106.6	140.8	76.6	97.1
0950, 0980	Ceilings & Acoustic Treatment	150.5	95.9	114.2	107.2	93.3	97.9	113.3	64.2	80.6	97.4	89.4	92.1	97.4	89.4	92.1	116.1	76.6	89.8
0960	Flooring	135.0	94.3	122.8	130.5	94.3	119.7	128.5	76.7	113.0	130.5	101.4	121.8	130.5	101.4	121.8	118.2	90.0	109.8
0970, 0990	Wall Finishes & Painting/Coating	114.6	112.4	113.3	109.1	97.5	102.2	112.6	67.2	85.3	109.0	93.7	99.8	109.0	93.7	99.8	113.9	82.0	94.7
09	FINISHES	133.3	98.5	113.9	118.9	95.0	105.6	121.4	68.1	91.7	114.5	92.8	102.4	114.9	92.8	102.6	117.2	81.2	97.2
COVERS	DIVS. 10 - 14, 25, 28, 41, 43, 44, 46	131.1	98.4	124.6	131.1	97.5	124.4	131.1	66.9	118.3	131.1	87.3	122.4	131.1	87.3	122.4	131.1	69.6	118.8
21, 22, 23	FIRE SUPPRESSION, PLUMBING & HVAC	101.2	92.2	97.6	102.9	101.0	102.2	102.6	81.1	94.0	102.9	93.0	98.9	102.5	93.0	98.7	100.7	77.7	91.5
26, 27, 3370	ELECTRICAL, COMMUNICATIONS & UTIL.	110.3	100.8	105.4	107.1	87.5	96.8	117.2	78.9	97.2	112.6	74.3	92.6	113.2	74.3	92.9	120.1	80.5	99.4
MF2010	WEIGHTED AVERAGE	125.0	95.4	112.1	124.1	94.2	111.1	118.1	74.0	98.9	112.5	89.2	102.3	112.8	89.1	102.4	119.9	80.6	102.8

CANADA

DIVISION		HAMILTON, ONTARIO			HULL, QUEBEC			JOLIETTE, QUEBEC			KAMLOOPS, BRITISH COLUMBIA			KINGSTON, ONTARIO			KITCHENER, ONTARIO		
		MAT.	INST.	TOTAL	MAT.	INST.	TOTAL	MAT.	INST.	TOTAL	MAT.	INST.	TOTAL	MAT.	INST.	TOTAL	MAT.	INST.	TOTAL
015433	CONTRACTOR EQUIPMENT		108.3	108.3		102.5	102.5		102.5	102.5		105.6	105.6		103.9	103.9		103.8	103.8
0241, 31 - 34	SITE & INFRASTRUCTURE, DEMOLITION	117.0	112.7	114.0	95.7	100.5	99.1	96.3	100.6	99.3	118.4	104.0	108.3	113.0	104.5	107.1	101.2	105.1	104.0
0310	Concrete Forming & Accessories	127.9	94.2	98.8	130.3	89.8	95.4	130.3	90.0	95.5	123.5	92.8	97.0	122.9	91.7	96.0	118.0	86.6	90.9
0320	Concrete Reinforcing	153.0	93.1	123.1	151.1	81.3	116.3	142.9	81.4	112.2	112.0	79.2	95.6	167.9	84.9	126.5	103.3	93.0	98.2
0330	Cast-in-Place Concrete	151.7	100.2	130.3	129.0	99.3	116.7	134.4	99.3	119.8	116.3	103.1	110.8	145.7	102.2	127.6	140.7	90.1	119.7
03	CONCRETE	140.5	96.0	118.6	129.2	91.7	110.7	130.4	91.7	111.3	136.9	93.9	115.7	141.2	94.1	118.0	118.8	89.2	104.2
04	MASONRY	193.0	99.7	135.3	163.6	88.6	117.2	164.0	88.6	117.3	170.7	96.6	124.9	173.6	95.7	125.4	159.0	95.3	119.6
05	METALS	121.5	92.7	112.6	103.8	88.7	99.2	103.8	88.8	99.2	106.2	88.7	100.8	107.2	90.7	102.1	113.9	92.5	107.3
06	WOOD, PLASTICS & COMPOSITES	105.6	93.7	98.9	131.6	89.9	108.1	131.6	89.9	108.1	101.3	91.3	95.7	118.6	91.1	103.1	109.7	85.3	96.0
07	THERMAL & MOISTURE PROTECTION	124.3	95.0	112.4	106.2	91.8	100.3	106.2	91.8	100.3	121.2	88.6	108.0	112.4	92.2	104.2	112.1	91.6	103.8
08	OPENINGS	91.9	92.1	91.9	94.7	78.2	90.8	94.7	83.0	91.9	91.0	87.7	90.2	94.7	87.9	93.1	85.7	85.8	85.7
0920	Plaster & Gypsum Board	172.8	93.5	118.9	140.5	89.4	105.8	172.3	89.4	115.9	124.3	90.6	101.4	211.3	90.8	129.4	141.4	84.9	102.9
0950, 0980	Ceilings & Acoustic Treatment	130.0	93.5	105.7	97.4	89.4	92.1	97.4	89.4	92.1	97.4	90.6	92.9	114.3	90.8	98.7	105.3	84.9	91.7
0960	Flooring	132.6	104.1	124.1	130.5	101.4	121.8	130.5	101.4	121.8	129.8	56.6	107.9	130.5	99.2	121.1	124.4	104.1	118.3
0970, 0990	Wall Finishes & Painting/Coating	114.2	102.5	107.2	109.0	93.7	99.8	109.0	93.7	99.8	109.0	85.8	95.0	109.0	86.8	95.6	107.9	92.5	98.6
09	FINISHES	129.3	97.1	111.3	114.5	92.8	102.4	118.9	92.8	104.4	115.0	86.0	98.9	128.7	92.9	108.7	114.3	90.1	100.8
COVERS	DIVS. 10 - 14, 25, 28, 41, 43, 44, 46	131.1	100.4	125.0	131.1	87.3	122.4	131.1	87.3	122.4	131.1	97.9	124.5	131.1	75.8	120.1	131.1	98.3	124.6
21, 22, 23	FIRE SUPPRESSION, PLUMBING & HVAC	101.4	85.5	95.1	102.5	93.0	98.7	102.5	93.0	98.7	102.5	96.5	100.1	102.9	102.5	102.7	100.5	87.6	95.3
26, 27, 3370	ELECTRICAL, COMMUNICATIONS & UTIL.	111.6	96.0	103.5	114.5	74.3	93.5	113.2	74.3	92.9	116.7	83.9	99.6	113.9	91.7	102.3	114.4	93.6	103.6
MF2010	WEIGHTED AVERAGE	119.3	95.3	108.8	112.6	89.2	102.4	113.0	89.4	102.7	114.9	92.4	105.1	116.6	95.2	107.3	111.6	92.0	103.1

City Cost Indexes

CANADA

DIVISION		LAVAL, QUEBEC			LETHBRIDGE, ALBERTA			LLOYDMINSTER, ALBERTA			LONDON, ONTARIO			MEDICINE HAT, ALBERTA			MONCTON, NEW BRUNSWICK		
		MAT.	INST.	TOTAL	MAT.	INST.	TOTAL	MAT.	INST.	TOTAL	MAT.	INST.	TOTAL	MAT.	INST.	TOTAL	MAT.	INST.	TOTAL
015433	CONTRACTOR EQUIPMENT		102.5	102.5		103.7	103.7		103.7	103.7		103.9	103.9		103.7	103.7		101.9	101.9
0241, 31 - 34	SITE & INFRASTRUCTURE, DEMOLITION	96.1	100.5	99.2	113.0	102.5	105.6	112.9	101.9	105.2	116.2	105.3	108.5	111.6	101.9	104.8	97.8	97.5	97.6
0310	Concrete Forming & Accessories	130.5	89.8	95.4	124.2	94.4	98.5	122.4	84.4	89.6	126.1	88.0	93.2	124.1	84.3	89.8	103.7	65.9	71.0
0320	Concrete Reinforcing	151.1	81.3	116.3	155.3	74.1	114.8	155.3	74.0	114.7	130.9	93.0	112.0	155.3	74.0	114.7	139.2	61.5	100.4
0330	Cast-in-Place Concrete	133.3	99.3	119.2	161.4	104.8	137.9	149.7	101.0	129.5	161.6	98.1	135.2	149.7	101.0	129.5	131.1	79.8	109.8
03	CONCRETE	131.2	91.7	111.7	144.7	94.4	119.9	139.1	88.6	114.2	141.5	92.5	117.3	139.2	88.6	114.2	128.5	70.8	100.1
04	MASONRY	163.8	88.6	117.3	181.6	89.6	124.7	163.2	82.9	113.5	196.0	97.0	134.7	163.2	82.9	113.5	165.2	66.2	103.9
05	METALS	103.9	88.7	99.2	124.2	89.0	113.4	106.4	88.9	101.0	122.9	92.0	113.4	106.4	88.8	100.9	104.4	81.5	97.4
06	WOOD, PLASTICS & COMPOSITES	131.8	89.9	108.2	117.3	93.8	104.1	113.7	83.8	96.9	108.5	86.4	96.0	117.3	83.8	98.4	97.8	65.4	79.5
07	THERMAL & MOISTURE PROTECTION	106.8	91.8	100.7	117.4	92.6	107.3	114.3	88.0	103.7	125.2	92.8	112.0	120.9	88.0	107.6	108.9	65.8	91.4
08	OPENINGS	94.7	78.2	90.8	94.7	84.6	92.3	94.7	79.2	91.0	91.1	87.0	90.1	94.7	79.2	91.0	89.2	62.4	82.8
0920	Plaster & Gypsum Board	143.3	89.4	106.7	131.4	93.3	105.5	126.2	83.0	96.8	173.0	86.0	113.8	129.2	83.0	97.7	151.8	64.2	92.2
0950, 0980	Ceilings & Acoustic Treatment	97.4	89.4	92.1	106.3	93.3	97.6	97.4	83.0	87.8	130.1	86.0	100.7	97.4	83.0	87.8	100.9	64.2	76.5
0960	Flooring	130.5	101.4	121.8	130.5	94.3	119.7	130.5	94.3	119.7	132.6	104.1	124.1	130.5	94.3	119.7	117.8	73.4	104.5
0970, 0990	Wall Finishes & Painting/Coating	109.0	93.7	99.8	109.0	106.5	107.5	109.1	83.0	93.4	112.6	99.3	104.6	109.0	83.0	93.4	108.4	52.7	74.9
09	FINISHES	114.9	92.8	102.6	116.5	95.9	105.0	113.9	85.7	98.2	129.0	91.9	108.3	114.2	85.7	98.3	113.4	65.9	86.9
COVERS	DIVS. 10 - 14, 25, 28, 41, 43, 44, 46	131.1	87.3	122.4	131.1	97.5	124.4	131.1	94.1	123.7	131.1	99.0	124.7	131.1	94.1	123.7	131.1	66.9	118.3
21, 22, 23	FIRE SUPPRESSION, PLUMBING & HVAC	100.5	93.0	97.5	102.7	97.6	100.7	102.9	97.6	100.8	101.5	82.8	94.0	102.5	94.2	99.2	102.5	71.6	90.1
26, 27, 3370	ELECTRICAL, COMMUNICATIONS & UTIL.	114.4	74.3	93.5	108.4	87.5	97.5	106.1	87.5	96.4	109.7	93.6	101.3	106.1	87.5	96.4	118.8	63.3	89.8
MF2010	WEIGHTED AVERAGE	112.4	89.2	102.3	118.7	93.7	107.8	113.9	90.3	103.6	119.5	91.9	107.5	114.0	89.6	103.4	112.3	71.4	94.5

CANADA

DIVISION		MONTREAL, QUEBEC			MOOSE JAW, SASKATCHEWAN			NEW GLASGOW, NOVA SCOTIA			NEWCASTLE, NEW BRUNSWICK			NORTH BAY, ONTARIO			OSHAWA, ONTARIO		
		MAT.	INST.	TOTAL	MAT.	INST.	TOTAL	MAT.	INST.	TOTAL	MAT.	INST.	TOTAL	MAT.	INST.	TOTAL	MAT.	INST.	TOTAL
015433	CONTRACTOR EQUIPMENT		104.0	104.0		100.2	100.2		101.5	101.5		101.9	101.9		101.6	101.6		103.8	103.8
0241, 31 - 34	SITE & INFRASTRUCTURE, DEMOLITION	107.7	100.0	102.3	112.7	96.5	101.3	104.4	98.9	100.5	98.4	97.3	97.6	119.5	100.4	106.1	112.9	104.5	107.0
0310	Concrete Forming & Accessories	131.4	93.1	98.4	107.3	61.9	68.1	98.8	73.2	76.8	103.7	65.3	70.6	127.4	89.0	94.3	123.8	91.1	95.6
0320	Concrete Reinforcing	135.8	96.4	116.1	109.6	63.8	86.7	173.8	48.2	111.1	139.2	58.4	98.8	205.4	84.4	145.0	163.7	87.1	125.4
0330	Cast-in-Place Concrete	174.5	100.5	143.8	145.3	72.1	114.9	164.2	73.2	126.4	136.1	62.9	105.7	154.2	88.1	121.6	162.7	89.2	132.2
03	CONCRETE	148.7	96.2	122.8	122.3	66.5	94.8	151.6	69.3	111.0	130.9	63.8	97.8	154.2	88.1	121.6	145.4	89.9	118.0
04	MASONRY	172.0	94.1	123.8	161.7	65.5	102.2	182.8	73.2	115.0	165.6	66.1	104.0	188.0	91.5	128.3	162.1	96.0	121.2
05	METALS	124.5	92.8	114.7	102.7	74.9	94.1	116.0	75.3	103.4	104.4	72.8	94.7	117.0	90.4	108.8	105.5	92.6	101.5
06	WOOD, PLASTICS & COMPOSITES	120.2	93.5	105.1	99.0	60.4	77.2	94.6	72.6	82.2	97.8	65.4	79.5	127.3	89.6	106.0	117.2	90.1	101.9
07	THERMAL & MOISTURE PROTECTION	118.4	96.5	109.5	105.6	65.5	89.3	110.4	71.4	94.6	108.9	63.6	90.5	115.7	87.4	104.2	113.1	89.2	103.4
08	OPENINGS	92.8	82.4	90.3	90.1	58.1	82.5	88.3	66.4	83.1	89.2	57.2	81.6	95.9	85.7	93.5	92.2	89.9	91.7
0920	Plaster & Gypsum Board	144.9	92.8	109.5	121.3	59.1	79.0	154.0	71.7	98.0	151.8	64.2	92.2	151.5	89.2	109.1	146.6	89.8	108.0
0950, 0980	Ceilings & Acoustic Treatment	115.8	92.8	100.5	97.4	59.1	71.9	102.5	71.7	82.0	100.9	64.2	76.5	102.5	89.2	93.6	100.8	89.8	93.5
0960	Flooring	138.7	101.4	127.5	120.8	64.4	104.0	118.0	68.5	103.2	117.8	73.4	104.5	136.3	99.2	125.2	127.7	106.8	121.5
0970, 0990	Wall Finishes & Painting/Coating	112.9	105.7	108.6	109.0	68.2	84.5	113.0	65.5	84.4	108.4	52.7	74.9	113.0	93.1	101.1	107.9	106.6	107.1
09	FINISHES	123.1	96.7	108.4	110.3	62.7	83.8	116.0	71.8	91.4	113.4	65.9	86.9	121.6	91.8	105.0	115.7	95.7	104.5
COVERS	DIVS. 10 - 14, 25, 28, 41, 43, 44, 46	131.1	88.6	122.6	131.1	66.1	118.1	131.1	68.2	118.5	131.1	66.9	118.3	131.1	74.5	119.8	131.1	99.7	124.8
21, 22, 23	FIRE SUPPRESSION, PLUMBING & HVAC	101.3	93.8	98.3	102.9	77.8	92.8	102.5	86.3	96.0	102.5	71.3	90.0	102.5	100.3	101.6	100.5	102.9	101.5
26, 27, 3370	ELECTRICAL, COMMUNICATIONS & UTIL.	113.8	86.5	99.6	115.4	64.3	88.7	117.7	65.9	90.7	113.4	63.3	87.3	117.7	93.0	104.8	115.6	92.6	103.6
MF2010	WEIGHTED AVERAGE	119.2	93.4	107.9	111.2	70.8	93.6	117.7	76.1	99.6	112.1	69.3	93.5	120.5	92.9	108.5	114.6	96.1	106.5

CANADA

DIVISION		OTTAWA, ONTARIO			OWEN SOUND, ONTARIO			PETERBOROUGH, ONTARIO			PORTAGE LA PRAIRIE, MANITOBA			PRINCE ALBERT, SASKATCHEWAN			PRINCE GEORGE, BRITISH COLUMBIA		
		MAT.	INST.	TOTAL	MAT.	INST.	TOTAL	MAT.	INST.	TOTAL	MAT.	INST.	TOTAL	MAT.	INST.	TOTAL	MAT.	INST.	TOTAL
015433	CONTRACTOR EQUIPMENT		103.8	103.8		101.6	101.6		101.6	101.6		103.9	103.9		100.2	100.2		105.6	105.6
0241, 31 - 34	SITE & INFRASTRUCTURE, DEMOLITION	110.8	105.0	106.7	115.3	100.9	105.2	114.9	100.8	105.0	113.7	99.9	104.0	107.8	96.7	100.0	121.8	104.0	109.3
0310	Concrete Forming & Accessories	126.4	90.9	95.8	125.1	87.5	92.6	124.9	90.1	94.9	124.3	73.6	80.6	107.3	61.7	67.9	113.0	87.5	91.0
0320	Concrete Reinforcing	144.0	93.0	118.5	174.2	86.5	130.4	167.9	84.9	126.5	155.3	54.9	105.2	114.6	63.8	89.2	112.0	79.2	95.6
0330	Cast-in-Place Concrete	161.6	99.0	135.6	166.0	84.3	132.1	162.0	90.1	132.2	149.7	77.1	119.6	131.6	72.0	106.9	145.8	103.1	128.0
03	CONCRETE	143.6	94.1	119.2	151.0	86.4	119.2	147.1	89.3	118.6	132.7	72.0	102.7	116.7	66.3	91.9	150.0	91.5	121.2
04	MASONRY	175.1	97.0	126.8	165.2	97.3	123.2	167.9	98.4	124.9	166.3	67.7	105.3	160.8	65.5	101.8	172.9	96.6	125.7
05	METALS	123.6	91.9	113.8	108.2	91.2	103.0	105.5	90.9	101.0	106.4	77.7	97.5	102.8	74.7	94.1	106.2	88.8	100.8
06	WOOD, PLASTICS & COMPOSITES	108.8	90.5	98.5	120.6	86.2	101.2	119.8	88.2	102.0	117.1	75.1	93.4	99.0	60.4	77.2	101.3	83.9	91.5
07	THERMAL & MOISTURE PROTECTION	127.5	92.7	113.4	112.4	88.2	102.6	112.6	93.1	104.7	106.1	72.8	92.6	105.5	64.4	88.8	115.3	87.9	104.1
08	OPENINGS	93.8	89.2	92.7	92.5	85.0	90.7	93.6	87.5	92.2	94.7	66.3	88.0	88.9	58.1	81.6	91.0	83.7	89.3
0920	Plaster & Gypsum Board	192.8	90.2	123.0	151.2	85.7	106.7	142.7	87.8	105.4	123.6	73.9	89.8	121.3	59.1	79.0	124.3	83.0	96.2
0950, 0980	Ceilings & Acoustic Treatment	134.7	90.2	105.1	95.2	85.7	88.9	97.4	87.8	91.0	97.4	73.9	81.8	97.4	59.1	71.9	97.4	83.0	87.8
0960	Flooring	126.9	99.2	118.6	130.7	100.7	121.7	130.5	99.2	121.1	130.5	71.5	112.8	120.8	64.4	104.0	126.1	77.6	111.6
0970, 0990	Wall Finishes & Painting/Coating	112.4	94.1	101.4	111.9	91.8	99.8	109.0	95.5	100.9	109.1	60.0	79.6	109.0	58.2	78.5	109.0	85.8	95.0
09	FINISHES	130.7	92.9	109.7	117.3	90.6	102.4	115.6	92.5	102.7	113.4	72.3	90.5	110.3	61.6	83.2	113.9	85.1	97.9
COVERS	DIVS. 10 - 14, 25, 28, 41, 43, 44, 46	131.1	97.1	124.3	139.2	75.0	126.4	131.1	76.0	120.1	131.1	68.7	118.6	131.1	66.1	118.1	131.1	97.1	124.3
21, 22, 23	FIRE SUPPRESSION, PLUMBING & HVAC	101.5	83.2	94.2	102.2	100.0	101.4	102.5	103.9	103.1	102.5	85.4	95.6	102.9	70.1	89.7	102.5	96.5	100.1
26, 27, 3370	ELECTRICAL, COMMUNICATIONS & UTIL.	109.0	94.4	101.4	117.9	91.7	104.2	112.9	92.6	102.3	115.1	61.5	87.1	115.4	64.3	88.7	113.1	83.9	97.8
MF2010	WEIGHTED AVERAGE	119.2	92.5	107.5	117.4	93.0	106.8	115.5	94.9	106.5	113.9	75.6	97.2	110.3	69.0	92.3	115.9	91.7	105.3

CANADA

DIVISION		QUEBEC, QUEBEC			RED DEER, ALBERTA			REGINA, SASKATCHEWAN			RIMOUSKI, QUEBEC			ROUYN-NORANDA, QUEBEC			SAINT HYACINTHE, QUEBEC		
		MAT.	INST.	TOTAL	MAT.	INST.	TOTAL	MAT.	INST.	TOTAL	MAT.	INST.	TOTAL	MAT.	INST.	TOTAL	MAT.	INST.	TOTAL
015433	CONTRACTOR EQUIPMENT		104.4	104.4		103.7	103.7		100.2	100.2		102.5	102.5		102.5	102.5		102.5	102.5
0241, 31 - 34	SITE & INFRASTRUCTURE, DEMOLITION	103.7	100.0	101.1	111.6	101.9	104.8	123.5	98.4	105.9	96.1	99.7	98.6	95.7	100.5	99.1	96.1	100.5	99.2
0310	Concrete Forming & Accessories	131.8	93.4	98.6	139.3	84.3	91.9	114.1	90.4	93.7	130.3	92.8	98.0	130.3	89.8	95.4	130.3	89.8	95.4
0320	Concrete Reinforcing	136.6	96.4	116.5	155.3	74.0	114.7	132.1	83.4	107.8	107.7	96.4	102.1	151.1	81.3	116.3	151.1	81.3	116.3
0330	Cast-in-Place Concrete	142.8	100.9	125.4	149.7	101.0	129.5	173.6	94.9	140.9	135.7	99.2	120.5	129.0	99.3	116.7	133.3	99.3	117.3
03	CONCRETE	133.9	96.4	115.4	140.3	88.6	114.8	150.3	90.6	120.9	125.3	95.6	110.7	129.2	91.7	110.7	131.2	91.7	111.7
04	MASONRY	172.0	94.1	123.8	163.2	82.9	113.5	184.7	94.4	128.8	163.4	94.1	120.5	163.6	88.6	117.2	163.8	88.6	117.3
05	METALS	124.4	93.0	114.7	106.4	88.8	100.9	125.6	85.7	113.3	103.4	92.3	100.0	103.8	88.7	99.2	103.8	88.7	99.2
06	WOOD, PLASTICS & COMPOSITES	119.9	93.5	105.0	117.3	83.8	98.4	98.3	91.3	94.4	131.6	93.2	110.0	131.6	89.9	108.1	131.6	89.9	108.1
07	THERMAL & MOISTURE PROTECTION	118.9	96.6	109.9	130.7	88.0	113.4	117.9	85.6	104.8	106.2	95.9	102.0	106.2	91.8	100.3	106.6	91.8	100.6
08	OPENINGS	94.0	90.3	93.1	94.7	79.2	91.0	90.8	80.2	88.3	94.2	80.5	91.0	94.7	78.2	90.8	94.7	78.2	90.8
0920	Plaster & Gypsum Board	164.8	92.8	115.8	129.2	83.0	97.7	147.8	91.0	109.2	172.1	92.8	118.1	140.3	89.4	105.7	142.7	89.4	106.5
0950, 0980	Ceilings & Acoustic Treatment	122.8	92.8	102.8	97.4	83.0	87.8	123.9	91.0	102.0	96.5	92.8	94.0	96.5	89.4	91.8	96.5	89.4	91.8
0960	Flooring	134.3	101.4	124.5	133.2	94.3	121.6	132.5	66.7	112.8	130.5	101.4	121.8	130.5	101.4	121.8	130.5	101.4	121.8
0970, 0990	Wall Finishes & Painting/Coating	115.4	105.7	109.5	109.0	83.0	93.4	112.9	90.9	99.7	109.0	105.7	107.0	109.0	93.7	99.8	109.0	93.7	99.8
09	FINISHES	126.3	96.7	109.8	115.0	85.7	98.7	125.5	86.8	103.9	118.7	96.5	106.3	114.3	92.8	102.3	114.6	92.8	102.5
COVERS	DIVS. 10 - 14, 25, 28, 41, 43, 44, 46	131.1	88.7	122.6	131.1	94.1	123.7	131.1	73.5	119.6	131.1	88.0	122.5	131.1	87.3	122.4	131.1	87.3	122.4
21, 22, 23	FIRE SUPPRESSION, PLUMBING & HVAC	101.2	93.8	98.3	102.5	94.2	99.2	100.7	84.2	94.1	102.5	93.7	99.0	102.5	93.0	98.7	98.9	93.0	96.5
26, 27, 3370	ELECTRICAL, COMMUNICATIONS & UTIL.	110.9	86.5	98.2	106.1	87.5	96.4	115.4	91.4	102.9	113.2	86.5	99.3	113.2	74.3	92.9	114.0	74.3	93.3
MF2010	WEIGHTED AVERAGE	117.5	93.8	107.2	114.5	89.6	103.6	120.3	88.4	106.4	112.3	93.1	103.9	112.5	89.2	102.3	111.9	89.2	102.0

CANADA

DIVISION		SAINT JOHN, NEW BRUNSWICK			SARNIA, ONTARIO			SASKATOON, SASKATCHEWAN			SAULT STE MARIE, ONTARIO			SHERBROOKE, QUEBEC			SOREL, QUEBEC		
		MAT.	INST.	TOTAL	MAT.	INST.	TOTAL	MAT.	INST.	TOTAL	MAT.	INST.	TOTAL	MAT.	INST.	TOTAL	MAT.	INST.	TOTAL
015433	CONTRACTOR EQUIPMENT		101.9	101.9		101.6	101.6		100.2	100.2		101.6	101.6		102.5	102.5		102.5	102.5
0241, 31 - 34	SITE & INFRASTRUCTURE, DEMOLITION	98.5	98.5	98.5	113.4	100.9	104.6	108.7	98.4	101.5	103.7	100.4	101.4	96.2	100.5	99.2	96.3	100.6	99.3
0310	Concrete Forming & Accessories	123.2	66.3	74.1	123.7	97.4	101.0	107.4	90.4	92.7	113.0	87.0	90.6	130.3	89.8	95.4	130.3	90.0	95.5
0320	Concrete Reinforcing	139.2	61.9	100.6	119.4	86.3	102.9	115.5	83.4	99.5	107.8	84.6	96.2	151.1	81.3	116.3	142.9	81.4	112.2
0330	Cast-in-Place Concrete	134.1	80.7	111.9	149.5	103.7	130.5	141.4	94.9	122.1	134.3	88.5	115.3	133.3	99.3	119.2	134.4	99.3	119.8
03	CONCRETE	131.4	71.4	101.8	133.3	97.4	115.6	122.5	90.6	106.7	117.3	87.3	102.5	131.2	91.7	111.7	130.4	91.7	111.3
04	MASONRY	185.8	72.2	115.5	179.3	101.2	131.0	167.2	94.4	122.2	164.3	94.5	121.1	163.9	88.6	117.3	164.0	88.6	117.3
05	METALS	104.3	82.6	97.6	105.5	91.3	101.1	101.9	85.7	96.9	104.7	90.8	100.4	103.8	88.7	99.2	103.8	88.8	99.2
06	WOOD, PLASTICS & COMPOSITES	121.4	64.5	89.3	118.9	96.8	106.4	98.0	91.3	94.3	106.0	86.5	95.0	131.6	89.9	108.1	131.6	89.9	108.1
07	THERMAL & MOISTURE PROTECTION	109.2	69.6	93.1	112.6	96.7	106.2	106.8	85.6	98.2	111.5	89.4	102.5	106.2	91.8	100.3	106.2	91.8	100.3
08	OPENINGS	89.1	60.8	82.4	95.7	91.5	94.7	90.1	80.2	87.7	87.2	85.3	86.8	94.7	78.2	90.8	94.7	83.0	91.9
0920	Plaster & Gypsum Board	169.4	63.3	97.2	164.7	96.7	118.4	129.7	91.0	103.4	131.7	86.0	100.6	142.7	89.4	105.7	172.1	89.4	115.9
0950, 0980	Ceilings & Acoustic Treatment	107.2	63.3	78.0	102.7	96.7	98.7	119.7	91.0	100.6	97.4	86.0	89.8	96.5	89.4	91.8	96.5	89.4	91.8
0960	Flooring	128.4	73.4	112.0	130.5	108.5	123.9	120.7	66.7	104.6	123.6	102.7	117.3	130.5	101.4	121.8	130.5	101.4	121.8
0970, 0990	Wall Finishes & Painting/Coating	108.4	78.8	90.6	109.0	108.0	108.4	109.9	90.9	98.5	109.0	100.0	103.6	109.0	93.7	99.8	109.0	93.7	99.8
09	FINISHES	120.2	68.5	91.4	119.8	101.1	109.4	116.5	86.8	99.9	111.4	91.3	100.2	114.6	92.8	102.5	118.7	92.8	104.3
COVERS	DIVS. 10 - 14, 25, 28, 41, 43, 44, 46	131.1	67.3	118.3	131.1	77.5	120.4	131.1	73.5	119.6	131.1	98.4	124.6	131.1	87.3	122.4	131.1	87.3	122.4
21, 22, 23	FIRE SUPPRESSION, PLUMBING & HVAC	102.5	81.0	93.9	102.5	110.2	105.6	100.6	84.2	94.0	102.5	96.8	100.2	102.9	93.0	98.9	102.5	93.0	98.7
26, 27, 3370	ELECTRICAL, COMMUNICATIONS & UTIL.	121.9	90.3	105.4	115.7	94.9	104.8	117.1	91.4	103.7	114.4	93.0	103.2	113.2	74.3	92.9	113.2	74.3	92.9
MF2010	WEIGHTED AVERAGE	114.6	78.3	98.8	115.3	99.5	108.4	111.3	88.4	101.3	110.7	93.1	103.0	112.8	89.2	102.5	113.0	89.4	102.7

CANADA

DIVISION		ST CATHARINES, ONTARIO			ST JEROME, QUEBEC			ST JOHNS, NEWFOUNDLAND			SUDBURY, ONTARIO			SUMMERSIDE, PRINCE EDWARD ISLAND			SYDNEY, NOVA SCOTIA		
		MAT.	INST.	TOTAL	MAT.	INST.	TOTAL	MAT.	INST.	TOTAL	MAT.	INST.	TOTAL	MAT.	INST.	TOTAL	MAT.	INST.	TOTAL
015433	CONTRACTOR EQUIPMENT		101.6	101.6		102.5	102.5		103.1	103.1		101.6	101.6		101.5	101.5		101.5	101.5
0241, 31 - 34	SITE & INFRASTRUCTURE, DEMOLITION	101.8	101.8	101.8	95.7	100.5	99.1	116.4	99.9	104.8	101.9	101.3	101.5	112.2	96.4	101.1	100.1	98.9	99.2
0310	Concrete Forming & Accessories	115.9	93.9	96.9	130.3	89.8	95.4	113.8	82.4	86.7	111.9	87.4	90.7	99.1	59.6	65.0	98.8	73.2	76.8
0320	Concrete Reinforcing	104.3	93.0	98.7	151.1	81.3	116.3	161.9	74.4	118.2	105.1	93.0	99.0	171.5	48.3	113.0	173.8	48.2	111.7
0330	Cast-in-Place Concrete	134.4	100.1	120.1	129.0	99.3	116.7	166.6	87.6	133.8	135.5	96.2	119.2	155.8	62.0	116.9	126.6	73.2	104.5
03	CONCRETE	115.8	95.8	105.9	129.2	91.7	110.7	159.3	83.0	121.6	116.2	91.6	104.0	156.5	59.1	108.5	133.8	69.3	102.0
04	MASONRY	158.6	99.7	122.1	163.6	88.6	117.2	187.1	89.8	126.9	158.6	94.9	119.2	181.9	63.7	108.8	180.0	73.2	113.9
05	METALS	104.6	92.4	100.8	103.8	88.7	99.2	126.2	83.4	113.0	104.6	91.9	100.7	116.0	68.6	101.4	116.0	75.3	103.4
06	WOOD, PLASTICS & COMPOSITES	107.4	93.6	99.6	131.6	89.9	108.1	101.4	80.9	89.8	103.5	86.5	93.9	94.9	59.1	74.7	94.6	72.6	82.2
07	THERMAL & MOISTURE PROTECTION	112.1	95.9	105.5	106.2	91.8	100.3	118.6	84.9	105.0	111.5	90.3	102.9	109.9	62.5	90.7	110.4	71.4	94.6
08	OPENINGS	85.2	90.7	86.5	94.7	78.2	90.8	99.3	73.4	93.2	86.0	85.3	85.8	99.1	51.1	87.8	88.3	66.4	83.1
0920	Plaster & Gypsum Board	129.0	93.4	104.8	140.3	89.4	105.7	154.5	80.1	103.9	133.6	86.0	101.2	154.4	57.7	88.6	154.0	71.7	98.0
0950, 0980	Ceilings & Acoustic Treatment	100.8	93.4	95.9	96.5	89.4	91.8	116.8	80.1	92.4	95.5	86.0	89.2	102.5	57.7	72.7	102.5	71.7	82.0
0960	Flooring	123.0	100.7	116.3	130.5	101.4	121.8	122.3	60.3	103.8	120.9	102.7	115.4	118.1	64.0	101.9	118.0	68.5	103.2
0970, 0990	Wall Finishes & Painting/Coating	107.9	102.5	104.7	109.0	93.7	99.8	112.8	75.8	90.6	107.9	93.5	99.3	113.0	43.9	71.4	113.0	65.5	84.4
09	FINISHES	111.2	96.4	103.0	114.3	92.8	102.3	121.1	78.0	97.1	110.1	90.7	99.3	117.0	59.1	84.7	116.0	71.8	91.4
COVERS	DIVS. 10 - 14, 25, 28, 41, 43, 44, 46	131.1	76.3	120.1	131.1	87.3	122.4	131.1	73.2	119.5	131.1	98.5	124.6	131.1	66.4	118.2	131.1	68.2	118.5
21, 22, 23	FIRE SUPPRESSION, PLUMBING & HVAC	100.5	84.4	94.1	102.5	93.0	98.7	100.8	73.9	90.0	102.5	85.8	95.8	102.5	65.2	87.6	102.5	86.3	96.0
26, 27, 3370	ELECTRICAL, COMMUNICATIONS & UTIL.	116.0	94.5	104.7	113.8	74.3	93.2	115.9	72.4	93.2	113.1	94.8	103.6	116.7	53.6	83.7	117.7	65.9	90.7
MF2010	WEIGHTED AVERAGE	109.7	93.0	102.4	112.5	89.2	102.3	122.0	80.4	103.9	109.9	91.7	101.9	119.5	64.1	95.4	115.6	76.1	98.4

CANADA

DIVISION		THUNDER BAY, ONTARIO			TIMMINS, ONTARIO			TORONTO, ONTARIO			TROIS RIVIERES, QUEBEC			TRURO, NOVA SCOTIA			VANCOUVER, BRITISH COLUMBIA		
		MAT.	INST.	TOTAL	MAT.	INST.	TOTAL	MAT.	INST.	TOTAL	MAT.	INST.	TOTAL	MAT.	INST.	TOTAL	MAT.	INST.	TOTAL
015433	CONTRACTOR EQUIPMENT		101.6	101.6		101.6	101.6		103.9	103.9		102.5	102.5		101.5	101.5		112.1	112.1
0241, 31 - 34	SITE & INFRASTRUCTURE, DEMOLITION	106.8	101.7	103.2	114.9	100.4	104.7	137.0	105.8	115.1	100.9	100.6	100.7	100.1	98.9	99.2	120.3	108.2	111.8
0310	Concrete Forming & Accessories	123.7	90.8	95.3	124.9	89.0	93.9	128.5	99.5	103.4	133.2	90.0	95.9	97.1	73.3	76.5	122.0	91.6	95.8
0320	Concrete Reinforcing	93.2	91.9	92.5	167.9	84.4	126.2	151.3	93.2	122.3	173.8	81.4	127.6	142.9	48.2	95.6	142.2	81.7	112.0
0330	Cast-in-Place Concrete	147.9	98.5	127.4	162.0	88.4	131.5	150.7	108.2	133.1	131.1	99.3	117.9	168.3	73.3	128.8	157.7	99.2	133.4
03	CONCRETE	124.2	93.7	109.2	147.1	88.1	118.0	139.8	101.1	120.7	136.8	91.7	114.6	145.5	69.3	107.9	148.1	92.7	120.8
04	MASONRY	159.3	99.0	122.0	167.9	91.5	120.6	194.2	104.1	138.4	183.8	88.6	124.9	163.4	73.2	107.6	182.3	93.0	127.0
05	METALS	104.4	91.3	100.4	105.5	90.4	100.9	125.1	93.1	115.2	115.1	88.8	107.0	104.6	75.3	95.6	141.4	91.4	126.0
06	WOOD, PLASTICS & COMPOSITES	117.2	89.5	101.6	119.8	89.6	102.7	111.5	98.7	104.3	139.8	89.9	111.7	89.2	72.6	79.9	104.1	91.7	97.1
07	THERMAL & MOISTURE PROTECTION	112.4	93.0	104.5	112.6	87.4	102.4	124.3	99.6	114.2	109.3	91.8	102.2	107.5	71.4	92.9	130.0	88.5	113.2
08	OPENINGS	84.3	87.8	85.1	93.6	85.7	91.7	91.8	96.8	93.0	97.0	83.0	93.7	86.6	66.4	81.8	94.5	87.9	93.0
0920	Plaster & Gypsum Board	162.4	89.2	112.6	142.7	89.2	106.3	155.3	98.6	116.7	186.1	89.4	120.3	141.8	71.7	94.1	140.0	90.9	106.6
0950, 0980	Ceilings & Acoustic Treatment	95.5	89.2	91.3	97.4	89.2	91.9	125.4	98.6	107.6	101.6	89.4	93.5	97.4	71.7	80.3	150.0	90.9	110.7
0960	Flooring	127.7	107.8	121.7	130.5	99.2	121.1	132.8	110.4	126.1	136.3	101.4	125.8	113.1	68.5	99.8	129.2	97.7	119.8
0970, 0990	Wall Finishes & Painting/Coating	107.9	92.1	98.4	109.0	93.1	99.5	114.8	106.6	109.9	113.0	93.7	101.4	109.0	65.5	82.9	114.0	97.7	104.2
09	FINISHES	116.4	94.2	104.0	115.6	91.8	102.4	127.3	102.5	113.5	125.3	92.8	107.2	109.9	71.8	88.7	129.1	93.6	109.3
COVERS	DIVS. 10 - 14, 25, 28, 41, 43, 44, 46	131.1	76.0	120.1	131.1	74.5	119.8	131.1	102.1	125.3	131.1	87.3	122.4	131.1	68.2	118.5	131.1	96.9	124.3
21, 22, 23	FIRE SUPPRESSION, PLUMBING & HVAC	100.5	84.3	94.0	102.5	100.3	101.6	101.2	94.6	98.6	102.5	93.0	98.7	102.5	86.3	96.0	101.3	82.3	93.7
26, 27, 3370	ELECTRICAL, COMMUNICATIONS & UTIL.	114.4	93.0	103.2	114.4	93.0	103.2	111.5	96.6	103.7	118.0	74.3	95.2	112.9	65.9	88.4	111.3	81.3	95.6
MF2010	WEIGHTED AVERAGE	110.9	91.7	102.6	115.6	92.9	105.7	120.2	99.0	111.0	117.9	89.4	105.5	113.0	76.1	96.9	123.3	90.0	108.8

CANADA

DIVISION		VICTORIA, BRITISH COLUMBIA			WHITEHORSE, YUKON			WINDSOR, ONTARIO			WINNIPEG, MANITOBA			YARMOUTH, NOVA SCOTIA			YELLOWKNIFE, NWT		
		MAT.	INST.	TOTAL	MAT.	INST.	TOTAL	MAT.	INST.	TOTAL	MAT.	INST.	TOTAL	MAT.	INST.	TOTAL	MAT.	INST.	TOTAL
015433	CONTRACTOR EQUIPMENT		108.7	108.7		101.7	101.7		101.6	101.6		105.9	105.9		101.5	101.5		101.6	101.6
0241, 31 - 34	SITE & INFRASTRUCTURE, DEMOLITION	121.5	107.7	111.8	123.0	97.4	105.0	97.3	101.6	100.3	119.5	101.3	106.7	104.2	98.9	100.5	138.7	101.7	112.8
0310	Concrete Forming & Accessories	112.9	91.0	94.0	117.7	60.9	68.7	123.7	90.0	94.6	131.5	68.1	76.8	98.8	73.2	76.8	116.1	82.0	86.7
0320	Concrete Reinforcing	113.0	81.6	97.3	153.9	61.9	107.9	102.2	93.0	97.6	141.0	57.4	99.3	173.8	48.2	111.1	154.5	64.7	109.6
0330	Cast-in-Place Concrete	146.4	98.6	126.6	191.7	71.3	141.7	137.7	100.3	122.1	181.5	73.8	136.8	162.4	73.2	125.4	231.5	89.4	172.5
03	CONCRETE	152.5	91.9	122.6	158.2	65.4	112.4	117.6	94.1	106.0	153.4	68.7	111.6	150.8	69.3	110.6	176.9	81.7	129.9
04	MASONRY	170.1	93.0	122.4	205.6	63.9	117.9	158.7	97.8	121.0	179.6	69.3	111.4	182.6	73.2	114.9	209.1	76.2	126.8
05	METALS	104.3	87.4	99.1	129.3	74.6	112.5	104.5	91.8	100.6	143.3	74.6	122.1	116.0	75.3	103.4	129.3	79.8	114.0
06	WOOD, PLASTICS & COMPOSITES	101.6	91.6	96.0	100.8	59.6	77.5	117.2	89.1	101.4	111.1	69.0	87.3	94.6	72.6	82.2	100.3	83.7	90.9
07	THERMAL & MOISTURE PROTECTION	115.8	88.3	104.7	125.8	63.4	100.5	112.2	92.2	104.0	118.7	70.7	99.2	110.4	71.4	94.6	122.1	80.0	105.0
08	OPENINGS	91.8	84.1	90.0	95.4	56.8	86.3	84.1	88.1	85.0	93.1	61.6	85.6	88.3	66.4	83.1	94.3	70.5	88.7
0920	Plaster & Gypsum Board	121.7	90.9	100.7	146.1	58.2	86.3	147.7	88.8	107.6	139.7	67.5	90.6	154.0	71.7	98.0	176.0	83.1	112.8
0950, 0980	Ceilings & Acoustic Treatment	99.3	90.9	93.7	127.7	58.2	81.4	95.5	88.8	91.0	143.6	67.5	93.0	102.5	71.7	82.0	133.5	83.1	99.9
0960	Flooring	125.9	77.6	111.5	140.3	62.5	117.0	127.7	105.0	120.9	131.3	74.0	114.1	118.0	68.5	103.2	134.7	94.2	122.6
0970, 0990	Wall Finishes & Painting/Coating	109.9	97.7	102.6	124.2	57.2	83.9	107.9	95.4	100.4	112.9	55.4	78.4	113.0	65.5	84.4	121.6	82.0	97.8
09	FINISHES	114.1	90.1	100.7	130.9	60.6	91.7	114.0	93.5	102.6	127.8	68.3	94.6	116.0	71.8	91.4	134.9	83.7	106.4
COVERS	DIVS. 10 - 14, 25, 28, 41, 43, 44, 46	131.1	72.9	119.5	131.1	65.4	118.0	131.1	75.4	120.0	131.1	67.9	118.5	131.1	68.2	118.5	131.1	68.7	118.6
21, 22, 23	FIRE SUPPRESSION, PLUMBING & HVAC	102.5	82.2	94.4	102.9	76.4	92.3	100.5	83.9	93.9	101.2	65.7	87.0	102.5	86.3	96.0	103.0	96.0	100.2
26, 27, 3370	ELECTRICAL, COMMUNICATIONS & UTIL.	113.8	81.3	96.8	134.3	63.7	97.5	119.3	94.5	106.4	112.9	66.9	88.9	117.7	65.9	90.7	132.1	87.2	108.7
MF2010	WEIGHTED AVERAGE	115.9	88.1	103.8	126.3	69.8	101.7	110.2	91.7	102.2	123.6	70.8	100.6	117.6	76.1	99.6	128.8	85.8	110.1

Location Factors

Costs shown in RSMeans cost data publications are based on national averages for materials and installation. To adjust these costs to a specific location, simply multiply the base cost by the factor and divide by 100 for that city. The data is arranged alphabetically by state and postal zip code numbers. For a city not listed, use the factor for a nearby city with similar economic characteristics.

STATE/ZIP	CITY	MAT.	INST.	TOTAL
ALABAMA				
350-352	Birmingham	97.5	74.1	87.3
354	Tuscaloosa	96.7	62.0	81.6
355	Jasper	97.0	56.7	79.4
356	Decatur	96.6	59.1	80.3
357-358	Huntsville	96.7	70.8	85.4
359	Gadsden	96.7	60.8	81.1
360-361	Montgomery	97.9	58.1	80.5
362	Anniston	96.5	63.0	81.9
363	Dothan	96.9	50.5	76.7
364	Evergreen	96.5	51.9	77.1
365-366	Mobile	97.8	65.9	83.9
367	Selma	96.7	50.8	76.7
368	Phenix City	97.3	55.7	79.2
369	Butler	96.8	50.5	76.6
ALASKA				
995-996	Anchorage	121.3	114.3	118.3
997	Fairbanks	120.7	115.0	118.2
998	Juneau	120.6	113.5	117.5
999	Ketchikan	132.0	113.5	124.0
ARIZONA				
850,853	Phoenix	99.4	74.8	88.7
851,852	Mesa/Tempe	98.8	73.8	87.9
855	Globe	99.0	71.2	86.9
856-857	Tucson	97.6	73.6	87.1
859	Show Low	99.1	73.5	88.0
860	Flagstaff	101.0	72.9	88.8
863	Prescott	98.9	69.7	86.2
864	Kingman	97.3	73.2	86.8
865	Chambers	97.3	71.9	86.3
ARKANSAS				
716	Pine Bluff	96.9	62.9	82.1
717	Camden	94.5	50.4	75.3
718	Texarkana	95.7	49.9	75.7
719	Hot Springs	93.8	52.3	75.8
720-722	Little Rock	98.0	63.8	83.1
723	West Memphis	95.6	62.7	81.2
724	Jonesboro	96.3	59.4	80.2
725	Batesville	94.2	55.1	77.2
726	Harrison	95.5	51.1	76.1
727	Fayetteville	93.0	52.9	75.6
728	Russellville	94.1	54.4	76.8
729	Fort Smith	96.8	61.7	81.5
CALIFORNIA				
900-902	Los Angeles	100.1	116.5	107.3
903-905	Inglewood	95.7	113.4	103.4
906-908	Long Beach	97.1	113.4	104.2
910-912	Pasadena	96.3	113.9	104.0
913-916	Van Nuys	99.1	113.9	105.5
917-918	Alhambra	98.2	113.9	105.0
919-921	San Diego	100.2	109.1	104.1
922	Palm Springs	96.7	111.6	103.2
923-924	San Bernardino	94.6	111.2	101.9
925	Riverside	98.9	114.0	105.5
926-927	Santa Ana	96.5	111.6	103.1
928	Anaheim	98.9	114.1	105.6
930	Oxnard	99.6	114.2	105.9
931	Santa Barbara	98.9	114.6	105.7
932-933	Bakersfield	100.8	110.6	105.1
934	San Luis Obispo	99.3	111.6	104.7
935	Mojave	96.8	108.6	101.9
936-938	Fresno	100.0	114.5	106.3
939	Salinas	100.2	120.3	108.9
940-941	San Francisco	106.1	143.8	122.5
942,956-958	Sacramento	101.2	118.6	108.8
943	Palo Alto	99.5	133.1	114.2
944	San Mateo	101.7	132.7	115.2
945	Vallejo	100.6	127.2	112.2
946	Oakland	103.9	133.1	116.6
947	Berkeley	103.4	133.1	116.4
948	Richmond	102.5	131.2	115.0
949	San Rafael	104.2	133.6	117.0
950	Santa Cruz	104.1	120.4	111.2

STATE/ZIP	CITY	MAT.	INST.	TOTAL
CALIFORNIA (CONT'D)				
951	San Jose	102.2	134.6	116.3
952	Stockton	100.5	115.5	107.0
953	Modesto	100.4	114.9	106.7
954	Santa Rosa	100.3	133.4	114.7
955	Eureka	101.6	111.6	106.0
959	Marysville	100.8	115.1	107.0
960	Redding	103.6	114.6	108.4
961	Susanville	102.6	114.6	107.8
COLORADO				
800-802	Denver	101.6	82.6	93.3
803	Boulder	98.6	82.0	91.3
804	Golden	100.6	79.6	91.4
805	Fort Collins	102.1	79.6	92.3
806	Greeley	99.7	76.1	89.4
807	Fort Morgan	99.1	79.6	90.6
808-809	Colorado Springs	101.3	79.3	91.7
810	Pueblo	100.9	78.6	91.2
811	Alamosa	102.0	74.6	90.1
812	Salida	101.7	76.2	90.6
813	Durango	102.4	76.8	91.2
814	Montrose	101.2	76.5	90.5
815	Grand Junction	104.4	76.7	92.4
816	Glenwood Springs	102.2	79.3	92.2
CONNECTICUT				
060	New Britain	100.8	120.4	109.3
061	Hartford	102.0	120.6	110.1
062	Willimantic	101.4	120.6	109.7
063	New London	97.7	120.5	107.6
064	Meriden	99.6	120.5	108.7
065	New Haven	102.2	120.5	110.2
066	Bridgeport	101.8	120.2	109.8
067	Waterbury	101.4	120.1	109.6
068	Norwalk	101.4	126.9	112.5
069	Stamford	101.5	127.9	113.0
D.C.				
200-205	Washington	101.6	91.6	97.2
DELAWARE				
197	Newark	98.8	108.1	102.8
198	Wilmington	99.4	108.1	103.2
199	Dover	99.7	108.1	103.3
FLORIDA				
320,322	Jacksonville	97.2	67.7	84.3
321	Daytona Beach	97.4	74.4	87.3
323	Tallahassee	98.7	58.0	81.0
324	Panama City	98.5	59.1	81.3
325	Pensacola	100.8	62.4	84.1
326,344	Gainesville	98.7	68.0	85.3
327-328,347	Orlando	99.3	71.4	87.1
329	Melbourne	99.9	77.9	90.3
330-332,340	Miami	97.7	74.6	87.6
333	Fort Lauderdale	96.4	73.9	86.6
334,349	West Palm Beach	95.3	72.3	85.3
335-336,346	Tampa	97.9	79.8	90.0
337	St. Petersburg	100.2	64.7	84.7
338	Lakeland	97.1	79.3	89.4
339,341	Fort Myers	96.4	74.1	86.7
342	Sarasota	99.3	75.3	88.8
GEORGIA				
300-303,399	Atlanta	96.8	75.3	87.5
304	Statesboro	96.5	56.9	79.2
305	Gainesville	95.2	62.8	81.1
306	Athens	94.7	65.1	81.8
307	Dalton	96.4	60.1	80.6
308-309	Augusta	95.6	64.8	82.2
310-312	Macon	96.2	65.9	83.0
313-314	Savannah	98.4	62.0	82.6
315	Waycross	97.3	60.7	81.3
316	Valdosta	97.5	62.6	82.3
317,398	Albany	97.5	62.5	82.3
318-319	Columbus	97.4	66.6	84.0

Location Factors

STATE/ZIP	CITY	MAT.	INST.	TOTAL
HAWAII				
967	Hilo	110.4	121.0	115.0
968	Honolulu	114.9	121.0	117.6
STATES & POSS.				
969	Guam	131.2	58.9	99.7
IDAHO				
832	Pocatello	100.8	78.4	91.1
833	Twin Falls	101.9	68.5	87.4
834	Idaho Falls	99.6	75.5	89.1
835	Lewiston	108.3	85.5	98.4
836-837	Boise	99.8	79.4	90.9
838	Coeur d'Alene	107.6	83.3	97.0
ILLINOIS				
600-603	North Suburban	98.5	135.9	114.8
604	Joliet	98.4	140.7	116.8
605	South Suburban	98.5	135.9	114.8
606-608	Chicago	98.9	141.9	117.6
609	Kankakee	94.8	130.8	110.5
610-611	Rockford	98.9	123.5	109.6
612	Rock Island	96.6	99.8	98.0
613	La Salle	97.7	125.1	109.6
614	Galesburg	97.6	107.6	102.0
615-616	Peoria	99.9	110.4	104.5
617	Bloomington	96.9	109.9	102.6
618-619	Champaign	100.2	108.0	103.6
620-622	East St. Louis	95.5	109.3	101.5
623	Quincy	96.9	101.6	99.0
624	Effingham	96.3	106.3	100.6
625	Decatur	98.2	105.9	101.6
626-627	Springfield	99.0	107.2	102.5
628	Centralia	94.1	108.4	100.4
629	Carbondale	93.9	106.2	99.2
INDIANA				
460	Anderson	95.5	83.1	90.1
461-462	Indianapolis	98.3	85.1	92.6
463-464	Gary	96.8	110.1	102.6
465-466	South Bend	95.7	84.2	90.7
467-468	Fort Wayne	96.0	79.2	88.7
469	Kokomo	93.3	82.0	88.4
470	Lawrenceburg	93.3	79.3	87.2
471	New Albany	94.4	77.0	86.8
472	Columbus	96.6	80.9	89.7
473	Muncie	97.3	81.8	90.6
474	Bloomington	98.7	81.5	91.2
475	Washington	95.0	83.3	89.9
476-477	Evansville	96.5	86.6	92.1
478	Terre Haute	97.2	85.8	92.2
479	Lafayette	96.3	82.9	90.5
IOWA				
500-503,509	Des Moines	99.4	83.9	92.7
504	Mason City	96.5	66.6	83.5
505	Fort Dodge	96.6	58.8	80.2
506-507	Waterloo	98.3	70.9	86.4
508	Creston	96.7	77.9	88.5
510-511	Sioux City	99.1	73.6	88.0
512	Sibley	97.7	57.5	80.2
513	Spencer	99.2	57.5	81.0
514	Carroll	96.4	72.2	85.9
515	Council Bluffs	100.2	78.8	90.9
516	Shenandoah	97.1	72.1	86.2
520	Dubuque	98.5	80.4	90.6
521	Decorah	97.4	65.6	83.5
522-524	Cedar Rapids	99.4	83.4	92.4
525	Ottumwa	97.3	73.0	86.7
526	Burlington	96.6	76.9	88.0
527-528	Davenport	98.4	93.4	96.2
KANSAS				
660-662	Kansas City	99.4	95.7	97.7
664-666	Topeka	99.4	66.5	85.1
667	Fort Scott	97.7	74.3	87.5
668	Emporia	97.8	70.0	85.7
669	Belleville	99.4	65.6	84.7
670-672	Wichita	99.9	65.1	84.8
673	Independence	99.9	70.3	87.0
674	Salina	100.4	67.0	85.9
675	Hutchinson	95.8	65.4	82.5
676	Hays	99.6	65.6	84.8
677	Colby	100.2	65.6	85.1

STATE/ZIP	CITY	MAT.	INST.	TOTAL
KANSAS (CONT'D)				
678	Dodge City	101.7	66.5	86.4
679	Liberal	99.5	66.4	85.1
KENTUCKY				
400-402	Louisville	97.8	84.2	91.9
403-405	Lexington	97.0	82.4	90.7
406	Frankfort	97.9	82.4	91.1
407-409	Corbin	94.4	73.3	85.2
410	Covington	95.2	93.2	94.3
411-412	Ashland	94.0	100.1	96.6
413-414	Campton	95.1	80.2	88.6
415-416	Pikeville	96.2	90.0	93.5
417-418	Hazard	94.6	79.9	88.2
420	Paducah	93.2	86.2	90.2
421-422	Bowling Green	95.5	84.8	90.8
423	Owensboro	95.6	88.9	92.7
424	Henderson	93.0	87.9	90.8
425-426	Somerset	92.7	81.5	87.8
427	Elizabethtown	92.2	83.7	88.5
LOUISIANA				
700-701	New Orleans	101.5	69.8	87.7
703	Thibodaux	98.7	64.9	84.0
704	Hammond	96.3	54.9	78.3
705	Lafayette	98.5	62.7	82.9
706	Lake Charles	98.6	65.0	84.0
707-708	Baton Rouge	100.4	63.6	84.4
710-711	Shreveport	98.4	59.6	81.5
712	Monroe	96.7	56.4	79.2
713-714	Alexandria	96.8	57.8	79.8
MAINE				
039	Kittery	95.1	85.7	91.0
040-041	Portland	100.8	91.2	96.6
042	Lewiston	98.3	91.2	95.2
043	Augusta	100.3	80.8	91.8
044	Bangor	97.6	90.8	94.7
045	Bath	96.1	83.0	90.4
046	Machias	95.7	86.5	91.7
047	Houlton	95.9	86.6	91.8
048	Rockland	95.0	86.5	91.3
049	Waterville	96.2	80.8	89.5
MARYLAND				
206	Waldorf	97.5	82.2	90.9
207-208	College Park	97.6	83.9	91.7
209	Silver Spring	96.9	83.8	91.2
210-212	Baltimore	100.5	82.8	92.8
214	Annapolis	100.3	81.8	92.3
215	Cumberland	96.0	81.9	89.9
216	Easton	97.4	69.3	85.2
217	Hagerstown	96.9	82.8	90.7
218	Salisbury	97.8	63.3	82.8
219	Elkton	95.1	81.9	89.4
MASSACHUSETTS				
010-011	Springfield	100.0	109.8	104.3
012	Pittsfield	99.6	109.6	103.9
013	Greenfield	97.5	110.2	103.0
014	Fitchburg	96.3	124.6	108.6
015-016	Worcester	100.0	124.6	110.7
017	Framingham	95.5	131.0	111.0
018	Lowell	99.4	130.1	112.8
019	Lawrence	100.1	131.3	113.7
020-022, 024	Boston	101.8	138.1	117.6
023	Brockton	100.4	126.3	111.7
025	Buzzards Bay	94.9	126.7	108.8
026	Hyannis	97.6	126.7	110.3
027	New Bedford	99.6	126.8	111.4
MICHIGAN				
480,483	Royal Oak	94.2	107.5	100.0
481	Ann Arbor	96.4	107.9	101.4
482	Detroit	97.9	109.3	102.8
484-485	Flint	96.1	96.8	96.4
486	Saginaw	95.7	92.4	94.2
487	Bay City	95.8	92.5	94.4
488-489	Lansing	97.7	94.1	96.1
490	Battle Creek	96.8	87.4	92.7
491	Kalamazoo	97.1	85.9	92.2
492	Jackson	95.0	95.9	95.4
493,495	Grand Rapids	98.1	84.5	92.2
494	Muskegon	95.6	85.5	91.2

Location Factors

STATE/ZIP	CITY	MAT.	INST.	TOTAL
MICHIGAN (CONT'D)				
496	Traverse City	94.6	81.0	88.6
497	Gaylord	95.5	84.4	90.7
498-499	Iron mountain	97.5	87.4	93.1
MINNESOTA				
550-551	Saint Paul	100.2	118.8	108.3
553-555	Minneapolis	100.6	119.9	109.0
556-558	Duluth	99.0	108.6	103.2
559	Rochester	98.8	104.9	101.5
560	Mankato	96.6	102.4	99.1
561	Windom	95.3	93.3	94.4
562	Willmar	94.9	103.0	98.4
563	St. Cloud	96.3	117.8	105.7
564	Brainerd	96.3	102.3	98.9
565	Detroit Lakes	98.3	96.7	97.6
566	Bemidji	97.7	99.5	98.5
567	Thief River Falls	97.3	93.8	95.7
MISSISSIPPI				
386	Clarksdale	95.8	53.8	77.5
387	Greenville	99.4	63.1	83.6
388	Tupelo	97.3	56.1	79.4
389	Greenwood	97.0	53.3	78.0
390-392	Jackson	99.1	63.5	83.6
393	Meridian	96.2	65.3	82.7
394	Laurel	97.2	57.1	79.7
395	Biloxi	97.7	59.1	80.9
396	Mccomb	95.7	52.9	77.1
397	Columbus	97.1	55.1	78.8
MISSOURI				
630-631	St. Louis	99.6	107.6	103.1
633	Bowling Green	98.1	94.7	96.6
634	Hannibal	97.1	92.6	95.1
635	Kirksville	100.3	90.0	95.8
636	Flat River	99.0	95.8	97.6
637	Cape Girardeau	99.1	90.6	95.4
638	Sikeston	97.5	90.6	94.5
639	Poplar Bluff	97.0	90.3	94.1
640-641	Kansas City	101.6	106.7	103.8
644-645	St. Joseph	100.7	93.9	97.8
646	Chillicothe	97.7	96.2	97.1
647	Harrisonville	97.3	102.2	99.5
648	Joplin	99.5	81.0	91.5
650-651	Jefferson City	98.4	93.4	96.2
652	Columbia	98.6	93.5	96.4
653	Sedalia	98.1	92.6	95.7
654-655	Rolla	96.3	95.6	96.0
656-658	Springfield	99.9	82.1	92.1
MONTANA				
590-591	Billings	102.2	77.9	91.6
592	Wolf Point	101.7	74.9	90.0
593	Miles City	99.5	74.7	88.7
594	Great Falls	103.4	77.1	92.0
595	Havre	100.6	74.2	89.1
596	Helena	102.0	75.1	90.2
597	Butte	102.0	77.2	91.2
598	Missoula	99.4	76.4	89.4
599	Kalispell	98.4	76.3	88.8
NEBRASKA				
680-681	Omaha	99.6	79.3	90.7
683-685	Lincoln	99.5	75.3	89.0
686	Columbus	97.5	77.9	88.9
687	Norfolk	99.2	77.5	89.8
688	Grand Island	99.1	77.8	89.9
689	Hastings	98.5	81.2	90.9
690	Mccook	98.1	72.1	86.8
691	North Platte	98.5	79.6	90.2
692	Valentine	100.6	73.6	88.9
693	Alliance	100.4	71.6	87.9
NEVADA				
889-891	Las Vegas	100.2	109.4	104.2
893	Ely	98.7	103.4	100.8
894-895	Reno	99.0	93.8	96.7
897	Carson City	99.1	93.8	96.8
898	Elko	97.6	86.1	92.6
NEW HAMPSHIRE				
030	Nashua	100.6	93.6	97.6
031	Manchester	102.1	93.6	98.4

STATE/ZIP	CITY	MAT.	INST.	TOTAL
NEW HAMPSHIRE (CONT'D)				
032-033	Concord	100.8	92.3	97.1
034	Keene	97.4	74.0	87.2
035	Littleton	97.1	77.2	88.4
036	Charleston	96.9	70.1	85.2
037	Claremont	96.0	70.1	84.7
038	Portsmouth	98.2	94.2	96.4
NEW JERSEY				
070-071	Newark	101.9	125.6	112.2
072	Elizabeth	99.5	125.3	110.7
073	Jersey City	98.5	125.5	110.2
074-075	Paterson	100.2	125.2	111.1
076	Hackensack	98.4	125.5	110.2
077	Long Branch	97.8	124.1	109.2
078	Dover	98.7	125.4	110.3
079	Summit	98.7	125.3	110.3
080,083	Vineland	97.5	123.4	108.8
081	Camden	99.4	123.6	109.9
082,084	Atlantic City	98.1	123.5	109.2
085-086	Trenton	100.8	124.0	110.9
087	Point Pleasant	99.2	121.4	108.8
088-089	New Brunswick	99.7	125.2	110.8
NEW MEXICO				
870-872	Albuquerque	99.2	73.6	88.0
873	Gallup	99.3	73.6	88.1
874	Farmington	99.7	73.6	88.3
875	Santa Fe	100.5	73.6	88.8
877	Las Vegas	97.7	73.6	87.2
878	Socorro	97.3	73.6	87.0
879	Truth/Consequences	97.0	70.4	85.4
880	Las Cruces	95.8	70.4	84.7
881	Clovis	98.1	73.5	87.4
882	Roswell	99.8	73.6	88.4
883	Carrizozo	100.1	73.6	88.5
884	Tucumcari	98.8	73.5	87.8
NEW YORK				
100-102	New York	103.8	166.4	131.1
103	Staten Island	99.7	163.9	127.6
104	Bronx	98.0	163.9	126.7
105	Mount Vernon	97.9	133.3	113.3
106	White Plains	98.0	133.3	113.4
107	Yonkers	102.5	133.4	116.0
108	New Rochelle	98.2	133.3	113.5
109	Suffern	98.0	126.2	110.3
110	Queens	100.8	162.9	127.8
111	Long Island City	102.2	162.9	128.6
112	Brooklyn	102.6	162.9	128.9
113	Flushing	102.3	162.9	128.7
114	Jamaica	100.6	162.9	127.7
115,117,118	Hicksville	100.7	146.6	120.7
116	Far Rockaway	102.4	162.9	128.7
119	Riverhead	101.4	146.6	121.1
120-122	Albany	98.6	100.2	99.3
123	Schenectady	97.8	100.2	98.8
124	Kingston	100.7	118.3	108.4
125-126	Poughkeepsie	100.0	127.5	112.0
127	Monticello	99.4	116.5	106.8
128	Glens Falls	92.6	95.0	93.6
129	Plattsburgh	97.3	88.4	93.4
130-132	Syracuse	98.5	97.0	97.9
133-135	Utica	96.7	93.2	95.1
136	Watertown	98.1	91.9	95.4
137-139	Binghamton	98.1	99.4	98.6
140-142	Buffalo	99.7	105.8	102.4
143	Niagara Falls	96.9	103.9	100.0
144-146	Rochester	100.3	95.6	98.3
147	Jamestown	96.0	87.8	92.4
148-149	Elmira	95.9	93.1	94.7
NORTH CAROLINA				
270,272-274	Greensboro	98.8	56.3	80.3
271	Winston-Salem	98.5	57.1	80.5
275-276	Raleigh	98.2	55.1	79.4
277	Durham	100.2	54.4	80.2
278	Rocky Mount	96.0	53.2	77.4
279	Elizabeth City	96.9	52.2	77.4
280	Gastonia	98.4	56.1	80.0
281-282	Charlotte	98.7	57.6	80.8
283	Fayetteville	100.9	58.5	82.5
284	Wilmington	97.2	56.6	79.5
285	Kinston	95.3	53.7	77.2

793

Location Factors

STATE/ZIP	CITY	MAT.	INST.	TOTAL
NORTH CAROLINA (CONT'D)				
286	Hickory	95.6	54.9	77.9
287-288	Asheville	97.6	55.9	79.4
289	Murphy	96.4	49.2	75.8
NORTH DAKOTA				
580-581	Fargo	101.7	67.6	86.9
582	Grand Forks	101.8	51.6	79.9
583	Devils Lake	101.0	58.6	82.5
584	Jamestown	101.0	45.1	76.7
585	Bismarck	102.0	64.0	85.5
586	Dickinson	101.9	57.9	82.7
587	Minot	101.8	71.0	88.4
588	Williston	100.3	58.0	81.9
OHIO				
430-432	Columbus	98.6	89.7	94.7
433	Marion	95.0	83.7	90.1
434-436	Toledo	98.7	96.4	97.7
437-438	Zanesville	95.5	85.6	91.2
439	Steubenville	96.8	94.5	95.8
440	Lorain	98.8	90.4	95.2
441	Cleveland	98.9	100.0	99.4
442-443	Akron	99.8	93.4	97.0
444-445	Youngstown	99.1	88.3	94.4
446-447	Canton	99.2	85.0	93.0
448-449	Mansfield	96.6	85.6	91.8
450	Hamilton	97.4	84.5	91.8
451-452	Cincinnati	97.8	84.8	92.1
453-454	Dayton	97.5	83.2	91.3
455	Springfield	97.5	84.2	91.7
456	Chillicothe	96.4	92.2	94.5
457	Athens	99.1	80.6	91.1
458	Lima	99.6	84.4	93.0
OKLAHOMA				
730-731	Oklahoma City	97.3	65.4	83.4
734	Ardmore	95.2	62.3	80.9
735	Lawton	97.5	63.3	82.6
736	Clinton	96.5	63.6	82.2
737	Enid	97.2	60.9	81.4
738	Woodward	95.3	63.8	81.6
739	Guymon	96.3	60.5	80.7
740-741	Tulsa	97.4	62.2	82.1
743	Miami	94.0	68.3	82.8
744	Muskogee	96.6	56.3	79.0
745	Mcalester	93.7	61.1	79.5
746	Ponca City	94.3	62.5	80.5
747	Durant	94.3	64.0	81.1
748	Shawnee	95.7	62.2	81.1
749	Poteau	93.5	62.1	79.8
OREGON				
970-972	Portland	97.2	101.4	99.1
973	Salem	99.0	100.5	99.7
974	Eugene	97.1	100.4	98.5
975	Medford	98.4	98.2	98.3
976	Klamath Falls	98.2	98.2	98.2
977	Bend	97.3	100.5	98.7
978	Pendleton	93.1	102.5	97.2
979	Vale	91.3	89.8	90.7
PENNSYLVANIA				
150-152	Pittsburgh	99.7	105.8	102.3
153	Washington	96.7	103.2	99.5
154	Uniontown	97.1	102.2	99.4
155	Bedford	98.0	92.6	95.7
156	Greensburg	98.0	101.6	99.5
157	Indiana	96.9	100.1	98.3
158	Dubois	98.4	97.1	97.8
159	Johnstown	97.9	97.3	97.7
160	Butler	92.1	102.2	96.5
161	New Castle	92.1	97.2	94.4
162	Kittanning	92.5	103.4	97.3
163	Oil City	92.1	97.0	94.3
164-165	Erie	94.1	95.0	94.5
166	Altoona	94.3	92.7	93.6
167	Bradford	95.3	96.8	96.0
168	State College	94.9	93.0	94.1
169	Wellsboro	95.9	92.3	94.3
170-171	Harrisburg	99.6	95.9	98.0
172	Chambersburg	96.0	89.7	93.2
173-174	York	96.5	96.0	96.3
175-176	Lancaster	94.8	89.3	92.4

STATE/ZIP	CITY	MAT.	INST.	TOTAL
PENNSYLVANIA (CONT'D)				
177	Williamsport	93.6	79.3	87.4
178	Sunbury	95.5	96.3	95.8
179	Pottsville	94.7	98.0	96.1
180	Lehigh Valley	95.4	112.5	102.9
181	Allentown	97.6	108.8	102.4
182	Hazleton	95.0	98.8	96.7
183	Stroudsburg	94.9	102.0	98.0
184-185	Scranton	98.3	99.7	98.9
186-187	Wilkes-Barre	94.7	99.2	96.7
188	Montrose	94.4	97.1	95.6
189	Doylestown	94.6	120.8	106.0
190-191	Philadelphia	98.9	133.4	113.9
193	Westchester	95.8	121.7	107.1
194	Norristown	94.9	129.5	110.0
195-196	Reading	97.1	101.1	98.8
PUERTO RICO				
009	San Juan	122.1	24.6	79.7
RHODE ISLAND				
028	Newport	99.0	116.6	106.6
029	Providence	101.5	116.6	108.1
SOUTH CAROLINA				
290-292	Columbia	97.2	57.3	79.8
293	Spartanburg	96.4	57.4	79.5
294	Charleston	97.7	66.4	84.1
295	Florence	96.2	57.8	79.4
296	Greenville	96.2	56.5	78.9
297	Rock Hill	95.6	51.2	76.3
298	Aiken	96.4	70.4	85.1
299	Beaufort	97.1	45.7	74.7
SOUTH DAKOTA				
570-571	Sioux Falls	100.0	58.8	82.1
572	Watertown	98.5	50.2	77.5
573	Mitchell	97.5	49.5	76.6
574	Aberdeen	100.1	50.6	78.6
575	Pierre	100.8	59.2	82.7
576	Mobridge	98.1	49.8	77.1
577	Rapid City	100.0	60.3	82.7
TENNESSEE				
370-372	Nashville	97.9	74.1	87.5
373-374	Chattanooga	99.5	65.5	84.7
375,380-381	Memphis	98.5	71.3	86.7
376	Johnson City	99.2	56.7	80.7
377-379	Knoxville	96.2	60.5	80.6
382	Mckenzie	96.6	60.4	80.9
383	Jackson	98.3	62.5	82.7
384	Columbia	95.3	67.5	83.2
385	Cookeville	96.4	60.4	80.7
TEXAS				
750	Mckinney	99.3	48.9	77.3
751	Waxahackie	99.3	56.4	80.6
752-753	Dallas	100.1	65.8	85.2
754	Greenville	99.4	42.2	74.5
755	Texarkana	98.4	49.7	77.2
756	Longview	99.0	40.5	73.5
757	Tyler	98.9	54.6	79.6
758	Palestine	95.4	55.8	78.2
759	Lufkin	95.9	59.1	79.9
760-761	Fort Worth	99.6	62.5	83.5
762	Denton	98.2	46.6	75.7
763	Wichita Falls	97.8	55.0	79.2
764	Eastland	96.5	49.1	75.9
765	Temple	95.0	52.7	76.6
766-767	Waco	97.2	57.3	79.8
768	Brownwood	98.5	48.4	76.7
769	San Angelo	98.2	49.5	77.0
770-772	Houston	98.7	70.9	86.6
773	Huntsville	97.2	56.9	79.6
774	Wharton	98.1	53.8	78.8
775	Galveston	96.3	69.7	84.7
776-777	Beaumont	96.7	61.2	81.2
778	Bryan	94.1	63.0	80.5
779	Victoria	98.2	42.7	74.1
780	Laredo	97.1	53.7	78.2
781-782	San Antonio	97.5	64.5	83.1
783-784	Corpus Christi	99.7	53.7	79.6
785	Mc Allen	99.7	46.6	76.6
786-787	Austin	98.6	59.1	81.4

Location Factors

STATE/ZIP	CITY	MAT.	INST.	TOTAL	STATE/ZIP	CITY	MAT.	INST.	TOTAL
TEXAS (CONT'D)					**WISCONSIN (CONT'D)**				
788	Del Rio	99.4	46.2	76.3	538	Lancaster	97.4	93.5	95.7
789	Giddings	96.4	55.6	78.6	539	Portage	96.1	97.9	96.9
790-791	Amarillo	98.2	60.0	81.6	540	New Richmond	96.2	95.9	96.1
792	Childress	97.9	56.9	80.0	541-543	Green Bay	100.5	94.1	97.7
793-794	Lubbock	100.0	56.3	81.0	544	Wausau	95.7	94.4	95.2
795-796	Abilene	98.3	53.6	78.8	545	Rhinelander	98.7	92.4	95.9
797	Midland	99.9	53.6	79.7	546	La Crosse	97.2	95.0	96.3
798-799,885	El Paso	97.2	50.6	76.9	547	Eau Claire	98.7	96.4	97.7
					548	Superior	96.1	97.6	96.7
UTAH					549	Oshkosh	96.3	92.4	94.6
840-841	Salt Lake City	102.2	66.8	86.8					
842,844	Ogden	97.9	68.8	85.2	**WYOMING**				
843	Logan	99.7	68.8	86.2	820	Cheyenne	100.1	65.7	85.2
845	Price	100.1	65.3	84.9	821	Yellowstone Nat'l Park	97.7	65.2	83.5
846-847	Provo	100.1	66.7	85.6	822	Wheatland	98.7	64.6	83.9
					823	Rawlins	100.2	67.8	86.1
VERMONT					824	Worland	98.3	64.1	83.4
050	White River Jct.	97.9	79.7	90.0	825	Riverton	99.3	64.9	84.3
051	Bellows Falls	96.6	94.7	95.8	826	Casper	100.4	60.7	83.1
052	Bennington	96.9	95.3	96.2	827	Newcastle	98.2	67.8	84.9
053	Brattleboro	97.2	94.5	96.0	828	Sheridan	100.9	65.2	85.4
054	Burlington	101.5	85.1	94.4	829-831	Rock Springs	101.8	65.4	85.9
056	Montpelier	99.2	84.3	92.7					
057	Rutland	99.2	85.1	93.0	**CANADIAN FACTORS** (reflect Canadian currency)				
058	St. Johnsbury	97.9	79.2	89.8	**ALBERTA**				
059	Guildhall	96.8	79.2	89.1		Calgary	124.7	95.4	111.9
						Edmonton	125.0	95.4	112.1
VIRGINIA						Fort McMurray	124.1	94.2	111.1
220-221	Fairfax	99.3	84.4	92.8		Lethbridge	118.7	93.7	107.8
222	Arlington	100.6	84.7	93.6		Lloydminster	113.9	90.3	103.6
223	Alexandria	99.8	85.4	93.5		Medicine Hat	114.0	89.6	103.4
224-225	Fredericksburg	98.2	83.0	91.6		Red Deer	114.5	89.6	103.6
226	Winchester	98.7	82.1	91.5					
227	Culpeper	98.6	80.8	90.9	**BRITISH COLUMBIA**				
228	Harrisonburg	98.8	68.1	85.5		Kamloops	114.9	92.4	105.1
229	Charlottesville	99.2	67.3	85.3		Prince George	115.9	91.7	105.3
230-232	Richmond	100.4	68.9	86.7		Vancouver	123.3	90.0	108.8
233-235	Norfolk	100.0	68.8	86.4		Victoria	115.9	88.1	103.8
236	Newport News	99.2	68.2	85.7					
237	Portsmouth	98.6	66.1	84.5	**MANITOBA**				
238	Petersburg	98.6	68.9	85.6		Brandon	118.7	77.3	100.7
239	Farmville	97.8	53.3	78.5		Portage la Prairie	113.9	75.6	97.2
240-241	Roanoke	100.2	66.0	85.3		Winnipeg	123.6	70.8	100.6
242	Bristol	98.1	55.6	79.6					
243	Pulaski	97.7	58.3	80.6	**NEW BRUNSWICK**				
244	Staunton	98.4	62.7	82.9		Bathurst	112.1	68.6	93.1
245	Lynchburg	98.6	66.1	84.5		Dalhousie	112.1	68.8	93.2
246	Grundy	98.0	53.4	78.6		Fredericton	118.1	74.0	98.9
						Moncton	112.3	71.4	94.5
WASHINGTON						Newcastle	112.1	69.3	93.5
980-981,987	Seattle	102.5	104.8	103.5		St. John	114.6	78.3	98.8
982	Everett	102.1	99.6	101.0					
983-984	Tacoma	102.3	100.0	101.3	**NEWFOUNDLAND**				
985	Olympia	101.0	100.0	100.6		Corner Brook	122.2	69.0	99.0
986	Vancouver	103.1	93.2	98.8		St Johns	122.0	80.4	103.9
988	Wenatchee	102.0	87.1	95.5					
989	Yakima	102.5	94.4	99.0	**NORTHWEST TERRITORIES**				
990-992	Spokane	102.5	82.7	93.8		Yellowknife	128.8	85.8	110.1
993	Richland	102.2	89.6	96.7					
994	Clarkston	100.6	80.7	92.0	**NOVA SCOTIA**				
						Bridgewater	113.4	76.1	97.2
WEST VIRGINIA						Dartmouth	119.7	76.1	100.7
247-248	Bluefield	97.1	91.7	94.7		Halifax	119.9	80.6	102.8
249	Lewisburg	98.4	91.4	95.4		New Glasgow	117.7	76.1	99.6
250-253	Charleston	99.0	94.1	96.9		Sydney	115.6	76.1	98.4
254	Martinsburg	98.3	86.1	93.0		Truro	113.0	76.1	96.9
255-257	Huntington	99.8	95.2	97.8		Yarmouth	117.6	76.1	99.6
258-259	Beckley	96.9	92.0	94.8					
260	Wheeling	99.8	93.8	97.2	**ONTARIO**				
261	Parkersburg	98.9	91.4	95.6		Barrie	117.3	94.9	107.5
262	Buckhannon	98.2	93.6	96.2		Brantford	115.5	98.8	108.2
263-264	Clarksburg	98.8	93.5	96.5		Cornwall	115.5	95.1	106.7
265	Morgantown	98.8	92.6	96.1		Hamilton	119.3	95.3	108.8
266	Gassaway	98.2	92.8	95.8		Kingston	116.6	95.2	107.3
267	Romney	98.2	90.4	94.8		Kitchener	111.6	92.0	103.1
268	Petersburg	98.0	90.1	94.6		London	119.5	91.9	107.5
						North Bay	120.5	92.9	108.5
WISCONSIN						Oshawa	114.6	96.1	106.5
530,532	Milwaukee	100.9	107.9	104.0		Ottawa	119.2	92.5	107.5
531	Kenosha	100.2	102.9	101.4		Owen Sound	117.4	93.0	106.8
534	Racine	99.7	102.6	101.0		Peterborough	115.5	94.9	106.5
535	Beloit	99.6	101.9	100.6		Sarnia	115.3	99.5	108.4
537	Madison	99.5	99.8	99.6					

Location Factors

STATE/ZIP	CITY	MAT.	INST.	TOTAL
ONTARIO (CONT'D)				
	Sault Ste Marie	110.7	93.1	103.0
	St. Catharines	109.7	93.0	102.4
	Sudbury	109.9	91.7	101.9
	Thunder Bay	110.9	91.7	102.6
	Timmins	115.6	92.9	105.7
	Toronto	120.2	99.0	111.0
	Windsor	110.2	91.7	102.2
PRINCE EDWARD ISLAND				
	Charlottetown	120.5	64.0	95.9
	Summerside	119.5	64.1	95.4
QUEBEC				
	Cap-de-la-Madeleine	112.8	89.4	102.6
	Charlesbourg	112.8	89.4	102.6
	Chicoutimi	111.9	93.1	103.7
	Gatineau	112.5	89.2	102.3
	Granby	112.8	89.1	102.4
	Hull	112.6	89.2	102.4
	Joliette	113.0	89.4	102.7
	Laval	112.4	89.2	102.3
	Montreal	119.2	93.4	107.9
	Quebec	117.5	93.8	107.2
	Rimouski	112.3	93.1	103.9
	Rouyn-Noranda	112.5	89.2	102.3
	Saint Hyacinthe	111.9	89.2	102.0
	Sherbrooke	112.8	89.2	102.5
	Sorel	113.0	89.4	102.7
	St Jerome	112.5	89.2	102.3
	Trois Rivieres	117.9	89.4	105.5
SASKATCHEWAN				
	Moose Jaw	111.2	70.8	93.6
	Prince Albert	110.3	69.0	92.3
	Regina	120.3	88.4	106.4
	Saskatoon	111.3	88.4	101.3
YUKON				
	Whitehorse	126.3	69.8	101.7

R011105-05   Tips for Accurate Estimating

1. Use pre-printed or columnar forms for orderly sequence of dimensions and locations and for recording telephone quotations.

2. Use only the front side of each paper or form except for certain pre-printed summary forms.

3. Be consistent in listing dimensions: For example, length x width x height. This helps in rechecking to ensure that, the total length of partitions is appropriate for the building area.

4. Use printed (rather than measured) dimensions where given.

5. Add up multiple printed dimensions for a single entry where possible.

6. Measure all other dimensions carefully.

7. Use each set of dimensions to calculate multiple related quantities.

8. Convert foot and inch measurements to decimal feet when listing. Memorize decimal equivalents to .01 parts of a foot (1/8″ equals approximately .01′).

9. Do not "round off" quantities until the final summary.

10. Mark drawings with different colors as items are taken off.

11. Keep similar items together, different items separate.

12. Identify location and drawing numbers to aid in future checking for completeness.

13. Measure or list everything on the drawings or mentioned in the specifications.

14. It may be necessary to list items not called for to make the job complete.

15. Be alert for: Notes on plans such as N.T.S. (not to scale); changes in scale throughout the drawings; reduced size drawings; discrepancies between the specifications and the drawings.

16. Develop a consistent pattern of performing an estimate. For example:
    a. Start the quantity takeoff at the lower floor and move to the next higher floor.
    b. Proceed from the main section of the building to the wings.
    c. Proceed from south to north or vice versa, clockwise or counterclockwise.
    d. Take off floor plan quantities first, elevations next, then detail drawings.

17. List all gross dimensions that can be either used again for different quantities, or used as a rough check of other quantities for verification (exterior perimeter, gross floor area, individual floor areas, etc.).

18. Utilize design symmetry or repetition (repetitive floors, repetitive wings, symmetrical design around a center line, similar room layouts, etc.). Note: Extreme caution is needed here so as not to omit or duplicate an area.

19. Do not convert units until the final total is obtained. For instance, when estimating concrete work, keep all units to the nearest cubic foot, then summarize and convert to cubic yards.

20. When figuring alternatives, it is best to total all items involved in the basic system, then total all items involved in the alternates. Therefore you work with positive numbers in all cases. When adds and deducts are used, it is often confusing whether to add or subtract a portion of an item; especially on a complicated or involved alternate.

R011105-50 Metric Conversion Factors

Description: This table is primarily for converting customary U.S. units in the left hand column to SI metric units in the right hand column. In addition, conversion factors for some commonly encountered Canadian and non-SI metric units are included.

	If You Know		Multiply By		To Find
Length	Inches	x	25.4[a]	=	Millimeters
	Feet	x	0.3048[a]	=	Meters
	Yards	x	0.9144[a]	=	Meters
	Miles (statute)	x	1.609	=	Kilometers
Area	Square inches	x	645.2	=	Square millimeters
	Square feet	x	0.0929	=	Square meters
	Square yards	x	0.8361	=	Square meters
Volume (Capacity)	Cubic inches	x	16,387	=	Cubic millimeters
	Cubic feet	x	0.02832	=	Cubic meters
	Cubic yards	x	0.7646	=	Cubic meters
	Gallons (U.S. liquids)[b]	x	0.003785	=	Cubic meters[c]
	Gallons (Canadian liquid)[b]	x	0.004546	=	Cubic meters[c]
	Ounces (U.S. liquid)[b]	x	29.57	=	Milliliters[c, d]
	Quarts (U.S. liquid)[b]	x	0.9464	=	Liters[c, d]
	Gallons (U.S. liquid)[b]	x	3.785	=	Liters[c, d]
Force	Kilograms force[d]	x	9.807	=	Newtons
	Pounds force	x	4.448	=	Newtons
	Pounds force	x	0.4536	=	Kilograms force[d]
	Kips	x	4448	=	Newtons
	Kips	x	453.6	=	Kilograms force[d]
Pressure, Stress, Strength (Force per unit area)	Kilograms force per square centimeter[d]	x	0.09807	=	Megapascals
	Pounds force per square inch (psi)	x	0.006895	=	Megapascals
	Kips per square inch	x	6.895	=	Megapascals
	Pounds force per square inch (psi)	x	0.07031	=	Kilograms force per square centimeter[d]
	Pounds force per square foot	x	47.88	=	Pascals
	Pounds force per square foot	x	4.882	=	Kilograms force per square meter[d]
Bending Moment Or Torque	Inch-pounds force	x	0.01152	=	Meter-kilograms force[d]
	Inch-pounds force	x	0.1130	=	Newton-meters
	Foot-pounds force	x	0.1383	=	Meter-kilograms force[d]
	Foot-pounds force	x	1.356	=	Newton-meters
	Meter-kilograms force[d]	x	9.807	=	Newton-meters
Mass	Ounces (avoirdupois)	x	28.35	=	Grams
	Pounds (avoirdupois)	x	0.4536	=	Kilograms
	Tons (metric)	x	1000	=	Kilograms
	Tons, short (2000 pounds)	x	907.2	=	Kilograms
	Tons, short (2000 pounds)	x	0.9072	=	Megagrams[e]
Mass per Unit Volume	Pounds mass per cubic foot	x	16.02	=	Kilograms per cubic meter
	Pounds mass per cubic yard	x	0.5933	=	Kilograms per cubic meter
	Pounds mass per gallon (U.S. liquid)[b]	x	119.8	=	Kilograms per cubic meter
	Pounds mass per gallon (Canadian liquid)[b]	x	99.78	=	Kilograms per cubic meter
Temperature	Degrees Fahrenheit	(F-32)/1.8		=	Degrees Celsius
	Degrees Fahrenheit	(F+459.67)/1.8		=	Degrees Kelvin
	Degrees Celsius	C+273.15		=	Degrees Kelvin

[a]The factor given is exact
[b]One U.S. gallon = 0.8327 Canadian gallon
[c]1 liter = 1000 milliliters = 1000 cubic centimeters
 1 cubic decimeter = 0.001 cubic meter
[d]Metric but not SI unit
[e]Called "tonne" in England and
 "metric ton" in other metric countries

R011105-60   Weights and Measures

Measures of Length
1 Mile = 1760 Yards = 5280 Feet
1 Yard = 3 Feet = 36 inches
1 Foot = 12 Inches
1 Mil = 0.001 Inch
1 Fathom = 2 Yards = 6 Feet
1 Rod = 5.5 Yards = 16.5 Feet
1 Hand = 4 Inches
1 Span = 9 Inches
1 Micro-inch = One Millionth Inch or 0.000001 Inch
1 Micron = One Millionth Meter + 0.00003937 Inch

Surveyor's Measure
1 Mile = 8 Furlongs = 80 Chains
1 Furlong = 10 Chains = 220 Yards
1 Chain = 4 Rods = 22 Yards = 66 Feet = 100 Links
1 Link = 7.92 Inches

Square Measure
1 Square Mile = 640 Acres = 6400 Square Chains
1 Acre = 10 Square Chains = 4840 Square Yards = 43,560 Sq. Ft.
1 Square Chain = 16 Square Rods = 484 Square Yards = 4356 Sq. Ft.
1 Square Rod = 30.25 Square Yards = 272.25 Square Feet = 625 Square Lines
1 Square Yard = 9 Square Feet
1 Square Foot = 144 Square Inches
An Acre equals a Square 208.7 Feet per Side

Cubic Measure
1 Cubic Yard = 27 Cubic Feet
1 Cubic Foot = 1728 Cubic Inches
1 Cord of Wood = 4 x 4 x 8 Feet = 128 Cubic Feet
1 Perch of Masonry = 16½ x 1½ x 1 Foot = 24.75 Cubic Feet

Avoirdupois or Commercial Weight
1 Gross or Long Ton = 2240 Pounds
1 Net or Short ton = 2000 Pounds
1 Pound = 16 Ounces = 7000 Grains
1 Ounce = 16 Drachms = 437.5 Grains
1 Stone = 14 Pounds

Shipping Measure
For Measuring Internal Capacity of a Vessel:
1 Register Ton = 100 Cubic Feet

For Measurement of Cargo:
Approximately 40 Cubic Feet of Merchandise is considered a Shipping Ton, unless that bulk would weigh more than 2000 Pounds, in which case Freight Charge may be based upon weight.

40 Cubic Feet = 32.143 U.S. Bushels = 31.16 Imp. Bushels

Liquid Measure
1 Imperial Gallon = 1.2009 U.S. Gallon = 277.42 Cu. In.
1 Cubic Foot = 7.48 U.S. Gallons

R011110-10   Architectural Fees

Tabulated below are typical percentage fees by project size, for good professional architectural service. Fees may vary from those listed depending upon degree of design difficulty and economic conditions in any particular area.

Rates can be interpolated horizontally and vertically. Various portions of the same project requiring different rates should be adjusted proportionately. For alterations, add 50% to the fee for the first $500,000 of project cost and add 25% to the fee for project cost over $500,000.

Architectural fees tabulated below include Structural, Mechanical and Electrical Engineering Fees. They do not include the fees for special consultants such as kitchen planning, security, acoustical, interior design, etc.

Civil Engineering fees are included in the Architectural fee for project sites requiring minimal design such as city sites. However, separate Civil Engineering fees must be added when utility connections require design, drainage calculations are needed, stepped foundations are required, or provisions are required to protect adjacent wetlands.

Building Types	Total Project Size in Thousands of Dollars						
	100	250	500	1,000	5,000	10,000	50,000
Factories, garages, warehouses, repetitive housing	9.0%	8.0%	7.0%	6.2%	5.3%	4.9%	4.5%
Apartments, banks, schools, libraries, offices, municipal buildings	12.2	12.3	9.2	8.0	7.0	6.6	6.2
Churches, hospitals, homes, laboratories, museums, research	15.0	13.6	12.7	11.9	9.5	8.8	8.0
Memorials, monumental work, decorative furnishings	—	16.0	14.5	13.1	10.0	9.0	8.3

General Requirements | R0111 Summary of Work

R011110-30 Engineering Fees

Typical **Structural Engineering Fees** based on type of construction and total project size. These fees are included in Architectural Fees.

Type of Construction	Total Project Size (in thousands of dollars)			
	$500	$500-$1,000	$1,000-$5,000	Over $5000
Industrial buildings, factories & warehouses	Technical payroll times 2.0 to 2.5	1.60%	1.25%	1.00%
Hotels, apartments, offices, dormitories, hospitals, public buildings, food stores		2.00%	1.70%	1.20%
Museums, banks, churches and cathedrals		2.00%	1.75%	1.25%
Thin shells, prestressed concrete, earthquake resistive		2.00%	1.75%	1.50%
Parking ramps, auditoriums, stadiums, convention halls, hangars & boiler houses		2.50%	2.00%	1.75%
Special buildings, major alterations, underpinning & future expansion	↓	Add to above 0.5%	Add to above 0.5%	Add to above 0.5%

For complex reinforced concrete or unusually complicated structures, add 20% to 50%.

Typical **Mechanical and Electrical Engineering Fees** are based on the size of the subcontract. The fee structure for both are shown below. These fees are included in Architectural Fees.

Type of Construction	Subcontract Size							
	$25,000	$50,000	$100,000	$225,000	$350,000	$500,000	$750,000	$1,000,000
Simple structures	6.4%	5.7%	4.8%	4.5%	4.4%	4.3%	4.2%	4.1%
Intermediate structures	8.0	7.3	6.5	5.6	5.1	5.0	4.9	4.8
Complex structures	10.1	9.0	9.0	8.0	7.5	7.5	7.0	7.0

For renovations, add 15% to 25% to applicable fee.

General Requirements | R0121 Allowances

R012153-10 Repair and Remodeling

Cost figures are based on new construction utilizing the most cost-effective combination of labor, equipment and material with the work scheduled in proper sequence to allow the various trades to accomplish their work in an efficient manner.

The costs for repair and remodeling work must be modified due to the following factors that may be present in any given repair and remodeling project.

1. Equipment usage curtailment due to the physical limitations of the project, with only hand-operated equipment being used.

2. Increased requirement for shoring and bracing to hold up the building while structural changes are being made and to allow for temporary storage of construction materials on above-grade floors.

3. Material handling becomes more costly due to having to move within the confines of an enclosed building. For multi-story construction, low capacity elevators and stairwells may be the only access to the upper floors.

4. Large amount of cutting and patching and attempting to match the existing construction is required. It is often more economical to remove entire walls rather than create many new door and window openings. This sort of trade-off has to be carefully analyzed.

5. Cost of protection of completed work is increased since the usual sequence of construction usually cannot be accomplished.

6. Economies of scale usually associated with new construction may not be present. If small quantities of components must be custom fabricated due to job requirements, unit costs will naturally increase. Also, if only small work areas are available at a given time, job scheduling between trades becomes difficult and subcontractor quotations may reflect the excessive start-up and shut-down phases of the job.

7. Work may have to be done on other than normal shifts and may have to be done around an existing production facility which has to stay in production during the course of the repair and remodeling.

8. Dust and noise protection of adjoining non-construction areas can involve substantial special protection and alter usual construction methods.

9. Job may be delayed due to unexpected conditions discovered during demolition or removal. These delays ultimately increase construction costs.

10. Piping and ductwork runs may not be as simple as for new construction. Wiring may have to be snaked through walls and floors.

11. Matching "existing construction" may be impossible because materials may no longer be manufactured. Substitutions may be expensive.

12. Weather protection of existing structure requires additional temporary structures to protect building at openings.

13. On small projects, because of local conditions, it may be necessary to pay a tradesman for a minimum of four hours for a task that is completed in one hour.

All of the above areas can contribute to increased costs for a repair and remodeling project. Each of the above factors should be considered in the planning, bidding and construction stage in order to minimize the increased costs associated with repair and remodeling jobs.

R012909-80   Sales Tax by State

State sales tax on materials is tabulated below (5 states have no sales tax). Many states allow local jurisdictions, such as a county or city, to levy additional sales tax.

Some projects may be sales tax exempt, particularly those constructed with public funds.

State	Tax (%)	State	Tax (%)	State	Tax (%)	State	Tax (%)
Alabama	4	Illinois	6.25	Montana	0	Rhode Island	7
Alaska	0	Indiana	7	Nebraska	5.5	South Carolina	6
Arizona	5.6	Iowa	6	Nevada	6.85	South Dakota	4
Arkansas	6	Kansas	6.3	New Hampshire	0	Tennessee	7
California	7.25	Kentucky	6	New Jersey	7	Texas	6.25
Colorado	2.9	Louisiana	4	New Mexico	5.13	Utah	5.95
Connecticut	6.35	Maine	5	New York	4	Vermont	6
Delaware	0	Maryland	6	North Carolina	4.75	Virginia	5
District of Columbia	6	Massachusetts	6.25	North Dakota	5	Washington	6.5
Florida	6	Michigan	6	Ohio	5.5	West Virginia	6
Georgia	4	Minnesota	6.88	Oklahoma	4.5	Wisconsin	5
Hawaii	4	Mississippi	7	Oregon	0	Wyoming	4
Idaho	6	Missouri	4.23	Pennsylvania	6	Average	5.06%

Sales Tax by Province (Canada)

GST - a value-added tax, which the government imposes on most goods and services provided in or imported into Canada. PST - a retail sales tax, which three of the provinces impose on the price of most goods and some

services. QST - a value-added tax, similar to the federal GST, which Quebec imposes. HST - Five provinces have combined their retail sales tax with the federal GST into one harmonized tax.

Province	PST (%)	QST (%)	GST(%)	HST(%)
Alberta	0	0	5	0
British Columbia	7	0	5	0
Manitoba	7	0	5	0
New Brunswick	0	0	0	13
Newfoundland	0	0	0	13
Northwest Territories	0	0	5	0
Nova Scotia	0	0	0	15
Ontario	0	0	0	13
Prince Edward Island	0	0	5	14
Quebec	0	9.975	5	0
Saskatchewan	5	0	5	0
Yukon	0	0	5	0

R012909-85   Unemployment Taxes and Social Security Taxes

State unemployment tax rates vary not only from state to state, but also with the experience rating of the contractor. The federal unemployment tax rate is 6.0% of the first $7,000 of wages. This is reduced by a credit of up to 5.4% for timely payment to the state. The minimum federal unemployment tax is 0.6% after all credits.

Social security (FICA) for 2014 is estimated at time of publication to be 7.65% of wages up to $115,800.

R013113-40   Builder's Risk Insurance

Builder's Risk Insurance is insurance on a building during construction. Premiums are paid by the owner or the contractor. Blasting, collapse and underground insurance would raise total insurance costs above those listed. Floater policy for materials delivered to the job runs $.75 to $1.25 per $100 value. Contractor equipment insurance runs $.50 to $1.50 per $100 value. Insurance for miscellaneous tools to $1,500 value runs from $3.00 to $7.50 per $100 value.

Tabulated below are New England Builder's Risk insurance rates in dollars per $100 value for $1,000 deductible. For $25,000 deductible, rates can be reduced 13% to 34%. On contracts over $1,000,000, rates may be lower than those tabulated. Policies are written annually for the total completed value in place. For "all risk" insurance (excluding flood, earthquake and certain other perils) add $.025 to total rates below.

Coverage	Frame Construction (Class 1)		Brick Construction (Class 4)		Fire Resistive (Class 6)	
	Range	Average	Range	Average	Range	Average
Fire Insurance	$.350 to $.850	$.600	$.158 to $.189	$.174	$.052 to $.080	$.070
Extended Coverage	.115 to .200	.158	.080 to .105	.101	.081 to .105	.100
Vandalism	.012 to .016	.014	.008 to .011	.011	.008 to .011	.010
Total Annual Rate	$.477 to $1.066	$.772	$.246 to $.305	$.286	$.141 to $.196	$.180

R013113-50   General Contractor's Overhead

There are two distinct types of overhead on a construction project: Project Overhead and Main Office Overhead. Project Overhead includes those costs at a construction site not directly associated with the installation of construction materials. Examples of Project Overhead costs include the following:

1. Superintendent
2. Construction office and storage trailers
3. Temporary sanitary facilities
4. Temporary utilities
5. Security fencing
6. Photographs
7. Clean up
8. Performance and payment bonds

The above Project Overhead items are also referred to as General Requirements and therefore are estimated in Division 1. Division 1 is the first division listed in the CSI MasterFormat but it is usually the last division estimated. The sum of the costs in Divisions 1 through 49 is referred to as the sum of the direct costs.

All construction projects also include indirect costs. The primary components of indirect costs are the contractor's Main Office Overhead and profit. The amount of the Main Office Overhead expense varies depending on the the following:

1. Owner's compensation
2. Project managers and estimator's wages
3. Clerical support wages
4. Office rent and utilities
5. Corporate legal and accounting costs
6. Advertising
7. Automobile expenses
8. Association dues
9. Travel and entertainment expenses

These costs are usually calculated as a percentage of annual sales volume. This percentage can range from 35% for a small contractor doing less than $500,000 to 5% for a large contractor with sales in excess of $100 million.

R013113-60   Workers' Compensation Insurance Rates by Trade

The table below tabulates the national averages for workers' compensation insurance rates by trade and type of building. The average "Insurance Rate" is multiplied by the "% of Building Cost" for each trade. This produces the "Workers' Compensation" cost by % of total labor cost, to be added for each trade by building type to determine the weighted average workers' compensation rate for the building types analyzed.

Trade	Insurance Rate (% Labor Cost) Range		Average	% of Building Cost Office Bldgs.	Schools & Apts.	Mfg.	Workers' Compensation Office Bldgs.	Schools & Apts.	Mfg.
Excavation, Grading, etc.	3.9 % to	18.7%	9.7%	4.8%	4.9%	4.5%	0.47%	0.48%	0.44%
Piles & Foundations	5.8 to	37	14.7	7.1	5.2	8.7	1.04	0.76	1.28
Concrete	4.6 to	38.6	13.1	5.0	14.8	3.7	0.66	1.94	0.48
Masonry	5.1 to	35	13.5	6.9	7.5	1.9	0.93	1.01	0.26
Structural Steel	5.8 to	108.2	34.6	10.7	3.9	17.6	3.70	1.35	6.09
Miscellaneous & Ornamental Metals	5.3 to	31.2	12.0	2.8	4.0	3.6	0.34	0.48	0.43
Carpentry & Millwork	5.5 to	34.9	15.4	3.7	4.0	0.5	0.57	0.62	0.08
Metal or Composition Siding	5.8 to	68.3	18.2	2.3	0.3	4.3	0.42	0.05	0.78
Roofing	5.8 to	93.3	31.3	2.3	2.6	3.1	0.72	0.81	0.97
Doors & Hardware	4.2 to	34.8	11.1	0.9	1.4	0.4	0.10	0.16	0.04
Sash & Glazing	5.3 to	36.8	13.1	3.5	4.0	1.0	0.46	0.52	0.13
Lath & Plaster	3.7 to	35	11.6	3.3	6.9	0.8	0.38	0.80	0.09
Tile, Marble & Floors	3.3 to	27.1	8.5	2.6	3.0	0.5	0.22	0.26	0.04
Acoustical Ceilings	3.4 to	36.7	8.1	2.4	0.2	0.3	0.19	0.02	0.02
Painting	5 to	33	11.5	1.5	1.6	1.6	0.17	0.18	0.18
Interior Partitions	5.5 to	34.9	15.4	3.9	4.3	4.4	0.60	0.66	0.68
Miscellaneous Items	2.5 to	150	14.4	5.2	3.7	9.7	0.75	0.53	1.40
Elevators	1.6 to	14.4	5.7	2.1	1.1	2.2	0.12	0.06	0.13
Sprinklers	3.2 to	18.3	7.2	0.5	—	2.0	0.04	—	0.14
Plumbing	2.6 to	17.5	7.1	4.9	7.2	5.2	0.35	0.51	0.37
Heat., Vent., Air Conditioning	4 to	18.8	8.8	13.5	11.0	12.9	1.19	0.97	1.14
Electrical	2.8 to	13.2	5.8	10.1	8.4	11.1	0.59	0.49	0.64
Total	1.6 % to	150%	—	100.0%	100.0%	100.0%	14.01%	12.66%	15.81%

Overall Weighted Average   14.16%

Workers' Compensation Insurance Rates by States

The table below lists the weighted average workers' compensation base rate for each state with a factor comparing this with the national average of 14%.

State	Weighted Average	Factor	State	Weighted Average	Factor	State	Weighted Average	Factor
Alabama	20.3%	145	Kentucky	14.9%	106	North Dakota	9.6%	69
Alaska	14.3	102	Louisiana	19.3	138	Ohio	8.6	61
Arizona	13.1	94	Maine	12.7	91	Oklahoma	12.9	92
Arkansas	8.6	61	Maryland	14.6	104	Oregon	12.3	88
California	26.8	191	Massachusetts	12.0	86	Pennsylvania	18.1	129
Colorado	7.5	54	Michigan	16.9	121	Rhode Island	12.6	90
Connecticut	24.6	176	Minnesota	23.5	168	South Carolina	19.6	140
Delaware	12.4	89	Mississippi	13.8	99	South Dakota	15.5	111
District of Columbia	11.5	82	Missouri	15.4	110	Tennessee	12.5	89
Florida	11.1	79	Montana	8.9	64	Texas	9.5	68
Georgia	29.2	209	Nebraska	18.3	131	Utah	9.1	65
Hawaii	8.4	60	Nevada	9.0	64	Vermont	13.6	97
Idaho	10.7	76	New Hampshire	20.8	149	Virginia	9.9	71
Illinois	28.1	201	New Jersey	15.0	107	Washington	10.9	78
Indiana	5.7	41	New Mexico	15.0	107	West Virginia	8.3	59
Iowa	15.1	108	New York	17.9	128	Wisconsin	13.6	97
Kansas	8.7	62	North Carolina	17.4	124	Wyoming	6.3	45

Weighted Average for U.S. is   14.2% of payroll = 100%

Rates in the following table are the base or manual costs per $100 of payroll for workers' compensation in each state. Rates are usually applied to straight time wages only and not to premium time wages and bonuses.

The weighted average skilled worker rate for 35 trades is 14%. For bidding purposes, apply the full value of workers' compensation directly to total labor costs, or if labor is 38%, materials 42% and overhead and profit 20% of total cost, carry 38/80 × 14% =6.6% of cost (before overhead and profit) into overhead. Rates vary not only from state to state but also with the experience rating of the contractor.

Rates are the most current available at the time of publication.

R013113-60 Workers' Compensation Insurance Rates by Trade and State (cont.)

State	Carpentry — 3 stories or less 5651	Carpentry — interior cab. work 5437	Carpentry — general 5403	Concrete Work — NOC 5213	Concrete Work — flat (flr., sdwk.) 5221	Electrical Wiring — inside 5190	Excavation — earth NOC 6217	Excavation — rock 6217	Glaziers 5462	Insulation Work 5479	Lathing 5443	Masonry 5022	Painting & Decorating 5474	Pile Driving 6003	Plastering 5480	Plumbing 5183
AL	34.03	17.01	24.59	13.79	10.37	8.87	16.42	16.42	19.75	19.84	9.24	23.79	15.91	18.57	15.88	8.73
AK	17.14	9.44	11.58	10.41	9.44	5.63	8.23	8.23	32.03	14.36	11.73	10.86	10.79	21.68	11.31	6.20
AZ	21.40	9.27	20.28	10.31	6.93	6.08	7.07	7.07	10.80	14.99	5.47	13.01	12.78	10.80	8.64	6.84
AR	12.80	4.77	9.18	6.63	5.16	4.03	6.82	6.82	8.14	7.67	3.99	8.30	7.08	8.10	13.00	4.55
CA	34.87	34.83	34.86	16.55	16.55	13.24	18.65	18.65	24.16	16.48	17.83	25.13	23.59	23.18	35.04	17.48
CO	8.95	4.93	6.07	6.68	4.75	2.92	5.49	5.49	6.00	7.27	3.95	8.29	6.56	6.51	5.69	4.16
CT	30.95	18.48	31.07	26.49	14.43	7.89	16.02	16.02	20.24	20.60	9.92	31.53	18.60	20.17	18.75	11.28
DE	12.46	12.46	9.93	10.07	8.80	4.53	7.70	7.70	10.90	9.93	6.60	11.53	13.39	15.03	10.90	6.60
DC	8.92	7.25	6.94	12.65	7.38	4.69	8.02	8.02	9.61	6.63	9.83	9.32	5.82	17.36	8.00	7.80
FL	11.32	8.62	11.92	12.51	6.20	6.17	7.30	7.30	10.56	10.45	5.53	10.92	10.23	17.84	9.68	5.63
GA	68.34	20.32	28.40	21.36	15.09	12.05	17.32	17.32	19.39	18.80	11.94	35.11	33.04	26.44	19.65	12.76
HI	8.51	6.92	12.69	7.05	4.02	4.47	5.40	5.40	8.22	5.20	6.26	7.01	6.19	7.32	8.33	5.31
ID	14.63	6.84	12.43	11.48	5.28	4.43	7.25	7.25	8.81	9.06	4.46	10.55	9.38	7.65	8.43	5.10
IL	33.34	21.75	28.57	38.59	16.83	10.03	14.53	14.53	25.55	21.41	14.32	28.94	18.57	24.53	32.84	12.51
IN	8.36	4.21	6.98	4.56	4.15	2.83	3.92	3.92	5.29	6.15	3.85	5.14	4.97	7.23	3.71	2.56
IA	15.46	11.35	19.21	14.85	11.16	5.20	11.01	11.01	15.76	9.89	6.48	14.30	10.13	11.38	21.73	7.80
KS	14.92	7.39	9.74	8.07	5.70	4.46	5.55	5.55	7.54	8.17	4.09	8.38	7.75	7.56	6.20	5.23
KY	18.75	13.00	20.00	8.50	6.50	6.00	14.00	14.00	22.12	11.15	7.60	7.50	9.00	16.03	12.93	5.00
LA	31.05	16.86	25.02	13.35	12.37	7.85	14.11	14.11	19.19	15.06	7.99	17.31	17.64	18.85	14.84	7.10
ME	12.24	8.87	16.18	16.43	8.70	4.74	12.34	12.34	14.82	12.79	5.09	10.88	12.44	9.00	9.99	5.90
MD	11.40	15.89	15.00	19.22	6.00	5.23	8.11	8.11	13.77	12.42	6.15	10.11	6.40	15.19	9.17	6.65
MA	8.68	5.23	9.61	18.85	6.24	2.84	4.35	4.35	9.58	7.78	5.27	10.55	5.09	12.92	4.68	3.50
MI	18.41	10.45	18.41	18.27	12.58	5.82	13.28	13.28	11.67	10.92	10.45	18.82	13.49	37.00	10.88	7.18
MN	20.27	20.82	34.13	11.58	13.15	5.83	11.00	11.00	36.85	18.37	11.55	15.59	17.55	27.58	11.58	8.09
MS	22.76	9.99	13.34	9.60	6.67	6.18	9.49	9.49	14.94	10.15	5.94	13.12	11.01	13.14	10.43	8.17
MO	19.66	11.10	12.81	12.38	10.34	6.15	9.96	9.96	9.47	11.55	7.44	15.13	11.42	13.38	12.15	9.00
MT	9.67	6.59	10.80	6.22	5.67	3.71	7.41	7.41	7.50	8.67	4.15	7.62	8.22	7.95	6.80	4.79
NE	21.80	13.15	21.48	18.23	11.20	8.03	17.38	17.38	12.05	21.53	8.35	18.73	13.00	13.93	13.68	8.73
NV	10.41	6.82	12.39	10.83	5.26	4.33	8.75	8.75	6.55	7.55	3.41	6.63	7.10	8.43	6.21	6.76
NH	24.24	11.06	19.63	28.40	16.47	5.63	12.61	12.61	14.12	12.63	7.30	16.19	20.93	18.53	11.20	9.49
NJ	18.69	13.18	18.69	15.51	11.69	5.13	10.83	10.83	11.21	12.63	15.13	18.71	11.28	15.79	15.13	6.96
NM	25.01	9.56	18.92	11.73	9.43	6.05	7.22	7.22	10.95	10.56	6.11	15.74	12.91	12.66	14.20	6.70
NY	12.54	10.74	19.18	23.71	17.15	7.85	12.16	12.16	18.72	10.88	12.86	21.24	14.99	20.13	10.02	10.83
NC	30.12	9.54	15.76	16.11	9.31	10.56	15.41	15.41	14.28	13.03	8.11	13.05	14.08	16.61	14.12	10.73
ND	9.54	4.31	9.54	5.43	5.43	3.75	4.13	4.13	10.50	10.50	9.93	6.52	6.00	10.59	9.93	6.11
OH	7.73	4.31	5.52	4.67	4.92	3.43	4.79	4.79	8.83	11.38	36.65	6.93	8.15	6.99	7.80	3.52
OK	18.82	10.32	12.49	13.50	7.66	6.82	9.48	9.48	11.79	11.31	5.13	14.63	10.66	11.24	14.01	6.82
OR	22.30	8.52	11.92	10.51	10.42	5.35	9.08	9.08	12.64	10.88	6.09	14.37	11.81	11.44	10.81	6.35
PA	19.22	19.22	15.60	19.54	13.58	7.39	11.11	11.11	14.34	15.60	14.34	16.04	17.13	19.44	14.34	9.19
RI	9.84	11.55	13.75	12.56	9.68	4.58	8.16	8.16	10.61	12.48	5.17	10.07	8.82	19.30	8.69	6.75
SC	29.32	13.80	17.10	12.84	8.21	9.82	12.01	12.01	12.92	14.13	9.57	15.39	16.10	15.67	14.47	9.40
SD	20.86	17.96	20.35	16.10	10.49	5.08	9.75	9.75	10.84	14.71	6.95	14.65	11.22	12.63	10.35	10.02
TN	22.71	10.14	11.54	10.75	7.08	5.49	10.05	10.05	11.07	10.34	6.60	11.69	8.27	12.08	11.04	5.17
TX	10.12	7.33	10.12	8.08	5.99	5.98	7.60	7.60	8.25	9.27	4.15	8.69	7.28	10.26	7.28	5.27
UT	14.72	6.59	7.50	7.34	6.57	3.56	6.79	6.79	7.45	7.15	6.41	8.96	7.73	6.72	5.56	4.17
VT	15.69	10.21	13.77	13.60	11.57	4.37	11.83	11.83	12.40	15.34	5.79	11.92	8.78	10.43	9.35	7.38
VA	12.38	8.14	8.89	10.51	5.76	4.50	7.40	7.40	8.02	7.27	5.45	7.98	8.93	8.31	6.69	5.07
WA	9.18	9.18	9.18	8.55	8.55	3.18	6.68	6.68	13.99	6.79	9.18	13.26	12.26	21.68	10.43	4.33
WV	14.85	5.54	8.34	7.68	4.51	3.53	6.46	6.46	6.74	6.29	4.33	8.39	6.03	8.09	6.54	3.52
WI	12.52	13.14	17.06	11.98	7.59	5.08	7.84	7.84	13.88	11.22	4.00	13.69	12.43	28.24	10.16	5.95
WY	5.82	5.82	5.82	5.82	5.82	5.82	5.82	5.82	5.82	5.82	5.82	5.82	5.82	5.82	5.82	5.82
AVG.	18.19	11.07	15.38	13.15	8.92	5.83	9.69	9.69	13.15	11.67	8.12	13.49	11.54	14.65	11.55	7.08

R013113-60   Workers' Compensation Insurance Rates by Trade and State (cont.)

State	Roofing 5551	Sheet Metal Work (HVAC) 5538	Steel Erection — door & sash 5102	Steel Erection — inter., ornam. 5102	Steel Erection — structure 5040	Steel Erection — NOC 5057	Tile Work — (interior ceramic) 5348	Waterproofing 9014	Wrecking 5701	Boiler-making 3726	Mill-wrights 3724	Structural Painters 5037	Elevator Constructor 5160	Truck Drivers 7219	Sprinkler Installer 5188
AL	54.71	10.34	12.52	12.52	40.75	21.56	12.35	9.27	40.75	11.93	12.83	55.64	10.09	23.31	8.40
AK	25.49	8.05	7.82	7.82	29.28	26.40	5.33	5.77	29.28	8.56	8.24	31.37	4.06	11.75	5.13
AZ	29.22	10.31	13.61	13.61	26.91	12.89	4.50	6.21	26.91	9.07	7.41	59.76	5.09	8.01	5.48
AR	16.03	4.74	8.34	8.34	15.40	11.28	6.69	2.58	15.40	4.94	5.76	25.69	2.73	10.96	5.72
CA	71.13	18.78	18.41	18.41	35.28	19.69	14.59	23.59	19.69	8.98	13.58	35.28	5.07	27.13	18.32
CO	15.60	4.16	5.36	5.36	23.64	10.59	4.10	3.23	18.40	4.37	3.87	22.88	2.78	7.22	3.85
CT	58.74	12.93	21.24	21.24	65.13	29.83	15.63	6.43	65.13	19.44	14.12	66.07	11.07	22.67	10.49
DE	26.71	5.55	13.16	13.16	23.27	13.16	8.00	11.53	23.27	6.17	6.19	23.27	6.19	11.13	6.60
DC	17.05	6.45	23.33	23.33	26.02	7.91	6.08	4.38	26.02	15.31	7.62	35.16	9.65	14.34	4.00
FL	18.17	7.69	9.91	9.91	23.04	12.59	5.63	5.26	23.04	9.07	6.05	39.44	3.54	9.24	6.41
GA	93.33	16.61	22.17	22.17	60.89	25.88	13.50	11.64	60.89	19.54	14.79	72.60	7.53	19.39	15.17
HI	17.24	4.93	7.60	7.60	21.77	6.88	6.52	5.40	21.77	4.82	7.71	24.83	2.28	10.54	3.49
ID	24.73	7.46	12.31	12.31	25.42	10.44	6.15	4.84	25.42	5.30	5.61	29.98	3.26	9.46	4.65
IL	47.55	15.21	31.16	31.16	84.68	19.36	27.09	7.88	84.68	23.23	15.10	101.23	14.42	19.73	16.65
IN	11.57	4.32	5.32	5.32	11.59	4.80	3.26	2.77	11.59	3.85	3.70	13.20	1.58	5.75	3.20
IA	28.01	8.53	9.15	9.15	52.79	14.30	9.38	6.15	25.61	14.19	8.59	87.69	6.14	13.60	7.75
KS	16.26	5.64	6.71	6.71	18.97	11.93	5.23	4.63	11.96	6.01	7.60	26.96	3.22	7.88	5.30
KY	34.00	12.00	11.72	11.72	36.00	11.02	16.73	3.50	36.00	12.15	8.35	150.00	9.56	10.00	10.32
LA	43.53	14.84	20.14	20.14	44.26	12.79	9.99	7.91	44.20	15.48	10.94	55.57	6.11	23.25	11.22
ME	22.72	6.77	8.92	8.92	37.18	12.21	5.76	4.64	37.18	8.08	6.58	54.29	4.39	8.15	6.70
MD	29.05	11.90	11.92	11.92	59.02	17.92	6.49	5.84	32.91	14.58	9.95	43.60	4.46	16.02	11.88
MA	30.99	5.72	6.89	6.89	54.08	33.00	5.81	2.48	23.75	15.42	5.98	23.51	4.21	8.28	4.13
MI	41.18	9.83	12.28	12.28	37.00	11.27	11.73	6.46	37.00	9.41	8.67	11.27	5.13	9.09	8.21
MN	67.71	17.30	9.82	9.82	108.16	7.70	14.69	7.95	7.70	10.92	12.24	36.60	6.41	11.39	7.62
MS	31.61	7.46	15.08	15.08	38.45	7.53	8.45	5.85	38.45	7.77	9.97	38.74	4.78	52.03	7.53
MO	36.73	8.64	12.33	12.33	47.55	24.29	10.41	5.92	47.55	14.45	9.66	60.85	6.20	12.44	8.43
MT	29.42	4.80	6.98	6.98	18.72	5.89	5.47	4.64	5.89	5.03	5.91	28.63	3.01	6.06	3.67
NE	35.08	12.88	14.80	14.80	59.03	14.13	8.68	6.73	67.83	16.33	11.35	66.18	7.13	15.98	10.30
NV	16.59	7.34	7.06	7.06	19.32	12.20	4.42	4.23	12.20	4.79	6.15	28.67	4.30	10.30	5.47
NH	36.82	8.93	14.28	14.28	95.03	28.57	12.35	7.17	95.03	8.91	9.04	54.18	6.29	36.82	10.68
NJ	40.10	7.22	12.87	12.87	17.25	13.36	9.55	6.63	16.86	4.18	9.20	23.37	7.00	15.75	5.89
NM	35.07	9.63	11.79	11.79	45.52	16.76	7.73	7.53	45.52	8.00	8.00	42.38	8.41	14.60	7.75
NY	35.96	13.56	19.25	19.25	35.26	19.08	10.35	7.49	18.10	21.41	10.22	42.40	12.20	14.37	6.45
NC	35.39	11.87	14.43	14.43	45.05	22.54	7.62	6.10	45.05	18.41	9.71	78.32	8.90	17.84	10.60
ND	17.63	6.11	10.59	10.59	10.90	10.59	10.50	17.63	8.18	3.33	10.50	10.59	3.33	8.79	6.11
OH	14.89	4.00	6.58	6.58	11.33	5.84	4.85	4.58	5.84	2.76	4.52	24.79	2.13	10.02	3.68
OK	22.44	9.62	10.98	10.98	29.21	15.15	6.69	6.41	32.94	9.25	6.21	52.38	3.88	11.26	6.40
OR	27.22	6.85	7.08	7.08	22.04	13.44	9.10	6.73	22.04	9.10	9.28	11.81	3.70	14.41	6.02
PA	38.35	8.92	19.10	19.10	30.01	19.10	11.69	16.04	30.01	7.95	8.85	30.01	8.85	16.69	9.19
RI	23.59	8.48	7.37	7.37	35.11	24.46	5.33	4.98	22.15	11.33	6.32	39.60	4.85	10.13	5.85
SC	46.45	10.88	15.24	15.24	31.33	24.73	7.98	5.42	31.33	11.24	10.59	66.07	8.64	15.07	10.12
SD	34.39	7.29	14.74	14.74	33.52	23.05	6.19	5.30	33.52	22.67	11.38	66.74	6.69	10.62	8.14
TN	29.78	8.13	13.42	13.42	16.07	18.88	7.46	4.09	16.07	8.10	7.46	40.34	4.92	10.23	6.10
TX	16.22	11.69	7.60	7.60	22.99	9.48	4.68	5.57	7.13	4.30	5.95	7.34	3.34	12.75	5.27
UT	23.93	5.78	5.71	5.71	24.61	11.81	5.75	4.31	20.14	5.91	4.77	21.36	3.71	7.05	4.16
VT	27.01	7.30	12.01	12.01	34.39	18.99	7.01	7.90	34.39	8.67	7.28	48.29	6.07	13.40	6.27
VA	25.97	5.47	7.46	7.46	29.39	10.80	5.76	3.30	29.39	4.92	7.38	27.90	5.39	9.03	5.30
WA	21.14	4.47	8.09	8.09	8.09	8.09	7.86	21.14	8.09	2.77	6.15	12.26	2.46	8.52	4.70
WV	19.62	5.62	7.13	7.13	19.39	9.55	4.86	3.11	20.70	5.62	6.64	35.86	4.23	8.93	3.76
WI	28.04	9.43	12.08	12.08	20.72	16.12	13.78	5.07	20.72	9.68	8.34	24.08	4.11	10.15	4.64
WY	5.82	5.82	5.82	5.82	5.82	5.82	5.82	5.82	5.82	5.82	5.82	5.82	5.82	5.82	5.82
AVG.	31.29	8.79	11.95	11.95	34.64	15.21	8.54	6.86	29.21	9.87	8.39	41.47	5.67	13.67	7.24

R013113-60 Workers' Compensation (cont.) (Canada in Canadian dollars)

Province		Alberta	British Columbia	Manitoba	Ontario	New Brunswick	Newfndld. & Labrador	Northwest Territories	Nova Scotia	Prince Edward Island	Quebec	Saskat-chewan	Yukon
Carpentry—3 stories or less	Rate	5.71	3.27	3.98	4.55	3.17	7.81	4.99	6.85	6.42	12.03	3.43	6.63
	Code	42143	721028	40102	723	238130	4226	4-41	4226	403	80110	B1226	202
Carpentry—interior cab. work	Rate	1.89	2.80	3.98	4.55	3.17	4.07	4.99	5.87	3.94	12.03	3.43	6.63
	Code	42133	721021	40102	723	238350	4279	4-41	4274	402	80110	B1127	202
CARPENTRY—general	Rate	5.71	3.27	3.98	4.55	3.17	4.07	4.99	6.85	6.42	12.03	3.43	6.63
	Code	42143	721028	40102	723	238130	4299	4-41	4226	403	80110	B1202	202
CONCRETE WORK—NOC	Rate	3.88	3.57	6.50	18.31	3.17	7.81	4.99	5.75	3.94	1.92	2.99	6.63
	Code	42104	721010	40110	748	238110	4224	4-41	4224	402	80100	B1314	203
CONCRETE WORK—flat (flr. sidewalk)	Rate	3.88	3.57	6.50	18.31	3.17	7.81	4.99	5.75	3.94	11.92	2.99	6.63
	Code	42104	721010	40110	748	238110	4224	4-41	4224	402	80100	B1314	203
ELECTRICAL Wiring—inside	Rate	1.56	1.18	1.65	3.69	1.28	2.29	2.44	1.97	3.94	5.04	1.83	3.89
	Code	42124	721019	40203	704	238210	4261	4-46	4261	402	80170	B1105	206
EXCAVATION—earth NOC	Rate	1.86	3.79	4.00	5.29	3.17	2.93	3.88	3.89	3.94	6.40	2.19	3.89
	Code	40604	721031	40706	711	238190	4214	4-43	4214	402	80030	R1106	207
EXCAVATION—rock	Rate	1.86	3.79	4.00	5.29	3.17	2.93	3.88	3.89	3.94	6.40	2.19	3.89
	Code	40604	721031	40706	711	238190	4214	4-43	4214	402	80030	R1106	207
GLAZIERS	Rate	2.23	3.79	3.98	10.25	3.17	5.10	4.99	5.22	3.94	15.02	2.99	3.89
	Code	42121	715020	40109	751	238150	4233	4-41	4233	402	80150	B1304	212
INSULATION WORK	Rate	1.62	9.87	3.98	10.25	3.17	5.10	4.99	5.22	3.94	12.03	3.43	6.63
	Code	42184	721029	40102	751	238310	4234	4-41	4234	402	80110	B1207	202
LATHING	Rate	4.20	7.84	3.98	4.55	3.17	4.07	4.99	5.87	3.94	12.03	2.99	6.63
	Code	42135	721042	40102	723	238390	4279	4-41	4271	402	80110	B1316	202
MASONRY	Rate	3.88	3.30	3.98	12.70	3.17	5.10	4.99	5.22	3.94	11.92	2.99	6.63
	Code	42102	721037	40102	741	238140	4231	4-41	4231	402	80100	B1318	202
PAINTING & DECORATING	Rate	3.16	3.62	3.11	7.51	3.17	4.07	4.99	5.87	3.94	12.03	3.43	6.63
	Code	42111	721041	40105	719	238320	4275	4-41	4275	402	80110	B1201	202
PILE DRIVING	Rate	3.88	3.42	4.00	7.03	3.17	2.93	3.88	5.75	6.42	6.40	2.99	6.63
	Code	42159	722004	40706	732	238190	4129	4-43	4221	403	80030	B1310	202
PLASTERING	Rate	4.20	7.84	4.45	7.51	3.17	4.07	4.99	5.87	3.94	12.03	3.43	6.63
	Code	42135	721042	40108	719	238390	4271	4-41	4271	402	80110	B1221	202
PLUMBING	Rate	1.56	2.55	2.78	4.16	1.28	2.47	2.44	2.81	3.94	5.89	1.83	3.89
	Code	42122	721043	40204	707	238220	4241	4-46	4241	401	80160	B1101	214
ROOFING	Rate	4.71	5.42	7.22	14.80	3.17	7.81	4.99	9.43	3.94	18.52	2.99	6.63
	Code	42118	721036	40403	728	238160	4236	4-41	4236	402	80130	B1320	202
SHEET METAL WORK (HVAC)	Rate	1.56	2.55	7.22	4.16	1.28	2.47	2.44	2.81	3.94	5.89	1.83	3.89
	Code	42117	721043	40402	707	238220	4244	4-46	4244	401	80160	B1107	208
STEEL ERECTION—door & sash	Rate	1.62	10.62	6.82	18.31	3.17	7.81	4.99	5.22	3.94	16.70	2.99	6.63
	Code	42106	722005	40502	748	238120	4227	-37	4227	402	80080	B1322	202
STEEL ERECTION—inter., ornam.	Rate	1.62	10.62	6.82	18.31	3.17	7.81	4.99	5.22	3.94	16.70	2.99	6.63
	Code	42106	722005	40502	748	238120	4227	4-41	4227	402	80080	B1322	202
STEEL ERECTION—structure	Rate	1.62	10.62	6.82	18.31	3.17	7.81	4.99	5.22	3.94	16.70	2.99	6.63
	Code	42106	722005	40502	748	238120	4227	4-41	4227	402	80080	B1322	202
STEEL ERECTION—NOC	Rate	1.62	10.62	6.82	18.31	3.17	7.81	4.99	5.22	3.94	16.70	2.99	6.63
	Code	42106	722005	40502	748	238120	4227	4-41	4227	402	80080	B1322	202
TILE WORK—inter. (ceramic)	Rate	3.02	3.65	1.86	7.51	3.17	4.07	4.99	5.87	3.94	12.03	2.99	6.63
	Code	42113	721054	40103	719	238340	4276	4-41	4276	402	80110	B1301	202
WATERPROOFING	Rate	3.16	3.62	3.98	4.55	3.17	4.07	4.99	5.22	3.94	18.52	3.13	6.63
	Code	42139	721016	40102	723	238190	4299	4-41	4239	402	80130	B1217	202
WRECKING	Rate	1.86	5.64	6.90	18.31	3.17	2.93	3.88	3.89	3.94	12.03	2.19	6.63
	Code	40604	721005	40106	748	238190	4211	4-43	4211	402	80110	R1125	202

R013113-80 Performance Bond

This table shows the cost of a Performance Bond for a construction job scheduled to be completed in 12 months. Add 1% of the premium cost per month for jobs requiring more than 12 months to complete. The rates are "standard" rates offered to contractors that the bonding company considers financially sound and capable of doing the work. Preferred rates are offered by some bonding companies based upon financial strength of the contractor. Actual rates vary from contractor to contractor and from bonding company to bonding company. Contractors should prequalify through a bonding agency before submitting a bid on a contract that requires a bond.

Contract Amount	Building Construction Class B Projects			Highways & Bridges					
				Class A New Construction			Class A-1 Highway Resurfacing		
First $ 100,000 bid	$25.00 per M			$15.00 per M			$9.40 per M		
Next 400,000 bid	$ 2,500	plus $15.00	per M	$ 1,500	plus $10.00	per M	$ 940	plus $7.20	per M
Next 2,000,000 bid	8,500	plus 10.00	per M	5,500	plus 7.00	per M	3,820	plus 5.00	per M
Next 2,500,000 bid	28,500	plus 7.50	per M	19,500	plus 5.50	per M	15,820	plus 4.50	per M
Next 2,500,000 bid	47,250	plus 7.00	per M	33,250	plus 5.00	per M	28,320	plus 4.50	per M
Over 7,500,000 bid	64,750	plus 6.00	per M	45,750	plus 4.50	per M	39,570	plus 4.00	per M

R015423-10 Steel Tubular Scaffolding

On new construction, tubular scaffolding is efficient up to 60' high or five stories. Above this it is usually better to use a hung scaffolding if construction permits. Swing scaffolding operations may interfere with tenants. In this case, the tubular is more practical at all heights.

In repairing or cleaning the front of an existing building the cost of tubular scaffolding per S.F. of building front increases as the height increases above the first tier. The first tier cost is relatively high due to leveling and alignment.

The minimum efficient crew for erecting and dismantling is three workers. They can set up and remove 18 frame sections per day up to 5 stories high. For 6 to 12 stories high, a crew of four is most efficient. Use two or more on top and two on the bottom for handing up or hoisting. They can also set up and remove 18 frame sections per day. At 7' horizontal spacing, this will run about 800 S.F. per day of erecting and dismantling. Time for placing and removing planks must be added to the above. A crew of three can place and remove 72 planks per day up to 5 stories. For over 5 stories, a crew of four can place and remove 80 planks per day.

The table below shows the number of pieces required to erect tubular steel scaffolding for 1000 S.F. of building frontage. This area is made up of a scaffolding system that is 12 frames (11 bays) long by 2 frames high.

For jobs under twenty-five frames, add 50% to rental cost. Rental rates will be lower for jobs over three months duration. Large quantities for long periods can reduce rental rates by 20%.

Description of Component	Number of Pieces for 1000 S.F. of Building Front	Unit
5' Wide Standard Frame, 6'-4" High	24	Ea.
Leveling Jack & Plate	24	
Cross Brace	44	
Side Arm Bracket, 21"	12	
Guardrail Post	12	
Guardrail, 7' section	22	
Stairway Section	2	
Stairway Starter Bar	1	
Stairway Inside Handrail	2	
Stairway Outside Handrail	2	
Walk-Thru Frame Guardrail	2	

Scaffolding is often used as falsework over 15' high during construction of cast-in-place concrete beams and slabs. Two foot wide scaffolding is generally used for heavy beam construction. The span between frames depends upon the load to be carried with a maximum span of 5'.

Heavy duty shoring frames with a capacity of 10,000#/leg can be spaced up to 10' O.C. depending upon form support design and loading.

Scaffolding used as horizontal shoring requires less than half the material required with conventional shoring.

On new construction, erection is done by carpenters.

Rolling towers supporting horizontal shores can reduce labor and speed the job. For maintenance work, catwalks with spans up to 70' can be supported by the rolling towers.

R015423-20   Pump Staging

Pump staging is generally not available for rent. The table below shows the number of pieces required to erect pump staging for 2400 S.F. of building frontage. This area is made up of a pump jack system that is 3 poles (2 bays) wide by 2 poles high.

Item	Number of Pieces for 2400 S.F. of Building Front	Unit
Aluminum pole section, 24' long	6	Ea.
Aluminum splice joint, 6' long	3	
Aluminum foldable brace	3	
Aluminum pump jack	3	
Aluminum support for workbench/back safety rail	3	
Aluminum scaffold plank/workbench, 14" wide x 24' long	4	
Safety net, 22' long	2	
Aluminum plank end safety rail	2	

The cost in place for this 2400 S.F. will depend on how many uses are realized during the life of the equipment.

R015433-10   Contractor Equipment

Rental Rates shown elsewhere in the book pertain to late model high quality machines in excellent working condition, rented from equipment dealers. Rental rates from contractors may be substantially lower than the rental rates from equipment dealers depending upon economic conditions; for older, less productive machines, reduce rates by a maximum of 15%. Any overtime must be added to the base rates. For shift work, rates are lower. Usual rule of thumb is 150% of one shift rate for two shifts; 200% for three shifts.

For periods of less than one week, operated equipment is usually more economical to rent than renting bare equipment and hiring an operator.

Costs to move equipment to a job site (mobilization) or from a job site (demobilization) are not included in rental rates, nor in any Equipment costs on any Unit Price line items or crew listings. These costs can be found elsewhere. If a piece of equipment is already at a job site, it is not appropriate to utilize mob/demob costs in an estimate again.

Rental rates vary throughout the country with larger cities generally having lower rates. Lease plans for new equipment are available for periods in excess of six months with a percentage of payments applying toward purchase.

Rental rates can also be treated as reimbursement costs for contractor-owned equipment. Owned equipment costs include depreciation, loan payments, interest, taxes, insurance, storage, and major repairs.

Monthly rental rates vary from 2% to 5% of the cost of the equipment depending on the anticipated life of the equipment and its wearing parts. Weekly rates are about 1/3 the monthly rates and daily rental rates about 1/3 the weekly rate.

The hourly operating costs for each piece of equipment include costs to the user such as fuel, oil, lubrication, normal expendables for the equipment, and a percentage of mechanic's wages chargeable to maintenance. The hourly operating costs listed do not include the operator's wages.

The daily cost for equipment used in the standard crews is figured by dividing the weekly rate by five, then adding eight times the hourly operating cost to give the total daily equipment cost, not including the operator. This figure is in the right hand column of the Equipment listings under Equipment Cost/Day.

Pile Driving rates shown for pile hammer and extractor do not include leads, crane, boiler or compressor. Vibratory pile driving requires an added field specialist during set-up and pile driving operation for the electric model. The hydraulic model requires a field specialist for set-up only. Up to 125 reuses of sheet piling are possible using vibratory drivers. For normal conditions, crane capacity for hammer type and size are as follows.

Crane Capacity	Hammer Type and Size		
	Air or Steam	Diesel	Vibratory
25 ton	to 8,750 ft.-lb.		70 H.P.
40 ton	15,000 ft.-lb.	to 32,000 ft.-lb.	170 H.P.
60 ton	25,000 ft.-lb.		300 H.P.
100 ton		112,000 ft.-lb.	

Cranes should be specified for the job by size, building and site characteristics, availability, performance characteristics, and duration of time required.

Backhoes & Shovels rent for about the same as equivalent size cranes but maintenance and operating expense is higher. Crane operators rate must be adjusted for high boom heights. Average adjustments: for 150' boom add 2% per hour; over 185', add 4% per hour; over 210', add 6% per hour; over 250', add 8% per hour and over 295', add 12% per hour.

Tower Cranes of the climbing or static type have jibs from 50' to 200' and capacities at maximum reach range from 4,000 to 14,000 pounds. Lifting capacities increase up to maximum load as the hook radius decreases.

Typical rental rates, based on purchase price are about 2% to 3% per month.

Erection and dismantling runs between 500 and 2000 labor hours. Climbing operation takes 10 labor hours per 20' climb. Crane dead time is about 5 hours per 40' climb. If crane is bolted to side of the building add cost of ties and extra mast sections. Climbing cranes have from 80' to 180' of mast while static cranes have 80' to 800' of mast.

Truck Cranes can be converted to tower cranes by using tower attachments. Mast heights over 400' have been used.

A single 100' high material **Hoist and Tower** can be erected and dismantled in about 400 labor hours; a double 100' high hoist and tower in about 600 labor hours. Erection times for additional heights are 3 and 4 labor hours per vertical foot respectively up to 150', and 4 to 5 labor hours per vertical foot over 150' high. A 40' high portable Buck hoist takes about 160 labor hours to erect and dismantle. Additional heights take 2 labor hours per vertical foot to 80' and 3 labor hours per vertical foot for the next 100'. Most material hoists do not meet local code requirements for carrying personnel.

A 150' high **Personnel Hoist** requires about 500 to 800 labor hours to erect and dismantle. Budget erection time at 5 labor hours per vertical foot for all trades. Local code requirements or labor scarcity requiring overtime can add up to 50% to any of the above erection costs.

Earthmoving Equipment: The selection of earthmoving equipment depends upon the type and quantity of material, moisture content, haul distance, haul road, time available, and equipment available. Short haul cut and fill operations may require dozers only, while another operation may require excavators, a fleet of trucks, and spreading and compaction equipment. Stockpiled material and granular material are easily excavated with front end loaders. Scrapers are most economically used with hauls between 300' and 1-1/2 miles if adequate haul roads can be maintained. Shovels are often used for blasted rock and any material where a vertical face of 8' or more can be excavated. Special conditions may dictate the use of draglines, clamshells, or backhoes. Spreading and compaction equipment must be matched to the soil characteristics, the compaction required and the rate the fill is being supplied.

R024119-10   Demolition Defined

Whole Building Demolition - Demolition of the whole building with no concern for any particular building element, component, or material type being demolished. This type of demolition is accomplished with large pieces of construction equipment that break up the structure, load it into trucks and haul it to a disposal site, but disposal or dump fees are not included. Demolition of below-grade foundation elements, such as footings, foundation walls, grade beams, slabs on grade, etc., is not included. Certain mechanical equipment containing flammable liquids or ozone-depleting refrigerants, electric lighting elements, communication equipment components, and other building elements may contain hazardous waste, and must be removed, either selectively or carefully, as hazardous waste before the building can be demolished.

Foundation Demolition - Demolition of below-grade foundation footings, foundation walls, grade beams, and slabs on grade. This type of demolition is accomplished by hand or pneumatic hand tools, and does not include saw cutting, or handling, loading, hauling, or disposal of the debris.

Gutting - Removal of building interior finishes and electrical/mechanical systems down to the load-bearing and sub-floor elements of the rough building frame, with no concern for any particular building element, component, or material type being demolished. This type of demolition is accomplished by hand or pneumatic hand tools, and includes loading into trucks, but not hauling, disposal or dump fees, scaffolding, or shoring. Certain mechanical equipment containing flammable liquids or ozone-depleting refrigerants, electric lighting elements, communication equipment components, and other building elements may contain hazardous waste, and must be removed, either selectively or carefully, as hazardous waste, before the building is gutted.

Selective Demolition - Demolition of a selected building element, component, or finish, with some concern for surrounding or adjacent elements, components, or finishes (see the first Subdivision (s) at the beginning of appropriate Divisions). This type of demolition is accomplished by hand or pneumatic hand tools, and does not include handling, loading,

storing, hauling, or disposal of the debris, scaffolding, or shoring. "Gutting" methods may be used in order to save time, but damage that is caused to surrounding or adjacent elements, components, or finishes may have to be repaired at a later time.

Careful Removal - Removal of a piece of service equipment, building element or component, or material type, with great concern for both the removed item and surrounding or adjacent elements, components or finishes. The purpose of careful removal may be to protect the removed item for later re-use, preserve a higher salvage value of the removed item, or replace an item while taking care to protect surrounding or adjacent elements, components, connections, or finishes from cosmetic and/or structural damage. An approximation of the time required to perform this type of removal is 1/3 to 1/2 the time it would take to install a new item of like kind (see Reference Number R220105-10). This type of removal is accomplished by hand or pneumatic hand tools, and does not include loading, hauling, or storing the removed item, scaffolding, shoring, or lifting equipment.

Cutout Demolition - Demolition of a small quantity of floor, wall, roof, or other assembly, with concern for the appearance and structural integrity of the surrounding materials. This type of demolition is accomplished by hand or pneumatic hand tools, and does not include saw cutting, handling, loading, hauling, or disposal of debris, scaffolding, or shoring.

Rubbish Handling - Work activities that involve handling, loading or hauling of debris. Generally, the cost of rubbish handling must be added to the cost of all types of demolition, with the exception of whole building demolition.

Minor Site Demolition - Demolition of site elements outside the footprint of a building. This type of demolition is accomplished by hand or pneumatic hand tools, or with larger pieces of construction equipment, and may include loading a removed item onto a truck (check the Crew for equipment used). It does not include saw cutting, hauling or disposal of debris, and, sometimes, handling or loading.

R024119-20   Dumpsters

Dumpster rental costs on construction sites are presented in two ways.

The cost per week rental includes the delivery of the dumpster; its pulling or emptying once per week, and its final removal. The assumption is made that the dumpster contractor could choose to empty a dumpster by simply bringing in an empty unit and removing the full one. These costs also include the disposal of the materials in the dumpster.

The Alternate Pricing can be used when actual planned conditions are not approximated by the weekly numbers. For example, these lines can be used when a dumpster is needed for 4 weeks and will need to be emptied 2 or 3 times per week. Conversely the Alternate Pricing lines can be used when a dumpster will be rented for several weeks or months but needs to be emptied only a few times over this period.

R024119-30   Rubbish Handling Chutes

To correctly estimate the cost of rubbish handling chute systems, the individual components must be priced separately. First choose the size of the system; a 30-inch diameter chute is quite common, but the sizes range from 18 to 36 inches in diameter. The 30-inch chute comes in a standard weight and two thinner weights. The thinner weight chutes are sometimes chosen for cost savings, but they are more easily damaged.

There are several types of major chute pieces that make up the chute system. The first component to consider is the top chute section (top intake hopper) where the material is dropped into the chute at the highest point. After determining the top chute, the intermediate chute pieces called the regular chute sections are priced. Next, the number of chute control door sections (intermediate intake hoppers) must be determined. In the more complex systems, a chute control door section is provided at each floor level. The last major component to consider is bolt down frames; these are usually provided at every other floor level.

There are a number of accessories to consider for safe operation and control. There are covers for the top chute and the chute door sections. The top

chute can have a trough that allows for better loading of the chute. For the safest operation, a chute warning light system can be added that will warn the other chute intake locations not to load while another is being used. There are dust control devices that spray a water mist to keep down the dust as the debris is loaded into a Dumpster. There are special breakaway cords that are used to prevent damage to the chute if the dumpster is removed without disconnecting from the chute. There are chute liners that can be installed to protect the chute structure from physical damage from rough abrasive materials. Warning signs can be posted at each floor level that is provided with a chute control door section.

In summary, a complete rubbish handling chute system will include one top section, several intermediate regular sections, several intermediate control door (intake hopper) sections and bolt down frames at every other floor level starting with the top floor. If so desired, the system can also include covers and a light warning system for a safer operation. The bottom of the chute should always be above the Dumpster and should be tied off with a breakaway cord to the Dumpster.

R026510-20   Underground Storage Tank Removal

Underground Storage Tank Removal can be divided into two categories: Non-Leaking and Leaking. Prior to removing an underground storage tank, tests should be made, with the proper authorities present, to determine whether a tank has been leaking or the surrounding soil has been contaminated.

To safely remove Liquid Underground Storage Tanks:
1. Excavate to the top of the tank.
2. Disconnect all piping.
3. Open all tank vents and access ports.
4. Remove all liquids and/or sludge.
5. Purge the tank with an inert gas.
6. Provide access to the inside of the tank and clean out the interior using proper personal protective equipment (PPE).
7. Excavate soil surrounding the tank using proper PPE for on-site personnel.
8. Pull and properly dispose of the tank.
9. Clean up the site of all contaminated material.
10. Install new tanks or close the excavation.

R028213-20   Asbestos Removal Process

Asbestos removal is accomplished by a specialty contractor who understands the federal and state regulations regarding the handling and disposal of the material. The process of asbestos removal is divided into many individual steps. An accurate estimate can be calculated only after all the steps have been priced.

The steps are generally as follows:
1. Obtain an asbestos abatement plan from an industrial hygienist.
2. Monitor the air quality in and around the removal area and along the path of travel between the removal area and transport area. This establishes the background contamination.
3. Construct a two part decontamination chamber at entrance to removal area.
4. Install a HEPA filter to create a negative pressure in the removal area.
5. Install wall, floor and ceiling protection as required by the plan, usually 2 layers of fireproof 6 mil polyethylene.
6. Industrial hygienist visually inspects work area to verify compliance with plan.
7. Provide temporary supports for conduit and piping affected by the removal process.
8. Proceed with asbestos removal and bagging process. Monitor air quality as described in Step #2. Discontinue operations when contaminate levels exceed applicable standards.
9. Document the legal disposal of materials in accordance with EPA standards.
10. Thoroughly clean removal area including all ledges, crevices and surfaces.
11. Post abatement inspection by industrial hygienist to verify plan compliance.
12. Provide a certificate from a licensed industrial hygienist attesting that contaminate levels are within acceptable standards before returning area to regular use.

R028319-60   Lead Paint Remediation Methods

Lead paint remediation can be accomplished by the following methods.

1. Abrasive blast
2. Chemical stripping
3. Power tool cleaning with vacuum collection system
4. Encapsulation
5. Remove and replace
6. Enclosure

Each of these methods has strengths and weakness depending on the specific circumstances of the project. The following is an overview of each method.

1. **Abrasive blasting** is usually accomplished with sand or recyclable metallic blast. Before work can begin, the area must be contained to ensure the blast material with lead does not escape to the atmosphere. The use of vacuum blast greatly reduces the containment requirements. Lead abatement equipment that may be associated with this work includes a negative air machine. In addition, it is necessary to have an industrial hygienist monitor the project on a continual basis. When the work is complete, the spent blast sand with lead must be disposed of as a hazardous material. If metallic shot was used, the lead is separated from the shot and disposed of as hazardous material. Worker protection includes disposable clothing and respiratory protection.

2. **Chemical stripping** requires strong chemicals be applied to the surface to remove the lead paint. Before the work can begin, the area under/adjacent to the work area must be covered to catch the chemical and removed lead. After the chemical is applied to the painted surface it is usually covered with paper. The chemical is left in place for the specified period, then the paper with lead paint is pulled or scraped off. The process may require several chemical applications. The paper with chemicals and lead paint adhered to it, plus the containment and loose scrapings collected by a HEPA (High Efficiency Particulate Air Filter) vac, must be disposed of as a hazardous material. The chemical stripping process usually requires a neutralizing agent and several wash downs after the paint is removed. Worker protection includes a neoprene or other compatible protective clothing and respiratory protection with face shield. An industrial hygienist is required intermittently during the process.

3. **Power tool cleaning** is accomplished using shrouded needle blasting guns. The shrouding with different end configurations is held up against the surface to be cleaned. The area is blasted with hardened needles and the shroud captures the lead with a HEPA vac and deposits it in a holding tank. An industrial hygienist monitors the project, protective clothing and a respirator is required until air samples prove otherwise. When the work is complete the lead must be disposed of as a hazardous material.

4. **Encapsulation** is a method that leaves the well bonded lead paint in place after the peeling paint has been removed. Before the work can begin, the area under/adjacent to the work must be covered to catch the scrapings. The scraped surface is then washed with a detergent and rinsed. The prepared surface is covered with approximately 10 mils of paint. A reinforcing fabric can also be embedded in the paint covering. The scraped paint and containment must be disposed of as a hazardous material. Workers must wear protective clothing and respirators.

5. **Remove and replace** is an effective way to remove lead paint from windows, gypsum walls and concrete masonry surfaces. The painted materials are removed and new materials are installed. Workers should wear a respirator and tyvek suit. The demolished materials must be disposed of as hazardous waste if it fails the TCLP (Toxicity Characteristic Leachate Process) test.

6. **Enclosure** is the process that permanently seals lead painted materials in place. This process has many applications such as covering lead painted drywall with new drywall, covering exterior construction with tyvek paper then residing, or covering lead painted structural members with aluminum or plastic. The seams on all enclosing materials must be securely sealed. An industrial hygienist monitors the project, and protective clothing and a respirator is required until air samples prove otherwise.

All the processes require clearance monitoring and wipe testing as required by the hygienist.

R031113-10   Wall Form Materials

Aluminum Forms

Approximate weight is 3 lbs. per S.F.C.A. Standard widths are available from 4″ to 36″ with 36″ most common. Standard lengths of 2′, 4′, 6′ to 8′ are available. Forms are lightweight and fewer ties are needed with the wider widths. The form face is either smooth or textured.

Metal Framed Plywood Forms

Manufacturers claim over 75 reuses of plywood and over 300 reuses of steel frames. Many specials such as corners, fillers, pilasters, etc. are available. Monthly rental is generally about 15% of purchase price for first month and 9% per month thereafter with 90% of rental applied to purchase for the first month and decreasing percentages thereafter. Aluminum framed forms cost 25% to 30% more than steel framed.

After the first month, extra days may be prorated from the monthly charge. Rental rates do not include ties, accessories, cleaning, loss of hardware or freight in and out. Approximate weight is 5 lbs. per S.F. for steel; 3 lbs. per S.F. for aluminum.

Forms can be rented with option to buy.

Plywood Forms, Job Fabricated

There are two types of plywood used for concrete forms.

1. Exterior plyform which is completely waterproof. This is face oiled to facilitate stripping. Ten reuses can be expected with this type with 25 reuses possible.
2. An overlaid type consists of a resin fiber fused to exterior plyform. No oiling is required except to facilitate cleaning. This is available in both high density (HDO) and medium density overlaid (MDO). Using HDO, 50 reuses can be expected with 200 possible.

Plyform is available in 5/8″ and 3/4″ thickness. High density overlaid is available in 3/8″, 1/2″, 5/8″ and 3/4″ thickness.

5/8″ thick is sufficient for most building forms, while 3/4″ is best on heavy construction.

Plywood Forms, Modular, Prefabricated

There are many plywood forming systems without frames. Most of these are manufactured from 1-1/8″ (HDO) plywood and have some hardware attached. These are used principally for foundation walls 8′ or less high. With care and maintenance, 100 reuses can be attained with decreasing quality of surface finish.

Steel Forms

Approximate weight is 6-1/2 lbs. per S.F.C.A. including accessories. Standard widths are available from 2″ to 24″, with 24″ most common. Standard lengths are from 2′ to 8′, with 4′ the most common. Forms are easily ganged into modular units.

Forms are usually leased for 15% of the purchase price per month prorated daily over 30 days.

Rental may be applied to sale price, and usually rental forms are bought. With careful handling and cleaning 200 to 400 reuses are possible.

Straight wall gang forms up to 12′ x 20′ or 8′ x 30′ can be fabricated. These crane handled forms usually lease for approx. 9% per month.

Individual job analysis is available from the manufacturer at no charge.

R031113-40   Forms for Reinforced Concrete

Design Economy

Avoid many sizes in proportioning beams and columns.

From story to story avoid changing column dimensions. Gain strength by adding steel or using a richer mix. If a change in size of column is necessary, vary one dimension only to minimize form alterations. Keep beams and columns the same width.

From floor to floor in a multi-story building vary beam depth, not width, as that will leave slab panel form unchanged. It is cheaper to vary the strength of a beam from floor to floor by means of steel area than by 2″ changes in either width or depth.

Cost Factors

Material includes the cost of lumber, cost of rent for metal pans or forms if used, nails, form ties, form oil, bolts and accessories.

Labor includes the cost of carpenters to make up, erect, remove and repair, plus common labor to clean and move. Having carpenters remove forms minimizes repairs.

Improper alignment and condition of forms will increase finishing cost. When forms are heavily oiled, concrete surfaces must be neutralized before finishing. Special curing compounds will cause spillages to spall off in first frost. Gang forming methods will reduce costs on large projects.

Materials Used

Boards are seldom used unless their architectural finish is required. Generally, steel, fiberglass and plywood are used for contact surfaces. Labor on plywood is 10% less than with boards. The plywood is backed up with

2 x 4′s at 12″ to 32″ O.C. Walers are generally 2 - 2 x 4′s. Column forms are held together with steel yokes or bands. Shoring is with adjustable shoring or scaffolding for high ceilings.

Reuse

Floor and column forms can be reused four or possibly five times without excessive repair. Remember to allow for 10% waste on each reuse.

When modular sized wall forms are made, up to twenty uses can be expected with exterior plyform.

When forms are reused, the cost to erect, strip, clean and move will not be affected. 10% replacement of lumber should be included and about one hour of carpenter time for repairs on each reuse per 100 S.F.

The reuse cost for certain accessory items normally rented on a monthly basis will be lower than the cost for the first use.

After fifth use, new material required plus time needed for repair prevent form cost from dropping further and it may go up. Much depends on care in stripping, the number of special bays, changes in beam or column sizes and other factors.

Costs for multiple use of formwork may be developed as follows:

2 Uses	3 Uses	4 Uses
$\frac{\text{(1st Use + Reuse)}}{2} = \text{avg. cost/2 uses}$	$\frac{\text{(1st Use + 2 Reuse)}}{3} = \text{avg. cost/3 uses}$	$\frac{\text{(1st use + 3 Reuse)}}{4} = \text{avg. cost/4 uses}$

R031113-60   Formwork Labor-Hours

Item	Unit	Fabricate	Erect & Strip	Clean & Move	Total Hours 1 Use	Multiple Use 2 Use	3 Use	4 Use
Beam and Girder, interior beams, 12" wide	100 S.F.	6.4	8.3	1.3	16.0	13.3	12.4	12.0
Hung from steel beams		5.8	7.7	1.3	14.8	12.4	11.6	11.2
Beam sides only, 36" high		5.8	7.2	1.3	14.3	11.9	11.1	10.7
Beam bottoms only, 24" wide		6.6	13.0	1.3	20.9	18.1	17.2	16.7
Box out for openings		9.9	10.0	1.1	21.0	16.6	15.1	14.3
Buttress forms, to 8' high		6.0	6.5	1.2	13.7	11.2	10.4	10.0
Centering, steel, 3/4" rib lath			1.0		1.0			
3/8" rib lath or slab form	↓		0.9		0.9			
Chamfer strip or keyway	100 L.F.		1.5		1.5	1.5	1.5	1.5
Columns, fiber tube 8" diameter			20.6		20.6			
12"			21.3		21.3			
16"			22.9		22.9			
20"			23.7		23.7			
24"			24.6		24.6			
30"			25.6		25.6			
Columns, round steel, 12" diameter			22.0		22.0	22.0	22.0	22.0
16"			25.6		25.6	25.6	25.6	25.6
20"			30.5		30.5	30.5	30.5	30.5
24"	↓		37.7		37.7	37.7	37.7	37.7
Columns, plywood 8" x 8"	100 S.F.	7.0	11.0	1.2	19.2	16.2	15.2	14.7
12" x 12"		6.0	10.5	1.2	17.7	15.2	14.4	14.0
16" x 16"		5.9	10.0	1.2	17.1	14.7	13.8	13.4
24" x 24"		5.8	9.8	1.2	16.8	14.4	13.6	13.2
Columns, steel framed plywood 8" x 8"			10.0	1.0	11.0	11.0	11.0	11.0
12" x 12"			9.3	1.0	10.3	10.3	10.3	10.3
16" x 16"			8.5	1.0	9.5	9.5	9.5	9.5
24" x 24"			7.8	1.0	8.8	8.8	8.8	8.8
Drop head forms, plywood		9.0	12.5	1.5	23.0	19.0	17.7	17.0
Coping forms		8.5	15.0	1.5	25.0	21.3	20.0	19.4
Culvert, box			14.5	4.3	18.8	18.8	18.8	18.8
Curb forms, 6" to 12" high, on grade		5.0	8.5	1.2	14.7	12.7	12.1	11.7
On elevated slabs		6.0	10.8	1.2	18.0	15.5	14.7	14.3
Edge forms to 6" high, on grade	100 L.F.	2.0	3.5	0.6	6.1	5.6	5.4	5.3
7" to 12" high	100 S.F.	2.5	5.0	1.0	8.5	7.8	7.5	7.4
Equipment foundations		10.0	18.0	2.0	30.0	25.5	24.0	23.3
Flat slabs, including drops		3.5	6.0	1.2	10.7	9.5	9.0	8.8
Hung from steel		3.0	5.5	1.2	9.7	8.7	8.4	8.2
Closed deck for domes		3.0	5.8	1.2	10.0	9.0	8.7	8.5
Open deck for pans		2.2	5.3	1.0	8.5	7.9	7.7	7.6
Footings, continuous, 12" high		3.5	3.5	1.5	8.5	7.3	6.8	6.6
Spread, 12" high		4.7	4.2	1.6	10.5	8.7	8.0	7.7
Pile caps, square or rectangular		4.5	5.0	1.5	11.0	9.3	8.7	8.4
Grade beams, 24" deep		2.5	5.3	1.2	9.0	8.3	8.0	7.9
Lintel or Sill forms		8.0	17.0	2.0	27.0	23.5	22.3	21.8
Spandrel beams, 12" wide		9.0	11.2	1.3	21.5	17.5	16.2	15.5
Stairs			25.0	4.0	29.0	29.0	29.0	29.0
Trench forms in floor		4.5	14.0	1.5	20.0	18.3	17.7	17.4
Walls, Plywood, at grade, to 8' high		5.0	6.5	1.5	13.0	11.0	9.7	9.5
8' to 16'		7.5	8.0	1.5	17.0	13.8	12.7	12.1
16' to 20'		9.0	10.0	1.5	20.5	16.5	15.2	14.5
Foundation walls, to 8' high		4.5	6.5	1.0	12.0	10.3	9.7	9.4
8' to 16' high		5.5	7.5	1.0	14.0	11.8	11.0	10.6
Retaining wall to 12' high, battered		6.0	8.5	1.5	16.0	13.5	12.7	12.3
Radial walls to 12' high, smooth		8.0	9.5	2.0	19.5	16.0	14.8	14.3
2' chords		7.0	8.0	1.5	16.5	13.5	12.5	12.0
Prefabricated modular, to 8' high		—	4.3	1.0	5.3	5.3	5.3	5.3
Steel, to 8' high		—	6.8	1.2	8.0	8.0	8.0	8.0
8' to 16' high		—	9.1	1.5	10.6	10.3	10.2	10.2
Steel framed plywood to 8' high		—	6.8	1.2	8.0	7.5	7.3	7.2
8' to 16' high	↓	—	9.3	1.2	10.5	9.5	9.2	9.0

Concrete   R0321 Reinforcing Steel

R032110-10   Reinforcing Steel Weights and Measures

Bar Designation No.**	Nominal Weight Lb./Ft.	U.S. Customary Units			SI Units			
		Nominal Dimensions*			Nominal Dimensions*			
		Diameter in.	Cross Sectional Area, in.²	Perimeter in.	Nominal Weight kg/m	Diameter mm	Cross Sectional Area, cm²	Perimeter mm
3	.376	.375	.11	1.178	.560	9.52	.71	29.9
4	.668	.500	.20	1.571	.994	12.70	1.29	39.9
5	1.043	.625	.31	1.963	1.552	15.88	2.00	49.9
6	1.502	.750	.44	2.356	2.235	19.05	2.84	59.8
7	2.044	.875	.60	2.749	3.042	22.22	3.87	69.8
8	2.670	1.000	.79	3.142	3.973	25.40	5.10	79.8
9	3.400	1.128	1.00	3.544	5.059	28.65	6.45	90.0
10	4.303	1.270	1.27	3.990	6.403	32.26	8.19	101.4
11	5.313	1.410	1.56	4.430	7.906	35.81	10.06	112.5
14	7.650	1.693	2.25	5.320	11.384	43.00	14.52	135.1
18	13.600	2.257	4.00	7.090	20.238	57.33	25.81	180.1

* The nominal dimensions of a deformed bar are equivalent to those of a plain round bar having the same weight per foot as the deformed bar.
** Bar numbers are based on the number of eighths of an inch included in the nominal diameter of the bars.

R032110-80   Shop-Fabricated Reinforcing Steel

The material prices for reinforcing, shown in the unit cost sections of the book, are for 50 tons or more of shop-fabricated reinforcing steel and include:

1. Mill base price of reinforcing steel
2. Mill grade/size/length extras
3. Mill delivery to the fabrication shop
4. Shop storage and handling
5. Shop drafting/detailing
6. Shop shearing and bending
7. Shop listing
8. Shop delivery to the job site

Both material and installation costs can be considerably higher for small jobs consisting primarily of smaller bars, while material costs may be slightly lower for larger jobs.

Concrete   R0322 Welded Wire Fabric Reinforcing

R032205-30   Common Stock Styles of Welded Wire Fabric

This table provides some of the basic specifications, sizes, and weights of welded wire fabric used for reinforcing concrete.

	New Designation	Old Designation		Steel Area per Foot				Approximate Weight per 100 S.F.	
	Spacing — Cross Sectional Area (in.) — (Sq. in. 100)	Spacing — Wire Gauge (in.) — (AS & W)		Longitudinal		Transverse			
				in.	cm	in.	cm	lbs	kg
Rolls	6 x 6 — W1.4 x W1.4	6 x 6 — 10 x 10		.028	.071	.028	.071	21	9.53
	6 x 6 — W2.0 x W2.0	6 x 6 — 8 x 8	1	.040	.102	.040	.102	29	13.15
	6 x 6 — W2.9 x W2.9	6 x 6 — 6 x 6		.058	.147	.058	.147	42	19.05
	6 x 6 — W4.0 x W4.0	6 x 6 — 4 x 4		.080	.203	.080	.203	58	26.91
	4 x 4 — W1.4 x W1.4	4 x 4 — 10 x 10		.042	.107	.042	.107	31	14.06
	4 x 4 — W2.0 x W2.0	4 x 4 — 8 x 8	1	.060	.152	.060	.152	43	19.50
	4 x 4 — W2.9 x W2.9	4 x 4 — 6 x 6		.087	.227	.087	.227	62	28.12
	4 x 4 — W4.0 x W4.0	4 x 4 — 4 x 4		.120	.305	.120	.305	85	38.56
Sheets	6 x 6 — W2.9 x W2.9	6 x 6 — 6 x 6		.058	.147	.058	.147	42	19.05
	6 x 6 — W4.0 x W4.0	6 x 6 — 4 x 4		.080	.203	.080	.203	58	26.31
	6 x 6 — W5.5 x W5.5	6 x 6 — 2 x 2	2	.110	.279	.110	.279	80	36.29
	4 x 4 — W1.4 x W1.4	4 x 4 — 4 x 4		.120	.305	.120	.305	85	38.56

NOTES: 1. Exact W—number size for 8 gauge is W2.1
2. Exact W—number size for 2 gauge is W5.4

R033105-10   Proportionate Quantities

The tables below show both quantities per S.F. of floor areas as well as form and reinforcing quantities per C.Y. Unusual structural requirements would increase the ratios below. High strength reinforcing would reduce the steel weights. Figures are for 3000 psi concrete and 60,000 psi reinforcing unless specified otherwise.

Type of Construction	Live Load	Span	Per S.F. of Floor Area				Per C.Y. of Concrete		
			Concrete	Forms	Reinf.	Pans	Forms	Reinf.	Pans
Flat Plate	50 psf	15 Ft.	.46 C.F.	1.06 S.F.	1.71 lb.		62 S.F.	101 lb.	
		20	.63	1.02	2.40		44	104	
		25	.79	1.02	3.03		35	104	
	100	15	.46	1.04	2.14		61	126	
		20	.71	1.02	2.72		39	104	
		25	.83	1.01	3.47		33	113	
Flat Plate (waffle construction) 20" domes	50	20	.43	1.00	2.10	.84 S.F.	63	135	53 S.F.
		25	.52	1.00	2.90	.89	52	150	46
		30	.64	1.00	3.70	.87	42	155	37
	100	20	.51	1.00	2.30	.84	53	125	45
		25	.64	1.00	3.20	.83	42	135	35
		30	.76	1.00	4.40	.81	36	160	29
Waffle Construction 30" domes	50	25	.69	1.06	1.83	.68	42	72	40
		30	.74	1.06	2.39	.69	39	87	39
		35	.86	1.05	2.71	.69	33	85	39
		40	.78	1.00	4.80	.68	35	165	40
Flat Slab (two way with drop panels)	50	20	.62	1.03	2.34		45	102	
		25	.77	1.03	2.99		36	105	
		30	.95	1.03	4.09		29	116	
	100	20	.64	1.03	2.83		43	119	
		25	.79	1.03	3.88		35	133	
		30	.96	1.03	4.66		29	131	
	200	20	.73	1.03	3.03		38	112	
		25	.86	1.03	4.23		32	133	
		30	1.06	1.03	5.30		26	135	
One Way Joists 20" Pans	50	15	.36	1.04	1.40	.93	78	105	70
		20	.42	1.05	1.80	.94	67	120	60
		25	.47	1.05	2.60	.94	60	150	54
	100	15	.38	1.07	1.90	.93	77	140	66
		20	.44	1.08	2.40	.94	67	150	58
		25	.52	1.07	3.50	.94	55	185	49
One Way Joists 8" x 16" filler blocks	50	15	.34	1.06	1.80	.81 Ea.	84	145	64 Ea.
		20	.40	1.08	2.20	.82	73	145	55
		25	.46	1.07	3.20	.83	63	190	49
	100	15	.39	1.07	1.90	.81	74	130	56
		20	.46	1.09	2.80	.82	64	160	48
		25	.53	1.10	3.60	.83	56	190	42
One Way Beam & Slab	50	15	.42	1.30	1.73		84	111	
		20	.51	1.28	2.61		68	138	
		25	.64	1.25	2.78		53	117	
	100	15	.42	1.30	1.90		84	122	
		20	.54	1.35	2.69		68	154	
		25	.69	1.37	3.93		54	145	
	200	15	.44	1.31	2.24		80	137	
		20	.58	1.40	3.30		65	163	
		25	.69	1.42	4.89		53	183	
Two Way Beam & Slab	100	15	.47	1.20	2.26		69	130	
		20	.63	1.29	3.06		55	131	
		25	.83	1.33	3.79		43	123	
	200	15	.49	1.25	2.70		41	149	
		20	.66	1.32	4.04		54	165	
		25	.88	1.32	6.08		41	187	

R033105-10   Proportionate Quantities (cont.)

Item	Size	Forms	Reinforcing	Minimum	Maximum
	4000 psi Concrete and 60,000 psi Reinforcing—Form and Reinforcing Quantities per C.Y.				
Columns (square tied)	10" x 10"	130 S.F.C.A.	#5 to #11	220 lbs.	875 lbs.
	12" x 12"	108	#6 to #14	200	955
	14" x 14"	92	#7 to #14	190	900
	16" x 16"	81	#6 to #14	187	1082
	18" x 18"	72	#6 to #14	170	906
	20" x 20"	65	#7 to #18	150	1080
	22" x 22"	59	#8 to #18	153	902
	24" x 24"	54	#8 to #18	164	884
	26" x 26"	50	#9 to #18	169	994
	28" x 28"	46	#9 to #18	147	864
	30" x 30"	43	#10 to #18	146	983
	32" x 32"	40	#10 to #18	175	866
	34" x 34"	38	#10 to #18	157	772
	36" x 36"	36	#10 to #18	175	852
	38" x 38"	34	#10 to #18	158	765
	40" x 40"	32	#10 to #18	143	692

Item	Size	Form	Spiral	Reinforcing	Minimum	Maximum
Columns (spirally reinforced)	12" diameter	34.5 L.F.	190 lbs.	#4 to #11	165 lbs.	1505 lb.
		34.5	190	#14 & #18	—	1100
	14"	25	170	#4 to #11	150	970
		25	170	#14 & #18	800	1000
	16"	19	160	#4 to #11	160	950
		19	160	#14 & #18	605	1080
	18"	15	150	#4 to #11	160	915
		15	150	#14 & #18	480	1075
	20"	12	130	#4 to #11	155	865
		12	130	#14 & #18	385	1020
	22"	10	125	#4 to #11	165	775
		10	125	#14 & #18	320	995
	24"	9	120	#4 to #11	195	800
		9	120	#14 & #18	290	1150
	26"	7.3	100	#4 to #11	200	729
		7.3	100	#14 & #18	235	1035
	28"	6.3	95	#4 to #11	175	700
		6.3	95	#14 & #18	200	1075
	30"	5.5	90	#4 to #11	180	670
		5.5	90	#14 & #18	175	1015
	32"	4.8	85	#4 to #11	185	615
		4.8	85	#14 & #18	155	955
	34"	4.3	80	#4 to #11	180	600
		4.3	80	#14 & #18	170	855
	36"	3.8	75	#4 to #11	165	570
		3.8	75	#14 & #18	155	865
	40"	3.0	70	#4 to #11	165	500
		3.0	70	#14 & #18	145	765

R033105-10 Proportionate Quantities (cont.)

3000 psi Concrete and 60,000 psi Reinforcing—Form and Reinforcing Quantities per C.Y.						
Item	Type	Loading	Height	C.Y./L.F.	Forms/C.Y.	Reinf./C.Y.
Retaining Walls	Cantilever	Level Backfill	4 Ft.	0.2 C.Y.	49 S.F.	35 lbs.
			8	0.5	42	45
			12	0.8	35	70
			16	1.1	32	85
			20	1.6	28	105
		Highway Surcharge	4	0.3	41	35
			8	0.5	36	55
			12	0.8	33	90
			16	1.2	30	120
			20	1.7	27	155
		Railroad Surcharge	4	0.4	28	45
			8	0.8	25	65
			12	1.3	22	90
			16	1.9	20	100
			20	2.6	18	120
	Gravity, with Vertical Face	Level Backfill	4	0.4	37	None
			7	0.6	27	
			10	1.2	20	
		Sloping Backfill	4	0.3	31	
			7	0.8	21	
			10	1.6	15	

		Live Load in Kips per Linear Foot							
	Span	Under 1 Kip		2 to 3 Kips		4 to 5 Kips		6 to 7 Kips	
		Forms	Reinf.	Forms	Reinf.	Forms	Reinf.	Forms	Reinf.
Beams	10 Ft.	—	—	90 S.F.	170 #	85 S.F.	175 #	75 S.F.	185 #
	16	130 S.F.	165 #	85	180	75	180	65	225
	20	110	170	75	185	62	200	51	200
	26	90	170	65	215	62	215	—	—
	30	85	175	60	200	—	—	—	—

Item	Size	Type	Forms per C.Y.	Reinforcing per C.Y.
Spread Footings	Under 1 C.Y.	1,000 psf soil	24 S.F.	44 lbs.
		5,000	24	42
		10,000	24	52
	1 C.Y. to 5 C.Y.	1,000	14	49
		5,000	14	50
		10,000	14	50
	Over 5 C.Y.	1,000	9	54
		5,000	9	52
		10,000	9	56
Pile Caps (30 Ton Concrete Piles)	Under 5 C.Y.	shallow caps	20	65
		medium	20	50
		deep	20	40
	5 C.Y. to 10 C.Y.	shallow	14	55
		medium	15	45
		deep	15	40
	10 C.Y. to 20 C.Y.	shallow	11	60
		medium	11	45
		deep	12	35
	Over 20 C.Y.	shallow	9	60
		medium	9	45
		deep	10	40

R033105-10   Proportionate Quantities (cont.)

3000 psi Concrete and 60,000 psi Reinforcing — Form and Reinforcing Quantities per C.Y.

Item	Size	Pile Spacing	50 T Pile	100 T Pile	50 T Pile	100 T Pile
Pile Caps (Steel H Piles)	Under 5 C.Y.	24″ O.C.	24 S.F.	24 S.F.	75 lbs.	90 lbs.
		30″	25	25	80	100
		36″	24	24	80	110
	5 C.Y. to 10 C.Y.	24″	15	15	80	110
		30″	15	15	85	110
		36″	15	15	75	90
	Over 10 C.Y.	24″	13	13	85	90
		30″	11	11	85	95
		36″	10	10	85	90

		8″ Thick		10″ Thick		12″ Thick		15″ Thick	
	Height	Forms	Reinf.	Forms	Reinf.	Forms	Reinf.	Forms	Reinf.
Basement Walls	7 Ft.	81 S.F.	44 lbs.	65 S.F.	45 lbs.	54 S.F.	44 lbs.	41 S.F.	43 lbs.
	8		44		45		44		43
	9		46		45		44		43
	10		57		45		44		43
	12		83		50		52		43
	14		116		65		64		51
	16				86		90		65
	18						106		70

R033105-20   Materials for One C.Y. of Concrete

This is an approximate method of figuring quantities of cement, sand and coarse aggregate for a field mix with waste allowance included.

With crushed gravel as coarse aggregate, to determine barrels of cement required, divide 10 by total mix; that is, for 1:2:4 mix, 10 divided by 7 = 1-3/7 barrels.

If the coarse aggregate is crushed stone, use 10-1/2 instead of 10 as given for gravel.

To determine tons of sand required, multiply barrels of cement by parts of sand and then by 0.2; that is, for the 1:2:4 mix, as above, 1-3/7 x 2 x .2 = .57 tons.

Tons of crushed gravel are in the same ratio to tons of sand as parts in the mix, or 4/2 x .57 = 1.14 tons.

1 bag cement = 94#	1 C.Y. sand or crushed gravel = 2700#	1 C.Y. crushed stone = 2575#
4 bags = 1 barrel	1 ton sand or crushed gravel = 20 C.F.	1 ton crushed stone = 21 C.F.

Average carload of cement is 692 bags; of sand or gravel is 56 tons.

Do not stack stored cement over 10 bags high.

R033105-70   Placing Ready-Mixed Concrete

For ground pours allow for 5% waste when figuring quantities.

Prices in the front of the book assume normal deliveries. If deliveries are made before 8 A.M. or after 5 P.M. or on Saturday afternoons add 30%. Negotiated discounts for large volumes are not included in prices in front of book.

For the lower floors without truck access, concrete may be wheeled in rubber-tired buggies, conveyer handled, crane handled or pumped. Pumping is economical if there is top steel. Conveyers are more efficient for thick slabs.

At higher floors the rubber-tired buggies may be hoisted by a hoisting tower and wheeled to location. Placement by a conveyer is limited to three floors

and is best for high-volume pours. Pumped concrete is best when building has no crane access. Concrete may be pumped directly as high as thirty-six stories using special pumping techniques. Normal maximum height is about fifteen stories.

Best pumping aggregate is screened and graded bank gravel rather than crushed stone.

Pumping downward is more difficult than pumping upward. Horizontal distance from pump to pour may increase preparation time prior to pour. Placing by cranes, either mobile, climbing or tower types, continues as the most efficient method for high-rise concrete buildings.

R033105-85   Lift Slabs

The cost advantage of the lift slab method is due to placing all concrete, reinforcing steel, inserts and electrical conduit at ground level and in reduction of formwork. Minimum economical project size is about 30,000 S.F. Slabs may be tilted for parking garage ramps.

It is now used in all types of buildings and has gone up to 22 stories high in apartment buildings. Current trend is to use post-tensioned flat plate slabs with spans from 22' and 35'. Cylindrical void forms are used when deep slabs are required. One pound of prestressing steel is about equal to seven pounds of conventional reinforcing.

To be considered cured for stressing and lifting, a slab must have attained 75% of design strength. Seven days are usually sufficient with four to five days possible if high early strength cement is used. Slabs can be stacked using two coats of a non-bonding agent to insure that slabs do not stick to each other. Lifting is done by companies specializing in this work. Lift rate is 5' to 15' per hour with an average of 10' per hour. Total areas up to 33,000 S.F. have been lifted at one time. 24 to 36 jacking columns are common. Most economical bay sizes are 24' to 28' with four to fourteen stories most efficient. Continuous design reduces reinforcing steel cost. Use of post-tensioned slabs allows larger bay sizes.

R033543-10   Polished Concrete Floors

A polished concrete floor has a glossy mirror-like appearance and is created by grinding the concrete floor with finer and finer diamond grits, similar to sanding wood, until the desired level of reflective clarity and sheen are achieved. The technical term for this type of polished concrete is bonded abrasive polished concrete. The basic piece of equipment used in the polishing process is a walk-behind planetary grinder for working large floor areas. This grinder drives diamond-impregnated abrasive discs, which progress from coarse- to fine-grit discs.

The process begins with the use of very coarse diamond segments or discs bonded in a metallic matrix. These segments are coarse enough to allow the removal of pits, blemishes, stains, and light coatings from the floor surface in preparation for final smoothing. The condition of the original concrete surface will dictate the grit coarseness of the initial grinding step which will generally end up being a three- to four-step process using ever finer grits. The purpose of this initial grinding step is to remove surface coatings and blemishes and to cut down into the cream for very fine aggregate exposure, or deeper into the fine aggregate layer just below the cream layer, or even deeper into the coarse aggregate layer. These initial grinding steps will progress up to the 100/120 grit. If wet grinding is done, a waste slurry is produced that must be removed between grit changes and disposed of properly. If dry grinding is done, a high performance vacuum will pick up the dust during grinding and collect it in bags which must be disposed of properly.

The process continues with honing the floor in a series of steps that progress from 100-grit to 400-grit diamond abrasive discs embedded in a plastic or resin matrix. At some point during, or just prior to, the honing step, one or two coats of stain or dye can be sprayed onto the surface to give color to the concrete, and two coats of densifier/hardener must be applied to the floor surface and allowed to dry. This sprayed-on densifier/hardener will penetrate about 1/8" into the concrete to make the surface harder, denser and more abrasion-resistant.

The process ends with polishing the floor surface in a series of steps that progress from resin-impregnated 800-grit (medium polish) to 1500-grit (high polish) to 3000-grit (very high polish), depending on the desired level of reflective clarity and sheen.

The Concrete Polishing Association of America (CPAA) has defined the flooring options available when processing concrete to a desired finish. The first category is aggregate exposure, the grinding of a concrete surface with bonded abrasives, in as many abrasive grits necessary, to achieve one of the following classes:

A. Cream – very little surface cut depth; little aggregate exposure

B. Fine aggregate (salt and pepper) – surface cut depth of 1/16"; fine aggregate exposure with little or no medium aggregate exposure at random locations

C. Medium aggregate – surface cut depth of 1/8"; medium aggregate exposure with little or no large aggregate exposure at random locations

D. Large aggregate – surface cut depth of 1/4"; large aggregate exposure with little or no fine aggregate exposure at random locations

The second CPAA defined category is reflective clarity and sheen, the polishing of a concrete surface with the minimum number of bonded abrasives as indicated to achieve one of the following levels:

1. Ground – flat appearance with none to very slight diffused reflection; none to very low reflective sheen; using a minimum total of 4 grit levels up 100-grit

2. Honed – matte appearance with or without slight diffused reflection; low to medium reflective sheen; using a minimum total of 5 grit levels up to 400-grit

3. Semi-polished – objects being reflected are not quite sharp and crisp but can be easily identified; medium to high reflective sheen; using a minimum total of 6 grit levels up to 800-grit

4. Highly-polished – objects being reflected are sharp and crisp as would be seen in a mirror-like reflection; high to highest reflective sheen; using a minimum total of up to 8 grit levels up to 1500-grit or 3000-grit

The CPAA defines reflective clarity as the degree of sharpness and crispness of the reflection of overhead objects when viewed 5' above and perpendicular to the floor surface; and reflective sheen as the degree of gloss reflected from a surface when viewed at least 20' from and at an angle to the floor surface. These terms are relatively subjective. The final outcome depends on the internal makeup and surface condition of the original concrete floor, the experience of the floor polishing crew, and expectations of the owner. Before the grinding, honing, and polishing work commences on the main floor area, it might be beneficial to do a mock-up panel in the same floor but in an out of the way place to demonstrate the sequence of steps with increasingly fine abrasive grits and to demonstrate the final reflective clarity and reflective sheen. This mock-up panel will be within the area of, and part of, the final work.

R034105-30 Prestressed Precast Concrete Structural Units

Type	Location	Depth	Span in Ft.		Live Load Lb. per S.F.
Double Tee 8' to 10'	Floor	28" to 34"	60 to 80		50 to 80
	Roof	12" to 24"	30 to 50		40
	Wall	Width 8'	Up to 55' high		Wind
Multiple Tee 8'	Roof	8" to 12"	15 to 40		40
	Floor	8" to 12"	15 to 30		100
Plank	Roof		Roof	Floor	40 for Roof
		4"	13	12	
		6"	22	18	
or	or	8"	26	25	
		10"	33	29	100 for Floor
	Floor	12"	42	32	
Single Tee 8' to 10'	Roof	28"	40		
		32"	80		
		36"	100		40
		48"	120		
AASHO Girder	Bridges	Type 4	100		
		5	110		Highway
		6	125		
Box Beam 4'	Bridges	15"	40		
		27"	to		Highway
		33"	100		

The majority of precast projects today utilize double tees rather than single tees because of speed and ease of installation. As a result casting beds at manufacturing plants are normally formed for double tees. Single tee projects will therefore require an initial set up charge to be spread over the individual single tee costs.

For floors, a 2" to 3" topping is field cast over the shapes. For roofs, insulating concrete or rigid insulation is placed over the shapes.

Member lengths up to 40' are standard haul, 40' to 60' require special permits and lengths over 60' must be escorted. Over width and/or over length can add up to 100% on hauling costs.

Large heavy members may require two cranes for lifting which would increase erection costs by about 45%. An eight man crew can install 12 to 20 double tees, or 45 to 70 quad tees or planks per day.

Grouting of connections must also be included.

Several system buildings utilizing precast members are available. Heights can go up to 22 stories for apartment buildings. Optimum design ratio is 3 S.F. of surface to 1 S.F. of floor area.

R035216-10   Lightweight Concrete

Lightweight aggregate concrete is usually purchased ready mixed, but it can also be field mixed.

Vermiculite or Perlite comes in bags of 4 C.F. under various trade names. Weight is about 8 lbs. per C.F. For insulating roof fill use 1:6 mix. For structural deck use 1:4 mix over gypsum boards, steeltex, steel centering, etc., supported by closely spaced joists or bulb trees. For structural slabs use 1:3:2 vermiculite sand concrete over steeltex, metal lath, steel centering, etc., on joists spaced 2'-0" O.C. for maximum L.L. of 80 P.S.F. Use same mix for slab base fill over steel flooring or regular reinforced concrete slab when tile, terrazzo or other finish is to be laid over.

For slabs on grade use 1:3:2 mix when tile, etc., finish is to be laid over. If radiant heating units are installed use a 1:6 mix for a base. After coils are in place, cover with a regular granolithic finish (mix 1:3:2) to a minimum depth of 1-1/2" over top of units.

Reinforce all slabs with 6 x 6 or 10 x 10 welded wire mesh.

R042110-20   Common and Face Brick

Common building brick manufactured according to ASTM C62 and facing brick manufactured according to ASTM C216 are the two standard bricks available for general building use.

Building brick is made in three grades; SW, where high resistance to damage caused by cyclic freezing is required; MW, where moderate resistance to cyclic freezing is needed; and NW, where little resistance to cyclic freezing is needed. Facing brick is made in only the two grades SW and MW. Additionally, facing brick is available in three types; FBS, for general use; FBX, for general use where a higher degree of precision and lower permissible variation in size than FBS is needed; and FBA, for general use to produce characteristic architectural effects resulting from non-uniformity in size and texture of the units.

In figuring the material cost of brickwork, an allowance of 25% mortar waste and 3% brick breakage was included. If bricks are delivered palletized with 280 to 300 per pallet, or packaged, allow only 1-1/2% for breakage. Packaged or palletized delivery is practical when a job is big enough to have a crane or other equipment available to handle a package of brick. This is so on all industrial work but not always true on small commercial buildings.

The use of buff and gray face is increasing, and there is a continuing trend to the Norman, Roman, Jumbo and SCR brick.

Common red clay brick for backup is not used that often. Concrete block is the most usual backup material with occasional use of sand lime or cement brick. Building brick is commonly used in solid walls for strength and as a fire stop.

Brick panels built on the ground and then crane erected to the upper floors have proven to be economical. This allows the work to be done under cover and without scaffolding.

R042110-50   Brick, Block & Mortar Quantities

Type Brick	Nominal Size (incl. mortar) L H W	Modular Coursing	Number of Brick per S.F.	C.F. of Mortar per M Bricks, Waste Included 3/8" Joint	1/2" Joint
Standard	8 x 2-2/3 x 4	3C=8"	6.75	10.3	12.9
Economy	8 x 4 x 4	1C=4"	4.50	11.4	14.6
Engineer	8 x 3-1/5 x 4	5C=16"	5.63	10.6	13.6
Fire	9 x 2-1/2 x 4-1/2	2C=5"	6.40	550 # Fireclay	—
Jumbo	12 x 4 x 6 or 8	1C=4"	3.00	23.8	30.8
Norman	12 x 2-2/3 x 4	3C=8"	4.50	14.0	17.9
Norwegian	12 x 3-1/5 x 4	5C=16"	3.75	14.6	18.6
Roman	12 x 2 x 4	2C=4"	6.00	13.4	17.0
SCR	12 x 2-2/3 x 6	3C=8"	4.50	21.8	28.0
Utility	12 x 4 x 4	1C=4"	3.00	15.4	19.6

Running Bond — Number of Brick per S.F. of Wall - Single Wythe with 3/8" Joints

For Other Bonds Standard Size — Add to S.F. Quantities in Table to Left

Bond Type	Description	Factor
Common	full header every fifth course	+20%
	full header every sixth course	+16.7%
English	full header every second course	+50%
Flemish	alternate headers every course	+33.3%
	every sixth course	+5.6%
Header = W x H exposed		+100%
Rowlock = H x W exposed		+100%
Rowlock stretcher = L x W exposed		+33.3%
Soldier = H x L exposed		—
Sailor = W x L exposed		-33.3%

Concrete Blocks Nominal Size	Approximate Weight per S.F. Standard	Lightweight	Blocks per 100 S.F.	Mortar per M block, waste included Partitions	Back up
2" x 8" x 16"	20 PSF	15 PSF	113	27 C.F.	36 C.F.
4"	30	20		41	51
6"	42	30		56	66
8"	55	38		72	82
10"	70	47		87	97
12"	85	55		102	112

R050521-20 Welded Structural Steel

Usual weight reductions with welded design run 10% to 20% compared with bolted or riveted connections. This amounts to about the same total cost compared with bolted structures since field welding is more expensive than bolts. For normal spans of 18' to 24' figure 6 to 7 connections per ton.

Trusses — For welded trusses add 4% to weight of main members for connections. Up to 15% less steel can be expected in a welded truss compared to one that is shop bolted. Cost of erection is the same whether shop bolted or welded.

General — Typical electrodes for structural steel welding are E6010, E6011, E60T and E70T. Typical buildings vary between 2# to 8# of weld rod per

ton of steel. Buildings utilizing continuous design require about three times as much welding as conventional welded structures. In estimating field erection by welding, it is best to use the average linear feet of weld per ton to arrive at the welding cost per ton. The type, size and position of the weld will have a direct bearing on the cost per linear foot. A typical field welder will deposit 1.8# to 2# of weld rod per hour manually. Using semiautomatic methods can increase production by as much as 50% to 75%.

R051223-10 Structural Steel

The bare material prices for structural steel, shown in the unit cost sections of the book, are for 100 tons of shop-fabricated structural steel and include:
1. Mill base price of structural steel
2. Mill scrap/grade/size/length extras
3. Mill delivery to a metals service center (warehouse)
4. Service center storage and handling
5. Service center delivery to a fabrication shop
6. Shop storage and handling
7. Shop drafting/detailing
8. Shop fabrication
9. Shop coat of primer paint
10. Shop listing
11. Shop delivery to the job site

In unit cost sections of the book that contain items for field fabrication of steel components, the bare material cost of steel includes:
1. Mill base price of structural steel
2. Mill scrap/grade/size/length extras
3. Mill delivery to a metals service center (warehouse)
4. Service center storage and handling
5. Service center delivery to the job site

R051223-15 Structural Steel Estimating for Repair and Remodeling Projects

The correct approach to estimating structural steel is dependent upon the amount of steel required for the particular project. If the project is a sizable addition to a building, the data can be used directly from the cost data book. This is not the case however if the project requires a small amount of steel, for instance to reinforce existing roof or floor structural systems. To better understand this, please refer to the unit price line for a W16x31 beam with bolted connections. Assume your project requires the reinforcement of the structural members of the roof system of a 3 story building required for the installation a new piece of HVAC equipment. The project will need 4 pieces of W16x31 that are 30' long. After pricing this 120 L.F. job using the unit prices for a W16x31, an analysis will reveal that the price is wholly inadequate.

The first problem is apparent if you examine the amount of steel that can be installed per day. The unit price line indicates 900 linear feet per day can be installed by a 5 man crew with an 90 ton crane. This productivity is correct for new construction but certainly is not for repair and remodeling work. Installation of new structural steel considers that each member is installed from the foundation to the roof of the structure in a planned and systematic manner with a crane having unrestricted access to all parts of the project. Additionally each connection is planned and detailed with full field access for fit-up and final bolting. The erection is planned and progresses such that interferences and conflicts with other structural members are minimized, if not completely eliminated. All of these assumptions are clearly not the case with a repair and remodeling job, and a significant decrease in the stated productivity will be observed.

A crane will certainly be needed to lift the members into the general area of the project but in most cases will not be able to place the beams into

their final position. An opening in the existing roof may not be large enough to permit the beams to pass through and it may be necessary to bring them into the building through existing windows or doors. Moving the beams to the actual area where they will be installed may involve hand labor and the use of dollies. Finally, hoists and/or jacks may be needed for final positioning.

The connection of new members to existing can often be accomplished by field bolting with accurate field measurements and good planning but in many cases access to both sides of existing members is not possible and field welding becomes the only alternative. In addition to the cost of the actual welding, protection of existing finishes, systems and structure and fire protection must be considered.

New beams can never be installed tight to the existing decks or floors which they must support and the use of shims and tack welding becomes necessary. Additionally, further planning and cost is involved in assuring that existing loads are minimized during the installation and shimming process.

It is apparent that installation of structural steel as part of a repair and remodeling project involves more than simply installing the members and estimating the cost in the same manner as new construction. The best procedure for estimating the total cost is adequate planning and coordination of each process and activity that will be needed. Unit costs for the materials, labor and equipment can then be attached to each needed activity and a final, complete price can be determined.

R053100-10   Decking Descriptions

General - All Deck Products

Steel deck is made by cold forming structural grade sheet steel into a repeating pattern of parallel ribs. The strength and stiffness of the panels are the result of the ribs and the material properties of the steel. Deck lengths can be varied to suit job conditions, but because of shipping considerations, are usually less than 40 feet. Standard deck width varies with the product used but full sheets are usually 12", 18", 24", 30", or 36". Deck is typically furnished in a standard width with the ends cut square. Any cutting for width, such as at openings or for angular fit, is done at the job site.

Deck is typically attached to the building frame with arc puddle welds, self-drilling screws, or powder or pneumatically driven pins. Sheet to sheet fastening is done with screws, button punching (crimping), or welds.

Composite Floor Deck

After installation and adequate fastening, floor deck serves several purposes. It (a) acts as a working platform, (b) stabilizes the frame, (c) serves as a concrete form for the slab, and (d) reinforces the slab to carry the design loads applied during the life of the building. Composite decks are distinguished by the presence of shear connector devices as part of the deck. These devices are designed to mechanically lock the concrete and deck together so that the concrete and the deck work together to carry subsequent floor loads. These shear connector devices can be rolled-in embossments, lugs, holes, or wires welded to the panels. The deck profile can also be used to interlock concrete and steel.

Composite deck finishes are either galvanized (zinc coated) or phosphatized/painted. Galvanized deck has a zinc coating on both the top and bottom surfaces. The phosphatized/painted deck has a bare (phosphatized) top surface that will come into contact with the concrete. This bare top surface can be expected to develop rust before the concrete is placed. The bottom side of the deck has a primer coat of paint.

Composite floor deck is normally installed so the panel ends do not overlap on the supporting beams. Shear lugs or panel profile shape often prevent a tight metal to metal fit if the panel ends overlap; the air gap caused by overlapping will prevent proper fusion with the structural steel supports when the panel end laps are shear stud welded.

Adequate end bearing of the deck must be obtained as shown on the drawings. If bearing is actually less in the field than shown on the drawings, further investigation is required.

Roof Deck

Roof deck is not designed to act compositely with other materials. Roof deck acts alone in transferring horizontal and vertical loads into the building frame. Roof deck rib openings are usually narrower than floor deck rib openings. This provides adequate support of rigid thermal insulation board.

Roof deck is typically installed to endlap approximately 2" over supports. However, it can be butted (or lapped more than 2") to solve field fit problems. Since designers frequently use the installed deck system as part of the horizontal bracing system (the deck as a diaphragm), any fastening substitution or change should be approved by the designer. Continuous perimeter support of the deck is necessary to limit edge deflection in the finished roof and may be required for diaphragm shear transfer.

Standard roof deck finishes are galvanized or primer painted. The standard factory applied paint for roof deck is a primer paint and is not intended to weather for extended periods of time. Field painting or touching up of abrasions and deterioration of the primer coat or other protective finishes is the responsibility of the contractor.

Cellular Deck

Cellular deck is made by attaching a bottom steel sheet to a roof deck or composite floor deck panel. Cellular deck can be used in the same manner as floor deck. Electrical, telephone, and data wires are easily run through the chase created between the deck panel and the bottom sheet.

When used as part of the electrical distribution system, the cellular deck must be installed so that the ribs line up and create a smooth cell transition at abutting ends. The joint that occurs at butting cell ends must be taped or otherwise sealed to prevent wet concrete from seeping into the cell. Cell interiors must be free of welding burrs, or other sharp intrusions, to prevent damage to wires.

When used as a roof deck, the bottom flat plate is usually left exposed to view. Care must be maintained during erection to keep good alignment and prevent damage.

Cellular deck is sometimes used with the flat plate on the top side to provide a flat working surface. Installation of the deck for this purpose requires special methods for attachment to the frame because the flat plate, now on the top, can prevent direct access to the deck material that is bearing on the structural steel. It may be advisable to treat the flat top surface to prevent slipping.

Cellular deck is always furnished galvanized or painted over galvanized.

Form Deck

Form deck can be any floor or roof deck product used as a concrete form. Connections to the frame are by the same methods used to anchor floor and roof deck. Welding washers are recommended when welding deck that is less than 20 gauge thickness.

Form deck is furnished galvanized, prime painted, or uncoated. Galvanized deck must be used for those roof deck systems where form deck is used to carry a lightweight insulating concrete fill.

824

Wood, Plastics & Comp.   R0611 Wood Framing

R061110-30   Lumber Product Material Prices

The price of forest products fluctuates widely from location to location and from season to season depending upon economic conditions. The bare material prices in the unit cost sections of the book show the National Average material prices in effect Jan. 1 of this book year. It must be noted that lumber prices in general may change significantly during the year.

Availability of certain items depends upon geographic location and must be checked prior to firm-price bidding.

Wood, Plastics & Comp.   R0616 Sheathing

R061636-20   Plywood

There are two types of plywood used in construction: interior, which is moisture-resistant but not waterproofed, and exterior, which is waterproofed.

The grade of the exterior surface of the plywood sheets is designated by the first letter: A, for smooth surface with patches allowed; B, for solid surface with patches and plugs allowed; C, which may be surface plugged or may have knot holes up to 1″ wide; and D, which is used only for interior type plywood and may have knot holes up to 2-1/2″ wide. "Structural Grade" is specifically designed for engineered applications such as box beams. All CC & DD grades have roof and floor spans marked on them.

Underlayment-grade plywood runs from 1/4″ to 1-1/4″ thick. Thicknesses 5/8″ and over have optional tongue and groove joints which eliminate the need for blocking the edges. Underlayment 19/32″ and over may be referred to as Sturd-i-Floor.

The price of plywood can fluctuate widely due to geographic and economic conditions.

Typical uses for various plywood grades are as follows:

AA-AD Interior — cupboards, shelving, paneling, furniture

BB Plyform — concrete form plywood

CDX — wall and roof sheathing

Structural — box beams, girders, stressed skin panels

AA-AC Exterior — fences, signs, siding, soffits, etc.

Underlayment — base for resilient floor coverings

Overlaid HDO — high density for concrete forms & highway signs

Overlaid MDO — medium density for painting, siding, soffits & signs

303 Siding — exterior siding, textured, striated, embossed, etc.

Thermal & Moist. Protec.   R0751 Built-Up Bituminous Roofing

R075113-20   Built-Up Roofing

Asphalt is available in kegs of 100 lbs. each; coal tar pitch in 560 lb. kegs. Prepared roofing felts are available in a wide range of sizes, weights and characteristics. However, the most commonly used are #15 (432 S.F. per roll, 13 lbs. per square) and #30 (216 S.F. per roll, 27 lbs. per square).

Inter-ply bitumen varies from 24 lbs. per sq. (asphalt) to 30 lbs. per sq. (coal tar) per ply, MF4@ 25%. Flood coat bitumen also varies from 60 lbs. per sq. (asphalt) to 75 lbs. per sq. (coal tar), MF4@ 25%. Expendable equipment (mops, brooms, screeds, etc.) runs about 16% of the bitumen cost. For new, inexperienced crews this factor may be much higher.

Rigid insulation board is typically applied in two layers. The first is mechanically attached to nailable decks or spot or solid mopped to non-nailable decks; the second layer is then spot or solid mopped to the first layer. Membrane application follows the insulation, except in protected membrane roofs, where the membrane goes down first and the insulation on top, followed with ballast (stone or concrete pavers). Insulation and related labor costs are NOT included in prices for built-up roofing.

Reference Tables

Thermal & Moist. Protec. | **R0752 Modified Bituminous Membrane Roofing**

R075213-30   Modified Bitumen Roofing

The cost of modified bitumen roofing is highly dependent on the type of installation that is planned. Installation is based on the type of modifier used in the bitumen. The two most popular modifiers are atactic polypropylene (APP) and styrene butadiene styrene (SBS). The modifiers are added to heated bitumen during the manufacturing process to change its characteristics. A polyethylene, polyester or fiberglass reinforcing sheet is then sandwiched between layers of this bitumen. When completed, the result is a pre-assembled, built-up roof that has increased elasticity and weatherablility. Some manufacturers include a surfacing material such as ceramic or mineral granules, metal particles or sand.

The preferred method of adhering SBS-modified bitumen roofing to the substrate is with hot-mopped asphalt (much the same as built-up roofing). This installation method requires a tar kettle/pot to heat the asphalt, as well as the labor, tools and equipment necessary to distribute and spread the hot asphalt.

The alternative method for applying APP and SBS modified bitumen is as follows. A skilled installer uses a torch to melt a small pool of bitumen off the membrane. This pool must form across the entire roll for proper adhesion. The installer must unroll the roofing at a pace slow enough to melt the bitumen, but fast enough to prevent damage to the rest of the membrane.

Modified bitumen roofing provides the advantages of both built-up and single-ply roofing. Labor costs are reduced over those of built-up roofing because only a single ply is necessary. The elasticity of single-ply roofing is attained with the reinforcing sheet and polymer modifiers. Modifieds have some self-healing characteristics and because of their multi-layer construction, they offer the reliability and safety of built-up roofing.

Thermal & Moist. Protec. | **R0784 Firestopping**

R078413-30   Firestopping

Firestopping is the sealing of structural, mechanical, electrical and other penetrations through fire-rated assemblies. The basic components of firestop systems are safing insulation and firestop sealant on both sides of wall penetrations and the top side of floor penetrations.

Pipe penetrations are assumed to be through concrete, grout, or joint compound and can be sleeved or unsleeved. Costs for the penetrations and sleeves are not included. An annular space of 1" is assumed. Escutcheons are not included.

Metallic pipe is assumed to be copper, aluminum, cast iron or similar metallic material. Insulated metallic pipe is assumed to be covered with a thermal insulating jacket of varying thickness and materials.

Non-metallic pipe is assumed to be PVC, CPVC, FR Polypropylene or similar plastic piping material. Intumescent firestop sealant or wrap strips are included. Collars on both sides of wall penetrations and a sheet metal plate on the underside of floor penetrations are included.

Ductwork is assumed to be sheet metal, stainless steel or similar metallic material. Duct penetrations are assumed to be through concrete, grout or joint compound. Costs for penetrations and sleeves are not included. An annular space of 1/2" is assumed.

Multi-trade openings include costs for sheet metal forms, firestop mortar, wrap strips, collars and sealants as necessary.

Structural penetrations joints are assumed to be 1/2" or less. CMU walls are assumed to be within 1-1/2" of metal deck. Drywall walls are assumed to be tight to the underside of metal decking.

Metal panel, glass or curtain wall systems include a spandrel area of 5' filled with mineral wool foil-faced insulation. Fasteners and stiffeners are included.

Openings — R0813 Metal Doors

R081313-20   Steel Door Selection Guide

Standard steel doors are classified into four levels, as recommended by the Steel Door Institute in the chart below. Each of the four levels offers a range of construction models and designs, to meet architectural requirements for preference and appearance, including full flush, seamless, and stile & rail. Recommended minimum gauge requirements are also included.

For complete standard steel door construction specifications and available sizes, refer to the Steel Door Institute Technical Data Series, ANSI A250.8-98 (SDI-100), and ANSI A250.4-94 Test Procedure and Acceptance Criteria for Physical Endurance of Steel Door and Hardware Reinforcements.

Level		Model	Construction	For Full Flush or Seamless		
				Min. Gauge	Thickness (in)	Thickness (mm)
I	Standard Duty	1	Full Flush	20	0.032	0.8
		2	Seamless			
II	Heavy Duty	1	Full Flush	18	0.042	1.0
		2	Seamless			
III	Extra Heavy Duty	1	Full Flush	16	0.053	1.3
		2	Seamless			
		3	*Stile & Rail			
IV	Maximum Duty	1	Full Flush	14	0.067	1.6
		2	Seamless			

*Stiles & rails are 16 gauge; flush panels, when specified, are 18 gauge

Openings — R0851 Metal Windows

R085123-10   Steel Sash

Ironworker crew will erect 25 S.F. or 1.3 sash unit per hour, whichever is less.

Mechanic will point 30 L.F. per hour.

Painter will paint 90 S.F. per coat per hour.

Glazier production depends on light size.

Allow 1 lb. special steel sash putty per 16″ x 20″ light.

Openings — R0853 Plastic Windows

R085313-20   Replacement Windows

Replacement windows are typically measured per United Inch.

United Inches are calculated by rounding the width and height of the window opening up to the nearest inch, then adding the two figures.

The labor cost for replacement windows includes removal of sash, existing sash balance or weights, parting bead where necessary and installation of new window.

Debris hauling and dump fees are not included.

R087110-10   Hardware Finishes

This table describes hardware finishes used throughout the industry. It also shows the base metal and the respective symbols in the three predominate systems of identification. Many of these are used in pricing descriptions in Division Eight.

US″	BMHA*	CDN	Base	Description
US P	600	CP	Steel	Primed for Painting
US 1B	601	C1B	Steel	Bright Black Japanned
US 2C	602	C2C	Steel	Zinc Plated
US 2G	603	C2G	Steel	Zinc Plated
US 3	605	C3	Brass	Bright Brass, Clear Coated
US 4	606	C4	Brass	Satin Brass, Clear Coated
US 5	609	C5	Brass	Satin Brass, Blackened, Satin Relieved, Clear Coated
US 7	610	C7	Brass	Satin Brass, Blackened, Bright Relived, Clear Coated
US 9	611	C9	Bronze	Bright Bronze, Clear Coated
US 10	612	C10	Bronze	Satin Bronze, Clear Coated
US 10A	641	C10A	Steel	Antiqued Bronze, Oiled and Lacquered
US 10B	613	C10B	Bronze	Antiqued Bronze, Oiled
US 11	616	C11	Bronze	Satin Bronze, Blackened, Satin Relieved, Clear Coated
US 14	618	C14	Brass/Bronze	Bright Nickel Plated, Clear Coated
US 15	619	C15	Brass/Bronze	Satin Nickel, Clear Coated
US 15A	620	C15A	Brass/Bronze	Satin Nickel Plated, Blackened, Satin Relieved, Clear Coated
US 17A	621	C17A	Brass/Bronze	Nickel Plated, Blackened, Relieved, Clear Coated
US 19	622	C19	Brass/Bronze	Flat Black Coated
US 20	623	C20	Brass/Bronze	Statuary Bronze, Light
US 20A	624	C20A	Brass/Bronze	Statuary Bronze, Dark
US 26	625	C26	Brass/Bronze	Bright Chromium
US 26D	626	C26D	Brass/Bronze	Satin Chromium
US 20	627	C27	Aluminum	Satin Aluminum Clear
US 28	628	C28	Aluminum	Anodized Dull Aluminum
US 32	629	C32	Stainless Steel	Bright Stainless Steel
US 32D	630	C32D	Stainless Steel	Stainless Steel
US 3	632	C3	Steel	Bright Brass Plated, Clear Coated
US 4	633	C4	Steel	Satin Brass, Clear Coated
US 7	636	C7	Steel	Satin Brass Plated, Blackened, Bright Relieved, Clear Coated
US 9	637	C9	Steel	Bright Bronze Plated, Clear Coated
US 5	638	C5	Steel	Satin Brass Plated, Blackened, Bright Relieved, Clear Coated
US 10	639	C10	Steel	Satin Bronze Plated, Clear Coated
US 10B	640	C10B	Steel	Antique Bronze, Oiled
US 10A	641	C10A	Steel	Antiqued Bronze, Oiled and Lacquered
US 11	643	C11	Steel	Satin Bronze Plated, Blackened, Bright Relieved, Clear Coated
US 14	645	C14	Steel	Bright Nickel Plated, Clear Coated
US 15	646	C15	Steel	Satin Nickel Plated, Clear Coated
US 15A	647	C15A	Steel	Nickel Plated, Blackened, Bright Relieved, Clear Coated
US 17A	648	C17A	Steel	Nickel Plated, Blackened, Relieved, Clear Coated
US 20	649	C20	Steel	Statuary Bronze, Light
US 20A	650	C20A	Steel	Statuary Bronze, Dark
US 26	651	C26	Steel	Bright Chromium Plated
US 26D	652	C26D	Steel	Satin Chromium Plated

* - BMHA Builders Hardware Manufacturing Association
″ - US Equivalent
^ - Canadian Equivalent
Japanning is imitating Asian lacquer work

Openings   R0871 Door Hardware

R087120-10   Hinges

All closer equipped doors should have ball bearing hinges. Lead lined or extremely heavy doors require special strength hinges. Usually 1-1/2 pair of hinges are used per door up to 7'-6" high openings. Table below shows typical hinge requirements.

Use Frequency	Type Hinge Required	Type of Opening	Type of Structure
High	Heavy weight	Entrances	Banks, Office buildings, Schools, Stores & Theaters
	ball bearing	Toilet Rooms	Office buildings and Schools
Average	Standard	Entrances	Dwellings
	weight	Corridors	Office buildings and Schools
	ball bearing	Toilet Rooms	Stores
Low	Plain bearing	Interior	Dwellings

Door Thickness	Weight of Doors in Pounds per Square Foot				
	White Pine	Oak	Hollow Core	Solid Core	Hollow Metal
1-3/8"	3psf	6psf	1-1/2psf	3-1/2 — 4psf	6-1/2psf
1-3/4"	3-1/2	7	2-1/2	4-1/2 — 5-1/4	6-1/2
2-1/4"	4-1/2	9	—	5-1/2 — 6-3/4	6-1/2

Openings   R0881 Glass Glazing

R088110-10   Glazing Productivity

Some glass sizes are estimated by the "united inch" (height + width). The table below shows the number of lights glazed in an eight-hour period by the crew size indicated, for glass up to 1/4" thick. Square or nearly square lights are more economical on a S.F. basis. Long slender lights will have a high S.F. installation cost. For insulated glass reduce production by 33%. For 1/2" float glass reduce production by 50%. Production time for glazing with two glaziers per day averages: 1/4" float glass 120 S.F.; 1/2" float glass 55 S.F.; 1/2" insulated glass 95 S.F.; 3/4" insulated glass 75 S.F.

Glazing Method	United Inches per Light							
	40"	60"	80"	100"	135"	165"	200"	240"
Number of Men in Crew	1	1	1	1	2	3	3	4
Industrial sash, putty	60	45	24	15	18	—	—	—
With stops, putty bed	50	36	21	12	16	8	4	3
Wood stops, rubber	40	27	15	9	11	6	3	2
Metal stops, rubber	30	24	14	9	9	6	3	2
Structural glass	10	7	4	3	—	—	—	—
Corrugated glass	12	9	7	4	4	4	3	—
Storefronts	16	15	13	11	7	6	4	4
Skylights, putty glass	60	36	21	12	16	—	—	—
Thiokol set	15	15	11	9	9	6	3	2
Vinyl set, snap on	18	18	13	12	12	7	5	4
Maximum area per light	2.8 S.F.	6.3 S.F.	11.1 S.F.	17.4 S.F.	31.6 S.F.	47 S.F.	69 S.F.	100 S.F.

R092000-50　Lath, Plaster and Gypsum Board

Gypsum board lath is available in 3/8″ thick x 16″ wide x 4′ long sheets as a base material for multi-layer plaster applications. It is also available as a base for either multi-layer or veneer plaster applications in 1/2″ and 5/8″ thick–4′ wide x 8′, 10′ or 12′ long sheets. Fasteners are screws or blued ring shank nails for wood framing and screws for metal framing.

Metal lath is available in diamond mesh pattern with flat or self-furring profiles. Paper backing is available for applications where excessive plaster waste needs to be avoided. A slotted mesh ribbed lath should be used in areas where the span between structural supports is greater than normal. Most metal lath comes in 27″ x 96″ sheets. Diamond mesh weighs 1.75, 2.5 or 3.4 pounds per square yard, slotted mesh lath weighs 2.75 or 3.4 pounds per square yard. Metal lath can be nailed, screwed or tied in place.

Many **accessories** are available. Corner beads, flat reinforcing strips, casing beads, control and expansion joints, furring brackets and channels are some examples. Note that accessories are not included in plaster or stucco line items.

Plaster is defined as a material or combination of materials that when mixed with a suitable amount of water, forms a plastic mass or paste. When applied to a surface, the paste adheres to it and subsequently hardens, preserving in a rigid state the form or texture imposed during the period of elasticity.

Gypsum plaster is made from ground calcined gypsum. It is mixed with aggregates and water for use as a base coat plaster.

Vermiculite plaster is a fire-retardant plaster covering used on steel beams, concrete slabs and other heavy construction materials. Vermiculite is a group name for certain clay minerals, hydrous silicates or aluminum, magnesium and iron that have been expanded by heat.

Perlite plaster is a plaster using perlite as an aggregate instead of sand. Perlite is a volcanic glass that has been expanded by heat.

Gauging plaster is a mix of gypsum plaster and lime putty that when applied produces a quick drying finish coat.

Veneer plaster is a one or two component gypsum plaster used as a thin finish coat over special gypsum board.

Keenes cement is a white cementitious material manufactured from gypsum that has been burned at a high temperature and ground to a fine powder. Alum is added to accelerate the set. The resulting plaster is hard and strong and accepts and maintains a high polish, hence it is used as a finishing plaster.

Stucco is a Portland cement based plaster used primarily as an exterior finish.

Plaster is used on both interior and exterior surfaces. Generally it is applied in multiple-coat systems. A three-coat system uses the terms scratch, brown and finish to identify each coat. A two-coat system uses base and finish to describe each coat. Each type of plaster and application system has attributes that are chosen by the designer to best fit the intended use.

Gypsum Plaster Quantities for 100 S.Y.	2 Coat, 5/8″ Thick		3 Coat, 3/4″ Thick		
	Base	Finish	Scratch	Brown	Finish
	1:3 Mix	2:1 Mix	1:2 Mix	1:3 Mix	2:1 Mix
Gypsum plaster	1,300 lb.		1,350 lb.	650 lb.	
Sand	1.75 C.Y.		1.85 C.Y.	1.35 C.Y.	
Finish hydrated lime		340 lb.			340 lb.
Gauging plaster		170 lb.			170 lb.

Vermiculite or Perlite Plaster Quantities for 100 S.Y.	2 Coat, 5/8″ Thick		3 Coat, 3/4″ Thick		
	Base	Finish	Scratch	Brown	Finish
Gypsum plaster	1,250 lb.		1,450 lb.	800 lb.	
Vermiculite or perlite	7.8 bags		8.0 bags	3.3 bags	
Finish hydrated lime		340 lb.			340 lb.
Gauging plaster		170 lb.			170 lb.

Stucco–Three-Coat System Quantities for 100 S.Y.	On Wood Frame	On Masonry
Portland cement	29 bags	21 bags
Sand	2.6 C.Y.	2.0 C.Y.
Hydrated lime	180 lb.	120 lb.

R092910-10   Levels of Gypsum Drywall Finish

In the past, contract documents often used phrases such as "industry standard" and "workmanlike finish" to specify the expected quality of gypsum board wall and ceiling installations. The vagueness of these descriptions led to unacceptable work and disputes.

In order to resolve this problem, four major trade associations concerned with the manufacture, erection, finish and decoration of gypsum board wall and ceiling systems have developed an industry-wide *Recommended Levels of Gypsum Board Finish*.

The finish of gypsum board walls and ceilings for specific final decoration is dependent on a number of factors. A primary consideration is the location of the surface and the degree of decorative treatment desired. Painted and unpainted surfaces in warehouses and other areas where appearance is normally not critical may simply require the taping of wallboard joints and 'spotting' of fastener heads. Blemish-free, smooth, monolithic surfaces often intended for painted and decorated walls and ceilings in habitated structures, ranging from single-family dwellings through monumental buildings, require additional finishing prior to the application of the final decoration.

Other factors to be considered in determining the level of finish of the gypsum board surface are (1) the type of angle of surface illumination (both natural and artificial lighting), and (2) the paint and method of application or the type and finish of wallcovering specified as the final decoration. Critical lighting conditions, gloss paints, and thin wall coverings require a higher level of gypsum board finish than do heavily textured surfaces which are subsequently painted or surfaces which are to be decorated with heavy grade wall coverings.

The following descriptions were developed jointly by the Association of the Wall and Ceiling Industries-International (AWCI), Ceiling & Interior Systems Construction Association (CISCA), Gypsum Association (GA), and Painting and Decorating Contractors of America (PDCA) as a guide.

Level 0: Used in temporary construction or wherever the final decoration has not been determined. Unfinished. No taping, finishing or corner beads are required. Also could be used where non-predecorated panels will be used in demountable-type partitions that are to be painted as a final finish. .

Level 1: Frequently used in plenum areas above ceilings, in attics, in areas where the assembly would generally be concealed, or in building service corridors and other areas not normally open to public view. Some degree of sound and smoke control is provided; in some geographic areas, this level is referred to as "fire-taping," although this level of finish does not typically meet fire-resistant assembly requirements. Where a fire resistance rating is required for the gypsum board assembly, details of construction should be in accordance with reports of fire tests of assemblies that have met the requirements of the fire rating acceptable.

All joints and interior angles shall have tape embedded in joint compound. Accessories are optional at specifier discretion in corridors and other areas with pedestrian traffic. Tape and fastener heads need not be covered with joint compound. Surface shall be free of excess joint compound. Tool marks and ridges are acceptable.

Level 2: It may be specified for standard gypsum board surfaces in garages, warehouse storage, or other similar areas where surface appearance is not of primary importance.

All joints and interior angles shall have tape embedded in joint compound and shall be immediately wiped with a joint knife or trowel, leaving a thin coating of joint compound over all joints and interior angles. Fastener heads and accessories shall be covered with a coat of joint compound. Surface shall be free of excess joint compound. Tool marks and ridges are acceptable.

Level 3: Typically used in areas that are to receive heavy texture (spray or hand applied) finishes before final painting, or where

commercial-grade (heavy duty) wall coverings are to be applied as the final decoration. This level of finish should not be used where smooth painted surfaces or where lighter weight wall coverings are specified. The prepared surface shall be coated with a drywall primer prior to the application of final finishes.

All joints and interior angles shall have tape embedded in joint compound and shall be immediately wiped with a joint knife or trowel, leaving a thin coating of joint compound over all joints and interior angles. One additional coat of joint compound shall be applied over all joints and interior angles. Fastener heads and accessories shall be covered with two separate coats of joint compound. All joint compounds shall be smooth and free of tool marks and ridges. The prepared surface shall be covered with a drywall primer prior to the application of the final decoration.

Level 4: This level should be used where residential grade (light duty) wall coverings, flat paints, or light textures are to be applied. The prepared surface shall be coated with a drywall primer prior to the application of final finishes. Release agents for wall coverings are specifically formulated to minimize damage if coverings are subsequently removed.

The weight, texture, and sheen level of the wall covering material selected should be taken into consideration when specifying wall coverings over this level of drywall treatment. Joints and fasteners must be sufficiently concealed if the wall covering material is lightweight, contains limited pattern, has a glossy finish, or has any combination of these features. In critical lighting areas, flat paints applied over light textures tend to reduce joint photographing. Gloss, semi-gloss, and enamel paints are not recommended over this level of finish.

All joints and interior angles shall have tape embedded in joint compound and shall be immediately wiped with a joint knife or trowel, leaving a thin coating of joint compound over all joints and interior angles. In addition, two separate coats of joint compound shall be applied over all flat joints and one separate coat of joint compound applied over interior angles. Fastener heads and accessories shall be covered with three separate coats of joint compound. All joint compounds shall be smooth and free of tool marks and ridges. The prepared surface shall be covered with a drywall primer like Sheetrock first coat prior to the application of the final decoration.

Level 5: The highest quality finish is the most effective method to provide a uniform surface and minimize the possibility of joint photographing and of fasteners showing through the final decoration. This level of finish is required where gloss, semi-gloss, or enamel is specified; when flat joints are specified over an untextured surface; or where critical lighting conditions occur. The prepared surface shall be coated with a drywall primer prior to the application of final decoration.

All joints and interior angles shall have tape embedded in joint compound and be immediately wiped with a joint knife or trowel, leaving a thin coating of joint compound over all joints and interior angles. Two separate coats of joint compound shall be applied over all flat joints and one separate coat of joint compound applied over interior angles. Fastener heads and accessories shall be covered with three separate coats of joint compound.

A thin skim coat of joint compound shall be trowel applied to the entire surface. Excess compound is immediately troweled off, leaving a film or skim coating of compound completely covering the paper. As an alternative to a skim coat, a material manufactured especially for this purpose may be applied such as Sheetrock Tuff-Hide primer surfacer. The surface must be smooth and free of tool marks and ridges. The prepared surface shall be covered with a drywall primer prior to the application of the final decoration.

R142000-10   Freight Elevators

Capacities run from 2,000 lbs. to over 100,000 lbs. with 3,000 lbs. to 10,000 lbs. most common. Travel speeds are generally lower and control less intricate than on passenger elevators. Costs in the unit price sections are for hydraulic and geared elevators.

R142000-20   Elevator Selective Costs   See R142000-40 for cost development.

	Passenger		Freight		Hospital	
A. Base Unit	Hydraulic	Electric	Hydraulic	Electric	Hydraulic	Electric
Capacity	1,500 lb.	2,000 lb.	2,000 lb.	4,000 lb.	4,000 lb.	4,000 lb.
Speed	100 F.P.M.	200 F.P.M.	100 F.P.M.	200 F.P.M.	100 F.P.M.	200 F.P.M.
#Stops/Travel Ft.	2/12	4/40	2/20	4/40	2/20	4/40
Push Button Oper.	Yes	Yes	Yes	Yes	Yes	Yes
Telephone Box & Wire	"	"	"	"	"	"
Emergency Lighting	"	"	No	No	"	"
Cab	Plastic Lam. Walls	Plastic Lam. Walls	Painted Steel	Painted Steel	Plastic Lam. Walls	Plastic Lam. Walls
Cove Lighting	Yes	Yes	No	No	Yes	Yes
Floor	V.C.T.	V.C.T.	Wood w/Safety Treads	Wood w/Safety Treads	V.C.T.	V.C.T.
Doors, & Speedside Slide	Yes	Yes	Yes	Yes	Yes	Yes
Gates, Manual	No	No	No	No	No	No
Signals, Lighted Buttons	Car and Hall	Car and Hall	Car and Hall	Car and Hall	Car and Hall	Car and Hall
O.H. Geared Machine	N.A.	Yes	N.A.	Yes	N.A.	Yes
Variable Voltage Contr.	"	"	N.A.	"	"	"
Emergency Alarm	Yes	"	Yes	"	Yes	"
Class "A" Loading	N.A.	N.A.	"	"	N.A.	N.A.

R142000-30   Passenger Elevators

Electric elevators are used generally but hydraulic elevators can be used for lifts up to 70' and where large capacities are required. Hydraulic speeds are limited to 200 F.P.M. but cars are self leveling at the stops. On low rises, hydraulic installation runs about 15% less than standard electric types but on higher rises this installation cost advantage is reduced. Maintenance of hydraulic type is about the same as electric type but underground portion is not included in the maintenance contract.

In electric elevators there are several control systems available, the choice of which will be based upon elevator use, size, speed and cost criteria. The two types of drives are geared for low speeds and gearless for 450 F.P.M. and over.

The tables on the preceding pages illustrate typical installed costs of the various types of elevators available.

R142000-40   Elevator Cost Development

To price a new car or truck from the factory, you must start with the manufacturer's basic model, then add or exchange optional equipment and features. The same is true for pricing elevators.

Requirement: One-passenger elevator, five-story hydraulic, 2,500 lb. capacity, 12' floor to floor, speed 150 F.P.M., emergency power switching and maintenance contract.

Example:

Description	Adjustment
A. Base Elevator: Hydraulic Passenger, 1500 lb. Capacity, 100 fpm, 2 Stops, Standard Finish	1 Ea.
B. Capacity Adjustment (2,500 lb.)	1 Ea.
C. Excess Travel Adjustment: 48' Total Travel (4 x 12') minus 12' Base Unit Travel =	36 V.L.F.
D. Stops Adjustment: 5 Total Stops minus 2 Stops (Base Unit) =	3 Stops
E. Speed Adjustment (150 F.P.M.)	1 Ea.
F. Options:	
1. Intercom Service	1 Ea.
2. Emergency Power Switching, Automatic	1 Ea.
3. Stainless Steel Entrance Doors	5 Ea.
4. Maintenance Contract (12 Months)	1 Ea.
5. Position Indicator for main floor level (none indicated in Base Unit)	1 Ea.

R220102-20   Labor Adjustment Factors

Labor Adjustment Factors are provided for Divisions 21, 22, and 23 to assist the mechanical estimator account for the various complexities and special conditions of any particular project. While a single percentage has been entered on each line of Division 22 01 02.20, it should be understood that these are just suggested midpoints of ranges of values commonly used by mechanical estimators. They may be increased or decreased depending on the severity of the special conditions.

The group for "existing occupied buildings", has been the subject of requests for explanation. Actually there are two stages to this group: buildings that are existing and "finished" but unoccupied, and those that also are occupied. Buildings that are "finished" may result in higher labor costs due to the

workers having to be more careful not to damage finished walls, ceilings, floors, etc. and may necessitate special protective coverings and barriers. Also corridor bends and doorways may not accommodate long pieces of pipe or larger pieces of equipment. Work above an already hung ceiling can be very time consuming. The addition of occupants may force the work to be done on premium time (nights and/or weekends), eliminate the possible use of some preferred tools such as pneumatic drivers, powder charged drivers etc. The estimator should evaluate the access to the work area and just how the work is going to be accomplished to arrive at an increase in labor costs over "normal" new construction productivity.

R220105-10   Demolition (Selective vs. Removal for Replacement)

Demolition can be divided into two basic categories.

One type of demolition involves the removal of material with no concern for its replacement. The labor-hours to estimate this work are found under "Selective Demolition" in the Fire Protection, Plumbing and HVAC Divisions. It is selective in that individual items or all the material installed as a system or trade grouping such as plumbing or heating systems are removed. This may be accomplished by the easiest way possible, such as sawing, torch cutting, or sledge hammer as well as simple unbolting.

The second type of demolition is the removal of some item for repair or replacement. This removal may involve careful draining, opening of unions,

disconnecting and tagging of electrical connections, capping of pipes/ducts to prevent entry of debris or leakage of the material contained as well as transport of the item away from its in-place location to a truck/dumpster. An approximation of the time required to accomplish this type of demolition is to use half of the time indicated as necessary to install a new unit. For example; installation of a new pump might be listed as requiring 6 labor-hours so if we had to estimate the removal of the old pump we would allow an additional 3 hours for a total of 9 hours. That is, the complete replacement of a defective pump with a new pump would be estimated to take 9 labor-hours.

R221113-50   Pipe Material Considerations

1. Malleable fittings should be used for gas service.
2. Malleable fittings are used where there are stresses/strains due to expansion and vibration.
3. Cast fittings may be broken as an aid to disassembling of heating lines frozen by long use, temperature and minerals.
4. Cast iron pipe is extensively used for underground and submerged service.
5. Type M (light wall) copper tubing is available in hard temper only and is used for nonpressure and less severe applications than K and L.

6. Type L (medium wall) copper tubing, available hard or soft for interior service.
7. Type K (heavy wall) copper tubing, available in hard or soft temper for use where conditions are severe. For underground and interior service.
8. Hard drawn tubing requires fewer hangers or supports but should not be bent. Silver brazed fittings are recommended, however soft solder is normally used.
9. Type DMV (very light wall) copper tubing designed for drainage, waste and vent plus other non-critical pressure services.

Domestic/Imported Pipe and Fittings Cost

The prices shown in this publication for steel/cast iron pipe and steel, cast iron, malleable iron fittings are based on domestic production sold at the normal trade discounts. The above listed items of foreign manufacture may be available at prices of 1/3 to 1/2 those shown. Some imported items after minor machining or finishing operations are being sold as domestic to further complicate the system.

Caution: Most pipe prices in this book also include a coupling and pipe hangers which for the larger sizes can add significantly to the per foot cost and should be taken into account when comparing "book cost" with quoted supplier's cost.

R224000-40   Plumbing Fixture Installation Time

Item	Rough-In	Set	Total Hours	Item	Rough-In	Set	Total Hours
Bathtub	5	5	10	Shower head only	2	1	3
Bathtub and shower, cast iron	6	6	12	Shower drain	3	1	4
Fire hose reel and cabinet	4	2	6	Shower stall, slate		15	15
Floor drain to 4 inch diameter	3	1	4	Slop sink	5	3	8
Grease trap, single, cast iron	5	3	8	Test 6 fixtures			14
Kitchen gas range		4	4	Urinal, wall	6	2	8
Kitchen sink, single	4	4	8	Urinal, pedestal or floor	6	4	10
Kitchen sink, double	6	6	12	Water closet and tank	4	3	7
Laundry tubs	4	2	6	Water closet and tank, wall hung	5	3	8
Lavatory wall hung	5	3	8	Water heater, 45 gals. gas, automatic	5	2	7
Lavatory pedestal	5	3	8	Water heaters, 65 gals. gas, automatic	5	2	7
Shower and stall	6	4	10	Water heaters, electric, plumbing only	4	2	6

Fixture prices in front of book are based on the cost per fixture set in place. The rough-in cost, which must be added for each fixture, includes carrier, if required, some supply, waste and vent pipe connecting fittings and stops. The lengths of rough-in pipe are nominal runs which would connect to the larger runs and stacks. The supply runs and DWV runs and stacks must be accounted for in separate entries. In the eastern half of the United States it is common for the plumber to carry these to a point 5' outside the building.

R233100-20   Ductwork

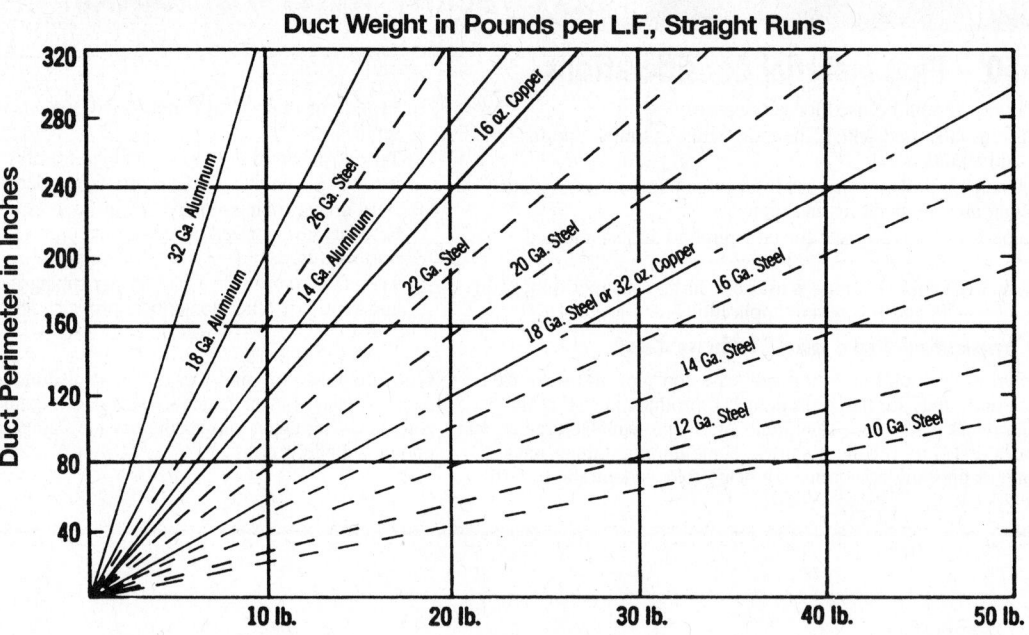

Duct Weight in Pounds per L.F., Straight Runs

Add to the above for fittings; 90° elbow is 3 L.F.; 45° elbow is 2.5 L.F.; offset is 4 L.F.; transition offset is 6 L.F.; square-to-round transition is 4 L.F.; 90° reducing elbow is 5 L.F. For bracing and waste, add 20% to aluminum and copper, 15% to steel.

R260105-30 Electrical Demolition (Removal for Replacement)

The purpose of this reference number is to provide a guide to users for electrical "removal for replacement" by applying the rule of thumb: 1/3 of new installation time (typical range from 20% to 50%) for removal. Remember to use reasonable judgment when applying the suggested percentage factor. For example:

Contractors have been requested to remove an existing fluorescent lighting fixture and replace with a new fixture utilizing energy saver lamps and electronic ballast:

In order to fully understand the extent of the project, contractors should visit the job site and estimate the time to perform the renovation work in accordance with applicable national, state and local regulation and codes.

The contractor may need to add extra labor hours to his estimate if he discovers unknown concealed conditions such as: contaminated asbestos ceiling, broken acoustical ceiling tile and need to repair, patch and touch-up paint all the damaged or disturbed areas, tasks normally assigned to general contractors. In addition, the owner could request that the contractors salvage the materials removed and turn over the materials to the owner or dispose of the materials to a reclamation station. The normal removal item is 0.5 labor hour for a lighting fixture and 1.5 labor-hours for new installation time. Revise the estimate times from 2 labor-hours work up to a minimum 4 labor-hours work for just fluorescent lighting fixture.

For removal of large concentrations of lighting fixtures in the same area, apply an "economy of scale" to reduce estimating labor hours.

Electrical   R2605 Common Work Results for Electrical

R260533-22 Conductors in Conduit

Table below lists maximum number of conductors for various sized conduit using THW, TW or THWN insulations.

Copper Wire Size	1/2"			3/4"			1"			1-1/4"			1-1/2"			2"			2-1/2"			3"		3-1/2"		4"	
	TW	THW	THWN	TW	THW	THWN	TW	THW	THWN	TW	THW	THWN	TW	THW	THWN	TW	THW	THWN	TW	THW	THWN	THW	THWN	THW	THWN	THW	THWN
#14	9	6	13	15	10	24	25	16	39	44	29	69	60	40	94	99	65	154	142	93		143		192			
#12	7	4	10	12	8	18	19	13	29	35	24	51	47	32	70	78	53	114	111	76	164	117		157			
#10	5	4	6	9	6	11	15	11	18	26	19	32	36	26	44	60	43	73	85	61	104	95	160	127		163	
#8	2	1	3	4	3	5	7	5	9	12	10	16	17	13	22	28	22	36	40	32	51	49	79	66	106	85	136
#6		1	1		2	4		4	6		7	11		10	15		16	26		23	37	36	57	48	76	62	98
#4		1	1		1	2		3	4		5	7		7	9		12	16		17	22	27	35	36	47	47	60
#3		1	1		1	1		2	3		4	6		6	8		10	13		15	19	23	29	31	39	40	51
#2		1	1		1	1		2	3		4	5		5	7		9	11		13	16	20	25	27	33	34	43
#1					1	1		1	1		3	3		4	5		6	8		9	12	14	18	19	25	25	32
1/0					1	1		1	1		2	3		3	4		5	7		8	10	12	15	16	21	21	27
2/0					1	1		1	1		1	2		3	3		5	6		7	8	10	13	14	17	18	22
3/0					1	1		1	1		1	1		2	3		4	5		6	7	9	11	12	14	15	18
4/0						1		1	1		1	1		1	2		3	4		5	6	7	9	10	12	13	15
250 kcmil								1	1		1	1		1	1		2	3		4	4	6	7	8	10	10	12
300								1	1		1	1		1	1		2	3		3	4	5	6	7	8	9	11
350									1		1	1		1	1		1	2		3	3	4	5	6	7	8	9
400											1	1		1	1		1	1		2	3	4	5	5	6	7	8
500											1	1		1	1		1	1		1	2	3	4	4	5	6	7
600												1		1	1		1	1		1	1	3	3	4	4	5	5
700														1	1		1	1		1	1	2	3	3	4	4	5
750														1	1		1	1		1	1	2	2	3	3	4	4

R312316-40　Excavating

The selection of equipment used for structural excavation and bulk excavation or for grading is determined by the following factors.

1. Quantity of material
2. Type of material
3. Depth or height of cut
4. Length of haul
5. Condition of haul road
6. Accessibility of site
7. Moisture content and dewatering requirements
8. Availability of excavating and hauling equipment

Some additional costs must be allowed for hand trimming the sides and bottom of concrete pours and other excavation below the general excavation.

Number of B.C.Y. per truck = 1.5 C.Y. bucket x 8 passes = 12 loose C.Y.

$$= 12 \times \frac{100}{118} = 10.2 \text{ B.C.Y. per truck}$$

Truck Haul Cycle:

Load truck, 8 passes	=	4 minutes
Haul distance, 1 mile	=	9 minutes
Dump time	=	2 minutes
Return, 1 mile	=	7 minutes
Spot under machine	=	1 minute
		23 minute cycle

Add the mobilization and demobilization costs to the total excavation costs. When equipment is rented for more than three days, there is often no mobilization charge by the equipment dealer. On larger jobs outside of urban areas, scrapers can move earth economically provided a dump site or fill area and adequate haul roads are available. Excavation within sheeting bracing or cofferdam bracing is usually done with a clamshell and production

When planning excavation and fill, the following should also be considered.

1. Swell factor
2. Compaction factor
3. Moisture content
4. Density requirements

A typical example for scheduling and estimating the cost of excavation of a 15′ deep basement on a dry site when the material must be hauled off the site is outlined below.

Assumptions:

1. Swell factor, 18%
2. No mobilization or demobilization
3. Allowance included for idle time and moving on job
4. No dewatering, sheeting, or bracing
5. No truck spotter or hand trimming

Fleet Haul Production per day in B.C.Y.

$$4 \text{ trucks} \times \frac{50 \text{ min. hour}}{23 \text{ min. haul cycle}} \times 8 \text{ hrs.} \times 10.2 \text{ B.C.Y.}$$

$$= 4 \times 2.2 \times 8 \times 10.2 = 718 \text{ B.C.Y./day}$$

is low, since the clamshell may have to be guided by hand between the bracing. When excavating or filling an area enclosed with a wellpoint system, add 10% to 15% to the cost to allow for restricted access. When estimating earth excavation quantities for structures, allow work space outside the building footprint for construction of the foundation and a slope of 1:1 unless sheeting is used.

R312316-45 Excavating Equipment

The table below lists THEORETICAL hourly production in C.Y./hr. bank measure for some typical excavation equipment. Figures assume 50 minute hours, 83% job efficiency, 100% operator efficiency, 90° swing and properly sized hauling units, which must be modified for adverse digging and loading conditions. Actual production costs in the front of the book average about 50% of the theoretical values listed here.

Equipment	Soil Type	B.C.Y. Weight	% Swell	1 C.Y.	1-1/2 C.Y.	2 C.Y.	2-1/2 C.Y.	3 C.Y.	3-1/2 C.Y.	4 C.Y.
Hydraulic Excavator	Moist loam, sandy clay	3400 lb.	40%	165	195	200	275	330	385	440
"Backhoe"	Sand and gravel	3100	18	140	170	225	240	285	330	380
15' Deep Cut	Common earth	2800	30	150	180	230	250	300	350	400
	Clay, hard, dense	3000	33	120	140	190	200	240	260	320
Power Shovel Optimum Cut (Ft.)	Moist loam, sandy clay	3400	40	170 (6.0)	245 (7.0)	295 (7.8)	335 (8.4)	385 (8.8)	435 (9.1)	475 (9.4)
	Sand and gravel	3100	18	165 (6.0)	225 (7.0)	275 (7.8)	325 (8.4)	375 (8.8)	420 (9.1)	460 (9.4)
	Common earth	2800	30	145 (7.8)	200 (9.2)	250 (10.2)	295 (11.2)	335 (12.1)	375 (13.0)	425 (13.8)
	Clay, hard, dense	3000	33	120 (9.0)	175 (10.7)	220 (12.2)	255 (13.3)	300 (14.2)	335 (15.1)	375 (16.0)
Drag Line Optimum Cut (Ft.)	Moist loam, sandy clay	3400	40	130 (6.6)	180 (7.4)	220 (8.0)	250 (8.5)	290 (9.0)	325 (9.5)	385 (10.0)
	Sand and gravel	3100	18	130 (6.6)	175 (7.4)	210 (8.0)	245 (8.5)	280 (9.0)	315 (9.5)	375 (10.0)
	Common earth	2800	30	110 (8.0)	160 (9.0)	190 (9.9)	220 (10.5)	250 (11.0)	280 (11.5)	310 (12.0)
	Clay, hard, dense	3000	33	90 (9.3)	130 (10.7)	160 (11.8)	190 (12.3)	225 (12.8)	250 (13.3)	280 (12.0)

				Wheel Loaders				Track Loaders		
				3 C.Y.	4 C.Y.	6 C.Y.	8 C.Y.	2-1/4 C.Y.	3 C.Y.	4 C.Y.
Loading Tractors	Moist loam, sandy clay	3400	40	260	340	510	690	135	180	250
	Sand and gravel	3100	18	245	320	480	650	130	170	235
	Common earth	2800	30	230	300	460	620	120	155	220
	Clay, hard, dense	3000	33	200	270	415	560	110	145	200
	Rock, well-blasted	4000	50	180	245	380	520	100	130	180

R312323-30 Compacting Backfill

Compaction of fill in embankments, around structures, in trenches, and under slabs is important to control settlement. Factors affecting compaction are:

1. Soil gradation
2. Moisture content
3. Equipment used
4. Depth of fill per lift
5. Density required

Production Rate:

$$\frac{1.75' \text{ plate width x 50 F.P.M. x 50 min./hr. x .67' lift}}{27 \text{ C.F. per C.Y.}} = 108.5 \text{ C.Y./hr.}$$

Production Rate for 4 Passes:

$$\frac{108.5 \text{ C.Y.}}{4 \text{ passes}} = 27.125 \text{ C.Y./hr. x 8 hrs.} = 217 \text{ C.Y./day}$$

Example:

Compact granular fill around a building foundation using a 21" wide x 24" vibratory plate in 8" lifts. Operator moves at 50 F.P.M. working a 50 minute hour to develop 95% Modified Proctor Density with 4 passes.

R314116-40   Wood Sheet Piling

Wood sheet piling may be used for depths to 20' where there is no ground water. If moderate ground water is encountered Tongue & Groove sheeting will help to keep it out. When considerable ground water is present, steel sheeting must be used.

For estimating purposes on trench excavation, sizes are as follows:

Depth	Sheeting	Wales	Braces	B.F. per S.F.
To 8'	3 x 12's	6 x 8's, 2 line	6 x 8's, @ 10'	4.0 @ 8'
8' x 12'	3 x 12's	10 x 10's, 2 line	10 x 10's, @ 9'	5.0 average
12' to 20'	3 x 12's	12 x 12's, 3 line	12 x 12's, @ 8'	7.0 average

Sheeting to be toed in at least 2' depending upon soil conditions. A five person crew with an air compressor and sheeting driver can drive and brace 440 SF/day at 8' deep, 360 SF/day at 12' deep, and 320 SF/day at 16' deep.

For normal soils, piling can be pulled in 1/3 the time to install. Pulling difficulty increases with the time in the ground. Production can be increased by high pressure jetting.

Earthwork | R3163 Drilled Caissons

R316326-60   Caissons

The three principal types of cassions are:

(1) Belled Caissons, which except for shallow depths and poor soil conditions, are generally recommended. They provide more bearing than shaft area. Because of its conical shape, no horizontal reinforcement of the bell is required.

(2) Straight Shaft Caissons are used where relatively light loads are to be supported by caissons that rest on high value bearing strata. While the shaft is larger in diameter than for belled types this is more than offset by the saving in time and labor.

(3) Keyed Caissons are used when extremely heavy loads are to be carried. A keyed or socketed caisson transfers its load into rock by a combination of end-bearing and shear reinforcing of the shaft. The most economical shaft often consists of a steel casing, a steel wide flange core and concrete. Allowable compressive stresses of .225 f'c for concrete, 16,000 psi for the wide flange core, and 9,000 psi for the steel casing are commonly used. The usual range of shaft diameter is 18" to 84". The number of sizes specified for any one project should be limited due to the problems of casing and auger storage. When hand work is to be performed, shaft diameters should not be less than 32". When inspection of borings is required a minimum shaft diameter of 30" is recommended. Concrete caissons are intended to be poured against earth excavation so permanent forms which add to cost should not be used if the excavation is clean and the earth sufficiently impervious to prevent excessive loss of concrete.

Soil Conditions for Belling		
Good	Requires Handwork	Not Recommended
Clay	Hard Shale	Silt
Sandy Clay	Limestone	Sand
Silty Clay	Sandstone	Gravel
Clayey Silt	Weathered Mica	Igneous Rock
Hard-pan		
Soft Shale		
Decomposed Rock		

Exterior Improvements | R3292 Turf & Grasses

R329219-50   Seeding

The type of grass is determined by light, shade and moisture content of soil plus intended use. Fertilizer should be disked 4" before seeding. For steep slopes disk five tons of mulch and lay two tons of hay or straw on surface per acre after seeding. Surface mulch can be staked, lightly disked or tar emulsion sprayed. Material for mulch can be wood chips, peat moss, partially rotted hay or straw, wood fibers and sprayed emulsions. Hemp seed blankets with fertilizer are also available. For spring seeding, watering is necessary. Late fall seeding may have to be reseeded in the spring. Hydraulic seeding, power mulching, and aerial seeding can be used on large areas.

R331113-80 Piping Designations

There are several systems currently in use to describe pipe and fittings. The following paragraphs will help to identify and clarify classifications of piping systems used for water distribution.

Piping may be classified by schedule. Piping schedules include 5S, 10S, 10, 20, 30, Standard, 40, 60, Extra Strong, 80, 100, 120, 140, 160 and Double Extra Strong. These schedules are dependent upon the pipe wall thickness. The wall thickness of a particular schedule may vary with pipe size.

Ductile iron pipe for water distribution is classified by Pressure Classes such as Class 150, 200, 250, 300 and 350. These classes are actually the rated water working pressure of the pipe in pounds per square inch (psi). The pipe in these pressure classes is designed to withstand the rated water working pressure plus a surge allowance of 100 psi.

The American Water Works Association (AWWA) provides standards for various types of **plastic pipe.** C-900 is the specification for polyvinyl chloride (PVC) piping used for water distribution in sizes ranging from 4″ through 12″. C-901 is the specification for polyethylene (PE) pressure pipe, tubing and fittings used for water distribution in sizes ranging from 1/2″ through 3″. C-905 is the specification for PVC piping sizes 14″ and greater.

PVC pressure-rated pipe is identified using the standard dimensional ratio (SDR) method. This method is defined by the American Society for Testing and Materials (ASTM) Standard D 2241. This pipe is available in SDR numbers 64, 41, 32.5, 26, 21, 17, and 13.5. Pipe with an SDR of 64 will have the thinnest wall while pipe with an SDR of 13.5 will have the thickest wall. When the pressure rating (PR) of a pipe is given in psi, it is based on a line supplying water at 73 degrees F.

The National Sanitation Foundation (NSF) seal of approval is applied to products that can be used with potable water. These products have been tested to ANSI/NSF Standard 14.

Valves and strainers are classified by American National Standards Institute (ANSI) Classes. These Classes are 125, 150, 200, 250, 300, 400, 600, 900, 1500 and 2500. Within each class there is an operating pressure range dependent upon temperature. Design parameters should be compared to the appropriate material dependent, pressure-temperature rating chart for accurate valve selection.

Change Orders

Change Order Considerations

A change order is a written document, usually prepared by the design professional, and signed by the owner, the architect/engineer, and the contractor. A change order states the agreement of the parties to: an addition, deletion, or revision in the work; an adjustment in the contract sum, if any; or an adjustment in the contract time, if any. Change orders, or "extras" in the construction process occur after execution of the construction contract and impact architects/engineers, contractors, and owners.

Change orders that are properly recognized and managed can ensure orderly, professional, and profitable progress for all who are involved in the project. There are many causes for change orders and change order requests. In all cases, change orders or change order requests should be addressed promptly and in a precise and prescribed manner. The following paragraphs include information regarding change order pricing and procedures.

The Causes of Change Orders

Reasons for issuing change orders include:

- Unforeseen field conditions that require a change in the work
- Correction of design discrepancies, errors, or omissions in the contract documents
- Owner-requested changes, either by design criteria, scope of work, or project objectives
- Completion date changes for reasons unrelated to the construction process
- Changes in building code interpretations, or other public authority requirements that require a change in the work
- Changes in availability of existing or new materials and products

Procedures

Properly written contract documents must include the correct change order procedures for all parties—owners, design professionals and contractors—to follow in order to avoid costly delays and litigation.

Being "in the right" is not always a sufficient or acceptable defense. The contract provisions requiring notification and documentation must be adhered to within a defined or reasonable time frame.

The appropriate method of handling change orders is by a written proposal and acceptance by all parties involved. Prior to starting work on a project, all parties should identify their authorized agents who may sign and accept change orders, as well as any limits placed on their authority.

Time may be a critical factor when the need for a change arises. For such cases, the contractor might be directed to proceed on a "time and materials" basis, rather than wait for all paperwork to be processed—a delay that could impede progress. In this situation, the contractor must still follow the prescribed change order procedures including, but not limited to, notification and documentation.

All forms used for change orders should be dated and signed by the proper authority. Lack of documentation can be very costly, especially if legal judgments are to be made, and if certain field personnel are no longer available. For time and material change orders, the contractor should keep accurate daily records of all labor and material allocated to the change.

Owners or awarding authorities who do considerable and continual building construction (such as the federal government) realize the inevitability of change orders for numerous reasons, both predictable and unpredictable. As a result, the federal government, the American Institute of Architects (AIA), the Engineers Joint Contract Documents Committee (EJCDC) and other contractor, legal, and technical organizations have developed standards and procedures to be followed by all parties to achieve contract continuance and timely completion, while being financially fair to all concerned.

In addition to the change order standards put forth by industry associations, there are also many books available on the subject.

Pricing Change Orders

When pricing change orders, regardless of their cause, the most significant factor is when the change occurs. The need for a change may be perceived in the field or requested by the architect/engineer *before* any of the actual installation has begun, or may evolve or appear *during* construction when the item of work in question is partially installed. In the latter cases, the original sequence of construction is disrupted, along with all contiguous and supporting systems. Change orders cause the greatest impact when they occur *after* the installation has been completed and must be uncovered, or even replaced. Post-completion changes may be caused by necessary design changes, product failure, or changes in the owner's requirements that are not discovered until the building or the systems begin to function.

Specified procedures of notification and record keeping must be adhered to and enforced regardless of the stage of construction: *before*, *during*, or *after* installation. Some bidding documents anticipate change orders by requiring that unit prices including overhead and profit percentages—for additional as well as deductible changes—be listed. Generally these unit prices do not fully take into account the ripple effect, or impact on other trades, and should be used for general guidance only.

When pricing change orders, it is important to classify the time frame in which the change occurs. There are two basic time frames for change orders: *pre-installation change orders*, which occur before the start of construction, and *post-installation change orders*, which involve reworking after the original installation. Change orders that occur between these stages may be priced according to the extent of work completed using a combination of techniques developed for pricing *pre-* and *post-installation* changes.

The following factors are the basis for a check list to use when preparing a change order estimate.

Factors To Consider When Pricing Change Orders

As an estimator begins to prepare a change order, the following questions should be reviewed to determine their impact on the final price.

General

- *Is the change order work* pre-installation *or* post-installation?

Change order work costs vary according to how much of the installation has been completed. Once workers have the project scoped in their minds, even though they have not started, it can be difficult to refocus.

Consequently they may spend more than the normal amount of time understanding the change. Also, modifications to work in place, such as trimming or refitting, usually take more time than was initially estimated. The greater the amount of work in place, the more reluctant workers are to change it. Psychologically they may resent the change and as a result the rework takes longer than normal. Post-installation change order estimates must include demolition of existing work as required to accomplish the change. If the work is performed at a later time, additional obstacles, such as building finishes, may be present which must be protected. Regardless of whether the change

occurs pre-installation or post-installation, attempt to isolate the identifiable factors and price them separately. For example, add shipping costs that may be required pre-installation or any demolition required post-installation. Then analyze the potential impact on productivity of psychological and/or learning curve factors and adjust the output rates accordingly. One approach is to break down the typical workday into segments and quantify the impact on each segment. The following chart may be useful as a guide:

Task	Activities (Productivity) Expressed as Percentages of a Workday		
	Means Mechanical Cost Data (for New Construction)	Pre-Installation Change Orders	Post-Installation Change Orders
1. Study plans	3%	6%	6%
2. Material procurement	3%	3%	3%
3. Receiving and storing	3%	3%	3%
4. Mobilization	5%	5%	5%
5. Site movement	5%	5%	8%
6. Layout and marking	8%	10%	12%
7. Actual installation	64%	59%	54%
8. Clean-up	3%	3%	3%
9. Breaks—non-productive	6%	6%	6%
Total	100%	100%	100%

Change Order Installation Efficiency

The labor-hours expressed (for new construction) are based on average installation time, using an efficiency level of approximately 60%–65%. For change order situations, adjustments to this efficiency level should reflect the daily labor-hour allocation for that particular occurrence.

If any of the specific percentages expressed in the above chart do not apply to a particular project situation, then those percentage points should be reallocated to the appropriate task(s). Example: Using data for new construction, assume there is no new material being utilized. The percentages for Tasks 2 and 3 would therefore be reallocated to other tasks. If the time required for Tasks 2 and 3 can now be applied to installation, we can add the time allocated for *Material Procurement* and *Receiving and Storing* to the *Actual Installation* time for new construction, thereby increasing the Actual Installation percentage.

This chart shows that, due to reduced productivity, labor costs will be higher than those for new construction by 5%–15% for pre-installation change orders and by 15%–25% for post-installation change orders. Each job and change order is unique and must be examined individually. Many factors, covered elsewhere in this section, can each have a significant impact on productivity and change order costs. All such factors should be considered in every case.

- *Will the change substantially delay the original completion date?*

  A significant change in the project may cause the original completion date to be extended. The extended schedule may subject the contractor to new wage rates dictated by relevant labor contracts. Project supervision and other project overhead must also be extended beyond the original completion date. The schedule extension may also put installation into a new weather season. For example, underground piping scheduled for October installation was delayed until January. As a result, frost penetrated the trench area, thereby changing the degree of difficulty of the task. Changes and delays may have a ripple effect throughout the project. This effect must be analyzed and negotiated with the owner.

- *What is the net effect of a deduct change order?*

  In most cases, change orders resulting in a deduction or credit reflect only bare costs. The contractor may retain the overhead and profit based on the original bid.

Materials

- *Will you have to pay more or less for the new material, required by the change order, than you paid for the original purchase?*

  The same material prices or discounts will usually apply to materials purchased for change orders as new construction. In some instances, however, the contractor may forfeit the advantages of competitive pricing for change orders. Consider the following example:

  A contractor purchased over $20,000 worth of fan coil units for an installation, and obtained the maximum discount. Some time later it was determined the project required an additional matching unit. The contractor has to purchase this unit from the original supplier to ensure a match. The supplier at this time may not discount the unit because of the small quantity, and the fact that he is no longer in a competitive situation. The impact of quantity on purchase can add between 0% and 25% to material prices and/or subcontractor quotes.

- *If materials have been ordered or delivered to the job site, will they be subject to a cancellation charge or restocking fee?*

  Check with the supplier to determine if ordered materials are subject to a cancellation charge. Delivered materials not used as result of a change order may be subject to a restocking fee if returned to the supplier. Common restocking charges run between 20% and 40%. Also, delivery charges to return the goods to the supplier must be added.

Labor

- *How efficient is the existing crew at the actual installation?*

  Is the same crew that performed the initial work going to do the change order? Possibly the change consists of the installation of a unit identical to one already installed; therefore, the change should take less time. Be sure to consider this potential productivity increase and modify the productivity rates accordingly.

- *If the crew size is increased, what impact will that have on supervision requirements?*

  Under most bargaining agreements or management practices, there is a point at which a working foreman is replaced by a nonworking foreman. This replacement increases project overhead by adding a nonproductive worker. If additional workers are added to accelerate the project or to perform changes while maintaining the schedule, be sure to add additional supervision time if warranted. Calculate the hours involved and the additional cost directly if possible.

- *What are the other impacts of increased crew size?*

  The larger the crew, the greater the potential for productivity to decrease. Some of the factors that cause this productivity loss are: overcrowding (producing restrictive conditions in the working space), and possibly a shortage of any special tools and equipment required. Such factors affect not only the crew working on the elements directly involved in the change order, but other crews whose movement may also be hampered.

As the crew increases, check its basic composition for changes by the addition or deletion of apprentices or nonworking foreman, and quantify the potential effects of equipment shortages or other logistical factors.

- *As new crews, unfamiliar with the project, are brought onto the site, how long will it take them to become oriented to the project requirements?*

  The orientation time for a new crew to become 100% effective varies with the site and type of project. Orientation is easiest at a new construction site, and most difficult at existing, very restrictive renovation sites. The type of work also affects orientation time. When all elements of the work are exposed, such as concrete or masonry work, orientation is decreased. When the work is concealed or less visible, such as existing electrical systems, orientation takes longer. Usually orientation can be accomplished in one day or less. Costs for added orientation should be itemized and added to the total estimated cost.

- *How much actual production can be gained by working overtime?*

  Short term overtime can be used effectively to accomplish more work in a day. However, as overtime is scheduled to run beyond several weeks, studies have shown marked decreases in output. The following chart shows the effect of long term overtime on worker efficiency. If the anticipated change requires extended overtime to keep the job on schedule, these factors can be used as a guide to predict the impact on time and cost. Add project overhead, particularly supervision, that may also be incurred.

Days per Week	Hours per Day	Production Efficiency					Payroll Cost Factors	
		1 Week	2 Weeks	3 Weeks	4 Weeks	Average 4 Weeks	@ 1-1/2 Times	@ 2 Times
5	8	100%	100%	100%	100%	100%	100%	100%
	9	100	100	95	90	96.25	105.6	111.1
	10	100	95	90	85	91.25	110.0	120.0
	11	95	90	75	65	81.25	113.6	127.3
	12	90	85	70	60	76.25	116.7	133.3
6	8	100	100	95	90	96.25	108.3	116.7
	9	100	95	90	85	92.50	113.0	125.9
	10	95	90	85	80	87.50	116.7	133.3
	11	95	85	70	65	78.75	119.7	139.4
	12	90	80	65	60	73.75	122.2	144.4
7	8	100	95	85	75	88.75	114.3	128.6
	9	95	90	80	70	83.75	118.3	136.5
	10	90	85	75	65	78.75	121.4	142.9
	11	85	80	65	60	72.50	124.0	148.1
	12	85	75	60	55	68.75	126.2	152.4

Effects of Overtime

Caution: Under many labor agreements, Sundays and holidays are paid at a higher premium than the normal overtime rate.

The use of long-term overtime is counterproductive on almost any construction job; that is, the longer the period of overtime, the lower the actual production rate. Numerous studies have been conducted, and while they have resulted in slightly different numbers, all reach the same conclusion. The figure above tabulates the effects of overtime work on efficiency.

As illustrated, there can be a difference between the *actual* payroll cost per hour and the *effective* cost per hour for overtime work. This is due to the reduced production efficiency with the increase in weekly hours beyond 40. This difference between actual and effective cost results from overtime work over a prolonged period. Short-term overtime work does not result in as great a reduction in efficiency and, in such cases, effective cost may not vary significantly from the actual payroll cost. As the total hours per week are increased on a regular basis, more time is lost due to fatigue, lowered morale, and an increased accident rate.

As an example, assume a project where workers are working 6 days a week, 10 hours per day. From the figure above (based on productivity studies), the average effective productive hours over a 4-week period are:

$$0.875 \times 60 = 52.5$$

Depending upon the locale and day of week, overtime hours may be paid at time and a half or double time. For time and a half, the overall (average) *actual* payroll cost (including regular and overtime hours) is determined as follows:

$$\frac{40 \text{ reg. hrs.} + (20 \text{ overtime hrs.} \times 1.5)}{60 \text{ hrs.}} = 1.167$$

Based on 60 hours, the payroll cost per hour will be 116.7% of the normal rate at 40 hours per week. However, because the effective production (efficiency) for 60 hours is reduced to the equivalent of 52.5 hours, the effective cost of overtime is calculated as follows:

For time and a half:

$$\frac{40 \text{ reg. hrs.} + (20 \text{ overtime hrs.} \times 1.5)}{52.5 \text{ hrs.}} = 1.33$$

Installed cost will be 133% of the normal rate (for labor).

Thus, when figuring overtime, the actual cost per unit of work will be higher than the apparent overtime payroll dollar increase, due to the reduced productivity of the longer workweek. These efficiency calculations are true only for those cost factors determined by hours worked. Costs that are applied weekly or monthly, such as equipment rentals, will not be similarly affected.

Equipment

- *What equipment is required to complete the change order?*

Change orders may require extending the rental period of equipment already on the job site, or the addition of special equipment brought in to accomplish the change work. In either case, the additional rental charges and operator labor charges must be added.

Summary

The preceding considerations and others you deem appropriate should be analyzed and applied to a change order estimate. The impact of each should be quantified and listed on the estimate to form an audit trail.

Change orders that are properly identified, documented, and managed help to ensure the orderly, professional and profitable progress of the work. They also minimize potential claims or disputes at the end of the project.

Estimating Tips

- The cost figures in this Square Foot Cost section were derived from approximately 11,000 projects contained in the RSMeans database of completed construction projects. They include the contractor's overhead and profit, but do not generally include architectural fees or land costs. The figures have been adjusted to January of the current year. New projects are added to our files each year, and outdated projects are discarded. For this reason, certain costs may not show a uniform annual progression. In no case are all subdivisions of a project listed.

- These projects were located throughout the U.S. and reflect a tremendous variation in square foot (S.F.) and cubic foot (C.F.) costs. This is due to differences, not only in labor and material costs, but also in individual owners' requirements. For instance, a bank in a large city would have different features than one in a rural area. This is true of all the different types of buildings analyzed. Therefore, caution should be exercised when using these square foot costs. For example, for courthouses, costs in the database are local courthouse costs and will not apply to the larger, more elaborate federal courthouses. As a general rule, the projects in the 1/4 column do not include any site work or equipment, while the projects in the 3/4 column may include both equipment and site work. The median figures do not generally include site work.

- None of the figures "go with" any others. All individual cost items were computed and tabulated separately. Thus, the sum of the median figures for plumbing, HVAC and electrical will not normally total up to the total mechanical and electrical costs arrived at by separate analysis and tabulation of the projects.

- Each building was analyzed as to total and component costs and percentages. The figures were arranged in ascending order with the results tabulated as shown. The 1/4 column shows that 25% of the projects had lower costs and 75% had higher. The 3/4 column shows that 75% of the projects had lower costs and 25% had higher. The median column shows that 50% of the projects had lower costs and 50% had higher.

- There are two times when square foot costs are useful. The first is in the conceptual stage when no details are available. Then square foot costs make a useful starting point. The second is after the bids are in and the costs can be worked back into their appropriate categories for information purposes. As soon as details become available in the project design, the square foot approach should be discontinued and the project priced as to its particular components. When more precision is required, or for estimating the replacement cost of specific buildings, the current edition of *RSMeans Square Foot Costs* should be used.

- In using the figures in this section, it is recommended that the median column be used for preliminary figures if no additional information is available. The median figures, when multiplied by the total city construction cost index figures (see city cost indexes) and then multiplied by the project size modifier at the end of this section, should present a fairly accurate base figure, which would then have to be adjusted in view of the estimator's experience, local economic conditions, code requirements, and the owner's particular requirements. There is no need to factor the percentage figures, as these should remain constant from city to city. All tabulations mentioning air conditioning had at least partial air conditioning.

- The editors of this book would greatly appreciate receiving cost figures on one or more of your recent projects, which would then be included in the averages for next year. All cost figures received will be kept confidential, except that they will be averaged with other similar projects to arrive at square foot cost figures for next year's book. See the last page of the book for details and the discount available for submitting one or more of your projects.

50 17 00 | S.F. Costs			UNIT COSTS			% OF TOTAL			
		UNIT	1/4	MEDIAN	3/4	1/4	MEDIAN	3/4	
01	0010	**APARTMENTS Low Rise (1 to 3 story)**	S.F.	73	92.50	123				**01**
	0020	Total project cost	C.F.	6.55	8.70	10.75				
	0100	Site work	S.F.	5.35	8.55	15	6.05%	10.55%	13.95%	
	0500	Masonry		1.44	3.55	5.80	1.54%	3.92%	6.50%	
	1500	Finishes		7.75	10.65	13.15	9.05%	10.75%	12.85%	
	1800	Equipment		2.40	3.63	5.40	2.71%	3.99%	5.95%	
	2720	Plumbing		5.70	7.30	9.30	6.65%	8.95%	10.05%	
	2770	Heating, ventilating, air conditioning		3.63	4.47	6.55	4.20%	5.60%	7.60%	
	2900	Electrical		4.25	5.65	7.65	5.20%	6.65%	8.35%	
	3100	Total: Mechanical & Electrical		15.10	19.60	24	16.05%	18.20%	23%	
	9000	Per apartment unit, total cost	Apt.	68,000	104,000	153,500				
	9500	Total: Mechanical & Electrical	"	12,900	20,300	26,500				
02	0010	**APARTMENTS Mid Rise (4 to 7 story)**	S.F.	97	117	144				**02**
	0020	Total project costs	C.F.	7.55	10.45	14.30				
	0100	Site work	S.F.	3.88	7.85	15.15	5.25%	6.70%	9.20%	
	0500	Masonry		4.05	8.90	12.15	5.10%	7.25%	10.50%	
	1500	Finishes		12.70	17	20	10.70%	13.50%	17.70%	
	1800	Equipment		2.71	4.22	5.55	2.54%	3.47%	4.31%	
	2500	Conveying equipment		2.20	2.70	3.26	2.05%	2.27%	2.69%	
	2720	Plumbing		5.70	9.10	9.65	5.70%	7.20%	8.95%	
	2900	Electrical		6.40	8.70	10.55	6.35%	7.20%	8.95%	
	3100	Total: Mechanical & Electrical		20.50	25.50	31	18.25%	21%	23%	
	9000	Per apartment unit, total cost	Apt.	109,500	129,500	214,000				
	9500	Total: Mechanical & Electrical	"	20,700	24,000	25,100				
03	0010	**APARTMENTS High Rise (8 to 24 story)**	S.F.	110	127	152				**03**
	0020	Total project costs	C.F.	10.70	12.45	14.65				
	0100	Site work	S.F.	3.99	6.45	9	2.58%	4.84%	6.15%	
	0500	Masonry		6.35	11.55	14.40	4.74%	9.65%	11.05%	
	1500	Finishes		12.20	15.25	18	9.75%	11.80%	13.70%	
	1800	Equipment		3.54	4.35	5.75	2.78%	3.49%	4.35%	
	2500	Conveying equipment		2.50	3.79	5.15	2.23%	2.78%	3.37%	
	2720	Plumbing		7.05	9.55	11.70	6.80%	7.20%	10.45%	
	2900	Electrical		7.55	9.55	12.90	6.45%	7.65%	8.80%	
	3100	Total: Mechanical & Electrical		22.50	29	35	17.95%	22.50%	24.50%	
	9000	Per apartment unit, total cost	Apt.	114,000	126,000	174,500				
	9500	Total: Mechanical & Electrical	"	22,700	28,200	29,900				
04	0010	**AUDITORIUMS**	S.F.	115	158	230				**04**
	0020	Total project costs	C.F.	7.15	9.95	14.30				
	2720	Plumbing	S.F.	6.80	10	11.95	5.85%	7.20%	8.70%	
	2900	Electrical		9.20	13.30	22	6.85%	9.50%	11.40%	
	3100	Total: Mechanical & Electrical		61	81.50	99	24.50%	27.50%	31%	
05	0010	**AUTOMOTIVE SALES**	S.F.	84.50	115	143				**05**
	0020	Total project costs	C.F.	5.55	6.70	8.65				
	2720	Plumbing	S.F.	3.86	6.70	7.30	2.89%	6.05%	6.50%	
	2770	Heating, ventilating, air conditioning		5.95	9.10	9.80	4.61%	10%	10.35%	
	2900	Electrical		6.80	10.70	15.70	7.25%	8.80%	12.15%	
	3100	Total: Mechanical & Electrical		19	30.50	36.50	17.30%	20.50%	22%	
06	0010	**BANKS**	S.F.	166	207	263				**06**
	0020	Total project costs	C.F.	11.85	16.10	21				
	0100	Site work	S.F.	19	30	42.50	7.90%	12.95%	17%	
	0500	Masonry		7.55	16.15	29	3.36%	6.90%	10.05%	
	1500	Finishes		14.85	22.50	28	5.85%	8.65%	11.70%	
	1800	Equipment		6.25	13.75	28	1.34%	5.55%	10.50%	
	2720	Plumbing		5.20	7.45	10.85	2.82%	3.90%	4.93%	
	2770	Heating, ventilating, air conditioning		9.85	13.20	17.60	4.86%	7.15%	8.50%	
	2900	Electrical		15.75	21	27.50	8.25%	10.20%	12.20%	
	3100	Total: Mechanical & Electrical		38	50.50	61	16.55%	19.45%	24%	
	3500	See also division 11020 & 11030 (MF2004 11 16 00 & 11 17 00)								

		**50 17 00	S.F. Costs**	UNIT	UNIT COSTS			% OF TOTAL		
				1/4	MEDIAN	3/4	1/4	MEDIAN	3/4
13	0010	**CHURCHES**	S.F.	112	143	185				13
	0020	Total project costs	C.F.	6.90	8.75	11.50			
	1800	Equipment	S.F.	1.21	3.17	6.80	.93%	2.11%	4.31%
	2720	Plumbing		4.35	6.10	8.95	3.51%	4.96%	6.25%
	2770	Heating, ventilating, air conditioning		10.15	13.25	18.75	7.50%	10%	12%
	2900	Electrical		9.55	12.95	17.65	7.30%	8.80%	10.90%
	3100	Total: Mechanical & Electrical		29.50	39	51.50	18.30%	22%	24.50%
	3500	See also division 11040 (MF2004 11 91 00)							
15	0010	**CLUBS, COUNTRY**	S.F	120	144	182				15
	0020	Total project costs	C.F.	9.65	11.75	16.25			
	2720	Plumbing	S.F.	7.25	10.75	24.50	5.60%	7.90%	10%
	2900	Electrical		9.40	12.90	16.80	7%	8.95%	11%
	3100	Total: Mechanical & Electrical		50	62.50	66	19%	26.50%	29.50%
17	0010	**CLUBS, SOCIAL Fraternal**	S.F.	101	138	184				17
	0020	Total project costs	C.F.	5.95	9.05	10.80			
	2720	Plumbing	S.F.	6	7.50	11.30	5.60%	6.90%	8.55%
	2770	Heating, ventilating, air conditioning		7.05	10.50	13.45	8.20%	9.25%	14.40%
	2900	Electrical		6.85	11.80	13.55	5.95%	9.30%	10.55%
	3100	Total: Mechanical & Electrical		37	40	51	21%	23%	23.50%
18	0010	**CLUBS, Y.M.C.A.**	S.F.	132	164	247				18
	0020	Total project costs	C.F.	5.55	9.25	13.80			
	2720	Plumbing	S.F.	7.60	15.10	16.95	5.65%	7.60%	10.85%
	2900	Electrical		9.85	12.75	22	6.45%	8%	9.20%
	3100	Total: Mechanical & Electrical		40	45.50	74.50	20.50%	21.50%	28.50%
19	0010	**COLLEGES Classrooms & Administration**	S.F.	116	164	212				19
	0020	Total project costs	C.F.	6.95	12.35	19.85			
	0500	Masonry	S.F.	9.15	16.85	20.50	5.10%	8.05%	10.50%
	2720	Plumbing		5.20	12.65	23.50	5.10%	6.60%	8.95%
	2900	Electrical		9.85	15.55	21.50	7.70%	9.85%	12%
	3100	Total: Mechanical & Electrical		41.50	57	76	23%	28%	31.50%
21	0010	**COLLEGES Science, Engineering, Laboratories**	S.F.	225	264	305				21
	0020	Total project costs	C.F.	12.95	18.85	21.50			
	1800	Equipment	S.F.	6.10	28.50	31	2%	6.45%	12.65%
	2900	Electrical		18.60	26.50	40.50	7.10%	9.40%	12.10%
	3100	Total: Mechanical & Electrical		69	82	127	28.50%	31.50%	41%
	3500	See also division 11600 (MF2004 11 53 00)							
23	0010	**COLLEGES Student Unions**	S.F.	144	195	236				23
	0020	Total project costs	C.F.	8	10.50	13			
	3100	Total: Mechanical & Electrical	S.F.	54	58.50	69	23.50%	26%	29%
25	0010	**COMMUNITY CENTERS**	S.F.	120	147	199				25
	0020	Total project costs	C.F.	7.75	11.05	14.35			
	1800	Equipment	S.F.	2.40	4.70	7.75	1.47%	3.01%	5.30%
	2720	Plumbing		5.60	9.85	13.45	4.85%	7%	8.95%
	2770	Heating, ventilating, air conditioning		8.45	13.10	18.80	6.80%	10.35%	12.90%
	2900	Electrical		10.05	13.25	19.50	7.15%	8.90%	10.40%
	3100	Total: Mechanical & Electrical		33	42	60	18.80%	23%	30%
28	0010	**COURT HOUSES**	S.F.	171	202	278				28
	0020	Total project costs	C.F.	13.15	15.70	19.80			
	2720	Plumbing	S.F.	8.15	11.35	12.90	5.95%	7.45%	8.20%
	2900	Electrical		18.20	20.50	30	9.05%	10.65%	12.15%
	3100	Total: Mechanical & Electrical		51	66.50	73	22.50%	26.50%	30%
30	0010	**DEPARTMENT STORES**	S.F.	63.50	85.50	108				30
	0020	Total project costs	C.F.	3.39	4.40	5.95			
	2720	Plumbing	S.F.	1.97	2.49	3.78	1.82%	4.21%	5.90%
	2770	Heating, ventilating, air conditioning		4.79	8.90	13.35	8.20%	9.10%	14.80%

		50 17 00	S.F. Costs	UNIT	UNIT COSTS			% OF TOTAL			
					1/4	MEDIAN	3/4	1/4	MEDIAN	3/4	
30	2900	Electrical	S.F.	7.25	9.95	11.75	9.05%	12.15%	14.95%	30
	3100	Total: Mechanical & Electrical	↓	12.80	16.35	28.50	13.20%	21.50%	50%	
31	0010	**DORMITORIES Low Rise (1 to 3 story)**	S.F.	120	166	208				31
	0020	Total project costs	C.F.	6.80	10.95	16.45				
	2720	Plumbing	S.F.	7.20	9.65	12.20	8.05%	9%	9.65%	
	2770	Heating, ventilating, air conditioning		7.65	9.15	12.20	4.61%	8.05%	10%	
	2900	Electrical		7.95	12.10	16.55	6.40%	8.65%	9.50%	
	3100	Total: Mechanical & Electrical	↓	41.50	44.50	69	22%	25%	27%	
	9000	Per bed, total cost	Bed	51,000	56,500	121,000				
32	0010	**DORMITORIES Mid Rise (4 to 8 story)**	S.F.	147	192	237				32
	0020	Total project costs	C.F.	16.25	17.85	21.50				
	2900	Electrical	S.F.	15.65	17.80	24	8.20%	10.20%	11.95%	
	3100	Total: Mechanical & Electrical	"	44	87.50	88.50	25%	30.50%	35.50%	
	9000	Per bed, total cost	Bed	21,000	47,900	277,000				
34	0010	**FACTORIES**	S.F.	55.50	83	128				34
	0020	Total project costs	C.F.	3.58	5.35	8.85				
	0100	Site work	S.F.	6.35	11.60	18.40	6.95%	11.45%	17.95%	
	2720	Plumbing		3.01	5.60	9.25	3.73%	6.05%	8.10%	
	2770	Heating, ventilating, air conditioning		5.85	8.40	11.35	5.25%	8.45%	11.35%	
	2900	Electrical		6.95	10.95	16.75	8.10%	10.50%	14.20%	
	3100	Total: Mechanical & Electrical	↓	19.80	30.50	40	21%	28.50%	35.50%	
36	0010	**FIRE STATIONS**	S.F.	111	153	209				36
	0020	Total project costs	C.F.	6.45	8.90	11.85				
	0500	Masonry	S.F.	15.10	29	37.50	7.50%	10.95%	15.55%	
	1140	Roofing		3.61	9.75	11.10	1.90%	4.94%	5.05%	
	1580	Painting		2.80	4.18	4.28	1.37%	1.57%	2.07%	
	1800	Equipment		1.38	2.64	4.87	.62%	1.63%	3.42%	
	2720	Plumbing		6.20	9.85	13.95	5.85%	7.35%	9.45%	
	2770	Heating, ventilating, air conditioning		6.15	9.95	15.35	5.15%	7.40%	9.40%	
	2900	Electrical		7.95	14.10	19	6.90%	8.60%	10.60%	
	3100	Total: Mechanical & Electrical	↓	40.50	52	59	18.40%	23%	27%	
37	0010	**FRATERNITY HOUSES & Sorority Houses**	S.F.	111	142	195				37
	0020	Total project costs	C.F.	11	11.50	13.85				
	2720	Plumbing	S.F.	8.35	9.60	17.55	6.80%	8%	10.85%	
	2900	Electrical	↓	7.30	15.80	19.35	6.60%	9.90%	10.65%	
38	0010	**FUNERAL HOMES**	S.F.	117	159	289				38
	0020	Total project costs	C.F.	11.90	13.25	25.50				
	2900	Electrical	S.F.	5.15	9.45	10.35	3.58%	4.44%	5.95%	
39	0010	**GARAGES, COMMERCIAL (Service)**	S.F.	66	102	141				39
	0020	Total project costs	C.F.	4.35	6.40	9.35				
	1800	Equipment	S.F.	3.73	8.40	13.05	2.21%	4.62%	6.80%	
	2720	Plumbing		4.58	7.05	12.85	5.45%	7.85%	10.65%	
	2730	Heating & ventilating		4.51	7.80	9.95	5.25%	6.85%	8.20%	
	2900	Electrical		6.30	9.60	13.80	7.15%	9.25%	10.85%	
	3100	Total: Mechanical & Electrical	↓	11.85	26.50	39	12.35%	17.40%	26%	
40	0010	**GARAGES, MUNICIPAL (Repair)**	S.F.	97	129	182				40
	0020	Total project costs	C.F.	6.05	7.70	13.25				
	0500	Masonry	S.F.	5.10	17.85	27.50	4.03%	9.15%	12.50%	
	2720	Plumbing		4.36	8.35	15.75	3.59%	6.70%	7.95%	
	2730	Heating & ventilating		7.45	10.80	21	6.15%	7.45%	13.50%	
	2900	Electrical		7.15	11.30	16.40	6.65%	8.15%	11.15%	
	3100	Total: Mechanical & Electrical	↓	33	46	66.50	21.50%	23%	28.50%	
41	0010	**GARAGES, PARKING**	S.F.	38.50	55	95				41
	0020	Total project costs	C.F.	3.55	4.82	7				

50 17 00 | S.F. Costs		UNIT	UNIT COSTS			% OF TOTAL		
			1/4	MEDIAN	3/4	1/4	MEDIAN	3/4
41 2720	Plumbing	S.F.	.65	1.66	2.56	1.72%	2.70%	3.85%	**41**
2900	Electrical		2.08	2.74	4	4.52%	5.40%	6.35%
3100	Total: Mechanical & Electrical	↓	4.03	5.90	7.35	7%	8.90%	11.05%
3200								
9000	Per car, total cost	Car	16,000	20,000	25,500			
43 0010	**GYMNASIUMS**	S.F.	105	140	193				**43**
0020	Total project costs	C.F.	5.25	7.10	8.75			
1800	Equipment	S.F.	2.50	4.68	8.45	1.76%	3.26%	6.70%
2720	Plumbing		5.75	7.75	10.20	4.65%	6.40%	7.75%
2770	Heating, ventilating, air conditioning		6.25	10.90	22	5.15%	9.05%	11.10%
2900	Electrical		8.35	11	14.65	6.75%	8.50%	10.30%
3100	Total: Mechanical & Electrical	↓	28.50	40	48.50	19.75%	23.50%	29%
3500	See also division 11480 (MF2004 11 67 00)							
46 0010	**HOSPITALS**	S.F.	202	253	350				**46**
0020	Total project costs	C.F.	15.30	19.05	27			
1800	Equipment	S.F.	5.10	9.85	17	.80%	2.53%	4.80%
2720	Plumbing		17.40	24.50	31.50	7.60%	9.10%	10.85%
2770	Heating, ventilating, air conditioning		25.50	32.50	45.50	7.80%	12.95%	16.65%
2900	Electrical		22.50	30	44.50	10%	11.75%	14.10%
3100	Total: Mechanical & Electrical	↓	65	90.50	134	28%	33.50%	37%
9000	Per bed or person, total cost	Bed	233,500	322,000	371,000			
9900	See also division 11700 (MF2004 11 71 00)							
48 0010	**HOUSING For the Elderly**	S.F.	99	126	154				**48**
0020	Total project costs	C.F.	7.10	9.85	12.55			
0100	Site work	S.F.	6.90	10.75	15.75	5.05%	7.90%	12.10%
0500	Masonry		1.87	11.30	16.50	1.30%	6.05%	11%
1800	Equipment		2.40	3.30	5.25	1.88%	3.23%	4.43%
2510	Conveying systems		2.24	3.24	4.40	1.78%	2.20%	2.81%
2720	Plumbing		7.40	9.40	11.85	8.15%	9.55%	10.50%
2730	Heating, ventilating, air conditioning		3.78	5.35	8	3.30%	5.60%	7.25%
2900	Electrical		7.40	10.05	12.85	7.30%	8.50%	10.25%
3100	Total: Mechanical & Electrical	↓	25.50	31.50	40.50	18.10%	22.50%	29%
9000	Per rental unit, total cost	Unit	92,500	108,000	120,000			
9500	Total: Mechanical & Electrical	"	20,600	23,600	27,600			
50 0010	**HOUSING Public (Low Rise)**	S.F.	83.50	116	151				**50**
0020	Total project costs	C.F.	6.60	9.25	11.50			
0100	Site work	S.F.	10.60	15.30	25	8.35%	11.75%	16.50%
1800	Equipment		2.27	3.70	5.65	2.26%	3.03%	4.24%
2720	Plumbing		6	7.95	10.05	7.15%	9.05%	11.60%
2730	Heating, ventilating, air conditioning		3.02	5.85	6.40	4.26%	6.05%	6.45%
2900	Electrical		5.05	7.50	10.45	5.10%	6.55%	8.25%
3100	Total: Mechanical & Electrical	↓	24	31	34.50	14.50%	17.55%	26.50%
9000	Per apartment, total cost	Apt.	91,500	104,000	131,000			
9500	Total: Mechanical & Electrical	"	19,500	24,100	26,700			
51 0010	**ICE SKATING RINKS**	S.F.	71.50	167	183				**51**
0020	Total project costs	C.F.	5.25	5.35	6.20			
2720	Plumbing	S.F.	2.66	5	5.10	3.12%	3.23%	5.65%
2900	Electrical	↓	7.65	11.70	12.40	6.30%	10.15%	15.05%
52 0010	**JAILS**	S.F.	185	280	360				**52**
0020	Total project costs	C.F.	19.60	27.50	32			
1800	Equipment	S.F.	8.45	25	42.50	2.80%	6.95%	9.80%
2720	Plumbing		21	28	37	7%	8.90%	13.35%
2770	Heating, ventilating, air conditioning		19.60	26	50.50	7.50%	9.45%	17.75%
2900	Electrical		23	31	39	9.40%	11.70%	15.25%
3100	Total: Mechanical & Electrical	↓	61	108	128	28%	30%	34%
53 0010	**LIBRARIES**	S.F.	140	186	243				**53**
0020	Total project costs	C.F.	9.40	11.75	15			

		50 17 00 | S.F. Costs		UNIT COSTS			% OF TOTAL			
			UNIT	1/4	MEDIAN	3/4	1/4	MEDIAN	3/4	
53	0500	Masonry	S.F.	9.30	19	31.50	5.60%	7.15%	10.95%	53
	1800	Equipment		1.88	5.05	7.60	.28%	1.39%	4.07%	
	2720	Plumbing		5.05	7.20	10	3.38%	4.60%	5.70%	
	2770	Heating, ventilating, air conditioning		11.20	19	23	7.80%	10.95%	12.80%	
	2900	Electrical		14.10	18.65	25	8.40%	10.55%	12%	
	3100	Total: Mechanical & Electrical		46	56	65.50	21%	24%	28%	
54	0010	**LIVING, ASSISTED**	S.F.	127	151	176				54
	0020	Total project costs	C.F.	10.70	12.50	14.20				
	0500	Masonry	S.F.	3.68	4.44	5.45	2.36%	3.16%	3.86%	
	1800	Equipment		2.81	3.35	4.30	2.12%	2.45%	2.87%	
	2720	Plumbing		10.65	14.25	14.75	6.05%	8.15%	10.60%	
	2770	Heating, ventilating, air conditioning		12.65	13.20	14.45	7.95%	9.35%	9.70%	
	2900	Electrical		12.45	14	16.15	9%	9.95%	10.65%	
	3100	Total: Mechanical & Electrical		34	40.50	47	24%	28.50%	31.50%	
55	0010	**MEDICAL CLINICS**	S.F.	129	159	203				55
	0020	Total project costs	C.F.	9.45	12.25	16.30				
	1800	Equipment	S.F.	1.65	7.35	11.40	1.05%	2.94%	6.35%	
	2720	Plumbing		8.60	12.10	16.15	6.15%	8.40%	10.10%	
	2770	Heating, ventilating, air conditioning		10.25	13.40	19.70	6.65%	8.85%	11.35%	
	2900	Electrical		11.10	15.75	20.50	8.10%	10%	12.20%	
	3100	Total: Mechanical & Electrical		35.50	48	66	22%	27%	33.50%	
	3500	See also division 11700 (MF2004 11 71 00)								
57	0010	**MEDICAL OFFICES**	S.F.	121	151	185				57
	0020	Total project costs	C.F.	9.05	12.30	16.60				
	1800	Equipment	S.F.	4.01	7.95	11.15	.66%	4.87%	6.50%	
	2720	Plumbing		6.70	10.35	13.95	5.60%	6.80%	8.50%	
	2770	Heating, ventilating, air conditioning		8.10	11.70	15.45	6.10%	8%	9.70%	
	2900	Electrical		9.70	14.20	19.75	7.50%	9.80%	11.70%	
	3100	Total: Mechanical & Electrical		26.50	38.50	55	19.30%	23%	28.50%	
59	0010	**MOTELS**	S.F.	76.50	111	145				59
	0020	Total project costs	C.F.	6.80	9.15	14.95				
	2720	Plumbing	S.F.	7.75	9.90	11.80	9.45%	10.60%	12.55%	
	2770	Heating, ventilating, air conditioning		4.74	7.05	12.65	5.60%	5.60%	10%	
	2900	Electrical		7.25	9.15	11.40	7.45%	9.05%	10.45%	
	3100	Total: Mechanical & Electrical		21.50	31	53	18.50%	24%	25.50%	
	5000									
	9000	Per rental unit, total cost	Unit	39,000	74,000	80,000				
	9500	Total: Mechanical & Electrical	"	7,600	11,500	13,400				
60	0010	**NURSING HOMES**	S.F.	120	155	193				60
	0020	Total project costs	C.F.	9.45	11.80	16.15				
	1800	Equipment	S.F.	3.28	5	8.40	2%	3.62%	4.99%	
	2720	Plumbing		10.30	15.60	18.80	8.75%	10.10%	12.70%	
	2770	Heating, ventilating, air conditioning		10.85	16.45	22	9.70%	11.45%	11.80%	
	2900	Electrical		11.90	14.95	20.50	9.40%	10.60%	12.50%	
	3100	Total: Mechanical & Electrical		28.50	39.50	66.50	26%	28%	30%	
	9000	Per bed or person, total cost	Bed	53,500	67,000	86,000				
61	0010	**OFFICES Low Rise (1 to 4 story)**	S.F.	101	132	172				61
	0020	Total project costs	C.F.	7.25	9.95	13.10				
	0100	Site work	S.F.	8.15	14.20	21	5.95%	9.70%	13.55%	
	0500	Masonry		3.92	7.90	14.40	2.61%	5.40%	8.45%	
	1800	Equipment		.91	2.11	5.75	.57%	1.50%	3.42%	
	2720	Plumbing		3.62	5.60	8.20	3.66%	4.50%	6.10%	
	2770	Heating, ventilating, air conditioning		8	11.15	16.35	7.20%	10.30%	11.70%	
	2900	Electrical		8.30	11.85	16.85	7.45%	9.65%	11.40%	
	3100	Total: Mechanical & Electrical		23	31.50	48	18.20%	22%	27%	
62	0010	**OFFICES Mid Rise (5 to 10 story)**	S.F.	107	130	176				62
	0020	Total project costs	C.F.	7.60	9.70	13.75				

			UNIT	UNIT COSTS			% OF TOTAL			
		50 17 00 | S.F. Costs		1/4	MEDIAN	3/4	1/4	MEDIAN	3/4	
62	2720	Plumbing	S.F.	3.24	5	7.20	2.83%	3.74%	4.50%	62
	2770	Heating, ventilating, air conditioning		8.15	11.65	18.60	7.65%	9.40%	11%	
	2900	Electrical		7.95	10.20	15.40	6.35%	7.80%	10%	
	3100	Total: Mechanical & Electrical	↓	20.50	26.50	50.50	18.95%	21%	27.50%	
63	0010	**OFFICES High Rise (11 to 20 story)**	S.F.	132	166	204				63
	0020	Total project costs	C.F.	9.20	11.50	16.50				
	2900	Electrical	S.F.	8	9.75	14.50	5.80%	7.85%	10.50%	
	3100	Total: Mechanical & Electrical	↓	26	34.50	58.50	16.90%	23.50%	34%	
64	0010	**POLICE STATIONS**	S.F.	158	208	265				64
	0020	Total project costs	C.F.	12.60	15.40	21				
	0500	Masonry	S.F.	15.80	26	33	7.80%	9.10%	11.35%	
	1800	Equipment		2.27	11.05	17.50	.98%	3.35%	6.70%	
	2720	Plumbing		8.85	17.60	22	5.65%	6.90%	10.75%	
	2770	Heating, ventilating, air conditioning		12.95	18.35	26	5.85%	10.55%	11.70%	
	2900	Electrical		17.25	25	32.50	9.80%	11.70%	14.50%	
	3100	Total: Mechanical & Electrical	↓	65.50	69	92	28.50%	31.50%	32.50%	
65	0010	**POST OFFICES**	S.F.	125	154	196				65
	0020	Total project costs	C.F.	7.50	9.50	10.80				
	2720	Plumbing	S.F.	5.05	6.95	8.80	4.24%	5.30%	5.60%	
	2770	Heating, ventilating, air conditioning		7.85	10.85	12.05	6.65%	7.15%	9.35%	
	2900	Electrical		10.30	14.50	17.20	7.25%	9%	11%	
	3100	Total: Mechanical & Electrical	↓	29.50	39	44	16.25%	18.80%	22%	
66	0010	**POWER PLANTS**	S.F.	865	1,150	2,100				66
	0020	Total project costs	C.F.	24	52	111				
	2900	Electrical	S.F.	61	130	193	9.30%	12.75%	21.50%	
	8100	Total: Mechanical & Electrical	↓	152	495	1,100	32.50%	32.50%	52.50%	
67	0010	**RELIGIOUS EDUCATION**	S.F.	101	131	161				67
	0020	Total project costs	C.F.	5.60	8	10				
	2720	Plumbing	S.F.	4.20	5.95	8.40	4.40%	5.30%	7.10%	
	2770	Heating, ventilating, air conditioning		10.60	12	16.95	10.05%	11.45%	12.35%	
	2900	Electrical		7.40	11.25	14.85	7.60%	9.05%	10.35%	
	3100	Total: Mechanical & Electrical	↓	32.50	42.50	52	22%	23%	27%	
69	0010	**RESEARCH Laboratories & Facilities**	S.F.	154	217	315				69
	0020	Total project costs	C.F.	11.20	22	26.50				
	1800	Equipment	S.F.	6.70	13.15	32	.94%	4.58%	9.10%	
	2720	Plumbing		10.95	19.30	31	6.15%	8.30%	10.80%	
	2770	Heating, ventilating, air conditioning		13.55	45.50	54	7.25%	16.50%	17.50%	
	2900	Electrical		18.10	29	47.50	9.55%	11.15%	14.60%	
	3100	Total: Mechanical & Electrical	↓	57.50	102	144	29.50%	37%	41%	
70	0010	**RESTAURANTS**	S.F.	146	188	245				70
	0020	Total project costs	C.F.	12.25	16.10	21				
	1800	Equipment	S.F.	8.65	23	35	6.10%	13%	15.65%	
	2720	Plumbing		11.55	14	18.40	6.10%	8.15%	9%	
	2770	Heating, ventilating, air conditioning		14.70	20.50	24.50	9.20%	12%	12.40%	
	2900	Electrical		15.40	19	24.50	8.35%	10.55%	11.55%	
	3100	Total: Mechanical & Electrical	↓	47.50	51	66	21%	25%	29.50%	
	9000	Per seat unit, total cost	Seat	5,350	7,125	8,450				
	9500	Total: Mechanical & Electrical	"	1,350	1,775	2,100				
72	0010	**RETAIL STORES**	S.F.	68	91.50	121				72
	0020	Total project costs	C.F.	4.62	6.60	9.15				
	2720	Plumbing	S.F.	2.47	4.12	7.05	3.26%	4.60%	6.80%	
	2770	Heating, ventilating, air conditioning		5.35	7.30	10.95	6.75%	8.75%	10.15%	
	2900	Electrical		6.15	8.40	12.10	7.25%	9.90%	11.60%	
	3100	Total: Mechanical & Electrical	↓	16.30	21	28	17.05%	21%	23.50%	
74	0010	**SCHOOLS Elementary**	S.F.	111	138	169				74
	0020	Total project costs	C.F.	7.25	9.30	12.05				
	0500	Masonry	S.F.	7.85	16.95	25	4.89%	10.50%	14%	
	1800	Equipment	↓	2.58	4.93	9.30	1.83%	3.13%	4.61%	

		50 17 00 | S.F. Costs	UNIT	UNIT COSTS			% OF TOTAL			
				1/4	MEDIAN	3/4	1/4	MEDIAN	3/4	
74	2720	Plumbing	S.F.	6.40	9.05	12.05	5.70%	7.15%	9.35%	74
	2730	Heating, ventilating, air conditioning		9.60	15.25	21.50	8.15%	10.80%	14.90%	
	2900	Electrical		10.50	14	17.85	8.45%	10.05%	11.85%	
	3100	Total: Mechanical & Electrical	↓	38	46.50	59	25%	27.50%	30%	
	9000	Per pupil, total cost	Ea.	12,800	19,000	42,500				
	9500	Total: Mechanical & Electrical	"	3,600	4,550	11,500				
76	0010	**SCHOOLS Junior High & Middle**	S.F.	115	142	173				76
	0020	Total project costs	C.F.	7.30	9.40	10.55				
	0500	Masonry	S.F.	12.30	18.40	22.50	7.55%	11.10%	14.30%	
	1800	Equipment		3.14	5.90	8.65	1.80%	3.03%	4.80%	
	2720	Plumbing		6.70	8.25	10.20	5.30%	6.80%	7.25%	
	2770	Heating, ventilating, air conditioning		13.35	16.20	28.50	8.90%	11.55%	14.20%	
	2900	Electrical		11.70	14.45	18.25	8.05%	9.55%	10.60%	
	3100	Total: Mechanical & Electrical	↓	36.50	47	58.50	23%	25.50%	29.50%	
	9000	Per pupil, total cost	Ea.	14,500	19,100	25,600				
78	0010	**SCHOOLS Senior High**	S.F.	120	147	184				78
	0020	Total project costs	C.F.	7.20	10.10	17.05				
	1800	Equipment	S.F.	3.17	7.40	10.25	1.88%	2.67%	4.30%	
	2720	Plumbing		6.70	10.05	18.35	5.60%	6.90%	8.30%	
	2770	Heating, ventilating, air conditioning		11.50	15.65	24	8.95%	11.60%	15%	
	2900	Electrical		12.05	16.05	23.50	8.70%	10.35%	12.50%	
	3100	Total: Mechanical & Electrical	↓	39.50	47	76	24%	26.50%	28.50%	
	9000	Per pupil, total cost	Ea.	11,200	22,900	28,600				
80	0010	**SCHOOLS Vocational**	S.F.	96.50	140	173				80
	0020	Total project costs	C.F.	6	8.60	11.90				
	0500	Masonry	S.F.	4.24	14	21.50	3.20%	4.61%	10.95%	
	1800	Equipment		3.02	7.50	10.35	1.24%	3.10%	4.26%	
	2720	Plumbing		6.15	9.20	13.55	5.40%	6.90%	8.55%	
	2770	Heating, ventilating, air conditioning		8.65	16.05	27	8.60%	11.90%	14.65%	
	2900	Electrical		10.05	13.75	18.80	8.45%	11%	13.20%	
	3100	Total: Mechanical & Electrical	↓	38	66.50	85	27.50%	29.50%	31%	
	9000	Per pupil, total cost	Ea.	13,400	36,000	53,500				
83	0010	**SPORTS ARENAS**	S.F.	84.50	113	174				83
	0020	Total project costs	C.F.	4.58	8.20	10.60				
	2720	Plumbing	S.F.	4.22	7.40	15.65	4.35%	6.35%	9.40%	
	2770	Heating, ventilating, air conditioning		10.55	12.45	17.30	8.80%	10.20%	13.55%	
	2900	Electrical	↓	7.80	11.90	15.40	7.65%	9.75%	11.90%	
85	0010	**SUPERMARKETS**	S.F.	78	90	106				85
	0020	Total project costs	C.F.	4.34	5.25	7.95				
	2720	Plumbing	S.F.	4.35	5.50	6.40	5.40%	6%	7.45%	
	2770	Heating, ventilating, air conditioning		6.40	8.50	10.35	8.60%	8.65%	9.60%	
	2900	Electrical		9.15	11.15	13.25	10.40%	12.45%	13.60%	
	3100	Total: Mechanical & Electrical	↓	25	26.50	35.50	23.50%	27.50%	28.50%	
86	0010	**SWIMMING POOLS**	S.F.	126	295	450				86
	0020	Total project costs	C.F.	10.10	12.60	13.75				
	2720	Plumbing	S.F.	11.65	13.35	17.90	4.80%	9.70%	20.50%	
	2900	Electrical		9.60	15.35	34	6.05%	6.95%	7.60%	
	3100	Total: Mechanical & Electrical	↓	60	79	104	11.15%	14.10%	23.50%	
87	0010	**TELEPHONE EXCHANGES**	S.F.	157	238	310				87
	0020	Total project costs	C.F.	10.40	16.75	23				
	2720	Plumbing	S.F.	7.05	10.90	16	4.52%	5.80%	6.90%	
	2770	Heating, ventilating, air conditioning		16.40	33	41	11.80%	16.05%	18.40%	
	2900	Electrical		17.05	27	48	10.90%	14%	17.85%	
	3100	Total: Mechanical & Electrical	↓	50.50	95.50	135	29.50%	33.50%	44.50%	
91	0010	**THEATERS**	S.F.	99.50	135	199				91
	0020	Total project costs	C.F.	4.87	7.20	10.55				

		50 17 00 | S.F. Costs	UNIT	UNIT COSTS			% OF TOTAL			
				1/4	MEDIAN	3/4	1/4	MEDIAN	3/4	
91	2720	Plumbing	S.F.	3.28	3.80	15.55	2.92%	4.70%	6.80%	91
	2770	Heating, ventilating, air conditioning		10.25	12.40	15.35	8%	12.25%	13.40%	
	2900	Electrical		9.20	12.45	25.50	8.05%	9.35%	12.25%	
	3100	Total: Mechanical & Electrical	↓	23.50	32	37.50	21.50%	25.50%	27.50%	
94	0010	**TOWN HALLS City Halls & Municipal Buildings**	S.F.	110	149	195				94
	0020	Total project costs	C.F.	7.95	12.40	18.10				
	2720	Plumbing	S.F.	4.91	9.20	16.10	4.31%	5.95%	7.95%	
	2770	Heating, ventilating, air conditioning		8.85	17.60	26	7.05%	9.05%	13.45%	
	2900	Electrical		11.15	15.40	21	8.05%	9.45%	11.65%	
	3100	Total: Mechanical & Electrical	↓	38.50	49	75	22%	26.50%	31%	
97	0010	**WAREHOUSES & Storage Buildings**	S.F.	44	63	93				97
	0020	Total project costs	C.F.	2.30	3.60	5.95				
	0100	Site work	S.F.	4.53	9	13.55	6.05%	12.95%	19.55%	
	0500	Masonry		2.49	6.25	13.45	3.60%	7.35%	12%	
	1800	Equipment		.67	1.52	8.55	.72%	1.69%	5.55%	
	2720	Plumbing		1.46	2.62	4.91	2.90%	4.80%	6.55%	
	2730	Heating, ventilating, air conditioning		1.67	4.71	6.30	2.41%	5%	8.90%	
	2900	Electrical		2.60	4.89	8	5.15%	7.20%	10.05%	
	3100	Total: Mechanical & Electrical	↓	7.25	11.10	22	13.30%	18.90%	26%	
99	0010	**WAREHOUSE & OFFICES Combination**	S.F.	54	72	99				99
	0020	Total project costs	C.F.	2.76	4.01	5.90				
	1800	Equipment	S.F.	.93	1.81	2.69	.42%	1.19%	2.40%	
	2720	Plumbing		2.08	3.63	5.40	3.74%	4.76%	6.30%	
	2770	Heating, ventilating, air conditioning		3.29	5.15	7.20	5%	5.65%	10.05%	
	2900	Electrical		3.68	5.45	8.50	5.85%	8%	10%	
	3100	Total: Mechanical & Electrical	↓	10.25	15.55	24.50	14.55%	19.95%	24.50%	

Square Foot Project Size Modifier

One factor that affects the S.F. cost of a particular building is the size. In general, for buildings built to the same specifications in the same locality, the larger building will have the lower S.F. cost. This is due mainly to the decreasing contribution of the exterior walls, plus the economy of scale usually achievable in larger buildings. The area conversion scale shown below will give a factor to convert costs for the typical size building to an adjusted cost for the particular project.

The square foot base size table lists the median costs, most typical project size in our accumulated data, and the range in size of the projects.

The size factor for your project is determined by dividing your project area in S.F. by the typical project size for the particular building type. With this factor, enter the area conversion scale at the appropriate size factor and determine the appropriate cost multiplier for your building size.

Example: Determine the cost per S.F. for a 100,000 S.F. Mid-rise apartment building.

$$\frac{\text{Proposed building area} = 100,000 \text{ S.F.}}{\text{Typical size from below} = 50,000 \text{ S.F.}} = 2.00$$

Enter area conversion scale at 2.0, intersect curve, read horizontally the appropriate cost multiplier of .94. Size adjusted cost becomes .94 × $117.00 = $110.00 based on national average costs.

Note: For size factors less than .50, the cost multiplier is 1.1
For size factors greater than 3.5, the cost multiplier is .90

Square Foot Base Size							
Building Type	**Median Cost per S.F.**	**Typical Size Gross S.F.**	**Typical Range Gross S.F.**	**Building Type**	**Median Cost per S.F.**	**Typical Size Gross S.F.**	**Typical Range Gross S.F.**
Apartments, Low Rise	$ 92.50	21,000	9,700 - 37,200	Jails	$ 280.00	40,000	5,500 - 145,000
Apartments, Mid Rise	117.00	50,000	32,000 - 100,000	Libraries	186.00	12,000	7,000 - 31,000
Apartments, High Rise	127.00	145,000	95,000 - 600,000	Living, Assisted	151.00	32,300	23,500 - 50,300
Auditoriums	158.00	25,000	7,600 - 39,000	Medical Clinics	159.00	7,200	4,200 - 15,700
Auto Sales	115.00	20,000	10,800 - 28,600	Medical Offices	151.00	6,000	4,000 - 15,000
Banks	207.00	4,200	2,500 - 7,500	Motels	111.00	40,000	15,800 - 120,000
Churches	143.00	17,000	2,000 - 42,000	Nursing Homes	155.00	23,000	15,000 - 37,000
Clubs, Country	144.00	6,500	4,500 - 15,000	Offices, Low Rise	132.00	20,000	5,000 - 80,000
Clubs, Social	138.00	10,000	6,000 - 13,500	Offices, Mid Rise	130.00	120,000	20,000 - 300,000
Clubs, YMCA	164.00	28,300	12,800 - 39,400	Offices, High Rise	166.00	260,000	120,000 - 800,000
Colleges (Class)	164.00	50,000	15,000 - 150,000	Police Stations	208.00	10,500	4,000 - 19,000
Colleges (Science Lab)	264.00	45,600	16,600 - 80,000	Post Offices	154.00	12,400	6,800 - 30,000
College (Student Union)	195.00	33,400	16,000 - 85,000	Power Plants	1150.00	7,500	1,000 - 20,000
Community Center	147.00	9,400	5,300 - 16,700	Religious Education	131.00	9,000	6,000 - 12,000
Court Houses	202.00	32,400	17,800 - 106,000	Research	217.00	19,000	6,300 - 45,000
Dept. Stores	85.50	90,000	44,000 - 122,000	Restaurants	188.00	4,400	2,800 - 6,000
Dormitories, Low Rise	166.00	25,000	10,000 - 95,000	Retail Stores	91.50	7,200	4,000 - 17,600
Dormitories, Mid Rise	192.00	85,000	20,000 - 200,000	Schools, Elementary	138.00	41,000	24,500 - 55,000
Factories	83.00	26,400	12,900 - 50,000	Schools, Jr. High	142.00	92,000	52,000 - 119,000
Fire Stations	153.00	5,800	4,000 - 8,700	Schools, Sr. High	147.00	101,000	50,500 - 175,000
Fraternity Houses	142.00	12,500	8,200 - 14,800	Schools, Vocational	140.00	37,000	20,500 - 82,000
Funeral Homes	159.00	10,000	4,000 - 20,000	Sports Arenas	113.00	15,000	5,000 - 40,000
Garages, Commercial	102.00	9,300	5,000 - 13,600	Supermarkets	90.00	44,000	12,000 - 60,000
Garages, Municipal	129.00	8,300	4,500 - 12,600	Swimming Pools	295.00	20,000	10,000 - 32,000
Garages, Parking	55.00	163,000	76,400 - 225,300	Telephone Exchange	238.00	4,500	1,200 - 10,600
Gymnasiums	140.00	19,200	11,600 - 41,000	Theaters	135.00	10,500	8,800 - 17,500
Hospitals	253.00	55,000	27,200 - 125,000	Town Halls	149.00	10,800	4,800 - 23,400
House (Elderly)	126.00	37,000	21,000 - 66,000	Warehouses	63.00	25,000	8,000 - 72,000
Housing (Public)	116.00	36,000	14,400 - 74,400	Warehouse & Office	72.00	25,000	8,000 - 72,000
Ice Rinks	167.00	29,000	27,200 - 33,600				

Abbreviations

A	Area Square Feet; Ampere	Brk., brk	Brick	Csc	Cosecant
AAFES	Army and Air Force Exchange Service	brkt	Bracket	C.S.F.	Hundred Square Feet
ABS	Acrylonitrile Butadiene Stryrene; Asbestos Bonded Steel	Brng.	Bearing	CSI	Construction Specifications Institute
		Brs.	Brass		
		Brz.	Bronze	CT	Current Transformer
A.C., AC	Alternating Current; Air-Conditioning; Asbestos Cement; Plywood Grade A & C	Bsn.	Basin	CTS	Copper Tube Size
		Btr.	Better	Cu	Copper, Cubic
		Btu	British Thermal Unit	Cu. Ft.	Cubic Foot
		BTUH	BTU per Hour	cw	Continuous Wave
ACI	American Concrete Institute	Bu.	bushels	C.W.	Cool White; Cold Water
ACR	Air Conditioning Refrigeration	BUR	Built-up Roofing	Cwt.	100 Pounds
ADA	Americans with Disabilities Act	BX	Interlocked Armored Cable	C.W.X.	Cool White Deluxe
AD	Plywood, Grade A & D	°C	degree centegrade	C.Y.	Cubic Yard (27 cubic feet)
Addit.	Additional	c	Conductivity, Copper Sweat	C.Y./Hr.	Cubic Yard per Hour
Adj.	Adjustable	C	Hundred; Centigrade	Cyl.	Cylinder
af	Audio-frequency	C/C	Center to Center, Cedar on Cedar	d	Penny (nail size)
AFUE	Annual Fuel Utilization Efficiency	C-C	Center to Center	D	Deep; Depth; Discharge
AGA	American Gas Association	Cab	Cabinet	Dis., Disch.	Discharge
Agg.	Aggregate	Cair.	Air Tool Laborer	Db	Decibel
A.H., Ah	Ampere Hours	Cal.	caliper	Dbl.	Double
A hr.	Ampere-hour	Calc	Calculated	DC	Direct Current
A.H.U., AHU	Air Handling Unit	Cap.	Capacity	DDC	Direct Digital Control
A.I.A.	American Institute of Architects	Carp.	Carpenter	Demob.	Demobilization
AIC	Ampere Interrupting Capacity	C.B.	Circuit Breaker	d.f.t.	Dry Film Thickness
Allow.	Allowance	C.C.A.	Chromate Copper Arsenate	d.f.u.	Drainage Fixture Units
alt., alt	Alternate	C.C.F.	Hundred Cubic Feet	D.H.	Double Hung
Alum.	Aluminum	cd	Candela	DHW	Domestic Hot Water
a.m.	Ante Meridiem	cd/sf	Candela per Square Foot	DI	Ductile Iron
Amp.	Ampere	CD	Grade of Plywood Face & Back	Diag.	Diagonal
Anod.	Anodized	CDX	Plywood, Grade C & D, exterior glue	Diam., Dia	Diameter
ANSI	American National Standards Institute			Distrib.	Distribution
		Cefi.	Cement Finisher	Div.	Division
APA	American Plywood Association	Cem.	Cement	Dk.	Deck
Approx.	Approximate	CF	Hundred Feet	D.L.	Dead Load; Diesel
Apt.	Apartment	C.F.	Cubic Feet	DLH	Deep Long Span Bar Joist
Asb.	Asbestos	CFM	Cubic Feet per Minute	dlx	Deluxe
A.S.B.C.	American Standard Building Code	CFRP	Carbon Fiber Reinforced Plastic	Do.	Ditto
Asbe.	Asbestos Worker	c.g.	Center of Gravity	DOP	Dioctyl Phthalate Penetration Test (Air Filters)
ASCE	American Society of Civil Engineers	CHW	Chilled Water; Commercial Hot Water		
A.S.H.R.A.E.	American Society of Heating, Refrig. & AC Engineers			Dp., dp	Depth
		C.I., CI	Cast Iron	D.P.S.T.	Double Pole, Single Throw
ASME	American Society of Mechanical Engineers	C.I.P., CIP	Cast in Place	Dr.	Drive
		Circ.	Circuit	DR	Dimension Ratio
ASTM	American Society for Testing and Materials	C.L.	Carload Lot	Drink.	Drinking
		CL	Chain Link	D.S.	Double Strength
Attchmt.	Attachment	Clab.	Common Laborer	D.S.A.	Double Strength A Grade
Avg., Ave.	Average	Clam	Common maintenance laborer	D.S.B.	Double Strength B Grade
AWG	American Wire Gauge	C.L.F.	Hundred Linear Feet	Dty.	Duty
AWWA	American Water Works Assoc.	CLF	Current Limiting Fuse	DWV	Drain Waste Vent
Bbl.	Barrel	CLP	Cross Linked Polyethylene	DX	Deluxe White, Direct Expansion
B&B, BB	Grade B and Better; Balled & Burlapped	cm	Centimeter	dyn	Dyne
		CMP	Corr. Metal Pipe	e	Eccentricity
B&S	Bell and Spigot	CMU	Concrete Masonry Unit	E	Equipment Only; East; emissivity
B.&W.	Black and White	CN	Change Notice	Ea.	Each
b.c.c.	Body-centered Cubic	Col.	Column	EB	Encased Burial
B.C.Y.	Bank Cubic Yards	CO₂	Carbon Dioxide	Econ.	Economy
BE	Bevel End	Comb.	Combination	E.C.Y	Embankment Cubic Yards
B.F.	Board Feet	comm.	Commercial, Communication	EDP	Electronic Data Processing
Bg. cem.	Bag of Cement	Compr.	Compressor	EIFS	Exterior Insulation Finish System
BHP	Boiler Horsepower; Brake Horsepower	Conc.	Concrete	E.D.R.	Equiv. Direct Radiation
		Cont., cont	Continuous; Continued, Container	Eq.	Equation
B.I.	Black Iron	Corr.	Corrugated	EL	elevation
bidir.	bidirectional	Cos	Cosine	Elec.	Electrician; Electrical
Bit., Bitum.	Bituminous	Cot	Cotangent	Elev.	Elevator; Elevating
Bit., Conc.	Bituminous Concrete	Cov.	Cover	EMT	Electrical Metallic Conduit; Thin Wall Conduit
Bk.	Backed	C/P	Cedar on Paneling		
Bkrs.	Breakers	CPA	Control Point Adjustment	Eng.	Engine, Engineered
Bldg., bldg	Building	Cplg.	Coupling	EPDM	Ethylene Propylene Diene Monomer
Blk.	Block	CPM	Critical Path Method		
Bm.	Beam	CPVC	Chlorinated Polyvinyl Chloride	EPS	Expanded Polystyrene
Boil.	Boilermaker	C.Pr.	Hundred Pair	Eqhv.	Equip. Oper., Heavy
bpm	Blows per Minute	CRC	Cold Rolled Channel	Eqlt.	Equip. Oper., Light
BR	Bedroom	Creos.	Creosote	Eqmd.	Equip. Oper., Medium
Brg.	Bearing	Crpt.	Carpet & Linoleum Layer	Eqmm.	Equip. Oper., Master Mechanic
Brhe.	Bricklayer Helper	CRT	Cathode-ray Tube	Eqol.	Equip. Oper., Oilers
Bric.	Bricklayer	CS	Carbon Steel, Constant Shear Bar Joist	Equip.	Equipment
				ERW	Electric Resistance Welded

855

E.S.	Energy Saver	H	High Henry	Lath.	Lather
Est.	Estimated	HC	High Capacity	Lav.	Lavatory
esu	Electrostatic Units	H.D., HD	Heavy Duty; High Density	lb.; #	Pound
E.W.	Each Way	H.D.O.	High Density Overlaid	L.B., LB	Load Bearing; L Conduit Body
EWT	Entering Water Temperature	HDPE	High density polyethelene plastic	L. & E.	Labor & Equipment
Excav.	Excavation	Hdr.	Header	lb./hr.	Pounds per Hour
excl	Excluding	Hdwe.	Hardware	lb./L.F.	Pounds per Linear Foot
Exp., exp	Expansion, Exposure	H.I.D., HID	High Intensity Discharge	lbf/sq.in.	Pound-force per Square Inch
Ext., ext	Exterior; Extension	Help.	Helper Average	L.C.L.	Less than Carload Lot
Extru.	Extrusion	HEPA	High Efficiency Particulate Air	L.C.Y.	Loose Cubic Yard
f.	Fiber stress		Filter	Ld.	Load
F	Fahrenheit; Female; Fill	Hg	Mercury	LE	Lead Equivalent
Fab., fab	Fabricated; fabric	HIC	High Interrupting Capacity	LED	Light Emitting Diode
FBGS	Fiberglass	HM	Hollow Metal	L.F.	Linear Foot
F.C.	Footcandles	HMWPE	high molecular weight	L.F. Nose	Linear Foot of Stair Nosing
f.c.c.	Face-centered Cubic		polyethylene	L.F. Rsr	Linear Foot of Stair Riser
f'c.	Compressive Stress in Concrete;	HO	High Output	Lg.	Long; Length; Large
	Extreme Compressive Stress	Horiz.	Horizontal	L & H	Light and Heat
F.E.	Front End	H.P., HP	Horsepower; High Pressure	LH	Long Span Bar Joist
FEP	Fluorinated Ethylene Propylene	H.P.F.	High Power Factor	L.H.	Labor Hours
	(Teflon)	Hr.	Hour	L.L., LL	Live Load
F.G.	Flat Grain	Hrs./Day	Hours per Day	L.L.D.	Lamp Lumen Depreciation
F.H.A.	Federal Housing Administration	HSC	High Short Circuit	lm	Lumen
Fig.	Figure	Ht.	Height	lm/sf	Lumen per Square Foot
Fin.	Finished	Htg.	Heating	lm/W	Lumen per Watt
FIPS	Female Iron Pipe Size	Htrs.	Heaters	LOA	Length Over All
Fixt.	Fixture	HVAC	Heating, Ventilation & Air-	log	Logarithm
FJP	Finger jointed and primed		Conditioning	L-O-L	Lateralolet
Fl. Oz.	Fluid Ounces	Hvy.	Heavy	long.	longitude
Flr.	Floor	HW	Hot Water	L.P., LP	Liquefied Petroleum; Low Pressure
FM	Frequency Modulation;	Hyd.; Hydr.	Hydraulic	L.P.F.	Low Power Factor
	Factory Mutual	Hz	Hertz (cycles)	LR	Long Radius
Fmg.	Framing	I.	Moment of Inertia	L.S.	Lump Sum
FM/UL	Factory Mutual/Underwriters Labs	IBC	International Building Code	Lt.	Light
Fdn.	Foundation	I.C.	Interrupting Capacity	Lt. Ga.	Light Gauge
FNPT	Female National Pipe Thread	ID	Inside Diameter	L.T.L.	Less than Truckload Lot
Fori.	Foreman, Inside	I.D.	Inside Dimension; Identification	Lt. Wt.	Lightweight
Foro.	Foreman, Outside	I.F.	Inside Frosted	L.V.	Low Voltage
Fount.	Fountain	I.M.C.	Intermediate Metal Conduit	M	Thousand; Material; Male;
fpm	Feet per Minute	In.	Inch		Light Wall Copper Tubing
FPT	Female Pipe Thread	Incan.	Incandescent	M²CA	Meters Squared Contact Area
Fr	Frame	Incl.	Included; Including	m/hr.; M.H.	Man-hour
F.R.	Fire Rating	Int.	Interior	mA	Milliampere
FRK	Foil Reinforced Kraft	Inst.	Installation	Mach.	Machine
FSK	Foil/scrim/kraft	Insul., insul	Insulation/Insulated	Mag. Str.	Magnetic Starter
FRP	Fiberglass Reinforced Plastic	I.P.	Iron Pipe	Maint.	Maintenance
FS	Forged Steel	I.P.S., IPS	Iron Pipe Size	Marb.	Marble Setter
FSC	Cast Body; Cast Switch Box	IPT	Iron Pipe Threaded	Mat; Mat'l.	Material
Ft., ft	Foot; Feet	I.W.	Indirect Waste	Max.	Maximum
Ftng.	Fitting	J	Joule	MBF	Thousand Board Feet
Ftg.	Footing	J.I.C.	Joint Industrial Council	MBH	Thousand BTU's per hr.
Ft lb.	Foot Pound	K	Thousand; Thousand Pounds;	MC	Metal Clad Cable
Furn.	Furniture		Heavy Wall Copper Tubing, Kelvin	MCC	Motor Control Center
FVNR	Full Voltage Non-Reversing	K.A.H.	Thousand Amp. Hours	M.C.F.	Thousand Cubic Feet
FVR	Full Voltage Reversing	kcmil	Thousand Circular Mils	MCFM	Thousand Cubic Feet per Minute
FXM	Female by Male	KD	Knock Down	M.C.M.	Thousand Circular Mils
Fy.	Minimum Yield Stress of Steel	K.D.A.T.	Kiln Dried After Treatment	MCP	Motor Circuit Protector
g	Gram	kg	Kilogram	MD	Medium Duty
G	Gauss	kG	Kilogauss	MDF	Medium-density fibreboard
Ga.	Gauge	kgf	Kilogram Force	M.D.O.	Medium Density Overlaid
Gal., gal.	Gallon	kHz	Kilohertz	Med.	Medium
gpm, GPM	Gallon per Minute	Kip	1000 Pounds	MF	Thousand Feet
Galv., galv	Galvanized	KJ	Kiljoule	M.F.B.M.	Thousand Feet Board Measure
GC/MS	Gas Chromatograph/Mass	K.L.	Effective Length Factor	Mfg.	Manufacturing
	Spectrometer	K.L.F.	Kips per Linear Foot	Mfrs.	Manufacturers
Gen.	General	Km	Kilometer	mg	Milligram
GFI	Ground Fault Interrupter	KO	Knock Out	MGD	Million Gallons per Day
GFRC	Glass Fiber Reinforced Concrete	K.S.F.	Kips per Square Foot	MGPH	Thousand Gallons per Hour
Glaz.	Glazier	K.S.I.	Kips per Square Inch	MH, M.H.	Manhole; Metal Halide; Man-Hour
GPD	Gallons per Day	kV	Kilovolt	MHz	Megahertz
gpf	Gallon per flush	kVA	Kilovolt Ampere	Mi.	Mile
GPH	Gallons per Hour	kVAR	Kilovar (Reactance)	MI	Malleable Iron; Mineral Insulated
GPM	Gallons per Minute	KW	Kilowatt	MIPS	Male Iron Pipe Size
GR	Grade	KWh	Kilowatt-hour	mj	Mechanical Joint
Gran.	Granular	L	Labor Only; Length; Long;	m	Meter
Grnd.	Ground		Medium Wall Copper Tubing	mm	Millimeter
GVW	Gross Vehicle Weight	Lab.	Labor	Mill.	Millwright
GWB	Gypsum wall board	lat	Latitude	Min., min.	Minimum, minute

Abbreviations

Abbreviation	Meaning
Misc.	Miscellaneous
ml	Milliliter, Mainline
M.L.F.	Thousand Linear Feet
Mo.	Month
Mobil.	Mobilization
Mog.	Mogul Base
MPH	Miles per Hour
MPT	Male Pipe Thread
MRGWB	Moisture Resistant Gypsum Wallboard
MRT	Mile Round Trip
ms	Millisecond
M.S.F.	Thousand Square Feet
Mstz.	Mosaic & Terrazzo Worker
M.S.Y.	Thousand Square Yards
Mtd., mtd., mtd	Mounted
Mthe.	Mosaic & Terrazzo Helper
Mtng.	Mounting
Mult.	Multi; Multiply
M.V.A.	Million Volt Amperes
M.V.A.R.	Million Volt Amperes Reactance
MV	Megavolt
MW	Megawatt
MXM	Male by Male
MYD	Thousand Yards
N	Natural; North
nA	Nanoampere
NA	Not Available; Not Applicable
N.B.C.	National Building Code
NC	Normally Closed
NEMA	National Electrical Manufacturers Assoc.
NEHB	Bolted Circuit Breaker to 600V.
NFPA	National Fire Protection Association
NLB	Non-Load-Bearing
NM	Non-Metallic Cable
nm	Nanometer
No.	Number
NO	Normally Open
N.O.C.	Not Otherwise Classified
Nose.	Nosing
NPT	National Pipe Thread
NQOD	Combination Plug-on/Bolt on Circuit Breaker to 240V.
N.R.C., NRC	Noise Reduction Coefficient/ Nuclear Regulator Commission
N.R.S.	Non Rising Stem
ns	Nanosecond
nW	Nanowatt
OB	Opposing Blade
OC	On Center
OD	Outside Diameter
O.D.	Outside Dimension
ODS	Overhead Distribution System
O.G.	Ogee
O.H.	Overhead
O&P	Overhead and Profit
Oper.	Operator
Opng.	Opening
Orna.	Ornamental
OSB	Oriented Strand Board
OS&Y	Outside Screw and Yoke
OSHA	Occupational Safety and Health Act
Ovhd.	Overhead
OWG	Oil, Water or Gas
Oz.	Ounce
P.	Pole; Applied Load; Projection
p.	Page
Pape.	Paperhanger
P.A.P.R.	Powered Air Purifying Respirator
PAR	Parabolic Reflector
P.B., PB	Push Button
Pc., Pcs.	Piece, Pieces
P.C.	Portland Cement; Power Connector
P.C.F.	Pounds per Cubic Foot
PCM	Phase Contrast Microscopy
PDCA	Painting and Decorating Contractors of America
P.E., PE	Professional Engineer; Porcelain Enamel; Polyethylene; Plain End
P.E.C.I.	Porcelain Enamel on Cast Iron
Perf.	Perforated
PEX	Cross linked polyethylene
Ph.	Phase
P.I.	Pressure Injected
Pile.	Pile Driver
Pkg.	Package
Pl.	Plate
Plah.	Plasterer Helper
Plas.	Plasterer
plf	Pounds Per Linear Foot
Pluh.	Plumbers Helper
Plum.	Plumber
Ply.	Plywood
p.m.	Post Meridiem
Pntd.	Painted
Pord.	Painter, Ordinary
pp	Pages
PP, PPL	Polypropylene
P.P.M.	Parts per Million
Pr.	Pair
P.E.S.B.	Pre-engineered Steel Building
Prefab.	Prefabricated
Prefin.	Prefinished
Prop.	Propelled
PSF, psf	Pounds per Square Foot
PSI, psi	Pounds per Square Inch
PSIG	Pounds per Square Inch Gauge
PSP	Plastic Sewer Pipe
Pspr.	Painter, Spray
Psst.	Painter, Structural Steel
P.T.	Potential Transformer
P. & T.	Pressure & Temperature
Ptd.	Painted
Ptns.	Partitions
Pu	Ultimate Load
PVC	Polyvinyl Chloride
Pvmt.	Pavement
PRV	Pressure Relief Valve
Pwr.	Power
Q	Quantity Heat Flow
Qt.	Quart
Quan., Qty.	Quantity
Q.C.	Quick Coupling
r	Radius of Gyration
R	Resistance
R.C.P.	Reinforced Concrete Pipe
Rect.	Rectangle
recpt.	receptacle
Reg.	Regular
Reinf.	Reinforced
Req'd.	Required
Res.	Resistant
Resi.	Residential
RF	Radio Frequency
RFID	Radio-frequency identification
Rgh.	Rough
RGS	Rigid Galvanized Steel
RHW	Rubber, Heat & Water Resistant; Residential Hot Water
rms	Root Mean Square
Rnd.	Round
Rodm.	Rodman
Rofc.	Roofer, Composition
Rofp.	Roofer, Precast
Rohe.	Roofer Helpers (Composition)
Rots.	Roofer, Tile & Slate
R.O.W.	Right of Way
RPM	Revolutions per Minute
R.S.	Rapid Start
Rsr	Riser
RT	Round Trip
S.	Suction; Single Entrance; South
SBS	Styrene Butadiere Styrene
SC	Screw Cover
SCFM	Standard Cubic Feet per Minute
Scaf.	Scaffold
Sch., Sched.	Schedule
S.C.R.	Modular Brick
S.D.	Sound Deadening
SDR	Standard Dimension Ratio
S.E.	Surfaced Edge
Sel.	Select
SER, SEU	Service Entrance Cable
S.F.	Square Foot
S.F.C.A.	Square Foot Contact Area
S.F. Flr.	Square Foot of Floor
S.F.G.	Square Foot of Ground
S.F. Hor.	Square Foot Horizontal
SFR	Square Feet of Radiation
S.F. Shlf.	Square Foot of Shelf
S4S	Surface 4 Sides
Shee.	Sheet Metal Worker
Sin.	Sine
Skwk.	Skilled Worker
SL	Saran Lined
S.L.	Slimline
Sldr.	Solder
SLH	Super Long Span Bar Joist
S.N.	Solid Neutral
SO	Stranded with oil resistant inside insulation
S-O-L	Socketolet
sp	Standpipe
S.P.	Static Pressure; Single Pole; Self-Propelled
Spri.	Sprinkler Installer
spwg	Static Pressure Water Gauge
S.P.D.T.	Single Pole, Double Throw
SPF	Spruce Pine Fir; Sprayed Polyurethane Foam
S.P.S.T.	Single Pole, Single Throw
SPT	Standard Pipe Thread
Sq.	Square; 100 Square Feet
Sq. Hd.	Square Head
Sq. In.	Square Inch
S.S.	Single Strength; Stainless Steel
S.S.B.	Single Strength B Grade
sst, ss	Stainless Steel
Sswk.	Structural Steel Worker
Sswl.	Structural Steel Welder
St.; Stl.	Steel
STC	Sound Transmission Coefficient
Std.	Standard
Stg.	Staging
STK	Select Tight Knot
STP	Standard Temperature & Pressure
Stpi.	Steamfitter, Pipefitter
Str.	Strength; Starter; Straight
Strd.	Stranded
Struct.	Structural
Sty.	Story
Subj.	Subject
Subs.	Subcontractors
Surf.	Surface
Sw.	Switch
Swbd.	Switchboard
S.Y.	Square Yard
Syn.	Synthetic
S.Y.P.	Southern Yellow Pine
Sys.	System
t.	Thickness
T	Temperature; Ton
Tan	Tangent
T.C.	Terra Cotta
T & C	Threaded and Coupled
T.D.	Temperature Difference
Tdd	Telecommunications Device for the Deaf
T.E.M.	Transmission Electron Microscopy
temp	Temperature, Tempered, Temporary
TFFN	Nylon Jacketed Wire

TFE	Tetrafluoroethylene (Teflon)	U.L., UL	Underwriters Laboratory	w/	With
T. & G.	Tongue & Groove;	Uld.	unloading	W.C., WC	Water Column; Water Closet
	Tar & Gravel	Unfin.	Unfinished	W.F.	Wide Flange
Th., Thk.	Thick	UPS	Uninterruptible Power Supply	W.G.	Water Gauge
Thn.	Thin	URD	Underground Residential	Wldg.	Welding
Thrded	Threaded		Distribution	W. Mile	Wire Mile
Tilf.	Tile Layer, Floor	US	United States	W-O-L	Weldolet
Tilh.	Tile Layer, Helper	USGBC	U.S. Green Building Council	W.R.	Water Resistant
THHN	Nylon Jacketed Wire	USP	United States Primed	Wrck.	Wrecker
THW.	Insulated Strand Wire	UTMCD	Uniform Traffic Manual For Control	W.S.P.	Water, Steam, Petroleum
THWN	Nylon Jacketed Wire		Devices	WT., Wt.	Weight
T.L., TL	Truckload	UTP	Unshielded Twisted Pair	WWF	Welded Wire Fabric
T.M.	Track Mounted	V	Volt	XFER	Transfer
Tot.	Total	VA	Volt Amperes	XFMR	Transformer
T-O-L	Threadolet	V.C.T.	Vinyl Composition Tile	XHD	Extra Heavy Duty
tmpd	Tempered	VAV	Variable Air Volume	XHHW,	Cross-Linked Polyethylene Wire
TPO	Thermoplastic Polyolefin	VC	Veneer Core	XLPE	Insulation
T.S.	Trigger Start	VDC	Volts Direct Current	XLP	Cross-linked Polyethylene
Tr.	Trade	Vent.	Ventilation	Xport	Transport
Transf.	Transformer	Vert.	Vertical	Y	Wye
Trhv.	Truck Driver, Heavy	V.F.	Vinyl Faced	yd	Yard
Trlr	Trailer	V.G.	Vertical Grain	yr	Year
Trlt.	Truck Driver, Light	VHF	Very High Frequency	Δ	Delta
TTY	Teletypewriter	VHO	Very High Output	%	Percent
TV	Television	Vib.	Vibrating	~	Approximately
T.W.	Thermoplastic Water Resistant	VLF	Vertical Linear Foot	Ø	Phase; diameter
	Wire	VOC	Volitile Organic Compound	@	At
UCI	Uniform Construction Index	Vol.	Volume	#	Pound; Number
UF	Underground Feeder	VRP	Vinyl Reinforced Polyester	<	Less Than
UGND	Underground Feeder	W	Wire; Watt; Wide; West	>	Greater Than
UHF	Ultra High Frequency			Z	zone
U.I.	United Inch				

Index

Index

Index

Index

Index

Reed Construction Data/RSMeans—
a tradition of excellence in construction cost information and services since 1942

Table of Contents
Annual Cost Guides
Seminars
New Titles
Reference Books
Order Form

or more information visit the RSMeans website at **www.rsmeans.com**　　　　Unit prices according to the latest MasterFormat!

Book Selection Guide The following table provides definitive information on the content of each cost data publication. The number of lines of data provided in each unit price or assemblies division, as well as the number of reference tables and crews, is listed for each book. The presence of other elements such as equipment rental costs, historical cost indexes, city cost indexes, square foot models, or cross-referenced indexes is also indicated. You can use the table to help select the RSMeans book that has the quantity and type of information you most need in your work.

Unit Cost Divisions	Building Construction	Mechanical	Electrical	Commercial Renovation	Square Foot	Site Work Landsc.	Green Building	Interior	Concrete Masonry	Open Shop	Heavy Construction	Light Commercial	Facilities Construction	Plumbing	Residential
1	582	395	411	508		521	196	319	463	581	511	244	1054	411	180
2	789	279	85	741		1005	180	399	222	788	746	481	1233	289	257
3	1689	347	231	1087		1477	995	329	2040	1688	1685	479	1787	317	385
4	963	21	0	932		729	179	620	1159	931	621	521	1176	0	435
5	1873	158	155	1068		811	1779	1073	716	1873	1034	954	1874	204	723
6	2404	18	18	2062		110	560	1523	278	2400	126	2085	2076	22	2612
7	1531	215	128	1569		584	747	516	509	1528	26	1282	1633	227	1018
8	2107	81	45	2530		268	1140	1768	112	2093	0	2109	2842	0	1511
9	1929	72	26	1726		313	449	2014	387	1870	15	1644	2179	54	1430
10	1006	17	10	623		215	27	818	158	1006	29	511	1098	235	224
11	1026	208	165	489		126	54	878	28	1010	0	230	1046	169	110
12	557	0	2	327		248	151	1669	12	545	19	364	1718	23	317
13	729	117	114	246		347	128	253	66	728	253	82	756	71	80
14	277	36	0	224		0	0	261	0	277	0	12	297	16	6
21	90	0	16	37		0	0	250	0	87	0	68	427	432	220
22	1159	7329	156	1170		1578	1099	849	20	1123	1687	861	7171	9082	712
23	1182	6901	586	886		160	898	741	38	1106	111	759	5013	1830	434
26	1379	499	10134	1039		816	661	1142	55	1351	562	1305	10083	444	621
27	72	0	298	34		13	0	60	0	72	39	52	280	0	4
28	97	58	137	72		0	21	79	0	100	0	41	152	44	26
31	1498	735	610	803		3206	289	7	1208	1443	3285	600	1560	660	611
32	782	54	8	859		4396	352	362	286	753	1824	407	1660	166	455
33	509	1020	542	209		2036	41	0	231	508	2024	120	1585	1211	118
34	109	0	47	4		192	0	0	31	64	195	0	130	0	0
35	18	0	0	0		327	0	0	0	18	442	0	83	0	0
41	60	0	0	32		0	0	22	0	60	30	0	67	14	0
44	75	83	0	0		0	0	0	0	0	0	0	0	75	0
46	23	16	0	0		274	151	0	0	23	264	0	33	33	0
48	12	0	27	0		0	27	0	0	12	19	12	12	0	12
Totals	**24527**	**18659**	**13951**	**19277**		**19752**	**10124**	**15952**	**8019**	**24038**	**15547**	**15223**	**49100**	**16029**	**12501**

Assem Div	Building Construction	Mechanical	Electrical	Commercial Renovation	Square Foot	Site Work Landscape	Assemblies	Green Building	Interior	Concrete Masonry	Heavy Construction	Light Commercial	Facilities Construction	Plumbing	Asm Div	Residential
A		15	0	188	150	577	598	0	0	536	571	154	24	0	1	368
B		0	0	848	2498	0	5658	56	329	1975	368	2089	174	0	2	211
C		0	0	647	872	0	1251	0	1576	146	0	762	249	0	3	588
D		1067	943	712	1856	72	2532	330	822	0	0	1342	1106	1081	4	851
E		0	0	86	260	0	300	0	5	0	0	257	5	0	5	392
F		0	0	0	114	0	114	0	0	0	0	114	3	0	6	357
G		522	442	318	262	3740	663	0	0	534	1558	199	288	758	7	307
															8	760
															9	80
															10	0
															11	0
															12	0
Totals		**1604**	**1385**	**2799**	**6012**	**4389**	**11116**	**386**	**2732**	**3191**	**2497**	**4917**	**1849**	**1839**		**3914**

Reference Section	Building Construction Costs	Mechanical	Electrical	Commercial Renovation	Square Foot	Site Work Landscape	Assem.	Green Building	Interior	Concrete Masonry	Open Shop	Heavy Construction	Light Commercial	Facilities Construction	Plumbing	Resi.
Reference Tables	yes	yes	yes	yes	no	yes	yes	yes	yes	yes	yes	yes	yes	yes	yes	yes
Models					111			25					50			28
Crews	561	561	561	540		561		558	561	561	538	561	538	540	561	538
Equipment Rental Costs	yes	yes	yes	yes		yes		yes	yes	yes	yes	yes	yes	yes	yes	yes
Historical Cost Indexes	yes	yes	yes	yes		yes		yes	yes	yes	yes	yes	yes	yes	yes	no
City Cost Indexes	yes	yes	yes	yes		yes	yes	yes	yes	yes	yes	yes	yes	yes	yes	yes

RSMeans Building Construction Cost Data 2014

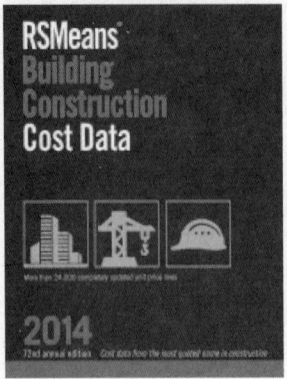

Offers you unchallenged unit price reliability in an easy-to-use format. Whether used for verifying complete, finished estimates or for periodic checks, it supplies more cost facts better and faster than any comparable source. More than 24,000 unit prices have been updated for 2014. The City Cost Indexes and Location Factors cover more than 930 areas, for indexing to any project location in North America. Order and get *RSMeans Quarterly Update Service* FREE.

$194.95 | Available Sept. 2013 | Catalog no. 60014

RSMeans Mechanical Cost Data 2014

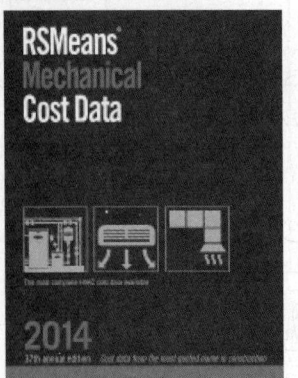

Total unit and systems price guidance for mechanical construction . . . materials, parts, fittings, and complete labor cost information. Includes prices for piping, heating, air conditioning, ventilation, and all related construction.

Plus new 2014 unit costs for:

- Thousands of installed HVAC/controls assemblies components
- "On-site" Location Factors for more than 930 cities and towns in the U.S. and Canada
- Crews, labor, and equipment

$191.95 | Available Oct. 2013 | Catalog no. 60024

RSMeans Square Foot Costs 2014
Accurate and Easy-to-Use

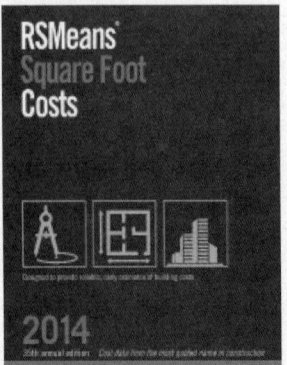

- **Updated price information** based on nationwide figures from suppliers, estimators, labor experts, and contractors
- New green building models
- Realistic graphics, offering true-to-life illustrations of building projects
- Extensive information on using square foot cost data, including sample estimates and alternate pricing methods

$205.95 | Available Oct. 2013 | Catalog no. 60054

RSMeans Green Building Cost Data 2014

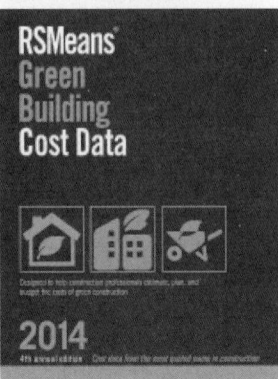

Estimate, plan, and budget the costs of green building for both new commercial construction and renovation work with this fourth edition of *RSMeans Green Building Cost Data*. More than 10,000 unit costs for a wide array of green building products plus assemblies costs. Easily identified cross references to LEED and Green Globes building rating systems criteria.

$160.95 | Available Nov. 2013 | Catalog no. 60554

RSMeans Facilities Construction Cost Data 2014

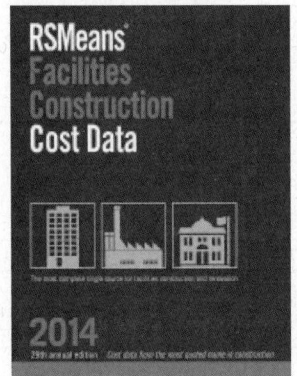

For the maintenance and construction of commercial, industrial, municipal, and institutional properties. Costs are shown for new and remodeling construction and are broken down into materials, labor, equipment, and overhead and profit. Special emphasis is given to sections on mechanical, electrical, furnishings, site work, building maintenance, finish work, and demolition.

More than 49,000 unit costs, plus assemblies costs and a comprehensive Reference Section are included.

$496.95 | Available Nov. 2013 | Catalog no. 60204

RSMeans Commercial Renovation Cost Data 2014
Commercial/Multifamily Residential

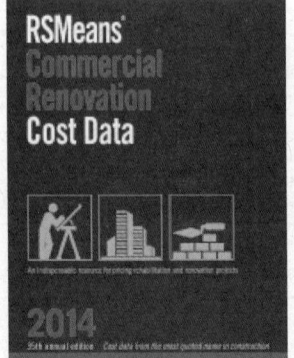

Use this valuable tool to estimate commercial and multifamily residential renovation and remodeling.

Includes: New costs for hundreds of unique methods, materials, and conditions that only come up in repair and remodeling, PLUS:

- Unit costs for more than 19,000 construction components
- Installed costs for more than 2,000 assemblies
- More than 930 "on-site" localization factors for the U.S. and Canada

$156.95 | Available Oct. 2013 | Catalog no. 60044

RSMeans Electrical Cost Data 2014

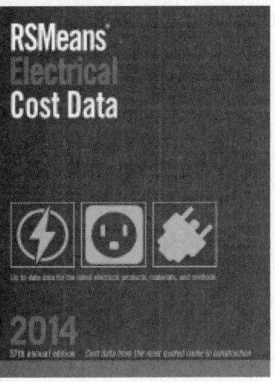

Pricing information for every part of electrical cost planning. More than 13,000 unit and systems costs with design tables; clear specifications and drawings; engineering guides; illustrated estimating procedures; complete labor-hour and materials costs for better scheduling and procurement; and the latest electrical products and construction methods.

- A variety of special electrical systems, including cathodic protection
- Costs for maintenance, demolition, HVAC/mechanical, specialties, equipment, and more

$196.95 | Available Oct. 2013 | Catalog no. 60034

RSMeans Electrical Change Order Cost Data 2014

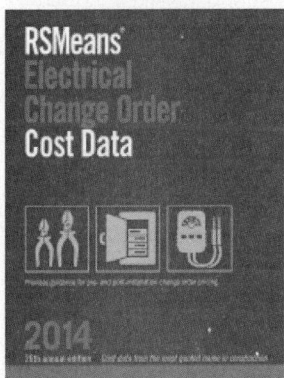

RSMeans Electrical Change Order Cost Data provides you with electrical unit prices exclusively for pricing change orders—based on the recent, direct experience of contractors and suppliers. Analyze and check your own change order estimates against the experience others have had doing the same work. It also covers productivity analysis and change order cost justifications. With useful information for calculating the effects of change orders and dealing with their administration.

$187.95 | Available Dec. 2013 | Catalog no. 60234

RSMeans Assemblies Cost Data 2014

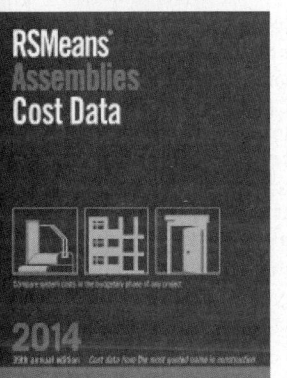

RSMeans Assemblies Cost Data takes the guesswork out of preliminary or conceptual estimates. Now you don't have to try to calculate the assembled cost by working up individual component costs. We've done all the work for you.

Presents detailed illustrations, descriptions, specifications, and costs for every conceivable building assembly— over 350 types in all—arranged in the easy-to-use UNIFORMAT II system. Each illustrated "assembled" cost includes a complete grouping of materials and associated installation costs, including the installing contractor's overhead and profit.

$315.95 | Available Sept. 2013 | Catalog no. 60064

RSMeans Open Shop Building Construction Cost Data 2014

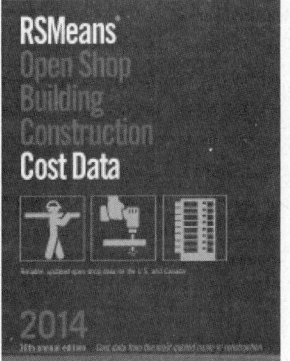

The latest costs for accurate budgeting and estimating of new commercial and residential construction . . . renovation work . . . change orders . . . cost engineering.

RSMeans Open Shop "BCCD" will assist you to:

- Develop benchmark prices for change orders
- Plug gaps in preliminary estimates and budgets
- Estimate complex projects
- Substantiate invoices on contracts
- Price ADA-related renovations

$165.95 | Available Dec. 2013 | Catalog no. 60154

RSMeans Residential Cost Data 2014

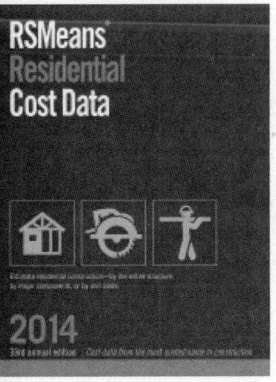

Contains square foot costs for 28 basic home models with the look of today, plus hundreds of custom additions and modifications you can quote right off the page. Includes costs for more than 700 residential systems. Complete with blank estimating forms, sample estimates, and step-by-step instructions.

Contains line items for cultured stone and brick, PVC trim lumber, and TPO roofing.

$139.95 | Available Oct. 2013 | Catalog no. 60174

RSMeans Site Work & Landscape Cost Data 2014

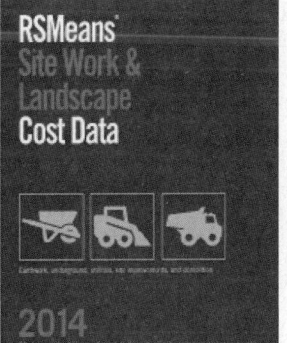

Includes unit and assemblies costs for earthwork, sewerage, piped utilities, site improvements, drainage, paving, trees and shrubs, street openings/repairs, underground tanks, and more. Contains 78 types of assemblies costs for accurate conceptual estimates.

Includes:

- Estimating for infrastructure improvements
- Environmentally-oriented construction
- ADA-mandated handicapped access
- Hazardous waste line items

$187.95 | Available Dec. 2013 | Catalog no. 60284

RSMeans Facilities Maintenance & Repair Cost Data 2014

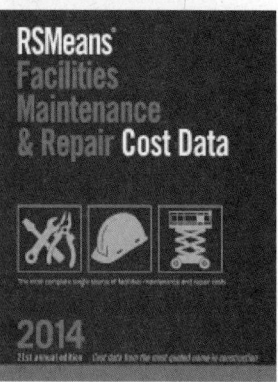

RSMeans Facilities Maintenance & Repair Cost Data gives you a complete system to manage and plan your facility repair and maintenance costs and budget efficiently. Guidelines for auditing a facility and developing an annual maintenance plan. Budgeting is included, along with reference tables on cost and management, and information on frequency and productivity of maintenance operations.

The only nationally recognized source of maintenance and repair costs. Developed in cooperation with the Civil Engineering Research Laboratory (CERL) of the Army Corps of Engineers.

$434.95 | Available Nov. 2013 | Catalog no. 60304

RSMeans Concrete & Masonry Cost Data 2014

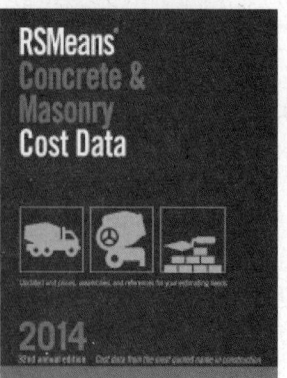

Provides you with cost facts for virtually all concrete/masonry estimating needs, from complicated formwork to various sizes and face finishes of brick and block—all in great detail. The comprehensive Unit Price Section contains more than 8,000 selected entries. Also contains an Assemblies [Cost] Section, and a detailed Reference Section that supplements the cost data.

$177.95 | Available Dec. 2013 | Catalog no. 60114

RSMeans Construction Cost Indexes 2014

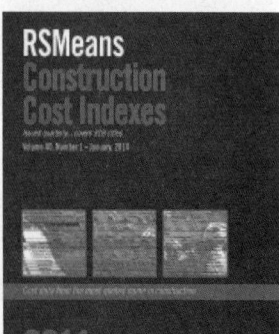

What materials and labor costs will change unexpectedly this year? By how much?

- Breakdowns for 318 major cities
- National averages for 30 key cities
- Expanded five major city indexes
- Historical construction cost indexes

$362.00 per year (subscription) | Catalog no. 50144
$93.50 individual quarters | Catalog no. 60144 A,B,C,D

RSMeans Light Commercial Cost Data 2014

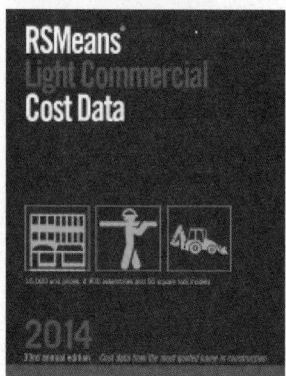

Specifically addresses the light commercial market, which is a specialized niche in the construction industry. Aids you, the owner/designer/contractor, in preparing all types of estimates—from budgets to detailed bids. Includes new advances in methods and materials.

Assemblies Section allows you to evaluate alternatives in the early stages of design/planning.

More than 15,000 unit costs ensure that you have the prices you need . . . when you need them.

$144.95 | Available Nov. 2013 | Catalog no. 60184

RSMeans Labor Rates for the Construction Industry 2014

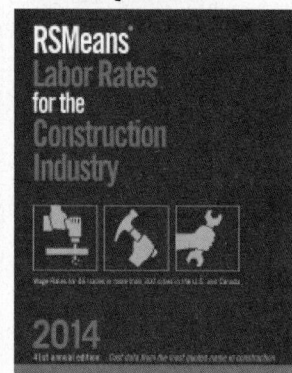

Complete information for estimating labor costs, making comparisons, and negotiating wage rates by trade for more than 300 U.S. and Canadian cities. With 46 construction trades listed by local union number in each city, and historical wage rates included for comparison. Each city chart lists the county and is alphabetically arranged with handy visual flip tabs for quick reference.

$424.95 | Available Dec. 2013 | Catalog no. 60124

RSMeans Interior Cost Data 2014

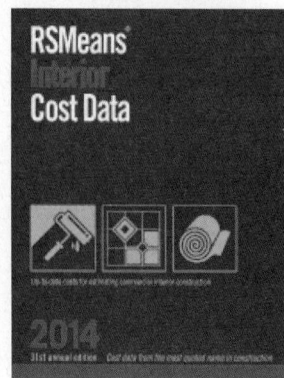

Provides you with prices and guidance needed to make accurate interior work estimates. Contains costs on materials, equipment, hardware, custom installations, furnishings, and labor costs . . . for new and remodel commercial and industrial interior construction, including updated information on office furnishings, and reference information.

$196.95 | Available Nov. 2013 | Catalog no. 60094

Annual Cost Guides

For more information visit the RSMeans website at **www.rsmeans.com**

Unit prices according to the latest MasterFormat!

RSMeans Heavy Construction Cost Data 2014

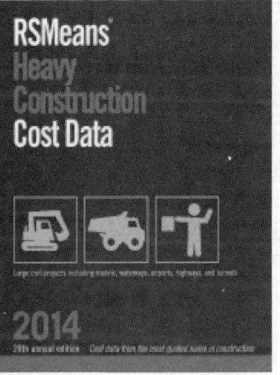

A comprehensive guide to heavy construction costs. Includes costs for highly specialized projects such as tunnels, dams, highways, airports, and waterways. Information on labor rates, equipment, and materials costs is included. Features unit price costs, systems costs, and numerous reference tables for costs and design.

$192.95 | Available Dec. 2013 | Catalog no. 60164

RSMeans Plumbing Cost Data 2014

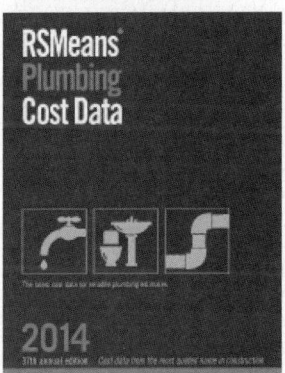

Comprehensive unit prices and assemblies for plumbing, irrigation systems, commercial and residential fire protection, point-of-use water heaters, and the latest approved materials. This publication and its companion, *RSMeans Mechanical Cost Data*, provide full-range cost estimating coverage for all the mechanical trades.

Now contains updated costs for potable water and radiant heat systems and high efficiency fixtures.

$194.95 | Available Oct. 2013 | Catalog no. 60214

2014 RSMeans Seminar Schedule

Note: call for exact dates and details.

Location	Dates	Location	Dates
Seattle, WA	January and August	Jacksonville FL	September
Dallas/Ft. Worth, TX	January	Dallas, TX	September
Austin, TX	February	Charleston, SC	October
Anchorage, AK	March and September	Houston, TX	October
Las Vegas, NV	March and October	Atlanta, GA	November
Washington, DC	April and September	Baltimore, MD	November
Phoenix, AZ	April	Orlando, FL	November
Kansas City, MO	April	San Diego, CA	December
Toronto	May	San Antonio, TX	December
Denver, CO	May	Raleigh, NC	December
San Francisco, CA	June		
Bethesda, MD	June		
Columbus, GA	June		
El Segundo, CA	August		

1-800-334-3509, Press 1

Professional Development

For more information visit the RSMeans website at **www.rsmeans.com**

eLearning Training Sessions

Learn how to use *RSMeans Online*™ or *RSMeans CostWorks*® CD from the convenience of your home or office. Our eLearning training sessions let you join a training conference call and share the instructors' desktops, so you can view the presentation and step-by-step instructions on your own computer screen. The live webinars are held from 9 a.m. to 4 p.m. eastern standard time, with a one-hour break for lunch.

For these sessions, you must have a computer with high speed Internet access and a compatible Web browser. Learn more at www.rsmeansonline.com or call for a schedule: 1-800-334-3509 and press 1. Webinars are generally held on selected Wednesdays each month.

RSMeans Online™
$299 per person

RSMeans CostWorks® CD
$299 per person

Professional Development

For more information visit the RSMeans website at **www.rsmeans.com**

RSMeans Online™ Training

Construction estimating is vital to the decision-making process at each state of every project. RSMeansOnline works the way you do. It's systematic, flexible and intuitive. In this one day class you will see how you can estimate any phase of any project faster and better.

Some of what you'll learn:
- Customizing RSMeansOnline
- Making the most of RSMeans "Circle Reference" numbers
- How to integrate your cost data
- Generate reports, exporting estimates to MS Excel, sharing, collaborating and more

Also available: RSMeans Online™ training webinar

Facilities Construction Estimating

In this *two-day* course, professionals working in facilities management can get help with their daily challenges to establish budgets for all phases of a project.

Some of what you'll learn:
- Determining the full scope of a project
- Identifying the scope of risks and opportunities
- Creative solutions to estimating issues
- Organizing estimates for presentation and discussion
- Special techniques for repair/remodel and maintenance projects
- Negotiating project change orders

Who should attend: facility managers, engineers, contractors, facility tradespeople, planners, and project managers.

Scheduling with Microsoft Project

Two days of hands-on training gives you a look at the basics to putting it all together with MS Project to create a complete project schedule. Learn to work better and faster, manage changes and updates, enhance tracking, generate actionable reports, and boost control of your time and budget.

Some of what you'll learn:
- Defining task/activity relationships: link tasks, establish predecessor/successor relationships and create logs
- Baseline scheduling: the essential what/when
- Using MS Project to determine the critical path
- Integrate RSMeans data with MS Project
- The dollar-loaded schedule: enhance the reliability of this "must-know" technique for scheduling public projects.

Who should attend: contractors' project-management teams, architects and engineers, project owners and their representatives, and those interested in improving their project planning prod scheduling and management skills.

Maintenance & Repair Estimating for Facilities

This *two-day* course teaches attendees how to plan, budget, and estimate the cost of ongoing and preventive maintenance and repair for existing buildings and grounds.

Some of what you'll learn:
- The most financially favorable maintenance, repair, and replacement scheduling and estimating
- Auditing and value engineering facilities
- Preventive planning and facilities upgrading
- Determining both in-house and contract-out service costs
- Annual, asset-protecting M&R plan

Who should attend: facility managers, maintenance supervisors, buildings and grounds superintendents, plant managers, planners, estimators, and others involved in facilities planning and budgeting.

Practical Project Management for Construction Professionals

In this *two-day* course, acquire the essential knowledge and develop the skills to effectively and efficiently execute the day-to-day responsibilities of the construction project manager.

Covers:
- General conditions of the construction contract
- Contract modifications: change orders and construction change directives
- Negotiations with subcontractors and vendors
- Effective writing: notification and communications
- Dispute resolution: claims and liens

Who should attend: architects, engineers, owner's representatives, project managers.

Mechanical & Electrical Estimating

This *two-day* course teaches attendees how to prepare more accurate and complete mechanical/electrical estimates, avoiding the pitfalls of omission and double-counting, while understanding the composition and rationale within the RSMeans mechanical/electrical database.

Some of what you'll learn:
- The unique way mechanical and electrical systems are interrelated
- M&E estimates—conceptual, planning, budgeting, and bidding stages
- Order of magnitude, square foot, assemblies, and unit price estimating
- Comparative cost analysis of equipment and design alternatives

Who should attend: architects, engineers, facilities managers, mechanical and electrical contractors, and others who need a highly reliable method for developing, understanding, and evaluating mechanical and electrical contracts.

890

Professional Development

Unit Price Estimating

This interactive *two-day* seminar teaches attendees how to interpret project information and process it into final, detailed estimates with the greatest accuracy level.

The most important credential an estimator can take to the job is the ability to visualize construction and estimate accurately.

Some of what you'll learn:
- Interpreting the design in terms of cost
- The most detailed, time-tested methodology for accurate pricing
- Key cost drivers—material, labor, equipment, staging, and subcontracts
- Understanding direct and indirect costs for accurate job cost accounting and change order management

Who should attend: corporate and government estimators and purchasers, architects, engineers, and others who need to produce accurate project estimates.

RSMeans CostWorks® CD Training

This one-day course helps users become more familiar with the functionality of *RSMeans CostWork*s program. Each menu, icon, screen, and function found in the program is explained in depth. Time is devoted to hands-on estimating exercises.

Some of what you'll learn:
- Searching the database using all navigation methods
- Exporting RSMeans data to your preferred spreadsheet format
- Viewing crews, assembly components, and much more
- Automatically regionalizing the database

This training session requires you to bring a laptop computer to class.

When you register for this course you will receive an outline for your laptop requirements.

Also offering web training for CostWorks CD!

Facilities Est. Using RSMeans CostWorks® CD

Combines hands-on skill building with best estimating practices and real-life problems. Brings you up-to-date with key concepts, and provides tips, pointers, and guidelines to save time and avoid cost oversights and errors.

Some of what you'll learn:
- Estimating process concepts
- Customizing and adapting RSMeans cost data
- Establishing scope of work to account for all known variables
- Budget estimating: when, why, and how
- Site visits: what to look for—what you can't afford to overlook
- How to estimate repair and remodeling variables

This training session requires you to bring a laptop computer to class.

Who should attend: facility managers, architects, engineers, contractors, facility tradespeople, planners, project managers and anyone involved with JOC, SABRE, or IDIQ.

Conceptual Estimating Using RSMeans CostWorks® CD

This *two day* class uses the leading industry data and a powerful software package to develop highly accurate conceptual estimates for your construction projects. All attendees must bring a laptop computer loaded with the current year *Square Foot Model Costs* and the *Assemblies Cost Data* CostWorks titles.

Some of what you'll learn:
- Introduction to conceptual estimating
- Types of conceptual estimates
- Helpful hints
- Order of magnitude estimating
- Square foot estimating
- Assemblies estimating

Who should attend: architects, engineers, contractors, construction estimators, owner's representatives, and anyone looking for an electronic method for performing square foot estimating.

Assessing Scope of Work for Facility Construction Estimating

This *two-day* practical training program addresses the vital importance of understanding the SCOPE of projects in order to produce accurate cost estimates for facility repair and remodeling.

Some of what you'll learn:
- Discussions of site visits, plans/specs, record drawings of facilities, and site-specific lists
- Review of CSI divisions, including means, methods, materials, and the challenges of scoping each topic
- Exercises in SCOPE identification and SCOPE writing for accurate estimating of projects
- Hands-on exercises that require SCOPE, take-off, and pricing

Who should attend: corporate and government estimators, planners, facility managers, and others who need to produce accurate project estimates.

Unit Price Est. Using RSMeans CostWorks® CD

Step-by-step instruction and practice problems to identify and track key cost drivers—material, labor, equipment, staging, and subcontractors—for each specific task. Learn the most detailed, time-tested methodology for accurately "pricing" these variables, their impact on each other and on total cost.

Some of what you'll learn:
- Unit price cost estimating
- Order of magnitude, square foot, and assemblies estimating
- Quantity takeoff
- Direct and indirect construction costs
- Development of contractor's bill rates
- How to use *RSMeans Building Construction Cost Data*

This training session requires you to bring a laptop computer to class.

Who should attend: architects, engineers, corporate and government estimators, facility managers, and government procurement staff.

891

Professional Development

For more information visit the RSMeans website at **www.rsmeans.com**

Registration Information

Register early . . . Save up to $100! Register 30 days before the start date of a seminar and save $100 off your total fee. *Note: This discount can be applied only once per order. It cannot be applied to team discount registrations or any other special offer.*

How to register Register by phone today! The RSMeans toll-free number for making reservations is **1-800-334-3509, Press 1.**

Two day seminar registration fee - $935. One-day *RSMeans CostWorks*® training registration fee - $375. To register by mail, complete the registration form and return, with your full fee, to: RSMeans Seminars, 700 Longwater Drive, Norwell, MA 02061.

Government pricing All federal government employees save off the regular seminar price. Other promotional discounts cannot be combined with the government discount.

Team discount program for two to four seminar registrations. Call for pricing: 1-800-334-3509, Press 1

Multiple course discounts When signing up for two or more courses, call for pricing.

Refund policy Cancellations will be accepted up to ten business days prior to the seminar start. There are no refunds for cancellations received later than ten working days prior to the first day of the seminar. A $150 processing fee will be applied for all cancellations. Written notice of cancellation is required. Substitutions can be made at any time before the session starts. **No-shows are subject to the full seminar fee.**

AACE approved courses Many seminars described and offered here have been approved for 14 hours (1.4 recertification credits) of credit by the AACE International Certification Board toward meeting the continuing education requirements for recertification as a Certified Cost Engineer/Certified Cost Consultant.

AIA Continuing Education We are registered with the AIA Continuing Education System (AIA/CES) and are committed to developing quality learning activities in accordance with the CES criteria. Many seminars meet the AIA/CES criteria for Quality Level 2. AIA members may receive (14) learning units (LUs) for each two-day RSMeans course.

Daily course schedule The first day of each seminar session begins at 8:30 a.m. and ends at 4:30 p.m. The second day begins at 8:00 a.m. and ends at 4:00 p.m. Participants are urged to bring a hand-held calculator, since many actual problems will be worked out in each session.

Continental breakfast Your registration includes the cost of a continental breakfast, and a morning and afternoon refreshment break. These informal segments allow you to discuss topics of mutual interest with other seminar attendees. (You are free to make your own lunch and dinner arrangements.)

Hotel/transportation arrangements RSMeans arranges to hold a block of rooms at most host hotels. To take advantage of special group rates when making your reservation, be sure to mention that you are attending the RSMeans seminar. You are, of course, free to stay at the lodging place of your choice. **(Hotel reservations and transportation arrangements should be made directly by seminar attendees.)**

Important Class sizes are limited, so please register as soon as possible.

Note: Pricing subject to change.

Registration Form

ADDS-1000

Call 1-800-334-3509, Press 1 to register or FAX this form 1-800-632-6732. Visit our website: www.rsmeans.com

Please register the following people for the RSMeans construction seminars as shown here. We understand that we must make our own hotel reservations if overnight stays are necessary.

☐ Full payment of $_____ enclosed.

☐ Bill me.

Please print name of registrant(s).

(To appear on certificate of completion)

_____
_____
_____
_____

P.O. #: _____
GOVERNMENT AGENCIES MUST SUPPLY PURCHASE ORDER NUMBER OR TRAINING FORM.

Firm name_____

Address_____

City/State/Zip_____

Telephone no._____ Fax no._____

E-mail address_____

Charge registration(s) to: ☐ MasterCard ☐ VISA ☐ American Express

Account no._____ Exp. date_____

Cardholder's signature_____

Seminar name_____

Seminar City_____

Please mail check to: RSMeans Seminars, 700 Longwater Drive, Norwell, MA 02061 USA

New Titles - Reference Books

For more information visit the RSMeans website at **www.rsmeans.com**

Solar Energy: Technologies & Project Delivery for Buildings

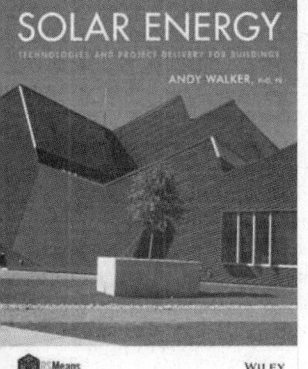

by Andy Walker

An authoritative reference on the design of solar energy systems in building projects, with applications, operating principles, and simple tools for the construction, engineering, and design professionals, the book simplifies the solar design and engineering process and provides sample documentation for the complete design of a solar energy system for buildings.

$85.00 | 320 pages, hardover | Catalog no. 67365

Project Scheduling & Management for Construction, 4th Edition

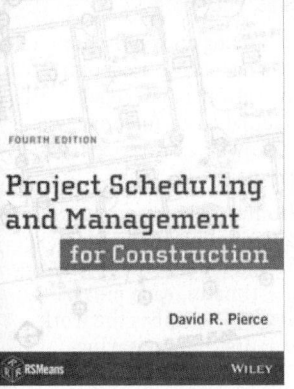

by David R. Pierce

First published in 1988 by RSMeans, the new edition of *Project Scheduling and Management for Construction* has been substantially revised for both professionals and students enrolled in construction management and civil engineering programs. While retaining its emphasis on developing practical, professional-level scheduling skills, the new edition is a relatable, real world case study.

$95.00 | 272 pages, softcover | Catalog no. 67367

Estimating Building Costs, 2nd Edition
For the Residential & Light Commercial Construction Professional

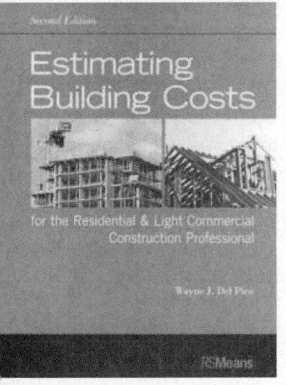

by Wayne J. Del Pico

This book guides readers through the entire estimating process, explaining in detail how to put together a reliable estimate that can be used not only for budgeting, but also for developing a schedule, managing a project, dealing with contingencies, and ultimately making a profit.

Completely revised and updated to reflect the CSI MasterFormat 2010 system, this practical guide describes estimating techniques for each building system and how to apply them according to the latest industry standards.

$75.00 | 398 pages, softcover | Catalog no. 67343A

Project Control: Integrating Cost & Schedule in Construction

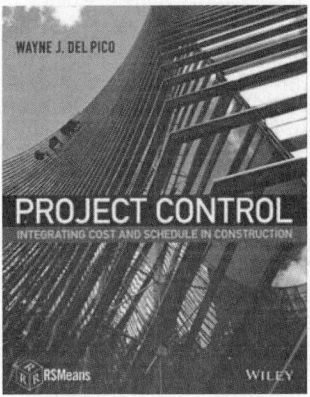

by Wayne J. Del Pico

Written by a seasoned professional in the field, *Project Control: Integrating Cost and Schedule in Construction* fills a void in the area of project control as applied in the construction industry today. It demonstrates how productivity models for an individual project are created, monitored, and controlled, and how corrective actions are implemented as deviations from the baseline occur.

$95.00 | 240 pages, softcover | Catalog no. 67366

How to Estimate with Means Data & CostWorks, 4th Edition

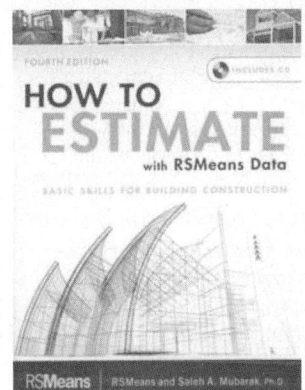

by RSMeans and Saleh A. Mubarak, Ph.D.

This step-by-step guide takes you through all the major construction items with extensive coverage of site work, concrete and masonry, wood and metal framing, doors and windows, and other divisions. The only construction cost estimating handbook that uses the most popular source of construction data, RSMeans, this indispensible guide features access to the instructional version of CostWorks in electronic form, enabling you to practice techniques to solve real-world estimating problems.

$75.00 | 292 pages, softcover | Includes CostWorks CD
Catalog no. 67324C

RSMeans Cost Data, Student Edition

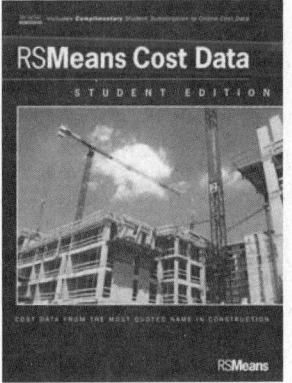

This book provides a thorough introduction to cost estimating in a self-contained print and online package. With clear explanations and a hands-on, example-driven approach, it is the ideal reference for students and new professionals.

Features include:

- Commercial and residential construction cost data in print and online formats
- Complete how-to guidance on the essentials of cost estimating
- A supplemental website with plans, problem sets, and a full sample estimate

$99.00 | 512 pages, softcover | Catalog no. 67363

Reference Books

For more information visit the RSMeans website at www.rsmeans.com

Value Engineering: Practical Applications

For Design, Construction, Maintenance & Operations

by Alphonse Dell'Isola, PE

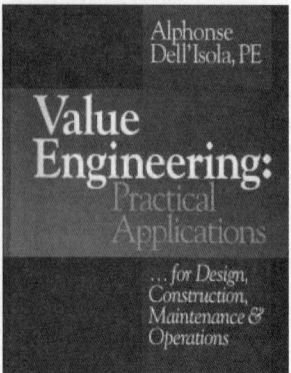

A tool for immediate application—for engineers, architects, facility managers, owners, and contractors. Includes making the case for VE—the management briefing; integrating VE into planning, budgeting, and design; conducting life cycle costing; using VE methodology in design review and consultant selection; case studies; VE workbook; and a life cycle costing program on disk.

$85.00 | Over 450 pages, illustrated, softcover | Catalog no. 67319A

Risk Management for Design & Construction

Introduces risk as a central pillar of project management and shows how a project manager can prepare to deal with uncertainty. Experts in the field use clear, straightforward terminology to demystify the concepts of project uncertainty and risk. Includes:

• Integrated cost and schedule risk analysis

• An introduction to a ready-to-use system of analyzing a project's risks and tools to proactively manage risks

• A methodology that was developed and used by the Washington State Department of Transportation

• Case studies and examples on the proper application of principles

• Information about combining value analysis with risk analysis

$125.00 | Over 250 pages, softcover | Catalog no. 67359

How Your House Works, 2nd Edition

by Charlie Wing

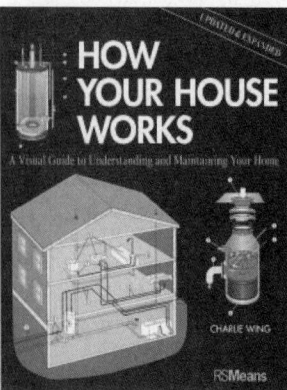

Knowledge of your home's systems helps you control repair and construction costs and makes sure the correct elements are being installed or replaced. This book uncovers the mysteries behind just about every major appliance and building element in your house. See-through, cross-section drawings in full color show you exactly how these things should be put together and how they function, including what to check if they don't work. It just might save you having to call in a professional.

$22.95 | 192 pages, softcover | Catalog no. 67351A

Complete Book of Framing, 2nd Edition

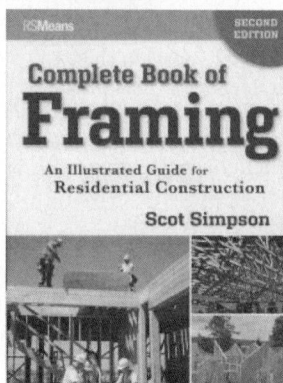

by Scot Simpson

This updated, easy-to-learn guide to rough carpentry and framing is written by an expert with more than thirty years of framing experience. Starting with the basics, this book begins with types of lumber, nails, and what tools are needed, followed by detailed, fully illustrated steps for framing each building element. Framer-Friendly Tips throughout the book show how to get a task done right—and more easily.

$29.95 | 352 pages, softcover | Catalog no. 67353A

Green Home Improvement

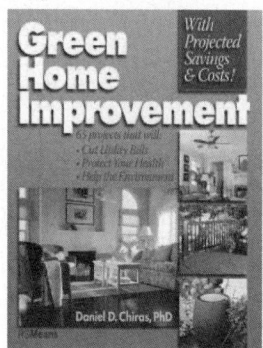

by Daniel D. Chiras, PhD

With energy costs rising and environmental awareness increasing, people are looking to make their homes greener. This book, with 65 projects and actual costs and projected savings help homeowners prioritize their green improvements.

Projects range from simple water savers that cost only a few dollars, to bigger-ticket items such as HVAC systems. With color photos and cost estimates, each project compares options and describes the work involved, the benefits, and the savings.

$34.95 | 320 pages, illustrated, softcover | Catalog no. 67355

Life Cycle Costing for Facilities

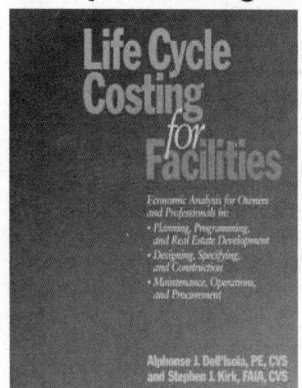

by Alphonse Dell'Isola and Dr. Steven Kirk

Guidance for achieving higher quality design and construction projects at lower costs! Cost-cutting efforts often sacrifice quality to yield the cheapest product. Life cycle costing enables building designers and owners to achieve both. The authors of this book show how LCC can work for a variety of projects — from roads to HVAC upgrades to different types of buildings.

$99.95 | 396 pages, hardcover | Catalog no. 67341

Builder's Essentials: Plan Reading & Material Takeoff
For Residential and Light Commercial Construction

by Wayne J. DelPico

A valuable tool for understanding plans and specs, and accurately calculating material quantities. Step-by-step instructions and takeoff procedures based on a full set of working drawings.

$45.00 | Over 420 pages, softcover | Catalog no. 67307

Means Unit Price Estimating Methods, 4th Edition

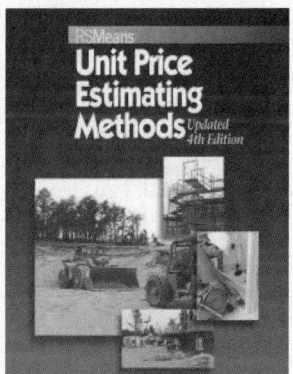

Includes cost data and estimating examples, updated to reflect changes to the CSI numbering system and new features of RSMeans cost data. It describes the most productive, universally accepted ways to estimate, and uses checklists and forms to illustrate shortcuts and timesavers. A model estimate demonstrates procedures. A new chapter explores computer estimating alternatives.

$75.00 | Over 350 pages, illustrated, softcover | Catalog no. 67303B

Concrete Repair & Maintenance Illustrated

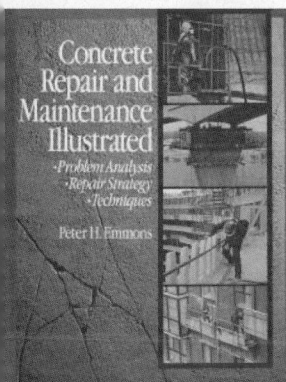

by Peter Emmons

Hundreds of illustrations show users how to analyze, repair, clean, and maintain concrete structures for optimal performance and cost effectiveness. From parking garages to roads and bridges to structural concrete, this comprehensive book describes the causes, effects, and remedies for concrete wear and failure. Invaluable for planning jobs, selecting materials, and training employees, this book is a must-have for concrete specialists, general contractors, facility managers, civil and structural engineers, and architects.

$75.00 | 300 pages, illustrated, softcover | Catalog no. 67146

Square Foot & UNIFORMAT Assemblies Estimating Methods, 3rd Edition

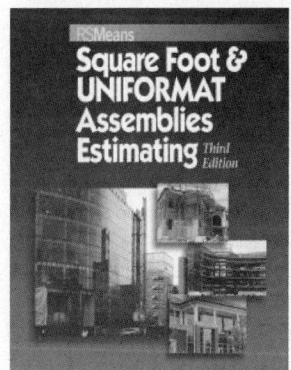

Develop realistic square foot and assemblies costs for budgeting and construction funding. The new edition features updated guidance on square foot and assemblies estimating using UNIFORMAT II. An essential reference for anyone who performs conceptual estimates.

$75.00 | Over 300 pages, illustrated, softcover | Catalog no. 67145B

Electrical Estimating Methods, 3rd Edition

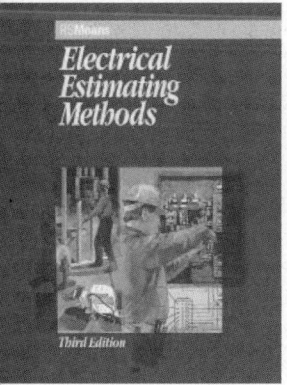

Expanded edition includes sample estimates and cost information in keeping with the latest version of the CSI MasterFormat and UNIFORMAT II. Complete coverage of fiber optic and uninterruptible power supply electrical systems, broken down by components, and explained in detail. Includes a new chapter on computerized estimating methods. A practical companion to *RSMeans Electrical Cost Data*.

$75.00 | Over 325 pages, hardcover | Catalog no. 67230B

Residential & Light Commercial Construction Standards, 3rd Edition

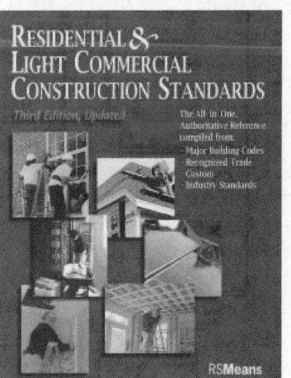

Updated by RSMeans and contributing authors

This book provides authoritative requirements and recommendations compiled from leading professional associations, industry publications, and building code organizations. This all-in-one reference helps establish a standard for workmanship, quickly resolve disputes, and avoid defect claims. Updated third edition includes new coverage of green building, seismic, hurricane, and mold-resistant construction.

$65.00 | Over 550 pages, illustrated, softcover | Catalog no. 67322B

Reference Books

For more information visit the RSMeans website at **www.rsmeans.com**

Construction Business Management

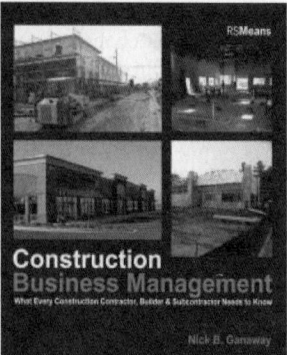

by Nick Ganaway

Only 43% of construction firms stay in business after four years. Make sure your company thrives with valuable guidance from a pro with 25 years of success as a commercial contractor. Find out what it takes to build all aspects of a business that is profitable, enjoyable, and enduring. With a bonus chapter on retail construction.

$55.00 | 200 pages, softcover | Catalog no. 67352

The Practice of Cost Segregation Analysis

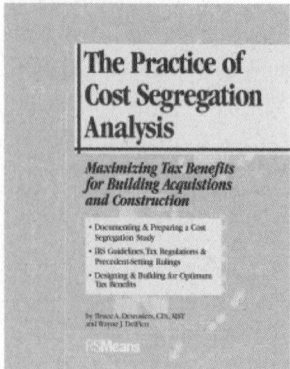

by Bruce A. Desrosiers and Wayne J. DelPico

This expert guide walks you through the practice of cost segregation analysis, which enables property owners to defer taxes and benefit from "accelerated cost recovery" through depreciation deductions on assets that are properly identified and classified.

With a glossary of terms, sample cost segregation estimates for various building types, key information resources, and updates via a dedicated website, this book is a critical resource for anyone involved in cost segregation analysis.

$105.00 | Over 225 pages | Catalog no. 67345

Green Building: Project Planning & Cost Estimating, 3rd Edition

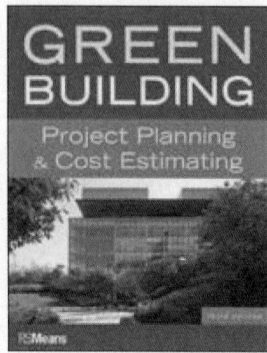

Since the widely read first edition of this book, green building has gone from a growing trend to a major force in design and construction.

This new edition has been updated with the latest in green building technologies, design concepts, standards, and costs. Full-color with all new case studies—plus a new chapter on commercial real estate.

$110.00 | Over 450 pages, softcover | Catalog no. 67338B

Project Scheduling & Management for Construction, 3rd Edition

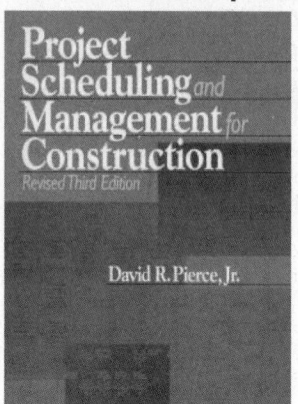

by David R. Pierce, Jr.

A comprehensive yet easy-to-follow guide to construction project scheduling and control—from vital project management principles through the latest scheduling, tracking, and controlling techniques. The author is a leading authority on scheduling, with years of field and teaching experience at leading academic institutions. Spend a few hours with this book and come away with a solid understanding of this essential management topic.

$64.95 | Over 300 pages, illustrated, hardcover | Catalog no. 67247B

Preventive Maintenance for Multi-Family Housing

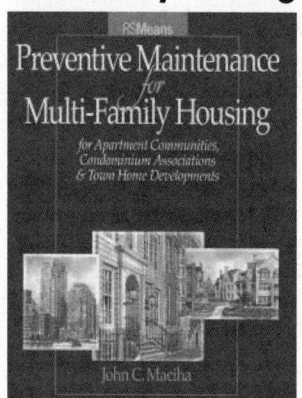

by John C. Maciha

Prepared by one of the nation's leading experts on multi-family housing.

This complete PM system for apartment and condominium communities features expert guidance, checklists for buildings and grounds maintenance tasks and their frequencies, a reusable wall chart to track maintenance, and a dedicated website featuring customizable electronic forms. A must-have for anyone involved with multi-family housing maintenance and upkeep.

$95.00 | 225 pages | Catalog no. 67346

Job Order Contracting: Expediting Construction Project Delivery

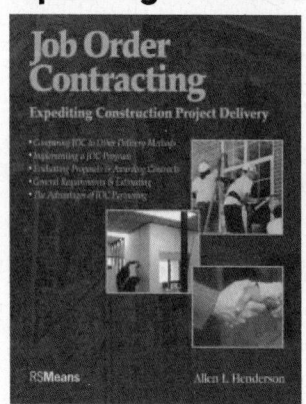

by Allen L. Henderson

Expert guidance to help you implement JOC—fast becoming the preferred project delivery method for repair and renovation, minor new construction, and maintenance projects in the public sector and in many states and municipalities. The author, a leading JOC expert and practitioner, shows how to:

- Establish a JOC program
- Evaluate proposals & award contracts
- Handle general requirements and estimating
- Partner for maximum benefits

$89.95 | 192 pages, illustrated, hardcover | Catalog no. 67348

Reference Books

For more information visit the RSMeans website at **www.rsmeans.com**

Construction Supervision

This brand new title inspires supervisory excellence with proven tactics and techniques applied by thousands of construction supervisors over the past decade. Recognizing the unique and critical role the supervisor plays in project success, the book's leadership guidelines carve out a practical blueprint for motivating work performance and increasing productivity through effective communication.

Features:

- A unique focus on field supervision and crew management
- Coverage of supervision from the foreman to the superintendent level
- An overview of technical skills whose mastery will build confidence and success for the supervisor
- A detailed view of "soft" management and communication skills

$95.00 | Over 450 pages, softcover | Catalog no. 67358

The Homeowner's Guide to Mold

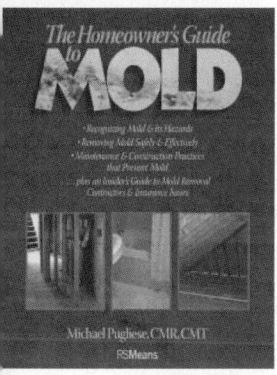

By Michael Pugliese

Expert guidance to protect your health and your home.

Mold, whether caused by leaks, humidity or flooding, is a real health and financial issue—for homeowners and contractors.

This full-color book explains:

- Construction and maintenance practices to prevent mold
- How to inspect for and remove mold
- Mold remediation procedures and costs
- What to do after a flood
- How to deal with insurance companies

$21.95 | 144 pages, softcover | Catalog no. 67344

Landscape Estimating Methods, 5th Edition

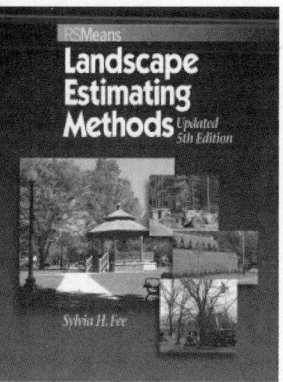

Answers questions about preparing competitive landscape construction estimates, with up-to-date cost estimates and the new MasterFormat classification system. Expanded and revised to address the latest materials and methods, including new coverage on approaches to green building. Includes:

- Step-by-step explanation of the estimating process
- Sample forms and worksheets that save time and prevent errors

$75.00 | Over 350 pages, softcover | Catalog no. 67295C

Building & Renovating Schools

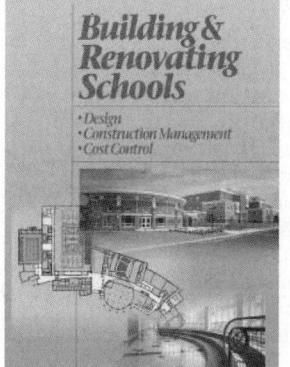

This all-inclusive guide covers every step of the school construction process—from initial planning, needs assessment, and design, right through moving into the new facility. A must-have resource for anyone concerned with new school construction or renovation. With square foot cost models for elementary, middle, and high school facilities, and real-life case studies of recently completed school projects.

The contributors to this book—architects, construction project managers, contractors, and estimators who specialize in school construction—provide start-to-finish, expert guidance on the process.

$99.95 | Over 425 pages, hardcover | Catalog no. 67342

Universal Design Ideas for Style, Comfort & Safety

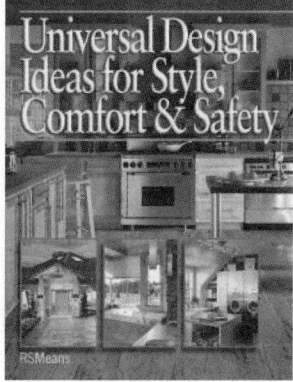

by RSMeans and Lexicon Consulting, Inc.

Incorporating universal design when building or remodeling helps people of any age and physical ability more fully and safely enjoy their living spaces. This book shows how universal design can be artfully blended into the most attractive homes. It discusses specialized products like adjustable countertops and chair lifts, as well as simple ways to enhance a home's safety and comfort. With color photos and expert guidance, every area of the home is covered. Includes budget estimates that give an idea how much projects will cost.

$21.95 | 160 pages, illustrated, softcover | Catalog no. 67354

Plumbing Estimating Methods, 3rd Edition

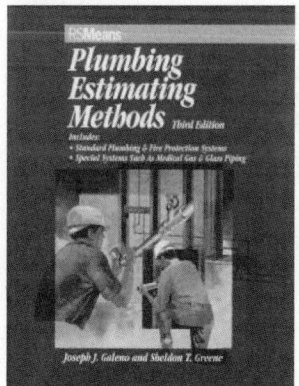

by Joseph J. Galeno and Sheldon T. Greene

Updated and revised! This practical guide walks you through a plumbing estimate, from basic materials and installation methods through change order analysis. *Plumbing Estimating Methods* covers residential, commercial, industrial, and medical systems, and features sample takeoff and estimate forms and detailed illustrations of systems and components.

$65.00 | 330+ pages, softcover | Catalog no. 67283B

Understanding & Negotiating Construction Contracts

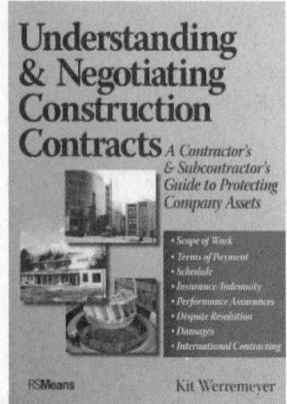

by Kit Werremeyer

Take advantage of the author's 30 years' experience in small-to-large (including international) construction projects. Learn how to identify, understand, and evaluate high risk terms and conditions typically found in all construction contracts—then negotiate to lower or eliminate the risk, improve terms of payment, and reduce exposure to claims and disputes. The author avoids "legalese" and gives real-life examples from actual projects.

$80.00 | 300 pages, softcover | Catalog no. 67350

The Gypsum Construction Handbook

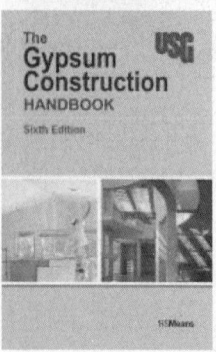

by USG

An invaluable reference of construction procedures for gypsum drywall, cement board, veneer plaster, and conventional plaster. This new edition includes the newest product developments, installation methods, fire- and sound-rated construction information, illustrated framing-to-finish application instructions, estimating and planning information, and more. Great for architects and engineers; contractors, builders, and dealers; apprentices and training programs; building inspectors and code officials; and anyone interested in gypsum construction. Features information on tools and safety practices, a glossary of construction terms, and a list of important agencies and associations. Also available in Spanish.

$40.00 | Over 575 pages, illustrated, softcover | Catalog no. 67357A

Mechanical Estimating Methods, 4th Edition

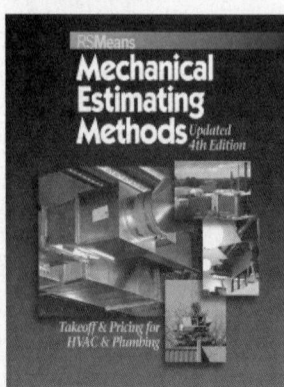

Completely updated, this guide assists you in making a review of plans, specs, and bid packages, with suggestions for takeoff procedures, listings, substitutions, and pre-bid scheduling for all components of HVAC. Includes suggestions for budgeting labor and equipment usage. Compares materials and construction methods to allow you to select the best option.

$70.00 per copy | Over 350 pages, illustrated, softcover | Catalog no. 67294B

Means Illustrated Construction Dictionary

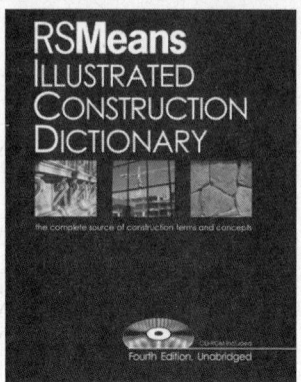

Unabridged 4th Edition, with CD-ROM

Long regarded as the industry's finest, *Means Illustrated Construction Dictionary* is now even better. With nearly 20,000 terms and more than 1,400 illustrations and photos, it is the clear choice for the most comprehensive and current information. The companion CD-ROM that comes with this new edition adds extra features such as: larger graphics and expanded definitions.

$99.95 | Over 790 pages, illust., hardcover | Catalog no. 67292B

RSMeans Estimating Handbook, 3rd Edition

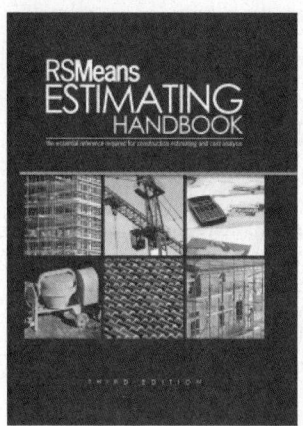

Widely used in the industry for tasks ranging from routine estimates to special cost analysis projects, this handbook has been completely updated and reorganized with new and expanded technical information.

RSMeans Estimating Handbook will help construction professionals:

- Evaluate architectural plans and specifications
- Prepare accurate quantity takeoffs
- Compare design alternatives and costs
- Perform value engineering
- Double-check estimates and quotes
- Estimate change orders

$110.00 | Over 900 pages, hardcover | Catalog No. 67276B

2014 Order Form

For more information visit the RSMeans website at **www.rsmeans.com**

Qty.	Book no.	COST ESTIMATING BOOKS	Unit Price	Total
	60064	Assemblies Cost Data 2014	$315.95	
	60014	Building Construction Cost Data 2014	194.95	
	60044	Commercial Renovaion Cost Data 2014	156.95	
	60114	Concrete & Masonry Cost Data 2014	177.95	
	50144	Construction Cost Indexes 2014 (subscription)	362.00	
	60144A	Construction Cost Index–January 2014	93.50	
	60144B	Construction Cost Index–April 2014	93.50	
	60144C	Construction Cost Index–July 2014	93.50	
	60144D	Construction Cost Index–October 2014	93.50	
	60344	Contr. Pricing Guide: Resid. R & R Costs 2014	39.95	
	60234	Electrical Change Order Cost Data 2014	187.95	
	60034	Electrical Cost Data 2014	196.95	
	60204	Facilities Construction Cost Data 2014	496.95	
	60304	Facilities Maintenance & Repair Cost Data 2014	434.95	
	60554	Green Building Cost Data 2014	160.95	
	60164	Heavy Construction Cost Data 2014	192.95	
	60094	Interior Cost Data 2014	196.95	
	60124	Labor Rates for the Const. Industry 2014	424.95	
	60184	Light Commercial Cost Data 2014	144.95	
	60024	Mechanical Cost Data 2014	191.95	
	60154	Open Shop Building Const. Cost Data 2014	165.95	
	60214	Plumbing Cost Data 2014	194.95	
	60174	Residential Cost Data 2014	139.95	
	60284	Site Work & Landscape Cost Data 2014	187.95	
	60054	Square Foot Costs 2014	205.95	
	62013	Yardsticks for Costing (2013)	185.95	
	62014	Yardsticks for Costing (2014)	189.95	
		REFERENCE BOOKS		
	67329	Bldrs Essentials: Best Bus. Practices for Bldrs	40.00	
	67307	Bldrs Essentials: Plan Reading & Takeoff	35.95	
	67342	Building & Renovating Schools	99.95	
	67261A	The Building Prof. Guide to Contract Documents	75.00	
	67339	Building Security: Strategies & Costs	95.00	
	67353A	Complete Book of Framing, 2nd Ed.	29.95	
	67146	Concrete Repair & Maintenance Illustrated	75.00	
	67352	Construction Business Management	55.00	
	67364	Construction Law	110.00	
	67358	Construction Supervision	95.00	
	67363	Cost Data Student Edition	99.00	
	67314	Cost Planning & Est. for Facil. Maint.	95.00	
	67230B	Electrical Estimating Methods, 3rd Ed.	75.00	
	67343A	Est. Bldg. Costs for Resi. & Lt. Comm., 2nd Ed.	75.00	
	67276B	Estimating Handbook, 3rd Ed.	110.00	
	67318	Facilities Operations & Engineering Reference	115.00	
	67301	Facilities Planning & Relocation	89.95	
	67338B	Green Building: Proj. Planning & Cost Est., 3rd Ed.	110.00	
	67355	Green Home Improvement	34.95	
	67357A	The Gypsum Construction Handbook	40.00	
	67148	Heavy Construction Handbook	110.00	
	67308E	Home Improvement Costs–Int. Projects, 9th Ed.	24.95	
	67309E	Home Improvement Costs–Ext. Projects, 9th Ed.	24.95	

Qty.	Book no.	REFERENCE BOOKS (Cont.)	Unit Price	Total
	67344	Homeowner's Guide to Mold	21.95	
	67324C	How to Est.w/Means Data & CostWorks, 4th Ed.	75.00	
	67351A	How Your House Works, 2nd Ed.	22.95	
	67282A	Illustrated Const. Dictionary, Condensed, 2nd Ed.	65.00	
	67292B	Illustrated Const. Dictionary, w/CD-ROM, 4th Ed.	99.95	
	67362	Illustrated Const. Dictionary, Student Ed.	55.00	
	67348	Job Order Contracting	89.95	
	67295C	Landscape Estimating Methods, 5th Ed.	75.00	
	67341	Life Cycle Costing for Facilities	99.95	
	67294B	Mechanical Estimating Methods, 4th Ed.	70.00	
	67283B	Plumbing Estimating Methods, 3rd Ed.	65.00	
	67345	Practice of Cost Segregation Analysis	105.00	
	67366	Project Control: Integrating Cost & Sched.	95.00	
	67346	Preventive Maint. for Multi-Family Housing	95.00	
	67367	Project Scheduling & Manag. for Constr., 4th Ed.	95.00	
	67322B	Resi. & Light Commercial Const. Stds., 3rd Ed.	65.00	
	67359	Risk Management for Design & Construction	125.00	
	67365	Solar Energy: Technology & Project Delivery	85.00	
	67145B	Sq. Ft. & Assem. Estimating Methods, 3rd Ed.	75.00	
	67321	Total Productive Facilities Management	85.00	
	67350	Understanding and Negotiating Const. Contracts	80.00	
	67303B	Unit Price Estimating Methods, 4th Ed.	75.00	
	67354	Universal Design	21.95	
	67319A	Value Engineering: Practical Applications	85.00	

MA residents add 6.25% state sales tax

Shipping & Handling**

Total (U.S. Funds)*

Prices are subject to change and are for U.S. delivery only. *Canadian customers may call for current prices. **Shipping & handling charges: Add 7% of total order for check and credit card payments. Add 9% of total order for invoiced orders.

Send order to: ADDV-1000

Name (please print) _____

Company _____

☐ Company

☐ Home Address _____

_____

City/State/Zip _____

Phone # _____ P.O. # _____

(Must accompany all orders being billed)

Mail to: RSMeans, 700 Longwater Drive, Norwell, MA 02061

RSMeans Project Cost Report

By filling out this report, your project data will contribute to the database that supports the RSMeans® Project Cost Square Foot Data. When you fill out this form, RSMeans will provide a $50 discount off one of the RSMeans products advertised in the preceding pages. Please complete the form including all items where you have cost data, and all the items marked (☑).

$50.00 Discount per product for each report you submit

Project Description (NEW construction only, please)

☑ Building Use (Office School . . .) _____

☑ Address (City, State)_____

_____

☑ Total Building Area (SF) _____

☑ Ground Floor (SF) _____

☑ Frame (Wood, Steel . . .) _____

☑ Exterior Wall (Brick, Tilt-up . . .) _____

☑ Basement: (check one)   ☐ Full   ☐ Partial   ☐ None

☑ Number of Stories _____

☑ Floor-to-Floor Height_____

☑ Volume (C.F.)_____

% Air Conditioned _____ Tons_____

Total Project Cost $ _____

Owner _____

Architect_____

General Contractor _____

☑ Bid Date _____

☑ Typical Bay Size _____

☑ Occupant Capacity_____

☑ Labor Force: _____ % Union   _____ % Non-Union

☑ Project Description (Circle one number in each line.)

   1. Economy   2. Average   3. Custom   4. Luxury

   1. Square   2. Rectangular 3. Irregular 4. Very Irregular

Comments _____

_____

A	☑	General Conditions	$	
B	☑	Site Work	$	
C	☑	Concrete	$	
D	☑	Masonry	$	
E	☑	Metals	$	
F	☑	Wood & Plastics	$	
G	☑	Thermal &Moisture Protection	$	
GR		Roofing & Flashing	$	
H	☑	Doors and Windows	$	
J	☑	Finishes	$	
JP		Painting & Wall Covering	$	

K	☑	Specialties	$	
L	☑	Equipment	$	
M	☑	Furnishings	$	
N	☑	SpecialConstruction	$	
P	☑	ConveyingSystems	$	
Q	☑	Mechanical	$	
QP		Plumbing	$	
QB		HVAC	$	
R	☑	Electrical	$	
S	☑	Mech./Elec. Combined	$	

Please specify the RSMeans product you wish to receive.
Complete the address information.

Product Name _____

Product Number _____

Your Name _____

Title _____

Company_____

   ☐ Company
   ☐ Home   Street Address_____

City, State, Zip _____

Email Address _____

Return by mail or fax 888-492-6770.

Method of Payment:

Credit Card # _____

Expiration Date _____

Check_____

Purchase Order _____

Phone Number _____
(if you would prefer a sales call)

RSMeans
a division of Reed Construction Data
Square Foot Costs Department
700 Longwater Drive
Norwell, MA 02061
www.RSMeans.com